The Good Pub Guide
2006

The Good Pub Guide 2006

Edited by

Alisdair Aird and Fiona Stapley

Managing Editor: Karen Fick
Senior Associate Editor: Robert Unsworth
Associate Editor: Tim Locke
Editorial Assistance: Fiona Wright

EBURY PRESS
LONDON

Please send reports on pubs to

The Good Pub Guide
FREEPOST TN1569
WADHURST
East Sussex
TN5 7BR

or contact our website:
www.goodguides.co.uk

Good Guide publications are available at special discounts for bulk
purchases or for sales promotions or premiums. Special editions,
including personalized covers, excerpts of existing Guides and corporate
imprints, can be created in large quantities for special needs. Enquiries
should be sent to the Sales Development Department, Random House,
20 Vauxhall Bridge Road, London SW1V 2SA (020 7840 8400).

This edition first published in 2005 by Ebury Press,
Random House, 20 Vauxhall Bridge Road,
London SW1V 2SA

The Random House Group Limited Reg. No. 954009

www.randomhouse.co.uk

1 3 5 7 9 10 8 6 4 2

A CIP catalogue record for this book is available from the British Library.

ISBN 0 091 90590 7

Typeset from author's disks by Clive Dorman
Edited by Pat Taylor Chalmers
Printed and bound in Great Britain by Cox and Wyman Ltd, Reading, Berkshire

Contents

Introduction

REAL ALE ON THE REBOUND

Cask-conditioned ale has crept back into fashion in the last year or so. After two decades of falling sales and an upsurge in the demand for lager instead, the more distinctive styles of real ale have now seen their sales start increasing again. Real ale brewers including Adnams, Banks's, Greene King, Timothy Taylors and Youngs have all seen rising demand this year.

Among the thousands of reports we get from readers each month, nearly half now specifically mention a pub's real ale. Interestingly, reports from our many women readers are now increasingly mentioning real ale rather than some other drink.

The great majority of good pubs are run by landlords or landladies who really care about their beer. In some, this is almost a passion. They search out interesting beers from small breweries far and wide, serve their wide and quickly changing variety in top condition, and are helpful with advice. The Bhurtpore at Aston (Cheshire), Watermill at Ings (Cumbria), Bridge at Topsham (Devon), Fat Cat in Norwich (Norfolk), Halfway House at Pitney (Somerset), Market Porter (London) and Bon Accord in Glasgow (Scotland) all fit this bill. The Watermill at Ings, its cheerful and enthusiastic landlord carefully checking each new cask as it comes on stream and maybe asking customers for a second opinion, is **Beer Pub of the Year 2006**.

THE £3 PINT

This year beer prices have continued their dizzy upwards spiral. In Great Britain as a whole, the average price of a pint is now £2.24. This marks an increase over last year of 4% – about double the rate of inflation. We even found a handful of pubs charging £3 a pint for their cheapest real ale. In Surrey, the most expensive county, the average price of a pint is now over £2.50. So people in Surrey are now paying just over 50p a pint more for their beer than people in the cheapest area – Lancashire.

The Table below shows how prices compare, county by county – these are average prices for the cheapest real ale stocked by each pub.

	£/pint
Lancashire	2.00
Cheshire, Nottinghamshire	2.03
Staffordshire	2.06
Cumbria	2.08
West Midlands, Yorkshire	2.10
Derbyshire	2.12
Herefordshire, Northumbria	2.13
Shropshire	2.14
Worcestershire	2.17
Wales	2.18

	£/pint
Leicestershire and Rutland	2.21
Cornwall, Devon, Gloucestershire, Wiltshire	2.23
Lincolnshire, Somerset	2.24
Dorset	2.26
Essex	2.27
Cambridgeshire, Warwickshire	2.28
Hertfordshire, Norfolk	2.29
Bedfordshire, Northamptonshire	2.30
Oxfordshire, Scotland	2.32
Hampshire, Isle of Wight, Kent, Suffolk	2.33
Sussex	2.35
Buckinghamshire	2.42
Berkshire	2.43
London	2.46
Surrey	2.51

Our survey is a very precise indication of how beer prices are actually moving, as it is the only price survey which compares the price in each pub with the price in that same pub 12 months earlier, in a sample of over 1,100 pubs nationwide. This gives a truer picture than the usual simpler system of comparing an average price in a sample of pubs one year with an average in a rather different sample the next.

For sheer value, one answer is to track down one of the growing number of pubs which brews its own beer. In our price survey, these generally undercut the price of beer in other pubs in their area by about 30p a pint. So, in effect, own-brew pubs are selling their beers at 2002 prices.

Nearly 50 of the main entries now brew their own beer. Sometimes, these own brews are of exceptional quality – so good that other pubs stock them too. Pots from the Flower Pots at Cheriton (Hampshire), Oakham from the Brewery Tap in Peterborough (Cambridgeshire), Grainstore from the pub of that name in Oakham (Leicestershire and Rutland), Burton Bridge from the Burton Bridge Inn in Burton upon Trent (Staffordshire), Kelham Island from the Fat Cat in Sheffield (Yorkshire) and Houston ales from the Fox & Hounds at Houston (Scotland) all fall into this exalted category. With a window to the brewery from its comfortable lounge, and a fine range of tasty beers including seasonal specials such as Big Lusty May, the Fox & Hounds at Houston is **Own Brew Pub of the Year 2006**.

Some breweries manage to match or even better the low prices charged in pubs which brew their own. Among our main entries, we found beers averaging under £2 a pint from 17 brewers. Here is the role of honour, starting with the cheapest: Holts, Wyre Piddle, Sam Smiths, Burton Bridge, Castle Rock, Reepham, Barngates, Coach House, Blackpool, Hydes, Clarks, Church End, Whim, John Roberts, Highwood, Woods and York.

Castle Rock is the house brewery for the small Tynemill group of mainly East Midlands pubs. Their pubs (we have five among the main entries) are normally quite down-to-earth and straightforward, with some concentration on good beers. Their food, like their drinks, is attractively priced, and can be interesting. For their consistently good value, Tynemill is **Pub Group of the Year 2006**.

Of course low price is not everything. Good value can mean exceptional quality, even if the price is not rock-bottom. One brewery which stands out for this is Black Sheep. We found their excellent beers sold regularly by nearly a hundred of the main entries – and in three dozen of these, it was the cheapest beer on sale. They also have a splendid brewery centre (in Masham, Yorkshire), with a café-bar which serves well as a substitute pub – for the first time we have included it as a main entry. Black Sheep is **Brewery of the Year 2006**.

THE WINE LAKE

No, that's not some vagary of the Common Agricultural Policy – that's the glass of pub wine in front of you. This year we have spotted an unnerving trend for pubs to push up the size of their wine glasses (and of course the price of what's inside them). Time was when a standard glass of wine was 125ml – that's six glasses out of a bottle. That's the basis for the Unit of Alcohol, the measure that people reckon on, for safe driving, for diets, and for the amounts of alcohol that men and women can drink in a week without risk to health.

Now, many pubs use a 175ml glass as standard – that's nearly quarter of a bottle. To them, a large glass is 250ml, or a third of a bottle. This isn't generosity, it's just a way of getting more money into their tills. And it leaves many customers drinking more than they want to – and perhaps, if they are driving, more than is safe.

We would like to see all pubs selling wine use the 125ml glass as their standard size. They should call 175ml glasses 'large', and 250ml glasses 'giant'.

On a happier note, there's no doubt that the quality of wine sold in pubs has improved no end. When good pubs now take so much interest in the quality of their wines, who needs wine bars? The choice can be amazing, too. Dozens of the main entries now offer ten or more by the glass, some up to 50 or more, often with a choice of rosé, champagne and sparkling wines, sweet wines and ports. Several import their own, some run a wine retail business in tandem.

Taking quality, value and sheer enjoyment into account, the four best wine pubs in Britain are the Culm Valley in Culmstock and Harris Arms at Portgate (both in Devon), the Penhelig Arms in Aberdovey (Wales) and the Stagg at Titley (Herefordshire). The Penhelig Arms in Aberdovey, keeping its wide and interesting range by the glass perfectly fresh with a good air exclusion system, giving helpful guidance, and not being at all greedy on price, is **Wine Pub of the Year 2006**.

… AND WHISKY

Besides the many pubs in Scotland which stock mind-boggling arrays of interesting malt whiskies, England and Wales both have a surprising number of pubs that offer several shelf-fuls. The Britons Protection in Manchester (Lancashire chapter) with 235 and the Nobody Inn at Doddiscombsleigh (Devon) with 270 would both keep even the most adventurous whisky-taster busy for quite a while. In Yorkshire the

Marton Arms at Thornton in Lonsdale is a connoisseur's delight, with a superlative and carefully listed collection of some 350 choice malts; it is **Whisky Pub of the Year 2006**.

PUB FOOD

The food served in good pubs now falls into three styles – we call them the bargain, the traditional and the fancy.

Roughly one in ten of the main entries goes in for bargain food. Here, the key is low price. Being cheap doesn't have to be boring. What is served could range from a hearty soup or doorstep sandwiches with chips to stir fries, pasta dishes, hot pots and casseroles showing real imagination. The Brewery Tap in Peterborough (Cambridgeshire), Black Dog in Dalton in Furness (Cumbria), Basketmakers Arms in Brighton (Sussex) and Fat Cat in Sheffield (Yorkshire) all show that flair and low price can go hand in hand. The Brewery Tap in Peterborough, its Thai chefs' tasty food going really well with its interesting ales, is **Bargain Pub of the Year 2006**.

Of the other main entries, around a quarter now mainly cook what we and readers think of as fancy food – that's to say, bass isn't just plain grilled, but comes with cherry tomato tarte tatin and vermouth cream. This style of pub food can be pretty expensive. No complaints if the results justify the prices – as they do in our 200-plus fancy-food main entries.

There are however two big dangers with this approach. Occasionally, what was a perfectly good pub, though it still has good food, takes on too many airs and graces, and pushes up its prices so high, that from our point of view it has simply got too big for its boots. The second more common problem is that as this style of restauranty cooking has gained a foothold in pubs, too many places without the necessary talent are jumping on the bandwagon. All too often, that ambitious menu turns out to be just a come-on, and what's on your plate is a bitter disappointment, at such a high price. Places like that might as well forget their pavé of yellowfin tuna on carrageen mousse, and go back to something fitting their abilities, like chicken nuggets.

When the fancy style works well, it can be terrific – just the thing for a special meal out, with the bonus of a warmer-hearted atmosphere than you'll find in many restaurants. Their wonderful imaginative food brings diners rich rewards at the top pubs cooking in this style. They are the Cock at Hemingford Grey (Cambridgeshire), Dartmoor Union at Holbeton (Devon), Stagg at Titley (Herefordshire), Alford Arms at Frithsden (Hertfordshire), Olive Branch at Clipsham (Leicestershire and Rutland), Half Moon at Cuxham (Oxfordshire), Jolly Sportsman at East Chiltington (Sussex), Vine Tree at Norton (Wiltshire), and Star at Harome and Blacksmiths at Westow (both in Yorkshire).

To recognise the coming of age of this more elaborate style of pub cooking, we are this year introducing a new award: the Vine Tree at Norton takes this new title of **Pub Restaurant of the Year 2006**.

Traditional food is still the mainstay of most good pubs. Their menus may include one or two fancy dishes, but what their customers go for is straightforward treatment of first-class fresh ingredients – a really good vegetable soup with home-baked bread, carefully thought-out salads, proper steak and kidney pie (not a silly puff pastry lid plonked on to some stew), home-baked ham with local free-range eggs, beer-battered fresh fish with crisp hand-cut chips.

Fine examples of this traditional style are the Dundas Arms at Kintbury (Berkshire), Polecat at Prestwood (Buckinghamshire), Red Hart at Awre and Five Mile House at Duntisbourne Abbots (both in Gloucestershire), Eagle & Child at Bispham Green (Lancashire), Crown at Hopton Wafers (Shropshire), King William IV at Mickleham (Surrey) and Plockton Hotel (Scotland). For the landlord's excellent homely yet individual cooking, served in charming pub surroundings, the Five Mile House at Duntisbourne Abbots is **Dining Pub of the Year 2006**.

IS THE UNSPOILT TRADITIONAL TAVERN DOOMED?

Among people who enjoy good simple pubs, this has been a favourite worry for over 150 years. Now as then, the answer is clear: good simple pubs are in no danger, though indifferent or bad ones will fall by the wayside.

By our calculation, at least 4% of the main entries would count as truly unspoilt taverns, town or country. And we are talking about really simple here. Think outside lavatories, maybe no bar counter, minimal if any food, third or fourth generation landladies and landlords, customers who might arrive on a horse or a tractor, or with muddy boots and dogs. What gains such pubs a place in the *Guide* is the genuine warmth of their unpretentious welcome (and as like as not their good log, coal or peat fire), the quality of their beer or cider (and indeed any simple food that they do), and their sheer individuality and atmosphere.

The Bell up on the Berkshire downs at Aldworth, in the same family for over 200 years and an absolute classic, is **Unspoilt Pub of the Year 2006**.

WHERE ARE PUBS HEADING?

One direction is clear: they are heading towards being entirely no smoking. In last year's edition, we noted that the number of main entries which were already no smoking throughout had doubled within that year. This year, there are three times as many as last year. From spring 2006, all the pubs in Scotland will by law be entirely no smoking (the Republic of Ireland's pubs have been no smoking for more than a year now). It's only a matter of time before England and Wales follow suit.

In parallel, pubs have become far less dependent on drinking than they used to be. Food has become an important element, and in many pubs it's now paramount. However, it is still vital for any good pub to have a good range of drinks, non-alcoholic as well as alcoholic – and for it to seem truly welcoming for people who do want just a drink and a chat.

The new entries to this edition – over a hundred – show how pubs are meeting today's demands.

They fall broadly into two types: pubs which have taken a strongly contemporary line, in their stylish décor and often innovative food; and in marked contrast pubs which show that an entirely traditional approach when it's done well can bring first-class results. In both groups there have been some really rewarding discoveries.

Stand-outs among the new wave of stylish up-to-date places are the Dartmoor Union at Holbeton (Devon), Falcon at Poulton (Gloucestershire),

Running Horse at Littleton (Hampshire) and Crabmill at Preston Bagot (Warwickshire). A sub-group would include the so-called gastropubs that are mushrooming in London particularly – former locals stripped down to bare boards and minimal decoration, with a lively informality and trendy young customers for their modern strong-flavoured food. The Anchor & Hope (near Waterloo in South London) is a good example.

In the traditional camp, top finds are the Sandy Park Inn (Devon), Bottle at Marshwood and Shave Cross Inn (both in Dorset), the Wheatsheaf at Braishfield (Hampshire), Wheatsheaf at Dry Doddington (Lincolnshire), Lord Nelson in Southwold (Suffolk), and Bridge Inn at Grinton and Rose & Crown at Sutton-on-the-Forest (both in Yorkshire).

Then there are some outstanding new pubs which at first glance look traditional but show great attention to today's ideas about food and style: the Three Horse Shoes at Breedon on the Hill (Leicestershire and Rutland), Red Lion at Tetsworth (Oxfordshire), Red Lion at Babcary (Somerset), and Star at North Dalton and Blacksmiths at Westow (both in Yorkshire).

For us, this final approach is the ideal. With its flagstoned locals' bar and comfortably relaxed lounge bar, well kept beers, super food, personable young landlord and genuine fresh-feeling individuality, the Red Lion at Babcary is **Newcomer of the Year 2006**.

WHERE TO STAY

Massive investment in pub accommodation in the last few years is now paying off handsomely for customers. Nearly 40% of the main entries now have bedrooms. These are usually comfortable and well equipped, with their own bathrooms – perfect for a night or two. The informality and individuality strongly appeals to many readers, in preference to similarly priced hotels.

Some outstanding inns to stay in are the Frog at Skirmett (Buckinghamshire), Anchor at Sutton Gault (Cambridgeshire), Pheasant at Bassenthwaite Lake (Cumbria), Inn at Whitewell (Lancashire), Royal Oak at Luxborough (Somerset), General Tarleton at Ferrensby, Star at Harome, Charles Bathurst near Langthwaite, Boars Head at Ripley and Sportsmans Arms at Wath in Nidderdale (all in Yorkshire), and Plockton Hotel (Scotland).

The Charles Bathurst in the glorious scenery of Arkengarthdale near Langthwaite, with good food, beer and atmosphere, comfortable rooms and a nice landlord, is **Inn of the Year 2006**.

PUB OF THE YEAR

On the national canvas, 22 pubs stand out as really special, winning the warmest praise from dozens of readers. They are the Bell at Aldworth (Berkshire), White Horse at Hedgerley (Buckinghamshire), Anchor at Sutton Gault (Cambridgeshire), Trengilly Wartha near Constantine (Cornwall), Drewe Arms at Broadhembury, Duke of York at Iddesleigh, Kings Arms at Stockland and Bridge at Topsham (all in Devon), West Bay at West Bay (Dorset), Five Mile House near Duntisbourne Abbots (Gloucestershire), Sun at Bentworth (Hampshire), Olive Branch at Clipsham (Leicestershire and Rutland), Adam & Eve in Norwich and Rose & Crown at Snettisham (both in Norfolk), Old Green Tree in Bath

(Somerset), Tempest Arms at Elslack, General Tarleton at Ferrensby, Star at Harome and Wellington at Lund (both in Yorkshire), Jerusalem Tavern (Central London), Plockton Hotel at Plockton (Scotland) and Groes at Ty'n-y-groes (Wales).

The Duke of York at Iddesleigh is, like hundreds of other main entries, an appealing country pub with good food and drink, welcoming service and plenty of happy locals. It also has that magic extra something which makes it memorably enjoyable; the Duke of York is **Pub of the Year 2006**.

LANDLORDS AND LANDLADIES – THE REAL STARS

The publican is always the key to a pub's success – or otherwise. Readers who have found themselves at bad pubs are always quick to let us know. Some of their experiences leave us amazed that such people can still be running pubs.

This is the sort of thing we mean:

Our food took 50 minutes to come. It was missing a side order. No apologies from the manageress who said that it must have been our fault, and when I asked how long it would take to reorder it, because we had already been waiting 50 minutes, she just glared and said, 'So has everybody else'.

Very unwelcoming landlord, inhospitable in the extreme.

Kneeling next to my friends (no chair free), I was kicked in the leg by the landlord and told 'Move your bloody legs!'. I suggested that he reword his comment. I was told to 'Piss off!'.

Landlady is rude to customers and makes them feel unwelcome; she treats her staff badly and all the good ones have left.

We ordered lemon sole, to eat at 7.30. At 6.45 we asked how it would be cooked. 'In butter' was the reply. My husband (who does not eat dairy products) asked if it could be plain grilled, and was told it was already cooking! At 6.45 for a meal at 7.30! When this was queried the owner said that in French there was a word for people like us and promptly broke into a stream of French – by the tone we gathered it was not pleasant! He then asked us to leave the pub. Our drinks were in front of us. Shocked, we asked for the bill and he produced two – one for the drinks and the other for the lemon soles. My husband said if we were being charged we should have the fish served to us. This was declined and we were escorted out of the pub and told in an aggressive manner not to come back.

New owners are abrasive and arrogant – when I asked for a light meal, owner told me 'This is a restaurant not a snack bar', and asked me to drink up and leave. Local tourist office told us they had had several complaints.

The men and women who run our main entries are quite the opposite of these disgraces to the pub world. Some are very special indeed:

Brian Coulthwaite of the Watermill at Ings (Cumbria), Jamie Stuart and Pippa Hutchinson of the Duke of York at Iddesleigh, Andy and Rowena Whiteman of the Harris Arms at Portgate and Simon Saunders of the Sandy Park Inn (both in Devon), André and Liz Large of the Cross House at Doynton, Jo and Jon Carrier of the Five Mile House at Duntisbourne Abbots and Kathryn Horton of the Ostrich at Newland (both in Gloucestershire), Bob and Josie Dyer of the Wheatsheaf at Dry Doddington (Lincolnshire), Lucille and Barry Carter of the Woolpack at Terrington St John (Norfolk), Maggie Chandler of the George at Kilsby (Northamptonshire), Chris and Celestine Roche of the Horse & Groom at Caulcott, Josh and Kay Reid of the Chequers in Chipping Norton and Peter and Assumpta Golding of the Chequers at Churchill (all in Oxfordshire), John and Trudy Greaves of the Bell at Pensax (Worcestershire), and the Key family of the Nags Head in Usk (Wales).

Though they've not been there long, the warmth of their enthusiasm and friendly welcome wins Andy and Rowena Whiteman of the Harris Arms at Portgate the top title of **Licensees of the Year 2006.**

What is a Good Pub?

The main entries in the *Guide* have been through a two-stage sifting process. First of all, some 2,000 regular correspondents keep in touch with us about the pubs they visit, and nearly double that number report occasionally. We are now also getting quite a flow of reports through our **www.goodguides.co.uk** web site. This keeps us up-to-date about pubs included in previous editions – it's their alarm signals that warn us when a pub's standards have dropped (after a change of management, say), and it's their continuing approval that reassures us about keeping a pub as a main entry for another year. Very important, though, are the reports they send us on pubs we don't know at all. It's from these new discoveries that we make up a shortlist, to be considered for possible inclusion as new main entries. The more people that report favourably on a new pub, the more likely it is to win a place on this shortlist – especially if some of the reporters belong to our hard core of about 600 trusted correspondents whose judgement we have learned to rely on. These are people who have each given us detailed comments on dozens of pubs, and shown that (when we ourselves know some of those pubs too) their judgement is closely in line with our own.

This brings us to the acid test. Each pub, before inclusion as a main entry, is inspected anonymously by one of the editorial team. They have to find some special quality that would make strangers enjoy visiting it. What often marks the pub out for special attention is good value food (and that might mean anything from a well made sandwich, with good fresh ingredients at a low price, to imaginative cooking outclassing most restaurants in the area). The drinks may be out of the ordinary (pubs with several hundred whiskies, with remarkable wine lists, with home-made country wines or good beer or cider made on the premises, with a wide range of well kept real ales or bottled beers from all over the world). Perhaps there's a special appeal about it as a place to stay, with good bedrooms and obliging service. Maybe it's the building itself (from centuries-old parts of monasteries to extravagant Victorian gin-palaces), or its surroundings (lovely countryside, attractive waterside, extensive well kept garden), or what's in it (charming furnishings, extraordinary collections of bric-a-brac).

Above all, though, what makes the good pub is its atmosphere – you should be able to feel at home there, and feel not just that *you're* glad you've come but that *they're* glad you've come. A good landlord or landlady makes a huge difference here – they can make or break a pub.

It follows from this that a great many ordinary locals, perfectly good in their own right, don't earn a place in the *Guide*. What makes them attractive to their regular customers (an almost clubby chumminess) may even make strangers feel rather out-of-place.

Another important point is that there's not necessarily any link between charm and luxury – though we like our creature comforts as much as anyone. A basic unspoilt village tavern, with hard seats and a flagstone floor, may be worth travelling miles to find, while a deluxe pub-restaurant may not be worth crossing the street for. Landlords can't buy the Good Pub accolade by spending thousands on thickly padded banquettes, soft music and menus boasting about signature dishes nesting on beds of trendy vegetables drizzled by a jus of this and that – they can only win it, by having a genuinely personal concern for both their customers and their pub.

Using the *Guide*

THE COUNTIES

England has been split alphabetically into counties, mainly to make it easier for people scanning through the book to find pubs near them. Each chapter starts by picking out the pubs that are currently doing best in the area, or are specially attractive for one reason or another.

The county boundaries we use are those for the administrative counties (not the old traditional counties, which were changed back in 1976). We have left the new unitary authorities within the counties that they formed part of until their creation in the most recent local government reorganisation. Metropolitan areas have been included in the counties around them – for example, Merseyside in Lancashire. And occasionally we have grouped counties together – for example, Rutland with Leicestershire, and Durham with Northumberland to make Northumbria. If in doubt, check the Contents.

Scotland and Wales have each been covered in single chapters, and London appears immediately before them at the end of England. Except in London (which is split into Central, East, North, South and West), pubs are listed alphabetically under the name of the town or village where they are. If the village is so small that you probably wouldn't find it on a road map, we've listed it under the name of the nearest sizeable village or town instead. The maps use the same town and village names, and additionally include a few big cities that don't have any listed pubs – for orientation.

We always list pubs in their true locations – so if a village is actually in Buckinghamshire that's where we list it, even if its postal address is via some town in Oxfordshire. Just once or twice, when the village itself is in one county but the pub is just over the border in the next-door county, we have used the village county, not the pub one.

STARS ★

Really outstanding pubs are picked out with a star after their name. In a few cases, pubs have two stars: these are the aristocrats among pubs, really worth going out of your way to find. The stars do NOT signify extra luxury or specially good food – in fact some of the pubs which appeal most distinctively and strongly of all are decidedly basic in terms of food and surroundings. The detailed description of each pub shows what its particular appeal is, and this is what the stars refer to.

FOOD AND STAY AWARDS 🍴 🛏

The knife-and-fork rosette shows those pubs where food is quite outstanding. The bed symbol shows pubs which we know to be good as places to stay in – bearing in mind the price of the rooms (obviously you can't expect the same level of luxury at £50 a head as you'd get for £100 a head). Pubs with bedrooms are marked on the maps as a square.

This wine glass symbol marks out those pubs where wines are a cut above the usual run, and/or offer a good choice of wines by the glass.

◖

The beer tankard symbol shows pubs where the quality of the beer is quite exceptional, or pubs which keep a particularly interesting range of beers in good condition.

£

This symbol picks out pubs where we have found decent snacks at £2.50 or less, or worthwhile main dishes at £5.95 or less.

RECOMMENDERS

At the end of each main entry we include the names of readers who have recently recommended that pub (unless they've asked us not to).

Important note: the description of the pub and the comments on it are our own and not the recommenders'; they are based on our own personal inspections and on later verification of facts with each pub. As some recommenders' names appear quite often, you can get an extra idea of what a pub is like by seeing which other pubs those recommenders have approved. In the rare instances where we have discovered a good pub which has no reader recommenders, or judge that a pub deserves to stay in the main entries despite a very recent management change we include the acronym BOB (buyer's own brand) as a recommender.

LUCKY DIPS

The Lucky Dip section at the end of each county chapter includes brief descriptions of pubs that have been recommended by readers, with the readers' names in brackets. As the flood of reports from readers has given so much solid information about so many pubs, we have been able to include only those which seem really worth trying. Where only one single reader's name is shown, in most cases that pub has been given a favourable review by other readers in previous years, so its inclusion does not depend on a single individual's judgement. In all cases, we have now not included a pub in the list unless readers' descriptions make the nature of the pub quite clear, and give us good grounds for trusting that other readers would be glad to know of the pub. So the descriptions normally reflect the balanced judgement of a number of different readers, increasingly backed up by similar reports on the same pubs from other readers in previous years. Many have been inspected by us. In these cases, LYM means the pub was in a previous edition of the *Guide*. The usual reason that it's no longer a main entry is that, although we've heard nothing really condemnatory about it, we've not had enough favourable reports to be sure that it's still ahead of the local competition. BB means that, although the pub has never been a main entry, we have inspected it, and found nothing against it. In both these cases, the description is our own; in others, it's based on the readers' reports. This year, we have deleted many previously highly rated pubs from the *Guide* simply because we have no very recent reports on them. This may well mean that we have left out some favourites – please tell us if we have!

Lucky Dip pubs marked with a ☆ are ones where the information we have (either from our own inspections or from trusted reader/reporters) suggests a firm recommendation. Roughly speaking, we'd say that these pubs are as much worth considering, at least for the virtues described for them, as many of the main entries themselves. Note that in the Dips we always commend food if we have information supporting a positive recommendation. So a bare mention that food is served shouldn't be taken to imply a recommendation of the food. The same is true of accommodation and so forth.

The Lucky Dips (particularly, of course, the starred ones) are under consideration for inspection for a future edition – so please let us have any comments you can make on them. You can use the report forms at the end of the book, the report card which should be included in it, or just write direct (no stamp needed if posted in the UK). Our address is The Good Pub Guide, FREEPOST TN1569, WADHURST, East Sussex TN5 7BR. Alternatively, you can get reports to us immediately, through our web site **www.goodguides.co.uk**.

MAP REFERENCES

All pubs outside the big cities are given four-figure map references. On the main entries, it looks like this: SX5678 Map 1. Map 1 means that it's on the first map in the book (see first colour section). SX means it's in the square labelled SX on that map. The first figure, 5, tells you to look along the grid at the top and/or bottom of the SX square for the figure 5. The third figure, 7, tells·you to look down the grid at the side of the square to find the figure 7. Imaginary lines drawn down and across the square from these figures should intersect near the pub itself.

The second and fourth figures, the 6 and the 8, are for more precise pin-pointing, and are really for use with larger-scale maps such as road atlases or the Ordnance Survey 1:50,000 maps, which use exactly the same map reference system. On the relevant Ordnance Survey map, instead of finding the 5 marker on the top grid you'd find the 56 one; instead of the 7 on the side grid you'd look for the 78 marker. This makes it very easy to locate even the smallest village.

Where a pub is exceptionally difficult to find, we include a six-figure reference in the directions, such as OS Sheet 102 map reference 654783. This refers to Sheet 102 of the Ordnance Survey 1:50,000 maps, which explain how to use the six-figure references to pin-point a pub to the nearest 100 metres.

MOTORWAY PUBS

If a pub is within four or five miles of a motorway junction, and reaching it doesn't involve much slow traffic, we give special directions for finding it from the motorway. And the Special Interest Lists at the end of the book include a list of these pubs, motorway by motorway.

PRICES AND OTHER FACTUAL DETAILS

The *Guide* went to press during the summer of 2005. As late as possible, each pub was sent a checking sheet to get up-to-date food, drink and bedroom prices and other factual information. By the summer of 2006 prices are bound to have increased a little – to be prudent, you should probably allow around 5% extra by then. But if you find a significantly different price please let us know.

Breweries or independent chains to which pubs are 'tied' are named at the beginning of the italic-print rubric after each main entry. That generally means the pub has to get most if not all of its drinks from that brewery or chain. If the brewery is not an independent one but just part of a combine, we name the combine in brackets. When the pub is tied, we have spelled out whether the landlord is a tenant, has the pub on a lease, or is a manager. Tenants and leaseholders of breweries generally have considerably greater freedom to do things their own way, and in particular are allowed to buy drinks including a beer from sources other than their tied brewery.

Free houses are pubs not tied to a brewery, so in theory they can shop around to get the drinks their customers want, at the best prices they can find. But in practice many free houses have loans from the big brewers, on terms that bind them to sell those breweries' beers. So don't be too surprised to find that so-called free houses may be stocking a range of beers restricted to those from a single brewery.

Real ale is used by us to mean beer that has been maturing naturally in its cask. We do not count as real ale beer which has been pasteurised or filtered to remove its natural yeasts. If it is kept under a blanket of carbon dioxide to preserve it, we still generally mention it – as long as the pressure is too light for you to notice any extra fizz, it's hard to tell the difference. (For brevity, we use the expression 'under light blanket pressure' to cover such pubs; we do not include among them pubs where the blanket pressure is high enough to force the beer up from the cellar, as this does make it unnaturally fizzy.) If we say a pub has, for example, 'Whitbreads-related real ales', these may include not just beers brewed by the national company and its subsidiaries but also beers produced by independent breweries which the national company buys in bulk and distributes alongside its own.

Other drinks: we've also looked out particularly for pubs doing enterprising non-alcoholic drinks (including good tea or coffee), interesting spirits (especially malt whiskies), country wines (elderflower and the like), freshly squeezed juices, and good farm ciders.

Bar food refers to what is sold in the bar, not in any separate restaurant. It means a place serves anything from sandwiches and ploughman's to full meals, rather than pork scratchings or packets of crisps. We always mention sandwiches in the text if we know that a pub does them – if you don't see them mentioned, assume you can't get them.

The **food listed** in the description of each pub is an example of the sort of thing you'd find served in the bar on a normal day, and generally includes the dishes which are currently finding most favour with readers. We try to indicate any difference we know of between lunchtime and evening, and between summer and winter (on the whole stressing summer food more).

In winter, many pubs tend to have a more restricted range, particularly of salads, and tend then to do more in the way of filled baked potatoes, casseroles and hot pies. We always mention barbecues if we know a pub does them. Food quality and variety may be affected by holidays – particularly in a small pub, where the licensees do the cooking themselves (May and early June seems to be a popular time for licensees to take their holidays).

What we call OAP meals are usually available for all 'seniors', not only people of pensionable age.

Any separate **restaurant** is mentioned. But in general all comments on the type of food served, and in particular all the other details about bar food at the end of each entry, relate to the pub food and not to the restaurant food.

Children's Certificates exist, but in practice **children** are allowed into at least some part of almost all the pubs included in this *Guide* (there is no legal restriction on the movement of children over 14 in any pub, though only people over 18 may get alcohol). As we went to press, we asked the main-entry pubs a series of detailed questions about their rules. **Children welcome** means the pub has told us that it simply lets them come in, with no special restrictions. In other cases we report exactly what arrangements pubs say they make for children. However, we have to note that in readers' experience some pubs make restrictions that they haven't told us about (children only if eating, for example). Also, very occasionally pubs which have previously allowed children change their policy altogether, virtually excluding them. If you come across this, please let us know, so that we can clarify the information for the pub concerned in the next edition. Beware that if children are confined to the restaurant, they may occasionally be expected to have a full restaurant meal. Also, please note that a welcome for children does not necessarily mean a welcome for breast-feeding in public. If we don't mention children at all, assume that they are not welcome. All but one or two pubs (we mention these in the text) allow children in their garden or on their terrace, if they have one. In the Lucky Dip entries we mention children only if readers have found either that they are allowed or that they are not allowed – the absence of any reference to children in a Dip entry means we don't know either way.

We asked all main entries what their policy was about **dogs**, and if they allow them we say so. Generally, if you take a dog into a pub you should have it on a lead. We also mention in the text any pub dogs or cats (or indeed other animals) that we've come across ourselves, or heard about from readers.

Parking is not mentioned if you should normally be able to park outside the pub, or in a private car park, without difficulty. But if we know that parking space is limited or metered, we say so.

We now say if a pub does **not** accept **credit cards**; some which do may put a surcharge on credit card bills, as the card companies take quite a big cut. We also say if we know that a pub tries to retain customers' credit cards while they are eating. This is a reprehensible practice, and if a pub tries it on you, please tell them that all banks and card companies frown on it – and please let us know the pub's name, so that we can warn readers in future editions.

Telephone numbers are given for all pubs that are not ex-directory.

Opening hours are for summer; we say if we know of differences in winter, or on particular days of the week. In the country, many pubs may open rather later and close earlier than their details show unless there are plenty of customers around (if you come across this, please let us know – with details). Pubs are allowed to stay open all day Mondays to Saturdays from 11am (earlier, if the area's licensing magistrates have permitted) till 11pm. However, outside cities most English and Welsh pubs close during the afternoon. Scottish pubs are allowed to stay open until later at night. The Licensing Act 2003 comes into force on 24 November 2005, after this edition is published. Some pubs may have changed or extended their opening hours; we'd be very grateful to hear of any differences from the hours we quote. You are allowed 20 minutes' drinking-up time after the quoted hours – half an hour if you've been having a meal in the pub.

Bedroom prices normally include full English breakfasts (if these are available, which they usually are), VAT and any automatic service charge that we know about. If we give just one price, it is the total price for two people sharing a double or twin-bedded room for one night. Otherwise, prices before the / are for single occupancy, prices after it for double. A capital B against the price means that it includes a private bathroom, a capital S a private shower. As all this coding packs in quite a lot of information, some examples may help to explain it:

£70	on its own means that's the total bill for two people sharing a twin or double room without private bath; the pub has no rooms with private bath, and a single person might have to pay that full price.
£70B	means exactly the same – but all the rooms have private bath
£65(£70B)	means rooms with private baths cost £5 extra
£40/£65(£70B)	means the same as the last example, but also shows that there are single rooms for £40, none of which has a private bathroom

If there's a choice of rooms at different prices, we normally give the cheapest. If there are seasonal price variations, we give the summer price (the highest). During the winter, many inns, particularly in the country, will have special cheaper rates. And at other times, especially in holiday areas, you will often find prices cheaper if you stay for several nights. On weekends, inns that aren't in obvious weekending areas often have bargain rates for two- or three-night stays.

MEAL TIMES

Bar food is commonly served from 12-2 and 7-9, at least from Monday to Saturday (food service often stops a bit earlier on Sundays). If we don't give a time against the *Bar food* note at the bottom of a main entry, that means that you should be able to get bar food at those times. However, we do spell out the times if we know that bar food service starts after 12.15 or after 7.15; if it stops before 2 or before 8.45; or if food is served for significantly longer than usual (say, till 2.30 or 9.45).

Though we note days when pubs have told us they don't do food, experience suggests that you should play safe on Sundays, and check first with any pub before planning an expedition that depends on getting a meal there. Also, out-of-the-way pubs often cut down on cooking during the week, especially the early part of the week, if they're quiet – as they tend to be, except at holiday times. Please let us know if you find anything different from what we say!

NO SMOKING

We say in the text of each entry what, if any, provision a pub makes for non-smokers. Pubs which are completely no smoking are also listed county by county in the Special Interest Lists at the back of the book.

DISABLED ACCESS

Deliberately, we do not ask pubs questions about this, as their answers would not give a reliable picture of how easy access is. Instead, we depend on readers' direct experience. If you are able to give us help about this, we would be particularly grateful for your reports.

PLANNING ROUTES WITH THE GOOD PUB GUIDE

Computer users may like to know of a route-finding programme, Microsoft® MapPoint™ European Edition, which shows the location of *Good Pub Guide* pubs on detailed maps, works out the quickest routes for journeys, adds diversions to nearby pubs – and shows our text entries for those pubs on screen.

OUR WEB SITE (www.goodguides.co.uk)

Our Internet web site uses material from *The Good Pub Guide* in a way that gives people who do not yet know it at least a taste of it. The site is being continually improved and expanded. It now includes a little map for each pub, including Lucky Dips. And we have added postcodes to help people with satnav route finding. You can use the site to send us reports – this way they get virtually immediate attention.

CHANGES DURING THE YEAR – PLEASE TELL US

Changes are inevitable during the course of the year. Landlords change, and so do their policies. And, as we've said, not all returned our fact-checking sheets. We very much hope that you will find everything just as we say. But if you find anything different, please let us know, using the tear-out card in the middle of the book (which doesn't need an envelope), the report forms at the back of the book, or just a letter. You don't need a stamp: the address is The Good Pub Guide, FREEPOST TN1569, WADHURST, East Sussex TN5 7BR. As we have said, you can also send us reports by using our web site **www.goodguides.co.uk**

Authors' Acknowledgements

The *Guide* owes its strength and authority to the extraordinarily generous help we have from the many thousands of readers who report to us on the pubs they visit, often in great detail. For the special help they have given us this year, we are deeply grateful to Ian Phillips, Michael and Jenny Back, George Atkinson, the Didler, Michael Doswell, Kevin Thorpe, Steve Whalley, Guy Vowles, Michael Dandy, Joan and Michel Hooper-Immins, Phyl and Jack Street, Susan and John Douglas, CMW, JJW, Tracey and Stephen Groves, Martin and Karen Wake, Gerry and Rosemary Dobson, Paul and Ursula Randall, LM, Dennis Jenkin, Dr and Mrs M E Wilson, Peter Meister, G Coates, Richard Lewis, Pete Baker, Paul A Moore, Joe Green, Ann and Colin Hunt, Paul Humphreys, Tom Evans, Roland and Wendy Chalu, Phil and Jane Hodson, Tony and Wendy Hobden, Rona Murdoch, W W Burke, Derek and Sylvia Stephenson, Pamela and Merlyn Horswell, John Foord, John Beeken, Martin Grosberg, A P Seymour, Nick Holding, Jenny and Brian Seller, John Wooll, Howard Dell, Val and Alan Green, Comus and Sarah Elliott, Simon Collett-Jones, Roger and Jenny Huggins, Tom McLean, Dave Irving, Ewan McCall, Michael and Alison Sandy, Phil and Sally Gorton, Michael Butler, Andy and Jill Kassube, June and Mike Coleman, John and Joan Nash, Neil and Anita Christopher, Margaret Dickinson, MDN, John Evans, Peter and Audrey Dowsett, Keith and Chris O'Neill, Esther and John Sprinkle, Charles and Pauline Stride, Anthony Longden, Alan and Paula McCully, Mr and Mrs Colin Roberts, B and K Hypher, Peter F Marshall, Mike Gorton, Mr and Mrs G S Ayrton, Barry and Anne, Mike Ridgway, Sarah Miles, Bob and Margaret Holder, KC, Dr and Mrs C W Thomas, Bert Newman, Pat and Tony Martin, Bruce Bird, Mike and Mary Carter, MLR, David Crook, Peter Scillitoe, B and M Kendall, John Saville, Tony Hobden, Martin and Pauline Jennings, Brian and Anna Marsden, Colin Moore, Ted George, Tina and David Woods-Taylor, Andy Sinden, Louise Harrington, Lynda and Trevor Smith, R T and J C Moggridge, J R Ringrose, Fred and Lorraine Gill, J F M and M West, Brian and Janet Ainscough, N R White, Dick and Madeleine Brown, M G Hart, Roy and Lindsey Fentiman, Ian and Nita Cooper, Tim and Ann Newell, David Barnes, Fr Robert Marsh and Meg and Colin Hamilton.

Sadly we report the deaths of three readers who gave us great guidance over the years, and whose continued help in the months before their deaths underpins this edition as it did many previous ones: E G Parish, Margaret Ross and Stephen Buckley.

Warm thanks to John Holliday of Trade Wind Technology, who built and looks after our database; and above all to the thousands of devoted publicans, who give us all so much pleasure.

Alisdair Aird and Fiona Stapley

The Good Pub Guide's just got even better!

TWO NIGHTS FOR THE PRICE OF ONE
AT PARTICIPATING PUBS ACROSS THE UK

What could be better than a couple of nights at one of *The Good Pub Guide*'s recommended pubs? Two nights for the price of one! Listed below, you'll find selected pubs from all over the country which are participating in *The Good Pub Guide*'s promotion, together with the page on which their listing can be found. You can also look out for the ♙ symbol throughout the Guide, which indicates those pubs included in the promotion. All you have to do is quote 'The Good Pub Guide two-nights-for-the-price-of-one offer' when you contact them to make your booking. So, what are you waiting for? Choose a fantastic pub, pack your overnight bag and prepare for a great time!

Terms & Conditions:
1 The offer is available from October 2005 to October 2006 inclusive and is subject to availability.
2 The offer is based on two people sharing a double or twin-bedded room; it is also subject to the terms and conditions of the participating pub.
3 Each pub has its own individual terms & conditions for your stay – please check these with the pub when making your booking.
4 You may take advantage of the 'two-nights-for-the-price-of-one offer' at any of the pubs marked with the ♙ symbol, but you cannot use the offer at the same pub more than once throughout the promotional period.
5 You must quote 'The Good Pub Guide two-nights-for-the-price-of-one offer' when making your booking.
6 The pubs listed below, and marked with the ♙ symbol throughout *The Good Pub Guide* are the only pubs participating in this offer.

Please note, a featured pub's participation in this promotion has no bearing whatsoever on its inclusion or otherwise in *The Good Pub Guide*.

County	Pub	Town	Page
Berkshire	Bull	Stanford Dingley	45
	Crown & Garter	Inkpen	41
	Royal Oak	Ruscombe	44
Buckinghamshire	Nags Head	Great Missenden	70
	Three Horseshoes	Bennett End	54
Cambridgeshire	Anchor	Sutton Gault	87
Cornwall	Port Gaverne Inn	Port Isaac	122
	Royal Oak	Lostwithiel	117
Cumbria	Queens Head	Tirril	159
	Wheatsheaf	Beetham	145
Derbyshire	Plough	Hathersage	178

County	Pub	Town	Page
Devon	Durant Arms	Ashprington	197
	Rising Sun	Woodland	228
Gloucestershire	Bathurst Arms	North Cerney	307
	Plough	Ford	301
	Red Hart	Awre	292
Hampshire	Trooper	Petersfield	339
Herefordshire	Stagg	Titley	371
	Three Horseshoes	Little Cowarne	368
Kent	Beacon	Tunbridge Wells	412
Lancashire	Horns	Goosnargh	429
	White Hart	Lydgate	431
Lincolnshire	Lea Gate Inn	Coningsby	477
Norfolk	Rose & Crown	Snettisham	496
	Crown	Wells-Next-The-Sea	502
Northumbria	Allenheads Inn	Allenheads	527
	Morritt Arms	Greta Bridge	532
	Pheasant	Stannersburn	539
Oxfordshire	Duke of Cumberlands Head	Clifton	568
	Falkland Arms	Great Tew	571
	Merrymouth	Fifield	570
	Sun	Hook Norton	574
	Gate Hangs High	Hook Norton	574
	Trout	Tadpole Bridge	581
Shropshire	Malthouse	Ironbridge	601
Somerset	Carew Arms	Crowcombe	620
	Rose & Crown	Stoke St Gregory	630
	Royal Oak	Luxborough	625
Suffolk	Angel	Lavenham	666
	Crown	Snape	669
Surrey	Running Horses	Mickleham	690
Warwickshire	Golden Lion	Easenhall	746
Wiltshire	Angel	Heytesbury	774
	Lamb	Hindon	774
	Neeld Arms	Grittleton	773
	Spread Eagle	Stourton	783
Worcestershire	Walter de Cantelupe	Kempsey	804
Yorkshire	Black Bull	Boroughbridge	818
	Shibden Mill	Halifax	828
	White Swan	Pickering	843
Scotland	Wheatsheaf	Swinton	947
Wales	Druid	Llanferres	975
Channel Islands	Old Court House Inn	St Aubin	1006

ENGLAND

Bedfordshire

In Bedfordshire's pubs the choice of food tends to be pretty uniform – the general rule is standard repertoire rather than anything special. Pubs where honest straightforward food is given particular care, adding real value, include the Three Tuns in Biddenham, the cosy and wonderfully unspoilt Cock at Broom, the Rose & Crown at Ridgmont (brought back into the *Guide* by new licensees, after a long absence), the cheerful Fox & Hounds in Riseley with its excellent steaks and frequently changing menu, and the reliably friendly Chequers at Keysoe (a particular favourite with readers for a meal out). A few other pubs here put special effort into lifting their food right out of the ordinary. The Red Lion in Milton Bryan (another pub making a welcome return to the Guide after a break, with a lovely garden and a fine range of drinks) now puts strong emphasis on local and seasonal ingredients, to very good effect. So does the attractive and rather elegant Hare & Hounds at Old Warden, and its scotch beef is well worth knowing about; its choice of wines by the glass is excellent. It is the Hare & Hounds which takes the top county award of Bedfordshire Dining Pub of the Year. On the drinks front, besides pubs mentioned above, an outstanding find for us this year has been yet another new entry, the Engineers Arms in Henlow. Its quickly changing range of beautifully kept real ales is both extensive and full of rarities, and this neatly kept and comfortable pub has some bargain snacks, too. In the Lucky Dip section at the end of the chapter, the Black Horse at Ireland is particularly well worth noting; after inspection we were minded to make this dining pub a main entry, and very likely would have done if the fact-checking questionnaires we sent the pub had been returned. Another hot tip here is the Olde Plough at Bolnhurst; and we'd also pick out the French Horn at Steppingley. Drinks prices are around the national average here, with those pubs taking the trouble to get beers from small breweries some way off tending to show the smallest price increase over the last year. The county's major brewer is Charles Wells, with Potton, Old Stables and B&T local microbreweries to look out for.

BIDDENHAM TL0249 Map 5
Three Tuns
Village signposted from A428 just W of Bedford

Since the last edition of this *Guide*, this pleasantly straightforward thatched village pub has had its public bar redone in oak panelling, but it continues to serve good value enjoyable bar food. It can draw a crowd (particularly at lunchtime) so it's worth booking. The low-beamed lounge is fairly straightforward with wheelback chairs round dark wood tables, window seats and pews on a red turkey carpet, and country paintings. The green-carpeted public bar (readers have found it a bit smoky in here, but the dining area and lounge bar are no smoking) has photographs of local sports teams, darts, table skittles, cribbage and dominoes; piped music. Standard but tasty food is served in generous helpings and includes dishes such as soup (£3), sandwiches (from £3; soup and sandwich £5.50), ploughman's (£4.50), home-made dishes such as quiche of the day (£7), steak and kidney pie, steak braised in tarragon and red wine, poached salmon, and meat or vegetable lasagne (£7.50), daily specials, and puddings (£3.50). On handpump, Greene King Abbot is kept under a light blanket pressure alongside a guest such as Wadworths 6X. There are seats in the attractively sheltered spacious garden, and a big decked terrace has lots of picnic-sets. The very good children's play area has swings for all ages, and a new climbing frame; more reports please. *(Recommended by Bob and Maggie Atherton, Michael Dandy, Richard Greaves)*

Greene King ~ Tenant Kevin Bolwell ~ Real ale ~ Bar food (11.30(12 Sun)-2, 6-9; not Sun evening) ~ Restaurant ~ (01234) 354847 ~ Children in eating area of bar and restaurant ~ Dogs welcome ~ Open 11.30-2.30, 6-11; 12-3, 7-10.30 Sun

BROOM TL1743 Map 5

Cock ★ £

High Street; from A1 opposite northernmost Biggleswade turn-off follow Old Warden 3, Aerodrome 2 signpost, and take first left signposted Broom

You get the feeling that little has changed over three centuries at this simple, four-room pub by the village green. Original latch doors lead from one little room to another, where you'll find warming winter open fires, low ochre ceilings, stripped panelling, and farmhouse tables and chairs on antique tiles. There's no bar counter, and the very well kept Greene King IPA, Abbot and Ruddles County are tapped straight from casks by the cellar steps off a central corridor. Straightforward bar food includes sandwiches (from £3.25), soup (£3.75), ploughman's (from £5.75), scampi or vegetarian curry (£5.95), breaded plaice (£7.95), chicken balti or filled yorkshire pudding (£7.25). The restaurant is no smoking; piped (perhaps classical) music, darts, table skittles, cribbage and dominoes. There are picnic-sets and flower tubs on the terrace by the back lawn; caravanning and camping facilities are available. *(Recommended by the Didler, Pete Baker, Peter and Jean Hoare, Mark and Ruth Brock, Geoff and Carol Thorp)*

Greene King ~ Tenants Gerry and Jean Lant ~ Real ale ~ Bar food (12-2.30, 7-9; not Sun evening) ~ Restaurant ~ (01767) 314411 ~ Children in restaurant and family room ~ Dogs allowed in bar ~ Open 12-3(4 Sat), 6-11; 12-4, 7-10.30 Sun

HENLOW TL1738 Map 5

Engineers Arms ◖ £

A6001 S of Biggleswade; High Street

The special thing here is the fabulous collection of quickly changing esoteric real ales from small breweries, in a splendid range of styles, strengths and regions, and all in top condition. On our visit Bartrams, Fenland, Leadmill, Northumberland, Old Stables, Rhymney, Rugby and Salamander were all represented on their great bank of handpumps, along with their regular house beer, Everards Tiger. If you'd expect an unreconstructed beer-gut alehouse from this, you'd be disappointed. It's full of charm, with everything spick and span (and a most stylish ladies'). The comfortable green-carpeted front room has lots of old local photographs on its green fleur-de-lys wallpaper, tidy and interesting bric-a-brac collections, traditional green-cushioned wall seats, settles and other dark seats, armchair-style bar stools, daily papers and a good log fire. A small tiled inner area has wide-screen sports TV, and beyond is a step up to another comfortable carpeted area, with a second TV, cribbage and dominoes, juke box, silenced fruit machine and games such as table football. They do sausage rolls (£1), pork pies (£1.50), hot pies (£1.60) and panini (£2.40), and also have farm cider and perry, many belgian and german bottled beers, decent wines by the glass, a good value wine of the month by the bottle, good coffee, and those splendid Tyrrells crisps. Service is hospitable and helpful; the good-natured spaniel is called Chico. They run quarterly bank holiday beer festivals, and a bigger one in mid-October. The back terrace has picnic-sets and heaters. *(Recommended by Conor McGaughey, Kevin Thorpe, Bruce Bird)*

Free house ~ Licensees Kevin Machin and Claire Sturgeon ~ Real ale ~ Bar food (during opening hours) ~ No credit cards ~ (01462) 812284 ~ Children welcome away from the bar ~ Dogs welcome ~ Live blues Fri, stand-up comic or live music Sat ~ Open 12-11(10.30 Sun)

HOUGHTON CONQUEST TL0441 Map 5

Knife & Cleaver

Between B530 (old A418) and A6, S of Bedford

In an attractive 17th-c building opposite an interesting church, this has a comfortably civilised bar with dark panelling which is reputed to have come from nearby ruined Houghton House, as well as maps, drawings and old documents on the walls, and a blazing fire in winter. The airy white-walled no smoking conservatory restaurant has rugs on the tiled floor and lots of hanging plants. There's also a family room and tables on the terrace alongside a neatly kept appealing garden. You may well have to book, and on Saturday evenings and Sunday lunchtimes if the restaurant is full they may not serve bar meals, which include soup of the day such as carrot and ginger (£3.75), ploughman's (£4.50), filled breads such as crab hummous in toasted pitta bread (£6.25), a dish of the day such as scottish smoked salmon and gravadlax with scrambled eggs (£7.95), and puddings such as apple brioche and butter pudding with calvados custard or home-made ice-cream (£4). Well kept Batemans XB and Fullers London Pride on handpump, Stowford Press farm cider, around 30 good wines by the glass, and over 20 well aged malt whiskies; unobtrusive piped music. Although the general flavour of readers' reports of this pub, which has long been a favourite for special meals out, continues to be favourable, we have noted an undercurrent of occasional disappointments. Given the prices, one or two meals have been not as special as they should be. And one or two people would have liked a warmer welcome. More reports please. *(Recommended by David and Ruth Shillitoe, Blaise Vyner, Ryta Lyndley, Bob and Maggie Atherton, Michael Dandy, Andrew Kell, Iain R Hewitt, Karen Eliot)*

Free house ~ Licensees David and Pauline Loom ~ Real ale ~ Bar food (12-2.30(2 Sat), 7-9.30; not Sun evenings but see text about weekends) ~ Restaurant ~ (01234) 740387 ~ Children in restaurant and family room ~ Dogs allowed in bedrooms ~ Open 12-2.30 (2 Sat, 2.30 Sun), 7-11; closed Sun evening, 27-30 Dec ~ Bedrooms: £53B/£68B

KEYSOE TL0762 Map 5

Chequers

Pertenhall Road, Brook End (B660)

Owned by the same publicans for more than a quarter of a century, this dependable village local continues to generate praise from readers for its friendliness and tasty food. It is usually fairly quiet at lunchtime (unless a group is in). From outside it really stands out with its recent repainting in sunny yellow and cherry brown, but inside feels less changed, with two neat and simple beamed rooms divided by an unusual stone-pillared fireplace. Comfortable seats in one room and piped local radio or music lend a homely 1960s air. Good value bar food includes sandwiches, plain or toasted (£2.75), home-made soup (£3), garlic mushrooms on toast (£3.95), ploughman's (£4), chilli (£6.50), home-made steak and ale pie (£6.50), chicken breast stuffed with stilton in chive sauce (£8.50), steaks (from £10) and blackboard specials such as leek and blue cheese tart (£6.50). The handpumps on the stone bar counter serve well kept Fullers London Pride and Hook Norton Best, and they have some malt whiskies, wines starting at £8 a bottle, and mulled wine in winter; darts, shove-ha'penny and dominoes. Tables and chairs on the back terrace look over the garden, which has a play tree and swings. *(Recommended by Michael and Jenny Back, Gordon Tong, Margaret and Roy Randle)*

Free house ~ Licensee Jeffrey Kearns ~ Real ale ~ Bar food (12-2, 7-9.30 (Sun 9); closed Tues) ~ No credit cards ~ (01234) 708678 ~ Children in eating area of bar and family room ~ Open 12-2.30, 6.30-11; 12-2.30, 7-10.30 Sun; closed Tues and two weeks in summer

MILTON BRYAN SP9730 Map 4

Red Lion 🍴

Toddington Road, off B528 S of Woburn

More than seventy hanging baskets of flowers make a spectacular show as you arrive here. The pub has repeatedly won Greene King's pub garden competition, thanks largely to the green fingers of Marilyn, the landlord's partner. The beamed bar area has cream-coloured walls, some exposed brickwork, polished wood and part flagstoned floors, and fresh flowers on the round wooden tables. Using many seasonal ingredients, such as asparagus and fresh fish from Devon, and local meat and vegetables, the food is nearly all home-made, with basic lunchtime bar food and more elaborate lunch and dinner served in the bar or restaurant. Lunchtime food includes soup (£3.95), sandwiches (from £3.95), ploughman's or caramelised onion and cherry tomato tartlet with melted taleggio cheese or thai fishcakes with asian coleslaw and sweet chilli dip (£4.95), steak and kidney pudding (£10.50) and slow cooked blade of beef; some dinner items are also available on the lunch menu, such as fillet of natural smoked haddock in butter sauce with poached egg on a bed of savoy cabbage or rib-eye steak (£12.50). Greene King IPA, Abbot and Old Speckled Hen and a monthly changing guest such as St Austell Tribute are kept under a light blanket pressure on handpump; local apple juice from Watergull Orchards is sold by the glass. There are plenty of tables, chairs and picnic-sets out on the terrace and lawn, which looks across to a delightful row of thatched black and white timbered cottages, and Woburn Abbey and Safari Park are a short drive away. *(Recommended by Mr and Mrs R A Buckler, Michael Dandy, Brian Staton, B R and M F Arnold)*

Greene King ~ Tenant Paul Ockleford ~ Real ale ~ Bar food (12-2.30, 7-9.30) ~ Restaurant ~ (01525) 210044 ~ Children in eating area of bar and restaurant ~ Open 11-3(4 Sat), 6.30-11; 12-4 Sun; closed Mon evening in winter

NORTHILL TL1446 Map 5

Crown

Ickwell Road; village signposted from B658 W of Biggleswade

As we went to press, new licensees were about to take over the running of this black and white pub. It stands just across from the church in a green and peaceful village, with picnic-sets under cocktail parasols out in front looking over the village pond. The smallish bar has a big open fire, flagstones and low heavy beams, comfortable bow window seats, and well kept Greene King IPA and Abbot, and Batemans XXB on handpump from the copper-topped counter. On the left is a small smoking dining area while on the right, the airy main dining room has elegantly laid tables on bare boards, with steps up to a smaller more intimate side room. Throughout, the atmosphere is warm and relaxed; fairly unobtrusive piped music. Bar food includes lunchtime sandwiches and baguettes (from £3.95), daily roast or sausage and mash (£7.95), with daily specials such as grilled tuna and niçoise salad (£9.95) or duck breast and orange segment salad (£10.95); daily puddings (£4.50) are good; no smoking restaurant. Outside, a sheltered side terrace has more picnic-sets, and opens into a very large garden with a few widely spaced canopied tables, plenty of trees and shrubs, a good play area, and masses of room for children to run around. More reports on the new regime please. *(Recommended by Pete Baker, K Stringer, Michael Dandy, Jeff Rix, John Cadge)*

Greene King ~ Real ale ~ Bar food (12-2.30, 6.30-9.30; not Sun evening) ~ Restaurant ~ (01767) 627337 ~ Children in eating area of bar and restaurant ~ Dogs allowed in bar ~ Open 11.30-3, 6-11; 12-4 (maybe later in summer) Sun

---

Looking for a pub with a really special garden, or in lovely countryside, or with an outstanding view, or right by the water? They are listed separately, at the back of the book.

OLD WARDEN TL1343 Map 5
Hare & Hounds 🍴 ♀
Village signposted off A600 S of Bedford and B658 W of Biggleswade

Bedfordshire Dining Pub of the Year

Although the accent is firmly on dining here, this pub also makes a welcoming spot for a drink. The village itself is part of the Shuttleworth estate and was built about 200 years ago in a swiss style. The glorious sloping garden, which stretches up to pine woods behind the pub, dates back to the same period and style (more tables at the side on a small terrace, and a couple in front), and there are some substantial walks nearby. Breads and ice-cream are home-made, and where possible they use local ingredients such as pork from the Shuttleworth estate. The changing bar menu might include bruschetta (£6.95), haddock with chips and peas, pie of the day or pork sausage and red wine casserole (£8.95), and you can eat from the pricier restaurant menu in the bar: chicken liver pâté (£5.95), lamb shank with grilled mediterranean vegetables and roast garlic polenta (£11.95), and bass with garlic and rosemary (£13.95); as founder members of the Scotch Beef Club the publicans pride themselves on their scotch sirloin steak with pepper butter (£14.95); puddings include lemon tart, vanilla crème brûlée and cheese platter (£4.95). Wells Eagle and Bombardier and a guest from a brewery such as Adnams are well kept on handpump, and ten or so wines by the glass include some from the local Southill estate. Rambling around a central servery, and painted warmly cosy red and cream, the four beamed rooms have dark standing timbers, comfortable upholstered armchairs and sofas on stripped flooring, light wood tables and coffee tables, a woodburning stove in an inglenook fireplace and fresh flowers on the bar. Prints and photographs depict the historic aircraft in the Shuttleworth Collection just up the road. Service from well turned out staff is attentive and friendly, and two rooms are no smoking; piped music. Though there's an ample car park, they sometimes need to commandeer the grounds of the village hall as an overflow. *(Recommended by Michael Dandy, Sarah Markham, John Saul, Dr G and Mrs J Kelvin, Bill Newton, Emma Watts, Alex and Irene Harvey, Bob and Maggie Atherton, B and M Kendall)*

Charles Wells ~ Lease Jane Hasler ~ Real ale ~ Bar food (12-2(3 Sun), 6.30-9.30; not Sun evening) ~ Restaurant ~ (01767) 627225 ~ Children in family room ~ Dogs allowed in bar ~ Open 12-3, 6-11; 12-10.30 Sun; closed Mon except bank hols

RIDGMONT SP9736 Map 4
Rose & Crown
2 miles from M1 junction 13: A507, follow Ampthill signs – High Street

Once part of the Duke of Bedford's estate, this attractive 17th-c brick house underwent a major refurbishment when the new licensee took over in 2004. Its neat lounge is pleasantly arranged with a sofa and other comfortable chairs, pictures of hunting scenes and an open fire in its sizeable brick fireplace. If you just want a drink, there's plenty of standing room in the low-ceilinged traditional public bar (with fruit machine and dominoes), hung with pictures and antique mirrors, while the no smoking dining area takes waterfowl for its pictorial theme. Besides well kept Adnams, Charles Wells Eagle and Bombardier on handpump, they usually have two guests such as Mauldons Suffolk Pride and Courage Directors, as well as six wines by the glass and half a dozen malt whiskies; piped music (provided separately to each area of the pub; can be turned off if requested). Reasonably priced bar food (last orders 7.30; sometimes later by request) includes soup (£3.25), sandwiches (£3.95), sausage and mash (£4.95), curries (£6.95) and pies (from £7.95); puddings (£3.95) include apple crumble and lemon meringue pie. In summer the long and attractive suntrap tree-lined garden behind, full of flowers and shrubs, is a big plus; there are also some picnic-sets out in front, below the pretty hanging baskets. There's easy parking and good wheelchair access, and it's handy for Woburn Abbey. The pub grounds offer plenty of room for reasonably priced camping and caravanning. More reports on the changes please. *(Recommended by Michael and Alison Sandy, Michael Dandy)*

Charles Wells ~ Tenant Jane Brazier ~ Real ale ~ Bar food (12-2.30, 6-7.30 (except Sun))
~ Restaurant ~ (01525) 280245 ~ Children in eating area of bar and restaurant ~ Dogs
allowed in bar ~ Live acoustic music first Fri evening of month ~ Open 12-11(Sun 10.30);
12-4, 6-11, Sat 12-11, Sun 12-10.30 winter

RISELEY TL0362 Map 5
Fox & Hounds
High Street; village signposted off A6 and B660 N of Bedford

For some 16 years the same landlord and his wife have stamped their own
character on this bustling, cheerful pub. They pride themselves on steak: you choose
your own piece and pay by weight – say, £11.60 for 8oz rump, £12.60 for 8oz of
sirloin and £14.20 for 8oz of fillet – and watch it cooked on an open grill. Other
dishes are listed on blackboards and might include parsnip and ginger soup (£3.75),
whitebait (£4.95), ploughman's (£6.95), beef curry (£8.95), steak and stilton pie
(£9.50), salmon in champagne sauce or chicken with pesto (£9.75), beef stroganoff
(£11.25) and desserts such as jam roly-poly or spotted dick and custard (£3.75).
Even if you don't see anything you fancy, it's worth asking: they're very obliging
here, and will try to cope with particular food requests. Service is normally very
attentive, but it does get busy, and as they don't take bookings on Saturday night
you may have to wait for your table and food. A relaxing lounge area, with
comfortable leather chesterfields, lower tables and wing chairs, contrasts with the
more traditional pub furniture spread among timber uprights under the heavy low
beams; unobtrusive piped classical or big band piped music. Charles Wells Eagle
and Bombardier with perhaps a changing guest such as Shepherd Neame Spitfire
are kept well on handpump, alongside a decent collection of other drinks including
bin-end wines and a range of malts and cognacs. An attractively decked terrace
with wooden tables and chairs has outside heating, and the pleasant garden has
shrubs and a pergola. *(Recommended by J WAC, Sarah Flynn, Michael Sargent, Margaret and
Roy Randle, A J Bowen, Michael Dandy)*

Charles Wells ~ Managers Jan and Lynne Zielinski ~ Real ale ~ Bar food (12-1.45, 6.30-9.30
(10 Fri; 12-2, 7-9 Sun)) ~ Restaurant ~ (01234) 708240 ~ Children welcome ~ Dogs
allowed in bar ~ Open 11.30-2.30, 6.30-11; 12-3, 7-10.30 Sun

STANBRIDGE SP9623 Map 4
Five Bells
Station Road, at junction with A505 – and pub signposted off A5 N of Dunstable

Five real bells form the pub sign, and the cream frontage with its striking grey
woodwork is an attractive backdrop to more tables nestling under a big tree.
Although it's a perfectly traditional pub building from outside, its interior has been
comprehensively updated with a stylish, contemporary look. Very low exposed
beams are complemented by careful spotlighting, and rugs on wooden floors,
armchairs and sofas, and neatly polished tables contribute to the atmosphere. Newly
refurbished, the airy, elegant no smoking restaurant leads into a large garden with
plenty of good wooden tables and chairs, and big perfectly mown lawns with fruit
trees. Bar food includes soup (£3.95), smoked pepper mackerel (£4.95), sandwiches
(£5.95), grilled chicken supreme or grilled tuna steak (£8.95) and items from the
restaurant which you can eat at the bar, such as king scallops (£8.95), fillet of
haddock (£9.95) and asparagus and spinach risotto (£8.95); puddings (£4.95)
include lemon cheesecake, crème brûlée and rich chocolate mousse with fresh
raspberries. Well kept Fullers London Pride and Timothy Taylor Landlord, and a
monthly changing guest such as Hook Norton or Charles Wells on handpump; half
a dozen malt whiskies and seven wines by the glass; one reader found the piped
music obtrusive. More reports on the new regime please. *(Recommended by Gerry and
Rosemary Dobson, Mel Smith, M and GR, Annabel Viney, Michael Dandy)*

Free house ~ Licensee Patrice Pollet ~ Real ale ~ Bar food (12-2.30, 6-9(9.30 Fri and Sat);
12-8 summer, 12-6 winter(Sun)) ~ Restaurant ~ (01525) 210224 ~ Children in eating area
of bar and restaurant ~ Dogs allowed in bar ~ Open 12-11(10.30 Sun)

LUCKY DIP

Besides the fully inspected pubs, you might like to try these Lucky Dips recommended to us and described by readers (if you do, please send us reports: www.goodguides.co.uk).

AMPTHILL [TL0338]
Queens Head [Woburn St]: Friendly little old-fashioned local with cosy lounge, rather bigger bar, good simple cheap home-made food, well kept Charles Wells Bombardier, homely furnishings, welcoming licensees and dog; quiz night, may be folk music and other evening events *(Conor McGaughey)*

BIGGLESWADE [TL1844]
Brown Bear [Hitchin St; from A6001 follow sign for Hitchin Street shops]: Local worth knowing for its wide range of real ales *(LYM, Pete Baker)*

BLETSOE [TL0157]
Falcon [Rushden Rd (A6)]: Welcoming ex-coaching inn dating from 17th c, Charles Wells Eagle and Bombardier, several wines by the glass, good coffees, enjoyable food from good lunchtime sandwiches and ploughman's to steaks, wider evening choice, pleasant service, buoyant atmosphere in carpeted L-shaped main bar with banquettes, open fires each end, copper jugs and so forth, small snug with leather settee and armchairs, quiet dining room; big riverside garden *(Sarah Flynn, Michael Dandy)*

BOLNHURST [TL0858]
☆ *Olde Plough* [Kimbolton Rd]: Charming squint-walled medieval cottage in lovely tree-shaded garden with long crazy-paved terrace overlooking former moat, closed for years and just reopened after major reworking into restaurant and bar by new owners – former chef patrons of the Old Bridge in Huntingdon and previously Pheasant at Keyston; the reopening came too late for us to check out the changes here, but the Lees' track record is so good, and the building so attractive, that this should be very well worth knowing *(LYM)*

CLOPHILL [TL0838]
Stone Jug [N on A6 from A507 roundabout, after 200 yds 2nd turn on right into Back St]: Secluded stone-built local, cosy and welcoming, with good value lunchtime food and well kept B&T Bitter, Courage Directors and a couple of guest beers, pleasantly unpretentious front bar, comfortable side lounge and family area; couple of tables among flowers on small back terrace, roadside picnic-sets *(Geoff and Carol Thorp)*

COLMWORTH [TL1057]
☆ *Cornfields* [Wilden Rd]: Early 17th-c, restaurant rather than pub, interesting stylish if not cheap food, friendly service, good house wines, big log fire and low armchairs in small low-beamed bar; front picnic-sets, small garden, comfortable bedroom extension *(Michael Sargent)*

GREAT BARFORD [TL1351]
Anchor [High St; off A421]: Usual food from sandwiches and baked potatoes up, wider evening choice, Charles Wells and changing guest beers such as Adnams and St Austell, good wine choice, quick friendly service, open-plan bar with small no smoking area down steps and back restaurant; piped music; roadside picnic-sets overlooking River Ouse by medieval bridge and church, bedrooms *(Michael Dandy, Ryta Lyndley)*

HUSBORNE CRAWLEY [SP9635]
White Horse [Mill Rd, just off A507]: Open-plan, part for eating, part with pool and games, Flowers and Tetleys, reasonable wine choice, usual bar food from baguettes and baked potatoes to scampi, lancashire hotpot and so forth; a few seats outside, lovely hanging baskets, open all day wknds *(Michael Dandy)*

IRELAND [TL1341]
☆ *Black Horse* [off A600 Shefford—Bedford]: Busy and attractive dining pub consistently reliable for wide choice of plentiful piping hot food from good value ciabattas to interesting restauranty dishes, good fresh ingredients, up-to-date presentation, wider evening menu, comfortable seats and plenty of space including stylish garden-view extension, well kept ales such as Fullers London Pride and Greene King IPA and Old Speckled Hen, good range of wines and good coffee, attentive service from helpful friendly staff; plenty of tables in neat front garden with play area, cottage bedrooms – nice peaceful rural setting *(Eithne Dandy, BB, John Branston, Gwyn Jones, Brian Root, Bob and Maggie Atherton, John Saul)*

KEMPSTON [TL0347]
Slaters Arms [Box End Rd (A5134, off A4218 W of Bedford)]: Low-beamed bar with separate eating area, wide food choice from sandwiches, baguettes and baked potatoes up, separate evening menu, Greene King ales and good choice of wines by the glass; piped music, pub games; big garden with play area *(Michael Dandy)*

LANGFORD [TL1840]
Plough [Church St]: Enjoyable home-made food with enterprising touches and traditional puddings, reasonable prices, Greene King IPA, decent wines *(Emma Chippendale)*

MAULDEN [TL0538]
Dog & Badger [Clophill Rd]: Attractive thatched village pub, refurbished bare-boards bar, steps down to two carpeted areas and no smoking restaurant, Fullers London Pride and Greene King IPA, good choice of wines by the glass, wide range of good value food (all day Sun – best to book wknds) from sandwiches to steaks, quick welcoming service, dominoes Mon; piped music; tables in front garden *(Michael Dandy)*

White Hart [Ampthill Rd]: Thatch and low beams, large dining area split into more intimate sections inc no smoking, big fireplace dividing bar; wide food choice from baguettes, hot sandwiches and baked potatoes up, Adnams Broadside, Greene King IPA and

Fullers London Pride, good choice of wines by the glass, friendly service; tables outside front and back, open all day wknds *(Michael Dandy)*

MILLBROOK [TL0138]
Chequers: Two-room village pub opp golf club, log fire and plate collection in small low-beamed carpeted bar, Flowers IPA and Stonehenge Great Bustard, good coffee, reasonably priced food, quick cheerful service, back restaurant; cl Sun/Mon *(Michael Dandy)*

ODELL [SP9657]
Bell [off A6 S of Rushden; via Sharnbrook; High St]: Several low-beamed rooms around central servery, well kept Greene King IPA and Abbot and perhaps a guest beer, mix of old settles and neat modern furniture, three log or coal fires (not always lit); usual food from sandwiches and baked potatoes up (not Sun evening); children welcome away from counter, delightful big garden backing on to River Ouse, handy for Harrold-Odell country park *(LYM, Michael Dandy, George Atkinson)*

PEGSDON [TL1130]
☆ *Live & Let Live* [B655 W of Hitchin]: Architecturally charming, much extended as posh high-end dining pub from snug traditional tiled and panelled core (you might not feel happy just having a drink here, despite the good wine choice and well kept Brakspears, Fullers London Pride and Marstons Pedigree), pleasant helpful waiting staff; piped music; attractive hanging baskets and garden below Deacon Hill, chalet bedrooms, open all day *(Michael Dandy, Phil and Heidi Cook, B and M Kendall, LYM)*

PULLOXHILL [TL0634]
Cross Keys [High St; off A6 N of Barton le Clay]: Friendly local, lots of timbering and flower baskets, rambling front bars, very welcoming long-serving landlord and family, good value usual food inc tasty pies and OAP bargain lunches, children in big back no smoking dining room, well kept Adnams Broadside and Charles Wells Bombardier and Eagle; popular jazz sessions; garden with play area (and field for caravans), pretty part of village in nice countryside *(Phil and Heidi Cook, Geoff and Carol Thorp, Michael Dandy, Gerry and Rosemary Dobson)*

RADWELL [TL0057]
☆ *Swan* [Felmersham Rd]: Charming beamed and partly thatched pub recently smartly refurbished for dining, two spacious eating rooms either side of small comfortable flagstoned bar, usual lunchtime pub food from sandwiches and baked potatoes up, wider evening menu inc good interesting cooking, friendly service, well kept Charles Wells Eagle, decent wines by the glass and coffee, interesting photographs; garden with tables and play area, attractive quiet village *(Michael Dandy, John Saville)*

SHARPENHOE [TL0630]
☆ *Lynmore*: Low partly open beams and end woodburner in traditional pub's long rambling warmly refurbished family lounge, good value food from sandwiches, hot hobs and baked

potatoes up, views of The Clappers from big back no smoking dining area, well kept Fullers London Pride, Greene King IPA and Potton Clappers, friendly landlady and good service, darts and other games in public bar; good garden for children, popular with walkers *(Phil and Heidi Cook, David Gough, Michael Dandy)*

SHILLINGTON [TL1234]
Crown [High Rd, S end]: Well run nicely decorated pub, small flagstoned bar with carpeted lounge area, Greene King IPA and Youngs, good value generous straightforward food from baguettes and baked potatoes up, quick helpful service, no smoking restaurant; pleasant garden with heaters *(Michael Dandy)*
Musgrave Arms [Apsley End Rd, towards Pegsdon and Hexton]: Well kept Greene King IPA, Abbot and Old Speckled Hen tapped from cooled casks in low-beamed village local with settles, tables, prints and horsebrasses in friendly and civilised lounge, woodburner in comfortable public bar, small no smoking dining room, wide choice of generous home-made usual food from sandwiches and baguettes up, cheerful service; big back garden with picnic-sets *(Michael Dandy, Geoff and Carol Thorp)*

SILSOE [TL0835]
Star & Garter [High St]: Smart pub by village church, large bar and raised no smoking dining area, enjoyable usual bar food from sandwiches and baguettes up, separate evening menu, quick service, well kept ales such as Adnams, Banks's, Greene King IPA and Timothy Taylors, darts; piped music; nice good-sized terrace *(Phil and Heidi Cook, Dudley and Moira Cockroft, Michael Dandy)*

SOUTHILL [TL1542]
White Horse [off B658 SW of Biggleswade]: Friendly and comfortable country pub with extensive eating area, wide range of enjoyable food inc lunchtime favourites, well kept Greene King IPA, Shepherd Neame Spitfire and Youngs, reasonable wine choice; piped music; lots of tables in large pleasant neatly kept garden with good play area *(LYM, Michael Dandy, Jane Ratcliff)*

STANFORD [TL1541]
Green Man [Southill rd]: L-shaped bar with big fireplace, adjoining games area with pool, bar food from generous sandwiches, hot baguettes and baked potatoes up, OAP lunchtime bargains, friendly service, Courage Best and Theakstons Best, smart new separate restaurant with beams and stripped brick; terrace with barbecue, big garden with lots of play equipment, 11 bedrooms in new chalet block *(Michael Dandy)*

STEPPINGLEY [TL0135]
☆ *French Horn* [Church End]: Good up-to-date food with plenty of choice from ciabattas up, Greene King IPA and Abbot, full range of wines by the glass, good friendly service, old beams but minimalist new décor – bare boards or paving stones, brown leather tub chairs, dining chairs with brown tables, perhaps a single flower on each, no pictures; tables

outside front and back *(Michael Dandy, Ian Phillips)*

STREATLEY [TL0728]

Chequers [just off A6 N of Luton; Sharpenhoe Rd]: Popular partly panelled open-plan L-shaped local, mix of chairs and table sizes, old-fashioned prints, books and old local photographs, good value food, four Greene King real ales, cheerful staff, open fire in public bar; piped music, games, TV, Tues quiz night; nice front terrace, small back garden *(Phil and Heidi Cook, Michael Dandy)*

TEMPSFORD [TL1652]

Wheatsheaf [Church St]: 18th-c village pub with open fire in cosy lounge, Special Operations Executive memorabilia (nearby World War II base), friendly service, home-made usual pub food from sandwiches and baked potatoes up, Potton Shambles and Charles Wells Eagle, reasonably priced restaurant; garden tables *(John Lammie, Michael Dandy)*

THURLEIGH [TL0558]

Jackal [High St]: Unassuming village pub, friendly and welcoming, with roaring winter fires in tiled-floor bar (where dogs allowed) and comfortable lounge/dining room, enjoyable food with plenty of choice from rolls and ploughman's up, well priced three-course meals, good service, well kept Charles Wells Eagle and Bombardier, interesting wines; piped music; roadside seats out in front, more in nice rambling back garden *(Mark Kiteley, Michael Dandy)*

TILSWORTH [SP9824]

Anchor [just off A5 NW of Dunstable]: Bright and airy, good value quickly served food from sandwiches and baked potatoes to Sun lunch, friendly staff, well kept Fullers, daily papers, dining conservatory; pool and TV in games end; side lawn with picnic-sets on paving stones, more paddocky part with play area *(Michael Dandy)*

TODDINGTON [TL0128]

Angel [Luton Rd]: Tucked away by green, part 16th-c but largely Victorian and recently refurbished in contemporary style, sofas, comfortable seats and log fire in one area, good-sized no smoking eating area, Greene King IPA, Abbot and a seasonal beer, good choice of wines by the glass, wide range of food, daily papers, pub games; tables in garden with terrace and heaters, overlooking village pond *(Michael Dandy)*

TURVEY [SP9452]

Three Cranes [off A428 W of Bedford]: Roomy two-level dining pub under newish management, wide range of quickly served food all day from bar snacks up, well kept Greene King ales with one or two guest beers and good choice of other drinks, daily papers, log fire; may be piped pop music; children in no smoking restaurant area, tables in secluded tree-shaded garden with climber, bedrooms *(Steve Godfrey, George Atkinson, Michael Dandy, LYM, Stephen Buckley)*

WESTONING [SP0332]

Chequers [Park Rd (A5120 N of M1 junction 12)]: Attractive multi-gabled thatched pub with black bargeboards, Adnams, Greene King IPA, Shepherd Neame Spitfire and Youngs, enjoyable food from sandwiches and salads up, set lunch deals, quick attentive service, settees and new tables and chairs in good-sized refurbished back bar, piped music and sports TV in locals' small low-beamed front bar; courtyard tables *(Phil and Heidi Cook, Michael Dandy)*

WOBURN [SP9433]

Bell [Bedford St]: Small bar area, longer bare-boards dining lounge up steps, good value generous food from baguettes and ploughman's to steaks, nice cheese board, well kept Greene King IPA and Abbot, good choice of wines by the glass, good coffee, efficient friendly service, pleasant décor and furnishings inc fireplace fish tank; children welcome at lunchtime; tables on back terrace, hotel part across road, handy for Woburn Park *(Michael Dandy, Ian Phillips)*

Birch [Newport Rd]: Well run country dining pub with small front bar, large eating area opening into conservatory, enjoyable up-to-date food from ciabattas up, well kept Adnams and Fullers London Pride, good choice of wines by the glass, friendly helpful staff *(Michael Dandy)*

☆ *Black Horse* [Bedford St]: Friendly and roomy 19th-c food pub, wide choice from sandwiches and baked potatoes to steaks and fish cut to order and grilled in the bar, well kept Greene King ales, good choice of wines by the glass, coal fire, several areas with steps down to pleasant back restaurant; children in eating areas, summer barbecues in attractive sheltered courtyard, open all day *(John and Joyce Snell, LYM, Michael Dandy)*

Berkshire

Five new entries here this year include two that were both in the *Guide* some years ago, but are very different now. On the surface the Hinds Head in Bray is physically much as we remember it from before, with handsome old fittings and furnishings. Given its new owner, now world-famous for his trend-setting modern cooking at the top-rated Fat Duck restaurant, we'd expected very good food, and that's what we found – the surprise was that the food at the Hinds Head turned out to be so traditional, really returning to the golden age of English innkeeping. By contrast, another pub to return to our fold this year, the Little Angel in Remenham, was quite unrecognisable inside. It's been thoroughly reworked in the best easy-going relaxing contemporary style – a very nice place indeed, with good food and drink. The final three newcomers, the Swan in East Ilsley, the Green Man in Hurst and the Beehive in White Waltham, are best described as classic traditional country pubs which have kept up well with today's tastes, good all-rounders. Among our other main entries, two which stand out for particularly good food are the very well run waterside Dundas Arms at Kintbury and the stylish and restauranty Red House at Marsh Benham. Both are rewarding for special meals out; for the second year running, the Dundas Arms takes the title of Berkshire Dining Pub of the Year. Other pubs here on fine form this year span a wide range of styles from quaintly unspoilt to smart and foody: that unchanging favourite the 14th-c Bell up at Aldworth (a very special place), the Sun in the Wood at Ashmore Green (hard-working licensees always striving to do better, well liked food and a new Wine Award this year), the Pot Kiln at Frilsham (still serving its fine own-brewed beers at an alluring price, and new licensees attractively upgrading both the pub itself and its food), the charming Magpie & Parrot, an unusual pub-cum-nursery on the edge of Shinfield, and the smart and comfortable Royal Oak at Yattendon (good wines, imaginative food, and an attentive new landlord). In the Lucky Dip section at the end of the chapter, current front-runners are the Flower Pot at Aston, Crown at Burchetts Green, Bel & the Dragon in Cookham, Crown & Horns and Star, both at East Ilsley, Bird in Hand at Knowl Hill, Hare & Hounds near Lambourn, Royal Oak at Paley Street, Pheasant at Shefford Woodlands, Bull in Sonning, Bell at Waltham St Lawrence and Five Bells at Wickham. Although this is generally one of the most expensive areas for drinks, there are big variations from pub to pub, with the Bell at Aldworth and Hobgoblin in Reading (a good place for beer) both much cheaper than the county norm. And you can often save significantly by looking out for beer from the local West Berkshire brewery. We found it was the cheapest beer on offer in quite a few of the pubs we surveyed – good value, as it's also one of the best.

ALDWORTH SU5579 Map 2
Bell ★ ♀ 🍺 £
A329 Reading—Wallingford; left on to B4009 at Streatley

Quite a few things make this 14th-c country pub so special: the diverse mix of customers spanning all age groups, the unspoilt simplicity of the furnishings, the fact that mobile phones, piped music and games machines are banned, and the genuinely friendly welcome from the long-standing licensees whose family have run the place for over 200 years. At its quietest on weekday lunchtimes, it has benches around the panelled walls, an ancient one-handed clock, beams in the shiny ochre ceiling, and a woodburning stove – and rather than a bar counter for service, there's a glass-panelled hatch. Well priced Arkells BBB and Kingsdown are superbly kept alongside Old Tyler, Dark Mild and a monthly guest on handpump from the local West Berkshire Brewery; no draught lager. They also serve good house wines and winter mulled wine (£2). Excellent value bar food is limited to filled hot crusty rolls such as honey-roast ham, wild mushroom and port pâté, cheddar, stilton or brie (£2), smoked salmon, crab, tongue or salt beef (£2.30), and a variety of ploughman's (from £4.50); in winter they also do home-made soup (£2.95). Darts, shove-ha'penny, and dominoes. The quiet, old-fashioned pub garden is by the village cricket ground, and behind the pub there's a paddock with farm animals. In summer morris dancers visit sometimes, while at Christmas local mummers perform in the road by the ancient well-head (the shaft is sunk 365 feet through the chalk). It tends to get very busy at weekends; dogs must be kept on leads. *(Recommended by Stan Edwards, Derek and Sylvia Stephenson, A P Seymour, Rob Winstanley, Susan and John Douglas, Dick and Madeleine Brown, the Didler, Colin McKerrow, Doreen and Haydn Maddock, Kevin Thorpe, Paul Humphreys, Keith Wright, Angela Copeland, Anthony Longden, Pete Baker, Guy Vowles)*

Free house ~ Licensee H E Macaulay ~ Real ale ~ Bar food (11-2.30, 6-10; 12-2.45, 7-10 Sun; not Mon) ~ No credit cards ~ (01635) 578272 ~ Children must be well behaved ~ Dogs welcome ~ Open 11-3, 6-11; 12-3, 7-10.30 Sun; closed Mon, 25 Dec

ASHMORE GREEN SU5069 Map 2
Sun in the Wood ♀

NE of Newbury, or off A4 at Thatcham; off A34/A4 roundabout NW of Newbury, via B4009 Shaw Hill, then right into Kiln Road, then left into Stoney Lane after nearly 0.5 miles; or get to Stoney Lane sharp left off Ashmore Green Road, N of A4 at W end of Thatcham via Northfield Road and Bowling Green Road

The hard-working and welcoming licensees at this very popular country pub are always striving to make the place even more attractive to their customers. The nine-hole woodland crazy golf course has proved an enormous success with all ages, a new decking terrace with outdoor heaters and old-fashioned street lights was being added as we went to press, and they have introduced a Privilege Club card for regular customers with all sorts of enticing offers. The high-beamed front bar has bare boards on the left, carpet on the right, with a mix of nice old chairs, padded dining chairs and stripped pews around sturdy tables. It opens into a big back dining area which has the same informal feel, candles on tables, and some interesting touches like the big stripped bank of apothecary's drawers. There's a small conservatory sitting area by the side entrance. Smoking is allowed only in the small front bar area. Served by friendly, helpful staff, the enjoyable bar food might include lunchtime choices such as home-made soup (£3.75), good freshly baked filled baguettes (£4.95), and brie and bacon omelette, battered haddock or chicken breast in a spinach and cheese sauce (all £7.95); also, garlic mushrooms in a creamy white wine sauce (£4.85), duck and apricot pâté with plum and apple chutney (£4.95), slow roasted crispy belly of pork on a bubble and squeak cake with baked apple fritters (£12.50), chargrilled fillet of tuna in garlic butter on spring onion and smoked fish risotto (£13.50), and chargrilled 10oz sirloin steak (£13.95), with evening specials like spinach and tomato lasagne (£9.75), venison and red wine sausages in port sauce (£10.50), and crispy skin-on organic scottish salmon on baby spinach and wild mushrooms (£12.95). Thursday is steak night (from £10.50), there's a good children's menu (£4.50), and traditional Sunday roasts. Well kept Wadworths IPA, 6X and JCB on handpump and a fine choice of 15 wines by the glass. The big woodside garden has plenty of picnic-sets, and there's a play area with swings. It's hard to believe the pub is only a few minutes away from the centre of Newbury. More reports please. *(Recommended by Mike and Heather Watson, James Goldwood, Veronica Turner, P Price, Mr and Mrs A Silver, Tim Hawkins)*

Wadworths ~ Tenant Philip Davison ~ Real ale ~ Bar food (12-2(3 Sun), 6-9.30; not Mon) ~ Restaurant ~ (01635) 42377 ~ Children in eating area of bar and restaurant ~ Open 12-3, 5.30-11; 12-11 Sat; 12-4, 7-10.30 Sun; 12-3, 5.30-11 Sat in winter; closed Mon

BRAY SU9079 Map 2

Crown

1¼ miles from M4 junction 9; A308 towards Windsor, then left at Bray signpost on to B3028; High Street

You can be sure of a friendly welcome and good food at this bustling 14th-c pub, and it is particularly cosy in winter as they have three roaring log fires. Throughout, there are lots of beams (some so low you have to mind your head), and plenty of old timbers handily left at elbow height where walls have been knocked through. The partly panelled main bar has oak tables and leather backed armchairs, and one dining area has photographs of WWII aeroplanes. Served by helpful staff, the enjoyable dishes might include home-made soup (£4.50), pâté of the day (£6.85), deep-fried brie with home-made onion marmalade (£8.50), a platter of cheese (£8.95), pasta with fresh tomato, mushrooms, basil and 'angry chilli' sauce (£9.25), wild boar sausages (£9.95), home-made beef and Guinness pie (£11.85), oriental warm chicken salad (£11.95), moules marinière and frites or fresh crab salad (£12.95), sirloin steak with a green peppercorn sauce and tomato and shallot salad (£16.95), and daily specials such as fresh halibut fillets with caper and red pepper sauce (£15.75), rack of english lamb with garlic and rosemary jus (£16.75), and fillet of scottish beef with wild mushroom sauce (£16.95). Best to arrive early as it does get busy, and they recommend you book if you want to eat in the restaurant. Well kept Brakspears Special, and Courage Best and Directors on handpump along with a decent choice of wines. There are tables and benches out in a sheltered flagstoned front courtyard (which has a flourishing grape vine), and in the large back garden. (Recommended by Jarrod and Wendy Hopkinson, Michael Dandy, Susan and John Douglas, Phyl and Jack Street, Dr and Mrs A K Clarke, Chris and Susie Cammack)

Scottish Courage ~ Lease John and Carole Noble ~ Real ale ~ Bar food (not Sun or Mon evenings) ~ Restaurant ~ (01628) 621936 ~ Children at weekends only in restaurant and eating area of bar ~ Open 11-3, 6-11; 12-3, 7-10.30 Sun; closed 25, 26, 31 Dec, 1 Jan

Hinds Head 🍴 ♀

High Street; car park opposite (exit rather tricky)

This handsome old pub is now under the same ownership as the highly praised Fat Duck restaurant nearby. But the food could hardly be more different from the extremely and intriguingly experimental flavour combinations which have made Heston Blumenthal so famous. Here, the good food is firmly traditional: starters such as pea and ham soup or soused herrings (£7.50), rabbit and bacon terrine (£7.75), mussels (£7.75/£11), potted shrimps (£8.25) or half a dozen oysters (£9.50), main dishes such as gloucester old spot chop with pease pudding (£12.50), skate with lemon and capers or lemon sole with brown shrimps (£13.50), oxtail and kidney pudding (£12.50), lamb hotpot (£14.75), old-fashioned puddings (£4.95) like trifle, eton mess or quaking pudding, and a plate of proper english cheeses (£5). At lunchtime (not Sunday) they do a few good sandwiches such as bacon, tomato and rocket (£4.50) and tender steak (£6); their triple-cooked chips (£4.50) are a treat. The L-shaped bar itself is thoroughly traditional, too, with blazing log fires, dark beams and panelling, polished oak parquet, red-cushioned built-in wall seats and studded leather carving chairs around small round tables, and latticed windows. The atmosphere is relaxed and decorous. They have a splendid choice of interesting wines by the glass (12 plus rosé and two champagnes), well kept Greene King IPA and Abbot and a changing guest beer such as Hampshire Thunderbolt on handpump, an excellent bloody mary, and Sheppy's farm cider; service is quick and efficient, and the lavatories are smart and stylish. A spacious restaurant area spreads off to the left. You may smoke only in the bar. It's worth knowing that at least on our lunchtime inspection visit an efficient hand car wash was operating at the far end of the car park. *(Recommended by Jarrod and Wendy Hopkinson, Simon Collett-Jones, Ian Phillips, Susan and John Douglas)*

Free house ~ Licensees Mr and Mrs A Proctor ~ Real ale ~ Bar food (12-2.30, 6.30-9.30; Sun 12-4; not Sun evening) ~ Restaurant ~ (01628) 626151 ~ Children welcome ~ Dogs allowed in bar ~ Open 11-11; 12-10.30 Sun; closed 25 Dec, 1 Jan

EAST ILSLEY SU4981 Map 2
Swan

Just off A34 Newbury—Abingdon; High Street

Run by friendly licensees, this traditional pub dates back to the 17th c and is just the place for a quiet pint. There's a welcoming atmosphere, and the open-plan bar has straightforward pubby furniture with some distinctive touches in the nooks and corners such as a clock made from copper and oak salvaged from HMS *Britannia* (the last wooden three-deck battleship, 1862-1916), local photographs on the walls of the elegant main area, and a gracefully arched 1930s fireplace. The separate pool room doubles as a function room; fruit machine, TV, and juke box. Served by cheerful staff, the well liked bar food includes soup (£3.50), sandwiches and freshly baked baguettes (from £3.95), whitebait (£4.95), filled baked potatoes (£5.50), home-cooked ham and egg (£6.50), vegetable quiche or sausage and mash with onion gravy (£7.95), irish stew (£8.95), steak and kidney pie (£9.25), and daily specials such as salads served in a filo pastry basket or home-made burger (£7.50), and poached salmon with new potatoes (£9.95). Well kept Greene King Morlands Original and IPA and a guest such as Wadworths 6X on handpump. There's a covered terrace, and picnic-sets on a sheltered lawn with a play area. The pub is a meeting place for two classic car clubs and the Harley Davidson Motor Cycle Club. *(Recommended by Val and Alan Green, Philip Goddard, Evelyn and Derek Walter)*

Greene King ~ Lease Andrew Venning ~ Real ale ~ Bar food (11-6 Mon, 12-9 Tues-Sat, 12-6 Sun) ~ Restaurant ~ (01635) 281238 ~ Children welcome ~ Dogs allowed in bar ~ Live jazz/blues/contemporary every month ~ Open 11-11; 12-10.30 Sun; closed 25 Dec

FRILSHAM SU5573 Map 2
Pot Kiln ★ ◀

From Yattendon take turning S, opposite church, follow first Frilsham signpost, but just after crossing motorway go straight on towards Bucklebury ignoring Frilsham signposted right; pub on right after about half a mile

The new, helpful and friendly licensees have made quite a few changes here but they have been done with a lot of care and readers have been quick to voice their enthusiasm. Now completely no smoking, the comfortable bar area still has wooden floorboards, bare benches and pews, and a good winter log fire, but the lounge has been extended and is open-plan at the back and now leads into a large, pretty dining room with russet painted walls, a nice jumble of old tables and chairs, and an old-looking stone fireplace. From the West Berkshire brewery behind, they serve well kept Brick Kiln Bitter, Maggs Mild, Full Circle and Mr Chubbs Lunchtime Bitter on handpump; an extensive wine list, and delicious home-made lemonade. Darts. Enjoyable food now includes bar snacks such as filled rolls, french onion soup with croûtons and melted gruyère (£5), and home-made cornish pasty (£5.50), as well as wild crayfish bisque, croûtons and rouille (£4.50), rabbit, lemon and thyme terrine with home-made chutney (£4.75), fresh tagliatelle with wild venison ragû (£5.25), a meaty or vegetarian plate of salads, pickles, terrines and so forth (£12.95 or £13.75), slow-roasted pork belly stuffed with rosemary and garlic (£13.75), coq au vin (£13.95), and grilled cod with saffron and shellfish broth (£14.75), with puddings like honey-roasted spiced fruits with marsala and mascarpone or crème brûlée (£4.75); two-course lunch of steak or stuffed aubergine with frites plus home-made ice-cream (£10), and Sunday roasts or barbecues, depending on the weather. We would expect the food here to deserve a Food Award but, as we went to press, did not have quite enough feedback to be absolutely sure. This is a charming rural spot, and seats in the big suntrap garden have good views of the nearby forests and meadows; plenty of nearby walks. *(Recommended by Brenda and Rob Fincham, P Price, the Didler, Gaynor Gregory, Lynn Sharpless, Paul Bruford, Dr D Scott, Susan and John Douglas, Anthony Longden)*

Own brew ~ Licensees Mr & Mrs Michael Robinson ~ Real ale ~ Bar food ~ Restaurant ~ (01635) 201366 ~ Children in eating area of bar and restaurant ~ Dogs allowed in bar ~ Open 12-3, 6-11; 12-11 Sat; 12-10.30 Sun

HURST SU8074 Map 2

Green Man

Hinton Road, off A321 just outside village

The oldest part of this busy pub dates back to the 17th c, built using timbers of decommissioned ships from Portsmouth. It has been much extended since then, and some recent changes have been to knock down the old kitchen and convert the cellar into seating space, add a new dining room, and (this year) refurbish and redecorate the place. The old-fashioned bar has black standing timbers and dark oak beams around cosy alcoves, cushioned wall seats and built-in settles around copper-topped and other pub tables, attractive prints, Edwardian enamels and decorative plates on cream or terracotta walls, a hot little fire in one fireplace, and a nice old iron stove in another, below the menu blackboards. Beyond these is a light and airy no smoking dining room, and the appealing cellar room, with just four tables and lots of pictures on its cream-painted brickwork, is also no smoking. Well kept Brakspears PA, Special, and a seasonal ale on handpump, and half a dozen wines by the glass. Popular bar food (which can be eaten in the bar, dining room or garden) includes lunchtime sandwiches (from £2.95; the hot sausage baguette is good) and filled baked potatoes (from £3.40), as well as soup (£2.95), deep-fried camembert with cranberry coulis (£3.95), ploughman's (£6.45), steak in ale pie (£7.25), vegetarian pasta (£7.75), caesar salad with cajun chicken breast (£8.45), lamb tagine (£9.25), steaks (from £9.25), and daily specials like lunchtime home-cooked ham and egg (£5.95), chargrilled lamb rump steaks (£8.95), and fresh bass, swordfish or tuna (£12.95); puddings such as home-made fruit crumble or spotted dick (from £3.25), and children's menu (£3.75). There are plenty of picnic-sets under big oak trees in the large garden, with tables and chairs under outdoor heaters on a sheltered terrace, and a good sturdy children's play area. *(Recommended by D J and P M Taylor, John Baish, Mrs L M Beard, Paul Humphreys)*

Brakspears ~ Tenants Simon and Gordon Guile ~ Real ale ~ Bar food (12-2.30(3 Sun), 6.30(7 winter Sun)-9.30) ~ Restaurant ~ (0118) 934 2599 ~ Children in eating area of bar and in restaurant until 8.30pm ~ Open 11-3, 5.30-11; 12-3.30, 6(7 in winter)-10.30 Sun

INKPEN SU3864 Map 2 ⌂

Crown & Garter ◨ ⇌

Inkpen signposted with Kintbury off A4; in Kintbury turn left into Inkpen Road, then keep on into Inkpen Common

James II is reputed to have used this 16th-c brick pub on his way to visit his mistress locally. It is surprisingly substantial for somewhere so remote-feeling, and has an appealing low-ceilinged bar with a few black beams, and a relaxed central bar serving well kept Archers Golden and West Berkshire Mr Chubbs Lunchtime Bitter and Good Old Boy on handpump. Three areas radiate from here; our pick is the parquet-floored part by the raised log fire, which has a couple of substantial old tables, a huge old-fashioned slightly curved settle, and a neat little porter's chair decorated in commemoration of the Battle of Corunna (the cats' favourite seat – they've two). Other parts are slate and wood, with a good mix of well spaced tables and chairs, and nice lighting; the no smoking dining room has been totally refurbished this year. Using local produce when possible, the enjoyable food includes home-made soup (£4.45), fried field mushrooms on garlic bread with pesto dressing (£4.65), chicken liver parfait with red onion marmalade (£4.95), various curries, beer battered cod or chinese pork with stir-fried vegetables (£8.95), local cumberland sausages (£9.15), grilled monkfish with roasted garlic risotto and shellfish sauce (£12.95), steaks (from £13.95), and puddings like pear crumble with cinnamon custard (£4.50). The long side garden is lovely in summer, with picnic-sets and a play area, and the pub is handy for good downland walks. In a separate single-storey building, the well equipped and freshly redecorated bedrooms form an L around a pretty garden. More reports please. *(Recommended by John and Joyce Snell, Ian Phillips, A P Seymour, Paul Humphreys, Paul Bruford, Bruce and Sharon Eden)*

Free house ~ Licensee Gill Hern ~ Real ale ~ Bar food (not Mon-Tues lunchtime) ~ Restaurant ~ (01488) 668325 ~ Children in eating area of bar and restaurant ~ Dogs allowed in bar ~ Open 12-3, 5.30-11; 12-3, 7-10.30 Sun; closed Mon and Tues lunchtime ~ Bedrooms: £55B/£80B

KINTBURY SU3866 Map 2
Dundas Arms 🍴 ☖ 🛏

Station Road

Berkshire Dining Pub of the Year

Built for canal workers in the early 19th c, this bustling pub takes its name from Admiral Lord Dundas who, along with his brother, was responsible for the creation of the Kennet & Avon Canal. On a warm day you must get here early to bag one of the seats on the canalside jetty or on the riverside terrace. Inside, the partly panelled and carpeted bar is well liked by locals, and one of the walls has a splendid collection of blue and white plates. Good bar food includes sandwiches, grilled goats cheese on italian bread (£5.50), home-potted shrimps (£6.60), salad of hot spicy chicken with chilli and peanut sauce or dressed dorset crab salad (£7), cumberland sausages (£7.50), home-baked ham and eggs (£7.95), lamb tagine (£10), steak and kidney pie (£10.50), calves liver and bacon (£11.75), blackened sea trout with red pepper and prawn sauce (£12), rib-eye steak (£13.50), and puddings like chocolate pavé with coffee bean sauce, treacle sponge or iced orange soufflé (£5). Well kept Adnams Southwold, West Berkshire Mr Chubbs Lunchtime Bitter and a couple of changing guests on handpump, and a good range of wines. The former barge-horse stables have been converted into comfortable, quiet bedrooms, which look out through french windows on to their own secluded terrace. *(Recommended by Mayur Shah, Paul Humphreys, V Brogden, Colin Wood, James Morrell, Craig Turnbull, Tom Evans, J Stickland, Paul Bruford, Angus and Rosemary Campbell, Susan and John Douglas)*

Free house ~ Licensee David Dalzell-Piper ~ Real ale ~ Bar food (not Sun evening) ~ Restaurant ~ (01488) 658263 ~ Well behaved children in eating area of bar ~ Open 11-2.30, 6-11; 12-2.30 Sun; closed Sun evening ~ Bedrooms: £75B/£85B

MARSH BENHAM SU4267 Map 2
Red House 🍴 ☖

Village signposted from A4 W of Newbury

This smart thatched dining pub is perhaps more of a place for a special meal than a casual drink, though they do serve well kept Fullers London Pride on handpump – as well as a good wine list with nine by the glass. The comfortable bar has a light stripped wood floor, and a mix of Victorian and older settles. The appealing library-style front restaurant (which is no smoking) is lined with bookcases and hung with paintings; piped music. Imaginative (though certainly not cheap) restaurant-style dishes include cream of celery soup flavoured with curry (£5.95), roast quail stuffed with wild rice, and apple and cider emulsion (£6.95), terrine of foie gras with spicy apple compote (£8.95), tomato, basil and goats cheese parcel with red pepper coulis (£13.95), free range chicken ballotine with lemon and thyme stuffing, parsnip and potato rösti and madeira jus (£16.25), roasted medallion of venison with parmentière galette and redcurrant sauce (£17.25), chargrilled whole bass with singapore-style noodle stir fry and sweet chilli sauce (£18.50), and puddings such as warm chocolate and red berry fondant, fresh banana banoffi and chocolate papillote with dark chocolate sauce or iced Kahlua parfait with espresso crème anglaise and almond tuile (£5.50). They also offer a two-course (£13.95) or three-course (£16.95) menu. A terrace with teak tables and chairs overlooks the long lawns that slope down to water meadows and the River Kennet. More reports please. *(Recommended by Brenda and Rob Fincham, Michael Kaye)*

Free house ~ Licensee Bruno Gaultier ~ Real ale ~ Bar food (not Sun evening) ~ Restaurant ~ (01635) 582017 ~ Children in eating area of bar and restaurant ~ Open 11.30-3.30, 6-11; closed Sun evenings

READING SU7272 Map 2
Hobgoblin ◖
2 Broad Street

There's a fine choice of eight regularly changing real ales on offer at this basic but cheerful pub. Served by friendly staff, the choice includes three beers from the West Berkshire Brewery alongside five interesting guests such as Acorn Legend, Buffys Mild, Itchen Valley Pure Gold, Merlin Vision, and Triple fff After Glow. If that isn't enough, they've also lots of different bottled beers, czech lager on tap, Weston's farm cider, and country wines. Pump clips cover practically every inch of the walls and ceiling of the simple bare-boards bar – a testament to the enormous number of brews that have passed through the pumps over the past few years (now over 4,750). Up a step is a small seating area, but the best places to sit are the three or four tiny panelled rooms reached by a narrow corridor leading from the bar; cosy and intimate, each has barely enough space for one table and a few chairs or wall seats, but they're very appealing if you're able to bag one; the biggest also manages to squeeze in a fireplace. It does get very busy, especially at weekends. They don't do any food at all, and they don't allow children or mobile phones. Piped music (very much in keeping with the rough and ready feel of the place), and TV. *(Recommended by the Didler, Catherine Pitt)*

Community Taverns ~ Manager Rob Wain ~ Real ale ~ No credit cards ~ (0118) 950 8119 ~ Open 11-11; 12-10.30 Sun; closed 25 and 26 Dec and 1 Jan

REMENHAM SU7682 Map 2
Little Angel ♀
A4130, just over bridge E of Henley

This has recently been most attractively reworked, with well spaced seats and tables in several areas – each distinct enough to feel individual, yet linking openly together so that you feel part of what's going on. Furnishings are mainly in pale fabrics or soft suede, running from comfortable bar seats through tub chairs to deep sofas, with just a few prints on walls painted mainly in gentle seaside pastels, spreads of bare boards or ochre tiles, lowered ceilings and subtle lighting – all very roomy and relaxed. In one corner a case of art books and the like helps to set the tone. In the no smoking conservatory, we were taken with the unusual patterned tablecloths and the grey Lloyd Loom wicker seating. Good modern food at lunchtime includes well liked eggs benedict (£4.50; large £6.95), prawn and salmon fishcake (£5.95; main course £10.95), home-made pasta of the day (£6.50), sandwiches on daily-changing breads (from £6.50; rib-eye steak and dijon mustard with caramelised red onions £7.50), ploughman's (£7.50), baked cromer crab or grilled tiger prawns with tomato and avocado salsa (£8.95), slow-roasted shoulder of lamb on a mint and sour cream mash (£10.95), and seared yellow fin tuna on warm niçoise salad (£14.50); evening choices such as home-made soup (£4.50), home hickory smoked chicken caesar salad (£6.95), crab and asparagus terrine with roast red peppers and pink grapefruit salad (£7.25), aubergine and mozzarella bake with pine nuts, tomato and basil (£9.95), pot-roasted guinea fowl, smoked bacon and baby vegetable casserole (£11.50), and breaded veal escalope, black pudding and wild mushrooms with madeira jus (£13.75), with puddings like white chocolate and vanilla crème caramel with orange compote or frozen zabaglione and raspberry terrine (£4.95). The attractive curved bar counter has a good choice of a dozen wines by the glass (plus champagne), and Brakspears Bitter and Special on handpump; board games. Service is friendly, helpful and unhurried – mildly continental in style. There may be unobtrusive piped music. A sheltered floodlit back terrace has tables under cocktail parasols, looking over to the local cricket ground. *(Recommended by Dave Braisted, Tom and Ruth Rees, Michael Dandy)*

Brakspears ~ Lease Douglas Green ~ Real ale ~ Bar food (12-3, 7-10; 12-4, 7-9 Sun) ~ Restaurant ~ (01491) 411008 ~ Children in eating area of bar ~ Dogs allowed in bar ~ Live music Weds ~ Open 11-11; 12-10.30 Sun

RUSCOMBE SU7976 Map 2 🏠

Royal Oak

Ruscombe Lane (B3024 just E of Twyford)

The hard-working licensees in this smartened up village pub are keen to offer a warm welcome to all their customers. It's open plan and carpeted throughout (not the cheerful side garden room), and well laid out so that each bit is fairly snug, yet keeps the overall feel of a lot of people enjoying themselves. A good variety of furniture runs from dark oak tables to big chunky pine ones, with mixed seating to match – the two sofas facing one another are popular. Contrasting with the exposed ceiling joists, mostly unframed modern paintings and prints decorate the walls, mainly dark terracotta over a panelled dado; one back area has a big bright fruity cocktail mural. Well liked bar food includes home-made soup (£3.95), sandwiches (1½ rounds £4.50; panini £5.95; triple decker steak with chips £9.95), home-made burgers (from £6.95), ham and egg (£7.95), bangers and mash with caramelised onion gravy (£8.95), and daily specials such as moules marinière (£5.95), very good stir-fried chicken with a light thai green curry sauce (£7.25), lamb shank with minted jus (£11.95), calves liver (£13.95), and baked monkfish wrapped in parma ham with a green peppercorn cream (£14.50); they use local meat and vegetables, and their own fresh eggs. Well kept Fullers London Pride, Greene King Abbot, and Youngs on handpump, and half a dozen nicely chosen wines in two glass sizes; the restaurant and conservatory are no smoking. Service is quick and friendly; piped music. Picnic-sets are ranged around a venerable central hawthorn in the garden behind, which has a barbecue area, and in summer they have morris dancing and spit roasts. *(Recommended by Paul Humphreys, Susan and John Douglas)*

Enterprise ~ Lease Jenny and Stefano Buratta ~ Real ale ~ Bar food (12-2.30, 6-9.30; 12-9 Sun) ~ Restaurant ~ (0118) 934 5190 ~ Children in eating area of bar and restaurant ~ Dogs welcome ~ Open 12-3, 5.30-11; 12-10.30 Sun ~ Bedrooms: £35/£50

SHINFIELD SU7367 Map 2

Magpie & Parrot 🍺

2.6 miles from M4 junction 11, via B3270; A327 just SE of Shinfield – heading out on Arborfield Road, keep eyes skinned for small hand-painted green Nursery sign on left, and Fullers 'bar open' blackboard

A charming and relaxed place to while away an hour or so in the afternoon! It's an unexpected combination of pub and plant nursery, and they raise good value alpines, perennials and bedding plants in the glasshouses and shade house here. Unless you already knew you'd never guess that the little brick roadside cottage includes a genuine pub (as indeed it did in the early 18th c.). Go in through the lobby (with its antiquated telephone equipment), and you find a cosy and inviting high-raftered room with a handful of small polished tables – each with a bowl of peanuts – and a comfortable mix of individualistic seats from Victorian oak thrones to a red velveteen sofa, not to mention the armchair with the paw-printed cushion reserved for Spencer the rescue collie cross. Everything is spick and span, from the brightly patterned carpet to the plethora of interesting bric-a-brac covering the walls: miniature and historic bottles, dozens of model cars and vans, veteran AA badges and automotive instruments, mementoes of a pranged Spitfire (ask about its story – they love to chat here). Well kept Fullers London Pride and Triple fff Altons Pride on handpump from the small corner counter, a good range of malt whiskies and of soft drinks; very hospitable landlady; a warm log or coal fire. There are teak tables on the back terrace, and an immaculate lawn beyond. In the summer they

have hog roasts. Note the unusual opening hours; no children inside.
(Recommended by Tom McLean, Martin and Pauline Jennings)

Free house ~ Licensee Mrs Carole Headland ~ Real ale ~ No credit cards ~
(0118) 988 4130 ~ Dogs allowed in bar ~ Open 12-7; 12-3 Sun

STANFORD DINGLEY SU5771 Map 2 🏠
Bull 🛏

Off A340 via Bradfield, coming from A4 just W of M4 junction 12

After a walk in the pretty surrounding countryside, this attractive 15th-c brick pub
is a fine place to end up. The beamed tap room is firmly divided into two by
standing timbers hung with horsebrasses. The main part has an old brick fireplace,
cushioned seats carved out of barrels, a window settle, wheelback chairs on the red
quarry tiles, and an old station clock; a carpeted section has an exposed wattle and
daub wall. The half-panelled lounge bar reflects the motorsport and classic car
interests of the licensees; on some summer Saturdays owners of classic cars and
motorcycles gather in the grounds. Well kept Brakspears Bitter, and West Berkshire
Good Old Boy, Dr Hexters Healer, and Skiff on handpump, and half a dozen wines
by the glass. Besides tasty lunchtime snacks such as filled crispy rolls (£2.50;
sandwiches, toasties, and filled baguettes from £3.50), home-made soups (£3.50;
filled roll and soup £5), filled baked potatoes (from £5), ploughman's (£6), and
ham, egg and chips (£7), there might be chicken liver parfait with port jelly (£4.50),
fresh crab cakes with thai curry sauce (£6.50), broccoli and stilton pasta bake
(£9.50), and steaks (from £14), as well as daily specials such as roasted duck leg on
walnut and balsamic salad (£5.50), grilled scallops with wild rocket and sweet chilli
sauce (£6.50), steak in ale pie (£9.50), and red mullet fillets on couscous with
Pernod and dill sauce (£10.50); puddings like home-made fruit crumble, melting
mocha pot or a changing crème brûlée (from £4), and Sunday roasts (£8). The
dining room and saloon bar are no smoking; dominoes, ring-the-bull and piped
music. In front of the building are some big rustic tables and benches, and to the
side the big garden has plenty of seats. Morris men visit in August, and on St
George's Day and New Year's Day. *(Recommended by John and Joan Nash, Philip and
June Caunt, P Price, M Sage, Julia and Richard Tredgett, Martin and Pauline Jennings,
B and M Kendall, Paul Humphreys, Dr D Scott, Nigel Clifton)*

Free house ~ Licensees Robert and Kate Archard, Robin and Carol Walker ~ Real ale ~
Bar food (12-2.30, 6.30-9.30) ~ Restaurant ~ (0118) 974 4409 ~ Children in eating area of
bar and restaurant ~ Dogs allowed in bar ~ Folk/blues second Weds of month ~ Open
12-3, 6-11; 12-3, 7-10.30 Sun ~ Bedrooms: £65S/£80S

Old Boot

Off A340 via Bradfield, coming from A4 just W of M4 junction 12

Everything in this stylish 18th-c pub is neatly kept, and there's a warm welcome for
customers (and their children). The beamed bar has two welcoming fires (one in an
inglenook), fine old pews, settles, old country chairs, and well polished tables. The
fabrics for the old-fashioned wooden-ring curtains are attractive, and there are
some striking pictures and hunting prints, and bunches of fresh flowers. Enjoyable
bar food might include home-made soup and filled baguettes (£4.95), lasagne
(£8.50), cod, chips and mushy peas (£9.50), and steak and kidney pudding (£9.95).
The dining conservatory is no smoking. Well kept Bass, local Loddon Hoppit and
West Berkshire Good Old Boy on handpump, and good, generously poured wine.
The tranquil sloping back garden and terrace have pleasant rural views, and there
are more tables out in front of the pub. *(Recommended by Martin and Karen Wake,
John Baish, Dick and Madeleine Brown, John and Glenys Wheeler, E M Probyn, P Price,
Paul Humphreys)*

Free house ~ Licensees John and Jeannie Haley ~ Real ale ~ Bar food ~ Restaurant ~
(0118) 974 4292 ~ Children in eating area of bar and restaurant ~ Dogs allowed in bar ~
Open 11-3, 6-11; 11(12 Sun)-11 Sat

WHITE WALTHAM SU8477 Map 2

Beehive ◖

Waltham Road (B3024 W of Maidenhead)

In summer, this cottagey country local's garden is an extra draw. Besides the few picnic-sets and teak seats out by the topiary on the front grass, there are more on a good-sized sheltered back lawn. It's just by the village cricket field. Inside, the relaxed and neatly kept bar on the left is brightened up by cheerful scatter cushions on its comfortable seats – built-in wall seats, captain's chairs and a leather wing armchair. It has well kept Brakspears, Fullers London Pride, Greene King Abbot and a seasonal guest beer such as Hogs Back Summer on handpump, welcoming service, and a good choice of soft drinks, nuts and so forth; piped music, fruit machine, cribbage and dominoes. On the right there's a lot more space, with country kitchen chairs around sturdy tables in several comfortably carpeted areas including a conservatory. The eating areas are no smoking. Honest bar food includes sandwiches (from £3.25), soup or pâté (£4.50), ploughman's, home-cooked ham and eggs or home-made lasagne (£7.95), warm goats cheese caesar salad (£8.95), home-made pie or fishcakes with chilli dip (£9.95), 10oz rib-eye steak (£12.95), and puddings (from £3.95). Good disabled access and facilities. *(Recommended by Mike and Sue Richardson, D Crook)*

Enterprise ~ Lease Guy Martin ~ Real ale ~ Bar food (11.30-2.30, 5.30-9.30; all day weekends) ~ Restaurant ~ (01628) 822877 ~ Children in eating area of bar ~ Dogs allowed in bar ~ Open 11-3, 5-11; 11-11 Sat; 12-10.30 Sun

WINDSOR SU9676 Map 2

Two Brewers ♀ ◖

Park Street, off High Street next to Mews

Handily set next to the entrance to Windsor Great Park's Long Walk (there are plenty of big car parks nearby), this bustling old-fashioned pub has lots to look at. Chalkboards record events of the day in history, some of the old pews and tables are quite distinctive, and around the bar are a plethora of tickets, for everything from Royal Ascot to the final of *Pop Idol*. Rambling around a central servery, each of the three quaint but cosily civilised bare-board rooms has a different feel. The red room on the left is our favourite, with a big armchair, wooden floors, and sizeable piles of magazines. The back bar leading off has a champagne theme, with hundreds of corks lining the walls, particularly around a big mirror above the fireplace. The bar on the right has stripped tables, and a stack of daily papers. Well kept Courage Best, Fullers London Pride and a guest such as Wadworths 6X on handpump, and up to 14 wines by the glass, including champagne. As there are only eight tables inside, it's best to book if you wish to eat: sandwiches, home-made soup (£3), home-made chicken liver pâté (£4.75), home-made chilli or fishcakes (£8.50), lamb shank (£9.50), calves liver and bacon with onion gravy (£10), steaks (from £11.50), and a weekly changing pasta and fish dish. Piped jazz, shove-ha'penny, cribbage and dominoes. There are a few tables out in front, under an array of hanging baskets; dogs are treated to a bowl of water. Please note that they don't allow children. *(Recommended by Kevin Thorpe, Tracey and Stephen Groves, John Saville, Ian Phillips, Simon Collett-Jones)*

Enterprise ~ Lease Robert Gillespie ~ Real ale ~ Bar food (12-2.30 (12-4 weekends), 6.30-10; not weekends evenings) ~ Restaurant ~ (01753) 855426 ~ Dogs welcome ~ Open 11.30-11; 12-10.30 Sun

WINTERBOURNE SU4572 Map 2

Winterbourne Arms ♀

3.7 miles from M4 junction 13; A34 S, then cutting across to B4494 Newbury—Wantage from first major slip road (bearing left in Chieveley towards North Heath when the main road bends round to the right), and follow Winterbourne signs

The surrounding countryside here is lovely and there are nearby walks to Snelsmore and Donnington. In summer, flowering tubs and hanging baskets brighten up the picnic-sets, and there's a big weeping willow in the garden. The bars, newly redecorated this year, have a collection of old irons around the fireplace, early prints and old photographs of the village, and a log fire; piped music. The peaceful view over the rolling fields from the big bar windows cleverly avoids the quiet road, which is sunken between the pub's two lawns. There's a good wine list with 13 wines by the glass (served in elegant glasses and including sparkling and sweet wines), and well kept Fullers London Pride, Greene King Old Speckled Hen, Wadworths 6X, and West Berkshire Good Old Boy on handpump. Bar food includes soup (£3.50), smoked haddock and chive fishcake with butter sauce (£5.75), a pot of garlic mushrooms in a white wine and cream sauce (£5.95), and mixed vegetable terrine with apricot compote (£6.95), with lunchtime dishes such as sandwiches (from £4.20), gammon and eggs (£6.95), sausage and mash with onion gravy (£7.50), and battered haddock and mushy peas (£7.95), evening choices like wild mushroom stroganoff (£9.50), steaks (from £12.95), braised lamb shank with celeriac mash and a port and redcurrant sauce (£13.25), and roast breast of duck with cherry sauce (£15.95); daily specials, and rather steeply priced puddings that might include sticky toffee pudding or raspberry crème brûlée (£5.95); coffee is £2 per cup. The little no smoking restaurant area was once a bakery, and you can still see the original bakers' ovens. *(Recommended by Sebastian and Paris Leach, Jenny Major, Mike Pugh, Dick and Madeleine Brown, Colin Wood, Michael and Judy Buckley, Basil and Jarvis, J R Parker, P Price, W J Taylor)*

Free house ~ Licensee Frank Adams ~ Real ale ~ Bar food (not Mon except bank hols) ~ Restaurant ~ (01635) 248200 ~ Children in restaurant ~ Dogs allowed in bar ~ Open 12-3, 6-11; 12-10.30 Sun; closed Mon except bank hols (under review as we went to press)

YATTENDON SU5574 Map 2
Royal Oak ♀ ⇔
The Square; B4009 NE from Newbury; turn right at Hampstead Norreys, village signposted on left

Under a new licensee and now a free house, this handsome inn is just as welcoming if all you want is a quiet drink – though it would be a pity to miss out on the particularly good food. Inside, the panelled and prettily decorated brasserie/bar has a nice log fire and striking flower arrangements. Staff are attentive and welcoming, and the lunchtime bar food comes in the form of a two or three-course set menu with five choices of starter, main course, and pudding (though if someone just wanted, say, a bowl of soup they could be flexible). The starters might include farmhouse soup, pigeon breast with figs and port wine jus or millefeuilles of spinach and gorgonzola with a creamy mushroom sauce; main courses such as poached haddock with mussel cream, whole roasted poussin with bacon, beans and a tomato and pumpkin salsa or braised lamb shank with provençal vegetables; puddings like a trio of apple puddings (crumble, thin tartlet and calvados and chocolate brûlée), hot treacle sponge pudding or pecan pie with bitter chocolate sauce and amaretto sorbet. It's best to book for the no smoking restaurant. Well kept Wadworths 6X and West Berkshire Good Old Boy, and a good wine list. In summer, you can eat at tables in the pleasant walled garden, and there are more in front by the peaceful village square. The bedrooms are attractive and well appointed, and some overlook the garden. The poet Robert Bridges once lived in the village. *(Recommended by John Braine-Hartnell, Mr and Mrs G Swire, Brenda and Rob Fincham, the Didler, Len and Di Bright, Heather Couper, Mrs E A Macdonald, V Brogden, Dr D Scott, Denise White, Karen and Graham Oddey)*

Free house ~ Licensee William Boyle ~ Real ale ~ Bar food (not served evenings or Sun lunch) ~ Restaurant ~ (01635) 201325 ~ Children in eating area of bar ~ Open 11-3, 5-11; 12-2.30, 7-10.30 Sun; closed 1 Jan ~ Bedrooms: £95B/£110B

Post Office address codings confusingly give the impression that some pubs are in Berkshire, when they're really in Oxfordshire or Hampshire (which is where we list them).

LUCKY DIP

Besides the fully inspected pubs, you might like to try these Lucky Dips recommended to us and described by readers (if you do, please send us reports: www.goodguides.co.uk).

ALDWORTH [SU5579]
☆ *Four Points* [B4009 towards Hampstead Norreys]: Country pub with low beams and standing timbers, good value home-made food from baguettes up, well kept Adnams Best and Wadworths 6X, quick service, tidy array of polished tables in good-sized eating area (bar area not so big), no piped music, games room; children very welcome, neat garden over road *(LYM, Stan Edwards)*

ARBORFIELD [SU7666]
Swan [Arborfield Cross, A327 Eversley Rd]: Friendly and attractive small pub, above-average enterprising food in two peaceful dining bars, good range of real ales *(Dr and Mrs A K Clarke, Martin and Pauline Jennings)*

ASCOT [SU9268]
Stag [High St]: Relaxed and friendly, with small comfortable lounge bar, extended bistro-feel dining area, Greene King beers and good wine and food choice *(Robert Hay)*

ASTON [SU7884]
☆ *Flower Pot* [small signpost off A4130 Henley—Maidenhead at top of Remenham Hill]: Roomy old-fashioned two-bar pub with fine array of stuffed fish and other river-inspired decorations in bright bare-boards public bar and (children allowed here) bigger blue-carpeted saloon, tiled-floor adult dining area, well kept Brakspears inc a seasonal beer, good unusual reasonably priced food from sandwiches to lots of fish and game in season, cheerful welcoming staff; may be unobtrusive piped music, friendly siamese cats and spaniel, very busy with walkers and families wknds; lots of picnic-sets giving quiet country views from nice big orchard garden (dogs allowed there), side field with chickens, ducks and guinea fowl *(BB, Richard Greaves, Susan and John Douglas, Jeremy Woods)*

BINFIELD [SU8271]
Bullfinch [Forest Rd (B3034 W)]: Family-oriented Vintage Inn (former Warren House), well laid out and spacious, with good friendly service, decent food from enterprising ciabattas up, good house wines and good range of soft and hot drinks; plenty of garden tables *(Paul Humphreys, Jack Clark, Alistair Forsyth)*
Victoria Arms [Terrace Rd N]: Neat and welcoming no-frills Fullers local with good choice of seating areas, well kept ales from central bar, good reasonably priced bar food, shelves filled with beer bottle collection, children's room; summer barbecues in quiet garden *(Richard Houghton, LYM, Paul Humphreys)*

BOXFORD [SU4271]
☆ *Bell* [back road Newbury—Lambourn]: Massive choice of wines and champagnes by the glass as well as four real ales and plenty of other drinks in relaxed and civilised country local with racing pictures, some interesting bric-a-brac and wide choice of bar food from

sandwiches and snacks to steak, rather smart no smoking restaurant area, pool, cribbage, shove-ha'penny, dominoes; advertising TV, piped music, children and dogs welcome, attractive covered and heated prettily lit terrace, bedrooms, open all day (Sun afternoon break) *(Andy and Yvonne Cunningham, Mayur Shah, Dr and Mrs M Savidge, Dr D and Mrs B Woods, LYM)*

BRACKNELL [SU8566]
Golden Retriever [Nine Mile Ride (junction A3095/B3430)]: Attractively done largely thatched Vintage Inn, olde-worlde farmhouse-style décor, lots of young well trained staff, decent food all day, well kept Bass and Fullers London Pride, plenty of wines by the glass, log fires, daily papers; open all day *(Ian Phillips, Martin Wilson)*

BURCHETTS GREEN [SU8381]
☆ *Crown* [side rd from A4 after Knowl Green on left, linking to A404]: Comfortable dining pub with high-backed chairs and soft piped music, new chef/landlord doing wide choice of enjoyable and attractively served food using local organic supplies and (most days) fresh Brixham fish, well kept Greene King IPA and Ruddles County, lots of wines by the glass, friendly staff; plans to enlarge the small bar, tables out in pleasant quiet garden *(Philip and June Caunt, Rod and Chris Pring, Paul Humphreys)*

CHEAPSIDE [SU9469]
Thatched Tavern [off A332/A329, then off B383 at Village Hall sign]: Civilised dining pub, part of a small group, with big inglenook log fire, low beams and polished flagstones in cottagey core, three smart carpeted dining rooms off, good interesting up-to-date food, friendly service, good choice of wines by the glass, well kept Brakspears and Fullers London Pride, daily papers, no games or piped music; children in restaurant, rustic tables on attractive sheltered back lawn, open all day wknds, handy for Virginia Water *(LYM, Robert Hay)*

CHIEVELEY [SU4773]
☆ *Olde Red Lion* [handy for M4 junction 13 via A34 N-bound; Green Lane]: Bustling local with good value straightforward food, welcoming staff, well kept Arkells beers, comfortable low-beamed L-shaped bar with well worn furnishings, lots of brassware, couple of old sewing machines, roaring log fire, back restaurant with paintings for sale, pool; piped music, fruit machine, TV; parking immediately outside can be a squeeze – easier in overflow opp *(BB, Roger and Jenny Huggins)*

COLD ASH [SU5169]
Spotted Dog [Gladstone Lane]: Consistently good choice of well cooked dishes in comfortable modern pub, bright and roomy, with several well kept ales and friendly efficient

staff, small restaurant off bar *(Stan Edwards)*

COMPTON [SU5180]

Swan [High St]: Welcoming new young couple, good food choice in lounge bar and dining area, well kept beers, locals' public bar *(Stan Edwards)*

COOKHAM [SU8985]

☆ *Bel & the Dragon* [High St (B4447)]: Smart old dining pub with heavy Tudor beams, open fires, thoughtful furnishings, pastel walls and modern lighting, good interesting if not cheap food, lunchtime sandwiches and baguettes, crisp napery, indoor barbecue in back room, well kept Brakspears, Courage Best and Marstons Pedigree, good choice of wines; piped music may be loud on nights when the young people come, esp Sat; children welcome, dogs allowed in bar, garden with terrace tables, Stanley Spencer Gallery almost opposite, open all day *(Peter and Eleanor Kenyon, Paul Humphreys, LYM, Colin Wood, JMC, Craig Turnbull)*

Ferry [Sutton Rd]: Stylish modernisation of splendidly placed riverside pub popular with families and young couples, dark décor and small servery in beamed core, light and airy waterside extension with contemporary artwork and bright sofas and armchairs, italian-theme Thames-view restaurants upstairs and down, friendly young staff; piped music may be rather loud; attractive waterside garden and decking *(BB, Susan and John Douglas)*

COOKHAM DEAN [SU8785]

☆ *Jolly Farmer* [Church Rd, off Hills Lane]: Carefully kept traditional by the village consortium which owns it, with old-fashioned bar, pine-furnished extension, stylish dining room, open fires, well kept ales such as Brakspears and Courage Best, enjoyable food, pub games, no music or machines; well behaved children welcome away from bar, good quiet garden with play area *(LYM, David Tindal, Susan and John Douglas)*

CRAZIES HILL [SU7980]

☆ *Horns* [Warren Row Rd off A4 towards Cockpole Green, then follow Crazies Hill signs]: Comfortable and civilised beamed bars with stripped furniture and open fires, plenty of character and warm décor in dark colours, raftered no smoking barn room where children allowed, enterprising food (not Sun evening) from lunchtime baguettes to Billingsgate fish, Brakspears Bitter, Special and seasonal ales, thoughtful wine list, a good bloody mary; dogs allowed lunchtime, pleasant seats in large garden with play area, cl Sun evening in winter *(Tracey and Stephen Groves, LYM, Wombat, Claire George, Michael Porter, T R and B C Jenkins, Stephen McCormick, Simon Collett-Jones, P Price, Roy and Gay Hoing)*

DATCHET [SU9877]

Royal Stag [not far from M4 junction 5; The Green]: Interesting timber-framed pub with mixed chairs and tables, beautiful beams and ecclesiastical windows overlooking churchyard, local memorabilia, log fire, Fullers London Pride, Greene King IPA and three guest beers, good sandwich choice, some interesting

blackboard specials; small outside seating area *(Peter and Margaret Glenister)*

EAST ILSLEY [SU4981]

☆ *Crown & Horns* [just off A34; Compton Rd]: No-frills bustling racing-country pub with rambling snug beamed rooms, soft lighting, blazing log fire, tables tucked into intimate corners, no smoking snug with big oval table, no smoking dining room – can be smoky elsewhere; lots of interesting racing prints and photographs, perhaps TV racing in the locals' bar, well kept ales such as Black Sheep, Brakspears, Fullers London Pride and Youngs Special, impressive collection of whiskies, wines by the glass, food from sandwiches, baguettes and baked potatoes to popular Sun lunch; fruit machine, piped music; children and dogs allowed, tables in pretty paved stable yard under two chestnut trees, bedrooms, open all day *(Val and Alan Green, Dennis Jenkin, LYM, P and J Shapley, Dick and Madeleine Brown, Colin Wood, David Cannings, Gerry and Rosemary Dobson, Howard and Margaret Buchanan, Jack Clark, Andrea and Guy Bradley, A P Seymour, Gill and Keith Croxton)*

☆ *Star* [High St, leaving village S]: Partly 15th-c, attractive and comfortable, with beams and black woodwork, inglenook log fire, good choice of good value fresh food, well kept ales inc West Berkshire, good choice of other drinks, sensible prices, friendly efficient service, books, board games and shove-ha'penny (no machines), separate dining room; children and dogs welcome, garden behind with picnic-sets and play area, comfortable bedrooms *(Alan London, BB, Ned Kelly, Stan Edwards)*

ETON [SU9677]

George [High St]: Friendly well staffed family dining pub with neat dining tables on stripped wood, seats for drinkers too (Brakspears, Fullers London Pride and Wadworths 6X, good wine choice), food from ciabattas and baked potatoes up; piped music; children welcome, big back terrace with heaters *(Simon Collett-Jones, Esther and John Sprinkle)*

☆ *Gilbeys* [High St]: Not a pub, but well worth knowing for good imaginative home-cooked light bar meals, nice sensibly priced house wines, friendly unstuffy family service; can be very busy if there's an event at the school, best to book for light and airy back restaurant down long corridor *(Mrs Ann Gray, BB)*

New College [High St]: Pleasantly refurbished local with friendly staff, well kept Badger ales and well done straightforward food; nice terrace *(anon)*

FIFIELD [SU9076]

Fifield Inn [just off B3024 W of Windsor]: Neat and attractive old stone-built village local with chatty atmosphere, well kept Greene King IPA and Abbot, lots of wines by the glass, friendly interested staff, fairly limited choice of good value generous fresh restaurant and bar food inc interesting dishes (no snacks on Sun), daily papers, flame-effect fire; live jazz Sun evening; children welcome, picnic-sets in lovely garden *(D J and P M Taylor, Karen and Steve Brine, Simon Collett-Jones)*

GREAT SHEFFORD [SU3875]

Swan [2 miles from M4 junction 14 – A338 towards Wantage]: Low-ceilinged bow-windowed pub with good range of lunchtime snacks and evening meals (can have just a starter), well kept Courage Best and Wadworths 6X, good wine choice, good welcoming service, good log fire, daily papers and magazines, no smoking river-view restaurant; good wheelchair access, children in eating areas, tables on attractive waterside lawn and terrace *(Mark and Ruth Brock, LYM, A and B D Craig, Ann and Colin Hunt)*

HAMSTEAD MARSHALL [SU4165]

☆ *White Hart* [off A4 W of Newbury]: Comfortable dining pub with good colourfully presented food, french influences on english menu and adaptable chef happy to modify recipes, Hook Norton Best and Wadworths 6X, log fire; children welcome, no smoking restaurant, pretty tree-sheltered walled garden, quiet and comfortable beamed bedrooms in converted barn *(A J Murray, J L A Gimblett, LYM, N R White)*

HARE HATCH [SU8078]

Queen Victoria [Blakes Lane; just N of A4 Reading—Maidenhead]: Two low-beamed and panelled bars with pleasant décor, usual food from well filled sandwiches up, well kept Brakspears ales, a fair choice of wines by the glass, pub games, no smoking conservatory; children in eating area, one or two tables outside, open all day Sun *(LYM, Paul Humphreys, D J and P M Taylor)*

HOLYPORT [SU8977]

☆ *Belgian Arms* [handy for M4 junction 8/9, via A308(M) and A330]: Traditional chatty low-ceilinged bar under new management, interesting belgian military uniform prints, cricketing memorabilia and a good log fire, quick cheerful service, decent straightforward food from good sandwiches up (small helpings for children available), Brakspears Bitter and Special; children in eating areas, pleasant outlook over pond and charming green from garden *(Stan Edwards, LYM, Simon Collett-Jones, Kevin Blake, M G Hart, Gordon Prince, KC)*

George [1½ miles from M4 junction 8/9, via A308(M)/A330; The Green]: Extended open-plan low-beamed carpeted pub with pleasant décor and nice old fireplace, wide choice of enjoyable generous sensibly priced food from baguettes, baked potatoes and light lunchtime dishes up, some more restauranty evening dishes, Adnams, Courage Directors and Fullers London Pride, friendly helpful service, daily papers, no smoking area; piped radio; picnic-sets outside, lovely village green *(Michael Dandy, Mr T J and Mrs L Baddeley)*

HUNGERFORD [SU3368]

Bear [3 miles from M4 junction 14; town signed at junction]: Chain hotel worth knowing for varied, reasonably priced and plentiful bar food, decorous period

atmosphere, fantastic huge clock, open fires, well kept real ales such as Wadworths 6X, nice house wines, efficient service; restaurant, bedrooms comfortable and attractive *(Colin and Janet Roe, LYM, Keith and Sally Jackson, Ann and Colin Hunt)*

John o' Gaunt [Bridge St (A338)]: Friendly pleasantly refurbished town pub with generous cheap food from well garnished sandwiches up, good service, well kept Greene King IPA, Abbot and Ruddles, decent wines, daily papers; quiet piped music; outside seating area with play things, open all day *(Sue and Mike Todd, LYM, Ann and Colin Hunt)*

Plume of Feathers [High St]: Big well run open-plan family pub, lots of tables around central bar, bare boards and lack of fabrics giving a slight brasserie feel, good food from soup and well made sandwiches up, very large helpings and imaginative recipes, well kept Greene King, friendly staff, cosy fire towards the back; bedrooms *(A P Seymour, Charles and Pauline Stride, Stan Edwards)*

HURLEY [SU8183]

Black Boy [A4130 E of Henley]: Former cottagey pub reopened after refurbishment as smart dining place, new furniture on wooden floors, woodburner separating main eating area from small bar, up-to-date food, Brakspears Bitter; piped music; garden tables, bedrooms, walks to Thames *(Michael Dandy)*

HURST [SU7973]

Castle [opp church]: New rather more homely and pubby feel (had been through a restauranty phase), with good welcoming service, good helpings of enjoyable food from new chef inc good value Sun lunch *(Paul Humphreys)*

KNOWL HILL [SU8178]

☆ *Bird in Hand* [A4, quite handy for M4 junction 8/9]: Relaxed civilised atmosphere and good home-made straightforward food even Sun evening from sandwiches and baguettes up in spacious heavy-beamed and panelled main bar with splendid log fire, cosy alcoves, much older side bar; well kept Brakspears and Shepherd Neame Spitfire, good wines by the glass, good choice of other drinks, polite prompt staff in colourful waistcoats, no smoking buffet area (children allowed), smart restaurant; tables out on front terrace, tidy modern bedrooms *(LYM, Mrs E A Macdonald, Tracey and Stephen Groves, M G Hart)*

LAMBOURN [SU3175]

☆ *Hare* [aka Hare & Hounds; Lambourn Woodlands, well S of Lambourn itself (B4000/Hilldrop Lane)]: Tastefully furnished dining pub, young chef doing good sophisticated lunchtime food and more elaborate evening menu at a price, several nicely individual rooms inc popular bar, friendly efficient service, well kept Bass and Wadworths IPA or 6X, nice wines, exemplary lavatories; piped music; children welcome, garden behind with decent play area, cl Sun evening *(Mark and Ruth Brock, Simon and Mandy King, LYM, Dr and Mrs Geoff Ayrey)*

LECKHAMPSTEAD [SU4376]

Stag: Welcoming pub with enjoyable attractively priced food in bar and restaurant, short choice of good value wines; quiet village *(G Harper)*

LITTLEWICK GREEN [SU8379]

☆ *Cricketers* [not far from M4 junction 9; A404(M) then left on to A4, from which village signed on left; Coronation Rd]: Welcoming new dutch landlady and daughter in proper old-fashioned pub, well kept Badger and Harveys, fine choice of wines by the glass, reasonably priced food from good range of sandwiches to some imaginative dishes and Sun roast, spick-and-span housekeeping, lots of cricketing pictures, cosy local atmosphere; charming spot opp cricket green *(LYM, Paul Humphreys, Susan and John Douglas)*

MAIDENHEAD [SU8683]

Lemon Tree [Golden Ball Lane, Pinkneys Green – off A308 N]: Refurbished as smart dining pub, low-ceilinged bar, airy larger dining area, Marlow Rebellion and a guest beer, food inc light lunchtime dishes such as sandwiches and wraps; tables outside *(Michael Dandy)*

MORTIMER [SU6464]

Turners Arms [Fairfield Park, West End Rd, Mortimer Common]: Open-plan L-shaped pub with friendly helpful service, good value generous food (Sun bar nibbles), Brakspears beers, nice coffee, log fire, no smoking dining area; tables in garden *(Andy Coleby, Paul Humphreys)*

OAKLEY GREEN [SU9276]

Olde Red Lion [B3024 just W of Windsor]: Compact low-beamed dining pub with good interesting reasonably priced food from wide sandwich range up, welcoming helpful staff, well kept Adnams, Bass and Flowers IPA in small bar, two separate eating areas, mix of seating from homely old chairs to trendy modern ones; piped music; comfortable bedrooms, good breakfast, good-sized pleasant back garden *(June and Robin Savage, Simon Collett-Jones)*

OLD WINDSOR [SU9874]

☆ *Union* [Crimp Hill Rd, off B3021 – itself off A308/A328]: Friendly and comfortable old pub, well kept Courage Best, Marstons Pedigree and Theakstons Best, consistently good service from long-serving staff, big woodburner, dated black and white show-business photographs, bank notes on beams, good reasonably priced traditional bar food from sandwiches and omelettes up, attractive copper-decorated restaurant; soft piped music, fruit machine; tables under cocktail parasols on heated front terrace, country views; comfortable bedrooms with own bathrooms *(BB, Ian Phillips, K Hutchinson, D M and B K Moores)*

PALEY STREET [SU8676]

☆ *Royal Oak* [B3024 W]: Friendly helpful service in simply but stylishly refurbished restaurant pub, well kept Fullers London Pride and good wide choice of wines by the glass (vintage port at a price), good food, smallish front part by bar with easy chairs and piano, pleasantly relaxed gingham-and-linen country eating area stretching back with bare boards, flagstones and some stripped brick, cricketing prints mixed with photographs of celebrity friends of landlord's father Michael Parkinson; piped jazz *(BB, June and Robin Savage, Susan and John Douglas)*

READING [SU7272]

☆ *Fishermans Cottage* [Kennet Side – easiest to walk from Orts Rd, off Kings Rd]: Friendly local in nice spot by canal lock and towpath, waterside tables, lovely big back garden and light and airy conservatory; modern furnishings of character, pleasant stone snug behind woodburning range, good value lunches inc lots of hot or cold sandwiches (very busy then but service quick), full Fullers beer range kept well, small choice of wines, small darts room, SkyTV; dogs allowed (not in garden) *(the Didler)*

Griffin [Church Rd, Caversham]: Roomy chain dining pub, sound food value, with Courage, Theakstons and a guest beer, good friendly service, separate areas with several log fires; tables in attractive courtyard garden, beautiful spot on Thames overlooking swan sanctuary *(Tony Hobden, D J and P M Taylor)*

☆ *Sweeney & Todd* [Castle St]: Successful cross between café and pub with exceptional value home-made pies all day, also ploughman's, casseroles and roasts, in warren of little period-feel alcoves and other areas on various levels, small well stocked bar with well kept Adnams Best, Badger Tanglefoot, Wadworths 6X and a changing guest beer, children welcome in restaurant area, open all day (cl Sun and bank hols) *(Ian Phillips, D J and P M Taylor, P Price, Susan and John Douglas, the Didler, LYM)*

SHEFFORD WOODLANDS [SU3673]

☆ *Pheasant* [less than ½ mile from M4 junction 14 – A338 towards Wantage then 1st left on to B4000]: Isolated country pub with lots of horse-racing pictures and cartoons and horsey customers, enjoyable regularly changing food inc interesting dishes in end dining area with burgundy décor and bistro atmosphere, welcoming old-school landlord and friendly staff, well kept real ales, log fires, four neat rooms inc public bar with games inc ring the bull; attractive views from pleasant garden *(LYM, Stan Edwards, Ceri Jenkins, Guy Vowles, Tony and Tracy Constance)*

SHURLOCK ROW [SU8274]

Royal Oak [Hungerford Lane]: Gently smartened up under newish management, sensible prices, usual food from lunchtime baguettes and baked potatoes up, well kept beer *(Paul Humphreys)*

SLOUGH [SU9779]

Herschel Arms [Park St]: Well run irish pub with irish emphasis to juke box, live music nights too *(Jack Clark)*

SONNING [SU7575]

☆ *Bull* [off B478, by church; village signed off A4 E of Reading]: Classic old-fashioned inn in pretty setting nr Thames, low heavy beams, cosy alcoves, cushioned antique settles and low-slung chairs, inglenook log fires, no smoking back dining area (children allowed); well kept Gales GB, HSB and Butser and a guest beer, lots of country wines, separate food order counter with broad if not cheap choice from baguettes and baked potatoes to steaks, friendly efficient service, charming courtyard; picnic-sets out in car park, open all day summer wknds, nice bedrooms *(A P Seymour, Karen and Steve Brine, LYM, Paul Humphreys, Simon Collett-Jones, P and J Shapley, Susan and John Douglas)*

SWALLOWFIELD [SU7364]

☆ *George & Dragon* [Church Rd, towards Farley Hill]: Relaxed and cottagey pub very popular with business diners, stripped beams, red walls, rugs on flagstones and big log fire, plenty of character and atmosphere, enjoyable fresh food inc reasonably priced lunchtime specials and some good interesting recipes, well kept Adnams, Fullers London Pride and Wadworths 6X, good wines, charming friendly young overseas staff; piped music; well behaved children welcome, open all day *(Colin Wood, Mike and Jayne Bastin, LYM, John and Glenys Wheeler, KC, Peter B Brown, John Baish, Ian Phillips, David Tindal, Stephen Allford)*

THEALE [SU6168]

Winning Hand [A4 W, opp Sulhamstead turn; handy for M4 junction 12]: Friendly pub with good service, well kept Arkells and Hook Norton, varied wine list, enjoyable food from sandwiches, baguettes and light meals to interesting main dishes, restaurant; quiet piped music; bright gardens, four bedrooms *(Mike and Sue Richardson)*

WALTHAM ST LAWRENCE [SU8376]

☆ *Bell* [B3024 E of Twyford; The Street]: Classic heavy-beamed and timbered village pub with good log fire, good value pubby bar food (not Sun evening) from good sandwich range up, fine choice of well kept changing ales inc West Berkshire Mild, plenty of malt whiskies, good wine, friendly attentive service, daily papers, compact panelled lounge, no smoking front snug, cheery local public bar, big sofa (enjoyed by pub dog – other dogs welcome); children in eating areas and family room, tables in back garden with extended terrace, open all day wknds *(Tracey and Stephen Groves, Simon Collett-Jones, Bob and Laura Brock, LYM, Mike and Sue Richardson, Anthony Longden, A P Seymour)*

WARGRAVE [SU7878]

☆ *Bull* [off A321 Henley—Twyford; High St]: Good friendly atmosphere in olde-worlde low-beamed two-bar pub with interesting choice of enjoyable food from good value lunchtime filled baguettes up, friendly young staff, well kept Brakspears, good wine choice, good log fires; tables on neat partly covered terrace, bedrooms *(Paul Humphreys, LYM, Doreen and Haydn Maddock)*

WEST ILSLEY [SU4782]

Harrow [signed off A34 at E Ilsley slip road]: Appealing knocked-through bar with Victorian prints on deep-coloured walls, some antique furnishings, log fire, well kept Greene King Abbot, IPA and Morlands Original, decent wines; children in eating areas, dogs allowed in bar, picnic-sets in big garden, more seats on pleasant terrace – peaceful spot overlooking cricket pitch and pond; cl Sun evening *(R M Sparkes, David Handforth, Susan and John Douglas, John Hale, Dr D Taub, Emma Rampton, Colin Wood, Toppo Todhunter, LYM, Ian Phillips)*

WICKHAM [SU3971]

☆ *Five Bells* [3 miles from M4 junction 14, via A338, B4000; Baydon Rd]: Newly thatched pub in racehorse-training country, enjoyable home-made food from proper sandwiches and generous baguettes up, consistently friendly service, well kept ales such as Adnams, Fullers London Pride and ESB and Ringwood, good choice of reasonably priced wines, good lunchtime mix from regulars to family groups, big log fire, tables tucked into low eaves, no smoking at bar; children in eating area, informal garden with new decking and good play area, good value bedrooms, interesting church nearby with overhead elephants *(Mark, Amanda, Luke and Jake Sheard, Paul Humphreys, G W A Pearce, LYM, J Iorwerth Davies)*

WINDSOR [SU9676]

Carpenters Arms [Market St]: Pretty pub with helpful service and enjoyable pubby food inc good sausage choice and children's dishes; tables outside, handy for castle and Legoland bus stop *(Esther and John Sprinkle)*

Three Tuns [Market St]: Big bar with well kept ales from central servery, kind helpful service, food from good sandwiches up; piped music; relaxing tables out on pedestrianised street *(Esther and John Sprinkle)*

Windsor Castle [Kings Rd]: Pleasant atmosphere, areas for drinkers and diners, decent food inc innovative specials, real ales such as Adnams, Caledonian Deuchars IPA and Courage, log fire; sports TV; dogs very welcome (handy for the Park with view over Royal Paddocks to Frogmore House), good parking, small outside deck *(Jeremy Woods)*

WINNERSH [SU7870]

☆ *Wheelwrights Arms* [off A329 Reading—Wokingham at Winnersh crossroads by Sainsbury's, signed Hurst, Twyford; then right into Davis Way]: Cheerfully bustling beamed local with big woodburner, bare black boards and flagstones, well kept Wadworths IPA, 6X and guest beers, enjoyable lunchtime food from huge doorstep sandwiches up, quick friendly service, cottagey no smoking dining area; may keep your credit card, can be a bit smoky by bar; children welcome, picnic-sets in smallish garden with maybe disabled parking and facilities *(June and Robin Savage, BB, D J and P M Taylor, Paul Humphreys)*

WOKINGHAM [SU7967]

Olde Leathern Bottel [Barkham Rd]: Extensive Chef & Brewer with very wide food choice, plenty of wines by the glass, staff working hard to please *(Alistair Forsyth)*

WOODSIDE [SU9271]

Duke of Edinburgh [Woodside Rd, off A332 Windsor—Ascot S of B3034]: Warmly welcoming local with well kept Arkells 2B, 3B and Kingsdown, cheerful service, solidly furnished main bar, sofas in middle lounge, no smoking area, usual bar food from proper sandwiches and baguettes up, small no smoking area and separate no smoking bistro restaurant; big-screen TV, quiz night; children welcome, tables out in front and in pleasant garden with summer marquee *(Tracey and Stephen Groves, Gerry and Rosemary Dobson)*

☆ *Rose & Crown* [Woodside Rd, Winkfield, off A332 Ascot—Windsor]: Thriving pub with low-beamed bar and extended no smoking dining area, food (not Sun or Mon evening) from lunchtime sandwiches and baguettes to more elaborate evening restaurant dishes and popular Sun lunch, Greene King IPA and Morlands Original and a guest beer; piped music, fruit machine; children in eating areas, tables and swing in side garden backed by woodland, bedrooms, open all day, cl Sun evening *(Gerry and Rosemary Dobson, Bob and Margaret Holder, LYM)*

Buckinghamshire

This is now splendid territory for finding good pubs, often in lovely spots, and often with notable food, too. Of the three new main entries here this year, the Palmer Arms at Dorney (nicely set despite being so handy for the M4) has such good food that it's clearly in the running for one of our Food Awards, and we also liked the food in the 16th-c Black Boy in Oving (completely no smoking, a nice all-rounder with a charming garden), and the Woolpack in Stoke Mandeville (a warmly relaxing mix of ancient pub with contemporary design and comforts). Other pubs with high meal appeal include the ambitious Royal Oak at Bovingdon Green (a great choice of wines by the glass, and lots of attention to detail), the attractively furnished Swan in Denham (good big garden, another fine wine choice), the Mole & Chicken at Easington (plenty of atmosphere in this snug and chatty dining pub, a favourite with many readers), the friendly and imaginative Green Dragon in Haddenham, the consistently well run and enjoyable Polecat at Prestwood (gaining its Food Award this year), and the nicely individual Frog in Skirmett (very good all round, and recommended as a place to stay). All these are great for a special meal out; it's the Mole & Chicken at Easington which takes the title of Buckinghamshire Dining Pub of the Year. Other pubs here currently earning high praise are the Red Lion at Chenies (good all round), the bustling and properly pubby Full Moon on Hawridge Common (enjoyable food and particularly good on the drinks side), the cheerful White Horse at Hedgerley (pleasing us all so much that this year it wins a Star), the ancient Crown at Penn (an outstanding Chef & Brewer, run exceptionally well), and the well run old Bull & Butcher in the honeypot Chilterns village of Turville (good food and wine). Some of entries in the Lucky Dip section at the end of the chapter also deserve a special mention: the Old Thatched Inn at Adstock, Pheasant at Brill, Ivy House in Chalfont St Giles, Chester Arms at Chicheley, Red Lion at Coleshill, Crown at Cuddington, Prince Albert at Frieth, Cross Keys in Great Missenden, Rising Sun at Little Hampden, Kings Head at Little Marlow, Blackwood Arms on Littleworth Common, Swan in Olney, Old Swan at The Lee, George & Dragon at West Wycombe and Royal Standard on Wooburn Common. Drinks in the county tend to be higher than the national average, even among pubs going out of their way to ship in beers from distant small breweries (often the cheapest). Good local brews to look out for include Vale and Rebellion.

BENNETT END SU7897 Map 4 🏠
Three Horseshoes

Horseshoe Road; from Radnage follow unclassified road towards Princes Risborough and turn left into Bennett End Road, then right into Horseshoe Road

The location of this unpretentious old country inn is a major draw for many of our readers. It's set in a tranquil village and overlooks a lovely wooded valley and the hillside beyond, and the friendly licensees tell us you would be really unlucky not to see a number of the magnificent red kites circling overhead. There are tables and benches in the garden and a rather endearing red telephone box that is gradually sinking into one of the duck ponds; it's lit up at night and you can watch the ducks swimming in and around it. Inside, the pub is cosy with five separate seating areas. To the left of the entrance (mind your head) is the flagstoned snug bar – fine for walking boots and well behaved dogs, with a log fire in the raised stone fireplace, and original brickwork and bread oven. To the right of the entrance are two further sitting areas, one with a long wooden winged settle and the other enclosed by standing timbers with wooden flooring and a woodburning stove. The areas are decorated with some antiques and sporting prints, wartime silk postcards, horsebrasses, and ancient bottles and lamps. The carpeted two-part no smoking restaurant overlooks the garden and valley beyond. Well kept Adnams, Brakspears, and Hop Back Summer Lightning on handpump, plus six wines by the glass. Traditional bar food at lunchtime might include soup (£3.95), sandwiches (£3.95; filled baguettes and ciabatta £4.95), home-cooked ham and egg or sausage and mash with red onion gravy (£6.25), ploughman's or moules marinière (£6.95), field mushrooms with goats cheese and tomato (£7.25), and home-made steak in ale pie (£9.95); evening choices such as home-made chicken pâté (£3.95), king scallops with lemon butter (£5.95), chicken curry (£6.95), vegetable and nut stir fry (£7.25), steaks (from £12.95), rack of lamb with mint gravy or beef stroganoff (£14.95), and half a crispy roast duck with orange and Cointreau sauce (£15.95), and puddings like apple and fruit crumble or banoffi pie (£3.95). Readers have enjoyed staying here and the breakfasts are good. Children must be well behaved. *(Recommended by Derek and Sylvia Stephenson, Peter Abbott, J Simmonds, Heather Couper, Mr and Mrs R J Timberlake, Bruce and Sharon Eden, Roy and Gay Hoing, Paul Humphreys)*

Free house ~ Licensee Richard Howard ~ Real ale ~ Bar food (not Sun evening) ~ Restaurant ~ (01494) 483273 ~ Children in eating area of bar and restaurant ~ Open 12-3, 5-11; 12-11 Sat; 12-10.30 Sun ~ Bedrooms: £65S/£78B

BOVINGDON GREEN SU8286 Map 2

Royal Oak 🍽 ♀

¾ mile N of Marlow, on back road to Frieth signposted off West Street (A4155) in centre

This is a well organised and civilised country pub in a pleasant rural spot with quite an emphasis placed on the seasonally changing food. Several attractively decorated areas open off the central bar, the half-panelled walls variously painted in pale blue, green or cream: the cosiest part is the low-beamed room closest to the car park, with three small tables, a woodburner in an exposed brick fireplace, and a big pile of logs. Throughout there's a mix of church chairs, stripped wooden tables and chunky wall seats, with rugs on the partly wooden, partly flagstoned floors, co-ordinated cushions and curtains, and a very bright, airy feel; thoughtful extra touches set the tone, with a big, square bowl of olives on the bar, smart soaps and toiletries in the lavatories, and carefully laid out newspapers – most tables have fresh flowers or candles. The raised dining area is no smoking. Using as much local produce as possible, the popular food might include soup (£4), goats cheese, toasted pine nut and spinach empanadilla (a small stuffed patty) with black olive and red onion salsa (£5.75), smoked salmon and prawn roulade with bloody mary dressing (£6.50), free-range pork and herb sausages with onion gravy (£10), field mushroom and asparagus pastry with watercress sauce and green beans (£10.75), smoked haddock on spinach and potato pancake with sorrel cream sauce (£12.50), slow-cooked local lamb parcel on braised puy lentil stew (£13.25), daily specials like smoked coarse pork and cranberry terrine with red onion and orange relish (£5.75), duck breast, chorizo and spring onion salad (£6.25), gruyère, rocket and slow-roasted tomato risotto (£10.25), and roasted monkfish on clam, mussel and parsley broth (£13.50), and puddings such as warm chocolate brownie with chocolate sauce, poached pear and pistachio crumble or honey and cinnamon rice pudding with roast fig (from £4.75); side orders of vegetables (from £2.50). A good few tables may have reserved signs (it's worth booking ahead, especially on Sundays). Well kept Brakspears, Fullers London Pride and Marlow Rebellion on handpump, and up to 15 wines by the glass plus a further 11 pudding wines; quick, helpful service, and piped music. A terrace with good solid tables leads to an appealing garden with plenty more, and there's a smaller garden at the side as well. The pub is part of a little group which comprises the Alford Arms in Frithsden (see Hertfordshire main entries) and the Swan at Denham (see opposite page). *(Recommended by Susan and John Douglas, Mrs Ann Gray, DM, Howard Dell, David Edwards, Phil Roberts, Tracey and Stephen Groves, Mrs E A Macdonald, Heather Couper, Michael Dandy, Jeff and Wendy Williams)*

Enterprise ~ Lease Trasna Rice Giff and David Salisbury ~ Real ale ~ Bar food (12-2.30 (3 Sun), 7-10) ~ (01628) 488611 ~ Children welcome ~ Dogs allowed in bar ~ Open 11-11; 12-10.30 Sun; closed 25-26 Dec

CADMORE END SU7892 Map 4
Old Ship ◀
B482 Stokenchurch—Marlow

There's plenty of unpretentious charm in this tiny and carefully restored 17th-c cottage. The two little low-beamed rooms of the bar are separated by standing timbers and simply furnished with scrubbed country tables and bench and church chair seating (one still has a hole for a game called five-farthings). Well kept Brakspears, Butts, Vale and Youngs tapped straight from the cask; unobtrusive piped music and shove-ha'penny. Outside, there are seats in the sheltered garden with a large pergola and a terrace at the end of the bar with cushioned seats and clothed tables. Simple bar food includes home-made soup or pâté (£4.95), filled organic baguettes with chips or caramelised red onion and goats cheese tart, local sausages and mash or local ham and eggs, and home-made steak and ale pie (£7.95), with puddings such as treacle sponge or spotted dick (£2.95); the small dining room is no smoking. Parking is on the other side of the road. More reports please. *(Recommended by Tracey and Stephen Groves, the Didler, Pete Baker, Angus Johnson, Carol Bolden)*

Free house ~ Licensee Philip Butt ~ Real ale ~ Bar food (12-2, 6-9, not Mon lunch) ~ Restaurant ~ (01494) 883496 ~ Open 11.30-2.30, 5-11; 11.30-3, 7-10.30 Sun; closed Mon lunchtime

CHALFONT ST GILES SU9893 Map 4
White Hart
Three Households (main street, W)

Although the civilised front bar is where the friendly, chatty locals like to gather for a drink at the barstools, one or two pub tables, and couple of liberally cushioned dark green settees, the main emphasis is on the dining area. This extended, spreading room has been newly decorated this year, and is mainly bare boards (the bright acoustics make for a lively medley of chatter – sometimes rather on the noisy side when it's busy) with leather seating and modern art on the walls. As well as sandwiches, the good modern food at lunchtime might include salad of warm confit of duck with asparagus, pine nuts, and avocado (£6.75), moules marinière or smoked salmon and haddock fishcakes with a tomato and herb sauce (£7.95), and stir-fried peppered chicken with oriental vegetables (£9.25); also, warmed speciality breads with tapenade, roasted garlic and rosemary oil (£3.95), lobster, crab and crayfish open ravioli in a light cucumber fish broth (£8.50), fried foie gras with fig sauterne chutney and toasted brioche (£10.50), a trio of sausages with caramelised onion gravy and streaky bacon crisps (£10.75), cod in beer batter with minted mushy peas and home-made tartare sauce (£10.95), braised lamb shank of cheesy bubble and squeak with rosemary infused jus (£13.95), paupiettes of sole stuffed with a prawn and lobster mousse with mussel and saffron cream (£15.75), and puddings such as sticky toffee pudding with butterscotch sauce, mango crème brûlée with berry fruits or warm chocolate fondant with vanilla crème fraîche (from £4.95). Well kept Greene King IPA, Morlands Original and Old Speckled Hen on handpump, and several wines by the glass; broadsheet daily papers, piped music, and neatly dressed young staff. A sheltered back terrace has squarish picnic-sets under cocktail parasols, with more beyond in the garden, which has a neat play area. *(Recommended by Howard Dell, Alison Cook, Ann Gray, Tracey and Stephen Groves, Roy and Gay Hoing)*

Greene King ~ Lease Scott MacRae ~ Real ale ~ Bar food (12-2, 6.30(7 Sun)-9.30) ~ Restaurant ~ (01494) 872441 ~ Children in eating area of bar and restaurant ~ Dogs allowed in bar ~ Open 11.30-2.30, 6-11; 12-10.30 Sun; 12-3, 7-10.30 Sun in winter ~ Bedrooms: £77.50S/£97.50S

CHENIES TQ0198 Map 3
Red Lion ★ 🍺

2 miles from M25 junction 18; A404 towards Amersham, then village signposted on right; Chesham Road

'As good as ever' is a comment we get regularly about this well run pub. The bustling, unpretentious L-shaped bar has comfortable built-in wall benches by the front windows, other traditional seats and tables, and original photographs of the village and traction engines; there's also a small no smoking back snug and a dining room. Very well kept Marlow Rebellion Lion Pride (brewed for the pub), Vale Best Bitter, Wadworths 6X, and a guest beer on handpump, and at least ten wines by the glass. Popular food from quite a wide menu includes filled baguettes or wholemeal baps (from £3.65; hot steak and onion £6.50), filled baked potatoes (from £4.95), several starters and snacks in two sizes such as pasta carbonara (£5.50 starter, £7.75 main course), antipasti with a tomato and onion salad or various dips with corn chips (£5.50 starter, £8.25 main course), and chicken liver pâté (£5.50 starter, £8.75 main course), balti potatoes with spinach and feta cheese (£7.50), lamb pie (£8.50), bangers and bubble and squeak in a rich red wine gravy (£8.95), moroccan chicken with couscous (£10.95), huge ham hock with parsley sauce (£11.95), mahi mahi with chilli sauce (£12.95), daily specials such as monkfish wrapped in bacon on a bed of asparagus, rocket and tomato (£5.95) or ham, leek and potato bake in cheese sauce (£7.95), and puddings like key lime pie (from £2.95). The hanging baskets and window boxes are pretty in summer, and there are picnic-sets on a small side terrace. No children, games machines or piped music. *(Recommended by Val and Alan Green, Derek and Sylvia Stephenson, Mrs Pamela Quinn, Peter and Giff Bennett, LM, Tracey and Stephen Groves, Ian Phillips, Michael B Griffith, M G Hart, L Elliott, Peter Abbott, Susan and John Douglas, Roy and Gay Hoing, Charles Gysin)*

Free house ~ Licensee Mike Norris ~ Real ale ~ Bar food (12-2, 7-10(9.30 Sun)) ~ (01923) 282722 ~ Dogs allowed in bar ~ Open 11-2.30, 5.30-11; 12-3, 6.30-10.30 Sun; closed 25 Dec

DENHAM TQ0486 Map 3
Swan 🍽️ 🍷

¾ mile from M40 junction 1 or M25 junction 16; follow Denham Village signs

In May when the wisteria is flowering, this civilised pub and the other old tiled village buildings here are a very pretty sight. The stylish furnishings include a nice mix of antique and old-fashioned chairs and solid tables, with individually chosen pictures on the cream and warm green walls, rich heavily draped curtains, inviting open fires (usually lit), newspapers to read, and fresh flowers. Promptly served by courteous staff, the interesting food includes soup (£4), potted brown shrimps (£6), home-smoked duck breast with piccalilli (£6.25), free-range pork and grain mustard sausages with caramelised onion gravy (£10), home-made spaghetti with wild mushrooms, sun-dried tomatoes and truffle oil (£10.50), oak-smoked bacon on bubble and squeak with hollandaise sauce and poached egg (£11.50), chargrilled calves liver with cumin spiced potatoes and soured cream (£13), grilled bass fillets on niçoise salad (£13.25), daily specials like chive, spring onion and smoked cheese risotto (£5.75), and warm chicken and black pudding salad with herb dressing (£10.75), and puddings such as croissant bread and butter pudding with brown bread ice-cream or rich chocolate fondant with tonka bean ice-cream (from £4.25); the dining room is no smoking. A good wine list includes over a dozen by the glass plus 11 sweet wines, and they keep Courage Best, Morrells Oxford Blue and

Wadworths 6X on handpump; piped music. The extensive garden is floodlit at night, and leads from a sheltered terrace with tables to a more spacious lawn. It can get busy at weekends, and parking may be difficult. The pub is part of a little group which comprises the Royal Oak, Bovingdon Green (also in this chapter) and the Alford Arms in Frithsden (see Hertfordshire main entries). *(Recommended by Jill Bickerton, Ian Phillips, Howard Dell, A P Seymour, Jane Pritchard, Karen Barr, Mrs Ann Gray, Tracey and Stephen Groves, Peter Saville, Geoffrey Kemp, Susan and John Douglas, Nigel Howard)*

Scottish Courage ~ Lease Mark Littlewood and David Salisbury ~ Real ale ~ Bar food (12-2.30(3 Sun), 7-10) ~ Restaurant ~ (01895) 832085 ~ Children welcome ~ Dogs allowed in bar ~ Open 11-11; 12-10.30 Sun; closed 25 and 26 Dec

DORNEY SU9279 Map 2

Palmer Arms ♀

2.7 miles from M4 junction 7; turn left on to A4, then left on B3026; Village Road

In an attractive conservation village yet handy for the motorway, this smartly modernised and extended pub is currently drawing very high praise for its excellently prepared and presented food. Lunchtime meals might include a platter of smoked meats, fish and cheese or home-made burgers with brie and parma ham glaze (£8.50), mussels from Cornwall with Plymouth gin, thyme, and crème fraîche (£9), and open tart of portobello mushrooms with sweet red onions and a soft cheese glaze (£12.50), while evening dishes typically take in roast duck breast with potato rösti, or slow roast lamb shank with butterbean and chorizo cassoulet (£15), and seared bass with creamed potato and spring onion dressing (£16). They also have a variety of set menus, at lunchtime (£11 for two courses, £14 for three), dinner (two courses £15.50, £18.50 for three), and their monthly 'Bubbles with Jazz' nights (when dinner includes unlimited champagne), as well as a separate menu for afternoon teas. Service is impeccable, though in the evenings may incur a 10% surcharge. Relaxed and civilised, the bar has several separate-seeming areas around a central counter, with a nicely polished wooden floor, newspapers, a couple of fireplaces and the occasional sofa, fresh flowers, mirrors, and art for sale on the walls; piped music. At the back is a more elegant no smoking dining room, with exposed brick walls, long red curtains, solid wooden tables and brown leather armchairs. It opens on to a terrace overlooking a very attractively landscaped palm-filled garden, with plenty of stylish tables and chairs. Well kept Greene King IPA, Abbot, Old Speckled Hen and seasonal beers on handpump, home-made lemonade, various teas and coffees, and a good, extensive range of wines; despite the emphasis on food, this is still the kind of place where locals come to drink. The drive from here to Eton throws up splendid views of Windsor Castle. *(Recommended by I D Barnett, Susan and John Douglas, Michael Dandy, E B Ireland)*

Greene King ~ Tenant Elizabeth Dax ~ Real ale ~ Bar food (12-2(3 Sun), 6.30-9.30; no food Sun evenings) ~ Restaurant ~ (01628) 666612 ~ Children in restaurant ~ Jazz Thurs evenings and monthly Suns ~ Open 11-11; 12-10 Sun; closed Sun evenings Jan-Mar

EASINGTON SP6810 Map 4

Mole & Chicken ⑪ ♀ ⇌

From B4011 in Long Crendon follow Chearsley, Waddesdon signpost into Carters Lane opposite the Chandos Arms, then turn left into Chilton Road

Buckinghamshire Dining Pub of the Year

This is very much somewhere to come for a special meal, and readers have particularly enjoyed their visits here recently. The open-plan layout is cleverly done, so that all the different parts seem quite snug and self-contained without being cut off from what's going on, and the atmosphere is relaxed and sociable. The beamed bar curves around the serving counter in a sort of S-shape, and there are pink walls with lots of big antique prints, flagstones, and (even at lunchtime) lit candles on the medley of tables to go with the nice mix of old chairs; good winter log fires. Delicious, generously served food might include sandwiches, home-made soup such as roasted baby marrow and stilton (£3.50), skewers of chicken and prawn with peanut dip, chilli, and garlic mayonnaise, deep-fried brie with redcurrant jelly or chicken livers with bacon and onions (£5.95), baked field mushrooms with spinach and mascarpone cheese wrapped in filo pastry (£8.95), popular rack of pork ribs in barbecue sauce or home-made smoked chicken and asparagus puff pastry pie (£9.95), bass fillet stuffed with roasted vegetables (£10.95), thai prawn curry or crispy gressingham duck with orange sauce (£12.95), slow-roasted shoulder of lamb (£13.95), and seasonal puddings (£4.95). They serve a good choice of wines (with decent french house wines), over 40 malt whiskies, and well kept Greene King Old Speckled Hen, Hook Norton Best, and Wadworths 6X on handpump; piped music. The garden, where they sometimes hold summer barbecues and pig and lamb roasts, has quite a few tables and chairs. *(Recommended by Neil and Angela Huxter, R E Dixon, Richard Siebert, Martin and Karen Wake, Jenny and Peter Lowater, Peter D B Harding, Ian Phillips, John Reilly, Angus Johnson, Carol Bolden, David and Pam Lewis, Jeff and Wendy Williams, Karen and Graham Oddey)*

Free house ~ Licensees A Heather and S Ellis ~ Real ale ~ Bar food ~ Restaurant ~ (01844) 208387 ~ Children in restaurant ~ Dogs allowed in bar ~ Open 12-3, 6.30-11; 12-10.30 Sun; closed 25 Dec ~ Bedrooms: £50B/£65B

FORD SP7709 Map 4
Dinton Hermit ◿
SW of Aylesbury

Although locals do still drop into this neat 16th-c stone cottage for just a drink, there's quite an emphasis on the enjoyable food. The bar has scrubbed tables and comfortable cushioned and wicker-backed mahogany-look chairs on a nice old black and red tiled floor, a huge inglenook fireplace, and white-painted plaster on very thick uneven stone walls. There's an old print of John Bigg, the supposed executioner of King Charles I and the man later known as the Dinton Hermit. The extended back dining area is very much in character, with similar furniture on quarry tiles. A nice touch is the church candles lit throughout the bar and restaurant, and there are hundreds of bottles of wine decorating the walls and thick oak bar counter. As well as lunchtime sandwiches (from £3.95) and salads (from £5.50), the generously served dishes might include home-made soup (£4.95), tempura of fresh squid rings with oriental dressing and herb salad (£5.95), chicken livers fried with mushrooms, shallots, garlic and chilli (£6.95), corn fed chicken legs with spring vegetables (£12.95), pork mignons with prunes and armagnac (£15.95), whole lemon sole grilled with prawns (£16.95), and daily specials such as moules marinière (£6.95), marinated fillets of bass with chilli, garlic and coriander (£14.50), and fillet of beef wellington (£17.50). Well kept Adnams, Batemans XB, and Brakspears on handpump, and a decent choice of wines; friendly and attentive service, and a congenial atmosphere. The huge garden has plenty of seats, and the comfortable, well decorated bedrooms are in a sympathetically converted barn. *(Recommended by Michael Jones, L Graham, Peter and Pat Branchflower, Nigel Ward, John and Pauline Day, Peter and Gill Helps, Helen Hodson, Barry Collett, Julia and Richard Tredgett)*

Free house ~ Licensees John and Debbie Colinswood ~ Real ale ~ Bar food (not Sun evening) ~ Restaurant ~ (01296) 747473 ~ Children in eating area of bar and restaurant, must be over 13 in evening ~ Open 11-11; 12-10.30 Sun; closed 25-26 Dec, 1 Jan ~ Bedrooms: /£100S

FORTY GREEN SU9292 Map 2
Royal Standard of England
3 miles from M40 junction 2, via A40 to Beaconsfield, then follow sign to Forty Green, off B474 ¾ mile N of New Beaconsfield; keep going through village

As the oldest free house in England, this ancient place certainly has plenty to look at – both in the layout of the building itself and in the fascinating collection of antiques which fills it. The rambling rooms have huge black ship's timbers, finely carved old oak panelling, roaring winter fires with handsomely decorated iron firebacks, and there's a massive settle apparently built to fit the curved transom of an Elizabethan ship; you can also see rifles, powder-flasks and bugles, ancient pewter and pottery tankards, lots of brass and copper, needlework samplers, and stained glass. Under the new licensee bar food includes sandwiches (from £3.95), cottage pie (£6.50), liver and bacon (£7.50), ham and eggs or pork sausages and gravy (£7.95), cod and chips (£9.95), rib-eye steak (£14.95), and puddings (£3.95). Well kept Brakspears Bitter, Marstons Pedigree, Rebellion IPA, and a couple of guest beers on handpump; the main dining bar and one other area are no smoking. There's a story that Charles II hid in the priest's hole here on his escape to France in 1651 after the Battle of Worcester. There are seats outside in a neatly hedged front rose garden, or in the shade of a tree. (Recommended by Tracey and Stephen Groves, Susan and John Douglas, Nigel Howard, Mrs Ann Gray, the Didler, Ian Phillips, Jarrod and Wendy Hopkinson, John Reilly, Michael Dandy)

Free house ~ Licensee Matthew O'Keeffe ~ Real ale ~ Bar food (all day) ~ (01494) 673382 ~ Children welcome ~ Dogs welcome ~ Open 11-11; 12-10.30 Sun; 25 Dec evening

HADDENHAM SP7408 Map 4

Green Dragon 🍴 ♀

Village signposted off A418 and A4129, E/NE of Thame; then follow Church End signs

There's no doubt that most customers come to this well run and warmly welcoming dining pub to enjoy the imaginative modern cooking. The whole place is now no smoking, and the neatly kept opened-up bar, in colours of pale olive and antique rose, has an open fireplace towards the back of the building and attractive furnishings throughout; the dining area has a fine mix of informal tables and chairs. From the imaginative menu there might be home-made soup or pork rillette with a pear and mandarin chutney (£4.25), goats cheese and sun-dried tomato parcel with an orange infused ratatouille (£5.75), salmon and crab fishcake with a lemon and basil rouille (£6), confit of duck glazed with local honey and black pepper on pineapple chutney (£6.75), open wild mushroom and leek ravioli with a thyme velouté (£9.95), home-made steak and kidney suet pudding in local ale (£10.50), corn fed chicken on asparagus risotto with baby morel sauce (£10.95), calves liver and bacon on spring onion mash with caramelised baby onion sauce (£11.50), fish and chips in beer batter with home-made chips and mushy peas (£12), daily specials such as pork and leek sausages with onion jus (£7.95) or fillet of salmon on country vegetables with fish bisque (£9.75), and puddings like home-made sticky toffee and date pudding with toffee sauce, cappuccino crème brûlée and hand-made chocolates or a duo of chocolate and raspberry mousse with raspberry sorbet (£5.50); a discretionary 10% service charge is added to the bill. On Tuesday and Thursday evenings, they do an excellent value two-course dinner (£11.95), best to book. Well kept Vale Wychert Ale on handpump, and around eight wines by the glass. A big sheltered gravel terrace behind the pub has white tables and picnic-sets under cocktail parasols, with more on the grass, and a good variety of plants. This part of the village is very pretty, with a duck pond unusually close to the church. (Recommended by B H and J I Andrews, Tracey and Stephen Groves, Stuart Turner, Brian Root, B Brewer, Tim and Janet Mears, Jeff and Wendy Williams, Jeremy Woods, Tim and Ann Newell, Paul Coleman, John and Claire Pettifer, Phyl and Jack Street, J Woollatt, Mike and Sue Richardson, Keith Rutter, Inga Davis, Jonathan and Virginia West, John Reilly, Ian Arthur)

Enterprise ~ Lease Peter Moffat ~ Real ale ~ Bar food ~ Restaurant ~ (01844) 291403 ~ Children over 7 in restaurant lunchtime only ~ Open 11.30-2.30, 6.30-11; 12-2.30 Sun; closed Sun evening, 1 Jan

---

We checked prices with the pubs as we went to press in summer 2005. They should hold until around spring 2006 – when our experience suggests that you can expect an increase of around 10p in the £.

HAWRIDGE COMMON SP9406 Map 4
Full Moon 🍺

Hawridge Common; left fork off A416 N of Chesham, then follow for 3.5 miles towards Cholesbury

This is a proper country pub with a smashing mix of customers and a happy, bustling atmosphere. It's in a pretty setting and there are plenty of walks over the common from here; in summer, you can sit at seats on the terrace (which has an awning and outside heaters for cooler evenings) and gaze over the windmill nestling behind. The low-beamed rambling bar is the heart of the building, with oak built-in floor-to-ceiling settles, ancient flagstones and flooring tiles, hunting prints, and an inglenook fireplace. A fine choice of six real ales might include Adnams, Bass, Brakspears Special, and Fullers London Pride, and weekly changing guests such as Shepherd Neame Spitfire or Wells Bombardier on handpump, and there are eight wines by the glass; good service, and piped music. Enjoyable lunchtime bar food such as sandwiches (from £3.50), home-made soup (£4.50), pâté of the day (£5.25), ginger and lemon grass chicken kebabs with sweet chilli dip (£5.50), filled baked potatoes (£5.95), home-cooked ham and egg (£8.25), beer battered cod (£8.95), and a vegetarian dish or pork and apple sausages with roasted shallot gravy (£9.25); in the evening, there might be smoked haddock, spinach and emmenthal gratin (£5.75), duck and potato millefeuille (£5.95), fresh fish of the day (£9.25), steak and kidney pudding (£9.95), guinea fowl, pomegranate, spinach and thyme casserole (£12.95), leg steak of organic spring lamb marinated in tomato, garlic and basil (£13.95), and steaks (from £13.95); puddings (£4.50). Both the restaurants are no smoking. *(Recommended by Tracey and Stephen Groves, Mark Percy, Lesley Mayoh, Sue Rowland, Paul Mallett, Brian Root, Peter and Giff Bennett, Mel Smith, D J and P M Taylor, Roy and Gay Hoing)*

Enterprise ~ Lease Peter and Annie Alberto ~ Real ale ~ Bar food (not Sun evening) ~ Restaurant ~ (01494) 758959 ~ Children welcome ~ Dogs allowed in bar ~ Open 12-11; 12-10.30 Sun; closed 25 Dec

HEDGERLEY SU9686 Map 2
White Horse ★ 🍺

2.4 miles from M40 junction 2; at exit roundabout take Slough turn-off then take Hedgerley Lane (immediate left) following alongside M40; after 1.5 miles turn right at T junction into Village Lane

'If all main entries had to match this pub, the *Good Pub Guide* would be very small' said one long-standing reporter about this particularly well run pub. It's a reliably enjoyable country local with hard-working and enthusiastic licensees, and a fine range of seven real ales all tapped from the cask in a room behind the tiny hatch counter: Greene King IPA and Rebellion IPA are well kept alongside five daily changing guests from anywhere in the country, with good farm cider and perry, and belgian beers too; their regular ale festivals are very popular. The cottagey main bar has plenty of character, with lots of beams, brasses and exposed brickwork, low wooden tables, some standing timbers, jugs, ballcocks and other bric-a-brac, a log fire, and a good few leaflets and notices about future village events. There is a little flagstoned public bar on the left; darts. On the way out to the garden, which has tables and occasional barbecues, they have a canopy extension to help during busy periods. The atmosphere is jolly with warmly friendly service from the cheerful staff. At lunchtimes they do bar food such as sandwiches (from £3.25), ploughman's (from £5), and changing straightforward hot dishes. In front are lots of hanging baskets, with a couple more tables overlooking the quiet road. There are good walks nearby, and the pub is handy for the Church Wood RSPB reserve. It can get crowded at weekends. *(Recommended by Tracey and Stephen Groves, Susan and John Douglas, the Didler, Stuart Turner, Dennis Jenkin, Simon Collett-Jones, Michael B Griffith, Nina Randall, Anthony Longden, N R White, Roy and Gay Hoing)*

Free house ~ Licensees Doris Hobbs and Kevin Brooker ~ Real ale ~ Bar food (lunchtime

only) ~ (01753) 643225 ~ Children in canopy extension area ~ Dogs allowed in bar ~
Open 11-2.30, 5-11; 11-11 Sat; 12-10.30 Sun

LEY HILL SP9802 Map 4

Swan 🍺

Village signposted off A416 in Chesham

This charming little timbered 16th-c pub has a chatty mix of locals and visitors and
a nice old-fashioned pubby atmosphere. The main bar has black beams (mind your
head) and standing timbers, an old range, a log fire and a collection of old local
photographs, and a cosy snug. Under the new licensees, bar snacks might include
baked brie wrapped in filo pastry with cranberry sauce (£6.95), plate of cold
charcuterie with tomato chutney and focaccia (£7.50), and duck pâté with
raspberry vinaigrette, smoked ham and gruyère omelette or minute steak baguette
with creamed horseradish (all £7.95), as well as home-made soup (£3.95),
fishcakes with lemon and dill mayonnaise (£4.95), seared scallops wrapped in
parma ham with pawpaw, mango and coriander salsa (£7.95), herb pancake
stuffed with mediterranean vegetables and mozzarella with garlic and tomato sauce
(£9.50), corn-fed chicken breast on dauphinoise potatoes (£10.50), grilled loin of
tuna on chive mash with pepper and tomato sauce (£12.50), roast lamb on chorizo
and shallot potatoes with marsala jus (£14.95), and puddings such as raspberry and
white chocolate cheesecake with raspberry coulis or orange and lemon tart with
meringue and lemon sorbet (from £4.25); they also offer two-course (£9.95) and
three-course (£12.50) menus. The restaurant is no smoking. Well kept Adnams,
Brakspears, Fullers London Pride, Hook Norton, Timothy Taylors Landlord and
Youngs Ordinary on handpump, and seven wines by the glass. In front of the pub
amongst the flower tubs and hanging baskets, there are picnic-sets with more in the
large back garden. There's a cricket pitch, a nine-hole golf course, and a common
opposite. *(Recommended by Anthony Barnes, B Brewer, Conor McGaughey, Susan and
John Douglas, Hunter and Christine Wright, Roy and Gay Hoing)*

Punch ~ Lease Nigel Byatt ~ Real ale ~ Bar food ~ Restaurant ~ (01494) 783075 ~
Children in eating area of bar and in restaurant but no small children in evening ~ Open
12-11; 12-10.30 Sun

LITTLE MISSENDEN SU9298 Map 4

Crown ★ 🍺 £

Crown Lane, SE end of village, which is signposted off A413 W of Amersham

This small brick cottage has been run by the same family now for more than 90
years. It's popular locally, has a proper traditional pubby feel (sometimes cheerfully
boisterous), and the friendly licensee keeps the bustling bars spotlessly clean. There
are old red flooring tiles on the left, oak parquet on the right, built-in wall seats,
studded red leatherette chairs, and a few small tables. You'll find darts, shove-
ha'penny, cribbage, and dominoes, but no piped music or machines. Adnams,
Fullers London Pride, and a guest or two from brewers such as Batemans,
Brakspears, and Vale on handpump, and decent malt whiskies. Straightforward bar
food includes good fresh sandwiches (from £3), ploughman's (from £4.50), buck's
bite (a special home-made pizza-like dish) or steak and kidney pie (£4.95), and
winter soup (£3.75). The large attractive sheltered garden behind has picnic-sets
and other tables, and the interesting church in the pretty village is well worth a
visit. No children. More reports please. *(Recommended by Tracey and Stephen Groves,
E A and D C T Frewer, Mr and Mrs John Taylor, Brian Root, P Price, Anthony Longden)*

Free house ~ Licensees Trevor and Carolyn How ~ Real ale ~ Bar food (lunchtime only) ~
No credit cards ~ (01494) 862571 ~ Open 11-2.30(3 Sat), 6-11; 12-3, 7-11 Sun

---

The 🍺 symbol shows pubs which keep their beer unusually well,
have a particularly good range or brew their own.

MARLOW SU8586 Map 2
Hare & Hounds ♀
Henley Road (A4155 W)

The quarry-tiled cream-walled bar here is heavily black-beamed and – like much of the rest of the pub – pretty minuscule: a few bar stools, a leather sofa and a couple of housekeeper's chairs, with a winter log fire in the big inglenook, and well kept Brakspears Bitter on handpump. There is a small carpeted eating room on the left, and a much bigger dining area on the right, also carpeted and snugly divided, with one or two steps up and down here and there, and little balustrades across door-sized wall openings; this part, no smoking, has a warmly relaxed feel, helped along by its gentle lighting. Bar food includes home-made soup (£4.25), chicken liver pâté with apple and apricot chutney (£5.25), sandwiches (from £5.50; steak sandwich with caramelised onion and roasted tomato on warm ciabatta £7.50), lamb and mint burger with rocket and endive salad (£7.25), asparagus, mushroom and cheese strudel (£10.75), chicken supreme filled with buffalo mozzarella wrapped in parma ham on wilted spinach with cherry tomato and red onion chutney (£11.25), tournedos of salmon with seared scallops and a mussel and chervil cream (£13.50), and herb crusted lamb cutlet and saddle of lamb with a sun-dried tomato farce and light lamb jus (£13.95). Monday mussels deal (as much as you can possibly eat, £10). They have a good choice of wines in several glass sizes, and good coffees including espresso; fruit machine and piped music. The front terrace has half a dozen picnic-sets under cocktail parasols (the road isn't too busy), with a few more in the little side garden. (*Recommended by Michael Dandy, John and Glenys Wheeler, Catherine and Richard Preston, Ian Phillips, Fr Robert Marsh*)

Enterprise ~ Lease Bryan and Barry Evans ~ Real ale ~ Bar food (12-2.30(3.30 Sun), 6.30-9.30) ~ Restaurant ~ (01628) 483343 ~ Children in restaurant early evening only ~ Open 11.45-3, 6-11; 11.45-11 Sat; 12-10.30 Sun

MENTMORE SP9119 Map 4
Stag ♀
Village signposted off B488 S of Leighton Buzzard; The Green

As well as champagne cocktails, you can choose from around 50 different wines by the glass in this pretty village pub. There's a small, civilised lounge bar with a relaxed atmosphere, low oak tables, attractive fresh flower arrangements, and an open fire; at times, this may be mainly used by customers heading for the restaurant. The more simple public bar leading off has shove-ha'penny, cribbage and dominoes, and well kept Wells Bombardier, Eagle and IPA and maybe a guest such as Adnams on handpump. Bar food at lunchtime includes sandwiches (£5.50), salads (£6.50), and hot meals such as smoked haddock with kedgeree and fried egg or cheese and mushroom omelette (£8.50), while in the evening there might be lamb curry, fishcakes and fried or vegetarian pasta (£8.50), with puddings such as home-made bread and butter pudding (£4.50). The restaurant is no smoking. There are seats out on the pleasant flower-filled front terrace looking across towards Mentmore House, and a charming, well tended, sloping garden. More reports please. (*Recommended by Mrs Ann Gray, Mrs J Ekins-Daukes, Doreen and Haydn Maddock, Ian Phillips*)

Charles Wells ~ Lease Jenny and Mike Tuckwood ~ Real ale ~ Bar food ~ Restaurant ~ (01296) 668423 ~ Children in eating area of bar and restaurant ~ Dogs allowed in bar ~ Open 12-11(10.30 Sun); may be shorter opening hours in winter

OVING SP7821 Map 4
Black Boy
Village signposted off A413 out of Whitchurch, N of Aylesbury

A distinctive tiled and timbered house near the village church, this appealing 16th-c pub boasts a particularly impressive garden, the tables on its spacious sloping lawns and terrace giving remarkable views down over the Vale of Aylesbury. Now completely no smoking, the building stretches further back than you might expect from the outside, with the old parts at the front the most atmospheric, especially the cosy red and black-tiled area around the enormous inglenook. The low heavy beams have mottoes chalked on, and, up a couple of steps, another snug corner has a single table, some exposed stonework, and a mirror over a small brick fireplace. The long, light wooden bar counter is covered with posters advertising sales of agricultural land; opposite, two big, comfortable leather armchairs lead into the lighter, more modern dining room, with good-sized country kitchen pine tables set for eating, and picture windows offering the same view of the gardens. Throughout are plenty of candles and fresh flowers. There's some emphasis on food, and particularly on their good aberdeen angus steaks (from £12.75), but the monthly changing menu might also typically include sandwiches, soup (£4.25), ploughman's (£6.50), cheese and onion filo parcel with a saffron sauce (£9.75), herb-coated rack of lamb with a red wine and rosemary jus (£12.25), supreme of barbary duck with a morello cherry and port jus or smoked haddock fillet with bubble and squeak and poached egg (£12.75), and daily specials; choice of Sunday roasts (£8.50), and children's meals. Service is friendly, but as meals are cooked to order can slow down at weekends. Two well kept real ales such as Caledonian Deuchars IPA and Hook Norton Old Hooky on handpump (usually cheaper than the norm around here), and a good range of wines by the glass; piped music. The licensees breed and train chocolate labradors. (Recommended by R E Dixon, B H and J I Andrews, Brian Root)

Free house ~ Licensees Sally and David Hayle ~ Real ale ~ Bar food (12(12.30 Sun/bank hols)-2, 6.30-9 (not Sun)) ~ Restaurant ~ (01296) 641258 ~ Well behaved children welcome ~ Dogs allowed in bar ~ Open 12-3, 6-11; 12-4.30 Sun; closed Sun evening, and all day Mon (exc bank hols)

PENN SU9193 Map 4

Crown

B474 Beaconsfield—High Wycombe

This is one of the best Chef & Brewer pubs we've come across. It's a welcoming, creeper-covered dining pub, and the nicely decorated bars are unusually laid out in an old-fashioned style; one comfortable low-ceilinged room used to be a coffin-maker's workshop. The food here is popular, and the menu has a good range of enjoyable dishes. Snacks that are available until 6pm might include cold sandwiches and focaccia (from £2.95), filled baked potatoes (£3.95), hot crusty baguettes (from £4.10), and ploughman's (£4.65); also, home-made soup (£2.95), pork and chicken liver pâté with apple chutney or goats cheese and tomato tart (£3.95), pork and leek sausages with red wine gravy (£5.95), steak and kidney pudding (£6.95), mushroom, spinach, leek and stilton pie (£7.25), chicken breast stuffed with camembert and wrapped in bacon (£8.35), blackened cajun salmon fillet with a sweet soy sauce (£8.95), steaks (from £9.95), and daily specials like italian-style antipasti or garlic prawns (£4.95), duck, orange and apricot sausages (£8.95), pork medallions on mustard mash with red wine sauce (£11.95), and sweet chilli swordfish loin on sweet pepper couscous (£13.95). Well kept Courage Best and a couple of guests such as Fullers London Pride and Wells Bombardier on handpump, and a decent short wine list (they serve all their wines by the glass); maybe piped classical music, and two roaring log fires. The staff are friendly and helpful, and there's a pleasant atmosphere; look out for Toby the pub labrador. Tables in front of the building, amongst pretty roses, face a 14th-c church which has a fine old painting of the Last Judgement. There are pleasant country views and maybe summer weekend barbecues. (Recommended by Geoff Pidoux, Dr D and Mrs B Woods, Ian Phillips, Sean and Sharon Pines, Mrs Ann Gray, D Reay, B Brewer, Geoff and Sylvia Donald, Roy and Gay Hoing)

Spirit Group ~ Manager Peter Douglas ~ Real ale ~ Bar food (12-10) ~ Restaurant ~ (01494) 812640 ~ Children away from bar ~ Open 11-11; 12-10.30 Sun

Our web site (www.goodguides.co.uk) now includes postcodes for pubs.

PRESTWOOD SP8700 Map 4

Polecat 🍴

170 Wycombe Road (A4128 N of High Wycombe)

With its friendly, relaxed atmosphere this bustling pub attracts a loyal following, and at lunchtime there tend to be chatty crowds of middle-aged diners, with a broader mix of ages in the evening. Opening off the low-ceilinged bar are several smallish rooms with an assortment of tables and chairs, various stuffed birds as well as the stuffed white polecats in one big cabinet, small country pictures, rugs on bare boards or red tiles, and a couple of antique housekeeper's chairs by a good open fire; the Gallery room and Drover Bar are no smoking. Enjoyable, home-made dishes from a popular menu could include good lunchtime sandwiches (from £3.50), filled baked potatoes (from £4.90), and ploughman's (£5.50), as well as soup (£3.80), smoked salmon terrine with creamed avocado and melba toast or crab cakes in lemon crumb with chilli jam (£4.90), home-made steak and kidney pie (£8.50), nice greek spinach and feta pie with tomato and basil sauce (£8.90), poached halibut in a mushroom and dill cream sauce (£10.60), calves liver with sage, bacon and cream sauce (£10.80), daily specials like stilton soufflé with red onion marmalade (£4.90), braised shoulder of lamb with tomato, rosemary and olives (£9.40), and corn fed chicken breast stuffed with wild mushrooms in a tarragon cream sauce (£9.90), and puddings such as chocolate torte with cherry coulis or bread and butter pudding (£4.10). Well kept Brakspears, Flowers IPA, Greene King Old Speckled Hen, and Marstons Pedigree on handpump, quite a few wines by the glass, and 20 malt whiskies. The attractive garden has lots of bulbs in spring, and colourful hanging baskets, tubs, and herbaceous plants; quite a few picnic-sets under parasols on neat grass out in front beneath a big fairy-lit pear tree, with more on a big well kept back lawn. *(Recommended by Michael Dandy, Alan and Anne Driver, Chris Hoy, M G Hart, Ken Richards, Tracey and Stephen Groves, B Brewer, Mel Smith, John Branston, Heather Couper, Roy and Lindsey Fentiman, Roy and Gay Hoing)*

Free house ~ Licensee John Gamble ~ Real ale ~ Bar food (12-2, 6.30-9; not Sun evening) ~ Restaurant ~ No credit cards ~ (01494) 862253 ~ Children in family room ~ Dogs welcome ~ Open 11.30-2.30, 6-11; 12-3 Sun; closed Sun evening, evenings 24 and 31 Dec, all day 25-26 Dec, 1 Jan

SKIRMETT SU7790 Map 2

Frog 🍴 ♟ 🛏

From A4155 NE of Henley take Hambleden turn and keep on; or from B482 Stokenchurch—Marlow take Turville turn and keep on

Readers enjoy staying at this bustling country inn and the breakfasts (and home-made biscuits in the room) are very good. The neatly kept beamed bar area has a mix of comfortable furnishings, a striking hooded fireplace with a bench around the edge (and a pile of logs sitting beside it), big rugs on the wooden floors, and sporting and local prints around the salmon painted walls. The function room leading off is sometimes used as a dining overflow. Although brightly modernised, there is still something of a local feel with leaflets and posters near the door advertising raffles and so forth. Served by friendly staff, the good, imaginative food could include lunchtime baguettes, soup (£3.75), delicious caesar salad (£5.75), a risotto of the day (£7.25), lasagne of wild mushrooms and asparagus with chervil cream sauce (£10.50), roast chicken supreme with a tarragon and shallot jus (£11.50), rump steak with a port and stilton sauce (£13.95), and daily specials like grilled mackerel fillet with marinated cucumber and dill crème fraîche (£5.95), salad of avocado, quails egg and hot crispy bacon (£6.25), ham hock and lentil terrine, rocket salad, poached egg and sauce gribiche (£6.85), calves liver and bacon with caramelised onion gravy (£12.95), slow-roasted belly pork with apple mash and cider sauce (£14.50), and steamed halibut on a bed of spinach with a mussel and marjoram broth (£14.95). They also offer a good value two and three-course set menu (£13.95 and £17.50); you must book to be sure of a table. All the food areas are no smoking; piped music. Well kept Adnams, Fullers London Pride, and

Rebellion IPA on handpump, a dozen wines by the glass (including champagne), 20 malt whiskies, and good coffees with generous refills. A side gate leads to a lovely garden with a large tree in the middle, and the unusual five-sided tables are well placed for attractive valley views; lots of surrounding hiking routes. Henley is close by, and just down the road is the delightful Ibstone windmill. *(Recommended by Jeremy Woods, Colin McKerrow, Mike and Sue Richardson, Tracey and Stephen Groves, Michael Dandy, Howard Dell, Paul Humphreys, Martin and Karen Wake, Peter Abbott, Ned Kelly, Anthony Longden, Mike and Mary Carter)*

Free house ~ Licensees Jim Crowe and Noelle Greene ~ Real ale ~ Bar food (12-2.30, 6.30-9.30; not winter Sun evening) ~ Restaurant ~ (01491) 638996 ~ Children in eating area of bar, restaurant and family room ~ Dogs allowed in bar ~ Open 11.30(11 Sat)-3, 6-11; 12-4, 6-10.30 Sun; closed Sun evening Sept-May ~ Bedrooms: £55B/£65B

SOULBURY SP8827 Map 4

Boot ♀

B4032 W of Leighton Buzzard

A fantastic choice of up to 40 wines plus a couple of champagnes is available by the glass in this brightly modernised, civilised village pub. The partly red-tiled bar has a light, sunny feel, thanks mainly to its cream ceilings and pale green walls, and there's a nice mix of smart and individual furnishings, as well as sporting prints and houseplants, and neat blinds on the windows. Friendly, smartly dressed staff serve well kept Greene King IPA and Abbot, and Shepherd Neame Spitfire on handpump from the modern, light wood bar counter, and they've organic fruit juices. One end of the room, with a fireplace and wooden floors, is mostly set for diners, and then at the opposite end, by some exposed brickwork, steps lead down to a couple of especially cosy rooms for eating – a yellow one with beams and another fireplace, and a tiny red one. All the eating areas are no smoking; piped music. As well as pubby choices such as filled ciabatta, onion baps or wholemeal baguettes (from £5.25), home-made minted lamb burger or local sausages (£7.95), and beer-battered fish and chips (£8.50), the good choice of food might include home-made soup (£3.95), chicken liver pâté (£5.25), melting goats cheese, aubergine, basil and tomato stack with sun-dried tomato salad (£5.75), five bean chilli (£9.75), salmon fishcakes with parsley sauce (£10.25), braised pork steak with honey and mustard sauce and baked apple (£10.50), and steak and kidney pie (£11.50), with puddings like cappuccino and irish whiskey brûlée, chocolate and butterscotch brownie or summer berry pudding (from £3.95). Overlooking peaceful fields, there are tables behind in a small garden and on a terrace (with heaters for cooler weather), and a couple more in front. More reports please. *(Recommended by Brian Root, Bob and Maggie Atherton, Susan and John Douglas)*

Pubmaster ~ Lease Greg Nichol, Tina and Paul Stevens ~ Real ale ~ Bar food (12-2.30, 6.30-9.30; 12-4, 6.30-9 Sun) ~ Restaurant ~ (01525) 270433 ~ Children welcome ~ Open 11-11; 12-10.30 Sun; closed 25-26 Dec

STOKE MANDEVILLE SP8310 Map 4

Woolpack

Risborough Road (A4010 S of Aylesbury)

Dramatically transformed over the last couple of years, this partly thatched old pub is a triumphant blend of the traditional with the trendy. Original stripped beams, timbers and a massive inglenook log fireplace comfortably jostle for attention with gleaming round copper-topped tables, low leather armchairs, and rich purple walls; stylish and warmly relaxing, it's an audacious example of contemporary pub design at its best. In the comfortable, knocked-through front areas by the bar it's the wood and low beams that make the deepest impression, but there are also substantial candles artfully arranged around the fireplace, and illuminated Mouton Rothschild wine labels (designed by top artists) on the walls. Beyond here is a big, busily chatty dining room with chunky wooden tables, a dividing wall made up of logs of wood, thick columns with ornate woodcarvings, and a real mix of customers; it's no smoking in here. The menu has an emphasis on home-made wood-fired pizzas like mozzarella, sweetcorn, crayfish and tuna (£7.95) or thai chicken, mango, chilli and rocket (£8.95), and various pasta dishes, but also includes cod with belgian beer in its batter (£9.95), a daily risotto (£10.95), lamb shank with chorizo and mash or calves liver and smoked bacon (£13.95), and fillet steak with béarnaise sauce (£17.95); prompt obliging service from uniformed young staff. Fullers London Pride and Greene King IPA on handpump, decent wines, various coffees; piped light pop or easy listening. The enormous car park filled up quickly on our inspection visit, but there's plenty of room to accommodate everyone comfortably inside, as well as a good few further tables in a neatly landscaped back garden, or in front. *(Recommended by B H and J I Andrews, Susan and John Douglas)*

Mitchells & Butlers ~ Manager Abby Selby ~ Real ale ~ Bar food (12-2.30, 6-9.30; 12-8 Sun) ~ Restaurant ~ (01296) 615970 ~ Children in restaurant ~ Dogs allowed in bar ~ Open 12-11; 12-10.30 Sun

TURVILLE SU7691 Map 2
Bull & Butcher ♀
Off A4155 Henley—Marlow via Hambleden and Skirmett

Even when really busy, the hard-working South African licensees and their helpful staff in this black and white timbered pub remain as cheerful and efficient as ever. There are two low-ceilinged, oak-beamed rooms (the Windmill lounge is no smoking), and the bar has a deep well incorporated into a glass-topped table, with tiled floor, cushioned wall settles and an inglenook fireplace. Well kept Brakspears Bitter, Special, and a seasonal guest on handpump, a good choice of wines by the glass, and Addlestone's cider; piped music. Popular bar food includes five bean salad with quail eggs (£6.95; main course £10.95), crayfish cocktail or seared strips of sirloin with mango dressing (£7.95; main course £11.95), bangers and mash (£10.95), pork medallions with a honey citrus sauce (£12.95), T-bone steak with peppercorn sauce (£16.95), daily specials such as grilled halibut on baby leeks (£7.95; main course £11.95), and duck and ginger stir fry (£11.95), and home-made puddings (£4.95). They do children's helpings (£6.95) and readers are keen on their roast rib-eye Sunday lunch. Cream teas and light bar snacks are served through the day during the summer months; maybe barbecues in good weather. There are seats on the lawn by fruit trees in the attractive garden and a children's play area. The village is popular with television and film companies; *The Vicar of Dibley*, *Midsomer Murders* and *Chitty Chitty Bang Bang* were all filmed here. A fine place to end up after a walk (though no muddy boots), the pub does get crowded at weekends. *(Recommended by Dominic Lucas, Gill and Keith Croxton, Martin and Karen Wake, M Thomas, Susan and John Douglas, Bob and Margaret Holder, Ian Phillips, LM, Piotr Chodzko-Zajko, John and Glenys Wheeler, Simon Collett-Jones, Torrens Lyster, Darren and Jane Staniforth, Jeremy Woods, Angus Johnson, Carol Bolden, Carolyn Dixon, Tracey and Stephen Groves)*

Brakspears ~ Tenants Hugo and Lydia Botha ~ Real ale ~ Bar food (12-2.30, 6.30-9.30; 12-4, 7-9.30 Sun and bank hol Mon) ~ Restaurant ~ (01491) 638283 ~ Children in eating area of bar and restaurant ~ Dogs allowed in bar ~ Open 12-11; 12-10.30 Sun

WOOBURN COMMON SU9187 Map 2
Chequers 🛏

From A4094 N of Maidenhead at junction with A4155 Marlow road keep on A4094 for another ¾ mile, then at roundabout turn off right towards Wooburn Common, and into Kiln Lane; if you find yourself in Honey Hill, Hedsor, turn left into Kiln Lane at the top of the hill; OS Sheet 175 map reference 910870

There's usually quite a mix of customers in the bar here, many drawn from the hotel and restaurant side. Standing timbers and alcoves break up the low-beamed room that is furnished with comfortably lived-in sofas (just right for settling into) on its bare boards, a bright log-effect gas fire, and various pictures, plates, a two-man saw, and tankards. One room is no smoking. They offer a sizeable wine list (with champagne and good wines by the glass), a fair range of malt whiskies and brandies, and well kept Greene King Abbot, IPA, Ruddles County and a guest on handpump; piped music. Bar food includes sandwiches (from £4.95; steak and stilton baguette £7.50), chicken caesar salad (£8.95), salmon and crayfish risotto or home-made burger (£9.95), slow-roasted lamb shank (£10.95), and tuna steak with tomato salsa (£11.95). The spacious garden, set away from the road, has cast-iron tables. The attractive stripped-pine bedrooms are in a 20th-c mock-Tudor wing. More reports please. *(Recommended by A J Murray, John and Glenys Wheeler, Mrs Ann Gray, Edward Mirzoeff, John Saville, Peter and Giff Bennett, Chris Glasson, Steve Derbyshire, Fr Robert Marsh)*

Free house ~ Licensee Peter Roehrig ~ Real ale ~ Bar food ~ Restaurant ~ (01628) 529575 ~ Children welcome ~ Open 10.30-11; 10.30-10.30 Sun ~ Bedrooms: £99.50B/£107.50B

LUCKY DIP

Besides the fully inspected pubs, you might like to try these Lucky Dips recommended to us and described by readers (if you do, please send us reports: www.goodguides.co.uk).

ADSTOCK [SP7229]

Folly [A413 SE of Buckingham]: Refurbished under newish licensees, dining tables in roomy beamed bar, nice light furniture in bright and airy further dining area, wide choice of enjoyable popular food inc tempting puddings, Brakspears and Tetleys, quick friendly service; may be piped music; play area in good-sized garden with fruit and other trees, bedrooms, handy for Buckingham *(Gill and Keith Croxton)*

☆ *Old Thatched Inn* [Main St, off A413]: Beams and flagstones, cosy corners and open fires, part pubby, and part with easy chairs and settees leading to modern restaurant; friendly and comfortable, with generous food from interesting doorstep sandwiches to game and theme nights, well kept Bass and Hook Norton Best, decent wines, good service; seats out in sheltered back garden, children in restaurant and eating area *(LYM, Jess and George Cowley, Ken and Jenny Simmonds)*

AMERSHAM [SU9597]

☆ *Saracens Head* [Whielden St (A404)]: Friendly unspoilt 17th-c local, neat, clean and largely no smoking, with beams, gentle lighting, massive inglenook with roaring fire in ancient decorative fire-basket, interesting décor, enjoyable generous fresh food from baguettes to good locally sourced lamb, well kept Greene King IPA, Old Speckled Hen and Ruddles Best and Hook Norton Old Hooky, winter mulled wine, pleasant staff, cheery chatty landlord; soft piped music; little back terrace, bedrooms *(LYM)*

ASTON ABBOTS [SP8519]

Royal Oak [off A418 NE of Aylesbury; Wingrave Rd]: 14th-c thatched pub with enjoyable generous food, real ales; garden tables, bedrooms *(R E Dixon)*

ASTWOOD [SP9547]

Old Swan [Main Rd]: Smartly refurbished adding an up-to-date touch of style to its low beams, flagstones, inglenook woodburner and nice collection of blue china, two well decorated dining areas, well kept Badger

Tanglefoot, Everards Tiger and Beacon and Fullers London Pride, warm cosy atmosphere, friendly quick service; large garden *(LYM, Michael Dandy, John Saul)*

AYLESBURY [SP8113]

Kings Head [Kings Head Passage]: Well preserved 15th-c inn owned by NT, now completely no smoking after lease taken on by Chiltern Brewery, three of their ales kept well, good limited food choice, wonderful early Tudor window lighting lofty pleasantly overhauled bar, more seats in side room and restaurant; tables out in original courtyard shared with corner arts and crafts shop *(Tim and Ann Newell)*

BEACONSFIELD [SU9489]

Greyhound [a mile from M40 junction 2, via A40; Windsor End, Old Town]: Well run rambling former coaching inn, well kept ales inc Marlow Rebellion, daily papers, small no smoking middle bar room, some emphasis on modern cooking in partly no smoking back bistro area *(Tracey and Stephen Groves, LYM)*

BRILL [SP6514]

☆ *Pheasant* [off B4011 Bicester—Long Crendon; Windmill St]: Simply furnished beamed pub in marvellous spot looking over to ancient working windmill, nearby view over nine counties, friendly service, good choice of food inc sophisticated dishes and popular Sun lunch, well kept ales such as Shepherd Neame Spitfire, good value house wines, attractive dining room up a step; piped music, no dogs; children welcome, verandah tables, superior picnic-sets in garden with decking, bedrooms, open all day wknds *(Ian Phillips, Geoff Pidoux, LYM, Andy Trafford, Louise Bayly, J A Ellis)*

CADSDEN [SP8204]

Plough [Cadsden Rd]: Welcoming, mellow and comfortable, very popular with families and Chilterns ramblers, good range of well kept beers, enjoyable and attractively presented inexpensive food from sandwiches to hearty shoulder of lamb, sensible prices; lots of tables in delightful quiet front and back garden, pretty spot on Ridgeway Path *(Howard C R Shaw)*

CALVERTON [SP7939]

Shoulder of Mutton [just S of Stony Stratford]: Friendly open-plan pub with beams and stripped brickwork, wide range of decent food from sandwiches up inc bargain offers, half a dozen or more well kept ales, good soft drinks choice, quick attentive service, darts; quiet piped music, games machines, quiz and live music nights; big attractive garden with pleasant view and play area, well equipped bedrooms, open all day wknds *(CMW, JJW)*

CHACKMORE [SP6835]

Queens Head [Main St]: Comfortable village pub by Stowe Gardens, with nice local feel in bar, prompt pleasant service, enjoyable lunchtime food, well kept ales such as Palmers, good house wines, small separate dining room *(Guy Vowles)*

CHALFONT ST GILES [SU9895]

☆ *Ivy House* [A413 S]: Smart 18th-c dining pub, wide range of good freshly cooked food, prompt friendly service, well kept changing ales such as Bass and Fullers London Pride, good wines by the glass, espresso coffee, attractive open-plan layout with comfortable fireside armchairs in elegantly cosy L-shaped tiled bar, lighter flagstoned no smoking dining extension; pleasant terrace and sloping garden (can be traffic noise) *(Simon Collett-Jones, BB, J and S French)*

CHALFONT ST PETER [SU9990]

Village Hall [Gold Hill W]: Doing well under newish landlords, good mix of customers, buoyant atmosphere, well kept changing real ales, enjoyable grill-based food; tables out on pleasant deck *(Christine Brown)*

White Hart [High St]: Old low-beamed pub, said to be haunted, pleasantly updated, with civilised atmosphere, some sofas, primrose walls above panelled dado, nice inglenook and large back dining area; well kept Greene King ales, wide choice of decent food, efficient service, daily papers *(Conor McGaughey, Simon Collett-Jones)*

CHEARSLEY [SP7110]

☆ *Bell* [The Green]: Traditional cosy beamed bar with enormous fireplace, well kept Fullers Chiswick, London Pride and seasonal brews, good wines by the glass, bar food from sandwiches up, cribbage, dominoes; children in eating area, dogs welcome, plenty of tables (and play equipment) in spacious back garden, terrace and attractive play area *(LYM, Barry Collett)*

CHICHELEY [SP9045]

☆ *Chester Arms* [quite handy for M1 junction 14]: Cosy and pretty low-beamed pub with rooms off semi-circular bar inc plenty of no smoking space, log fire, comfortable settles and chairs, wide choice of good popular home-made meals inc daily fresh fish (they do lobster with notice) and aberdeen angus beef, children's helpings, good friendly service, well kept Greene King ales, decent wines, good coffee, daily papers, interesting back dining room down steps; darts, fruit machine, quiet

piped music; picnic-sets in small back garden and out in front *(B A Lord, Ryta Lyndley, BB, Gerry and Rosemary Dobson, Michael Dandy, Mr and Mrs D S Price)*

COLESHILL [SU9495]

☆ *Red Lion* : Sensible food prices make this relaxed and unspoilt two-room local well worth knowing – a wide choice of good home-made dishes (not Sun evening) and great sandwiches too, two or three well kept changing ales such as Greene King IPA and Vale Wychert, amiable and interesting helpful licensees, blazing fire, thriving darts and dominoes teams, Tues quiz nights; TV for racing, fruit machine; picnic-sets out in front and in back garden with sturdy dining frames outside, good walks, open all day wknds *(Ann Gray, Howard Dell, Jarrod and Wendy Hopkinson, Michael B Griffith, BB, Roy and Gay Hoing)*

CUDDINGTON [SP7311]

☆ *Crown* [village signed off A418 Thame—Aylesbury; Spurt St]: Small convivial village pub, attractively olde-worlde with candles, low beams, good tables, nicely cushioned settles, pleasant décor and inglenook log fire, prompt friendly service, unusual choice of good food inc interesting hot sandwiches and specials, Fullers Chiswick, London Pride and ESB; appealing small terrace *(R E Dixon, B Brewer, Susan and John Douglas)*

DENHAM [TQ0487]

☆ *Green Man* [Village Rd]: Warm and lively 18th-c pub, beams and flagstones in original part, conservatory dining extension, enjoyable good value main dishes, well kept Fullers London Pride, Greene King IPA and Abbot and Charles Wells Bombardier, decent wines, cheerful willing service, very reasonable prices; piped music; picnic-sets under cocktail parasols on small back terrace, many more in quiet garden beyond *(Jill Bickerton, John and Glenys Wheeler)*

DINTON [SP7610]

Seven Stars [signed off A418 Aylesbury—Thame, nr Gibraltar turn-off; Stars Lane]: Pretty pub with inglenook bar, comfortable beamed lounge and spacious dining room, well kept Fullers London Pride and Charles Wells Bombardier, usual bar food (not Sun evening) from sandwiches and baked potatoes up; tables under cocktail parasols in sheltered garden with terrace, pleasant village, handy for Quainton Steam Centre, has been cl Tues *(Marjorie and David Lamb, LYM, Richard C Morgan)*

DORNEY [SU9279]

Pineapple [off A4 Maidenhead—Cippenham by Sainsburys; Lake End Rd]: Old-fashioned beamery and panelling, gleaming bar, scrubbed tables and woodburner one end, carpeted dining tables opposite, great range of outstanding sandwiches (shame about their names), other food inc Sun roasts, well kept Fullers London Pride, Greene King IPA and Tetleys, decent house wine, quick friendly service even when busy; piped radio, pub games; disabled access, verandah, picnic-sets in garden, good walks, open all day *(Mike and Sue Richardson, Michael Dandy)*

FINGEST [SU7791]

☆ *Chequers* [signed off B482 Marlow—Stokenchurch]: Proper traditional Chilterns local with several rooms around old-fashioned Tudor core, roaring fire in vast fireplace, sunny lounge by good-sized charming and immaculate country garden with lots of picnic-sets, small no smoking room, interesting furniture, Brakspears full range kept well, dominoes and cribbage, lunchtime food (not Mon, and can take a while when busy) from sandwiches up, reasonable prices, cheerful service, attractive restaurant; children in eating area; interesting church opp, picture-book village, good walks – can get crowded wknds *(Clare and Peter Pearse, LYM, the Didler, M G Hart, Roy and Gay Hoing)*

FRIETH [SU7990]

☆ *Prince Albert* [off B482 SW of High Wycombe]: Welcoming landlord and locals in old-fashioned and cottagey Chilterns local with low black beams and joists, high-backed settles, big black stove in inglenook, big log fire in larger area on the right, good value pubby food from low-priced baguettes up, well kept Brakspears ales; children and dogs welcome, nicely planted informal side garden with views of woods and fields, open all day *(Pete Baker, the Didler, LYM, Paul Humphreys, Anthony Longden)*

Yew Tree [signed off B482 N of Marlow]: Enjoyable if not cheap traditional food from baguettes up in peaceful bar and pleasant dining conservatory (service charge), well kept ales such as Brakspears PA and Fullers London Pride, good coffee, friendly landlord and exemplary service, huge log fire, scrubbed pine tables, attractive back restaurant; piped music; walkers with dogs welcome, lovely setting *(LYM, Paul Humphreys)*

GREAT BRICKHILL [SP9029]

☆ *Red Lion* [Ivy Lane]: Friendly pub with simple décor, Greene King IPA and a guest such as Batemans XXXB, reasonably priced nicely presented food from sandwiches and baked potatoes up, good service, daily papers, log fire in small bar, woodburner in restaurant; fabulous view over Buckinghamshire and beyond from neat walled back lawn *(Ian Phillips, LYM, Roy and Lindsey Fentiman, Michael Dandy)*

GREAT HAMPDEN [SP8401]

☆ *Hampden Arms* [off A4010 N and S of Princes Risborough]: Civilised dining pub opp village cricket pitch, enjoyable food from lunchtime sandwiches to substantial main dishes, quick friendly service, Adnams and Hook Norton and Addlestone's cider from small corner bar, big woodburner in more spacious back room; children and dogs welcome, tree-sheltered garden, good walks nearby *(Peter Saville, Marjorie and David Lamb, LYM, Tracey and Stephen Groves, William Goodhart, Anthony Longden, Paul Humphreys)*

GREAT HORWOOD [SP7731]

Crown [off B4033 N of Winslow; The Green]:

Comfortable Georgian pub with striking inglenook fireplace, Adnams and Greene King IPA and Abbot, pleasant service, good value usual food from sandwiches up, daily papers, dining room with big wooden tables; piped music; tables on neat front lawn, pretty village, very handy for Winslow Hall *(BB, Michael Dandy)*

Swan [B4033 N of Winslow]: Recently refurbished former low-beamed coaching inn, two feature fireplaces (one a big inglenook) in open-plan lounge/dining area, well kept Greene King IPA, Marstons Pedigree and Charles Wells Bombardier, usual food from sandwiches up, friendly landlord, back bar with darts and pool; TV; nice side garden, open all day wknds *(Michael Dandy)*

GREAT KIMBLE [SP8206]

☆ *Bernard Arms* [Risborough Rd (A4010)]: Friendly and homely, with photographs of fairly recent Prime Ministers dropping in for a drink, daily papers, popular freshly-made food in bar and restaurant, up to four changing real ales, decent wines, good range of malt whiskies and bottled beer, good log fire, games room, live piano Sat evenings and Sun lunch; children welcome, no dogs, particularly attractive fairy-lit gardens, well equipped bedrooms *(Alastair McKay, George Atkinson, BB, Mel Smith)*

Swan [Grove Lane (B4009, nr A4010)]: Popular country local with simple beamed and tiled tap room, log fires and lots of panelling, wide choice of good value fresh food from sandwiches and baked potatoes up, well kept ales such as Adnams and Fullers London Pride, friendly staff, pleasant end dining area; soft piped music; children allowed if well behaved, small well kept garden and tables out on village green, bedrooms *(Mel Smith, B Brewer, Marjorie and David Lamb, BB, N R White)*

GREAT LINFORD [SP8542]

Nags Head [High St]: Thatched 16th-c pub with big inglenook fireplace in low-beamed lounge, Greene King IPA and Tetleys, food all week inc various deals, attentive service, darts and TV in public bar; picnic-sets outside, pleasant walks, open all day *(Tony Hobden, CMW, JJW)*

GREAT MISSENDEN [SP8901]

☆ *Cross Keys* [High St]: Relaxed and unspoilt beamed bar divided by standing timbers, bric-a-brac, traditional furnishings inc high-backed settle and open fire in huge fireplace, well kept Fullers Chiswick, London Pride and ESB, good wines, good interesting modern food from tasty baguettes to the more upmarket style of its attractive and spacious no smoking beamed restaurant (children allowed here), cheerful helpful staff; back terrace *(Tracey and Stephen Groves, David Hoare, LYM, Howard Dell, J B C Williams, Roy and Gay Hoing)*

☆ *Nags Head* [old London rd, E – beyond 🏠 Abbey]: Cosy creeper-covered pub with welcoming new licensees, well kept Flowers IPA and guest beers such as Brakspears and Fullers London Pride, good choice of wines by the glass, lunchtime bar food from sandwiches and baguettes up, nice mix of furnishings, big log fire, small restaurant (children allowed); dogs welcome, picnic-sets on back lawn, bedrooms, open all day *(anon)*

White Lion [High St]: Recently refurbished, with enjoyable food inc some good unusual dishes *(anon)*

GROVE [SP9122]

☆ *Grove Lock* : Newish canalside dining pub on several levels, enjoyable food inc good Sun lunch, friendly staff, well kept Fullers ales, comfortable leather seating on oak boards, modern artwork and décor, big log fire; tables out in neat garden *(David Eagles, Lynda Payton, Sam Samuells)*

HAMBLEDEN [SU7886]

☆ *Stag & Huntsman* [off A4155 Henley—Marlow]: Handsome brick and flint pub in pretty Chilterns village not far from the river, attractively simple and old-fashioned front public bar and cosy snug, big fireplace in low-ceilinged partly panelled lounge bar, well kept Rebellion IPA, Wadworths 6X and a guest beer, farm cider, good wines, friendly efficient staff, popular food (not Sun evening), darts, dominoes, cribbage, shove-ha'penny; piped music; provision for children and dogs, spacious suntrap country garden with some raised areas and decking, bedrooms with own bathrooms *(Peter Saville, Paul Humphreys, Iwan and Sion Roberts, Roy and Lindsey Fentiman, Susan and John Douglas, Gill and Keith Croxton, M Thomas, LYM, Anthony Longden, Robert Turnham, Roy and Gay Hoing)*

LACEY GREEN [SP8201]

☆ *Pink & Lily* [from A4010 High Wycombe—Princes Risboro follow Loosley sign, then Gt Hampden, Gt Missenden one]: Charming little old-fashioned tap room (celebrated sillily by Rupert Brooke – poem framed here) in much-extended Chilterns pub with airy and plush main dining bar, well presented good food; well kept Brakspears and other changing beers, good well priced wines, friendly efficient service, log fires, dominoes, cribbage, ring the bull; piped music; children and dogs now welcome, conservatory, big garden *(Heather Couper, LYM, the Didler, B Brewer, Mike and Jennifer Marsh, Mel Smith, Roy and Gay Hoing)*

LAVENDON [SP9153]

Green Man [A428 Bedford—Northampton]: Recently refurbished attractive thatched 17th-c pub in pretty village, roomy and relaxed open-plan wood-floored bar with no smoking area, beams, lots of stripped stone and woodburner, Greene King IPA, Abbot, Ruddles County and Old Speckled Hen, good choice of wines by the glass, good coffee, generous food, quick friendly service, big carpeted evening/wknd restaurant with no smoking area; children welcome, may be unobtrusive piped music; open all day, tables out in neatly kept good-sized secluded garden behind, some with heaters *(Michael Dandy, Mike Ridgway, Sarah Miles)*

Horseshoe [A428 Bedford—Northampton; High St]: Sizeable spotlessly kept low-beamed village pub with restaurant off small lounge, decent food from baguettes and baked potatoes to lots of fish, well kept Charles Wells Eagle and a guest such as Marstons Pedigree, small but interesting wine list, quick cheerful service, skittles in public bar; piped music; appealing good-sized garden behind with terrace and play area *(BB, George Atkinson)*

LITTLE HAMPDEN [SP8503]

☆ *Rising Sun* [off A4128 or A413 NW of Gt Missenden; OS Sheet 165 map ref 856040]: Comfortable no smoking dining pub in delightful setting, opened-up bar with woodburner and log fire, interesting choice of good food (can take a while – may be very busy wknds), well kept Adnams, Brakspears Bitter and a seasonal beer, short but decent wine list, home-made mulled wine and spiced cider in winter, prompt friendly service; piped music, and they may try to keep your credit card if you eat outside; prime walking area (but no walkers' boots), tables out on terrace, bedrooms with own bathrooms, cl Sun evening and all Mon exc bank hols *(Kevin Thomas, Nina Randall, Mrs Ann Gray, Peter and Giff Bennett, M G Hart, LYM, John and Glenys Wheeler, B Brewer, John and Joyce Snell)*

LITTLE HORWOOD [SP7930]

Old Crown [Mursley Rd]: Friendly old thatched and beamed village pub, small bar, dining area with small room off, good value freshly made food (not Sun evening, Mon lunch) inc children's, two or three real ales, daily papers; fruit machine, TV, quiz nights; picnic-sets in side garden *(Marjorie and David Lamb)*

LITTLE KINGSHILL [SU8999]

☆ *Full Moon* [Hare Lane]: Picturesque hidden-away country pub with pleasantly traditional front bar and bigger carpeted side room, big helpings of well served fresh food (not Mon lunchtime), Adnams and Youngs, friendly landlord, quiet on wkdy lunchtimes, buoyant atmosphere evenings and wknds; may be piped radio; neat attractive garden *(Tracey and Stephen Groves)*

LITTLE MARLOW [SU8788]

☆ *Kings Head* [A4155 about 2 miles E of Marlow; Church Rd]: Long low flower-covered pub with homely and bustling open-plan beamed bar, wide blackboard choice of good value food from substantial sandwiches to some unusual main dishes and popular Sun roasts, smart red dining room, no smoking areas, well kept Adnams Broadside, Fullers London Pride, Caledonian Deuchars IPA and Timothy Taylors Landlord, quick cheerful service, log fire, Sun bar nibbles, no smoking room; children welcome, can get crowded wknds; big attractive garden behind popular with families, nice walk down to church *(BB, Richard List, Paul Humphreys, Howard Dell, Michael Dandy, Edward Mirzoeff, Tracey and Stephen Groves, Ian Phillips)*

☆ *Queens Head* [Church Rd/Pound Lane; cul de

sac off A4155 nr Kings Head]: Charming small quietly placed pub with interestingly varied good food (not Mon/Tues evening) from sandwiches to unusual and exotic dishes, well kept Adnams Broadside, Greene King IPA and a changing guest beer, cosy lighter no smoking dining room on right, helpful service, lots of books in saloon; darts and TV in public bar on left (can get smoky), no dogs; picnic-sets in appealing cottagey front garden, a couple more tables on secluded terrace across lane – short walk from River Thames *(Mark Percy, Lesley Mayoh, Paul Humphreys, Michael Dandy, BB, Ian Phillips)*

LITTLE MISSENDEN [SU9298]

☆ *Red Lion* : Small traditional 15th-c local, two coal fires, well kept real ales, decent wines, generous good value standard food inc nice fairly priced proper sandwiches, preserves for sale; piped music; tables and busy aviary in sunny side garden by river with ducks, swans and fat trout *(Brian Root, Mike Turner, B Shelley, Roy and Gay Hoing)*

LITTLEWORTH COMMON [SP9386]

☆ *Blackwood Arms* [3 miles S of M40 junction 2; Common Lane, OS Sheet 165 map ref 937864]: Gently smartened up rustic local tucked away in lovely spot on edge of beech woods – good walks; up-to-date stylish décor in cream and mulberry, dark woodwork and blinds, almost all tables now set for the good home cooking from open sandwiches (enough for two) and simple lunchtime dishes to pricier evening meals and great puddings, well kept Brakspears and a guest beer such as Hook Norton from handsome oak counter, prompt pleasant service, roaring log fire; quiet piped music; children and dogs welcome, views from chunky tables in pleasant back garden *(Jarrod and Wendy Hopkinson, Nick Binns, Michael Dandy, LYM, Simon Collett-Jones, Steve Derbyshire)*

MAIDS MORETON [SP7035]

☆ *Wheatsheaf* [Main St, just off A413 Towcester—Buckingham]: Thatched and low-beamed old-world pub, very clean, with friendly atmosphere and service, wide choice of good attractively priced food from sandwiches up, well kept Hook Norton Best and a guest beer, farm cider, decent choice of wines, lots of pictures and bric-a-brac in old part, two inglenooks, settles and chairs, conservatory restaurant with woodburner; unobtrusive piped music; pleasant quiet enclosed garden behind *(Bob and Marilyn Baylis)*

MARLOW [SU8486]

Chequers [High St]: Attractive pub with large air-conditioned front bar, bare boards and heavy beams, leather settees, daily papers, Brakspears ales, friendly service, good food range from basics to more exotic things in bright and pleasant back restaurant area, children welcome; piped music, games – popular with young people (stays open late at wknds); homely tables on pavement, bedrooms *(Michael Dandy)*

Hand & Flowers [West St (A4155)]: Gently spruced-up bar with new log fireplace, brasses and old prints, home-made food from sandwiches and baguettes up, well kept Greene King IPA and Abbot, helpful service, daily papers, darts, bar billiards, big sympathetically lit dining area; piped music; small garden with play area *(Michael Dandy)*

☆ *Two Brewers* [St Peter St, first right off Station Rd from double roundabout]: Busy low-beamed pub with plenty of atmosphere and character, most tables set for good imaginative food from good choice of sandwiches, baguettes and light snacks up (may have to book Sun lunch), shiny black woodwork, nautical pictures, gleaming brassware, an unusual crypt-like area, well kept Brakspears, Fullers London Pride, Greene King Old Speckled Hen and Marlow Rebellion, good wines, welcoming service, relaxed atmosphere; children in eating area, unobtrusive piped music; tables in sheltered back courtyard with more in converted garage, front seats with glimpse of the Thames (pub right on Thames Path) *(Charles Davey, David Tindal, Gerry and Rosemary Dobson, LYM, Michael Dandy)*

MARSWORTH [SP9114]

Red Lion [village signed off B489 Dunstable—Aylesbury; Vicarage Rd]: Low-beamed partly thatched village pub with cheerful service, well kept ales such as Fullers London Pride and Vale Notley, decent wines, good value food from the kitchen door, quiet lounge with two open fires, steps up to snug parlour and games area, nice variety of seating inc traditional settles, no smoking areas; sheltered garden, not far from impressive flight of canal locks *(LYM, Tony Hobden, Roy and Gay Hoing)*

MILTON KEYNES [SP8739]

Barge [Newport Rd, Woolstone]: Large beamed Vintage Inn in untouched corner of an original village just off central Milton Keynes, rustic furnishings in various rooms and alcoves, no smoking areas inc modern conservatory, well kept Bass, lots of wines by the glass, wide food choice, daily papers, friendly staff, good food service (not in garden); piped music; picnic-sets on spacious tree-dotted lawns *(Tony Hobden, Michael Dandy)*

Lloyds No 1 [Savoy Cres]: Handy Wetherspoons for reasonably priced pre-theatre snack, with three real ales, wines and good soft drinks range; piped pop music may be loud *(CMW, JJW)*

☆ *Old Beams* [Osier Lane, Shenley Lodge; in grounds tucked into curve of ridge-top Paxton Cres, off Fulmer St or Childs Way]: Comfortably modernised and extended former farmhouse, relaxing beamed and flagstoned bar with through fireplace, matching chairs around handsome candlelit tables, big fireplaces, lots of brick and wood, old photographs, paintings and brass, good value enjoyable food inc light dishes and Sun roasts, usually something available all day, well kept McMullens ales, welcoming and attentive young staff, speciality coffees, no smoking areas; business faxes sent and received free, very popular with local office staff; piped music; children in dining area; large pleasant garden perhaps with swans and ducks in former moat – a striking oasis in vast tracts of new red-brick housing *(BB, Margaret and Roy Randle, George Atkinson)*

Olde Swan [Newport rd, Woughton on the Green]: Spacious and picturesque timber-framed thatched Chef & Brewer, largely no smoking, with attractive furnishings, roaring log fires and nice nooks and corners, their usual wide food, good management, good wine choice and real ales; picnic-sets in back garden, footpaths to nearby lakes *(Heather Couper)*

Ship Ashore [Granville Sq, Willen]: Well designed late 1980s Ember Inn, half a dozen distinct areas each with lounge, dining part and big log-effect gas fire, Fullers London Pride, Greene King Old Speckled Hen and Charles Wells Bombardier, their usual decent food; picnic-sets under parasols on small lawn *(Ian Phillips)*

MOULSOE [SP9141]

☆ *Carrington Arms* [1¼ miles from M1, junction 14: A509 N, first right signed Moulsoe; Cranfield Rd]: Good interesting if not cheap pub majoring on meats and fresh fish sold by weight (priced per 100g) from refrigerated display then cooked on indoor barbecue, good puddings, three well kept real ales, champagnes by the glass, friendly helpful staff, comfortable mix of wooden chairs and cushioned banquettes; children allowed, long pretty garden behind, open all day Sun, decent bedrooms *(Alan Sutton, John Saville, David and Ruth Shillitoe, LYM, Mr and Mrs D S Price)*

NEWTON LONGVILLE [SP8431]

☆ *Crooked Billet* [off A421 S of Milton Keynes; Westbrook End]: Thatched dining pub notable for its extraordinary choice of wines by the glass – literally hundreds; lunchtime sandwiches and wraps as well as the enterprising restaurant dishes it focuses on, brightly modernised extended bar with well kept Greene King IPA and Abbot, a couple of guest beers and splendid choice of spirits; children allowed in no smoking restaurant (which may not be open lunchtime), dogs in bar, tables out on lawn, open all day Sat, cl Mon lunchtime *(LYM, Karen and Graham Oddey)*

OLNEY [SP8851]

Bull [Market Pl/High St]: Recently smartened up, with two small front bar rooms (can be smoky) and more spacious no smoking eating area, Charles Wells ales with a guest beer and flourishing Aug bank hol beer festival, good coffee, popular pubby food from sandwiches and baguettes up, log-effect gas fires, very friendly chatty landlord, lots of games; small courtyard (no dogs), big back garden with big climbing frame; HQ of the famous Shrove Tuesday pancake race *(Mike Ridgway, Sarah Miles, George Atkinson)*

☆ *Swan* [High St S]: Cosy beamed and timbered pub with good choice of excellent value generous food from sandwiches, baguettes and

baked potatoes up, well kept ales such as Adnams Best, Eccleshall Slaters, Fullers London Pride and Shepherd Neame Best, good value wines by the glass, quick helpful service, daily papers, attractive flowers; several rooms off bar, candles on pine tables, log fires, small no smoking back bistro dining room (booking advised for this); very busy at lunchtime, no under-10s; back courtyard tables, one under cover *(Michael Sargent, BB, Michael Dandy, Sue and Keith Campbell)*

Two Brewers [High St (A509)]: Large straightforward double-fronted pub, large public bar and lounge, big dining area with plenty of different-sized tables, enjoyable home-made traditional food at fair prices, keen and welcoming landlord, well kept beers, decent wines by the glass; attractive courtyard interestingly decorated to show its brewery past, tables in small garden too *(Earl and Chris Pick)*

PENN [SU9093]

Red Lion [Elm Rd]: Attractive low-ceilinged traditional bar with vast log fire and plenty of bric-a-brac, no smoking area, wide choice of generous well priced food showing imagination, five real ales, friendly landlord and efficient service, separate games room; piped music; children welcome, nice spot opp green and duck pond *(Tracey and Stephen Groves, Roy and Gay Hoing)*

PENN STREET [SU9295]

☆ *Hit or Miss* [off A404 SW of Amersham, then keep on towards Winchmore Hill]: Well laid out low-beamed pub with own cricket ground, enjoyable freshly made food (can take a while when busy) inc good fish and popular Sun lunch, well kept Badger ales, decent wines, attentive staff, cheerful atmosphere in three clean linked rooms, log fire, charming décor inc interesting cricket and chair-making memorabilia, good-sized no smoking area; shame about the piped music; picnic-sets out in front, pleasant setting *(Mrs Ann Gray, Tracey and Stephen Groves, LYM)*

PRESTON BISSETT [SP6529]

☆ *White Hart* [off A421 or A4421 SW of Buckingham; Pound Lane]: Charming little thatched, timbered and low-beamed 18th-c pub refurbished under welcoming new owners, with enjoyable home-made food from simple sandwiches and good ciabattas to dishes with imaginative italian touches, popular Tues pasta night, well kept Fullers London Pride and Oxfordshire Marshmellow, good choice of wines by the glass, three cosy rooms (the biggest is a no smoking restaurant), log fire, daily papers; some seats outside *(LYM, MJB, Canon Michael Bourdeaux, Michael Dandy)*

PRINCES RISBOROUGH [SP8003]

Whiteleaf Cross [Market Sq]: Refurbished in the current style of leather sofas and bare boards, civilised atmosphere, friendly local service, usual food, daily papers *(Heather Couper)*

QUAINTON [SP7420]

George & Dragon [The Green]: Traditional pub with real ales such as Fullers London

Pride, home-made food, friendly staff; tables outside, good view of windmill *(Steve and Larraine Gooch)*

SAUNDERTON [SU8099]

Rose & Crown [Wycombe Rd]: Comfortably if slightly starkly modernised pub/hotel with contemporary décor and artwork in L-shaped bar, nice log fire, cosy alcove with sofa, Timothy Taylors Landlord, good choice of wines and teas, friendly staff, smart upmarket restaurant with good food inc well presented modern dishes and good value set meals; piped music; tables out in front, good Chilterns walks, comfortable bedrooms *(John and Glenys Wheeler, BB)*

SHABBINGTON [SP6606]

Old Fisherman [off A418 Oxford—Thame; Mill Rd]: Prettily placed recently extended riverside dining pub, roomy and attractive, with generous home-made food inc children's dishes and popular all-day Sun lunch, well kept Greene King ales, good choice of wines by the glass, no smoking areas; lots of tables in waterside garden with play area, open all day wknds and summer *(anon)*

SHERINGTON [SP8946]

White Hart [off A509; Gun Lane]: Friendly and well run, with four well kept ales, attentive landlord, enjoyable food from sandwiches up, bright fire, two-room bar and pleasantly rustic restaurant; children and dogs welcome, picnic-sets in garden with terrace, pretty hanging baskets *(Michael B Griffith)*

STOKE GOLDINGTON [SP8348]

Lamb [High St]: Cosy lounge with log fire and sheepish décor, well kept changing ales such as Caledonian Deuchars IPA, Church End Vicars Ruin and Nethergate IPA and Old Growler, farm cider, good choice of good generous home-made food (not Sun/Tues evenings) at appealing prices from baguettes up, friendly welcoming staff and dogs, table skittles, no smoking dining room; quiet piped radio, TV; sizeable garden and terrace *(George Atkinson, Gerry and Rosemary Dobson, CMW, JJW)*

STOKE POGES [SU9885]

Fox & Pheasant [Gerrards Cross Rd (B416, Stoke Common)]: Popular for its carvery restaurant, with other decent food too; smartly well appointed bar, but welcoming, with a relaxed atmosphere and good service *(Marjorie and David Lamb)*

STONE [SP7912]

Bugle Horn [Hartwell; A418 SW of Aylesbury]: Long low 17th-c stone-built family dining pub, warm and friendly series of comfortable rooms, pleasant furnishings, good choice of decent food, well kept Bass and Hook Norton Old Hooky, good wines by the glass, log fire and prettily planted well furnished conservatory; lovely trees in large pretty garden, horses grazing in pastures beyond *(Tim and Ann Newell, Mel Smith, Michael Dandy)*

STONY STRATFORD [SP7840]

☆ *Cock* [High St]: Comfortable old-fashioned hotel, quiet at lunchtime but lively in the evenings, with leather settles and library chairs

on bare boards, decent standard bar food from filled baps to chargrills, friendly prompt service, well kept Greene King IPA and Abbot, interesting old local photographs and memorabilia; may be barbecues in attractive back courtyard, bedrooms *(David and Ruth Hollands, LYM, George Atkinson)*

☆ *Crown* [Market Sq]: Smart informal pub/bistro, contemporary light colours and local artwork for sale, pre-meal area on left with comfortable leather sofas, more traditional bar on right (smoking allowed only here), extensive back dining area with enjoyable and enterprising fresh food from lunchtime sandwiches and light dishes up, wider evening choice, good puddings, interesting and fairly priced wine range, real ales, friendly helpful staff; open all day, cl Sun evening *(Mrs J Groom, Chris Shaw)*

TAPLOW [SU9185]

Feathers [Taplow Common, opp Cliveden entrance]: Rambling olde-worlde Chef & Brewer family dining pub opp Cliveden entrance (NT), wide food choice from sandwiches, crusty rolls and baguettes up, Courage Directors, Fullers London Pride and Theakstons Old Peculier, good choice of decent wines, good coffee, quick helpful service; piped music, games; courtyard tables, play area, dogs allowed only by front picnic-sets *(Bob and Laura Brock, Michael Dandy, John and Sue Woodward, Meg and Colin Hamilton)*

THE LEE [SP8904]

☆ *Old Swan* [Swan Bottom, back rd ¾ mile N of The Lee]: Charming civilised 16th-c dining pub well off the beaten track, with very good interesting food esp seafood cooked by long-serving landlord, good value, and sandwiches too; four simply but attractively furnished linked rooms, low beams and flagstones, cooking-range log fire in inglenook, particularly well kept Adnams and Brakspears, decent wines, cheerful landlady, friendly relaxed service, TV etc tucked nicely away; spacious prettily planted back lawns with play area, good walks *(CMW, JJW, LYM, John and Glenys Wheeler, Marjorie and David Lamb, Tracey and Stephen Groves, Victoria Taylor, Anthony Longden, Mike Turner)*

WADDESDON [SP7416]

☆ *Five Arrows* [High St (A41)]: Elegant and civilised series of light and airy well furnished high-ceilinged rooms with Rothschild family portrait engravings and lots of old estate-worker photographs, more restaurant-with-rooms or small hotel than pub, but worth knowing for its excellent wines (well kept Fullers London Pride too) and friendly staff; no smoking area, children allowed; appealing back garden, comfortable bedrooms, handy for Waddesdon Manor; has been cl last wknd Aug *(Neil and Angela Huxter, David and Jean Hall, Bob and Maggie Atherton, David and Ruth Hollands, Michael Dandy, Mr and Mrs John Taylor, LYM, Karen and Graham Oddey)*

Lion [High St]: Newly refurbished village pub with lively bar and tasteful linked dining areas, friendly staff, good food, friendly staff, good choice of beers *(Mr and Mrs Bentley-Davies)*

WEST WYCOMBE [SU8394]

☆ *George & Dragon* [High St; A40 W of High Wycombe]: Handsome and popular centrepiece of beautifully preserved Tudor village, thriving atmosphere in rambling bar with massive beams, sloping rust-coloured walls, interesting 1890s village picture over its big log fire, well kept Adnams, Courage Best and Charles Wells Bombardier, prompt friendly service even when busy, good fairly priced food choice from fresh lunchtime sandwiches and wraps to some exotic specials, small no smoking family dining room (wknd children's menu); spacious peaceful garden with fenced play area, neatly kept character bedrooms (magnificent oak staircase) and good breakfast, handy for West Wycombe Park *(Paul Humphreys, M G Hart, LYM, Tracey and Stephen Groves, Piotr Chodzko-Zajko, Ian Phillips)*

WESTON TURVILLE [SP8510]

Chequers [Church Lane]: Traditional relaxing low-beamed two-level bar with well kept Adnams, Boddingtons, Fullers London Pride, Gales HSB and Wadworths 6X, enjoyable bar food, flagstones, large open fire and stylish solid wooden furniture, adjoining restaurant (not cheap) with good food esp fish and good friendly service; tucked away in attractive part of village, tables in nice garden *(Peter and Jan Humphreys, Lin Carroll, Tricia North)*

WHEELER END [SU8093]

☆ *Chequers* [off B482 NW of Marlow]: Neatly kept 17th-c pub with inglenook log fire in convivial low-ceilinged little bar, bigger back no smoking room, candlelit tables and hunting prints, enjoyable bar food (not Sun evening) from sandwiches up using their garden herbs, good fish choice and local game, well kept Fullers London Pride, ESB and a guest beer, decent wines, brisk friendly service, dominoes and cribbage; children welcome in eating areas, dogs in bar, two charmingly kept gardens (M40 noise), open all day *(Michael Dandy, Tracey and Stephen Groves, LYM, Martin and Karen Wake)*

WINCHMORE HILL [SU9394]

Plough [The Hill]: Chic upmarket dining place, restaurant rather than pub now, comfortable, spacious and sensitively modernised, with several interconnecting low-beamed areas, carefully cooked and presented enterprising food inc good value set lunch, neat helpful staff, fashionable imported lagers; piped music turned off if you ask; tables on lawn with wishing well *(John Faircloth, BB, Tracey and Stephen Groves)*

WING [SP8822]

Cock [off A418 SW of Leighton Buzzard; High St]: Partly 16th-c, with well kept ales inc Fullers London Pride and Greene King IPA, decent wines, good coffee, friendly attentive service, cottage armchairs and roaring fire, lots of books, partly no smoking dining areas with good reasonably priced food choice from pubby things and lunchtime carvery to bistro evening menu; garden with picnic-sets and play area *(Craig Turnbull, J Iorwerth Davies, Tony and Wendy Hobden)*

WINSLOW [SP7327]

☆ *Verney Arms* [2 miles W, towards Steeple Claydon; Verney Junction, Addington]: New young licensees doing good interesting food in cheery and cottagey bistroish pub with Shaker-style furniture, small bar area around tiny brick counter with well kept Greene King ales, smartly relaxed atmosphere and attractive clean décor, open fire, attentive service; garden tables *(BB, R N L Broome)*

WOOBURN COMMON [SU9387]

☆ *Royal Standard* [about 3½ miles from M40 junction 2]: Thriving low-ceilinged down-to-earth local with welcoming helpful staff, wide choice of enjoyable good value straightforward food from low-priced baguettes up, up to ten well kept changing ales such as Adnams Broadside, Black Sheep, Caledonian Deuchars IPA, Flowers, Fullers London Pride, Hop Back Summer Lightning and seasonal specials, well chosen wines, lots of daily papers, open fire, daily papers and crossword reference books, popular refurbished dining area; picnic-sets on pretty front terrace and in back garden, open all day *(Roy and Lindsey Fentiman, LYM, Michael Dandy, Jarrod and Wendy Hopkinson, Steve Derbyshire, Roy and Gay Hoing)*

WOOBURN GREEN [SU9188]

Glory Mill [Wycombe Lane (A4094)]: Former Rose & Crown, now neatly refurbished with leather settees by log fire, pleasant décor, enjoyable food, real ales inc guest beers, reasonably priced wines, no smoking restaurant area *(D and M T Ayres-Regan)*

WORMINGHALL [SP6308]

☆ *Clifden Arms* [Clifden Rd]: 16th-c beamed, timbered and thatched pub in pretty gardens, enchanting inside too with its unpretentiously old-fashioned seats, rustic memorabilia and roaring log fires, attractive lounge bar leading to further no smoking dining area, decent food inc bargain wkdy lunches, well kept changing ales, traditional games in public bar, children allowed; good play area, aunt sally, attractive village *(LYM, Dick and Madeleine Brown, Marjorie and David Lamb, Susan and John Douglas)*

Please tell us if any Lucky Dips deserve to be upgraded to a main entry – and why. No stamp needed: The Good Pub Guide, FREEPOST TN1569, Wadhurst, E Sussex TN5 7BR.

Cambridgeshire

Plenty of choice nowadays in this well served county, from properly pubby places to smarter more upmarket styles, with a good deal of individual character. Food is often a high point, from simple pub meals at bargain prices (several of our town pubs stand out for this, perhaps most notably the Free Press in Cambridge, as does that unspoilt country favourite the Queens Head at Newton) to delicious inventive cooking. Strong tips for enjoyable meals out include the pretty Black Horse at Elton (ambitious cooking, and it gains a Wine Award this year), the welcoming and well run Ancient Shepherds at Fen Ditton, the restaurantly White Pheasant at Fordham, the unusual Exhibition in Godmanchester with its interior 'shop fronts', the King William IV at Heydon (full of character and interesting knick-knacks), the stylish Old Bridge Hotel in Huntingdon (not cheap but a rewarding experience), the Pheasant at Keyston (another top-notch stylish dining place), the welcoming and well cared for Red House at Longstowe, the exemplary Dyke's End at Reach (interesting and not at all pricey), and the Anchor at Sutton Gault (justly a favourite both for meals and as a place to stay in). It's a new entry though which takes our top award of Cambridgeshire Dining Pub of the Year: the Cock in the lovely village of Hemingford Grey is best thought of as a place for an excellent meal in its relaxed dining room (or pretty garden), though it also has good beers – and splendid wines by the glass – in its pleasant side bar. Many of these pubs have good beers, but the Brewery Tap in Peterborough deserves a special mention for the fine Oakham beers it brews and sells so cheaply, and its interesting guest beers (good thai food, too); its equally good value sister pub Charters is fascinating – a converted dutch barge. Otherwise, drinks prices in the county tend to be somewhat higher than the national average. In the Lucky Dip section at the end of the chapter, pubs to note particularly this year are the Duke of Wellington at Bourn, George in Buckden, John Barleycorn in Duxford, White Horse at Eaton Socon, Blue Lion at Hardwick, George in Huntingdon and Haycock at Wansford.

CAMBRIDGE TL4658 Map 5
Cambridge Blue ♦ ■ £
85 Gwydir Street

Completely no smoking, this quiet back street pub has two uncluttered rooms that are simply decorated with old-fashioned bare-boards style furnishings, candles on the tables, and a big collection of oars; there's also the bow section of the Cambridge boat that famously rammed a barge and sank before the start of the 1984 boat race, and such a nice selection of rowing photographs you feel you're browsing through someone's family snaps. Cribbage and dominoes. An interesting range of seven regularly changing well kept real ales on handpump might include Adnams Bitter, City of Cambridge Hobsons Choice, Elgoods Black Dog Mild, Iceni Fine Soft Day, Nethergate IPA, Oakham JHB, and Woodfordes Wherry; they also have cider, malt whiskies and fresh orange juice. Reasonably priced straightforward bar food is served in an attractive little conservatory dining area: home-made soup (from £2.95), filled baked potatoes (from £3), filled ciabatta rolls (from £4), chickpea and vegetable casserole (£6), courgette and spinach lasagne (£6.25), california chicken or beef in beer (£6.50), and smoked salmon, prawn and spinach pie or game casserole (£6.75); Sunday roast (£6.50). Children like the surprisingly rural feeling and large back garden. More reports please. *(Recommended by Rona Murdoch, Clare and Peter Pearse, the Didler, Eric Robinson, Jacqueline Pratt)*

Free house ~ Licensees Chris and Debbie Lloyd ~ Real ale ~ Bar food (12-2.30, 6-9.30; not 25 Dec) ~ (01223) 505110 ~ Children welcome in conservatory ~ Dogs welcome ~ Open 12-2.30(3 Sat), 5.30-11; 12-3, 6-10.30 Sun

Eagle ♀ £
Bene't Street

The rambling rooms of this old coaching inn have many charming original architectural features, from the lovely worn wooden floors to plenty of pine panelling, two fireplaces dating back to around 1600, two medieval mullioned windows, and the remains of two possibly medieval wall paintings. The creaky old furniture is nicely in keeping; no smoking areas. Don't miss the high dark red ceiling which has been left unpainted since World War II to preserve the signatures of British and American airmen worked in with Zippo lighters, candle smoke and lipstick. You queue at the servery for the straightforward but good value bar food which comes in generous helpings and includes filled baked potatoes (from £4.70), filled baguettes (from £5.45), and vegetarian quiche, steak in ale pie, ham and eggs or lasagne (all £6.45); evening dishes such as salmon fishcakes (£6.45), giant battered cod (£8.25), and steaks (from £9.85); Sunday carvery. Well kept Greene King IPA, Abbot, Old Speckled Hen and Ruddles County on handpump, and around a dozen wines by the glass. An attractive cobbled and galleried courtyard, screened from the street by sturdy wooden gates and with heavy wooden seats and tables and pretty hanging baskets, takes you back through the centuries – especially at Christmas, when they serve mulled wine and you can listen to the choristers from King's College singing here. No children inside. *(Recommended by John Wooll, Kevin Thorpe, the Didler, Gwyn Jones, Christine and Neil Townend, Eric Robinson, Jacqueline Pratt, Hazel Morgan, Bernard Patrick)*

Greene King ~ Managers Steve Ottley and Sian Crowther ~ Real ale ~ Bar food (12-3.30, 5-9(8 Fri and Sat), 12-4 Sun (not Sun evening)) ~ Restaurant ~ (01223) 505020 ~ Open 11-11; 12-10.30 Sun

Free Press £
Prospect Row

There's a good, cheerful pubby atmosphere in this unspoilt old place, helped by having no piped music or games machines. It is completely no smoking, and in winter you can read a newspaper by the log fire which warms its simple but characterfully sociable bare-board rooms, and in summer the sheltered paved garden at the back is quite a suntrap. Over the years loyal customers have donated little items that are displayed in old printing trays, which are hung up amongst old newspapers and printing memorabilia. Well kept Greene King IPA, Abbot and Mild and a guest such as Batemans on handpump, several malt whiskies, and winter mulled wine; cribbage, dominoes, and assorted board games. Good value tasty bar food is served in generous helpings: soup or filled ciabattas (£3.25), ploughman's (from £5.75), spinach and ricotta tortellini or stuffed peppers (£5.95), gammon with bubble and squeak (£6.25), and lamb shank (£7.95). *(Recommended by John Wooll, Mark Harrington, the Didler, A J Bowen)*

Greene King ~ Tenant Donna Thornton ~ Real ale ~ Bar food (12-2, 6-8.30; not Sun evening) ~ (01223) 368337 ~ Children welcome ~ Dogs welcome ~ Open 12-2.30, 6-11; 12-2.30, 7-10.30 Sun; closed 25-26 Dec, 1 Jan

---

We say if we know a pub allows dogs.

Live & Let Live 🍺 £

40 Mawson Road; off Mill Road SE of centre

Down to earth but popular, the heavily timbered brickwork rooms in this friendly old local have sturdy varnished pine tables with pale wood chairs on bare boards, and real gas lighting; also, lots of interesting old country bric-a-brac, some steam railway and brewery memorabilia, and posters about local forthcoming events. Well kept Everards Tiger and Nethergate Umbel, and guests from brewers such as Cropton, Three Rivers, and Tring on handpump, plus 20 belgian beers, and a dozen malt whiskies; cribbage and dominoes. The eating area of the bar is no smoking until 9pm, and simple but good value home-made food includes sandwiches and filled baked potatoes (from £2.50), home-made soup (£3.50), ploughman's (£5), sausage or ham and egg (£6), lambs liver and bacon with bubble and squeak or vegetable lasagne (£6.50), chicken and mushroom pie (£7.50), and puddings (£3.75); all day breakfast on Saturday and roast lunch on Sunday. *(Recommended by John Wooll, Alan Dickinson, Giles and Annie Francis, Keith and Janet Morris)*

Burlison Inns ~ Lease Peter Wiffin ~ Real ale ~ Bar food (12-2, 6(7 Sun)-9) ~ (01223) 460261 ~ Children in eating area of bar ~ Dogs welcome ~ Local musician Sat ~ Open 11.30-2.30, 5.30(6 Sat)-11; 12-2.30, 7-10.30 Sun

ELTON TL0893 Map 5

Black Horse ♀

B671 off A605 W of Peterborough and A1(M); Overend

Although there's quite an emphasis on the enjoyable food in this handsome honey brick dining pub, regulars do drop in for a pint of well kept Bass, Everards Tiger, Nethergate Suffolk County, and Youngs Bitter on handpump. And there's all you'd expect in a country inn from the welcoming atmosphere to roaring fires, hop-strung beams, a homely and comfortable mix of furniture (no two tables and chairs seem the same), antique prints, and lots of ornaments and bric-a-brac including an intriguing ancient radio set. Dining areas at each end of the bar have parquet flooring and tiles, and the stripped stone back lounge towards the partly no smoking restaurant has an interesting fireplace. Served in generous helpings by helpful staff, the popular food includes bar snacks such as filled baked potatoes (from £3.50), sandwiches (from £4.95; warm filled baguettes from £6.45), ploughman's or caesar salad (£8.25), and a home-made pie of the day (£8.95); also, soup (£3.95), home-made pâté (£5.45), fried pigeon breast with a cherry kirsch compote (£5.95), mushroom tartlet (£6.50), bangers and mash (£10.95), smoked haddock with rosemary and garlic roast potatoes or chicken stuffed with asparagus and wrapped with bacon in a black pepper sauce (£12.95), steaks (from £12.95), goose breast with pear and ginger chutney (£13.95), and seasonal game pie (£14.95); around a dozen wines by the glass. The big garden has super views across to Elton Hall park and the village church; there are seats on the terrace, some tables shaded by horse chestnut trees, and a couple of acres of grass for children to play. *(Recommended by Stephen and Jean Curtis, Gene and Kitty Rankin, Oliver and Sue Rowell, Simon and Sally Small, Phil and Jane Hodson, Fiona McElhone, Gerry and Rosemary Dobson)*

Free house ~ Licensee John Clennell ~ Real ale ~ Bar food (12-2.30, 6-9; not Sun evening) ~ Restaurant ~ (01832) 280240 ~ Children welcome ~ Dogs allowed in bar ~ Open 12-11; 12-6 Sun; closed Sun evening

ELY TL5380 Map 5

Fountain 🍺

Corner of Barton Square and Silver Street

Somehow, despite being very close to the cathedral, this simple but genteel town corner pub manages to escape the tourists. Old cartoons, local photographs, regional maps and mementoes of the neighbouring King's School punctuate the elegant dark pink walls, and neatly tied-back curtains hang from golden rails above the big windows. Above one fireplace is a stuffed pike in a case, and there are a few antlers dotted about – not to mention a duck at one end of the bar; everything is very clean and tidy, and there's no music, fruit machines or even food. Well kept Adnams Bitter and Broadside, Fullers London Pride and a changing guest such as Youngs Special on handpump. A couple of tables are squeezed on to a tiny back terrace. Note the limited opening times. More reports please. *(Recommended by the Didler)*

Free house ~ Licensees John and Judith Borland ~ Real ale ~ No credit cards ~ (01353) 663122 ~ Children welcome away from bar until 8pm ~ Dogs welcome ~ Open 5-11; 12-2, 6-11 Sat; 12-2, 7-10.30 Sun

FEN DITTON TL4860 Map 5
Ancient Shepherds
Off B1047 at Green End, The River signpost, just NE of Cambridge

Even when busy, the friendly staff will take time to welcome you into this solidly beamed old pub. Many people come to enjoy the generously served good food, but you will feel just as at home enjoying a pint and a chat. Perhaps the nicest room is the softly lit central lounge, where you can't fail to be comfortable on one of the big fat dark red button-back leather settees or armchairs at low solid indonesian tables, by the warm coal fire, and all tucked in by heavy drapes around the window seat with its big scatter cushions. Above a black dado the walls (and ceiling) are dark pink, and decorated with little steeplechasing and riding prints, and comic fox and policeman ones. On the right the smallish convivial more pubby bar with its coal fire serves Adnams and Greene King IPA and Old Speckled Hen on handpump, while on the left is a pleasant no smoking restaurant (piped music in here). Using good quality ingredients, the popular food includes home-made soup (£3.95), filled baguettes (from £4.40), ploughman's (from £5.95), home-made fishcakes, sausage and mash or spinach and ricotta cheese cannelloni (£8.95), steak and ale pie (£10.75), braised lamb shank in minted rosemary gravy (£11.25), half a duck in orange sauce (£12.95), fresh fish that is delivered on Tuesdays and Fridays, such as bass, scallops or scampi provençale (from £8.95). The licensees' west highland terrier, Billie, might be around outside food service times. *(Recommended by Mr and Mrs T B Staples, Roger and Anne Newbury, Dr Phil Putwain, Helen and Ian Jobson)*

Punch ~ Tenant J M Harrington ~ Real ale ~ Bar food (not Sun evening) ~ Restaurant ~ (01223) 293280 ~ Children in eating area of bar and restaurant ~ Dogs allowed in bar ~ Open 12-2.30, 6-11; 12-5 Sun; closed Sun evening; bank hol Mons; 1 Jan

FORDHAM TL6270 Map 5
White Pheasant
A142 (may be bypassed by the time this edition is published) at junction with B1102 to Burwell, north of Newmarket; Market Street

Knowledgeable and friendly licensees and their helpful staff will ensure you are made welcome and comfortable in this bustling roadside dining pub. The exterior is somewhat unassuming, but once inside, it's smallish but open plan and airy, and has a mix of well spaced big farmhouse tables and chairs on bare boards, some stripped brickwork, and a cheery log fire at one end. One or two steps lead down to a small similarly furnished but carpeted room. Fenland Rabbit Poacher and a guest such as Wissey Valley are well kept on handpump, and a dozen carefully chosen wines (including champagne) by the glass are served from the horseshoe bar that faces the entrance. Food here is very good, and you can choose from the bar or restaurant menu or specials board. The bar menu (not available on Sunday) includes crispy whitebait (£4.50), lunchtime sandwiches (from £5.50; fillet steak and onion £7.25), pasta carbonara (£7.95), home-made lamb and mint burger with home-made chips or bangers and mash with onion gravy (£7.95), and chicken breast topped with barbecue sauce or a huge lunchtime breakfast (£9.95); from the restaurant menu, there might be caesar salad (£4.50), grilled field mushroom topped with welsh rarebit and pancetta (£5.25), crab and coriander spring roll with thai dipping and hoisin sauces (£5.50), chargrilled aubergine baked with peppers, tomatoes and smoked cheddar sauce (£13.95), and beef stroganoff (£14.95), and specials such as scottish mussels with beer and bacon (£5.95; main course £9.95), fish pie (£9.95), and yellow fin tuna, king scallop and tiger prawn kebab (£8.50; main course £16.95). The restaurant is no smoking. The garden tables will benefit greatly from the new bypass. *(Recommended by Richard Storey, Molly and Arthur Aldersey-Williams, John Saville, Mr and Mrs S Wilson, David and Judith Stewart, Michael Dandy, Ben and Helen Ingram, Stephen Woad)*

Free house ~ Licensee Elizabeth Meads ~ Real ale ~ Bar food (12-2.30, 6-9.30) ~ Restaurant ~ (01638) 720414 ~ Children allowed until 8pm ~ Open 12-3, 6-11(7-10.30 Sun); closed 25-30 Dec

FOWLMERE TL4245 Map 5

Chequers 🍽 ♀
B1368

In 1660, Pepys had dinner in this 16th-c coaching inn – roast veal and a bottle of port – and today, it remains somewhere special for a good meal out. The two comfortably furnished downstairs rooms are warmed by an open log fire, and upstairs there are beams, wall timbering and some interesting moulded plasterwork above the fireplace. One area is no smoking. The airy conservatory overlooks white tables under cocktail parasols among flowers and shrub roses in an attractive well tended floodlit garden – in summer overhead you might see historic aeroplanes flying from Duxford. Under the new licensees, the good, popular food might include soup (£4.40), duck pâté with home-made tomato and apple chutney (£5.95), smoked haddock baked with cream and cheese or warm mussel tart (£6.45), scallops, pancetta and roasted cherry tomatoes (£8.50), pasta with roasted red peppers, artichokes and goats cheese (£9.95), salmon fishcakes or beef tagine (£10.95), loin of marinated pork topped with sage butter (£11.80), mango and prawn curry with saffron rice (£12.30), and puddings such as hot date sponge with hot toffee sauce or baked white chocolate cheesecake with dark chocolate sauce (from £5); Sunday roast.Well kept Adnams, and a couple of guests from Nethergate and Springhead tapped from the cask, ten wines by the glass, and 30 malt whiskies. More reports on the new regime, please. *(Recommended by Mike and Jennifer Marsh, Adele Summers, Alan Black, John and Enid Morris, Tony and Shirley Albert, Mr and Mrs W E Cross, Eric Robinson, Jacqueline Pratt, Gerry and Rosemary Dobson)*

Free house ~ Licensees Paul Beaumont and Philip Daley ~ Real ale ~ Bar food ~ Restaurant ~ (01763) 208369 ~ Children in family room ~ Open 12-3, 6-11; 12-3, 7-10.30 Sun; closed 25 Dec

GODMANCHESTER TL2470 Map 5

Exhibition
London Road

Although this looks rather ordinary from outside, it's quite a surprise once you step through the door. There's an unexpectedly attractive choice of rooms, and the main bar has its walls humorously decorated with re-created shop-fronts – a post office, gallery, and wine and spirit merchant – complete with doors and stock in the windows. It's a cosy room with big flagstones on the floor, cushioned wall benches, fresh flowers and candles on each of the tables and white fairy lights on some of the plants; piped music. Enjoyable, popular food at lunchtime might include sandwiches (from £3.50; steak baguette with teriyaki sauce £5.25), soup (£3.95), chargrilled burger in a seeded bun (£4.95), duck and chicken liver terrine with home-made chutney (£5.75), pasta of the day (£8.95), thai salmon fishcakes with soured cream and sweet chilli jam (£10.95), vegetarian bake (£10.95), and cornfed chicken supreme wrapped in pancetta with a wild mushroom and mixed herb sauce (£11.25); evening choices such as emmenthal cheese and vegetable terrine (£4.95), prawn and crab tian with fresh gazpacho sauce (£5.45), globe artichoke with butter bean cassoulet (£9.75), duck breast glazed with orange and soya sauce (£13.35), chargrilled sirloin steak (£13.75), and halibut fillet with spinach, potato purée, muscat grapes and fish cream sauce (£14.85). The dining room, with smart candelabra and framed prints, is no smoking. Well kept Fullers London Pride, Greene King IPA and a changing guest beer like Hook Norton Old Hooky on handpump, eight wines by the glass, and several malt whiskies. There are picnic-sets on the back lawn, some shaded by pergolas, and a couple in front as well, and they hold barbecues in summer. Every year the Exhibition and its sister pub, the nearby White Hart, organise a gathering of steam engines. *(Recommended by Karen Eliot, Michael Dandy, A C English, George Atkinson, Keith and Chris O'Neill, Christopher Turner, Richard Siebert)*

Enterprise ~ Lease Willem Middlemiss ~ Real ale ~ Bar food ~ Restaurant ~ (01480) 459134 ~ Children in eating area of bar and restaurant ~ Monthly live jazz or blues on Tues ~ Open 11.30-3, 5-11; 11.30-11 Sat; 12-10.30 Sun

HELPSTON TF1205 Map 5
Blue Bell ⚑
Woodgate; off B1443

There have been quite a few changes to the layout and décor here this year. The entrance hall now has matching stonework and tiles, a big round table with chairs, and books in the new bookcase, and the lounge has comfortable cushioned chairs and settles, with the bar counter in one corner. To one side is the Smoking Parlour, and to the other, the snug. The new no smoking dining extension is light and airy with a sloping glass roof. Plenty of pictures, ornaments, mementoes, and cart-wheel displays throughout; there may be jam and marmalade for sale. The friendly bustle is as good as ever, and the food remains popular. As well as the good value two-course lunch (£5.95), there are lunchtime sandwiches (£3.75), ploughman's (£5.95), and small helpings of main meals (from £4.25). Also, soup (£2.25), creamy garlic mushrooms (£3.75), salmon and dill fishcakes (£3.95), home-cooked ham with eggs (£6.75), home-made steak in ale pie (£7.45), stuffed haddock (£7.75), lamb in rosemary and redcurrant sauce (£7.95), sirloin steak (£9.95), and daily specials such as liver and bacon hotpot (£7.45), and chicken breast with orange and ginger or lamb rogan josh (£8.25). Well kept Adnams Southwold, Everards Tiger and Old Original and a guest such as Mauldons Suffolk Pride on handpump, and the good coffee comes with fresh cream; helpful, efficient service. Piped music, darts, pool, cribbage, and dominoes. John Clare the early 19th-c peasant poet was born next door and originally worked here. Wheelchair access. A sheltered terrace has plastic garden tables under outdoor heaters. *(Recommended by Michael and Jenny Back, Ian Stafford)*

Free house ~ Licensee Aubrey Sinclair Ball ~ Real ale ~ Bar food (not Sun or Mon evenings) ~ Restaurant ~ (01733) 252394 ~ Children welcome ~ Dogs allowed in bar ~ Open 11.30-2.30, 5-11; 11.30-3, 6-11 Sat; 12-10.30 Sun

HEMINGFORD GREY TL2970 Map 5
Cock ⊗ ♀ ⚑
Village signposted off A14 eastbound, and (via A1096 St Ives road) westbound; High Street

Cambridgeshire Dining Pub of the Year
In a delightful village on the River Ouse, this pretty little pub is doing extremely well at the moment. And although there's quite an emphasis on the very good food, the public bar on the left is a proper place to drink in, with an open woodburning stove in the raised hearth, bar stools, wall seats and one carver, some cock photographs, and steps down to more seating below black beams. There's a bustling, friendly atmosphere, a good mix of locals and visitors, well kept Elgoods Black Dog, Wolf Golden Jackal, Woodfordes Wherry, and a guest from Nethergate on handpump, and ten good wines by the glass from an extensive list. The stylishly simple spotless restaurant on the right has pale bare boards, canary walls above a powder-blue dado, and another woodburning stove. Served by well trained young staff, the imaginative food at lunchtime includes good sandwiches (from £4.95),

and a two-course (£8.95) or three-course (£11.95) menu; also, soup (£3.95), roasted pumpkin and red onion salad with rocket, balsamic dressing and parmesan or rare breed pork and apple terrine with corn salad, grain mustard and honey (£4.95), baked duck parcel with sweet and sour cucumber (£5.95), very popular home-made sausages with flavoured mash, wild mushroom parcel with wilted spinach, creamed salsa verde and lentils (£10.95), calves liver with sage mash and onion sauce, rib-eye steak with good hand-cut chips, and chicken supreme with bacon, savoy cabbage, sautéed mushrooms and goats cheese cream (all £13.95), and puddings such as frozen peanut butter parfait with berry sorbet, chocolate tart or rhubarb and apple crumble. There are tables out behind in a neat garden, and the nearby manor house is possibly the second oldest continuously inhabited domestic house in the country. *(Recommended by Dr David Cockburn, George Atkinson, John Saul, P Clements)*

Free house ~ Licensees Oliver Thain and Richard Bradley ~ Real ale ~ Bar food (12-2.30, 7-9.30) ~ Restaurant ~ (01480) 463609 ~ Children in restaurant ~ Dogs allowed in bar ~ Open 11.30-3, 6-11; 11.30-11 Sat; 12-10.30 Sun; weekend hours as weekdays in winter

HEYDON TL4340 Map 5
King William IV 🍴
Off A505 W of M11 junction 10

The beamed rambling rooms in this neatly kept dining pub are warmed by a winter log fire, and the nooks and crannies are filled with a charming assortment of rustic jumble: ploughshares, yokes and iron tools, cowbells, beer steins, samovars, brass or black wrought-iron lamps, copper-bound casks and milk ewers, harness, horsebrasses, and smith's bellows – as well as decorative plates, cut-glass and china ornaments. It all rather reflects the landlady's abundant character. Well liked bar food at lunchtime includes filled baguettes, tortilla wraps, and baked potatoes (from £4.95), and ploughman's (£5.45), as well as soup (£4.25 – wiser not to order this if you sit at one of the tables suspended from the ceiling), duck liver and game terrine with fig compote or filo parcels filled with sesame chicken and pak choi with a sweet and sour dip (£6.25), good vegetarian choices such as lentil shepherd's pie or fresh ravioli stuffed with mozzarella, tomato and basil in a pepper and olive sauce (£9.95), and roasted winter root vegetable and three bean casserole (£10.65), moules marinière or thai green chicken curry (£9.95), steaks (from £11.95), rack of pork ribs with a hickory-smoked barbecue sauce or king prawns in garlic butter (£12.25), braised lamb shank with a port and redcurrant jus (£12.95), and rather pricey puddings (from £5.45). Part of the restaurant is no smoking. Well kept real ales such as Adnams Best, Fullers London Pride, and Greene King IPA on handpump. Fruit machine and piped music. In summer, the wooden deck has teak furniture and outdoor heaters, and there are more seats in the pretty garden. *(Recommended by Mike and Shelley Woodroffe, Richard Siebert, Alan and Carolin Tidbury, Mrs Margo Finlay, Jörg Kasprowski, Margaret and Roy Randle, M R D Foot, B N F and M Parkin)*

Free house ~ Licensee Elizabeth Nicholls ~ Real ale ~ Bar food (12-2, 6.30-10; 12-3, 7-10 Sun) ~ Restaurant ~ (01763) 838773 ~ Children welcome ~ Dogs allowed in bar ~ Open 12-2.30(3 Sat), 6-11; 12-3, 7-10.30 Sun

HINXTON TL4945 Map 5
Red Lion
2 miles off M11 junction 9 northbound; take first exit off A11, A1301 N, then left turn into village – High Street; a little further from junction 10, via A505 E and A1301 S

With its twin gables and pink-washed walls, this carefully extended 16th-c inn is most attractive. The dusky mainly open-plan bar has leather chesterfields on wooden floors, well kept Adnams Best, Greene King IPA, and Woodfordes Wherry and Nelsons Revenge on handpump, nine wines by the glass, and Aspall's cider; cribbage, dominoes. Off here there are high-backed upholstered settles in an informal dining area (no smoking on Sundays), and the smart no smoking restaurant is filled with mirrors, pictures and assorted clocks. Enjoyable bar food served by helpful, friendly staff might include home-made soup (£3.95), sandwiches (from £3.95; fresh baked baguettes from £5.50), and filled baked potatoes (from £4.50), with lunchtime choices like ham and egg (£7.25), field mushrooms stuffed with caramelised red onion and stilton, lasagne or grilled local sausages of the day (£7.95), and chicken curry or steak in ale pie (£8.95); there's also home-made soup (£3.95), chicken liver terrine (£5.25), king prawn curry (£9.95), breast of chicken wrapped in bacon with a cream sauce (£10.95), red bream fillets topped with roast cherry tomatoes, red onion and courgette (£12.50), steaks (from £12.95), and puddings such as sticky date and ginger pudding with butterscotch sauce or banoffi pie (from £4.95). In the tidy, attractive garden there's a pleasant terrace with picnic-sets, a dovecote and views of the village church. The pub is not far from the Imperial War Museum, Duxford. *(Recommended by Sue Rowland, Paul Mallett, Mrs Margo Finlay, Jörg Kasprowski, Martin Webster, Peter and Jean Dowson, Anthony Barnes, Eric Robinson, Jacqueline Pratt, Stephen and Jean Curtis, LM)*

Free house ~ Licensee Alex Clarke ~ Real ale ~ Bar food ~ Restaurant ~ (01799) 530601 ~ Well behaved children welcome ~ Dogs allowed in bar ~ Open 11-3, 6-11; 12-4.30, 7-10.30 Sun

HUNTINGDON TL2371 Map 5
Old Bridge Hotel ★ ⊕ ♀ ⇌

1 High Street; ring road just off B1044 entering from easternmost A14 slip road

Although this is not a pub, the bar in the very civilised ivy-covered Georgian hotel is still somewhere that customers are happy to drop into for a pint. It has fine polished floorboards, a good log fire, a quietly chatty atmosphere, and well kept Adnams Bitter, and a couple of guests such as Batemans XXXB and Potton Village Bike on handpump; 17 wines by the glass, ten sweet ones, and two champagnes. But it's the excellent imaginative food served by friendly, efficient staff that most people come to enjoy. You can eat in the big no smoking airy Terrace (an indoor room, but with beautifully painted verdant murals suggesting the open air) or in the slightly more formal panelled no smoking restaurant. As well as a bargain lunch menu (£13.50 two courses, £16.75 three courses), there might be sandwiches (from £5; steak with fried onions £8.50), home-made soup (£5.50), tuna carpaccio with wasabi and sesame and soy dressing (£5.95), caesar salad (£6.50; main course £10.95), crab ravioli with crab bisque and coriander (£6.95), pork sausages with onion and mustard sauce or asparagus tart with roast young vegetables (£9.95), fish and chips with pease pudding (£11.95), braised ham hock with vegetable hash and thyme and grain mustard (£13.95), corn-fed goosnargh chicken with braised fennel, tomato and garlic roast potatoes (£15.25), and roast loin of Denham Estate venison with redcurrant chutney (£17.95); good coffee. The bar is the only place you may smoke. The building is tucked away in a good spot by the River Great Ouse with its own landing stage, and tables on the waterside terraces (unfortunately there may be traffic noise, too). *(Recommended by Michael Sargent, J F M and M West, Alan Clark, Martin and Pauline Jennings, Les and Barbara Owen, Fred and Lorraine Gill, Christopher Turner, Anthony Longden, Richard Siebert)*

Huntsbridge ~ Licensee John Hoskins ~ Real ale ~ Bar food (12-2.30, 7-10) ~ Restaurant ~ (01480) 424300 ~ Children welcome ~ Dogs allowed in bar ~ Open 11-11; 12-10.30 Sun ~ Bedrooms: £95B/£125B

KEYSTON TL0475 Map 5
Pheasant ⊕ ♀

Just off A14 SE of Thrapston; village loop road, off B663

The emphasis in this long low thatched white inn is very much on the highly thought-of modern cooking. The oak-beamed spreading bar has a comfortably civilised atmosphere, open fires, simple wooden tables and chairs on deep coloured carpets, guns on the pink walls, and country paintings. The excellent wine list includes an interesting choice of reasonably priced bottles and 16 wines by the glass (plus eight sweet wines and two champagnes); fine port and sherry too. Well kept Adnams Bitter with changing guests such as Shepherd Neame Spitfire and Potton Village Bike on handpump, and freshly squeezed juices. The only place you can smoke is in the bar. Using carefully sourced ingredients, the food might include sandwiches and some snacks, mushroom and madeira soup with truffle oil (£5.50), pressed terrine of rabbit, roast hazelnuts and tarragon wrapped in prosciutto with hazelnut dressing (£6.50), crab with caviar, cucumber and coriander jelly (£6.95), spinach, ricotta and parmesan tart with artichoke, rocket and sun-blush tomato salad (£9.95), roast quail with thyme, parmesan polenta and girolle mushroom sauce with baby leeks (£13.95), aberdeenshire steaks (from £15.75), seared tuna with roast aubergine purée, chilli, lemon and basil (£16.75), and puddings like chocolate terrine with white chocolate and coffee ice-cream or banana and toffee crumble (£5.95). Seats out in front of the building (which has been owned by the Hoskins family for over 40 years). *(Recommended by Martin and Pauline Jennings, Michael Sargent, Oliver and Sue Rowell, Brenda and Rob Fincham, J F M and M West, Gerry and Rosemary Dobson, DRH and KLH, John and Enid Morris, Mr and Mrs D S Price, Martin and Sue Day)*

Huntsbridge ~ Licensees Johnny Dargue and John Hoskins ~ Real ale ~ Bar food (12-2.30, 7-10) ~ Restaurant ~ (01832) 710241 ~ Children welcome ~ Dogs allowed in bar ~ Open 12-2.30, 6ª11

KIMBOLTON TL0967 Map 5
New Sun ♀
High Street

A nice old pub fitting in well with Kimbolton's delightfully harmonious High Street. The low-beamed front lounge is perhaps the cosiest, with a couple of comfortable armchairs and a sofa beside the fireplace, standing timbers and exposed brickwork, books, pottery and brasses, and maybe mid-afternoon sun lighting up the wonkiest corners. This leads into a narrower locals' bar, with well kept Charles Wells Bombardier and Eagle, and a guest such as Greene King Old Speckled Hen, and quite a few wines by the glass; fruit machine and piped music. Opening off here are a dining room and a bright, busy tiled conservatory, with wicker furniture, an unusual roof like a red and yellow striped umbrella, and plenty of tables for eating. As well as lunchtime sandwiches (from £2.75) and filled baked potatoes (from £2.95), the menu might include chicken liver pâté with home-made fruit chutney (£5.25), grilled field mushroom, herb crumb, crispy pancetta and creamed garlic sauce (£5.50), parma ham, rocket salad and antipasti (£5.95; main course £8.95), home-made steak and kidney pudding (£8.25), roast mediterranean vegetable tart (£8.75), slow-braised belly pork with sultana, apple and sage stuffing (£9.25), fried halibut with creamed spinach, gnocchi, basil and cherry tomatoes (£12.75), roast rack of english spring lamb with redcurrant jus (£16.75), and puddings like baked lemon tart with raspberry coulis, Malteser cheesecake or syrup sponge and custard (from £4.25); popular tapas are listed on the specials board and they serve fresh battered haddock on Fridays. There's a very pleasant garden behind, with plastic tables and chairs. Some of the nearby parking spaces have a 30-minute limit. *(Recommended by John Picken, Sarah Flynn, Michael Dandy)*

Charles Wells ~ Tenant Stephen Rogers ~ Real ale ~ Bar food (12-2.15, 7-9.30; not Sun or Mon evenings) ~ Restaurant ~ (01480) 860052 ~ Children in eating area of bar and restaurant ~ Dogs allowed in bar ~ Open 11(11.30 Sat)-2.30, 6(6.30 Sat)-11; 12-10.30 Sun

LONGSTOWE TL3154 Map 5
Red House ◖
Old North Road; A1198 Royston—Huntingdon, S of village

The friendly licensees are sure to give you a warm welcome in this very easy-going creeper-covered place. From the bar with its red-tiled floor, you go round to the right, past the big log fire with its fat back kettle and a couple of tables beside it, and step down into another dark-tiled area with chintzy easy chairs and settees; a very comfortable haunt, looking out into a sheltered and attractive little garden with picnic-sets. The décor includes a fox mask and horse tack, quite a few good hunting prints, and rosettes mounted proudly behind the bar, and there are daily papers to read. On the left is an attractive restaurant area; a warm fire and maybe piped music. Well kept Greene King IPA and three or four interesting guests from breweries such as Archers and Cottage on handpump, and a good choice of wines by the glass. As well as lunchtime sandwiches, there might be sausage and mash, beef in ale pie or cajun chicken (£9.50), vegetarian open ravioli (£9.95), gammon and egg (£10.95), and steaks (from £13.95). The largest doll's house museum in the world is nearby. *(Recommended by Clive Jones, Michael Dandy, Phil and Jane Hodson)*

Free house ~ Licensee Martin Willis ~ Real ale ~ Bar food (12-2, 6-9.30; 12-9.30 Sat; 12-8 Sun) ~ Restaurant ~ (01954) 718480 ~ Children in eating area of bar and restaurant ~ Dogs allowed in bar ~ Open 12-3, 5.30-11; 12-11(10.30 Sun) Sat; closed Mon am

NEWTON TL4349 Map 5
Queens Head ★ ◼ £
2½ miles from M11 junction 11; A10 towards Royston, then left on to B1368

David Short has now been joined by his son Robert – which marks the beginning of the third generation to run this unspoilt and genuinely welcoming pub. It's so popular that you will need to get here early for a seat during busy times, and there may be a queue of people waiting for the doors to open on a Sunday. The well-worn main bar has a low ceiling and crooked beams, bare wooden benches and seats built into the walls, paintings on the cream walls, and bow windows. A curved high-backed settle stands on yellow tiles, a loudly ticking clock marks the unchanging time, and a lovely big log fire happily warms the place. The little carpeted saloon is similar but even cosier. Adnams Bitter and Broadside are tapped straight from the barrel, with any one of the Adnams range on as a guest, ten wines by the glass, and interesting fruit juices. Darts in a no smoking side room, with shove-ha'penny, table skittles, dominoes, cribbage, and nine men's morris. The pubby food here is very simple and there's only a limited range but it's very fairly priced, well liked, and comes in hearty helpings: toast and beef dripping (£2), good value lunchtime sandwiches (from £2.20, including things like banana with sugar and lemon or herb and garlic), a mug of their famous home-made brown soup (£2.80), and filled Aga-baked potatoes (£2.80). In the evening and on Sunday lunchtime you can get plates of excellent cold meat, smoked salmon, cheeses and pâté (from £3.80). There are seats in front of the pub, with its vine trellis. *(Recommended by Howard Selina, Conor McGaughey, Patrick Hancock, Mr and Mrs T B Staples, Mark Harrington, Keith and Janet Morris, Eric Robinson, Jacqueline Pratt, Annabel Viney, Michael and Marion Buchanan)*

Free house ~ Licensees David and Robert Short ~ Real ale ~ Bar food ~ No credit cards ~ (01223) 870436 ~ Very well behaved children in games room ~ Dogs welcome ~ Open 11.30-2.30, 6-11; 12-2.30, 7-10.30 Sun; closed 25 Dec

PETERBOROUGH TL1999 Map 5
Brewery Tap ◼ £
Opposite Queensgate car park

The very good Oakham beers are produced here in what is said to be one of the largest microbreweries in Europe. A two storey high glass wall running down one side of this enormous pub gives a fascinating view of the massive copper-banded stainless brewing vessels. These provide Bishops Farewell, JHB, and White Dwarf plus four seasonal Oakham beers. The pub also serves six guest ales from breweries scattered all over the country, eight bottled belgian beers, and quite a few wines by the glass. There's an easy going relaxed feel to the design of the place which is a striking conversion of an old labour exchange, with blue-painted iron pillars holding up a steel-corded mezzanine level; light wood and stone floors, and hugely enlarged and framed newspaper cuttings on light orange or burnt red walls. It's stylishly lit by a giant suspended steel ring with bulbs running around the rim, and steel-meshed wall lights. A band of chequered floor tiles traces the path of the long sculpted light wood bar counter, which is boldly backed by an impressive display of bottles in a ceiling-high wall of wooden cubes. A sofa seating area downstairs provides a comfortable corner for a surprisingly mixed bunch of customers from young to old; there's a big screen TV for sporting events. It gets very busy in the evening. The extensive choice of good bar food is prepared by Thai chefs and includes snacks (£1.50-£3.95), stir fries (£4.95-£6.50), curries (£4.95-£5.95), set menus (from £10.95) and buffets (from £11.95). The pub is owned by the same people as Charters. More reports please. *(Recommended by Patrick Hancock, Evelyn and Derek Walter, the Didler, Steve Nye, Pat and Tony Martin, Mike and Sue Loseby, Andy Lickfold)*

Own brew ~ Licensees Stuart Wright, Jessica Loock, Paul Hook ~ Real ale ~ Bar food (12-2.30, 6-9.30; all day weekends) ~ Restaurant ~ (01733) 358500 ~ Dogs allowed in bar ~ Open 12-11(till 1.30am Fri and Sat); 12-10.30 Sun; closed 25-26 Dec, 1 Jan

Charters ✿ £
Town Bridge, S side

As well as having what is perhaps the biggest pub garden in the city, this rather unusual place is also interesting for the fact that it is housed in a remarkable conversion of a sturdy 1907 commercial dutch grain barge. There's plenty of seating in the well timbered sizeable nautically themed bar, which is down in the cargo holds, and above deck a glazed oriental restaurant replaces the tarpaulins that used to cover the hold; piped music. A third of the bar and the restaurant are no smoking. As well as their own Oakham beers, Bass and Elgoods Black Dog, they keep up to eight quickly changing guests from many widely spread breweries on handpump, have around 30 foreign bottled beers, and hold regular beer festivals. Good value oriental-style bar food lunchtime includes snacks such as crispy seaweed, spring rolls, tempura prawns or salt and pepper crispy squid (£1.95-£4.65), pitta bread with fillings such as oriental duck or beef in black bean sauce (£3.95), and singapore chicken curry or lamb rendang curry (£5.65). More reports please. *(Recommended by Steve Nye, the Didler, Pat and Tony Martin, Patrick Hancock, Barry Collett, Alastair Gibson)*

Free house ~ Licensees Stuart Wright and Paul Hook ~ Real ale ~ Bar food (12-2.30 (restaurant only in evening)) ~ Restaurant ~ No credit cards ~ (01733) 315700 ~ Children in restaurant ~ Dogs allowed in bar ~ Live bands Fri and Sat ~ Open 12-11(2am Fri and Sat, 10.30 Sun)

REACH TL5666 Map 5
Dyke's End ✿
From B1102 E of A14/A1103 junction, follow signpost to Swaffham Prior and Upware – keep on through Swaffham Prior (Reach signposted from there); Fair Green

At the heart of this village pub is a 17th-c farmhouse which is in a charming village-green setting and next to the church. A high-backed winged settle screens off the door, and the simply decorated ochre-walled bar has stripped heavy pine tables and pale kitchen chairs on dark boards with one or two rugs, a few rather smarter dining tables on parquet flooring in a panelled section on the left, and on the right a step down to a red-carpeted bit with the small red-walled servery, and sensibly placed darts at the back. All the tables have lit candles in earthenware bottles, and there may be a big bowl of lilies to brighten up the serving counter: well kept Adnams Bitter and Greene King IPA and a couple of guests from breweries such as Fenland or Woodfordes on handpump, a good wine list, and Aspall's cider. Enjoyable bar food includes sandwiches, soup or spare ribs marinated in cola and bourbon (£4.50), potted ham and toast (£4.95), local bangers and mash with onion gravy or baked ham and egg (£6.95), cod in beer batter with mushy peas (£8.50), roast tomato and vegetable tart with caramelised red onion (£8.95), venison casserole with parsley dumplings or roast chicken with grappa and sweet potato mash (£9.95), and steaks (from £9.95). The dining area is no smoking during mealtimes, and the evening restaurant is upstairs. Service is pleasant and efficient, the atmosphere chatty and relaxed, and piped music (such as Bach cello suites) unobtrusive. The front grass has picnic-sets under big green canvas parasols. *(Recommended by M and GR, Pam and David Bailey)*

Free house ~ Licensee Simon Owers ~ Real ale ~ Bar food (not Sun or Mon evenings) ~ Restaurant ~ (01638) 743816 ~ Children in eating area of bar ~ Dogs allowed in bar ~ Open 12-2.30, 6-11; 12-2, 7-10.30 Sun; closed Mon lunchtime

STILTON TL1689 Map 5
Bell ♀ ⇌
High Street; village signposted from A1 S of Peterborough

This elegant 16th-c stone coaching inn (now mainly no smoking) has two neatly kept bars with bow windows, sturdy upright wooden seats on flagstone floors as well as plush button-back built-in banquettes, and there's a good big log fire in one handsome stone fireplace. The partly stripped walls have big prints of sailing and winter coaching scenes, and a giant pair of blacksmith's bellows hangs in the middle of the front bar; shove-ha'penny, dominoes, cribbage, and piped music. There's also a residents' bar and a bistro. Bar food includes sandwiches, home-made soup (£3.95), chicken liver pâté with walnut brioche and apple chutney (£4.95), burger with home-made bap (£8.50), pasta with a chunky tomato and chilli sauce (£9.25), slow braised lamb in beer with stilton dumplings (£10.50), chicken in grain mustard sauce (£11.50), and 10oz sirloin steak (£14.95). Well kept Fullers London Pride, Greene King IPA, and a couple of Oakham ales on handpump, and a decent choice of wines by the glass. Through the fine coach arch is a very pretty sheltered courtyard with tables, and a well which supposedly dates back to Roman times. More reports please. *(Recommended by Charles and Pauline Stride, Peter Abbott, Ian Phillips)*

Free house ~ Licensee Liam McGivern ~ Real ale ~ Bar food ~ Restaurant ~ (01733) 241066 ~ Children in eating area of bar only ~ Open 12-2.30(3 Sat), 6-11; 12-3, 7-10.30 Sun; closed evenings 25-26 Dec ~ Bedrooms: £72.50B/£99.50B

SUTTON GAULT TL4279 Map 5 ⌂
Anchor ★ ⑪ ♀ ⇌
Village signed off B1381 in Sutton

Tucked away off the beaten track, this very well run inn cleverly manages to appeal to a wide mix of customers. As well as being a fine place to drop into for a pint and a chat (though drinks prices are high), much emphasis is on the very popular, imaginative food; it's also particularly comfortable to stay in (and we have given them a new Stay Award this year). Four heavily timbered rooms are stylishly simple with a nice informal pubby atmosphere, three log fires, antique settles and well spaced scrubbed pine tables on the gently undulating old floors, good lithographs and big prints on the walls, and lighting by gas and candles; three of the four rooms are no smoking. As well as a weekday lunch menu offering one-course (£7.50), two-course (£10), and three-course choices (£14.50), the lovely food might include a changing soup (£4.95), super grilled dates wrapped in bacon on a mild mustard cream sauce (£5.95), lamb sweetbreads on potato rösti with red onion jam and sherry jus (£6.50), seared king scallops with chorizo sausage on creamed celeriac purée with watercress (£8.50), root vegetable and cashew nut risotto with parsnip crisps (£11.50), roast leg of lamb on black olive mash with wilted greens and red wine jus (£13.50), lemon and tarragon chicken with mushroom basmati and green beans (£13.95), baked halibut on a minted pea, broad bean, tomato and potato broth with Noilly Prat (£14.95), sirloin steak with home-made chips (£15.95), and puddings such as liquorice parfait with lime syrup, sticky toffee pudding with butterscotch sauce and warm dark chocolate mousse with coffee ice-cream (from £5.50). Service is friendly and helpful. Well kept City of Cambridge Boathouse Bitter or Hobson's Choice are tapped straight from the cask, there's a thoughtful wine list with quite a few (including champagne) by the glass, winter mulled wine and freshly squeezed fruit juice. There are pleasant seats outside, nice walks along the high embankment by the river, and the bird-watching is said to be good. *(Recommended by Jeff and Wendy Williams, Bob and Maggie Atherton, M and GR, John Saville, Earl and Chris Pick, A J Bowen, Glenys and John Roberts, Richard Siebert, Jill Hurley, Stephen Woad, Carolyn Dixon, Anthony Longden, Paul and Annette Hallett)*

Free house ~ Licensees Robin Moore and Carlene Bunten ~ Real ale ~ Bar food (12-2, 7-9; 6.30-9.30 Sat) ~ Restaurant ~ (01353) 778537 ~ Children welcome ~ Open 12-3.30, 7(6.30 Sat)-11; closed 26 Dec ~ Bedrooms: £55S(£65B)/£85S(£110B)

THRIPLOW TL4346 Map 5

Green Man

3 miles from M11 junction 10; A505 towards Royston, then first right; Lower Street

Handy for Duxford, this comfortably cheery Victorian pub has a good mix of furniture – mostly sturdy stripped tables and attractive high-backed dining chairs and pews on a flowery red carpet, and shelves on strongly coloured walls with pewter mugs and decorated china. To the right of the bar a cosy little room has comfortable sofas and armchairs, while two arches lead through to a no smoking restaurant on the left. Using local produce, the home-made bar food includes lunchtime baguettes (from £5), home-made burger (£5.50) and sausage and mash (£7.50) and daily specials such as sautéed potato, chorizo sausage and spinach salad or beef in beer on olive mash (£6), lamb curry (£8.50), pork loin with mustard mash and cider gravy (£9.50), and calves liver with crispy pancetta with roasted shallots (£11). In the evening you can choose your own combination of sauce and meal, such as creamy mushroom or port sauce with chicken, stuffed pepper, steak and so on (from £7.50). Regularly changing real ales come from brewers such as Milton, Oldershaw, Slaters, and Woodfordes; piped music. There are tables and an outdoor heater outside. More reports please. *(Recommended by Eric Robinson, Jacqueline Pratt, Gerry and Rosemary Dobson)*

Free house ~ Licensee Ian Parr ~ Real ale ~ Bar food (not Mon or Sun evening) ~ Restaurant ~ (01763) 208855 ~ Children welcome ~ Open 12-3, 6-11; closed Sun evening, all day Mon

---

LUCKY DIP

Besides the fully inspected pubs, you might like to try these Lucky Dips recommended to us and described by readers (if you do, please send us reports: www.goodguides.co.uk).

BARRINGTON [TL3849]
Royal Oak [turn off A10 about 3¾ miles SW of M11 junction 11, in Foxton; West Green]: Rambling thatched Tudor pub with tables out overlooking classic village green, heavy low beams and timbers, bar food from sandwiches to steak and special offers, children's helpings, friendly helpful landlord, prompt service, well kept Greene King IPA, Morlands and Old Speckled Hen, light and airy no smoking dining conservatory; may be piped music; children welcome *(P and D Carpenter, LYM, Michael Dandy, Jill McLaren)*
BOURN [TL3256]
☆ *Duke of Wellington* [signed off B1046 and A1198 W of Cambridge; at N end of village]: Consistently good, generous and imaginative freshly made food in quiet and civilised relaxing bar divided by arches and so forth – where the locals come to dine out; well spaced tables, pleasant attentive staff, well kept Greene King; cl Mon *(David Collison, BB)*
BROUGHTON [TL2877]
☆ *Crown* [off A141 opp RAF Wyton; Bridge

Rd]: Well kept ales such as Elgoods Black Dog and good enterprising food in bar with restaurant end, good service; disabled access and facilities; attractive village – pub owned by village consortium *(Nick and Ginny Law, Dr and Mrs Irvine Loudon)*
BUCKDEN [TL1967]
☆ *George* [Old Gt North Rd]: Stylish and elegant modern revamp of handsome former coaching inn, good upmarket brasserie food all day inc interesting dishes, good wines (and choice of champagnes) by the glass, Adnams and a guest ale, attentive service, log fire; large integral boutique, tables out on sheltered pretty terrace, bedrooms *(Karen and Steve Brine, Michael Sargent, BB, Michael Dandy, Gerry and Rosemary Dobson)*
☆ *Lion* [High St]: Handsome partly 15th-c coaching inn, black beams and big inglenook log fire in airy and relaxed bow-windowed entrance bar with plush bucket seats, wing armchairs and settees, decent bar food inc good value lunchtime sandwiches, good choice of wines, well kept Adnams and Greene King

IPA, courteous staff, no music or machines, panelled no smoking back dining room beyond latticed window partition; children welcome, bedrooms with own bathrooms *(BB, Michael Sargent, Sarah Flynn, Anthony Double, Gerry and Rosemary Dobson)*

CAMBRIDGE [TL4458]

Anchor [Silver St]: Well laid out if touristy pub in beautiful riverside position by a punting station, fine river views from upper bar and suntrap terrace, bar lunches from sandwiches up, evening baguettes; children in eating areas, open all day *(Dr and Mrs A K Clarke, LYM, MDN)*

☆ *Castle* [Castle St]: Large, airy and well appointed, with full Adnams range kept well and guests such as Wadworths, wide range of good value quick pubby food, friendly staff, peaceful no smoking area upstairs (downstairs can be noisy, with piped pop music); picnic-sets in good walled garden *(Dr David Cockburn, Mark O'Sullivan, P and D Carpenter, the Didler, Abi Benson)*

Flying Pig [Hills Rd]: Original small pub with good mix of people inc solicitors, journalists, students and locals, pig emblems everywhere, well kept Adnams, Fullers London Pride and Greene King Old Speckled Hen, young friendly staff, daily papers, back games room with pool; piped music from great blues and soul to customers' occasionally very amateur tapes; seats outside front and back *(Dr David Cockburn)*

Green Dragon [Water St, Chesterton]: Attractive late medieval timber-framed building, comfortable linked areas with beams, huge inglenook fireplace now housing secondhand books and videos, substantial bargain basic food all day, well kept Everards Tiger and Greene King ales, prompt friendly service even if crowded; waterside tables across quiet street, easy parking *(MLR, P and D Carpenter)*

☆ *Kingston Arms* [Kingston St]: U-shaped pub with some emphasis on the food side (many tables booked for this) inc popular light lunches, ten well kept real ales inc four changing guest beers, good choice of wines by the glass, friendly service, no music children inside; wkdy lunchtime free internet access (two terminals and wireless access); small torch-lit back terrace *(Louise Symons, Dr David Cockburn, JHBS, John Wooll, Steve Nye)*

Lawyers [Lensfield Rd]: Wine bar with enjoyable food and drinks *(Jeff and Wendy Williams)*

CHATTERIS [TL3986]

Cross Keys [Market Hill]: Welcoming and attractive 16th-c coaching inn opp church in fenland market town, open fire in long bar with armchair area, good value food in bar and comfortable candlelit restaurant inc good Sun lunches, friendly service, Greene King beers, inexpensive wine, tea and coffee; pleasant back courtyard, comfortable bedrooms *(Christine and Neil Townend)*

DRY DRAYTON [TL3862]

Black Horse [signed off A428 (was A45) W of Cambridge; Park St, opp church]: Roomy olde-worlde village pub, well kept Adnams Bitter and Broadside and Greene King IPA, enjoyable reasonably priced food inc good Sun lunch, friendly prompt service, welcoming fire in central fireplace, no smoking dining area; tables on pretty back terrace and neat lawn *(BB, Keith and Janet Morris, Ian and Nita Cooper)*

DULLINGHAM [TL6357]

Boot [Brinkley Rd]: Welcoming staff, well kept Adnams, good food choice, buoyant atmosphere with Newmarket types checking the racing form *(Charles Gysin)*

DUXFORD [TL4745]

☆ *John Barleycorn* [handy for M11 junction 10; signed off A505 E at Volvo junction]: Thatch, shutters, low beams, appealing old furnishings, prints and china, gentle lighting, good home-made food from open sandwiches up all day (cooked to order, so may be a wait), Greene King IPA and Abbot and a guest beer, decent wines; may be piped music; tables out among flowers, open all day, pleasantly simple beamed bedrooms *(David Twitchett, Erica Castle, LYM, Paul and Marion Watts)*

EATON SOCON [TL1658]

☆ *White Horse* [B4128]: Rambling, comfortable and interestingly furnished low-beamed rooms dating from 13th c, nice high-backed traditional settles around fine log fire in end room, relaxing atmosphere, well kept ales such as Flowers IPA and Original, Tetleys and Wadworths 6X, decent wines, quick friendly service and enjoyable fresh food from nachos and baked potatoes to good proper pies and tender steaks; play area in back garden, children in eating areas, bedrooms in more recent back extension *(LYM, Mr and Mrs W E Cross, Michael Dandy)*

ELLINGTON [TL1671]

Mermaid [High St]: Quaint old building in lovely spot by church, good food and helpful service, friendly and chatty atmosphere, comfortable seating and appealing understated décor *(Margaret and Roy Randle)*

ELSWORTH [TL3163]

☆ *George & Dragon* [off A14 NW of Cambridge, via Boxworth, or off A428]: Neatly furnished dining pub very popular with older regulars (OAP wkdy lunchtime discount card), panelled main bar and back dining area, enjoyable generous food, well kept Greene King IPA and Old Speckled Hen, decent wines, friendly helpful service, open fire; disabled access (step down to lavatories), nice terraces, play area in garden, attractive village *(Michael and Jenny Back, LYM, M and GR)*

Poacher [Brockley Rd]: 17th-c thatched and beamed pub with polished pine and neat settles, lots of carving inc nicely done birds on bar front, nice pictures, well kept changing ales such as Greene King and Shepherd Neame Spitfire, welcoming landlord and friendly staff, enjoyable food from baked potatoes up, no smoking area; plenty of tables in pretty garden with play area and barbecues, good walks *(BB, Michael Alcott)*

ELTISLEY [TL2759]

☆ *Leeds Arms* [signed off A428; The Green]: Pleasantly old-fashioned beamed bar overlooking peaceful village green, enjoyable generous food from nicely presented sandwiches to more adventurous evening dishes, well kept changing ales such as Charles Wells Bombardier, Stowford Press cider, quick friendly service, huge log fire, no smoking restaurant; darts, unobtrusive piped music; children in eating area, attractive garden with play area, simple comfortable bedrooms in separate block *(LYM, Michael Alcott, D and M T Ayres-Regan)*

ELTON [TL0893]

☆ *Crown* [Duck St]: Carefully rebuilt stone pub opp green in beautiful small village, long-serving landlord and cheerful welcoming service, pleasant layout with big log fire, banknotes on beams, artwork for sale and more formal no smoking conservatory restaurant (cl Sun pm and Mon), wide choice of above-average food from good proper sandwiches (wknd baguettes instead) to enjoyable hot dishes and tempting puddings trolley, well kept Greene King IPA and quickly changing seasonal and guest beers, well chosen wines; lavatories upstairs *(Michael and Jenny Back, H Bramwell)*

FEN DRAYTON [TL3468]

☆ *Three Tuns* [off A14 NW of Cambridge at Fenstanton; High St]: Well preserved thatched pub in charming village, heavy Tudor beams and timbers, inglenook fireplaces, tiled-floor bar, comfortable settles and other seats, well kept Greene King IPA and Abbot or Old Speckled Hen, sensibly placed darts, usual bar food (not Sun evening) from lunchtime sandwiches to steaks; piped music; children welcome in partly no smoking dining room, tables on covered terrace and neat back lawn, good play area, open all day *(Martin and Pauline Jennings, LYM, Comus and Sarah Elliott, Christopher Turner)*

FENSTANTON [TL3168]

King William IV [off A14 nr St Ives; High St]: Hospitable low-beamed pub with wide choice of above-average food, well kept Greene King ales, good range of wines, cosy bar with adjoining restaurant; pretty outside *(R E Dixon)*

GIRTON [TL4262]

☆ *Old Crown* [High St]: Roomy and popular restaurant/pub, antique pine on polished boards, good generous food (best to book wknds), well chosen menu with fish emphasis, well kept Greene King IPA, good wine choice, prompt smiling service even when crowded, real fires; children welcome, disabled facilities, pleasant terrace overlooking countryside *(Eric George)*

GODMANCHESTER [TL2470]

Black Bull [signed off A14 (was A604) just E of Huntingdon; Post St]: Heavily beamed old pub by church, big inglenook log fire, settles forming booths by leaded-light windows, side

room with lots of black rustic ironwork, Adnams, Fullers London Pride, Greene King IPA and Wadworths 6X, food from baguettes to pheasant, daily papers, steps down to no smoking dining room; big courtyard, pretty garden *(LYM, Michael Dandy)*

GRANTCHESTER [TL4355]

Red Lion [High St]: Good welcoming atmosphere in comfortable and spacious family food pub, well balanced menu with some emphasis on fresh fish, quick friendly service, good beer and wine choice; sheltered terrace, good-sized lawn *(LYM, P and D Carpenter, J A West)*

Rupert Brooke [Broadway; junction Coton rd with Cambridge—Trumpington rd]: Friendly beamed bar with central log fire, usual food from baguettes and lunchtime light dishes up, good staff, Greene King Old Speckled Hen and Charles Wells Bombardier, good choice of wines by the glass, sympathetic extension mainly for eating in – crisp white tablecloths; piped music *(Sarah Flynn, Michael Dandy)*

GRAVELEY [TL2463]

Three Horseshoes [High St]: Pleasantly furnished long narrow bar with two fish tanks, good choice of usual food from baguettes to steaks, Adnams Bitter and Old and Marstons Pedigree, good coffee, helpful licensees, low-beamed restaurant; piped music *(Michael Dandy)*

GREAT GRANSDEN [TL2655]

Crown & Cushion [off B1046 Cambridge—St Neots; West St]: Thatch, old beams, log fire, enjoyable food, well kept real ales, warm welcome; small garden, pretty thatched village *(Ron Deighton)*

GREAT PAXTON [TL2063]

Bell [High St]: Friendly straightforward local, very popular for its Weds fresh fish night (takeaways too) *(Margaret and Roy Randle)*

GUYHIRN [TF3903]

☆ *Oliver Twist* [follow signs from A47/A141 junction S of Wisbech]: Comfortable open-plan lounge with cheerful welcoming licensees, well kept sturdy furnishings, good range of home-made generous food from huge crusty warm rolls to steaks, well kept changing ales such as Shepherd Neame Spitfire, big open fires, no smoking restaurant; may be piped music; six bedrooms *(BB, Phil and Jane Hodson)*

HARDWICK [TL3758]

☆ *Blue Lion* [signed off A428 (was A45) W of Cambridge; Main St]: Friendly and attractive old local with lots of beams, open fire and woodburner, good food from lunchtime sandwiches and baguettes to wide choice of home-made dishes in bar and extended restaurant area (evening booking recommended), children's helpings, cheerful service, well kept Greene King IPA and Abbot tapped from the cask, old farm tools, pleasant conservatory; may be piped music; pretty roadside front garden, handy for Wimpole Way walkers *(Kevin Malam, BB)*

HISTON [TL4363]

Red Lion [High St]: Popular and friendly, with plain public bar, comfortably well used lounge, several well kept ales inc Greene King (autumn beer festival), good value pub food; big garden *(Peter and Liz Holmes)*

HOLYWELL [TL3370]

☆ *Old Ferry Boat* [signed off A1123]: Much refurbished partly thatched pub, low beams, open fires and side areas, dozens of carpenter's tools, window seats overlooking Great Ouse, Greene King IPA, Abbot and Old Speckled Hen, decent wines by the glass, enjoyable generous food from sandwiches to full meals (all day in summer), friendly and helpful young staff, good no smoking areas; quiet piped music, games; children welcome, tables and cocktail parasols on front terrace and riverside lawn, moorings, bedrooms, open all day wknds *(Michael Dandy, LYM, J Stickland, Peter and Jean Dowson)*

HORNINGSEA [TL4962]

Crown & Punchbowl [just NE of Cambridge]: Stylish dining place, restaurant-with-rooms rather than pub these days, with good food inc plenty of fresh fish (cooked to order so can take quite a while), well kept ales, decent wine, helpful management; piped music; refurbished bedrooms with good bathrooms *(Phil and Helen Holt, Dr David Cockburn, Patrick and Phillipa Vickery, LYM)*

HOUGHTON [TL2872]

Three Horseshoes [The Green]: Cosy village pub with low black beams and inglenook, good-sized L-shaped eating area with no smoking conservatory, Adnams Broadside, Greene King IPA and Old Speckled Hen, Smiles Best and Theakstons Best, good choice of wines by the glass, lunchtime food from baguettes and baked potatoes up, different evening menu, friendly service, pool in small second bar, darts, two cats; quiet piped music; tables outside, next to Houghton watermill (NT) and Ouse walks *(LYM, Michael Dandy)*

Three Jolly Butchers [A1123, Wyton]: Log fire in L-shaped beamed pub redone with leather sofas and new tables and chairs, Adnams and Greene King IPA and Old Speckled Hen, friendly attentive service; bar food from baguettes and baked potatoes up (not Sun/Mon evenings), separate restaurant area, piped music and games; children and dogs allowed in one area, pool table on covered back terrace, huge back garden with play area and occasional barbecues, pretty village *(Lucien Perring, Michael Dandy)*

HUNTINGDON [TL2371]

☆ *George* [George St]: Relaxed, friendly and comfortable hotel lounge bar, generous reasonably priced sandwiches and simple bar meals, wider choice in brasserie, well kept Greene King IPA and Abbot, decent choice of wines by the glass, good coffee (or tea and pastries), staff eager to please; magnificent galleried central courtyard, comfortable bedrooms *(LYM, Nigel Blackhall, Michael Dandy)*

ISLEHAM [TL6474]

Merry Monk [West St]: Now a dining pub, with enjoyable home-made food in big

helpings inc cheaper lunchtime dishes *(Richard Haw)*

MADINGLEY [TL3960]

☆ *Three Horseshoes* [off A1303 W of Cambridge; High St]: Pretty thatched pub, the most restaurany of the good local Huntsbridge group of dining pubs, and among the most expensive, with really ambitious food; small airy bar (which can be a bit of a crush at busy times), open fire, simple wooden tables and chairs on bare boards, stools at the bar and pictures on the green walls, no smoking conservatory restaurant, well kept Adnams and Timothy Taylors Landlord, and a fine list of around 20 wines by the glass inc sweet ones; children allowed, sunny garden *(Michael Dandy, LYM, Colin McKerrow, J F M and M West, Charles and Isabel Cooper, Ryta Lyndley, Richard Siebert)*

OFFORD D'ARCY [TL2166]

Horseshoes [High St]: Bought by local families for preservation as village pub, well presented straightforward food, Greene King beer, welcoming service *(Anthony Barnes)*

PAMPISFORD [TL4948]

Chequers [Town Lane]: Picturesque pub with lovely window boxes and hanging baskets, comfortable décor and atmosphere combining restaurant feel with traditional bar friendliness, good standard popularly priced food inc fresh fish and Sun lunch, well kept Greene King IPA, helpful licensee; tables in pleasant garden, handy for M11 *(D and M T Ayres-Regan)*

PETERBOROUGH [TL1897]

Coalheavers Arms [Park St, Woodston]: Small friendly traditional flagstoned pub, Milton ales and guest beers, farm cider, good range of continental imports and malt whiskies; pleasant garden *(Richard Houghton, the Didler, Steve Nye)*

Goodbarns Yard [St Johns St, behind Passport Office]: Cosy and friendly two-room pub with well kept Adnams, Black Sheep and changing guest beers tapped from the cask, annual beer festival, enjoyable wkdy bar lunches, big-screen sports TV, big conservatory; open all day *(the Didler)*

Gordon Arms [Oundle Rd (A605), Orton Longueville]: Friendly informal service, food cooked to order from pubby menu, also some unusual main courses, good choice of wine by the glass, no smoking eating area (popular bar can be smoky) *(Margaret McPhee)*

Palmerston Arms [Oundle Rd]: Old-fashioned 16th-c stone-built pub with well kept Batemans and lots of guest ales tapped from the cask, good choice of malt whiskies, good pork pies, welcoming service, old tables, chairs, benches and a sofa in carpeted lounge, tiled-floor public bar, no music or machines; step down into pub, steps to lavatory; picnic-sets in small garden, open all day *(the Didler)*

SAWSTON [TL4849]

Greyhound [High St (Cambridge Rd)]: Smart grey banquettes in cosy L-shaped bar, light and airy high glass-roofed dining room overlooking good big garden, friendly service, wide choice of enjoyable food from sandwiches up, local ales as well as the mainstream ones, big open fires, games room down steps, good facilities for children; quiet piped music *(P and D Carpenter)*

ST NEOTS [TL1859]

Chequers [St Marys St, Eynesbury]: Charming 16th-c beamed inn, interesting antique furnishings in small bar, good varied bar food from sandwiches and baked potatoes to steaks, good friendly service, well kept Tetleys and interesting guest beers, separate restaurant menu; sheltered terrace and garden *(Michael Dandy)*

STILTON [TL1689]

Stilton Cheese [signed off A1; North St]: Tasty food from sandwiches up inc imaginative dishes and lots of fish, well kept Bass, Elgoods Greyhound and Tetleys, decent wines, welcoming staff, interesting old interior with log fire in unpretentious central bar, good tables in two rooms off (one no smoking), and separate two-room restaurant; piped music; bedrooms, tables out on decking and garden *(Oliver and Sue Rowell, Michael Dandy)*

STOW CUM QUY [TL5159]

Quy Mill [Newmarket Rd]: Best Western hotel (not a pub) with neat friendly staff in its well appointed bar, wide choice of enjoyable food, well kept Adnams, Greene King Abbot, Marstons Pedigree and a small-brewery guest beer, plenty of whiskies; comfortable bedrooms *(Jerry Brown)*

STRETHAM [TL5174]

Fish & Duck [from A1123 E of Stretham turn left on to long signed track just after railway]: Excellent fenland spot at junction of two water-courses, enjoyable food, good service, interesting old photographs; cl Mon *(Robert Turnham, Dave Lowe)*

Red Lion [High St (off A10)]: Neat village pub with wide daily-changing choice of good generous food inc children's and Sun lunch, solid pine furniture and old village photographs, friendly attentive service, five well kept real ales, marble-topped tables in pleasant no smoking dining conservatory; children welcome, picnic-sets and barbecues in garden, new bedrooms, open all day bank hols *(Abi Benson, Keith and Janet Morris)*

SWAFFHAM PRIOR [TL5663]

Red Lion [B1102 NE of Cambridge; High St]: Attractive and spotless ancient building, wide range of generous fresh food from sandwiches and baked potatoes to steaks, Mon two-course bargains, prompt friendly service, good value house wines, Greene King Old Speckled Hen and Abbot, comfortably divided dining area, interesting old local photographs; tables in courtyard *(Stephen Woad)*

SWAVESEY [TL3565]

☆ *Trinity Foot* [by A14 eastbound, NW of Cambridge]: Comfortably worn in pub with

well spaced tables, well kept Elgoods, decent wines, broad choice of food inc sandwiches, light lunches and good fish and seafood, helpful staff, attractive conservatory; piped music; outside tables (traffic noise here) *(Peter and Jean Hoare, R M Corlett, Adam and Joan Bunting, LYM, Irene and Ray Atkin)*

TRUMPINGTON [TL4455]

Coach & Horses [High St (A1309)]: Roomy and tastefully restored, decent fairly priced food from sandwiches to good value meals, friendly prompt service, well kept beers, dining area, open fire *(P and D Carpenter)*

TYDD GOTE [TF4517]

Tydd Gote Inn [Main Rd (A1101 N of Wisbech)]: Fresh and clean, with attractive beamed dining rooms, well kept beers such as Courage Directors and John Smiths; terrace tables overlooking play area and bowling green, bedrooms *(anon)*

WANSFORD [TL0799]

☆ *Haycock* [just off A1 W of Peterborough]: Handsome old coaching inn greatly extended and frequently updated as hotel and conference centre, useful break for enjoyable bar food all day from good sandwiches and ciabattas up, well kept Adnams and Bass, good wines, relaxed seating areas with character, big log fire, no smoking restaurant; children in eating areas, courtyard and garden, dogs allowed in bar and comfortable bedrooms, open all day *(Dr and Mrs R G J Telfer, LYM, Mrs M E Mills, Phil and Jane Hodson, Eithne Dandy, Eric Robinson, Jacqueline Pratt)*

Paper Mills [London Rd]: Front bar with two woodburners, no smoking eating area, Bass, Everards Perfick and Hancocks HB, usual bar food inc good baguettes and baked potatoes, good friendly service, separate menu for larger back restaurant; piped music; outside tables *(Michael Dandy)*

WARESLEY [TL2454]

☆ *Duncombe Arms* [Eltisley Rd (B1040, 5 miles S of A428)]: Welcoming old pub, long main bar, fire one end, good range of good value generous food from lunchtime sandwiches up, nice fresh veg and salads, consistently well kept Greene King ales, good service, no smoking back room and restaurant; garden picnic-sets *(JWAC, Margaret and Roy Randle, Gerald and Valerie Pepper)*

WHITTLESFORD [TL4648]

Bees in the Wall [North Rd; handy for M11 junction 10]: Comfortable timbered lounge, small public bar with darts and old wall settles, good food choice from sandwiches up, well kept Fullers London Pride, Timothy Taylors Landlord and a guest beer, open fires; may be piped classical music; no dogs, picnic-sets in attractive garden, bees' nest visible in wall, open all day wknds *(Kevin Thorpe)*

Post Office address codings confusingly give the impression that some pubs are in Cambridgeshire, when they're really in the Leicestershire or Midlands groups of counties (which is where we list them).

Cheshire

Pubs on top form here this year are the Grosvenor Arms at Aldford
(imaginative food all day now, a fine choice of drinks, appealing surroundings),
the enthusiastically run Bhurtpore at Aston (outstanding on the drinks side,
good curries too – and interesting décor), the timeless old thatched White Lion
in Barthomley (down to earth value), the Cholmondeley Arms near Bickley
Moss (run with a good deal of character, memorable food and a cheerful bar),
the civilised Dysart Arms at Bunbury (interesting food all day and good drinks
choice), the highly traditional Albion in Chester (tremendous character,
interesting World War I memorabilia), the canalside Old Harkers Arms there
(virtues very much as its sister pubs at Aldford and Bunbury), the calm and
immaculate Nags Head at Haughton Moss (good value meals, especially its
lunchtime buffet), and the warmly welcoming and genial Swan at Wybunbury
(good value food and beer). Going from strength to strength under the Keigans
over the few years that they've had it, it's the Nags Head at Haughton Moss
which now deserves our award of Cheshire Dining Pub of the Year. After
several years in which there has been quite a turnover of pubs in this chapter
we have no new main entries for you here this year, but in the Lucky Dip
section at the end of the chapter we'd particularly point you towards the Bears
Head at Brereton Green, Mill in Chester, Duke of Portland at Lach Dennis,
Roebuck in Mobberley, recently reworked Dun Cow at Ollerton, Swettenham
Arms at Swettenham, Crag at Wildboarclough and Boot at Willington. Cheshire
drinks prices are well below the national average; the Hydes beer in the Dog at
Peover Heath and Plough at Eaton was particularly cheap. With a host of small
more or less local breweries jostling with the major regional firm Robinsons of
Stockport, there's always been a good deal of healthy competition to keep
prices fair. And now that the Midlands regional brewery Wolverhampton &
Dudley are taking over both Cheshire's own Burtonwood and Jennings (based
in Cumbria, but active too down here), competition here may hot up even
more.

ALDFORD SJ4259 Map 7
Grosvenor Arms ★ ⑪ ⏦ ◧

B5130 Chester—Wrexham

The really enjoyable food at this tightly run ship is very handily served all day. It's a
hugely popular place so it's worth going just outside peak times – otherwise it's best
to book. Children are welcome until 7pm, and though this is a popular place for
family gatherings there's a fairly grown-up atmosphere, so no highchairs, but they
do have cribbage, dominoes, Trivial Pursuit and Scrabble. Traditional furnishings,
plenty of interesting pictures, and skilfully welcoming lighting soften the spacious
open-plan interior. A buoyantly chatty atmosphere prevails in the huge no smoking
panelled library area, with its tall book shelves lining one wall, and lots of
substantial tables well spaced on the handsomely boarded floor. Several quieter
areas are well furnished with good individual pieces. Lovely on summer evenings,
the airy terracotta-floored no smoking conservatory has lots of huge low hanging
flowering baskets and chunky pale wood garden furniture. It opens on to a large

elegant suntrap terrace, and a neat lawn with picnic-sets, young trees and a tractor. A great choice of drinks includes around 20 wines (largely new world and all served by the glass, a tempting range of whiskies (including 100 malts, 30 bourbons, and 25 irish whiskeys) as well as Flowers IPA, Caledonian Deuchars IPA and Robinsons Best, which are well kept on handpump alongside a couple of guests from brewers such as Blackawton and Worfield. A balanced menu of well presented interesting dishes might include tomato and basil soup (£3.95), good sandwiches such as brie with waldorf salad on walnut bread (from £4.25), chicken liver parfait with red onion and plum chutney (£4.95), ploughman's (£6.45), butternut and lemon grass risotto with spring onions, pine nuts and balsamic dressing or steakburger topped with bacon and mozzarella (£8.45), duck breast with parsnip dauphinoise, savoy cabbage and spinach or chicken breast with creamed leeks and black pudding potato (£11.95), grilled bass with oriental noodles and hoisin dressing (£15.95) and puddings such as cheshire farm ice-creams (£3.25) or cherry crumble tart with custard (£4.75). Swift service is friendly and attentive. *(Recommended by A P Seymour, Peter Abbott, Mike Marsh, Angie Coles, Revd D Glover, Mr and Mrs A H Young, Stephen Funnell, Paul Boot, Mrs P J Carroll, Therese Flanagan, Bruce and Sharon Eden, Derek and Sylvia Stephenson)*

Brunning & Price ~ Managers Gary Kidd and Jeremy Brunning ~ Real ale ~ Bar food (12-10(9 Sun and bank hols)) ~ (01244) 620228 ~ Children welcome till 7pm ~ Dogs allowed in bar ~ Open 11.30-11; 12-10.30 Sun; closed 25, 26 Dec, 1 Jan evenings

ASTBURY SJ8461 Map 7

Egerton Arms 🛏

Village signposted off A34 S of Congleton

Very much a family run place – look out for the sociable pub dogs – this friendly village inn is in a pretty spot overlooking an attractive old church. Rambling round the bar, the bright yellow-painted rooms have a cheery pub atmosphere. Walls sport the odd piece of armour, shelves of books, and mementoes of the Sandow Brothers, who performed as 'the World's Strongest Youths' (one of them was the landlady's father). In summer dried flowers fill the big fireplace; parts of the bar and restaurant are no smoking. Robinsons Double Hop, Hartleys XB and Unicorn are well kept on handpump; piped music, fruit machine, TV. A wide choice of straightforward reasonably priced bar meals could include soup (£2.50), sandwiches (from £2.95), sardines grilled in garlic butter (£3.95), spicy bean and vegetable pasta, steak, kidney and mustard pie, roast ham with cranberry glaze or battered cod with mushy peas (all £6.25), a handful of daily specials such as fried squid with lemon ginger (£7.95), and puddings such as chocolate rum truffle (£3.25). They also do OAP lunches Mon-Thurs (two courses £4.75, three £5.75), as well as children's meals (£2.95). Out in front, you'll find a few well placed tables, and a play area with wooden fort. Despite the large car park, at Sunday lunchtime you might struggle to get a place. Their refurbished en-suite bedrooms are very good value. More reports please. *(Recommended by K M Crook)*

Robinsons ~ Tenants Alan and Grace Smith ~ Real ale ~ Bar food (11.30-2, 6.30-9) ~ Restaurant ~ (01260) 273946 ~ Children in eating area of bar, restaurant and family room ~ Open 11.30-11; 12-3, 6.30-10.30 Sun ~ Bedrooms: £40S/£60S

ASTON SJ6147 Map 7

Bhurtpore ★ ♀ ◖

Off A530 SW of Nantwich; in village follow Wrenbury signpost

Each year, more than 1,000 different superbly kept real ales – anything from Abbeydale to Weetwood – pass through the 11 handpumps at this enthusiastically run red brick freehouse. They also stock dozens of unusual bottled beers and fruit beers, lots of bottled ciders and perries, over 100 different whiskies, a good wine list (with fine wines and fruit wines) and plenty of soft drinks. The pub takes its unusual name from the town in India, where a local landowner, Lord Combermere, won a battle. In the carpeted lounge bar a collection of exotic artefacts has an indian influence, with one turbaned statue behind the counter proudly sporting any sunglasses left behind by customers; also good local period photographs, and some attractive furniture. At lunchtime or early weekday evenings the atmosphere is cosy and civilised, but even on weekends, when it gets packed, the cheery staff cope superbly. Tables in the comfortable public bar are reserved for people not eating, and the snug and dining room are no smoking; darts, dominoes, cribbage, pool, TV, and fruit machine. The enjoyable menu has snacks (not Friday or Saturday night) such as sandwiches (from £2.65, hot filled baguettes £3.95) and sausage, egg and chips (£4.95), as well as a choice of five different tasty curries (from £7.95), cheese and leek cakes with creamy dijon sauce (£8.25), steak and kidney pie (£8.50) and steaks (from £10.95), with daily changing specials such as black pudding on sweet potato mash with madeira sauce (£4.75) and monkfish in red wine sauce with mushrooms and bacon (£10.95), as well as puddings such as banoffi pie with toffee sauce (£3.50). *(Recommended by Dr B and Mrs P B Baker, Mrs P J Carroll, E G Parish, the Didler, John and Helen Rushton, Martin Grosberg)*

Free house ~ Licensee Simon George ~ Real ale ~ Bar food (12-2(2.30 Sat), 6.45-9.30; 12-9 Sun) ~ Restaurant ~ (01270) 780917 ~ Children welcome (not Fri, Sat evening) ~ Dogs allowed in bar ~ Open 12-2.30(3 Sat), 6.30-11; 12-10.30 Sun; closed 25-26 Dec, 1 Jan ~ Bedrooms: £30S/£40S

BARTHOMLEY SJ7752 Map 7
White Lion ★ £

A mile from M6 junction 16; from exit roundabout take B5078 N towards Alsager, then Barthomley signposted on left

Deservedly popular, this lovely 17th-c black and white thatched place has a happy traditional atmosphere. The main bar feels timeless, with its blazing open fire, heavy low oak beams dating back to Stuart times, attractively moulded black panelling, cheshire watercolours and prints on the walls, latticed windows, and thick wobbly old tables. Up some steps, a second room has another welcoming open fire, more oak panelling, a high-backed winged settle, a paraffin lamp hinged to the wall, and shove-ha'penny, cribbage and dominoes; local societies make good use of a third room. Outside, seats and picnic-sets on the cobbles have a charming view of the attractive village, and the early 15th-c red sandstone church of St Bertiline across the road is well worth a visit. Very good value lunchtime food includes sandwiches (from £4.40), sausage and mash or fresh salmon (£5.50), beef and yorkshire pudding (£5.90) and ploughman's for two (£7.95). It's best to arrive early on weekends to be sure of a table. Well kept real ales on handpump include Burtonwood Bitter and Top Hat, with a couple of guests such as Marstons Pedigree and Wychwood Hobgoblin. The cottage behind the pub is available to rent. *(Recommended by MLR, Edward Mirzoeff, Richard Greaves, the Didler, Michael and Marion Buchanan, J B R Ashley, Dr D J and Mrs S C Walker, G Coates, John Saul, Philip and Cheryl Hill, Roger Thornington, John and Yvonne Davies, Jack Clark, Simon Jones, Peter and Gill Helps)*

Union Pub Company ~ Tenant Terence Cartwright ~ Real ale ~ Bar food (lunchtime only) ~ (01270) 882242 ~ Children welcome away from bar ~ Dogs welcome ~ Open 11.30-11(5-11 only Thurs); 12-10.30 Sun; closed Thurs afternoon

BICKLEY MOSS SJ5650 Map 7
Cholmondeley Arms 🍴 🍷 🛏

Cholmondeley; A49 5½ miles N of Whitchurch; the owners would like us to list them under Cholmondeley Village, but as this is rarely located on maps we have mentioned the nearest village which appears more often

Run with good-natured individuality, this imaginatively converted Victorian schoolhouse welcomes a happy mix of locals who chat cheerily at the bar, diners visiting for the very good food (it's best to book at peak times) and guests enjoying the comfortable accommodation. The building's scholarly past is evident in the cross-shaped high-ceilinged bar, with its high gothic windows, huge old radiators and old school desks on a gantry above the bar. A medley of seats runs from cane and bentwood to pews and carved oak settles, and the patterned paper on the shutters matches the curtains. There's a stag's head over one of the side arches, an open fire and masses of Victorian portraits and military pictures. Most enjoyable generously served bar food includes delicious lunchtime sandwiches (£4.75) and steak baguettes (£6.50), stuffed pancakes (£7.25) and lasagne (£8.50), with daily specials such as watercress soup (£3.95), beef carpaccio (£5.95), tagliatelle with spicy tomato and red pepper sauce (£8.25), lamb stew with pearl barley (£9.25), gressingham duck breast with port, spring onion and ginger sauce (£11.25) and cod from Whitby (£11.95). Well kept Adnams, Banks's, Marstons Pedigree and Weetwood and perhaps a guest such as Greene King Abbot on handpump. Around eight interesting and reasonably priced wines by the glass are listed on a blackboard; they also do good coffees (liqueur ones too), and some speciality teas. There are seats outside on the sizeable lawn, and more in front overlooking the quiet road. The pub is handy for Cholmondeley Castle Gardens. *(Recommended by J S Burn, Mrs P Dewhurst, Rod Stoneman, Ray and Winifred Halliday, Susie Symes, Jane Thomas, Mrs P J Carroll, Mike Ridgway, Sarah Miles, Mike and Mary Carter, A G Roby, Peter Neate, Susan Brookes)*

Free house ~ Licensees Guy and Carolyn Ross-Lowe ~ Real ale ~ Bar food (12-2.30, 6.30-10) ~ Restaurant ~ (01829) 720300 ~ Children welcome ~ Dogs welcome ~ Open 11(12 Sun)-4, 6.30-11 ~ Bedrooms: £50B/£65B

BUNBURY SJ5758 Map 7

Dysart Arms 🍴 ♀

Bowes Gate Road; village signposted off A51 NW of Nantwich; and from A49 S of Tarporley – coming this way, coming in on northernmost village access road, bear left in village centre

A civilised but relaxed dining atmosphere prevails in the thoughtfully laid out spaces that ramble around the pleasantly lit central bar at this popular place – you may need to book. Though you can equally pop in for just a drink, it's not the sort of place with a gathering of locals at the bar. Under deep venetian red ceilings, the knocked-through cream-walled rooms have red and black tiles, some stripped boards and some carpet, a comfortable variety of well spaced big sturdy wooden tables and chairs, a couple of tall bookcases, some carefully chosen bric-a-brac, properly lit pictures, and good winter fires. They've lowered the ceiling in the more restauranty end room (with its book-lined back wall), and there are lots of plants on the window sills. Two rooms are no smoking. Thwaites and Weetwood and a couple of guests such as Deuchars IPA and Titanic Anchor are well kept on handpump, alongside a good selection of 16 wines by the glass. Now served all day, interesting, nicely presented dishes (using local produce where possible) from a changing menu could include soup (£3.95), sandwiches such as hot bacon and brie with cranberry sauce (from £4.50), baked goats cheese leek and walnut tart (£5.25), linguini with roast butternut, shi-itake mushrooms, tomatoes and red pesto sauce (£8.50), braised shoulder of lamb with tomato and marjoram sauce and dauphinoise potatoes (£11.95), sweet potato, green lentil and spinach curry with coriander rice (£8.50), grilled bass on wok-fried greens and noodles with an oriental dressing (£13.95), puddings such as apple and almond tart with raspberry coulis and clotted cream (£4.75), and a very interesting local cheeseboard (£6.50). Sturdy wooden tables on the terrace and picnic sets on the lawn in the neatly kept slightly elevated garden are lovely in summer, with views of the splendid church at the end of the pretty village, and the distant Peckforton Hills beyond. *(Recommended by Revd D Glover, John Kane, Mrs P J Carroll, Stephen Funnell, E G Parish, Brian and Anna Marsden, Stephen Buckley, Gwyn and Anne Wake, J S Burn, Paul Davies, Dennis Jones, JWAC, Dave Irving, Dr D Scott, H and P Cate, Steve Whalley, Joyce and Maurice Cottrell, Selwyn Roberts, Gerry and Rosemary Dobson, A Darroch Harkness)*

Brunning & Price ~ Managers Darren and Elizabeth Snell ~ Real ale ~ Bar food (12-9.30 (9 Sun)) ~ (01829) 260183 ~ No children under 10 after 6pm ~ Dogs allowed in bar ~ Open 11.30(12 Sun)-11; closed 25 Dec

CHESTER SJ4166 Map 7

Albion ★ ◧

Park Street

The strongly traditional atmosphere, absence of piped music, noisy machines and children make this firmly run pub especially popular with a loyal following of older visitors – even a handful of World War I veterans during commemorative events. Leased by the same landlord for over 34 years, with a layout that's little changed since Victorian times, it's tucked away on a quiet street corner just below the Roman Wall. Throughout the peacefully quiet rooms you'll find an absorbing collection of World War I memorabilia from big engravings of men leaving for war, and similarly moving prints of wounded veterans (even the pub cat is called Kitchener) to flags, advertisements and so on. The post-Edwardian décor is appealingly muted, with dark floral William Morris style wallpaper, a cast-iron fireplace, appropriate lamps, leatherette and hoop-backed chairs, a period piano, a large mangle, and cast-iron-framed tables; there's an attractive side dining room too. Service is friendly, though groups of race-goers are discouraged (opening times may be limited during meets), and they don't like people rushing in just before closing time. Well kept Banks's, Jennings Cumberland, and Timothy Taylors Landlord on handpump and maybe a guest from a brewer such as Titanic, with over 25 malt whiskies, new world wines, and fresh orange juice. Big helpings of hearty home-made bar food (made with lots of local ingredients) include doorstep sandwiches (£3.50, club sandwiches £3.75), filled staffordshire oatcakes (£3.90), haggis and tatties, cottage pie or lambs liver, bacon and onions in cider gravy with creamed potatoes (all £6.95), and daily specials such as hot thai chicken curry (£6.95). It can get very busy at lunchtime. If you stay here please tell us about the bedrooms. *(Recommended by Michael Butler, Joe Green, Brenda and Rob Fincham, the Didler, Patrick Hancock, Angie Coles, A Darroch Harkness)*

Punch ~ Lease Michael Edward Mercer ~ Real ale ~ Bar food (12-2, 7-8; not Sun evening) ~ Restaurant ~ No credit cards ~ (01244) 340345 ~ Dogs allowed in bar ~ Open 12-3, 5(6 Sat)-11(7-10.30 Sun); 12-11 Fri ~ Bedrooms: /£65B

Old Harkers Arms ♀ ◧

Russell Street, down steps off City Road where it crosses canal – under Mike Melody antiques

This converted early Victorian canalside warehouse takes its name from a Mr Harker, who once ran a canal-boat chandler's in the building. Lofty ceilings and tall windows (you can watch canal and cruise boats glide past on the water outside) give an appealing sense of space and light, though tables are carefully arranged to create a sense of privacy. Walls are covered with frame to frame old prints, and the typical Brunning & Price wall of books features at one end. Attractive lamps add cosiness, and the bar counter is apparently constructed from salvaged doors. Imaginative bar food (now served all day) from a changing menu could include starters or light meals such as cream of tomato soup (£3.95), sandwiches (from £4.45) and fried squid with lime and rocket mayonnaise (£7.25), main courses such as spinach and ricotta cannelloni (£7.25), steak and mushroom suet pudding (£9.95), grilled cod fillet with caper butter (£11.95), fried calves liver and treacle bacon with black pudding mash (£13.95), puddings such as chocolate chip sponge pudding with white chocolate sauce or coconut, lime and mint crème brûlée with shortbread biscuit (£4.95), and a cheese board (£5.75). An impressive range of nine real ales on handpump includes Cains IPA, Wapping and Weetwood and up to six regularly changing guests from brewers such as Moorhouse, Northern and Whim. They also do around 50 malt whiskies, farmhouse ciders and decent well described wines. *(Recommended by Darren and Jane Staniforth, Oliver and Sue Rowell, Jo Lilley, Simon Calvert, Simon J Barber, Andrew York, Roger and Anne Newbury, Joe Green, Mrs Hazel Rainer, Mrs Maricar Jagger, A Darroch Harkness)*

Brunning & Price ~ Manager John Thomas ~ Real ale ~ Bar food (12-9.30(9 Sun)) ~ (01244) 344525 ~ Children in eating area of bar till 6pm ~ Open 12-11(10.30 Sun); closed 25, 26 Dec

COTEBROOK SJ5865 Map 7

Fox & Barrel

A49 NE of Tarporley

Snug areas at this bar restaurant are interestingly furnished, with a good mix of tables and chairs including two seats like Victorian thrones, an oriental rug in front of a very big log fireplace, a comfortable banquette corner, and a part with shelves of rather nice ornaments and china jugs; silenced fruit machine, unobtrusive piped music. Beyond the bar a huge uncluttered candlelit no smoking dining area has varying-sized tables, comfortable dining chairs, attractive rugs on bare boards, rustic pictures above the panelled dado, and a more extensively panelled section. Under a new licensee since the last edition, neatly uniformed staff serve well kept Bass, John Smiths, Marstons Pedigree and a guest such as Charles Wells Bombardier through a sparkler (though you can ask for it to be taken off), and there's a decent choice of wines. As well as lunchtime bar snacks such as sandwiches or baguettes (from £4.25), ploughman's (£6.35), and chicken fajitas (£7.50), well presented dishes from a changing menu might include home-made soup (£3.50), smoked haddock and chorizo risotto (£5.50), steak, ale and mushroom pie (£9.25), goats cheese tart (£9.75), parma ham wrapped chicken breast stuffed with dolcelatte, on tagliatelle with basil pesto (£11.75), king prawn thai green curry (£14.50) and 8oz fillet (£15.95); it's a good idea to book for Sunday lunch. *(Recommended by Simon J Barber, E G Parish, J S Burn, Mrs P J Carroll, Brian and Anna Marsden, Peter Fitton)*

Punch ~ Tenant Chris Crossley ~ Real ale ~ Bar food (12-2.30, 6.30(6 Sat)-9; 12-3, 6-9 Sun) ~ Restaurant ~ (01829) 760529 ~ Children in restaurant ~ Live entertainment Mon evening ~ Open 12-3, 6-11; 12-11 Sat(10.30 Sun); closed 25 Dec

EATON SJ8765 Map 7

Plough 🛏

A536 Congleton—Macclesfield

Well run, with a nicely civilised feel, this handsome 17th-c village pub is smart but comfortably welcoming. The neatly converted bar has plenty of beams and exposed brickwork, a couple of snug little alcoves, comfortable armchairs and cushioned wooden wall seats on red patterned carpets, long red curtains leading off to a cosy no smoking room, mullioned windows, and a big stone fireplace. Moved here piece by piece from its original home in Wales, the raftered barn at the back is used as a restaurant. The big tree-filled garden is attractive, with good views of the nearby hills, and there are picnic-sets on the lawn and a smaller terrace. Very good home-made bar food relying on local ingredients includes lunchtime sandwiches (from £2.95), soup (£2.95), prawns in garlic butter (£5.15), steak and kidney pudding or chilli (£7.95), thai green curry (£8.50), 10oz rib-eye steak (£11.95), some interesting daily specials, and a three-course Sunday lunch (£11.95). Well kept Boddingtons, Hydes Bitter and a guest such as Greene King Ruddles County on handpump, and a decent wine list; they have a happy hour between 4 and 7 (not Sun). Service is friendly and attentive, and spare a few words for Thunder, the resident black labrador; piped music, TV. The appealingly designed bedrooms are in a converted stable block. *(Recommended by Jack Morley, E G Parish, Mrs P J Carroll)*

Free house ~ Licensee Mujdat Karatas ~ Real ale ~ Bar food (12-2, 6-9) ~ Restaurant ~ (01260) 280207 ~ Dogs allowed in bedrooms ~ Quiz Mon evening ~ Open 12-11; closed 25, 26 Dec evenings ~ Bedrooms: £50B/£70B

Post Office address codings confusingly give the impression that some pubs are in Cheshire, when they're really in Derbyshire (and therefore included in this book under that chapter) or in Greater Manchester (see the Lancashire chapter).

HAUGHTON MOSS SJ5855 Map 7

Nags Head 🏠 ♀ £

Turn off A49 S of Tarporley into Long Lane, at 'Beeston, Haughton' signpost

Cheshire Dining Pub of the Year

Readers very much enjoy this immaculately kept black and white pub, which is nicely tucked away down winding country lanes. Dating back in parts to the 16th c, it has gleaming black and white tiles by the serving counter, pews and a heavy settle by the fire in a small quarry-tiled room on the left, and button-back wall banquettes in the carpeted room on the right, which also has logs burning in a copper-hooded fireplace. Below the heavy black beams are shelves of pewter mugs, attractive Victorian prints and a few brass ornaments, and the front window of the pub is full of charmingly arranged collector's dolls. On the right is a sizeable carpeted dining area, and an oak beamed conservatory extension serves as the dining room; may be very quiet piped music. Alongside a well chosen wine list (with ten by the glass) and a dozen malts, Flowers and Wadworths 6X and a guest such as Marstons Pedigree are well kept on handpump. The generously served tasty bar food is popular – attentive service and atmosphere remain calm even when it's busy – particularly between 12 and 2 on weekdays when they run the bargain-priced self-service buffet (£6.20). Snacks, which are served till 4.30, include sandwiches (£4.25), filled baked potatoes (£4.25), omelettes (£3.60) and ploughman's (£6.20). Main menu items include soup (£3.25), fishcakes (£4.15), roasted peppers filled with vegetable risotto (£7.60), gammon and egg (£8.50), pork medallions on roasted peppers with sweet soy sesame sauce (£9.80), fried monkfish on stir-fried vegetables with thai cream sauce (£10.25), and steak (£11.70); there's a puddings trolley (£3.75) and various ice-cream sundaes (£3.35). A big immaculately kept garden has well spaced picnic-sets and a bowling green. *(Recommended by Leo and Barbara Lionet, Mrs P J Carroll, E G Parish, Dr G B Carter, Gill and Keith Croxton)*

Free house ~ Licensees Rory and Deborah Keigan ~ Real ale ~ Bar food (12-9.30(10 Fri, Sat)) ~ Restaurant ~ (01829) 260265 ~ Children in eating area of bar and restaurant ~ Open 12-11(10.30 Sun); closed evening 25 Dec

HIGHER BURWARDSLEY SJ5256 Map 7

Pheasant

Burwardsley signposted from Tattenhall (which itself is signposted off A41 S of Chester) and from Harthill (reached by turning off A534 Nantwich—Holt at the Copper Mine); follow pub's signpost on up hill from Post Office; OS Sheet 117 map reference 523566

The interior of this half-timbered and sandstone 17th-c pub has a bright modern feel, with wooden floors and well spaced light furniture. They say the see-through fireplace houses the largest log fire in the county, and there's a pleasant no smoking conservatory. On a clear day the telescope on the terrace lets you make out the pier head and cathedrals in Liverpool, while from inside you can see right across the Cheshire plain. Four local Weetwood beers are well kept on handpump alongside a guest from Firkin, and around 20 malts; piped music, daily newspapers. A big side lawn has picnic-sets, and on summer weekends they sometimes have barbecues. Besides sandwiches (from £3.95, steak £5.95), the menu might include soup (£3.75), chicken satay (£4.50), spinach and ricotta cannelloni or sausage and mash (£6.95), battered cod (£8.95) and braised lamb shank with roast garlic and mint gravy or bass on thai-style vegetables with cream sauce (£12.95), and puddings such as chocolate rum and raisin cheesecake or syrup sponge pudding (from £4.25). Popular with walkers, the pub is well placed for the Sandstone Trail along the Peckforton Hills. *(Recommended by Dave Irving)*

Free house ~ Licensee Andrew Nelson ~ Real ale ~ Bar food (12-9.30; 12-3, 6-9.30 Mon) ~ (01829) 770434 ~ No children evenings ~ Dogs allowed in bar ~ Open 12-11(10.30 Sun) ~ Bedrooms: £65B/£80B

LANGLEY SJ9569 Map 7

Hanging Gate

Meg Lane, Higher Sutton; follow Langley signpost from A54 beside Fourways Motel, and that road passes the pub; from Macclesfield, heading S from centre on A523 turn left into Byrons Lane at Langley, Wincle signpost; in Sutton (½ mile after going under canal bridge, ie before Langley) fork right at Church House Inn, following Wildboarclough signpost, then 2 miles later turn sharp right at steep hairpin bend; OS Sheet 118 map reference 952696

High on a Peak District ridge, this welcoming old drover's inn was first licensed around 300 years ago, but is thought to have been built long before that. Still in their original layout, three cosy little low-beamed rooms are simply furnished, and have attractive old prints of Cheshire towns, and big coal fires. The first traditional room houses the bar (with well kept Hydes Bitter, Jekylls Gold, a Hydes on handpump, quite a few malt whiskies and eight wines by the glass) and is so small there's barely space for seating; the second room has a section of bar in the corner and three or four tables, and the third, the appealingly snug blue room, with its little chaise longue, is no smoking. Down some stone steps, an airy garden room extension has panoramic views over a patchwork of valley pastures to distant moors and the tall Sutton Common transmitter above; piped music. Good straightforward bar food served by very friendly attentive staff could include soup (£3.20), prawns in filo parcels or deep-fried camembert (£4.25), fried cod or gammon and pineapple (£7.95), steaks (from £8.95), and delicious lamb chops (£12.95), with puddings such as crème caramel (£3.95); best to book on weekends. Seats out on the crazy-paved terrace also have terrific views. *(Recommended by the Didler, Mandy and Simon King, M and GR, Mr and Mrs Colin Roberts, Derek and Heather Manning, DJH)*

Hydes ~ Tenants Peter and Paul McGrath ~ Real ale ~ Bar food (not Sun evening) ~ Restaurant ~ (01260) 252238 ~ Children in restaurant ~ Open 12-3, 7-11; 12-11 Sat; 12-10.30 Sun

MACCLESFIELD SJ9271 Map 7

Sutton Hall Hotel ★ 🛏

Leaving Macclesfield southwards on A523, turn left into Byrons Lane signposted Langley, Wincle, then just before canal viaduct fork right into Bullocks Lane; OS Sheet 118 map reference 925715

This charming 16th-c baronial hall is in lovely grounds, with tables on a tree-sheltered lawn, and ducks and moorhens swimming in the pond. Divided into separate areas by tall oak timbers, the bar has some antique squared oak panelling, lightly patterned art nouveau stained-glass windows, broad flagstones around the bar counter (carpet elsewhere), and a raised open fire. It's mostly furnished in a straightforward way with ladderback chairs around sturdy thick-topped cast-iron-framed tables, but there are a few unusual touches such as a suit of armour by a big stone fireplace, a longcase clock, a huge bronze bell, and a brass cigar-lighting gas taper on the bar counter itself. There's a good relaxed atmosphere, and the staff are friendly and efficient. Enjoyable bar food might include soup (£3.25), welsh rarebit (£4.65), sandwiches (from £3.65, toasties from £4.75), mediterranean vegetable lasagne (£6.95), grilled gammon and pineapple (£8.50), and battered cod and chips (£8.55), changing specials such as sweet and sour pork (£8.65) and grilled haddock on spinach with cheese sauce and poached egg (£8.95), and puddings such as crème brûlée and sticky toffee pudding (£3.50). Well kept Bass, Greene King IPA, Marstons Best and a guest such as Moorhouses Pride of Pendle are well kept on handpump, and they also stock over 40 malt whiskies, decent wines and freshly squeezed fruit juice, and serve a well prepared Pimms. If you're lucky enough to be staying here, they can arrange clay shooting, golf or local fishing; there's access to canal moorings at Gurnett Aqueduct 200 yards away. *(Recommended by MLR, Mart Lawton, the Didler, Derek and Sylvia Stephenson, Mrs P J Carroll, Dennis Jones)*

Free house ~ Licensee Robert Bradshaw ~ Real ale ~ Bar food (12-2.30, 7-10) ~

Restaurant ~ (01260) 253211 ~ Children in restaurant ~ Dogs allowed in bedrooms ~
Open 11-11; 12-10.30 Sun ~ Bedrooms: £79.95B/£94.95B

PEOVER HEATH SJ7973 Map 7

Dog

**Off A50 N of Holmes Chapel at the Whipping Stocks, keep on past Parkgate into
Wellbank Lane; OS Sheet 118 map reference 794735; note that this village is called
Peover Heath on the OS map and shown under that name on many road maps, but the
pub is often listed under Over Peover instead**

It can be busy here, so it's worth arriving early to try for a seat in the slightly more
spacious feeling main bar. This is comfortably furnished with easy chairs and wall
seats (including one built into a snug alcove around an oak table), and two wood-
backed seats built in either side of a coal fire, opposite which logs burn in an old-
fashioned black grate. You may have a short wait for the generous helpings of bar
food, which might include soup (£2.95), sandwiches (from £3.05, hot baguettes
from £4.15), ploughman's (from £4.55), chilli (£6.55), sausage of the day and mash
(£8.25), steak and kidney pie (£10.25), braised lamb shank (£10.45), roast of the
day (£10.75), and king cod with chips and mushy peas (£10.95), and puddings such
as strawberry pavlova (£3.95). The dining room is no smoking. Reasonably priced
Copper Dragon Scotts 1816, Hydes, Moorhouses Black Cat and Weetwood Best
are well kept on handpump. They also have Addlestone's cider, 35 different malt
whiskies and eight wines by the glass; darts, pool, dominoes, TV and piped music.
There are picnic-sets underneath colourful hanging baskets on the peaceful lane,
and more out in a pretty back garden. It's a pleasant walk from here to the Jodrell
Bank Centre and Arboretum. *(Recommended by John Wooll, David Field, Revd D Glover,
Roger and Anne Newbury, E G Parish, Steve Whalley, Andy Sinden, Louise Harrington,
Maurice and Della Andrew, Mrs P J Carroll, Peter F Marshall, Dr Phil Putwain, Gerry and
Rosemary Dobson, Dave Braisted, H and P Cate)*

Free house ~ Licensee Steven Wrigley ~ Real ale ~ Bar food (12-2.30, 6-9; 12-8.30 Sun) ~
Restaurant ~ (01625) 861421 ~ Children in eating area of bar and restaurant ~ Dogs
allowed in bar ~ Live music monthly Fri ~ Open 11.30-3, 4.30-11; 11.30-11 Sat; 12-10.30
Sun ~ Bedrooms: £55B/£75B

PRESTBURY SJ8976 Map 7

Legh Arms 🛏

A538, village centre

This white painted 16th-c building has been smartly refurbished in a traditional
style. The relaxing bar, though opened up, is well divided into several distinctive
areas: muted tartan fabric over a panelled dado on the right, with ladderback
dining chairs, good solid dark tables, elegant french steam train prints, italian
costume engravings and a glass case of china and books; brocaded bucket seats
around similar tables, antique steeplechase prints, staffordshire dogs on the stone
mantelpiece and a good coal fire on the left; a snug panelled back part has cosy
wing armchairs and a grand piano, and a narrow side offshoot has pairs of art deco
leather armchairs around small granite tables, and antique costume prints of french
tradesmen. The bar, towards the back on the left, has well kept Robinsons Best and
Hatters Mild on handpump and nice house wines, a good range of malts and
whiskies, good coffee, and maybe genial regulars perched on the comfortable
leather bar stools; this part looks up to an unusual balustraded internal landing.
There are daily papers on a coffee table, and magazines on an antique oak dresser;
piped music. Service by uniformed staff is pleasantly informal. Popular with
families at the weekend, and the interesting changing bar food might include soup
(£2.95), spicy fishcakes with sweet chilli sauce or warm goats cheese with sweet
onion and apple chutney (£4.75), mild thai chicken curry or steak and kidney pie
(£7.25), wild mushroom risotto with asparagus (£7.95), salmon fillet with wilted
spinach and tomato concasse (£9.25), with puddings such as home-made apple pie
(£4.25). A garden behind has a terrace with outdoor heating, tables and chairs.

(Recommended by Mrs P J Carroll, DJH, Mr and Mrs Robert Jamieson)

Robinsons ~ Tenant Peter Myers ~ Real ale ~ Bar food (12-10 Sun) ~ Restaurant ~
(01625) 829130 ~ Children in eating area of bar ~ Open 12-11(10.30 Sun) ~
Bedrooms: /£95B

TARPORLEY SJ5563 Map 7

Rising Sun

High Street; village signposted off A51 Nantwich—Chester

The cosy bustling pub rooms at this friendly old place have well chosen tables
surrounded by eye-catching old seats including creaky 19th-c mahogany and oak
settles, an attractively blacked iron kitchen range, sporting and other old-fashioned
prints on the walls, and a big oriental rug in the back room. The wide-ranging
menu (with around a dozen vegetarian dishes) includes soup (£2.50), sandwiches
(from £2.65), toasties and filled baked potatoes (from £3.10), a variety of tasty pies
(from £6.65), poached salmon with prawn and tomato sauce (£8.25), black bean
sizzler, spinach pancakes and lasagne (all £8.50) and beef stroganoff (£8.95); no
smoking dining room, helpful service, piped music. Well kept Robinsons Best and
Double Hop on handpump. *(Recommended by Maurice and Della Andrew, the Didler,
Mrs P J Carroll)*

Robinsons ~ Tenant Alec Robertson ~ Real ale ~ Bar food ~ Restaurant (evening) ~
(01829) 732423 ~ Children in restaurant and family room ~ Open 11.30-3, 5.30-11;
11.30-11 Sat; 12-10.30 Sun

WETTENHALL SJ6261 Map 7

Boot & Slipper

From B5074 on S edge of Winsford, turn into Darnhall School Lane, then right at Wettenhall signpost: keep on for 2 or 3 miles; OS Sheet 118 map reference 625613

The knocked-through beamed main bar of this pleasant old pub has three shiny old
dark settles, straightforward chairs, and a fishing rod above the deep low fireplace
with its big log fire. The modern bar counter also serves the left-hand
communicating beamed room with its shiny pale brown tiled floor, cast-iron-
framed long table, panelled settle and bar stools; darts, dominoes, and piped music.
An unusual trio of back-lit arched pseudo-fireplaces forms one stripped-brick wall,
and there are two further areas on the right, as well as an attractive back restaurant
with big country pictures. Bass and Tetleys on handpump, a good choice of malt
whiskies and a decent wine list; the landlady and staff are friendly. Tasty lunchtime
dishes could include home-made soup (£2.75), good sandwiches (from £3.40), roast
of the day, braised beef in red wine with shallots and baby mushrooms or poached
scottish salmon with rich butter cream parsley sauce (all £5.95), with evening dishes
such as deep-fried breaded brie with tangy cumberland sauce (£4.75), leek and
potato bake (£8.50), trout grilled with garlic butter and herbs (£9.95), cannon of
pork fillet with black pudding and black peppercorn sauce (£10.85), and mixed
grill (£14.50), with puddings such as fruit pie (£3.50); children's meals (£3.80). You
may need to book at the weekend. There are picnic-sets out on the cobbled front
terrace by the big car park; children's play area. *(Recommended by Mrs P J Carroll,
Alec and Joan Laurence, E G Parish)*

Free house ~ Licensee Joan Jones ~ Real ale ~ Bar food ~ Restaurant ~ (01270) 528238 ~
Children in eating area of bar and restaurant ~ Dogs allowed in bar ~ Open 12-3, 5.30-11;
12-11(10.30 Sun) Sat ~ Bedrooms: £40S/£60S

'Children welcome' means the pub says it lets children inside without any special
restriction. If it allows them in, but to restricted areas such as an eating area or family
room, we specify this. Some pubs may impose an evening time limit. We do not
mention limits after 9pm as we assume children are home by then.

WINCLE SJ9666 Map 7

Ship ◖

Village signposted off A54 Congleton—Buxton

Handy for walkers (they sell their own book of local walks, £3), this attractive 16th-c pub in scenic countryside is one of Cheshire's oldest. Free of piped music and games machines (dominoes are the order of the day here), its two simple little tap rooms have a welcoming atmosphere, thick stone walls and a coal fire. A couple of thoughtfully sourced guest beers such as Eccleshall Slaters Monkey Magic and York Yorkshire Terrier are well kept alongside Fullers London Pride and Timothy Taylors Landlord, belgian beers, Weston's farm cider, and fruit wines. Served by efficient young staff, tasty bar food could include home-made soup (£3.25), lunchtime sandwiches (from £3.95), oak-smoked bacon on bubble and squeak with hollandaise sauce and poached egg (£5.50), spinach, ricotta and roasted vegetable cannelloni (£8.95), grilled trout with tarragon and citrus butter (£9.95), lamb shank pie with rosemary mash and red wine gravy (£11.50), steak (£14.95) and specials such as home-made fishcakes with mushy peas (£5.25) and venison steak with rosemary mash, black pudding and red wine jus (£13.50); puddings might include home-made banoffi pie (£3.95). It's best to book at the weekends, when parking may overflow to the steep narrow road. A small garden has wooden tables. *(Recommended by Mrs P J Carroll, the Didler, M and GR, E G Parish)*

Free house ~ Licensee Giles Henry Meadows ~ Real ale ~ Bar food (12-3, 6.30-9.30 Sat) ~ Restaurant ~ (01260) 227217 ~ Children in family room ~ Dogs allowed in bar ~ Open 12-3, 6.30-11; 12-11(10.30 Sun) Sat; closed Mon (except bank hols)

WRENBURY SJ5948 Map 7

Dusty Miller

Village signposted from A530 Nantwich—Whitchurch

Right next to the Shropshire Union Canal, this substantial brick building is a neatly converted 19th-c corn mill – you can still see the old lift hoist up under the rafters. Rather surprisingly, the River Weaver runs in an aqueduct under the canal at this point, and it was the river that once powered the millrace. These days a constant stream of boats slipping through the striking counter-weighted canal drawbridge, just outside here, provide entertainment if you're sitting at picnic-sets among rose bushes on the gravel terrace or at one of the tables inside by the series of tall glazed arches. The modern main bar area is comfortably welcoming, with long low-hung hunting prints on green walls, and a mixture of seats flanking the rustic tables – tapestried banquettes, oak settles and wheelback chairs. Further in, a quarry-tiled part by the bar counter has an oak settle and refectory table. There's quite an emphasis on the changing menu. Good, well presented dishes (using local ingredients where possible) could include soup (£3.20), grilled sardines with garlic butter (£3.95), gravadlax (£4.75), pasta with roast tomatoes, rocket, cheshire cheese and double cream sauce (£7.50), chicken stuffed with black pudding with creamy mustard sauce (£10.25), baked bass (£11.95), and puddings such as Baileys bread and butter pudding or sticky toffee pudding (from £3.50). Don't get here late as they do stop food service very promptly. The upstairs restaurant and six tables in the bar are no smoking. Friendly staff serve well kept Robinsons Hartleys XB, Old Tom, Unicorn and a Robinsons guest on handpump; eclectic piped music and dominoes. The pub can get very crowded in fine weather. *(Recommended by Mrs P J Carroll, Gwyn and Anne Wake, E G Parish, Philip and Cheryl Hill, Roger and Pauline Pearce)*

Robinsons ~ Tenant Mark Sumner ~ Real ale ~ Bar food (12-2, 7-9.30(9 Sun)) ~ Restaurant ~ (01270) 780537 ~ Children in eating area of bar till 8.30pm ~ Dogs allowed in bar ~ Open 11.30-3, 6.30-11(all day bank holiday weekends); 12-3, 7-10.30 Sun

WYBUNBURY SJ6950 Map 7

Swan

B5071

In winter two big fires warm the cosy bar of this pretty pub, and a good local following adds to the genial atmosphere. It's full of bric-a-brac, with lots of copper and brass, ornate lamps and a magnificent model galleon. Comfortable seats in the no smoking lounge area include good bays built into the windows. Jennings Bitter, Cumberland and Cocker Hoop and a couple of guests such as Greene King Abbot and local Woodlands are well kept on handpump, and the wine list is reasonably priced; piped music, darts, fruit machine, cribbage and dominoes. Served by friendly staff, enjoyable food includes soup (£2.95), thick cut sandwiches (from £3.95), hot baps (from £6.95), ploughman's (£7.25), beef and ale pie (£7.75), good salmon and smoked haddock fishcakes (£8.50), penne with roast vegetables and goats cheese (£7.95), battered haddock (£8.25), lamb shoulder with redcurrant jus (£11.95), and puddings such as caramel apple pie (£3.95); they do a two-course lunch (Tuesday to Friday) for £6.95. There are picnic-sets under cocktail parasols in a neat garden, with a couple more in the sheltered back yard. The pub stands next to a lovely sloping churchyard with great lime trees. For those who have been here before, the unusual leaning stone-built church tower has recently been straightened. (*Recommended by Sue Holland, Dave Webster, M and GR, E G Parish, Roy and Lindsey Fentiman, Martin Grosberg, John and Sylvia Harrop*)

Jennings (W & D) ~ Lease Richard and Fiona Fitzgerald ~ Real ale ~ Bar food (12-2, 6.30-9.30; 12-8 Sun and bank hols) ~ Restaurant ~ (01270) 841280 ~ Children welcome ~ Dogs allowed in bar ~ Open 12(5 Mon)-11(10.30 Sun) ~ Bedrooms: £40B/£65B

LUCKY DIP

Besides the fully inspected pubs, you might like to try these Lucky Dips recommended to us and described by readers (if you do, please send us reports: www.goodguides.co.uk).

ALDERLEY EDGE [SJ8176]
Stags Head [Mill Lane, off A535 SW]: Relaxing and welcoming traditional pub in lovely countryside, well kept beer, pleasant service, enjoyable food inc proper steak pie, fresh fish and local specialities (*John Trevor and Susan Rispin*)
ALPRAHAM [SJ5859]
Tollemache Arms [Chester Rd (A51)]: Comfortable family pub with country décor, interesting pictures and bric-a-brac, cheerful bar, separate dining areas, reasonably priced food all day, real ales inc Greene King Old Speckled Hen, good service, open fires; big play area, bedroom extension (*Pete Baker, E G Parish*)
Travellers Rest [A51 Nantwich—Chester]: Unspoilt four-room country local with veteran landlady (same family for three generations), particularly well kept Tetleys Bitter and Mild and a guest such as Lees, low prices, leatherette, wicker and Formica, some flock wallpaper, fine old brewery mirrors, darts and dominoes, back bowling green; no machines, piped music or food (apart from crisps and nuts), cl wkdy lunchtimes (*the Didler, Pete Baker*)
BEESTON [SJ5559]
☆ *Beeston Castle Hotel* [A49 S of Tarporley]: Comfortably restored pub in good walking country below the castle, friendly staff, good choice of attractively presented food, small

wing chairs and nicely placed tables in spacious bar, well kept ales such as Shepherd Neame Spitfire, short but well chosen wine list, restaurant; children till 8pm, comfortable bedrooms, open all day Sun (*E G Parish*)
BELL O' TH' HILL [SJ5245]
☆ *Blue Bell* [just off A41 N of Whitchurch]: Heavily beamed partly 14th-c country local with relaxed atmosphere, friendly licensees, well kept changing ales such as Black Sheep, Hanby Drawell, Old Swan Mrs Pardoes Original and Woods, well priced food from sandwiches and baguettes up, two cosy and attractive rooms, well behaved alsatian; pleasant garden and surroundings, cl Mon (*John and Wendy Allin, LYM, MLR*)
BICKERTON [SJ5254]
Bickerton Poacher [A534 E of junction with A41]: Rambling 17th-c poacher-theme pub, linked beamed rooms with open fires, copper-mining memorabilia and a talkative parrot, good range of reasonably priced food, Courage Directors, Greene King Ruddles and Theakstons Old Peculier; attractive barbecue extension around sheltered courtyard, play area (*LYM, Mike Jones, Edward Leetham*)
BOLLINGTON [SJ9477]
☆ *Poachers* [Mill Lane]: Friendly stone-built village local, well kept Boddingtons, Timothy Taylors Landlord and two guest beers such as local Storm, decent wines, good home-made food with appealingly priced lunches attracting

older people and more upscale evening choice, helpful and attentive young licensees; attractive secluded garden and terrace behind, pretty setting, handy for walkers, cl Mon lunchtime *(Brian and Anna Marsden, Stephen Buckley)*

Vale [heading N off B5091 by railway viaduct]: Pleasantly modernised local reopened under friendly and enthusiastic young licensees, well kept local Storm Silk Amnesia and Timothy Taylors Landlord, good atmosphere, home-made food (all day Sat), log fire; children welcome till 7pm, neat woodside lawn, canal walks nearby *(LYM, Brian and Anna Marsden)*

BOTTOM OF THE OVEN [SJ9872]

☆ *Stanley Arms* [A537 Buxton—Macclesfield, 1st left past Cat & Fiddle]: Isolated moorland pub, small, friendly and cosy, lots of shiny black woodwork, plush seats, dimpled copper tables, good coal fires in all rooms inc dining room, generous well cooked traditional food, well kept Marstons and guest beers; children welcome, piped music; picnic-sets on grass behind, may close Mon in winter if weather bad *(Stephen Buckley, LYM)*

BRADFIELD GREEN [SJ6859]

☆ *Coach & Horses* [A530 NW of Crewe]: Welcoming service in well run family pub, interesting blackboard food choice from sandwiches up in comfortable bar and pleasant restaurant section, well kept real ales, good value house wine, horse-racing pictures; discreet piped music *(E G Parish)*

BRERETON GREEN [SJ7864]

☆ *Bears Head* [handy for M6 junction 17; set back off A50 S of Holmes Chapel]: Beautiful and thoughtfully developed heavily timbered inn, welcoming and civilised linked rooms with old-fashioned furniture, flagstones, carpets and hop-hung low beams, good choice of well prepared enjoyable fresh food inc big sandwiches (till 5pm) and varying sizes of hot dishes, good service, well kept ales and decent wines by the glass, cheerful log fires, daily papers; open all day, good value bedrooms in modern block *(Dr and Mrs T E Hothersall, Brenda and Stuart Naylor, E G Parish, LYM)*

BROWNLOW [SJ8360]

Brownlow Inn [Brownlow Heath Lane, off A34 S of Congleton]: Tucked-away well furnished traditional country dining pub, wide choice of good value food from baguettes to daily roasts (should book for the popular Sun lunch), choice of beers, good value house wine, good friendly service, log fire, conservatory *(Pauline and Terry James)*

BUTLEY TOWN [SJ9177]

Butley Ash [A523 Macclesfield—Stockport]: Popular dining pub with well kept ales, wide choice of generous food, interlinked areas inc 'library', attentive staff *(Mr and Mrs P J Barlow, LYM, Stephen Buckley)*

CHELFORD [SJ8175]

Egerton Arms [A537 Macclesfield—Knutsford]: Good rambling Chef & Brewer, candles on oak tables, bottles on shelves, bric-a-brac, wide choice of reasonably priced blackboard food, well kept Theakstons and a guest such as Greene King Old Speckled Hen,

plenty of well organised friendly young staff; garden tables, open all day *(John Wooll)*

CHESTER [SJ4166]

Boot [Eastgate Row N]: Down-to-earth and relaxed pub in lovely 17th-c Rows building, heavy beams, lots of dark woodwork, oak flooring, flagstones, some exposed Tudor wattle and daub, black-leaded kitchen range in lounge beyond good value food servery, old-fashioned settles and oak panelling in no smoking upper area popular with families, good service, cheap well kept Sam Smiths; piped music; children allowed *(the Didler, Joe Green, LYM)*

☆ *Falcon* [Lower Bridge St]: Striking ancient building with handsome beams and brickwork, well kept Sam Smiths, good value lunches (not Sun), friendly helpful staff; piped music, fruit machine; children allowed lunchtime (not Sat) in airy and attractive no smoking room upstairs; open all day Sat (can get packed then, with lunchtime jazz), interesting tours of the vaults *(Andrew York, LYM, Patrick Hancock, Angie Coles, Mrs Maricar Jagger)*

☆ *Mill* [Milton St]: Early 19th-c mill converted to hotel, neat and comfortable sizeable bar on right, five regular beers inc ones brewed for them by Coach House and Phoenix, up to nine changing guest ales, reasonable prices, good value ciabattas and enjoyable hot dishes till late evening, friendly efficient staff, relaxed mix of customers, restaurant overlooking water and now canal barge dining too; quiet piped music, unobtrusively placed big-screen SkyTV, jazz Mon; children looked after well, waterside benches, good bedrooms, open all day *(Martin Grosberg, Joe Green, BB, Colin Moore, the Didler, Patrick Hancock)*

Stanley Arms [Brook St]: Light and airy décor, good beer choice inc a guest, reasonably priced wines, good value food *(Paul Baker)*

Talbot [Walter St]: Friendly two-bar corner local, well kept beers, welcoming service, reasonable prices, pool and table skittles *(Colin Moore)*

Telfords Warehouse [Tower Wharf, behind Northgate St nr rly]: Converted canal building, bare brick and boards, high pitched ceiling, big wall of windows overlooking water, massive iron winding gear in bar, some old enamelled advertisements, good photographs for sale; good choice of well kept ales and of wines, freshly made generous up-to-date food, efficient friendly staff, steps to heavy-beamed restaurant area with more artwork; live music Fri/Sat (very busy then), tables out by water *(Sue Holland, Dave Webster, BB, Angie Coles, Colin Moore)*

Union Vaults [Francis St/Egerton St]: Corner alehouse with well kept and reasonably priced Timothy Taylors Landlord and guest beers (suggestions book), friendly knowledgeable staff, bagatelle, dominoes, cards and two TV sports channels, back games room with pool, two quieter upper rooms with old local photographs; piped music; open all day *(Patrick Hancock, Martin Grosberg, the Didler, Joe Green)*

CONGLETON [SJ8663]

Beartown Tap [Willow St (A54)]: Light and airy tap for nearby Beartown small brewery, their beers well priced and perhaps a guest microbrew, changing farm cider, bottled belgians, bare boards in friendly bar and two pleasant rooms off, no games or music; upstairs lavatories; open all day Fri-Sun *(the Didler)*

Railway Inn [Biddulph Rd (A527)]: Well kept frequently changing real ales and popular home-made food *(Rob Pointon)*

COTEBROOK [SJ5765]

☆ *Alvanley Arms* [A49/B5152 N of Tarporley]: Fine old sandstone inn, 16th-c behind its Georgian façade, with three attractive beamed rooms (two no smoking areas), big open fire, chintzy little hall, shire horse décor (plenty of tack and pictures – adjacent stud open in season), generous food inc baguettes, light lunches and good value specials, well kept Robinsons ales; garden with pond and trout, seven comfortable bedrooms with own bathrooms *(Michael and Jenny Back, Jean and Douglas Troup, LYM, Olive and Ray Hebson, Susie Symes, Denis Golden)*

CREWE [SJ7055]

Borough Arms [Earle St]: Now brewing its own good beers, alongside interesting guest beers from small breweries in top condition, five or six foreign beers on tap and dozens in bottle, friendly enthusiastic landlord, two small plain rooms off central bar, railway theme, green décor, enjoyable home-made food in new dining room; games machine, TV, cl wkdy lunchtimes *(Martin Grosberg, the Didler)*

Gaffers Row [Victoria St]: Spacious and well fitted Wetherspoons, decent food all day, well spaced tables, bargain beer from invitingly long bar counter, prompt polite service, reasonable prices, pleasant family section; soft piped music, games machines *(E G Parish, B J Harding)*

Rising Sun [Middlewich Rd (A530), Wolstanwood]: Chef & Brewer comfortably done out in olde-worlde style with beamery, panelling, prints and lots of separate areas, particularly well kept real ales inc Courage and one brewed for the pub by Titanic, occasional beer festivals, enthusiastic new licensees supporting local charities, wide choice of enjoyable food from doorstep sandwiches and melts up, raised eating area; children's facilities, good disabled access (inc lift), tables and play area outside, open all day, quiet countryside *(E G Parish, Martin Grosberg)*

Three Lamps [Earle St, by town hall]: Good eating place with comfortably pubby bar, lots of woodwork and attractive prints, relaxed atmosphere, friendly staff; back food area, well kept Banks's ales inc Mild; piped music, games machines, live music some nights; open all day, overlooking Town Lawn and handy for Lyceum Theatre; very busy lunchtime, esp market days – Mon, Fri, Sat *(E G Parish)*

DARESBURY [SJ5782]

Ring o' Bells [B5356, handy for M56 junction 11]: Rambling Chef & Brewer with wide choice of food all day from sandwiches, baguettes and baked potatoes up, well kept Courage Directors, Greenalls, Theakstons and a couple of guest beers, lots of wines by the glass, generous coffee, comfortable library-style areas (largely no smoking) and part more suited to walkers (canal is not far); children in eating areas, good disabled access, plenty of tables in long partly terraced garden, pretty village, church with *Alice in Wonderland* window, open all day *(June and Ken Brooks, Mrs P J Carroll, David A Hammond, Andrew York, Roger Thornington, LYM, Mrs Hazel Rainer)*

DAVENHAM [SJ6670]

Bulls Head [London Rd]: Picturesque old coaching inn with several rooms up upstairs no smoking dining room, large blackboard choice of good value food inc light dishes, Theakstons and a guest beer such as Caledonian Deuchars IPA, decent wines, good helpful service, nicely placed tables, low beams, sympathetic décor, interesting prints, small library under stairs; tables out on back terrace *(E G Parish)*

FRODSHAM [SJ5177]

Helter Skelter [Church St]: Good choice of well kept beers inc one brewed locally for the pub from long counter on right, imported beers too, wide range of freshly made imaginative food (not Sun evening), nice atmosphere with tall stools, leaning-post seating, window tables and raised deck, real fire, upstairs restaurant Thurs-Sat; open all day *(Dr B and Mrs P B Baker)*

GAWSWORTH [SJ8969]

☆ *Harrington Arms* [Church Lane]: Rustic 17th-c farm pub with two small basic rooms (children allowed in one), bare boards and panelling, fine carved oak bar counter, well kept Robinsons Best and Hatters Mild, friendly service, pickled eggs or onions, pork pies, fresh chunky lunchtime sandwiches; Fri folk night; sunny benches on small front cobbled terrace *(LYM, the Didler)*

GRAPPENHALL [SJ6386]

Parr Arms [nr M6 junction 20; A50 towards Warrington, left after 1½ miles; Church Lane]: Good atmosphere in several different areas off central bar, wide choice of good reasonably priced home-made food, pleasant efficient service, real ales, no piped music, Rugby League photographs – landlord was St Helens captain and an international; tables out by church, picture-postcard setting *(Pete and Josephine Cropper, Mr and Mrs E Shingler)*

GREAT BUDWORTH [SJ6677]

☆ *George & Dragon* [signed off A559 NE of Northwich; High St]: Attractive and unusual 17th/18th-c building in delightful village, rambling panelled lounge, beams hung with copper jugs, interesting old pictures, red plush button-back banquettes and older settles, three well kept quickly changing guest beers (over a hundred a year), farm cider, decent coffee, sensibly priced bar food inc good Sun lunch and (not Sun) two-for-one early evening bargains, upstairs restaurant and family dining

area, no smoking area, games in public bar;
open all day Sat/Sun *(LYM, Edward Leetham)*

HELSBY [SJ4874]

New Helsby Arms [Chester Rd (A56, handy
for M56 junction 14)]: Black Sheep and three
changing real ales, good wine choice,
imaginative fresh food from home-made soups
through thai fishcakes to steak, bass and
venison, young friendly staff, good log fire, no
smoking area *(Sue and Alex)*

HIGH LEGH [SJ7084]

Bears Paw [Warrington Rd (A50 E of M6
junction 20)]: Comfortable and welcoming,
two carpeted dining rooms off bar, popular for
enjoyable food cooked to order (so may take a
while), well kept Marstons Pedigree; tables out
behind *(Mr and Mrs Colin Roberts)*

HOLMES CHAPEL [SJ7667]

George & Dragon [Middlewich Rd]:
Attractively refurbished, with well done pubby
food inc good puddings, pleasant helpful staff,
well kept Robinsons, decent house wines,
choice of coffees *(Mrs P J Carroll)*

KERRIDGE [SJ9276]

Lord Clyde [Clarke Lane, off A523]: Recently
reopened, with small friendly bar, interesting
food (ten or so tables for diners), Adnams and
Black Sheep *(Stephen Buckley)*

LACH DENNIS [SJ7072]

☆ *Duke of Portland* [B5082]: Roomily
refurbished as smart country dining pub by
newish owners (noted Knutsford
restaurateurs), leather seats and sofas,
attractive L-shaped bar with balustraded eating
areas (one no smoking), beautifully presented
fresh traditional food with some interesting
choices (using local supplies) from sandwiches
and light lunches up, pleasant efficient service,
Banks's and Marstons Pedigree, good if not
cheap wine choice *(Mrs P J Carroll,
Simon J Barber)*

LANGLEY [SJ9471]

☆ *Leathers Smithy* [off A523 S of Macclesfield,
OS Sheet 118 map ref 952715]: Isolated pub
up in fine walking country, spotless flagstoned
bar and carpeted dining room, interesting local
prints and photographs, pleasant relaxing
atmosphere, good choice of enjoyable food (all
day Sun) from sandwiches to exotic fish, good
steaks and good value Sun roasts, log fire,
winter gluhwein and lots of whiskies, well kept
Courage Directors, Marstons Pedigree,
Theakstons Best and a guest beer, farm cider,
quick cheerful service; unobtrusive piped
music; family room, no dogs *(Michael Porter,
LYM, Mr and Mrs R P Begg, Stephen Buckley)*

LITTLE BOLLINGTON [SJ7286]

☆ *Swan With Two Nicks* [2 miles from M56
junction 7 – A56 towards Lymm, then first
right at Stamford Arms into Park Lane; use
A556 to get back on to M56 westbound]:
Beamed village pub full of brass, copper and
bric-a-brac, some antique settles, log fire,
welcoming helpful service, good choice of
generous above-average food from filling
baguettes up, several well kept ales inc one
brewed for the pub, decent wines, good coffee;
tables outside, open all day, attractive hamlet

by Dunham Hall deer park, walks by
Bridgewater Canal *(LYM, Mr and
Mrs Colin Roberts, John and Sylvia Harrop)*

LOWER PEOVER [SJ7474]

☆ *Bells of Peover* [just off B5081; The Cobbles]:
Wisteria-covered Chef & Brewer on quiet
cobbled lane opposite fine black and white
14th-c church, old-fashioned largely no
smoking interior with panelling, antiques and
two small coal fires, well kept Courage
Directors, Theakstons and a guest such as
Charles Wells Bombardier, lots of wines by the
glass, good tea, food all day from sandwiches
and baked potatoes to steak, dominoes and
cribbage; piped music; children in family room,
terrace tables and big side lawn with trees, rose
pergolas and a little stream, open all day
*(Nikki Wild, Spider Newth, the Didler,
Catherine and Rob Dunster, Patrick Hancock,
Dr and Mrs T E Hothersall, LYM, Revd D
Glover)*

LYMM [SJ6787]

☆ *Spread Eagle* [not far from M6 junction 20;
Eagle Brow (A6144, in centre)]: Big cheerful
rambling beamed pub, charming black and
white façade, good value home-made food all
day from sandwiches and baguettes through
two-course bargains to steaks, particularly well
kept Lees Bitter and Red Dragon, good choice
of wines, good service, comfortable two-level
lounge, proper drinking area by central bar,
coal fire, lots of brasses, separate games room
with pool; piped music; attractive village, open
all day *(BB, Pete Baker, Caroline and
Gavin Callow)*

MACCLESFIELD [SJ9272]

Railway View [Byrons Lane (off A523)]: Half
a dozen or more unusual changing ales in pair
of 1700 cottages knocked into roomy pub with
lots of intimate attractively furnished areas,
farm cider, good value simple food (may be
free sandwiches late Fri/Sat night), friendly
staff and locals; back terrace overlooking
railway, remarkably shaped gents';
cl lunchtime Mon-Thurs, open all day Fri
and Sun *(the Didler)*

Waters Green Tavern [Waters Green, opp stn]:
Well kept quickly changing interesting ales in
large L-shaped open-plan local, home-made
lunchtime food (not Sun), friendly staff and
locals, back pool room; open all day
(the Didler)

MARBURY [SJ5645]

Swan [NNE of Whitchurch]: Old-fashioned
unpretentious pub with welcoming licensees,
well presented fresh food from lunchtime
sandwiches to good choice of specials and
imaginative puddings, well kept Adnams,
decent wines, several dozen malt whiskies,
partly panelled lounge, log fire in copper-
canopied fireplace; venerable oak on green
opposite, delightful village a half-mile's
country walk from the Llangollen Canal,
Bridges 23 and 24 *(Tom and Diane Harker,
LYM)*

MARTON [SJ8568]

Davenport Arms [A34 N of Congleton]:
Comfortable, roomy and tasteful pub doing

well under newish management, with good choice of home-made food in bar and restaurant inc good value Sun lunch, friendly obliging service, well kept real ales, no smoking area; nr ancient half-timbered church (and Europe's widest oak tree); no dogs *(Mr and Mrs Colin Roberts, E G Parish, Dr D J and Mrs S C Walker)*

MOBBERLEY [SJ7879]

Bulls Head [Mill Lane]: Comfortable low-beamed pub with old pictures, soft lighting, enjoyable straightforward reasonably priced food from hot baguettes up, well kept ales such as Boddingtons, Timothy Taylors Landlord and Tetleys Bitter and Mild, quick friendly service, central open fire and another one end, games room; piped music; immaculate bowling green *(BB, H and P Cate)*

☆ *Roebuck* [Mill Lane; down hill from sharp bend on B5085 at E edge of 30mph limit]: Reliably good fresh food from lunchtime sandwiches to interesting modern dishes in spacious and appealing open-plan bar with brasses, pews, polished boards, panelling and alcoves, upstairs restaurant, welcoming staff, well kept real ales, good wine choice, no smoking area; piped music can obtrude, can get noisy wknds; children welcome, pretty outside, with tables in cobbled courtyard and pleasant extended two-level garden behind, play area *(Mrs P J Carroll, LYM, H and P Cate, Dr D Scott)*

MOULDSWORTH [SJ5170]

Goshawk [Station Rd (B5393)]: Plushly comfortable dining pub with character décor, attentive uniformed staff, enjoyable generous food, family room; good spot nr Delamere Forest with big outdoor area inc good play area and bowling green *(Rachel Morrison)*

NANTWICH [SJ6552]

☆ *Black Lion* [Welsh Row]: Three little rooms alongside main bar, old-fashioned nooks and crannies, beams, bare floors and brickwork, big grandfather clock, coal fire; three well kept local Weetwood ales, Titanic White Star and guest beers, farm cider, cheap sandwiches, very friendly cat, chess; live music Fri/Sat night, busy then; dogs welcome, open all day *(the Didler, Edward Leetham, BB, Ken Flawn, Pete Baker)*

Cronkinsons Farm [corner Pear Tree Field and new link road]: New pub on new suburban development nr Stapeley Water Gardens, large central bar serving several different lounge areas, food all day for all ages, Banks's, Marstons Pedigree and a guest beer *(Edward Leetham)*

☆ *Crown* [High St, free public parking behind]: Striking and attractively placed three-storey timbered Elizabethan hotel with overhanging upper galleries, cosy rambling beamed bar with antique tables and chairs on sloping creaky floors, enjoyable generous food from sandwiches and baked potatoes to steak, italian evening restaurant (and all day Sat), well kept Boddingtons and Flowers IPA, staff very helpful with children; very busy wknd evenings, piped music, fruit machine and TV;

open all day, comfortable bedrooms *(LYM, E G Parish, John and Yvonne Davies)*

Curshaws at the Cat [Welsh Row]: Fine old black and white building, former Cheshire Cat reworked as bar/restaurant with interestingly contemporary mix of modern glass and steel with medieval wattle and daub; good range of food (tapas recommended) and wines, decent beer, friendly efficient service; good hotel bedrooms *(P Burns)*

Globe [Audlem Rd]: Traditional landlady and generous home cooking (all day wknds) inc lunchtime and early evening bargains, Flowers real ale, good wine choice, service very welcoming and helpful even when busy, comfortable seating inc some small room areas, good civilised pub atmosphere, quaint rooms with old prints; tables in garden, pretty floral displays *(Stuart Paulley)*

☆ *Red Cow* [Beam St]: Well renovated and welcoming proper pub in low-ceilinged former Tudor farmhouse, three well kept Robinsons ales and a guest beer, good value coffee, good log or coal fire, good value home-made food inc less usual dishes in no smoking dining area away from the bar, smallish lounge; terrace with pergola and play area, bedrooms *(Gwyn and Anne Wake, Edward Leetham, Keith and Maureen Trainer)*

Vine [Hospital St]: Dates from 17th c, sympathetically modernised and stretching far back with old prints and dimly lit quiet corners, well kept Hydes beers inc seasonal ones, friendly service and locals, pub games, lunchtime sandwiches, baguettes, wraps, baked potatoes and simple hot dishes, raised back no smoking area; piped music; children welcome, open all day Sat, cl Mon lunchtime *(BB, Roger and Anne Newbury, Gwyn and Anne Wake, Martin Grosberg)*

Wickstead Arms [Mill St]: Friendly local atmosphere in roomy carpeted bar with pool room, well kept Tetleys and Charles Wells Bombardier, good value food, separate dining area *(Gwyn and Anne Wake)*

NESTON [SJ2976]

Harp [Quayside, SW of Little Neston; keep on along track at end of Marshlands Rd]: Tucked-away country local with particularly well kept ales such as Beartown, Holts and Titanic, good malt whiskies, woodburner in pretty fireplace, pale quarry tiles and simple furnishings (children allowed in room on right), home-made lunchtime food; picnic-sets up on grassy front sea wall look out over the marshes of the Dee to Wales, glorious sunsets with wild calls of wading birds; open all day from noon *(BB, Paul Davies, Derek and Sylvia Stephenson)*

Hinderton Arms [Chester High Rd (A540)]: Large tastefully decorated bar/dining area, enjoyable pub food all day from sandwiches and baguettes up, friendly service, well kept Courage Directors and good choice of other drinks *(Paul Humphreys)*

NORLEY [SJ5772]

Tigers Head [Pytchleys Hollow]: Pleasantly refurbished and cheerful 17th-c inn nr Delamere Forest, good value straightforward food, well kept changing real ales inc a Mild, friendly service, no smoking area *(J S Burn)*

OLLERTON [SJ7776]

☆ *Dun Cow* [Chelford Rd; outskirts of Knutsford towards Macclesfield]: Attractive country pub, recently comfortably upgraded with thoroughly modern décor, leather sofas and easy chairs, two fine log fires, good changing choice of up-to-date food, long-serving character barmaid and other pleasant well trained staff, well kept real ales inc a guest beer, decent wines; open all day in summer *(Mrs P J Carroll, LYM, H and P Cate, Simon J Barber)*

OVER PEOVER [SJ7873]

Olde Park Gate [Stocks Lane; off A50 N of Holmes Chapel at the Whipping Stock]: Country pub particularly popular at lunchtime for generous food from sandwiches to changing pies, fish and daily roast (particularly good roast potatoes), Sam Smiths beers *(Hilary Forrest, LYM, Mrs P J Carroll)*

Whipping Stocks [Stocks Lane]: Several neatly kept rooms, good oak panelling and fittings, solid furnishings, well kept cheap Sam Smiths, neat friendly staff, big log fire, wide choice of low-priced popular straightforward food all day; children in eating area, picnic-sets in good-sized garden with safe play area, easy parkland walks *(E G Parish, Mike Marsh, LYM)*

PARKGATE [SJ2778]

Boathouse [village signed off A540]: Black and white timbered family dining pub with several interesting linked rooms, generous food inc popular Sun lunch, well spaced tables, well kept Tetleys tapped from the cask, big conservatory with spectacular views to Wales over estuary and silted marshes *(E G Parish)*

Ship [The Parade]: Bow-window estuary views from long bar of large hotel, well kept Theakstons and interesting guest beers, good value bar food inc local fish (and afternoon teas), quick pleasant service, open fire, restaurant, quizzes, perhaps karaoke; 24 bedrooms, open all day *(MLR, E G Parish)*

PLUMLEY [SJ7275]

☆ *Golden Pheasant* [Plumley Moor Lane (off A556 by the Smoker)]: Wide food choice inc interesting dishes, well kept Lees Bitter and Mild, spacious series of comfortably modernised rooms, roomy restaurant and conservatory; children welcome, extensive gardens inc play area and bowling green, good well equipped bedrooms *(LYM, Mike Jones)*

☆ *Smoker* [A556 S of M6 junction 19]: Attractive 16th-c pub with dark panelling, open fires in impressive period fireplaces, deep sofas as well as other seating in three partly no smoking linked rooms, good choice of wines and whiskies, well kept Robinsons and a guest ale, food (all day Sun) from sandwiches up in bar and restaurant; piped music, wheelchair access tricky; children welcome, good-sized garden with good play area, open all day Sun *(LYM, Martin and Jane Bailey, Pat and Sam Roberts, Mart Lawton, J Silcock, Dennis Jones, Hugh and Susan Ellison)*

POYNTON [SJ9483]

Boars Head [Shrigley Rd N, Higher Poynton, off A523]: Friendly and unpretentious Victorian country pub, well refurbished with button-back leather seats (and darts) in bar, lounge with good value home-made food (all day wknds) inc speciality pies, well kept reasonably priced Boddingtons and a guest beer, coffee etc, big open fire; next to ex-railway Middlewood Way walk and cycle route and Macclesfield Canal, handy for Lyme Park *(Pete and Kate Holford, Tom Halsall)*

PRESTBURY [SJ8878]

Bulls Head [Wilmslow Rd (A538)]: Beamery, rough plaster and some oak panelling for rustic old-look décor, comfortable seating inc some armchairs, enjoyable food, Greene King Old Speckled Hen and Marstons Pedigree, good coffee, friendly atmosphere *(Mr and Mrs Colin Roberts)*

RAINOW [SJ9576]

☆ *Highwayman* [A5002 Whaley Bridge—Macclesfield, NE of village]: Cheerfully unchanging 17th-c moorside pub with cosy low-beamed rooms, well kept Thwaites ales, decent low-priced bar food inc good sandwiches and ideal black pudding, lovely winter fires, plenty of atmosphere, lovely views *(LYM, Stephen Buckley, the Didler, Peter F Marshall)*

RUNCORN [SJ5081]

Prospect [Weston Rd, just off A557 expressway]: Cains and other well kept real ales and reasonably priced standard food lunchtime and early evening in village local with partly no smoking lounge bar and good public bar with darts, dominoes and cribbage *(Pete Baker)*

SANDBACH [SJ7560]

Lower Chequer [Crown Bank]: Refurbished 16th-c pub just off cobbled square, eight well kept ales from island servery inc some from small breweries, good value generous home-made food, friendly staff, coal-effect gas fire; TV in original small bar *(David Hunter)*

SHOCKLACH [SJ4349]

Bull [off A534 from Wrexham at crossroads with Farndon]: Good fresh food changing daily inc interesting dishes, wide range of puddings and big fun ice-creams, Marstons Pedigree, good value house wines, charming service, conservatory; can be very busy *(Rita and Keith Pollard, Mrs P J Carroll, Esther and John Sprinkle)*

SPROSTON GREEN [SJ7366]

Fox & Hounds [very handy for M6 junction 18 – A54 towards Middlewich]: Attractive pub with decent food in bar and dining area, friendly service, well kept Boddingtons, open fire, low beams and varnished flagstones *(Edward Mirzoeff)*

STRETTON [SJ6282]

☆ *Stretton Fox* [Spark Hall Cl, Tarporley Rd, just off M56 junction 10 exit roundabout]: Particularly good Vintage Inn in spaciously and sympathetically converted farmhouse, surprisingly rural setting, interesting variety of rooms, generous well priced food, quick friendly service, real ales and good choice of wines *(Simon J Barber, Pat and Stewart Gordon)*

SUTTON [SJ9469]

☆ *Ryles Arms* [Hollin Lane, Higher Sutton]: Popular dining pub in fine countryside, consistently good generous food from sandwiches and juicy home-made burgers to game and interesting dishes, well kept ales inc local Storm, decent well priced wines, good choice of whiskies, pleasant décor and some attractively individual furnishings, hill-view no smoking dining room, no music or games; french windows to terrace, bedrooms in converted barn *(Mrs P J Carroll, Mr and Mrs Colin Roberts, LYM)*

SWETTENHAM [SJ8067]

☆ *Swettenham Arms* [off A54 Congleton— Holmes Chapel or A535 Chelford—Holmes Chapel]: Attractive old country pub very popular for its pretty setting next to its own scenic wildlife area (they are adding a lavender and sunflower meadow), wide choice of good food from sandwiches up in charming line of individually furnished rooms from sofas and easy chairs to no smoking dining area (must book Sun), well spaced tables, good changing choice of well kept real ales and of wines, log fires; children welcome, picnic-sets on quiet side lawn, open all day wknds *(Mrs P J Carroll, LYM, K M Crook, Edward Leetham)*

TARPORLEY [SJ5561]

☆ *Red Fox* [A49/A51, a mile S]: Stylishly extended and decorated country pub with comfortable and spacious low-beamed core, leather sofas in lounge area, wide range of enjoyable food cooked to individual preferences (best to book Fri/Sat evenings), real ales, friendly staff, pleasant conservatory; children welcome, bedrooms, handy for Beeston and Peckforton castles, open all day Sun *(E G Parish)*

☆ *Swan* [High St, off A49]: Tastefully modernised Georgian inn with rambling linked beamed areas, decent food from lunchtime sandwiches and snacks to restaurant dishes (afternoon teas too), good welcoming service, Lees Bitter, Timothy Taylors Landlord and Theakstons, coal fires; provision for children, tables outside, 16 charming well equipped bedrooms, good breakfast in sunny former kitchen *(LYM, Susie Symes, E G Parish)*

TILSTON [SJ4651]

Carden Arms [Malpas Rd]: Good reasonably priced food choice from baguettes and baked potatoes to steak, Bass, Jennings Cumberland and Tetleys, helpful staff; children welcome; interesting inn sign *(Esther and John Sprinkle)*

TIVERTON [SJ5360]

☆ *Shady Oak* [Bates Mill Lane]: Canalside family pub looking up to Beeston Castle, well kept Theakstons and Greene King Ruddles, reasonably priced food all day from sandwiches to enjoyable blackboard dishes, comfortable timbered bar, airy lounge with leather chesterfields, small carpeted and heated no smoking conservatory, games room; plenty of tables in waterside garden with covered

decking, good play area, summer barbecues, moorings, open all day *(LYM, Edward Leetham)*

WARRINGTON [SJ6091]

Winwick Quay [Woburn Rd, just off M62 junction 9]: Comfortable Brewers Fayre popular for its proximity to retail park and motorway, with good value food, pleasant service though busy *(Mr and Mrs Colin Roberts)*

WILDBOARCLOUGH [SJ9868]

☆ *Crag*: Straightforward old stone-built pub notable for its position in charming little sheltered valley below the moors, good basic fresh home cooking using local ingredients, well kept Worthington and a guest beer, help-yourself coffee; walkers welcome (boot covers available), tables on pretty terrace *(LYM, Pete Yearsley)*

WILLINGTON [SJ5367]

☆ *Boot* [Boothsdale, off A54 at Kelsall]: Good dining pub in terrific hillside setting, views over Cheshire plain to Wales, good if rather pricey food (all day wknds and bank hols), good service, well kept ales such as Greene King and Weetwood, decent wine list, plenty of malt whiskies, small unpretentiously furnished areas around central bar, woodburner, no smoking area, log fire in charming restaurant; no under-8s; garden with picnic-sets on suntrap raised stone terrace (they do make you pay as you order course by course out here), two donkeys, golden retriever H and cat called Sooty *(Mrs P J Carroll, LYM, Olive and Ray Hebson, Mike Tucker, Derek and Sylvia Stephenson)*

WILMSLOW [SJ8381]

Boddington Arms [Racecourse Rd (A538)]: Big, modern and comfortable, well kept Everards Tiger and Theakstons, quick pleasant food service; fairly unobtrusive piped music *(Mr and Mrs Colin Roberts)*

Unicorn [Adlington Rd (B5358 E)]: Appetising freshly made food worth the wait in busy pub, very neatly kept *(Tom Halsall)*

WINTERLEY [SJ7557]

Forresters Arms [A534]: Cosy and welcoming low-beamed village local with cheerful attentive landlord, inventive good value bar lunches from open-view kitchen, well kept Tetleys ales inc Dark Mild; darts and quiz night, Weds raffle; pleasant garden with dovecote and retired tractor *(E G Parish)*

Holly Bush [nr Sandbach on A534]: Warm, comfortable and civilised, with enjoyable food from light dishes to Sunday roasts, real ales inc Tetleys, good value wines, hospitable staff, ample seating, sensible tables and picture windows; large garden, play area, handy for canal *(E G Parish)*

WRENBURY [SJ5948]

Cotton Arms [Cholmondeley Rd]: Appealing beamed and timbered village pub in popular spot by canal locks and boatyard, with good value interesting food in two large comfortable dining areas, friendly staff, well kept real ales inc a guest beer, lots of brass, open fire, side games room *(Mrs P J Carroll, Joyce and Maurice Cottrell)*

Cornwall

Plenty of good pubs here, in great variety, include two new main entries that are interesting because of their appealing modern style: the 5 Degrees West overlooking Falmouth harbour, an airy largely no smoking bar with good up-to-date food and drinks, and the Blue at Porthtowan, also light and airy, refreshingly informal, with picture-window sea views and nice food. Other more traditional pubs scoring highly here this year are the Trengilly Wartha near Constantine (a fine all-rounder), the very well run Olde Plough House at Duloe (once readers find it, they go back again and again), the beautifully placed Halzephron near Helston (nice to eat at or stay in), the Royal Oak at Perranwell (particularly good landlord, good food including popular tapas), the bustling harbourside Ship in Porthleven (good fresh local fish, plenty of character), and the Old Ale House in Truro (really well run – a model town pub, with bargain food, thriving local atmosphere and a fine ale range). As we've said, food quality is a plus at several of these top pubs; for a really enjoyable meal out the Trengilly Wartha near Constantine takes the title of Cornwall Dining Pub of the Year. The Lucky Dip section at the end of the chapter is a particularly rich one. Pubs to note specially here are the Trelowarren Arms at Budock Water, Cross Keys in Cawsand, Old Quay House at Devoran, Quayside Inn and Seven Stars in Falmouth, King of Prussia in Fowey, Fishermans Arms at Golant, Blue Anchor in Helston, Lamorna Wink at Lamorna, Red Lion at Mawnan Smith, Fountain in Mevagissey, Bush at Morwenstow, Ship in Mousehole, Cornish Arms at Pendoggett, Admiral Benbow and Dolphin in Penzance, Victoria at Perranuthnoe, Kings Head at Ruan Lanihorne, Crown at St Ewe, Sloop in St Ives, London at St Neot, Wheel at Tresillian, New Inn at Veryan and Tinners Arms at Zennor. In the Isles of Scilly, look out for the Fraggle Rock on Bryher, Seven Stones on St Martin's and Bishop & Wolf on St Mary's. Beer prices in the county tend to be around the national average, with local brews from Sharps very popular and widely available, though the brewery was started little more than ten years ago. Skinners, an even newer brewery, is also doing well, alongside long-established St Austell and several good smaller outfits such as Ales of Scilly, Organic, Ring o' Bells and Blackawton (now brewed in Cornwall despite its Devon name).

ALTARNUN SX2182 Map 1
Rising Sun ■ £
Village signposted off A39 just W of A395 junction; pub itself NW of village, so if coming instead from A30 keep on towards Camelford

Whatever the weather, you'll be sure to find this straightforward ex-farmhouse busy with jolly locals – and probably their dogs, too. The low-beamed L-shaped main bar has bare boards and polished delabole slate flagstones, some stripped stone, a couple of coal fires, guns on the wall, and plain traditional furnishings. The central bar has well kept Bass, Cotleigh Barn Owl, Eagle and Tawny, Fullers London Pride, Greene King IPA, Marstons Pedigree, and Sharps Cornish Coaster, Doom Bar and Eden Ale on handpump, and decent house wines. The food is hearty home cooking: soup or local pasty (£2.50), sandwiches (£2.50; baguettes with home-cooked ham £4.50), three-egg omelette (£3.50), pork and smoky bacon sausages (£4), home-cooked meat pie or vegetable chilli (£6.50), home-made seafood pie or greek-style lamb casserole (£7.50), steaks (from £8), and puddings (£2.50). A small back area has darts, fruit machine, juke box, and a pool table, with a second pool table in the carpeted room beyond (no dogs allowed in that one); cribbage and dominoes. The main bar can get a bit smoky sometimes. There are tables outside and, screened off by high evergreens, the field opposite has space for caravans. The village itself (with its altarless church – hence the name) is well worth a look. *(Recommended by Guy Vowles, Gordon Briggs, Dr and Mrs M W A Haward, Dennis Jenkin)*

Free house ~ Licensee Jim Manson ~ Real ale ~ Bar food ~ Restaurant ~ No credit cards ~ (01566) 86636 ~ Children in restaurant ~ Dogs allowed in bar ~ Open 11-3, 5.30-11; 11-11 Sat; 12-10.30 Sun ~ Bedrooms: £17/£34

BLISLAND SX0973 Map 1
Blisland Inn 🍺
Village signposted off A30 and B3266 NE of Bodmin

Every inch of the beams and ceiling in this welcoming local is covered with beer badges (or their particularly wide-ranging collection of mugs), and the walls are similarly filled with beer-related posters and memorabilia. A blackboard lists the day's range, which has a firm emphasis on brews from Cornwall – and at any one time, they stock a fine choice of up to eight well kept on handpump or tapped from the cask. They also have a changing farm cider, fruit wines, and real apple juice. Above the fireplace another blackboard has the choice of enjoyable, hearty home-made food, which might include hot meat baps (£3.75; bacon, brie and cranberry wrap £5.95; breakfast bap of bacon, egg, sausage, mushroom and tomato £4.95), lasagne, moussaka or leek and mushroom bake (£6.95), and various pies like rabbit or steak in ale (from £6.95); service is cheerful and friendly. The carpeted no smoking lounge has a number of barometers on the walls, a rack of daily newspapers for sale, a few standing timbers, and a good chatty atmosphere. The family room has pool, table skittles, cribbage and dominoes; piped music. Plenty of picnic-sets outside. The Camel Trail cycle path is close by. As with many pubs in this area, it's hard to approach without negotiating several single-track roads. *(Recommended by the Didler, Rona Murdoch, Gordon Briggs, Matthew Lidbury, DAV, Canon Michael Bourdeaux, A P Seymour)*

Free house ~ Licensees Gary and Margaret Marshall ~ Real ale ~ Bar food (12-2.15, 6.30-9.30; 12-2.15, 7-9 Sun) ~ Restaurant ~ (01208) 850739 ~ Children in eating area of bar, restaurant and family room ~ Dogs welcome ~ Live music Sat evening ~ Open 11.30-11; 12-10.30 Sun

BODINNICK SX1352 Map 1
Old Ferry ★
Across the water from Fowey; coming by road, to avoid the ferry queue turn left as you go down the hill – car park on left before pub

In warm weather you can make the most of this old inn's location and bag one of the seats on the front terrace that have views of the pretty Fowey river. Inside, there are binoculars and a telescope in the guest lounge to make the most of any water activity or birdlife. Three simply furnished little rooms have quite a few bits of nautical memorabilia, a couple of half model ships mounted on the wall, and several old photographs, as well as wheelback chairs, built-in plush pink wall seats, and an old high-backed settle; there may be several friendly cats and a dog. The family room at the back is actually hewn into the rock, and the restaurant is no smoking; piped music. Decent bar food includes home-made soup (£3.60), sandwiches (from £2.75; toasties 40p extra), quite a few dishes with chips (from £4.60; home-cooked ham and egg £6.10), home-made cream cheese and broccoli pasta bake or curry of the day (£6.95), home-made steak and kidney in ale pie (£7.60), fresh smoked haddock with scrambled egg (£8.50), puddings (£3.50), and daily specials like home-made pâté (£5.25), fresh scallop and prawn au gratin

(£5.75), local sausages with root mash and madeira and red onion gravy (£8.95), and roast duck breast with fruits of the forest sauce (£11.25). Sharps Own on handpump, kept under light blanket pressure; TV. The lane beside the pub, in front of the ferry slipway, is extremely steep and parking is limited, and some readers suggest parking in the public car park in Fowey and taking the little ferry to the pub. *(Recommended by Jim Abbott, John Taylor, Nick Lawless, Michael Butler, Patrick Hancock, Christopher Turner, J V Dadswell, Sue Demont, Tim Barrow, Cathy Robinson, Ed Coombe, Brian and Rosalie Laverick, Reg Fowle, Helen Rickwood, Mr and Mrs A H Young, Gill and Keith Croxton, Charles and Pauline Stride, A P Seymour)*

Free house ~ Licensees Royce and Patricia Smith ~ Real ale ~ Bar food (12-3, 6-9; 12-2.30, 6.30-8.30 in winter) ~ Restaurant ~ (01726) 870237 ~ Children welcome ~ Dogs allowed in bar ~ Open 11-11; 12-10.30 Sun; 12-10.30 weekdays in winter; closed 25 Dec ~ Bedrooms: /£60(£70B)

CADGWITH SW7214 Map 1
Cadgwith Cove Inn
Down very narrow lane off A3083 S of Helston; no nearby parking

This old-fashioned, bustling local is set at the bottom of a steep working fishing cove; you can park at the top and walk down but it's quite a hike back up again. The two snugly dark front rooms have plain pub furnishings on their mainly parquet flooring, a log fire in one stripped stone end wall, lots of local photographs including gig races, cases of naval hat ribands and of fancy knot-work, and a couple of compass binnacles. Some of the dark beams have ship's shields and others have spliced blue rope hand-holds. Well kept Flowers IPA, Greene King Abbot, and Sharps Doom Bar on handpump. A plusher pink back room has a huge and colourful fish mural. The daily specials tend to be the things to go for in the food line: home-made sausages (£7.50), moules marinière (£8.50), skate wing (£9.50), fish casserole or red mullet (£10.50), and seasonal lobster and game. From the menu, there might be home-made soup (£3.85; crab soup £6.45), sandwiches (from £3.95; white crab £5.50), home-made stilton and broccoli quiche (£7.50), home-made lasagne (£7.55), sirloin steak (£11.45), and puddings such as fruit crumble or rich chocolate mousse with chocolate sauce and clotted cream (£3.85); best to check food times in winter. The left-hand room has darts, euchre, and maybe 1960s piped music. A good-sized front terrace has green-painted picnic-sets, some under a fairy-lit awning, looking down to the fish sheds by the bay. Coast Path walks are superb in both directions. More reports please. *(Recommended by Sarah Trayers, Pete Walker, Ian and Liz Rispin, Charles Gysin, Derek and Heather Manning)*

Punch ~ Lease David and Lynda Trivett ~ Real ale ~ Bar food ~ Restaurant ~ (01326) 290513 ~ Children in restaurant ~ Dogs welcome ~ Folk club Tues, Cornish singing Fri ~ Open 12-3, 7-11 (all day August); 12-11 Fri and Sat; 12-10.30 Sun ~ Bedrooms: £50/£50(£70S)

CONSTANTINE SW7328 Map 1
Trengilly Wartha ★ ⑪ ⌷ ◧ ⇥
Simplest approach is from A3083 S of Helston, signposted Gweek near RNAS Culdrose, then fork right after Gweek; coming instead from Penryn (roads narrower), turn right in Constantine just before Minimarket (towards Gweek), then pub signposted left in nearly a mile; at Nancenoy, OS Sheet 204 map reference 731282

Cornwall Dining Pub of the Year

Down narrow lanes and not far from the Helford river, this tucked away inn is popular with a wide mix of customers. It cleverly appeals to those who want just a pint after a walk, a particularly good meal with a glass of their many wines for a special occasion, and as somewhere to spend a comfortable overnight stay. The long low-beamed main bar has a woodburning stove and attractive built-in high-backed settles boxing in polished heavy wooden tables, and at one end, shelves of interesting wines with drink-in and take-out price labels (they run their own retail and wholesale wine business). The bright no smoking conservatory is popular with families; shove-ha'penny and dominoes. The enjoyable food might include daily changing soups and risottos, chicken liver and port pâté with home-made chutney (£5.80), ploughman's (from £6.90), local sausages with caramelised onions (£7.80), crab open sandwich (£8.60), butternut squash gratin (£9.20), pad thai (noodles, pork, prawns, chicken and dried shrimps) or lasagne (£9.80), duck breast and chargrilled halloumi cheese with fresh figs and an orange, clove and honey dressing (£12.10), and specials such as mussels steamed with white wine and served with a provençale sauce (£6.20), simply cooked, daily fresh fish (£7.50), local scallops with pasta, crème fraîche and pickled ginger (£8.40), goats cheese and herb soufflé (£8.80), and confit shoulder of cornish lamb stuffed with anchovies, lemon and garlic on black pudding mash with an armagnac cream sauce (£13.80); puddings like green apple sorbet with home-made lavender shortbread, sticky toffee pudding or a trio of brûlées (from £3.80). You can eat the restaurant food in the bar but not vice versa. Well kept Sharps Cornish Coaster and Skinners Betty Stogs on handpump or tapped from the cask, 16 wines by the glass from a list of over 200, and over 30 malt whiskies. There's a pretty landscaped garden with some tables under large parasols, an international sized piste for boules, and a lake; lots of surrounding walks. The pub does get very busy at peak times and there may be a wait for a table then. *(Recommended by Gene and Kitty Rankin, Mike Green, David Tindal, Ian and Celia Abbott, Cathy Robinson, Ed Coombe, Lyn Huxtable, Richard Seers, the Didler, Mandy and Simon King, A J Atyeo, Andrea Rampley, Neal Wills, Mr and Mrs N Knapman, J V Dadswell, Jill McLaren, John and Bryony Coles, Chris and Susie Cammack, M A Borthwick, Paul and Shirley White, Dennis Jenkin, David and Nina Pugsley, Sue Demont, Tim Barrow, H W Roberts, Jan and Alan Summers, A S and M E Marriott)*

Free house ~ Licensees Nigel Logan and Michael Maguire ~ Real ale ~ Bar food (12-2.15 (2 Sun), 6.30(7 Sun)-9.30; not 25 or 31 Dec) ~ Restaurant ~ (01326) 340332 ~ Children welcome ~ Dogs allowed in bar and bedrooms ~ Open 11-3, 6.30-11; 12-3, 7-10.30 Sun ~ Bedrooms: £50B/£80B

DULOE SX2358 Map 1
Olde Plough House
B3254 N of Looe

Once holidaymakers have discovered this very well run and neatly kept pub, they tend to come back several times. The three communicating rooms have lovely dark polished delabole slate floors, some turkey rugs, a mix of pews, modern high-backed settles and smaller chairs, foreign banknotes on the beams, and three woodburning stoves. The décor is restrained – prints of waterfowl and country scenes, and a few copper jugs and a fat wooden pig perched on window sill. Good, popular food at lunchtime includes home-made soup (£3.10), local pasty (£3.45), white or granary filled baguettes (from £4.05; sausage, bacon and egg £5.35), ploughman's (from £5.80), home-cooked ham and egg (£6.15), vietnamese sweet chilli chicken (£6.95), vegetable lasagne (£7.15), and scallops in garlic butter (£7.85); also, devilled whitebait (£4.95), mushroom, bacon and peppercorn crumble or smoked chicken, duck, orange and black olive salad (£4.85), gammon and egg (£7.75), goats cheese and sunblush tomato tart or beef and stilton pie (£7.85), meat cooked on hot stones (readers like this a lot; from £8.95), half a slow roasted duckling with plum and oyster sauce (£11.75), roasted shoulder of lamb with a fresh rosemary, redcurrant and beer sauce (£12.95), and daily specials like fillets of bass wrapped in lettuce leaves with hollandaise (£11.95) or john dory fillets baked in a foil parcel with tomatoes and herbs and a lemon sauce (£12.25). The small more modern restaurant is no smoking; piped music. Well kept Bass and Sharps Doom Bar on handpump, and eight wines by the glass. There are a few picnic-sets out by the road. The two friendly jack russells are called Jack and Spot, and the cat, Willow. *(Recommended by Jim Abbott, Paul and Shirley White, Michael Butler, Mr and Mrs R P Welch, Prof and Mrs Tony Palmer, Nick Lawless, John Edwards, Mark Flynn, John Hale, David Lewis, John and Joan Calvert, Geoff Calcott, Glenwys and Alan Lawrence)*

Free house ~ Licensees Gary and Alison Toms ~ Real ale ~ Bar food ~ Restaurant ~ (01503) 262050 ~ Children in eating area of bar ~ Dogs allowed in bar ~ Open 12-2.30, 6.30-11; 12-2.30, 7-10.30 Sun; closed evenings 25-26 Dec

EGLOSHAYLE SX0172 Map 1

Earl of St Vincent £

Off A389, just outside Wadebridge

It's worth tracking down this pretty pub if you can find it tucked away in a narrow, quiet back street – just head for the church. They now have 200 antique clocks, all in working order, so it is pretty noisy at midday when they all start chiming. They also have some golfing memorabilia, art deco ornaments, and all sorts of rich furnishings. Well kept St Austell HSD, Tinners and Tribute, and a guest like Dartmoor Best Bitter on handpump; piped music. Bar food (with prices unchanged since last year) includes soup (£3.50), sandwiches (from £4), ploughman's (from £5), mushroom and broccoli au gratin or ham and egg (£6.50), fish dishes (from £7.50), and grills (from £11.50). The snug is no smoking. In summer, there are picnic-sets in the lovely garden and marvellous flowering baskets and tubs.
(Recommended by David Crook, R J Herd, the Didler, Canon Michael Bourdeaux, George Tucker, Mike Tucker, R M Corlett, Kevin Blake, Liz and Tony Colman)

St Austell ~ Tenants Edward and Anne Connolly ~ Real ale ~ Bar food (not Sun evening) ~ Restaurant ~ (01208) 814807 ~ Well behaved children allowed at lunchtime ~ Open 11-3, 6.30-11; 12-3, 7-10.30 Sun

FALMOUTH SW8132 Map 1

5 Degrees West ♀

Grove Place, by main harbourside car park

Across the road from the waterfront and marina, this is an up-to-date light and airy bar. It's all open-plan (and two-thirds no smoking), an expanse of stripped wood flooring divided into different areas: squashy sofas around low tables, some modern leatherette cushioned dining chairs around chunky pine tables, a few leather-topped high steel benches and stools dotted about (one table has a nice metal fish leg), and a log fire in a driftwood-effect fireplace. The young staff (all neatly clad in black) are helpful and friendly, the contemporary artwork and photographs are local, there's a relaxed informal atmosphere, and the lighting is good – lots of steel and etched glass. From the long bar counter they serve St Austell Tribute and IPA on handpump, a dozen good wines by the glass, plus three sparkling ones, and lots of coffees, hot chocolate with marshmallows and a flake, and several teas. Using local seasonal produce, the enjoyable food might include nibbles such as garlic ciabatta topped with mature cheddar and mixed leaves (£3.25), toasted ciabatta with chargrilled chicken or minute steak and onion (from £4.95), tapas (home-made hummous, marinated olives, guacamole, balsamic, olive oil and local bread £5.95), tortilla chips topped with melted mozzarella and home-made chilli con carne or vegetarian salsa (from £5.95), and italian and german salami and cheese with crusty bread (£6.95), as well as home-made soup (£3.95), scallops with crispy bacon and new potatoes or chunky greek salad with feta (£6.95), home-made leek and mushroom risotto cake with red pesto dressing and a quail egg (£7.95), popular double burger layered with bacon, mozzarella and fried egg or a trio of local sausages with caramelised onion and ale gravy (£8.95), mussels provençale (£10.95), pork chops with cider cream sauce (£11.95), puddings (£4.50), and a good children's menu (from £4.50). A back dining area is similar in style with long built-in side pews and a couple of little semi-open booths; doors lead to a sheltered back terraced area with seating. They plan to open a downstairs bar soon. A side ramp gives good wheelchair access; disabled facilities. There's a useful short-term car park across the road.
(Recommended by David Crook)

St Austell ~ Managers James and Justine Stockton ~ Bar food (all day) ~ Restaurant ~ (01326) 311288 ~ Children welcome ~ Dogs welcome ~ Live entertainment Fri evenings ~ Open 11-11; 12-10.30 Sun

There are report forms at the back of the book.

HELFORD SW7526 Map 1

Shipwrights Arms ♀

Off B3293 SE of Helston, via Mawgan

The terraces which drop down from this thatched pub to the water's edge give a lovely view of this beautiful wooded creek (at its best at high tide). You can get here by foot ferry (open April to the end of October) from Helford Passage – (01326) 250770 – or by car, though it is quite a walk from the nearest car park. There are seats on the terrace making the most of the water views, and plenty of surrounding walks, including a long distance coastal path that goes right past the door. Inside, there's quite a nautical theme, with navigation lamps, models of ships, sea pictures, drawings of lifeboat coxswains, and shark fishing photographs. A dining area has oak settles and tables; winter open fire. Well kept Camerons Castle Eden and Sharps Doom Bar on handpump, a good wine list, and bar food such as home-made soup (£4), buffet lunch platters (from £5.50), summer evening barbecue dishes that include steaks (from £11), marinated lamb chops (£12.50), and monkfish marinated with chilli, lime and coriander (£12.75), and home-made puddings; piped music. Dogs must be kept on a lead. *(Recommended by Geoff Pidoux, the Didler, Paul and Shirley White, J V Dadswell, Andrea Rampley)*

Free house ~ Licensee Charles Herbert ~ Real ale ~ Bar food (not Sun or Mon evenings in winter) ~ Restaurant ~ (01326) 231235 ~ Dogs welcome ~ Open 11-2.30, 6-11; 12-2.30, 7-10.30 Sun; closed Sun and Mon evenings in winter

HELSTON SW6522 Map 1

Halzephron 🍴 ♀ 🛏

Gunwalloe, village about 4 miles S but not marked on many road maps; look for brown sign on A3083 alongside perimeter fence of RNAS Culdrose

There's always a good mix of regulars and visitors in this former smugglers' haunt, and although it does get packed at the height of the season, the really friendly feeling in the bustling bar remains. It is kept spotlessly clean, and has comfortable seating, copper on the walls and mantelpiece, and a warm winter fire in the big hearth; there's also a family room. Particularly enjoyable food might include lunchtime sandwiches (from £3.20; the seasonal crab are delicious, £7.95), as well as home-made soup (£4.40), ploughman's (from £5.50), pâté of the day with home-made toasted brioche (£5.70), local smoked fish selection (£7.80), tagliatelle bolognese (£8.50), evening sirloin steak (£12.95), and crab platter (£13.60), with specials like prawn bisque with a welsh rarebit croûte (£4.95), seared scallops on a seafood risotto (£6.25), wild mushroom and nut stroganoff (£9.50), beef bourguignon or lamb tagine with apricot and sultana couscous (£10.90), seared supreme of salmon on fresh pasta tossed with spinach, asparagus and herbs and a white wine velouté sauce (£12.50), and caramelised gressingham duck breast with a rosemary and garlic potato rösti drenched in cassis sauce (£13.50); half helpings for children where possible. All the eating areas are no smoking. Well kept Organic Halzephron Gold (this local brewer supplies only organic beers), and Sharps Own, Doom Bar and Will's Resolve on handpump, a good wine list, lots of malt whiskies, and around 25 liqueurs; darts and dominoes. This is a smashing place to stay with sea views in some rooms and good breakfasts. There are lots of lovely surrounding unspoilt walks with fine views of Mount's Bay; Gunwalloe fishing cove is just 300 yards away; and there's a sandy beach one mile away at Church Cove. The church of St Winwaloe (built into the dunes on the seashore) is also only a mile away, and well worth a visit. *(Recommended by Mike Green, R and S Bentley, Jacquie and Jim Jones, Patrick Hancock, Andrea Rampley, Brian and Bett Cox, A J Atyeo, Nick Lawless, Susie Symes, Derek and Heather Manning, P Hennessey, Karl and Julie Stamper, Tom McLean, J K and S M Miln, Stuart Turner, Mel Smith, Sue Demont, Tim Barrow, J and S French, Jan and Alan Summers)*

Free house ~ Licensee Angela Thomas ~ Real ale ~ Bar food ~ Restaurant ~ (01326) 240406 ~ Children in family room ~ Open 11-2.30, 6(6.30 winter)-11; 12-2.30, 6(6.30 in winter)-10.30 Sun; closed Sun and Mon evenings (apart from Christmas period) in winter ~ Bedrooms: £50B/£90B

LANLIVERY SX0759 Map 1

Crown ◗

Signposted off A390 Lostwithiel—St Austell (tricky to find from other directions)

The extensions and improvements here are well liked by readers, and it is certainly a nice place to stay. You can also be sure of a friendly welcome from both the licensees and the regulars. The small, dimly lit public bar has heavy beams, a slate floor and built-in wall settles, and an attractive alcove of seats in the dark former chimney. A much lighter room leads off, with beams in the white boarded ceiling, cushioned black settles, and a little fireplace with an old-fashioned fire; there's also another similar small room. No noisy games machines or music, and smoking is permitted only in the bar. Lunchtime bar food includes pasties (£3.75), sandwiches (from £3.95), steak in ale or apricot, mushroom and chestnut pies (£7.95), and fresh local crab salad (small £8.95; large £12.95), with evening choices such as smoked mackerel pâté (£3.95), fish pie or chicken with a honey and ginger sauce (£9.95), and lamb chops with redcurrant and mint dressing (£11.95). Well kept Sharps Cornish Coaster, Doom Bar, and a beer named for the pub, Crown Inn Glory, on handpump; local cider. Darts and dominoes. The slate-floored porch room has lots of succulents and a few cacti, and wood-and-stone seats, and at the far end of the restaurant is a sun room, full of more plants, with tables and benches. There's a sheltered garden with granite faced seats, white cast-iron furniture, and several solid wooden tables. The Eden Project is only ten minutes away. *(Recommended by John Evans, Dr and Mrs M W A Haward, M and R Thomas, Mrs Sally Kingsbury, Martin and Karen Wake, Dr Graham Thorpe, Jenny and Brian Seller, Dennis Jenkin, Mrs Joy Griffiths, Prof and Mrs Tony Palmer, Jacquie and Jim Jones, Keith and Maureen Trainer, Charles and Pauline Stride, Brian Dawes, David Crook)*

Wagtail Inns ~ Licensee Andrew Brotheridge ~ Real ale ~ Bar food (12-9 in summer) ~ Restaurant ~ (01208) 872707 ~ Children in eating area of bar and restaurant ~ Dogs allowed in bar ~ Open 12-11; 12-10.30 Sun; 12-3, 6-11 in winter ~ Bedrooms: £50S/£80S

LOSTWITHIEL SX1059 Map 1 🏠

Royal Oak ◗

Duke Street; pub just visible from A390 in centre – best to look out for Royal Talbot Hotel

The well kept real ales in this bustling and friendly town local are quite a draw, and might include Bass, Fullers London Pride and Marstons Pedigree, and changing guests such as Sharps Doom Bar and Will's Resolve on handpump – as well as lots of bottled beers from around the world. Bar food includes lunchtime sandwiches (from £2.20; toasties 50p extra), ploughman's (from £5.10), and fried chicken (£5.95), as well as soup (£3.10), stuffed mushrooms (£4.75), vegetarian lasagne (£7.95), fresh local trout (£9.75), steaks (from £10.75), and daily specials like curry or steak and kidney in ale pie (£9.25), barbary duck with orange and ginger sauce (£13.95), and fresh whole lemon sole (£14.50); the restaurant is no smoking. The neat lounge is spacious and comfortable, with captain's chairs and high-backed wall benches on its patterned carpet, and a couple of wooden armchairs by the log-effect gas fire; there's also a delft shelf, with a small dresser in one inner alcove. The flagstoned and beamed back public bar has darts, fruit machine, TV and juke box, and is liked by younger customers. On a raised terrace by the car park are some picnic-sets. *(Recommended by Paul and Shirley White, David Crook, Tom Bottinga, A and B D Craig, John Taylor, David M Cundy, Jodie Phillips, B J Harding)*

Free house ~ Licensees Malcolm and Eileen Hine ~ Real ale ~ Bar food (12-2, 6.30-9.15) ~ Restaurant ~ (01208) 872552 ~ Children in restaurant and family room ~ Dogs allowed in bar ~ Open 11-11; 12-10.30 Sun ~ Bedrooms: £43B/£75B

If we know a pub does sandwiches we always say so – if they're not mentioned, you'll have to assume you can't get one.

MALPAS SW8442 Map 1

Heron

Trenhaile Terrace, off A39 S of Truro

The main draw here is the lovely creekside location, and if you are lucky enough to bag one of the seats on the terrace or one of the window tables inside, you can enjoy a drink and watch the sunset. The bar is long and narrow with several areas leading off and a raised area at one end, and it's all very light and airy with blue and white décor and furnishings throughout. Two gas fires, mainly wooden floors with flagstones by the bar, modern yacht paintings on the wood-planked walls, some brass nautical items, heron pictures and a stuffed heron in a cabinet, and a chatty brasserie-type atmosphere; half the pub is no smoking. Straightforward bar food (they keep your credit card behind the bar), well kept St Austell IPA, HSD, and Tribute on handpump, good wines by the glass, and several malt whiskies; piped music. Parking is extremely difficult at peak times. *(Recommended by Malcolm Taylor, Ian Phillips, Andrea Rampley, Di and Mike Gillam, Debbie and Neil Hayter, David and Sally Cullen, Jenny and Brian Seller, David Crook, A P Seymour)*

St Austell ~ Tenant F C Kneebone ~ Real ale ~ Bar food ~ (01872) 272773 ~ Children welcome ~ Open 11-4, 6-11; 12-3, 7-10.30 Sun

MITCHELL SW8654 Map 1

Plume of Feathers 🛏

Just off A30 Bodmin—Redruth, by A3076 junction; take the southwards road then turn first right

The contemporary interior and pillared entrance here are quite a surprise given that the village is pretty sleepy. It's all very appealing, and the attractive bars have stripped old beams, painted wooden dado, Farrow & Ball pastel-coloured walls with paintings by local artists, and two fireplaces. The restaurant is no smoking. Well presented bar food served by helpful, friendly staff includes lunchtime specials such as sandwiches, home-made chicken, leek and ham pie (£6.95), fish pie with parmesan mash (£7.25), home-cooked ham with local free range eggs (£5.50), and locally shot rabbit braised in cider (£11), with evening choices like home-cured bresaola with pink grapefruit (£5.75), local scallops with five spice (£6.95), poached corn-fed chicken breast in a wild garlic and baby vegetable broth (£13.25), and roasted whole bass with crispy fennel salad and herb crushed potatoes (£14.50). From the menu, there might be home-made soup (£3.95), greek mezze plate (£5.25), chargrilled angus burger with red onion jam (£8.75), fresh pasta with wild mushrooms, truffle oil and parmesan (£8.95), and chargrilled angus rib-eye steak (£14.95). Oakham JHB and Sharps Doom Bar with guests like Shepherd Neame Spitfire and Skinners Betty Stogs on handpump, eight wines by the glass from a comprehensive list, and their own bottled spring water. Piped music, fruit machine and TV. The well planted garden areas have plenty of seats. The bedrooms are very comfortable and readers have enjoyed staying here. *(Recommended by Bernard Stradling, Sheila Brooks, Kevin Mayne, Guy Vowles, Charles and Isabel Cooper, B and M Kendall, Mandy and Simon King, Reg Fowle, Helen Rickwood, R J Herd, Callum and Letitia Smith-Burnett, Andy Sinden, Louise Harrington, Dr C C S Wilson, R M Corlett, Mayur Shah, Paul and Shirley White, Betsy and Peter Little, Roger and Anne Newbury, H W Roberts, A P Seymour)*

Free house ~ Licensees M F Warner and J Trotter ~ Real ale ~ Bar food (12-3, 6-10) ~ Restaurant ~ (01872) 510387/511125 ~ Children in eating area of bar and restaurant ~ Dogs allowed in bar ~ Open 10.30-11(10.30 Sun); closed evening 25 Dec ~ Bedrooms: £63.75S(£71.25B)/£85S(£95B)

Places with gardens or terraces usually let children sit there – we note in the text the very few exceptions that don't.

MITHIAN SW7450 Map 1

Miners Arms

Just off B3285 E of St Agnes

Friendly new licensees again for this 16th-c pub. Several cosy little rooms and passages are warmed by winter open fires, and the small back bar has an irregular beam and plank ceiling, a wood block floor, and bulging squint walls (one with a fine old wall painting of Elizabeth I); another small room has a decorative low ceiling, lots of books and quite a few interesting ornaments. The restaurant areas are no smoking; piped music. Bar food at lunchtime now includes home-made soup (£3.95), filled ciabattas (from £4.95), omelettes (from £6.95), chicken caesar salad (£8.95), and popular lime, crab and prawn salad (£9.95), with evening dishes such as lemon and thyme risotto or red pepper en croûte (from £6.95), fish of the day (from £8), chicken with stilton wrapped in bacon (£8.95), and local lobster (from £12). Well kept Greene King Old Speckled Hen and Sharps Doom Bar on handpump, and several wines by the glass. There are seats on the back terrace, with more on the sheltered front cobbled forecourt. More reports please. *(Recommended by Ian Phillips, Stephen Buckley, Andrea Rampley, Ken Arthur, Dennis Jenkin, Mike Tucker, Stephen and Jean Curtis, Paul and Shirley White)*

Inn Partnership (Pubmaster) ~ Lease Dyanne Hull and Christ Mitchell ~ Real ale ~ Bar food (all day in summer; 12-2.30, 6-9 in winter) ~ (01872) 552375 ~ Children in restaurant ~ Dogs allowed in bar ~ Open 12-11; 12-10.30 Sun; only open 4-11 Mon in winter

MOUSEHOLE SW4726 Map 1

Old Coastguard 🛏

The Parade (edge of village, coming in on coast road from Newlyn – street parking just before you reach the inn); village also signposted off B3315

This is a light and airy bar attached to a seaside hotel and is certainly not a traditional pub, but many readers enjoy their visits and they do keep Bass and Sharps Doom Bar on handpump, and a fair choice of wines by the glass.The position is lovely, and the neat and attractive sizeable garden (now lit at night) has palms and dracaenas, marble-look tables on decking, and a path leading down to the water's-edge rock pools. There's a mediterranean feel inside with plenty of blue and white décor, modern metal and wicker seats around well spaced matching tables on wood strip flooring, modern light watercolours on the walls, and palms, potted plants and fresh flowers. Its lower dining part has a glass wall giving a great view out over the garden to Mounts Bay; a quiet back area is darker. Good modern food at lunchtime might include sandwiches (from £4.50; open sandwiches on grilled ciabatta from £7), beetroot and butternut squash soup (£5), caesar salad (£6), salmon and sorrel fishcakes with smoked paprika hollandaise or steamed scallops with pickled ginger, bamboo shoots and straw mushrooms (£12.50), and roast honey glazed duck breast with sour cherry sauce (£14), with evening choices such as lobster and star anise soup (£6), fresh local oysters grilled with hazelnut butter (£7), baked filo pastry and parmesan basket filled with balsamic roasted vegetables, local blue cheese and roast garlic sauce (£12), skate wings with capers and brown butter (£15), and venison fillet with a juniper and thyme sauce or roast rack of lamb with rosemary, mint and garlic and a fresh fig sauce (£16). You can smoke only in the top bar. *(Recommended by David Glynne-Jones, Barry and Anne, Susie Symes, Sue Demont, Tim Barrow, Mike and Heather Watson, Ken Arthur, Dr R A Smye, Callum and Letitia Smith-Burnett, Ian and Liz Rispin, Simon J Barber, Stuart Turner, David and Nina Pugsley, Andy and Ali, David Booth)*

Free house ~ Licensee Bill Treloar ~ Real ale ~ Bar food (12-2.30, 7-9) ~ Restaurant ~ (01736) 731222 ~ Children in eating area of bar and restaurant ~ Dogs allowed in bar ~ Open 11-11(10.30 Sun) ~ Bedrooms: £48B/£100B

MYLOR BRIDGE SW8137 Map 1

Pandora ★★ ♀

Restronguet Passage: from A39 in Penryn, take turning signposted Mylor Church, Mylor
Bridge, Flushing and go straight through Mylor Bridge following Restronguet Passage
signs; or from A39 further N, at or near Perranarworthal, take turning signposted
Mylor, Restronguet, then follow Restronguet Weir signs, but turn left down hill at
Restronguet Passage sign

The position of this lovely medieval thatched pub is very special, and in fine
weather you can sit with your drink on the long floating pontoon and watch
children catching buckets of crabs and visiting dinghies pottering about in the
sheltered waterfront. Inside, the several rambling, interconnecting rooms have low
wooden ceilings (mind your head on some of the beams), beautifully polished big
flagstones, cosy alcoves with leatherette benches built into the walls, old race
posters, two large log fires in high hearths (to protect them against tidal floods);
part of the bar area is no smoking – as is the restaurant. Bar food includes
lunchtime sandwiches (from £4.50), baked potatoes (from £5.95), and platters
(from £6.95), as well as home-made soup (£4.50), local mussels (£5.25), vegetarian
pasta (£7.50), cod in ale batter (£9.95), and pot-braised lamb shank (£11.25), with
specials such as grilled lambs liver and smoked bacon (£11.95), local seabream on
dill risotto with asparagus spears and herb oil (£12.50), and sirloin steak (£12.95).
They also serve afternoon teas in summer. Well kept Bass, and St Austell HSD,
Tinners and Tribute on handpump, several wines by the glass, and local cider. It
does get very crowded in summer, and parking is difficult at peak times. Good
surrounding walks. *(Recommended by John Whiting, Mike Green, Gene and Tony
Freemantle, Robert Coates, A J Atyeo, Andrea Rampley, J M Tansey, Gene and
Kitty Rankin, Geoff Pidoux, Patrick Hancock, Ken Arthur, Philip and Ann Board, Jenny and
Brian Seller, David Crook, Kevin Thorpe, Guy Vowles, Ian and Celia Abbott, Dr Michael Smith,
John Close, Paul and Shirley White, Reg Fowle, Helen Rickwood, the Didler, Andy Sinden,
Louise Harrington, Mr and Mrs A H Young, Chris and Susie Cammack, Michael and
Jeanne Shillington, Malcolm Taylor, Mayur Shah, Bernard Stradling, A P Seymour,
Simon Cleasby)*

St Austell ~ Tenant John Milan ~ Real ale ~ Bar food (12-3, 6.30-9) ~ Restaurant ~
(01326) 372678 ~ Children welcome ~ Dogs allowed in bar ~ Occasional local choirs
and live jazz ~ Open 11-11; 12-10.30 Sun

PENZANCE SW4730 Map 1

Turks Head

At top of main street, by big domed building (Lloyds TSB), turn left down Chapel Street

There's always a cheerful mix of both regulars and visitors at this reliably friendly
local. The bustling bar has old flat irons, jugs and so forth hanging from the beams,
pottery above the wood-effect panelling, wall seats and tables, and a couple of
elbow rests around central pillars; piped music. Well liked bar food includes soup
(£3.50), lunchtime sandwiches and baguettes (from £4.50), and filled baked
potatoes (from £4.95), omelettes (£5.50), various ciabattas (from £6.50), a pie of
the day (£7.95), steaks (from £10.50), popular sizzler dishes (£10.50 chicken,
£11.95 tandoori monkfish), and white crabmeat salad (£12.50). The restaurant
area is no smoking. Well kept Greene King IPA, Sharps Doom Bar, Wadworths 6X,
and a guest on handpump; helpful service. The suntrap back garden has big urns of
flowers. There has been a Turks Head here for over 700 years – though most of the
original building was destroyed by a Spanish raiding party in the 16th c.
*(Recommended by Andrea Rampley, Susie Symes, Gordon Tong, Callum and Letitia Smith-
Burnett, Gene and Kitty Rankin, Barry and Anne, Michael and Alison Sandy, Pam and
Alan Neale, Catherine Pitt, Paul and Shirley White)*

Punch ~ Lease Jonathan Gibbard ~ Real ale ~ Bar food (11.30-2.30, 6-10) ~
(01736) 363093 ~ Children in eating area of bar and restaurant ~ Dogs welcome ~
Open 11-11; 12-10.30 Sun; may close afternoons in winter

PERRANWELL SW7739 Map 1

Royal Oak

Village signposted off A393 Redruth—Falmouth and A39 Falmouth—Truro

There's no doubt that much of the emphasis in this pretty and quietly set stone-built village pub is on the very good food – though drinkers do get a look in, with well kept Bass, Flowers IPA, and Sharps Special on handpump from the small serving counter and good wines by the glass (the wine list is well balanced and not over-long); prompt, friendly service and a particularly helpful landlord. The roomy, carpeted bar is welcoming and relaxed, with a buoyant, gently upmarket atmosphere, horsebrasses and pewter and china mugs on its black beams and joists, plates and country pictures on its cream-painted stone walls, and cosy wall and other seats around its tables. It rambles around beyond a big stone fireplace (with a good log fire in winter) into a snug little nook of a room behind, with just a couple more tables. Well presented, the interesting bar food includes super tapas like smoked anchovies, chorizo and olives, artichoke hearts in garlic butter, stuffed vine leaves, guacamole, and even occasional sushi (from £3.25), home-made soup (£4.25), smoked duck salad (£6.25), crab bake (£6.50), moules marinière or smoked salmon and crab gateau (£6.75), teriyaki chicken (£9.75), a trio of local fish (£10.25), steaks (from £11.95), and specials such as crab and sweetcorn bisque (£4.25), fresh steamed cockles (£6.95), paella (£9.95), and lobster in garlic butter (£22). The restaurant area is no smoking; piped music and shove-ha'penny. There are some picnic-sets out by the quiet village lane. *(Recommended by David Crook, Andy Sinden, Louise Harrington, Gene and Tony Freemantle, Mayur Shah, Dennis Jenkin, J M Tansey)*

Free house ~ Licensee Richard Rudland ~ Real ale ~ Bar food (12-2.30, 7-9.30) ~ Restaurant ~ (01872) 863175 ~ Children in restaurant ~ Dogs allowed in bar ~ Open 11-3, 6-11; 12-3, 6-10.30 Sun

POLKERRIS SX0952 Map 1

Rashleigh

Signposted off A3082 Fowey—St Austell

This year, a large part of the sun terrace here has been rebuilt and a big awning with outside heaters has been installed. This means that even in cooler weather you can make the most of the fine views towards the far side of St Austell and Mevagissey bays; the splendid beach with its restored jetty is only a few steps away and there are safe moorings for small yachts in the cove. Inside, the bar is snug and cosy, and the front part has comfortably cushioned seats and half a dozen or so well kept real ales on handpump such as Sharps Doom Bar and a beer named for the pub, Timothy Taylors Landlord, and guests like Badger Tanglefoot, Cotleigh Tawny and Skinners Cornish Knocker; two ciders, several whiskies, and eight wines by the glass. The more simply furnished back area has local photographs on the brown panelling, and a winter log fire; fruit machine and shove-ha'penny. Reasonably priced popular bar food includes sandwiches (from £3.20; open salad sandwiches from £6.50), home-made soup (£3.30), local mushrooms stuffed with pâté and fried in a light batter (£4.80), ploughman's (from £5.50), hazelnut and vegetable crumble (£7.50), home-made fish pie (£8.25), home-made steak pie (£8.50), daily specials such as vegetable lasagne (£7.50), locally shot pheasant pie or grilled bass or grey mullet with lemon butter (£8.50), and local scallops in garlic butter (£12.50), and puddings like jam roly-poly or treacle tart (£3.95). Plenty of parking either at the pub's own car park or the large village one. This whole section of the Cornish Coast Path is renowned for its striking scenery. *(Recommended by Bob and Margaret Holder, Sue Demont, Tim Barrow, Brian and Rosalie Laverick, Geoff Pidoux, Mrs M Granville-Edge, Prof and Mrs Tony Palmer, Val and Alan Green, Mayur Shah, the Didler, Reg Fowle, Helen Rickwood, Patrick Hancock, David Lewis, Charles and Pauline Stride, Alan Sutton, A P Seymour)*

Free house ~ Licensees Jon and Samantha Spode ~ Real ale ~ Bar food (12-2, 6-9; snacks on summer afternoons from 3pm) ~ Restaurant ~ (01726) 813991 ~ Children in eating area of bar and restaurant ~ Open 11-11; 12-10.30 Sun; closed 25 Dec and evening 26 Dec

PORT ISAAC SX0080 Map 1 ⌂

Port Gaverne Inn ♀ ⇤

Port Gaverne signposted from Port Isaac, and from B3314 E of Pendoggett

Several of the bedrooms have been refurbished recently in this popular 17th-c seaside inn, and there's a new terraced garden with outside heaters. The bar has a bustling atmosphere, big log fires and low beams, flagstones as well as carpeting, some exposed stone, and lots of chatty locals. In spring, the lounge is usually filled with pictures from the local art society's annual exhibition, and at other times there are interesting antique local photographs. Bar food includes sandwiches, chicken liver pâté (£5.25), ploughman's (from £5.50), roasted mediterranean vegetables topped with goats cheese or smoked haddock and spring onion fishcakes (£7), ham and egg (£7.20), seafood pie (£7.60), and chargrilled sirloin steak with herb butter (£11.50); children's meals (from £3.50); you can eat in the bar, the 'Captain's Cabin' – a little room where everything is shrunk to scale (old oak chest, model sailing ship, even the prints on the white stone walls) or on a balcony overlooking the sea. The restaurant is no smoking. Well kept St Austell Eden Ale and Sharps Doom Bar, Cornish Coaster and Will's Resolve on handpump, a good wine list, and several whiskies; cribbage and dominoes. Splendid clifftop walks all around. *(Recommended by Rona Murdoch, Earl and Chris Pick, P R Morley, M A Borthwick, Mrs Angela McArt, John and Vivienne Rice, Alan Sadler, Charles Gysin, Hugh Roberts, Chris Glasson, Liz and Tony Colman, A P Seymour)*

Free house ~ Licensee Graham Sylvester ~ Real ale ~ Bar food ~ Restaurant ~ (01208) 880244 ~ Children in eating area of bar and restaurant ~ Dogs allowed in bar and bedrooms ~ Open 12-11; 12.30-10.30 Sun ~ Bedrooms: /£79B

Slipway

Middle Street; limited foreshore parking, or use top car park and walk down

At the foot of this delightful steep conservation village and just across from the slipway down to the beach where crabbing boats are pulled up for the night, is this small family run hotel. There's a crazy-paved terrace at the front under an awning and with outside heaters, and plenty of tables and chairs. Inside, the little bar has low dark beams, delabole slate flagstones and some stripped stone walling that give something of a cellar feel, and it's all entirely unpretentious and not at all 'hotelish' though pleasantly civilised, with one or two nice touches like the appealing local watercolours (for sale). Sharps Doom Bar and Will's Resolve on handpump, and decent wines by the glass. Lunchtime bar snacks such as home-made soup (£3.50), sandwiches (from £3.95), filled baked potatoes (from £5.50), pasties (£5.95), ploughman's or home-made salmon and broccoli fishcakes (£6.95), battered fresh haddock (£7.95), and seasonal crab salad (£12.50), with evening dishes like sardines with rosemary and garlic (£6.45), duck liver and port pâté (£6.95), rack of cornish lamb (£14.75), and line caught bass on a clam and prawn risotto (£15.50); smaller helpings for children. The restaurant is no smoking; piped music and TV. The bedrooms have been refurbished this year. *(Recommended by Mrs Sally Kingsbury, Neil and Beverley Gardner, Earl and Chris Pick)*

Free house ~ Licensees Mark and Kep Forbes ~ Real ale ~ Bar food (12-2.30, 6-9) ~ Restaurant ~ (01208) 880264 ~ Children in restaurant and family room ~ Dogs allowed in bedrooms ~ Open 11-11; 12-10.30 Sun; 11-3, 6-11 in winter; closed 25 Dec ~ Bedrooms: /£90B

The details at the end of each main entry start by saying whether the pub is a free house, or if it's tied to a brewery or pub group (which we name).

PORTHLEVEN SW6225 Map 1

Ship

Village on B3304 SW of Helston; pub perched on edge of harbour

This is such an enjoyable pub and it's usually packed with tourists and characterful
locals, with plenty of lively banter between the two. There's a marvellous view over
the pretty working harbour and out to sea, and if you are lucky, you might be able
to bag a window seat inside or one of the tables out in the terraced garden; at night,
the harbour is interestingly floodlit. The knocked-through bar has log fires in big
stone fireplaces and some genuine individuality. The no smoking family room is a
conversion of an old smithy and has logs burning in a huge open fireplace; piped
music, fruit machine, cribbage and dominoes. Good, popular bar food includes
sandwiches or toasties (from £4.95; crusties from £5.95), smoked haddock fishcake
with lime chilli salsa (£5.25), plump moules marinière (£5.95), filled baked potatoes
(from £5.95), ploughman's (from £7.50), mediterranean vegetable bake (£9.95),
steaks (from £10.95), crab and prawn mornay or chargrilled lamb steak in
rosemary and garlic sauce (£12.95), and home-made specials such as lasagne
(£9.95), beef in beer (£10.50), lemon sole (£12.95), and monkfish in bacon
(£13.95); the candlelit dining room also enjoys the good view. Well kept Courage
Best and Sharps Cornish Coaster, Doom Bar and Special on handpump, and
friendly service. *(Recommended by Andrea Rampley, Reg Fowle, Helen Rickwood,
Dr and Mrs M W A Haward, Susie Symes, Paul and Shirley White, Brian Skelcher, Mike and
Heather Watson, the Didler, Tom McLean, Catherine Pitt, Ann and Bob Westbrook, David and
Nina Pugsley, Andy and Ali)*

Free house ~ Licensee Colin Oakden ~ Real ale ~ Bar food (12-9 in summer) ~
(01326) 564204 ~ Children in family room ~ Dogs allowed in bar ~ Open 11.30-11;
12-10.30 Sun

PORTHTOWAN SW6948 Map 1

Blue

Beach Road, East Cliff; use the car park (fee in season), not the slippy sand

Certainly not a traditional pub, this bustling bar is in a fantastic beach location and
has a real mixture of customers, from serious surfers to dog walkers to families. It's
all very light and airy with huge picture windows looking across the terrace to the
huge expanse of sand and sea. There are built-in pine seats in the front bays,
chrome and wicker chairs around plain wooden tables on the stripped wood floor,
quite a few high-legged chrome and wooden bar stools, and plenty of standing
space around the bar counter; powder blue painted walls, ceiling fans, some big
ferny plants, two large TVs showing silent surfing videos, and fairly quiet piped
music; pool table. Perky, busy young staff and a chatty informal atmosphere. Good
modern bar food includes home-made soup (£3.50), stone-baked pizzas (from
£4.50), tortillas with tomato salsa, sour cream and guacamole or chilli beef, melted
cheese and sour cream or lunchtime filled ciabatta and panini (from £4.75),
chargrilled chicken and bacon with creamy caesar dressing (£5; main course £8.50),
beer-battered king prawns with lemon mayonnaise (£5.50), meaty or vegetarian
burgers (£7), chorizo, smoked paprika, white bean and tomato stew (£8), meaty or
vegetarian thai green curries (from £8.50), sirloin steak (£9.50), and puddings like
chilled toffee apple custard pots or banana, honey and roasted almond cheesecake
(£4); children's meals (from £3.50); all-day breakfasts at weekends. Quite a few
wines by the glass, cocktails and shots, and giant cups of coffee. *(Recommended by
Dr R A Smye, Andy Sinden, Louise Harrington, Tim and Ann Newell)*

Free house ~ Licensees Tara Roberts, Luke Morris and Alexandra George ~ Bar food
(12-3(4 weekends), 6-9) ~ Restaurant ~ (01209) 890329 ~ Children in eating area of
bar ~ Dogs welcome ~ Live bands Sat evening and summer Fri evening ~ Open 11-11;
11-10.30 Sun; closed Jan

SENNEN COVE SW3526 Map 1

Old Success

Off A30 Land's End road

In summer, given its position, this old-fashioned seaside hotel does get very busy; it's much less hectic out of season. From seats in the terraced garden there are marvellous views of the surf of Whitesands Bay; it's an attractive and clean beach, and Land's End is a pleasant walk away. The beamed and timbered bar has plenty of lifeboat memorabilia, including an RNLI flag hanging on the ceiling; elsewhere are ship's lanterns, black and white photographs, dark wood tables and chairs, and a big ship's wheel that doubles as a coat stand. Reasonably priced bar food includes sandwiches (from £2.75; hot panini from £4.25), pasty (£2.85), soup (£3.25), filled baked potatoes (from £4.50), beer battered fresh cod (£6.75), vegetable lasagne (£7.75), home-made seafood pie (£7.95), steaks (from £8.50), and puddings like jam roly-poly (£3.50). Well kept Sharps Doom Bar and Skinners Heligan Honey and a beer exclusive to the inn called Head Launcher on handpump. The upper bar and restaurant are no smoking; piped music. Bedrooms are basic but comfortable, enjoying the sound of the sea, and they have four self-catering suites. (*Recommended by A and B D Craig, Roger and Jenny Huggins, Callum and Letitia Smith-Burnett, Margaret Booth, Michael and Alison Sandy, Simon J Barber*)

Free house ~ Licensee Martin Brooks ~ Real ale ~ Bar food ~ Restaurant ~ (01736) 871232 ~ Children welcome ~ Dogs allowed in bar ~ Live music Sat and sometimes Thurs ~ Open 11-11; 12-10.30 Sun ~ Bedrooms: £31S/£88B

ST AGNES SV8807 Map 1

Turks Head 🍺 🛏

This is the St Agnes in the Isles of Scilly; The Quay

An easy boat trip from St Marys, this converted little boathouse is held dear in the hearts of many of our readers. In summer, you can sit on the extended area across the sleepy lane or on terraces down towards the sea, and there are steps down to the slipway so you can take your drinks and food and sit right on the shore; the hanging baskets are very pretty. The simply furnished but cosy and very friendly pine-panelled bar has quite a collection of flags, helmets and headwear, as well as maritime photographs and model ships. The real ale arrives in St Agnes via a beer supplier in St Austell and two boat trips, and the two well kept on handpump might include St Austell Dartmoor Best and a beer named for the pub, Ales of Scilly Scuppered (from a local microbrewery), and Sharps Doom Bar or Skinners Heligan Honey; decent house wines, a good range of malt whiskies, and hot chocolate with brandy. At lunchtime, the well liked bar food includes open rolls (from £3.25; local crab £6.25), ploughman's (£4.95), salads (from £6.50; local crab £9.95), cold ham with chips (£6.75), vegetable pasta bake (£7.50), and puddings (£3.20), with evening dishes like chicken curry (£7.75), wild rice, spinach and honey roast (£7.95), crab cakes with sweet chilli dip (£8.25), and blackened swordfish steak or sirloin steak (£10.95). Ice-cream and cakes are sold through the afternoon, and in good weather they may do evening barbecues. The dining extension is no smoking, and the cats are called Taggart and Lacey, and the collie, Tess. Darts, cribbage, dominoes and piped music. If you wish to stay here, you must book months ahead. Winter opening hours tend to be quite sporadic, given that only some 70 people live on the island. (*Recommended by Pete and Rosie Flower, R J Herd, David Crook, Michael Butler, Mr and Mrs P Dix, Paul Hopton, Ian and Liz Rispin, Paul Humphreys, Val and Alan Green, Catherine Pitt, Andy Sinden, Louise Harrington, David Hoult*)

Free house ~ Licensees John and Pauline Dart ~ Real ale ~ Bar food (12-2.30, 6-9) ~ (01720) 422434 ~ Children welcome ~ Dogs allowed in bar ~ Open 10.30-11; 10.30-10.30 Sun; three days per week in winter ~ Bedrooms: /£64S

It's very helpful if you let us know up-to-date food prices when you report on pubs.

ST ANNS CHAPEL SX4170 Map 1

Rifle Volunteer

A390

Although there's some emphasis on the popular food in this ex-coaching inn, the two front bars have kept a pleasantly pubby feel. The main one on the left has a log fire in its big stone fireplace, cushioned pews and country kitchen chairs, a turkey rug on its parquet floor, and a relaxed ochre and green décor; on the right, the Chapel Bar has similar furnishings on its dark boards, another open fire, and motorcycle prints on its cream walls. Well kept Sharps Doom Bar, Cornish Coaster and Will's Resolve are tapped from the cask, there are over 70 whiskies, local farm cider, and decent wines by the glass; piped music, darts, pool, dominoes, TV and skittle alley. Well liked bar food might include lunchtime sandwiches, home-made soup (£4.25), moules marinière or chicken liver pâté (£4.95), curries, steak and kidney pie or wild mushroom pasta (£8.95), fish crumble, lemon ginger chicken, lamb burgundy or honeyed pork (all £9.95), steaks (from £11.50), and specials such as oriental vegetable stir fry or seafood cocktail (£5.50), lamb steak with orange and spring onion sauce (£10.50), pheasant breasts in bacon and red wine (£10.95), and seared tuna steak with fresh mint oil (£12.75). The modern back dining room has picture windows to take advantage of a very wide view that stretches down to the Tamar estuary and Plymouth. An elevated Astroturf deck beside it has some tables, with more in the garden which slopes away below. *(Recommended by Ted George, Alan and Paula McCully, Mark Rogers, Jacquie and Jim Jones, Dave Maunder, Paul and Sue Merrick)*

Free house ~ Licensees Frank and Lynda Hilldrup ~ Real ale ~ Bar food ~ Restaurant ~ (01822) 832508 ~ Children in eating area of bar and restaurant ~ Dogs allowed in bar ~ Open 12-2.30, 6-11 ~ Bedrooms: £35S/£50B

ST KEW SX0276 Map 1

St Kew Inn

Village signposted from A39 NE of Wadebridge

Relaxed and friendly, this rather grand-looking old stone building (now no smoking except for the public bar) has a neatly kept bar with winged high-backed settles and varnished rustic tables on the lovely dark delabole flagstones, black wrought-iron rings for lamps or hams hanging from the high ceiling, and a handsome window seat; there's also an open kitchen range under a high mantelpiece decorated with earthenware flagons. At lunchtime, the good, popular bar food includes home-made soup (£3.25), cornish pasty (£3.95), ploughman's (£6.25), filled baked potatoes (from £6.25), chicken kiev (£6.95), and 10oz sirloin steak (£12.95), with evening choices such as home-made chicken liver pâté, deep-fried camembert or garlic mushrooms (£4.25), king prawns in garlic butter (£5.25), vegetarian curry (£7.50), beef in Guinness with herb dumplings (£8.75), breast of chicken in a smoked bacon, cider and mushroom sauce (£8.75), lamb casserole (£9.50), and honey-roast duck (£12.95). Well kept St Austell Tinners, HSD and Tribute tapped from wooden casks behind the counter (lots of tankards hang from the beams above it), a couple of farm ciders, a good wine list, and several malt whiskies; darts, cribbage, dominoes and shove-ha'penny. The big garden has a small summer marquee, seats on the grass and picnic-sets on the front cobbles. *(Recommended by R T and J C Moggridge, M A Borthwick, Jacquie and Jim Jones, the Didler, Rona Murdoch, J S Burn, Andrea Rampley, DAV, Michael B Griffith, David Eberlin, Mike Tucker, Mick and Moira Brummell, M Hosegood, Kevin Blake, Liz and Tony Colman, Brian and Bett Cox)*

St Austell ~ Tenant Desmond Weston ~ Real ale ~ Bar food ~ (01208) 841259 ~ Children in dining room ~ Open 11-2.30, 6-11(all day July and Aug); 12-3, 7-10.30 (all day in July and Aug) Sun; closed 25 Dec

ST MAWGAN SW8766 Map 1

Falcon

NE of Newquay, off B3276 or A3059

Under a new licensee, this wisteria-clad old stone inn is in a very pretty village. The neatly kept big bar has a log fire, large antique coaching prints and falcon pictures on the walls, and well kept St Austell Tinners, HSD and Tribute on handpump. As well as lunchtime sandwiches (from £3.75) and filled baked potatoes (from £4.25), bar food might include home-made soup (£3.50), salmon, watercress and tomato terrine (£4.25), vegetarian pasta (£6.95), a trio of local sausages or a curry (£7.95), steak and mushroom pie or honey glazed ham with mango and pineapple chutney (£8.25), local fresh cod in beer batter (£8.95), and puddings like home-made apple pie or chocolate mousse (from £3.75). The restaurant is no smoking and has paintings and pottery by local artists for sale; darts. There are seats in the front cobbled courtyard and a peaceful garden with plenty of seats, a wishing well and play equipment for children. *(Recommended by David Crook, A and B D Craig, Mark Flynn, David Eberlin, Val and Alan Green, Bob and Margaret Holder, Brian Skelcher, Tim and Rosemary Wells, Brian and Bett Cox, Robert Coates, Ray and Winifred Halliday, Louise Daler-Finch, David Hoult, Brian Dawes, Ron and Sheila Corbett, Mrs J R Williams)*

St Austell ~ Tenant Andy Marshall ~ Real ale ~ Bar food (12-2.30, 6-9.30 (slightly less in winter)) ~ Restaurant ~ (01637) 860225 ~ Children welcome ~ Dogs allowed in bar ~ Open 11-3, 6-11; 12-3, 7-11 Sun ~ Bedrooms: £26S/£68S

TREBURLEY SX3477 Map 1

Springer Spaniel

A388 Callington—Launceston

There have been several changes of licensee here over the last couple of years, so we are hoping that Mr Hall stays for a while. The relaxed bar has a lovely, very high-backed settle by the woodburning stove in the big fireplace, high-backed farmhouse chairs and other seats, and pictures of olde-worlde stage-coach arrivals at inns; this leads into a cosy room with big solid teak tables. Up some steps from the main bar is the beamed, attractively furnished restaurant. Bar food includes lunchtime sandwiches (from £3.95; ciabattas from £4.95), mushroom pot (£4.95), home-cooked ham and egg or sausage, mash and onion gravy (£6.50), stilton beef (£8.95), chicken strips with a sun-dried tomato, paprika, herb and cream sauce (£10.95), local crab salad (£11.95), local scallops and roasted pepper tagliatelle (£13.95), a whole rack of local lamb with a mustard and herb crust and redcurrant and mint dressing (£14.25), and puddings like dark chocolate tart or home-made gingerbread with toffee sauce (£4.95). Well kept Sharps Doom Bar, Cornish Coaster and a beer named for the pub on handpump. More reports please. *(Recommended by Jacquie and Jim Jones, John Whiting, Pamela and Merlyn Horswell, Alan Sadler, Brian and Bett Cox, Paul and Philippa Ward, Gene and Kitty Rankin, Mr and Mrs G M Pearson, Ryta Lyndley, Stephen Gutteridge, Mary Ellen Cummings, Tim and Sue Halstead, Alan Wilcock, Christine Davidson, W F C Phillips)*

Wagtail Inns ~ Licensee John Hall ~ Real ale ~ Bar food ~ Restaurant ~ (01579) 370424 ~ Children in eating area of bar and restaurant ~ Dogs allowed in bar ~ Open 12-3, 6-11; 12-3, 7-10.30 Sun

TREGADILLETT SX2984 Map 1

Eliot Arms

Village signposted off A30 at junction with A395, W end of Launceston bypass

The series of small softly lit rooms in this creeper-covered inn is full of interest: 72 antique clocks (including seven grandfathers), 400 snuffs, hundreds of horsebrasses, old prints, old postcards or cigarette cards grouped in frames on the walls, quite a few barometers, and shelves of books and china. Also, a fine old mix of furniture on the delabole slate floors, from high-backed built-in curved settles, through plush Victorian dining chairs, armed seats, chaise longues and mahogany housekeeper's chairs, to more modern seats, and open fires. Under the new licensee, the decent bar food includes lunchtime baguettes and filled baked potatoes (from £4.95), home-made soup (£3.25), chicken liver pâté with apple chutney (£4.25), wild mushroom and herb risotto topped with a poached egg (£5.95; main course £8.50), ploughman's (from £5.95), meat pie (£6.75), local pork sausages with mustard mash and onion gravy (£6.95), lambs liver and bacon (£7.25), chicken breast with roast shallots and red wine jus (£8.95), and steaks (from £11.95); an area of the restaurant is no smoking. Well kept Courage Best, Greene King Old Speckled Hen and Sharps Doom Bar on handpump; darts and piped music. There are seats in front of the pub and at the back of the car park. *(Recommended by Nigel Long, Philip and Ann Board, Dorsan Baker, Mr and Mrs P Dix, Dr D and Mrs B Woods, Dr D Taub, the Didler, Alan Sadler, David Crook, Steve Whalley, Chris Glasson, J and S French)*

Coast & Country Inns ~ Managers Karen and Mark Jenkins ~ Real ale ~ Bar food ~ Restaurant ~ (01566) 772051 ~ Children in eating area of bar ~ Dogs allowed in bar ~ Open 11.30-3, 6-11; 11-11 Sat; 12-10.30 Sun ~ Bedrooms: /£60S(£55B)

TREMATON SX3959 Map 1
Crooked Inn
Off A38 just W of Saltash

Reached down a long drive past several old caravans, this relaxed place is liked as a lunch stop on the way to west Cornwall. The bar is more or less open-plan, with high bar stools by the curved stone counter, mate's chairs and brocaded stools around a mix of tables in front of the big open fireplace, and a piano for impromptu entertainment. Down a step is the lower lounge with heavier stripped beams, upholstered settle seating, and another fireplace with a woodburning stove. A conservatory leads off this, and there are doors that open out onto a decked area which looks over the garden and valley below. For children there are swings, a slide built into the hillside, a tree house, and trampoline. Sheep, ducks, a pig, and two dogs roam the grounds, and two horses may be nibbling the lawn. Well kept Fullers London Pride, Sharps Own, Skinners Cornish Knocker and St Austell HSD on handpump, and a decent wine list; piped music. Generous helpings of bar food include sandwiches (from £2.75), home-made soup (£2.95), pâté (£4.75), ploughman's (from £5.50), lunchtime ham and eggs (£5.95), home-made curry of the day (£6.75), pie of the day (£6.95), steaks (from £10.95), and daily specials such as pork creole (£6.95) or smoked salmon and prawn linguini (£10.95). The bedrooms overlook the courtyard where there are seats. *(Recommended by Ted George, Michael Lamm)*

Free house ~ Licensees Sandra and Tony Arnold ~ Real ale ~ Bar food (12-2.30, 6-9.30) ~ (01752) 848177 ~ Children welcome ~ Dogs welcome ~ Open 11-11; 12-10.30 Sun; closed 25 Dec ~ Bedrooms: £25(£45B)/£49(£70B)

TRESCO SV8915 Map 1
New Inn ♀ ◧ ⇦
New Grimsby; Isles of Scilly

There's not much competition, so this attractive inn does get very busy in high season. The locals' bar has a good chatty atmosphere, while visitors enjoy the main bar room or the light, airy dining extension. There are some comfortable old sofas, banquettes, planked partition seating, and farmhouse chairs and tables, a few standing timbers, boat pictures, a large model sailing boat, a collection of old telescopes, and plates on the delft shelf. The Pavilion extension has plenty of seats and tables on the blue wooden floors, and cheerful yellow walls; it looks over the flower-filled terrace where there's plenty of teak furniture and views of the sea. Good bar food at lunchtime might include pasty (£5), sandwiches (from £5.50; fresh local crab £10), honey-glazed ham and eggs (£7.50), trio of sausages or beef in ale casserole (£8), gnocchi with mediterranean vegetables (£9), and local beer battered fish (£9.50); evening choices such as soup (£3.50), salmon and smoked haddock fishcakes (£5; main course £10), pizzas (from £6.50), mussels in cider and cream sauce (£8; main course £16), chicken and oyster mushroom stroganoff, slow roasted belly pork with red wine and thyme jus or curries (£10), and chargrilled 10oz rump steak (£15.50). Three well kept beers on handpump from Ales of Scilly, Skinners and St Austells, quite a few malt whiskies, interesting wines by the large glass, and up to ten vodkas; good coffee, piped music, darts, pool, cribbage and dominoes. Note that the price below is for dinner, bed and breakfast. *(Recommended by Bernard Stradling, Gwyn Jones, Roger and Jenny Huggins, Michael Butler, R J Herd, Paul Hopton, Andy Sinden, Louise Harrington, Paul Humphreys, Val and Alan Green, Catherine Pitt)*

Free house ~ Licensee Alan Baptist ~ Real ale ~ Bar food ~ Restaurant ~ (01720) 422844 ~ Children in eating area of bar and restaurant ~ Dogs allowed in bar ~ Open 11-11; 12-10.30 Sun; 11-3, 6-11 in winter ~ Bedrooms: /£219.90B

TRURO SW8244 Map 1
Old Ale House ☕ £
Quay Street

Extremely popular and very well run, this bustling place has a fine choice of real ales and a tremendous local atmosphere. On handpump or tapped from the cask, the well kept, regularly changing beers might include Skinners Kiddlywink plus seven changing guests from breweries such as Courage, Everards, Fullers, Hobgoblin, Otter, Sharps and Skinners; 21 country wines. Tasty wholesome bar food prepared in a spotless kitchen in full view of the bar includes doorstep sandwiches (from £2.75; 'hands' or half bloomers with toppings such as bacon, onions and melted cheese or tuna, mayonnaise and melted cheese), sautéed potatoes with bacon and mushroom in creamy sauce, cauliflower and bacon mornay and potato skins topped with stilton and mushrooms (all £3.50), and beef stew or pork and apple casserole (£3.75). The dimly lit bar has an engaging diversity of furnishings, some interesting 1920s bric-a-brac, beer mats pinned everywhere, matchbox collections, and newpapers and magazines to read. Giant Jenga, giant Connect Four, and piped music. *(Recommended by Ted George, Joyce and Maurice Cottrell, R T and J C Moggridge, Ian Phillips, Jacquie and Jim Jones, Callum and Letitia Smith-Burnett, the Didler, Di and Mike Gillam, Mark Flynn, Mike Gorton, David Crook, Klaus and Elizabeth Leist)*

Enterprise ~ Tenants Mark Jones and Beverley Jones ~ Real ale ~ Bar food (12-2.45, 6.30-9; not Sat or Sun evenings) ~ (01872) 271122 ~ Jazz every second Weds, live band every second Thurs ~ Open 11-11; 12-10.30 Sun

LUCKY DIP

Besides the fully inspected pubs, you might like to try these Lucky Dips recommended to us and described by readers (if you do, please send us reports: www.goodguides.co.uk).

ALTARNUN [SX2280]
Kings Head [Five Lanes]: Good choice of food, guest beers, enthusiastic licensees, traditional lounge with big log fire and small padded settles, simple public bar; open all day *(John Whiting)*
ANGARRACK [SW5838]
Angarrack Inn [Steamers Hill]: Welcoming village local tucked below railway viaduct in little secluded valley, new licensees making good choice of food to order, well kept St Austell beers; picnic-sets outside *(Mick and Moira Brummell)*
ASHTON [SW6028]
Lion & Lamb [A394 Helston—Penzance]: Welcoming pub with wide range of food from good sandwiches and panini up (just roast

lunches on Sun), half a dozen well kept ales such as Greene King IPA and Old Speckled Hen and Sharps Doom Bar, occasional mini beer festivals, friendly staff, no smoking areas; dogs welcome in bar, lovely hanging baskets and flower beds, open all day, handy for SW Coastal Path *(Dennis Jenkin, Ann and Bob Westbrook)*
BOSCASTLE [SX0990]
Cobweb [B3263, just E of harbour]: Well used dim-lit local with plenty of character, hundreds of old bottles hanging from heavy beams, two or three high-backed settles, flagstones and dark stone walls, cosy log fire, real ales such as Dartmoor and St Austell, usual food, good prices, decent wine choice; darts, dominoes, cribbage, pool, fruit machine and juke box,

more machines and another fire in sizeable no smoking family room; live music Sat, open all day *(Glenn and Gillian Miller, LYM, the Didler, Mayur Shah, Geoff Pidoux, Betsy and Peter Little, Ted George)*

BREAGE [SW6128]

Queens Arms [3 miles W of Helston]: L-shaped local with well kept changing ales such as Bass, Caledonian Deuchars IPA, Sharps Doom Bar, Shepherd Neame Bishops Finger and Charles Wells Bombardier, farm cider, decent wine, wide range of good value food from sandwiches and tasty baguettes (not Sun) up, quick polite service even when busy, daily papers, good coal fires, ceiling festooned with interesting decorative plates, Queen Victoria memorabilia one end, plush banquettes, back games area with pool, paperback sales for silver band; piped pop music, quiz night Weds, jazz Thurs; dogs welcome, some picnic-sets outside, bedrooms, medieval wall paintings in church opp, open all day Sun *(Alan Bowker, Dennis Jenkin, BB, Patrick Renouf)*

BRIDGE [SW6744]

Bridge Inn [B3300 Redruth—Portreath]: L-shaped bar with newish landlord, good value food (dining area on left), well kept ales such as Greene King IPA, local Ring o' Bells D'reckly and One & All and Sharps Doom Bar; garden with dovecote *(Alan Bowker)*

BUDOCK WATER [SW7832]

☆ *Trelowarren Arms*: Cheerful proper landlord makes for good atmosphere in comfortable turkey-carpeted pub with wide range of good value food inc fresh fish in split-level dining area, well kept Greene King IPA and guest beers such as Exmoor Hound Dog, Sharps Doom Bar and Skinners Cornish Knocker from central bar, efficient service, lots of jugs on dark beams, snaps of regulars, darts and well lit pool table in nice little back games room; piped radio, picnic-sets on small back terrace *(BB, Alan Bowker)*

CALLINGTON [SX3569]

☆ *Coachmakers Arms* [A388 towards Launceston]: Imposing 18th-c pub, beams and timbers, ceilings with flags from around the world matching clock collection with differing time zones, bric-a-brac and tropical fish, friendly service, good value standard food from baguettes and baked potatoes to chargrills, restaurant; piped music, Weds quiz night; children in eating areas, bedrooms due for refurbishment, good breakfast *(LYM, Val and Alan Green, Robin and Tricia Walker)*

CALSTOCK [SX4368]

Tamar [Quay]: Spotless pub in lovely setting yards from the river, good reasonably priced standard food, well kept ales such as Sharps Special, friendly service; shiny tables and chairs on sunny decking, hilly walk or ferry to Cotehele (NT) *(David Crook)*

CARGREEN [SX4362]

☆ *Crooked Spaniard* [off A388 Callington—Saltash]: Much-altered pub in grand spot by Tamar, with smart river-view dining extension and waterside terrace – always some river

activity, esp at high tide; cosy and comfortable panelled bar, huge fireplace in another room, good generous food inc Sun carvery, well kept ales; under same management as Crooked Inn at Trematon *(Andy and Ali)*

CAWSAND [SX4350]

☆ *Cross Keys* [The Square]: Friendly unpretentious pub opp boat club, well kept west country ales such as Blackawton and Teignworthy alongside mainstream brands, wide range of enjoyable generous reasonably priced food esp fish and shellfish (well worth booking in season) in bar and attractive stripped-pine dining room, flexible service; pool, may be piped music; dogs welcome, pleasant bedrooms *(Neil Doak, Pat and Derek Westcott, Kathleen Henry, S P Watkin, P A Taylor)*

CHAPEL AMBLE [SW9975]

☆ *Maltsters Arms* [off A39 NE of Wadebridge]: Friendly new licensees in appealing well lit country food pub with beams, panelling, stripped stone and partly carpeted flagstones, well kept ales inc one brewed by Sharps for the pub, good wines, upstairs family room, attractive restaurant; dogs welcome in bar, benches out in sheltered sunny corner; more reports on new regime, please *(LYM, Jacquie and Jim Jones, Dr D Smith)*

CHARLESTOWN [SX0351]

Rashleigh Arms [Quay Rd]: Roomy pub recently tastefully refurbished with nautical touches, well kept St Austell ales, good coffee, cheery quick helpful service, generous food inc all-day carvery, good waterside family room; piped music, on the coach circuit; lots of terrace tables (dogs allowed here) and garden above little harbour, good value bedrooms *(M Joyner)*

CONSTANTINE [SW7329]

Queens Arms [Fore St]: Comfortable, friendly and unpretentious, with good value simple food from good proper sandwiches up, well kept Sharps Doom Bar, decent house wine, interesting collection of ancient tools; dogs allowed, handy for 15th-c church, good walks *(Dennis Jenkin)*

COVERACK [SW7818]

Paris [The Cove]: Friendly old-fashioned pub above harbour in beautiful fishing village, spectacular bay views, well kept real ales, enjoyable generous food esp local fish and seafood, also children's, good Sun lunch, nautical items inc large model of namesake ship, interesting wooden moulds from Falmouth churchyard, no mobile phones; garden, bedrooms *(Paul and Shirley White)*

CRACKINGTON HAVEN [SX1496]

Coombe Barton [off A39 Bude—Camelford]: Much-extended old inn in beautiful setting opposite splendid craggy bay popular with surfers and walkers; side terrace with plenty of tables, big modernised bar with plenty of room for summer crowds, lots of local pictures, surfboard hanging from plank ceiling, smartly uniformed young staff, wide range of simple bar food (can take a time) inc fresh fish and children's menu, well kept Sharps Safe Haven (brewed specially for the pub) and St Austell, decent wines, big plain family room, enjoyable no smoking restaurant; darts, glazed-off pool table, fruit machines, piped music, TV; dogs allowed in bar, comfortable bedrooms, open all day Sun, also Sat in school hols *(LYM, Betsy and Peter Little, DAV, Michael H Legge)*

CRAFTHOLE [SX3654]

☆ *Finnygook*: Clean and comfortable much-modernised lounge bar, light and airy, well kept Skinners Betty Stogs, reasonably priced wines, wide food choice from good generous baguettes up, friendly expert service, restaurant; discreet piped music; one car park is steep; dogs on leads allowed, tables in yard, good sea views from residents' lounge, low-priced bedrooms *(BB, Dennis Jenkin)*

CREMYLL [SX4553]

☆ *Edgcumbe Arms*: Super setting by foot-ferry to Plymouth, with good views of Tamar and picnic-sets out by water; attractive layout and décor, with slate floors, big settles, comfortable fireside sofas and other old-fashioned furnishings, old pictures and china, no smoking area, plentiful food from sandwiches up, well kept St Austell ales, cheerful staff, good family room/games area; children in eating area, bedrooms, *(LYM, S P Watkin, P A Taylor, Andy and Ali)*

CROWN TOWN [SW6330]

Crown [B3303 N of Helston]: Friendly open-plan roadside local with particularly well kept Greene King Abbot, Ring o' Bells D'reckly and Skinners Betty Stogs tapped from stillroom casks, welcoming licensees, enjoyable food running up to duck and steaks, side eating area, fine collection of brassware, giant Jenga (great fun) and pool; bedrooms in lodges *(Roger and Jenny Huggins, Tom McLean)*

CUBERT [SW7858]

☆ *Smugglers Den* [village signed off A3075 S of Newquay, then brown sign to pub (and Trebellan holiday park) on left]: Big open-plan 16th-c thatched pub, lots of well ordered tables, dim lighting, stripped stone and heavy beam and plank ceilings, west country pictures and seafaring memorabilia, small barrel seats, steps down to no smoking area with enormous inglenook woodburner, another step to big side family dining room; neat helpful friendly staff, fresh generous enjoyable food inc local seafood, well kept Sharps, Skinners and St Austell ales, farm cider, well lit pool area, darts; piped music, fruit machine; picnic-sets in small courtyard and on lawn with climbing frame, has been cl winter Mon-Weds lunchtime *(BB, the Didler)*

DEVORAN [SW7938]

☆ *Old Quay House* [Quay Rd – brown sign to pub off A39 Truro—Falmouth]: Friendly new couple running this relaxing old local at end of coast to coast cycle way, he does the cooking – good reasonably priced food from tasty baguettes to specials such as ling with prawn sauce and garlic mash; well kept changing ales such as Fullers London Pride and Greene King Old Speckled Hen, quick friendly service, two small unpretentious rooms, one with daily

papers and big coal fire, boating bric-a-brac, evening restaurant; steeply terraced garden behind making the most of the idyllic spot – peaceful creekside village, lovely views, walks nearby; good value bedrooms, open all day in summer *(David Crook, J V Dadswell, BB, Andy Sinden, Louise Harrington, David Billington, Dr and Mrs M W A Haward, Guy Vowles, R and M Willes)*

DOWNDERRY [SX3153]

Inn on the Shore: Generous good value food inc carvery, helpful friendly staff, well kept Courage, restaurant with views over Whitsand Bay and boats; good garden *(anon)*

EDMONTON [SW9672]

☆ *Quarryman* [off A39 just W of Wadebridge bypass]: Unusual three-room beamed bar, partly no smoking, around courtyard of former quarrymen's quarters, and part of a small holiday complex; some interesting decorations inc old sporting memorabilia, well kept Sharps, Skinners and a couple of good guest beers, some good individual cooking besides lunchtime snacks such as sandwiches, home-made burgers and ploughman's, attentive staff; pool, cribbage and dominoes, friendly dog called Floyd (visiting dogs welcome), cosy no smoking bistro; well behaved children in eating area, open all day *(Mrs Sylvia Elcoate, Andrin Cooper, M A Borthwick, LYM)*

FALMOUTH [SW8132]

☆ *Chain Locker* [Custom House Quay]: Fine spot by inner harbour with window tables and lots outside, well kept ales such as Sharps Doom Bar and Skinners, well priced generous food from sandwiches to fresh local fish, quick service, strongly nautical bare-boards décor, darts alley; fruit machine, piped music; well behaved children welcome, open all day, self-catering accommodation *(LYM, the Didler, Patrick Hancock, M Joyner, Dr and Mrs M E Wilson)*

☆ *Quayside Inn & Old Ale House* [Arwenack St/Fore St]: Popular bare-boards dark-panelled bar with good range of well kept ales inc Sharps, Skinners and more distant favourites, decent wines, efficient service, reasonably priced food (all day in summer) from good value doorstep sandwiches to Sun roasts, upstairs harbour-view lounge with armchairs and sofas one end; lots of pub games, piped music, TV, busy with young people evenings – esp Fri/Sat for live music; children welcome, plenty of waterside picnic-sets, open all day *(Callum and Letitia Smith-Burnett, David Crook, Patrick Hancock, Gene and Kitty Rankin, LYM, the Didler, Barry Collett, Dr and Mrs M E Wilson)*

☆ *Seven Stars* [The Moor (centre)]: Classic unchanging and unsmart 17th-c local with long-serving and entertaining vicar-landlord, no gimmicks (nor machines or mobile phones), warm welcome, Bass, Sharps and Skinners tapped from the cask, home-made rolls, chatty regulars, big key-ring collection, quiet back snug; corridor hatch serving tables on prime-site roadside courtyard *(Patrick Hancock,*

Kevin Thorpe, the Didler, Giles and Annie Francis, BB, Dr and Mrs M E Wilson)

FLUSHING [SW8033]

Royal Standard [off A393 at Penryn (or foot ferry from Falmouth); St Peters Hill]: Trim waterfront local with veteran welcoming landlord, plenty of genuine characters, great views to Falmouth from front terrace, neat bar with pink plush and copper, alcove with pool and darts, simple well cooked food inc good baked potatoes, home-made pasties and fruit pies, well kept Bass and Sharps Doom Bar; outside gents' *(Di and Mike Gillam, the Didler)*

Seven Stars [Trefusis Rd]: Particularly well kept Skinners ales, welcoming local atmosphere, enjoyable food in bar and separate dining room, darts and pool; outside gents'; great views of Falmouth from out in front *(Steve Mills)*

FOWEY [SX1252]

☆ *Galleon* [Fore St; from centre follow Car Ferry signs]: Superb spot overlooking harbour and estuary, spotless solid pine and modern nautical décor with lots of wood, dining areas off, well kept and priced Flowers IPA, Sharps Cornish Coaster and a guest beer, generous good value food from good sandwiches to plenty of fish, fast service; pool, jazz Sun lunchtime, children welcome, disabled facilities, tables out on attractive extended waterside terrace and in sheltered courtyard with covered heated area, good estuary-view bedrooms *(Jim and Maggie Cowell, Nick Lawless, BB, Michael Lamm, Ann and Bob Westbrook)*

☆ *King of Prussia* [Town Quay]: Handsome quayside building under new management, good welcoming service, good food inc splendid local seafood and meats in side family food bar and new restaurant concentrating on local produce, large neat upstairs bar with bay windows looking over harbour to Polruan, St Austell ales, sensibly priced wines; may be piped music, occasional live; seats outside, open all day at least in summer, pleasant bedrooms *(Patrick Hancock, Geoff Pidoux, LYM, Martin and Karen Wake, Sue Demont, Tim Barrow, Jodie Phillips)*

Lugger [Fore St]: Spotless and interesting family-friendly pub with good mix of locals and visitors in unpretentious bar, comfortable small candlelit dining area, wide choice of good generous food inc lots of seafood, cheap well kept St Austell ales, friendly service, big waterfront mural; piped music; pavement tables, bedrooms *(BB, Nick Lawless, Jim and Maggie Cowell, the Didler, Alan Sutton)*

☆ *Ship* [Trafalgar Sq]: Friendly, clean and tidy local, good choice of good value generous food from sandwiches up inc fine local seafood, lots of sea pictures, coal fire, pool/darts room, family dining room with big stained-glass window, well kept St Austell beers; juke box or piped music, small TV for sports; dogs allowed, old-fashioned bedrooms, some oak-panelled *(Nick Lawless, LYM, Patrick Hancock, Alan Sutton)*

GOLANT [SX1155]

☆ *Fishermans Arms* [Fore St (B3269)]: Bustling partly flagstoned waterside local with lovely views across River Fowey from front bar and terrace, good value generous home-made standard food from sandwiches to curry specials and fresh local fish, all day in summer (cl Sun afternoon), well kept Sharps Doom Bar and Ushers Best, good wines by the glass, friendly service (can slow on busy days), log fire, interesting pictures, fancy goldfish, back family room; piano, TV, may be piped radio; pleasant garden *(BB, Tim and Rosemary Wells, Mrs M Granville-Edge, Martin and Karen Wake, the Didler, B and M Kendall, Charles and Pauline Stride)*

GOLDSITHNEY [SW5430]

☆ *Crown* [B3280]: Roomy and comfortable local with good value food inc local fresh fish and bargain Thurs and Sun lunches, well kept St Austell ales, decent house wines, good friendly service, L-shaped beamed bar and small attractive no smoking dining room; pretty sun-trap glass-roofed front loggia and pavement tables, masses of hanging baskets *(Dr Phil Putwain)*

GOONHAVERN [SW7853]

New Inn [A3075 S of Newquay]: Neatly kept roadside village pub with generous lunchtime food inc popular Sun carvery in three good value helping sizes, good choice of wines and beers, friendly service; tables and play area outside, huge car park *(Mick and Moira Brummell, Klaus and Elizabeth Leist)*

GORRAN CHURCHTOWN [SW9942]

Barley Sheaf [follow Gorran Haven signs from Mevagissey]: Welcoming old pub, reputedly haunted but extensively modernised, central servery for three areas, back pool room, long-serving landlord, good food choice in bar and restaurant, real ales such as Flowers IPA and Original, Skinners Betty Stogs and Sharps Doom Bar, good range of ciders; children welcome, disabled facilities, garden with summer barbecues, nice village *(Christopher Wright)*

GORRAN HAVEN [SX0141]

☆ *Llawnroc* [Chute Lane]: Comfortable and relaxed family-friendly granite hotel, good choice of home-made food inc local fish and good value Sun lunch in expanded dining area, well kept Sharps Doom Bar and a bargain beer brewed for the pub, good wine selection; sunny tables in good-sized garden overlooking the cove and quiet fishing village, barbecues, good value bedroom block, open all day *(Christopher Wright)*

GUNNISLAKE [SX4371]

☆ *Rising Sun* [lower Calstock Rd, just S of village]: Cosy and attractive 17th-c two-room pub with red plush seats, beams, stripped stone, panelling and flagstones, lots of china, brasses and prints, log fires, good straightforward food using seasonal produce inc good value Sun lunch, cheerful service, well kept Bass, Sharps Cornish Coaster and Wills Resolve and Skinners Betty Stogs, decent wine choice; pleasant valley views from charming terraced garden with play area *(Alan and Paula McCully, Betty Petheram, DAV, BB)*

GWEEK [SW7026]

Gweek Inn [back roads E of Helston]: Cheerful family chain pub, large comfortable open-plan low-ceilinged bar with woodburner, quick good-humoured service, well kept Greene King Old Speckled Hen, John Smiths and Wadworths 6X, decent wines, reasonably priced standard food inc good puddings choice, decent wines, lots of motoring trophies (enthusiast licensees), bright and roomy back restaurant; live music Fri, children welcome, tables on grass (safe for children), summer kiosk with all-day snacks, short walk from seal sanctuary *(Mick and Moira Brummell)*

HARROWBARROW [SX4069]

☆ *Cross House* [off A390 E of Callington; School Rd – over towards Metherell]: Substantial stone building, spreading carpeted bar with some booth seating, cushioned wall seats and stools around pub tables, newish family doing decent pubby bar food, well kept Sharps Wills Resolve and Cornish Coaster and Skinners Betty Stogs, friendly service, good coal fire, darts area, no smoking restaurant; children welcome, plenty of picnic-sets out on good-sized lawn, good play area *(DAV, BB)*

HELSTON [SW6527]

☆ *Blue Anchor* [Coinagehall St]: 15th-c basic thatched local, very popular for the Spingo IPA, Middle and specials they still brew in their ancient brewhouse; quaint rooms off corridor, flagstones, stripped stone, low beams and simple old-fashioned furniture, traditional games, family room, cheap lunchtime food (if not, they let you bring your own); seats out behind, bedrooms, open all day *(Andrea Rampley, Roger and Jenny Huggins, Patrick Hancock, Rona Murdoch, LYM, Tom McLean, the Didler)*

HESSENFORD [SX3057]

Copley Arms [A387 Looe—Torpoint]: Emphasis on good food from sandwiches, baguettes and baked potatoes to popular Sun lunch and restaurant dishes using local produce in modernised linked areas, well kept St Austell ales, nice wine choice, variety of teas and coffee, log fires, one part with sofas and easy chairs; piped music, dogs allowed in one small area, big plain family room; sizeable and attractive streamside garden and terrace (but by road), play area, bedrooms *(Gill and Keith Croxton, S P Watkin, P A Taylor)*

KINGSAND [SX4350]

☆ *Halfway House* [Fore St, towards Cawsand]: Attractive well sited inn popular with locals, simple mildly Victorian bar rambling around huge central fireplace, low ceilings and soft lighting, well kept Courage Best, Marstons Pedigree and Sharps Doom Bar, decent wines, bar food, morning coffee, perhaps summer afternoon teas, no smoking restaurant; children and dogs welcome, picturesque village, marvellous walks, bedrooms, open all day in summer *(Mrs Sylvia Elcoate, Allegra Taylor, B Forster, Chris Pelley, Richard and*

Anne Ansell, Charles and Pauline Stride, Geoff Calcott, LYM)

Rising Sun [The Green]: Welcoming civilised local, quite smart, with generous food from sandwiches and pasties to good local seafood, well kept Courage Best, Sharps Eden and Skinners Cornish Knocker, good sensibly priced wine choice, good coffee, open fire, fishing gear; subtle piped music, popular live music nights; on one of Cornwall's best walks *(S P Watkin, P A Taylor)*

LAMORNA [SW4424]

☆ *Lamorna Wink* [off B3315 SW of Penzance]: Unspoilt no-frills country local short stroll above pretty cove, with good coast walks; good collection of warship mementoes, sea photographs, nautical brassware and hats, well kept Sharps Own and Doom Bar and Skinners Cornish Knocker, nice house wine, enormous sandwich platters and other simple lunchtime food from homely kitchen area (may not be available out of season), coal fire, pool table, books and perhaps lots of local produce for sale; children in eating area, picnic-sets outside, open all day in summer *(Adrian Johnson, LYM, David Crook)*

LANNER [SW7240]

☆ *Fox & Hounds* [Comford; A393/B3298]: Relaxed and rambling low-beamed pub, stripped stone and dark panelling, high-backed settles and cottagey chairs on flagstones, warm fires, good choice of generous reasonably priced food from sandwiches and baguettes up, well kept St Austell ales tapped from the cask, decent house wines, good service, children welcome in no smoking dining room; pub games, dogs allowed in bar, piped music; great floral displays in front, neat back garden with pond and play area, open all day wknds *(Charles Gysin, Paul and Shirley White, LYM)*

LAUNCESTON [SX3384]

White Horse [Newport Sq/Dutson Rd]: Limited choice of good if not cheap food, well kept beers, good wines *(DAV)*

LELANT [SW5437]

Badger [village signed off A30 W of Hayle; Fore St]: Spaciously extended dining pub with wide range of enjoyable food from sandwiches to fresh fish and OAP lunches, well kept St Austell ales, cheerful efficient service, attractive softly lit modern L-shaped interior, partly no smoking, with panelled recesses, some high-backed settles, airy back conservatory; may be piped music; children welcome, good value pretty bedrooms, wonderful breakfast *(Callum and Letitia Smith-Burnett, A P Seymour)*

☆ *Old Quay House* [Griggs Quay, Lelant Saltings; A3047/B3301 S of village]: Large neatly kept modern pub in marvellous spot overlooking bird sanctuary estuary, good value wholesome usual food, real ales, good service, dining area off open-plan bar, children allowed upstairs; garden tables, decent motel-type bedrooms *(J V Dadswell, Alan Bowker, Mel Smith)*

LERRYN [SX1457]

Ship [signed off A390 in Lostwithiel; Fore St]:

Lovely spot especially when tide's in, near famous stepping-stones and three well signed waterside walks, picnic-sets and pretty play area outside; well kept ales such as Bass, Skinners and Sharps Eden, local farm cider, good wines, fruit wines and malt whiskies, wide food choice using local produce from pasties and good sandwiches up inc popular Sun carvery, no smoking area, huge woodburner, attractive adults-only dining conservatory (booked quickly evenings and wknds), games room with pool; dogs on leads and children welcome, bedrooms in adjoining building *(David Crook, LYM, Ann and Bob Westbrook, Clive and Vivienne Locks, Richard and Jean Phillips, A P Seymour)*

LIZARD [SW7012]

☆ *Top House* [A3083]: Spotless well run pub in same friendly helpful family for over 40 years, lots of interesting local sea pictures, fine shipwreck relics and serpentine craftwork (note the handpumps) in neat bar with well kept ales such as Flowers IPA, Sharps Doom Bar and Wadworths 6X, reasonably priced wines, roaring log fire, generous food (particularly popular with older people) inc good crab sandwiches, big no smoking area, no piped music (occasional live); tucked-away fruit machine, darts, pool; dogs welcome, tables on sheltered terrace, interesting nearby serpentine shop, and handy for Goonhilly *(A and B D Craig, Pat and Robert Watt, BB, B Pike, Paul and Shirley White, J K and S M Miln)*

LUDGVAN [SW5033]

☆ *White Hart* [off A30 Penzance—Hayle at Crowlas]: Friendly, unpretentious and well worn in 19th-c pub with considerable unspoilt appeal, great atmosphere in small beamed rooms, paraffin lamps, masses of mugs, jugs and pictures, rugs on bare boards, two big blazing woodburners, well kept Bass, Flowers IPA and Marstons Pedigree tapped from the cask, sensibly priced home cooking (not Mon evenings exc high season) from sandwiches up, no piped music; no high chairs *(the Didler, Pat and Roger Fereday, Andrea Rampley, Callum and Letitia Smith-Burnett, Paul and Shirley White, LYM)*

LUXULYAN [SX0458]

Kings Arms [Bridges]: Friendly open-plan village pub by bridge, simple décor with light oak fittings and beams, friendly helpful staff, good range of good value home-made food, well kept St Austell ales, back games area with pool; tables on small front terrace and in back garden, handy for Eden Project, open all day *(Steve Felstead)*

MANACCAN [SW7624]

☆ *New Inn* [down hill signed to Gillan and St Keverne]: Thatched village pub in attractive setting above sea, not far from Helford or St Anthony; bar with beam and plank ceiling, traditional built-in wall seats, individually chosen chairs, Flowers IPA and Sharps Doom Bar, bar food (may take a time when busy), cribbage, dominoes; children and dogs welcome, picnic-sets in rose-filled garden *(John Hale, Ian and Liz Rispin, LYM,*

Susie Symes, Andrea Rampley, the Didler, Ned Kelly)

MARAZION [SW5130]

Godolphin Arms [West End]: Redeveloped hotel with great views across beach and Mounts Bay towards St Michael's Mount, good food, well kept ales inc Sharps, good service, comfortable and civilised upper lounge bar and no smoking dining room, family room with play area, informal lower bar, roomy terrace; good carefully decorated bedrooms, most with sea view *(Mel Smith)*

Kings Arms [The Square]: Enjoyable freshly made food cooked to order, well kept real ale, reasonable prices and good friendly service *(Mr and Mrs D Bullman)*

MARHAMCHURCH [SS2203]

☆ *Bullers Arms*: Oak beams and settles in pleasant rambling L-shaped bar, good choice of well prepared food and of well kept local and national beers, decent wine by the glass, obliging staff, darts in flagstoned back part, restaurant; children welcome; tables and play area in sizeable garden, a mile's walk to the sea, bedrooms *(LYM, Robert Wivell)*

MAWNAN SMITH [SW7728]

☆ *Red Lion* [W of Falmouth, off former B3291 Penryn—Gweek; The Square]: Attractive old thatched pub with open-view kitchen doing wide choice of enjoyable food inc seafood (should book summer evening), friendly helpful service, lots of wines by the glass, well kept real ales, good coffee, fresh flowers, dark woodwork, pictures, plates and bric-a-brac in cosy softly lit linked beamed rooms inc back no smoking area; piped music, live Sat, TV; children welcome, handy for Glendurgan and Trebah Gardens *(Roger Fox, LYM, Cathy Robinson, Ed Coombe)*

MEVAGISSEY [SX0145]

☆ *Fountain* [Cliff St, down alley by Post Office]: Unpretentious and interesting fishermen's pub, low beams, slate floor and some stripped stone, well kept St Austell ales, lovely coal fire, lots of old local pictures, small fish tank, good value simple bar food, good fish in upstairs evening restaurant, back locals' bar with glass-topped cellar and pool, games machine and sports TV); occasional live music; dogs welcome, bedrooms, pretty frontage, open all day *(Ted George, B and M Kendall, J V Dadswell, Gill and Tony Morriss, Mayur Shah, the Didler, BB, David Crook, Christopher Wright, J M Tansey)*

Ship [Fore St, nr harbour]: Lively 16th-c pub with interesting alcove areas in big open-plan bar, low ceilings, flagstones, nice nautical décor, open fire, friendly helpful staff, good range of generous quickly served food inc good crab sandwiches, full St Austell range kept well; games machines, piped music, occasional live; comfortable bedrooms, open all day *(DF, NF, Mrs Maricar Jagger, Mayur Shah, Christopher Wright)*

MORWENSTOW [SS2015]

☆ *Bush* [signed off A39 N of Kilkhampton; Crosstown]: One of Britain's most ancient pubs, beguiling, individual and unchanging;

part Saxon, with serpentine Celtic basin in one wall, ancient built-in settles, beams and flagstones, and big stone fireplace, upper bar with interesting bric-a-brac, well kept St Austell HSD tapped from the cask, Inch's cider, friendly veteran landlady and staff, darts, no piped music; limited lunchtime food (not Sun), no children or dogs, seats out in yard; lovely setting, interesting village church with good nearby teashop, great cliff walks; cl Mon in winter *(Nigel Long, the Didler, LYM, Anthony Longden)*

MOUSEHOLE [SW4626]

☆ *Ship* [Harbourside]: Bustling harbourside local, the heart of the village, with beams, panelling, flagstones and open fire, well kept St Austell ales, good-natured service; prominent TV and machines in one part, restaurant area – busy early evening with families eating; children and dogs welcome, plastic glasses for beach drinks, nice bedrooms, open all day *(Andrea Rampley, Geoff Marston, LYM, Ian and Liz Rispin, Dr R A Smye, Gill and Tony Morriss, Mike and Heather Watson, Barry and Anne, Sue Demont, Tim Barrow, Stuart Turner, Paul and Shirley White)*

MYLOR BRIDGE [SW8036]

Lemon Arms [Lemon Hill]: Friendly traditional village pub, three well kept St Austell ales, good value mainly blackboard food; handy for start or finish of very pretty walk *(J M Tansey)*

NEWLYN [SW4629]

Tolcarne [Tolcarne Pl]: Clean and well kept traditional 17th-c pub, wide choice of good value home-made food inc good seafood and vegetarian choice, friendly staff, well kept Greene King Old Speckled Hen and Sharps Doom Bar; terrace by sea wall, good parking – useful here *(Mick and Moira Brummell, Derek and Heather Manning)*

NEWQUAY [SW8061]

☆ *Fort* [Fore St]: Massive recently built pub in magnificent setting high above surfing beach and small harbour, decent food all day from sandwiches, hot baguettes and baked potatoes up through the full price range, open-plan areas well divided by balustrades and surviving fragments of former harbourmaster's house, good solid furnishings from country kitchen to button-back settees, soft lighting and one panelled area, friendly service, well kept St Austell HSD and Tribute, games area with two well lit pool tables, excellent indoor play area; great views from long glass-walled side section and from sizeable garden with terrace and play areas, good bedrooms, open all day *(BB, Steve Kirby)*

Lewinnick Lodge [Pentire headland, off Pentire Rd]: Modern bar/restaurant built into the bluff above the sea – an outstanding spot, with big picture windows for the terrific views; furnished in open uncluttered style, with good interesting if not cheap food, friendly staff, good outside seating *(Brian Skelcher, Andy Sinden, Louise Harrington)*

NORTH HILL [SX2776]

Racehorse [North Hill, off B3254 Launceston—Liskeard]: Pleasantly reworked

two-bar beamed pub (once the gabled village school) with a careful balance between eating and drinking, friendly owners, good sensibly priced food in bar and restaurant, attentive staff, several Sharps real ales, two coal fires; views from tables out on decking *(David C West, Peter Stanning, John and Sarah Perry)*

PADSTOW [SW9175]

Golden Lion [Lanadwell St]: Friendly black-beamed front bar, high-raftered back lounge with plush banquettes against ancient white stone walls, cheerful local bustle, reasonably priced simple bar lunches (not Sat if landlord playing football) inc very promptly served good crab and other sandwiches, evening steaks and fresh seafood, well kept Bass, Sharps Doom Bar and Skinners, friendly service, coal fire; pool in family area, piped music or juke box, fruit machines; terrace tables, bedrooms, open all day *(Michael Butler, the Didler, BB, Michael B Griffith, Chris and Susie Cammack)*

Harbour Inn [Strand St]: Attractive harbourside pub, long room with nautical bric-a-brac, front area with comfy sofas, well kept St Austell beers, enjoyable food (may be a wait), family room *(Kevin Blake)*

☆ *London* [Llanadwell St]: Down-to-earth fishermen's local with flower-filled façade, lots of pictures and nautical memorabilia, buoyant atmosphere, St Austell beers, decent choice of malt whiskies, wknd lunchtime bar food inc good if pricey crab sandwiches, fresh local fish, more elaborate evening choice (small bar dining area – get there early for a table), great real fire; games machines but no piped music – home-grown live music Sun night; dogs welcome in bar, open all day, bedrooms good value *(LYM, Gordon Briggs, Alan Sadler, Chris and Susie Cammack, Kevin Blake)*

Old Custom House [South Quay]: Large airy open-plan seaside bar, well divided, with rustic décor and cosy corners, bare boards, raised section, big family area and conservatory, well kept St Austell ales, good food choice from sandwiches and baguettes up, adjoining fish restaurant, good service, pool; big-screen TV, some live music; good spot by harbour, open all day, attractive sea-view bedrooms *(BB, Chris and Susie Cammack, Ted George, Chris Glasson)*

Old Ship [Mill Sq, just off North Quay/Broad St]: Cheery mix of locals and visitors in hotel's bustling open-plan bar with well kept St Austell ales, good range of reasonably priced food from sandwiches to plenty of fresh fish, upstairs restaurant; back games room with SkyTV, may be piped radio, good live music Fri/Sat; tables in heated front courtyard tucked away just off harbour, open all day from breakfast on at least in summer, 15 bedrooms *(George Atkinson, BB, D W Stokes, Robert Wivell)*

Shipwrights [North Quay; aka the Blue Lobster]: Big low-ceilinged quayside bar, stripped brick, lots of wood, flagstones, lobster pots and nets, quick popular food, St Austell ales, friendly service, upstairs restaurant; busy with young people evenings; a few tables out by water (Mrs Sylvia Elcoate, BB, Paul and Shirley White, D W Stokes, Brian Skelcher)

PAUL [SW4627]

☆ *Kings Arms*: Lively and appealing beamed local opp church, a true cornish pub, with friendly licensees, well kept St Austell ales, enjoyable sensibly priced food; bedrooms (Dr R A Smye, Stuart Turner, Giles and Annie Francis, J and D Waters)

PENDEEN [SW3834]

North: Small, friendly and interesting, with tin-mining memorabilia, well kept St Austell ales, food inc good ploughman's and curries; bedrooms (Peter Salmon, Sheila Newbury)

PENDOGGETT [SX0279]

☆ *Cornish Arms* [B3314]: Picturesque old coaching inn doing well under welcoming helpful new licensees, above-average food from good soup and sandwiches to fresh fish and splendid steaks, well kept St Austell ales, good wines by the glass, traditional oak settles on civilised front bar's handsome polished slate floor, fine prints, comfortably spaced tables in small dining room, back locals' bar with woodburner, pool, TV and piped music (live Sat); provision for children, terrace with distant sea view, open all day, bedrooms (LYM, Mick and Moira Brummell, M A Borthwick, Gloria Bax)

PENELEWEY [SW8240]

☆ *Punch Bowl & Ladle* [B3289]: Well run thatched dining pub in picturesque setting handy for Trelissick Gardens, comfortable olde-worlde bar with big settees, rustic bric-a-brac, several room areas, wide choice of good value generous food from good sandwiches up (Thurs very popular with elderly lunchers), children's helpings, efficient helpful service, St Austell ales, good wine choice; unobtrusive piped music; children and dogs on leads welcome, small back sun terrace, open all day summer (LYM, Simon Cottrell, Paul and Shirley White, Mick and Moira Brummell, Gill and Keith Croxton, Ian and Celia Abbott)

PENTEWAN [SX0147]

Trewhiddle Inn [Trewhiddle Holiday Estate, B3273 towards St Austell]: Large open-plan pub on touring caravan park, popular daily carvery and other food inc take-away pizzas, Sharps Doom Bar and Eden and a guest beer such as St Austell Trelawny, Thatcher's farm cider, several wines by the glass (Jane and Mark Hooper)

PENZANCE [SW4730]

☆ *Admiral Benbow* [Chapel St]: Well run pub with elaborately nautical décor in interesting maze of areas, cosy corners, friendly staff and welcoming atmosphere, good value above-average food inc local fish, well kept ales such as Sharps, Skinners and St Austell, decent wines, downstairs restaurant, upper floor with pool, juke box and pleasant view from back room; children allowed, open all day summer (LYM, Louise Symons, Gordon Tong, Catherine Pitt)

Crown [Victoria Sq]: Fresh and bright, under charming new licensees, with sofa and open fire in small back candlelit snug, large antique mirror, Otter and a guest beer such as Ales of Scilly; gentle piped jazz (Catherine Pitt)

☆ *Dolphin* [The Barbican; Newlyn road, opp harbour after swing-bridge]: Roomy and welcoming, part old-fashioned pub and part bistro, with attractive nautical décor, good harbour views, good value food from baguettes to steaks and fresh local fish (landlady's husband is a fisherman), well kept St Austell ales, generous wine glasses, helpful service, great fireplace, dining area a few steps down, cosy family room; big pool room with juke box etc, no obvious nearby parking; pavement picnic-sets, open all day (the Didler, LYM, Michael and Alison Sandy, Anne Morris, Valerie Baker)

☆ *Globe & Ale House* [Queen St]: Well kept Bass, Sharps Own and Skinners Betty Stogs and Bettys Mild with guest beers, some tapped from the cask, in small low-ceilinged tavern, lots of old pictures and artefacts, bare boards and dim lighting, enthusiastic helpful landlord, enjoyable simple prompt food; TV sports (the Didler, Catherine Pitt)

Navy [Queen St]: Interesting historic house with atmosphere, new chef/landlord putting emphasis on good restaurany food (sandwiches, ploughman's and light dishes too, and brunch from 10am), Batemans and Sharps Doom Bar, decent choice of wines, reasonable prices, pleasant service and setting (Brian and Genie Smart, Anne Morris)

Pirate [Alverton]: Reasonably priced food (not Sun evening), changing real ales usually from Cornwall, live music Sat; picnic-sets in good-sized sloping garden with barbecues and good play area, two bedrooms with own bathrooms (anon)

PERRANARWORTHAL [SW7738]

☆ *Norway* [A39 Truro—Penryn]: Large pub revitalised under new licensees, quietly efficient helpful service, typical food choice using local produce, all-day Sun carvery, three St Austell real ales, good wine choice, half a dozen linked areas, beams hung with farm tools, lots of prints and rustic bric-a-brac, old-style wooden seating and big tables on slate flagstones, open fires; tables outside, open all day (BB, Mr and Mrs Ian Davidson, Andy Sinden, Louise Harrington, David Crook, Mark Flynn)

PERRANUTHNOE [SW5329]

☆ *Victoria* [signed off A394 Penzance—Helston]: Comfortable and relaxed L-shaped pub, cosy low-beamed bar, some stripped stonework and no smoking part, coastal and wreck photographs, good food from freshly baked lunchtime baguettes to good venison, interesting evening specials, friendly efficient service, well kept ales such as Bass and Sharps Doom Bar, nice wine choice, neat coal fire, second good-sized no smoking room useful for families; quiet piped music; picnic-sets in sheltered pretty sunken garden, good bedrooms, handy for Mounts Bay (Peter Salmon, LYM, Eileen Goddard)

PHILLEIGH [SW8739]

Roseland [off A3078 NE of St Mawes]: Beautifully tranquil classic country pub, long a favourite both with readers and with us, with plenty of character esp in lower flagstoned back bar, open fires and old local photographs, well kept Bass, Greene King Old Speckled Hen, Ringwood Best and Sharps Doom Bar, good wines by the glass, dominoes and cribbage, simple restaurant, and pretty front courtyard; though many readers have still found it good, over the last year there have been quite a few dissenters (particularly on the price/quality equation), and talk of a possible sale – we look forward to it recovering its former unbroken record of approval; dogs and children welcome, bedrooms, open all day summer *(LYM)*

POLGOOTH [SW9950]

☆ *Polgooth Inn* [well signed off A390 W of St Austell; Ricketts Lane]: Popular and attractive country pub with well kept St Austell ales, good wine choice, efficient friendly service, enjoyable food from good value generous sandwiches to some interesting modern dishes (only roasts on Sun), children's helpings, good big family room and (up steps) outside play area; fills quickly in summer (handy for nearby caravan parks), eating area around biggish bar (can be smoky); tables out on grass, pretty countryside *(LYM, Geoff Ziola, Mark Flynn, Jane and Mark Hooper, Christopher Wright)*

POLMEAR [SX0853]

☆ *Ship* [A3082 Par—Fowey]: Good friendly atmosphere, chatty locals and welcoming uniformed staff, good straightforward food using fresh produce from sandwiches and baked potatoes to steaks and stir fries, Fullers London Pride, Marstons Pedigree and guests such as Sharps Doom Bar and Shepherd Neame Spitfire, farm cider, good choice of other drinks, roomy bar with nice shipping photographs, lots of hanging whisky-water jugs and big stove, back dining area still in keeping with dark furniture, big conservatory opening to tables in sizeable gardens (one with summer bandstand); nr holiday camps *(Mrs Maricar Jagger, Bob and Pam Breens)*

POLPERRO [SX2051]

☆ *Blue Peter* [Quay Rd]: Dark and cosy, in great setting up narrow steps above harbour; unpretentious little low-beamed wood-floored local, well kept Sharps Doom Bar and Cornish Coaster, St Austell and guest beers, farm cider, quick friendly service, log fire, basic bar food, nautical memorabilia, traditional games, family area upstairs with video game; can get crowded, piped music, may be live Sat; dogs and children welcome, some seats outside, open all day *(Mrs Yvette Bateman, LYM, the Didler, Geoff Calcott)*

☆ *Old Mill House* [Mill Hill; bear right approaching harbour]: Cheery bar with stripped pine, bare boards and flagstones, nautical décor, big log fireplace, four or five well kept Sharps and other ales, decent bar food inc low-priced crab baguettes, no smoking dining room; quiz nights, games area

with darts and pool, TV, piped music (some live), no nearby parking; children in eating areas, dogs in bar, picnic-sets out in streamside garden, open all day *(Michael Butler, George Atkinson, LYM, Gene and Kitty Rankin, Geoff Calcott)*

☆ *Three Pilchards* [Quay Rd]: Welcoming fishermen's local behind the fish quay, good value food from baguettes to nicely cooked local fish and seafood, well kept real ales, low beams, lots of black woodwork, dim lighting, simple furnishings, open fire in big stone fireplace, regulars' photographs; piped music, can get very busy; tables on upper terrace (no sea view) up steep steps, open all day *(Jim Abbott, Mrs Yvette Bateman, Edward Leetham, Prof and Mrs Tony Palmer, BB)*

POLRUAN [SX1250]

Russell [West St]: Fishermen's local, lively yet relaxing, with no smoking section in large tidy bar, sensibly priced straightforward food using local produce, well kept St Austell beers, friendly staff, log fire and interesting photographs; lovely hanging baskets *(Tim and Rosemary Wells, Nick Lawless)*

PORT ISAAC [SW9980]

☆ *Golden Lion* [Fore Street]: It's the position that draws here, with window seats and terrace looking down on rocky harbour and lifeboat slip far below; simply furnished rooms, open fire in back one, local atmosphere, straightforward bar food, well kept St Austell Tinners, HSD and Tribute, darts, dominoes, cribbage; piped music, fruit machine; children in eating areas, open all day *(LYM, Simon Collett-Jones, Mrs M Granville-Edge, Mr and Mrs John Taylor, the Didler, Michael Butler, Michael H Legge)*

PORTHLEVEN [SW6225]

Harbour Inn [Commercial Rd]: Large well looked-after pub/hotel in outstanding setting, tables out on big quayside terrace; good value simple food in impressive dining area off expansive lounge and bar, quick service, well kept St Austell ales, comprehensive wine list, restaurant; decent bedrooms, some with harbour view, good breakfast *(Sue Demont, Tim Barrow, David and Nina Pugsley)*

PORTLOE [SW9339]

☆ *Ship*: Comfortable, bright and friendly L-shaped local, masses of interesting nautical and local memorabilia and photographs, sensibly priced generous food from basic lunchtime sandwiches to good local seafood, beef and veg, three well kept St Austell ales, decent wines, happy staff; piped music; sheltered and attractive streamside picnic-sets over road, pretty fishing village with lovely cove and coast path above, open all day Fri-Sun in summer *(BB, Jenny and Brian Seller, Derek and Gillian Henshaw, Mark Flynn, Christopher Wright)*

PORTMELLON COVE [SX0143]

☆ *Rising Sun* [just S of Mevagissey]: Particularly good food from interesting bar snacks (inc home-made pork pies and cakes) to upmarket dishes in pleasant evening restaurant, friendly flagstoned bar with unusual open fire, well kept changing ales such as Adnams and Sharps, decent largely new world wines, faultless service, charming cool plant-filled conservatory, big upper family/games room (no children after 6pm); a few tables outside, fine spot overlooking quiet sandy cove *(BB, Tom Gondris, M J Bourke, Mrs M Granville-Edge, Jane and Mark Hooper)*

PORTREATH [SW6545]

Basset Arms [Tregea Terr]: Reliable village pub at end of Mineral Tramways cycle path to Devoran, enjoyable food inc fresh fish and good value Sun lunch in comfortable bar, polite friendly service, well kept beers inc Sharps Doom Bar, no smoking dining room and big bright conservatory; unobtrusive piped music; picnic-sets on sunny terrace and grass with play area, short stroll from beach, open all day Sun and summer *(Brian Skelcher, David Crook, Lawrence Pearse, Mick and Moira Brummell)*

PORTSCATHO [SW8735]

☆ *Plume of Feathers* [The Square]: Comfortable and cheerful largely stripped stone pub in pretty fishing village, sea-related bric-a-brac in linked room areas, side locals' bar (can be very lively evenings), well kept St Austell and other ales, good staff, pubby bar food inc bargain Fri fish night and off-season two-for-one deals Mon-Weds, restaurant; very popular with summer visitors but perhaps at its best with warm local atmosphere out of season; dogs welcome, open all day in summer (and other times if busy) *(Jenny and Brian Seller, LYM, Kevin Thorpe, Mark Flynn, Paul and Shirley White)*

PRAZE AN BEEBLE [SW6336]

St Aubyn Arms [The Square]: Simple country local, well kept Ring o' Bells, Sharps and Skinners, wide choice of good value food inc lunchtime bargains (particularly for OAPs) and Fri steak specials, purple décor and some interesting decorations, two restaurants, one upstairs; public bar with games; piped music; children warmly welcomed, picnic-sets in large attractive garden, perhaps with marquee *(Guy Vowles, Tony and Maggie Harwood, David M Cundy, Mark Flynn)*

REDRUTH [SW6842]

☆ *Tricky Dickys* [Tolgus Mount; OS Sheet 203 map ref 686427]: Spotless and well run modern conversion of isolated former tin-mine smithy, dark inside, with forge bellows, painting of how it might have looked; buoyant atmosphere, well kept Ring o' Bells Bodmin Boar and Sharps Own and Doom Bar, good wines and spirits choice, good value food, friendly staff, immaculate lavatories; piped music, games machines; children welcome, partly covered terrace with barbecues, jazz Tues and Thurs, quiz alternate Suns; bedroom block, squash and fitness centre *(Mick and Moira Brummell, Alan Bowker)*

ROCHE [SW9860]

Rock [Fore St]: Roomy originally 14th-c pub with welcoming new management, wide choice of enjoyable food using mainly local produce

from open kitchen in dining and restaurant areas, popular Sun carvery, well kept real ales, good atmosphere *(Peter Yorke)*

RUAN LANIHORNE [SW8942]

☆ *Kings Head* [off A3078]: Cheerful and popular new landlady in attractive beamed pub opp fine old church, comfortable and interesting, with sofa by good log fire in front bar, pleasant family room, some unusual dishes as well as old favourites using local ingredients, well kept ales inc ones brewed for the pub by Sharps and Skinners, decent wines, efficient service, no smoking eating area with plenty to look at; piped music, traditional games – for children too; suntrap sunken garden, views over the Fal estuary, cl Mon lunchtime (and Mon evening in winter) *(Mr and Mrs P Hill, LYM, D J Elliott, Kevin Thorpe, Jane and Mark Hooper, Basil and Sylvia Walden, Gordon Stevenson)*

SCORRIER [SW7244]

Fox & Hounds [B3298, off A30 just outside Redruth]: Long partly panelled well divided bar, big log or coal fires each end, red plush banquettes, hunting prints, stripped stonework and creaky joists, large no smoking section, wide choice of generous food, well kept Sharps Doom Bar; unobtrusive piped music; picnic-sets out in front, handy for Portreath—Devoran cycle trail *(Paul and Shirley White, LYM)*

SLADESBRIDGE [SX0171]

Slades House: Neatly kept and friendly, with decent pub food, good service, well kept St Austell ales, no smoking dining area; children welcome *(R M Corlett)*

ST BLAZEY [SX0654]

Cornish Arms [Church St]: Neatly furnished local, well kept St Austell ales and popular food from generous sandwiches and snacks up, games area with pool; bedrooms *(Jennifer Banks)*

ST BREWARD [SX0977]

☆ *Old Inn* [off B3266 S of Camelford; Churchtown]: Broad slate flagstones, low oak beams, stripped stonework, two massive granite fireplaces dating from 11th c, straightforward bar food, Bass and Sharps Doom Bar and Eden, lots of wines by the glass, sensibly placed darts, roomy no smoking extended restaurant with tables out on deck; piped music, fruit machine; provision for dogs and children, moorland behind (cattle and sheep wander freely into the village), open all day Fri-Sun and summer *(Guy Vowles, Rona Murdoch, David Crook, Simon Collett-Jones, Mick and Moira Brummell, the Didler, Andrea Rampley, A and B D Craig, Jacquie and Jim Jones, LYM, Liz and Tony Colman)*

ST DOMINICK [SX4067]

☆ *Who'd Have Thought It* [off A388 S of Callington]: Large comfortable country pub with plenty of individuality and superb views of Tamar, esp from no smoking conservatory; plush lounge areas with antique bric-a-brac and open fires (not always lit), prompt service, Sharps Doom Bar and Skinners Betty Stogs, great range of wines by the glass, usual food from sandwiches and baked potatoes to steaks, partly no smoking dining area; dogs allowed in public bar, garden tables, handy for Cotehele (NT) *(Ted George, Pamela and Merlyn Horswell, LYM, Mary Ellen Cummings, Roger Martin, Dennis Jenkin)*

ST EWE [SW9746]

☆ *Crown* [off B3287]: Attractive cottagey dining pub, smartly traditional, airy and spacious, with beams, 16th-c flagstones, church pews and a fine settle, lovely log fire, voluble parrot, St Austell ales kept well, good house wines, quick welcoming service, generous food from sandwiches to more pricey main dishes with some emphasis on fish, large back dining room up steps (heavily booked in season); outside gents', children in eating areas, dogs in public bar (two friendly pub jack russells), stone tables in good garden, handy for the Lost Gardens of Heligan, open all day in summer *(Jenny and Brian Seller, LYM, Andrea Rampley, Peter and Anne Hollindale, Gill and Tony Morriss, David Eberlin, M Joyner, Jane and Mark Hooper, Dennis Jenkin, Christopher Wright, Sue Demont, Tim Barrow, Klaus and Elizabeth Leist)*

ST ISSEY [SW9271]

Ring o' Bells [A389 Wadebridge—Padstow; Churchtown]: Cheerful village pub with leather sofas and open fire at one end of beamed bar, darts and pool the other, well kept Bass and local beers, decent wines, friendly service, long narrow no smoking side dining room with good value fresh food – can take a while; no dogs, can get packed in summer, car park across rd; some tables in flowery courtyard, bedrooms *(LYM, A and B D Craig, Gill and Keith Croxton)*

ST IVE [SX3067]

Butchers Arms [A390 Liskeard—Callington]: 16th-c pub with well kept beers, reasonably priced food, prompt service, cosy cottage-style dining lounge, bar with pub games; lovely area *(DAV)*

ST IVES [SW5441]

Castle [Fore St]: Cosy and spotless, with good range of well kept ales tapped from the cask (beer festivals), good friendly service, ample fairly priced usual food, good value coffee, comfortable plain seats and lots of dark panelling in one long low-ceilinged room, stained glass, local photographs, maritime memorabilia; unobtrusive piped music; bustling in summer, relaxing out of season *(Pat and Roger Fereday, Ted George)*

Golden Lion [High St]: Lively and welcoming, standard lunchtime food inc filling pasties, well kept beers such as Courage Best and Sharps Doom Bar *(J M Tansey)*

Lifeboat [Wharf Rd]: Recently refurbished harbourside pub, good atmosphere, wide choice of all-day food, three St Austell real ales, friendly staff, cosy corners, nautical theme, good views; open all day *(Geoff Calcott)*

☆ *Sloop* [The Wharf]: Low-beamed and flagstoned harbourside pub crowded all year

(the friendly staff cope well), with bright St Ives School pictures and attractive portrait drawings in front bar, booth seating in panelled back bar, well cooked down-to-earth food from sandwiches and baguettes to lots of fresh local fish, well kept Bass, John Smiths, Greene King Old Speckled Hen and Sharps Doom Bar, good wine list and coffee; juke box or piped music, TV; children in eating area, a few beach-view seats out on cobbles, open all day (breakfast from 9am), clean cosy bedrooms, handy for Tate Gallery *(LYM, Mrs Yvette Bateman, Gene and Kitty Rankin, Peter Salmon, Dr J Barrie Jones, Paul and Shirley White, the Didler, Alan Johnson, Callum and Letitia Smith-Burnett, David Glynne-Jones, David Crook)*

Union [Fore St]: Spotless friendly pub, roomy but cosy dark interior, low beams, small fire, masses of old local photographs, good value food worth waiting for from good soup and filled baguettes to local seafood specials, well kept ales inc Bass and Sharps, decent wines, coffee, roaring fire, broadsheet papers; piped music, can get crowded *(Dr J Barrie Jones, Alan Johnson, Barry Collett, Tim and Ann Newell)*

ST JUST IN PENWITH [SW3631]

Kings Arms [Market Sq]: Old-fashioned local with friendly relaxed service, comfortable elderly furniture, plenty of character, good local photographs, good value bar meals from tasty baguettes up, well kept St Austell ales, some tapped from the cask; popular live music nights, Sun quiz; dogs welcome, reasonably priced bedrooms with own bathrooms, prodigious breakfast *(the Didler, Peter and Anne Hollindale, Ann and Bob Westbrook, David Crook)*

☆ *Star* [Fore St]: Relaxed and informal dimly lit low-beamed local with regulars clustered around the bar, good value home-made food from sandwiches and pasties up (if no food, they let you bring your own), well kept St Austell ales, farm cider in summer, mulled wine in winter, coal fire; traditional games inc bar billiards, nostalgic juke box, singalong Mon; tables in attractive back yard, simple bedrooms, good breakfast *(Barry and Anne, the Didler, Callum and Letitia Smith-Burnett, LYM, Paul and Shirley White)*

ST MAWES [SW8433]

Idle Rocks [Tredenham Rd (harbour edge)]: Comfortable waterfront hotel with superb sea views, well kept Skinners Betty Stogs, good house wines, friendly helpful young foreign staff, lunchtime food inc pricey sandwiches in bar and adjoining informal brasserie, smart leisurely evening restaurant; well behaved dogs allowed on terrace, good bedrooms *(Dennis Jenkin, BB, Mark Flynn)*

☆ *Rising Sun* [The Square]: Long nicely fitted bare-boards bar with nice bow-window seat, good coal fire, well kept St Austell ales, decent wines, good coffee, prompt good-natured service, interesting choice of reasonably priced good food here and in restaurant with pleasant conservatory, proper sandwiches and unusual seafood snacks, great puddings; dogs allowed, teak seats and slate-topped tables on handsome sunny terrace just across lane from harbour wall, open all day summer, good value attractive bedrooms *(Jenny and Brian Seller, Mr and Mrs P Hill, LYM, Mr and Mrs A H Young, Mark Flynn)*

☆ *Victory* [Victory Hill]: Cheerful local bareboards bar on left (can be smoky), simply furnished no smoking dining area on right, enjoyable if pricey food from good crab sandwiches to carefully cooked fresh local fish, well kept ales such as Sharps Doom Bar, good service, warm log fires, upstairs restaurant in season; piped music; pleasant picnic-sets outside, good value bedrooms, open all day *(David Crook, LYM, Jodie Collins, D S and J M Jackson, Guy Vowles, Mr and Mrs A H Young, C J Jones, Stephen and Jean Curtis, Paul and Shirley White, Barry Collett, Jenny and Brian Seller)*

ST MERRYN [SW8874]
Cornish Arms [Churchtown (B3276 towards Padstow)]: Well kept St Austell ales, good value generous food inc good fresh fish and steaks (may be a wait at busy times), also more extensive evening menu, in spotless local with fine slate floor, some 12th-c stonework, RNAS memorabilia, good games room; children over 6 may be allowed in eating area, picnic-sets out under cocktail parasols *(LYM, Paul and Shirley White, Gill and Keith Croxton)*

ST NEOT [SX1867]
☆ *London* [N of A38 Liskeard—Bodmin]: Spotless 16th-c beamed country pub on Bodmin Moor, comfortable and airy with almost more the feel of an upmarket hotel than a pub; cheerful efficient staff, good home-made food from sandwiches (normal or doorstep) up, well kept Fullers London Pride and Sharps Doom Bar tapped from the cask, decent house wines (choice of glass sizes), two log fires, dining area behind trellis; unobtrusive piped music; attractive village in wooded valley, 15th-c church with outstanding medieval stained glass *(DAV, Charles Gysin)*

ST TUDY [SX0676]
Cornish Arms [off A391 nr Wadebridge]: Attractive low-beamed 16th-c local with largish flagstoned front bar, pool room and restaurant, well kept Bass, Sharps and St Austell, home-made bar food; children welcome *(the Didler)*

STITHIANS [SW7037]
Golden Lion [Stithians Lake, Menherion]: Welcoming pub with large well maintained garden and lakeside terrace, good sensibly priced food from sandwiches and other bar food to restaurant meals (neat white linen – busy Fri and wknds), well kept St Austell ales, friendly helpful licensees, no smoking area *(David Crook)*

TREBARWITH [SX0586]
☆ *Mill House* [signed off B3263 and B3314 SE of Tintagel]: Marvellously placed in own steep streamside woods above sea, convivial blackbeamed bar with fine delabole flagstones, well worn mix of furnishings and interesting local

pictures, good rather upmarket food, well kept ales inc Sharps Doom Bar, welcoming service, restaurant; piped music; provision for dogs and children, tables out on terrace and by stream, 12 bedrooms, open all day *(DB, BB, Canon Michael Bourdeaux, Robert Wivell, A P Seymour)*

TREEN [SW3824]
☆ *Logan Rock* [just off B3315 Penzance—Lands End]: Relaxed local nr fine coast walks, lowbeamed traditional bar with inglenook seat by hot coal fire, well kept if not cheap local ales, wide food choice (all day in summer) from good sandwiches up, courteous service, lots of games in family room, no smoking in small back snug with cricket memorabilia, gorgeous pub dog (others allowed on leads); may be juke box or piped music, no children inside; tables in small and pretty sheltered garden *(Celia Minoughan, the Didler, Barry and Anne, LYM, David Crook, Callum and Letitia Smith-Burnett, Paul and Shirley White)*

TREGONY [SW9245]
☆ *Kings Arms* [Fore St (B3287)]: Well run 16th-c local, long chatty comfortable main bar with well kept ales such as Sharps Doom Bar and Skinners Betty Stogs, decent wine, friendly licensees, good value quickly served standard food using local produce inc fresh fish and Sun lunch, woodburners in two smart beamed and panelled front rooms, one a no smoking dining room, the other for families, pool and juke box in back games room; tables in pleasant garden, charming village, open all day *(Reg Fowle, Helen Rickwood, Kevin Thorpe, Christopher Wright)*

TRESILLIAN [SW8646]
☆ *Wheel* [A39 Truro—St Austell]: Friendly bustle in neatly thatched roadside pub, steps between two compact main areas with plush seating, timbering, stripped stone and low ceiling joists, plenty of spotless bric-a-brac, strong local following for good value food, particularly well kept ales such as Adnams Broadside and John Smiths, welcoming service; piped music, narrow entrance to car park; children welcome, play area in neat garden stretching down to tidal inlet *(Simon Cottrell, Phil and Jane Hodson, BB)*

TREVAUNANCE COVE [SW7251]
Driftwood Spars [off B3285 in St Agnes; Quay Rd]: 17th-c inn just up from beach and dramatic cove, great coastal walks; slate, granite and massive timbers, lots of nautical and wreck memorabilia, brews its own Cuckoo Ale, plus Sharps Doom Bar, Skinners Betty Stogs, St Austell HSD and Tetleys, over 100 malt whiskies, Addlestone's cider, 15 wines by the glass, log fires, bar food at a price (all day in summer), separate residents' areas and new fish restaurant; juke box, pool, fruit machine, TV; piped music may be loud (some live, open till midnight Fri/Sat), can get crowded; children welcome, dogs allowed in bar, garden tables, nautical-theme bedrooms, open all day *(Mrs Yvette Bateman, R L R Nicholson, Gill and Tony Morriss, Philip and Ann Board, the Didler, John and Vivienne Rice, LYM,*

Cathy Robinson, Ed Coombe, Kev and Gaye Griffiths, Steve Felstead, Jan and Alan Summers)

TREWELLARD [SW3733]

Trewellard Arms Hotel [Trewellard Rd (B3306 Pendeen—St Just)]: Pleasantly relaxed beamed village pub, warm and friendly, with welcoming staff, well kept Sharps ales inc RV brewed for the pub, bar food using local produce, log fires; cosy bedrooms, open all day from noon *(LYM, Rina Matthews)*

TRURO [SW8244]

Barley Sheaf [Old Bridge St, behind cathedral]: Smartly modernised without being brash, stretching back through linked beamed areas, lots of wood and slight art deco feel, two fireside chesterfields, well kept Boddingtons, Sharps Doom Bar and Skinners Cornish Knocker, enjoyable food inc bargain meals, conservatory; piped music, big-screen TV; suntrap terrace *(Mrs Angela McArt, Patrick Hancock, Ted George)*

TYWARDREATH [SX0854]

New Inn [off A3082; Fore St]: Friendly and informal conversion of private house in nice village setting, busy local atmosphere, well kept Bass tapped from the cask and St Austell ales on handpump, food (till 8 evening), games and children's room; large secluded garden behind, bedrooms *(Mrs Maricar Jagger, Jim and Maggie Cowell, BB, the Didler)*

VERYAN [SW9139]

☆ *New Inn* [village signed off A3078]: Neat and comfortably homely one-bar beamed local with good nourishing food using local produce (try the steak sandwich), popular Sun lunch, well kept St Austell ales, good value house wines, good coffee, leisurely atmosphere, inglenook woodburner, lots of polished brass and old pictures, no smoking dining area, friendly staff, alsatian and burmese cat; piped music, quiet garden behind the pretty house, bedrooms, interesting partly thatched village – nearby parking unlikely in summer *(David Crook, the Didler, BB, Nick Lawless, Mark Flynn, Gordon Stevenson, Barry Collett, Christopher Wright, Glenn and Julia Smithers)*

WIDEMOUTH [SS2002]

Bay View [Marine Drive]: Open-plan and unpretentious, with fine views over beach, good value food, well kept Sharps Doom Bar and Own, Skinners Betty Stogs and a beer brewed for the pub; tables on front decking, open all day in summer, bedrooms *(A and B D Craig, the Didler)*

ZENNOR [SW4538]

☆ *Tinners Arms* [B3306 W of St Ives]: Enthusiastic new owners perking up the food side, with new back dining room and reworked kitchen doing enjoyable food from good sandwiches up, long unspoilt bar with flagstones, granite, stripped pine and real fires each end, real ales such as Sharps Doom Bar and Wadworths 6X kept well in casks behind counter, Lane's farm cider, decent coffee, relaxed informal service, no music; tables in small suntrap courtyard, lovely peaceful windswept setting by church nr coast path

(Pete Walker, Andrea Rampley, David Crook, LYM, Guy Vowles, Roger and Jenny Huggins, the Didler, Jacquie and Jim Jones, Brian and Genie Smart)

ISLES OF SCILLY

BRYHER [SV8715]

☆ *Fraggle Rock*: Tiny welcoming waterside local, unpretentious and owner-run, the only 'off-island' pub with a piano; well kept Timothy Taylors Landlord in season, popular hot drinks (a cut goes to local charity), good range of attractively priced bar food inc outstanding crab sandwiches, good pizzas and Fri night fish and chips, fine views from upstairs eating area, miniature juke box; attractive terrace, self-catering accommodation, campsite a field away; odd opening hours out of season *(O G D Goldfinch, Val and Alan Green, Paul Humphreys)*

ST MARTIN'S [SV9215]

☆ *Seven Stones* [Lower Town]: Stunning location and sea-and-islands view, 11 steps up to big main bar (after 111 paces up the hill) unpretentiously reworked inside, friendly landlord, new chef doing good fresh food from baguettes and home-made burgers and fishcakes to splendid local seafood, local organic veg, summer teas and sandwiches, well kept Skinners Heligan Honey and St Austell Tribute, perhaps Ales of Scilly as a guest beer, decent wines, bar billiards, local art for sale, nice window seats; lots of terrace tables, lovely walks, limited winter opening *(Andy Sinden, Louise Harrington, Pete and Rosie Flower, Paul Humphreys, Michael Butler, Catherine Pitt, J and S French)*

ST MARY'S [SV9010]

Atlantic Inn [The Strand; next to but independent from Atlantic Hotel]: Spreading cosily dark bar with nice little room at one end, low beams, hanging boat and lots of nautical bits and pieces, flowery-patterned seats, bar food, reasonably priced St Austell ales, friendly efficient service, mix of locals and tourists – busy evenings, quieter on sunny lunchtimes; darts, pool, fruit machines; little terrace with green cast-iron furniture and wide views, good bedrooms *(Val and Alan Green, R J Herd, BB, Michael Butler, Tom McLean, Mayur Shah)*

☆ *Bishop & Wolf* [Hugh St/Silver St (A3110)]: Lively and friendly local atmosphere, interesting sea/boating décor with secluded corners and gallery above road, nets, lots of woodwork and maritime bric-a-brac, lifeboat photographs, friendly helpful staff, well kept St Austell Tinners and HSD, very wide choice of good generous food with plenty of seafood (should book, attractive relaxed upstairs restaurant – no bar food after 7.30pm), games area with pool; piped music, popular summer live music, handy for day-trippers (nr coach tour start) *(Michael Butler, David Crook, Tom McLean, Stuart Turner, J and S French)*

Mermaid [The Bank]: Thorough-going nautical theme in unpretentious bar with ceiling flags, lots of seafaring relics, rough timber, stone floor, dim lighting, big stove; real ales such as Ales of Scilly Scuppered and Skinners Betty Stogs, simple bar food, picture-window all-day back restaurant extension (not Tues) with views across town beach and harbour; packed on Weds and Fri when the gigs race; cellar bar with boat counter, pool table, TV and music for young people (live wknds) *(Pete and Rosie Flower, Michael Butler, David Crook, Catherine Pitt)*

If a pub tries to make you leave a credit card behind the bar, be on your guard. The credit card firms and banks which issue them condemn this practice. After all, the publican who asks you to do this is in effect saying: 'I don't trust you'. Have you any more reason to trust his staff? If your card is used fraudulently while you have let it be kept out of your sight, the card company could say you've been negligent yourself – and refuse to make good your losses. So say that they can 'swipe' your card instead, but must hand it back to you. Please let us know if a pub does try to keep your card.

Cumbria

Cumbrian pubs are these days taking more and more account of the riches on their doorsteps – well reared local meats often from well flavoured rare breeds, good fresh fish, and a growing range of distinctive locally brewed beers at attractive prices (which helps to keep the cost of drinks here well below the national average). And though Jennings, the popular local pub-owning brewery, is being taken over by the Wolverhampton & Dudley combine, they plan to keep it going very much as before. Quite a few of the places we include are given special appeal by their surroundings – pubs which are perfectly pleasant for a drink or a lunch, and are lifted out of the ordinary by glorious scenery. And there is a good range of styles, from proper basic walkers' pubs to good bars in smart hotels. The aristocrats among Cumbrian pubs are those far fewer pubs which add some unforgettable element of their own appeal. Currently, places doing particularly well are the Pheasant near Bassenthwaite Lake (with a lovely little bar, great drinks range, good food and a comfortable hotel side), the Kings Arms nicely placed in Cartmel (new licensees since it was last in the *Guide* some years ago, with well kept beers and enjoyable rather restauranty food), Wainwrights in a lovely spot at Chapel Stile (another pub returning to these pages after a break, much enjoyed these days by walkers and families), the friendly Bitter End in Cockermouth (brewing its own good low-priced beers, with good value food), the picturesque Britannia at Elterwater (massively popular, with nice food and comfortable bedrooms), the Highland Drove at Great Salkeld (a new entry, gaining ground rapidly as word of its good food gets around), the Watermill at Ings (a great place for beer, with a super enthusiastic landlord never content to rest on his laurels), the prettily placed Mill Inn at Mungrisdale (a friendly all-rounder, where the daughter cooks marvellous pies), the Blacksmiths Arms at Talkin (another well run all-rounder in a nice spot), and the Gate Inn at Yanwath, with good food from its cheerful new landlord – bringing this nice pub back into the *Guide* after a break. If a special meal out is what you want, we'd add to this top shortlist the Drunken Duck near Hawkshead, the Queens Head at Troutbeck, and the Bay Horse near Ulverston and Farmers Arms in that town. But our overall choice as Cumbria Dining Pub of the Year is the interesting newcomer, the Highland Drove at Great Salkeld. Places which currently stand out in the Lucky Dip section at the end of the chapter are the Kirkstone Pass Inn up above Ambleside, Sun at Bassenthwaite, New Inn at Blencogo, Coledale Hotel at Braithwaite, Wheatsheaf at Brigsteer, Black Bull and Sun in Coniston, Sun at Crook, Prince of Wales at Foxfield, Station Inn at Oxenholme, White Horse at Scales and Greyhound at Shap.

AMBLESIDE NY3804 Map 9
Golden Rule

Smithy Brow; follow Kirkstone Pass signpost from A591 on N side of town

There's always a good mix of customers in this friendly, no frills town local. The bar has lots of local country pictures decorating the butter-coloured walls, horsebrasses on the black beams, built-in leatherette wall seats, and cast-iron-framed tables. There is a no smoking back room with TV (not much used), and a left-hand room with darts and a fruit machine, and a further room down a few steps on the right, with lots of seats and an internet cubicle. Well kept Robinsons Hatters Mild, Hartleys XB, Cumbrian Way, Old Stockport, and Cwmbran Double Hop or a seasonal beer on handpump; pickled eggs (50p), pork pies (55p or 85p), cockles or jumbo scotch eggs (£1.20), and filled rolls (£2.50). There's a back yard with benches, and especially colourful window boxes. The golden rule referred to in its name is a brass measuring yard mounted over the bar counter. *(Recommended by David A Hammond, Sue Holland, Dave Webster, MLR, James Woods, Patrick Hancock, Richard and Anne Ansell, Mark Harrington, Mike and Sue Loseby)*

Robinsons ~ Tenant John Lockley ~ Real ale ~ Bar food ~ No credit cards ~ (015394) 32257 ~ Children welcome until 9pm ~ Dogs welcome ~ Open 11-11; 12-10.30 Sun

Wateredge ♀ 🛏

Borrans Road

A fine sunny day is perhaps the best time to visit this busy place as you can make the most of the sizeable garden that runs right down to the edge of Windermere. There are enough tables and garden furniture to cope comfortably with plenty of visitors, and some bench swings look past the boats on the water to the hills beyond. You get the same view through the big windows of the modernised bar – and from some of the bedrooms. The building was originally two 17th-c cottages, though the knocked-through, partly no smoking bar gives few clues to its age; the main part, with a mix of polished floorboards and carpet, has a mix of contemporary and more traditional lighting, solid wooden tables, a long curved bar counter, and plenty of hops. Down a couple of steps is a cosier area with beams and timbers, and a sofa in front of the log fire; piped music. Well kept Coniston Bluebird, Greene King Old Speckled Hen, and Marstons Pedigree on handpump, a dozen wines by the glass, and maybe jugs of Pimms or mulled wine; fast, helpful service. New kitchens and a new chef will be in place by the time this book is published, but the bar food has included home-made soup (£3.95), chicken liver pâté (£4.25), local cumberland sausage (£7.95), mediterranean vegetable tart (£8.45), battered haddock or steak in ale pie (£8.95), confit of duck with Grand Marnier sauce (£10.50), steaks (from £12.95), and puddings such as sticky toffee pudding or apple crumble (from £4.25). Between meals you can usually get teas, scones and so on; you can't eat at the tables on the grass, but there are plenty of other outdoor tables on a gravelled terrace, or in a nicely landscaped area. Some bedrooms are in an adjacent extension, and as we went to press, a separate entrance for residents, and a dining lounge and bar for them, were under construction. More reports please. *(Recommended by Margaret and Roy Randle, Michael Dandy, Hugh Roberts, Margaret Dickinson)*

Free house ~ Licensee Derek Cowap ~ Real ale ~ Bar food (12-4, 5-8.30) ~ (015394) 32332 ~ Children in eating area of bar until 9pm ~ Dogs allowed in bar ~ Folk music Mon evening ~ Open 11-11; 12-10.30 Sun ~ Bedrooms: £50B/£100B

APPLEBY NY6921 Map 10
Royal Oak

B6542/Bongate is E of the main bridge over the River Eden

This old-fashioned coaching inn has a bustling atmosphere and a good mix of both locals and visitors. The oak-panelled public bar is relaxed and chatty and has a good open fire, and the beamed lounge has old pictures on the timbered walls, some armchairs and a carved settle, and a panelling-and-glass snug enclosing the bar counter. Popular bar food includes lunchtime filled ciabattas or baguettes (from £4.45), home-made salmon and crab fishcakes with a sweet chilli dip (£5.25; main course £9.25), spinach and ricotta cannelloni or cumberland sausage ring (£7.45), home-made pancakes with mixed vegetable filling (£7.95), steak in ale pie (£8.95), baked cod (£9.50), lamb cutlets with honey, mint and rosemary sauce (£10.45), and roast rabbit (£11). The restaurant is no smoking. Well kept Black Sheep Bitter,

Dent Aviator and a beer from Derwent Rose on handpump. There are seats on the front terrace, and attractive flowering tubs, troughs and hanging baskets. You can get here on the scenic Leeds/Settle/Carlisle railway (best to check times and any possible delays to avoid missing lunch). *(Recommended by A and B D Craig, Paul Boot, John and Wendy Allin, J S Burn, Tony and Betty Parker, Dr D G Twyman, Roger Braithwaite, Ms M F Chandler, Karen Eliot, B and M Kendall, Pat and Tony Martin)*

Landmark Inns ~ Manager Nigel Duffin ~ Real ale ~ Bar food (12-2.30, 6-9; all day Sun) ~ Restaurant ~ (01768) 351463 ~ Children in eating area of bar and restaurant ~ Dogs allowed in bar ~ Open 11-11; 12-10.30 Sun ~ Bedrooms: £35B/£69B

ARMATHWAITE NY5046 Map 10
Dukes Head
Off A6 S of Carlisle

In a quiet Eden Valley village below the Pennines, this village inn offers a warm welcome to both regulars and visitors. The civilised lounge bar has oak settles and little armchairs among more upright seats, oak and mahogany tables, antique hunting and other prints, and some brass and copper powder-flasks above the open fire. Using as much local produce as possible, the good, popular food includes sandwiches (from £3.25), home-made soup with croûtons (£3.45), butter bean and black olive pâté with pesto dressing (£3.95), hot potted solway shrimps (£4.25), cold meat platter with gooseberry preserve (£4.95), ploughman's (£6.95), filo parcels filled with roasted red pepper, red onion and a mild goats cheese (£8.25), fresh cod in a light basil and olive crumb with home-made tartare sauce (£8.45), local steaks (from £8.25), daily specials such as goats cheese and spinach tart with caramelised onions (£3.80; main course £7.95), skewered salmon, scallops and smoked bacon (£4.25), lamb, haggis and leek pie (£8.25), and grilled halibut with butter sauce (£12.75), and home-made puddings like treacle tart and custard (£3), orange and ginger tiramisu or rich chocolate and rum torte (from £3.25). The restaurant is no smoking. Well kept Black Sheep and Jennings Cumberland on handpump, home-made lemonade and blackcurrant liqueur; dominoes, and a separate public bar with fruit machine, darts and table skittles. There are tables out on the lawn behind; boules. There are day tickets for fishing available.
(Recommended by Dr and Mrs T E Hothersall, Kay and Alistair Butler, Richard J Holloway, Greg Bridges, David and Ruth Shillitoe, Hugh and Susan Ellison, Fred and Lorraine Gill, Mr and Mrs A Campbell, M Sharp, Mr and Mrs W D Borthwick, John and Margaret Priestley, JWAC)

Punch ~ Tenant Henry Lynch ~ Real ale ~ Bar food ~ Restaurant ~ (016974) 72226 ~ Children in eating area of bar and restaurant ~ Dogs allowed in bar and bedrooms ~ Open 12-11; 12-10.30 Sun ~ Bedrooms: £35.50B/£55.50B

BARBON SD6282 Map 10
Barbon Inn 🛏
Village signposted off A683 Kirkby Lonsdale—Sedbergh; OS Sheet 97 map reference 628826

The quiet and comfortable little bedrooms in this friendly 17th-c coaching inn remain very popular with our readers; some overlook the lovely sheltered and prettily planted garden. Several small rooms lead off the simple bar with its blackened range, each individually and comfortably furnished: carved 18th-c oak settles, comfortable sofas and armchairs, a Victorian fireplace. Reasonably priced bar food includes hot and cold filled baguettes (from £3.95), morecambe bay potted shrimps (£4.95), home-made lasagne (£6.75), steak in ale pie (£7.50), and specials such as mixed bean casserole or black pudding with light mustard sauce (£6.95), and seafood lasagne (£7.25); the restaurant is no smoking. Well kept Greene King Old Speckled Hen, Theakstons Black Bull and a guest beer on handpump; dominoes and piped music. There are plenty of surrounding tracks and paths all around to walk along. *(Recommended by Mrs Hilarie Taylor, Lee and Liz Potter, Michael Dugdale, Dr and Mrs T E Hothersall, Maurice and Gill McMahon)*

Free house ~ Licensee Lindsey MacDiarmid ~ Real ale ~ Bar food ~ Restaurant ~
(015242) 76233 ~ Children welcome ~ Dogs allowed in bar ~ Open 11.30-3,
6.30-11.30(11 Sun) ~ Bedrooms: £45B/£70B

BASSENTHWAITE LAKE NY1930 Map 9
Pheasant ★ ⊕ ⊈ ⇌

Follow Pheasant Inn sign at N end of dual carriageway stretch of A66 by Bassenthwaite Lake

The little bar in this civilised hotel remains as pleasantly old-fashioned and pubby
as ever, with plenty of customers enjoying a quiet pint or informal lunch. There are
mellow polished walls, cushioned oak settles, rush-seat chairs and library seats,
hunting prints and photographs, and well kept Bass, Jennings Cumberland and
Theakstons Best on handpump; 14 good wines by the glass and over 50 malt
whiskies. Several comfortable lounges have log fires, fine parquet flooring, antiques,
and plants; one is no smoking – as is the restaurant. Enjoyable lunchtime bar food
includes freshly made soup with home-made bread (£3.95), open sandwiches with
home-made crisps (from £5.95; prawn with basil and garlic mayonnaise, watercress
and a mango and chilli salsa £6.75), their own potted silloth shrimps (£6.25),
ploughman's (£6.95), braised cumberland sausage and mash (£8.75), parmesan and
sun-dried tomato risotto (£8.95), casserole of wild venison (£9.95), and braised
shank of local lamb in tomato, garlic, and haricot beans (£10.95), and puddings
(£4.55). There are seats in the garden, attractive woodland surroundings, and
plenty of walks in all directions. *(Recommended by Pat and Stewart Gordon,
Helen Clarke, Andy and Jill Kassube, Tina and David Woods-Taylor, R A K Crabtree,
Mr and Mrs Woodhead, Peter F Marshall, Jack Clark, Mike and Sue Loseby, Patrick and
Phillipa Vickery, Mrs Phoebe A Kemp, Martin and Sue Day)*

Free house ~ Licensee Matthew Wylie ~ Real ale ~ Bar food (not in evening – restaurant
only) ~ Restaurant ~ (017687) 76234 ~ Children in eating area of bar if over 8 ~ Dogs
allowed in bar and bedrooms ~ Open 11-2.30, 5.30-10.30(11 Sat); 12-2.30, 6-10.30 Sun;
closed 25 Dec ~ Bedrooms: £82B/£144B

BEETHAM SD5079 Map 7 ⌂
Wheatsheaf ⊈ ⇌

Village (and inn) signposted just off A6 S of Milnthorpe

Opposite a pretty 14th-c church, this bustling 16th-c coaching inn is neatly kept
with fresh flowers and candles on the tables. The opened-up front lounge bar has
lots of exposed beams and joists, and the main bar is behind on the right, with well
kept Jennings Cumberland, Tirril Brougham Ale, and a changing guest beer on
handpump, eight wines by the glass, and quite a few malt whiskies; there's also a
cosy and relaxing smaller room for drinkers, a roaring log fire, and Charlie the
yellow headed parrot. The pub is no smoking apart from the tap room; piped
music. Bar food includes sandwiches, home-made soup (£3.60), potted shrimps
(£5.70), cod and prawn fishcakes (£6.25), sausages and mash or steak and
mushroom pie (£7.95), a dish of the day such as fish pie, hotpot or coq au vin
(£8.95), wild mushrooms, layered pasta, asparagus and chervil (£11.95), and fillet
steak or breast of chicken filled with cumin, garlic and gruyère wrapped in bacon
with a vermouth cream sauce (£13.95); they also offer an early bird menu (6-7pm
Monday-Thursday, two courses £10.95) and a two-course Sunday lunch (£10.95).
More reports please. *(Recommended by Mr and Mrs C R Little, Malcolm Taylor, Jo Lilley,
Simon Calvert, Richard Greaves, R M Corlett, Michael Doswell, T Walker, Graham and
Doreen Holden, J F M and M West, Maurice and Gill McMahon)*

Free house ~ Licensees Mark and Kath Chambers ~ Real ale ~ Bar food (12-2, 6-9; not Sun
evening) ~ Restaurant ~ (015395) 62123 ~ Well behaved children in eating area of bar
and restaurant before 7pm ~ Open 11.30-3, 5.30-11; 12-4, 6-10.30 Sun; closed Sun evening
in winter ~ Bedrooms: £55B/£69.50B

BOUTH SD3386 Map 9
White Hart ✦
Village signposted off A590 near Haverthwaite

After enjoying one of the surrounding walks, you can quench your thirst on quite a choice of real ales here. On handpump, there might be Black Sheep, Castle Rock Black Gold, Hawkshead Bitter, Jennings Cumberland, Tetleys and Yates Bitter. The whole pub is now no smoking. The sloping ceilings and floors show the building's age, and there are lots of old local photographs and bric-a-brac – farm tools, stuffed animals, a collection of long-stemmed clay pipes – and two woodburning stoves. The games room has darts, pool, dominoes, fruit machine, TV and juke box; piped music. Bar food (using local meat) includes home-made soup (£3.75), sandwiches (from £4.75; ciabattas £4.95), five bean chilli (£8.25), home-made steak and Guinness pie (£8.25), halibut steak in garlic and parsley butter (£9.75), cumberland sausage with rich onion and cranberry gravy (£8.75), rare breed sirloin steak (£12.95), daily specials such as medallions of pork fillet in sweet chilli and coconut sauce (£9.95), and lamb in fresh thyme and red wine or beef in hoisin, oyster and soy sauces (£11.95); a good children's menu (from £4.25). Thirty-five malt whiskies, Weston's cider, and eight wines by the glass. There are some seats outside. *(Recommended by Pat and Stewart Gordon, Ian and Sue Wells, J S Burn, Patrick Hancock, Charles and Pauline Stride, Ron Gentry, JDM, KM, Malcolm Taylor, Dennis Jones, Mike Pugh)*

Free house ~ Licensees Nigel and Peter Barton ~ Real ale ~ Bar food (12-2, 6-8.45; not Mon or Tues lunchtime except bank hols) ~ Restaurant ~ (01229) 861229 ~ Children in eating area of bar and restaurant ~ Dogs allowed in bedrooms ~ Live acoustic music Sun evening ~ Open 12-2, 6-11; 12-11 Sat; 12-10.30 Sun; closed Mon and Tues lunchtimes (except bank hols) ~ Bedrooms: £47.50S(£37.50B)/£80S(£60B)

BROUGHTON MILLS SD2190 Map 9
Blacksmiths Arms
Off A593 N of Broughton-in-Furness

With friendly licensees and enthusiastic locals, this charming little pub is an enjoyable place to spend some time. Three of the four simply but attractively decorated small rooms have open fires and ancient slate floors. Well kept Hawkshead Bitter, Jennings Cumberland and Moorhouses Pride of Pendle on handpump, and summer farm cider. Bar food is very good and they use meat from local farms, and local game and fish. At lunchtime, there might be sandwiches or filled baguettes (from £3.50), ploughman's (£5.75), cajun chicken salad (£5.95), baked cumberland sausage with red onion gravy (£6.95), deep-fried cod (£7.45), and home-made steak in ale pie (£7.60), with evening choices such as chicken, duck and Cointreau pâté with red onion marmalade, crab cakes with tomato and coriander salsa or baked goats cheese with thyme (all £3.95), belly pork braised in cider with wholegrain mustard and spinach (£8.50), shoulder of lamb marinated in mint (£9.50), and fillet of beef with gorgonzola and herb crust and a roasted shallot, thyme and port sauce (£14.95); daily specials like marinated pigeon breast (£4.65), fish of the day, filled vegetarian puff pastry parcel (£7.45), and duck marinated in ginger, lime and chilli (£10.50), and puddings such as home-made sticky toffee pudding or chocolate and hazelnut torte with raspberry sauce (£3.95). There are three smallish dining rooms (the back one is no smoking). Darts, dominoes, and cribbage. Pretty summer hanging baskets and tubs of flowers in front of the building, and some fine walks nearby. *(Recommended by Michael Doswell, Tina and David Woods-Taylor, Richard and Anne Ansell, Derek Harvey-Piper, Kevin Thorpe, Peter F Marshall, Karen Eliot, Christine and Phil Young)*

Free house ~ Licensees Mike and Sophie Lane ~ Real ale ~ Bar food (12-2, 6-9; not Mon lunchtime) ~ Restaurant ~ (01229) 716824 ~ Children welcome ~ Dogs allowed in bar ~ Open 12-11; 12-10.30 Sun; 5-11 Mon (closed winter Mon), 12-2.30, 5-11 Tues-Fri in winter; closed 25 Dec

---

Tipping is not normal for bar meals, and not usually expected.

BUTTERMERE NY1817 Map 9
Bridge Hotel 🛏
Just off B5289 SW of Keswick

In some of the best steep countryside in the county and with Crummock Water and Buttermere just a stroll away, it's not surprising that the flagstoned area in the beamed bar of this bustling inn is popular with walkers. There are built-in wooden settles and farmhouse chairs around traditional tables, a panelled bar counter, and a few horsebrasses – as well as a dining bar with brocaded armchairs around copper-topped tables and brass ornaments hanging from the beams, a no smoking restaurant, and a guest lounge. Given that the inn is well liked by our many readers, it seems a shame that the owners are so uninterested in helping us, but bar food has included interesting sandwiches, filled baguettes or toasties, home-made burgers with different toppings, ploughman's, cumberland sausage, and a meaty or vegetarian hotpot. Well kept Black Sheep, Theakstons Old Peculier, and a guest beer on handpump, several malt whiskies, and a decent wine list. Outside, a flagstoned terrace has white tables by a rose-covered sheltering stone wall. The views from the bedrooms are marvellous; please note, the bedroom prices are for dinner, bed and breakfast; self-catering, too. *(Recommended by Helen Clarke, Jarrod and Wendy Hopkinson, Duncan Cloud, Len Beattie, Michael Dandy, A S and M E Marriott, Geoff and Angela Jaques, Patrick and Phillipa Vickery, John Foord, Geoff and Carol Thorp)*

Free house ~ Licensees Adrian and John McGuire ~ Real ale ~ Bar food (12-9.30) ~ Restaurant ~ (017687) 70252 ~ Children in eating area of bar and, if over 7, in restaurant ~ Dogs allowed in bedrooms ~ Open 10.30-11; 10.30-10.30 Sun ~ Bedrooms: £75B/£150B

CARTMEL SD3879 Map 7
Kings Arms
The Square

Doing well under its present licensees, this rather grand little black and white pub (recently refurbished) has seats outside that make the most of the lovely square. Inside, the rambling bar has a mixture of seats including old country chairs, settles and wall banquettes, small antique prints on the walls, and tankards hanging over the bar counter. As well as sandwiches, the well liked food might include roast mediterranean vegetables topped with goats cheese (£9.95), scottish salmon fillet with prawn hollandaise (£10.75), roast half duck with orange and brandy sauce (£12.50), local bass with lime and coriander dressing or sautéed pork fillet with stilton (£12.95), and lamb shoulder marinated in mint (£13.95). The snug and restaurant are no smoking. Well kept Black Sheep, Coach House Honeypot Bitter, Coniston Bluebird, Hawkshead Bitter and Timothy Taylors Landlord on handpump, and nine wines by the glass; piped music and dominoes. This ancient village has a grand priory church, and close to the pub is a fine medieval stone gatehouse; the race track is 200 yards away. *(Recommended by John Foord, Matthew Lidbury, Dennis Jones, Steve and Liz Tilley)*

Enterprise ~ Lease Richard Grimmer ~ Real ale ~ Bar food (12-2.30, 5.30-8.45; 12-8.45 weekends) ~ Restaurant ~ (01539) 536220 ~ Children in restaurant and family room ~ Dogs allowed in bar ~ Open 11-11; 12-10.30 Sun; 11-3, 5-11 in winter; closed 25 Dec

CARTMEL FELL SD4189 Map 9
Masons Arms 🍽
Strawberry Bank, a few miles S of Windermere between A592 and A5074; perhaps the simplest way of finding the pub is to go uphill W from Bowland Bridge (which is signposted off A5074) towards Newby Bridge and keep right then left at the staggered crossroads – it's then on your right, below Gummer's How; OS Sheet 97 map reference 413895

From the rustic benches and tables on the terrace here, there's an unrivalled view overlooking the Winster Valley to the woods below Whitbarrow Scar. Inside, the main bar has plenty of character, with low black beams in the bowed ceiling, and country chairs and plain wooden tables on polished flagstones. A small lounge has oak tables and settles to match its fine Jacobean panelling, there's a plain little room beyond the serving counter with pictures and a fire in an open range, a family room with an old-parlourish atmosphere, and a no smoking upstairs dining room; piped music and TV. Well kept Black Sheep, Hawkshead Bitter and Gold, Moorhouses Pride of Pendle and Timothy Taylors Best on handpump; belgian fruit beer, quite a range of foreign bottled beers, and locally produced damson gin and strawberry vodka. Bar food includes home-made soup (£3.65), sandwiches (£4.95; ciabattas from £5.95), grilled black pudding and crushed new potatoes topped with a poached egg with grain mustard sauce (£5.95), vegetarian pasta (£9.95), honey and mustard chicken (£10.95), rump steak or slow roasted shoulder of lamb (£13.95), seared fresh tuna with warm spinach, rocket, red onion, cucumber, and sour cream (£14.25), and puddings like sticky toffee pudding (£4.25). Self-catering cottages and apartments behind. *(Recommended by Clive and Fran Dutson, Michael Doswell, Dr and Mrs R G J Telfer, Jo Lilley, Simon Calvert, Peter Abbott, Malcolm Taylor, Mark Harrington, Nigel Stevenson, Dennis Jones, Tom Halsall, Ewan McCall, Simon Cleasby, Ewan and Moira McCall)*

Free house ~ Licensees John and Diane Taylor ~ Real ale ~ Bar food (12-2(3 Sun), 6-9 (8 Sun) ~ Restaurant ~ (015395) 68486 ~ Children welcome ~ Open 11.30-11; 12-10.30 Sun; 11.30-3, 6-11 in winter

CASTERTON SD6279 Map 7

Pheasant ♀ 🚗

A683 about 1 mile N of junction with A65, by Kirkby Lonsdale; OS Sheet 97 map reference 633796

The neatly kept and attractively modernised beamed rooms of the main bar here have wheelback chairs, cushioned wall settles, a nicely arched oak framed fireplace, and Black Sheep, Theakstons Bitter and a guest such as Dent Aviator on handpump; over 20 malt whiskies and an extensive wine list. There's quite an emphasis on the restauranty food which might include sandwiches, waldorf salad (£3.95), mixed seafood platter (£4.75), spicy lamb curry (£8.95), chicken en croûte with wild mushrooms and brandy sauce (£9.95), whole lemon sole grilled with herbed butter or slow roasted shoulder of lamb (£10.95), and chargrilled swordfish steak (£12.95). The restaurant is no smoking; piped music and dominoes. There are some tables with cocktail parasols outside by the road, with more in the pleasant garden. The nearby church (built for the girls' school of Brontë fame here) has some attractive pre-Raphaelite stained glass and paintings. More reports please. *(Recommended by G Dobson, John and Yvonne Davies, Brian and Anita Randall, Jo Lilley, Simon Calvert)*

Free house ~ Licensee The Dixon Family ~ Real ale ~ Bar food (12-2, 6-9) ~ Restaurant ~ (015242) 71230 ~ Children in eating area of bar ~ Open 11-3, 6-11(10.30 Sun); closed evening 25 Dec ~ Bedrooms: £35S/£70B

CHAPEL STILE NY3205 Map 9

Wainwrights

B5343

In a delightful fellside spot, this white-rendered lakeland house is surrounded by good walks, and you can enjoy the views from the picnic-table sets out on the terrace. Inside, the characterful slate-floored bar has plenty of room, and it is here that walkers and their dogs are welcomed. There's a relaxed and friendly atmosphere, an old kitchen range, cushioned settles, and well kept Jennings Cumberland Ale, Sneck Lifter, Golden Host and Robinsons Cumbria Way on handpump or tapped from the cask. Reasonably priced bar food includes soup (£2.50), lunchtime sandwiches (from £3.50), filled baked potatoes (from £4.60), chicken or beef burgers (£7.75), ploughman's, vegetable stroganoff or curry of the day (£7.95), cumberland sausage (£8.75), and daily specials like cottage pie, steak and kidney pudding, and chicken breast or pork chops with various sauces (all £7.95). The family dining area is no smoking; piped music, darts, fruit machines, dominoes, and TV. *(Recommended by Ewan and Moira McCall, John and Caroline, Jack Clark, W W Burke)*

Free house ~ Licensees M Darbyshire and D Banks ~ Real ale ~ Bar food (12-2(2.30 Sun), 6-9) ~ (015394) 38088 ~ Children welcome ~ Dogs allowed in bar ~ Open 11.30-3, 6-11; 11.30-11 Sat; 12-10.30 Sun

COCKERMOUTH NY1231 Map 9

Bitter End 🍺

Kirkgate, by cinema

It's not surprising that there is such a good, bustling atmosphere in this own brew pub. You can be sure of a friendly welcome from the courteous staff and their own beers (you can view the little brewery through a tiny Victorian-style window) are very popular: Cuddy Luggs, Farmers Ale and Cockermouth Pride. The licensee also keeps guests from Derwent, Hawkshead and Jennings on handpump in good condition; quite a few bottled beers from around the world, and seven wines by the glass. The three main rooms have a different atmosphere in each – from quietly chatty to sporty, with the décor reflecting this, such as unusual pictures of a Cockermouth that even Wordsworth might have recognised, to more up-to-date sporting memorabilia, various bottles, jugs and books, and framed beer mats. The snug is no smoking. Good value traditional bar food includes toasted panini bread with fillings (from £2.95), filled baked potatoes (£3.75), chilli lamb (£5.25), pasta in a spicy tomato sauce (£6.25), cumberland sausage (£6.75), battered haddock (£6.95), steak, mushroom and ale pie (£7.25), and puddings such as sticky toffee pudding (£2.30); piped music. The public car park round the back is free after 7pm. *(Recommended by Helen Clarke, Kevin Thorpe, C A Hall, Paul Davies, Edward Mirzoeff, Steve Kirby, P S Hoyle, John Foord, Barry Collett)*

Own brew ~ Licensee Susan Askey ~ Real ale ~ Bar food (12-2, 6-8.30) ~ (01900) 828993 ~ Children in eating area of bar ~ Open 12-2.30, 6-11; 11.30-11 Sat; 12-2.30, 6-10.30 Sun; 11.30-3, 6-11 Sat in winter

DALTON-IN-FURNESS SD2376 Map 7

Black Dog 🍺 £

Holmes Green, Broughton Road; 1 mile N of town, beyond A590

This is an unpretentious local with a fine range of real ales, and a particularly friendly and cheery licensee; access is from the terrace in the car park. The simple bar has beer mats and brasses around the beams, two log fires, partly tiled and flagstoned floor, and plain wooden tables and chairs; the eating area is no smoking, as is the breakfast room. Good value hearty bar food – all home-made – includes sandwiches (from £2.25), soup (£1.95), leek and potato bake (£4.50), chilli beef (£4.95), curries (from £4.95), cumberland sausage (£5.25), poached haddock mornay (£5.75), daily specials such as seafood chowder (£2.50), black pudding platter with bacon and fruit sauce topped with melted cheese (£3.95), cauliflower and macaroni pie with garlic bread (£4.95), beef casserole (£5.95), and roast lamb with mint and redcurrant sauce (£6.25), and puddings such as apple crumble (£2.75). The six real ales change constantly but might include Archers Best Bitter, Barngates Cat Nap, Dent Bitter, Exmoor Gold, Moorhouses Pride of Pendle, Abraham Thompson Lickerish Stout and Wychwood Hobgoblin on handpump; they also have four farm ciders and a perry, and several interesting cordials. Table skittles, darts, shove-ha'penny, cribbage, and dominoes. A side terrace has a few plastic tables and chairs. The pub is handy for the South Lakes Wild Animal Park. More reports please. *(Recommended by Kevin Thorpe, Harry Clegg, Geoffrey Tyack, Hugh Roberts)*

Free house ~ Licensee Jack Taylor ~ Real ale ~ Bar food (5-9 weekdays in winter; 12-2.30, 5-9 weekdays in summer; 12-9 weekends all year) ~ No credit cards ~ (01229) 462561 ~ Children welcome ~ Dogs allowed in bar and bedrooms ~ Open 12-11; 12-10.30 Sun;

4.30-11 weekdays in winter; may be closed winter weekday lunchtimes ~ Bedrooms:
£17.50(£25S)/£40S

ELTERWATER NY3305 Map 9

Britannia 🍷 🛏

Off B5343

Walkers and their dogs are welcome here – which is just as well since this very
popular, friendly inn is in a beautiful part of Cumbria with tracks over the fells to
Grasmere and Easedale. As well as a small and traditionally furnished back bar,
there's a front one with a couple of window seats looking across to Elterwater itself
through the trees: cosy coal fires, oak benches, settles, windsor chairs, a big old
rocking chair, and well kept Coniston Bluebird, Isle of Skye Coruisk, Jennings
Bitter, Timothy Taylors Landlord and Yates Sun Goddess on handpump. Quite a
few malt whiskies, country wines, and winter mulled wine; the lounge is
comfortable. Bar food includes lunchtime filled rolls, home-made soup (£3.30),
home-made cumberland pâté (£4.70), red pesto with sweet pepper filo tart topped
with cheese (£8.70), cumberland sausage with onion gravy (£9.30), home-made
steak in ale pie or lamb rogan josh (£9.70), daily specials such as wild mushroom
stroganoff (£9.25), baked red snapper fillet on a tomato and artichoke salad
(£10.95), breast of local chicken stuffed with sun-dried tomatoes and brie with
provençale sauce (£11.25), and puddings like home-made chocolate bread and
butter pudding or treacle sponge (£4.40). There are queues at peak times but service
is pretty efficient. The main bar, dining room and residents' lounge are no smoking.
In summer, people flock to watch the morris and step and garland dancers. Plenty
of seats outside. (Recommended by Tina and David Woods-Taylor, Ron Gentry, Malcolm and
Jane MacDonald, Jonathan Shephard, Tim Maddison, Richard and Anne Ansell, Andy and
Ali, J S Burn, Ewan and Moira McCall, David A Hammond, Alan Sadler, Peter and
Eleanor Kenyon, Mr and Mrs Richard Osborne, Jack Clark, TOH, W W Burke,
Steve and Liz Tilley)

Free house ~ Licensees Clare Woodhead and Christopher Jones ~ Real ale ~ Bar food
(all day) ~ Restaurant ~ (015394) 37210 ~ Children welcome ~ Dogs allowed in bar and
bedrooms ~ Quiz most Sun evenings ~ Open 10-11; 11-10.30 Sun ~ Bedrooms:
£78B/£88B

GREAT SALKELD NY5536 Map 10

Highland Drove 🍴

B6412, off A686 NE of Penrith

Cumbria Dining Pub of the Year

The hard-working and cheerful licensees here are actually father and son and are
natives of this attractive old village. It's a 300-year-old inn with lovely views over
the Eden Valley and the Pennines – best enjoyed from seats on the upstairs
verandah. The convivial bar, lounge and games room have been carefully renovated
with new floors and exposed old fireplaces, and they keep John Smiths, Theakstons
Black Bull and a guest beer on handpump, and a good choice of wines; piped
music, juke box, darts, pool, fruit machine and dominoes. The food is highly
thought of and in the bar might include home-made soup (£3.95), home-made pâté
(£4.95), filled baguettes (from £4.95), charcuterie plate (£5.95), a dish of crayfish
cocktail, smoked salmon, fried calamari, soused herring and crispy whitebait
(£6.50), cumberland sausage (£6.95), wild mushroom and risotto bake with stilton
topping (£7.25), and chicken in white wine, onions and mushrooms (£7.95); you
can also choose from the restaurant menu – warm leek and dolcelatte tartlet
(£5.50), crispy home-made duck spring roll with sweet chilli dipping sauce (£5.75),
pasta with a tomato and roasted vegetable and goats cheese sauce (£9.95), pork
tenderloin stuffed with black pudding, wrapped with pancetta and served with
apple and grain mustard mash (£12.50), and roasted fillet of red snapper on
roasted mediterranean vegetables with sun-dried tomato pesto dressing (£13.50).
As we went to press, they were working on a new dining extension. The upstairs

restaurant is no smoking and very attractive. More reports please. *(Recommended by Kevin Tea, Richard J Holloway, Helen Clarke, Tony and Maggie Harwood)*

Free house ~ Licensees Donald and Paul Newton ~ Real ale ~ Bar food (12-1.45, 6.45-8.45; not Mon lunchtime) ~ Restaurant ~ (01768) 898349 ~ Children welcome ~ Dogs allowed in bar ~ Open 12-2.30, 6-11; 11-11 Sat; 12-10.30 (may shut in afternoon if not busy) Sun; closed Mon lunchtime ~ Bedrooms: £30B/£55B

HAWKSHEAD NY3501 Map 9

Drunken Duck 🍽 ♀ ◀

Barngates; the hamlet is signposted from B5286 Hawkshead—Ambleside, opposite the Outgate Inn; or it may be quicker to take the first right from B5286, after the wooded caravan site; OS Sheet 90 map reference 350013

As a stylish place to enjoy imaginative modern cooking, this civilised inn is hard to beat. There's also a thriving hotel side and the country house style bedrooms are beautifully appointed and very popular. The only place you may smoke is in the small smart bar area with its beams and oak floorboards, high chairs and stools clustered around the slate-topped bar counter, and hunting pictures, photographs, coaching prints, fox masks and kentish hop bines. Here they serve their own-brewed Barngates Cat Nap, Chesters Strong & Ugly, Cracker Ale and Tag Lag, with a guest such as Hawkshead Bitter on handpump, and 20 wines by the glass. We get a lot of reports from readers on the Drunken Duck; the many who like it generally emphasise its qualities as an upmarket place to stay or eat in. It does cater too for people who want a lunchtime sandwich (hearty ones using home-cooked meats from named, traditionally reared herds, local cheeses, and free-range eggs, and wrapped in greaseproof paper, from £4.25, and much appreciated by groups of walkers), but doesn't do bar food in the style of other pubs. From the restaurant menu, there might be pigeon marinated with liquorice on prune and parmesan risotto (£6.25), tempura battered okra with lime, ginger and cardamom marmalade (£6.95), beer-battered cod with salt and vinegar butter sauce (£9.50), layers of grilled pasta with roasted red peppers, red onions, fennel, chestnut purée and spinach on a red pepper sauce (£14.45), noisette of herdwick shearling with wild mushroom and spinach roulade and madeira glaze (£15.95), and diver-caught seared king scallops with a rocket, black pudding, black pepper beignet soufflé and chilli jam salad (£17.95), with puddings like melting dark chocolate pudding with white chocolate panna cotta and chocolate and orange parfait or rum soaked savarin and pink peppercorn poached pineapple with passion fruit ice-cream (from £5.95). Rustic seating on the grass bank opposite the building offers spectacular views across the fells, and there are thousands of spring and summer bulbs. *(Recommended by Dr D G Twyman, Frazer and Louise Smith, Revd D Glover, Ray and Winifred Halliday, Tim Maddison, Mrs J A Taylar, Pierre Richterich, Duncan Cloud, Steve Cawthray, Dr Terry Murphy, Pat and Sam Roberts, Mark Harrington, Nigel Stevenson, Mr and Mrs Woodhead, Alan Sadler, Ms M F Chandler, Jo Lilley, Simon Calvert, T Walker, Tina and David Woods-Taylor, Mike and Sue Loseby, Derek and Heather Manning, W W Burke, Janet Walters, Karen and Graham Oddey)*

Own brew ~ Licensee Steph Barton ~ Real ale ~ Restaurant ~ (015394) 36347 ~ Children welcome ~ Dogs allowed in bar ~ Open 11.30-11; 12-10.30 Sun ~ Bedrooms: £71.25B/£95B

Kings Arms ◀

The Square

Travellers have been welcomed here since Elizabethan times, and there are some fine original features. It's on a glorious square, and has traditional pubby furnishings, Archers Best Bitter, Coniston Bluebird, Hawkshead Bitter and a changing guest on handpump, 29 malt whiskies, summer cider and a decent wine list. Piped music, fruit machine, shove-ha'penny, dominoes and cribbage. Generous helpings of bar food at lunchtime include soup (£2.95), filled focaccia, baps or ciabatta (£4.75), filled baked potatoes (£5.25), and hot meals such as gammon and egg, cumberland sausage or haddock with parsley and lemon (£6.95); evening choices like goats cheese and onion marmalade tart or thai prawns (£4.95), leek, broccoli and stilton quiche (£7.50), honey and ginger turkey steak (£7.95), beef goulash (£8.25), and minted lamb steak (£10.50). The restaurant is no smoking. Picnic-sets outside. As well as bedrooms, they offer self-catering cottages. More reports please. *(Recommended by Brian and Anna Marsden, Angus Lyon, Ron Gentry, Andy and Ali)*

Free house ~ Licensees Rosalie and Edward Johnson ~ Real ale ~ Bar food (12-2.30, 6-9.30) ~ Restaurant ~ (015394) 36372 ~ Children in eating area of bar and restaurant ~ Dogs allowed in bar and bedrooms ~ Live music some Fri evenings ~ Open 11-11; 12-10.30 Sun; closed evening 25 Dec ~ Bedrooms: £43S/£78S

Queens Head
Main Street

There's always a good mix of locals and visitors in this lovely black and white timbered pub, and a friendly welcome to all from the pleasant, helpful staff. The bustling low-ceilinged bar has heavy bowed black beams, red plush wall seats and plush stools around heavy traditional tables, lots of decorative plates on the panelled walls, and an open fire; a snug little room leads off. Lunchtime food served in either the bar or no smoking restaurant includes home-made soup (£3.25), interesting baguettes, flavoured rolls, and bruschetta (from £4.95), chicken liver pâté with orange and tequila (£5.25), cumberland sausage with white onion sauce (£7.25), vegetarian pasta (£7.50), organic salmon, haddock and prawns in a lemon and parsley cream sauce (£9.50), and chicken and prawn thai green curry (£9.95); in the evening, there might be goats cheese and roast pepper tartlet with red onion marmalade (£4.95), game terrine with tomato chutney (£5.45), scottish mussels in cream and white wine (£6.45), a pastry case with wild mushroom and asparagus ragoût in a garlic cream sauce (£10.75), pork medallions on an apricot and cranberry compote (£13.50), slow-roasted lamb with rosemary scented sauce (£14.75), and calves liver on a herb potato cake with rich red wine sauce (£14.95). Well kept Robinsons Cumbria Way, Double Hop, Best, Hartleys XB and Unicorn on handpump, and 30 whiskies; dominoes, cribbage, and piped music. Walkers must take their boots off. As well as bedrooms in the inn, they have three holiday cottages to rent in the village. The summer window boxes are very pretty. No dogs. *(Recommended by Helen Clarke, Ray and Winifred Halliday, Brian and Anna Marsden, Andrew Crawford, Michael Dandy, Angus Lyon, Duncan Cloud, David Carr, W W Burke, Andy and Ali, Bruce and Sharon Eden)*

Robinsons ~ Tenants Mr and Mrs Tony Merrick ~ Real ale ~ Bar food (12-2.30, 6.15-9.30) ~ Restaurant ~ (015394) 36271 ~ Children welcome ~ Open 11-11; 12-10.30 Sun ~ Bedrooms: £60B/£90B

HESKET NEWMARKET NY3438 Map 10
Old Crown ◀
Village signposted off B5299 in Caldbeck

Very much enjoyed by readers, this is a bustling and friendly unfussy local with super own-brew beers. Well kept on handpump, these include Hesket Newmarket Blencathra Bitter, Doris's 90th Birthday Ale, Great Cockup Porter, Helvellyn Gold, Skiddaw Special Bitter, Old Carrock Strong Ale, Catbells Pale Ale and the new Scafell Blond. Reasonably priced bar food includes good home-made soup (£2.50), sandwiches (from £2.50), ham and egg (£5), steak in ale pie (£7.50), and lots of evening curries (£7.50). The dining room is no smoking. The little bar has a few tables, a coal fire and shelves of well thumbed books, and a friendly atmosphere; darts, pool, cribbage and dominoes. The pub is in a pretty setting in a remote, attractive village. You can book up tours to look around the brewery; £10 and a minimum of six people. *(Recommended by Helen Clarke, Patrick Hancock, Ian and Sue Wells, Peter F Marshall, Michael and Jennifer Wadsworth, Tina and David Woods-Taylor, Tony and Maggie Harwood, Steve Nye, G Coates, Mrs C E Godfrey, Martin and Sue Day, Simon Cleasby)*

Own brew ~ Licensees Lou and Linda Hogg ~ Real ale ~ Bar food (12-2, 6.30-8.30; not winter Mon or Tues evenings, not Sun evening) ~ Restaurant ~ No credit cards ~ (016974) 78288 ~ Children in eating area of bar and restaurant ~ Dogs allowed in bar ~ Folk first Sun of month ~ Open 12-3, 5.30-11; 12-3, 7-10.30 Sun; closed Mon and Tues lunchtimes

INGS SD4599 Map 9

Watermill ☕

Just off A591 E of Windermere

Never one to sit on his laurels, the enthusiastic and hard-working landlord here has embarked on an extension which will create a new beer cellar, two gardens, extra internal sitting, and their own five-barrel microbrewery. The car park has been re-arranged and they have gained an eighth bedroom. Around 800 different beers pass through the 16 handpumps a year, and as well as eight regulars, there might be guests such as Dent T'Owd Tup, Harviestoun Bitter & Twisted, Hambleton Knightmare, Hawkshead Gold, Isle of Skye Blaven, Oakham JHB, Orkney Dark Island and Phoenix White Monk; all the breweries and their beers are helpfully described on a board, and there are 60 foreign bottled beers and over 50 whiskies. The building is cleverly converted from a wood mill and joiner's shop, and the bars have a friendly, bustling atmosphere, a happy mix of chairs, padded benches and solid oak tables, bar counters made from old church wood, open fires, and interesting photographs and amusing cartoons by a local artist. The spacious lounge bar, in much the same traditional style as the other rooms, has rocking chairs and a big open fire; two areas are no smoking. Using locally sourced produce, the generous helpings of popular bar food include home-made soup (£3.30), lunchtime filled rolls or ciabatta (from £3.50), filled baked potatoes (from £4.25), and ploughman's (£5.95), as well as home-made pâté (£4.50), broccoli and onion pasta (£7), cumberland sausage with beer and onion gravy (£7.95), fresh beer battered haddock or home-made beef in ale pie (£8.25), chicken breast with fresh rosemary, english mustard, black pepper and cream (£8.50), mixed grill (£14.25), daily specials such as goats cheese tart (£4.50), vegetarian tortellini in a rich tomato, pepper and basil sauce (£7.95), pork escalope on a raspberry, elderflower and pink peppercorn cream sauce (£11.50), and local shoulder of lamb in red wine and mint (£12.75), with puddings such as chocolate and Cointreau mousse, home-made apple crumble or lemon cheesecake (£4.25). Darts, cribbage, and dominoes. Lots to do nearby. *(Recommended by Helen Clarke, Sue Holland, Dave Webster, Mrs B M Hill, Ray and Winifred Halliday, Paul Boot, Ian and Sue Wells, Peter Abbott, David Reid, J S Burn, Jo Lilley, Simon Calvert, JDM, KM, Brian and Anna Marsden, Kevin Thorpe, A S and M E Marriott, Lee and Liz Potter, Richard and Anne Ansell, Steve Whalley, M and GR, Tony Pope, Karen Bonham, Mark Harrington, Dennis Jones, MLR, Mike Pugh, Douglas Keith, Mr and Mrs Maurice Thompson, Paul and Gloria Howell)*

Free house ~ Licensee Brian Coulthwaite ~ Real ale ~ Bar food (12-4.30, 5-9) ~ (01539) 821309 ~ Children in family room ~ Dogs allowed in bar and bedrooms ~ First Tues of month storytelling club ~ Open 12-11(10.30 Sun); closed 25 Dec ~ Bedrooms: £35S/£65B

KESWICK NY2421 Map 9

Swinside Inn

Only pub in Newlands Valley, just SW; OS Sheet 90 map reference 242217

Seats in the garden and on the upper and lower terraces here make the most of the fine view down over the valley and up to the high crags and fells around Grisedale Pike. It's a warmly friendly inn with pleasant smiling staff and quite a few original 17th-c features. The long bright public bar has traditional wheelbacks and red and cream wall banquettes, and well kept Jennings Cumberland, Theakstons Best and a guest on handpump; a central chimney with an open fire divides off the games area, which has piped music, pool, fruit machine, cribbage and dominoes. There are two no smoking dining rooms and two further open fires. Popular, tasty bar food (best to book to be sure of a table) includes sandwiches, home-made soup (£2.65), spare ribs in barbecue sauce (£4.95), vegetable lasagne or home-made steak pie (£6.95), cod in their own beer batter (£7.50), chicken stuffed with cheese, wrapped in bacon and served with a mushroom and bacon sauce (£7.95), steaks (from £9.25), lamb shoulder marinated in fresh mint sauce (£9.95), and puddings such as hot chocolate fudge cake or lemon meringue roulade (£3.95). *(Recommended by Mrs M Hitchings, Tina and David Woods-Taylor, Geoff and Angela Jaques, Paul and Gloria Howell, J S Burn)*

S&N ~ Lease Joyce and Jim Henderson ~ Real ale ~ Bar food (12-2, 6-8.45) ~ (017687) 78253 ~ Children welcome ~ Dogs allowed in bar ~ Open 11-11; 12-10.30 Sun ~ Bedrooms: £45S/£60S

LANGDALE NY2906 Map 9
Old Dungeon Ghyll
B5343

Walkers and their dogs are welcomed into this straightforward local which is in a marvellous position at the heart of the Great Langdale Valley, and surrounded by fells including the Langdale Pikes flanking the Dungeon Ghyll Force waterfall. The whole feel of the place is basic but cosy – and once all the fell walkers and climbers crowd in, full of boisterous atmosphere. There's no need to remove boots or muddy trousers, and you can sit on the seats in old cattle stalls by the big warming fire, and enjoy the well kept real ales such as Black Sheep Special, Jennings Cumberland, Kelham Island Pale Rider, Theakstons Old Peculier and XB, Wells Eagle and Yates Bitter on handpump; up to 30 malt whiskies, and farm cider. Straightforward food includes lunchtime sandwiches, and home-made dishes such as soup (£3), a vegetarian choice (from £7), curries or stews (£7.50), and lasagne or pie of the day (£7.75). Darts, cribbage and dominoes. It may get lively on a Saturday night (there's a popular National Trust campsite opposite). *(Recommended by Helen Clarke, Richard and Anne Ansell, Tim Maddison, Sarah and Peter Gooderham, Hugh Roberts, B Shelley, Ewan and Moira McCall, Dr D J and Mrs S C Walker)*

Free house ~ Licensee Neil Walmsley ~ Real ale ~ Bar food (12-2, 6-9) ~ Restaurant ~ (015394) 37272 ~ Children in eating area of bar and restaurant ~ Dogs welcome ~ Folk first Weds of month ~ Open 11-11; 11-10.30 Sun; closed Christmas ~ Bedrooms: £45/£90(£96S)

LITTLE LANGDALE NY3204 Map 9
Three Shires 🛏
From A593 3 miles W of Ambleside take small road signposted The Langdales, Wrynose Pass; then bear left at first fork

The three shires are the historical counties Cumberland, Westmorland and Lancashire, which meet at the top of the nearby Wrynose Pass. There are lovely views over the valley to the partly wooded hills below Tilberthwaite Fells from seats on the terrace, with more seats on a well kept lawn behind the car park, backed by a small oak wood. Inside, the comfortably extended back bar has stripped timbers and a beam-and-joist stripped ceiling, antique oak carved settles, country kitchen chairs and stools on its big dark slate flagstones, lakeland photographs lining the walls, and a warm winter fire in the modern stone fireplace with a couple of recesses for ornaments; an arch leads through to a small, additional area. Enjoyable bar food at lunchtime includes sandwiches (£3.50; popular soup and a sandwich £5), home-made fishcake with lime and cucumber crème fraîche (£5.75), ploughman's (£6.50), and cumberland sausage or a home-made pie of the day (£7.95), with evening dishes such as crab tortelloni with a lightly spiced tomato sauce (£5.50), smoked sliced duck breast with a plum and raspberry sauce (£6.50), wild mushroom tagliatelle with truffle oil and cream sauce (£9.50), local cumberland sausage with lancashire cheese and home-made westmorland chutney (£9.95), and specials like smoked pheasant (£9.50), game pie (£9.95), and whole plaice with lemon and herb butter and capers (£12.95). The inn is no smoking at meal times (apart from the main bar). Well kept Jennings Bitter and Cumberland,

and a guest such as Coniston Old Man or Hawkshead Bitter on handpump, 40
malt whiskies, and a decent wine list; darts, cribbage and dominoes. *(Recommended
by Louise English, Tina and David Woods-Taylor, Ewan and Moira McCall, Mr and
Mrs John Taylor, Sarah and Peter Gooderham, Jo Lilley, Simon Calvert, Jack Clark, TOH,
Christine and Phil Young, Barry Collett)*

Free house ~ Licensee Ian Stephenson ~ Real ale ~ Bar food (12-2, 6-8.45; no evening
meals Dec and Jan) ~ Restaurant ~ (015394) 37215 ~ Children welcome until 9pm ~
Dogs allowed in bar ~ Open 11-10.30(11 Fri and Sat); 12-10.30 Sun; 11-3, 8-10.30
midweek in winter; closed 25 Dec ~ Bedrooms: /£78B

LOWESWATER NY1421 Map 9
Kirkstile Inn 🍺 🛏️
From B5289 follow signs to Loweswater Lake; OS Sheet 89 map reference 140210

There's a good bustling atmosphere, quite a mix of customers, and their own-
brewed ales in this well run 16th-c inn – now totally no smoking. The bar is low-
beamed and carpeted, with a roaring log fire, comfortably cushioned small settles
and pews, and partly stripped stone walls; slate shove-ha'penny board. Popular bar
food at lunchtime includes home-made soup (£3), filled baked potatoes (from
£3.50), filled baguettes (£3.95), home-made pâté with home-made cumberland
sauce (£4), smoked salmon and cream cheese tart (£5.95), home-made pasty
(£6.95), and wild mushroom and feta cheese lasagne or steak and mushroom pie
(£7), with evening dishes such as black pudding in their own beer batter with red
wine sauce (£4), broccoli and stilton bake (£7), chicken breast marinated in lemon
and coriander with a tomato and chilli jus (£8.50), baked lamb in honey and mint
sauce or grilled monkfish with capsicum sauce (£9.50), roast duckling with figs and
calvados sauce (£10.50), and puddings like sticky toffee pudding or fruit crumble
(£3.75); friendly staff. Well kept Loweswater Grasmere Dark and Melbreak Bitter
as well as Coniston Bluebird and Yates Bitter on handpump. You can enjoy the view
from picnic-sets on the lawn, from the very attractive covered verandah in front of
the building and from the bow windows in one of the rooms off the bar.
*(Recommended by G J and M M Hill, John Kane, Michael and Jennifer Wadsworth,
Michael Jones, Jenny Ellis, Edward Mirzoeff, Mr and Mrs John Taylor, Tim Maddison,
Dennis Jones, Mrs Judith Smith, T Walker, Geoff and Carol Thorp, Maurice and Gill McMahon)*

Own brew ~ Licensees Roger and Helen Humphreys ~ Real ale ~ Bar food (12-2, 6-9) ~
Restaurant ~ (01900) 85219 ~ Children welcome ~ Dogs allowed in bar and bedrooms ~
Open 11-11; 12-10.30 Sun; closed 25 Dec ~ Bedrooms: £45B/£74B

MUNGRISDALE NY3630 Map 10
Mill Inn
Off A66 Penrith—Keswick, a bit over 1 mile W of A5091 Ullswater turn-off

You can be sure of a warm, friendly welcome from the licensees and their helpful
staff in this bustling and popular inn. The traditionally furnished and neatly kept
bar has a wooden bar counter with an old millstone built into it, an open fire in the
stone fireplace, and well kept Jennings Bitter and Cumberland, and a guest like
Black Sheep on handpump; 30 malt whiskies and seven wines by the glass.
Enjoyable bar food includes 13 varieties of home-made shortcrust pastry pies such
as wild venison, pheasant and rabbit, particularly good locally sourced beef in ale,
herdwick lamb and redcurrants, and roasted vegetables in a sweet chilli and tomato
sauce (from £7.95; they have just opened the Pie Mill in Threlkeld from where they
will sell pies nationwide); also, lunchtime choices such as home-made soup (£2.90),
filled rolls (from £3.25; toasted muffins from £3.60; open sandwiches from £4.60),
three-egg omelette (£4.90), fishcakes with tartare sauce (£4.95), ploughman's
(£5.75), and lamb chops (£6.75), and daily evening specials such as smoked salmon
and mackerel pâté (£4.95), chicken breast stuffed with apricots and pesto with
spiced couscous (£9.95), and chargrilled tuna steak with pineapple chutney
(£11.95). The restaurant and part of the bar are no smoking. There are tables on
the gravel forecourt and neat lawn sloping to a little river; good walks nearby and

some strenuous hillwalking further on. The bedrooms are to be upgraded this year, to match the smart bathrooms. Please note that there's a quite separate Mill Hotel here. *(Recommended by G J and M M Hill, Helen Clarke, Steve Nye, Paul Davies, Tim Maddison, Geoff and Angela Jaques, Peter Abbott, Jim Abbott, Sally and Mark Bramall, Mike and Penny Sutton, Tracey and Stephen Groves, Mr and Mrs W D Borthwick, Mrs Phoebe A Kemp, Maurice and Gill McMahon, J S Burn)*

Free house ~ Licensees Jim and Margaret Hodge ~ Real ale ~ Bar food (12-2, 6-9) ~ Restaurant ~ (017687) 79632 ~ Children in eating area of bar ~ Dogs allowed in bar and bedrooms ~ Open 11-11; 12-10.30 Sun ~ Bedrooms: £40B/£65B

NEAR SAWREY SD3796 Map 9
Tower Bank Arms 🍺
B5285 towards the Windermere ferry

As it features in *The Tale of Jemima Puddleduck* and backs onto Beatrix Potter's Hill Top Farm (owned by the National Trust), this little country inn does get busy at peak times. The low-beamed main bar has a fine log fire in the big cooking range, high-backed settles on the rough slate floor, local hunting photographs, postcards of Beatrix Potter, and signed photographs of celebrities on the walls, a grandfather clock, and good traditional atmosphere. Well kept Theakstons Old Peculier and Best and guests such as Barngates Cat Nap or Caledonian Deuchars IPA on handpump, as well as lots of malt whiskies, and belgian fruit beers and other foreign beers. Bar food at lunchtime includes filled rolls (from £3.30), morecambe bay potted shrimps (£5.10), ploughman's (from £5.10), a vegetarian dish of the day (£6.95), and cumberland sausage or home-made pie (£7.25); in the evening, extras might include half a honey roast duck (£9.50) or steaks (from £11). Darts, dominoes and cribbage. Seats outside have pleasant views of the wooded Claife Heights. This is a good area for golf, sailing, birdwatching, fishing (they have a licence for two rods a day on selected waters in the area), and walking, but if you want to stay at the pub, you'll have to book well in advance. More reports please. *(Recommended by Dave and Sue Mitchell, Michael and Marion Buchanan, Michael Dandy, Tina and David Woods-Taylor, Catherine and Rob Dunster, Ron Gentry)*

Free house ~ Licensee Philip Broadley ~ Real ale ~ Bar food ~ Restaurant ~ (015394) 36334 ~ Children in eating area of bar lunchtime but in restaurant only, in evenings ~ Dogs welcome ~ Open 11-3, 5.30-11; 12-3, 5.30(6 in winter)-10.30 Sun; closed evening 25 Dec ~ Bedrooms: £40B/£59B

SANDFORD NY7316 Map 10
Sandford Arms 🍷 🍺 🛏
Village and pub signposted just off A66 W of Brough

This neat and welcoming little inn is tucked away in a very small village by the River Eden. The compact and comfortable no smoking dining area is on a slightly raised balustraded platform at one end of the L-shaped carpeted main bar, which has stripped beams and stonework, well kept Black Sheep and a guest like Hesket Newmarket Skiddaw Special Bitter on handpump, a good range of malt whiskies, and nice new world house wines (also ones from the Sandford Estate – no connection). The two sons do the cooking, and the food might include sandwiches, home-made soup (£2.95), grilled black pudding with mustard sauce (£3.85), hot spicy prawns (£5.65), local cumberland sausage with onion gravy (£7.75), home-made steak in ale pie (£7.95), mushroom and pepper stroganoff (£8.25), mediterranean salad (£8.50), chicken with mushrooms, smoked bacon and cream (£8.75), steaks (from £13.25), and puddings such as fruit crumble or sticky toffee pudding (from £3.50); popular three-course Sunday lunch (£10.50). There's also a more formal separate dining room (open if pre-booked), and a second bar area with broad flagstones, charming heavy-horse prints, an end log fire, and darts and piped music. The eating areas are no smoking. Some picnic-sets outside. Please note the restricted opening times; they may open longer at weekend lunchtimes if there are enough customers. More reports please. *(Recommended by Dr and Mrs R G J Telfer, Richard J Holloway)*

Free house ~ Licensee Susan Stokes ~ Real ale ~ Bar food ~ Restaurant ~
(017683) 51121 ~ Children welcome ~ Dogs allowed in bar ~ Open 6.30(7 Mon)-11;
12-1.30, 6.30-11 Sat; 12-1.45, 7-10.30 Sun; closed Tues and weekday lunchtimes ~
Bedrooms: £50B/£60B

SANTON BRIDGE NY1101 Map 9
Bridge Inn
Off A595 at Holmrook or Gosforth

Although this traditional little black and white place is more of a hotel than a pub,
it is none the worse for that. It has a friendly atmosphere, and cheerful, helpful
staff, and is in lovely countryside with plenty of surrounding walks. The turkey-
carpeted bar has stripped beams, joists and standing timbers, a coal and log fire,
and three rather unusual timbered booths around big stripped tables along its outer
wall, with small painted school chairs and tables elsewhere. Bar stools line the long
concave bar counter, which has well kept Jennings Bitter, Cumberland, Cocker
Hoop and Sneck Lifter, and a guest such as Golden Host on handpump; good big
pots of tea, speciality coffees, and eight wines by the glass; piped music, pool, darts,
TV and dominoes. Bar food includes filled baguettes, home-made soup (£2.50),
greek salad (£4.20), crab and prawn medley (£4.50), cumberland sausage, curry of
the day or steak and kidney pie (£7.95), a daily fish dish, and specials such as
crispy-coated camembert with cumberland sauce (£4.95), wild mushroom and
smoked bacon tagliatelle or vegetable pie (£9.95), pork medallions with stilton and
walnut sauce (£11.50), and organic lambs liver with celeriac mash (£11.95). The
back bistro is no smoking (children must be over 10 in here), the small reception
hall has a rack of daily papers, and there's a comfortable more hotelish lounge
(with an internet café) on the left. There are fell views and seats out in front by the
quiet road. *(Recommended by Tony and Maggie Harwood, Derek Harvey-Piper, Paul Davies,
Stuart Orton, Mary Kirman and Tim Jefferson)*

Jennings (W & D) ~ Lease John Morrow and Lesley Rhodes ~ Real ale ~ Bar food
(12-2.30, 6-9.30) ~ Restaurant ~ (01946) 726221 ~ Children welcome ~ Dogs allowed in
bar and bedrooms ~ Open 11-11; 12-10.30 Sun ~ Bedrooms: £45(£50B)/£55(£65B)

SEATHWAITE SD2396 Map 9
Newfield Inn 🍺
Duddon Valley, near Ulpha (ie not Seathwaite in Borrowdale)

With good walks from the doorstep of this cottagey 16th-c inn, it's not surprising
that walkers and climbers crowd in at weekends. It's well run and neatly kept with a
friendly welcome for all, and the slate-floored bar has a genuinely local and
informal atmosphere, with wooden tables and chairs, and some interesting pictures,
and well kept Jennings Bitter, Moorhouses Pride of Pendle, Theakstons Old
Peculier and a changing guest on handpump, and half a dozen wines by the glass.
There's a comfortable side room and a games room with shove-ha'penny, cribbage
and dominoes. Good value bar food includes soup (£2.55), filled rolls (from £3.10),
filled baked potatoes (from £3.95), home-cooked ham and egg or pasta in tomato
and basil sauce (£5.95), home-made lasagne (£7.25), home-made steak pie (£7.55),
steaks (from £11.95), daily specials such as hotpot (£6.45) or local trout (£9.25),
and home-made pear and chocolate crumble or bread and butter pudding (£3.10).
The grill room is no smoking; piped music. Tables outside in the nice garden with
good hill views. The pub owns and lets the next-door self-catering flats.
*(Recommended by Tony and Maggie Harwood, David Field, Derek Harvey-Piper, Mrs J Walker,
Tina and David Woods-Taylor, Christine and Phil Young, Nigel Howard)*

Free house ~ Licensee Paul Batten ~ Real ale ~ Bar food (12-9) ~ Restaurant ~
(01229) 716208 ~ Children welcome ~ Dogs allowed in bar ~ Open 11-11; 12-10.30 Sun

---

Please let us know of any pubs where the wine is particularly good.

STAVELEY SD4798 Map 9
Eagle & Child 🍺 🛏
Kendal Road; just off A591 Windermere—Kendal

With enjoyable food and four well kept real ales, this little inn is popular with our readers. There's a roughly L-shaped flagstoned main area with plenty of separate parts to sit in, and pews, banquettes, bow window seats and some high-backed dining chairs around polished dark tables; also, some nice photographs and interesting prints, just a few farm tools and a delft shelf of bric-a-brac, and two good log fires, one under an impressive mantelbeam. As well as interestingly filled baguettes and ciabattas, the well liked dishes from the menu might include home-made soup (£2.50), field mushrooms stuffed with stilton, breadcrumbed and deep-fried and served with a garlic and herb dip (£4.95), cumberland sausage with red wine onion gravy (£7.95), fresh local trout with lemon and prawn butter or home-made fresh spinach and ricotta puff pastry lattice with a creamy wild mushroom sauce (£8.50), braised lamb shank with sweet redcurrant and mint jus (£10.95), daily specials such as spinach and wild mushroom lasagne (£8.75), halibut steak on roast mediterranean vegetables (£9.95), chicken supreme stuffed with cumberland sausage wrapped in bacon with a warm cumberland sauce (£10.50), and well hung rump steak (£13.95), with puddings like home-made sticky toffee pudding with butterscotch sauce or apple crumble (£3.95); the Sunday lunch is good. On handpump, there might be Barngates Cat Nap, Black Sheep, Kelham Island Pale Rider and Yates Bitter; quite a few wines by the glass, draught wheat beer, bottled foreign beers and farm cider. Piped music, darts, TV, cribbage and dominoes. An upstairs barn-theme dining room (with its own bar for functions and so forth) doubles as a breakfast room. There are picnic-sets under cocktail parasols in a sheltered garden by the River Kent, with more on a good-sized back terrace, and second garden behind. *(Recommended by Stephen Gibbs, Rowena Lord, Bill Braithwaite, MLR, Michael Doswell, Alan and Carolin Tidbury, Jo Lilley, Simon Calvert, Mike Pugh, Paul and Gloria Howell)*

Free house ~ Licensees Richard and Denise Coleman ~ Bar food (12-2.30, 6-9) ~ Restaurant ~ (01539) 821320 ~ Children welcome ~ Dogs allowed in bar ~ Open 11-11; 12-10.30 Sun ~ Bedrooms: £40B/£60B

STONETHWAITE NY2613 Map 9
Langstrath 🍺 🛏
Off B5289 S of Derwent Water

If you stay overnight at this civilised, no smoking little inn, you can make the most of the good surrounding walks as this is a lovely spot in the heart of Borrowdale and en route for the Cumbrian Way and the Coast to Coast Walk. It's at its pubbiest at lunchtime, and the neat and simple bar has a welcoming coal and log fire in a big stone fireplace, just a handful of cast-iron-framed tables, plain chairs and cushioned wall seats, and on its textured white walls quite a few walking cartoons and attractive lakeland mountain photographs. Well kept Black Sheep and Jennings Bitter on handpump, with a couple of guest beers such as Coniston Bluebird or the new Hesket Newmarket Scafell Blond, eight wines by the glass, and over 25 malt whiskies; piped music and dominoes. A little oak-boarded room on the left reminded us almost of a doll's house living room in style – this is actually the original cottage built around 1590. Enjoyable bar food includes home-made soup (£2.95), sandwiches (from £3.95), mushrooms in creamy garlic sauce or morecambe bay potted shrimps (£4.95), vegetable pie (£8.25), local trout poached with tarragon (£9.25), local roast lamb with mint (£11.50), daily specials like cumberland sausage with onion gravy (£8.50), wild boar and duckling pie (£9.25), and fillet of halibut in pastry parcel with lemon butter sauce (£9.50). It is essential to book a table in advance. There is also a separate back restaurant, by the residents' lounge. Outside, a big sycamore shelters a few picnic-sets. *(Recommended by Fred and Lorraine Gill, Tina and David Woods-Taylor, Jarrod and Wendy Hopkinson, Peter J and Avril Hanson, J C Clark, John Knighton, John and Enid Morris, Christine and Phil Young, Glenys and John Roberts, Guy Vowles)*

Free house ~ Licensees Donna and Gary MacRae ~ Real ale ~ Bar food (12-2, 6-8) ~ Restaurant ~ (017687) 77239 ~ Children in eating area of bar ~ Open 11-11; 12-10.30 Sun; they may close late Dec and weekdays in Jan due to refurbishments ~ Bedrooms: £29/£58(£64S)(£78B)

TALKIN NY5557 Map 10

Blacksmiths Arms ♀ ⇰

Village signposted from B6413 S of Brampton

Well run and friendly, this bustling inn once housed the former blacksmith's. On the right is a warm, neatly kept lounge with a log fire, upholstered banquettes, tables and chairs, and country prints and other pictures on the walls; the no smoking restaurant to the left is pretty, there's a long lounge opposite the bar with smaller round tables, and a well lit garden room. All areas are no smoking except the bar. Well kept Black Sheep, Coniston Bluebird, Hawkshead Bitter and a guest such as Jennings Cumberland on handpump, over 20 wines by the glass, and 30 malt whiskies; piped music and dominoes. As well as lunchtime sandwiches and filled baguettes, the good, enjoyable food might include home-made soup (£2.30), chicken and pistachio pâté (£3.75), fresh haddock in home-made beer batter (£6.25), steak and kidney pie or vegetable curry (£6.55), chicken curry (£7.50), beef stroganoff (£11.55), steaks (from £12.95), and daily specials such as fishcakes (£4.45), venison in Guinness casserole (£8.95), and shoulder of lamb in mint, honey and garlic (£10.95); three-course Sunday lunch (£7.25; children £4.95), and nice breakfasts. There are a couple of picnic-sets outside the front door with more in the back garden. (*Recommended by Michael Doswell, Dr and Mrs R G J Telfer, Ian and Jane Irving, JWAC, Steve Whalley, Pat and Stewart Gordon*)

Free house ~ Licensees Donald and Anne Jackson ~ Real ale ~ Bar food (12-2, 6-9) ~ Restaurant ~ (016977) 3452 ~ Children welcome ~ Dogs allowed in bedrooms ~ Open 12-3, 6-11(10.30 Sun) ~ Bedrooms: £35B/£50B

TIRRIL NY5126 Map 10 ⌂

Queens Head ◀

3½ miles from M6 junction 40; take A66 towards Brough, A6 towards Shap, then B5320 towards Ullswater

The oldest parts of the bar in this busy inn have low bare beams, black panelling, original flagstones and floorboards, and high-backed settles; the little back bar has a lot of character, and there are four open fireplaces including one roomy inglenook. Their own beers, brewed at Brougham Hall a couple of miles away, include Bewshers Bitter, Academy Ale, Brougham Ale, Old Faithful and 1823, and there might be a guest from another local brewery on handpump; over 40 malt whiskies. At lunchtime when several of the dishes can be ordered in smaller helpings, the menu might include hot stuffed ciabattas (from £4.95), mushroom, hazelnut and a cream sauce with pasta (£7.95), ploughman's (£8.50), and battered cod or home-made pie of the day (£8.75), with more elaborate choices such as brie tartlet or chicken liver pâté (£4.50), chicken breast filled with smoked bacon and brandy stuffing on a coarse grain mustard sauce or shoulder of lamb in redcurrant gravy (£10.95), and venison in orange and port gravy (£14.95); puddings like sticky toffee pudding (from £4.25). The restaurant is no smoking; piped music. Pool, juke box and dominoes in the back bar. The pub is very close to a number of interesting places, such as Dalemain House at Dacre, and is just 2½ miles from Ullswater. (*Recommended by Dr and Mrs T E Hothersall, Derek and Sylvia Stephenson, Helen Clarke, Jo Lilley, Simon Calvert, John and Claire Pettifer, John and Wendy Allin, Dr D G Twyman, Dr and Mrs M W A Haward, Brian and Jacky Wilson, Richard Houghton, Paul Boot, Nigel Scott, Robert F Smith, Richard and Anne Ansell, Callum and Letitia Smith-Burnett, Mike and Lynn Robinson, Geoff and Angela Jaques, Malcolm Taylor, Sally and Mark Bramall, Ms M F Chandler, Tracey and Stephen Groves, Jonathan Tong, Catherine and Rob Dunster*)

Own brew ~ Licensees Chris Tomlinson, Daniel Ingham and Thomas Mitchell ~ Real ale ~ Bar food (12-2, 6-9.30) ~ Restaurant ~ (01768) 863219 ~ Children in eating area of bar and in restaurant; under 3 or over 13 for accommodation ~ Dogs allowed in bar and bedrooms ~ Open 12-11; 12-10.30 Sun; 12-3, 6-11 Mon-Thurs in winter ~ Bedrooms: £40B/£70B

TROUBECK NY4103 Map 9

Queens Head ★ ⑪ ♀ ◼ ⇦
A592 N of Windermere

Parts of this rather civilised, bustling inn date back 400 years and the various alterations over the past few years fit in well. The big rambling original U-shaped bar has a little no smoking room at each end, beams and flagstones, a very nice mix of old cushioned settles and mate's chairs around some sizeable tables (especially the one to the left of the door), and a log fire in the raised stone fireplace with horse harness and so forth on either side of it in the main part, and a log fire in the other; some trumpets, cornets and saxophones on one wall, country pictures on others, stuffed pheasants in a big glass case, and a stag's head with a tie around its neck, and a stuffed fox with a ribbon around its neck. A massive Elizabethan four-poster bed is the basis of the finely carved counter where they serve around four real ales well kept on handpump from local breweries such as Barngates, Coniston, Hawkshead, Jennings and Tirril. The newer dining rooms (where you can also drop in for just a drink) are similarly decorated to the main bar, with oak beams and stone walls, settles along big tables, and an open fire. Popular bar food includes home-made soup (£3.95), lunchtime filled baguettes (from £4.25), confit of duck leg on celeriac remoulade with field mushrooms and smoked garlic dressing (£6.25), grilled polenta with roast vine cherry tomatoes, goats cheese, rocket and pesto, skate wing on herbed new potatoes with crispy capers and beurre noisette, pheasant, honey and mustard sausages with caramelised apples and grain mustard sauce or roast breast of corn-fed chicken on fettuccine with a herb butter sauce (all £7.25), steak and mushroom in ale cobbler (£7.95), and grilled rib-eye of fell-bred beef with yorkshire pudding (£9.75). Piped music. Seats outside have a fine view over the Trout valley to Applethwaite moors. *(Recommended by Revd D Glover, Helen Clarke, Hugh Roberts, Sarah and Peter Gooderham, Richard and Anne Ansell, Fred and Lorraine Gill, Malcolm and Jane MacDonald, Ken Richards, Sue Holland, Dave Webster, Phil and Heidi Cook, Stephen Gibbs, Rowena Lord, Ron Gentry, Catherine and Rob Dunster, Dennis Jones, David Field, Mike Pugh, John and Enid Morris, Barry and Patricia Wooding, Mrs S E Griffiths, Mr and Mrs Hyde-Moxon, Patrick and Phillipa Vickery, Douglas Keith, Bruce and Sharon Eden)*

Free house ~ Licensees Mark Stewardson and Joanne Sherratt ~ Real ale ~ Bar food ~ Restaurant ~ (015394) 32174 ~ Children welcome ~ Dogs allowed in bar ~ Open 11-11; 12-10.30 Sun; closed 25 Dec ~ Bedrooms: /£105S(£120B)

ULVERSTON SD2978 Map 7

Bay Horse ⑪ ♀ ⇦
Canal Foot signposted off A590 and then you wend your way past the huge Glaxo factory

This smart and civilised hotel stands on the water's edge of the Leven Estuary and has commanding views of both the Lancashire and Cumbrian fells. It's at its most informal at lunchtime, and the bar, notable for its huge stone horse's head, has a relaxed atmosphere despite its smart furnishings: attractive wooden armchairs, some pale green plush built-in wall banquettes, glossy hardwood traditional tables, blue plates on a delft shelf, and black beams and props with lots of horsebrasses. Magazines are dotted about, there's a handsomely marbled green granite fireplace, and decently reproduced piped music; shove-ha'penny, cribbage and dominoes. Good, imaginative bar food might include home-made soup (£3.50), sandwiches (from £3.70), hot filled ciabattas, baguettes, baked potatoes or chicken liver pâté with cranberry and ginger purée (£6.25), deep-fried chilli prawns on a sweet and sour sauce (£7.95), red and green peppers stuffed with a mushroom and onion pâté, served on a tomato provençale with a garlic and chive cream, breadcrumb and pine nut topping (£9.50), fresh crab and salmon fishcakes in a white wine and fresh herb cream sauce or medallions of pork, leek and lancashire cheese on a rich madeira sauce (£10.50), lamb shank braised in red burgundy with rosemary, mushrooms and shallots (£11.50), aberdeen angus steak and kidney puff pastry pie (£12.50), and home-made puddings (£5.75). Well kept Jennings Best, Marstons Pedigree and Shepherd Neame Spitfire on handpump, and a dozen wines by the glass (champagne, too) from a carefully chosen and interesting wine list with quite a few from South Africa. The no smoking conservatory restaurant has fine views over Morecambe Bay (as do the bedrooms) and there are some seats out on the terrace. *(Recommended by Tina and David Woods-Taylor, W K Wood, Mary Kirman and Tim Jefferson, Jo Lilley, Simon Calvert, Michael Doswell)*

Free house ~ Licensee Robert Lyons ~ Real ale ~ Bar food (lunchtime only) ~ Restaurant ~ (01229) 583972 ~ Children in eating area of bar; not allowed in evening restaurant if under 12 ~ Dogs allowed in bar and bedrooms ~ Open 11-11; 12-10.30 Sun ~ Bedrooms: /£90B

Farmers Arms 🍴 ♀ 📖
Market Place

At the top of the main street, this friendly town pub looks pretty much unchanged from the outside since it was built in the 16th c, but inside it's managed to combine traditional and modern chic décor at the same time. The original fireplace and timbers blend in well with the more contemporary furnishings in the front bar – mostly wicker chairs on one side, comfortable sofas on the other; the overall effect is rather unusual, but somehow it still feels like a proper village pub. A table by the fire has newspapers, glossy magazines and local information, then a second smaller bar counter leads into a big raftered eating area, part of which is no smoking; piped music. Up to six swiftly changing well kept real ales on handpump: Courage Directors, Hawkshead Bitter, Marstons Pedigree, Theakstons Best, Timothy Taylors Landlord and Yates Bitter. They specialise in carefully chosen new world wines, with around a dozen by the glass. Good food includes lunchtime hot and cold sandwiches (from £4.25) and filled baked potatoes (from £5.95), plus home-made soup (£3.25), chicken caesar salad with parmesan and croûtons (£4.25), greek mezze or dim sum and samosas with a soy and sweet chilli dip (£6.95), stir-fried chicken strips with cajun spices, red onions and mushrooms, large fish, chips and mushy peas or mushrooms filled with pine nuts and couscous topped with cheddar cheese and caramelised red onion (all £7.95), full rack of chargrilled spare ribs or grilled salmon topped with whole green beans stir-fried in chilli marmalade (£8.95), and steaks (from £11.95). In front is a very attractive terrace with plenty of good wooden tables looking on to the market cross, big heaters, and lots of colourful plants in tubs and hanging baskets. If something's happening in town, the pub is usually a part of it, and they can be busy on Thursday market day. *(Recommended by Jo Lilley, Simon Calvert, David Carr, Michael Doswell)*

Free house ~ Licensee Roger Chattaway ~ Real ale ~ Bar food (11-3, 5.30-8.30) ~ Restaurant ~ (01229) 584469 ~ Children welcome ~ Open 10-11

YANWATH NY5128 Map 9
Gate Inn 🍴 ♀
2¼ miles from M6 junction 40; A66 towards Brough, then right on A6, right on B5320, then follow village signpost

The friendly and hard-working new landlord here is keen to restore this 350-year-old no smoking place back to being a proper country pub again – but at the same time is winning warm praise for his imaginative food. The emphasis is very much on that, but the atmosphere is relaxed and pubby, and you can be sure of a warm welcome from the helpful and cheerful staff – service is top-notch. Using local suppliers and producers, the menu at lunchtime might include soup (£4.25), bowl of moules marinière (£5.50; main course £9.50), open sandwich of avocado and crayfish tails with lemon aïoli and potato salad (£7.50), scrambled egg and chives with smoked salmon and fresh asparagus on a toasted bloomer or parsnip and chestnut crumble (£7.95), a platter of fish, meats and local cheese with chutney and freshly baked bread (£7.95; main course £13.95), a traditional lamb stew (£8.50), and corn-fed thai chicken burger with chilli mayonnaise (£8.95); evening choices such as squash, ricotta and basil tartlet with watercress sauce (£5.50), hot smoked salmon and spring onion crème brûlée (£6.95), seared scallops with pea purée (£7.95), beetroot risotto with cheese beignets and bean curd fritters (£11.95), seared tuna salad niçoise (£12.95), and pork fillet stuffed with smoked port and apricot with cider fondant potatoes and jus of leeks or goosnargh corn-fed duck breast with fig sauce (£13.95), and puddings like toffee apple crumble with crème anglaise or chocolate and sweet ginger tart with blood orange sorbet (from £5.50). The two restaurant areas have been carefully refurbished with oak floors, panelled oak walls and heavy beams, and the cosy bar has country pine and dark wood furniture, lots of brasses on the beams, church candles on all the tables, and a good log fire in the attractive stone inglenook. Well kept Hesket Newmarket Doris's 90th Birthday Ale, Jennings Crag Rat and Tirril Bewshers on handpump, and a good choice of wines (nine in handy 250ml bottles); piped music. There are seats on the terrace and in the garden. (Recommended by Helen Clarke, Hugh and Susan Ellison, Sally and Mark Bramall, J S Burn, Maurice and Gill McMahon, Richard J Holloway)

Free house ~ Licensee Matt Edwards ~ Real ale ~ Bar food (12-2.30, 6-9.30; not Mon) ~ Restaurant ~ (01768) 862386 ~ Children welcome ~ Dogs allowed in bar ~ Live music winter Mon evenings ~ Open 11-11; 12-10.30 Sun

LUCKY DIP

Besides the fully inspected pubs, you might like to try these Lucky Dips recommended to us and described by readers (if you do, please send us reports: www.goodguides.co.uk).

ALSTON [NY7146]
☆ *Angel* [Front St]: Friendly and busy 17th-c local on steep cobbled street of charming small Pennine market town, beams, timbers, big log and coal fire, traditional furnishings, good value homely food (not Tues evening), generous and quickly served, from well filled sandwiches to steaks, well kept Flowers IPA and Greene King Old Speckled Hen, decent house wines; no dogs; children welcome in eating area, tables in sheltered back garden; cheap bedrooms *(R T and J C Moggridge, LYM, Nick Holding)*

AMBLESIDE [NY4008]
☆ *Kirkstone Pass Inn* [A592 N of Troutbeck]: Majestic surrounding scenery for Lakeland's highest inn, doing well under current management and with atmosphere to match – flagstones, stripped stone and simple furnishings, lots of old photographs and bric-a-brac, two log fires, friendly service, cheap tasty food all day from 9.30, well kept Jennings and occasional guest beers, good coffee, hot chocolate, mulled wine, daily papers, games and books; piped music, pool room; dogs welcome, tables outside, three bedrooms, open all day *(John and Hiro Charles, Mrs B M Hill, Kevin Thorpe, LYM, Catherine and Rob Dunster)*

White Lion [Market Pl]: Large comfortable pub with popular quickly served food in bar and restaurant, well kept Bass and Worthington, friendly helpful well trained staff; tables out on sunny streetside terrace *(John Foord)*

APPLEBY [NY6820]
Tufton Arms [Market Sq/Boroughgate]: Family-run late Victorian hotel, bar well used by locals with enjoyable food, quick attentive service, real ales; seats out in cobbled yard, comfortable bedrooms *(John and Jackie Chalcraft)*

ARMATHWAITE [NY5045]
Fox & Pheasant: Cosy, comfortable and neatly kept 18th-c coaching inn overlooking River Eden, enjoyable generous food inc imaginative dishes, well kept Jennings and Hesket Newmarket ales, cafetière coffee, attractive beamed and flagstoned stripped-stone bar, shining brass, roaring fire, charming small dining room, helpful staff; picnic-sets outside, bedrooms *(Helen Clarke, Michael Doswell)*

BAMPTON [NY5118]
Mardale: Smart and neatly kept small village inn, entirely no smoking, with well kept ales such as Coniston, Hawkshead, Jennings or Tirril, lots of whiskies, good wines and coffee, small choice of enjoyable evening food inc splendid hearty puddings, informal friendly atmosphere, prompt helpful service, log fire and oak beams, dominoes, wooden puzzles and things to read left out; unobjectionable piped music; children welcome, three comfortable well equipped bedrooms, lovely countryside, cl wkdy lunchtimes *(Nigel Scott)*

BASSENTHWAITE [NY2332]
☆ *Sun* [off A591 N of Keswick]: Opened-up rambling bar popular for wide range of quickly served up-to-date food from sandwiches up,

friendly landlord and attentive service, well kept Jennings ales, good wines by the glass, two big log fires, low 17th-c beams, interesting local photographs, pool; provision for children, tables in pretty front yard with lovely fell views *(D F Lye, Simon J Barber, Mrs M Hitchings, LYM, Richard J Holloway, Paul Jeffery, Tony and Maggie Harwood, Roger and Maureen Kenning)*

BLENCOGO [NY1948]

☆ *New Inn* [signed off B5302 Wigton—Silloth]: Must book for fine choice of very good food – real serious cooking, in big helpings at good value prices – in bright and simply modernised former village local, log fire, real ale, decent wines and whiskies, a few big Cumbrian landscapes, pleasant service; cl Mon *(BB, Matthew and Pippa Oakeshott)*

BOOT [NY1700]

☆ *Brook House*: Converted small Victorian hotel with friendly family service, wide choice of good generous home-made food inc some interesting dishes on solid timber tables (breakfast for nearby campers too), small no smoking plushly modernised bar, comfortable hunting-theme lounge, log fires, four well kept ales such as Black Sheep, Coniston, Theakstons and Yates, decent wines, peaceful separate restaurant, good views; handy for Ravenglass railway and great walks, eight good bedrooms with own bathrooms – and good drying room *(Jenny and Brian Seller, Paul Davies, Annie Rosenthal, J S Burn, Jo Lilley, Simon Calvert, Robert Ager, Mark and Debra Davies)*

Burnmoor [aka Boot Inn; signed just off the Wrynose/Hardknott Pass rd]: Comfortably modernised beamed bar with ever-burning fire, well kept Black Sheep, Jennings Bitter and Cumberland and a guest beer, decent wines and malt whiskies, good mulled wine all year, reasonably priced home-made lunchtime bar food from sandwiches and baked potatoes up, no smoking restaurant and dining conservatory; booked minibus parties may have priority, games room with pool, TV and juke box; children welcome, seats out on sheltered front lawn with play area, open all day, good walks, lovely surroundings *(LYM, Tina and David Woods-Taylor, Jo Lilley, Simon Calvert, Mark and Debra Davies)*

BORROWDALE [NY2617]

Borrowdale Hotel [B5289, S end of Derwentwater]: A hotel, but very good choice of reasonably priced 'pub lunch' food from sandwiches up in smart, friendly and roomy bar, well kept Jennings Cumberland, pleasant service and attentive management, good value five-course meals in properly run restaurant, light conservatory; garden tables, good bedrooms *(Guy Consterdine, C A Hall)*

BOWLAND BRIDGE [SD4189]

☆ *Hare & Hounds* [signed from A5074]: Spick and span country dining pub with roaring log fire in small bar, attractive eating areas off with polished flagstones or red carpet, some stripped stone, wide range of enjoyable reasonably priced food from baguettes through

typical pub dishes to some tempting up-to-date specials, pleasant attentive service, real ales inc Black Sheep, Boddingtons and a bargain beer brewed for the pub; children welcome, picnic-sets in spacious side garden, bedrooms, quiet hamlet in lovely scenery *(Margaret and Roy Randle, Dr R C C Ward, LYM, Michael Doswell, Mrs P Gostling)*

BOWNESS-ON-WINDERMERE [SD4097]

☆ *Hole in t' Wall* [Lowside]: Ancient beams and flagstones, stripped stone, lots of country bric-a-brac and old pictures, lively bustle, splendid log fire under vast slate mantelpiece, upper room with attractive plasterwork (and dominoes and juke box), good value generous honest pub food from sandwiches to steak and good curries, well kept Robinsons ales, may be home-made lemonade or good winter mulled wine; very busy in tourist season; no dogs or prams, sheltered picnic-sets in tiny flagstoned front courtyard *(Tony Pope, Karen Bonham, Peter Abbott, LYM, Mrs J Walker, Ron Gentry)*

Royal Oak [Brantfell Rd]: Decent town pub with well kept beers, reasonably priced food, friendly service; children welcome, tables out in front, bedrooms with own bathrooms *(Dennis Jones)*

BRAITHWAITE [NY2323]

☆ *Coledale Hotel* [signed off A66 W of Keswick, pub then signed left off B5292]: Bustling inn below Whinlatter Pass, welcoming to walkers, with coal fire, little 19th-c Lakeland engravings, plush banquettes and studded tables, well kept Jennings, John Smiths and Theakstons XB, friendly staff, hearty promptly served food, no smoking dining room; darts, dominoes, piped music; fine views of Skiddaw, garden with slate terrace and sheltered lawn, pretty bedrooms, open all day *(LYM, Don and Shirley Parrish, Geoff and Angela Jaques, John and Angie Millar)*

Royal Oak: Flagstoned bar with good value food, prompt helpful service, well kept Jennings; dogs welcome exc at mealtimes *(Julia and Richard Tredgett, Tony and Maggie Harwood)*

BRIGSTEER [SD4889]

☆ *Wheatsheaf*: Decorous dining pub with good food from interesting sandwiches (they bake their own bread) and lunchtime snacks to good fresh fish and game (takeaways some nights – fish and steak and kidney pie), good value Sun lunch inc splendid fish hors-d'oeuvre, well kept local ales such as Barngates, Hawkshead, Jennings or Yates, well chosen wines, cheerful attentive staff, attractive dining room; quiet pretty village *(Michael Doswell, Malcolm Taylor, A C English, Maurice and Gill McMahon, Jonathan Shephard, Peter Abbott, Jim Abbott, Robert Ager, Pat and Graham Williamson)*

BROUGHTON-IN-FURNESS [SD2187]

☆ *Manor Arms* [The Square]: Outstanding choice of changing well kept ales from local microbreweries and further afield in neatly kept and comfortable open-plan pub on quiet sloping square, flagstones and bow window seats, coal fire in big stone fireplace, chiming clocks, good sandwiches, pizzas and bockwurst sausages, winter soup, pool table; children allowed, stairs down to lavatories (ladies' has baby-changing); well appointed good value bedrooms, big breakfast, open all day *(BB, Richard Houghton, Mr and Mrs Maurice Thompson)*

CALDBECK [NY3239]

☆ *Oddfellows Arms* [B5299 SE of Wigton]: Homely modernised split-level pub with fine old photographs and woodburner in comfortable front bar, big no smoking back dining room, generous home cooking from baked potatoes and lunchtime sandwiches to lots of blackboard specials, well kept Jennings Bitter and Cumberland and Youngers, decent wines, reasonable prices, affable landlord, obliging uniformed staff; piped music, games area with darts, pool and TV; children welcome, open all day Fri-Sun and summer, low-priced bedrooms, nice village *(Helen Clarke, Kevin Thorpe)*

CARLISLE [NY3458]

Drovers Rest [off B5307 W of Carlisle]: Small and spotless, with good range of Jennings beers, welcoming open fire and lots of polished wood, quick helpful service, good range of baguettes and enjoyable straightforward hot dishes, attractive no smoking side dining room, back games room; tables out in garden with play area *(A H C Rainier)*

Sportsmans [Heads Lane, nr Marks & Spencer]: Small, friendly and neatly kept, with good range of sensibly priced food 11.30-7 (12.30-5 Sun) from baguettes up, well kept Youngers; quiz night Mon *(David Carr, Tim and Rosemary Wells)*

CARTMEL [SD3778]

Cavendish Arms [Cavendish St, off main sq]: Good unpretentious local atmosphere in civilised bar with roaring fire, well kept real ales, good value food from sandwiches up, good service, no smoking restaurant; children truly welcome, tables out in front and behind by stream, ten comfortable bedrooms, good walks, open all day *(LYM, Margaret Dickinson)*

CASTLE CARROCK [NY5455]

Weary Sportsman: 17th-c building reworked as stylish pub/brasserie, comfortable sofas and bucket chairs on bare boards of light and airy bar with good prints and wall of glassware and objets, smart conservatory dining room, good choice of upmarket food, well kept Black Sheep, interesting wines, welcoming service; good tables in back japanese garden, comfortable well equipped bedrooms *(Michael Doswell, Nigel and Jean Eames)*

CONISTON [SD3098]

☆ *Black Bull* [Yewdale Rd (A593)]: Good Coniston Bluebird, XB and Old Man brewed here, Theakstons XB, lots of Donald Campbell water-speed memorabilia, bustling flagstoned back area (dogs allowed), banquettes and open fire in partly no smoking carpeted lounge bar (no smoking restaurant too), quick cheerful service, simple good value food inc children's, good sandwiches and more enterprising

specials, farm ciders, quite a few bottled beers and malt whiskies; children welcome in eating areas, tables out in suntrap former coachyard, bedrooms, open all day *(John Foord, Nikki Wild, Jarrod and Wendy Hopkinson, Peter Abbott, Patrick Hancock, Andrew Crawford, Len Beattie, LYM, Jo Lilley, Simon Calvert, Mike and Lynn Robinson, Mr and Mrs Maurice Thompson)*

Crown [Tilberthwaite Ave (B5285)]: Relaxed and welcoming, with good friendly staff, quickly served bar food, well kept real ale, reasonable prices, hot coal fire; bedrooms, open all day *(Sion Jair)*

☆ *Sun*: 16th-c pub in terrific setting below dramatic fells, interesting Donald Campbell and other Lakeland photographs in old-fashioned back bar with beams, flagstones, good log fire in 19th-c range, cask seats and old settles, big no smoking conservatory off carpeted lounge (children allowed here), friendly helpful staff, well kept Coniston Bluebird, Moorhouses Black Cat and interesting guest beers, decent wines, darts, cribbage, dominoes; dogs in bar, tables on pleasant front terrace, big tree-sheltered garden, simple comfortable bedrooms, good hearty breakfast, open all day *(Mr and Mrs Ireland, Michael and Marion Buchanan, Tina and David Woods-Taylor, Tim Maddison, Duncan Cloud, Steve Kirby, LYM, Len Beattie, Ray and Winifred Halliday, Ron Gentry, Patrick Hancock, Christine and Phil Young, Mrs Phoebe A Kemp, Mr and Mrs Maurice Thompson)*

COWGILL [SD7686]

☆ *Sportsmans* [nr Dent Station, on Dent— Garsdale Head rd]: Cosy Dentdale local with good nearby walks, friendly landlord, good standard home-made food lunchtime and evening, well kept Black Sheep and Tetleys, decent wine, log fires, simple bar/lounge with darts in snug at one end and pool room at the other, no piped music; bedrooms overlooking lovely river *(Mr and Mrs Maurice Thompson)*

CROOK [SD4795]

☆ *Sun* [B5284 Kendal—Bowness]: Good atmosphere and wide choice of good plentiful food (all day wknds) from unusual sandwiches to enterprising hot dishes, winter game and lovely puddings, two bustling no smoking dining areas off low-beamed bar, roaring log fire, fresh flowers, well kept Coniston Bluebird and Courage Directors, good value wines, cheerful helpful service *(Jean and Douglas Troup, LYM, E A and D C T Frewer, Hugh Roberts, Les and Barbara Owen, Michael Doswell)*

CROSTHWAITE [SD4491]

Punch Bowl [off A5074 SE of Windermere]: This formerly very popular dining pub has been taken over and remodelled by the owners of the Drunken Duck nr Hawkshead (see main entries); still under wraps with the builders in just before we went to press with this edition, so we can't yet give any rating, but we heard they might use the old dining room for people staying (comfortable bedrooms in this attractive quiet location), turning the snug into an eating area and keeping part of the bar for people who just want a drink; reports on the new regime please *(LYM)*

CUMWHITTON [NY5052]

☆ *Pheasant* [off B6413 Brampton—Kirkoswald]: Simple flagstoned bar with prompt friendly service, well kept changing ales such as Black Sheep, good value tasty generous food, buoyant atmosphere, back pool table and small no smoking dining room (best to book at wknds); children welcome, small garden *(Nick and Meriel Cox, Mrs Anne Henley)*

DACRE [NY4526]

Horse & Farrier [between A66 and A592 SW of Penrith]: 18th-c black-beamed village local with well kept Jennings inc a Mild, straightforward home-made pub food, small cheery front room with elderly stove, more modern dining extension down steps on the left, darts, dominoes, bridge and quiz nights; children welcome, integral post office, pretty village *(A H C Rainier, BB, Geoff and Angela Jaques)*

DENT [SD7086]

George & Dragon [Main St]: Comfortable hotel bar, dark panelling (but bright lights), flagstones, partitioned tables, good generously served food inc bargain Sun lunch and reasonably priced evening restaurant meals, helpful service, no smoking dining room, separate games room; bedrooms comfortable, lovely village *(Margaret Dickinson)*

Sun [Main St]: Old-fashioned local with pleasantly traditional beamed bar, plenty of character, its own good Dent ales brewed nearby, reasonably priced usual food from sandwiches up, darts; children welcome, open all day in summer *(Gerry and Rosemary Dobson, LYM, Margaret Dickinson, Mr and Mrs Maurice Thompson)*

ENNERDALE BRIDGE [NY0615]

☆ *Shepherds Arms* [off A5086 E of Egremont]: Walkers' inn well placed by car-free dale, with footpath plans, weather-forecast blackboard and appropriate books, lots of pictures, log fire and woodburner, no smoking bar extension, panelled dining room and conservatory, food from good sandwiches up using local produce, well kept Coniston Bluebird, Jennings, Timothy Taylors Landlord and guest beers, good wine choice; may be piped music; children and dogs welcome, bedrooms, open all day (may be winter afternoon break Mon-Thurs) *(Pat and Stewart Gordon, LYM, Evan and Marjorie Lisovskis, TOH, John and Enid Morris, Mark and Debra Davies, Paul and Gloria Howell)*

ESKDALE GREEN [NY1300]

☆ *Bower House* [½ mile W]: Civilised and friendly old-fashioned stone-built inn with good log fire in main lounge bar extended around beamed and alcoved core, well kept ales such as Theakstons, generous straightforward bar food, biggish no smoking restaurant; bar can be smoky, may be piped music; nicely tended sheltered garden by cricket field, charming spot with great walks, bedrooms, open all day *(Tina and David Woods-Taylor, LYM, TOH, Mark and Debra Davies)*

FOXFIELD [SD2185]

☆ *Prince of Wales* [opp stn]: Friendly and simple, with half a dozen well kept and served ales inc bargain beers brewed in the former stables here and at their associated Tigertops brewery, bottled imports, farm cider and regular beer festivals, enthusiastic licensees, enjoyable simple home-made food, hot coal fire, maps, customer snaps and beer awards, pub games inc bar billiards, daily papers and beer-related reading matter, back room with one huge table; children very welcome, games for them; steps up to door; cl Mon/Tues, opens 5 Weds/Thurs, open all day Fri-Sun, reasonably priced bedrooms with own bathrooms *(Richard Houghton, Dr B and Mrs P B Baker, BB, G Coates, Christopher Goddard, Mr and Mrs Maurice Thompson)*

GARRIGILL [NY7441]

☆ *George & Dragon* [off B6277 S of Alston]: Nicely set small 17th-c village inn with enjoyable food, well kept ales such as Black Sheep, good wines, great log fire in flagstoned bar and attractive stone-and-panelling dining room; pleasant bedrooms, open all day Sat *(LYM, Tony and Maggie Harwood, Mike and Lynn Robinson)*

GILSLAND [NY6366]

Samson [B6318, E end of village]: Weekly guest beer, good country cooking, walkers welcome (handy for Hadrian's Wall Trail); dogs allowed in part of bar *(Dr D J and Mrs S C Walker)*

GRASMERE [NY3307]

Red Lion [Red Lion Sq]: Plush seats and cast-iron pub tables in hotel's Lamb bar, open fire in slate fireplace, simple décor with some paintings, china and cider jugs, well kept Theakstons Best and XB, good range of malt whiskies, decent bar food inc all-day soup, good friendly service; pool and darts in back room, TV; cane-chair conservatory, well priced restaurant; comfortable bedrooms, good breakfast, lovely views, open all day *(Kevin Thorpe, Christine and Neil Townend)*

☆ *Travellers Rest* [A591 just N]: Cheerful and popular, with settles, banquettes, upholstered armchairs and log fire, local watercolours, old photographs, suggested walks, bar food (all day in summer), Greene King and Jennings ales, family games area with pool, big dining area; children in eating areas, dogs in bar, open all day, bedrooms *(Nikki Wild, Kevin Thorpe, Don and Shirley Parrish, Tina and David Woods-Taylor, LYM, Jack Clark, W W Burke, Mr and Mrs John Taylor, Mr and Mrs Maurice Thompson)*

HAVERTHWAITE [SD3284]

Anglers Arms [just off A590]: Busy and friendly split-level pub with good choice of fairly priced generous fresh food from sandwiches to steak, fine choice of well kept ales served by helpful staff, overflow upstairs dining room, lower area with pool *(Dennis Jones)*

HAYTON [NY5157]

☆ *Lane End* [A69 Carlisle—Brampton]: Well run stone-built pub with wide choice of good value generous food served quickly all day from sandwiches up, cosy softly lit low-beamed bar, rugs on flagstones, banquettes and settles, roaring log fire, good bustling atmosphere, friendly staff, well kept Jennings, good coffee, dining room and attractive conservatory; pool room, piped music; open all day, play area *(Pat and Stewart Gordon)*

HEVERSHAM [SD4983]

Blue Bell [A6]: Beamed and partly panelled lounge bar, warm log fire, big big-windowed no smoking area, Sam Smiths OB, bar food (all day during hols), no smoking restaurant, long public bar (games, TV, piped music); children and dogs welcome, comfortable bedrooms, open all day *(Dr and Mrs T E Hothersall, Mr and Mrs C R Little, David Mee, LYM, Roger and Maureen Kenning, JWAC)*

HIGH NEWTON [SD4082]

Crown [just off A590 Lindale—Newby Bridge, towards Cartmel Fell]: Friendly, well run and attractive former 18th-c coaching inn with changing well kept beers inc Jennings and Yates, enjoyable food inc quickly served Sun lunch, spacious bars and dining area; children welcome, comfortable bedrooms with own bathrooms *(Ron Gentry)*

KENDAL [SD5192]

Burgundys Wine Bar [Lowther St]: Small attractive multi-level bar with interesting changing local ales such as Dent, Derwent and Yates, enthusiastic landlord happy to talk about them, bottled imports, ciders and unusual wines too, welcoming service; cl Mon evening and Sun-Weds lunchtimes *(Mr and Mrs Maurice Thompson, Hugh Roberts, Christopher Goddard)*

Castle [Castle St]: Well run bustling two-bar local by River Kent and nr castle, good value popular bar lunches from sandwiches up, well kept Jennings, Tetleys and guests such as Black Sheep and Dent; TV and games area *(Mr and Mrs Maurice Thompson, MLR)*

Miles Thompson [Allhallows Lane]: Well appointed Wetherspoons in interesting conversion of substantial Victorian public baths with towering chimney, plain wood and chrome furniture, high-raftered stripped-stone upper room, ten reasonably priced real ales and speciality bottled beers, their usual food, family room; very popular with young people *(Hugh Roberts, Michael Doswell)*

KESWICK [NY2623]

Bank Tavern [Main St]: Low-beamed L-shaped carpeted bar, clean and comfortable, full Jennings range and a guest beer kept well, simple pub food (very popular for this at lunchtime), log-effect gas fire, children's room; bedrooms, open all day *(Tony and Maggie Harwood, Steve and Liz Tilley)*

Dog & Gun [Lake Rd]: Lively flagstoned town pub with well kept Theakstons Best and Old Peculier, Yates and several guest beers from afar (landlord really cares about his beer), log fires, generous straightforward bar food all day

from sandwiches up inc speciality goulash, close-set tables and some high settles, fine Abrahams mountain photographs, coins in lion beams and timbers by fireplace (collected for local mountain rescue), model cars; piped music, games machine, no dogs; children welcome, open all day *(Andy and Jill Kassube, Kevin Thorpe, LYM, A and B D Craig, P S Hoyle, MLR, Don and Shirley Parrish, Steve Kirby, David Carr, Tony and Maggie Harwood, John Foord)*

☆ *George* [St Johns St]: Fine old place with attractive traditional black-panelled side room, open-plan main bar, old-fashioned settles and modern banquettes under Elizabethan beams, daily papers, well kept Jennings Bitter, Cocker Hoop, Cumberland and Sneck Lifter, good plain bar food, big log fire, no smoking restaurant; piped music, fruit machine; children welcome in eating areas, dogs in bar, bedrooms with own bathrooms, open all day *(LYM, Mrs J Walker, Don and Shirley Parrish, Mike and Lynn Robinson, David Carr, B Shelley, Robert Ager, Mr and Mrs John Taylor, Paul and Gloria Howell)*

Kings Arms [Main St]: Comfortable hotel front bar, Black Sheep and Theakstons Best, good choice of food from good value toasties up, friendly if not always speedy staff, courtyard restaurant; quite a few steps here and there, lavatories upstairs; bedrooms, open all day *(George Atkinson)*

Oddfellows [Main St]: Long busy open-plan bar with masses of horse-racing memorabilia, pleasant staff, four well kept Jennings ales, plentiful food all day, upstairs dining room; piped music, live nightly; huge beer garden, open all day *(Kevin Thorpe, Tony and Maggie Harwood)*

☆ *Pack Horse* [Pack Horse Ct, off Market Sq]: Low-beamed pub in attractive alley courtyard, well kept Jennings (full range) and interesting guest beers, friendly service, cheery locals (bar can get smoky); worth booking for enjoyable food in two upper floors – an oasis of calm *(LYM, Mr and Mrs John Taylor)*

KIRKBY LONSDALE [SD6178]

Orange Tree [Fairbank]: Well stocked bar, good range of food inc speciality steaks, softly lit back restaurant, discreetly placed pool; SkyTV; comfortable bedrooms over road *(Jo Lilley, Simon Calvert)*

Snooty Fox [B6254]: Rambling partly panelled pub with interesting pictures and bric-a-brac, country furniture, two coal fires, no smoking dining annexe, Timothy Taylors Landlord, Theakstons Best and a guest beer, several country wines, reasonably priced straightforward food; piped music, machines; children in eating areas, tables in pretty garden, open all day *(LYM, Tony and Maggie Harwood, Jo Lilley, Simon Calvert, Brian and Anita Randall, Christine and Neil Townend, Drs M J and P M Cox, Bruce and Sharon Eden)*

☆ *Sun* [Market St (B6254)]: Low-beamed partly stripped-stone bar, cosy pews, two good log fires, well kept ales such as Black Sheep and

Timothy Taylors Landlord, lots of malt whiskies, good value generous food, cheerful staff, attractive no smoking back dining room; quiet piped music; bedrooms *(Roger Thornington, LYM, Jo Lilley, Simon Calvert)*

KIRKOSWALD [NY5541]

☆ *Crown*: Friendly 16th-c village local (darts, dominoes, pool and quizzes all taken seriously), beams covered with plates, brasses around fireplace, teapots over bar, good generous reasonably priced food from big sandwiches to italian specialities, plenty of local produce and fish (same menu in bar and small no smoking restaurant), well kept Jennings ales inc Dark Mild, proper coffees *(Kevin Tea, JWAC, Michael Doswell)*

LEVENS [SD4785]

Gilpin Bridge Inn [on cut-off from A590, nr A5074 junction]: Good reasonably priced food in bar and restaurant (wider choice here, booking advised), well trained cheerful service, Robinsons real ales *(Ron Gentry)*

LOWICK BRIDGE [SD2986]

☆ *Red Lion* [just off A5084]: Family food pub, warm, comfortable and clean, very busy in summer, with well kept Robinsons Hartleys XB, friendly landlord, reasonably priced home-made food, open fire, separate dining area; children and dogs welcome, tables outside, charming spot, good value bedrooms, good breakfast *(Susan Pierce)*

MELMERBY [NY6237]

Shepherds [A686 Penrith—Alston]: Country pub with comfortable heavy-beamed no smoking room off flagstoned bar, spacious end room with woodburner, generous food, well kept Black Sheep, Jennings and a guest beer such as Dent, quite a few malt whiskies, games area with pool and juke box; children welcome *(A and B D Craig, LYM, JWAC, John Foord, Mr and Mrs Maurice Thompson)*

MIDDLETON [SD6286]

☆ *Swan* [A683 Kirkby Lonsdale—Sedbergh]: Quaint two-roomed beamed pub built as a 16th-c farm, clean and friendly, with lots of individuality, real ales such as Black Sheep, Hawkshead, Timothy Taylors and Thwaites, log fire in lovely fireplace, decent food with some imaginative dishes *(LYM, Margaret Dickinson)*

NATEBY [NY7807]

Black Bull [B6259 Kirkby Stephen—Wensleydale]: Peaceful and welcoming old moors-edge inn with enjoyable reasonably priced food, well kept real ales, civilised landlord, pleasant layout, roaring log fire, nice decorations and beams; five bedrooms, lovely setting *(M and GR, R Halsey)*

NENTHEAD [NY7843]

Miners Arms: Friendly helpful service in stripped stone lounge with leather sofas among other seating, well kept changing ales, good range of coffees, good genuine home cooking at least in season, reasonable prices, no piped music, bar billiards in partly panelled flagstoned public bar, view from big conservatory; dogs welcome, picnic-sets out in front, homely family bedrooms, filling breakfast, also bunkhouse, open all day in summer, handy for Pennine Way and cycle path *(Tony and Maggie Harwood)*

NETHER WASDALE [NY1204]

Screes: Interesting public bar and steps up to long plush lounge, stunning views of mountains and along Wasdale, particularly well kept Black Sheep, Yates Best and an interesting guest beer, quick friendly service, good value home-made food inc lunchtime sandwiches and generous honest-to-goodness hot dishes, decent piped music; picnic-sets out on large front green, five bedrooms *(Tony and Maggie Harwood, David Field, Dr and Mrs S G Barber)*

NEWBY BRIDGE [SD3686]

Swan [just off A590]: Substantial hotel in fine setting below fells next to river with waterside picnic-sets under cocktail parasols by old stone bridge, extensive neatly kept rambling bar with all sorts of comfortable nooks and crannies inc no smoking areas, bar snacks and brasserie meals (all day wknds), Bass and Boddingtons, good coffee; piped music; children in eating areas, open all day, comfortable bedrooms with own bathrooms *(LYM, John and Sylvia Harrop)*

OULTON [NY2451]

Bird in Hand [N of Wigton]: Unpretentious and homely local, with enjoyable home-made food (especially the chips), Jennings ales, friendly service *(Helen Clarke)*

OXENHOLME [SD5390]

☆ *Station Inn* [½ mile up hill, B6254 towards Old Hutton]: Reliable generous home-made food inc hearty sandwiches and interesting dishes as well as the standards in spruce and roomy dining pub, thoughtful children's dishes, good friendly service, well kept ales such as Black Sheep, Flowers Original and Tirril, nice wine list, log fire; children welcome, large garden with extensive play area, bedrooms, good walks *(Michael Doswell, John and Gillian Scarisbrick, Clive Gibson, Jim Abbott)*

PATTERDALE [NY3915]

White Lion: Cheerful bar with a ready market of walkers and climbers (can be crowded wknds), well kept ales such as Castle Eden, substantial inexpensive food in long narrow room on left; dogs welcome, bedrooms *(John and Hiro Charles)*

PENRITH [NY5130]

Gloucester Arms [Cornmarket]: Friendly and ancient low-beamed local, lots of wood and panelling, comfortable seats, big open fire, well kept changing guest beers, cheap filling food; no dogs, open all day *(John and Hiro Charles)*
Lowther Arms [Queen St]: Handsome 17th-c local, friendly and comfortable, with reliable home cooking, well kept ales such as Courage Directors, Fullers London Pride and Theakstons, real fire *(John and Hiro Charles)*

PENRUDDOCK [NY4227]

Herdwick [off A66 Penrith—Keswick]: New management in attractively cottagey 18th-c inn with stripped stone and white paintwork, well kept Jennings and summer guest beers from unusual curved bar, decent wines, nice no smoking dining room with upper gallery, bar food from lunchtime sandwiches, baguettes and baked potatoes to more elaborate evening dishes, games room with pool and darts; children in eating areas, five bedrooms *(Geoff and Angela Jaques, LYM, Andy and Jill Kassube, Mike and Sue Loseby)*

POOLEY BRIDGE [NY4724]
Sun: Busy panelled pub with good value generous food from sandwiches and baked potatoes to nicely cooked main dishes, cheery young landlord, full Jennings range kept well, good wine choice, small no smoking lounge bar, steps past servery to bigger bar with games, TV and piped music, no smoking restaurant; bedrooms, plenty of garden tables, great views *(Michael Dandy, Geoff and Angela Jaques, Alison Hoy)*

PORTINSCALE [NY2423]
Farmers Arms [off A66 at Grane/Newlands Valley sign]: Comfortable dining pub with enjoyable food, tasteful orange-washed walls, small partly tiled bare-boards bar with Jennings ales and good stock of wines and spirits, friendly helpful staff; booking recommended *(Tony and Maggie Harwood)*

RAVENSTONEDALE [SD7401]
☆ *Fat Lamb* [Crossbank; A683 Sedbergh—Kirkby Stephen]: Remote pub with pews in cheerful relaxing bar, coal fire in traditional black inglenook range, good local photographs and bird plates, friendly helpful staff, wide choice of above-average hearty food from filled baguettes to enjoyable restaurant meals, well kept Tetleys, decent wines; facilities for disabled, children welcome; tables out by sheep pastures, good walks, bedrooms *(John and Yvonne Davies, E G Parish, M S Catling, M and GR, BB, Jack Clark, Margaret Dickinson)*

ROSTHWAITE [NY2514]
Scafell [B5289 S of Keswick]: Plain slate-floored bar in back extension, a few tables out overlooking beck, well kept Theakstons Best and XB, blazing log fire, usual food from sandwiches up, fast friendly service even when packed with walkers (weather forecasts up on a board); afternoon teas, piped music, pool; separate entrance to rather plush hotel with appealing cocktail bar/sun-lounge and dining room, bedrooms not big but good *(BB, Jack Clark)*

SATTERTHWAITE [SD3392]
Eagles Head: Attentive and friendly new owner for small unpretentious pub in beautiful scenery of Grizedale Forest, enjoyable sensibly priced food, well kept real ales, big log fire, lots of local photographs and maps; children welcome, picnic-sets outside, comfortable bedrooms *(Mr and Mrs Hughes)*

SCALES [NY3426]
☆ *White Horse* [A66 W of Penrith]: Light and airy no smoking beamed pub-restaurant under welcoming and hard-working new licensees, cosy corners, interesting farmhouse-kitchen memorabilia and good log fires, three well kept ales inc Camerons, wide choice of good food inc local fish and meats, reasonable prices;

quiet piped music; well behaved children welcome, lovely setting below Blencathra, open all day summer *(Angus Lyon, LYM, Mike and Penny Sutton, JWAC)*

SEATOLLER [NY2413]
☆ *Yew Tree*: Good value meals in attractive low-ceilinged dining area with nice prompt no-nonsense service, a couple of well kept ales such as Hesket Newmarket, reasonably priced house wines and good whisky choice, cosy beamed and slate-floored back bar with open range; garden behind *(Guy Vowles)*

SEDBERGH [SD6592]
☆ *Dalesman* [Main St]: Linked rooms with stripped stone and beams, log fire, sporting prints, no smoking buttery area with generous food (all day Sun) running up to aberdeen angus steaks, well kept Tetleys and their own Dalesman, dominoes; piped music, monthly jazz night; children in eating areas, picnic-sets out in front, bedrooms, open all day *(Clare and Peter Pearse, Jim Abbott, LYM, Derek Stafford, John and Yvonne Davies)*

SHAP [NY5615]
☆ *Greyhound* [A6, S end]: Bustling and unpretentious former coaching inn, good local food from sandwiches to slow-cooked local lamb and rather special puddings in open-plan bar or restaurant (chef happy to share his recipes), hearty helpings, well kept Jennings and up to half a dozen guest beers, good reasonably priced house wines, quick service by happy helpful staff; unobtrusive piped classical music, resident collie, dogs welcome; comfortable bedrooms, bunkhouse, popular with coast-to-coast walkers *(Mr and Mrs Maurice Thompson, John and Wendy Allin, Catherine and Rob Dunster, J S Burn, James Snowden, Michael Doswell, MLR, Alison Hoy, Evan and Marjorie Lisovskis, Andy and Jill Kassube)*

SOUTHWAITE [NY4146]
Crown [away from village, towards Gaitsgill]: Very welcoming, with good reasonably priced fresh food from sandwiches and home-made soup up, Theakstons Best and a guest beer, open fire, brightly decorated light and airy dining extension; handy for Carlisle races *(Hugh and Susan Ellison)*

STAINTON [NY4828]
Kings Arms [village signed off A66, handy for M6 junction 40]: Pleasant no smoking open-plan pub with cheery new landlord, reasonably priced simple pub food from home-made soup and well filled sandwiches up, well kept ales such as Greene King, Tetleys and Charles Wells Bombardier, no piped music; children welcome in eating areas, tables on side terrace and small lawn *(LYM, Dodie and Cliff Rutherford)*

THRELKELD [NY3225]
Horse & Farrier: Comfortably extended and neatly kept rather hotelish 17th-c pub with three well kept Jennings ales, good house wines, cosy snug, fairly close-set tables in eating area; open all day, dogs allowed when restaurant is closed, good bedrooms *(Michael Doswell, Tony and Maggie Harwood)*

Salutation [old main rd, bypassed by A66 W of Penrith]: Low-beamed pub below Blencathra, padded wall seats in three areas divided by standing timbers, good coal or log fire, well kept Jennings Cumberland, quite a few malt whiskies, pubby food from sandwiches and baguettes up, new back games room; piped music, TV; dogs welcome, spacious upper children's room, tables out on new decking *(Kevin Thorpe, Tina and David Woods-Taylor, LYM)*

TROUTBECK [NY4103]

☆ *Mortal Man* [A592 N of Windermere; Upper Rd]: Neatly kept partly panelled beamed hotel bar with big log fire, comfortable mix of seats inc a cushioned settle, copper-topped tables, well kept ales such as Jennings, John Smiths and Theakstons Best, friendly young staff, darts, dominoes, cosy eating room, no smoking picture-window restaurant; piped music, TV room, Sun folk/blues night; great views from gloriously sited tables in sunny garden, children welcome, open all day, comfortable bedrooms – lovely village *(Guy Consterdine, Don and Shirley Parrish, Ewan and Moira McCall, LYM, Jack Clark)*

Sportsman [B5288, just off A66]: Big bright rambling bar, Jennings ales and an interesting guest beer, good wine choice, good range of well prepared bar food, separate restaurant menu; children welcome, pretty back terrace overlooking valley, open all day *(Roger Braithwaite)*

ULDALE [NY2436]

Snooty Fox: Comfortable two-bar village inn, friendly helpful landlord, well kept changing beers inc one brewed for them in Hesket Newmarket, good value wines, wide choice of good generous food using local ingredients; good value bedrooms with own bathrooms *(Martin and Sue Day)*

WARWICK-ON-EDEN [NY4656]

Queens Arms [2 miles from M6, junction 43; signed off A69 towards Hexham]: Neatly kept unpretentious two-room bar, well kept Thwaites, good choice of good value wines and malt whiskies, warm log fires, reasonably priced freshly made food (so can take a time); children welcome, tables in attractive side garden with play area, comfortable bedrooms *(LYM, John and Angie Millar)*

WASDALE HEAD [NY1807]

Wasdale Head Inn [NE of Wast Water]: Mountain hotel in marvellous fellside setting, roomy walkers' bar with side hot food counter (all day in summer, may be restricted winter), well kept ales inc their own Great Gable brews, decent choice of wines and malt whiskies, interesting mountain photographs, traditional games, comfortably old-fashioned residents' bar, lounge and restaurant; children welcome, dogs allowed in bar, open all day, bedrooms *(Helen Clarke, LYM, Peter F Marshall, Tim Maddison)*

WATERMILLOCK [NY4523]

Brackenrigg [A592, Ullswater]: Opened-up 19th-c inn in lovely spot with spectacular Ullswater and mountain views, food from generous lunchtime filled rolls and sandwiches to some imaginative recipes, good value and unusual Sunday roasts and thoughtful children's dishes, particularly well kept Black Sheep Special, Tirril Old Faithful, Jennings Cumberland and Theakstons, good range of wines by the glass, friendly mix of holiday-makers and locals, pleasant partly panelled bar with log fire and darts (can be smoky), carpeted lounge and good-sized dining room; comfortable bedrooms, self-catering *(Malcolm and Jane MacDonald, Jane and Neil Kendrick, Geoff and Angela Jaques, Michael Doswell, BB)*

WINDERMERE [NY3902]

Holbeck Ghyll Hotel [Holbeck Ghyll, off A591 N]: Nicely placed hotel, worth knowing for its good fresh food *(Anthony Rickards Collinson)*

Bedroom prices normally include full English breakfast, VAT and any inclusive service charge that we know of. Prices before the '/' are for single rooms, after for two people in double or twin (B includes a private bath, S a private shower). If there is no '/', the prices are only for twin or double rooms (as far as we know there are no singles). If there is no B or S, as far as we know no rooms have private facilities.

Derbyshire

This is one of the best areas for finding traditional unspoilt taverns, in town or country. Splendid examples among the main entries are the timeless Olde Gate at Brassington, the chatty Olde Dolphin in the centre of Derby (splendid beer choice, food all day), the very rustic Quiet Woman at Earl Sterndale, the Dead Poets at Holbrook, the striking Barley Mow at Kirk Ireton, and the farm-side Three Stags Heads near Wardlow. The Lucky Dip section at the end of the chapter is a rich source of further examples. Pubs which are currently winning particularly warm approval for other reasons include the splendid old Bear at Alderwasley (good food all day in interesting and individual surroundings), the Brunswick in Derby (a real ale magnet, excellent value food), the cottagey Coach & Horses at Fenny Bentley (a fine all-rounder, serving its enjoyable food all day), the snug Barrel up on its ridge near Foolow (another all-rounder, gaining a Place to Stay Award this year), the stylish Chequers on Froggatt Edge (this smart dining pub is now no smoking throughout, and serves its good food all day at weekends), the Hardwick Inn, also no smoking, on the edge of the Hardwick Hall estate (food served all day, great drinks choice including two dozen wines by the glass and well over 200 malt whiskies), the friendly Plough just outside Hathersage (spotless bedrooms and very good upmarket food, all day at weekends – it too is entirely no smoking while food's being served), the popular Scotsmans Pack there, the appealing Red Lion on the Litton village green (good food, particularly friendly landlord), the restaurant Miners Arms in Milltown (yet another no smoking place), the Monsal Head Hotel (a favourite for its position and all-day food and drink), the Cock & Pullet at Sheldon (bargain food in a charming building), and the White Horse at Woolley Moor (new owners settling in well, good lunches and a lovely garden). As we have said, food is a strong point at several of these places – and quite often tends to be served throughout the day, particularly at weekends (other tourist areas please note). For a special meal out we'd have no hesitation in recommending the Chequers on Froggatt Edge, Plough near Hathersage or Monsal Head Hotel. However the charming individuality of the Bear at Alderwasley, coupled with its good cooking, makes it our choice as Derbyshire Dining Pub of the Year. In the Lucky Dip section at the end of the chapter, strong prospects include Smiths Tavern in Ashbourne, the Navigation at Buxworth, Olde Nags Head in Castleton, Flower Pot and Standing Order in Derby, Duke of York at Elton, Cheshire Cheese at Hope, Packhorse at Little Longstone, Holly Bush at Makeney, Bulls Head at Monyash, Royal Oak at Ockbrook, and Peacock at Rowsley (hotel not pub, but a splendid alternative). Both food and drinks prices in the area tend to be lower than the national average. Several pubs here now brew their own good value beers, and two local beers well worth looking out for are Whim and (from a new brewery on the Chatsworth estate) Peak.

ALDERWASLEY SK3153 Map 7

Bear ★ ⓦ ♀

Village signposted with Breanfield off B5035 E of Wirksworth at Malt Shovel; inn ½ mile SW of village, on Ambergate—Wirksworth high back road

Derbyshire Dining Pub of the Year

A wonderfully timeless atmosphere pervades the dark, low-beamed rooms of this strikingly unspoilt village pub. Partly lit by candles and stone fireplaces, it has a cheerful miscellany of antique furniture including high-backed settles, locally made antique oak chairs with derbyshire motifs, as well as staffordshire china ornaments, old paintings and engravings and a trio of grandfather clocks. One little room is filled right to its built-in wall seats by a single vast table. Despite the treasures, this is a proper easy-going country local, with dominoes players clattering about beside canaries trilling in a huge Edwardian-style white cage (elsewhere look out for the budgerigars and talkative cockatoos). The sensibly priced, imaginative food is popular so you may need to book (two weeks in advance is advised for Saturdays). Made mostly with ingredients from local farms and growers, and listed on a daily changing blackboard, dishes might include home-made soup (£3.50), japanese king prawns with a sweet chilli dip or smoked mackerel fishcakes (£4.95), melted stilton and crispy bacon en croûte with orange and strawberry chutney (£5.95), roast beef or cottage pie (£7.95), vegetarian chilli con carne with rice (£8.95), slow-cooked lamb in red wine, rosemary and tomato sauce (£9.95), tuna steak with lemon, lime and butter sauce (£10.95), duck breast with brandy and orange jus or venison steak in apricot and port jus (£12.95), 10oz fillet steak in pepper sauce with battered onion rings (£16.95), and puddings such as bakewell pudding or banana fritters with maple syrup (£4.50). Service is friendly and helpful. They have a fine range of interesting wines (including mulled wine and dessert wines by the glass) as well as malt whiskies, and six real ales on handpump – Bass, Black Sheep, Marstons Pedigree, Greene King Old Speckled Hen, Timothy Taylors Landlord and Whim Hartington. There are peaceful country views from well spaced picnic-sets out on the side grass, and it's popular with walkers. There's no obvious front door – you get in through the plain back entrance by the car park. Two dining rooms are no smoking. *(Recommended by Bernard Stradling, Peter F Marshall, Michael and Margaret Slater, Fred and Lorraine Gill, the Didler, CMW, JJW, Pat and Roger Fereday, Richard Cole, Dave and Sue Mitchell, Cathryn and Richard Hicks, Patrick Hancock, Andrew Pearson, Wendy Dye, Kevin Blake, Theocsbrian, Martha Hoyer Millar, R Brackenbury, Derek and Sylvia Stephenson)*

Free house ~ Licensee Nicky Fletcher-Musgrave ~ Real ale ~ Bar food (12-9.30) ~ Restaurant ~ (01629) 822585 ~ Children in family room ~ Dogs welcome ~ Open 12-12; 12-10.30 Sun ~ Bedrooms: £45S/£70S

BEELEY SK2667 Map 7

Devonshire Arms

B6012, off A6 Matlock—Bakewell

In a handsome stone-built estate village within strolling distance of Chatsworth and its huge park, this became a coaching inn in the 19th c – when Dickens is said to have been a regular. Big log fires cheerfully warm the cosy black-beamed rooms and antique settles and simpler wooden chairs stand on old flagstoned floors. There's a big emphasis on the tasty bar food, which is served all day, and could include soup (£3.75), generously filled baguettes (from £4.95), starters such as roasted field mushroom crumble (£5.25) or grilled goats cheese (£6.40), oak smoked salmon and orange salad, as a starter or main course (£6.95 or £10.95), vegetarian pie (£8.75) lamb casserole or derbyshire pigeon breasts (£9.95), salmon en croûte (£11.95) and fillet steak (£16.50), with puddings (from £4) such as apple and cider cake and bread and butter pudding; also a british cheese board with three to six cheeses (£5.95-£8.95). They have a Friday fish night, and on Sundays do a Victorian breakfast (£11.75); you'll need to book for both, and at weekends. Handpumps serve well kept Bass, Black Sheep Best and Special, Greene King Ruddles, Theakstons Old Peculier and a guest such as Peak Ales Swift Nick.

They've also decent good value house wine, and about 30 malt whiskies. All of the building is no smoking; shove-ha'penny; cribbage and dominoes. The excellent Chatsworth estate produce shop is to be found in nearby Pilsley. *(Recommended by Romayne and Donald Denham, Steve Whalley, Keith and Chris O'Neill, Mrs P J Carroll, Susan and John Douglas, the Didler, B M Eldridge, Wendy Dye, Dr P C Rea, A and B D Craig, Mike and Sue Loseby, Mike and Mary Carter)*

Free house ~ Licensee John A Grosvenor ~ Real ale ~ Bar food (12-9.30(Sun 9)) ~ Restaurant ~ (01629) 733259 ~ Children welcome ~ Dogs allowed in bar ~ Open 11-11; 12-10.30 Sun

BRASSINGTON SK2354 Map 7
Olde Gate ★
Village signposted off B5056 and B5035 NE of Ashbourne

'An absolute gem; an authentic, traditional, spotless pub': readers continue to enjoy the wonderfully ancient-feeling interior of this cosy ivy clad inn, which is prettily candlelit at night and does get very busy. The timelessly relaxing public bar is traditionally furnished, with a fine ancient wall clock, rush-seated old chairs, antique settles, including one ancient black solid oak one, and roaring log fires. Gleaming copper pots sit on a 17th-c kitchen range, pewter mugs hang from a beam, and a side shelf boasts a collection of embossed Doulton stoneware flagons. To the left of a small hatch-served lobby, another cosy beamed room has stripped panelled settles, scrubbed-top tables, and a blazing fire under a huge mantelbeam. Stone-mullioned windows look out across lots of tables in the pleasant garden (boules on Sunday evenings in summer) to small silvery-walled pastures, and in fine weather, the small front yard with a few benches is a nice place to sit (listen out for the village bell-ringers practising on Friday evenings). Although the date etched on the building reads 1874, it was originally built in 1616, from magnesian limestone and timbers salvaged from armada wrecks, bought in exchange for locally mined lead. Bar food, from a regularly changing menu, is mostly home-made (some with a new england influence: the landlady, Evie, is from Connecticut) and could include well presented lunchtime sandwiches, baguettes or soup (from £3.50), new england clam chowder (£4.50), ploughman's (£7.50), fidget pie, made of baked sliced potato, honey roast ham and cheese (£8.15), vegetarian chilli (£8.95), barbecued cajun spiced butterflied chicken (£10.95), rump steaks (from £12.95) and puddings such as boston brownie or treacle sponge (£3.95). The panelled room and bar area are no smoking. Well kept Marstons Pedigree and a guest such as Adnams Regatta on handpump, and a good selection of malt whiskies; cribbage and dominoes. The pub is a five-minute drive from Carsington Water. *(Recommended by Pat and Roger Fereday, Peter F Marshall, Jim Abbott, B Forster, Patrick Hancock, the Didler, Derek and Heather Manning, Brian and Julie Shurmer, John Dwane, Tich Critchlow)*

Marstons (W & D) ~ Tenant Paul Burlinson ~ Real ale ~ Bar food (12-1.45(2 Sat, Sun), 7-8.45(9 Fri and Sat), not Sun evening) ~ (01629) 540448 ~ Children over 10 ~ Dogs welcome ~ Open 12-2.30(possibly earlier if quiet; 3 Sat), 6-11; 12-3, 7-10.30 Sun; closed Mon except bank hols

CASTLETON SK1583 Map 7
Castle Hotel 🛏
High Street at junction with Castle Street

Right in the centre of the scenically placed village, beneath the soaring ruin of Peveril Castle, this neatly kept spacious historic hotel makes a useful stopping point during a walk or a visit to the area's many show caves. For entertainment value it's worth visiting on 29 May, when the colourful Garland Ceremony procession that commemorates the escape of Charles II takes place. The pub itself has plenty of history, and lots of spooky tales too, including one about the ghost of a bride who, instead of enjoying her planned wedding breakfast here, died broken-hearted when she was left at the altar. The inviting bar has stripped stone walls with built-in cabinets, lovely open fires, finely carved early 17th-c beams and, in one room, ancient flagstones. They have well kept Bass and Tetleys and a guest such as John Smiths on handpump, a range of malt whiskies, over 20 wines by the glass, and a selection of fruit juices. A good part of the pub is no smoking; piped music and fruit machine. Good value bar food is served all day and includes sandwiches (lunchtime and afternoon only, from £3.50), seafood salad or chicken and bacon salad (£6.50), hot prawn pasta (£8.75), lemon sole (£10.95), with blackboard specials such as chinese chargrilled chicken (£6.50), profiteroles (£2.95), caramel apple crumble (£3.85). From the heated terrace you get pleasant views of the village. *(Recommended by Duncan Cloud, Chris Smith, M G Hart, Guy Vowles, Mrs Julie Thomas, R Brackenbury, Ian and Nita Cooper)*

Vintage Inns ~ Manager Glen Mills ~ Real ale ~ Bar food (12-10(9.30 Sun)) ~ Restaurant ~ (01433) 620578 ~ Children welcome ~ Open 11-11; 12-10.30 Sun ~ Bedrooms: /£59.95B

DERBY SK3435 Map 7

Alexandra 🍺

Siddals Road, just up from station

Just a few minutes away from Derby station, this lively Victorian town pub deserves a visit for its outstanding array of well kept real ales. Besides Bass, Belvoir Star, Castle Rock Nottingham Gold and York Yorkshire Terrier, they have up to nine frequently changing guest beers from all sorts of small countrywide breweries such as Hadrian and Border, Cotleigh and Ringwood. They also have up to five continental beers on tap, country wines, cider tapped from the cask and around two dozen malt whiskies; their soft drinks are very good value too. Two simple rooms have a buoyantly chatty atmosphere, good heavy traditional furnishings on dark-stained floorboards, shelves of bottles, breweriana, and lots of railway prints and memorabilia about Derby's railway history. The lounge is no smoking; darts, dominoes and piped music. At lunchtime they serve good value rolls (from £2). *(Recommended by David Carr, Patrick Hancock, C J Fletcher, the Didler)*

Tynemill ~ Manager Mark Robins ~ Real ale ~ Bar food (lunchtimes only) ~ No credit cards ~ (01332) 293993 ~ Children in eating area of bar ~ Dogs welcome ~ Open 11-11; 12-3, 7-10.30 Sun ~ Bedrooms: £25S/£35S

Brunswick 🍺 £

Railway Terrace; close to Derby Midland station

At the end of a terrace of railway workers' cottages stands this 1840s tower, originally a railwaymen's hostelry. Restored in the 1980s by a local trust and now with its own brewery attached, it gives little clue to the treasure trove of beers inside. Up to 16 real ales, on handpump or tapped from the cask, include seven which are produced here (Father Mikes Dark Rich Ruby, Old Accidental, Second Brew Usual, Mild, Pilsner, Triple Hop and Triple Gold) as well as around ten regularly changing widely sourced guests such as Batemans, Everards Tiger, Holdens Golden Glow, Marstons Pedigree and Timothy Taylors Landlord; Weston's Old Rosie farm cider is tapped from the cask. You can tour the brewery (£7.50 including a meal and a pint). The welcoming high-ceilinged bar has heavy well padded leather seats, whisky-water jugs above the dado, and a dark blue ceiling and upper wall, with squared dark panelling below. The no smoking room is decorated with little old-fashioned prints and swan's neck lamps, and has a high-backed wall settle and a coal fire; behind a curved glazed partition wall is a chatty family parlour narrowing to the apex of the triangular building. Informative wall displays tell you about the history and restoration of the building, and there are interesting old train photographs; darts, dominoes, cribbage, fruit machine and TV. Tasty good value lunchtime bar food includes toasted sandwiches (from £1.25), filled rolls (from £1.90), soup (£2.25), filled baked potatoes (from £2.70), ploughman's (£3.70), home-made lasagne (£4.25), beef stew (£4.50) and beef pie (£4.80); on Sunday they do rolls only. There are two outdoor seating areas, including a terrace behind. They'll gladly give dogs a bowl of water. *(Recommended by David Carr, Keith and Chris O'Neill, Patrick Hancock,*

Brian and Rosalie Laverick, C J Fletcher, the Didler, Bob)

Everards ~ Licensee Graham Yates ~ Real ale ~ Bar food (12-2.30(5 Fri and Sat; Sun rolls only) ~ No credit cards ~ (01332) 290677 ~ Children in family room ~ Dogs welcome ~ Blues Mon evenings, jazz Thurs evenings ~ Open 11-11; 12-10.30 Sun

Olde Dolphin ◨ £

Queen Street; nearest car park King Street/St Michaels Lane

Just a few steps away from the cathedral, this characterful timber-framed hostelry is Derby's oldest, and a notable absence of piped music or fruit machines allows you to enjoy the chatty atmosphere. Its rambling layout encompasses four snug old-fashioned rooms (two with their own separate street doors), with big bowed black beams, shiny panelling, cast-iron-framed tables, opaque leaded windows, lantern lights, and coal fires; there are varnished wall benches in the tiled-floor public bar, and a brocaded seat in the little carpeted snug. The lounge bar and restaurant are no smoking. Up to nine real ales on handpump including Adnams, Bass, Black Sheep, Caledonian Deuchars IPA, Greene King Abbot and Marstons Pedigree, along with three guest beers, and there's a beer festival in the last week of July with some 80 brews. Good value tasty bar food includes triple-decker sandwiches (from £2.40), soup (£2.85), filled baguettes (from £3.45), all-day breakfast (£3.90), giant yorkshire pudding with pork sausage and onions (£3.65), battered cod (£4.85), home-made pie of the day (£4.95), 16oz rump steak (£9.50), specials such as home-made chicken madras (£4.25), and a changing pudding menu which might include rhubarb and ginger crumble (£2.30), spotted dick or apple strudel (£2.35). On warmer days the terrace makes a nice resting spot close to the bustle of the city centre. *(Recommended by David Carr, Patrick Hancock, C J Fletcher, Peter F Marshall, the Didler, Kevin Blake)*

Mitchells & Butlers ~ Lease James and Josephine Harris ~ Real ale ~ Bar food (11-10; 12-6 Sun) ~ Restaurant ~ (01332) 267711 ~ Children in restaurant ~ Open 10.30-11; 12-10.30 Sun

EARL STERNDALE SK0967 Map 7
Quiet Woman

Village signposted off B5053 S of Buxton

Quiet it is indeed in its character and setting, a thoroughly traditional, unfussy rural pub by a village green. Emphatically not a dining venue – bar food is limited to locally made pork pies – this stone-built cottage is for those who enjoy a good friendly down-to-earth pub and aren't too bothered about the housekeeping. A fun time to visit is during their Sunday lunchtime folk session, when you might encounter clog dancers or similar. It's very simple inside, with hard seats, plain tables (including a sunken one for dominoes or cards), low beams, quarry tiles, lots of china ornaments and a coal fire. There's a pool table in the family room (where you may be joined by two friendly jack russells eager for a place by the fire), cribbage, dominoes and darts. Mansfield Dark Mild and Marstons Best and Pedigree are well kept on handpump along with a couple of guests such as Archers and Leek Brewery Quiet Woman (the latter also is sold bottled). There are picnic-sets out in front, and the budgies, hens, turkeys, ducks and donkeys help keep children entertained. You can buy free-range eggs, local poetry books and even silage here, and sometimes local dry-cured bacon and raw sausages; they have a caravan for hire in the garden, and you can also arrange to stay at the small campsite next door. Needless to say, it's a popular place with walkers, with some very rewarding hikes across the Dove valley towards Longnor and Hollinsclough. *(Recommended by the Didler, Reg Fowle, Helen Rickwood, Patrick Hancock, Barry Collett)*

Free house ~ Licensee Kenneth Mellor ~ Real ale ~ No credit cards ~ (01298) 83211 ~ Children in family room ~ Jamming sessions most Sun lunchtimes ~ Open 12-3(Sat 4), 7-11; 12-5, 7-10.30 Sun

EYAM SK2276 Map 7

Miners Arms 🛏

Signposted off A632 Chesterfield—Chapel-en-le-Frith

Now under new licensees, this three-roomed old place has a thoroughly traditional character, with neatly kept plush beamed rooms each with its own stone fireplace. It gets nicely lively in the evening, when locals drop in for a well kept pint. Bar food includes soup (£3.95), sandwiches (from £3.95), grilled black pudding with dijon mustard sauce (£4.95), sausage of the day and mash or roast of the day (£7.95), pie of the day (£8.95), lunchtime specials such as vegetarian creamy tomato pasta (£7.25) and navarin of lamb (£8.25), and a monthly changing menu that includes items such as baked asparagus loaf (£7.95), wild mushroom pasta (£8.95), oriental duck breast (£11.25); puddings include chocolate fudge cake and lemon tart (£4.25); the restaurant is no smoking. They have guest ales from brewers such as Bass, Black Sheep and Everards on handpump; darts, dominoes and piped music. Bedrooms are nicely decorated. This is an excellent base for exploring the Peak District, and there are decent walks nearby, especially below Froggatt Edge. Eyam is famous for the altruism of its villagers, who isolated themselves during the plague to save the lives of others in the area. The Barmote Court which legislated over mining matters regularly used to meet here. More reports on the new regime please. *(Recommended by Catherine and Rob Dunster, the Didler, Betty and Cyril Higgs, M G Hart, Eric Robinson, Jacqueline Pratt, John and Hazel Williams)*

New Century Inns ~ Tenants Ian Jackson and Jessica Wales ~ Real ale ~ Bar food (12-2 (3 Sat, Sun), 6-9; not Sun evening) ~ Restaurant ~ (01433) 630853 ~ Children welcome ~ Dogs allowed in bar and bedrooms ~ Live entertainment once or twice a month ~ Open 12-11(10.30 Sun) ~ Bedrooms: £45S/£65S(£65B)

FENNY BENTLEY SK1750 Map 7

Coach & Horses

A515 N of Ashbourne

A short stroll away from the ever-popular Tissington Trail, this 17th-c rendered stone house provides welcome shelter from the elements, with exposed brick hearths, flagstone floors and blazing log fires setting a cosy theme. Hand-made pine furniture includes flowery-cushioned wall settles, and wagon wheels hang from the black beams, amid horsebrasses, pewter mugs and prints. There are prints on the stained pine panelling in the little back room, with country cottage furnishings; cribbage, dominoes and quiet piped music. Marstons Pedigree and Timothy Taylors, and a guest such as Caledonian Deuchars IPA, are well kept on handpump alongside about 20 whiskies. From a changing menu and served by efficient uniformed staff, tasty bar food uses local produce and might include home-made soup (£2.95), warmed goats cheese with wholegrain mustard vinaigrette (£4.25), sausage and mash (£6.95), roast butternut squash filled with chilli bean and vegetable casserole (£7.50), red bream fillet with tarragon butter (£8.95), venison haunch with horseradish and wild mushroom sauce (£9.50) and rib-eye steak (£10.50); home-made desserts include date and walnut pudding, and bread and butter pudding (£3.50); a wide range of fresh fish on Fridays, plus curries on Tuesdays in winter. The dining room and back bar are no smoking. Outside, there are views across fields from picnic-sets in the side garden by an elder tree, and wooden tables and chairs under cocktail parasols on the front terrace. *(Recommended by Joan and Tony Walker, Kevin Thorpe, Dave Braisted, Chris Smith, the Didler, Peter F Marshall, Mr and Mrs John Taylor, Jan and Alan Summers, Geoff and Linda Payne, Bob)*

Free house ~ Licensees John and Matthew Dawson ~ Real ale ~ Bar food (12-9) ~ Restaurant ~ (01335) 350246 ~ Children in eating area of bar and restaurant ~ Open 11-11; 12-10.30 Sun

---

Pubs brewing their own beers are listed at the back of the book.

FOOLOW SK2077 Map 7

Barrel ★ 🍺 🛏

Bretton; signposted from Foolow, which itself is signposted from A623 just E of junction with B6465 to Bakewell; can also be reached from either the B6049 at Great Hucklow, or the B6001 via Abney, from Leadmill just S of Hathersage

High up on a lonely spot on the top of Eyam Ridge, this magnificently placed stone-roofed turnpike inn has received praise from readers not only for its sweeping views over five counties, but as a place to enjoy a pint, a meal and a night's stay. The peacefully cosy oak-beamed bar has an old-fashioned charm, with flagstones, studded doors in low doorways, lots of pictures, antiques and a collection of bottles and gleaming copper. Stubs of massive knocked-through stone walls divide it into several areas: the cosiest is at the far end, with a log fire, a leather-cushioned settle, and a built-in corner wall-bench by an antique oak table; piped music. Hardys & Hansons Bitter and Olde Trip, Marstons Pedigree and a monthly changing guest perhaps from the Hardys & Hanson range are very well kept; also more than 25 malts. Bar food includes home-made soup (£2.65), sandwiches (from £3.20), roast of the day (£7.50), liver and bacon or cod and chips (£8.95), salmon with raspberry vinaigrette (£11.95), shank of lamb (£12.95), and puddings (£3.95). Seats out on the front terrace and a courtyard garden give good shelter from the inevitable breeze at this height. *(Recommended by Derek and Sylvia Stephenson, Jim Abbott, Keith and Chris O'Neill, Peter F Marshall, B and M Kendall, Betty and Cyril Higgs, the Didler, Richard Thornton, Ian Thurman, Jon and Donna Shaw, Kevin Blake, Darren Arnold, C E Reid, R Brackenbury)*

Free house ~ ~ Real ale ~ Bar food ~ (01433) 630856 ~ Children welcome ~ Dogs allowed in bar ~ Ceilidh Weds evening ~ Open 11-3, 6-11; 11-11 Sat, Sun ~ Bedrooms: £45S/£65B

Bulls Head 🍺 🛏

Village signposted off A623 Baslow—Tideswell

Welcoming and well run, this pub stands in a pleasantly unrushed village, ranged around a large green with an ancient stone cross by the pond. In addition to the simply furnished flagstoned bar are a couple of quieter areas set out for a relaxing meal. A step or two takes you down into what may once have been a stables, with its high ceiling joists, some stripped stone, and a woodburning stove. On the other side, a smart no smoking dining room has more polished tables set in cosy stalls. Interesting photographs include a good collection of Edwardian naughties. The wide range of enjoyable food is popular, so you may need to book at the weekend: lunchtime snacks such as sandwiches (from £3.95), hot filled baps (£5.25), ploughman's (£5.50), as well as soup (£3.25), thai fishcakes with sweet chilli sauce (£4.50), chicken with lemon cream sauce or minted lamb casserole (£7.25), rump steak (£10.75), and three succulent roasts on Sunday; the dining room is no smoking. Adnams and Shepherd Neame Spitfire are well kept alongside a couple of guests from brewers such as Fullers and Black Sheep; piped music, dominoes and darts. You can buy basic provisions here (milk, eggs, bread and so forth), which is handy as there's no shop in Foolow. Picnic-sets at the back have nice views, and from here you can follow paths out over rolling pasture enclosed by dry-stone walls. *(Recommended by John Wooll, B and M Kendall, Jim Abbott, Derek and Sylvia Stephenson, Patrick Hancock, Dick and Penny Vardy, Peter F Marshall, C E Reid, JWAC)*

Free house ~ Licensee William Bond ~ Real ale ~ Bar food (12-2, 6.30-9) ~ Restaurant ~ (01433) 630873 ~ Children welcome ~ Dogs allowed in bar ~ Live folk Fri evening ~ Open 12-3(2 Sat), 6.30-11; 12-10.30 Sun; closed Mon except bank hols ~ Bedrooms: £40S/£70S

Bedroom prices include full English breakfast, VAT and any inclusive service charge that we know of.

FROGGATT EDGE SK2476 Map 7

Chequers 🍴

A625 (busy even at night with quarry traffic), off A623 N of Bakewell; OS Sheet 119
map reference 247761

The wooded slopes of Froggatt Edge, rising to a breezy moorland rim dotted with
rocky outcrops, provide a wonderful backdrop to this smart and deservedly popular
dining pub. A path leading from the rustic garden up the hill makes it ideal for
combining a scenic walk with a good meal. Inside, the countrified bar has library
chairs or small high-backed winged settles on well waxed boards, an attractive richly
varnished beam-and-board ceiling, antique prints on white walls and some big dark
stone blocks, and a large solid-fuel stove. One corner has a nicely carved oak
cupboard. It's a good idea to book if you are going for the very well prepared and
attractively presented bar food (not cheap but readers continue to enthuse about the
quality). In addition to more elaborate restaurant food, bar food includes
imaginative sandwiches (from £4.75), with starters on the specials board such as
goats cheese and red onion terrine (£5.25) and chicken and mushroom roulade
(£5.50); main courses include smoked trout with celeriac, apple and endive salad
(£8.95), pasta with tomato and spinach sauce (£7.75), local pork sausage with mash,
red onion jam and gravy (£9.25), pesto crusted field mushroom with roast pepper
and caper relish, and pistachio mascarpone (£9.50), smoked haddock and brie
fishcakes (£10.25), rib-eye steak (£12.95), and specials such as fillet of pork wrapped
in basil and parma ham with apple jus, or duck breast with sweet potatoes and red
onion gratin (£14.95); puddings might include sticky toffee pudding or cappuccino
mousse (£4.50). Greene King IPA and Charles Wells Bombardier are well kept on
handpump; 20 malts and ten wines are served by the glass. Recent refurbishments
have included making the entire pub no smoking; piped music. The bedrooms have
also been redone and look most appealing; we would welcome reports from readers
who have stayed here. *(Recommended by David Carr, Mrs Brenda Calver, Richard Marjoram,
Peter F Marshall, Mike and Linda Hudson, Patrick Hancock, D J and P M Taylor, Geoff and
Kaye Newton, M G Hart, C E Reid, Dave Braisted)*

Pubmaster ~ Lease Jonathan and Joanne Tindall ~ Real ale ~ Bar food (12-2, 6-9.30;
12-9.30(9 Sun) Sat) ~ Restaurant ~ (01433) 630231 ~ Children welcome ~ Open 12-2.30,
6-11(12-11 bank hol Mon); 12-11 Sat; 12-10.30 Sun ~ Bedrooms: /£65B

HARDWICK HALL SK4663 Map 7

Hardwick Inn

3 miles from M1 junction 29: at roundabout A6175 towards Clay Cross; after ½ mile
turn left signed Stainsby and Hardwick Hall (ignore any further sign for Hardwick Hall);
at sign to Stainsby follow road to left; after 2½ miles turn left at staggered road junction

The National Trust's Hardwick Hall estate spreads southwards to encompass this
handsome old sandstone inn, built as a lodge for the great house itself, and with its
stone-mullioned latticed windows giving it the air of a manor house, so it's worth a
visit for the building alone – handy for the M1. The very pleasant back garden is a
useful place for children to let off steam. With plenty more tables in front, the pub
is geared for the crowds (you do need to book at the weekend). Of the cosy but
fairly old-fashioned rooms, though one has an attractive 18th-c carved settle, the
carpeted lounge is the most comfortable, with its upholstered wall settles, tub chairs
and stools around varnished wooden tables. The carvery restaurant and all rooms
are no smoking. It does get very busy (especially on weekends). Standard bar food
includes soup (£2.75), ploughman's (from £5.55), salads (from £6.99), roasts
(£6.99), daily specials, and an evening carvery from Tuesday to Saturday. As well
as a huge range of some 220 malt whiskies and 24 wines by the glass, they've well
kept Greene King Old Speckled Hen and Ruddles County, Marstons Pedigree and
Theakstons XB and Old Peculier on handpump; piped music. Reports praise the
friendliness of the staff, but some readers were disappointed with the food.
*(Recommended by D P and M A Miles, Andy and Ali, Fred and Lorraine Gill, the Didler,
J Stickland, Mrs G R Sharman, Patrick Hancock, Gerry and Rosemary Dobson, Brian and*

Janet Ainscough, Adam and Joan Bunting, Keith and Chris O'Neill, Dr and Mrs A K Clarke, Peter F Marshall, Alison and Pete)

Free house ~ Licensees Peter and Pauline Batty ~ Real ale ~ Bar food (11.30-9.30; 12-9 Sun) ~ Restaurant ~ (01246) 850245 ~ Children in restaurant and family room ~ Open 11.30-11; 12-10.30 Sun

HASSOP SK2272 Map 7

Eyre Arms

B6001 N of Bakewell

With a venerable longcase clock ticking away in the beamed dining bar, and an array of cushioned settles and plush chairs, there's a gracious atmosphere at this 17th-c stone-built inn. Lots of brass and copper is dominated by the Eyre coat of arms which is painted above a stone fireplace (coal fire in winter). A smaller public bar has an unusual collection of teapots, and another fire; apart from the tap room bar, all the areas are no smoking. Black Sheep, Marstons Pedigree and John Smiths are well kept on handpump; piped classical music, darts, cribbage and dominoes. Besides lunchtime sandwiches (from £3.75) and ploughman's (from £5.55), the menu includes soup (£3.85), deep-fried fillet of trout coated with almonds and breadcrumbs (£7.65), chicken korma (£7.75), steak and kidney pie (£7.95) and 8oz fillet steak (£13.65). They also do daily specials such as local braised pheasant (£9.75) or rabbit pie (£10.45), and service is obliging. There's a fountain in the small garden, which has tables looking out over beautiful peak district countryside. Colourful hanging baskets brighten up the exterior stonework in summer, and in autumn, virginia creeper. Although most readers recommend this as a main entry, and generally the ambience and beer have been admired, one or two have indicated that the food fell short of expectations; more reports please. *(Recommended by Jim Abbott, Susan and John Douglas, Derek and Sylvia Stephenson, Dick and Penny Vardy, the Didler, M G Hart, W W Burke, Kevin Blake, R Brackenbury)*

Free house ~ Licensee Lynne Smith ~ Real ale ~ Bar food (12-2, 6.30-9) ~ Restaurant ~ (01629) 640390 ~ Children in eating area of bar ~ Open 11.30-3, 6.30-11(10.30 Sun)

HATHERSAGE SK2380 Map 7 🏠

Plough 🍴 🍷 🛏

Leadmill; B6001 towards Bakewell, OS Sheet 110 map reference 235805

'On a miserable wet day it was delightful to see a roaring open fire and cheerful welcoming staff', remarked one reader: feedback has been unanimously favourable here. The emphasis at this former farmhouse is very firmly on the excellent choice of highly imaginative food, though it's not cheap. Unfortunately drinkers may have trouble finding a seat at busy times, and it is worth booking for Sunday lunch. The menu changes every three months but usually includes some pubby staples alongside more creative (and more expensive) dishes: home-made soup (£3.95), starters including feta cheese, artichoke and cashew nut salad with beetroot crisps (£5.95) or crab cream cheese and ginger gateau (£6.95), and main courses featuring toad in the hole (£7.25), steak and kidney pudding (£8.95), roast duck breast (£13.95), seared scallops on a red onion and tomato tatin (£15.95) and fillet steak (£16.95). They serve around 20 good value wines by the glass, alongside Theakstons Bitter and Old Peculier, and a guest such as Adnams, on hand or electric pump. Everything is spotlessly kept, and the attractive bar, with dark wood tables and chairs on a turkey carpet, is on two levels, with a big log fire at one end and a woodburning stove at the other. The atmosphere is pleasantly relaxed and airy, with all areas no smoking during food service hours (at other times you can smoke in the bar), and the service friendly and efficient; piped music. The pub is beautifully placed by the River Derwent with picnic-sets in the pretty secluded garden going right down to the water. Readers really enjoy staying in the very comfortable rooms, and the breakfasts are very satisfying. *(Recommended by Adrian White, M G Hart, Jeremy Hebblethwaite, M Sharp, Revd D Glover, Dr L Kaufman, Michael Doswell, Keith and Chris O'Neill, Mrs P J Carroll, D J and P M Taylor,*

Mrs Brenda Calver, Nigel Epsley, Barry and Anne, DC, Elizabeth Crabtree, Peter F Marshall, Gerry and Rosemary Dobson, John and Elizabeth Cox, Mike and Mary Carter, Bob)

Free house ~ Licensees Bob and Cynthia Emery ~ Real ale ~ Bar food (11.30-2.30, 6.30-9.30; 11.30-9.30 Sat; 12-9 Sun) ~ Restaurant ~ (01433) 650319 ~ Children in eating area of bar, and restaurant until 7.30pm ~ Open 11.30-11; 12-10.30 Sun ~ Bedrooms: £49.50S(£55B)/£69.50(£79.50B)

Scotsmans Pack 🛏

School Lane, off A6187

Walk down from the primeval-feeling moors that rise high around the village, and you'll find this welcoming, civilised place close to the church where Little John is said to be buried. There's been a pub on the spot for centuries, though the current building dates from around 1900. The most comfortable area is on the left as you enter, with a fireplace, and patterned wallpaper somewhat obscured by a splendid mass of brasses, stuffed animal heads and the like. Elsewhere there's plenty of dark panelling, lots of mugs and plates arranged around the bar, and a good few tables, many with reserved space (it's worth booking ahead, particularly at weekends). Much of the wide range of food is sourced from local produce; bar food includes a good choice of sandwiches, home-made soup (£2.75), deep-fried brie with hot cranberry sauce (£3.95), home-made steak pie (£8.25), sausage of the day (£7.80), grilled salmon steak with cream and prawn sauce (£9.25) and 10z sirloin steak (£10.95); the specials board has around six starters such as grilled flat cap mushroom filled with dolcelatte (£3.95) and octopus and crab salad (£4.25) and about a dozen main courses which might include rabbit stew (£10.95) or grilled haddock with scallops (£12.95). Well kept on handpump are Burtonwood, Marstons Pedigree and two or three guests such as Burtonwood Top Hat and Hop Back Summer Lightning, and they stock eight or nine malts; service remains prompt and cheery even when busy. Some dining areas are no smoking. Outside is a small but very pleasant patio, next to a trout-filled stream. We would particularly welcome reports from any readers who have stayed here. *(Recommended by David Carr, Jane Taylor, David Dutton, M G Hart, Peter F Marshall, Paul A Moore, Keith and Chris O'Neill)*

Burtonwood (W & D) ~ Lease Nick Beagrie, Steve Bramley and Susan Concannon ~ Real ale ~ Bar food (12-2, 6-9; 12-5, 6-9 Sat, Sun and bank hol Mons) ~ Restaurant ~ (01433) 650253 ~ Children welcome till 9pm ~ Dogs welcome ~ Jazz first Mon of month ~ Open 11-3, 5.30-11; 11-11 Sat; 12-10.30 Sun ~ Bedrooms: £38S/£62S(£62B)

HAYFIELD SK0388 Map 7

Lantern Pike 🛏

Glossop Road (A624 N) at Little Hayfield, just N of Hayfield

Friendly new licensees continue to make this a welcoming place to come to. The bar is unpretentious but cosy with a warm fire, plush seats, flowers on the tables, and lots of brass platters, china and toby jugs. Well kept Boddingtons and Timothy Taylors Landlord, plus guests such as Black Sheep and Theakstons Old Peculier on handpump, and about eight malt whiskies. Reasonably priced bar food includes home-made soup (£2.45), sandwiches (£3.75), salads (from £5.75), mixed vegetable balti (£6.25), home-made steak and kidney pie (£6.65) and 8oz rump steak (£9), while specials might feature hot braised steak muffin with onions (£4.95), green thai curry (£6.95), salmon fillet in hollandaise sauce (£7.25) or lamb on the bone (£8.95). TV and piped music. The restaurant is no smoking. Tables on a stonewalled back terrace, served from a window, look over a big-windowed weaver's house to the Lantern Pike itself, and the pub's very well placed for walks on to the moors of Kinder Scout. We would particularly welcome reports from any readers who have stayed here. *(Recommended by Michael Lamm, Christine Miller, Christine Mills, Derek and Sylvia Stephenson, Donald and Margaret Wood, Kevin Blake)*

Enterprise ~ Lease Chris and Katherine Middleton ~ Real ale ~ Bar food (12-9) ~

Restaurant ~ (01663) 747590 ~ Children welcome ~ Live entertainment monthly Sat ~
Open 12-11(Sun 10.30) ~ Bedrooms: £40B/£55B

Royal ◀

Market Street, just off A624 Chapel-en-le-Frith—Buxton

Next to the village cricket ground and previously a vicarage, this large, welcoming
and bustling inn is very much at the centre of local life and retains a genuinely
pubby feel. It can get busy, but with plenty of room easily absorbs the crowds.
They have half a dozen or so real ales well kept on handpump, with Hydes, Tetleys
and Boddingtons and guests such as Greene King IPA, Flowers Original and
Moorhouses Black Cat; 15 malt whiskies and a wide selection of brandies including
a Louis XIII which is over 100 years old and sells at £85 a measure. They have a
civilised beer festival in early October. The 18th-c building still has many of its
original features, so there's lots of dark panelling in the separate-seeming areas
around the central island bar counter, as well as several fireplaces, bookshelves,
brasses and house plants, and newspapers to read; piped music, cribbage and
dominoes. Good, tasty bar food is all sourced locally and includes sandwiches with
chips (from £4.50), roast turkey with cranberry stuffing (£7.95), roasted vegetable
lasagne (£8.95) or seared tuna with niçoise salad or poached salmon fillet with
lemon and lime sauce (£9.95). Service is prompt and friendly – walkers are made to
feel particularly welcome. On fine days drinkers spill out on to the terrace in front,
which has lots of picnic-sets. The restaurant and family room are no smoking. The
River Sett runs alongside the car park. Bedrooms are comfortable, and it's a useful
base for exploring the local scenery. More reports please. *(Recommended by Brian and
Anna Marsden, Derek and Sylvia Stephenson)*

Free house ~ Licensee David Ash ~ Real ale ~ Bar food (11-2.30, 5.30-9.30(12-9.30 Sun
and bank hols)) ~ Restaurant ~ (01663) 742721 ~ Children welcome until 9.30pm ~ Jazz
some Sun afternoons ~ Open 11-11; 12-10.30 Sun ~ Bedrooms: £45B/£60B

HOGNASTON SK2350 Map 7
Red Lion 🛏

Village signposted off B5035 Ashbourne—Wirksworth

With its three open fires and attractive open-plan oak-beamed bar and in a
delightfully peaceful spot, this dining pub is a relaxing place to drop in for a pint. It
has an attractive mix of old tables (candlelit at night) and old-fashioned settles and
other seats arranged on ancient flagstones. There are three open fires, and a
growing collection of teddy bears among other bric-a-brac; the conservatory
restaurant is no smoking. Food includes filled baguettes, focaccias and ciabattas
(£4.95), and such items as thai spiced pork patties with sweet chilli dipping sauce
(£4.95), italian meatballs in tomato sauce with tagliatelle (£8.95), tagine of
chickpeas, kidney beans and vegetables cooked in north african spices, with
couscous (£9.95), roast beef, pork or lamb (from £9.95), grilled fillet of salmon
with prawn and tarragon sauce (£10.95) and puddings such as sticky toffee
pudding (£4.50). They've well kept Bass and Marstons Pedigree, and a guest on
handpump; piped music and cribbage. It's handy for Carsington Water and
bedrooms are big and comfortable. *(Recommended by Ian and Jane Irving, Annette and
John Derbyshire, Fred and Lorraine Gill, Brian and Jacky Wilson, Mrs P J Carroll, Cathryn and
Richard Hicks, Jim Abbott, M G Hart, Jeff and Wendy Williams, R Brackenbury, Peter Cole)*

Free house ~ Licensee Pip Price ~ Real ale ~ Bar food (12-2, 6.30-9) ~ Restaurant ~
(01335) 370396 ~ Children in eating area of bar and restaurant ~ Dogs allowed in bar ~
Open 12-3, 6-11.30; 12-3 Sun; closed Mon ~ Bedrooms: £60S/£85S

Anyone claiming to arrange or prevent inclusion of a pub in the *Guide* is a fraud.
Pubs are included only if recommended by genuine readers and if our own
anonymous inspection confirms that they are suitable.

HOLBROOK SK3644 Map 7

Dead Poets ❤ £

Village signposted off A6 S of Belper; Chapel Street

A thoroughly atmospheric, old-fashioned place to enjoy sampling a range of eight real ales, the Dead Poets has a dark interior, with low black beams in its ochre ceiling, stripped stone walls with some smoked plaster, and broad flagstones. Candles burn on scrubbed tables, there's a big log fire in the end stone fireplace, high-backed winged settles form snug cubicles along one wall, and there are pews and a variety of chairs in other intimate corners and hideaways. Alongside well kept Bass, Greene King Abbot and Marstons Pedigree are guests from brewers such as Church End, Everards, Exmoor and Ossetts – on handpump or served by the jug from the cellar; also farm cider and about 20 country wines. The beer festivals (twice a year) here are very popular. It's very dark inside. The décor makes a few nods to the pub's present name (it used to be the Cross Keys) including a photo of W B Yeats and a poem dedicated to the pub by Les Baynton, and adds some old prints of Derby. Alongside cobs (from £2, nothing else on Sundays), bar food is limited to a few good value hearty dishes such as home-made soup (£2) and chilli con carne, casserole or chicken jalfrezi (£4.25). There's a good atmosphere, and a nice mix of customers, male and female; well reproduced piped music. Behind is a sort of verandah room, with lanterns, fairy lights and a few plants, and more seats out in the yard, with outdoor heaters. *(Recommended by Alan Bowker, MLR, the Didler, Derek and Sylvia Stephenson)*

Everards ~ Tenant William Holmes ~ Real ale ~ Bar food (lunchtime only) ~ No credit cards ~ (01332) 780301 ~ Children in family room ~ Dogs welcome ~ Open 12-3, 5-11; 12-11 Fri-Sat; 12-10.30 Sun

KIRK IRETON SK2650 Map 7

Barley Mow ❤ ⇌

Village signed off B5023 S of Wirksworth

Readers greatly appreciate how little has changed at this classic 17th-c pub, a drinking den since about 1800. The dimly lit passageways and narrow stairwells of this tall gabled Jacobean brown sandstone inn have a timeless atmosphere, helped along by traditional furnishings and civilised old-fashioned service. It's a place to sit and chat, and though the only games you'll find here are dominoes and cards, it still pulls in a good crowd of youngsters and local old folk at weekends, and walkers at other times. The small main bar has a relaxed pubby feel, with antique settles on the tiled floor or built into the panelling, a roaring coal fire, four slate-topped tables, and shuttered mullioned windows. Another room has built-in cushioned pews on oak parquet and a small woodburning stove, and a third room has more pews, a tiled floor, beams and joists, and big landscape prints. One room is no smoking. In casks behind a modest wooden counter are the well kept (and reasonably priced) real ales: Archers, Burton Bridge, Cottage, Eccleshall Slaters, Hook Norton Old Hooky, Storm and Whim Hartington IPA; Thatcher's farm cider too. Lunchtime filled rolls (85p) are the only food; the good home-made interesting evening meals are reserved for residents staying in the comfortable rooms. There's a decent-sized garden, and a couple of benches out in front, and they've opened a post office in what used to be the pub stables. Handy for Carsington Water, the pretty hilltop village is in good walking country. *(Recommended by Pete Baker, Kevin Thorpe, the Didler, Jim Abbott, Brian and Jacky Wilson, Tich Critchlow, Mark and Mary Fairman)*

Free house ~ Licensee Mary Short ~ Real ale ~ No credit cards ~ (01335) 370306 ~ Children in side rooms lunchtime only ~ Dogs allowed in bar and bedrooms ~ Open 12-2, 7-11(10.30 Sun); closed 25 Dec and 1 Jan ~ Bedrooms: £30S/£50B

LADYBOWER RESERVOIR SK1986 Map 7

Yorkshire Bridge ⇐

A6013 N of Bamford

The hills and dense forests surrounding the spectacular reservoirs of the Derwent valley are in view from this hotel, where readers enjoy the friendly service. One area has a country cottage feel, with floral wallpaper, sturdy cushioned wall settles, staffordshire dogs and toby jugs on a big stone fireplace with a warm coal-effect gas fire, china on delft shelves, a panelled dado and so forth. Another extensive area, with another fire, is lighter and more airy with pale wooden furniture, good big black and white photographs and lots of polished brass and decorative plates on the walls. The no smoking Bridge Room has yet another coal-effect fire and oak tables and chairs, and the no smoking Garden Room gives pleasant views across a valley to steep larch woods. The First Bar is no smoking too, and the restaurant is for residents only. In summer it's a good idea to arrive early, to be sure of a table. The menu includes soup (£3.25), lunchtime sandwiches (from £3.75), filled baked potatoes (from £3.80), ploughman's (£6.95), salads (from £7), home-made steak and kidney pie or red onion, sweet pepper and goats cheese tartlet (£7.75), italian chicken (£8.75), 12oz rib-eye steak (£12.50) with specials such as quiche of the day (£7), chicken, mushroom and asparagus pie (£7.75) and halibut steak with stir-fried vegetables (£8.95); puddings such as home-made apple and toffee crumble, chocolate brandy tulip basket or lemon meringue pie (from £3.70); children's meals (£3.50). Well kept on handpump are Black Sheep, Theakstons Old Peculier and Timothy Taylors Landlord; darts, fruit machine, and piped music; disabled lavatories. *(Recommended by Derek and Sylvia Stephenson, Dr and Mrs T E Hothersall, Michael Butler, Patrick Hancock, B M Eldridge, Alan and Paula McCully, Jan and Alan Summers, Irene and Ray Atkin, Bob)*

Free house ~ Licensees Trevelyan and John Illingworth ~ Real ale ~ Bar food (12-2, 6-9(9.30 Fri, Sat); 12-8.30 Sun) ~ Restaurant ~ (01433) 651361 ~ Children welcome ~ Dogs welcome ~ Open 11-11; 12-10.30 Sun ~ Bedrooms: £48B/£68B

LITTON SK1675 Map 7

Red Lion

Village signposted off A623, between B6465 and B6049 junctions; also signposted off B6049

The friendly landlord really makes everyone welcome at this stone-built 17th-c village pub facing the tree-shaded village green, and readers enjoy the food. The two inviting homely linked front rooms have low beams and some panelling, and blazing log fires. There's a bigger back room (no smoking during food service) with good-sized tables, and large antique prints on its stripped stone walls. The small bar counter has well kept Barnsley real ale on handpump, plus three guests that usually include Black Sheep, Timothy Taylors and another often from a small brewery such as Kelham Island, with decent wines and 30 malt whiskies; shove-ha'penny, darts, cribbage, dominoes and table skittles. Fresh tasting and good value bar food includes steak and ale pie or steak and kidney pudding (£6.60), rabbit casserole (£6.70), braised steak in Black Sheep ale (£6.95), pork and apricot casserole (£7.10) and garlic and rosemary lamb (£8.50). A particularly rewarding time to visit is during the annual village well-dressing carnival (usually the last weekend in June), when villagers create a picture from flower petals, moss and other natural materials, and at Christmas a brass band plays carols. It's such a small pub that it's not ideal for children. *(Recommended by Patrick Hancock, Keith and Chris O'Neill, the Didler, Mrs R McLauchlan, Derek and Sylvia Stephenson, Barry Collett)*

Free house ~ Licensees Terry and Michele Vernon ~ Real ale ~ Bar food (12-2, 6-8.30(not Sun evening)) ~ (01298) 871458 ~ No children under 6 ~ Dogs welcome ~ Open 12-3, 6-11; 12-11 Fri, Sat; 12-10.30 Sun ~ Bedrooms: /£65S(£60B)

If we know a pub has an outdoor play area for children, we mention it.

MELBOURNE SK3427 Map 7

John Thompson 🍺 £

Ingleby, which is NW of Melbourne; turn off A514 at Swarkestone Bridge or in Stanton by Bridge; can also be reached from Ticknall (or from Repton on B5008)

At the back of this converted 15th-c farmhouse is the pub's own brewery, set up by the welcoming landlord, John Thompson, in 1977 – eight years after he created the present public house here. It's well worth a visit for the good value beers: JTS XXX, Rich Porter and Summer Gold, plus a guest such as Shardlow Reverend Eatons. It's a simple but comfortable place. The big modernised lounge has ceiling joists, some old oak settles, button-back leather seats, sturdy oak tables, antique prints and paintings, and a log-effect gas fire; piped music. A couple of smaller cosier rooms open off, with a piano, fruit machine, pool and a juke box in the family room; there are two no smoking areas in the lounge. The menu is very short but the food is home-made and decidedly tasty: sandwiches (£1.50), soup (£2), delicious salads with cold ham or beef (£5), and mouthwatering puddings such as bread and butter pudding or rhubarb crumble (£2); they also do a carvery from Tuesday to Saturday (£6). Outside are lots of tables by flowerbeds on the well kept lawns, or you can sit on the partly covered outside terrace which has its own serving bar. *(Recommended by Brian and Jacky Wilson, Joan and Graham Varley, Geoff and Anne Sirett, the Didler, Lynn Sharpless, Rona Murdoch, Michael Lamm, Brian and Ruth Archer, Paul and Gloria Howell)*

Own brew ~ Licensee John Thompson ~ Real ale ~ Bar food (lunchtime; soup and sandwiches only Sun and Mon) ~ (01332) 862469 ~ Children in family room ~ Dogs allowed in bar ~ Open 10.30-2.30, 6-11; 11-11 Sat; 12-10.30 Sun

MILLTOWN SK3561 Map 7

Miners Arms

Off B6036 SE of Ashover; Oakstedge Lane

Old lead-mining workings dot the landscape around this stone-built, entirely no smoking pub, tucked away on the edge of Ashover. The accent is firmly on food here, and you will need to book. Listed on a board, the (fairly straightforward) changing dishes are very good value considering the quality, and typically include home-made soup (from £2.10), sandwiches (from £3.35), spinach-stuffed mushrooms (£3.75), chicken liver pâté (£3.95), pork, apple and sausage pie (£7.75), chicken breast with mustard cream sauce or grilled cod (£9.25), turkey escalope with herb butter (£9.65), and puddings such as chocolate crumble cheesecake and crème brûlée (£3.25); the vegetables are especially well cooked. Service is friendly and efficient. The layout of the building is basically L-shaped, with a local feel up nearer the door. They serve good value wines, and one or two guest ales, such as Archers, plus german wheat beer; at lunchtime there may be quiet piped classical music. Attractive country walks lead right from the door. Please note their opening times. *(Recommended by Tony Fisher, the Didler, Cathryn and Richard Hicks)*

Free house ~ Licensees Andrew and Yvonne Guest ~ Real ale ~ Bar food (12-2, 6-9.30) ~ Restaurant ~ (01246) 590218 ~ Children welcome ~ Open 12-3, 7-11; 12-3 Sun; closed Weds evening in winter; closed Sun evening and Mon, Tues

MONSAL HEAD SK1871 Map 7

Monsal Head Hotel 🍺 🛏

B6465

The view is one of the Peak District's classics: steeply down into a dramatic bend of the River Wye in Monsal Dale, spanned by a huge former railway viaduct that now provides a walkers' and cyclists' route along the Monsal Trail. Readers continue to enthuse about the good solidly inventive home-cooking as well as the panorama of this busy extended hotel. The cosy stable bar once housed the horses that used to haul guests and their luggage from the station down below; the stripped timber horse-stalls, harness and brassware, and lamps from the disused station itself, all hint at those days. There's a big warming woodburning stove in the inglenook, and cushioned oak pews around the tables on the flagstones. Eight well kept real ales on handpump include Lloyds, Timothy Taylors Landlord, Theakstons Best and Old Peculier, Whim Hartington and guests such as Abbeydale Moonshine and Absolution, or Caledonian Deuchars IPA, and they also keep a very good choice of bottled german beers, six malts, and sensibly priced wines with about a dozen by the glass. Very fairly priced given the high standard of cooking, the menu has items such as soup (£3.50), daytime sandwiches (from £4.20), duck spring rolls (£4.80), cod in beer batter (£7.50), vegetarian dishes such as roasted mediterranean vegetable tart (£8.10), steak pie (£8.90), chicken breast filled with stilton, wrapped in smoked bacon with white wine, cream and chive sauce (£9.50) and 10oz rib-eye steak (£10.50); children's meals (£4.20); specials might include mussels (£4.90), roasted red pepper filled with couscous, feta and coriander with tomato and cumin sauce (£8.20), navarin of lamb (£10.50), roasted scallops with tomato and chili jam and crème fraîche (£12.80). From 12 to 6 they offer a light menu, with sandwiches and baked potatoes. The boundary of the parishes of Little Longstone and Ashford runs through the hotel, and the spacious no smoking restaurant and smaller lounge are named according to which side of the line they sit; beer garden. The best place to admire the terrific view is from the big windows in the lounge, the garden, and from four of the seven bedrooms; good generous breakfasts. *(Recommended by Mike and Linda Hudson, Keith and Chris O'Neill, Brian and Jacky Wilson, Peter F Marshall, John and Wendy Allin, Simon and Amanda Southwell, Andrew Pearson, Paul and Margaret Baker, the Didler, Leigh and Gillian Mellor, M G Hart, Mike and Sue Loseby, Mr and Mrs R B Berry, R Brackenbury)*

Free house ~ Licensees Christine O'Connell and Victor Chandler ~ Real ale ~ Bar food (12-9.30(9 Sun)) ~ Restaurant ~ (01629) 640250 ~ Children in eating area of bar, restaurant and family room ~ Dogs allowed in bar and bedrooms ~ Open 11.30-11.30; 12-11 Sun ~ Bedrooms: £55B/£55B

OVER HADDON SK2066 Map 7
Lathkil
Village and inn signposted from B5055 just SW of Bakewell

A collection of walking boots might well greet you in the lobby of this beautifully placed pub, as walkers often call in here while hiking through Lathkill Dale, a gorgeously secretive limestone valley. The walled garden is a good place to sit and soak in the views. Five reasonably priced real ales include Charles Wells Bombardier and Whim Hartington, which are well kept alongside a couple of guests from brewers such as Cottage and Leek St Edwards. They have a few unusual malt whiskies and a good range of new world wines. The airy room on the right as you go in has a nice fire in the attractively carved fireplace, old-fashioned settles with upholstered cushions and chairs, black beams, a delft shelf of blue and white plates, original prints and photographs, and big windows. On the left, the spacious and sunny no smoking dining area doubles as a restaurant in the evenings. The buffet style lunch menu includes filled rolls (from £2.50), soup (£3), fish pie, a vegetarian dish or a cold dish such as quiche (£6), steak and kidney pie (£6.50) and smoked trout (£7.25); specials such as aubergine moussaka (£6) and beef and black peppercorn crumble (£6.25); puddings (from £3); more elaborate restaurant food in the evening. There are darts, bar billiards, shove-ha'penny, backgammon, dominoes, cribbage and piped music. *(Recommended by MLR, Patrick Hancock, the Didler, Ian and Liz Rispin, Don and Shirley Parrish, P Price, Matthew Shackle, Richard and Margaret McPhee, A and B D Craig, Alan and Paula McCully, R Brackenbury, Mark and Mary Fairman)*

Free house ~ Licensee Robert Grigor-Taylor ~ Real ale ~ Bar food (lunchtime) ~ Restaurant ~ (01629) 812501 ~ Children in restaurant ~ Dogs allowed in bar ~ Open 11.30-3, 6.30(7 winter)-11; 11.30-11 Sat; 12-10.30 Sun ~ Bedrooms: £40B/£65S(£80B)

SHELDON SK1768 Map 7

Cock & Pullet £

Village signposted off A6 just W of Ashford

A cheerful assembly of deliberately mismatched furnishings and a flagstoned bar successfully contrives to make the Cock and Pullet feel much older than it is, yet the building was converted into a pub only just over ten years ago. The friendly family that run it have created a proper traditional village local, taking great pains to include the sort of features that other pubs have taken decades to amass. As well as low beams, exposed stonework, and scrubbed oak tables and pews, the small, cosy rooms have 24 fully working clocks (one for every hour of the day), whose decorous chimes further add to the relaxed, peaceful atmosphere. Well kept Bass, Black Sheep, Timothy Taylors Landlord and a guest such as St Austell Tribute on handpump. As well as good sandwiches and a choice of popular Sunday roasts, the shortish, very reasonable menu includes steak in ale pie, gammon and home-made lasagne (£5.75), and specials might feature moussaka or broccoli bake (£5.75); the well presented meals are highly praised by readers. A fireplace is filled with flowers in summer, and around it are various representations of poultry, including some stuffed. A plainer room has pool and a TV; there's also a no smoking snug; darts and dominoes. At the back is a pleasant little terrace with tables and a water feature. The pub is a year-round favourite with walkers (it can be busy at weekends); the pretty village is just off the Limestone Way. More reports please.
(Recommended by Peter F Marshall, Guy Vowles, Patrick Hancock)

Free house ~ Licensees David and Kath Melland ~ Real ale ~ Bar food (12-2.30, 6-9) ~ No credit cards ~ (01629) 814292 ~ Children in eating area of bar ~ Dogs allowed in bar ~ Open 11-11; 12-10.30 Sun ~ Bedrooms: 1/£60B

WARDLOW SK1875 Map 7

Three Stags Heads

Wardlow Mires; A623 by junction with B6465

Readers appreciate the down to earth, unchanged décor of this place; one remarked that it hardly looks like a pub from outside. Genuinely traditional, this is a real find if you like your pubs basic and full of character, and enjoy a chat with friendly locals at the bar. It's situated in a natural sink, so don't be surprised to find the floors muddied by boots in wet weather (and the dogs even muddier). Warmed right through by a cast-iron kitchen range, the tiny flagstoned parlour bar has old leathercloth seats, a couple of antique settles with flowery cushions, two high-backed windsor armchairs and simple oak tables (look out for the petrified cat in a glass case). Four well kept real ales on handpump are Abbeydale Absolution, Black Lurcher (brewed for the pub at a hefty 8% ABV) and Matins, and Broadstone Charter Ale; they've lots of bottled continental and english beers (the stronger ones aren't cheap), and in winter they do a roaring trade in mugs of steaming tea – there might be free hot chestnuts on the bar; cribbage and dominoes, nine men's morris and backgammon. Food is hearty and home-made, and the seasonal menu notably countrified: possibly pasta (£6.50), cold pheasant pie or chicken and aubergine curry (£7.50) steak and kidney pie (£8.50), fried pigeon breasts (£9.50) and hare pie (£10.50); the hardy plates are home-made (the barn is a pottery workshop). You can book the tables in the small no smoking dining parlour. The front terrace looks across the main road to the distant hills. Please note the opening times.
(Recommended by Pete Baker, the Didler, Kevin Thorpe, Jim Abbott, Patrick Hancock, Derek and Sylvia Stephenson, R Brackenbury)

Free house ~ Licensees Geoff and Pat Fuller ~ Real ale ~ Bar food ~ No credit cards ~ (01298) 872268 ~ Dogs welcome ~ Folk music most Sat evenings and alternate Fri ~ Open 7-11 Fri; 12-11 Sat, Sun and bank hols; closed weekday lunchtimes

---

Prices of main dishes usually include vegetables or a side salad.

WOOLLEY MOOR SK3661 Map 7
White Horse
Badger Lane, off B6014 Matlock—Clay Cross

In lovely rolling countryside and looking over the Amber valley, this is as much a place to enjoy outside as inside. A very good play area with a wooden train, boat, climbing frame and swings, and a puzzle sheet and crayons with their meal means children are amply catered for, and the garden has picnic-sets as well as a boules pitch. A sign outside shows how horses and carts carried measures of salt along the toll road in front – the toll bar cottage still stands at the entrance of the Badger Lane (a badger was the haulier who transported the salt). Still very much in its original state, the tap room has a pleasant chatty atmosphere. Guest ales such as Black Sheep and Marstons Pedigree and Best are kept under a light blanket pressure; decent wines too, and efficient friendly service. There is piped music in the lounge and conservatory (great views of the Ogston reservoir from here); darts, dominoes. Bar food, which is enjoyable, good value and generously served, could include soup (£2.95), moules marinière (£4.50, or £7.25 as a main course), sandwiches (from £4.50), battered haddock or derbyshire sausage, ham and eggs (£6.95), home-made beef or vegetable lasagne (£7.25), steak and kidney pie (£7.50), 8oz sirloin steak (£12.50) and mixed grill (£14.95); puddings (£3.95). It's best to book for the linen laid restaurant. All eating areas are no smoking.
(Recommended by the Didler, Maurice and Della Andrew, Patrick Hancock, WAH, Keith and Chris O'Neill, Peter F Marshall, Robert F Smith)

Musketeers ~ Real ale ~ Bar food (12-2, 6-9; 12-7 Sun(3 winter); not Sun evening) ~ Restaurant ~ (01246) 590319 ~ Children welcome away from tap room ~ Dogs allowed in bar ~ Open 12-3, 6-11; 12-10.30 Sun

---

LUCKY DIP

Besides the fully inspected pubs, you might like to try these Lucky Dips recommended to us and described by readers (if you do, please send us reports: www.goodguides.co.uk).

ASHBOURNE [SK1846]
Careys [Workhouse Yard, Dig St/Compton St]: Friendly restored former workhouse, calls itself a wine bar but has good range of well kept ales, wines and spirits; stripped brick, big open fire, roomy conservatory, pleasant staff, good lunchtime bar food (quite quiet then, more lively evenings, with younger customers), good bistro upstairs; riverside garden *(B M Eldridge)*
☆ *Smiths Tavern* [bottom of market place]: Neatly kept traditional pub, friendly and relaxed, stretching back from heavily black-beamed bar to warmly refurbished light and airy end no smoking dining room, good value food, well kept Banks's, Marstons Pedigree and a guest beer, lots of whiskies and vodkas, daily papers, traditional games; children welcome, open all day summer Sun *(Michael Lamm, Patrick Hancock, DJH, LYM, Ken Richards)*
ASHFORD IN THE WATER [SK1969]
☆ *Bulls Head* [Church St]: Busy dining pub with cosy and homely lounge, thriving bar, friendly and helpful management, well kept Robinsons Best, Old Stockport and Hartleys XB, enjoyable meals, lunchtime sandwiches, daily papers; may be piped music; tables out behind and by front car park *(Mrs Sylvia Elcoate, Patrick Hancock, Jennifer Banks, Annette and John Derbyshire, Mrs Jennifer Hurst, Derek and Sylvia Stephenson)*
ASHOVER [SK3463]
Crispin [Church St]: Impressive new

refurbishment, enjoyable food, welcoming service, well kept Mansfield, real fires, several areas from beamed original core to back conservatory *(Barry Steele-Perkins)*
☆ *Old Poets Corner* [aka Red Lion; Butts Rd]: Well kept Greene King Abbot and Marstons Pedigree from the jug, half a dozen changing guest beers on handpump (and plans for on-site microbrewery), bottled belgian beers, farm ciders, decent wines and country wines, enjoyable home-made food, good faintly alternative atmosphere, comfortable turn-of-the-century décor, cheerful fire; landlord's rock band some nights; pleasant terrace *(the Didler)*
BAKEWELL [SK2168]
Castle Inn [Bridge St]: Homely Georgian-fronted 17th-c pub with three candlelit rooms, flagstones and lots of pictures, well kept ales inc a guest beer, enjoyable food, friendly staff, two real fires, daily papers; tables outside *(B M Eldridge)*
Peacock [Bridge St]: Clean, bright and cheerful, well kept Theakstons and guests such as Adnams Bitter and Broadside, good value food (not Mon-Weds evenings), friendly service *(Simon and Amanda Southwell, A and B D Craig)*
BARLBOROUGH [SK4777]
De Rodes Arms [handy for M1 junction 30 – A619 Chesterfield Rd roundabout]: Chain pub useful for usual food all day till 10pm, Marstons Pedigree, decent wine and soft drinks

choice, no smoking area; piped music; children allowed, picnic-sets outside *(CMW, JJW)*

Rose & Crown [handy for M1 junction 30; High St]: Extended village pub with elegant dining room, lots of crimson plush, generous fair-priced food (not Mon or Tues), Hardys & Hansons ales, good choice of soft drinks and wine; piped music, no dogs; picnic-sets and play area in side garden, rustic benches facing Norman cross in front, cl Mon/Tues lunchtimes *(CMW, JJW)*

BARLOW [SK3474]

☆ **Old Pump** [B6051 towards Chesterfield]: Comfortable lounge and bars with valley views, wide choice of good attractively priced food from well filled rolls to popular Sun lunch, well kept Everards, Mansfield and Marstons Pedigree, good value wines, polite service, restaurant; bedrooms, good walks *(David Carr, Keith and Chris O'Neill)*

BELPER [SK3547]

Cross Keys [Market Pl]: Two-room pub with Batemans and a guest beer, bar food, coal fire in lounge, bar billiards; summer beer festival, open all day *(the Didler)*

Queens Head [Chesterfield Rd]: Warm and cosy three-room pub with well kept Caledonian Deuchars IPA, Greene King IPA and guest beers, constant coal fire, local photographs; good upstairs wknd band nights, beer festivals; terrace tables, open all day *(the Didler)*

Thorntree [Chesterfield Rd (B6013)]: Comfortable two-bar local with well kept Bass and three changing guest beers *(the Didler)*

BIRCH VALE [SK0186]

Sycamore [Sycamore Rd; from A6015 take Station Rd towards Thornsett]: Reliable four-roomed dining pub, reasonable prices, well kept ales, friendly helpful service, fountain in downstairs drinking bar, restaurant open all day Sun; piped music; children welcome, spacious streamside gardens with good play area and summer bar, handy for Sett Valley trail *(Michael Lamm, LYM, Ian and Nita Cooper)*

Waltzing Weasel [New Mills Rd (A6015 E of New Mills)]: Wine-bar-style restaurant pub under new management, home-made food with some emphasis on fish, well kept Marstons Pedigree, decent wines, cosy fire, daily papers; children and dogs welcome, disabled access, bedrooms *(Craig Booth, LYM)*

BIRCHOVER [SK2362]

Druid [off B5056; Main St]: No smoking two-storey dining pub, spacious and airy, with very wide if not cheap food choice, real ale such as Marstons Pedigree, good choice of malt whiskies and reasonably priced wines; piped music; children welcome, picnic-sets out in front, good area for walks, has been cl Mon *(M L Rantzen, LYM, Richard Cole, Derek and Sylvia Stephenson, James A Waller)*

BONSALL [SK2858]

Barley Mow [off A6012 Cromford—Hartington; The Dale]: Friendly tucked-away pub with well kept Whim Hartington and guest beers, fresh sandwiches and other

popular food, character furnishings, coal fire; live music wknds inc landlord playing accordion, organises local walks; small terrace, cl wkdy lunchtimes (may open Fri by arrangement, open all day wknds) *(the Didler, Derek and Sylvia Stephenson, R Brackenbury, Mark and Mary Fairman)*

BRASSINGTON [SK2354]

Miners Arms [off B5035/B5056 NE of Ashbourne; Miners Hill]: Welcoming and lively local, with well kept Banks's Mild, Marstons Pedigree and two guest beers, friendly helpful staff, enjoyable home-made food inc good value daily roasts and hot meat rolls; children welcome, tables out among flower tubs, bedrooms, open all day *(Duncan Chappell)*

BUXTON [SK1266]

☆ **Bull i' th' Thorn** [Ashbourne Rd (A515) 6 miles S of Buxton, nr Flagg and Hurdlow]: Intriguing cross between medieval hall and straightforward roadside dining pub, all sorts of antique features to look at, handsome panelling, old flagstones and big open fire, also games room and simple no smoking family room; friendly licensees, wide range of food all day from baguettes to restaurant dishes, Robinsons Best; children and dogs welcome, terrace and big lawn, bedrooms with own bathrooms, big breakfast, open all day from 9.30am *(Dave Simmonds, Colin McKerrow, the Didler, Jenny Berki, B M Eldridge, Alan and Paula McCully, Paul and Margaret Baker)*

Old Sun [33 High St]: Well kept Banks's and Marstons Best and Pedigree, usual food from sandwiches up usefully served till 10pm, good choice of reasonably priced wines by the glass, farm cider, friendly helpful staff, open fires, several small dimly lit traditional areas off central bar, low beams, bare boards or tiles, stripped wood screens, old local photographs; piped music, TV; children in back bar, open all day *(Paul Goldman, the Didler, Roger and Anne Newbury, LYM, Barry Collett)*

BUXWORTH [SK0282]

☆ **Navigation** [S of village towards Silkhill, off B6062]: Popular and cheery pub by reopened canal basin, linked low-ceilinged flagstoned rooms with canalia and brassware, lacy curtains, coal and log fires, flagstone floors, well kept and attractively priced Marstons Pedigree, Timothy Taylors Landlord and Websters Yorkshire, summer farm ciders, winter mulled wine, enjoyable generous bar food all day from nice sandwiches up, no smoking restaurant, games room; quiet piped music; tables on sunken flagstoned terrace, play area and pets corner, open all day *(Michael Lamm, Bill Sykes, Keith and Chris O'Neill, Patrick Hancock, LYM, Derek and Sylvia Stephenson, Gerry and Rosemary Dobson, Peter F Marshall, Barry Collett)*

CALVER [SK2474]

Bridge Inn [Calver Bridge, off A623 N of Baslow]: Unpretentious two-room stone-built village local, short choice of good value plain food (not Mon evening or winter Sun evening), small separate eating area, particularly well kept Hardys & Hansons ales, quick friendly service, cosy comfortable corners, coal fires, bank notes on beams, local prints and bric-a-brac inc old fire-fighting equipment in lounge; picnic-sets in nice big garden by River Derwent *(Patrick Hancock, John Dwane, Kevin Blake)*

CASTLETON [SK1482]

☆ *George* [Castle St]: Friendly and relaxed, good value food from nourishing sandwiches to imaginative main dishes, well kept Wadworths 6X, two good-sized rooms, one mainly for eating, ancient beams and stripped stone, no music; tables on wide forecourt, lots of flower tubs; popular with young people – nr YHA; dogs, children and muddy boots welcome, may be cl Mon lunchtime *(B M Eldridge, A and B D Craig)*

Olde Cheshire Cheese [How Lane]: Two family-friendly linked beamed areas, cosy, welcoming and spotless, with cheery landlord, well kept real ales, good house wine, back lounge set for new chef's wide choice of enjoyable reasonably priced food all day, open fire, lots of photographs, toby jugs and local paintings, sensibly placed darts; piped music may obtrude; bedrooms each with a teddy bear *(BB, Simon and Amanda Southwell, Patrick Hancock, Lynda Payton, Sam Samuells, N R White)*

☆ *Olde Nags Head* [Cross St (A6187)]: Small but solid hotel dating from 17th c, interesting antique oak furniture and coal fire in small civilised bar with nice pictures on dark red walls, well kept ales such as Black Sheep, Edale and Timothy Taylors, good coffee, impressive sensibly priced bar food from sandwiches up, cosy Victorian restaurant; open all day, comfortable bedrooms *(LYM, Lynda Payton, Sam Samuells)*

CHELMORTON [SK1170]

Church Inn [between A6 and A515 SW of Buxton]: Comfortable split bar, ample space for diners, good range of reasonably priced generous food, friendly landlord and golden labrador, well kept Adnams, Marstons Pedigree and a guest beer; piped music, outside lavatories; tables out in pleasant sloping garden with terrace, well tended flower boxes, superb walking country, open all day summer wknds *(Patrick Hancock, Peter F Marshall, Michael Lamm, Barry Collett)*

CHESTERFIELD [SK3871]

Barley Mow [Saltergate]: Former Wards pub with original stained glass, wide choice of enjoyable food from sandwiches, cobs, baguettes and baked potatoes up, low prices, well kept Greene King IPA, Marstons Pedigree and John Smiths, good hot drinks; very active in charity work *(Keith and Chris O'Neill)*

Royal Oak [Chatsworth Rd, Brampton]: Large friendly local, well kept Greene King Ruddles Best, Theakstons Best and Old Peculier, Whim Hartington and Arbor Light and weekly guest beers; conservatory with pool and table football, big-screen sports TV, jazz Sun afternoon, Weds band night; tables outside, play area *(anon)*

Rutland [Stephenson Pl]: Ancient L-shaped pub next to crooked-spire church, well kept Badger Best, Timothy Taylors Landlord and three or more interesting guest beers, farm cider, good clear price and details boards, low-priced pub food all day from sandwiches and baguettes up, friendly polite service even when busy, rugs and assorted wooden furniture on bare boards, old photographs, no smoking eating area, darts; piped music; children welcome, open all day *(Keith and Chris O'Neill, Patrick Hancock, Andrew York, Tony Hobden)*

Spa Lane Vaults [St Marys Gate]: Reliable Wetherspoons, their usual pricing, food and good beer choice, smart lavatories *(Tony Hobden)*

CLIFTON [SK1645]

Cock: Comfortable two-bar family pub with friendly staff, jovial landlord, dark beams and period feel, good value home-made food, well kept ales inc Timothy Taylors Landlord, darts; children really welcome, garden tables, climber and slide *(David Tindal)*

COMBS [SK0378]

Beehive: Roomy, neat and comfortable, with good generous home cooking (good wkdy lunch deals, bargain suppers Mon, Weds/Thurs steak nights, food all day wknds), well kept ales such as Black Sheep, decent house wines, log fire; quiet piped jazz, live music Fri, quiz night Tues; bedrooms, tables outside, by lovely valley tucked away from main road *(Mr and Mrs B C McGee, Mrs P J Carroll)*

COWERS LANE [SK3147]

Railway Inn [Ashbourne Rd (A517/B5023 W of Belper)]: Neatly kept and comfortable traditional pub with enjoyable food, good beer choice, friendly staff, real fire, separate dining area, pool room with darts and machines; tables and play area outside *(Bob)*

CRICH [SK3454]

Cliff [Cromford Rd, Town End]: Cosy and unpretentious two-room pub with real fire, well kept Hardys & Hansons Bitter and Mild, good value generous straightforward food inc children's; great views, handy for National Tramway Museum *(the Didler, Stuart Paulley)*

CROMFORD [SK2956]

☆ *Boat* [Scarthin, off Mkt Pl]: Traditional 18th-c waterside pub (though no view of water) under friendly young brother and sister, well kept ales such as Marstons Pedigree and Whim Hartington, relaxed atmosphere, coal fire, good value food (not Sun/Mon eves), long narrow low-beamed bar with stripped stone, bric-a-brac and books, darts, cellar bar, recently refurbished restaurant; live music Tues and wknds; children welcome, back garden, open all day wknds *(the Didler, BB, Jeremy Beckett)*

CROWDECOTE [SK1065]

Packhorse: Small 16th-c two-bar pub, nicely cooked food (sandwiches too), three real ales inc local Hartington, tables in back garden, beautiful views, on popular walking route *(Peter F Beever, R Brackenbury)*

CUTTHORPE [SK3373]
Peacock [School Hill (B6050 NW of
Chesterfield)]: Neatly kept and comfortable,
pleasant service, good straightforward food
from sandwiches to good choice of roasts, well
kept Greene King IPA and Charles Wells
Bombardier, modest bookable dining area;
space for caravans in garden behind, well
placed for walks *(Peter F Marshall)*

DENBY [SK3847]
Old Stables [Park Hall Rd, just off B6179
(former A61) S of Ripley): Friendly tap for
Leadmill microbrewery in raftered former
stable barn in Park Hall grounds, their full
range, some from the cask, at low prices, two
or three guest beers, fresh filled cobs, bench
seating and sawdust on floor, plenty of
brewery memorabilia, visits of the 1800s
former mill brewery opposite; open only Fri
evening and all day wknds *(the Didler)*

DERBY [SK3438]
☆ *Abbey Inn* [Darley St, Darley Abbey]:
Conversion of surviving part of 11th-c abbey
into pub, massive stonework remnants, brick
floor, studded oak doors, big stone inglenook,
stone spiral stair to upper bar with handsome
oak rafters and tapestries (and the lavatories
with their beams, stonework and tiles are
worth a look too); well kept cheap Sam
Smiths, decent low-priced lunchtime bar food,
coal fire; piped music; children welcome, opp
Derwent-side park, pleasant riverside walk out
from centre *(the Didler, LYM)*
Babington Arms [Babington Lane]: Large well
run open-plan Wetherspoons, usual style and
comfortable seating, good welcoming service,
particularly good choice of well kept ales inc
some brewed for the pub, 20 whiskies; open all
day *(Richard Houghton, the Didler)*
Falstaff [Silver Hill Rd, off Normanton Rd]:
Basic bouncy local aka the Folly, brewing its
own good value ales such as 3 Faze and
Phoenix, guest beers too; right-hand bar with
coal fire usually quieter, games room on left;
open all day *(the Didler)*
☆ *Flower Pot* [King St]: Extended real ale pub
with up to a dozen or so well kept and
reasonably priced changing beers mainly from
small breweries – glazed panels show cellarage,
regular beer festivals; friendly staff, three
linked rooms inc comfortable back bar with
lots of books, side area with old photographs
of Derby and brewery memorabilia, good
value food cooked to order till early evening,
daily papers, pub games; piped music/juke box,
separate concert room – good live bands
wknds; disabled access and facilities, tables on
cherry-tree terrace, open all day
(Patrick Hancock, G Coates, Bob)
Rowditch [Uttoxeter New Rd (A516)]: Good
value friendly local with well kept Mansfield,
Marstons Pedigree and guest beers, country
wines, attractive small snug on right, coal fire,
piano, downstairs cellar bar; pleasant garden
(the Didler)
☆ *Smithfield* [Meadow Rd]: Friendly and
comfortable bow-fronted pub with big bar,
snug, back lounge full of old prints, curios and

breweriana, fine choice of well kept changing
ales, filled rolls and hearty lunchtime meals,
real fires, daily papers; piped music, pub games
inc table skittles, board games, TV and games
machines, quiz nights, summer blues nights;
children welcome, riverside terrace, open all
day *(Patrick Hancock, the Didler, C J Fletcher)*
☆ *Standing Order* [Irongate]: Imposing and
echoing banking hall converted to vast no
smoking Wetherspoons, central bar, booths
down each side, elaborately painted
plasterwork, pseudo-classical torsos, high
portraits of mainly local notables; usual
popular food all day (good steaks), good range
of well kept ales, reasonable prices, daily
papers, neat efficient young staff; good
disabled facilities *(David Carr, the Didler, BB,
Kevin Blake, Bob)*
Station Inn [Midland Rd, below station]:
Friendly and basic local with good food
lunchtime and early evening in large back
lounge, particularly well kept Bass in jugs from
cellar, Black Sheep on handpump, tiled floor
bar, side room with darts, pool and TV, ornate
façade; piped music, open all day Fri
(the Didler)

DRONFIELD [SK3378]
Jolly Farmer [Pentland Rd/Gorsey Brigg,
Dronfield Woodhouse; off B6056]: Spreading
bar done out with old pine, bare bricks, boards
and carpets, bric-a-brac, alcoves and cosy
corners, open fire, well kept changing ales from
glazed cellarage such as Batemans, Burton
Bridge, Tetleys and Charles Wells Bombardier,
good wine and soft drinks choice, enjoyable
fair-priced food (not Sun evening), very
friendly staff, daily papers, no smoking dining
area; piped music, games area with pool and
TV, quiz nights Tues and Sun; children
allowed if eating, picnic-sets outside, open all
day *(Patrick Hancock, Andrew Crawford,
CMW, JJW)*

EDALE [SK1285]
Old Nags Head [off A625 E of Chapel-en-le-
Frith; Grindsbrook Booth]: Popular well used
traditional pub at start of Pennine Way,
flagstoned area for booted walkers, open fire
(not always lit), real ales; TV; children in airy
back family room, tables on front terrace and
in garden, open all day, cl Mon/Tues
lunchtimes out of season *(LYM, N R White)*

EDLASTON [SK1842]
Shire Horse [off A515 S of Ashbourne, just
beside Wyaston]: Immaculate rambling
timbered pub run by hospitable sisters, blazing
fires and gleaming brass in long beamed bar,
good food inc some interesting recipes, efficient
attentive service, well kept Bass, Marstons
Pedigree and a guest such as Fullers London
Pride, back conservatory restaurant; tables
outside, peaceful spot *(D P and M A Miles,
Barrie Frost, Martin Grosberg)*

ELTON [SK2261]
☆ *Duke of York* [village signed off B5056 W of
Matlock; Main St]: Unspoilt old-fashioned
local in Peak District, charming village, very
long-serving friendly landlady, lovely little
quarry-tiled back tap room with coal fire in

massive fireplace, glazed bar and hatch to corridor, more fires in the two front ones – one like private parlour with piano and big dining table (no food, just crisps); Adnams and Mansfield, welcoming regulars, darts; lavatories out by the pig sty; open 8.30-11, and Sun lunchtime *(RWC, the Didler, Pete Baker, Tich Critchlow)*

FENNY BENTLEY [SK1850]

☆ *Bentley Brook* [A515 N of Ashbourne]: Big open-plan bare-boards bar/dining room, central log fire, communicating restaurant, well kept Banks's, Marstons Pedigree and perhaps their own Leatherbritches, enjoyable food inc some unusual dishes and their own herbs and garden produce (they sell kitchen/meat products too); piped music; terrace picnic-sets, barbecue, good play area, marquee for spring bank hol beer festival, 11 bedrooms, open all day *(Michael Butler, Cathryn and Richard Hicks, Guy Vowles, Derek and Sylvia Stephenson, Mr and Mrs A Campbell, John and Wendy Allin, the Didler, Patrick Hancock, Bob, Jim and Barbara Palmer, LYM)*

FLAGG [SK1167]

Duke of York [off A515 Buxton—Ashbourne, 5 miles from Buxton]: Popular low-ceilinged pub with well kept Robinsons ales, well priced enjoyable pub food, open fires, attractive bar, sun lounge and pretty no smoking dining room *(Alan and Paula McCully)*

FROGGATT EDGE [SK2577]

Grouse [Longshaw, off B6054 NE of Froggatt]: Plush front bar, log fire and wooden benches in back bar, big dining room, good home cooking from sandwiches to imaginative dishes, good value smaller helpings, Banks's and guest beers, friendly service, handsome views; verandah and terrace, clean bedrooms, good gritstone moorland walking country *(J S Bethell)*

GLOSSOP [SK0394]

Prince of Wales [off High St East (A57)]: Relaxing three-room local, three well kept mainly Marstons ales, friendly chatty regulars, real fires, lots of bric-a-brac, brasses and photographs; TV *(Dennis Jones)*

Star [Howard St]: Bare-boards alehouse opp station, up to a dozen well kept changing real ales inc small breweries, friendly helpful staff, shelves crammed with breweriana; shame about the piped music; open all day *(the Didler, Dennis Jones)*

GREAT HUCKLOW [SK1878]

Queen Anne: Comfortable 17th-c stone-built pub, beams, log fire and gleaming copper, well kept ales such as Adnams and Cottage, walkers' bar, good soft drinks choice, enjoyable blackboard food (may be just soup and sandwiches, winter lunchtimes), pub games; piped music; french windows to small back terrace and charming garden with picnic-sets and lovely views, two quiet bedrooms, good walks, cl Tues lunchtime *(Patrick Hancock, the Didler, Derek and Sylvia Stephenson, CMW, JJW, Mrs S Fairbrother, B M Eldridge, R Brackenbury)*

HARTINGTON [SK1260]

Devonshire Arms [Market Pl]: Good food choice from simple bar meals up in attractive old pub, well kept ales such as Greene King Abbot and Jennings Cumberland, friendly staff, log fires, flagstoned public bar welcoming walkers and dogs; comfortable bedrooms, tables out in front facing village duck pond, more in small garden behind, good walks *(Dr D J and Mrs S C Walker, R Brackenbury)*

HAYFIELD [SK0387]

Pack Horse [off A624 Glossop—Chapel-en-le-Frith; Market St]: Nicely (even luxuriously) furnished dining pub under new licensees, new chef doing good fresh food at reasonable prices from baguettes to some interesting main dishes, Greene King IPA and Fullers London Pride, good choice of spirits and wines; piped music may obtrude; has been open all day *(Dr M A Turner)*

HILTON [SK2430]

Old Talbot [Main St]: Attractive village pub, cosy and intimate, with usual food, reasonably priced changing guest beers, big fireplace in beamed lounge with bottles, earthenware jugs, old pictures and breweriana, pleasant bar; lots of flowers and hanging baskets *(Kevin Blake)*

HOLBROOK [SK3644]

Wheel [Chapel St]: Friendly beamed village local with well kept changing ales, some in jugs from the cellar, food from sandwiches and baguettes up, coal-fired stove, snug, family room, attractive back conservatory restaurant; pleasant secluded garden with covered terrace and barbecue, has been open all day Sat, cl Mon lunchtime *(Brian and Rosalie Laverick, the Didler, Derek and Sylvia Stephenson)*

HOLLINGTON [SK2238]

Red Lion [off A52 Derby—Ashbourne]: Enjoyable interesting food, well kept beer, good atmosphere, friendly attentive staff *(Michael B Griffith)*

HOLYMOORSIDE [SK3469]

Lamb [Loads Rd, just off Holymoor Rd]: Small, cosy and spotless two-room village pub in leafy spot, Bass, Theakstons XB and several guest beers, friendly landlady, coal fire, pub games; tables outside, cl wkdy lunchtimes *(the Didler, Patrick Hancock)*

HOPE [SK1783]

☆ *Cheshire Cheese* [off A6187, towards Edale]: 16th-c rather food-oriented pub handy for Pennine Way and Edale Valley, three snug beamed rooms each with a coal fire, no smoking lower dining room, well kept changing ales such as Edale, Kelham Island, Wentworth and Whim Hartington, good choice of house wines and malt whiskies, prompt service; piped music; children in eating areas, open all day Sat, attractive bedrooms *(DC, the Didler, C J Fletcher, LYM, Pete Baker, Michael Lamm, Mrs Julie Thomas, Peter F Marshall)*

HULLAND WARD [SK2647]

Black Horse [Hulland Ward; A517 Ashbourne—Belper]: 17th-c pub with good fresh food inc interesting dishes in low-beamed quarry-tiled bar or back dining room with popular Sun carvery, well kept changing beers such as Bass and Harviestoun, friendly licensees; children welcome, garden tables, comfortable bedrooms, nr Carsington Water *(the Didler)*

ILKESTON [SK4643]

Bridge Inn [Bridge St, Cotmanhay; off A609/A6007]: Welcoming two-room local by Erewash Canal, popular with fishermen and boaters for early breakfast and sandwich lunches; low-priced well kept Hardys & Hansons Best and Best Mild, interesting photographs in lounge, darts and dominoes, may have eggs for sale; well behaved children allowed, nice back garden with play area, open all day *(the Didler)*
Dewdrop [Station St, Ilkeston Junction, off A6096]: Large three-room Victorian pub in old industrial area, well kept changing ales such as Glentworth, Kelham Island, Mallards, Nottingham and Oakham, simple lunchtime bar food, pictures and plates, new woodburner in small public bar with darts and TV; sheltered outside seating, bedrooms, walks by former Nottingham Canal *(JP, PP)*
Ilford [Station Rd]: Club but open to all, welcoming local atmosphere, well kept Whim Hartington and one or two guest beers from small breweries, filled rolls, pool, TV, live music Sat; tables in pleasant area outside, open all day Sun, cl wkdy lunchtimes *(the Didler)*

KILBURN [SK3845]

Travellers Rest [Chapel St]: Two-room 1850s local with Carlsberg Burton, Greene King Abbot, Tetleys and a local Leadmill beer *(the Didler)*

KING'S NEWTON [SK3826]

Hardinge Arms [not far from M1 junction 23A, via A453 to Isley, then off Melbourne/Wilson rd; Main St]: Recently refurbished, bright and spacious yet warm and relaxing with its low beams and brick or wood floors, well prepared straightforward food inc good value Sun lunch, Timothy Taylors Landlord and guest beers, good wine range, quick friendly service, stately back lounge; children in eating area, motel bedrooms *(LYM, Roland Curtis, Elaine Thompson)*

KIRK LANGLEY [SK2937]

Bluebell [Adams Rd/B5020]: Two-bar country pub with enjoyable reasonably priced blackboard food, well kept Bass, Greene King Old Speckled Hen and Marstons Pedigree, friendly staff; garden picnic-sets, play area *(Deb and John Arthur)*

LITTLE LONGSTONE [SK1971]

☆ *Packhorse* [off A6 NW of Bakewell via Monsal Dale]: Chatty 16th-c cottage with old wooden chairs and benches in homely and appealing beamed rooms (one no smoking), delightful when it's not too busy, with well kept Marstons Best and Pedigree and a guest beer, good coffee, enjoyable simple food from doorstep sandwiches to good steak and kidney pie, breakfast 9.30-12, coal fire, welcoming informal service, pictures for sale, charity bookshelf; darts Mon, Weds folk night, quiz Thurs; hikers welcome (on Monsal Trail),

terrace in steep little back garden, open all day Sun *(LYM, Patrick Hancock, the Didler, Peter F Marshall, CMW, JJW)*

MAKENEY [SK3544]

☆ *Holly Bush* [from A6 heading N after Duffield, take 1st right after crossing R Derwent, then 1st left]: Unspoilt two-bar village pub, cosy and friendly, five well kept changing ales (may be brought from cellar in jugs), beer festivals, lots of brewing advertisements; three blazing coal fires (one in old-fashioned range by snug's curved settle), flagstones, beams, black panelling and tiled floors; cheap food from lunchtime rolls up inc Thurs steak night; games lobby; children allowed in rough and ready hatch-served back conservatory, picnic-sets outside, dogs welcome, open all day wknds *(Alan Bowker, BB, the Didler)*

MAPLETON [SK1647]

Okeover Arms [back rd just NW of Ashbourne]: Welcoming two-room pub, small and comfortable, doing well under newish owners, landlady using identified local produce for all her tasty food from baguettes to restaurant dishes, well kept Black Sheep ales, dozens of malt whiskies (some very rare), friendly efficient service, open fire and papers, magazines and books, restaurant; nice garden, pleasant village with interesting domed church, good riverside walks *(D P and M A Miles, A C Johnstone)*

MARSTON MONTGOMERY [SK1338]

Crown: Beamed bar/brasserie with interesting imaginatively presented food from excellent lunchtime sandwiches using six breads and two-course meals to enterprising evening menu, well kept Bass and Marstons Pedigree, friendly staff, cheerful atmosphere with log fire (even at breakfast); good garden, nice village, six large comfortable bedrooms *(L Elliott, John Dwane)*

MATLOCK [SK2960]

Crown [Crown Sq]: Welcoming child-friendly Wetherspoons, useful for real ales and their usual value food *(Fred and Lorraine Gill)*
Red Lion [Matlock Green]: Friendly family-run pub with enjoyable home-made food, good range of well kept real ales, open fires in lounge and games room, restaurant; pleasant terrace, bedrooms *(B M Eldridge)*
Thorn Tree [Jackson Rd, Matlock Bank]: Superb valley views to Riber Castle from homely and immaculate 19th-c stone-built two-room local, esp from front picnic-sets; well kept Bass and guest beers, sensibly priced enjoyable fresh lunchtime food from sandwiches up (Weds-Sun), quick friendly service, chatty licensees, interesting bric-a-brac, darts, dominoes; TV, piped nostalgic music, outside gents'; cl Mon/Tues lunchtime *(the Didler)*

MATLOCK BATH [SK2958]

Princess Victoria [South Parade]: Small Batemans pub with three of their beers and guest ales kept well, good value food all day in comfortable long beamed and panelled bar, chatty landlady, coal fire, upstairs evening restaurant; games machine, piped music, busy

wknds – live music Sat; open all day
(the Didler)

MILFORD [SK3545]

William IV [Milford Bridge]: Relaxing stone-built pub now tied to Leadmill, with their ales and guest beers, some tapped ingeniously from casks in back room, low beams, bare boards and quarry tiles, blazing coal fire, good filled rolls *(the Didler)*

MILLERS DALE [SK1473]

Anglers Rest [just down Litton Lane; pub is PH on OS Sheet 119 map ref 142734]: Friendly creeper-clad pub in lovely setting on Monsal Trail, wonderful gorge views and riverside walks; cosy lounge, ramblers' bar (dogs welcome here) and no smoking dining room, well kept ales such as Marstons Pedigree, Storm and Tetleys, open fire, lots of toby jugs, plates and teapots, food from cobs up, pool room; children welcome, attractive village *(John Wooll, Peter F Marshall, Patrick Hancock, the Didler)*

MILLTOWN [SK3562]

Nettle [Fallgate, Littlemoor]: Interesting old pub, several small rooms inc small good value carvery restaurant, enjoyable food, friendly service, Hardys & Hansons real ales, log fires *(R and M Tait)*

MONYASH [SK1566]

☆ *Bulls Head* [B5055 W of Bakewell]: Welcoming bustle in high-ceilinged old inn with lively local atmosphere, oak wall seats and panelled settle, horse pictures, shelf of china, mullioned windows, enthusiastic landlady, helpful staff, good value home cooking using local ingredients, sandwiches and help-yourself Sun buffet, well kept ales such as Carlsberg Burton, Tetleys Mild and Whim Hartington, good log fire; two-room dining room, darts, dominoes, pool in small back bar; may be quiet piped music; children and muddy dogs welcome, long pews out facing small green, simple bedrooms, attractive village in fine walking country, open all day *(Matthew Shackle, BB, Rona Murdoch, Mrs S Fairbrother, Alan and Paula McCully, Pam and John Smith, Mark and Mary Fairman)*

Royal Oak [Hurdlow, W of Monyash, on opposite side of A515 – towards Crowdecote]: Friendly beamed stone-built country pub with good choice of good value home-made food all day, esp pies and Thurs steak night, chatty atmosphere, well kept Bass and Marstons Pedigree, lower dining area; handy for High Peak/Tissington Trail, open all day *(Alan and Paula McCully)*

NEW MILLS [SJ9886]

Fox [Brookbottom; OS Sheet 109 map ref 985864]: Friendly traditional country local cared for well by long-serving landlord, particularly well kept Robinsons, good value sandwiches, baked potatoes and basic hot dishes (not Tues evening), log fire, darts and pool; children welcome, handy for walkers (can get crowded wknds), splendid tucked-away hamlet up single-track lane *(the Didler, Michael Lamm, Bob Broadhurst, John Fiander, David Hoult)*

Pack Horse [Mellor Rd]: Popular and friendly

family-run country pub with plentiful good value food, well kept real ales, sensibly priced wine, warm atmosphere and lovely views across broad Sett valley to Kinder Scout; bedrooms, open all day *(B M Eldridge)*

NEWTON SOLNEY [SK2825]

Brickmakers Arms [Main St (B5008 NE of Burton)]: Three comfortable rooms, beams and brasses, well kept Bass and Marstons Pedigree, enjoyable popular food; tables on small terrace, open all day (Sun afternoon break) *(the Didler)*

Unicorn [Repton Rd]: Friendly village local with well kept Bass and Marstons Pedigree, good value food in bar and small restaurant; good bedrooms, huge breakfast *(Ian and Jane Irving)*

OCKBROOK [SK4236]

☆ *Royal Oak* [village signed off B6096 just outside Spondon; Green Lane]: Quiet 18th-c village local run by same family for half a century, small unspoilt rooms (one no smoking), well kept Bass and four interesting guest beers (summer and Oct beer festivals), good soft drinks choice, tiled-floor tap room, turkey-carpeted snug, inner bar with Victorian prints, larger and lighter no smoking side room, nice old settle in entrance corridor, open fires, cheap popular food (not wknd evenings) from good fresh lunchtime rolls and sandwiches up, OAP bargains, good value Sun lunch, darts and dominoes, no music or machines; brass band night Sun; tables in sheltered cottage garden, more on cobbled front courtyard, separate play area *(CMW, JJW, BB, the Didler, Derek and Sylvia Stephenson, Pete Baker)*

OSMASTON [SK1943]

Shoulder of Mutton [off A52 SE of Ashbourne]: Snug and inviting down-to-earth pub in peaceful pretty village with thatched cottages, duckpond and good walks; enjoyable generous home-made food, pleasant smoke-free atmosphere, well kept Bass, Marstons Pedigree and a guest such as Greene King Abbot, attractive garden *(Nigel Long)*

OWLER BAR [SK2978]

☆ *Peacock* [A621 2 miles S of Totley]: Warm, welcoming and attractive Chef & Brewer in moorland setting with panoramic views of Sheffield and Peak District, keeping its original character; good food from huge sandwiches, rolls, baguettes and baked potatoes to extensive blackboard menu, big log fires, helpful attentive staff, good beer choice, large no smoking area away from central bar; open all day *(Kathy and Chris Armes, Matthew Lidbury, David and Ruth Hollands, Irene and Ray Atkin)*

PARWICH [SK1854]

Sycamore: Welcoming old country pub with jovial landlady, lively chat and roaring log fire in simply furnished but comfortable main bar, plain wholesome fresh food lunchtimes and most Weds-Sat evenings, big helpings, well kept Robinsons and Theakstons, lots of old local photographs, hatch-served tap room with games; tables out in front and on grass by car park, quiet village not far from Tissington *(the Didler, Pete Baker)*

PENTRICH [SK3852]

Dog [Main Rd (B6016 N of Ripley)]: Well run refurbished village pub, cosy and comfortable, with well kept Bass, Marstons Pedigree and a guest beer and enjoyable fresh food in restaurant area *(the Didler)*

PILSLEY [SK2371]

☆ *Devonshire Arms* [off A619 Bakewell—Baslow; High St]: Welcoming and well run, with good value generous home cooking worth waiting for inc interesting fish and Thurs-Sat evening carvery (may need to book), well kept Boddingtons, Mansfield and a guest beer, San Miguel on tap, appealing lounge bar with warm atmosphere and bric-a-brac, public bar area for walkers and children, open fires; quiz and music nights; bedrooms, handy for Chatsworth farm and craft shops, lovely village *(W W Burke, Peter F Marshall)*

RIPLEY [SK4050]

Moss Cottage [Nottingham Rd]: Welcoming straightforward pub with enjoyable home cooking inc good value two-for-one lunch deals, good helpful service, real ales such as Robinsons Old Stockport, good-sized no smoking dining areas *(John Wooll)*

Pear Tree [Derby Rd (B6179)]: Full Hardys & Hansons range kept well inc Mild and seasonal beers in friendly unspoilt two-room local, two good coal fires; open all day *(the Didler)*

ROWARTH [SK0189]

Little Mill [off A626 in Marple Bridge at Mellor sign, sharp left at Rowarth sign, then pub signed]: Beautiful tucked-away setting, unusual features inc working waterwheel; cheap cheerful plentiful bar food all day, bargain midweek meals, big open-plan bar with lots of little settees, armchairs and small tables, Banks's, Marstons Pedigree and a guest beer, big log fire, busy upstairs carvery restaurant evening and Sun lunchtime (good generous local beef), pub games; children welcome, pretty garden dell across stream great for them, with good play area; vintage Pullman-carriage bedrooms, open all day; talk of a possible sale recently – news please *(Michael Lamm, LYM, Dennis Jones)*

ROWSLEY [SK2565]

Grouse & Claret [A6 Bakewell—Matlock]: Attractively refurbished family dining pub in old stone building, spacious and comfortable, with enterprising food (all day wknd) from sandwiches and light dishes up as well as the usual pubby dishes, friendly helpful service, decent wines, open fires, no smoking area, tap room popular with walkers; tables outside, good value bedrooms *(P Price, David Carr)*

☆ *Peacock* [Bakewell Rd]: Civilised small 17th-c country hotel with comfortable chairs and sofas and a few antiques in spacious uncluttered lounge, interesting stone-floored inner bar, restful colours, enjoyable bar food from sandwiches up, Greene King IPA and a local guest beer, good wines, beautifully served coffee, well prepared restaurant meals; attractive riverside gardens, trout fishing, good

bedrooms *(Kathy and Chris Armes, W W Burke, LYM, Mrs S Fairbrother, Derek and Sylvia Stephenson)*

SHARDLOW [SK4330]

☆ *Malt Shovel* [3½ miles from M1 junction 24, via A6 towards Derby; The Wharf]: Busy old-world beamed pub in 18th-c former maltings, interesting odd-angled layout, well kept Banks's Best and Marstons Pedigree, quick friendly service, cheap lunchtime food from baguettes and baked potatoes up, good central open fire, farm tools and bric-a-brac; no small children; lots of tables out on canalside terrace, pretty hanging baskets *(LYM, the Didler)*

☆ *Old Crown* [off A50 just W of M1 junction 24; Cavendish Bridge, E of village]: Masses of jugs and mugs on the beams, lots of other interesting bric-a-brac, half a dozen or more real ales inc Burtonwood, Bass, Highgate Davenports, Marstons Pedigree and Wychwood Hobgoblin, nice choice of malt whiskies, very friendly service, sandwiches and low-priced standard pub dishes; children and dogs welcome, bedrooms, open all day *(Kay and Alistair Butler, Ian Phillips, the Didler, Alan and Sue Folwell, Kevin Blake, Brian and Ruth Archer, Mr and Mrs John Taylor, Bren and Val Speed, R T and J C Moggridge, Michael and Marion Buchanan, LYM)*

SHEEN [SK1160]

Staffordshire Knot [off B5054 at Hulme End]: Friendly stone-built village pub with good range of good value food from interesting snacks to perfectly cooked full meals, Mansfield and Marstons Pedigree, helpful staff, unusual décor with flagstones and two welcoming log fires *(Mr and Mrs B C McGee, Faith Smith)*

SMALLEY [SK4044]

☆ *Bell* [A608 Heanor—Derby]: Small comfortable two-room village pub, well kept low-priced Adnams, Mallard, Oakham, Whim Hartington and several guest beers, good choice of wines, pots of tea or coffee, smart efficient friendly staff, dining area with good reasonably priced changing food; post office annexe, tables in front and on big relaxing lawn with play area, beautiful hanging baskets, open all day wknds, attractive bedrooms behind *(Derek and Sylvia Stephenson, JP, PP)*

SMISBY [SK3419]

Smisby Arms [Nelsons Sq]: Friendly ancient beamed pub with well kept Marstons Pedigree, sensible shortish choice of enjoyable food inc delicious puddings, pleasant dining extension *(anon)*

SOUTH WINGFIELD [SK3755]

Old Yew Tree [B5035 W of Alfreton; Manor Rd]: Cosy and convivial local with good value food esp steaks and big Sun lunch, well kept Cottage, Marstons Pedigree and a couple of interesting guest beers, log fire, panelling, kettles and pans hanging from beams, separate restaurant area *(Derek and Sylvia Stephenson, Kevin Blake)*

SPARKLOW [SK1265]

Royal Oak [on Monyash—Longnor rd, just off A515 S of Buxton]: Relaxed country atmosphere in civilised open-plan pub with good value food inc interesting specials and busy Thurs steak night; two bar areas, well kept changing local ales, good wine range, quick friendly service, chatty landlord, log fire, restaurant; children welcome, on Tissington Trail *(DC)*

SPARROWPIT [SK0980]
Wanted Inn [junction A623/B6061]: Attractive easy-going 16th-c stone-built pub, all beams, copper and brasses one end, tidy plainer bar with local photographs (dogs allowed here), prompt friendly service, well kept Robinsons ales, sensibly priced simple home-made food from toasties to good Sun lunch, tiled floors, table football; piped music; picnic-sets by car park, beautiful countryside *(Guy Vowles)*

SPONDON [SK3935]
☆ *Malt Shovel* [off A6096 on edge of Derby, via Church Hill into Potter St]: Unspoilt traditional pub under newish landlord, decent cheap food, well kept Bass and Burtonwood Top Hat from hatch in tiled corridor with cosy panelled and quarry-tiled or turkey-carpeted rooms off (one no smoking), old-fashioned décor, gas heater in huge inglenook, steps down to big games bar with full-size pool table; lots of picnic-sets, some under cover, in big well used back garden with good play area *(the Didler, BB)*

STANTON IN PEAK [SK2464]
Flying Childers [off B5056 Bakewell—Ashbourne; Main Rd]: New licensees keeping settles by coal fire in cosy and unspoilt beamed right-hand bar, comfortable lounge, well kept Storm and changing guest beers, friendly service, good value lunchtime rolls, dominoes and cribbage; in delightful steep stone village overlooking rich green valley, good walks, may be cl Mon and Thurs lunchtimes *(Patrick Hancock, the Didler)*

STARKHOLMES [SK3058]
White Lion [Starkholmes Rd]: Well run open-plan village pub in exceptional location, views over Matlock Bath and Derwent valley, enjoyable imaginative food at reasonable prices, well kept Burtonwood, Marstons Pedigree, Whim Hartington and a guest beer, attentive staff, low ceilings and stripped stone, coal fire in restaurant; pleasant tables outside, boules, bedrooms, open all day wknds *(the Didler, B M Eldridge, Mark and Mary Fairman)*

STAVELEY [SK4374]
☆ *Speedwell* [Lowgates]: Basic pub brewing its own good keenly priced Townes beers, fine choice of bottle-conditioned belgian beers too, friendly staff, no smoking area, no juke box or machines (nor food); cl wkdy lunchtimes, open all day wknds *(Patrick Hancock, Keith and Chris O'Neill, Tony Hobden)*

STENSON [SK3229]
Bubble [by Trent & Mersey Canal, off A5132 E of Willington]: Newish pub in converted 19th-c barn, good value food served on upper level, real ales; plenty of seats outside, lawn by lock with its locally famous 'bubble' which gives the pub its name *(John Wooll)*

STONEY MIDDLETON [SK2375]
Moon [Townend (A623)]: Good sensibly priced food inc OAP lunchtime bargains, well kept ales such as Black Sheep and Charles Wells Bombardier, reasonably priced wines, friendly staff, nice décor with old photographs; handy for dales walks *(Patrick Hancock, A and B D Craig)*

SUTTON CUM DUCKMANTON [SK4371]
Arkwright Arms [A632 Bolsover—Chesterfield]: Friendly 1970s-style pub with bar, pool room and dining room, all with real fires, good value lunchtime food, changing ales such as Fullers London Pride and Woodfordes Wherry; quiet piped music; garden and play area, open all day *(Patrick Hancock, Derek and Sylvia Stephenson)*

SWANWICK [SK4053]
Steam Packet [Derby Rd (B6179/B6016)]: Chatty 19th-c local popular for its well kept Adnams, Jennings Cumberland and guest beers (and beer festivals Apr and Oct), comfortable traditional bar with coal fire, cosy lounge, food lunchtimes and (not Sun-Tues) evenings; open all day (not till 2 Mon-Weds) *(the Didler)*

TANSLEY [SK3259]
Tavern [A615 Matlock—Mansfield]: Well run dining pub with good value well prepared traditional food from lunchtime baguettes and baked potatoes to duck, bass, steaks and good Sun lunch, friendly relaxed atmosphere, pleasant staff, well kept Marstons Pedigree, Tetleys and another real ale, Weston's farm cider, reasonably priced wines, no smoking restaurant *(Steve Nye, Brian Coleman)*

TIDESWELL [SK1575]
☆ *George* [Commercial Rd (B6049, between A623 and A6 E of Buxton)]: Cheerful staff in pleasantly unpretentious inn, traditional L-shaped bar/lounge inc dining area and linked no smoking room, good value quick generous food from bar meals to wide choice of restaurant dishes, three well kept Hardys & Hansons ales, modestly priced wines, open fires; piped music, separate bar with darts, pool, juke box and machines; children really welcome, dogs too, live 60s music Fri; by remarkable church, tables in front overlooking pretty village, sheltered back garden; five comfortable bedrooms (church clock strikes the quarters), pleasant walks *(BB, the Didler, Mrs S Fairbrother)*

Star [High St]: Several unchanging rooms with local paintings (most for sale) and old photographs, three well kept real ales, short but eclectic and inexpensive wine list, brisk cheerful service; unobtrusive piped music, public bar with TV and games machine; reasonably priced bedrooms *(Dennis Jones)*

TINTWISTLE [SK0297]
Bulls Head [Old Rd (off A628, N side)]: Good value generous food, well kept ales and reasonable prices in low-beamed character 16th-c pub, suitable décor, big log fire, very friendly staff, no juke box or machines; children, dogs and walking groups welcome, handy for Woodhead Pass *(Greg Banks)*

WENSLEY [SK2661]

Red Lion [B5057 NW of Matlock]: Friendly and unspoilt no smoking farm pub with chatty brother and sister owners, assorted 1950s-ish furniture, piano in main bar (landlord likes sing-songs), unusual tapestry in second room (usually locked, so ask landlady), no games or piped music, just bottled beer, tea, coffee, soft drinks and filled sandwiches or home-baked rolls perhaps using fillings from the garden; outside lavatories; open all day *(Pete Baker, the Didler)*

WESSINGTON [SK3758]

Horse & Jockey [Brackenfield Lane (A615 Alfreton—Matlock)]: Open-plan around large central servery, beams, copper, brass and roaring fire giving character, ales such as Bass and Marstons Pedigree, enjoyable food with real chips, pool in separate area *(Kevin Blake)*
Three Horseshoes [The Green]: Comfortable traditional village-green pub with good range of well kept ales, wide choice of bar and restaurant food, welcoming service and atmosphere, log fires *(B M Eldridge)*

WESTON-UPON-TRENT [SK4028]

Old Plough [5 miles SE of Derby]: Rambling village pub with Edwardian décor and surprisingly wide food choice (all day wknds), with good-sized no smoking restaurant up steps; well kept Greene King Abbot and Old Speckled Hen and Marstons Pedigree, good choice of wines (take-away sales too), helpful staff, children's/games room; piped pop music, TV, popular quiz and karaoke nights; good back lawns with play area and barbecues *(CMW, JJW)*

WHITTINGTON [SK3875]

Cock & Magpie [Church Street N, behind museum]: Old stone-built dining pub with no smoking dining area/conservatory (children welcome here) and good choice of good food inc sandwiches and OAP bargains, friendly service, particularly well kept Banks's and Marstons Pedigree, good soft drinks choice, tap room, proper snug with own servery and games room; piped music, no dogs; next to Revolution House museum *(Keith and Chris O'Neill, CMW, JJW)*

WHITTINGTON MOOR [SK3873]

☆ *Derby Tup* [Sheffield Rd; B6057 just S of A61 roundabout]: Tynemill pub with well kept

Burton Bridge, Kelham Island, Oakham, Timothy Taylors and four guest beers, good choice of other drinks, simple furniture and lots of standing room, two small no smoking rooms (children allowed here), daily papers, good value straightforward bar lunches; can get very busy wknd evenings; dogs welcome, open all day Fri/Sat *(David Carr, Patrick Hancock, LYM, MLR, the Didler)*
Red Lion [Sheffield Rd (B6057)]: Friendly two-room 19th-c stone-built pub tied to Old Mill, their Bitter and Bullion kept well, hard-working landlady, thriving atmosphere, old local photographs; TV; open all day *(the Didler, Patrick Hancock, Keith and Chris O'Neill)*

WINSTER [SK2460]

Miners Standard [Bank Top (B5056 above village)]: Welcoming 17th-c local, friendly family service, well kept ales such as Storm, good value generous food inc huge pies, big open fires, lead-mining photographs and minerals, ancient well, restaurant; children allowed away from bar, attractive view from garden, interesting stone-built village below, open all day (at least Sun) *(the Didler, Reg Fowle, Helen Rickwood)*

WIRKSWORTH [SK2854]

Royal Oak [North End]: Traditional backstreet local, small and comfortable, with key fobs, old copper kettles and other bric-a-brac, friendly licensees and locals, well kept Bass, Timothy Taylors Landlord, Whim Hartington and two guest beers, may be filled cobs, back pool room; opens 8, cl lunchtime exc Sun *(the Didler)*

YOULGREAVE [SK2164]

☆ *George* [Alport Lane/Church St]: Handsome stone-built 17th-c inn opp Norman church, unpretentious local feel inside, with quick friendly service, good straightforward low-priced home cooking inc game, comfortable banquettes, well kept Courage Directors, Greene King Old Speckled Hen, John Smiths and Theakstons Mild; flagstoned walkers' side room, dogs welcome, games room, juke box, live music Sat; attractive village handy for Lathkill Dale and Haddon Hall, roadside tables, simple bedrooms, open all day *(Patrick Hancock, Des and Jen Clarke, the Didler)*

Real ale to us means beer which has matured naturally in its cask — not pressurised or filtered. We name all real ales stocked. We usually name ales preserved under a light blanket of carbon dioxide too, though purists — pointing out that this stops the natural yeasts developing — would disagree (most people, including us, can't tell the difference!)

Devon

Devon's pubs are particularly popular with our readers – this last year alone, they have sent us over 1,200 reports on them. This popularity is well deserved. A lot of real individuality gives plenty of interest and variety, with a splendid range from simple and unspoilt to chic and almost restaurenty. We have found some very good food this year, often using local ingredients – particularly fresh fish. A bonus is the strong drinks side: Devon publicans clearly like to stock West Country beers (often delicious), and there are some super wines to be found in pubs here now. Moreover, there always seem to be new discoveries to be made here. Last year we added seven new Devon main entries to the *Guide*, and this year in come another half dozen. In their wide variety, these six newcomers typify the range of good interesting pubs that's to be found here: the quirky Maritime above Brixham harbour (all sorts of interesting things to look at, great character, good drinks), the decorously old-fashioned Abbey Inn by the River Dart in Buckfast, the stylish and upscale Dartmoor Union at Holbeton (good modern food, good wines and now its own microbrewery), the attractive and enthusiastically run Harris Arms at Portgate (very good fresh local food, and super wine choice – they care passionately about it), the charming Sandy Park Inn (a delightful all-rounder), and the Kings Arms on the coast in Strete (top-notch fish cooking here, and it's a pretty building, with engaging family service). We'd have no hesitation in recommending the Dartmoor Union, Harris Arms and Kings Arms for a special meal out. Other fine Devon pubs that score consistently high marks on the food side include the attractive Masons Arms in Branscombe (positive early reports on its new licensees), the civilised yet nicely informal little Drewe Arms at Broadhembury (wonderful fish, very helpful service), the Merrie Harriers at Clayhidon (doing very well these days, strong on free range and local produce), the Anchor at Cockwood (very popular for its seafood, great on the drinks side too), the individualistic Culm Valley at Culmstock (good real ales too, and they import their own wines), the engaging Tower at Slapton, and the Kings Arms at Stockland (very well run, cleverly mixing its good restaurant and residents' side with a thriving much pubbier side). Against all this competition, it's the newcomer, the Dartmoor Union at Holbeton, which takes the title of Devon Dining Pub of the Year. More everyday Devon favourites include the charming little Drake Manor in Buckland Monachorum (unanimous reader approval for its beer), the appealing old Drewe Arms in Drewsteignton, the Rock at Haytor Vale on Dartmoor (good all round), the marvellous Duke of York at Iddesleigh (the sort of place that really warms your heart), the attractive Fox & Goose at Parracombe (friendly young new licensees doing well here), the very well run Peter Tavy Inn on the edge of Dartmoor, the gloriously unspoilt Bridge Inn just outside Topsham (lovely atmosphere, great beer choice), the Start Bay in Torcross (very popular for its unpretentious spanking-fresh fish), and the bustling Kings Arms in Winkleigh (a well run all-rounder). The Lucky Dip section at the end of the chapter is a rich trawling-ground, too. We'd particularly mention the Avon at Avonwick, Exeter Inn at Bampton, Sloop at Bantham, Barrel o' Beer and Dolphin in Beer, Chichester Arms at Bishop's Tawton (due to reopen after fire restoration), Rockford Inn at Brendon, Pilchard on Burgh Island, Claycutters Arms at Chudleigh Knighton, Churston Court at Churston Ferrers, Thatched Barn in Croyde, Ship in Exeter, Stags Head at Filleigh, Rock at Georgeham, Grampus at Lee, Dartmoor Inn near Lydford (really too restauranty now for the main entries, but very good for a special meal), Beer Engine at Newton St Cyres, Ring of Bells in North Bovey, Old Ship and Swan in Sidmouth, Ridgeway at Smallridge, Millbrook at South Pool, Tradesmans Arms at Stokenham, Golden Lion at Tipton St John, Globe and Lighter in Topsham, Steam Packet in Totnes, Rising Sun at Umberleigh and New Fountain at Whimple. Drinks prices in Devon are close to the national average, with much cheaper beer in the Imperial in Exeter than in any other Devon pub in our survey. The local beer that is now most widely available in good pubs here is Otter, and other popular good value Devon brews include Teignworthy, Summerskills, Branscombe Vale and Clearwater – with Sharps and St Austell Dartmoor (both from Cornwall) and Cotleigh and Exmoor (from Somerset) also very popular here.

ASHPRINGTON SX8156 Map 1 🏠

Durant Arms 🛏

Village signposted off A381 S of Totnes; OS Sheet 202 map reference 819571

Strictly, this attractive Victorian gabled building is now more of a small country hotel with a busy dining side and attached bar rather than a pub, but readers very much enjoy their visits here and they still stock well kept St Austell Dartmoor Best and Tribute on handpump. It's all spotlessly kept by the charming and helpful licensees, and there are three linked areas, turkey carpeted throughout, with comfortably upholstered red dining chairs around clothed tables, a small corner bar counter in one area with a couple of bar stools in front, and lots of pictures for sale. With quite an emphasis on dining and all the food cooked to order, there might be sandwiches (from £2.50), home-made soup (£3.95), home-cooked ham and eggs (£7), good liver and onions or spinach and mushroom lasagne (£8.50), steak and kidney pie (£8.95), scallops and tiger prawns in a cream and white wine sauce (£14), sirloin steak (£15), and home-made puddings such as blackberry and apple pie or crème brûlée (£4.50); best to book if you want to be sure of a table. The no smoking dining room has lots of oil and watercolours by local artists on the walls. Good, attentive service. The flagged back courtyard has teak furniture, and the bedrooms are carefully decorated and comfortable. *(Recommended by Richard and Margaret Peers, Mike and Heather Watson, John Mitchell, Dennis Jenkin, Mrs Anne Lowe, Richard Haw, Keith and Margaret Kettell, Doreen and Haydn Maddock, Cathy Robinson, Ed Coombe, Ann and Bob Westbrook, MP, Brian Green, Bob and Margaret Holder)*

Free house ~ Licensees Graham and Eileen Ellis ~ Real ale ~ Bar food ~ Restaurant ~ (01803) 732240 ~ Children in family room ~ Dogs allowed in bar ~ Open 11.30-2.30, 6.30-11; 12-2.30, 7-10.30 Sun; closed evenings 25 and 26 Dec ~ Bedrooms: £45B/£70B

BERRYNARBOR SS5646 Map 1

Olde Globe

Village signposted from A399 E of Ilfracombe

In a pretty village, this rambling 13th-c pub is bigger than it appears. There are several dimly lit homely rooms (and a sizeable no smoking family room) with low ceilings, curved deep-ochre walls, and floors of flagstones or ancient lime-ash (with silver coins embedded in them). Also, old high-backed oak settles (some carved), plush cushioned cask seats around antique tables, and lots of cutlasses, swords, shields and fine powder-flasks, a profusion of genuinely old pictures, priests (fish-coshes), thatcher's knives, sheep shears, gin-traps, pitchforks, antlers and copper warming pans. Well kept Bass, St Austell Dartmoor Best and maybe Shepherd Neame Spitfire on handpump; sensibly placed darts, pool, dominoes and cribbage. Bar food includes sandwiches (from £2.85), home-made soup (£3.50), filled baked potatoes (from £4), local ham and egg (£4.95), salads (from £4.95), meaty or vegetarian lasagne (£5.25), home-made steak and kidney pie (£6.75), and steaks (from £9.25); children's meals (from £1.65). The dining room is no smoking. The crazy-paved front terrace has some old-fashioned garden seats, and there is a children's activity area. *(Recommended by David Eberlin, Dorsan Baker, W W Burke, Ann Holdsworth, Chris and Ann Coy, Brian and Ruth Archer, Sue Demont, Tim Barrow, Andy and Ali)*

Enterprise ~ Lease Don and Edith Ozelton and family ~ Real ale ~ Bar food ~ (01271) 882465 ~ Children in family room ~ Dogs allowed in bar ~ Open 12-2.30, 6-11(10.30 Sun); evening opening time 7pm in winter

BRANSCOMBE SY1888 Map 1

Fountain Head 🍺

Upper village, above the robust old church; village signposted off A3052 Sidmouth—Seaton, then from Branscombe Square follow road up hill towards Sidmouth, and after about a mile turn left after the church; OS Sheet 192 map reference SY188889

The new licensee in this old-fashioned and unspoilt 500-year-old stone pub has made some gentle refurbishments and uncovered a fine inglenook fireplace. The Branscombe Brewery still supply their own-brewed beers such as Branoc, Jolly Geff, and summer Summa That, and there are guests such as Fullers London Pride or Loddon Hullabaloo on handpump; the annual beer festival takes place in June. The room on the left – formerly a smithy – has forge tools and horseshoes on the high oak beams, a log fire in the original raised firebed with its tall central chimney, and cushioned pews and mate's chairs. On the right, an irregularly shaped, more orthodox snug room has another log fire, white-painted plank ceiling with an unusual carved ceiling-rose, brown-varnished panelled walls, and rugs on its flagstone-and-lime-ash floor. Bar food includes soup (£3.50), lunchtime sandwiches (from £3.50), chicken satay (£4.25), ploughman's (£4.95), pasta of the day (£6.25), home-cooked ham and eggs (£6.95), beef in ale pie (£7.25), beer-battered cod (£7.95), and steaks (from £10.95). There are seats out on the front loggia and terrace, and a little stream rustling under the flagstoned path; pleasant nearby walks. More reports on the new regime please. *(Recommended by Mrs Sylvia Elcoate, Phil and Sally Gorton, Mrs C Lintott, Tom and Ruth Rees, Derek and Sylvia Stephenson, Pete Walker, Conor McGaughey, the Didler, Gordon Stevenson, Mary Kirman and Tim Jefferson, Mike and Mary Carter, John and Jane Hayter)*

Own brew ~ Licensee Andy Hearn ~ Real ale ~ Bar food ~ Restaurant ~ (01297) 680359 ~ Children in eating area of bar and restaurant ~ Dogs welcome ~ Open 11-2.30, 6-11; 11-11 Sat; 12-10.30 Sun

Masons Arms 🍴 🍷 🛏

Main Street; signed off A3052 Sidmouth—Seaton, then bear left into village

Efficient new licensees have taken over this thatched 14th-c longhouse and have told us that many of the staff have stayed on and that they don't plan any major changes. The rambling low-beamed main bar is the heart of the building, with a massive central hearth in front of the roaring log fire (they may still hold spit roasts), windsor chairs and settles, slate floors, ancient ship's beams, and a good bustling atmosphere. The no smoking Old Worthies bar also has a slate floor, a fireplace with a two-sided woodburning stove, and woodwork that has been stripped back to the original pine. There's also the original no smoking restaurant (warmed by one side of the woodburning stove), and the newer Waterfall Restaurant, set slightly away from the pub, and with an open kitchen so you can watch the chefs at work. Well liked bar food includes sandwiches (from £2.75), soup (£2.95), terrine of spinach with feta cheese and beef tomatoes or chicken liver parfait with toasted brioche and cumberland sauce (£4.75), ploughman's (from

£4.85), smoked haddock, salmon and herb fishcakes with spicy tomato salsa
(£7.95), mushroom and courgette lasagne or mild thai fish curry with chilli
salsa (£8.95), steak and kidney pudding (£9.25), shank of lamb in red wine and
herbs (£10.50), local pork tenderloin in cider and cream with caramelised apple
(£11.50), and free-range chicken breast on pasta with pesto, parma ham and
mozzarella (£11.95). Well kept Bass, Otter Ale and Bitter, and guests like
Branscombe Vale Branoc or St Austell Tribute on handpump, 14 wines by the glass,
33 malt whiskies, and farm cider; darts, TV, shove-ha'penny, cribbage and
dominoes. Outside, the quiet flower-filled front terrace has tables with little
thatched roofs, extending into a side garden. More reports on the new regime
please. *(Recommended by Chris and Ann Coy, Brenda and Stuart Naylor, Mike Gorton,
Brian and Bett Cox, Andrea Rampley, the Didler, Richard and Anne Ansell, Mrs J Poole,
Lyn Huxtable, Richard Seers, A P Seymour, Cathy Robinson, Ed Coombe, Conor McGaughey,
Pete Walker, Peter Craske, Liz and Alun Jones, John Knighton, D Stilgoe, Cathryn and
Richard Hicks, W W Burke, Barry Steele-Perkins, Alan and Paula McCully, Mike and
Chris Higgins, Melanie Ginger, Mrs Sylvia Elcoate, Anthony Moody, Simon J A Powis,
Canon Michael Bourdeaux, Nux, Neil and Lorna Mclaughlan)*

Free house ~ Licensees Colin and Carol Slaney ~ Real ale ~ Bar food ~ Restaurant ~
(01297) 680300 ~ Children welcome ~ Dogs welcome ~ Open 11-11; 12-10.30 Sun;
11-3, 6-11 weekdays in winter ~ Bedrooms: £30(£60B)/£50(£60B)

BRIXHAM SX9256 Map 1

Maritime

King Street (up steps from harbour – nearby parking virtually non-existent)

With fine views over the harbour and lots to look at inside, this enjoyable little pub
is well worth dropping into. There's just one bar crammed full of interest: hundreds
of key fobs and chamber-pots hang from the beams, there's a binnacle by the door,
cigarette cards and pre-war ensigns from different countries, toby jugs and
horsebrasses, mannequins, pictures of astronomical charts and plenty of mugs and
china jugs. There's an african grey parrot (mind your fingers) and a lively little
terrier, two warming coal fires, cushioned wheelback chairs and pink-plush
cushioned wall benches, flowery swagged curtains, and a small TV on if there's
something the landlady wants to watch. It's all very informal and relaxed. Well
kept Marstons Pedigree and St Austell Dartmoor on handpump, and 78 malt
whiskies; no food. Parking nearby is non-existent. *(Recommended by Kevin Blake)*

Free house ~ Licensee Mrs Pat Seddon ~ Real ale ~ (01803) 853535 ~ Dogs allowed in
bar ~ Open 11-3, 6.30-11; 12-3, 7-10.30 Sun ~ Bedrooms: £20/£40

BROADHEMBURY ST1004 Map 1

Drewe Arms ★ ⑪ ♀

Signposted off A373 Cullompton—Honiton

This civilised place remains consistently well run by the courteous and helpful
Burge family, and the small bar area is still somewhere to feel comfortable dropping
into for just a drink, despite the emphasis on the lovely fish dishes. The bar has
neatly carved beams in its high ceiling, and handsome stone-mullioned windows
(one with a small carved roundabout horse), and on the left, a high-backed stripped
settle separates off a little room with flowers on the three sturdy country tables,
plank-panelled walls painted brown below and yellow above with attractive
engravings and prints, and a big black-painted fireplace with bric-a-brac on a high
mantelpiece; some wood carvings, walking sticks and framed watercolours for sale.
The flagstoned entry has a narrow corridor of a room by the servery with a couple
of tables, and the cellar bar has simple pews on the stone floor; the dining room is
no smoking. Unfailingly good, the food might include open sandwiches (from £5;
crab £6.95), daily specials such as spicy crab soup (£5), cornish sardines or warm
salmon salad (£7; main course £13.50), smoked haddock with stilton rarebit (£7;
main course £12.50), whole langoustines (£7; main course £15.50), wing of skate
with black butter (£13.50), lyme bay crab (£14), seared tuna salad (£14.50), and

sea bream with orange and chilli (£15); there are a few meaty choices, and puddings such as bread pudding with whisky butter sauce or hazelnut parfait (£5). Best to book to be sure of a table. Well kept Otter Bitter, Ale and Bright tapped from the cask, and a very good wine list laid out extremely helpfully – including around half a dozen by the glass. There are picnic-sets in the lovely garden which has a lawn stretching back under the shadow of chestnut trees towards a church with its singularly melodious hour-bell. Thatched and very pretty, the 15th-c pub is in a charming village of similar cream-coloured cottages. *(Recommended by M G Hart, S J and B S Highmore, Mr and Mrs C Barwell, Mandy and Simon King, the Didler, Bob and Margaret Holder, W W Burke, Gene and Kitty Rankin, Howard and Margaret Buchanan, Alan and Jill Bull, Mark and Heather Williamson, Peter Burton, Francis Johnston, Mrs S Lyons, John and Sonja Newberry, Conor McGaughey, Dr and Mrs M E Wilson, Barry Steele-Perkins, John and Diana Head, R I C Skinner, John and Vivienne Rice)*

Free house ~ Licensees Kerstin and Nigel Burge ~ Real ale ~ Bar food (not Sun evening) ~ Restaurant ~ (01404) 841267 ~ Children in eating area of bar, restaurant and family room ~ Dogs allowed in bar ~ Open 11-3, 6-11; 12-3 Sun; closed Sun evening

BUCKFAST SX7467 Map 1

Abbey Inn ♀

Just off A38 at A384 junction; take B3380 towards Buckfastleigh, but turn right into Buckfast Road immediately after bridge

Down a steep little drive from the car park, this sizeable, pleasantly old-fashioned inn is right by the River Dart with picnic-sets on the terrace overlooking the water. Inside, the bar has partly panelled walls with some ships' crests there and over the gantry (friendly Mr Davison was in the Royal Navy for many years), two chequered green and beige wooden-armed settees, a mix of high-backed chairs and captain's chairs around a few circular tables, a woodburning stove in an ornate fireplace with books on the mantelpiece, and some nice leather-topped bar stools. The big no smoking dining room has a woodburning stove in a fireplace at one end, more panelling, and river views. For the good bar food they use local or west country fresh produce where possible: home-made soup (£2.95), filled rolls (from £3.95), scallops on celeriac mash and red pepper sauce or chicken liver pâté (£5.25), home-cooked ham and egg or sausage with sage mash (£6.95), home-made wild mushroom and asparagus lasagne (£8.50), loin of boneless lamb with spicy couscous and apricot and mint sauce or chicken breast in a creamy bacon, onion, mushroom and stilton sauce (£11.50), lemon sole fillets with butter, lemon and white wine (£11.95), roast duck on coconut risotto with a thai red curry sauce (£12.50), and puddings like home-made rich chocolate tart with Cointreau cream or caramelised rice pudding with caramel poached pear (£3.50); they also have a children and small appetites menu (from £4.50). Well kept St Austell Dartmoor Best, HSD and Tribute on handpump, 16 wines by the glass, and liqueur coffee; piped music. We have not yet had reports on the bedrooms here, but would expect this to be a nice place to stay in. *(Recommended by E B Ireland, Glenn and Gillian Miller)*

St Austell ~ Tenants Terence and Elizabeth Davison ~ Real ale ~ Bar food ~ Restaurant ~ (01364) 642343 ~ Children welcome ~ Dogs allowed in bar and bedrooms ~ Open 11-11; 12-10.30 Sun; 11-3, 6-11 Mon-Thurs in winter ~ Bedrooms: £40S/£70S

BUCKLAND BREWER SS4220 Map 1

Coach & Horses

Village signposted off A388 S of Monkleigh; OS Sheet 190 map reference 423206

There's a traditional village pub atmosphere in this 13th-c thatched house, and the heavily beamed bar has comfortable seats (including a handsome antique settle), a woodburning stove in the inglenook, and maybe Harding the friendly cat – who is now 19; a good log fire also burns in the big stone inglenook of the cosy lounge. A small back room has darts and pool. Bar food includes sandwiches (from £2.95), large pasty (£3.95), ploughman's (£5.50), home-made curries (£8.25), home-made daily specials such as lasagne (£7.50), butternut squash and chick pea curry, pork cooked with apples and cider or beef, ale and stilton pie (all £7.95), lamb in spicy red wine gravy or venison stew with herb dumplings (£8.95), salmon steak with honey and ginger sauce (£10.95), and skate wing with capers (£12.95), with puddings like sticky toffee pudding or chocolate sponge with hot chocolate sauce (£3.95). The restaurant is no smoking. Well kept Adnams Broadside, Clearwater Cavalier, Fullers London Pride and Shepherd Neame Spitfire on handpump, and around six wines by the glass; dominoes, cribbage, fruit machine, skittle alley, and piped music. There are tables on a terrace in front, and in the side garden. They have a self-contained flat above the pub to rent out. *(Recommended by Michael Bayne, Francis Johnston, Bob and Margaret Holder, the Didler, Gene and Kitty Rankin, Peter Robinson, Peter and Margaret Glenister, Rev D E and Mrs J A Shapland, W W Burke)*

Free house ~ Licensees Oliver Wolfe and Nicola Barrass ~ Real ale ~ Bar food (not 25 Dec) ~ Restaurant ~ (01237) 451395 ~ Children welcome ~ Dogs allowed in bar ~ Open 12-3, 6-11; 12-3, 7-10.30 Sun

BUCKLAND MONACHORUM SX4868 Map 1
Drake Manor ▰
Off A386 via Crapstone, just S of Yelverton roundabout

The floral displays at the front of this charming little pub are very attractive all year round and now that the exterior has been repainted, it all looks very smart. The heavily beamed public bar on the left (redecorated this year) has brocade-cushioned wall seats, prints of the village from 1905 onwards, some horse tack and a few ship badges on the wall, and a really big stone fireplace with a woodburning stove; a small door leads to a low-beamed cubbyhole. The snug Drakes Bar has beams hung with tiny cups and big brass keys, a woodburning stove in an old stone fireplace, horsebrasses and stirrups, a fine stripped pine high-backed settle with a partly covered hood, and a mix of other seats around just four tables (the oval one is rather nice). On the right is a small, beamed no smoking dining room with settles and tables on the flagstoned floor. Shove-ha'penny, darts, dominoes, cribbage and fruit machine. Well liked bar food includes lunchtime baguettes (from £3.95), ploughman's (from £4.50), and snacks like sausage and chips (£2.95), as well crab cakes with a lemon and dill cream dressing or home-made brie and broccoli filo parcels on a sweet pepper sauce (£3.95), spinach and mascarpone lasagne (£6.25), home-made steak and kidney pie (£6.50), and chicken wrapped in bacon with a three cheese, white wine and cream sauce (£8.95), with daily specials such as spare ribs with barbecue sauce or smoked chicken and feta salad (£4.25), venison in red wine with forest fruits (£8.50), whole grilled lemon sole with lemon and parsley butter (£9.75), and puddings such as treacle and orange tart (£3.25). Well kept Courage Best, Greene King Abbot and Sharps Doom Bar on handpump, around 50 malt whiskies, and a decent wine list with ten by the glass. The sheltered back garden – where there are picnic-sets – is prettily planted. *(Recommended by A Mathews, Brian and Bett Cox, Jacquie and Jim Jones, John and Elizabeth Cox, D M Heath)*

Punch ~ Lease Mandy Robinson ~ Real ale ~ Bar food (12-2, 7-10(9.30 Sun)) ~ Restaurant ~ (01822) 853892 ~ Children in restaurant ~ Dogs allowed in bar ~ Open 11.30-2.30 (3 Sat), 6.30-11; 12-3, 7-10.30 Sun

CHERITON BISHOP SX7793 Map 1
Old Thatch Inn
Village signposted from A30

What was the family room in this 16th-c pub has been decorated and furnished to the same standard as the restaurant, and children can now eat anywhere except the bar area. The lounge and the rambling beamed bar (the only place where you can smoke) are separated by a large open stone fireplace (lit in the cooler months), and have Otter Ale, Sharps Doom Bar and a guest like O'Hanlons Fire Fly or Port Stout or Princetown Jail Ale on handpump; ten wines by two sizes of glass. As well as daily specials such as courgette and oregano tart with provençale dressing (£4.95), warm pigeon breast with a strawberry and balsamic dressing (£5.50), a gateau of local crab and cucumber with lemon mayonnaise (£5.75), fresh fillets of plaice with garlic butter or chicken with fresh mussel and chardonnay sauce (£10.25), and breast of pheasant wrapped in bacon with fresh apple and thyme sauce or wild boar with green peppercorn and curried peach sauce and an apple fritter (£12.50), there are lunchtime bar snacks like sandwiches (from £3.50; filled baguettes from £4.25), and ploughman's (from £5.75), plus beer battered fish with home-made tartare sauce or gammon and egg (£8.50); children's meals (£4.75). The garden has been made a bit smaller but is more secluded with fencing providing a wind break, and lots of pretty flowering baskets and tubs. (*Recommended by Mark Flynn, Sheila Brooks, Adrian Johnson, Alan Sadler, John and Vivienne Rice, C W Burke, Mick and Moira Brummell, David Crook, Michael Butler, Mayur Shah, Geoff Pidoux, M G Hart, DAV, Dr C C S Wilson, DP and RA Pascoe, OPUS, Sue Demont, Tim Barrow*)

Free house ~ Licensees David and Serena London ~ Real ale ~ Bar food ~ Restaurant ~ (01647) 24204 ~ Children welcome ~ Dogs allowed in bar ~ Open 11.30-3, 6-11; 12-3, 6.30-10.30 Sun; closed winter Sun evenings ~ Bedrooms: £45B/£60B

CLAYHIDON ST1817 Map 1
Merry Harriers 🍴 ♀ 🍺

3 miles from M5 junction 26: head towards Wellington; turn left at first roundabout signposted Ford Street and Hemyock, then after a mile turn left signposted Ford Street; at hilltop T junction, turn left towards Chard – pub is 1½ miles on right

With a friendly welcome and a convivial atmosphere, it's not surprising that this well run and charmingly laid out dining pub is so popular. Several small linked green-carpeted areas have comfortably cushioned pews and farmhouse chairs, lit candles in bottles, a woodburning stove with a sofa beside it, and plenty of horsey and hunting prints and local wildlife pictures. Two dining areas have a brighter feel with quarry tiles and lightly timbered white walls; you can smoke only in the bar area. Using local produce, the food is consistently good, and starters or light lunches might include home-made soup (£3.95 or £5.75), sandwiches (from £4), brie roasted in almonds with home-made cranberry sauce or pork and venison pâté with quince jelly (£4.95; £9.50), and scallops wrapped in bacon with rosemary and garlic butter (£6 and £11.50); also, smoked ham and free-range eggs (£6.50), fresh fish in beer batter (£8.50), free-range chicken curry with home-made chutney (£10), home-made tortellini stuffed with goats cheese, pine nuts and shallots with tomato and pesto sauce (£11.50), local steaks (from £11.50), confit of local duck on onion marmalade (£14), rack of lamb on tarragon mustard mash with home-made lemon apple jelly (£15), and puddings such as dark chocolate orange mousse served in a chocolate cup, crème brûlée or sticky toffee pudding (from £4.50). Well kept Cotleigh Harrier, Otter Ale, and Palmers Tally Ho on handpump, ten wines by the glass, local cider and juice, vintage rum, 20 malt whiskies and several belgian bottled beers. There are two dogs, Annie who likes real ale, and Nipper who has only three legs. Picnic-sets on a small terrace, with more in a sizeable garden sheltered by shrubs and the old skittle alley; this is a good walking area. (*Recommended by B H and J I Andrews, Mr and Mrs W Mills, Christine and Neil Townend, Mike Gorton, Mr and Mrs Colin Roberts, Richard and Jean Phillips, M Incledon, M G Hart*)

Free house ~ Licensees Barry and Chris Kift ~ Real ale ~ Bar food (not Sun evening or Mon) ~ Restaurant ~ (01823) 421270 ~ No children under 6 in evening ~ Dogs allowed in bar ~ Open 12-3, 6.30-11; 12-3 Sun; closed Sun evening, Mon

CLYST HYDON ST0301 Map 1
Five Bells

West of the village and just off B3176 not far from M5 junction 28

This attractive thatched pub is reached down narrow lanes and some of the signposts can be hidden in the high hedges, so keep your eyes peeled. The partly no smoking bar is divided at one end into different seating areas by brick and timber pillars; china jugs hang from big horsebrass-studded beams, there are many plates lining the shelves, lots of copper and brass, and a nice mix of dining chairs around small tables, with some comfortable pink plush banquettes on a little raised area. Past the inglenook fireplace is another big (but narrower) room they call the Long Barn with a series of prints on the walls, a pine dresser at one end, and similar furnishings. Bar food includes soup (£3.95), filled baguettes or panini (from £4.50), creamy garlic mushrooms or chicken terrine with cumberland sauce (£4.95), ploughman's (£5.95), chicken curry (£7.95), roasted vegetables in filo pastry with red pepper sauce or cod in crispy beer batter (£8.95), supreme of chicken in sun-dried tomato and basil sauce (£9.95), beef, blackcurrant and pickled walnut pie (£10.50), and lamb shank with orange and rosemary (£10.95). Well kept Cotleigh Tawny, O'Hanlon's Yellowhammer and Otter Bitter on handpump, and eight wines by the glass; piped music. The immaculate cottagey front garden is a fine sight with its thousands of spring and summer flowers, big window boxes and pretty hanging baskets; up some steps is a sizeable flat lawn with picnic-sets, a play frame, and pleasant country views. *(Recommended by Gene and Tony Freemantle, Mike Gorton, Paul Boot, Dr and Mrs M W A Haward, John and Joan Nash, John and Vivienne Rice, Mr and Mrs W Mills, B H and J I Andrews, Alan and Jill Bull, Tim Gorringe, Canon Michael Bourdeaux, Mark and Heather Williamson, Ken and Barbara Turner, John and Sonja Newberry, John and Fiona McIlwain, D M Heath, Brian Dawes, Simon J A Powis, M Joyner)*

Free house ~ Licensees Mr and Mrs R Shenton ~ Real ale ~ Bar food ~ (01884) 277288 ~ Children in eating area of bar ~ Open 11.30-3, 6.30-11; 12-3, 7-10.30 Sun; evening opening 7pm in winter

COCKWOOD SX9780 Map 1

Anchor 🍴 ♀ 🍺

Off, but visible from, A379 Exeter—Torbay

It's pretty essential to arrive at this busy fishy place early – not just to get a table, but to find a parking space. There's often a queue to get in but they do two sittings in the restaurant on winter weekends and every evening in summer to cope with the crowds. But the good news is that a large extension (in keeping with the existing one) is to be built this year. There are 30 different ways of serving mussels (£7.50 normal size helping, £12.25 for a large one), 13 ways of serving scallops (from £5.75 for a starter, from £13.45 for a main course), and five ways of serving oysters (from £7.25 for a starter, from £14.25 for a main course), as well as crab and brandy soup (£3.15), and potted seafood pie or whole grilled plaice (£7.50). Non-fishy dishes feature as well, such as sandwiches (from £3.25), home-made chicken liver pâté (£4.25), cheese and potato pie (£5.25), home-made steak and kidney pudding (£7.25), rump steak (£8.50), and children's dishes (£4.50). But despite the emphasis on food, there's still a pubby atmosphere, and they keep six real ales on handpump or tapped from the cask: Bass, Fullers London Pride, Greene King IPA and Old Speckled Hen, Otter Ale and Timothy Taylors Landlord. Also, a fine wine list of 300 (bin ends and reserves and 12 by the glass), 20 brandies, and 100 malt whiskies. The small, low-ceilinged, rambling rooms have black panelling, good-sized tables in various alcoves, and a cheerful winter coal fire in the snug; the cosy restaurant is no smoking. Darts, dominoes, cribbage, fruit machine and piped music. From the tables on the sheltered verandah you can look across the road to the bobbing yachts and crabbing boats in the harbour. *(Recommended by John and Marion Tyrie, John Beeken, Pat and Robert Watt, Alain and Rose Foote, David Field, John and Vivienne Rice, Ann and Bob Westbrook, Mr and Mrs A H Young, John and Fiona McIlwain, Dr and Mrs M E Wilson, Dr A J and Mrs Tompsett, the Didler)*

Heavitree ~ Tenants Mr Morgan and Miss Sanders ~ Real ale ~ Bar food (12-3, 6.30-10(9.30 Sun)) ~ Restaurant ~ (01626) 890203 ~ Children in eating area of bar and restaurant ~ Dogs allowed in bar ~ Open 11-11; 12-10.30 Sun; closed evening 25 Dec

---

Planning a day in the country? We list pubs in really attractive scenery
at the back of the book.

COLEFORD SS7701 Map 1

New Inn 🍴 ♀ 🛏

Just off A377 Crediton—Barnstaple

At 600 years old, this is one of the oldest 'new' inns in the country. It has new licensees this year, though luckily little seems to have changed. It's an L-shaped building with the servery in the angle, and interestingly furnished areas leading off it: ancient and modern settles, spindleback chairs, plush-cushioned stone wall seats, some character tables – a pheasant worked into the grain of one – and carved dressers and chests; also, paraffin lamps, antique prints and old guns on the white walls, and landscape plates on one of the beams, with pewter tankards on another. The chatty resident parrot Captain is still here. As well as snacks such as filled baguettes and ciabattas (from £4), sausage and chips (£5.25), omelettes (from £5.25), and ploughman's (£7), the good food includes soup (£4), smoked bacon and liver pâté or warmed goats cheese salad with honey dressing and pine nuts (£5), spicy potato cakes with red pepper salsa (£7), creamy fish pie (£7.50), local pork sausages with onion gravy or parmesan crusted chicken goujons with a honey and mustard dip (£8), 6oz sirloin steak and fries (£8.50), lamb rogan josh (£9), pork schnitzel or seared tuna steak with tomato, garlic and olive sauce (£10), and puddings like double chocolate profiterole gateau, lime and raspberry mousse cake with raspberry coulis or sticky toffee pudding (£5). The restaurant is no smoking. Well kept Badger Best, Otter Ale and Wells Bombardier on handpump; fruit machine (out of the way up by the door), dominoes and piped music. There are chairs, tables and umbrellas on decking under the willow tree along the stream, and more on the terrace. *(Recommended by Mark Flynn, Sarah and Anthony Bussy, DRH and KLH, W W Burke, A P Seymour, Bob and Margaret Holder, Alan and Jill Bull, Mandy and Simon King, Richard and Margaret Peers, Mike and Mary Carter, J F Stackhouse)*

Free house ~ Licensees Simon and Melissa Renshaw ~ Real ale ~ Bar food (till 10(9.30 Sun)) ~ Restaurant ~ (01363) 84242 ~ Children welcome ~ Dogs allowed in bar ~ Open 12-3.30, 6-11; 12-3.30, 7-10.30 Sun; closed 25 and 26 Dec ~ Bedrooms: £55B/£70B

COMBEINTEIGNHEAD SX9071 Map 1

Wild Goose 🍺

Just off unclassified coast road Newton Abbot—Shaldon, up hill in village

There's certainly a marvellous range of drinks to choose from in this bustling place. They have seven well kept west country ales on handpump such as Archers Mild, Badger Tanglefoot, Otter Bright, Skinners Betty Stogs, Teignworthy Beachcomber and Old Moggie, and Westbury Pale Storm, 40 malt whiskies, nine wines by the glass, and two village-produced ciders and apple juices. The spacious back beamed lounge has a mix of wheelbacks, red plush dining chairs, a decent mix of tables, and french windows to the garden, with nice country views beyond; the front bar has some red Rexine seats in the window embrasures of the thick walls, flagstones in a small area by the door, some beams and standing timbers, and a step down on the right at the end, with dining chairs around the tables and a big old fireplace with an open log fire. There's a small carved oak dresser with a big white goose, cribbage, dominoes and shove-ha'penny, and also a cosy section on the left with an old settee and comfortably well used chairs; open fires in winter. As well as lunchtime filled baguettes, the well liked bar food includes home-made soup (£3.50), swedish meatballs in spicy tomato sauce and melted mozzarella (£5.50), thai crab cakes with zingy salsa (£6.95), spaghetti bolognese (£7.95), beef in ale or leek and mushroom crumble (£8.95), moroccan lamb or fresh cod in batter (£9.95), chicken breast wrapped in smoky bacon and smothered in stilton sauce (£10.25), steaks (from £10.95), and puddings (£3.75). The garden behind this bustling pub, overlooked by the 14th-c church, has plenty of seats, and there are outdoor heaters for chillier evenings. *(Recommended by the Didler, D M Heath)*

Free house ~ Licensees Jerry and Kate English ~ Real ale ~ Bar food ~ (01626) 872241 ~ Well behaved children in restaurant ~ Dogs allowed in bar ~ Live music first Fri of month ~ Open 11.30-2.30(3 Sat), 6.30-11; 12-3, 7-10.30 Sun

CORNWORTHY SX8255 Map 1
Hunters Lodge

Off A381 Totnes—Kingsbridge ½ mile S of Harbertonford, turning left at Washbourne; can also be reached direct from Totnes, on the Ashprington—Dittisham road

Popular with walkers – dogs are welcome, too – this friendly pub is tucked away down narrow lanes. The small low-ceilinged bar has two rooms with an engagingly pubby feel and a combination of wall seats, settles, and captain's chairs around heavy elm tables; there's also a small and pretty cottagey dining room with a good log fire in its big 17th-c stone fireplace. Half the pub is no smoking. As well as lunchtime sandwiches (from £3.50; brixham crab with lemon mayonnaise £6) and ploughman's (£6.50), the reasonably priced bar food might include soup (£3.50), grilled goats cheese and onion marmalade tartlet or chicken and duck pâté with apricot chutney (£4.50), sesame battered cod fillet with lime tartare sauce (£6.95), trio of local sausages with parmesan mash and onion gravy or wild mushroom pasta with shallots, parsley, pesto and garlic (£8.50), local mussels with smoked bacon, mushrooms, white wine and cream (£9.95), chicken breast with merlot chasseur sauce (£10.50), and puddings like walnut, stem ginger and rum dark chocolate terrine with raspberry coulis and cinnamon mascarpone or blueberry bread and butter pudding (£4.50); a good children's menu (£4.50). Well kept Teignworthy Reel Ale and a couple of guests on handpump, 50 malt whiskies, and Hogwash local cider; piped music. In summer, there is plenty of room to sit outside, either at the picnic-sets on a big lawn or on the flower-filled terrace closer to the pub. More reports please. *(Recommended by Brian and Bett Cox, Len Beattie, OPUS, M Sage, B J Harding)*

Free house ~ Licensees J Reen and G Rees ~ Real ale ~ Bar food ~ Restaurant ~ (01803) 732204 ~ Children welcome ~ Dogs allowed in bar ~ Open 11.30-3, 6.30-11; 12-3, 7-10.30 Sun; closed Mon in winter

CULMSTOCK ST1013 Map 1
Culm Valley

B3391, off A38 E of M5 junction 27

For those who like slightly quirky (the landlord's own words) places, this village inn is smashing. The food is exceptionally good, you'll get a genuinely warm welcome whether you are a local, a visitor, a child or a dog, and quite a few of our readers have enjoyed staying overnight. There's a thriving mix of customers in the salmon-coloured bar, which is a hotch-potch of modern and unrenovated, with very well worn upholstered chairs and stools, a big newly opened up fireplace with some china above it, newspapers, and a long stripped wooden bar counter; further along is a dining room with chalkboard menu, and a small room at the front. You may smoke in the bar but nowhere else. Cribbage, chess and dominoes. Old photographs show how the railway line used to run through what's now the car park. The landlord and his brother import wines from smaller french vineyards, so you can count on a few of those (they offer 50 wines by the glass), as well as some unusual french fruit liqueurs, somerset cider brandies, vintage rum, good sherries and madeira, local ciders, and an excellent range of real ales tapped from the cask. You'll usually find between four and ten mostly local brews, such as Blackawton Peninsula, Branscombe Vale Anniversary, Dorset Weymouth Harbour Master, Mauldons Black Adder, O'Hanlons Yellowhammer, Stonehenge Heel Stone and Teignworthy Amy's Ale tapped from the cask; their May bank holiday weekend beer festival features over 23 beers. Changing daily, the interesting food might include sandwiches, mushroom soup (£4), chicken and duck liver parfait with cognac (£6; main course £10), hot smoked wild bass roe with horseradish, lemon and cream, very popular tapas or italian pancakes with wild mushrooms (from £6), ham, free-range eggs and hand-cut chips (£7), moules marinière (£7; main course £11), hand-dived scallops with pomegranate molasses dressing (£8; main course £16), red thai duck, rump steak or lamb braised with ginger, cumin, garlic and fennel (£10), brill with basil cream sauce (£10; main course £15), local crab (from

£10), local organic, free-range duck peking-style with spiced orange sauce (£15), and puddings such as treacle and lemon tart, sticky toffee pudding, and crème brûlée (£4). Outside, tables are very attractively set overlooking the bridge and the River Culm. The gents' is in an outside yard. *(Recommended by David Collison, Simon Watkins, Paul and Philippa Ward, June and Peter Shamash, Conor McGaughey, B Phenin, M Fairbairn, John and Fiona McIlwain, R M Corlett, Ian and Meg Ainsworth, M G Hart)*

Free house ~ Licensee Richard Hartley ~ Real ale ~ Bar food (not Sun evening) ~ Restaurant ~ No credit cards ~ (01884) 840354 ~ Children in eating area of bar ~ Dogs welcome ~ Open 12-3, 7-11(may open all day in good weather); 12-11(10.30 Sun) Sat ~ Bedrooms: £30B/£55B

DALWOOD ST2400 Map 1

Tuckers Arms

Village signposted off A35 Axminster—Honiton; keep on past village

Parts of this pretty cream-washed thatched old hunting lodge date back to the 13th c, which makes it the oldest building in the parish. The fine flagstoned bar has a lot of atmosphere, plenty of beams, a random mixture of dining chairs, window seats and wall settles (including a high-backed winged black one), and a log fire in the inglenook fireplace. The back bar has an enormous collection of miniature bottles. Well liked bar food at lunchtime includes sandwiches (from £3.95), ploughman's (from £4.95), toasted rustic bread topped with things such as spanish meat balls and chorizo sausage or bacon, black pudding and fried egg or home-made fishcakes (£6.95), and seafood platter (£12.95); there's a two-course set lunch (£10.95). In the evening there's a more elaborate choice: smoked haddock rarebit, moules marinière, deep-fried calamari with citrus mayonnaise, roulade of spinach and tomato sauce filled with avocado, cheese and sweet peppers, braised kidneys, chicken with bacon, pesto and sherry glaze, and fillet of barramundi and tiger prawns with chilli and lime butter; two courses £16.95, three courses £19.95. The restaurant is no smoking. Well kept Otter Bitter, O'Hanlons Firefly and Palmers IPA on handpump, eight wines by the glass and farm cider; skittle alley. In summer, the hanging baskets, flowering tubs and window boxes in front of the building are lovely, and the covered pergola with its outdoor heating is proving a success. *(Recommended by Pete Walker, Bob and Margaret Holder, Brian and Bett Cox, Mrs C Lintott, Mark Flynn, John Waters, Stephen and Jean Curtis, Glenwys and Alan Lawrence)*

Free house ~ Licensees David and Kate Beck ~ Real ale ~ Bar food ~ Restaurant ~ (01404) 881342 ~ Children in restaurant and family room ~ Open 12-2.30, 6.30-11; 12-3, 7-10.30 Sun ~ Bedrooms: £39.50S/£65S

DARTMOUTH SX8751 Map 1

Cherub

Higher Street

Dating from around 1380, this lovely pub is Dartmouth's oldest building and in summer, particularly, it's a striking sight with each of the two heavily timbered upper floors jutting further out than the one below, and very pretty hanging baskets. The bustling bar has tapestried seats under creaky heavy beams, leaded-light windows, a big stone fireplace, and Sharps Doom Bar, a beer named for the pub, and a changing guest on handpump; quite a few malt whiskies and 14 wines by the glass. Upstairs is the fine, low-ceilinged and no smoking restaurant; piped music. Bar food includes soup (£3.90), sandwiches (from £3.95; open ones from £4.95), home-made chicken liver pâté with red onion marmalade or smoked haddock in white wine sauce and topped with cheese (£4.95), thai crab cakes with sweet chilli sauce (£5.95), seared scallops with black pudding and bacon or crayfish salad (£6.95), and steak, mushroom and Guinness pie or curry of the day (£7.95). It does get very crowded at peak times. *(Recommended by Geoff Calcott, John Evans, Ken Flawn, Margaret and Peter Brierley, David Swift, David Carr, DM, M Sage, Mr and Mrs Colin Roberts, Glenn and Gillian Miller, Jim and Janet Brown, Emma Kingdon)*

Free house ~ Licensee Laurie Scott ~ Real ale ~ Bar food ~ Restaurant ~ (01803) 832571 ~ Children over 5 in restaurant by appointment ~ Dogs allowed in bar ~ Open 11-11; 12-10.30 Sun; 11-2.30, 5-11 weekdays in winter

DODDISCOMBSLEIGH SX8586 Map 1
Nobody Inn ★ ♀ ◀ 🛏

Village signposted off B3193, opposite northernmost Christow turn-off

The wine list in this busy pub is probably the best pub wine cellar in the country. There are around 800 wines by the bottle and 25 by the glass kept oxidation-free, and they hold tutored tastings (they also sell wine retail, and the good tasting-notes in their detailed list are worth the £3.50 it costs – anyway refunded if you buy more than £30-worth). Also, 270 whiskies, local ciders, and well kept Otter Bitter, a beer named for the pub, and a changing guest on handpump or tapped from the cask. The two rooms of the lounge bar have handsomely carved antique settles, windsor and wheelback chairs, benches, carriage lanterns hanging from the beams, and guns and hunting prints in a snug area by one of the big inglenook fireplaces. Bar food includes soup (£4.20), a special toasted sandwich or filled ciabatta (from £4.90), duck liver pâté with tomato and apple chutney (£5), a choice of six local cheeses (£6.20), wild boar and apple sausages on cheese and garlic mash or ploughman's (£6.90), vegetarian shepherd's pie (£7.90), bass and ginger fishcake with tomato and fennel sauce or breast of chicken with wild mushroom risotto and red pepper sauce (£9.50), and puddings like chocolate soufflé cake with fudge sauce (£4.50). The restaurant is no smoking. There are picnic-sets on the terrace with views of the surrounding wooded hill pastures. The medieval stained glass in the local church is some of the best in the West Country. *(Recommended by Dr and Mrs T E Hothersall, Peter Salmon, John Whiting, Peter Burton, Andrea Rampley, Jim and Maggie Cowell, David Handforth, Mr and Mrs W Mills, Cathryn and Richard Hicks, Dr Martin Owton, Mr and Mrs Taylor, Simon Rodway, Michael Butler, JHW, Nick and Meriel Cox, the Didler, Canon Michael Bourdeaux, John and Christine Lowe, John Urquhart, D S and J M Jackson, Tim and Rosemary Wells, Patrick Hancock, Terry and Linda Moseley, John Close, DAV, Ann Holdsworth, Ann and Bob Westbrook, Steve Whalley, Ian and Jane Irving, Sue Demont, Tim Barrow, Simon Cleasby)*

Free house ~ Licensee Nick Borst-Smith ~ Real ale ~ Bar food (till 10pm) ~ Restaurant ~ (01647) 252394 ~ Children in restaurant ~ Open 12-2.30, 6-11; 12-3, 7-10.30 Sun; closed 25, 26, evening 31 Dec, 1 Jan ~ Bedrooms: £25(£45B)/£40(£80B)

DREWSTEIGNTON SX7390 Map 1
Drewe Arms

Signposted off A30 NW of Moretonhampstead

With welcoming licensees, this unpretentious old thatched pub remains very popular with many of our readers – and thankfully, little changes. The small, unspoilt room on the left has a serving hatch and basic seats, and the room on the right with its assorted tables and chairs has a log fire, and is not much bigger. Well kept Adnams Broadside, Bass and Otter Bitter kept on racks in the tap room behind, and local cider. At the back is a sizeable eating area, with well liked food such as lunchtime sandwiches and ploughman's, mixed vegetable and coconut curry or local butcher's sausages on bubble and squeak (£7.95), crab and mushroom bake (£8.95), steak and kidney pie, smoked haddock with stilton and a poached egg or honey roast hock of ham with parsley sauce (£10), half a crispy roast duck with spiced plum sauce (£14), and beef wellington (£14.95); home-made puddings and steak evening Tuesdays (£6.95). The restaurant is no smoking. Dominoes, cribbage, darts, shove-ha'penny and skittle alley. Castle Drogo nearby (open for visits) looks medieval, though it was actually built in the 20th century. *(Recommended by David Crook, John Hale, Mrs C Lintott, the Didler, Revd R P Tickle, Anthony Longden, Jennifer Hutchings, Michael and Margaret Slater, Mayur Shah, Peter Craske, Andy and Glenda Matheson, Mark Flynn, OPUS, Dr and Mrs M E Wilson, DAV, Derek Allpass, Andrea and Guy Bradley, Jim and Janet Brown, Gaynor Gregory, Klaus and Elizabeth Leist)*

Enterprise ~ Lease Dave Jermey ~ Real ale ~ Bar food (may not do food Sun evening) ~ Restaurant ~ (01647) 281224 ~ Children in eating area of bar and in restaurant until 8.30pm ~ Dogs allowed in bar ~ Open 12-11(10.30 Sun) ~ Bedrooms: /£70B

EAST BUDLEIGH SY0684 Map 1

Sir Walter Raleigh

High Street

Handy for Bicton Park gardens and in a pretty thatch-and-cob village, this pleasant local is run by friendly licensees. There's a low-beamed bar with lots of books on shelves, a cosily chatty atmosphere, and well kept Adnams Broadside, Otter Bitter and Wells Bombardier on handpump. The attractive restaurant down a step from the bar is no smoking. Bar food is very good and changes every couple of months: sandwiches or ploughman's, mussels in a white wine and cream broth (£4.75), cranberry and camembert en croûte (£4.95), mushroom tagliatelle with a walnut and blue cheese sauce (£7.95), steak in ale on a potato cake (£8.50), maize-fed chicken with chorizo and tomato or liver and bacon (£8.95), wild salmon on ratatouille (£9.95), whole lemon sole with lime and ginger (£10.95), and puddings such as mango bavarois or calvados rice pudding (£3.50). There's a fine church with a unique collection of carved oak bench ends, and the pub is handy for Bicton Park gardens. Raleigh himself was born at nearby Hayes Barton, and educated in a farmhouse 300 yards away. Parking is about 100 yards away. No children. *(Recommended by John and Doris Couper, M G Hart, Dr and Mrs M E Wilson, Barry Steele-Perkins, John Waters, Ian and Joan Blackwell, John and Jane Hayter)*

Enterprise ~ Lease Lindsay Mason ~ Real ale ~ Bar food ~ Restaurant ~ (01395) 442510 ~ Dogs allowed in bar ~ Open 11.45-3, 6-11; 12-3, 7-10.30 Sun

EXETER SX9292 Map 1

Imperial ◗ £

New North Road (St David's Hill on Crediton/Tiverton road, above St David's station)

The setting for this early 19th-c mansion is quite special – it's in its own six-acre hillside park with plenty of picnic-sets in the grounds and elegant garden furniture in the attractive cobbled courtyard. Inside, there's a light and airy former orangery with an unusual lightly mirrored end wall, and various different areas including a couple of little clubby side bars, a left-hand bar that looks into the orangery, and a fine ex-ballroom filled with elaborate plasterwork and gilding brought here in the 1920s from Haldon House (a Robert Adam stately home that was falling on hard times). One area is no smoking. The furnishings give Wetherspoons' usual solid well spaced comfort (some refurbishment this year), and there are plenty of interesting pictures and other things to look at. Well kept and very cheap Burton Bridge Bitter, Exmoor Stag or Fox, Greene King Abbot, Marstons Pedigree and four guest beers on handpump, and two farm ciders; friendly, efficient staff – even when the place is hopping with students. Standard bar food includes filled panini (from £2.99), battered cod or ham and eggs (£4.65), chicken caesar salad (£5.09), mediterranean pasta bake or sausages and mash (£5.29), burgers (from £5.35; after 5pm), and barbecue chicken melt (£6.15). *(Recommended by Pete Walker, Dr and Mrs A K Clarke, Joe Green, Jim and Maggie Cowell, Roger Huggins, Tom and Alex McLean, the Didler, Mike Gorton, Mrs Sylvia Elcoate, E B Ireland)*

Wetherspoons ~ Manager Paul Dixey ~ Real ale ~ Bar food (all day) ~ (01392) 434050 ~ Children in family area only until 6pm ~ Open 10-11; 11-10.30 Sun

---

Stars after the name of a pub show exceptional quality. One star means most people (after reading the report to see just why the star has been won) would think a special trip worth while. Two stars mean that the pub is really outstanding – many that for their particular qualities cannot be bettered.

EXMINSTER SX9686 Map 1

Turf Hotel ★

Follow the signs to the Swan's Nest, signposted from A379 S of village, then continue to end of track, by gates; park, and walk right along canal towpath – nearly a mile; there's a fine seaview out to the mudflats at low tide

Readers enjoy getting to this friendly pub as you cannot reach it by car, so it's a bit more of an adventure. You must either walk (which takes about 20 minutes along the ship canal) or cycle, and there's a 60-seater boat which brings people down the Exe estuary from Topsham quay (15-minute trip, adult £3, child £2); there's also a canal boat from Countess Wear Swing Bridge every lunchtime. Best to phone the pub for all sailing times. For those arriving in their own boat there is a large pontoon as well as several moorings. The decking area with outdoor rotisserie for chicken and pig roasts and outside bar is very popular (barbecue choices from £3.75). Inside, the pleasantly airy bar has church pews, wooden chairs and alcove seats on the polished bare floorboards, and pictures and old photographs of the pub and its characters over the years on the walls; woodburning stove and antique gas fire. From the bay windows there are views out to the mudflats (full of gulls and waders at low tide). Good bar food includes quite a choice of lunchtime sandwiches, toasties and baked potatoes (from £3.25; bacon and egg toastie £4.50; crab sandwich £6.50), as well as home-made soup (£3.75), nibbles like hummous and cracked olives or guacamole and spicy salsa (£4.25), a tart of the day (£6.25), shepherd's pie (£7), moules marinière (£7.50), chilli nachos (£7.95), thai green chicken and coconut curry (£8.95), and puddings like fruit crumble or sticky toffee pudding (from £4). The dining room and food bar are no smoking. Well kept Otter Bitter, Bright and Ale, and a guest beer on handpump, Green Valley cider, local apple juice and over 20 wines by two sizes of glass; cribbage, dominoes and piped music. The garden has a children's play area built using a lifeboat from a liner that sank off the Scilly Isles around 100 years ago. (*Recommended by Phil and Sally Gorton, Brenda and Stuart Naylor, John Beeken, Alain and Rose Foote, David Carr, Mike Gorton, the Didler, Mark and Heather Williamson, Dr and Mrs M E Wilson, David Field, Neil and Lorna Mclaughlan*)

Free house ~ Licensees Clive and Ginny Redfern ~ Real ale ~ Bar food (not Sun evening) ~ (01392) 833128 ~ Children welcome ~ Dogs welcome ~ Open 11.30-11; 11.30-10.30 Sun; closed Dec-Feb

HAYTOR VALE SX7677 Map 1

Rock ★ 🛏

Haytor signposted off B3387 just W of Bovey Tracey, on good moorland road to Widecombe

Although many evening customers in this civilised and neatly kept inn are here to stay overnight in the comfortable bedrooms or to enjoy the good restaurant food, at lunchtime it's a different story. As a place for a light meal or a quiet drink in the small bars or pretty garden after a walk or a visit to one of the most popular of the Dartmoor tors, this would be hard to beat, and the staff are very welcoming and helpful. The two communicating, partly panelled bar rooms have polished antique tables with candles and fresh flowers, old-fashioned prints and decorative plates on the walls, and warming winter log fires (the main fireplace has a fine Stuart fireback). Good lunchtime bar food includes home-made soup (£3.50), sandwiches (£4.95; soup and a sandwich £6.50), chicken liver parfait (£5.95), local mussels in chilli, lemon and parlsey or whole grilled sole (£7.95), pork and honey sausages (£7.50), asparagus pasta with tomato and basil sauce (£8.95), and chicken with dauphinoise potatoes and pesto dressing (£9.95), with evening choices such as duck risotto or warm goats cheese on confit tomatoes with basil and balsamic dressing (£6.95), scallops with roasted red pepper dressing (£8.95), wild mushroom risotto, rump of local lamb with roasted thyme potatoes and garlic and olive jus, monkfish on saffron fondant potato with a mussel and saffron sauce or duck breast with figs, ginger and redcurrant jus (all £14.95), and puddings like treacle and hazelnut tart or raspberry brûlée (£5.50); three courses £24.95. No smoking at all in the evenings. Well kept Bass, Greene King Old Speckled Hen and St Austell Dartmoor Best on handpump, and several malt whiskies. There are seats in the pretty, large garden opposite the inn, with tables and chairs on a small terrace next to the pub itself. Parking is not always easy. *(Recommended by Val and Alan Green, Ron Gentry, Brian and Bett Cox, John and Marion Tyrie, Andrea Rampley, Mark Flynn, Neil and Beverley Gardner, DF, NF, Peter Cole, Brian England, Mike Gorton, Mark and Heather Williamson, Hugh Roberts, M Sage, Dr C C S Wilson, Gene and Tony Freemantle)*

Free house ~ Licensee Christopher Graves ~ Real ale ~ Bar food (not 25 or 26 Dec) ~ Restaurant ~ (01364) 661305 ~ Children in restaurant ~ Dogs allowed in bedrooms ~ Open 11-11; 12-10.30 Sun; closed 25 and 26 Dec ~ Bedrooms: £66.95B/£95.95B

HOLBETON SX6150 Map 1

Dartmoor Union 🍴 ♀ ◀

Village signposted off A379 W of A3121 junction; Fore Street

Devon Dining Pub of the Year

It's quite a surprise to step into this smart and rather chic place from the little village street, as it all looks very unprepossessing from the outside. The civilised bar, with plenty of neat young staff dressed in black waiting to serve you, has a nice mix of dining chairs around several wooden tables on the stripped wood floor, squashy leather sofas and armchairs in front of the log fire in the brick fireplace, witticisms and old photographs of the village on the elegant, pale yellow walls, and a dark wood, brass and black slate bar counter with vases of yellow tulips on top; table skittles. The no smoking restaurant leads off here with big yachting photographs by Beken on the dark red walls, red arum lilies and red tulips on the white-clothed tables, and high-backed leather dining chairs. The atmosphere is chatty and relaxed, and there's a good mix of customers. Imaginative modern food might include home-made soup (£4.25), slow-roasted ham hock salad with toasted brioche and balsamic reduction or honey glazed goats cheese with confit of mushrooms (£5.25), corn-fed chicken breast with wild mushrooms and smoked bacon and potato hash or lemon and rosemary roasted vegetables with garlic sautéed potato (£9.95), local sirloin with béarnaise sauce (£10.95), roasted monkfish wrapped in parma ham and sage (£11.95), and specials such as goats cheese crostini with fresh pesto dressing (£4.95), crab salad with shallots and chives (£6.95), hand-dived scallops with champagne butter and crispy vegetables (£6.95; main course £11.95), gressingham duck breast niçoise style (£10.50), and local beef fillet with garlic tiger prawns (£13.95); three-course set lunch (£13.95), and puddings like caramelised banana tatin with clotted cream (£4.95). Nine wines by two sizes of glass from a carefully chosen list, and well kept Cotleigh Tawny and Otter Bitter. On our visit they were just putting the finishing touches to a state-of-the-art new back microbrewery, which should be in operation by now, and which you can see from the sheltered back terrace, with its smart teak furniture. There's a back car park, not signed from the street when we were there (and rather a tight squeeze in and out), and no inn sign – just a brass plaque. *(Recommended by J F Stackhouse, John Evans, Brian and Bett Cox)*

Free house ~ Licensee Sue Constantine ~ Real ale ~ Bar food (12-3.30, 6.30-9) ~ Restaurant ~ (01752) 830288 ~ Children welcome ~ Dogs allowed in bar ~ Open 12-3, 5.30-11; 12-10.30 Sun

HOLNE SX7069 Map 1

Church House

Signed off B3357 W of Ashburton

Originally built as a resting place for visiting clergy and worshippers at the church, this medieval Dartmoor inn was also used to brew ale for religious feast days. There are fine moorland views from the pillared porch (where regulars tend to gather), and plenty of surrounding walks. Inside, the lower bar has stripped pine panelling and an 18th-c curved elm settle, and is separated from the lounge bar by a 16th-c heavy oak partition; open log fires in both rooms. Bar food includes lunchtime filled baked potatoes (from £4), sandwiches and baguettes (from £4.25), and ploughman's (from £5.50), as well as soup (£3.95), home-made pâté (from £4.75), and favourites like steak in ale pie or rabbit casserole (£8); more elaborate choices in the evening. Part of the bar is no smoking. Well kept Butcombe Bitter, Summerskills Best Bitter and Teignworthy Reel Ale on handpump, several wines by the glass, and organic cider, apple juice and ginger beer; darts. Morris men and clog dancers in the summer. Charles Kingsley (of *Water Babies* fame) was born in the village. More reports please. *(Recommended by Neil and Beverley Gardner, Gene and Tony Freemantle, Simon and Jane Williams, Glenn and Gillian Miller)*

Free house ~ Licensee J Silk ~ Real ale ~ Bar food (not Sun evening or Mon in winter) ~ Restaurant ~ (01364) 631208 ~ Children in eating area of bar and restaurant ~ Dogs allowed in bar and bedrooms ~ Open 12-2.30(3 Sat), 7-11(10.30 in winter); 12-3, 7-10.30 Sun; closed Sun evening and Mon in winter ~ Bedrooms: £33S/£66B

HORNDON SX5280 Map 1

Elephants Nest 🍺

If coming from Okehampton on A386 turn left at Mary Tavy Inn, then left after about ½ mile; pub signposted beside Mary Tavy Inn, then Horndon signposted; on the Ordnance Survey Outdoor Leisure Map it's named as the New Inn

Originally three 16th-c miners' cottages, this isolated pub is surrounded by plenty of walks, and both walkers and their dogs are welcome. There are benches on the spacious lawn in front that look over dry-stone walls to the pastures and the rougher moorland above; they have their own cricket pitch. Inside, the bar has original stone walls, flagstones, three woodburning stoves (two have their doors wide open to provide open log fires), and a beam-and-board ceiling; there's a no smoking dining room and garden room, and children are welcome in both. Well kept Otter Bright, Palmers IPA and Copper Ale, and a guest such as Exmoor Hart or O'Hanlons Yellowhammer on handpump, farm cider and a few wines by the glass. Under the new licensee, bar food now includes soup (£3.50), lunchtime baguettes (not Sunday, from £4.25; local sirloin steak £6.75), chicken, pepper and leek terrine with tomato and basil chutney (£4.95), salad of local brie, figs and parma ham (£5.25), roasted red pepper tarts topped with goats cheese (£7.50), trio of sausages with onion gravy (£8.25), deep-fried natural smoked haddock (£8.95), slow-roasted belly of pork with sage reduction (£9.25), home-made steak and kidney pudding (£10.50), and chicken supreme wrapped in bacon and filled with apple and grapes with a champagne and wild mushroom velouté (£11.95); Sunday roasts. *(Recommended by Dr and Mrs M W A Haward, Oliver and Sue Rowell, John and Marion Tyrie, JHW, Mick and Moira Brummell, Neil and Beverley Gardner, DAV, Rev D E and Mrs J A Shapland)*

Free house ~ Licensee Hugh Cook ~ Real ale ~ Bar food (12-2.15, 7-9) ~ Restaurant ~ (01822) 810273 ~ Children in restaurant ~ Dogs welcome ~ Jazz first Weds of month and folk third Weds of month ~ Open 12-3, 6.30-11(10.30 Sun)

IDDESLEIGH SS5708 Map 1

Duke of York ★ ♒ 🛏

B3217 Exbourne—Dolton

Reports from readers on this little inn are always heart-warming – and this year is no exception. Indeed, one person feels that this should be a compulsory stopping-off point for every licensee in the country who wonders what the magic formula is for running a successful pub. Mr Stuart has the enviable knack of making visitors feel as welcome as regulars and he also keeps particularly good Adnams Broadside, Cotleigh Tawny and Sharps Doom Bar tapped from the cask. It helps, too, that the bar food is most enjoyable, and that it's a super place to stay overnight. The bar is full of friendly locals (plenty of chat and no noisy games machines or piped music) and has a lot of homely character: rocking chairs by the roaring log fire, cushioned wall benches built into the wall's black-painted wooden dado, stripped tables and other simple country furnishings, lots of wines by the glass and freshly squeezed orange and pink grapefruit juice. With prices virtually unchanged since last year, generous helpings of bar food include sandwiches, home-made soup such as pea and mint (£2.75 small, £4 large), sandwiches (from £4), chicken liver and brandy pâté (£5), grilled or battered fish and chips (£5.50; large £7.50), ham and eggs (£5), delicious scallops wrapped in smoked bacon or crab mayonnaise (£5.50 small, £9 large), cottage pie or ploughman's (£6), vegetable korma, smoked haddock or beef in Guinness (£7), steak and kidney pudding (£8.50), and double lamb chop with rosemary and garlic gravy (£9); it can get a bit cramped at peak times. Cribbage, dominoes and darts. Through a small coach arch is a little back garden with some picnic-sets. Fishing nearby. *(Recommended by Louise English, Jacquie and Jim Jones, Peter Craske, JHW, John and Marion Tyrie, Ron and Sheila Corbett, Michael and Ann Cole, Anthony Longden, the Didler, David and Pauline Brenner, Mark Flynn, Ann Holdsworth, DAV, Peter and Jean Dowson, Stuart Turner, Peter and Margaret Glenister, Rev D E and Mrs J A Shapland, Sue Demont, Tim Barrow, W W Burke)*

Free house ~ Licensees Jamie Stuart and Pippa Hutchinson ~ Real ale ~ Bar food (all day) ~ Restaurant ~ (01837) 810253 ~ Children welcome ~ Dogs allowed in bar and bedrooms ~ Open 11-11; 12-10.30 Sun ~ Bedrooms: £30B/£60B

LOWER ASHTON SX8484 Map 1

Manor Inn ♟

Ashton signposted off B3193 N of Chudleigh

Friendly, helpful new licensees have taken over this bustling creeper-covered pub but readers have been quick with their enthusiasm. There's a good mix of customers, although the left-hand room with its beer mats and brewery advertisements on the walls is more for locals enjoying the well kept Cottage Wheel Tappers, Princetown Jail Ale, RCH Pitchfork and Teignworthy Reel Ale or Tipple on handpump; 14 wines by the glass, Gray's farm cider, and Luscombe organic ginger beer and apple juice. On the right, two rather more discreet rooms have a wider appeal, bolstered by the good, popular home-made food which might include sandwiches (from £2.95; filled baguettes from £3), home-made soup (£3.50), lots of filled baked potatoes (from £3.95), home-made burger (£4.75), ploughman's (from £6.75), vegetable bake (£6.95), home-cooked ham and egg (£7.75), beef, mushroom and Guinness pie (£7.95), chicken in a creamy stilton sauce (£8.75), seafood pasta mornay (£8.95), steaks (from £9.95), duck breast in morello cherry sauce (£10.95), home-made puddings (£3.50), and a good cheese platter with five different local cheeses to share (£5.95). The garden has lots of picnic-sets under cocktail parasols (and a fine tall scots pine), and pretty hanging baskets. No children inside. *(Recommended by the Didler, Mike Gorton, David M Cundy, Ann Holdsworth, DAV, David and Jean Hall)*

Free house ~ Licensee Mark Quilter ~ Real ale ~ Bar food (12-1.30, 7-9.30; not Mon except bank hols) ~ (01647) 252304 ~ Dogs welcome ~ Open 12-2(2.30 Sat), 6.30-11; 12-2.30, 7-10.30 Sun; closed Mon (except bank hols)

LUSTLEIGH SX7881 Map 1

Cleave

Village signposted off A382 Bovey Tracey—Moretonhampstead

In summer, you can sit in the sheltered garden of this charming thatched no smoking 15th-c pub, and the hanging baskets and flower beds are lovely. It's deservedly popular with walkers, so it's best to arrive early to avoid a bit of a wait at the bar. The low-ceilinged lounge bar has attractive antique high-backed settles, cushioned wall seats, and wheelback chairs around the tables on its patterned carpet, granite walls and a roaring log fire. A second bar has similar furnishings, a large dresser, harmonium, an HMV gramophone and prints, and the family room has crayons, books and toys for children. Bar food includes sandwiches, home-made soup (£3.95), home-made chicken liver pâté (£4.95), local butcher's sausages (£6.95), spinach and feta cheese pie (£8.95), venison casserole (£9.95), poached salmon fillet with watercress sauce (£10.95), braised lamb shank with mint gravy (£11.95), half a honey roasted duckling with orange sauce (£14.95), and puddings (from £3.95). Well kept Greene King IPA, and Otter Ale on handpump kept under light blanket pressure, quite a few malt whiskies, and a dozen wines by the glass. Until the car parking field in the village is opened during the summer, parking can be very difficult. *(Recommended by C W Burke, Jim and Maggie Cowell, Andrea Rampley, Mike Turner, John and Marion Tyrie, Alice Harper, Jacquie and Jim Jones, DAV, Dr and Mrs M E Wilson, Geoff and Marianne Millin)*

Heavitree ~ Tenant A Perring ~ Real ale ~ Bar food (not Mon) ~ Restaurant ~ (01647) 277223 ~ Children in family room ~ Dogs welcome ~ Open 11-3, 6-11; closed Mon

LYDFORD SX5184 Map 1
Castle Inn
Off A386 Okehampton—Tavistock

Next to the daunting, ruined 12th-c castle this pink-washed Tudor inn has plenty of character and charm. The twin-roomed bar has country kitchen chairs, high-backed winged settles and old captain's chairs around mahogany tripod tables on big slate flagstones. One room has low lamp-lit beams, a sizeable open fire, masses of brightly decorated plates, some Hogarth prints and, near the serving counter, seven Lydford pennies hammered out in the old Saxon mint in the reign of Ethelred the Unready, in the 11th c. The bar area has a bowed ceiling with low beams, a polished slate flagstone floor and a stained-glass door with the famous Three Hares; there's also a snug with high-backed settles. Bar food includes sandwiches, filled baked potatoes (£4.95), chicken and wild mushroom pâté (£5.95), ploughman's or ham and eggs (£6.95), sausages and herb mash with creamed onion and leek sauce (£7.95), a pie of the day or vegetarian lasagne (£8.25), game casserole or minted lamb cutlets (£8.95), and cajun salmon (£9.50). The restaurant area is no smoking. Well kept Fullers London Pride, Greene King IPA and Otter Ale on handpump, and 11 wines by the glass; darts, cribbage and dominoes. You can walk in the beautiful nearby river gorge (owned by the National Trust; closed November-Easter). *(Recommended by Guy Vowles, John and Joan Nash, DRH and KLH, Andrea Rampley, Ian Clare, Adrian Johnson, Mary Ellen Cummings, David Crook, DAV, Dr and Mrs M E Wilson)*

Heavitree ~ Tenant Richard Davies ~ Real ale ~ Bar food ~ Restaurant ~ (01822) 820241 ~ Children in restaurant ~ Dogs allowed in bar and bedrooms ~ Open 11.30-11; 12-10.30 Sun ~ Bedrooms: £45B/£65B

MARLDON SX8663 Map 1
Church House 🍴 ♟
Just off A380 NW of Paignton

To find this attractive, bustling inn just head for the church. The spreading bar has several different areas that radiate off the big semicircular bar counter, and the main part has interesting windows, some beams, dark pine chairs around solid tables on the turkey carpet and yellow leather bar chairs; leading off here is a cosy little candlelit room with just four tables on the bare-boards floor, a dark wood dado and stone fireplace; next to this is the restaurant with a large stone fireplace. At the other end of the building, a similarly interesting room is split into two parts with a stone floor in one bit and a wooden floor in another (which has a big woodburning stove). All the pub is no smoking except for a few tables in the public bar. Popular bar food includes sandwiches, home-made soup (£5), home-made chicken liver pâté with date and apricot chutney (£5.50), quenelles of smoked fish with horseradish dressing (£6), mediterranean vegetable tart (£8.50), chicken supreme with spicy sauce and couscous or fillet of salmon on a potato rösti with a cherry tomato and cream sauce (£11.95), breast of duck with gooseberry sauce (£12.50), and shoulder of lamb with rosemary and garlic sauce, fillet of cod with a fresh herb crust and spring onion and dijon mustard sauce or sirloin steak (naturally reared on Exmoor) with a fresh tarragon cream sauce (£13.50); efficient service even when busy. Well kept Bass, Fullers London Pride, Greene King IPA and St Austell Dartmoor Best on handpump, and 12 wines by the glass; piped music. There are three grassy terraces with picnic-sets behind. Please note, they no longer have letting bedrooms. *(Recommended by Cathryn and Richard Hicks, Adrian White, John and Sonja Newberry, Mr and Mrs Colin Roberts, Dr and Mrs A K Clarke, John and Christine Lowe, JMC, Neil and Beverley Gardner, Felicity Stephens, David Fox, David M Cundy, Jim and Maggie Cowell, Pamela and Merlyn Horswell, Mike and Mary Carter, M Sage, Alan and Paula McCully, Emma Kingdon)*

Enterprise ~ Lease Julian Cook ~ Real ale ~ Bar food ~ Restaurant ~ (01803) 558279 ~ Children in restaurant ~ Dogs allowed in bar ~ Open 11.30-2.30, 5-11; 11.30-3, 5.30-11 Sat; 12-10.30 Sun

MOLLAND SS8028 Map 1

London ◖

Village signposted off B3227 E of South Molton, down narrow lanes

This is real old Exmoor: a water-bowl by the good log fire for the working dogs that come in with their keepers, proper farm cider as well as Cotleigh and Exmoor Ale tapped from casks, and an easy chatty mix of customers. The two small linked rooms by the old-fashioned central servery have lots of local stag-hunting pictures, tough carpeting or rugs on flagstones, cushioned benches and plain chairs around rough stripped trestle tables, a table of shooting and other country magazines, ancient stag and otter trophies, and darts, table skittles and dominoes. On the left an attractive beamed room has accounts of the rescued stag which lived a long life at the pub some 50 years ago, and on the right a panelled dining room with a great curved settle by its fireplace has particularly good hunting and gamebird prints, including ones by McPhail and Hester Lloyd. Honest bar food includes home-made soup (£3), sandwiches (from £3.50), ham and egg (£4.70), ploughman's (£4.90), filled baked potatoes (£5.20), savoury pancakes (£5.80), and a dish of the day such as cottage or steak and kidney pie or curry (£6.20). The dining room is no smoking. A small hall with stuffed birds and animals and lots of overhead baskets has a box of toys, and there are good country views from a few picnic-sets out in front. The low-ceilinged lavatories are worth a look, with their Victorian mahogany and tiling (and in the gents' a testament to the prodigious thirst of the village cricket team). And don't miss the next-door church, with its untouched early 18th-c box pews – and a spring carpet of tenby daffodils in the graveyard. *(Recommended by J C Brittain-Long, Jeremy Whitehorn, the Didler, Andrea Rampley, Geoff and Teresa, Barry Steele-Perkins, Bob and Margaret Holder, David and Sheila Pearcey)*

Free house ~ Licensees Mike and Linda Short ~ Real ale ~ Bar food ~ Restaurant ~ No credit cards ~ (01769) 550269 ~ Children in eating area of bar ~ Dogs allowed in bar and bedrooms ~ Open 11.30-2.30, 6-11; 12-2.30, 7-10.30 Sun ~ Bedrooms: /£50B

NEWTON ABBOT SX8468 Map 1

Two Mile Oak ◖

A381 2 miles S, at Denbury/Kingskerswell crossroads

This is an enjoyable old coaching inn with a friendly welcome and a bustling atmosphere. There's a beamed lounge and an alcove just for two, a mix of wooden tables and chairs, and a fine winter log fire. The beamed and black-panelled bar is traditionally furnished, again with a mix of seating, lots of horsebrasses, and another good log fire. Well kept Bass, Flowers IPA and Otter Ale tapped from the cask, and decent wines. Popular bar food includes soup (£3.50), filled baguettes (from £4.25), roast beef, lamb or turkey (£4.50), ploughman's (from £5.75), lasagne (£7.45), ham and eggs (£7.95), thai chicken curry (£8.25), steak and kidney pudding (£8.95), and daily specials such as butterfly chicken breast in cajun sauce (£8.95), lamb cutlets with rosemary and minted gravy (£9.50), pork medallions in a creamy mushroom and brandy sauce (£10.25), and puddings (£4.25). Part of the restaurant is no smoking; piped music, darts and cribbage. There are picnic-sets on the terrace where they hold summer barbecues, and a lawn with shrubs and tubs of flowers. *(Recommended by Mrs Sylvia Elcoate, Alan and Paula McCully, Dr and Mrs A K Clarke, the Didler, Mr and Mrs Colin Roberts, Pamela and Merlyn Horswell)*

Heavitree ~ Manager Karen Brown ~ Real ale ~ Bar food ~ (01803) 812411 ~ Children in eating area of bar, restaurant and family room ~ Dogs allowed in bar ~ Folk music Sun evening ~ Open 11-11; 11-11 Sat; 12-10.30 Sun

NEWTON FERRERS SX5447 Map 1
Dolphin
Riverside Road East – follow Harbour dead end signs

The two terraces across the lane from this friendly 18th-c pub are, not surprisingly, very popular in warm weather. By day they have a grandstand view of the boating action on the busy tidal River Yealm below the cottages on these steep hillsides, and at night the floodlit church over in Noss Mayo makes a lovely focal point. Inside, the L-shaped bar has a few low black beams, slate floors, some white-painted plank panelling and simple pub furnishings including cushioned wall benches and small winged settles; chatty and relaxed out of season, it can get packed in summer. Enjoyable food includes sandwiches (from £3.90; filled baguettes from £4.95), filled baked potatoes (from £4.50), ploughman's (from £5.95), home-made vegetable lasagne (£6.90), fresh cod (from £7.40), and daily specials such as scallops in garlic butter (£5.40), mixed fish curry, thai-style chicken or home-made steak and mushroom in ale pie (£8.95), and honey and mustard quarter shoulder of lamb (£10.95). Palmers IPA, Sharps Doom Bar and a Skinners brew for the pub are kept well on handpump, Heron Valley cider and eight wines by the glass; they have darts and a popular quiz night on Wednesdays in winter, and the pub is decorated with lots of coastal watercolours (for sale). The carpeted no smoking dining room is up a few steps at the back. Parking by the pub is very limited, with more chance of a space either below or above. *(Recommended by B J Harding, Geoff Pidoux, David M Cundy, MP)*

Free house ~ Licensee Sandra Dunbar Rees ~ Bar food ~ Restaurant ~ (01752) 872007 ~ Children in eating area of bar and restaurant ~ Dogs welcome ~ Open 12-2.30(3 Sat), 6-11; 12-3, 7-10.30 Sun; opens 12.30 in winter

NOMANSLAND SS8313 Map 1
Mount Pleasant
B3137 Tiverton—South Molton

Informal and friendly, this is a relaxed and pleasant place for either a drink or a meal. The long bar is divided into three with huge fireplaces each end, one with a woodburning stove under a low dark ochre black-beamed ceiling, the other with a big log fire, and there are tables in a sizeable bay window extension. A nice mix of furniture on the patterned carpet includes an old sofa with a colourful throw, old-fashioned leather dining chairs, pale country kitchen chairs and wall pews, and tables all with candles in attractive metal holders; there are country prints and local photographs including shooting parties. The bar, with plenty of bar stools, has well kept Cotleigh Tawny and Barn Owl and Greene King IPA on handpump, and decent wines. Sensibly priced popular food includes sandwiches, chicken liver pâté or whitebait (£4.95), steak and kidney pie, tortillas filled with chilli con carne and crème fraîche, or smoked salmon and pasta with a tomato and basil sauce (all £7.95), mushroom stroganoff (£8.95), chicken breast in several different sauces (£9.95), honey roast duck in plum and pear sauce (£12.95), steaks (from £12.95), and puddings such as treacle tart or chocolate brownie (£4.50). On the left, a high-beamed stripped stone no smoking dining room with a stag's head was once a smithy, and still has the raised forge fireplace. Piped music and darts; picnic-sets under smart parasols in the neat back garden. Samuel the spaniel comes in to say hello at closing time. *(Recommended by Shaun and Beccy Haydon, Richard and Anne Ansell, Jan Multon, Bob and Margaret Holder, Mr and Mrs M G Lipton)*

Free house ~ Licensees Anne, Karen and Sarah Butler ~ Real ale ~ Bar food (all day) ~ Restaurant ~ (01884) 860271 ~ Children welcome ~ Dogs allowed in bar ~ Open 11.30-11; 12-10.30 Sun; closed evening 25 Dec, 1 Jan

NOSS MAYO SX5447 Map 1
Ship ♀ ◖
Off A379 via B3186, E of Plymouth

In fine weather the terrace in front of this bustling pub is extremely popular. You can sit at the octagonal wooden tables under parasols and look over the inlet, and visiting boats can tie up alongside – with prior permission; outdoor heaters have been added for cooler evenings. Inside it's all no smoking now, and the two thick-walled bars have a happy mix of dining chairs and tables on the wooden floors, log fires (so hot you might not want to sit too close!), bookcases, dozens of local pictures, newspapers and magazines to read, and a friendly, chatty atmosphere; dominoes and cribbage. At its best, food is very good indeed and might include chunky seafood chowder (£4.25), sandwiches (from £4.50; filled panini from £4.95), chicken liver pâté with onion marmalade (£4.95), potted shrimps (£6.25), ploughman's (£7.25), tapas to share between two or local pork and prune sausages with black pudding, herb mash and onion gravy (£7.95), wild mushroom burger or crab fishcakes (£8.25), local haddock in real ale batter (£9.95), chicken stuffed with leek and tomato with a rich madeira sauce (£10.95), and warm tuna niçoise salad or local rib-eye steak with béarnaise sauce (£12.95). Well kept Butcombe Blonde, Princetown Jail Ale, St Austell Tribute and Summerskills Tamar on handpump, lots of malt whiskies, and ten wines by the glass. Parking is restricted at high tide. *(Recommended by John Evans, B J Harding, Christopher Turner, Gene and Kitty Rankin, Ian Wilson, Mrs C Sleight, Geoff Pidoux, Vanessa Stilwell, Richard and Margaret Peers, Mike Gorton, Brian and Bett Cox, John and Joan Nash, Alice Harper, Alan and Anne Driver, OPUS, B Forster, Lynda and Trevor Smith, Mr and Mrs J E C Tasker, Charles and Pauline Stride, Geoff and Marianne Millin, Steve Whalley, Karen and Graham Oddey)*

Free house ~ Licensees Lesley and Bruce Brunning ~ Real ale ~ Bar food (12-9.30) ~ Restaurant ~ (01752) 872387 ~ Children allowed before 7.30pm ~ Dogs allowed in bar ~ Open 11.30-11; 12-10.30 Sun

PARRACOMBE SS6644 Map 1
Fox & Goose ♀
Village signposted off A39 Blackmoor Gate—Lynton (actually a short cut, but winding and rather narrow)

Although new licensees have taken over this quietly placed inn, readers are happy to report that not much has changed. The young landlords are friendly and welcoming, and the beer and food are very good. The log fire, brown-varnished plank ceiling, assorted mounted antlers, horns and ex-wildlife in some variety give a proper Exmoor feel to the bar, and seating is mainly wheelback carver chairs around solid tables, with more tables at a comfortable height for people eating over on the left, and rambling around behind; there are some interesting black and white photographs. The good food relies strongly on local connections: home-made cream of broccoli soup with stilton and granary bread (£3.95), greek salad or home-made chicken liver or smoked mackerel pâté (£4.75), dressed crab salad (£5.95), mushroom stroganoff (£8.95), steak and kidney pie with a herb crust or venison casserole (£10.95), skate wing with warm green salsa or lamb steak and mint gravy (£11.95), steaks (from £11.95), cod fillet with tiger prawns grilled with bacon butter (£12.95), and puddings such as truffley peppermint and chocolate pots, rich toffee sauce sponge pudding or creamy rice pudding with fresh orange (£4.25). The restaurant and part of the bar are no smoking. Well kept Cotleigh Barn Owl and Exmoor Gold with a guest such as Archers Special tapped from the cask, local farm cider and ten wines by the glass including local ones; service is quick and friendly, the atmosphere relaxed and informal, and there's a juke box. The dining room on the right looks down on a little stream, and the front verandah has a couple of picnic-sets, with hanging baskets and flower tubs. *(Recommended by David Gibbs, Steve Godfrey, Geoff and Teresa, Rev D E and Mrs J A Shapland, Bob and Margaret Holder, Trevor and Diane Waite, David and Kay Griffiths, B M Eldridge, W W Burke)*

Free house ~ Licensees N Baxter and P Houle ~ Real ale ~ Bar food (12-2, 6-9) ~ Restaurant ~ (01598) 763239 ~ Well behaved children in eating area of bar ~ Dogs allowed in bar ~ Open 11-11; 12-10.30; though may shut afternoons if not busy Sun; 11-2.30, 6(7 Sun)-11 in winter ~ Bedrooms: £30S/£45S

PETER TAVY SX5177 Map 1
Peter Tavy Inn ♀
Off A386 near Mary Tavy, N of Tavistock

Friendly, helpful licensees and their efficient staff keep things running smoothly even when this attractive old stone inn is at its busiest. The low-beamed bar has a good bustling atmosphere, high-backed settles on the black flagstones by the big stone fireplace (a fine log fire on cold days), smaller settles in stone-mullioned windows, and a snug, no smoking side dining area. Popular food at lunchtime might include thai vegetable and noodle soup (£4.25), filled baguettes or baked potatoes (from £4.95), ham and egg (£5.75), roast stuffed shoulder of lamb with minted pear (£7.95), fillet of cod topped with banana and bacon, cumberland sausage, lasagne or lamb curry (all £8.95), and steak and stilton pie (£9.95); evening choices such as spicy prawn balls or duck liver and apricot pâté (£5.50), greek salad (£5.95), vegetable and coconut curry (£8.95), chicken strips in batter with honey and ginger sauce or game casserole (£11.95), halibut with stir-fried vegetables (£12.95), duck breast with cherry sauce (£13.45), pork medallions with roasted vegetables and brie or lamb cannon with redcurrant gravy (£13.95), and home-made puddings such as chocolate truffle torte, sticky toffee pudding or coconut and lime tart (£4.25). Well kept Princetown Jail Ale, Summerskills Tamar and Sharps Doom Bar, with a couple of guests from breweries like Burrington or Sutton on handpump, kept under light blanket pressure; local farm cider, 30 malt whiskies and nine wines by the glass; piped music. From the picnic-sets in the pretty garden there are peaceful views of the moor rising above nearby pastures. *(Recommended by Gillian Rodgers, Cathryn and Richard Hicks, D Hines, John and Christine Lowe, Gene and Kitty Rankin, John and Vivienne Rice, Jacquie and Jim Jones, Richard and Margaret Peers, Michael and Margaret Slater, Richard and Anne Ansell, Guy Vowles, Pam and Alan Neale, Alan and Paula McCully)*

Free house ~ Licensees Graeme and Karen Sim ~ Real ale ~ Bar food ~ Restaurant ~ (01822) 810348 ~ Children in family room ~ Dogs welcome ~ Open 12-3, 6-11(10.30 Sun); closed 25 Dec and evenings 24 and 31 Dec

PORTGATE SX4185 Map 1
Harris Arms ⊕ ♀
Turn off A30 E of Launceston at Broadwoodwidger turn-off (with brown Dingle Steam Village sign), and head S; Launceston Road (old A30 between Lewdown and Lifton)

The warmly friendly and chatty Whitemans run this white-painted roadside pub with infectious enthusiasm. They are passionate about wine and as qualified wine-makers were hoping to find a vineyard in France. Luckily for us, they bought this place instead. As well as a dozen of their favourite house wines (all available by the glass), they have a Special Selection and a Fine & Interesting wine list, and are keen to encourage customers to experiment; what you can't finish, they will seal up so you can take it home. With maroon end walls and cream ones in between, there are some rather fine photographic posters, a log fire in a big stone hearth with a woodburning stove in another, a huge table at one end (brought back from New Zealand) with a long red-plush built-in wall banquette and armed wheelbacks, a few other tables and a mix of dining chairs, and maybe piped salsa music; part of this bar is no smoking. On the left, steps lead down to a maroon-carpeted no smoking back dining room with country kitchen chairs and wheelbacks around stripped wooden tables. The food is very good and uses local seasonal produce. At lunchtime, there might be filled baguettes (from £5; wild boar sausage £5.50), liver and bacon with red wine gravy, ham and free-range eggs or bangers and mash (all £7.50), ploughman's with home-cooked ham and local cheese (£7.75), fish and chips (£7.95), steak frites (£8.95), and a vegetarian and a pasta dish; evening choices like home-made soup (£3.75), home-made game terrine (£5.50), grilled local goats cheese with olive oil croûtons and home-made onion marmalade (£5.75), six local snails in garlic butter (£7.50), corn-fed chicken breast with creamed leeks (£8.95), hake fillet with spring onion mash and roasted peppers (£9.50), and specials such as grilled, marinated cornish sardines (£6.50), seared scallops with sage, lemon and capers (£6.95), roasted leg of venison with chestnuts and spiced red cabbage (£9.95), and thai fish casserole (£12.50), and puddings such as stem ginger pudding, very berry brûlée or dark chocolate torte (from £4.50). Well kept Sharps Doom Bar and Skinners Border Bitter (brewed exclusively for the pub) on handpump, and a pile of country magazines. There are picnic-sets in the sloping back garden that look out over wooded pasture hills. *(Recommended by John Whiting, Peter Craske, David C West)*

Free house ~ Licensees Andy and Rowena Whiteman ~ Bar food ~ Restaurant ~ (01566) 783331 ~ Children in restaurant ~ Dogs allowed in bar ~ Open 12-3, 6(7 Sun)-11; closed Tues in winter, Mon in summer

POSTBRIDGE SX6780 Map 1
Warren House
B3212 ¾ mile NE of Postbridge

After a damp hike on Dartmoor this no-frills place is a valuable refuge. The cosy bar has a fireplace at either end (one is said to have been kept almost continuously alight since 1845), and is simply furnished with easy chairs and settles under a beamed ochre ceiling, wild animal pictures on the partly panelled stone walls, and dim lighting (fuelled by the pub's own generator); there's a no smoking family room. Decent, no-nonsense bar food includes home-made soup (£2.90), lunchtime sandwiches (from £3.75), filled baked potatoes (from £4.50), and good ploughman's (£5.95), spinach and mascarpone lasagne (£7.25), home-made steak in ale pie (£7.95), daily specials (from £6), and home-made puddings such as treacle tart (£3.95). Well kept Badger Tanglefoot, Otter Ale, Ringwood Old Thumper and a guest on handpump, local farm cider and malt whiskies. Darts, dominoes and piped music. There are picnic-sets on both sides of the road that enjoy the moorland views. *(Recommended by Peter Salmon, Andrea Rampley, Pat and Robert Watt, Ian and Ruth Laurence, Anthony Longden)*

Free house ~ Licensee Peter Parsons ~ Real ale ~ Bar food (all day summer and winter weekends) ~ (01822) 880208 ~ Children in family room ~ Dogs welcome ~ Open 11-11; 12-10.30 Sun; 11-2.30, 6-11 weekdays in winter

POUNDSGATE SX7072 Map 1
Tavistock Inn
B3357 continuation

As moorland walks start and finish at this picturesque 15th-c pub or pass it en route, boots and even waders are welcome, as are dogs on a lead – there's a bowl of water outside for them, and maybe if they are lucky, a dog biscuit behind the bar. Some original features include a narrow-stepped granite spiral staircase, flagstones, ancient log fireplaces and beams, and there's a friendly atmosphere and a good mix of locals and visitors; one small room is no smoking. Well kept Courage Best, Wadworths 6X and a guest such as Wychwood Hobgoblin Best on handpump, decent wines and a few malt whiskies. Tasty traditional bar food includes filled baguettes (from £3.50; sausage and onion £3.75), filled baked potatoes (from £4.50), basket meals (from £5), home-made lasagne or mushroom, broccoli and pasta bake with stilton and cream (£6.50), locally made burger (£6.75), beef in ale pie (£7.50), and steaks (from £10.50); summer afternoon teas. Tables on the front terrace and pretty flowers in stone troughs, hanging baskets, and window boxes, and more seats (and ducks) in the quiet back garden with a gazebo overlooking the children's play area; lovely scenery. Sir Arthur Conan-Doyle wrote *The Hound of the Baskervilles* while staying here. *(Recommended by David Landey, JHW, Geoff and Marianne Millin)*

InnSpired ~ Lease Peter and Jean Hamill ~ Real ale ~ Bar food ~ Restaurant ~ (01364) 631251 ~ Children in eating area of bar ~ Dogs allowed in bar ~ Open 11-3, 6-11; 11-11 Sat; 12-10.30 Sun

RATTERY SX7461 Map 1
Church House
Village signposted from A385 W of Totnes, and A38 S of Buckfastleigh

The original building here probably housed the craftsmen who built the Norman church, and may then have served as a hostel for passing monks. Dating back to 1028, it is one of Britain's oldest pubs, and the spiral stone steps behind a little stone doorway on your left as you come in date back to that time. There are massive oak beams and standing timbers in the homely open-plan bar, large fireplaces (one with a little cosy nook partitioned off around it), windsor armchairs, comfortable seats and window seats, and prints on the plain white walls; the dining room is separated from this room by heavy curtains, and there's also a no smoking lounge area. Bar food includes soup (£3.75), sandwiches (from £4.25; toasties £4.50; filled baguettes from £4.75), devilled whitebait (£4.95), ploughman's (from £5.75), sausages with onion gravy (£6.75), creamy coconut chicken curry or steak and kidney pie (£7.75), vegetable lasagne (£8.25), steaks (from £10.75), citrus and olive lamb shank (£11.75), and puddings (£3.50). Well kept Gales HSB, Greene King Abbot, Otter Ale and St Austell Dartmoor Best on handpump, several malt whiskies and eight wines by the glass. The garden has picnic benches on the large hedged-in lawn, and peaceful views of the partly wooded surrounding hills. *(Recommended by B J Harding, Mr and Mrs J Curtis, JHW, John Evans, Andrea Rampley, Simon and Jane Williams, John and Christine Lowe, Ron and Sheila Corbett, Jacquie and Jim Jones, Hugh Roberts, M Sage, Mick and Moira Brummell, George Atkinson, Richard May)*

Free house ~ Licensee Ray Hardy ~ Real ale ~ Bar food ~ Restaurant ~ (01364) 642220 ~ Children welcome ~ Dogs allowed in bar ~ Open 11-3, 6-11; 12-3, 6-10.30 Sun

ROCKBEARE SY0295 Map 1
Jack in the Green 🍽 ♀
Signposted from new A30 by-pass E of Exeter

Most customers come to this big, neatly kept roadside dining pub for a meal out rather than a drink and a chat. The neat and comfortable good-sized bar has wheelback chairs, sturdy cushioned wall pews and varying-sized tables on its dark blue carpet, with sporting prints, nice decorative china and a dark carved oak dresser; piped music. The larger dining side is air-conditioned but similarly traditional in style: some of its many old hunting and shooting photographs are well worth a close look, and it has button-back leather chesterfields by its big woodburning stove. You may smoke in only one bar. Popular, if not cheap, bar food includes soup (£3.95), chicken liver pâté (£4.25), four cheese tagliatelle (£7.50), BLT croissant (£7.95), beef in ale pie or bangers and mash (£9.25), smoked salmon and prawn salad (£10.50), parmesan fried courgettes with tomato relish (£11.50), smoked haddock with welsh rarebit (£13.50), and rib-eye steak with green peppercorn and garlic butter (£16.50), and puddings such as coconut rice pudding with ginger syrup or sticky toffee pudding with butterscotch sauce (£5.25); two-course Sunday lunch (£17.95). Well kept Branscombe Vale labelled as JIG for the pub, Cotleigh Tawny, Otter Ale and Greene King Ruddles Best on handpump, and 12 good wines by the glass. There are some tables out behind, by a back skittle alley. *(Recommended by Mick and Moira Brummell, Mrs Sylvia Elcoate, John Cadge, John and Vivienne Rice, John and Sonja Newberry, Oliver and Sue Rowell, Alan Sadler, Martin and Karen Wake, Dr and Mrs M E Wilson, Barry Steele-Perkins, John and Fiona McIlwain, Piotr Chodzko-Zajko, Gill and Keith Croxton, OPUS)*

Free house ~ Licensee Paul Parnell ~ Real ale ~ Bar food (12-2, 7-9 but all day Sun) ~ Restaurant ~ (01404) 822240 ~ Well behaved children in eating area of bar ~ Open 11-3, 5.30(6 Sat)-11; 12-10.30 Sun; closed 25 Dec-5 Jan

SANDY PARK SX7087 Map 1

Sandy Park Inn 🛏️

A382 Whiddon Down—Moretonhampstead

A warmly friendly and enthusiastic young landlord runs this small thatched inn. It's got a terrific bustling atmosphere with a super mix of customers and serves good beer and enjoyable food. The small bar on the right has rugs on the black-painted composition floor, black beams in the cream ceiling, varnished built-in wall settles forming separate areas around nice tables, and bar stools by the chatty bar with Otter Ale and St Austell Tribute, and perhaps a couple of guests like Exe Valley XXI and Sharps Doom Bar on handpump and a decent choice of wines by the glass; big blow-ups of old golfing pictures and some smaller interestingly annotated Dartmoor photographs. The back snug has one big table that a dozen people could just squeeze around, stripped stone walls and a cream-painted bright-cushioned built-in wall bench. On the left is a small dining room with golfing and other prints on the red walls and just a few tables, and an inner private no smoking dining room with lots of prints and one big table. Enjoyable food includes home-made soup (£4.50), hearty sandwiches (£4.95), salmon and blue cheese pasta (£6.50), vegetarian pies (£7), braised lamb shank (£9.50), and locally raised steak (£11); cribbage and dominoes. There's a large garden with fine views. This is a nice place to stay, with comfortable carefully decorated simple bedrooms, but perhaps best to choose a room away from the road; decent breakfasts cooked by the landlord. They may have preferential fishing rates on the River Teign. *(Recommended by Richard and Margaret Peers, Barry Steele-Perkins, Gordon and Glynis Casey, Sally Jenkin)*

Free house ~ Licensee Simon Saunders ~ Real ale ~ Bar food (12-2.30(3.30 Sun), 6-9) ~ Restaurant ~ (01647) 433267 ~ Children in restaurant ~ Dogs allowed in bar ~ Live entertainment Sun evening ~ Open 11-11; 12-10.30 Sun ~ Bedrooms: /£70B

SIDBURY SY1595 Map 1

Hare & Hounds 🍺

3 miles N of Sidbury, at Putts Corner; A375 towards Honiton, crossroads with B3174

So much bigger inside than you could have guessed from outside, this very well run roadside pub is extremely popular at mealtimes – but as it is open all day, the crowds can be avoided. Despite its rambling size, the very friendly and efficient staff will make you welcome and serve you promptly. There are two good log fires (and rather unusual wood-framed leather sofas complete with pouffes) heavy beams and fresh flowers throughout, some oak panelling, plenty of tables with red leatherette or red plush-cushioned dining chairs, window seats and well used bar stools too; it's mostly carpeted, with bare boards and stripped stone walls at one softly lit no smoking end. At the opposite end of the pub, on the left, another big dining area has huge windows looking out over the garden. As you come in, the first thing you see is the good popular daily carvery counter, with a choice of joints, and enough turnover to keep up a continuous supply of fresh vegetables (lunchtime £7.85, evening £8.35, Sunday lunch £8.50). Other food includes sandwiches or baguettes (from £3.75), home-made soup (£3.95), home-made chicken liver pâté (£4.45), filled baked potatoes (from £4.45), home-made pie of the day (£7.25), home-made curry (£7.45), nut roast or ploughman's (£7.50), home-made lasagne (£7.75), local steaks (from £10.75), and daily specials. Well kept Branscombe Vale Summa That, Otter Ale and Bitter, and a guest beer tapped from the cask; side room with a big-screen sports TV. Alley skittles and piped music. The big garden, giving good valley views, has picnic-sets, a play area enlivened by a pensioned-off fire engine, and a small strolling flock of peafowl. More reports please. *(Recommended by Howard and Margaret Buchanan, Brian and Bett Cox, Joyce and Maurice Cottrell, Michael and Marion Buchanan)*

Free house ~ Licensee Peter Cairns ~ Real ale ~ Bar food (all day) ~ Restaurant ~ (01404) 41760 ~ Children in eating area of bar ~ Dogs allowed in bar ~ Live music Sun lunchtimes in marquee ~ Open 10-11.30; 11.30-11 Sun

SIDFORD SY1390 Map 1
Blue Ball ★ 🍺 🛏

A3052 just N of Sidmouth

This busy thatched, cob and flint inn has been in the same family for 94 years now. The low, partly-panelled and neatly kept lounge bar has heavy beams, upholstered wall benches, plush cushioned stools and windsor chairs, three open fires and lots of bric-a-brac; the family room and part of the restaurant are no smoking. Bar food includes sandwiches (from £2.75), home-made soup (£3.50), local sausages (£4.50), ploughman's (£5.50), omelettes (£6.25), home-made vegetarian chilli (£7.25), steak in ale pudding (£8.50), fresh salmon fillet with lime, chilli and ginger dressing (£8.95), steaks (from £9.95), and daily specials. Bass, Flowers IPA, Greene King Old Speckled Hen, Otter Ale and a guest such as Wadworths JCB on handpump, kept well in a temperature-controlled cellar, summer Pimms and winter mulled wine. A plainer public bar has darts, dominoes, cribbage and a fruit machine; piped music. Tables on a terrace look out over a colourful front flower garden, and there are more seats on a bigger back lawn – as well as in a covered area next to the barbecue; see-saw and play house for children. Readers have enjoyed staying here. The large car park is across a very busy road. (*Recommended by Barry and Anne, Mr and Mrs P B Berry, KC, Warham St Leger-Harris, Mr and Mrs W D Borthwick, Alan and Paula McCully, Joyce and Maurice Cottrell, David and Julie Glover, Dennis Jenkin, Dr and Mrs M E Wilson, Nick Lawless, Mark Flynn, W K Wood, Colin Morgan, Gordon Prince, Irene and Ray Atkin, John and Jane Hayter*)

Punch ~ Lease Roger Newton ~ Real ale ~ Bar food (11-2, 6.30-9.30 but they also offer breakfast between 8 and 10am) ~ Restaurant ~ (01395) 514062 ~ Children in restaurant ~ Dogs allowed in bar ~ Occasional live entertainment Fri evening ~ Open 11-11; 12-10.30 Sun ~ Bedrooms: £30(£45B)/£50(£75B)

SLAPTON SX8244 Map 1
Tower ★ 🍴

Signposted off A379 Dartmouth—Kingsbridge

The picnic-sets on the neatly kept lawn in the pretty garden behind this fine old place are overlooked by the ivy-covered ruin of a 14th-c chantry. Inside, the low-ceilinged beamed bar has armchairs, low-backed settles and scrubbed oak tables on the flagstones or bare boards, open log fires, and well kept Adnams Best, Badger Tanglefoot and St Austell Tribute on handpump; several wines by the glass. At lunchtime, the popular food includes home-made soup (£3.95), sandwiches (from £4.50; hot bacon and brie with redcurrant mayonnaise £5.25), chicken liver and raspberry terrine with a bacon and pine nut salad (£5.95), antipasti (£6.95; large one to share £10.95), trio of local sausages with rich gravy (£8.95), beef in ale pie (£9.45), roasted butternut squash, spinach, sun-dried tomato and goats cheese risotto with red pepper coulis (£9.95), and red wine and plum braised lamb shank with horseradish creamed potatoes (£12.50); evening choices such as thai-style fishcakes with sweet chilli jam or crispy fried duck confit on caramelised vermicelli with spring onion, cucumber and plum sauce (£5.95), citrus, chilli and herb marinated scallop and king prawn kebab (£6.95), chicken supreme stuffed with mozzarella, sun-dried tomato and basil (£12.95), sirloin steak (£13.50), and seared venison steak with cranberry, port and ginger sauce or whole lemon and thyme roasted bass with asparagus fried rice and tomato and basil sauce (£14.95); piped music. The lane up to the pub is very narrow and parking can be pretty tricky. We would be grateful for views on the bedrooms here, which we would expect to be good. (*Recommended by Mr and Mrs J Curtis, Roger Wain-Heapy, Brian Kneale, Lynda and Trevor Smith, Brian and Bett Cox, Alice Harper, David Eberlin, Brian Root, Geoffrey and Karen Berrill, DRH and KLH, BOB, Richard and Margaret Peers, the Didler,*)

Marguerite Pointer, Richard and Anne Ansell, Nick Lawless, Ann Holdsworth, Lizzie Parker-Clarke, Mark Bramley, Mike Ambrose, Chris and Helena Cooke)

Free house ~ Licensees Annette and Andrew Hammett ~ Real ale ~ Bar food ~ Restaurant ~ (01548) 580216 ~ Children in eating area of bar and restaurant ~ Dogs welcome ~ Open 12-2.30, 6-11; 12-3, 7-10.30 Sun; closed Sun evening and Mon in winter ~ Bedrooms: £40S/£60S

STAVERTON SX7964 Map 1
Sea Trout ♀
Village signposted from A384 NW of Totnes

Just a few hundred yards from the River Dart, this friendly old village pub has a neatly kept rambling beamed lounge bar with a cheerful mix of locals and visitors. There are also sea trout and salmon flies and stuffed fish on the walls, cushioned settles and stools, and a stag's head above the fireplace; the main bar has low banquettes, soft lighting and an open fire, and there's also a public bar with darts, pool, fruit machine, TV, shove-ha'penny and a juke box. Well liked bar food includes lunchtime sandwiches, soup with home-made bread (£3.75), chicken caesar salad or plaice goujons with home-made tartare sauce (£5.25), smoked duck breast with gooseberry and elderflower compote (£5.50), spicy five bean cassoulet with chestnuts (£8.50), 10oz gammon steak with a honey and grain mustard sauce, steak and Guinness pie or lambs liver and bacon (£8.95), chicken breast stuffed with mozzarella and chorizo on mediterranean vegetables (£9.95), whole brixham plaice (£11.95), steaks (from £12.95), daily specials, and puddings such as apple and wild berry crumble or dark chocolate mousse (£4.50). The whole pub apart from one bar is no smoking. Well kept Palmers IPA, Copper and Gold on handpump, a dozen wines by the glass (the white is on ice on the counter for customers to try first), quite a few whiskies, and farm cider; efficient, helpful staff. There are seats under parasols on the attractive paved back garden. A station for the South Devon Steam Railway is not too far away. *(Recommended by Dennis Jenkin, Joyce and Maurice Cottrell, Simon Rodway, the Didler, Brian and Bett Cox, E B Ireland, Mrs A P Lee, Tony Baldwin, Henry and Fiona Dryden)*

Palmers ~ Tenants Nicholas and Nicola Brookland ~ Real ale ~ Bar food ~ Restaurant ~ (01803) 762274 ~ Children in eating area of bar and restaurant ~ Dogs allowed in bar and bedrooms ~ Open 11-4, 6-11; 12-4, 7-10.30 Sun; closed evenings 25 and 26 Dec ~ Bedrooms: £49.50B/£64B

STOCKLAND ST2404 Map 1
Kings Arms 🍴 ♀ 🛏
Village signposted from A30 Honiton—Chard; and also, at every turning, from N end of Honiton High Street

'As good as ever' is a phrase used by many of our readers to describe this spotlessly kept 16th-c inn. It's a friendly, welcoming place with a good mix of customers in the various bars, and is a pleasant place to stay, too. The dark beamed, elegant Cotley Bar has solid refectory tables and settles, attractive landscapes, a medieval oak screen (which divides the room into two), and a great stone fireplace across almost the whole width of one end; the cosy no smoking restaurant has a huge inglenook fireplace and bread oven. Enjoyable bar food is served at lunchtime only (not Sunday): sandwiches (from £2.50), home-made soup (£3), omelettes (from £4), duck liver pâté (£5), ploughman's (£5.50), various pasta dishes (small £4.50, large £7.50), sausage and mash with onion gravy (£6.50), curries (from £7.50), and daily specials. In the evening, only the restaurant menu is available and diners are invited to the Cotley Bar to have the menu explained in full detail. Well kept Exmoor Ale, O'Hanlons Fire Fly and Yellowhammer, and Otter Ale on handpump, over 40 malt whiskies (including island and west coast ones; large spirit measures), a comprehensive wine list, and farm ciders. At the back, a flagstoned bar has cushioned benches and stools around heavy wooden tables, and leads on to a carpeted darts area, another room with dark beige plush armchairs and settees (and a fruit machine), and a neat ten-pin skittle alley; TV, and quiet mainly classical piped music. There are tables under cocktail parasols on the terrace in front of the white-faced thatched pub and a lawn enclosed by trees and shrubs. *(Recommended by Dr and Mrs T E Hothersall, Mrs Angela McArt, KN-R, Martin and Karen Wake, Mike and Heather Watson, Andrew Shore, Maria Williams, Mr and Mrs W Mills, Anthony Barnes, Bob and Margaret Holder, Brian and Bett Cox, MLR, Richard and Margaret Peers, Comus and Sarah Elliott, David and Elizabeth Briggs, Alan Sadler, Michael B Griffith, Mike and Mary Carter, Dr and Mrs R Booth, Pat and Robert Watt, Derek and Heather Manning, Chris Bell)*

Free house ~ Licensees Heinz Kiefer and Paul Diviani ~ Real ale ~ Bar food ~ Restaurant ~ (01404) 881361 ~ Children welcome ~ Dogs allowed in bar ~ Live music Sat and Sun ~ Open 12-3, 6.30-11; closed 25 Dec ~ Bedrooms: £45B/£70B

STOKE FLEMING SX8648 Map 1

Green Dragon ♀
Church Road

At its best when the friendly landlord, Peter Crowther, is at the helm here (he is a long-distance yachtsman), this well liked pub has cuttings about him, maps of his races, and accounts of his sinking 800 miles out in the Atlantic. The main part of the flagstoned and beamed bar has two small settles, bay window seats and stools, boat pictures, and maybe Maia the burmese cat or Rhea the german shepherd; down on the right is a wooden-floored snug with throws and cushions on sofas and armchairs, a few books (50p to RNLI), adult board games, and a grandfather clock. Down some steps is the no smoking Mess Deck restaurant with an open winter fire, and old charts and lots of ensigns and flags; piped music, darts, shove-ha'penny, cribbage and dominoes. Enjoyable bar food includes lunchtime burgers (made by a local butcher, from £2.50) and filled baguettes (from £4; hand-picked crab when available £5), as well as devilled mushrooms topped with stilton (£4), crab cakes (£4.50), smoked gravadlax and kiln-roasted salmon with lemon crème fraîche or pasta with various sauces (£5), curry of the day or vegetarian sausages (£6), spicy venison and pork kofta with lemon and basil couscous, or fish, or steak in ale pies (£6.50), and daily specials. Well kept Bass, Flowers IPA, Otter Ale and Wadworths 6X on handpump (all except Bass kept under light blanket pressure), big glasses of good house wines, Addlestone's cider, and a decent range of spirits; you can take the beer away with you. Some seats outside and outdoor heaters on the front terrace under a suspended sail. The church opposite has an interesting tall tower. Parking can be tricky. *(Recommended by Roger Wain-Heapy, OPUS, Marguerite Pointer, D J Elliott, E B Ireland, George Atkinson)*

Heavitree ~ Tenants Peter and Alix Crowther ~ Real ale ~ Bar food (12-2.30, 6.30-9) ~ Restaurant ~ (01803) 770238 ~ Children in eating area of bar and in restaurant ~ Dogs allowed in bar ~ Open 11-3, 5.30-11; 12-3, 6.30-10.30 Sun

STOKE GABRIEL SX8457 Map 1

Church House
Village signposted from A385 just W of junction with A3022, in Collaton St Mary; can also be reached from nearer Totnes

There's always a good mix of cheerful customers in this friendly old local. The lounge bar has an exceptionally fine medieval beam-and-plank ceiling, as well as a black oak partition wall, window seats cut into the thick butter-coloured walls, decorative plates and vases of flowers on a dresser, and a huge fireplace still used in winter to cook the stew; darts. The mummified cat in a case, probably about 200 years old, was found during restoration of the roof space in the verger's cottage three doors up the lane – one of a handful found in the West Country and believed to have been a talisman against evil spirits. Straightforward, good value bar food includes home-made soup (£2.95), a big choice of sandwiches and toasties (from £2.95; ham, cheese, pineapple and onion toastie £3.95), filled baked potatoes (from £3.95), ploughman's (from £4.95), steak and kidney pie, turkey curry or stilton and leek bake (£6.95), and puddings (£3.75). Well kept Bass, Hancocks HB and Worthington Best on handpump, and 20 malt whiskies. Euchre in the little public locals' bar. There are picnic-sets on the little terrace in front of the building. No children inside. The church is very pretty, and relations with the Church of England and this pub go back a long way – witness the priest hole, dating from the Reformation, visible from outside. *(Recommended by Dr and Mrs A K Clarke, H Frank Smith, M Sage, Sheila Newbury, Alan and Paula McCully)*

Free house ~ Licensee T G Patch ~ Real ale ~ Bar food ~ No credit cards ~ (01803) 782384 ~ Dogs welcome ~ Open 11-11; 12-3.30, 7-11 Sun; 11-3, 6-11 in winter

STRETE SX8446 Map 1
Kings Arms 🍴 ♀
A379 SW of Dartmouth – car park is S of pub

For lovers of fish, this bustling, family run pub is just the place to head for. Mr Dawson has been passionate about fish cooking since he was a boy and a few years ago won our Fish Pub of the Year for the Victory in St Mawes, Cornwall. It's very pretty outside with wrought-iron work and a canopied upper balcony, and there's a back terrace and garden with views over Start Bay. Inside, the L-shaped bar has country kitchen chairs and tables, some comfortable brocaded dining chairs, very nice fish prints on the dark salmon pink walls, and bar stools by the attractively carved oak bar counter where the chatty locals gather. Well kept Adnams and Otter Ale on handpump, 15 wines by the glass (including sweet ones) from a carefully chosen list, a dozen malt whiskies, and local Heron Valley cider; piped classical music. Up some stairs is the little no smoking restaurant decorated in cool blue/green colours with dark green padded plush and pale wood chairs around wooden tables. Using local and regional produce and baking their own breads, brioche, oatcakes and biscuits, the menu is the same throughout. From the light bar menu there might be provençale fish soup, rouille and croûtons (£5.50), fried soft herring roes on green peppercorn toast or grilled goats cheese salad, roasted baby tomatoes and fresh pesto (£6.25), cod or plaice and chips (£6.95; mushy peas 60p extra), and treacle glazed ham, bubble and squeak, poached egg and home-made chutney (£8.95); also, ham hock and pigeon breast terrine with pistachio nuts and pickled baby beetroot (£6.25), escabeche of brixham mackerel with a tart rhubarb and ginger jelly (£6.75), aubergine slices with tomato sauce and spicy yoghurt raita (£6.95), whole local crab (£14.50; on our evening visit we ate the biggest crab we had ever seen), grilled fillet of sea bream with crispy pancetta, vanilla, white rum, apple and green peppercorn syrup (£14.95), roast rack of organic spring lamb on celeriac mash, truffled green beans and a port and rosemary jus (£16.50), and puddings such as chocolate marquise, glazed lemon tart or sticky toffee pudding (from £5.50). The pub is on the South West Coastal Path. *(Recommended by DM, Charles Moore, Roger Wain-Heapy)*

Heavitree ~ Tenant Rob Dawson ~ Real ale ~ Bar food ~ Restaurant ~ (01803) 770377 ~ Children in eating area of bar and restaurant ~ Dogs allowed in bar ~ Open 11.30-11; 12-10.30 Sun

TOPSHAM SX9688 Map 1
Bridge Inn 🍺
2¼ miles from M5 junction 30: Topsham signposted from exit roundabout; in Topsham follow signpost (A376) Exmouth on the Elmgrove Road, into Bridge Hill

The utterly old-fashioned layout and character of this 16th-c ex-maltings remains a firm favourite with many of our readers. It's run by the fifth generation of the same family and you can be quite sure of a genuinely warm welcome from the helpful and friendly licensee. There are fine old traditional furnishings (true country workmanship) in the little lounge partitioned off from the inner corridor by a high-backed settle; log fire, and a bigger lower room (the old malthouse) is open at busy times. The cosy regulars' inner sanctum keeps up to ten real ales tapped from the cask: Adnams Broadside, Blackawton Peninsula, Branscombe Vale Branoc and

Summa That, Exe Valley Spring Beer, Moor Old Freddy Walker, O'Hanlons Yellowhammer or Royal Oak, Otter Ale, Teignworthy Old Moggie or Maltsters, and Topsham Ferryman. Local farm cider and elderberry and gooseberry wines; friendly service. Simple, tasty bar food such as pasties (£2.50), sandwiches (from £3.50; the ham is particularly good), and various ploughman's (from £5.50); the local hand-fried crisps are excellent. No noisy music or machines – just a chatty, relaxed atmosphere. The pub is no smoking at lunchtime and only one room is available for smokers in the evening. Outside, riverside picnic-sets overlook the weir. *(Recommended by Phil and Sally Gorton, David Crook, OPUS, Mark and Heather Williamson, MLR, the Didler, Mrs C Lintott, Pete Baker, Dr and Mrs M E Wilson, Roger and Jenny Huggins, Michael Rowse, Mike Gorton, John and Fiona McIlwain, John and Jane Hayter)*

Free house ~ Licensee Mrs C Cheffers-Heard ~ Real ale ~ Bar food (not evenings) ~ No credit cards ~ (01392) 873862 ~ Children in room without bar ~ Dogs allowed in bar ~ Occasional live music ~ Open 12-2, 6(7 Sun)-10.30(11 Fri/Sat)

TORBRYAN SX8266 Map 1
Old Church House

Most easily reached from A381 Newton Abbot—Totnes via Ipplepen

Friendly new licensees – who have run quite a few successful inns and hotels in the West Country – have taken over this partly thatched, Grade II* listed early 15th-c inn. Bustling and neatly kept, the bar on the right of the door is particularly attractive, and has benches built into the fine old panelling as well as a cushioned high-backed settle and leather-backed small seats around its big log fire. On the left there are a series of comfortable and discreetly lit lounges, one with a splendid deep Tudor inglenook fireplace with a side bread oven. The restaurant is no smoking. Enjoyable bar food now includes sandwiches (from £3.75), home-made soup (£3.95), devilled whitebait (£5.25), ploughman's (from £5.95), a roast of the day, vegetable curry or pork fillet in barbecue sauce (all £9.95), deep-fried fillet of haddock with tartare sauce (£10.95), and rack of lamb or half a honey-roast duck with orange and black cherry sauce (£14.95). Well kept Skinners Betty Stogs and Cornish Knocker and a guest beer on handpump, 25 malt whiskies and farm cider. The pub once housed the workmen restoring the next-door part-Saxon church with its battlemented Norman tower. Plenty of nearby walks. *(Recommended by E B Ireland, Alan and Paula McCully, Ann and Bob Westbrook, Mr and Mrs T A Watson, Emma Kingdon, J D O Carter)*

Free house ~ Licensees Kane and Carolynne Clarke ~ Real ale ~ Bar food ~ Restaurant ~ (01803) 812372 ~ Children in eating area of bar and restaurant ~ Dogs allowed in bar ~ Open 11-11; 12-10.30 Sun ~ Bedrooms: £54B/£69B

TORCROSS SX8241 Map 1
Start Bay

A379 S of Dartmouth

Although this extremely popular dining pub is always packed (and there are often queues outside before it opens), the service is so speedy and efficient and the fish dishes so fresh and unpretentious, that no one really seems to mind. Local fishermen work off the beach right in front of the pub and deliver all kinds of fish, a local crabber drops the crabs at the back door, and the landlord enjoys catching plaice, scallops and bass: cod or haddock (medium £5.40; large £7.20; jumbo £9.20), whole lemon sole (from £6.95), skate wing in batter (£7.90), whole dover sole (in four sizes from £8.50), brill (from £8.90), and whole bass (small £9.50; medium £10.50; large £11.50). Other food includes sandwiches (from £2.95), ploughman's (from £4.75), vegetable lasagne (£5.95), gammon and pineapple (£7.50), steaks (from £8.90), and children's meals (£3.95); they do warn of delays at peak times. Well kept Bass and Flowers Original or Otter Ale on handpump, and maybe Heron Valley cider and fresh apple juice, and local wine from the Sharpham Estate. The unassuming main bar is very much set out for eating with wheelback chairs around plenty of dark tables or (round a corner) back-to-back settles forming booths; there are some photographs of storms buffeting the pub and country pictures on its cream walls, and a winter coal fire; a small chatty drinking area by the counter has a brass ship's clock and barometer. The winter games room has pool and darts; there's more booth seating in a no smoking family room with sailing boat pictures. There are seats (highly prized) out on the terrace overlooking the three-mile pebble beach, and the freshwater wildlife lagoon of Slapton Ley is just behind the pub. *(Recommended by Brian and Bett Cox, Brian Kneale, Jack Clark, Keith and Margaret Kettell, Mrs Sylvia Elcoate, Michael Porter, Cathryn and Richard Hicks, Geoff Calcott, Sheila Newbury, Fred and Lorraine Gill, Sue Demont, Tim Barrow)*

Whitbreads ~ Tenant Paul Stubbs ~ Real ale ~ Bar food (11.30-2, 6-10; they may serve some food through summer afternoons) ~ (01548) 580553 ~ Children in family room ~ Dogs allowed in bar ~ Open 11.30-11; 12-10.30 Sun; 11.30(12 Sun)-2.30, 6-11(10.30 Sun) in winter

WIDECOMBE SX7276 Map 1
Rugglestone
Village at end of B3387; pub just S – turn left at church and NT church house, OS Sheet 191 map reference 720765

Often very busy – it's just up the road from the bustling tourist village – this unspoilt local has a good mix of both regulars and visitors. The small bar has a strong rural atmosphere, just four small tables, a few window and wall seats, a one-person pew built into the corner by the nice old stone fireplace, and a rudimentary bar counter dispensing well kept Butcombe Bitter and St Austell Dartmoor Best tapped from the cask; local farm cider and a decent little wine list. The room on the right is a bit bigger and lighter-feeling with another stone fireplace, beamed ceiling, stripped pine tables, and a built-in wall bench. There's also a little no smoking room which is used for dining. Well liked bar food includes filled baked potatoes (from £3.95), home-made soup (£3.50), ploughman's (£6.95), and daily specials such as a vegetarian choice (from £4.40), steak and kidney pie (£6.95), and good liver and bacon casserole; service can slow down at peak times. Outside across the little moorland stream is a field with lots of picnic-sets. Tables and chairs in the garden. *(Recommended by Patrick and Phillipa Vickery, Mike Gorton, Steve and Liz Tilley, JHW, Phil and Sally Gorton, the Didler, Andrea Rampley, Michael Weston, Michael and Judy Buckley, Ann and Bob Westbrook)*

Free house ~ Licensees Rod and Diane Williams ~ Real ale ~ Bar food ~ No credit cards ~ (01364) 621327 ~ Children in dining room and second bar ~ Dogs welcome ~ Open 11.30-3.30ish(4 Sat), 6.30-11; 12-3.30, 6.30-10.30 Sun

WINKLEIGH SS6308 Map 1
Kings Arms
Village signposted off B3220 Crediton—Torrington; Fore Street

On the edge of the little village square, this bustling pub is very well run by its friendly and efficient licensees. There's an attractive beamed main bar with a good mix of customers, some old-fashioned built-in wall settles, scrubbed pine tables and benches on the flagstones, and a woodburning stove in a cavernous fireplace; another woodburning stove separates the bar from the dining rooms (one is no smoking). Popular bar food includes burgers (from £2.95), home-made soup (£3.50), sandwiches and baguettes (from £3.75; steak and onion £5.50), chicken liver and brandy pâté (£3.75), ploughman's (£5.95), filled baked potatoes or omelettes (from £5.95), a trio of sausages and eggs (£6.25), vegetable bolognese (£7.50), fish and chips or curry of the day (£7.95), steak and kidney parcel or chicken breast filled with brie and spinach (£9.50), steaks (from £10.75), and puddings such as marmalade bread and butter pudding, raspberry and mascarpone cheesecake or rich chocolate mousse (£3.75). Well kept Butcombe Bitter, Otter Bitter and Skinners Cornish Knocker on handpump, local cider, and decent wines; darts, cribbage, dominoes, shove-ha'penny and table skittles. There are seats out in the garden. *(Recommended by Mark Flynn, Rod Stoneman, D P and M A Miles)*

Enterprise ~ Lease Chris Guy and Julia Franklin ~ Real ale ~ Bar food (all day) ~ Restaurant
~ (01837) 83384 ~ Children welcome ~ Dogs welcome ~ Open 11-11; 12-10.30 Sun

WONSON SX6790 Map 1

Northmore Arms ♀ ◀

A30 at Merrymeet roundabout, take first left on old A30, through Whiddon Down; new
roundabout and take left on to A382; then right down lane signposted
Throwleigh/Gidleigh. Continue down lane over hump-back bridge; turn left to Wonson;
OS Sheet 191 map reference 674903

'Almost like visiting a long lost friend' is how one reader described this secluded
cottage. It does have a particularly easy atmosphere, and the two small connected
beamed rooms – modest and informal but civilised – have wall settles, up to three
tables in each room, and an open fire and woodburning stove; the granite stone
walls are hung with some attractive photographs. Well kept Adnams Broadside,
Cotleigh Tawny and Exe Valley Dobs tapped from the cask, and good house wines;
darts, cribbage and dominoes. Simple but reasonably priced food includes
sandwiches (from £1.75; toasties from £2.25), garlic mushrooms or pâté (£2.65),
ploughman's (£4.25), filled baked potatoes (from £4.25), ham and egg (£4.75),
feta, spinach and mushroom pie or liver and onions (£5.50), roast lamb with garlic
potatoes or Tuesday curries (£6.95), lamb shank in rosemary and red wine (£7.95),
and steak with stilton or peppercorn sauces (£8.25). The ladies' lavatory is up steep
steps. The sloping rustic and peaceful garden has several tables and seats; excellent
walking from the pub (or to it, perhaps from Chagford or Gidleigh Park). The car
park extension is unobtrusive but very welcome. Castle Drogo is close by.
*(Recommended by JHW, Anthony Longden, Andrea Rampley, the Didler, Mike Gorton,
Gordon Briggs, Ann Holdsworth)*

Free house ~ Licensee Mrs Mo Miles ~ Real ale ~ Bar food (all day Mon-Sat; 12-2.30, 7-9
Sun) ~ (01647) 231428 ~ Children in eating area of bar ~ Dogs allowed in bar ~ Open
11-11; 12-10.30 Sun ~ Bedrooms: /£40

WOODBURY SALTERTON SY0189 Map 1

Diggers Rest

3½ miles from M5 junction 30: A3052 towards Sidmouth, village signposted on right
about ½ mile after Clyst St Mary; also signposted from B3179 SE of Exeter

The friendly licensees in this thatched village pub are working hard to try and keep
a pubby atmosphere and a welcome for locals, despite the emphasis on the food.
The bars have antique furniture, local art on the walls, and Butcombe Bitter, Fullers
London Pride and Otter Bitter and Ale on handpump, and up to 14 wines by the
glass; there's a cosy seating area by an open fire with an extra large sofa and
armchair. Bar food, using local produce where possible, includes home-made soup
(£4.25), pheasant terrine (£5.50), home-made hummous and tzatziki with olives,
crudités and chargrilled pitta bread (£5.85), lunchtime ploughman's or home-
cooked ham and free-range egg (£6.95), pasta in a mushroom, garlic, parmesan and
cream sauce with fresh spinach (£7.95), fresh haddock and herb fishcakes with
crème fraîche and dill tartare sauce or local sausages and onion gravy (£8.75), thai
chicken curry or steak and kidney pie (£8.95), local steaks (from £11.75), and daily
specials. You may smoke only in the public bar; piped music. Contemporary garden
furniture under canvas parasols in the terraced garden, and lovely countryside
views. *(Recommended by Glenn and Gillian Miller, Brenda and Stuart Naylor, Dr and
Mrs M E Wilson, Joyce and Maurice Cottrell, Richard and Margaret Peers, Mike Gorton,
Diana Brumfit, John and Vivienne Rice, John and Sarah Perry, M and GR, David Hall,
Sue and Alex, Geoffrey Medcalf, Phil and Jane Hodson)*

Free house ~ Licensee Stephen Rushton ~ Real ale ~ Bar food (12-2.30, 6.30-9.30) ~
Restaurant ~ (01395) 232375 ~ Children welcome ~ Dogs allowed in bar ~ Open 11-3,
6-11; 11-11 Sat; 12-10.30 Sun

If we know a pub does summer barbecues, we say so.

WOODLAND SX7968 Map 1 🏠

Rising Sun ♀ 🛏

Village signposted off A38 just NE of Ashburton – then keep eyes peeled for Rising Sun signposts (which may be hidden in the hedges); pub N of village itself, near Combe Cross

Well worth the detour from the A38, this bustling pub is a friendly place with popular, enjoyable food. There's an expanse of softly lit red plush button-back banquettes and matching studded chairs, partly divided by wooden banister rails, masonry pillars and the odd high-backed settle. A forest of beams is hung with thousands of old doorkeys, and a nice part by the log fire has shelves of plates and books, and old pictures above the fireplace. Well kept Princetown Jail Ale, and a guest from a local brewery like Blackdown on handpump, 12 wines by the glass, and Luscombe cider; cheerful service. The no smoking family area has various toys (and a collection of cookery books). Bar food, using local meat and fish, includes home-made soup (£3.75), sandwiches (from £4.50), ham and pork terrine with apple jelly or leek, walnut and Devon Blue cheese tart (£4.95), home-made pies such as lamb with lemon and honey or steak in ale or tempura of vegetables with noodles and a sweet and sour dipping sauce (£7.95), honey roast pork sausages with roast onion mash (£8.95), breast of chicken with bacon and red wine risotto or two dabs roasted with lemon and butter (£11.50), sirloin steak with béarnaise sauce (£13.95), and home-made puddings like sticky toffee pudding with butterscotch sauce or chocolate marquise (£3.80). The dining area is no smoking. There are some picnic-sets (and some new seats) in the spacious garden which has a play area including a redundant tractor. They've added four new bedrooms this year. *(Recommended by E B Ireland, Brian and Bett Cox, D S and J M Jackson, David M Cundy, John and Marion Tyrie, John and Vivienne Rice, Melanie Ginger, S P Watkin, P A Taylor)*

Free house ~ Licensee Heather Humphreys ~ Real ale ~ Bar food (12-2.15(3 Sun), 6(7 Sun)-9.15; not Mon except bank hols) ~ Restaurant ~ (01364) 652544 ~ Children in restaurant and family room ~ Dogs allowed in bar ~ Open 11.45-3, 6-11; 12-3, 7-10.30 Sun; closed Mon (except bank hols) ~ Bedrooms: £38B/£60B

LUCKY DIP

Besides the fully inspected pubs, you might like to try these Lucky Dips recommended to us and described by readers (if you do, please send us reports: www.goodguides.co.uk).

APPLEDORE [SS4630]
☆ *Beaver* [Irsha St]: Pretty estuary views from raised area in thriving unpretentious harbourside pub, good value food esp fresh local fish and good puddings, friendly staff, well kept Bass and St Austell or other local ales, farm cider, decent house wines, great range of whiskies; pool in smaller games room; children really welcome, disabled access, tables on sheltered terrace *(Paul and Ursula Randall, Peter and Margaret Glenister, Mark Flynn)*
Coach & Horses [Market St]: Compact and cosy old three-room local in picturesque cobbled street just off quay, cheap food, well kept beer, open fire; dogs welcome, simple bedrooms *(Michael and Ann Cole)*
☆ *Royal George* [Irsha St]: Simple but good fresh food inc local fish in no smoking dining room with superb estuary views, well kept ales, decent wines, good friendly service, cosy unspoilt front bar (dogs allowed), attractive pictures (sensitive souls should steer clear of the postcards in the gents'), fresh flowers; disabled access, picnic-sets outside, picturesque

street sloping to sea *(Michael and Ann Cole, Rod Stoneman)*
ASHWATER [SX3895]
Village Inn: Roomy slate-floored bar, welcoming atmosphere, courteous service, wide choice of above-average generous food from sandwiches and baked potatoes up, realistic prices, well kept Exmoor and a guest beer, welcoming licensees, no smoking dining room, pool room, no music or machines, venerable grape vine in conservatory; tables on interestingly planted terrace *(Mrs S M Heard)*
AVETON GIFFORD [SX6947]
Fishermans Rest [Fore St]: Enjoyable food from good sandwiches to succulent fresh fish in bar and no smoking restaurant, happily cater for special needs; sensible prices, welcoming service *(David and Elizabeth Briggs, Ann and Bob Westbrook)*
AVONWICK [SX7158]
☆ *Avon* [off A38 at W end of South Brent bypass]: Comfortable fairly modern dining pub under new French chef/landlord, light and airy redecoration, open fire brought back into

action, good food in sensible helpings in restaurant and bar, some interesting specials, friendly smart staff, well kept ales such as Badger Best and Teignworthy, decent wine choice; picnic-sets in meadow by River Avon, adventure playground *(John Evans, LYM, John Riddell)*

AXMOUTH [SY2591]

Harbour Inn [B3172 Seaton—Axminster]: Prettily set thatched local, beams, flagstones, traditional settles and big log fires, well kept Flowers IPA and Original, pool and big simple summer family bar, food from sandwiches up, cheerful if not always speedy service, friendly cats; children in eating area, disabled access and facilities, tables in the neat back flower garden, cl winter Sun evenings *(Alain and Rose Foote, Mr and Mrs W Mills, LYM, Mrs C Lintott, Mrs Sylvia Elcoate)*

☆ *Ship* [Church St]: Comfortable, civilised and very welcoming, wide choice of attractively priced food from crab sandwiches through plenty of good fresh local fish and other tasty food using their own herbs to luscious puddings, well kept Bass and Otter, good wines and coffee, lots of embroidered folk dolls, one room devoted to Guinness memorabilia, tables (may be candlelit) in garden with long-established owl rescue home and a distant estuary view *(Michael Doswell, LYM, Perry Mills, Meg and Colin Hamilton)*

BAMPTON [SS9520]

☆ *Exeter Inn* [A396 some way S, at B3227 roundabout]: Long low stone-built roadside pub under steep hill overlooking River Exe, several friendly and comfortable linked rooms, mainly flagstoned, huge choice of good reasonably priced food inc local crab and fish, large pleasant carvery restaurant, well kept Cotleigh Tawny and Exmoor Ale and Gold tapped from the cask, quick service, early coffee, log fire, daily papers, no piped music; tables out in front, good value bedrooms with own bathrooms, open all day, fairly handy for Knightshayes Court *(BB, Peter and Audrey Dowsett, Jodie Phillips, Di and Mike Gillam)*

BANTHAM [SX6643]

☆ *Sloop* [off A379/B3197 NW of Kingsbridge]: Friendly 16th-c pub, recently gently refurbished but keeping character with black beams, flagstones and stripped stone, easy chairs in quieter side area, good food using local ingredients from sandwiches to enterprising specials, well kept ales such as Sutton Eddystone, good wines, woodburner, no smoking dining room (two evening sittings, 7 and 9), lots of (well behaved) children; dogs warmly welcomed, seats outside, bedrooms, plenty of surrounding walks *(Mr and Mrs J Curtis, Roger Wain-Heapy, Gordon Stevenson, David Eberlin, Lawrence Pearse, Norman and Sarah Keeping, LYM, Helen Sharpe, Lynda and Trevor Smith, Alan and Anne Driver, Ann and*

Bob Westbrook, W Taylor, Ian and Ruth Laurence, Geoff and Marianne Millin, Ian and Jane Irving, Martin and Sue Day)

BEER [ST2289]

Anchor [Fore St]: Sea-view dining pub with wide choice of food from baguettes and ciabattas to local and Brixham fish and massive mixed grill for two, Greene King IPA and Abbot and Otter, decent wines, genial management, prompt and friendly young staff, rambling open-plan layout with old local photographs, large no smoking eating area; sports TV, may be piped pop music, live Fri-Sun; reasonably priced bedrooms, lots of tables in garden opp, balcony harbour views, delightful seaside village – parking may not be easy *(Tony and Maggie Harwood, LYM, Ken Flawn, John Branston, Mary Kirman and Tim Jefferson, Neil and Lorna Mclaughlan)*

☆ *Barrel o' Beer* [Fore St]: Welcoming and comfortably straightforward family-run pub with surprisingly good generous food using fresh local organic ingredients from simple dishes to good interestingly cooked and served game, local fish and seafood (they cure and smoke their own), well kept Exe Valley Bitter and Devon Glory and Timothy Taylors Landlord, choice of ciders, cheerful efficient staff, log fire, very small no smoking back dining area; piped music; dogs welcome, open all day *(Alain and Rose Foote, Miss E M Ford, Martin and Jane Wright, Michael Doswell, Tony and Maggie Harwood, BB, Mrs L Wressel, Mike Gorton, Mike and Chris Higgins, Cynthia and Stephen Fisher)*

Dolphin [Fore St]: Open-plan local quite near sea, old-fashioned décor, oak panelling, nautical bric-a-brac and interesting nooks inc marvellous old distorting mirrors and antique boxing prints in corridors leading to back antique stalls, Bass and Cotleigh ales, decent wine, popular food from lunchtime sandwiches up; piped music, can be smoky, no credit cards; children and dogs welcome, one or two tables out by pavement, bedrooms *(Geoff Pidoux, Meg and Colin Hamilton, LYM, Barry and Anne, Ian and Joan Blackwell)*

BEESANDS [SX8140]

☆ *Cricket*: Friendly open-plan pub, really well run, in old-fashioned fishing village above a sandy beach (the parking's free); light and airy décor, interesting local photographs, enjoyable food inc good crab sandwiches and good choice of fresh local fish and shellfish, summer cream teas, well kept Bass and Fullers London Pride, local farm cider, decent wines, log fire, family room; unobtrusive piped music; dogs welcome, picnic-sets out by sea wall, bedrooms, at start of coast path to Hallsands and Start Point *(Mr and Mrs J Curtis, Mayur Shah, Roger Wain-Heapy, Matthew Shackle, Stephen Gutteridge, Mike and Shelley Woodroffe, Brian Root, BB, Fred and Lorraine Gill)*

BIDEFORD [SS4526]

Kings Arms [The Quay]: Cheerful old-fashioned 16th-c pub with Victorian harlequin floor tiles in alcovey front bar, reasonably priced usual food (not Fri/Sat evenings) from sandwiches to steaks, well kept Bass, Tetleys and four local ales, pleasant staff, back raised family area; piped music; pavement tables *(June and Robin Savage)*

BIGBURY [SX6647]

Royal Oak: Welcoming village pub with well kept Sharps Doom Bar, good atmosphere, friendly service, good restaurant *(E B Ireland)*

BISHOP'S TAWTON [SS5629]

☆ *Chichester Arms* [signed off A377 outside Barnstaple; East St]: After a ten-engine fire, restoration work on this friendly 15th-c cob and thatch pub started in June 2005; they hoped to reopen by Christmas and we look forward to that – it's been a nice place, with low bowed beams, large stone fireplace, old local photographs, plush banquettes, log fire, quick obliging service, well priced good generous food from home-made soup and sandwiches to fresh local fish, fine steaks and carvery (all meat from named local farms), well kept Dartmoor Best, Ind Coope Burton and Tetleys, decent wines, partly no smoking restaurant; children welcome, picnic-sets on front terrace and in back garden, open all day *(LYM, Mark Flynn, June and Robin Savage)*

BISHOPSTEIGNTON [SX9073]

Cockhaven Manor [Cockhaven Rd]: Friendly family and staff in 16th-c former manor, warm atmosphere, good range of well kept real ales and other drinks, food from bar snacks to bargain four-course Sun lunch; bedrooms *(B M Eldridge)*

BLACKAWTON [SX8050]

☆ *George* [signed off A3122 and A381]: Very welcoming two-bar family pub, enjoyable reasonably priced hearty food (not Mon lunchtime) inc fresh fish and some good specials, Teignworthy ales and a guest beer, good choice of belgian beers (early May and Aug beer festivals with live bands), woodburner in cosy end lounge, traditional games; children welcome, nice views from garden picnic-sets, cottagey bedrooms *(LYM, Marguerite Pointer, Howard and Lorna Lambert, Len Beattie, Brian Kneale)*

BLACKMOOR GATE [SS6443]

Old Station House [A39/A399]: Former station on redundant line interestingly converted into big family dining pub, wide choice of decent freshly made food from sandwiches and baguettes up inc takeaways, well kept ales, polite efficient service, carved pews, plush dining chairs, soft red lighting, lots of bric-a-brac, character no smoking area with grandfather clock; spacious games area with two well lit pool tables, darts, piped music; children allowed (small family room for under-5s), skittle alley, picnic-sets and play area in big garden with hens and good views, open all day *(CMW, JJW, BB)*

BOLBERRY [SX6939]

☆ *Port Light:* Alone on dramatic NT clifftop, bright, clean, spacious and busy, with superb picture-window views and conservatory, well kept ales such as Teignworthy Reel, friendly

efficient eager-to-please service, interesting memorabilia of its time as a radar station, decent lunchtime bar food, evening functions more as a restaurant; well behaved children and dogs welcome (they host dog wknds), picnic-sets on quiet terrace and in garden with splendid fenced play area; five bedrooms, nr fine beaches, right on the coast path *(Jack Clark, George Atkinson)*

BOVEY TRACEY [SX8178]

Cromwell Arms [Fore St]: Cheery and appealing old beamed local with reasonably priced generous food inc good value Sun lunch, welcoming staff, well kept well priced Marstons Pedigree and St Austell HSD, good wine choice, several areas with high-backed settles; piped music may obtrude; small terrace *(George Atkinson)*

BRAYFORD [SS7235]

☆ *Poltimore Arms* [Yarde Down; 3 miles towards Simonsbath]: Old-fashioned 17th-c yellow-painted two-bar local in isolated spot, cheerful obliging staff, enticing good value blackboard food inc good Sun roast, well kept Cotleigh Tawny and Exmoor tapped from the cask, basic traditional furnishings, fine woodburner in inglenook, interesting ornaments, two attractive restaurant areas (children allowed); picnic-sets in side garden, no dogs inside, has been cl winter lunchtimes *(LYM, Mark Flynn)*

BRENDON [SS7547]

☆ *Rockford Inn* [Lynton—Simonsbath rd, off B3223]: Unspoilt 17th-c inn well set for walkers (and fishermen) by East Lyn river, generous low-priced homely food from good proper sandwiches to fresh fish, cream teas (all day in summer), friendly staff, well kept Cotleigh Tawny and Barn Owl and St Austell HSD, good house wines, good choice of malt whiskies, farm cider, interesting layout, lots of local pictures, darts, pool, shove-ha'penny, cribbage, dominoes, restaurant; folk night every 3rd Sat; children in eating areas, quiet dogs on leads welcome (resident young springer), bedrooms, open all day summer, cl Sun evening and Mon out of season *(Gaynor Gregory, LYM, B M Eldridge, Dennis Jenkin)*

Staghunters: Hotel in idyllic setting with garden by East Lyn river, neat traditional bar with woodburner, generous popular food, well kept Wadworths 6X and Addlestone's cider, family room with pool table, restaurant; can get very busy; walkers and dogs welcome, good value bedrooms *(Gaynor Gregory, Lynda and Trevor Smith)*

BRIDESTOWE [SX5189]

☆ *White Hart* [Fore St (old A38, off A30/A386)]: Partly flagstoned beamed main bar, some nice old furnishings in lounge, freshly decorated panelled dining room, good value food inc good local ham and steaks, well kept ales such as Fullers London Pride, Rock and Sharps, decent wines, friendly helpful staff; informal streamside back garden, peaceful Dartmoor village, two comfortable bedrooms with own bathrooms *(Heather Roberts, Mrs Diane Smith)*

BRIXHAM [SX9255]
Blue Anchor [Fore St/King St]: Attractive
harbourside pub under new management, with
well kept Dartmoor Best, Greene King Abbot
and a guest such as Exmoor, banquettes and
plenty of nautical hardwear, cheerfully served
food from good value sandwiches to low-
priced hot meals in two small dining rooms –
one a former chapel, down some steps; no
children or credit cards, piped music, some
live; open all day *(Glenn and Gillian Miller,
Mike Turner, Kevin Blake)*
BROADHEMPSTON [SX8066]
☆ *Coppa Dolla*: Good ambitious food, also curry
nights and fine steaks, in comfortable and
welcoming beamed bar divided by sturdy
timber props, very reasonable prices, children's
helpings of all dishes, well kept ales such as
Bass, Dartmoor Best and Greene King Old
Speckled Hen, decent wines, cheery service, log
fires, pleasant upstairs restaurant; Sun quiz
night; well spaced picnic-sets in attractive
garden with country views, two apartments
(BB, Mr and Mrs S Smith)
BUCKFASTLEIGH [SX7466]
☆ *Dartbridge* [Totnes Rd, handy for A38]: Big
family pub prettily placed opp South Devon
Rly though just off busy main rd, enjoyable
generous food (all day at least in summer) inc
good crab sandwiches and choice of Sun
roasts, well kept Otter ales, good house wines,
cheerful efficient service even when busy;
reasonable disabled access, tables on neatly
kept front terrace, bedrooms, open all day
*(E B Ireland, John Evans, Dr D and
Mrs B Woods, Dr and Mrs A K Clarke,
Glenn and Gillian Miller, Tony Baldwin)*
BURGH ISLAND [SX6444]
☆ *Pilchard* [300 yds across tidal sands from
Bigbury-on-Sea; walk, or summer Tractor if
tide's in – unique bus on stilts]: Unbeatable
setting high above sea on tidal island with
unspoilt cliff walks, and now entirely no
smoking; lanterns, roaring log fire in back bar
and ancient beams and flagstones make for a
salty atmosphere despite the neat refurbishment;
Sharps, Thwaites Lancaster Bomber and an ale
brewed for the pub, friendly chatty staff, decent
food inc lunchtime baguettes, family room –
useful for trippers by day, friendly local
atmosphere at night; Sat evening barbecues,
some tables down by beach, open all day all
year *(David Eberlin, the Didler, Geoff Pidoux,
Neil and Beverley Gardner, LYM, Ian and
Ruth Laurence, Sue Demont, Tim Barrow,
George Atkinson)*
BUTTERLEIGH [SS9708]
☆ *Butterleigh Inn* [off A396 in Bickleigh]:
Appealing small-roomed country pub with nice
pictures, big fireplace, pine dining chairs
around country kitchen tables in one room,
attractive elm trestle tables and darts in another,
two no smoking areas (one a lunchtime family
room), Cotleigh and guest beers, attractive
gardens and up-to-date bedrooms; several
recent management changes, new licensees
arriving as this edition is printed – news of the
new regime please *(LYM)*

CHAGFORD [SX7087]
☆ *Ring o' Bells* [off A382 Moretonhampstead—
Whiddon Down]: Well run and welcoming
black-and-white medieval pub with appealing
oak-panelled bar, well kept Butcombe Bitter, St
Austell Dartmoor Best and Teignworthy Reel
Ale, Addlestone's cider, enjoyable bar food,
nice photographs, copper and brass, log-effect
fire, traditional games, small no smoking
candlelit dining room; dogs in bar, sunny
walled garden behind with seats on lawn,
bright clean bedrooms, good breakfast *(JMC,
LYM, J Poirrette, Sheila Newbury,
David Uren)*
CHALLACOMBE [SS6941]
☆ *Black Venus* [B3358 Blackmoor Gate—
Simonsbath]: Low-beamed 16th-c pub
reopened after renovation by friendly helpful
new owners, shortish choice of good varied
food from sandwiches and baguettes to
blackboard specials, two well kept changing
real ales, Thatcher's farm cider, pews and
comfortable chairs, woodburner and big open
fire, attractive big dining area; garden tables,
attractive countryside *(BB, P K Clark,
Merle Abbott)*
CHAWLEIGH [SS7112]
Earl of Portsmouth [B3042]: Current
chef/landlady doing good food using only local
meats and other produce and baking her own
bread, comfortable surroundings, friendly
landlord, good service, local real ales; children
welcome, skittle alley *(Nick)*
CHUDLEIGH [SX8679]
Bishop Lacey [Fore St, just off A38]: Quaint
partly 14th-c church house with good service,
well kept Branscombe Vale, Flowers IPA,
Fullers London Pride and a guest such as
Princetown Jail, some tapped from casks in
back bar, good strong coffee, two log fires,
good value food, no smoking dining room; live
bands in next-door offshoot; garden tables,
winter beer festival, bedrooms, open all day
(JDM, KM, the Didler)
Old Coaching House [Fore St]: Popular
flagstoned country pub with good value food
inc good curries and mixed grill in bar or
restaurant, well kept Greene King Abbot, Otter
and Teignworthy, friendly staff, local jazz Fri
(the Didler)
CHUDLEIGH KNIGHTON [SX8477]
☆ *Claycutters Arms* [just off A38 by B3344]:
Friendly and attractive 17th-c thatched two-
bar village pub with well kept ales such as
Fullers London Pride and a hefty Otter, home-
made food from good sandwiches and
ploughman's up, good service, stripped stone,
interesting nooks and crannies, pleasant
restaurant; dogs welcome, tables on side
terrace and in orchard *(LYM, David M Cundy,
Dennis Jenkin, E B Ireland)*
CHURCHSTOW [SX7145]
☆ *Church House* [A379 NW of Kingsbridge]:
Long character pub dating from 13th c, heavy
black beams, stripped stone, cushioned settles,
warm welcome, quickly served generous
sensibly priced food from sandwiches to mixed
grill and (Weds-Sat nights, Sun lunch) popular

carvery, well kept Bass and local ales, decent wines, back conservatory with floodlit well feature; well behaved children and dogs welcome, tables outside *(LYM, Ann and Bob Westbrook, Nick Lawless)*

CHURSTON FERRERS [SX9056]

☆ *Churston Court* [off A3022 S of Torquay; Church Rd]: Interesting converted manor house dating back to Saxon times in pretty spot next to ancient church; warren of largely no smoking candlelit rooms, plenty of beams, flagstones and open fires inc a massive inglenook, suits of armour, historic portraits, faded tapestries, long wooden tables, sofas, gilt-framed mirrors, Greene King Abbot, Princetown Dartmoor and Jail, huge carvery choice plus local fish; piped classical music; children allowed, lots of tables in attractive walled lawn, quirky individual bedrooms, good walks nearby, open all day *(John and Glenys Wheeler, LYM, David M Cundy, Alan and Paula McCully, Kevin Blake, Emma Kingdon)*

CLYST HONITON [SX9893]

Black Horse [Redhayes]: Enjoyable food inc good value lunchtime specials, good friendly service *(DAV)*

CLYST ST MARY [SX9791]

☆ *Half Moon* [under a mile from M5 junction 30 via A376]: Attractive and genuine old pub next to disused multi-arched bridge (Devon's oldest) over Clyst, well kept Bass, Fullers London Pride and Otter, enjoyable generous home-made food, cheerful and attentive new landlord, friendly unpretentious local atmosphere, red plush seating, log fire; wheelchair access, bedrooms *(Dr and Mrs M E Wilson)*

COLATON RALEIGH [SY0787]

Otter [A376 Newton Poppleford—Budleigh Salterton]: Friendly new management doing good choice of enjoyable food in long airy bar and restaurant; lovely big garden, handy for Bicton Park *(Grace and Michael Upton)*

COLYTON [SY2494]

Gerrard Arms [St Andrews Sq]: Friendly open-plan local with well kept Branscombe Vale Branoc and guest beers, good value home-made food inc Sun roasts, skittle alley; tables in pleasant courtyard and garden *(Pete Walker, the Didler)*

☆ *Kingfisher* [off A35 and A3052 E of Sidmouth; Dolphin St]: Village local under new licensees, popular food from generous baguettes and baked potatoes to fresh local crab, stripped stone, plush seats and elm settles, low beams and big open fire, well kept Otter beer, farm cider, pub games, upstairs family room, skittle alley; parking can be a problem, outside gents'; tables out on terrace, garden with water feature *(LYM, KN-R, Michael Doswell, the Didler)*

CREDITON [SS8300]

Three Little Pigs [Parliament St]: Eclectic pub with plenty of atmosphere, well kept Dartmoor ale, enjoyable food *(Leslie J Lyon)*

CROYDE [SS4439]

Manor House Inn [St Marys Rd, off B3231

NW of Braunton]: Friendly family pub with cheerful efficient service, good value food from baguettes and baked potatoes to a few less common dishes and lovely treacle pudding, well kept Bass, Wadworths 6X and a house beer, no smoking restaurant and dining conservatory; piped music, games end; skittle alley, disabled facilities, attractive terraced garden with good big play area *(Brian and Jennifer Salisbury)*

☆ *Thatched Barn* [B3231 NW of Braunton; Hobbs Hill]: Lively thatched pub nr great surfing beaches, with cheerful efficient young staff, laid-back feel and customers to match (can get packed in summer); rambling and roomy, with beams, settles and good seating, wide choice of generous food from sandwiches and baguettes up, well kept changing ales inc Bass, morning coffee, teas, smart restaurant with dressers and lots of china; piped music; children in eating areas, tables on flower-filled suntrap terraces, bedrooms simple but clean and comfortable, open all day *(LYM, Mark Flynn, Kevin Blake)*

DARTINGTON [SX7762]

Cott [Cott signed off A385 W of Totnes, opp A384 turn-off]: Picturesque long 14th-c thatched pub, heavy beams, steps, flagstones and big log fires, well kept Greene King IPA and Abbot and Otter, food (not cheap) from lunchtime sandwiches and baked potatoes up; children and dogs on leads welcome, picnic-sets in garden and on pretty terrace, open all day at least in summer *(E B Ireland, Daphne Barkhouse, LYM, Brian and Bett Cox, Ian and Ruth Laurence)*

DARTMOUTH [SX8751]

Royal Castle Hotel [the Quay]: Rambling 17th-c or older hotel behind Regency façade overlooking inner harbour, pleasant lounge-like Galleon bar on right, neatly reworked Harbour Bar on left (TV, piped music, dogs very welcome – no children), well kept Bass and Exe Valley Dobs Best, all-day bar food from plain sandwiches to good steaks, perhaps winter lunchtime spit-roasts from their 300-year-old Lidstone range; comfortable bedrooms with secure parking, open all day *(Russell Grimshaw, Kerry Purcell, J E Shackleton, David and Julie Glover, Norman and Sarah Keeping, Joyce and Maurice Cottrell, Keith and Margaret Kettell, LYM)*

DAWLISH WARREN [SX9778]

Mount Pleasant [Mount Pleasant Rd]: Marvellous view from lounge and garden over the Warren, Exe estuary and sea, welcoming staff, enjoyable food, good choice of well kept beers, two pool tables, darts *(anon)*

DREWSTEIGNTON [SX7489]

☆ *Anglers Rest* [E of village; OS Sheet 191 map ref 743899]: Idyllic wooded Teign valley spot by 16th-c pack-horse bridge, lovely walks; much extended former tea pavilion, with tourist souvenirs and airy café feel, but has well kept Exe Valley ales and reliable substantial food (not Sun) from baguettes and good local cheese ploughman's up, friendly helpful service and log fire; children and dogs welcome, waterside picnic-sets, has been cl winter evenings *(LYM, Robert Gomme, Ian and Ruth Laurence)*

DUNSFORD [SX8189]

☆ *Royal Oak* [signed from Moretonhampstead]: Relaxed village inn with good generous food (home-made so may take a while), well kept Greene King Abbot, Princetown Jail, Sharps Cornish Coaster and Doom Bar and changing guest beers, local farm ciders, friendly landlord, light and airy lounge bar with woodburner and view from small sunny dining bay, simple dining room, steps down to games room with pool; quiz nights, piped music; children welcome, Fri barbecues in sheltered tiered garden, good value bedrooms in converted barn *(the Didler, LYM, Barry Steele-Perkins, Dr and Mrs M E Wilson)*

EAST ALLINGTON [SX7648]

Fortescue Arms [off A381 Totnes—Kingsbridge]: Pretty village pub with popular food in traditional slate-floored bar and comfortable old-world dining room, well kept local ales; dogs very welcome, open all day in summer *(anon)*

EAST PORTLEMOUTH [SX7537]

Gara Rock: Comfortable family-friendly hotel not pub, but a handy stop on the South West Coast Path – non-residents welcome, with obliging service and enjoyable food all day inc barbecues in its extensive gardens; bedrooms *(Jack Clark)*

EAST PRAWLE [SX7836]

Pigs Nose [Prawle Green]: Cheery and homely, with low beams and flagstones, well kept real ales tapped from the cask, enjoyable if limited food from good ploughman's and sandwiches up, open fire, easy chairs and sofa, interesting bric-a-brac and local pictures, jars of wild flowers and candles on tables, bird log, darts, small family area with small box of unusual toys, nice dogs; unobtrusive piped music, hall for live bands; tables outside, nice spot on village green *(Roger Wain-Heapy, Brian Kneale)*

EXETER [SX9390]

☆ *Double Locks* [Canal Banks, Alphington, via Marsh Barton Industrial Estate; OS Sheet 192 map ref 933901]: Remote and unpretentious retreat by ship canal, great range of eight or so well kept ales often tapped straight from the cask, farm cider, good value plain home-made bar food from sandwiches and hot filled rolls up all day; piped music, live wknds; children welcome in eating areas, dogs very welcome too, distant view to city and cathedral from seats out on decking, good big play area, camping, open all day *(Phil and Sally Gorton, Steve Felstead, Ian and Deborah Carrington, the Didler, John and Vivienne Rice, John Prescott, A P Seymour, Brenda and Rob Fincham, Richard and Anne Ansell, LYM, David Carr, Andy Sinden, Louise Harrington, Dick Ward, Mrs Sylvia Elcoate)*

Georges Meeting House [South St]: Comfortable and flourishing new Wetherspoons, entirely no smoking, in awesome and echoic former 18th-c chapel (described by Pevsner as 'sombre but magnificent') dominated by tall pulpit one end; stained glass, original pews in three-side gallery, some leather settees, their usual food and good west country cheese, fish and meat, half a dozen real ales, good wine choice; children welcome when eating, quality furniture in attractive side garden *(Mike Gorton, Dr and Mrs M E Wilson)*

☆ *Great Western* [St Davids Hill]: Up to a dozen or more well kept changing ales usually inc Adnams, Bass, Exmoor, Fullers London Pride and Teignworthy in large hotel's small split-level convivial bar, wholesome good value fresh food all day from sandwiches and generous baked potatoes up (kitchen also supplies the hotel's restaurant), daily papers, no music; bedrooms fresh and warm *(Phil and Sally Gorton, Revd R P Tickle, Dr and Mrs A K Clarke, the Didler, Joe Green)*

Hour Glass [Melbourne St, above the quay]: Bistro-feel 19th-c pub under new management, beams, panelling, candles and open fire, well kept Adnams Broadside, Otter and Sharps Doom Bar, good house wine, enjoyable reasonably priced rather unusual bar food, friendly helpful staff *(the Didler, Dr and Mrs M E Wilson, Mike Gorton)*

Old Fire House [New North Rd]: Superb collection of Fire Service memorabilia in small busy flagstoned pub with Wadworths IPA and 6X and Youngs Special, good value coffee, enjoyable bargain food, further eating area upstairs; through high arched wrought-iron gates to block of flats or offices *(Dr and Mrs M E Wilson)*

Port Royal [Weirfield Path, off Weirfield Rd – left-bank path downstream from The Quay]: Low gabled waterside pavilion with sofas and settles in long convivial nautical-theme lounge, smart restaurant area, real ales such as Ringwood Fortyniner and Wadworths 6X, wide choice of reasonably priced fresh interesting food from ciabattas to good steaks, friendly service, public bar with darts, pool, machines and piped music; river-view tables *(Dr and Mrs M E Wilson, Michael and Alison Sandy)*

Prospect [The Quay (left bank, nr rowing club)]: Good quayside spot, comfortable seating, modern colour-scheme and prints contrasting with the old building's beams, sensibly priced up-to-date bar food from baguettes with chips and baked potatoes up, well kept Fullers London Pride and Otter, friendly helpful young staff, raised river-view dining area; gentle piped music – live Fri/Sat; tables out by water *(John and Vivienne Rice, Joe Green, Derek and Sylvia Stephenson, Michael and Alison Sandy)*

Royal Oak [Okehampton St]: Unpretentious L-shaped town local with lots of red plush and beamery, Bass and Wadworths 6X, end dining lounge, cheerful atmosphere; small river-view terrace *(Dr and Mrs M E Wilson)*

☆ *Ship* [Martins Lane, nr cathedral]: Pretty 14th-c building with genuine dark heavy beams, done up inside in olde-worlde city pub style, well kept Bass, Greene King Old Speckled Hen and Marstons Pedigree, farm cider, speedy friendly service, generous sandwiches only down here, reasonably priced meals in comfortable upstairs restaurant *(Alain and Rose Foote, Mark Flynn, Roger Huggins, Tom and Alex McLean, Dr and Mrs M E Wilson, Dr and Mrs A K Clarke, LYM, DAV, Pat and Robert Watt)*

Welcome [Haven Banks, off Haven Rd (which is first left off A377 heading S after Exe crossing)]: Old two-room pub near the gasometers and little changed since the 1960s (ditto the juke box), gas lighting and flagstones, very friendly old-school landlady, well kept changing real ales; a few tables out overlooking basin on Exeter Ship Canal, and can be reached on foot via footbridges from The Quay *(Phil and Sally Gorton, the Didler)*

Well House [Cathedral Yard, attached to Royal Clarence Hotel]: Big windows looking across to cathedral in open-plan bistro-look bar with tables divided by inner walls and partitions, lots of interesting Victorian prints, good choice of well kept local ales such as Otter, quick service, wide range of reasonably priced upscale lunchtime food inc good sandwiches and salads, daily papers; may be piped music, popular with young smokers; Roman well below (can be viewed when pub not busy) *(Derek and Sylvia Stephenson, Roger Huggins, Tom and Alex McLean, BB, R Michael Richards, Pete Walker, Michael and Alison Sandy)*

White Hart [South St]: Attractively old-fashioned largely no smoking rambling bar, heavy beams, oak flooring, nice furnishings inc antiques, charming inner cobbled courtyard, well kept Bass, Otter and a house beer not unlike Hook Norton Old Hooky, good wines and sherry, efficient cheerful staff, bar food inc good sandwich choice, bar billiards; bedrooms a bit dated now, but good breakfast and free parking *(Jim and Maggie Cowell, Roger Huggins, Tom and Alex McLean, Richard Pierce, LYM, Michael and Alison Sandy)*

EXMINSTER [SX9587]
Swans Nest [Station Rd, just off A379 on outskirts]: Huge well arranged mass-throughput food pub very popular for wide choice of reasonably priced food from sandwiches and children's dishes to extensive carvery, friendly staff, well kept Otter Best and Youngs Special, no smoking areas; especially good for family groups, handy for M5 *(LYM, Fr Robert Marsh, John Beeken, David Carr, Mrs Sylvia Elcoate)*

EXMOUTH [SX9980]
Beach [Victoria Rd]: Down-to-earth old quayside local with shipping and lifeboat memorabilia and photographs, beams, posts and panelling, cast-iron-framed tables, Bass, Greene King Old Speckled Hen and Otter, food, friendly landlord and staff; can be smoky *(Dr and Mrs M E Wilson)*

FILLEIGH [SS6727]
☆ *Stags Head* [off A361, via B3226 N of S Molton; large-scale maps name the hamlet Stags Head]: Welcoming new licensees in pretty 16th-c thatched and flagstoned pub, helpful staff, good value home-made food from sandwiches up, well kept real ales, reasonably priced wines, friendly local bar with crack darts team and very high-backed settle, separate lounge bar, good-sized cottagey dining room up a couple of steps; old rustic tables out in fairy-lit honeysuckle arbour by big tree-sheltered pond with lots of ducks and fish; children welcome, bedrooms comfortable and good value, good breakfast *(Mark, Amanda, Luke and Jake Sheard, BB, Mark Flynn, D A Walker, D G Brown, June and Robin Savage)*

FOLLY GATE [SX5798]
Crossways [A386 Hatherleigh—Okehampton]: Welcoming new licensees, homely comfortable atmosphere, generous good value food, well kept St Austell ales, faultless service *(Ron and Sheila Corbett)*

GALMPTON [SX8856]
Manor [village and pub signed off A3022; Stoke Gabriel Rd]: Large friendly open-plan Edwardian local with well kept Bass and Greene King Abbot, good value straightforward food inc local fish, two-part bar and family dining area, well spaced tables; open all day *(Alan and Paula McCully)*

GEORGEHAM [SS4639]
Kings Arms [B3231 Croyde—Woolacombe]: Well kept Bass, Fullers London Pride and a guest such as Exmoor Gold, shortish choice of modestly priced food inc popular good value Sun roast, fresh décor in open-plan bar and restaurant; children allowed in family room *(Paul and Ursula Randall)*

☆ *Rock* [Rock Hill, above village]: Well restored oak-beamed pub with well kept ales such as Bass, Cotleigh Golden Eagle, Fullers London Pride, Greene King IPA and Abbot and Timothy Taylors Landlord, local farm cider, good value generous straightforward food from baguettes up, quick cheerful service, old red quarry tiles, open fire, pleasant mix of rustic furniture, lots of bric-a-brac, separate vine-adorned back family conservatory (children allowed in pool room too); piped music, darts, fruit machine, juke box; dogs welcome, tables under cocktail parasols on front terrace, pretty hanging baskets *(Paul and Ursula Randall, Mark, Amanda, Luke and Jake Sheard, Kev and Gaye Griffiths, BB, Bob and Margaret Holder, Chris and Ann Coy, Peter and Margaret Glenister, Rona Murdoch)*

GOODLEIGH [SS5934]
New Inn: Welcoming pub with blackboard choice of enjoyable reasonably priced home-made food, changing ales such as Sharps Doom Bar and Wyre Piddle, log fire *(Mrs S Lyons)*

GRENOFEN [SX4971]
Halfway House [A386 near Tavistock]: Good choice of reasonably priced home-made food

using local produce, friendly efficient licensees, well kept Fullers London Pride, Sharps Doom Bar and a guest beer, farm cider, decent wines, lounge, restaurant and traditional bar with pool and darts; tables out overlooking Dartmoor, good value bedrooms, good breakfast *(anon)*

HARBERTON [SX7758]

☆ *Church House* [off A381 just S of Totnes]: Ancient partly Norman village pub, medieval latticed glass and oak panelling, attractive 17th- and 18th-c pews and settles, woodburner in big inglenook, no smoking family room, well kept Butcombe, Courage Best, Marstons Pedigree and St Austell Tribute, good choice of wines by the glass, farm cider, bar food (can take a while), traditional games; piped music; dogs welcome, bedrooms with own bathrooms *(B J Harding, LYM, JHW, Ann Holdsworth, M Sage, Ann and Bob Westbrook)*

HATHERLEIGH [SS5404]

☆ *George* [A386 N of Okehampton; Market St]: Timbered pub with huge oak beams, enormous fireplace, easy chairs, sofas and antique cushioned settles in original core, more modern monk-theme main bar, more settles and woodburner in L-shaped beamed back bar, good value simple generous bar food from sandwiches to steaks and fresh fish, welcoming staff, Bass, St Austell Dartmoor Best and a beer named for the pub, lots of malt whiskies, farm cider, restaurant; children in eating area, dogs in bar, rustic tables in pretty courtyard and walled cobbled garden, bedrooms, open all day *(John and Joan Nash, LYM, the Didler, Liz Tull)*

☆ *Tally Ho* [Market St (A386)]: Attractive heavy-beamed and timbered linked rooms, sturdy furnishings, big log fire and woodburner, ample enjoyable food from lunchtime sandwiches up, good real ales brewed for them locally by Clearwater, pleasant service, no smoking restaurant, traditional games; piped music; tables in nice sheltered garden, three cosy and prettily furnished bedrooms *(LYM, the Didler, Ron and Sheila Corbett, Brian Coleman, DAV)*

HEMERDON [SX5657]

Miners Arms: New generation of the family owning this for 120 years have added a high-standard garden restaurant to the friendly and attractive low-beamed former tin miner's cottage with its internal well; good pastoral views from restaurant and roomy and attractive flagstoned terrace *(Chris Drewitt)*

HEXWORTHY [SX6572]

Forest Inn [signed off B3357 Tavistock—Ashburton, E of B3212]: Gorgeous setting on Dartmoor, roomy plush-seated open-plan bar and back walkers' bar, short daily-changing choice of good generous bar and restaurant food using fresh local produce, prompt service, well kept Teignworthy ales with a guest such as Otter, local cider, friendly helpful staff, real fire, daily papers, no smoking area; may charge for tap water; dogs and boots welcome, comfortable bedrooms (also bunkhouse),

fishing permits, good walking and riding *(Gene and Kitty Rankin, LYM, Bruce Bird)*

HOLBETON [SX6150]

Mildmay Colours [off A379 W of A3121]: Friendly mix of locals and holidaymakers, a beer brewed for the pub by Skinners and guest beers, local farm cider, generous food from sandwiches and baguettes up, horse and racing memorabilia, stripped stone and timbers, pubby seats on turkey carpet, woodburner, small no smoking family room, games area with dominoes, cribbage, pinball and pool; piped music, TV, fruit machine, no credit cards; dogs and children welcome, colourful front terrace, well kept back garden with picnic-sets and aviary, bedrooms with own bathrooms *(LYM, Geoff and Marianne Millin, B J Harding, Bruce Bird)*

HOLSWORTHY [SS3408]

Kings Arms [Fore St/The Square]: 17th-c inn with Victorian fittings, etched windows and coal fires in three interesting traditional bars, old pictures and photographs, 40s and 50s beer advertisements, lots of optics behind ornate counter, particularly well kept Bass and Sharps Doom Bar, friendly locals; open all day, Sun afternoon closure *(the Didler)*

Rydon Inn [Rydon (A3072 W)]: Enjoyable food in comfortable dining pub with two no smoking dining rooms; disabled access and facilities, dogs welcome in part of bar *(anon)*

HONITON [SY1198]

Greyhound [Fenny Bridges, B3177 4 miles W]: Big busy thatched family dining pub with wide food choice from good open sandwiches and baked potatoes up, quick cheerful service, good choice of well kept beers inc Otter, heavy beams and stylish décor, attractive restaurant with no smoking area; bedrooms *(Meg and Colin Hamilton, LYM, Gill and Keith Croxton)*

Holt [High St]: Former Dominoes Bar reopened under Otter Brewery, with short choice of good interesting up-to-date food *(M C Stephenson)*

Honiton Motel [Turks Head Corner, Exeter Rd]: More pubby than many pubs, with well kept Otter in two bars, good value food *(Bob and Margaret Holder)*

☆ *Red Cow* [High St]: Welcoming local, very busy on Tues and Sat market days, scrubbed tables, pleasant alcoves, log fires, well kept Bass, Courage Directors and local Otter, decent wines and malt whiskies, good value quickly served no-nonsense food from sandwiches up in restaurant part, lots of chamber-pots and big mugs on beams; pavement tables, bedrooms *(Mark Flynn, BB, Colin and Janet Roe, Dr and Mrs M E Wilson)*

HOPE COVE [SX6740]

Hope & Anchor: Simple inn, friendly and comfortable, in lovely seaside spot, with good open fire, kind quick service, good value straightforward food inc good crab sandwiches, well kept Sharps Doom Bar, reasonably priced wines, flagstone floor, no piped music; children and dogs welcome in family room, games room with pool; great coast walks, good bay views from tables outside, bedrooms, open all day *(LYM, Lawrence Pearse)*

HORNS CROSS [SS3823]

Hoops [A39 Clovelly—Bideford, W of village]: Picturesque thatched inn under new management, cushioned window seats, oak settles, beams and inglenook log fires, pricey bar food (all day wknds), several real ales, good wine choice, welcoming staff, daily papers, darts, no smoking restaurant; piped music, TV; well behaved children in eating area till 8, dogs allowed in bar, bedrooms with own bathrooms, open all day *(LYM, John and Joan Calvert, JMC)*

HORSEBRIDGE [SX3975]

☆ *Royal* [off A384 Tavistock—Launceston]: Cheerful slate-floored rooms, interesting bric-a-brac and pictures, tasty reasonably priced food from baguettes and baked potatoes up, well kept ales inc Sharps Doom Bar and Special, farm cider, log fire, bar billiards, cribbage, dominoes, no smoking café-style side room, no music or machines; no children in evening, picnic-sets on back terrace and in big garden perhaps with summer salad bar *(Andrea Rampley, LYM, DAV, G Coates)*

IDE [SX8990]

Poachers [3 miles from M5 junction 31, via A30; High St]: Good generous food, both traditional and inventively individual, inc good fish choice (worth booking evenings), well kept Bass, Branscombe Vale Branoc, Otter and one brewed locally for the pub, good value house wines, sofas and open fire; blues night, picnic-sets in nice garden, attractive bedrooms, small quaint village, cl Mon lunchtime *(John and Vivienne Rice, Dr and Mrs M E Wilson, John and Marion Tyrie, John and Sonja Newberry, Mrs Jill Silversides, Barry Brown, the Didler)*

IDEFORD [SX8977]

☆ *Royal Oak* [2 miles off A380]: Cosy thatched and flagstoned village local brightened up but still unspoilt, interesting Nelson and Churchill memorabilia, welcoming service, well kept Otter and Timothy Taylors Landlord, good simple well priced bar snacks, log fire; children and dogs welcome *(Phil and Sally Gorton, the Didler, Ian and Ruth Laurence)*

ILFRACOMBE [SS5247]

☆ *George & Dragon* [Fore St]: Oldest pub here, handy for harbour, with good local atmosphere, proper pubby food inc Sun lunch, helpful friendly staff, well kept real ale, decent wines, attractive olde-worlde décor, soft lighting, lots of ornaments, china etc; may be piped music, cash machine but no credit cards *(Kevin Blake, Duncan Cloud)*

Prince of Wales [Fore St]: Low beams, pictures, earthenware on shelves, candlelit tables at night, good choice of food, well kept Butcombe, friendly character landlord, darts, pool; younger crowd at wknds; pleasant garden and terraces *(Kevin Blake)*

Ship & Pilot [Broad St, off harbour]: Light and airy open-plan pub near harbour, chatty and friendly, with decent food, well kept

mainstream ales, reasonable prices, nautical atmosphere and lots of Ilfracombe pictures, former indoor skittle alley *(Kevin Blake)*

INSTOW [SS4730]

☆ *Boat House* [Marine Parade]: Airy modern high-ceilinged café/bar with huge tidal beach just across lane and views to Appledore, big old-fashioned nautical paintings on stripped stone wall, well kept Bass, Flowers IPA and a local guest beer, good choice of popular food from sandwiches to steaks inc plentiful fish, open fire, friendly prompt service even when crowded, lively family bustle – children very welcome; gets very busy, piped music; roof terrace *(LYM, Rev D E and Mrs J A Shapland)*

Quay Inn [Marine Parade]: Friendly down-to-earth open-plan seaside pub just above quay, tables looking out over estuary, reasonably priced enjoyable food from baguettes to lobster tails, also afternoon teas, local real ales and strong farm cider; piped music may obtrude, inflexible menu, may try to keep your credit card behind bar; children (must behave well) and dogs welcome, disabled access, open all day *(J V Dadswell, Michael and Ann Cole, Ian Clare, June and Robin Savage)*

IVYBRIDGE [SX6356]

Sportsmans [Exeter Rd]: Large open-plan bar with big dining area, wide choice of food all day, well kept mainstream real ales, lots of panelling; bedrooms *(Dr and Mrs A K Clarke)*

KINGSKERSWELL [SX8666]

☆ *Bickley Mill* [Stoneycombe, Abbotskerswell—Compton/Marldon]: Tucked-away pub with wide choice of good reasonably priced food from sandwiches or baguettes to fine main dishes, sensible prices, well kept real ales, faultless service, buoyant atmosphere in spotless rambling beamed rooms with lots of copper and brass, log fire; children welcome, tables in courtyard, subtropical-style hillside garden, bedrooms *(LYM, Mrs Sylvia Elcoate)*

KINGSTON [SX6347]

☆ *Dolphin* [off B3392 or A379 SW of Modbury]: Several relaxed linked rooms in quietly set largely no smoking 16th-c inn, dark beams and stripped stone, inglenook woodburner, rustic tables and cushioned seats and settles, reasonably priced home-made bar food (not Mon in winter) from sandwiches to lots of fresh fish, cheerful service, well kept ales such as Courage Best, Sharps Doom Bar, Teignworthy and Wadworths 6X; children welcome, tables and swings outside, nice walks down to unspoilt beach, good value bedrooms, good generous breakfast *(LYM, Gene and Kitty Rankin, B J Harding, Jacquie and Jim Jones, David Uren, Sue Demont, Tim Barrow, George Atkinson)*

KNOWLE [SS4938]

☆ *Ebrington Arms* [A361 2 miles N of Braunton]: Comfortable olde-worlde pub doing well under current licensees, well kept Badger Tanglefoot, Bass and Flowers IPA, good food from ploughman's to delicately prepared salads and changing fresh hot dishes using local ingredients (booking now advisable evenings and wknds), cheerful helpful service, lots of bric-a-brac and relaxed atmosphere in cosy main bar, decent family room, attractive candlelit restaurant *(Paul and Ursula Randall, LYM)*

LAKE [SX5288]

☆ *Bearslake* [A386 just S of Sourton]: Welcoming thatched stone-built Dartmoor inn dating from 13th c, reopened after careful refurbishment in spring 2005, beams, flagstones, inglenook fireplace, pews and plenty of locals in friendly character bar, wide choice of enjoyable and popular home-made food from generous baguettes up, well kept mainstream and local ales, good cheerful family service; picnic-sets in sizeable streamside garden with terrace, six olde-worlde bedrooms, filling breakfast *(Francine Lee-Thompson, DAV)*

LANDKEY [SS5931]

Castle [signed off A361 E of Barnstaple; Blakeshill Rd]: Cosy flagstoned pub with warm welcome, decent beers, enjoyable reasonably priced food from good sandwiches and baked potatoes up inc lunchtime speciality bubble and squeak (booking recommended Fri/Sat nights); children's play area *(June and Robin Savage)*

LEE [SS4846]

☆ *Grampus* [signed off B3343/A361 W of Ilfracombe]: Attractive and comfortable 14th-c pub, nothing fancy, with friendly new owners, wide range of inexpensive tasty home-made food such as sandwiches, soups and pies, well kept real ales such as Exmoor Gold, pool in family room; dogs very welcome, lots of tables in appealing sheltered garden, short stroll from sea – superb coast walks *(Lynda and Trevor Smith, BB, Rona Murdoch, R L R Nicholson, Michael and Ann Cole)*

LIFTON [SX3885]

Arundell Arms [Fore St]: Substantial country-house fishing hotel run with charming individuality, rich décor, very agreeable welcoming atmosphere, good interesting lunchtime bar food and evening restaurant, good choice of wines by the glass, sophisticated service; can arrange fishing tuition – also shooting, deer-stalking and riding; bedrooms – a pleasant place to stay *(Mary Ellen Cummings, Oliver and Sue Rowell)*

LITTLEHEMPSTON [SX8162]

Pig & Whistle [Newton Rd (A381)]: Large pub with reasonably priced home-made food inc good value set meals, well kept local beer, long bar, big dining area *(E B Ireland)*

☆ *Tally Ho!* [off A381 NE of Totnes]: 14th-c low-beamed pub, neat and cosy, with interesting mix of chairs and settles, lots of cheerful bric-a-brac on stripped stone walls, some panelling, friendly family service, well kept Greene King IPA and perhaps a guest beer, bar food from sandwiches to steaks, duck and tuna, restaurant; piped music; several cats, children and dogs welcome, flower-filled terrace, bedrooms (main rail line nearby) *(George Atkinson, Ian and Ruth Laurence)*

LODDISWELL [SX7148]

Loddiswell Inn: Comfortable old village pub with friendly licensees, log fire, freshly made

generous simple food using local produce, two well kept ales; lovely walks along river and former railway line *(Lawrence Pearse)*

LUPPITT [ST1606]

Luppitt Inn [back roads N of Honiton]: Unspoilt little basic farmhouse pub, a real throwback, friendly chatty landlady who keeps it open because she (and her cats) like the company; tiny room with corner bar and a table, another not much bigger with fireplace, Otter tapped from the cask, metal puzzles made by neighbour, no food or music, lavatories across the yard; cl lunchtime and Sun evening *(the Didler, RWC, Conor McGaughey)*

LUTTON [SX5959]

Mountain [pub signed off Cornwood—Sparkwell rd]: Simply furnished beamed pub with log fires, some stripped stone, a high-backed settle, well priced traditional food, well kept local ales and farm cider, friendly service; children welcome, tables on verandah and vine-arbour terrace *(LYM, Geoff and Marianne Millin)*

LYDFORD [SX5285]

☆ *Dartmoor Inn* [Downton, A386]: Best thought of as a (good) restaurant-with-rooms though there is a small front log-fire bar; no smoking throughout, with interesting if pricey food in several small civilised and relaxed stylishly decorated areas, good wines by the glass, well organised friendly helpful service; children welcome, dogs in bar, terrace tables, cl Sun evening, Mon *(Jacquie and Jim Jones, Richard and Margaret Peers, Paul Hopton, Peter Craske, Mr and Mrs W Mills, John and Christine Lowe, Charles and Isabel Cooper, Rev D E and Mrs J A Shapland, LYM, David Hall, Gaynor Gregory, Cynthia and Stephen Fisher)*

LYMPSTONE [SX9984]

☆ *Redwing* [Church Rd]: Friendly two-bar pub with good value well prepared food inc lots of local fish and good puddings, well kept Greene King Abbot, Otter and Palmers Bitter and Dorset Gold, local farm ciders, good house wines, caring licensees and helpful efficient staff, brightly painted lounge, neat little no smoking dining area with wild flowers, open all day wknds; may be discreet piped music, quiz nights, live music most wknds, some bank hols, and jazz Tues; pretty garden behind (sometimes music here in fine weather), unspoilt village with shore walks *(Peter Burton, BB, Dr and Mrs M E Wilson, the Didler)*

LYNMOUTH [SS7249]

Rising Sun [Harbourside]: Wonderful position overlooking harbour, concentration on the upmarket hotel side and the attractive cosy no smoking restaurant; well kept west country ales, wide lunchtime choice of blackboard food inc plenty of fish, good fire; may be quiet piped classical music, parking can be a problem – expensive by day, sparse at night; children allowed away from bar, bedrooms (may be small) in cottagey old thatched terrace stepped up hills, gardens up behind *(Michael and*

Ann Cole, LYM, Comus and Sarah Elliott, Keith and Margaret Kettell, June and Robin Savage)

LYNTON [SS7249]

Crown [Market St/Sinai Hill]: Good relaxed atmosphere in hotel lounge bar, friendly and chatty staff and locals, open fire, decent reasonably priced bar food all day from baguettes to small comfortable restaurant, five well kept changing ales such as Cotleigh, Greene King Ruddles and Marstons Pedigree, farm cider, horse tack; good bedrooms, open all day (A and B D Craig, Bruce Bird, Comus and Sarah Elliott)

☆ *Hunters* [pub well signed off A39 W of Lynton]: Superb Heddon Valley position by NT information centre down very steep hill, great walks inc one, not too taxing, down to the sea; big spreading bar with some plush banquettes and so forth, enjoyable freshly prepared generous food from soup and baguettes to local seafood (may be a wait when crowded), cheerful young helpful staff, well kept Exmoor ales, woodburner (may be a dozing boxer dog), no smoking area; piped music; bedrooms, picnic-sets on balconied terrace overlooking attractively landscaped pondside garden with peacocks, open all day (Bruce Bird, Gillian Rodgers, BB, Andy and Ali)

Queens [Queen St]: Enjoyable varied food, and quite handy for both funicular railway and coast path; dogs welcome (Ian Clare)

MAIDENCOMBE [SX9268]

☆ *Thatched Tavern* [Steep Hill]: Friendly and spotless much extended three-level thatched pub, well kept Bass, Flowers IPA and Original and Fullers London Pride in pubby bar, well priced generous food inc local fish (can be a wait) and tempting puddings in two cosy eating areas, one no smoking, quick attentive service even when busy, big family room, pleasant restaurant; children allowed, no dogs inside, nice garden with small thatched huts, small attractive village above small beach (E B Ireland, Dr and Mrs M E Wilson, Brian and Ruth Archer)

MEAVY [SX5467]

☆ *Royal Oak* [off B3212 E of Yelverton]: Heavy-beamed partly 15th-c pub changing management as we went to press (it's actually owned by the Parish Council), pews from the next-door church, red plush banquettes, old agricultural prints and church pictures, smaller flagstoned bar with flagstones and big open hearth, tables out by the pretty green; has had decent bar food and well kept Princetown and guest beers, and a welcome for dogs; reports on new regime please (LYM)

MEETH [SS5408]

☆ *Bull & Dragon* [A386 Hatherleigh—Torrington]: 16th-c beamed and thatched village pub, well kept Fullers London Pride, decent wines, good freshly made food, friendly new management, interesting early 20th-c photographs; unobtrusive piped music; children and dogs welcome, handy for Tarka Trail (Ron and Sheila Corbett)

MERRIVALE [SX5475]

☆ *Dartmoor Inn* [B3357, 4 miles E of Tavistock]: Well run and sensitively refurbished pub in tranquil spot with high views of Dartmoor; generous lunchtime food from sandwiches and good ploughman's up, quick polite service, well kept Greene King IPA, decent wines, water from their 36-metre (120-ft) deep well, open fire; dogs on leads allowed, good views from tables out in front (very popular summer evenings) good walks – nr bronze-age hut circles, stone rows and pretty river (Dr and Mrs M E Wilson, Dennis Jenkin)

MODBURY [SX6551]

Modbury Inn [Brownston St]: Friendly helpful licensees, enjoyable food, small traditional bar with well kept Bass, Courage and Otter; attractive garden, comfortable bedrooms (John and Joan Calvert)

MONKLEIGH [SS4520]

☆ *Bell*: Laid-back beamed and partly thatched village local with good Civil War pictures by local artist (prints for sale), log fire, well kept changing ales often from interesting small West Country breweries, Thatcher's farm cider, bargain down-to-earth home-made food inc plenty of local produce and some interesting variations, friendly licensees and staff, woodburner, no smoking eating area beyond piano, children and dogs welcome – friendly boxer called Tasha; pleasant back room with Aga and pool table; piped music may be rather loud, Fri music night; attached shop with organic meats and local food, pleasant garden, good walks, low-priced bedrooms, open all day (BB, Mark Flynn)

MORELEIGH [SX7652]

New Inn [B3207, off A381 Kingsbridge—Totnes in Stanborough]: Busy country local with character old furniture, nice pictures, candles in bottles, limited choice of wholesome generous home cooking (book if you want a table nr the big inglenook log fire), reasonable prices, well kept Palmers tapped from the cask; may be cl Sat lunchtime/race days (Roger Wain-Heapy, LYM)

MORETONHAMPSTEAD [SX7586]

White Hart [A382 N of Bovey Tracey; The Square]: Well restored old coaching inn, stripped floor bar, elegant relaxing lounge, good friendly service, well kept real ales, enjoyable bar food from toasties and hot meat sandwiches up, attractive brasserie; courtyard tables, 13 well equipped country-style bedrooms with own bathrooms, well placed for Dartmoor, good walks (LYM, Mrs S Lyons, Sally Jenkin)

MORTEHOE [SS4545]

Chichester Arms [off A361 Ilfracombe—Braunton]: Interesting old local photographs in plush and leatherette panelled lounge and comfortable no smoking dining room, wide choice of pubby food, real ales such as local Barum Original, reasonably priced wine, pubby locals' bar with darts and pool, no piped music; skittle alley and games machines in summer children's room, tables out in front and in small garden, good coast walks

(Bruce Bird, Bob and Margaret Holder)

☆ **Ship Aground** [signed off A361 Ilfracombe—Braunton]: Welcoming open-plan beamed village pub; well kept ales such as Cotleigh Tawny, Burton Bridge and Greene King Abbot, Hancock's cider in summer, decent wine, good choice of inexpensive bar food from good crab sandwiches up (may be a wait when busy), upstairs carvery some days, big log fires, friendly service; massive rustic furnishings, interesting nautical brassware, children allowed in big back family room, pool, skittles and other games; tables on sheltered sunny terrace with good views, by interesting church, wonderful walking on nearby coast footpath *(Rona Murdoch, LYM, Comus and Sarah Elliott, Chris and Ann Coy)*

MORWELLHAM [SX4469]

Ship [part of Morwellham Quay restored village]: Part of this interesting English Heritage restored copper-mine and shipping village (well worth the admission fee), waitresses in Victorian dress, décor and drinks to suit (local farm cider and Sharps tapped from the cask), fresh good value filled buns, baked potatoes, cakes and cream teas – enjoyed by all the family *(Mark, Amanda, Luke and Jake Sheard)*

NEWTON ABBOT [SX8571]

Dartmouth [East St]: Thriving three-room pub with well kept changing local ales inc McBrides (started here but now brewed elsewhere), farm cider, decent wines, log fires, enjoyable food; children welcome till 7pm, tables and barbecues in nice outside area, open all day *(the Didler)*

Jolly Abbot [East St]: Olde-worlde country-pub atmosphere, with beams, friendly helpful staff and cheerful customers, enjoyable low-priced home-made standard food (must book Weds market day) from sandwiches and baked potatoes up, well kept ales inc guests, nice short wine list leaning to Australia *(Ken Flawn)*

☆ **Olde Cider Bar** [East St]: Casks of interesting low-priced farm ciders and a couple of perries, with more in bottles, in basic old-fashioned cider house, dark stools, barrel seats and wall benches, flagstones and bare boards; good country wines, baguettes and pasties etc, very low prices; small games room with machines *(the Didler)*

Pen [Torquay Rd (A380/A381 roundabout)]: Former Beefeater with several comfortable if functional areas off central bar, decent food, efficient friendly service, pool; good parking *(Mr and Mrs Colin Roberts)*

NEWTON ST CYRES [SX8798]

☆ **Beer Engine** [off A377 towards Thorverton]: Friendly helpful licensees in cheerful and roomy pub brewing its own good beers, with good home-made bar food esp fish and very popular Sun lunch, no smoking eating area welcoming children, traditional games; verandah and large sunny garden, popular summer barbecues, open all day *(John and Bryony Coles, LYM, J V Dadswell, Mark and Joanne Preston)*

NORTH BOVEY [SX7483]

☆ **Ring of Bells** [off A382/B3212 SW of

Moretonhampstead]: Attractive bulgy-walled 13th-c thatched inn, low beams, flagstones, slabby rustic tables and winding staircases, well kept ales inc Otter, Gray's farm cider and warm log fire, enjoyable interestingly cooked fresh food majoring on local produce, good set meals, friendly relaxed service, smart no smoking dining room, longer more functional room with pool and TV; by lovely tree-covered village green below Dartmoor, garden picnic-sets, good walks from the door, five big comfortably refurbished bedrooms with own bathrooms *(Brian and Bett Cox, Dr and Mrs M E Wilson, LYM, Stephen R Holman, Sybil Williams, Mr and Mrs Colin Roberts)*

NOSS MAYO [SX5447]

☆ **Swan** [off B3186 at Junket Corner]: Lovely waterside views from small welcoming two-room beamed pub right on the creek, redecorated in unpretentiously traditional style, plenty of individuality, wide choice of enjoyable food inc good low-priced fresh fish and popular Fri curry night, well kept Brakspears and Sharps Doom Bar, good-humoured newish landlord, open fire, Thurs quiz night with free sandwiches; can get crowded, with difficult parking; dogs on leads and children welcome, terrace tables facing the sunset *(Alice Harper, Nicola Hull, Alistair Milne, MP, Martin and Pauline Jennings)*

OAKFORD [SS9121]

Red Lion: 17th-c coaching inn partly rebuilt in Georgian times, simple local atmosphere, enthusiastic new management, well kept changing ales, Weston's farm cider, attractively priced hearty food, popular no smoking dining area off main bar with big inglenook fireplace, cigarette cards, rifles, swords and other bric-a-brac *(Guy Vowles, Philip Kingsbury)*

OKEHAMPTON [SX5895]

Plymouth [West St]: Matey beer-oriented local with attractive façade, cheerful staff, enterprising food at very reasonable prices, well kept Palmers IPA and St Austell Tribute tapped from the cask (May and Nov beer festivals), daily papers, no smoking area, provision for children; open all day wknds *(Dr and Mrs A K Clarke, BB, B C Head)*

OTTERY ST MARY [SY0995]

London [Gold St]: Cosy rambling village local, beams, timbers and brasses, reasonably priced standard food from sandwiches, baked potatoes and good ploughman's to mixed grill, well kept Adnams Bitter and Broadside and Bass, cheerful informal service, open fires, no smoking area; large back terrace, bedrooms *(Dr and Mrs M E Wilson, Robert Gomme, George Atkinson)*

PAIGNTON [SX8961]

Embassy [Colin Rd, Preston]: Wide choice of generous bargain food from sandwiches and baguettes through local fish to steak and choice of three roasts, OAP and children's deals, attentive service, real ales; terrace tables, open all day *(Mrs Rachel Wayth)*

Ship [Manor Rd, Preston]: Large yet homely mock-Tudor pub specialising in wide choice of cheap food (small helpings of any dish for children), dining areas on three levels, comfortable furnishings inc leather settees, soft lighting, well kept Badger Tanglefoot from very long bar, speedy cheerful service; piped music; children welcome, a minute's walk from Preston beach *(Mr and Mrs Colin Roberts, David Carr)*

PLYMOUTH [SX4755]

☆ *China House* [Sutton Harbour, via Sutton Rd off Exeter St (A374)]: Plymouth's oldest warehouse attractively restored as Vintage Inn, super boaty views day and night over harbour and Barbican, great beams and flagstones, bare slate and stone walls, good log fire, friendly helpful staff, great choice of wines by the glass, well kept Bass and Tetleys, food all day from ciabattas and filled baguettes up; piped music; good parking and disabled access and facilities, open all day *(B J Harding, LYM, Ken Flawn, Andy and Ali)*

Dolphin [Barbican]: Well used lively and unspoilt local, good range of beers inc particularly well kept Bass tapped from the cask, coal fire; colourful décor, Beryl Cook paintings inc one of the friendly landlord; open all day *(the Didler)*

Gog & Magog [Southside St]: Roomy new art deco Wetherspoons with most attractively priced well kept ales such as Courage Directors, Exmoor Best, Greene King Abbot, Shepherd Neame Spitfire and Theakstons Best and Old Peculier from long bar, plenty of big solid furniture *(Steve Whalley)*

Lounge [Stopford Pl, Stoke]: Unspoilt open-plan backstreet local, Bass and a guest beer from oak-panelled counter, popular lunchtime food, friendly landlord *(the Didler)*

Queens Arms [Southside St, Barbican]: Small cosily Victorian local, spotless and smartly decorated, with interesting Royal photographs, comfortable banquettes, well kept Bass, excellent sandwiches inc fresh crab from efficient servery, good friendly staff *(Steve Whalley)*

Thistle Park [Commercial Rd]: Welcoming pub nr National Maritime Aquarium, good range of well kept beers inc some from next-door Sutton brewery, tasty straightforward food all day, friendly landlady, interesting décor, children welcome; open all day till very late, live music wknds *(the Didler)*

POSTBRIDGE [SX6579]

East Dart [B3212]: Central Dartmoor hotel by pretty river, in same family since 1861; roomy and comfortable lightened-up open-plan bar, promptly served enjoyable generous food using local ingredients from sandwiches and chips up, well kept St Austell ales inc Dartmoor, good wines by the glass, good fire, hunting murals and horse tack, pool room; dogs welcome, tables out in front and behind, decent bedrooms, some 30 miles of fishing *(David Swift, Dennis Jenkin, BB, Mrs S Lyons)*

RACKENFORD [SS8518]

☆ *Stag* [pub signed off A361 NW of Tiverton]: 13th-c low-beamed pub recovered from bad thatch fire late 2004, intriguing ancient layout, original flagstoned and cobbled entry passage between massive walls, huge fireplace flanked by ancient settles; welcoming landlord, nicely served good value food, well kept Cotleigh Tawny and a local guest beer, farm cider, good soft drinks choice, cottagey dining room (children allowed); may be quiet piped radio, some live music; simple bedrooms *(CMW, JJW, Peter Webster, LYM, Guy Vowles, Michael Rowse)*

SALCOMBE [SX7438]

Ferry Inn [off Fore St nr Portlemouth Ferry]: Good visitors' pub in splendid estuary position, lovely view from tiers of stripped-stone bars rising from sheltered flagstoned waterside terrace, inc top one opening off street, and middle dining bar, classic seaside pub menu, well kept Palmers and farm cider, good house wine; piped music, can get busy, may be cl part of winter *(B J Harding, JMC, Jack Clark, LYM)*

☆ *Fortescue* [Union St, end of Fore St]: Sizeable but homely proper pub, popular for its enjoyable promptly served food inc hot pork rolls, well kept ales such as Bass, Courage Directors and Otter, decent wines, pleasant service, good woodburner, nautical theme in five interlinked rooms, lots of old local black and white shipping pictures, restaurant, big public bar with pool, darts etc, no piped music; children welcome, picnic-sets in courtyard *(Gordon Stevenson, Bruce Bird)*

Victoria [Fore St]: Neat and attractive 19th-c pub opp harbour car park, colourful window boxes, hard-working welcoming landlord and comfortable furnishings, enjoyable generous food from good sandwiches and chips up, well kept St Austell ales, decent wines, good coffee, no smoking area, good housekeeping, nautical décor; piped music may obtrude; large sheltered tiered garden behind with good play area, bedrooms *(Roger Wain-Heapy, David Eberlin, P Mason, Frances Mumford, Dudley and Moira Cockroft, J M Tansey, George Atkinson, Bruce Bird)*

SAMPFORD PEVERELL [ST0314]

☆ *Globe* [a mile from M5 junction 27, village signed from Tiverton turn-off; Lower Town]: Spacious and comfortable, with thriving atmosphere, enjoyable good value home-made food from sandwiches to steaks inc fish and popular Sun lunch, well kept Bass and local guest beers, good choice of wines; piped music; children and dogs welcome, picnic-sets out in front, open all day *(LYM, Mike and Jenny Beacon)*

SANDY GATE [SX9690]

Blue Ball [handy for M5 junction 30; 1st right off A376, towards Topsham]: Extended dining pub with good rather upmarket food (even the baked potatoes never see a microwave), good helpings, beams, old wood and tile floors, lovely settles, well kept Bass and well priced wine, no smoking section, friendly attentive young staff; good gardens inc good play area *(Dr and Mrs M E Wilson)*

SCORRITON [SX7068]

Tradesmans Arms: Good-sized Dartmoor-edge open-plan pub in attractive countryside,

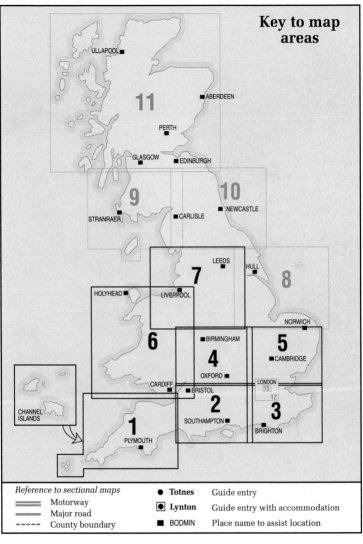

Key to map areas

ULLAPOOL

ABERDEEN

11

PERTH

GLASGOW   EDINBURGH

9   10

STRANRAER   CARLISLE   NEWCASTLE

LEEDS   HULL

7   8

HOLYHEAD   LIVERPOOL

6   BIRMINGHAM   5

4   CAMBRIDGE

CARDIFF   OXFORD   NORWICH

BRISTOL   LONDON

CHANNEL   13   12

ISLANDS   2   3

1   SOUTHAMPTON

PLYMOUTH   BRIGHTON

Reference to sectional maps	● Totnes	Guide entry
Motorway	⊡ Lynton	Guide entry with accommodation
Major road		
County boundary	■ BODMIN	Place name to assist location

MAPS IN THIS SECTION

For Maps 8 – 13 see later colour section

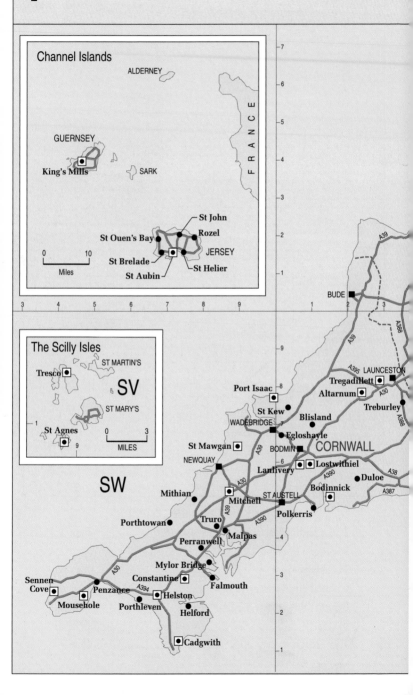

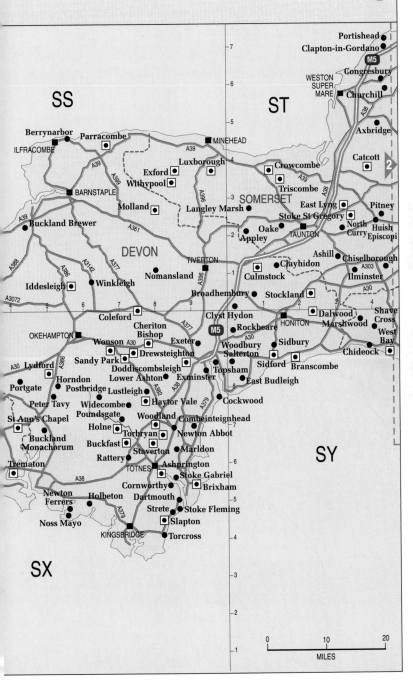

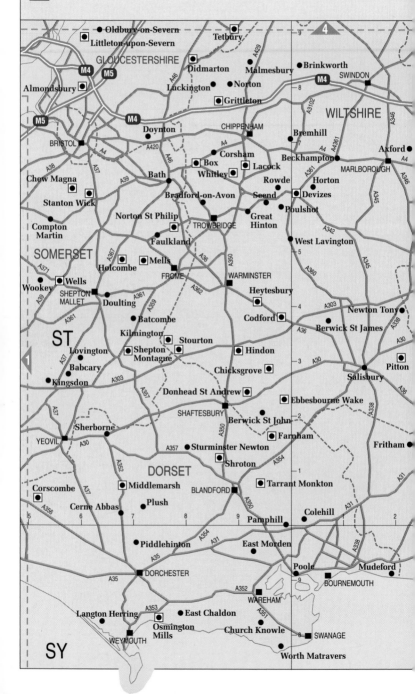

2

Oldbury-on-Severn
Littleton-upon-Severn
Tetbury

GLOUCESTERSHIRE
Didmarton
Malmesbury
Brinkworth
SWINDON

Almondsbury
Luckington
Norton
M4

M4
M5
Grittleton
WILTSHIRE

M5
Doynton
CHIPPENHAM
Bremhill
Axford

BRISTOL
A4
A420
Corsham
Beckhampton
MARLBOROUGH

Chew Magna
Box
Lacock
Rowde
Horton

Stanton Wick
Bath
Whitley
Seend
Devizes

Compton
Martin
Bradford-on-Avon
Great
Hinton
Poulshot

SOMERSET
Norton St Philip
TROWBRIDGE
West Lavington

Faulkland

Holcombe
Mells
FROME
WARMINSTER
Heytesbury

Wells
Doulting
Codford
Berwick St James
Newton Tony

Wookey
SHEPTON
MALLET
Batcombe
Pitton

ST
Kilmington
Stourton
Hindon
Salisbury

Lovington
Shepton
Montague
Chicksgrove

Babcary
Kingsdon
Donhead St Andrew
Ebbesbourne Wake

Sherborne
SHAFTESBURY
Berwick St John
Farnham
Fritham

YEOVIL
Sturminster Newton
Shroton

Corscombe
Middlemarsh
BLANDFORD
Tarrant Monkton

Cerne Abbas
Plush
Pamphill
Colehill

Piddlehinton
East Morden

Langton Herring
DORCHESTER
Poole
Mudeford
BOURNEMOUTH

Osmington
Mills
East Chaldon
WAREHAM

WEYMOUTH
Church Knowle
SWANAGE

SY
Worth Matravers

DORSET

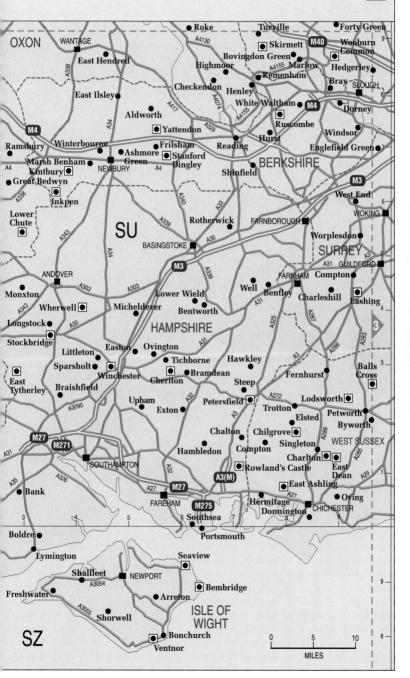

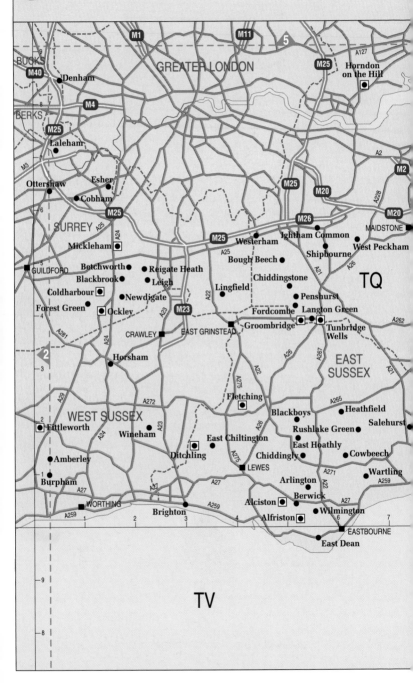

3

BUCKS
M40 ●Denham
BERKS
M4
M25
●Laleham
M3
Ottershaw● Esher●
●Cobham
M25
SURREY
Mickleham●
GUILDFORD
Betchworth● ●Reigate Heath
Blackbrook● ●Leigh
Coldharbour●
Newdigate●
Forest Green● ●Ockley
A261
A24
CRAWLEY
●Horsham
A29
WEST SUSSEX
●Fittleworth Wineham●
A24
Ditchling● ●East Chiltington
●Amberley
Burpham● A275
A27 WORTHING LEWES●
A259 1 2 Brighton 3

GREATER LONDON
M1 M11 5
A127
M25 Horndon on the Hill●
A2
M25 M20 M2
M26 M20
MAIDSTONE
M25 Westerham● Ightham Common●
A25 Bough Beech● Shipbourne● ●West Peckham
A21 A26 TQ
Chiddingstone●
Lingfield● Penshurst●
A22 Fordcombe● Langton Green●
EAST GRINSTEAD Groombridge● Tunbridge Wells
A262
M23 A26 A267 EAST SUSSEX A21
A22
A275
Fletching●
A26 Blackboys● ●Heathfield A265
Rushlake Green● Salehurst●
East Hoathly● ●Cowbeech
Chiddingly●
Arlington● Wartling● A259
A22 A271
Alciston● Berwick● A27
Alfriston● Wilmington●
4 5 6 7
EASTBOURNE
East Dean●

TV

9
8

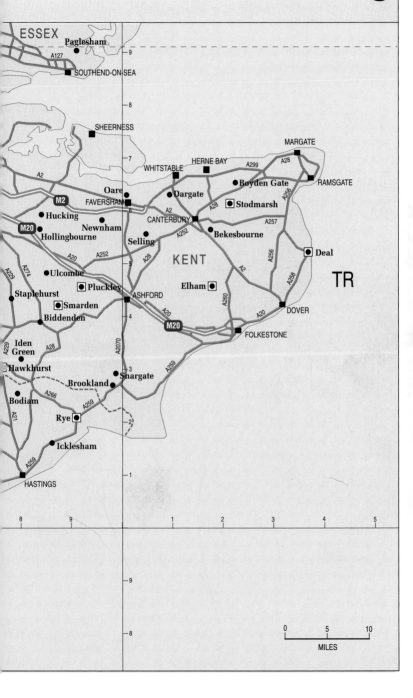

ESSEX

Paglesham

A127

SOUTHEND-ON-SEA

SHEERNESS

MARGATE

WHITSTABLE   HERNE BAY   A299   A28   RAMSGATE

Oare   Dargate   Boyden Gate

A2   M2   FAVERSHAM   A256

Hucking   A2   Stodmarsh

M20   Newnham   CANTERBURY   A257

Hollingbourne   Selling   Bekesbourne

A20   A252   KENT   A256   Deal

Ulcombe   A28   A2

Pluckley   Elham   A258   TR

Staplehurst   ASHFORD   A260   DOVER

A229   A274   Smarden

Biddenden   M20   A20

Iden   A2070   FOLKESTONE

Green   A28

Hawkhurst   Snargate   A259

A229

Brookland

A266   A259

Bodiam   Rye

A21   Icklesham

A259

HASTINGS

8   9   1   2   3   4   5

9

8   0   5   10

MILES

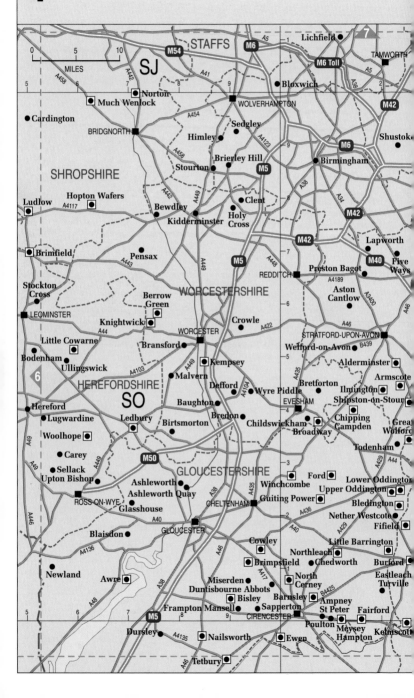

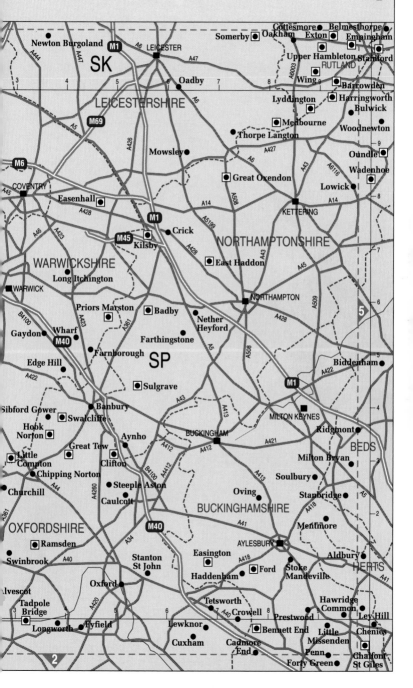

Newton Burgoland

M1 LEICESTER

SK

Somerby Oakham Cottesmore Belmesthorpe
Exton Empingham
Upper Hambleton Stamford
RUTLAND

Oadby

LEICESTERSHIRE

Wing Barrowden

Lyddington Harringworth
Bulwick

Medbourne

Thorpe Langton Woodnewtwon

Mowsley

M69

M6

COVENTRY

Great Oxendon

Oundle

Wadenhoe

Lowick

Easenhall

KETTERING

M1

M45 Crick

Kilsby

NORTHAMPTONSHIRE

WARWICKSHIRE

East Haddon

Long Itchington

NORTHAMPTON

WARWICK

Priors Marston Badby

Nether
Heyford

Gaydon Wharf

M40

Farnborough SP

Edge Hill

Farthingstone

Biddenham

Sulgrave

M1

Sibford Gower Banbury
Swalcliffe

Hook
Norton

MILTON KEYNES

Ridgmont

BEDS

Little
Compton

Great Tew Aynho

BUCKINGHAM

Milton Bryan

Clifton

Soulbury

Chipping Norton

Churchill Steeple Aston

Oving Stanbridge

Caulcott

BUCKINGHAMSHIRE

OXFORDSHIRE

M40

Menmore

Ramsden

Swinbrook

Easington

AYLESBURY Aldbury

HERTS

Alvescot

Stanton
St John

Ford Stoke
Mandeville

Tadpole
Bridge

Haddenham

Hawridge
Common

Ley Hill

Longworth Fyfield

Oxford

Tetsworth

Lewknor Crowell

Prestwood

Chenies

Cuxham

Bennett End Little
Missenden

Cadmore
End

Penn

Chalfont
St Giles

Forty Green

2

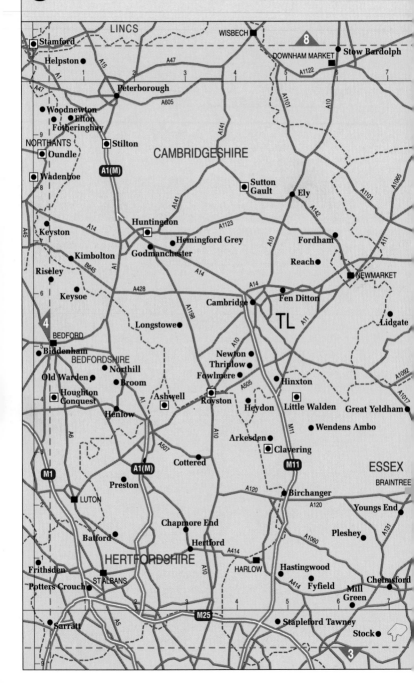

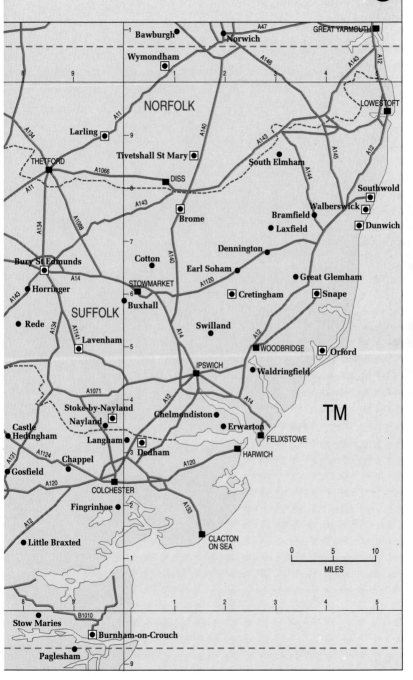

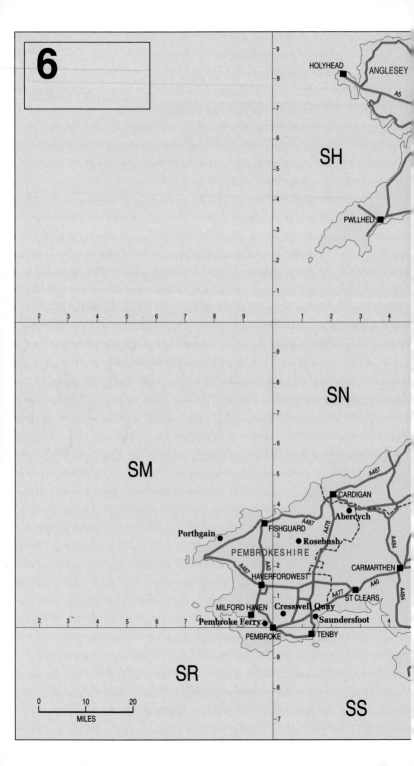

6

HOLYHEAD

ANGLESEY

A5

SH

PWLLHELI

SN

SM

CARDIGAN

Abercych

Porthgain

A487

FISHGUARD

A478

PEMBROKESHIRE

Rosebush

A487

A40

HAVERFORDWEST

CARMARTHEN

A484

A477

ST CLEARS

A40

A484

MILFORD HAVEN

Cresswell Quay

Pembroke Ferry

Saundersfoot

PEMBROKE

TENBY

SR

SS

0 10 20
MILES

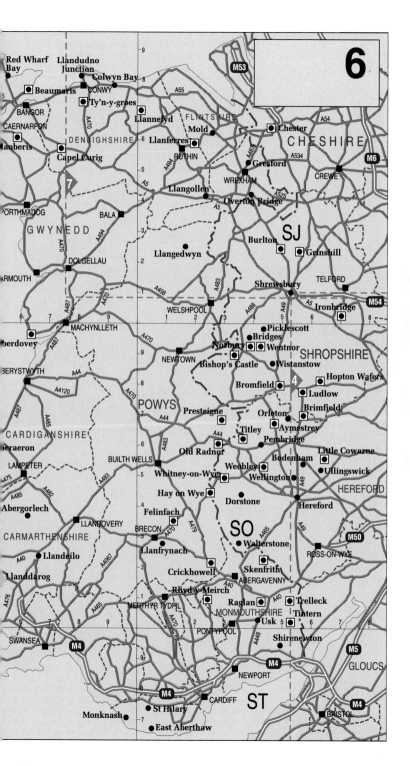

7

9

Ulverston
Beetham
Casterton
Chapel-le-Dale
Cartmel
Tunstall
Thornton in Lonsdale
Dalton-in-Furness
Yealand Conyers
M6
A683
A65
BARROW-IN-FURNESS

0 10 20
MILES

LANCASTER
SD
LANCASHIRE

Bay Horse
A6
Newton
Whitewell
Sawley
Chipping
Rimington
Little Eccleston
Goosnargh
Longridge
A59
BLACKPOOL
M55
Ribchester
Lytham
A584
PRESTON
M65
Wheelton
Belmont
SOUTHPORT
A59
Bu
Bispham Green
M61
A6
GREATER MANCHESTER
M
M58
A580
M6
MERSEYSIDE
M60
Liverpool
M62
Barnston
M53
M56
Llandudno Junction
CONWY
Colwyn Bay
CHESHIRE
Ty'n-y-groes
A55
M56
Llannefydd
FLINTSHIRE
Chester
A54
Peo Hea
A525
Mold
Cotebrook
Tarporley
DENBIGHSHIRE
RUTHIN
A494
Aldford
Wettenhall
A5
A49
Bunbury
Higher Burwardsley
Barthom
A5
Haughton Moss
WREXHAM
A534
Wybunbury
Bickley Moss
NANTWICH
M6
Llangollen
SJ
Wrenbury
A5
Overton Bridge
Aston
BALA
GWYNEDD
A483
A41
A53
A494
A528
6
POWYS
A49
A41
A5
A495
Burlton
Grinshill
A5
SHROPSHIRE
Shrewsbury

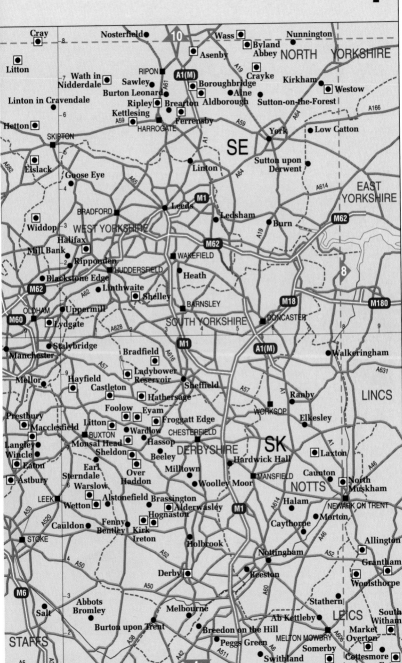

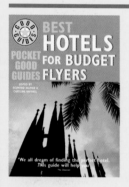 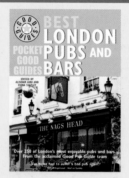 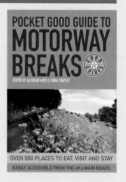

friendly licensees, good food using local produce inc some interesting dishes, Badger ales, farm cider, comfortbale leather sofas and open fire, big children's room, small conservatory with wonderful rolling hill views; bedrooms *(Miss M K Harper, Glenn and Gillian Miller)*

SHALDON [SX9372]

Ferryboat [Fore St]: Cosy and quaint little waterside local, basic but comfortable, long low-ceilinged bar overlooking estuary with Teignmouth ferry and lots of boats, welcoming helpful staff, Dartmoor, Greene King IPA and Old Speckled Hen, interesting wines, big helpings of good value varied home-made food, open fires, seafaring artefacts; children and dogs on leads welcome, tables on small sunny terrace across narrow road by sandy beach *(Meg and Colin Hamilton, Ian and Ruth Laurence)*

London [Bank St/The Green]: Well run and cheery village pub opp bowling green, good value generous food from good sandwiches up, well kept Greene King Abbot IPA and Abbot and Otter, decent wines, pleasant landlord; pool, juke box, can get smoky; children welcome, good value bedrooms with wholesome breakfast, pretty waterside village *(Mike Turner, Roy and Lindsey Fentiman)*

Royal Standard [Fore St]: Enjoyable home-made food inc local fish, good range of real ales, decent wines, warm atmosphere, welcoming staff; reasonably priced bedrooms, in centre of beautiful village handy for beach and ferry *(B M Eldridge)*

SIDMOUTH [SY1287]

Dukes [Market Pl]: Good central spot nr esplanade, one side no smoking with comfortable leather sofas and armchairs, the other side a modern coffee/wine bar with flagstones and big-screen TV; Branscombe Vale Branoc, Fullers London Pride and Otter, pubby food all day from lunchtime sandwiches and baked potatoes to steak, small conservatory; terrace tables, bedrooms with own bathrooms *(Joan and Michel Hooper-Immins)*

☆ *Old Ship* [Old Fore St]: Partly 14th-c, with low beams, mellow black woodwork and early 17th-c carved panelling, sailing ship prints, good inexpensive food (not Sun evening) from baked potatoes, local pasties and huge crab sandwiches to local fish, well kept ales such as Otter, St Austell Dartmoor and Wadworths 6X, decent wine choice, prompt courteous service even when busy, chatty manager and quietly friendly atmosphere, no piped music; close-set tables but roomier raftered upstairs bar with family room, dogs allowed; in pedestrian zone just moments from the sea (note that around here parking is limited to 30 mins) *(Dr and Mrs M E Wilson, Phil and Sally Gorton, Joan and Michel Hooper-Immins, BB, W W Burke, Mike Turner)*

☆ *Swan* [York St]: Lively and convivial backstreet local, pleasant staff, decent food from doorstep sandwiches to reasonably priced fresh fish, well kept Youngs, lounge bar with interesting pictures and memorabilia, bigger light and airy public bar with boarded walls and ceilings and thriving darts team, warm fire, separate dining area; nice small flower-filled garden *(Phil and Sally Gorton, Klaus and Elizabeth Leist, Alan and Paula McCully, B H and J I Andrews, Dr and Mrs M E Wilson)*

SILVERTON [SS9503]

Lamb [Fore St]: Friendly flagstoned local with two or three well kept changing ales such as Exe Valley Dobs Best tapped from the cask, food from sandwiches through straightforward main dishes to ostrich, helpful service, separate eating area; handy for Killerton (NT) *(Roger and Jenny Huggins, the Didler)*

Three Tuns [Exeter Rd]: 17th-c or older, with fair-sized public bar, comfortable settees, period furniture and log fire in attractively old-fashioned beamed lounge, food here or in cosy restaurant welcoming children, Exe Valley and guest beers; lovely flower displays, tables in pretty inner courtyard, handy for Killerton *(Jim and Maggie Cowell, Dr and Mrs M E Wilson, Mick and Moira Brummell, the Didler)*

SLAPTON [SX8245]

Queens Arms: Friendly modernised village local with snug comfortable corners, inexpensive straightforward food using local suppliers, well kept ales such as Princetown Dartmoor IPA, Sharps Doom Bar and Teignworthy Reel, interesting World War II pictures; parking needs skill; plenty of tables in lovely suntrap stepped back garden *(David Eberlin, Nick Lawless, Fred and Lorraine Gill, Bruce Bird)*

SMALLRIDGE [ST3000]

☆ *Ridgeway* [off A358 N of Axminster]: Friendly largely no smoking country bar with fresh flowers and chunky tables, more tables in back two-lane skittle alley, raftered upstairs dining room (no under-12s) with another skittle alley, very wide choice of good value generous food inc good fish range prepared to order (so may be a wait), well kept Branscombe Vale and Otter, good wines by the glass, good coffee, attentive very helpful service, woodburner, family atmosphere; piped music; ten bedrooms, pleasant two-level quiet terrace and garden, lovely views *(Michael Doswell, Michael and Jenny Back, BB, Meg and Colin Hamilton)*

SOURTON [SX5390]

☆ *Highwayman* [A386, S of junction with A30]: Marvellously eccentric décor in warren of dimly lit stonework and flagstone-floored burrows and alcoves, all sorts of things to look at and visual tricks to enjoy, even a make-believe sailing galleon; farm cider (and in season perhaps a real ale such as Bass), organic wines, food confined to sandwiches or pasties, friendly chatty service, old-fashioned penny fruit machine, 40s piped music, no smoking at bar counters; outside has fairy-tale pumpkin house and an old-lady-who-lived-in-the-shoe house – children allowed to look around pub but can't stay inside; period bedrooms with four-posters and half-testers, bunk rooms for walkers and cyclists *(the Didler, Mayur Shah, Dr D and Mrs B Woods, LYM, DAV)*

SOUTH POOL [SX7740]
☆ *Millbrook* [off A379 E of Kingsbridge]:
Charming little creekside pub opened up a bit
under welcoming newish owners, more open
dining space off the cheerful compact bar
areas, and new kitchen doing good food using
much local produce from generous lunchtime
crab sandwiches, ploughman's and so forth to
wider range of interesting simple modern
evening cooking, with well kept Bass, Fullers
London Pride, Wadworths 6X and a changing
guest beer tapped from the cask, local farm
cider, no piped music; children and dogs
welcome, covered seating and heaters for front
courtyard and waterside terrace, bedrooms
*(B J Harding, David Eberlin, Mr and
Mrs J Curtis, Roger Wain-Heapy, Brian and
Jean Hepworth, Richard and Anne Norris,
LYM, Geoffrey Townsend, Mrs C Lintott)*

SOUTH ZEAL [SX6493]
Kings Arms: Thatched medieval local with big
slate fireplace in long dark-beamed bar, well
kept Adnams, Otter and Charles Wells
Bombardier, enjoyable bar food; open all day
Sun *(Dr and Mrs M E Wilson)*
☆ *Oxenham Arms* [off A30/A382]: Marvellous
building, well worth a look, friendly beamed
and partly panelled front bar with elegant
mullioned windows and Stuart fireplaces (can
be smoky), small beamed family room with
another open fire, well kept Sharps Doom Bar
and a guest such as Archers, quite a few wines
by the glass, bar and restaurant food; dogs
allowed in bar, imposing garden with lovely
views, bedrooms with own bathrooms
*(Phil and Sally Gorton, Pete Baker,
Ann Holdsworth, Elizabeth and Roy Russell,
Ian and Jane Irving, the Didler, LYM,
Karen and Graham Oddey)*

SPARKWELL [SX5857]
Treby Arms: Unpretentiously old-world, with
very wide choice of reliable good value food,
friendly helpful service, good range of beers inc
unusual guests and Scutchers brewed locally
for the pub, decent house wines, small dining
room; disabled facilities, nearby wildlife park
(John Evans)

ST ANNS CHAPEL [SX4170]
Old Chapel: Charming service and relaxing
atmosphere in stylishly converted Gothic
chapel, beams, stripped stone, log fire in big
fireplace, good fresh and varied modern food
inc original children's dishes in bar and family
room, restaurant menu for elegant airy
conservatory, fine wine choice, five real ales;
neat garden, five bedrooms (furnished to suit
the building) with own bathrooms *(anon)*

ST GILES IN THE WOOD [SS5420]
Cranford [off B3227 NE of Torrington]:
Friendly pub with good nicely served food,
attractive dining room *(Michael and
Judy Buckley)*

STAPLE CROSS [ST0320]
Staplecross Inn [Holcombe Rogus—
Hockworthy]: Simple Exmoor-edge pub in
pleasant woodside setting, understated charm,
well kept real ales and good honest pub food
(Jeremy Whitehorn, Anthony Longden)

STOKEINTEIGNHEAD [SX9169]
☆ *Chasers Arms*: Good food inc interesting
dishes, imaginative veg, lots of fish and
unusual puddings, in long 16th-c thatched
pub/restaurant (you can't just go for a drink,
but they do bar snacks too and the style
emulates a country pub); fine range of house
wines, pleasant atmosphere, quick friendly
service *(Mr and Mrs S Smith)*
☆ *Church House* [signed from
Combeinteignhead, or off A379 N of
Torquay]: 13th-c thatched pub with heavy
beams, inglenook fireplace, antique
furnishings, ancient spiral stairs and relaxed
informal atmosphere, some emphasis on
enjoyable food from good sandwiches and
baked potatoes up, well kept Adnams, Bass
and Greene King Old Speckled Hen, farm
cider, good coffee, friendly obliging staff, smart
extended no smoking dining room, simple
public bar with traditional games and TV;
quiet piped music, children in eating area, neat
interestingly planted back garden, unspoilt
village *(Richard and Margaret Peers, LYM,
Tim and Rosemary Wells, David Field)*

STOKENHAM [SX8042]
☆ *Church House* [opp church, N of A379
towards Torcross]: Large comfortable open-
plan pub next to interesting church, enjoyable
food from proper generous sandwiches and
filled baked potatoes to fresh local seafood and
good steaks, four real ales, farm cider, no
smoking dining room; unobtrusive piped
music, Weds quiz night; attractive garden with
fishpond and appealing play area *(B J Harding,
Roger Wain-Heapy, LYM, Brian Root,
Fred and Lorraine Gill)*
☆ *Tradesmans Arms* [just off A379 Dartmouth—
Kingsbridge]: Friendly landlord in picturesque
15th-c thatched pub overlooking village green,
enjoyable reasonably priced food from pubby
favourites to lots of local fish, good Sun roasts
and good puddings, four well kept ales, local
farm cider, well chosen wines, nice antique
tables in beamed bar and no smoking dining
room; wknd live music, attractive garden, open
all day *(Roger Wain-Heapy, Keith and
Margaret Kettell, Marguerite Pointer, Mr and
Mrs J Curtis, Torrens Lyster, LYM,
Nick Lawless, Carolyn Dixon, Fred and
Lorraine Gill)*

TEIGNMOUTH [SX9372]
Molloys [Teign St]: Warmly welcoming town
pub well worth knowing for its lady chef's
short choice of good cheap food inc bargain
steaks, friendly staff, well kept beer, cosy
booth seating; no credit cards *(Ken Flawn,
Meg and Colin Hamilton)*
New Quay [New Quay St]: Doing well under
new landlord, good choice of beers and wines
by the glass, enjoyable food from new kitchen,
helpful staff, super waterside location
(Ken Flawn)

THURLESTONE [SX6743]
Village Inn: Small much refurbished pub
owned by neighbouring smart hotel and
emphasising wide food choice (cold cabinet,
open kitchen behind servery, blackboards, etc);

well kept ales such as Sharps Doom Bar, comfortable country-style furnishings, dividers forming alcoves; children and dogs catered for, darts, quiz nights, live music; handy for coast path *(M Thomas, Lawrence Pearse)*

TIPTON ST JOHN [SY0991]

☆ *Golden Lion* [signed off B3176 Sidmouth—Ottery St Mary]: Wide blackboard choice of sensibly priced good food from sandwiches to seafood and some interesting dishes (French chef/landlord), well kept Bass and Otter, limited but well chosen wine list, quick friendly service, blazing log fire, attractive décor and mix of furnishings in spacious relaxing bar with quiet back room, no smoking restaurant; piped music; children in eating areas, open all day wknds, garden and terrace tables, two comfortable bedrooms with showers *(W Perry, LYM, Mark and Heather Williamson, Dr and Mrs M E Wilson, John and Doris Couper, Mrs A P Lee)*

TIVERTON [SS9512]

Prince Regent [Lowman Green, opp old Blundells School building]: Welcoming traditional pub, well kept St Austell Trelawnys Pride and a beer brewed for the pub, helpful service, food arrangement with next-door restaurant – for instance, getting sandwiches made; open all day Fri *(Rona Murdoch)*

TOPSHAM [SX9688]

☆ *Globe* [Fore St; 2 miles from M5 junction 30]: Substantial traditional inn dating from 16th c, solid comfort in heavy-beamed bow-windowed bar, good interesting home-cooked food from tasty sandwiches and toasties up, reasonable prices, well kept Bass, Sharps Doom Bar and guest beers, good value house wines, prompt friendly helpful service, plenty of locals, log-effect gas fire, snug little dining lounge, good value separate restaurant, back extension; children in eating areas, open all day, good value attractive bedrooms *(Mark and Heather Williamson, LYM, Dr and Mrs M E Wilson, the Didler, Barry Steele-Perkins, David Field)*

☆ *Lighter* [Fore St]: Comfortably extended and refurbished, catering well for visitors; brisk service even when busy, well kept Badger Best and Tanglefoot, food from good sandwiches, baked potatoes and popular local cheese platter to mildly upmarket dishes and local fish, nautical décor, panelling and tall windows looking out over tidal flats, central log fire, raised enclosed no smoking area, good children's area; games machines, piped music; lots of tables out in lovely spot on old quay, handy for big antiques centre *(Mrs Sylvia Elcoate, Mark and Heather Williamson, David Carr, Michael and Alison Sandy, the Didler, BB, Barry Steele-Perkins, Dr and Mrs M E Wilson)*

☆ *Passage House* [Ferry Rd, off main street]: Quiet and attractive foody pub recently taken in hand by new landlord, good fresh fish choice, nice simple cooking, other dishes from sandwiches up, well kept Otter and other ales, good wines, traditional 18th-c black-beamed bar and no smoking slate-floored lower bistro

area (children welcome here), pleasant service; may be piped music; peaceful terrace looking over moorings and river (lovely at sunset) to nature reserve beyond, open all day wknds and summer *(LYM, Derek and Sylvia Stephenson, John and Vivienne Rice, David Carr, Peter Burton, Louise Symons, the Didler, Dr and Mrs M E Wilson, Barry Steele-Perkins)*

TORQUAY [SX9175]

Crown & Sceptre [Petitor Rd, St Marychurch]: Friendly two-bar local in 18th-c beamed and stone-built coaching inn, eight well kept changing ales, interesting naval memorabilia and chamber-pot collection, good-humoured long-serving landlord, basic good value lunchtime food (not Sun), snacks any time, frequent jazz nights; dogs very welcome, children too *(Jim and Maggie Cowell, John Haslam, Linda Drew, the Didler, Kevin Blake, Margaret Mason, David Thompson)*

☆ *Hole in the Wall* [Park Lane, opp clock tower]: Ancient unpretentious two-bar local nr harbour, consistently good value usual food, well kept Sharps Doom Bar and guest beers, Blackawton cider, proper old-fashioned landlord and friendly service, flagstones, low beams and alcoves, lots of nautical brassware, ship models, old local photographs, chamber-pots, restaurant/function room (band nights); small terrace, open all day *(Kevin Blake, Mr and Mrs R J Timberlake)*

TORRINGTON [SS4919]

☆ *Black Horse* [High St]: Unpretentious twin-gabled pub dating from 15th c, overhanging upper storeys, beams hung with stirrups, solid furniture, oak bar counter, no smoking lounge with striking ancient black oak partition wall and a couple of attractive oak seats, oak-panelled back restaurant with aquarium, good value generous food inc OAP wkdy lunchtime bargains and good evening dishes, friendly service, well kept Courage Best and Directors, John Smiths and changing guest beers, darts, shove-ha'penny, cribbage, dominoes; well reproduced piped music, friendly cat and dogs; children really welcome, disabled access, open all day Sat *(Lesley Hampson, Brian Brooks, LYM, Michael and Judy Buckley)*

Puffing Billy [Old Station House, A386 NW]: Popular family pub in former station building on Tarka Trail walk/cycle route, done out in old Southern Railway colours; well kept ales, decent wines and enjoyable food inc good value children's dishes, lots of train memorabilia and pictures; dogs welcome, garden with pets corner *(Ian Clare)*

Torridge [Mill St]: Welcoming, with well kept real ales *(Dr and Mrs A K Clarke)*

TOTNES [SX8060]

King William IV [Fore St]: Warm, spacious and comfortably carpeted Victorian pub, popular (esp with older people) for enjoyable bargain main dishes, quick cheerful service and obliging chef, real ales such as Flowers or Fullers London Pride, californian wines; big-screen sports TV; bedrooms with own bathrooms *(Mr and Mrs Colin Roberts, Ken Flawn)*

☆ *Steam Packet* [St Peters Quay, on W bank (ie not on Steam Packet Quay!)]: Appealing layout and décor, thriving atmosphere, well kept ales such as Courage Best, Marstons Pedigree and Otter, decent wines, cheerful efficient staff, tempting food from tasty lunchtime crab and other sandwiches up, good wines and coffee, log fire, restaurant with spectacular river view from no smoking conservatory; piped music, jazz Sun lunchtime, winter quiz night Mon; children welcome (games for them in side library area with squishy leather sofa), tables on big heated quay-view terrace, bedrooms, open all day *(Alain and Rose Foote, Comus and Sarah Elliott, George Atkinson, BB, Ken Flawn)*

TUCKENHAY [SX8156]
Maltsters Arms [Ashprington rd out of Totnes (signed left off A381 on outskirts)]: Such a lovely spot, with waterside tables out by peaceful wooded creek, that they scarcely need to try here, but it's usually friendly and most enjoyable, with some good interesting dishes, fresh local fish, local cheeses and real food for children, well kept Sharps Doom Bar and St Austell ales, lots of good wines by the glass and other good drinks, relaxed chatty atmosphere, interesting small rooms with simple up-to-date décor (a no smoking area would be appreciated), traditional games, compact restaurant (booking recommended; wknd barbecues with live music); children and dogs welcome, bedrooms (there may be a minimum wknd stay of two nights), open all day *(the Didler, Lorna Duff, Doreen and Haydn Maddock, Mike Gorton, OPUS, Felicity Stephens, David Fox, Mrs Susan Pritchard, John and Doris Couper, A P Seymour, LYM, Alan and Anne Driver, Lynda and Trevor Smith, Barry and Anne, M Sage, MP, Andrew Barker,Claire Jenkins)*

UGBOROUGH [SX6755]
Anchor [off A3121]: Village pub with log fire, locals and dogs in unpretentious beamed bar, well kept ales such as Bass, Shepherd Neame Spitfire and Suttons, partly no smoking restaurant, food from light lunchtime things to ambitious dishes with bison, ostrich and so forth; TV; children welcome, small outside seating area, open all day wknds *(Roger and Jenny Huggins, LYM, Mr and Mrs J E C Tasker, Oliver and Sue Rowell)*

UMBERLEIGH [SS6023]
Portsmouth Arms [A377 by Portsmouth Arms Stn]: Wider opening under new hard-working young licensees (still cl Mon), sensibly organised food – lunchtime emphasis on baguettes, short evening choice of starters and hot dishes etc, changing weekly, limited choice of well kept ale, log fire, amiable dog; plans for bathroom for each bedroom *(Mark Flynn)*

☆ *Rising Sun* [A377 S of Barnstaple]: Comfortable and civilised fishing inn with five salmon and sea trout beats on River Taw, lots of stuffed fish and fishing memorabilia in relaxed partly no smoking divided bar with

woodburner, flagstones and magazines to read; friendly staff, good food inc lunchtime sandwiches and light dishes, well kept real ales inc Cotleigh Barn Owl, good wines by the glass and farm cider; children in eating areas, tables outside, good bedrooms *(Dr and Mrs A K Clarke, LYM, David Gibbs, Mark Flynn, B M Eldridge, JMC)*

WALKHAMPTON [SX5369]
Walkhampton Inn: Cheerful 17th-c local, log fire each end of comfortable carpeted bar, stripped stone, beams and lots of horsebrasses, good value generous no-nonsense food inc good steaks and puddings, well kept Princetown and St Austell ales, friendly staff, no smoking area, games room; dogs welcome, nice Dartmoor-edge village *(DAV, Ron and Sheila Corbett)*

WEARE GIFFARD [SS4722]
Cyder Press: Homely and welcoming pub in pretty village overlooking River Torridge, good sensible food, friendly service, darts in public bar, separate dining area; handy for Tarka Trail, beautiful countryside *(David Whiter)*

WELCOMBE [SS2317]
Old Smithy [signed off A39 S of Hartland]: Much modernised newly re-thatched pub with new young chef doing enjoyable fresh food using local fish and other local produce, well kept real ales, buoyant atmosphere combining local regulars with the surfing contingent in simple open-plan family bar with rows of tables; plenty of seats in pretty terraced garden, self-catering, lovely setting by lane leading eventually to attractive rocky cove *(LYM, Tansy Spinks, Nick Rampley)*

WEMBWORTHY [SS6609]
☆ *Lymington Arms* [Lama Cross]: Large dining pub, clean and bright, with wide choice of good reasonably priced food (not Mon), friendly efficient service, well kept beers inc Sharps Doom Bar, Inch's cider, decent wines, agreeable restaurant (not Sun/Mon); children welcome, tables in garden, pleasant country setting *(Mark Flynn, Guy Vowles)*

WEST ALVINGTON [SX7243]
☆ *Ring o' Bells*: Extraordinarily wide choice of good attractively priced food inc children's and half helpings in extended modernised pub with wide views, helpful friendly staff, relaxing atmosphere, good housekeeping, Sharps Doom Bar; children and dogs welcome, terrace tables, comfortable bedrooms in motel-style upper bedroom wing with great breakfast – also B&B in licensees' own converted barn *(B J Harding, BB, George Atkinson, Gary Fairbairn)*

WESTLEIGH [SS4728]
Westleigh Inn [½ mile off A39 Bideford—Instow]: Excellent play area in big neat garden overlooking Torridge estuary, inglenook log fire, well kept Bass, enjoyable usual food from baguettes up, friendly prompt service, no smoking room; dogs welcome, Tarka Trail walks *(Ian Clare, LYM)*

WESTON [ST1400]
Otter [off A373, or A30 at W end of Honiton bypass]: Big pleasantly extended and

refurbished family pub with heavy low beams, enjoyable food, Fullers London Pride and Otter, good value wines, good log fire; children welcome, picnic-sets on big lawn leading to River Otter and its ducks and skipping-rocks, play area (*LYM, Bob and Margaret Holder, Dr and Mrs M E Wilson*)

WHIMPLE [SY0497]
☆ *New Fountain* [off A30 Exeter—Honiton; Church Rd]: Attractive, civilised and very friendly two-bar beamed village pub with cosy local atmosphere, good inexpensive food inc interesting dishes, well kept changing beers inc O'Hanlons brewed in the village, woodburner (*LYM, HP, Dr and Mrs M E Wilson*)

WITHERIDGE [SS8014]
Angel [The Square]: Bright, airy and spacious, with homely bric-a-brac, friendly licensees, well kept interesting changing beers, good range of malt whiskies, reasonably priced tasty food inc very fresh salads (*C R Cann, C T Baker*)

WOODBURY [SY0187]
White Hart [3½ miles from M5 junction 30; A376, then B3179; Church St]: Good unpretentious local atmosphere, good choice of good value food, well kept Bass and Everards Tiger, decent wines, plain public bar, comfortable quieter dining lounge, log fire; attractive small walled garden with aviary,

skittle alley, nice spot by church in peaceful village (*Dr and Mrs M E Wilson*)

WRAFTON [SS4935]
Williams Arms [A361 just SE of Braunton]: Modernised thatched family dining pub geared to holiday-makers and giving children free rein, two big comfortable subdivided bars, wide food choice majoring on very popular unlimited self-service carvery, children's helpings, very efficient friendly service, Bass, decent house wines; pool, darts, piped music, discreet TV; picnic-sets outside with play area and aviary (*K R Harris, Chris and Ann Coy*)

LUNDY ISLAND

LUNDY [SS1344]
☆ *Marisco*: One of England's most isolated pubs (yet full every night), great setting, galleried interior with lifebelts and other paraphernalia from local shipwrecks; brews its own two tasty beers, also others and Lundy spring water on tap, good value house wines, welcoming staff, good food using island produce and lots of seafood fresh from immaculate kitchen; children welcome, tables outside, self-catering and camping available; souvenir shop, and doubles as general store for the island's few residents (*D Cheesbrough*)

'Children welcome' means the pub says it lets children inside without any special restriction. If it allows them in, but to restricted areas such as an eating area or family room, we specify this. Places with separate restaurants often let children use them, hotels usually let them into public areas such as lounges. Some pubs impose an evening time limit – let us know if you find this.

Dorset

After finding no fewer than six new main entries here last year, we have another five this year (some of them returning to the fold after a break of several years, under go-ahead new licensees). These newcomers are the Elm Tree at Langton Herring (enjoyable food using good local supplies, in pleasant surroundings), the welcoming old low-beamed Bottle at Marshwood (enjoyable food here too), the comfortable Brace of Pheasants at Plush (impressive as a dining pub, good beer, friendly service and a nice garden), the interesting and relaxing modern-style Cow in Poole (enjoyable up-to-date food and drink), and in contrast the ancient Shave Cross Inn (brought back to life under a new landlord, with interesting caribbean food alongside all the virtues of a quintessentially English country pub). Other pubs on fine form here include the comfortably unpretentious old George in Chideock (nice food), the charmingly rustic Fox at Corscombe (imaginative cooking gains a Food Award this year, far from cheap but well worth it), the Cock & Bottle at East Morden (good food here too, with some inventive dishes, and a proper pubby public bar), the civilised Museum at Farnham (a stylish if pricey gastropub, great care over ingredients), the down-to-earth Digby Tap in Sherborne (good beers and bargain food), the welcoming Cricketers at Shroton (good all round, gaining a Place to Stay Award this year), the chatty West Bay in West Bay itself (superb fish cooking in pleasantly low-key surroundings), and the Square & Compass at Worth Matravers – many people's idea of a classic unspoilt country pub. Several of these pubs are good for a special meal out; for the third year on the trot, the West Bay takes the Dorset Dining Pub of the Year Award. Good prospects in the Lucky Dip section at the end of the chapter are the Worlds End at Almer, White Lion at Bourton, George in Bridport, Three Horseshoes at Burton Bradstock, Poet Laureate on the edge of Dorchester, Blackmore Vale at Marnhull, Three Horseshoes at Powerstock, Bankes Arms at Studland, Red Lion at Sturminster Marshall, Greyhound at Sydling St Nicholas, Ilchester Arms at Symondsbury and Crown at Uploders. Dorset drinks prices are close to the national average; the county's main brewers are Palmers and Badger.

CERNE ABBAS ST6601 Map 2
Royal Oak
Long Street

New licensees just as we went to press put this picturesque creeper-covered Tudor dining pub on probation this year, so do let us know about your visit. The three flagstoned communicating rooms have sturdy oak beams, lots of shiny black panelling, an inglenook with an oven, and warm winter log fires. Stone walls and the ceilings are packed with all sorts of small ornaments from local photographs to antique china, brasses and farm tools; candles on tables; fresh flowers; occasional piped music. Three Badger beers are served from handpumps on the uncommonly long bar counter. They also do around eight wines by the glass, 15 malt whiskies and a local cider. Bar food includes soup (£3.95), local pâté with gooseberry and coriander chutney (£4.95), spicy lambs kidneys (£5.95), ploughman's (£7.75), battered haddock or courgette and mushroom ragoût (£7.95), local venison sausages and mash (£8.95) and veal in cream, mustard and whisky or 10oz rib-eye steak (£11.95). The enclosed back garden is very pleasant, with comfortable chairs and tables under cocktail parasols, and outdoor heaters on purbeck stone terracing and cedarwood decking. On sunny summer afternoons they sometimes serve drinks and snacks out here. Readers tell us parking can be a problem at busy times. *(Recommended by the Didler)*

Badger ~ Tenants Tony and Christine Green ~ Real ale ~ Bar food ~ Restaurant ~ (01300) 341797 ~ Children welcome ~ Dogs welcome ~ Open 11.30-3, 6-11; 12-3, 6.30-10.30 Sun

CHIDEOCK SY4292 Map I

George
A35 Bridport—Lyme Regis

Unpretentious but comfy in its décor, this heavily thatched 17th-c inn has plenty of character and a good cheery welcome. Four well kept Palmers beers served on handpump from the horseshoe shaped counter. The dark-beamed lounge bar has comfortable red plush stools and wall and window seats, pewter tankards hanging from the mantelpiece above the big fireplace (with good winter log fires), boat drawings and attractively framed old local photographs on its cream walls, a collection of over 250 foreign banknotes, and high shelves of bottles, plates, mugs and so forth. Much enjoyed by readers, bar food includes lunchtime soup (£3.95), sandwiches (from £3.95), ploughman's (from £5.95), battered haddock (£9.25), irish stew (£9.45) and seafood pasta (£10.95). The evening blackboard menu might include additional dishes such as thai green curry (£9.45) and grilled tiger prawns (£11.95). The restaurant and dining room are no smoking; darts, table skittles, unobtrusive piped music. In summer, you can eat out on the patio, where they hold regular barbecues. *(Recommended by Jacqueline Waller, Mrs Jill Silversides, Barry Brown, Terry and Linda Moseley, Oz and Annette, W W Burke, Nick Lawless, Julie and Bill Ryan)*

Palmers ~ Tenant Paul Crisp ~ Real ale ~ Bar food (lunchtime only) ~ Restaurant ~ (01297) 489419 ~ Children welcome ~ Dogs allowed in bar ~ Live folk country and blues Fri, Sat ~ Open 11-3, 6-12; 12-3, 6-11 Sun; 12-2.30, 6(7 Sun)-11 winter

CHURCH KNOWLE SY9481 Map 2

New Inn ♀
Village signposted off A351 just N of Corfe Castle

Handy if you're in the Purbecks, this partly thatched 16th-c inn serves good food, including a great choice of fresh fish: half a pint of prawns (£7.50), fruits de mer (£9.50), large haddock (£13.50), locally caught sea bream (£13.95), and bass (£14.95). Other meals might include sandwiches (from £4), blue vinney soup (£4.25), ploughman's (from £6.25), steak and kidney pie (£8.95), and steaks (from £12.95). The two main areas, linked by an arch, are attractively furnished with farmhouse chairs and tables, lots of bric-a-brac (including a glass case with some interesting memorabilia) and a log fire at each end; one area is no smoking. You can choose wines from a tempting display in the wine cellar, which often includes interesting bin ends from their wine shack (they also do off sales from here), and they serve several wines by the glass. Well kept Flowers Original, Greene King Old Speckled Hen and Wadworths 6X on handpump, farmhouse cider and organic apple juices, and around a dozen malt whiskies. There are disabled facilities, though there's a step down to the gents'. The good-sized garden has plenty of tables and fine views of the Purbeck hills, and you can camp in two fields behind (you must book). *(Recommended by JDM, KM, Pat and Robert Watt, Gerry and Rosemary Dobson, Joan and Michel Hooper-Immins, Ned Kelly, Mike and Sue Loseby, John Balfour, Derek and Maggie Washington, Pam and Alan Neale)*

Punch ~ Tenants Maurice and Rosemary Estop ~ Real ale ~ Bar food (12-2, 6.30-9.15) ~ (01929) 480357 ~ Open 11-3, 6-11; 12-3, 6-10.30 Sun; closed Mon Jan-end Mar

COLEHILL SU0302 Map 2

Barley Mow

From roundabout junction of A31 Ferndown bypass and B3073 Wimborne road, follow Colehill signpost up Middlehill Road, pass Post Office, and at church turn right into Colehill Lane; OS Sheet 195 map reference 032024

This attractive part-thatched and part-tiled former drovers' cottage is a handy stop if you're in the area, though it can be very busy, at which times there may be a wait for your meal. With an emphasis on dining, the cosy low-beamed main bar has a good winter fire in the huge brick inglenook, attractively moulded oak panelling, some Hogarth prints. Sheltered by oak trees, there's a big pleasant, enclosed lawn at the back with a boules pitch. The pub is specially striking in summer, when colourful flowers in tubs and hanging baskets are set off vividly against the whitewash. Big helpings of bar food could include soup (£2.95), smoked haddock florentine (£4.25), fish and chips (£6.45), chicken, ham and leek or steak and ale pie (£7.45), brie and broccoli en croûte (£8.95), sirloin steak (£10.75) and daily specials such as moussaka and at least two fresh fish dishes of the day (£7.95), an extension to the main bar is set for diners. Badger Best, Tanglefoot and Fursty Ferret are well kept on handpump alongside a dozen fruit wines; unobtrusive piped music and a fruit machine. The cat is called Misty. (Recommended by W W Burke, David Cannings, Mr and Mrs R W Allan, B and K Hypher, John A Barker, M and R Thomas)

Badger ~ Manager Bruce Cichocki ~ Real ale ~ Bar food (12-2, 6(7 Sun)-9) ~ (01202) 882140 ~ Children in family room ~ Dogs allowed in bar ~ Open 11-2.30, 5.30-11; 12-3, 7-10.30 Sun

CORSCOMBE ST5205 Map 2

Fox 🍽 ♀ 🍺

Outskirts, towards Halstock

This picturesque old thatched pub (there are even roses over the door) delights readers. It's in a lovely country setting just out of the village, with seats across a quiet lane on a lawn by a little stream. A flagstoned room on the right has harness hanging from the beams, small Leech hunting prints and Snaffles prints, Spy cartoons of fox-hunting gentlemen, a long scrubbed pine table, and two open fires with large inglenooks. In the left-hand room there are built-in settles, candles on the blue-and-white gingham tablecloths or barrel tables, an assortment of chairs, lots of horse prints, antlers on the beams, two glass cabinets with a couple of stuffed owls in each, and an L-shaped wall settle by the inglenook fireplace. The dining room (which is open when they're busy and for winter breakfast) has an Aga, pine cupboards, and a welsh dresser. Apart from lunchtime baguettes and ploughman's (from £5.50), the rather good (though definitely not cheap) food is imaginative and several notches up on the usual pub menu. Served by professional staff, the menu includes fish soup or wild mushroom risotto (£5.50), roast aubergine baked with mozzarella, garlic, tomato and cream (£4.95), duck breast with cranberry and orange sauce (£15.95), rack of lamb with mustard mash and rosemary jus (£16.50) and specials such as aberdeen angus steak with shropshire blue, mushroom and vodka sauce (£21.95), around half a dozen fresh fish dishes such as john dory topped with garlic and lemon crust (£17.95), bass fillets with fennel and dill (£17.95), half a grilled lobster (£22.95), and home-made puddings such as chocolate torte or meringues and clotted cream (£3.95). Most of the dining areas are no smoking. Exmoor Ale and Butcombe Bitter are well kept on handpump alongside an occasional summer guest, a local cider, a thoughtful wine list and, as a nice touch, home-made elderflower cordial, damson vodka, and sloe gin. (Recommended by Joel Dobris, Mrs H Filmer, Francis Johnston, W W Burke, Paul Morris, Roland and Wendy Chalu, Conor McGaughey, Kim and Ann Miller, OPUS, John Hale, J S Burn, John A Barker, Douglas and Ann Hare, Marianne and Peter Stevens, Brian Hulme)

Free house ~ Licensees Clive Webb and Margaret Hannell ~ Real ale ~ Bar food ~ Restaurant ~ (01935) 891330 ~ Children over 5 in dining areas ~ Open 12-3, 7(10.30 Sun)-11 ~ Bedrooms: £55B/£80B

EAST CHALDON SY7983 Map 2
Sailors Return
Village signposted from A352 Wareham—Dorchester; from village green, follow
Dorchester, Weymouth signpost; note that the village is also known as Chaldon
Herring; OS sheet 194 map reference 790834

Picnic-sets, benches and log seats on the grass in front of this extended thatched pub
look down over fields to the village. Although fairly isolated, it gets very busy at
weekends, especially in fine weather. The flagstoned bar still keeps much of its
original country-tavern character, while the newer part has unfussy furnishings, old
notices for decoration, and open beams showing the roof. Half a dozen well kept real
ales include Hampshire Strongs Best and Ringwood Best, alongside guests from
brewers such as Badger, Hop Back and Palmers, and they also have country wines
and several malt whiskies. Straightforward bar food includes baguettes (£3.75),
ploughman's or filled baked potatoes (£5.75), egg and sausage or breaded plaice
(£7.25) and a handful of daily specials such as half a lamb shoulder (£9.95). The no
smoking restaurant has solid old tables in nooks and corners; cribbage, dominoes and
piped music. *(Recommended by Bruce Bird, Roy and Lindsey Fentiman, Alec and
Joan Laurence, Alex and Irene Harvey, Matthew Beard, Pat and Robert Watt, Alan M Pring,
Pam and Alan Neale)*

Free house ~ Licensees Mike Pollard, Claire Kelly and David Slater ~ Real ale ~ Bar food
(12-2, 6-9; 12-9.30 Fri-Sun) ~ Restaurant ~ (01305) 853847 ~ Children in restaurant ~
Dogs allowed in bar ~ Open 11-11; 12-10.30 Sun

EAST MORDEN SY9195 Map 2
Cock & Bottle 🍴 ♀ ◀
B3075 between A35 and A31 W of Poole

Chatty locals in the pubby wood-floored bar (fruit machine, and sensibly placed darts
alcove) make a healthy contrast to the strong culinary aspects of this welcoming pub
– in fact it's a good idea to book if you do want to eat. Mostly laid out for dining, the
rest of the interior is divided into several communicating areas (mostly laid out for
dining), with heavy rough beams, some stripped ceiling boards, squared panelling, a
mix of old furnishings in various sizes and degrees of antiquity, small Victorian prints
and some engaging bric-a-brac. There's a roaring log fire, and comfortably intimate
corners, each with just a couple of tables. From an imaginative changing bar menu
dishes might include roast butternut and thai coconut sauce with caramelised sweet
potatoes (£4.50), tempura prawns with sweet chilli sauce (£6.95), steak and kidney
pudding (£11.25), roast cornish rack of lamb with grilled vegetables and mint and
yoghurt dressing or seared king scallops with asian spiced cream sauce or steamed
brill fillet with baby spinach and mussel and smoked haddock cream sauce (£13.95)
and puddings such as glazed rhubarb crème brûlée or soft chocolate pudding with
chocolate sauce (£4.50). There's a children's menu, and they'll also do half helpings
of some main courses. Most of the restaurant is no smoking, and they have some
disabled facilities. As well as a good choice of decent house wines (including half a
dozen by the glass), they have well kept Badger Best, King and Barnes and Tanglefoot
on handpump; helpful service from the pleasant staff. There are a few picnic-sets
outside, a garden area, and an adjoining field with a nice pastoral outlook.
*(Recommended by Roy and Lindsey Fentiman, Tim and Rosemary Wells, A B Mason, John and
Joan Nash, Mrs H E Cunliffe, Peter Neate, Peter Meister, Betsy and Peter Little, Mr and
Mrs Peter Llewellyn, Dr Stephen Jolles, T and P)*

Badger ~ Tenant Peter Meadley ~ Real ale ~ Bar food (12-2, 6(7 Sun)-9) ~ Restaurant ~
(01929) 459238 ~ Children in restaurant ~ Dogs welcome ~ Open 11-2.30, 6-11; 12-3,
7-10.30 Sun

Post Office address codings confusingly give the impression that some pubs are in
Dorset, when they're really in Somerset (which is where we list them).

FARNHAM ST9515 Map 2

Museum Ⓦ ♀ ◧ ⌂

Village signposted off A354 Blandford Forum—Salisbury

Using local and organic produce where possible, and served with home-made bread, jams, chutneys and marmalades, the very well prepared inventive food is very much the focus at this informally civilised place. Apart from lunchtime baguettes (£6.50), the changing menu is by no means cheap, especially if you add a vegetable side dish (£2.50). It might include smoked haddock chowder (£6), seared foie gras with mushy peas, air dried ham and truffle oil (£9), spinach and ricotta tortellini (£12.50), grilled calves liver with smoked bacon, red wine and dijon (£15), grilled local lamb chump with spinach and aïoli (£17), and puddings such as black treacle tart or ice berry parfait with brandy snap biscuits (£5.50). It's a good idea to book if you want to eat in the stylish no smoking restaurant. Built in the 17th c by General Pitt Rivers to offer accommodation and refreshment for his nearby museum, this attractively extended building has been opened up into a series of appealing interconnecting rooms and bars. Cheery yellow walls and plentiful windows give the place a bright, fresh feel. The flagstoned bar has a big inglenook fireplace, light beams, good comfortably cushioned furnishings and fresh flowers on all the tables. To the right is a dining room with a fine antique dresser, while off to the left is a cosier room, with a very jolly hunting model and a seemingly sleeping stuffed fox curled in a corner. Another room feels rather like a contemporary baronial hall, soaring up to a high glass ceiling, with dozens of antlers and a stag's head looking down on a long refectory table and church-style pews. This leads to an outside terrace with more wooden tables. As well as an excellent choice of wines, with about a dozen by the glass, three well kept real ales will probably be Hop Back Summer Lightning, Ringwood and Timothy Taylors Landlord; prompt service from antipodean staff. *(Recommended by John and Vivienne Rice, Dr D G Twyman, Terry and Linda Moseley, Penny Simpson, Keith and Jean Symons, Gaynor Gregory, M N Sugarhood, Pat and Robert Watt, J Stickland, Karen Eliot)*

Free house ~ Licensees Vicky Elliot and Mark Stephenson ~ Real ale ~ Bar food (12-2.30, 7-9.30) ~ Restaurant (Fri and Sat evening and Sun lunch) ~ (01725) 516261 ~ Children over 8 ~ Dogs allowed in bar and bedrooms ~ Open 12-3, 6-11(10.30 Sun) ~ Bedrooms: £85B/£95B

LANGTON HERRING SY6182 Map 2

Elm Tree

Signed off B3157

The rambling interior of this lovely old beamed dining pub is spotlessly kept and full of character, with most people here for the wide range of very good food. Interesting daily specials might be creamed fennel and celery soup (£3.50), roasted red pepper and goats cheese bruschetta (£4.95), pasta with fresh asparagus, leeks and pecorino cheese (£6.95), pork tenderloin with port jus and red onion marmalade (£10.95) and grilled bass fillets with black pepper and balsamic (£11.95). The more pubby menu includes sandwiches (from £3.50), filled panini (from £5.75), ploughman's (£5.95), lasagne (£6.95), steak and ale pie (£7.45), baked crab mornay (£7.95) and 10oz sirloin steak (£11.95). Puddings might be treacle tart and clotted cream, dorset apple cake or chocolate rum pot (from £3.95); most of the pub is no smoking. The Portland spy ring is said to have met in the main beamed and carpeted rooms, which have walls festooned with copper, brass and bellows, cushioned window seats, red leatherette stools, windsor chairs, and lots of big old kitchen tables; one has some old-fashioned settles and an inglenook. The traditionally furnished extension gives more room for diners. Marstons Pedigree and a guest such as Wadworths 6X under light blanket pressure and a dozen wines by the glass; piped music, darts. Outside in the very pretty flower-filled sunken garden are colourful hanging baskets, flower tubs, and tables; a track leads down to the Dorset Coast Path, which here skirts the eight-mile lagoon enclosed by Chesil Beach. *(Recommended by Peter Neate, W W Burke, Fred and Lorraine Gill)*

Punch ~ Lease Paul and Jo-Ann Riddiough ~ Real ale ~ Bar food (12-2.15, 6.30-9.15(12-3,
7-9.15 Sun); 12-9.15 July-Aug) ~ Restaurant ~ (01305) 871257 ~ Children welcome ~ Jazz
second Sun in month ~ Open 11.30-11 July-Aug; 11.30-2.30, 6-11; 12-3, 7-10.30 Sun

MARSHWOOD SY3799 Map 1

Bottle

B3165 Lyme Regis—Crewkerne

The annual world stinging-nettle eating championships, held at the same time as their
beer festival, on the Saturday before the summer solstice, has achieved international
notoriety for this enjoyable village local. Other than that, this straightforward place,
with its strong local following, has changed little over the years. The simple cream-
walled interior has down-to-earth furnishings including cushioned benches and one
high-backed settle, and there's an inglenook fireplace with a big log fire in winter;
also pool, a skittle alley, and piped music. Otter Bitter and Greene King Old Speckled
Hen are well kept alongside a couple of guests (from the West Country in the
summer for visitors, and nationals for the locals in the winter). A wide range of tasty
bar food includes soup (£3.50), recommended baguettes, and ploughman's (from
£4.95), a vegetarian pie or roast of the day (£6.95), medallions of pork fillet with
stilton sauce (£10.50), chicken breast stuffed with smoked salmon in whisky cream
and mustard sauce (£11.50), fillet steak (£13.95) and puddings such as ginger and
white chocolate cheesecake (£2.75); the dining area is no smoking. A good big back
garden has a play area, and beyond it a field for camping. The pub is surrounded by
pretty walking country and close to Lambert's Castle (a National Trust hill fort).
*(Recommended by Pat and Tony Martin, OPUS, Meg and Colin Hamilton, Roland and
Wendy Chalu)*

Free house ~ Licensees Shane and Ellen Pym ~ Real ale ~ Bar food (12-2, 6.30-9) ~
(01297) 678254 ~ Children welcome ~ Live music alternate Sats ~ Open 12-3, 6.30
(7 Sun)-11; closed Mon except bank hols

MIDDLEMARSH ST6607 Map 2

Hunters Moon 🍺 🛏

A352 Sherborne—Dorchester

This happy country inn serves reasonably priced tasty food and a nice range of beers.
Well kept on handpump, and often from the West Country, they might include
Dorset Best, Sharps Doom Bar, St Austell Tribute and Otter. The comfortably
welcoming interior rambles around in several linked areas, with a great variety of
tables and chairs, plenty of bric-a-brac from decorative teacups, china ornaments and
glasses through horse tack and brassware, to quite a collection of spirits miniatures.
Beams, some panelling, soft lighting from converted oil lamps, three log fires (one in
a capacious inglenook), and the way that some attractively cushioned settles form
booths all combine to give a cosy relaxed feel. Bar food includes baked potatoes
(£4.95), lasagne (£7.25), fish pie (£7.50), steak and kidney pie (£8.25) and mixed
grill (£11.50). Also decent wines by the glass, proper coffee, and a good range of
spirits and soft drinks; faint piped pop music. A neat lawn has circular picnic-sets as
well as the more usual ones, and the bedrooms are in what was formerly a skittle
alley and stable block. *(Recommended by Joan and Michel Hooper-Immins, Ian and
Mary Logan, David Fulford-Brown)*

Free house ~ Licensee Brendan Malone ~ Real ale ~ Bar food ~ Restaurant ~
(01963) 210966 ~ Children welcome ~ Dogs allowed in bar ~ Open 11-3, 6-11; 12-10.30
Sun ~ Bedrooms: £45S/£60S

MUDEFORD SZ1892 Map 2
Ship in Distress ♀
Stanpit; off B3059 at roundabout

Cheery clutter and homely old leather sofas, alongside more orthodox pub
furnishings, might give you the idea that this is just an entertaining local. Don't be
fooled. The wide choice of carefully cooked fresh local fish and seafood is good and
imaginative: sandwiches (£4.50), breton-style fish soup or a pint of prawns (£6.50),
grilled scallops (£8), fish and chips (£8.95), tagliatelle with wild mushroom, garlic,
parsley, lemon and truffle oil or fried smoked haddock fishcake on rocket and tomato
salad with poached egg and chive butter sauce (£9.50), baked pollock fillet with crab,
tomato and pecorino crust on crushed potatoes with tuscan-style beans or seared tuna
with cajun pepper crust on aubergine and pesto salad (£13.50), grilled rib-eye steak
(£14.50) and puddings such as carrot and orange panna cotta torte with chocolate
sauce or chocolate, raspberry and mascarpone roulade with pistachio and chocolate
fudge (£5.50). It's well worth a close look round at quiet times, when you've room to
move freely – the décor in the bar's two cottagey rooms is good fun. All sorts of more
or less nautical bric-a-brac spans the gamut from rope fancywork and brassware
through lanterns, oars and ceiling nets and ensigns, to a somewhat murky aquarium,
boat models (we particularly liked the Mississippi steamboat), and the odd piratical
figure. Besides a good few boat pictures, the room on the right has masses of
snapshots of locals caught up in various waterside japes, under its glass tabletops.
Service is friendly, and they have well kept Adnams Broadside, Bass, Ringwood Best
and a guest such as Shepherd Neame Spitfire on handpump, and good wines by the
glass; darts, fruit machine, a couple of TV sets – the dated piped pop music seems to
fit in rather well. A spreading two-room restaurant area, as cheerful in its way as the
bar, has a light-hearted mural sketching out the impression of a window open on a
sunny boating scene, and another covering its dividing wall with vines. There are
tables out on the back terrace; look out for the two springer spaniels. More reports
please. *(Recommended by Michael and Robin Inskip, Brian and Ruth Archer)*

Punch ~ Tenants Sally Canning, Colin Pond, Ed Blanchard ~ Real ale ~ Bar food ~
Restaurant ~ (01202) 485123 ~ Children welcome ~ Dogs allowed in bar ~ Open 11-11;
12-10.30 Sun

OSMINGTON MILLS SY7381 Map 2
Smugglers
Off A353 NE of Weymouth

The interior of this popular partly thatched inn has recently been brightened up with
fresh décor, and the old pool table and other pub games have given way to additional
tables. It does get very busy in high season (there's a holiday settlement just up the
lane) so if you prefer a quieter atmosphere it may be better to visit off-peak, though
staff cope well with the crowds, and service remains friendly. Woodwork divides the
spacious bar into cosy, welcoming areas, with logs burning in two open stoves and
old local pictures scattered about. Some seats are tucked into alcoves and window
embrasures, with one forming part of an upended boat. The fruit machine is kept
sensibly out of the way; piped music. Handily served all day, bar food (they will do
smaller helpings for children) includes soup (£2.95), cod and parsley fishcake (£3.75),
fish and chips (£6.45), sausage and mash (£6.95), irish stew or basil and garlic
chicken (£7.25), butternut squash and spinach crumble (£7.75) and sirloin steak
(£10.75). Part of the restaurant is no smoking. Badger Dorset Best, Tanglefoot and a
guest are well kept on handpump. There are picnic sets out on crazy paving by a little
stream, with a thatched summer bar (where they sometimes have summer barbecues
and hog roasts) and a good play area over on a steep lawn. *(Recommended by John and
Joan Nash, Mark Percy, Lesley Mayoh, A J Batty, Joan and Michel Hooper-Immins, the Didler,
OPUS, John Fiander, Pam and Alan Neale)*

Badger ~ Manager Michael Rowe ~ Real ale ~ Bar food (12-9) ~ Restaurant ~
(01305) 833125 ~ Children in eating area of bar ~ Open 11-11; 12-10.30 Sun; 11-3, 6-11
Mon-Fri in winter ~ Bedrooms: /£90B

PAMPHILL ST9900 Map 2

Vine ◖

Off B3082 on NW edge of Wimborne: turn on to Cowgrove Hill at Cowgrove signpost, then turn right up Vine Hill

In 1991, this charmingly simple and unspoilt country pub, sited in the grounds of the Kingston Lacy estate, was bought by the National Trust from Whitbreads, though it continues to be independently run by the family who have been tenants here for three generations. Its two tiny bars have that well cared-for feel and friendly service that make little places like this feel so special. One, with a warm coal-effect gas fire, has only three tables, the other just half a dozen or so seats on its lino floor, some of them huddling under the stairs that lead up via narrow wooden stairs to an upstairs games room; darts. Local photographs (look out for the one of the regular with his giant pumpkin) and notices decorate the painted panelling. On our weekday inspection visit, piped Classic FM mingled quietly with a blackbird's song drifting in through the french window, though at weekends and in summer it can get very busy. Fullers London Pride and a guest are well kept on handpump, and good fresh sandwiches (from £1.80) and ploughman's (£3.50) are on offer if you're hungry. There are picnic-sets and benches out on a sheltered gravel terrace, and more share a fairy-lit, heated verandah with a grapevine. Round the back a patch of grass has a climbing frame; outside lavatories. *(Recommended by Phil and Sally Gorton, the Didler, John and Jane Hayter)*

Free house ~ Licensee Mrs Sweatland ~ Real ale ~ No credit cards ~ (01202) 882259 ~ Children in family room ~ Dogs welcome ~ Open 11-2.30, 7-11; 12-3, 7-10.30 Sun

PIDDLEHINTON SY7197 Map 2

Thimble £

B3143

This streamside pub is simpler inside than the partly thatched exterior suggests. It's spotlessly kept low-beamed bar is spacious and airy, even when the summer crowds roll in. There are two handsome brick fireplaces, and a deep glassed-over well; darts, shove-ha'penny, dominoes, cribbage. Badger Best and Tanglefoot, Palmers Copper and IPA, and Ringwood Old Thumper are well kept on handpump, along with quite a few fruit wines and 15 malt whiskies. Straightforward bar food includes sandwiches, and soup (from £2.95), filled baked potatoes (from £3.90), king prawn and chilli rolls with chilli mayonnaise dip (£4.25), ploughman's (from £4.50), mushroom and spinach lasagne (£6.10), breaded plaice (£6.10), steak pie (£6.90) and fillet steak (£13), with puddings such as lemon meringue pie (£4); they also do children's meals (£3.75), and a Sunday roast (£6.95). The garden is floodlit at night. *(Recommended by Tony Rose, Daphne Slater, Dennis Jenkin, Prof Keith and Mrs Jane Barber, Gene and Kitty Rankin, Norma and Noel Thomas, Peter Neate)*

Free house ~ Licensees N R White and V J Lanfear ~ Real ale ~ Bar food ~ Restaurant ~ (01300) 348270 ~ Children welcome ~ Dogs welcome ~ Open 12-2.30, 7-11(10.30 Sun)

PLUSH ST7102 Map 2

Brace of Pheasants

Off B3143 N of Dorchester

This handsome 16th-c thatched pub used to be two cottages and the village smithy, and is now a bustling, friendly place with good, popular beer and food. There's a fairly upmarket but relaxed atmosphere in the airy beamed bar, which has good solid tables, windsor chairs, fresh flowers, a huge heavy-beamed inglenook at one end with cosy seating inside, and a good warming log fire at the other. A usefully pubby bar menu includes snacks such as soup (£4.95), generous filled baguettes (from £6.95), cottage pie, ham and egg or eggs benedict (£7.95), and a more elaborate menu such as beer-battered scallops with salsa verde (£7.95; main course £14.50), twice-baked cheese soufflé with plum compote (£7.75), venison sausages with mash and red wine gravy (£9.95), fresh mackerel fillets (£15.95), fillet steak (£16), monkfish in a champagne sauce (£17.95), and puddings (£5.25). The restaurant and family room are no smoking. Well kept Butcombe Best Bitter, Sharps Doom Bar and Ringwood Best tapped from the cask. A decent-sized garden and terrace includes a lawn sloping up towards a rockery. The pub lies alongside Plush Brook, and an attractive bridleway behind goes to the left of the woods and over to Church Hill. *(Recommended by John and Joan Nash, Phil and Jane Hodson, Dave Morgan, Mrs Diane M Hall, John Coatsworth, the Didler, OPUS, Peter Neate, Stuart and Alison Ballantyne, Sue and Keith Campbell)*

Free house ~ Licensees Toby and Suzie Albu ~ Real ale ~ Bar food ~ Restaurant ~ (01300) 348357 ~ Children welcome ~ Dogs allowed in bar ~ Open 12-3, 7-11; 12-3, 7-10.30 Sun; closed Mon exc bank hols

POOLE SZ0391 Map 2

Cow ♀

Station Road, Ashley Cross, Parkstone; beside Parkstone Station

This is rather a surprise. Not much to look at from the outside and right next to the railway station means you might go straight past, but once inside it's a nicely modernised one-bar pub with interesting décor and a relaxed, informal atmosphere. The ochre ragged walls are hung with a vintage songsheet of *Three Acres and a Cow*, Twickenham Rugby Museum replicas of 1930s and 1940s rugby prints, and big modern cow prints in bright pinks, yellows and blues. There are a mix of wooden tables and dining chairs, a couple of low tables by some comfortable squashy sofas with huge colourful cushions, and high leatherette bar chairs. A gas-effect coal fire in a brick fireplace, with another in the entrance hall, and quite a discreet flat-screen TV in one corner. Well kept Fullers London Pride, Ringwood Best and a guest such as Palmers Tally Ho on handpump, and an extensive wine list with about ten wines by the glass and many remarkable bottles; piped music, TV. From a sensibly short menu, the good modern lunchtime bar food includes soup (£4.25), panini or baguettes such as warm roast chicken with dill mayonnaise (£5.25), club sandwich (£5.95), prawn and avocado salad (£6.95), wild mushroom risotto with poached beetroot (£7.50), fish stew (£7.95), tempura cod and chips (£8.95), lambs liver and bacon on mustard mash (£9.50), puddings such as sticky toffee with hot caramel sauce or iced banana parfait with poached pear (£4.50), and british cheeses (£6.50). In the evening you can eat in the sizeable no smoking bistro, where there are more heavy stripped tables on bare boards, and plenty of wine bottles lining the window sills. *(Recommended by W W Burke)*

Free house ~ Licensees David Sax, Simon Garbutt and David Alderson ~ Real ale ~ Bar food (lunchtime only) ~ Restaurant ~ (01202) 749569 ~ Children welcome ~ Dogs allowed in bar ~ Live bands bank hols ~ Open 11(12 Sat)-11(10.30 Sun)

SHAVE CROSS SY4198 Map 1

Shave Cross Inn

On back lane Bridport—Marshwood, signposted locally; OS Sheet 193 map reference 415980

Several satisfied readers feel this charming partly 14th-c flint and thatch inn is the essence of what an old English country pub should be. The original timbered bar is a lovely flagstoned room, surprisingly roomy and full of character, with country antiques, two armchairs either side of a warming fire in an enormous inglenook fireplace and hops round the bar – a scene little altered from the last century. A cheery barmaid serves three real ales from West Country brewers such as Branscombe Vale and Dorset, which are well kept alongside half a dozen wines by the glass, local farm cider and a caribbean beer; piped music. The caribbean origins of the chef show in the tasty home-made food which might include soup (£4.50), filled baguettes (£6.95), caribbean chicken, lamb curry with calypso rice, stewed pork, jerk chicken salad or onion tart (£8.95), though the home-made puddings such as dorset apple cake or lemon meringue pie (£3.95) are nicely English. The refurbished skittle alley has pool, darts and a juke box, and the no-smoking dining area and restaurant are stylishly decorated with crimson walls, Renaissance drawings in red chalk, and candles on the tables. Lovingly tended, the sheltered flower-filled garden with its thatched wishing-well, goldfish pool and children's play area is very pretty. *(Recommended by John and Joan Nash, Conor McGaughey, Marjorie and David Lamb, Joan and Michel Hooper-Immins, J S Davies, H Frank Smith, Terry and Linda Moseley, Mr and Mrs M Shirley, W W Burke, Mrs A P Lee, Revd L J and Mrs Melliss, Roland and Wendy Chalu)*

Free house ~ Licensee Roy Warburton ~ Real ale ~ Bar food (12-2.30, 6-9(8 Sun); not winter Sun evenings) ~ Restaurant ~ (01308) 868358 ~ Children in restaurant and skittle alley ~ Dogs allowed in bar ~ Local folk club third Thurs in month ~ Open 11-11; 12-10.30 Sun; 11-3, 6-11; 12-3, 7-10.30 Sun winter; closed winter Mon

SHERBORNE ST6316 Map 2
Digby Tap ◨ £
Cooks Lane; park in Digby Road and walk round corner

This down-to-earth old-fashioned ale house is not a pub for those seeking sophistication, the welcoming flagstoned bar is simple and full of character, with a good mix of chatty customers, with emphasis on the superbly kept beer. Mostly from West Country brewers such as Exmoor, Otter, Sharps and St Austell, they change regularly, with four pumps serving around 20 different ones a week. A little games room has pool, cribbage, dominoes and piped music and there's a TV room. Large helpings of reasonably priced, straightforward bar food might include tasty soup (£1.95), sandwiches or baguettes (from £1.75, toasted from £1.80), filled baked potatoes (from £2.80), potato wedges (£2.95), with daily specials such as lasagne, tuna mozzarella fishcakes or smoked plaice stuffed with mushrooms and prawns (£4.50) and steak and chips (£4.50); they don't do puddings. There are some seats outside. *(Recommended by W W Burke, Guy Vowles, Michael B Griffith, John A Barker, Mr and Mrs A Silver, Brian and Bett Cox)*

Free house ~ Licensees Peter Lefevre and Nick Whigham ~ Real ale ~ Bar food (lunchtimes only, not Sun) ~ No credit cards ~ (01935) 813148 ~ Children welcome lunchtimes only ~ Dogs welcome ~ Open 11-2.30, 5.30-11; 11-3, 6-11 Sat; 12-3, 7-10.30 Sun

Skippers
A352 link road, W of centre; car park, or park around corner, in Horsecastles

Along with up to ten fresh fish dishes such as grilled plaice (£10.95) and swordfish steak (£11.95), the changing bar food at this comfortably extended pub might include sandwiches (from £2.50), liver and bacon (£8.50), lasagne (£8.95), chicken supreme in stilton sauce (£11.95) and duck in ginger (£13.95), with puddings (£3.50). They do a bargain two-course OAP lunch (£5.95, not Sunday). Cheerfully decorated with puce Anaglypta walls, the interior is basically a line of three fairly snug rooms, partly separated by knocked-through stone walls, starting with the serving area – which has well kept Butcombe and Wadworths Henrys, IPA and 6X, and maybe a guest such as Greene King Abbot on handpump, and about eight wines by the glass. Tables on the turkey carpet vary from dark pub style to sturdy varnished pine. There's a rack of daily papers, a coal-effect gas fire, scatter cushions on a window seat and a lively collection of helicopter and other mainly RNAS photographs. Bright tablecloths continue the cheery decorations into the dining area at the far end; fruit machine, cribbage, shove-ha'penny, dominoes and maybe unobtrusive piped radio. There are tables outside. More reports please. *(Recommended by BOB)*

Wadworths ~ Tenants Sandra and Chris Frowde ~ Real ale ~ Bar food (11.30-2, 6.30-9.30(12-2, 7-9 Sun)) ~ Restaurant ~ (01935) 812753 ~ Children in eating area of bar and restaurant ~ Open 11-2.30, 6-11; 12-3, 7-10.30 Sun

---

Pubs in outstandingly attractive surroundings are listed at the back of the book.

SHROTON ST8512 Map 2

Cricketers ♀ 🍺 🛏

Off A350 N of Blandford (village also called Iwerne Courtney); follow signs

The bright divided bar at this welcoming red brick pub has a big stone fireplace, alcoves and cricketing memorabilia. Four well kept changing ales from brewers such as Butcombe, Felinfoel, Shepherd Neame and Wadworths are served from pumps made into little cricket bats. They've also a dozen wines by the glass, and quite a few malt whiskies; good friendly service from the attentive landlord and his neatly uniformed staff. Besides filled baguettes (£5.50), good, reasonably priced changing dishes could include soup (£3.95), sautéed lamb kidneys with balsamic vinegar cream (£3.75), crab filo tart with coriander mayonnaise (£3.95), faggots with wholegrain mash (£6.95), smoked haddock and coriander fishcakes with lemon mayonnaise (£8.25), spinach, mushroom and goats cheese filo tart (£7.95) and lamb hock with rosemary and red wine sauce (£9.95), with puddings such as raspberry meringue roulade or chocolate torte (£3.95). The comfortable no smoking back restaurant overlooks the garden and has a fresh neutral décor, and a sizeable games area has pool, darts, cribbage, dominoes, fruit machine and piped music. The pub faces the peaceful village green, and there are good walks from here over Hambledon Hill with its fine views (though you will need to leave your boots outside). Secluded and pretty, the garden has big sturdy tables under cocktail parasols, a fairy-lit clematis arbour, well tended shrubs, and a well stocked (and well used) herb garden by the kitchen door. *(Recommended by KN-R, Colin and Janet Roe, Terry and Linda Moseley, Peter Neate, Mrs H E Cunliffe, Mike and Shelley Woodroffe, W W Burke, J Stickland, Pat and Robert Watt, Richard and Nicola Tranter)*

Free house ~ Licensees George and Carol Cowie ~ Real ale ~ Bar food (not Sun evenings in mid-winter) ~ Restaurant ~ (01258) 860421 ~ Children welcome ~ Open 11.30-2.30, 6.30-11; 12-3, 7-10.30 ~ Bedrooms: £40S/£70S

STURMINSTER NEWTON ST7813 Map 2

Bull

A357 near junction with B3092, S of village centre

This cosily compact thatched local has a comfortable more or less L-shaped bar with soft lighting and some low beams. The joists by the serving counter are packed with key fobs, while others have lots of decorative mugs, and the swirly cream walls have anything from country prints and bull cartoons to snaps of happy regulars, and there are charity shelves of readable paperbacks at one end; skittle alley, piped Classic FM and local radio. Simple, but generously served bar food includes soup (£2.95), sandwiches (from £3.50), plaice and chips (£6.75), steak and stilton pie (£8.25), mushroom, brie and cranberry wellington (£9.25), sirloin steak (£13.95), and puddings could be syrup sponge or spotted dick (from £3.50). Badger Best and Harveys Sussex are well kept on handpump, along with good house wines including eight by the glass. You'll find picnic-sets out in front by rather totemic wooden statuary (and the busy road), and more in a fenced garden. *(Recommended by D Rossi, Colin and Janet Roe, Liz and Tony Colman, John A Barker, Paul Kelly)*

Badger ~ Tenant Fran Hussey ~ Real ale ~ Bar food ~ (01258) 472435 ~ Children in eating area of bar ~ Dogs welcome ~ Open 11-3, 6-11; 12-3, 7-10.30 Sun

TARRANT MONKTON ST9408 Map 2

Langton Arms 🍺 🛏

Village signposted from A354, then head for church

Following a fairly big fire last year, this pretty 17th-c thatched pub has undergone extensive refurbishment. The welcoming light oak beamed bar is now airier with cream walls, flagstone floors, a light oak counter with recessed lighting, and fresh flowers on light wood furniture. Two guest beers are well kept on handpump alongside Hop Back Best and Ringwood. The public bar has a juke box, darts, pool, a fruit machine, TV, cribbage and dominoes. The no smoking bistro restaurant is in an attractively reworked barn, and the skittle alley doubles as a no smoking family room during the day; piped music. Bar food includes soup (£3.75), baguettes (from £3.50), filo prawns (£5.95), ploughman's (from £5.95), pork and leek sausages and chips (£6.50), battered cod (£6.95), roast beef (£7.75), chicken curry (£7.95), steak and ale pie (£8.25), poached salmon fillet with white wine and dill sauce (£8.65), game pie or stuffed aubergines (£8.95) and local steaks (from £11.95), with puddings such as home-made steamed coffee and walnut pudding or local ice-creams (from £3.75). Tarrant Monkton is a charming village (with a ford that can flow quite fast in wet weather), and is well located for local walks and exploring the area. There's a very good wood-chip children's play area in the garden, and the comfortable ensuite bedrooms are in a modern block at the back; good breakfasts. *(Recommended by Dr J Puszet, John and Joan Nash, Pat and Robert Watt, Val and Alan Green, Francis Johnston, Mrs L M Beard, Mrs Pat Crabb)*

Free house ~ Licensees Barbara and James Cossins ~ Real ale ~ Bar food (11.30-2.30, 6.30-9.30; all day Sat, Sun) ~ Restaurant ~ (01258) 830225 ~ Children in restaurant and family room ~ Dogs allowed in bedrooms ~ Open 11.30-11; 12-10.30 Sun ~ Bedrooms: £60B/£80B

WEST BAY SY4690 Map 1

West Bay 🍴 🛏

Station Road

Dorset Dining Pub of the Year

This very well run seaside pub is a great favourite with readers, and is included with our heartiest recommendation. It's deservedly very popular (though its spaciousness means it never feels crowded) so booking is virtually essential. With around ten imaginatively prepared types to choose from, their speciality is fish, with a typical selection perhaps including skate wing with capers and black butter (£11.95), hot crab and shellfish platter (£15.50) and turbot fillet on spinach with scallops and light Pernod sauce (£15.95). As well as lunchtime bar snacks such as sandwiches (from £3.75), ploughman's (£6.75), steak and kidney casserole with mustard dumplings or chicken curry (£8.95), other delicious food might include fettuccine with roasted vegetables (£8.50) and pork tenderloin with cheese and oyster mushroom sauce (£12.95). Decent piped music, a chatty buzz, friendly hands-on licensees and cheerful staff help generate an enjoyably relaxed atmosphere. An island servery separates the fairly simple bare-boards front part, with its coal-effect gas fire and mix of sea and nostalgic prints, from a cosier carpeted no smoking dining area with more of a country kitchen feel. Palmers IPA, Copper and 200 are well kept on handpump alongside good house wines (with ten by the glass), and whiskies. A local team meets to play in the skittles alley. There are tables outside on a dining terrace, and there's plenty of parking. Readers very much like staying in the quiet comfortable bedrooms, and tell us the breakfasts are delicious. *(Recommended by Ann and Stephen Saunders, Peter Meister, Roland and Wendy Chalu, Charles Gysin, Bob and Margaret Holder, OPUS, J P Humphery, Mrs Veronica Duggan, Brian Thompson, Geoffrey Leather, Mayur Shah, Guy Vowles, Adrian White, David Thornton, Roderick and Jill Leslie, Pat and Tony Martin, David and Julie Glover, John and Hazel Deacon, Julie and Bill Ryan, Liz and Tony Colman, JMC, Mrs L M Beard, Roger and Maureen Kenning, Sheela Curtis, Ian and Jane Irving, Richard Wyld, Mrs A P Lee, John Coatsworth, Brian Loan Lord)*

Palmers ~ Tenants John Ford and Karen Trimby ~ Real ale ~ Bar food (12-2(2.30 Sun); 6.30-9.30) ~ Restaurant ~ (01308) 422157 ~ Children in restaurant ~ Dogs allowed in bar ~ Open 11-2.30, 6-11; 12-3 Sun; closed Sun evening ~ Bedrooms: £50B/£65B

WORTH MATRAVERS SY9777 Map 2

Square & Compass ★ 🍴

At fork of both roads signposted to village from B3069

Hardly anything has changed in the 90-odd years that the Newman family have been running this charmingly old-fashioned pub. To this day there's no bar counter, so the Ringwood Best, Palmers Dorset Gold and a guest from a brewer such as Archers, and the nine ciders they keep, are tapped from a row of casks and passed to you in a drinking corridor through two serving hatches. A couple of basic unspoilt rooms opposite have simple furniture on the flagstones, a woodburning stove and a loyal crowd of friendly locals; darts, cribbage, shove-ha'penny and table skittles. Bar food is limited to tasty home-made pasties and pies (£2.30, served till they run out). A little museum (free) exhibits local fossils and artefacts, mostly collected by the current friendly landlord and his father; mind your head on the way out. The pub is on a peaceful hilltop, with a fantastic view from benches out in front (you may find free-roaming hens, chickens and other birds clucking around your feet), looking down over the village rooftops to the sea between the East Man and the West Man (the hills that guard the coastal approach) and out beyond Portland Bill. There are good walks from the here, but you will need to park in the public car park 100 yards along the Corfe Castle road. *(Recommended by John and Joan Nash, Andrea Rampley, Phil and Sally Gorton, Pete Baker, MLR, Richard Siebert, John and Laney Woods, Chris Ferguson, Joan and Michel Hooper-Immins, JDM, KM, Jason Caulkin, the Didler, W W Burke, Mr and Mrs M Clark, Alex and Irene Harvey, Mike and Sue Loseby, Tich Critchlow, Paul Goldman, Derek and Maggie Washington)*

Free house ~ Licensee Charlie Newman ~ Real ale ~ Bar food (all day) ~ No credit cards ~ (01929) 439229 ~ Children welcome ~ Dogs welcome ~ Open 12-3, 6-11; 12-11 Sat; 12-3, 7-10.30 Sun

LUCKY DIP

Besides the fully inspected pubs, you might like to try these Lucky Dips recommended to us and described by readers (if you do, please send us reports: www.goodguides.co.uk).

ABBOTSBURY [SY5785]
Ilchester Arms [B3157]: Rambling stone-built pub with old pine tables and settles, lots of rustic bric-a-brac, prints of the famous swans; food from doorstep sandwiches, ciabattas or baked potatoes up, Courage Best, Gales HSB and Theakstons XB tapped from the cask, good house wines in three glass sizes, large games room, no smoking conservatory restaurant; can get smoky, service can falter at busy times, quiet piped music, TV, fruit machine; children in eating areas, nice views from suntrap terrace picnic-sets, ten bedrooms, open all day *(Paul Goldman, LYM, OPUS, Stephen R Holman, Sarah and Peter Gooderham, Roland and Wendy Chalu)*
ALDERHOLT [SU1112]
Churchill Arms [Daggons Rd (back rd Fordingbridge—Cranborne)]: Thriving local with brass cannons by fireplace of panelled bar, darts in second bar, family/games room with more darts, usual food from sandwiches and baked potatoes up, Badger Best and Tanglefoot, skittle alley; garden tables *(Neil and Anita Christopher)*
ALMER [SY9097]
☆ *Worlds End* [B3075, just off A31 towards Wareham]: Very long and busy open-plan thatched and partly flagstoned family dining pub, beams, panelled alcoves and candles, very wide choice of enjoyable reasonably priced food all day (you can choose generous or smaller helpings), well kept Badger ales, quick pleasant hard-working staff (lots of tables, even so you may have to wait), restaurant with no smoking area; open all day, picnic-sets and heaters in front and behind, outstanding play area *(BB, Lynn Sharpless, Michael and*

Robin Inskip)
ANSTY [ST7603]
Fox [NW of Milton Abbas]: Former home of the Hall & Woodhouse brewers (now trading as Badger), well worn in hotel rather than pub, with interesting family history in the high-ceilinged partly no smoking main bar; lots of toby jugs, well kept Badger Best, Tanglefoot and a seasonal beer, good wines by the glass, very wide choice of inexpensive food; piped music, separate bar with pool and TV, skittle alley; children welcome in no smoking restaurant, garden tables, bedrooms, attractive countryside, open all day *(LYM, David and Elizabeth Briggs, Joan and Michel Hooper-Immins, Stuart and Alison Ballantyne, Richard and Liz Dilnot)*
ASKERSWELL [SY5292]
Spyway [off A35 Bridport—Dorchester]: Beamed country pub with old-fashioned high-backed settles, cushioned wall and window seats, old-world décor, well kept ales such as Otter and Weymouth Best, good value food from fresh sandwiches and baguettes to standard cooked dishes inc good fresh local fish, friendly if not always speedy service, no smoking dining area with steps down to overflow area; may be soft piped music; disabled access though not ideal, children in eating areas, spectacular views from back terrace and large informal garden, good walks *(Roland and Wendy Chalu, LYM, Barry and Anne, N R White)*
BEAMINSTER [ST4801]
Greyhound [A3066 N of Bridport; The Square]: Flagstones and simple furnishings on right, plusher on left, coal-effect gas fires, well kept Palmers ales, wide blackboard choice of

decent reasonably priced standard food from sandwiches and baked potatoes up, congenial service, small back family room, darts; piped music; dogs welcome *(Marjorie and David Lamb, BB, Roland and Wendy Chalu)*

BERE REGIS [SY8494]

Drax Arms [West St; off A35 bypass]: Comfortable and welcoming village local with cheerful helpful service, well kept Badger Best and farm cider, limited choice of good generous home-made food from sandwiches up, esp pies and casseroles, big open fire on left, small dining area (busy in summer); good walking nearby *(John and Joan Nash)*

BLANDFORD FORUM [ST8806]

Crown [West St]: Best Western hotel's well furnished spacious bar areas used by locals as pub, large no smoking area, well kept Badger beers from nearby brewery, good range of reasonably priced straightforward bar food inc good sandwiches and light meals, separate restaurant; bedrooms *(Colin and Janet Roe, J C Poley, Craig Turnbull, W W Burke, Gerry and Rosemary Dobson)*

Dolphin [East St]: Interesting and friendly old pub with bare boards, rugs and panelling, pews, fireside sofa, well kept real ales inc guest beers, fruit wines, reasonably priced standard food *(John A Barker)*

BLANDFORD ST MARY [ST8805]

Hall & Woodhouse: Visitor centre for Badger brewery, their full beer range in top condition, popular food from well filled baguettes up, friendly staff; spectacular chandelier made of Badger beer bottles, lots of memorabilia in centre and upper gallery; popular brewery tours *(Meg and Colin Hamilton, Joan and Michel Hooper-Immins)*

BOURNEMOUTH [SZ0891]

Goat & Tricycle [West Hill Rd]: Comfortable and roomy two-level rambling local (actually two separate pubs knocked together) with well kept Wadworths and impressive range of half a dozen or more interesting guest beers that seem to change on Thurs, farm cider, inexpensive generous food inc splendid ploughman's, good coffee, coal fire, lots of bric-a-brac inc hundreds of hats and helmets; can be smoky, though not in games area *(Michael and Alison Sandy, Theocsbrian, Steve Jackson, Joan and Michel Hooper-Immins)*

Porterhouse [Poole Rd, Westbourne, just off A35]: Smallish old-fashioned tavern with full Ringwood ale range kept well at sensible prices (also takeaway jugs), changing farm ciders, good choice of malt whiskies and country wines, bare boards and dark panelling, lunchtime filled rolls, shelf of board games; disabled access *(Michael and Alison Sandy)*

BOURTON [ST7430]

☆ *White Lion* [High St, off old A303 E of Wincanton]: Plushly refurbished stripped stone dining pub, nicely lit pubby beamed bars with sporting equipment, well kept Fullers London Pride, Greene King IPA and a guest beer, good wines, friendly staff, tasty sensibly priced blackboard food using good fresh ingredients, good range of home-made puddings, efficient

no smoking beamed restaurant; dogs welcome, well spaced tables in pleasant garden, two neat bedrooms with own bathrooms *(Colin and Janet Roe, LYM, M Benjamin, John and Joan Calvert)*

BRIDPORT [SY4691]

Crown [West Bay Rd]: Pretty but unpretentious, with generous well presented food (children well catered for), good service, well kept Palmers ales, no smoking restaurant (best to book) *(Ron and Val Broom)*

☆ *George* [South St]: Unpretentious two-bar town local, traditional dark décor, assorted furnishings and floor rugs, bargain home-made pub food (not Sun) cooked in sight, filling sandwiches, well kept Palmers ales, good choice of wines by the glass, efficient service, cheerful fire, hatch-served family room; can get smoky, piped radio, upstairs lavatories; dogs welcome, open all day, from 9am for popular wkdy breakfast or coffee *(Roland and Wendy Chalu, Brenda and Rob Fincham, Phil and Sally Gorton, LYM, Brian Hulme, John Kearins)*

Hope & Anchor [St Michaels Lane]: Friendly refurbished local with four well kept ales and two farm ciders, popular cheap family Sun lunch *(David Ellerington, Jacqueline Hampton, Timothy Jan)*

BROADWINDSOR [ST4302]

☆ *White Lion* [The Square (B3163/B3164)]: 17th-c stone-built pub with friendly good-humoured landlord, good service, good choice of generous reasonably priced pubby food using local produce from good sandwiches to popular Sun roasts, Palmers beers, decent wines, pews and flagstones on left, pine booth seating and big inglenook with log fire in carpeted area on right, a modicum of china, local artwork for sale, traditional games; unobtrusive piped music; disabled facilities, picnic-sets in small courtyard *(BB, Roland and Wendy Chalu)*

BUCKLAND NEWTON [ST6804]

☆ *Gaggle of Geese*: Comfortable and well run country local with good atmosphere and attractive décor, friendly accommodating staff, well kept Badger Best, Butcombe and Ringwood Best and Fortyniner, decent wines and spirits, good reasonably priced usual bar food, smartish restaurant, no music; goose auction May and Sept, spacious pool/snooker and skittle rooms, small garden but sizeable grounds (room for caravans) *(OPUS, R J Davies, Peter Salmon, BB, Joan and Michel Hooper-Immins, Nick and Lynne Carter)*

BURTON BRADSTOCK [SY4889]

☆ *Anchor* [B3157 SE of Bridport]: Unusual mix of lively two-bar village pub (pub games, sports TV) and upmarket seafood meals, not cheap but usually very good; other generous food too (may be all day in summer) from baguettes up, great range of malt whiskies, decent wines by the glass, well kept beers such as Hampshire Strongs Best, Ringwood Best, Ushers and Wychwood Hobgoblin, Thatcher's farm cider, friendly staff, no smoking restaurant; children and dogs welcome, comfortable bedrooms, open all day *(Alec and Barbara Jones, Roland and Wendy Chalu, Conor McGaughey, K Hutchinson, Rob Winstanley, Terry and Linda Moseley, Tony Beaulah, Peter Meister, Joan and Michel Hooper-Immins, Mrs Hilarie Taylor, Oz and Annette, Martin and Jane Wright, Pamela and Merlyn Horswell, D Crook, LYM, Roger and Maureen Kenning, M A Lightfoot)*

☆ *Three Horseshoes* [Mill St]: Attractive thatched inn in charming village, comfortable, homely and roomy, with low beams and doorways, smiling helpful service, good honest quickly served food from sandwiches, baguettes and baked potatoes up, popular Sun lunches, well kept Palmers IPA and Ushers, good wines, log fire, nice no smoking dining room; may be piped music; picnic-sets out on lawn, pleasant shingle beach a few minutes' drive away (with NT car park), bedrooms *(LYM, Mrs C Lintott, Joan and Michel Hooper-Immins, Ron and Val Broom, Roger and Maureen Kenning, N R White, Roland and Wendy Chalu, Guy Vowles)*

CATTISTOCK [SY5999]

☆ *Fox & Hounds* [off A37 N of Dorchester]: Tucked-away 17th-c or older pub, flagstones and nicely moulded Jacobean beams, stripped stone, log fire in huge inglenook, minimal décor, friendly helpful service, Palmers ales from attractively carved counter, Taunton cider, good value wine choice, reasonably priced food from baguettes up inc generous OAP meals, table skittles, pleasant no smoking side dining room, back public bar with well lit darts and TV, immaculate skittle alley; piped pop music, live some Sats; dogs allowed on back terrace, comfortable bedrooms, cl Mon lunchtime, open all day wknds *(Joan and Michel Hooper-Immins, John and Joan Nash, Ron Shelton, BB, Mark and Sarah Desmond, J S Burn)*

CERNE ABBAS [ST6601]

☆ *New Inn* [14 Long Street]: Handsome Tudor inn with mullioned window seats in gently dated beamed bar, well kept ales such as Flowers IPA and Wadworths 6X, enjoyable food with some interesting dishes using local ingredients alongside nicely presented traditional favourites, no smoking dining area; children welcome, lots of tables in coachyard and on sheltered lawn behind, play area, eight bedrooms with own bathrooms, open all day wknds and summer *(LYM, Joan and Michel Hooper-Immins, John Coatsworth)*

CHARMOUTH [SY3693]

George [off A35 W of Bridport; The Street]: Friendly and comfortable open-plan village local, prompt cheerful service, good value usual food, well kept real ales, pool, table skittles; dogs welcome, garden with play area *(BB, Sarah and Peter Gooderham)*

Royal Oak [off A3052/A35 E of Lyme Regis; The Street]: Thorough-going gossipy three-room local with well kept Palmers, welcoming staff and regulars, traditional games, usual food (lunchtimes only), no TV or piped music *(John Joseph Smith)*

CHESIL [SY6873]

Cove House [follow Chiswell signposts]: Pleasantly refurbished beamed and bare-boarded 18th-c pub in superb position effectively built into the sea defences just above the miles-long Chesil pebble beach, great views from three-room bar, friendly staff, reasonably priced usual food from sandwiches, baguettes and baked potatoes up, some nice specials and good value local fish and seafood, well kept Bass, Courage Directors and Flowers; quiet piped music, steps down to gents'; picnic-sets out by sea wall *(Nigel Siesage, LYM, Pete and Rosie Flower, Roland and Wendy Chalu)*

CHICKERELL [SY6480]

Lugger [West St]: Recently reopened stone-built pub, olde-worlde beamed décor, enjoyable reasonably priced food (opens 8.30 for breakfast and coffee), fairly large two-part no smoking dining area; bedrooms and self-catering cottages *(Phil and Jane Hodson)*

CHIDEOCK [SY4191]

☆ *Anchor* [Seatown signed off A35 from Chideock]: Dramatic position and lovely sea and cliff views, with a spacious front terrace; small and simple inside (and crowded in season), with a no smoking family room, friendly young staff, well kept Palmers 200, IPA and Copper, local farm cider, bar food (all day in summer) from lunchtime sandwiches, baguettes and a good ploughman's with local cheeses up; unobtrusive piped music; children and dogs welcome, open all day in summer *(Roland and Wendy Chalu, Rob Winstanley, Roderick and Jill Leslie, John Coatsworth, Mrs C Lintott, David Crook, K Hutchinson, Marjorie and David Lamb, R M Corlett, Susan Loppert, Pamela and Merlyn Horswell, Mrs L M Beard, Andy Trafford, Louise Bayly, Dr Stephen Jolles, Steve Derbyshire, Barry and Anne, N R White)*

CHRISTCHURCH [SZ1592]

Olde George [Castle St]: Bustling 17th-c character pub, low beams, cosy bar, friendly staff, well kept Ringwood Best and Fortyniner and two changing ales such as Gales HSB, good choice of home-made standard food with unusual puddings and different evening menu; some music nights, tables in large former coach yard *(Joan and Michel Hooper-Immins, Diana Brumfit)*

Ship [High St]: Dark low-beamed pub with nautical décor, reasonably priced food featuring speciality sausages with unusual accompaniments, well kept ales *(Meg and Colin Hamilton)*

CORFE CASTLE [SY9681]

☆ *Fox* [West St]: Old-fashioned take-us-as-you-find us stone-built local with ancient origins inc pre-1300 stone fireplace, hatch service, tiny front bar, glassed-over well in lounge (many tables reserved for eaters), well kept ales such as Greene King Abbot, Fullers London Pride, Timothy Taylors Landlord and Wadworths 6X tapped from the cask, generous standard food from sandwiches and baguettes up; dogs but not children allowed inside, informal castleview garden *(Chris Ferguson, John and Laney Woods, the Didler, Tony Brace, LYM)*

Greyhound [A351]: Bustling much photographed old pub in centre of tourist village, three small low-ceilinged panelled rooms, several well kept changing ales such as Gales and Hook Norton, traditional games inc purbeck long board shove-ha'penny, friendly service, no smoking family room; piped music, live Fri; garden with fine castle and countryside views, pretty courtyard opening on to castle bridge, bedrooms, open all day wknds and summer *(LYM, the Didler, Geoff Pidoux, J M Tansey)*

CORFE MULLEN [SY9798]

Coventry Arms [A31 W of Wimborne; Mill St]: Enjoyable reasonably priced bistro-style food with nice light lunches, some unusual dishes and enterprising children's things in beamed dining pub, candlelit at night, with good service, things like olives to buy too, well kept changing ales such as Gales BB, Greene King Abbot and Timothy Taylors Landlord tapped from the cask, good service, four low-ceilinged rooms with large central open fire, flagstones and bare boards, fishing décor, board games and books to browse; tables out by small river *(John Haslam, Linda Drew, J S Davies, W W Burke)*

CRANBORNE [SU0513]

☆ *Fleur-de-Lys* [Wimborne St (B3078 N of Wimborne)]: 17th-c inn nicely set on the edge of Cranborne Chase, subject of a witty Rupert Brooke poem about going to the wrong pub framed above fire in panelled lounge, simpler beamed public bar, friendly new landlord, well kept Badger Best and Tanglefoot, farm cider, decent wines, good value bar food from good baguettes and sandwiches up inc children's, evening restaurant; pub games, piped music, TV; comfortable pretty bedrooms *(LYM, Mr and Mrs A H Young, Phyl and Jack Street, Martin and Alison Stainsby)*

DORCHESTER [SY6890]

☆ *Blue Raddle* [Church St, nr central short stay car park]: Thriving unpretentious local with good attractively priced food from generous sandwiches to game, well kept changing ales inc Otter, good wines, obliging landlord, cheery pub dog, coal-effect gas fire; no credit cards, piped music may be a bit loud; disabled access, but one step *(the Didler, David Swift, Dr and Mrs M E Wilson, BB)*

Kings Arms [High East St]: Hotel bar with thriving atmosphere, appealing décor, well kept Courage Directors, decent wines, enjoyable food from sandwiches up, two-for-one deals and Sun carvery, attentive service, open fire; close associations with Nelson and Hardy's *Mayor of Casterbridge;* bedrooms (the Lawrence of Arabia suite and the Tutenkhamen are pretty striking) *(the Didler, Dr and Mrs M E Wilson, LYM, Kathy Higley, John and Joan Nash)*

☆ *Poet Laureate* [Pummery Sq, Poundbury]: Substantial new building in the Prince of Wales's Poundbury development, largely no smoking light and airy L-shaped bar with lots

of chandeliers and quiet unhurried feel, leather chesterfields, good solid tables and chairs and fresh flowers, enjoyable traditional food from baguettes and baked potatoes to full meals (lamb and beef from named local farms), well kept Palmers ales, decent wines by the glass, proper coffee, pleasant attentive service, daily papers, flame-effect stove, agreeable restaurant area; unobtrusive piped music; wheelchair access, a few picnic-sets on side terrace *(Malcolm Taylor, D P and M A Miles, Ian and Deborah Carrington, Terry and Linda Moseley, Peter Neate, Marianne and Peter Stevens, John and Joan Nash, Alex and Irene Harvey, Roland and Wendy Chalu)*

EAST BURTON [SY8287]

Seven Stars: Old country pub with dining conservatory, good choice of consistently good value food (can be a wait – can get packed in summer), well kept real ales, nice fairly priced wine list, friendly welcome for families; tables outside, play area inc summer bouncy castle, handy for Bovington Tank Museum and Monkey World, parking for caravans *(Mrs H E Cunliffe)*

EAST KNIGHTON [SY8185]

☆ *Countryman* [just off A352 Dorchester—Wareham]: Big bustling family pub with popular carvery (not Mon, or lunchtime Tues), some comfortable sofas, log fires, Courage Best, Greene King Old Speckled Hen and Ringwood Best and Old Thumper, farm cider, good choice of wines, no smoking restaurant; piped music, service can slow at busy times; disabled lavatories, comfortable bedrooms, good breakfast *(M G Hart, OPUS, Renee and Dennis Ball, W W Burke, Roy and Lindsey Fentiman, Richard and Margaret Peers, Jason Caulkin, Mrs Pat Crabb, LYM, Cathy Robinson, Ed Coombe, Pam and Alan Neale)*

EVERSHOT [ST5704]

Acorn [off A37 S of Yeovil]: Modern redecoration alongside the oak panelling and log fires or woodburner, good restaurant and bar meals with a modern touch, well kept Branscombe Vale ales, interesting wines and other drinks, superior service, lively games bar with pool, darts, dominoes, cribbage, backgammon, chess, juke box, skittle alley; children allowed in eating areas, dogs in bar, terrace with dark oak furniture, bedrooms, charming village, good surrounding walks, open all day *(Guy Vowles, Colin and Janet Roe, LYM, Joan and Michel Hooper-Immins, Roland and Wendy Chalu)*

EYPE [SY4491]

New Inn: Unassuming two-bar village local, cheerful staff, well kept Palmers, popular food inc children's, coal fire, darts, two steps down to cottage dining room; piped radio; level access, magnificent views from back terrace, steps down to lawn *(Cathy Robinson, Ed Coombe, Marjorie and David Lamb, Roland and Wendy Chalu)*

FERNDOWN [SU0500]

Old Thatch [Wimborne Rd, Uddens Cross (old A31)]: Extended open-plan pub/restaurant with plenty of thatch, beams and boards, reliable food, good range of beers and wines, accommodating staff, open fires, no smoking area; nice secluded woodside seating out behind *(A and H Piper)*

FIDDLEFORD [ST8013]
Fiddleford Inn [A357 Sturminster Newton—Blandford Forum]: Spotless and comfortable, with three linked smartly refurbished areas (can get full despite all the space), ancient flagstones, some stripped stone, generous quickly served standard food (not Sun evening) from sandwiches up, Ringwood Best, Timothy Taylors Landlord and Youngs; unobtrusive piped music; big pleasant garden with play area safely fenced from busy road *(LYM, Ian Phillips)*

FURZEHILL [SU0102]
☆ *Stocks* [off B3078 N of Wimborne]: Partly thatched 17th-c dining pub extended as rambling set of comfortable low-beamed areas, soft lighting and attractive décor strong on local pictures and bric-a-brac, friendly helpful staff, well kept Ringwood Best and Fortyniner and a guest beer, huge food choice inc lunchtime sandwiches, hot baguettes and OAP bargains, largely no smoking restaurant with huge mirror, darts; piped music, fruit machine; children in eating area, dogs in bar, some outside tables, open all day *(Dr and Mrs A K Clarke, D Marsh, R T and J C Moggridge, LYM, Alec and Joan Laurence, Peter Neate, John A Barker)*

GILLINGHAM [ST8027]
Dolphin [Peacemarsh (B3082)]: Popular dining pub with good choice, partly no smoking restaurant area, well kept Badger beers in pleasant beamed bar; garden with play area *(Colin and Janet Roe, BB)*

GODMANSTONE [SY6697]
☆ *Smiths Arms* [A352 N of Dorchester]: This interesting and old-fashioned 15th-c thatched pub, famous as one of the smallest in the country, was closed due to illness as we went to press, with the sad suggestion that it might not reopen for quite some time – but if you do find it open, it's well worth a visit *(LYM)*

HIGHCLIFFE [SZ2193]
Hinton Oak [Lymington Rd]: Good choice of enjoyable home-made food all day in pleasant dining pub with good range of beers inc Ringwood Fortyniner, conservatory; terrace tables, open all day *(David M Cundy)*

HOLT [SU0304]
Old Inn: Well appointed beamed dining pub with generous standard food inc fresh fish, friendly attentive staff, winter fires, Badger beers, good atmosphere *(M and R Thomas)*

HORTON [SU0407]
Drusillas [Wigbeth]: Picturesque renovated 17th-c beamed pub, wide choice of food inc lots of fresh fish, unusual dishes, OAP bargains, thatched dining extension, Boddingtons, Flowers IPA and Wadworths 6X, good friendly service, log fire, separate games bar with pool; children welcome, adventure playground *(Dr Alan and Mrs Sue Holder)*

KINGSTAG [ST7210]
Green Man [B3143, S of A3030]: Bright and open, with well kept Exmoor and Hop Back Crop Circle, farm cider, varied food inc Sun roasts and Fri steak night, friendly staff, good local atmosphere, no smoking restaurant area down on left, skittle alley *(Nick and Lynne Carter)*

KINGSTON [SY9579]
☆ *Scott Arms* [West St (B3069)]: Much-used holiday pub with rambling warren-like rooms, panelling, stripped stone, beams, log fires and some fine antique prints, attractive room overlooking garden, decent family extension, well kept Courage Best and Ringwood Best, lots of wines, generally enjoyable food (may be queues to order and pay, and things do run out), summer cream teas, no smoking dining area; darts, dominoes, pool and fruit machine, piped music; attractive garden with superb views of Corfe Castle and the Purbeck Hills *(Joan and Michel Hooper-Immins, K H Frostick, LYM, the Didler, David H T Dimock, W W Burke)*

LITTON CHENEY [SY5590]
☆ *White Horse*: Relaxed and unpretentious, with cheerful new landlord, well prepared traditional food from sandwiches up, good fresh local ingredients, well kept Palmers ales, decent wines by the glass, big woodburner, lots of pictures, some pine panelling, stripped stone and flagstones, country kitchen chairs in dining area, table skittles; piped jazz; good spot on quiet lane into quaint village, picnic-sets on pleasant streamside front lawn *(D Marsh, BB, Roland and Wendy Chalu)*

LODERS [SY4994]
☆ *Loders Arms* [off A3066 just N of Bridport]: Extended 17th-c stone-built pub, welcoming and relaxed, friendly efficient service, good value changing food from huge baguettes and baked potatoes through interesting starters and light dishes to wide choice of main courses, both familiar and (at a higher price) innovative, Palmers real ales, farm cider, good choice of wines by the glass, log fire with parrot alongside, magazines and daily papers, thousands of corks on ceiling, pretty no smoking dining room, skittle alley; children in eating areas, pleasant views from picnic-sets in small informal back garden, pretty thatched village, open all day Sun *(LYM, Roland and Wendy Chalu, Joan and Michel Hooper-Immins, Steve Derbyshire)*

LONGBURTON [ST6412]
Rose & Crown [A352 Sherborne—Dorchester]: Welcoming pleasantly modernised village pub with good value straightforward food (limited Mon), freshly made and generous, from sandwiches to nice unusual puddings, Badger beers, main dining area nr inglenook fireplace, overflow in next room, skittle alley; disabled access *(Francis Johnston, Marjorie and David Lamb, Richard and Jean Green)*

LOWER BURTON [SY6891]
Sun [Old Sherborne Rd]: Comfortably extended beamed family dining pub with lots

of pictures, four well kept ales, decent wines, home-made food from baguettes to carvery; big well kept enclosed garden with play area, front terrace *(Alan M Pring)*

LYME REGIS [SY3391]

Harbour Inn [Marine Parade]: Clean-cut modern décor alongside original flagstones and stone walls, sea and coast views from front windows, good food inc fresh local fish, friendly service, Otter and St Austell real ale, farm cider *(Joan and Michel Hooper-Immins)*

Pilot Boat [Bridge St]: Popular all-day family food spot handily set nr waterfront, plenty of tables in cheery nautically themed bars with no smoking dining areas, Palmers real ales, several wines by the glass, low prices, skittle alley; piped music; children and dogs welcome, tables out on terrace, open all day *(Alain and Rose Foote, Meg and Colin Hamilton, Betsy and Peter Little, Dave Irving, Mrs C Lintott, LYM, Vanessa Stilwell, Pat and Tony Martin, Sarah and Peter Gooderham, Tim and Ann Newell)*

Royal Lion [Broad St]: Coaching inn dating from 17th c, old-fashioned dark-panelled many-roomed bar, well kept Bass, good value pub meals, knowledgeable bar staff, welcoming atmosphere, games room, restaurant; good bedrooms *(LYM, Tim and Ann Newell)*

Royal Standard [Marine Parade, The Cobb]: Right on broadest part of beach, lively bar serving area dominated by pool table and piped pop, but has some fine built-in stripped high settles, and there's a quieter no smoking area with stripped brick and pine; quick friendly service, three well kept Palmers ales, good choice of wines by the glass, reasonably priced popular food from sandwiches to local crab and fish, good cream teas, darts; children welcome, good-sized suntrap courtyard sheltered from the NE wind (own servery and wendy house – and you can keep an eye on your children on the beach just feet away) *(Marjorie and David Lamb, Howard and Lorna Lambert, BB, Dave Irving, Colin and Janet Roe, Peter Salmon, Tim and Ann Newell)*

MAIDEN NEWTON [SY5997]

Chalk & Cheese [Dorchester Rd]: Traditional village local with spacious lounge bar, hearty good value food (not Sun evening), pleasant warm atmosphere, well kept Bass, Flowers and a changing guest beer *(B M Eldridge)*

MANSTON [ST8116]

Plough [B3091 Shaftesbury—Sturminster Newton, just N]: Good-sized country pub with good choice of traditional food from sandwiches up, well kept Palmers ales with a guest such as Archers, richly decorated plasterwork, ceilings and bar front; garden tables *(Colin and Janet Roe)*

MARNHULL [ST7719]

☆ *Blackmore Vale* [Burton St, via Church Hill off B3092]: Comfortably modernised pub with pleasantly opened-up beamed and flagstoned no smoking dining bar with woodburner, cosy smaller bar with settles, sofas and pub games,

friendly helpful service, enjoyable generous home-made food inc OAP Tues and Thurs lunches, well kept Badger beers, good choice of reasonably priced wines; piped music, Weds quiz night; children welcome, tables in attractively reworked garden, open all day wknds *(Paul Humphreys, Pat and Robert Watt, LYM)*

Crown [about 3 miles N of Sturminster Newton; Crown Rd]: Part-thatched 17th-c dining pub, generous food with nice blackboard choice, well kept Badger Best and Tanglefoot, good wine choice, considerate service, linked rooms with oak beams, huge flagstones or bare boards, old settles, stuffed animals and old prints and plates, log fire in big stone hearth in oldest part, more modern furnishings and carpet elsewhere; skittle alley, may be piped music; tables in peaceful enclosed garden, children welcome *(Paul Humphreys, LYM)*

MELBURY OSMOND [ST58707]

Rest & Welcome [Yeovil Rd (A37)]: Unassuming roadside inn with well kept Palmers, good value home-made food, friendly service, cottagey décor, back skittle alley *(John Coatsworth)*

MELPLASH [SY4897]

Half Moon [A3066 Bridport—Beaminster]: Friendly 18th-c thatched pub, beams, brasses and pictures of local scenes and animals, good range of well presented reasonably priced standard food from sandwiches up, well kept Palmers ales, cheerful service, good choice of wines, inglenook eating area; may be unobtrusive piped music; tables and chairs in good-sized attractive garden with water feature, shares car park with cricket club next door *(Marjorie and David Lamb, Roland and Wendy Chalu)*

MILTON ABBAS [ST8001]

Hambro Arms [signed off A354 SW of Blandford]: In beautiful late 18th-c thatched landscaped village, good log fire, well kept Greene King Abbot, Ringwood and Tetleys, enjoyable generous food from sandwiches to popular Sunday carvery, prompt service even when busy, bright décor; darts, pool and TV in cosy back public bar; children in restaurant, tables out on terrace, comfortable bedrooms *(Joel Dobris, LYM, Norma and Noel Thomas, John Fiander)*

MOTCOMBE [ST8426]

Coppleridge: Former 18th-c farmhouse in good-sized grounds, enjoyable food from sandwiches to speciality steaks in bar/lounge and two smallish dining rooms, Boddingtons and Butcombe, decent wines, welcoming service; big airy bedrooms *(Colin and Janet Roe)*

NETTLECOMBE [SY5195]

☆ *Marquis of Lorne* [off A3066 Bridport—Beaminster, via W Milton]: Smart and well run, with neat and comfortable panelled front bar, coal fire, enjoyable food (can take a while) from sandwiches to steaks, fish and game, well kept Palmers BB, Copper and 200, good wines, friendly service, daily papers, cottagey front dining room with beams, stripped stone and candles, attractive carpeted back restaurant extension (candles here too); disabled access and facilities, children in eating areas, seven comfortable bedrooms with big breakfast, picnic-sets in big pretty garden with rustic-style play area *(Dorothy Clarkson, Howard and Lorna Lambert, Peter and Audrey Dowsett, Roland and Wendy Chalu, Conor McGaughey, Joan and Michel Hooper-Immins, LYM, R M Corlett, Mr and Mrs S Jones, David and Julie Glover)*

OSMINGTON [SY7282]

Sunray [A353 Weymouth—Wareham]: Pleasant fresh décor, generous good value food; children welcome, large garden and terrace, play area *(Cathy Robinson, Ed Coombe)*

PIDDLETRENTHIDE [SY7198]

☆ *European*: Unpretentiously old-fashioned oak-beamed pub with enjoyable food from fresh crisp baguettes up, well kept Courage Directors and Ringwood Best, decent wines, cheerful efficient staff, log fire in attractive copper-hooded fireplace, willow-pattern china, stylish chairs; dogs welcome, tables in neatly kept front garden, three bedrooms with own baths and good views *(BB, Dennis Jenkin)*

☆ *Piddle* [B3143 N of Dorchester]: Emphasis on good food inc whole board of imaginative fish specials, most tables set for eating, but comfortable leatherette sofas in refurbished bar; well kept Greene King ales, children's room, dining room, end pool room with SkyTV; informal streamside garden with picnic-sets and play area, good bedrooms *(Geoff Pidoux, BB, John Fiander, Marianne and Peter Stevens)*

Poachers [B3143 N of Dorchester]: Smart bright modern décor, well kept Butcombe, Palmers 200 and Ringwood Old Thumper, wide food choice from pub standards to plenty of more individual up-to-date dishes and leisurely Sunday lunch, welcoming service and good atmosphere in large bar and roomy refurbished beamed restaurant with local artwork; piped music; dogs welcome, terraced garden with stream at bottom, 20 comfortable good value motel-style bedrooms around residents' swimming pool *(Geoff Pidoux, Joan and Michel Hooper-Immins, Nick and Lynne Carter)*

PIMPERNE [ST9008]

Farquarson Arms [A354 NE of Blandford Forum]: Neat Badger pub with friendly staff, enjoyable reasonably priced food, four real ales inc Best and K&B *(Val and Alan Green, Richard May)*

POOLE [SZ0190]

Angel [Market St, opp Guildhall which is signed off A348]: Well run, spacious and relaxed, with light modern décor, four well kept Ringwood ales from visible back cellar, fairly priced up-to-date food 12-7 (just lunchtime Sun), decent wines, quick efficient service; disabled facilities, heated back courtyard, modern bedrooms *(LYM, G Coates)*

Bermuda Triangle [Parr St, Lower Parkstone]:

Four interesting and particularly well kept changing real ales, two or three good continental lagers on tap and many other beers from around the world, good lunchtime food, friendly landlady, good local atmosphere, various snug old corners and lots of nautical and other bric-a-brac on shelves and ceiling, back room with sports TV; a bit too steppy for disabled access *(G Coates)*

Blue Boar [Market Cl]: Comfortable former mansion house, a pub since the 1990s, with well kept changing ales, wide choice of inexpensive lunchtime food, lots of interesting nautical theme pictures and artefacts, cellar bar with wknd live music and Weds folk club *(David Carr)*

☆ *Guildhall Tavern* [Market St]: Largely attractively laid restaurant rather than pub, french-run and good (if not cheap), mainly fish; friendly service, small front bar, well kept Ringwood Best and decent house wine, bright nautical décor, lots of yachting memorabilia *(David Carr, Derek Thomas, LYM, Joan and Michel Hooper-Immins)*

☆ *Inn in the Park* [Pinewood Rd, off A338 towards Branksome Chine, via The Avenue]: Pleasantly decorated open-plan bar in substantial Edwardian villa (now a small hotel), popular with local residents and business people for well kept Wadworths and other ales and good value generous standard food (not Sun evening) from good sandwiches with chips to fresh seafood, cheerful young staff, log fire, oak panelling and big mirrors, airy and attractive restaurant (children allowed) and Sun carvery; tables on small sunny terrace, comfortable bedrooms, quiet pine-filled residential area just above sea, open all day *(LYM, Michael and Alison Sandy, W W Burke)*

Nightjar [Ravine Rd, Canford Cliffs]: Ember Inn attractively refurbished with leather armchairs, sofas and so forth, several separate areas, well kept Bass, Shepherd Neame Spitfire and Wadworths 6X from long bar, wide range of reasonably priced food from sandwiches up; piped music, machines, two quiz nights; picnic-sets on pleasant shaded lawn, nice quiet spot in upmarket district *(W W Burke, Michael and Alison Sandy)*

Queen Mary [West St]: Usual nautical pictures and bric-a-brac, two well kept Ringwood ales and a guest beer, roaring fire, wholesome pub food, darts, traditional dark wood furnishings; disabled access *(G Coates)*

Sandacres [Banks Rd]: Large open-plan bar below block of flats, plush banquettes in one part, tables and chairs in another, large family area, splendid harbour views, well kept Greene King Old Speckled Hen and Ringwood Best and Fortyniner, generous low-priced pub food; corner TV, live music Fri/Sat, adjoining pool hall *(Michael and Alison Sandy)*

PORTLAND [SY6872]

George [Reforne]: Well kept ales inc a guest such as Adnams Fisherman, chatty and knowledgeable local landlord, good value food (not Weds lunchtime) from big filled baps to cheap home-made hot dishes in 17th-c stone-built pub mentioned by Thomas Hardy and reputed to have smugglers' tunnels running to the cliffs; very low doorways and beams, flagstones, small rooms, scrubbed tables and interesting prints, children's room; picnic-sets in pleasant garden *(Joan and Michel Hooper-Immins, Roland and Wendy Chalu)*

POWERSTOCK [SY5196]
☆ *Three Horseshoes* [off A3066 Beaminster—Bridport via W Milton]: Plain country pub with landlord/chef cooking good enterprising meals using fresh fish and other local ingredients, generous interesting lunchtime baguettes too, well kept Palmers ales, good range of wines by the glass, friendly helpful landlady, good log fires and stripped panelling, children welcome in no smoking pine-plank dining room, no music; level access, dogs welcome (two resident springers), lovely views towards the sea from recently extended back terrace (steps down to this) and big sloping garden with picnic-sets and swings, three pleasant bedrooms with own bathrooms, good walks, open all day *(Pam and Alan Neale, LYM, Peter and Audrey Dowsett, Joan and Michel Hooper-Immins, Conor McGaughey, C W Burke, Roland and Wendy Chalu, R M Corlett, Barry and Anne)*

PUNCKNOWLE [SY5388]
Crown [off B3157 Bridport—Abbotsbury]: Newly refurbished 16th-c thatched inn, inglenook log fires each end of low-beamed stripped stone lounge with local paintings for sale, steps up to public bar with books and magazines, no smoking family room with children's books, Palmers full ale range, ten wines by the glass, straightforward food from sandwiches and baked potatoes to several casseroles; no credit cards; views from peaceful pretty back garden, good walks, bedrooms *(Mike and Shelley Woodroffe, Marjorie and David Lamb, Roland and Wendy Chalu, LYM, Colin and Janet Roe, Val and Alan Green, Ian and Deborah Carrington)*

PYMORE [SY4794]
Pymore Inn [off A3066 N of Bridport]: Attractive Georgian beamed and stone-built pub popular with older local people for good value generous traditional food (most tables laid for eating), lunchtime toasties and baguettes, friendly prompt service, well kept changing ales such as Badger Best and Youngs, good choice of wines by the glass, prints on panelled walls, woodburner, small pretty dining room; soft piped music; wheelchair access, big garden *(Bob and Margaret Holder, Roland and Wendy Chalu)*

SANDFORD ORCAS [ST6220]
☆ *Mitre* [off B3148 and B3145 N of Sherborne]: Tucked-away country local with flagstones and fresh flowers throughout, quick friendly service, good choice of attractively presented reasonably priced food, well kept real ales, country wines, small bar and larger pleasantly homely dining area; has been cl Mon lunchtime *(LYM, OPUS, Marjorie and David Lamb)*

SHAFTESBURY [ST8622]
Crown [High St]: Old coaching inn with friendly landlord and staff, Badger beer inc seasonal ones, huge open fireplace, window seats *(Alan and Paula McCully)*
Fountain [Breach Lane, Enmore Green]: Pleasantly refurbished by new licensees, roomy bar, small restaurant, sensibly short choice of imaginative english food, attentive service *(Colin and Janet Roe)*
Half Moon [Salisbury Rd (A30 E, by roundabout)]: Pleasantly enlarged family-friendly pub with large comfortable restaurant area off small bar, wide choice of good value generous food inc popular Sun lunch, quick helpful service, Badger beers; garden with adventure playground *(Nicholas and Dorothy Stephens)*
Mitre [High St]: Tastefully refurbished ancient pub with quickly served good value food from huge chunky sandwiches to enjoyable carvery, good friendly service, fine log fire, well kept Youngs, good choice of wines, daily papers, Blackmore Vale views from back dining room and three-tier suntrap back decking; piped music; children welcome *(BB, M Vlassova, J Longworth, Alan and Paula McCully, Steve and Liz Tilley, Colin and Janet Roe)*
Two Brewers [St James St]: Down steep famously photogenic Gold Hill, friendly well divided open-plan plush-seated bar, lots of decorative plates, well kept ales such as Courage Best, Fullers London Pride, Gales, Greene King or Ringwood, usual bar food from baguettes up (children's helpings of any dish), good value wines, no smoking back dining room, skittle alley; children in eating areas, dogs in bar, picnic-sets in attractive good-sized garden with pretty views *(LYM, Alan and Paula McCully)*

SHAPWICK [ST9301]
☆ *Anchor* [off A350 Blandford—Poole; West St]: Appealing pub in heart of pretty thatched village, varnished pine tables on quarry tiles, friendly new management, good freshly made food (not Mon; may take a while) from baguettes to some interesting hot dishes, good wine choice, Greene King Abbot and Ringwood Best, several small rooms with pleasant end dining room; piped music, occasional live; children welcome, brightly painted tables in front, more in attractive garden with terrace and play area behind, handy for Kingston Lacy *(BB, John and Joan Nash, A and H Piper)*

SHERBORNE [ST6316]
Half Moon [Half Moon St]: Standard food pub with prompt service and good choice of decent reasonably priced food from sandwiches and baked potatoes up, real ales such as Ringwood, bright and airy no smoking restaurants; 16 bedrooms with own bathrooms *(Joan and Michel Hooper-Immins, Guy Vowles)*

STOBOROUGH [SY9286]
Kings Arms [B3075 S of Wareham]: Neatly kept inside and out, enjoyable food with good choice of specials inc local fish, well kept Timothy Taylors Landlord, good service and

atmosphere; disabled access *(Peter Neate, Liz and Tony Colman, Pam and Alan Neale)*

STRATTON [SY6593]

Saxon Arms [off A37 NW of Dorchester; The Square]: Traditional (but recently built) thatched local under new management, open-plan, bright and spacious, with well kept Timothy Taylors Landlord and Charles Wells Bombardier, good value wines, enjoyable food, efficient service, open fire, part flagstones, part carpet, light oak tables and comfortable settles, large no smoking dining section on right, traditional games; children and dogs welcome, tables out overlooking village green *(LYM, Alec and Joan Laurence, James A Waller, Brian and Bett Cox, Mrs A P Lee)*

STUDLAND [SZ0382]

☆ *Bankes Arms* [off B3351, Isle of Purbeck; Manor Rd]: Very popular spot above fine beach, outstanding country, sea and cliff views from huge pleasant garden with masses of seating; comfortably basic, friendly and easy-going big bar with raised drinking area, very wide choice of decent food (at a price) all day from good baguettes to local fish and good crab salad, half a dozen or more changing real ales (it brews some of its own), local farm cider, good wines by the glass, efficient service, great log fire, darts and pool in side games area; they may try to keep your credit card while you eat, can get very busily trippery wknds and in summer, parking in season can be complicated or expensive if you're not a NT member, piped music, machines, big-screen sports TV – it could do with a no smoking area; children welcome, just off Coastal Path, big comfortable bedrooms *(Terry and Linda Moseley, Richard Fendick, Phil and Sally Gorton, John and Laney Woods, John Coatsworth, Roy and Lindsey Fentiman, Liz and Tony Colman, Gerry and Rosemary Dobson, Mr and Mrs John Taylor, Dr D E Granger)*

STURMINSTER MARSHALL [SY9499]

☆ *Red Lion* [N end of High St, opp church; off A350 Blandford—Poole]: Attractive and civilised village pub opp handsome church, old-fashioned roomy U-shaped bar, good friendly relaxed atmosphere, good value home-made food inc substantial interesting starters, limited-choice OAP two-course lunch, sandwiches on Sun too, smart efficient service, well kept Badger Best and Tanglefoot, log fire, team photographs and caricatures, cabinet of sports trophies, quiet end round corner, roomy no smoking restaurant/family room in skittle alley conversion *(BB, Marjorie and David Lamb, W W Burke, Michael and Ann Cole)*

STURMINSTER NEWTON [ST7814]

☆ *Swan* [off A357 Blandford—Sherborne, via B3092; Market Pl]: Traditional beamed bar with fireside sofa, panelling and stripped brick, well kept Badger Best and Tanglefoot, food all day from lunchtime sandwiches, baguettes and burgers up, daily papers to read, mainly no smoking eating areas (children over 5 welcome in restaurant); piped music, can be smoky;

dogs allowed, tables out on terrace and in garden, good value bedrooms, open all day *(Martin and Jane Wright, Paul Humphreys, D P and M A Miles, Colin and Janet Roe, Gene and Kitty Rankin, LYM)*

White Hart [Market Cross, B3092]: 18th-c thatched and black-beamed inn, compact and friendly, with well kept Badger ales, pleasant staff, reasonably priced bar food; garden beyond cobbled coach entry, bedrooms *(John A Barker)*

SUTTON POYNTZ [SY7083]

☆ *Springhead* [off A353 NE of Weymouth]: Appealingly placed smart pub, entirely no smoking, with friendly efficient service, enjoyable food from well filled lunchtime baguettes and baked potatoes up, well kept Greene King Old Speckled Hen and Otter, good value wines inc bin-ends, good range of malt whiskies, daily papers, beamed and panelled bar, wing chairs, sofas and coal fire in clubby lounge, nicely decorated dining room; well chosen piped music; wheelchair access, lovely spot opp willow stream in quiet village, entertaining ducks, good play area in big garden with fruit trees, walks to White Horse Hill and Dorset Coastal Path *(Roland and Wendy Chalu)*

SWANAGE [SZ0378]

Anchor [High St]: Unpretentious pub with lots of nautical memorabilia and wide food choice from good substantial sandwiches up *(Meg and Colin Hamilton)*

Pines [Burlington Rd]: Big hotel bar popular with older people for reliably good value lunches at hard-to-beat prices; well kept beers, good friendly service, excellent coast views from garden (a long way from bar); comfortable bedrooms *(A and B D Craig)*

SYDLING ST NICHOLAS [SY6399]

☆ *Greyhound* [High St]: Wide choice of attractively presented food (can take a while) from filled crusty rolls to good fish and delicious puddings, warm welcome and entertaining chatty landlord, well kept Otter and Palmers BB, fairly priced wines, long brick bar counter, beams, stripped stonework and flagstones, comfortable seating, pleasant bistro-style flagstoned conservatory, restaurant; pool, piped music; good tables in nice small garden with play area, very pretty streamside village *(Peter Neate, Dr D and Mrs B Woods, BB, George Atkinson, Richard and Nicola Tranter)*

SYMONDSBURY [SY4493]

☆ *Ilchester Arms* [signed off A35 just W of Bridport]: Attractive partly thatched old inn, snugly rustic open-plan low-beamed bar with high-backed settle built in by big inglenook, pretty no smoking dining area with another fire, carefully prepared good food strong on local fish and other local ingredients, moderate prices, friendly obliging service, well kept Palmers beers, reasonably priced wines, pub games, skittle alley; fairly quiet piped music; level entrance (steps from car park), children welcome, tables in nice informal brookside back garden with play area, peaceful village, good walks nearby (*J Radford, Mrs C Lintott, Roland and Wendy Chalu, LYM, Neil and Anita Christopher*)

THREE LEGGED CROSS [SU0905]

Old Barn Farm [Ringwood Rd, towards Ashley Heath and A31]: Picturesque thatched Vintage Inn, long and low, with good value usual food presented well, pleasant rambling layout, friendly attentive young staff, Bass real ale, decent wines; lots of tables on attractive terrace and front lawn by fish pond, some children's amusements, handy for Moors Valley Country Park (*Phyl and Jack Street*)

TOLPUDDLE [SY7994]

Martyrs [former A35 W of Bere Regis]: Relaxed creeper-covered pub with well kept Badger beers, wide food choice inc good local fish and seafood and lovely home-made ice-creams in bar and busy attractively laid out restaurant; children welcome, picnic-sets on heated front terrace, nice garden, open all day, quiet bypassed village (*Roy and Lindsey Fentiman, Derek and Maggie Washington*)

TRENT [ST5818]

Rose & Crown: Attractively old-fashioned ex-farmhouse pub with enjoyable food and atmosphere, well kept ales, decent wines, good service, log fire, flagstones, oak settles, dining conservatory; children welcome, picnic-sets behind – lovely peaceful surroundings, good walks (*OPUS, Peter Neate*)

UPLODERS [SY5093]

☆ *Crown* [signed off A35 E of Bridport]: Appealing low-beamed bar with cheerful décor, friendly prompt service, wide variety of good food from snacks to generous Sun roasts and seafood straight off the local boats, sensible prices, all Palmers ales kept well, ten wines by the glass, daily papers, table skittles and log fires, steps down to pretty no smoking restaurant with flowers and candles; piped music, quiz nights; picnic-sets in small attractive two-tier garden (*Brian and Bett Cox, Roland and Wendy Chalu, David Martin, LYM, David and Julie Glover*)

UPWEY [SY6785]

Old Ship [off A354; Ridgeway]: Quiet beamed pub with lots of alcoves and log fires each end, well kept Greene King Old Speckled Hen and a guest beer, food from lunchtime baguettes up, quick friendly service; picnic-table sets in garden with terrace, interesting walks nearby (*Marjorie and David Lamb, LYM, Joyce and Geoff Robson*)

☆ *Riverhouse* [B3159, nr junction A354]: Coal-effect gas fireplace dividing flagstoned bar side from neat carpeted no smoking dining side, main emphasis on wide range of good quickly served food from lunchtime baguettes through familiar dishes to italian specialities, good relaxed gently upmarket atmosphere, well kept (if cold) Courage Best and Wadworths 6X, adventurous wine choice, good coffees, friendly staff; well reproduced piped pop music; disabled access, sizeable garden with play area, cl Sun evening (*BB, Joan and Michel Hooper-Immins*)

Royal Standard [Dorchester Rd (A354)]: Proper 1940s alehouse, lots of railway pictures inc old Upwey station on former Abbotsbury line in public bar on right, more with railway books and even model trains in cream and teak lounge bar on right, well kept Butcombe, Fullers London Pride and Timothy Taylors Landlord (no food); eagle owl Hedwig in back enclosure (*Joan and Michel Hooper-Immins*)

WAREHAM [SY9287]

Black Bear [South St]: Well worn-in bow-windowed 18th-c hotel with old local prints and lots of brass in convivial bar off through corridor, lounge with settees and easy chairs, well kept ale, good choice of keenly priced usual food from sandwiches up, decent coffee, back eating room and restaurant; piped classical music; picnic-sets in pleasant flower-filled back yard, bedrooms, open all day (*Colin and Janet Roe, BB*)

Old Granary [The Quay]: Warm and comfortable compact bar with friendly staff, decent house wines and nicely served hot drinks (keg beers), large restaurant overlooking River Frome; pleasant tables outside, four bedrooms with own bathrooms (*anon*)

WAYTOWN [SY4797]

Hare & Hounds [between B3162 and A3066 N of Bridport]: Peaceful 17th-c country local, two small cottagey rooms and pretty dining room, good value well presented straightforward food from sandwiches, baguettes and baked potatoes up inc popular Sun lunch, friendly licensees and staff, well kept Palmers ales tapped from the cask, log fire, no music; step down to entrance, into bar, and into dining room; lovely views of Brit valley from picnic-sets in sizeable simple garden with good play area (*Roland and Wendy Chalu, Joan and Michel Hooper-Immins*)

WEST BAY [SY4690]

Bridport Arms: Newly refurbished 16th-c thatched pub on beach of Bridport's low-key holiday village, large new two-level no smoking bar besides original inglenook flagstoned bar, wide range of food inc filled triangular rolls and some up-to-date light dishes, well kept Palmers ales, friendly service; tables in adjoining hotel with own entrance; picnic-sets outside, paying public car park (*BB, John Coatsworth*)

George [George St]: Red plush banquettes, mate's chairs, masses of shipping pictures, some model ships and nautical hardware, roomy L-shaped public bar with games and juke box, separate no smoking back restaurant; food inc lots of good value local fish from prawn and crab sandwiches up, well kept Palmers IPA and Gold, cheery helpful staff; tables outside, bedrooms (*Geoff Pidoux, BB, N R White*)

WEST BEXINGTON [SY5386]

☆ *Manor Hotel* [off B3157 SE of Bridport; Beach Rd]: Relaxing quietly set hotel with long history and fine sea views, good no smoking restaurant with smart Victorian-style conservatory, comfortable log-fire lounge and bustling black-beamed cellar bar with another log fire, helpful staff kind to children, bar food from sandwiches up, well kept Butcombe Gold and Quay Harbour Master, quite a few malt whiskies and several wines by the glass; piped music; dogs allowed in bar, plenty of picnic-sets on lawns with play area, comfortable bedrooms, open all day *(OPUS, Mayur Shah, Andrea Rampley, Alice Harper, A P Seymour, Dennis Jenkin, Anthony Rogers, Mrs A P Lee, LYM, Roland and Wendy Chalu, John and Joan Nash, Alex and Irene Harvey)*

WEST KNIGHTON [SY7387]

New Inn [off A352 E of Dorchester]: Neat biggish pub with good sensibly priced food inc tempting puddings, friendly attentive staff, real ales, country wines, small restaurant, skittle alley, good provision for children; big colourful garden, pleasant setting in quiet village with wonderful views *(Jason Caulkin, Colin Watt)*

WEST LULWORTH [SY8280]

☆ *Castle Inn* [B3070 SW of Wareham]: Pretty thatched inn in lovely spot nr Lulworth Cove, good walks and lots of summer visitors; quaintly divided flagstoned bar concentrating on food (not cheap, and may take a while) from sandwiches to local crab inc children's dishes and summer salad bar, decent house wines, farm cider, Courage Best, Gales HSB and Ringwood Best, friendly chatty staff, maze of booth seating divided by ledges for board games and jigsaws, cosy more modern-feeling separate lounge bar and pleasant restaurant, splendid ladies'; piped music, video game; popular garden with terrace, giant chess boards, boules and barbecues, bedrooms *(Richard Fendick, Joan and Michel Hooper-Immins, LYM, Sarah and Peter Gooderham)*

WEST STAFFORD [SY7289]

Wise Man [signed off A352 Dorchester—Wareham]: 16th-c thatched and beamed village pub nr Hardy's cottage, up to five real ales, cheerful staff, enjoyable food inc some good imaginative dishes, coal fire, interesting displays inc masses of old pipes, sensibly placed darts, close-set tables in cottagey stripped-stone restaurant; piped music, big-screen sports TV; reasonable disabled access, dogs on leads welcome, solid tables out in front, picnic-sets in small back garden, lovely walks nearby *(BB, Dr D E Granger)*

WEST STOUR [ST7822]

Ship [A30]: Old-style pub with good value very generous food cooked by landlord, proper sandwiches, low prices, friendly landlady, well kept Palmers and Ringwood, spotless attractive furnishings, big log fire, lovely views from chatty bright and airy bar, intimate split-level dining area; dogs allowed in bar (two friendly pub labradors) but not garden behind, comfortable bedrooms *(Dennis Jenkin, Comus and Sarah Elliott, Colin and Janet Roe, Steve Jackson, Neil Crux)*

WEYMOUTH [SY6778]

Boot [High West St]: Bare-boards local nr harbour dating from early 1600s, beams and stone-mullioned windows, emphasis on well kept Ringwood ales with a guest beer, Cheddar Vale farm cider, cheap filled rolls, pork pies etc; pavement tables *(the Didler, Joan and Michel Hooper-Immins)*

Dorothy [Esplanade]: Big plain two-level open-plan bar, carpet and bare boards, Bass, Fullers London Pride, Greene King IPA and Abbot and Wadworths 6X, low-priced straightforward food (all day in summer); piped music may be loud, and turns into a nightclub late at night; children welcome, pavement tables, open all day, multi-occupancy bedrooms *(the Didler, Joan and Michel Hooper-Immins)*

☆ *Nothe Tavern* [Barrack Rd]: Roomy and comfortable local doing well under popular new local landlord, with good atmosphere, wide range of enjoyable food inc local fresh fish, friendly service, well kept ales such as Ringwood Best and Wadworths 6X, decent wines, good choice of malt whiskies, lots of whisky-water jugs on ceiling, interesting prints and photographs, no smoking restaurant (children welcome here); may be quiet piped music; distant harbour glimpses from garden *(BB, Joan and Michel Hooper-Immins, Phil and Jane Hodson)*

☆ *Red Lion* [Hope Sq]: Lively unsmart bare-boards pub with well kept Courage Best and Dorset beers from smart touristy complex in former brewery opp, quickly served limited bargain lunches, good crab sandwiches too, interesting RNLI and fishing stuff all over the walls and ceiling (even two boats), coal fire, daily papers, friendly family atmosphere, good staff, darts; can get a bit smoky, may be piped pop music; dogs welcome, plenty of picnic-sets on sunny front terrace (more than inside), open all day wkdys, food all day then too *(the Didler, BB, Mr and Mrs M Clark, Roland and Wendy Chalu)*

Sailors Return [St Nicholas St]: Old-fashioned local with RNLI and naval memorabilia, enjoyable food from baguettes through up-to-date snacks to bargain meals for two, Courage Directors, John Smiths and Weymouth ales *(Liz and John Soden)*

Ship [Custom House Quay]: Neat and spaciously extended waterfront pub, several open-plan levels inc no smoking area, well kept Badger ales from long bar, good choice of wines by the glass, good value usual food (only upstairs at night) from sandwiches, baguettes and ciabattas up, thorough-going nautical decoration; unobtrusive piped pop music; wheelchair access downstairs, pleasant back terrace *(LYM, Sue and Mike Todd, Roland and Wendy Chalu)*

Wellington Arms [St Alban St]: Unpretentious panelled town pub, good value lunchtime food (all day summer wkdys) from toasted sandwiches and baguettes to sensibly priced hot dishes inc daily roasts, well kept real ales, children welcome in no smoking back dining room *(Joan and Michel Hooper-Immins)*

WIMBORNE MINSTER [SU0000]

Kings Head [The Square]: Popular brasserie/bar in old-established hotel, enjoyable

honest food, plenty of room for drinkers in roomy bar areas, fast service; comfortable bedrooms *(Geoff Pidoux, John Branston)*
Oddfellows Arms [Church St]: Compact pub with well kept Badger beers and particularly obliging service *(John A Barker)*
WINFRITH NEWBURGH [SY8085]
Red Lion [A352 Wareham—Dorchester]: Comfortable and welcoming Badger family dining pub with wide food range, their usual beers, good service, reasonably priced wines; TV room, piped music; tables in big sheltered garden (site for caravans), bedrooms *(Marjorie and David Lamb, Paul and Penny Rampton, Pam and Alan Neale)*
WINKTON [SZ1696]
Fishermans Haunt [B3347 N of Christchurch]: Hotel with neat well divided partly no smoking big-windowed bar, well kept Gales GB and HSB and Ringwood Fortyniner, lots of country wines, standard food from sandwiches and filled baked potatoes up, wknd restaurant; disabled facilities, children and dogs welcome,

well kept gardens, comfortable bedrooms, open all day *(LYM, A and B D Craig, Richard Haw, Joan and Michel Hooper-Immins, Mr and Mrs A P Reeves, Francis Johnston, T and P)*
WINTERBORNE ZELSTON [SY8997]
Botany Bay [A31 Wimborne—Dorchester]: Spreading open-plan roadside dining pub, front part divided into areas by partly glazed partitions, back more restauranty, reliable food from sandwiches and baguettes through usual pubby dishes to steaks, sensible prices and good quick service, well kept Ringwood, decent house wines and coffee; tables on back terrace *(BB, Glenn and Gillian Miller, A and H Piper)*
YETMINSTER [ST5910]
White Hart [High St]: Lots of nooks and crannies in comfortable low-beamed stone and thatched village pub with well kept real ales, proper pub food, friendly staff and locals; well behaved children allowed, tables on back terrace, garden with play area *(OPUS)*

Essex

Essex pubs include quite a lot of fine ancient buildings. One such is the Sun in Dedham, an appealing new main entry this year, good all round, with award-level beer, wine and food quality. Other pubs on fine form here are the welcoming Axe & Compasses at Arkesden (good food, nice choice of wines and malt whiskies), the Three Willows at Birchanger (good value fresh fish), the Alma in Chelmsford (charm that you don't expect in a town pub, enjoyable food that they take real care over), the Cricketers at Clavering (a very good smart dining pub, comfortable bedrooms), the cheerful good value Rainbow & Dove just off the motorway at Hastingwood (now largely no smoking), the busy and well run Shepherd & Dog at Langham (reliable food), the unspoilt Viper surrounded by woodland at Mill Green (good beers), and the cheerful 15th-c White Horse at Pleshey (enjoyable food and interesting memorabilia). Run by Jamie Oliver's parents (he was obviously brought up in a good school, food-wise), the Cricketers at Clavering takes the award of Essex Dining Pub of the Year. In the Lucky Dip section at the end of the chapter, pubs gaining high praise these days are the Barge in Battlesbridge, Griffin in Danbury, Sun at Feering, Swan at Felsted, Red Lion at Finchingfield, Crooked Billet in Leigh-on-Sea, Blue Boar in Maldon, Ferry Boat at North Fambridge, Rose at Peldon, Plough at Radwinter, Cricketers Arms at Rickling Green and Bell at Woodham Walter. Drinks prices in the county are perhaps a touch above the national average, with Ridleys the main local brewer often attractively priced, and Crouch Vale, Mauldons and Mighty Oak other local brews to look out for.

ARKESDEN TL4834 Map 5
Axe & Compasses ★ ⑪ ♀

Village signposted from B1038 – but B1039 from Wendens Ambo, then forking left, is prettier

Comments from most readers continue to enthuse about this quintessentially English thatched village pub and its food. Home-made bar food might include soup (£3.50), lunchtime sandwiches (from £3.50, not Sunday), spinach and potato cake with tomato and basil sauce (£9.95), home-made steak and kidney pie or chicken supreme (£10.95), monkfish with roasted red pepper sauce (£13.95) and grilled sardines (£4.95); specials might include spicy home-made meatballs on fresh spaghetti (£10.95), grilled salmon steak with asparagus and lemon butter sauce (£11.95) or roast pheasant with rich madeira sauce (£11.95); on the puddings trolley you might find mouthwatering home-made puddings such as raspberry and hazelnut meringue or crème brûlée (£4.25). The no smoking restaurant has a more elaborate menu. The pub dates back to the 17th c, and the oldest part is the cosy carpeted lounge bar, which has beautifully polished upholstered oak and elm seats, easy chairs and wooden tables, a blazing fire and lots of gleaming brasses. A smaller quirky public bar (which can get a bit smoky, although there's no smoking around the bar areas themselves) is uncarpeted, with built-in settles, and darts. The atmosphere is welcoming and relaxed; friendly service from the pleasant staff. You'll find a very good wine list (with 14 wines by the glass) and around two dozen malt whiskies, along with Greene King Abbot, IPA and Old Speckled Hen served under a light blanket pressure on handpump. There are seats out on a side terrace with pretty hanging baskets; parking at the back. It's in a very pretty village. *(Recommended by Nick Lawless, Mr and Mrs T B Staples, John and Claire Pettifer, Bob and Maggie Atherton, David Barnes, Richard Siebert, Mrs Margo Finlay, Jörg Kasprowski, B and M Kendall, John Saville, Nigel Howard, Grahame Brooks, Eric Robinson, Jacqueline Pratt)*

Greene King ~ Tenants Themis and Diane Christou ~ Real ale ~ Bar food (not Sun evening in winter) ~ Restaurant ~ (01799) 550272 ~ Children in restaurant ~ Open 11.30(12 Sat)-2.30, 6-11; 12-3, 7-10.30 Sun

BIRCHANGER TL5022 Map 5
Three Willows

Under a mile from M11 junction 8: A120 towards Bishops Stortford, then almost immediately right to Birchanger Village; don't be waylaid earlier by the Birchanger Services signpost!

Liked by readers for its reasonable prices and excellent fish dishes, this pub has a cricketing theme – its name refers to cricket bats, and the spacious, carpeted main bar is full of cricketing prints, photographs, cartoons and other memorabilia. Generously served food brings plenty of people here, so it's best to arrive early if you want to eat. Besides a wide selection of more standard bar food such as lunchtime sandwiches (from £2.50), filled baked potatoes (from £3.50), ploughman's (£4.95), chilli con carne (£5.95), and other dishes such as steak and ale pie or vegetable curry (£8.95), and steaks (from £10.95), you can choose from a list of about 12 deliciously fresh simply cooked fish specials (served with chunky chips and plain salads) such as crab salad (£7.95), haddock (£8.95), and monkfish cutlets (£9.95); puddings (£3.90). Booking is a good idea if you want to eat in the no smoking restaurant. A small public bar has pool and sensibly placed darts, and there's a fruit machine. Friendly and attentive staff serve well kept Greene King IPA, Abbot and Ruddles County on handpump, and there are decent house wines. There are picnic-sets out on a terrace with heaters and on the lawn behind, with a sturdy climbing frame, swings and a basketball hoop (you can hear the motorway out here). No children are allowed inside. *(Recommended by Edward and Deanna Pearce, Matthew Shackle, Reg Fowle, Helen Rickwood, Ian Phillips, Mr and Mrs P L Spencer, George Atkinson, Mrs Margo Finlay, Jörg Kasprowski, Stephen and Jean Curtis, Dave Lowe, Eric Robinson, Jacqueline Pratt, Mrs Hazel Rainer, Charles Gysin, Neil Marshall, Peter and Jean Dowson)*

Greene King ~ Tenants Paul and David Tucker ~ Real ale ~ Bar food (12-2, 6-9.30, not Sun evening) ~ Restaurant ~ (01279) 815913 ~ Dogs allowed in bar ~ Open 11.30-3, 6-11; 12-3, 7-11 Sun

BURNHAM-ON-CROUCH TQ9596 Map 5
White Harte
The Quay

The views are really special here: this old hotel is right by the water's edge of the yacht-filled River Crouch, and on a warm evening it's a delightful spot for sipping a drink and taking in the scene. Throughout the partly carpeted bars, with cushioned seats around oak tables, are models of Royal Navy ships, and assorted nautical hardware such as a ship's wheel, a barometer, even a compass in the hearth. The other traditionally furnished high-ceilinged rooms have sea pictures on panelled or stripped brick walls; one room is no smoking. An enormous log fire makes it cosy in winter. Well kept Adnams and Crouch Vale Best are on handpump. From a straightforward menu, bar food includes sandwiches (from £2.30), a handful of daily specials such as steak and kidney pie (all £6.40), locally caught fish (£9.40), and puddings. It's popular with boaty types in summer, and can get very busy on Friday and Saturday evenings. *(Recommended by OPUS, Keith and Chris O'Neill, Ian Phillips)*

Free house ~ Licensee G John Lewis ~ Real ale ~ Bar food ~ Restaurant ~ (01621) 782106 ~ Children in eating area of bar and restaurant ~ Dogs welcome ~ Open 11-11; 12-10.30 Sun ~ Bedrooms: £19.80(£54B)/£39(£68B)

CASTLE HEDINGHAM TL7835 Map 5

Bell

B1058 E of Sible Hedingham, towards Sudbury

A delightful big walled garden is a special highlight of this interesting old coaching inn, with an acre or so of grass, trees and shrubs, as well as toys for children; there are more seats on a vine-covered terrace. Now run by the same welcoming family for more than 35 years, it is little changed inside, with its beamed and timbered saloon bar equipped with Jacobean-style seats and windsor chairs around sturdy oak tables and, beyond standing timbers left from a knocked-through wall, steps leading up to an unusual little gallery. Behind the traditionally furnished public bar, a games room has dominoes, cribbage and shove-ha'penny; piped music. Each of the rooms has a warming log fire, and one bar is no smoking; look out for Portia, the sociable german pointer. Well kept Adnams, Greene King IPA and Mighty Oak Oscar Wilde Mild are tapped from the cask along with a guest such as Batemans, and they stock a good selection of malts. Tasty, good value bar food includes home-made soup (£3.25), smoked prawns (£4.95), ploughman's (£6) or smoked haddock fishcakes (£6.50), spinach and mushroom filo parcel (£7.75), red thai curry (£8.95), and lamb chops (£9.25), specials such as south sea mussels (£4.95) or turkish lamb casserole (£8.25); puddings (£3.95); children's meals (from £3.25). On Monday night they have a fish barbecue. In the pretty village is one of the finest Norman keeps in the country. Dogs are welcome but you must phone first. More reports please. *(Recommended by Charles Gysin, Paul and Margaret Baker, Ian Phillips, David Randall)*

Grays ~ Tenants Penny Doe and Kylie Turkoz-Ferguson ~ Real ale ~ Bar food (12-2(2.30 Sat), 7-9(9.30 Sat)) ~ (01787) 460350 ~ Children welcome away from bar ~ Traditional jazz last Sun lunchtime of month, acoustic guitar group Fri evening ~ Open 12-3, 6-11; 11.30-11 Fri; 12-11 Sat; 12-10.30 Sun

CHAPPEL TL8927 Map 5

Swan

Wakes Colne; pub visible just off A1124 Colchester—Halstead

The River Colne runs through the garden of this friendly timbered and beautifully placed old pub, just upstream from a splendid Victorian viaduct. Big overflowing flower tubs and french street signs lend the sheltered suntrap cobbled courtyard a continental feel, and gas heaters mean that even on cooler evenings you can still sit outside. The spacious and low-beamed rambling bar has standing oak timbers dividing off side areas, plenty of dark wood chairs around lots of dark tables for diners, a couple of swan pictures and plates on the white and partly panelled walls, and a few attractive tiles above the very big fireplace. The central bar area keeps a pubbier atmosphere, with regulars dropping in for a drink; fruit machine, cribbage, dominoes and piped music. The restaurant and one of the lounge bars are no smoking. They do a range of fresh fish including scallops grilled with bacon (£6.95; large £13.95), fried rock eel (£8.45, large £10.95), haddock (£9.45, large £13.45), skate (£9.95) and specials such as fried tuna with garlic mushrooms or grilled lemon sole (from £13.95). Other bar food includes lunchtime filled baguettes or sandwiches (from £2.25), and ploughman's (from £4.45), as well as chicken kiev (£7.95, large £10.95), calves liver and bacon (£10.45), and sirloin steak (£12.45), with home-made puddings such as sticky toffee pudding (£3.95); they also do a simple children's menu (from £2.95). Well kept Greene King IPA and Abbot and a guest on handpump are swiftly served; they've just under two dozen malt whiskies. The Railway Centre (a must for train buffs) is only a few minutes' walk away. More reports please. *(Recommended by Tom Bottinga, Richard Siebert, Pete Bennett, Colin and Dot Savill, Matthew Eglise)*

Free house ~ Licensee Terence Martin ~ Real ale ~ Bar food (12-2.30, 6.30-10(10.30 Sat); 12-3, 6.30-9.30 Sun) ~ Restaurant ~ (01787) 222353 ~ Children in eating area of bar and restaurant ~ Dogs allowed in bar ~ Open 11-3, 6-11; 11-11 Sat; 12-10.30 Sun

CHELMSFORD TL7006 Map 5

Alma ♀

Arbour Lane, off B1137 (Springfield Road)

The staff put a great deal of enthusiasm into running this town centre pub, which continues to improve each year and puts on regular theme nights. The mainly carpeted beamed bar has a comfortable mix of tables and brocade-cushioned chairs and stools, a central brick fireplace with a club fender, a piano nearby, and a big mirror over a trompe l'oeil flanked by bookcases. One cosy alcove has a deeply cushioned button-back leather sofa and armchair, and above a dark dado is a nice collection of old advertising posters on the puce rough-cast walls. There are bar stools on flagstones by the brick-built serving counter – look out for another trompe l'oeil on the wall opposite. Besides the no smoking bar dining area, a comfortable restaurant (also no smoking) is prettily decorated in creams and blues, with an inglenook fireplace. They serve decent wines (with 11 by the glass), and Greene King IPA and a couple of guests such as Crouch Vale Brewers Gold and Nethergate Suffolk County are well kept on handpump; piped music. The menu changes monthly and uses seasonal produce; meat is bought from a local farmer, and game from a nearby game dealer, while fresh fish comes from Lowestoft and Billingsgate. As well as enjoyable changing evening specials such as soup (£3.50), mussels (£5.95), parma ham risotto (£10.95), roast cod with parsley mash, spinach and mussel broth (£12.95), and sirloin steak (£13.95), they also serve lunchtime (not Sunday) sandwiches (from £2.95), ploughman's (£4.50) and ciabattas (from £4.95), and on Sundays there's a choice of six roasts (£7.95); as the food is cooked to order, service may be slow when it's busy. They do a two-course evening meal (£11.95), and have occasional themed food nights with tribute acts such as Elvis. You'll find picnic-sets out on a crazy-paved terrace at the front and in a small garden at the back. (Recommended by Reg Fowle, Helen Rickwood, John Saville, Mr Taylor, Anthony Rogers, Ian Phillips, Sam and Christine Kilburn)

Free house ~ Licensees David and Sheila Hunt ~ Real ale ~ Bar food (12-2.30, 6-9.30, Sun 12-8.30) ~ Restaurant ~ (01245) 256783 ~ Children in eating area of bar and restaurant ~ Dogs allowed in bar ~ Open 11-11; 12-10.30 Sun; closed 25 Dec evening, 26 Dec

CLAVERING TL4731 Map 5

Cricketers ⊕ ⇔

B1038 Newport—Buntingford, Newport end of village

Essex Dining Pub of the Year

The food at this comfortably modernised 16th-c dining pub is not cheap, but is really special and changes with the seasons. Run by the same licensees (parents of TV chef Jamie Oliver) for nearly 30 years, it attracts a well heeled set; signed copies of Jamie Oliver's cookbook are on sale. The menu might include soup (£4), vegetable bhajis with mint, coriander and ginger yoghurt (£4.75), blue cheese fritots (£5.50), warm confit of rabbit with salad (£5.80), home-made beef and vegetable pie (£11.75), pancakes stuffed with spinach and four cheeses (£12.75), breast of duck (£14.75) and medallions of monkfish fillet in chopped herbs (£16.75); home-made puddings (£5); they also do sandwiches (from £3.75). You can get half price portions of some of the main meals for children, and there's a children's menu (£4.50). The spotlessly kept and roomy L-shaped beamed bar has standing timbers resting on new brickwork, and pale green plush button-backed banquettes, stools and windsor chairs around shiny wooden tables on a pale green carpet, gleaming copper pans and horsebrasses, dried flowers in the big fireplace (open fire in colder weather), and fresh flowers on the tables; the restaurant and most of the bar are no smoking; piped music. Adnams and Ridleys IPA are well kept on handpump, and they've decent wines (seven by the glass); the atmosphere can be really lively on busy lunchtimes, and the attentive staff cope with the crowds. The attractive front terrace has picnic-sets and umbrellas among colourful flowering shrubs. The no smoking bedrooms are in the adjacent cottage; readers have enjoyed staying here, and the complimentary sherry is a nice touch. It's pleasant to wander round the nearby village, especially the old cottages of Middle Street and its ford, and the 15th-c church and adjacent castle site. *(Recommended by Bob and Maggie Atherton, David Glynne-Jones, Paul Humphreys, David J Bunter, John Saville, Mike and Heather Watson, John and Claire Pettifer, M R D Foot, Martin and Karen Wake, John and Enid Morris, Alex and Irene Harvey)*

Free house ~ Licensee Trevor Oliver ~ Real ale ~ Bar food (12-2, 7-10) ~ Restaurant ~ (01799) 550442 ~ Children welcome ~ Open 11-11; 12-10.30 Sun; closed 25-26 Dec ~ Bedrooms: £70B/£100B

DEDHAM TM0533 Map 5
Sun 🍴 ♀ ⬛
High Street (B2109)

Since the *Guide*'s last edition, a new licensee has thoroughly overhauled this Tudor inn in a handsome village in the heart of Constable country, and we have been getting very favourable comments from readers, particularly on the food and beer. There are high carved beams, squared panelling and some wall timbers in the communicating bars, which are roomy and carpeted, with a variety of seats including high settles, easy chairs and a window seat looking across to the church which is at least glimpsed in several of Constable's paintings. It is all no smoking apart from the Oak Room and there are big log fires in splendid fireplaces. The menu changes daily and has a mediterranean slant, using local produce, garden herbs and fish from Billingsgate, and includes items such as soup (£4.50), smoked salmon salad (£4.50 or £9 as a main course), lunchtime sandwiches (from £5.50), grilled tuscan sausages with parmesan and spring greens (£9), tapas plate (£9.50), grilled mackerel (£10) and roast free-range duck with fig compote or roast rump of beef (£11), plus puddings such as chocolate and hazelnut torte or tiramisu (£4.50); children's portions are available. Adnams Broadside and Crouch Vale are well kept on handpump alongside a couple of guests such as Earl Soham Victoria Bitter, plus a very good selection of more than 50 wines (14 by the glass; they also do occasional wine-tasting dinners) and some interesting soft drinks; maybe piped music, cribbage and dominoes. There is a separate restaurant. On the way out to picnic-sets on the quiet and attractive back lawn, notice the unusual covered back staircase, with what used to be a dovecote on top. Beautiful walks lead out of the village, over water meadows towards Flatford Mill. The panelled bedrooms are nicely done and have abundant character; we would welcome reports from any readers who have stayed here. *(Recommended by Tim Wellock, Mike and Mary Carter, Peter and Margaret Glenister, Pam and David Bailey, J and D Boutwood, Simon Cleasby)*

Free house ~ Licensee Piers Baker ~ Real ale ~ Bar food (12-2.30(3 Sat and Sun), 6.30-9.30(10 Sat)) ~ Restaurant ~ (01206) 323351 ~ Children welcome ~ Dogs allowed in bar ~ Open 12-11(6 Sun) ~ Bedrooms: £55B/£120B

FINGRINGHOE TM0220 Map 5
Whalebone
Follow Rowhedge, Fingringhoe signpost off A134, the part that's just S of Colchester centre; or Fingringhoe signposted off B1025 S of Colchester

You can just call in for a drink at this easy-going pub, but the main focus is the imaginative food, and if you book you can get a tasty breakfast (10-11.30am; bookings only). The pale yellow-washed interior has been very nicely done out, its three room areas airily opened together, leaving some timber studs; stripped tables on the unsealed bare boards have a pleasant mix of chairs and cushioned settles. Roman blinds with swagged pelmets, neat wall lamps, a hanging chandelier and local watercolours (for sale) are good finishing touches. An enticing choice of dishes, listed on a blackboard over the small but warming coal fire, might include soup (£4.25), double baked cheese soufflé (£8.95), slow roast chinese glazed duck or home-made lamb meatballs with moroccan risotto (£9.95), steaks (from £10.50) and fresh lobster (£13.25); puddings (£4.50); they do weekday lunchtime sandwiches and baguettes (from £3.50) and children's meals (from £3.95).

Caledonian Deuchars and Greene King IPA are well kept alongside a couple of guests such as Mighty Oak on handpump, and there are decent house wines; no smoking dining area; piped music, and live music every month or so. Pleasant on a fine day, the back garden, with gravel paths winding through the grass around a sizeable old larch tree, has picnic-sets with a peaceful valley view; they sometimes have plays out here in summer. Readers recommend stopping off at the Fingringhoe Wick Nature Reserve. One reader found the service left something to be desired; more reports please. *(Recommended by Paul and Ursula Randall, Charles Gysin)*

Free house ~ Licensees Sam and Victoria Burroughes ~ Real ale ~ Bar food (10-2.30, 7-9.30) ~ Restaurant ~ (01206) 729307 ~ Children in eating area of bar, restaurant and family room ~ Dogs welcome ~ Open 11-3, 5.30-11; 11-11 Sat; 12-10.30 Sun

FYFIELD TL5706 Map 5
Queens Head ♀ ◖
Corner of B184 and Queen Street

They have six real ales at this characterful 15th-c pub, but the emphasis is mostly on serving very good food. The low-beamed, compact L-shaped bar has some exposed timbers in the terracotta-coloured walls, fresh flowers and pretty lamps on its nice sturdy elm tables, and comfortable seating from button-back wall banquettes to attractive and unusual high-backed chairs, some in a snug little side booth. Two facing log fireplaces have lighted church candles instead in summer. On handpump are Adnams Bitter and Broadside and several guests such as Caledonian Deuchars IPA, Crouch Vale Brewers Gold, Exe Valley Dobs Best, Hop Back Summer Lightning and Kings Red River, also Weston's Old Rosie farm cider, and good wines by the glass including champagne – most of the pictures have a humorous wine theme, including a series of Ronald Searle cartoons. Besides good lunchtime (not Sunday) sandwiches (from £3.25), toasted baguettes (£4.50), and baked potatoes or ploughman's (£6.25), well prepared generous food from the daily changing menu might include soup (£4.25), asparagus with smoked salmon (£6), fennel cooked in cream with mozzarella and herb crust (£8.95), steak and kidney pie (£9.95), smoked haddock on chive mash (£11.50), roast garlic rack of lamb (£13.95) or fillet steak (£15.95). The young licensees are enthusiastic and friendly; they've a cat and two dogs; occasional piped music (one reader found it too loud). At the back, a neat little prettily planted garden by a weeping willow has a teak bench and half a dozen picnic-sets under canvas parasols, and beyond a picket fence the sleepy River Roding flowing past. More reports please. *(Recommended by Mr and Mrs C F Turner, Dave Lowe)*

Free house ~ Licensees Daniel Lemprecht and Penny Miers ~ Real ale ~ Bar food (not Sun evenings) ~ Restaurant ~ (01277) 899231 ~ Open 11-3.30, 6-11; 12-3.30, 7-10.30 Sun

GOSFIELD TL7829 Map 5
Green Man ⊕ ♀
3 miles N of Braintree

New licensees have taken over at this smart dining pub, and they have refurbished the bar and dining area, but readers report the transition has been smooth. They do a help-yourself cold buffet table: you can choose from home-cooked ham and pork, turkey, tongue, beef and poached or smoked salmon, as well as game pie, salads and home-made pickles (from £7.95). If you want something hot, big portions from a mostly traditional english menu include home-made soup (£3.70), home-made steak and kidney pudding (£7.95), calves liver and bacon (£9.45), rump steak (£9.75) or lamb chops in a port and cranberry gravy (£10.25) and compote of duck with a warm potato salad (£11.95), plus puddings such as home-made fruit pie (£3.50); specials might include pork and apple casserole (£6.95) or fish pie (£7.50), or you can choose from bar food such as sandwiches (from £3), filled baked potatoes (from £3.25) and ploughman's (from £4.75). Even midweek it's a good idea to book. The two little bars have a happy relaxed atmosphere (or you can sit outside in the garden), and the staff are exceptionally friendly. Many of the decent nicely priced wines are available by the glass, and they've very well kept Greene King IPA Abbot, and maybe a guest on handpump. The main bar and restaurant are no smoking; piped music. *(Recommended by David Twitchett, Richard Siebert, David J Bunter, Richard and Margaret Peers, Ian Phillips)*

Greene King ~ Tenants Debbie With and Tony Bowen ~ Real ale ~ Bar food ~ Restaurant ~ (01787) 472746 ~ Children in eating area of bar and restaurant ~ Dogs allowed in bar ~ Open 11-3, 6-11; 12-4 Sun

GREAT YELDHAM TL7638 Map 5
White Hart ♀
Poole Street; A1017 Halstead—Haverhill

This splendid old black and white timbered dining pub was just taken over by new licensees as we went to press, and we had reservations that it might become too restauranty for the *Guide*, but it is still possible to pop in just for a drink. They focus mainly on set meals (£12.95 for two-course lunches on weekdays, £21.95 on Friday), with starters such as pillow of smoked salmon filled with crayfish and prawns, and main courses such as chicken supreme, fish pie or rib-eye steak. Lunchtime bar food (all £8.50) includes thai fishcakes, salad with crayfish tails, cashel blue cheese, bacon lardons and pine nuts, ploughman's and toasted scottish rump steak sandwich. They serve ten wines by the glass, and aside from well kept Adnams, they serve one or two continually changing guests such as Elgoods Black Dog Mild and Rebellion Zebedee; also a good choice of belgian bottled beers, organic fruit juices and a dozen malt whiskies. Watch your head as you come in: the door into the bar is very low. The main areas have stone and wood floors with some dark oak panelling, especially around the fireplace. In fine weather, the attractive landscaped garden is a pleasant place to sit, with well tended lawns and pretty seating. More reports on the new regime please. *(Recommended by David J Bunter, JWAC, B N F and M Parkin, Adele Summers, Alan Black)*

Free house ~ Licensee Mathew Mason ~ Real ale ~ Bar food (12-3, 6.30-9.30) ~ Restaurant ~ (01787) 237250 ~ Children in eating area of bar and restaurant ~ Fri night jazz and live music first Sun evening of month ~ Open 11-3, 6-11; 12-3, 7-10.30 Sun

HASTINGWOOD TL4807 Map 5
Rainbow & Dove £
¼ mile from M11 junction 7; Hastingwood signposted after Ongar signs at exit roundabout

In winter a roaring fire greets you as you step inside this 17th-c cottage-style pub, most of which is now no smoking. Three homely little low-beamed rooms open off the main bar area; the one on the left is particularly snug and beamy, with the lower part of its wall stripped back to bare brick and decorated with brass pistols and plates. It does get very busy, but the friendly staff cope well with the crowds, and the atmosphere remains relaxed; when it's quiet dogs are allowed in the bar. Good value, well presented bar food includes tasty sandwiches (from £2.50, readers recommend the crab), soup (£3.30), baked potatoes (from £4), ploughman's (from £5.50), home-made steak and ale pie or spinach and red pepper lasagne (£5.95), local sausages and mash (£6.15), and steaks (from £8.95), with fresh fish dishes such as skate wing (£8.95), and bass (£9.25); puddings might be treacle sponge and spotted dick (£3.40). Greene King IPA and a couple of weekly guest beers such as Youngs Special are well kept on handpump; piped music and darts. Hedged off from the car park, a stretch of grass has picnic-sets and you can also eat outside in front of the pub. This makes a very handy stop if you're on the nearby M11 and is not that far from Stansted Airport. *(Recommended by Bob Richardson, Alan and Paula McCully, R T and J C Moggridge, Sean and Sharon Pines, Ian Phillips, Tony Beaulah, Colin and Janet Roe, John and Wendy Allin, Jeremy King, Bob and Margaret Holder, Anthony Longden)*

Punch ~ Lease Andrew Keep ~ Real ale ~ Bar food (12-2.30, 7-9.30) ~ (01279) 415419 ~ Children in eating area of bar ~ Open 11.30-3, 6-11; 12-4, 7-10.30 Sun; closed Sun evening in Jan

HORNDON-ON-THE-HILL TQ6683 Map 3

Bell 🏮 ♀ 🍷 🛏️

M25 junction 30 into A13, then left into B1007 after 7 miles, village signposted from here

In addition to the ambitious food, this 15th-c village inn stocks seven real ales and over a hundred well chosen wines from all over the world, including 16 by the glass, and you can buy very fairly priced bottles off-sales. Food is not cheap (some readers thought it over-expensive), but they have had a recent change of chef, and still do reasonable bar food. The heavily beamed bar has some antique high-backed settles and benches, rugs on the flagstones or highly polished oak floorboards, and a curious collection of ossified hot cross buns hanging from a beam. Five swiftly rotating guests such as Archers Golden Bitter, Crouch Vale Brewers Gold and Shepherd Neame Spitfire are well kept on handpump alongside Bass and Greene King IPA, and the pub holds occasional beer festivals. The menu changes frequently, and is available in the bar and no smoking restaurant; you may need to book. Well presented dishes might include roast swede soup (£4.95), caramelised red onion tarte tatin with tarragon sorbet (£6.95), fried lamb chump with lentil jus, pearl barley and broad bean sauté (£11.95), fried trout fillet with tomato and dill sauté (£12.95) or garlic roast chicken with sweet potato fondant (£13.50); puddings such as orange curd tart or roast pear crumble with clotted cream and fresh mint (£5.95). The separate bar menu contains dishes such as lunchtime sandwiches (£4.95), smoked haddock fishcakes with basil (£7.50) and lambs kidneys with mustard and sage or cod fillet with white beans and watercress (£8.50). Note the accommodation is a couple of hundred yards away from the pub itself. Centuries ago, many important medieval dignitaries would have stayed here, as it was the last inn before travellers heading south could ford the Thames at Highams Causeway. *(Recommended by R E Dixon, Nick Lawless, John and Enid Morris, Bob Richardson, Richard Siebert, David J Bunter, Mike and Shelley Woodroffe, Ian Phillips, Adrian White, Geoff and Teresa Salt, W Andrew, Tina and David Woods-Taylor)*

Free house ~ Licensee John Vereker ~ Real ale ~ Bar food (12-2, 6.30(7 Sun)-9.45; not bank hol Mon) ~ Restaurant ~ (01375) 642463 ~ Children in eating area of bar and restaurant ~ Dogs allowed in bar and bedrooms ~ Open 11-2.30(3 Sat), 5.30(6 Sat)-11; 12-4, 7-10.30 Sun; closed 25-26 Dec ~ Bedrooms: /£64B

LANGHAM TM0233 Map 5

Shepherd & Dog ♀

Moor Road/High Street; village signposted off A12 N of Colchester

A former West Ham and Liverpool footballer runs this pleasant village pub with great panache, and even when it's busy the staff cope very well. The L-shaped bar has engaging collections of continental bottled beers and brass and copper fire extinguishers. The food here is deservedly popular: chalked on boards around the bar, the enjoyable menu changes regularly, but includes around ten fish specials such as chilli-glazed butterfish or tuna (£8.95), and hummous-crusted halibut or lemon sole (£9.95), with other dishes such as sandwiches (£2.30), soup (£3.25), chicken liver pâté (£4.25), ploughman's (from £4.20), lemon sole (£10.95) and fillet steak (£13.95), with puddings such as apple and apricot crumble (£4.25); they do children's meals (£3.95), and a Sunday roast (£7.50). Greene King IPA, Abbot and Ruddles County are well kept on handpump, or you can choose from a short but carefully selected wine list; piped music, and readers tell us it can get smoky. In summer, there are very pretty window boxes, and a shaded bar in the enclosed side garden; tables outside. They hold occasional theme nights. *(Recommended by Roy and Lindsey Fentiman, R E Dixon, Charles and Pauline Stride, Mr and Mrs W E Cross, Comus and Sarah Elliott)*

Free house ~ Licensee Julian Dicks ~ Real ale ~ Bar food (12-2, 6-9.30(10 Fri); 12-10 Sat; 12-9 Sun) ~ Restaurant ~ (01206) 272711 ~ Children in eating area of bar and restaurant ~ Dogs allowed in bar ~ Open 11-3, 5.30-11; 11-11 Sat; 12-10.30 Sun

LITTLE BRAXTED TL8314 Map 5
Green Man £
Kelvedon Road; village signposted off B1389 by NE end of A12 Witham bypass – keep on patiently

This friendly and pretty brick house, tucked well away on an isolated lane, makes an enticing spot for a quiet drink – either in the pleasant sheltered garden, or in the traditional welcoming little lounge. This has an interesting collection of bric-a-brac, including 200 horsebrasses, some harness, mugs hanging from a beam, and a lovely copper urn; it's especially cosy in winter when you'll really feel the benefit of the open fire. The tiled public bar has books, darts, cribbage and dominoes; part of the saloon bar is no smoking. Welcoming staff serve Ridleys IPA and Old Bob plus perhaps a guest ale on handpump, along with several malt whiskies. Reasonably priced, hearty bar food such as sandwiches (from £2.65), filled baguettes or baked potatoes (from £3.45), ploughman's (£5.50), cottage pie or prawn cocktail (£3.95), sausages and creamed potatoes (£4.95), lasagne (£6.75), and a couple of daily specials such as steak and ale pie (£7.95), and minted lamb shank (£8.95), while puddings might be treacle tart (£3.25). More reports please. *(Recommended by G Culliford, Alan and Carolin Tidbury)*

Ridleys ~ Tenant Neil Pharoah ~ Real ale ~ Bar food (not first Sun evening in month) ~ (01621) 891659 ~ Open 11.30-3, 6-11; 12-3.30, 7-10.30 Sun

LITTLE WALDEN TL5441 Map 5
Crown ◖
B1052 N of Saffron Walden

This extended white 18th-c cottage stands in tranquil countryside, and you can eat outside at tables on the patio. The cosy low-beamed bar has two log fires in brick fireplaces, bookroom-red walls, flowery curtains and a mix of bare boards and navy carpeting. Seats, ranging from high-backed pews to little cushioned armchairs, are spaced around a good variety of closely arranged tables, mostly big, some stripped. The small red-tiled room on the right has two little tables; piped local radio. The big draw is the four or five well kept real ales tapped straight from the cask, which might include Adnams Bitter, Greene King IPA, Mauldons Bitter and Wolfs, and a couple of changing guests, often local brews, such as City of Cambridge Boathouse or Hobson's Choice. Hearty bar food includes sandwiches (from £2.95), soup (£3.95), ploughman's (from £6.25) and steak and ale pie (£7.95), with daily specials on blackboards such as vegetable curry (£7.50), smoked haddock mornay (£8.25), home-made lasagne or chicken cacciatore (£8.95), cold seafood platter (£9.75), and beef stroganoff (£10.25); puddings might be tasty apple crumble or bread and butter pudding (from £4.25). There is a no smoking restaurant, and you can eat at tables out on a side patio. *(Recommended by the Didler, Dave Lowe, Eric Robinson, Jacqueline Pratt)*

Free house ~ Licensee Colin Hayling ~ Real ale ~ Bar food (not Mon evening) ~ (01799) 522475 ~ Children welcome ~ Dogs allowed in bar ~ Trad jazz Weds evening ~ Open 11.30-3, 6-11; 12-10.30 Sun ~ Bedrooms: £55B/£70B

MILL GREEN TL6401 Map 5
Viper ◖ £
The Common; from Fryerning (which is signposted off north-east bound A12 Ingatestone bypass) follow Writtle signposts

Even if you don't manage to time a visit to coincide with one of the pub's beer festivals, which feature around 60 barrels, this enchantingly down to earth pub keeps an interesting range of real beer. Five well kept beers on handpump, including Ridleys and Viper Ales, produced specially for the pub by local microbrewery Mighty Oak, and with names such as Hissed Off and Jake the Snake (they keep changing the recipes and the names), plus weekly changing guests; Wilkins's farm cider too, from the barrel. The two timeless cosy lounge rooms have spindleback seats, armed country kitchen chairs, and tapestried wall seats around neat little old tables, and there's a log fire. Booted walkers are directed towards the fairly basic parquet-floored tap room, which is more simply furnished with shiny wooden traditional wall seats, and beyond that another room has country kitchen chairs and sensibly placed darts; shove-ha'penny, dominoes, cribbage. There's an easy-going welcoming atmosphere, and it's the kind of place where you're quite likely to fall into casual conversation with the sociable locals or welcoming landlord; the friendly pub cats are Molly and Millie. Simple but tasty bar snacks might include sandwiches and home-made soup (from £3), ploughman's (from £4.95), chicken and leek pie or steak and ale pie (£5.95), puddings (£3) and the tasty bread comes from a local baker a mile or so down the road; Sunday roast (£7.95, and they do a popular barbecue at summer weekends. It stands in a wood, and tables on the lawn overlook a beautifully tended cottage garden which is a dazzling mass of colour in summer, further enhanced at the front by overflowing hanging baskets and window boxes. One reader rates it as 'the perfect place to stop off after a long cycle ride through the surrounding woods'. No children inside the pub. *(Recommended by Pete Baker, Anthony Rogers, Kevin Thorpe, the Didler, Nick Lawless, Reg Fowle, Helen Rickwood, Daniel Myers, Ian Phillips)*

Free house ~ Licensees Harry and Denise Torris ~ Real ale ~ Bar food (12-3(4 Sat and Sun); barbecue 2-9 summer weekends) ~ No credit cards ~ (01277) 352010 ~ Dogs allowed in bar ~ Open 12-3, 6-11; 12-11 Sat and bank hol Mon; 12-10.30 Sun

PAGLESHAM TQ9293 Map 5

Punchbowl

Church End; from the Paglesham road out of Rochford, Church End is signposted on the left

The view here is delightfully rural from this secluded white weatherboarded pub, and its position can be enjoyed from tables in the little garden, or at the front by the quiet road. Cosy and spotlessly kept, the beamed bar has pews, barrel chairs and other seats, and lots of pictures and memorabilia. They serve four well kept real ales which, besides Adnams and Ridleys Old Bob, might include guests such as Archers or Highwood Tom Woods Old Timber on handpump; cribbage, shove-ha'penny, darts (set up on Monday evenings in winter), and piped music playing mostly 1960s and 70s classic hits; the restaurant is no smoking. Straightforward priced bar food such as rolls, sandwiches and filled baguettes (from £2.95), soup (£3.25), filled baked potatoes (£4.50) and ploughman's (£4.95), with daily specials such as skate (£7.50), mild lamb curry (£7.95) and rump steak (from £10.50); puddings (from £3.50). Be warned that they sometimes close a few minutes early at lunchtime during the week. More reports please, particularly on the food. *(Recommended by Kevin Thorpe, George Atkinson)*

Free house ~ Licensees Bernie and Pat Cardy ~ Real ale ~ Bar food ~ Restaurant ~ (01702) 258376 ~ Children welcome till 9pm ~ Live entertainment Mon evening in winter ~ Open 11.30-3, 6.30-11; 12-3, 6.30-10.30 Sun

PLESHEY TL6614 Map 5

White Horse ♀

The Street

Full of interesting things to look at, this 15th-c pub has its own little art gallery, with works by local artists, and sells crafts. Nooks and crannies are filled with jugs, tankards, antlers, miscellaneous brass, prints, books, bottles – and even an old ship's bell. The rooms have a friendly feel and are furnished with wheelback and other chairs and a mix of dark wooden tables; a fireplace has an unusual curtain-like fireguard. The snug room by the tiny bar counter has brick and beamed walls, a comfortable sofa, some bar stools and a table with magazines to read. Well kept Youngs Best and maybe a Youngs guest are swiftly served by helpful staff, and there are 12 wines by the glass; piped music. At lunchtime you can choose from enjoyable home-made bar snacks such as toasted sandwiches (from £3.50), herring roes fried in butter or prawn cocktail (£5.25), ploughman's (£6), smoked ham and eggs (£6.75), cottage pie or home-made lasagne (£6.95) and steak and kidney pie or fried plaice (£7.75), with more elaborate dishes from the à la carte menu (available lunchtime and evenings) such as smoked salmon salad (£5.50), pork escalope or duckling casserole (£9.50), roast rack of lamb (£12.75), with puddings such as home-made fruit crumble or apple and spice pie (£3.75); at Sunday lunchtime they do a two-course set menu (£10.50). Glass cabinets in the big no smoking dining room are filled with lots of miniatures and silverware; also sturdy furniture, and flowers on tables. Doors from here open on to a terrace with a grass area with newly planted trees and shrubs, and tables. The pub hosts various events, including jazz buffets and barbecues. More reports please. *(Recommended by Tony Beaulah, Anthony Rogers, Tina and David Woods-Taylor, Sharon and Alan Corper)*

Free house ~ Licensees Mike and Jan Smail ~ Real ale ~ Bar food ~ Restaurant ~ (01245) 237281 ~ Children in eating area of bar and restaurant ~ Dogs allowed in bar ~ Open 11-5(3 Sat), 6.30-11; 12-5 Sun; closed Mon

STAPLEFORD TAWNEY TL5001 Map 5
Mole Trap ◗ £

Tawney Common, which is a couple of miles away from Stapleford Tawney and is signposted off A113 just N of M25 overpass – keep on; OS Sheet 167 map reference 500013

Popular with walkers and cyclists, this is an isolated country pub full of lively chatter and can get busy on Sundays when it's worth getting there early if you want to eat, as they often run out of food early. The smallish carpeted bar (mind your head as you go in) has black dado, beams and joists, brocaded wall seats, library chairs and bentwood elbow chairs around plain pub tables, and steps down through a partly knocked-out timber stud wall to a similar area. There are a few small pictures, 3-D decorative plates, some dried-flower arrangements and (on the sloping ceiling formed by a staircase beyond) some regulars' snapshots, with a few dozen beermats stuck up around the serving bar. It's especially cosy in winter, when you can fully appreciate the three blazing coal fires. As well as Fullers London Pride on handpump, they have three constantly changing guests, such as Holdens Black Country and Rebellion Mutiny; Fentimans botanically brewed soft drinks; piped radio; one area is no smoking. Besides sandwiches (from £2.95, baguettes from £3.50), bar food includes lasagne, lamb curry and chilli (all £5.95), and steak or fresh daily fish such as plaice, cod or salmon (all £7.50); they do a roast on Sunday (£6.95). Outside are some plastic tables and chairs and a picnic-set, and there's a growing tribe of resident animals, many rescued, including friendly cats, rabbits, a couple of dogs, hens, geese, a sheep, goats and horses. The pub is run with considerable individuality by forthright licensees. Do make sure children behave well here if you bring them, and note that they don't accept cheques. *(Recommended by H O Dickinson, the Didler, J H Wright, Nick Lawless, N R White)*

Free house ~ Licensees Mr and Mrs Kirtley ~ Real ale ~ Bar food (not Sun and Mon evening) ~ No credit cards or cheques ~ (01992) 522394 ~ Well behaved children over 14 allowed (not at bar) ~ Open 11.30-2.30(3 Sat), 6-11; 12-4, 6.30-10.30 Sun

STOCK TQ6998 Map 5
Hoop ◗

B1007; from A12 Chelmsford bypass take Galleywood, Billericay turn-off

This happily unsophisticated local has been an alehouse for the past 450 years, and the 15th-c building was originally a row of weavers' cottages. During ten days from late May to early June it hosts a popular May beer festival with more than 130 beers. At other times six well kept changing ales are tapped from the cask or on handpump: alongside Adnams, you'll find beers from brewers such as Archers, Exmoor and Youngs, and they've also changing farm ciders and perries, plus mulled wine in winter; no fruit machines or piped music. With a cheerfully inclusive atmosphere, the cosily bustling bar is very popular with locals; friendly and accommodating service. There's a coal-effect gas fire in the big brick fireplace, cushioned benches, brocaded stools and wooden-top tables; about a third of the pub is no smoking; darts and cribbage. The reasonably priced, mostly traditional menu includes tasty dishes such as sandwiches (from £3), soup (£3.25), filled baked potatoes (from £3.50), whitebait (£4.50), ploughman's (from £6.25), sausage pie or chicken curry (£6.50), and liver and bacon (£7), with around seven daily specials such as braised stuffed hearts (£7.50), pheasant casserole or grilled wing of skate (£8.50), and home-made puddings such as spotted dick or cherry bakewell (£3.50). Prettily bordered with flowers, the large sheltered back garden has picnic-sets, a covered seating area, and in fine weather an outside bar and weekend barbecues. More reports please. *(Recommended by Ian Phillips, John and Enid Morris)*

Free house ~ Licensees John Hawkes and Amanda Fenwick ~ Real ale ~ Bar food (12-9 (7 Sun)) ~ (01277) 841137 ~ Dogs welcome ~ Open 11-11; 12-10.30 Sun

STOW MARIES TQ8399 Map 5
Prince of Wales 🍺
B1012 between S Woodham Ferrers and Cold Norton Posters

'Great menu, well kept real ales, lovely beer garden; everything just right' commented one reader of this appealingly laid-back pub. Although the chatty low-ceilinged rooms appear unchanged since the turn of the last century, they've in fact been renovated in a traditional style. Few have space for more than one or two tables or wall benches on the tiled or bare-boards floors, though the room in the middle squeezes in quite a jumble of chairs and stools. As well as five interesting, frequently changing real ales on handpump from brewers such as Dark Star and Newby Wyke, you'll also find bottled and draught belgian beers; several bottled fruit beers and farm cider too. Besides sandwiches or ciabattas (from £3.95), enjoyable, generously served dishes (with good fish specials) could include ham or sausage, egg and chips (£5.95), beer-battered cod with mushy peas (£9.95), lamb shank with raspberry beer and mash (£9.75), and puddings such as sticky toffee pudding (£3.50); the restaurant and part of the bar area are no smoking. On Thursday evenings in winter they fire up the old bread oven to make pizzas in the room that used to be the village bakery (from £5.95), while in summer on some Sundays, they barbecue unusual fish such as saupe, mahi-mahi and black barracuda (there are also steaks for the less adventurous). There are seats and tables in the back garden, and between the picket fence and the pub's white weatherboarded frontage is a terrace with herbs in Victorian chimneypots, sheltered by a huge umbrella. There are live bands on most bank holidays and some Sundays. *(Recommended by Nick Lawless, Adrian White, Ian Phillips, Derek Thomas)*

Free house ~ Licensee Rob Walster ~ Real ale ~ Bar food (12-2.30, 7-9.30, 12-9 Sun) ~ No credit cards ~ (01621) 828971 ~ Children in family room ~ Dogs welcome ~ Live entertainment some Sun afternoons ~ Open 11-11; 12-10.30 Sun

WENDENS AMBO TL5136 Map 5
Bell
B1039 just W of village

The small cottagey low-ceilinged rooms of this village pub have brasses on ancient timbers, wheelback chairs around neat tables, comfortably cushioned seats worked into snug alcoves, quite a few pictures on the cream walls, and an inviting open fire. A real bonus in summer, the extensive back garden has plenty to keep children entertained, with crazy golf and a big tree-sheltered lawn; they've recently landscaped the meadow at the bottom. Nicely lit up in the evenings and a suntrap during the day, the patio is a nice spot for dining; look out for the pub's resident pigs. Adnams and Woodfordes Wherry are well kept on handpump, along with a couple of changing guests (they have 150 different ones throughout the year). Friendly service from the new landlord and his staff; cribbage, dominoes and piped music. Tasty bar food includes sandwiches (from £3.95), sausages and mash (£6.25), steak, mushroom and ale pie or fish pie (£7.95), and sirloin steak (£11.95), changing specials such as roasted mediterranean vegetables (£7.85) or slow-roasted shank of lamb (£9.10) with puddings (mostly £4-£4.25); the dining room is no smoking. The pub is handy for Audley End. *(Recommended by Mrs Margo Finlay, Jörg Kasprowski, Mr and Mrs T B Staples, Dave Lowe, Eric Robinson, Jacqueline Pratt, J L Wedel)*

Free house ~ Licensees Shaun and Elizabeth Fetzer ~ Real ale ~ Bar food (12-2, 6.30-9 (not Sun and Mon evenings)) ~ Restaurant ~ (01799) 540382 ~ Children in restaurant and family room ~ Dogs allowed in bar ~ Live music every third Weds evening of month ~ Open 11.30-2.30, 5-11; 11-11 Fri-Sat; 12-10.30 Sun

YOUNGS END TL7319 Map 5
Green Dragon
Former A131 Braintree—Chelmsford (off new bypass), just N of Essex Showground

Good reports from readers continue to endorse the Green Dragon, which manages to strike a successful balance as both a dining pub and as a pleasant, pubby local where you can just come in for a drink. Lunchtime dishes might include sandwiches (from £2.95, baguettes from £3.95), home-made soup (£3.50), cottage pie (£5.65), ploughman's (£5.95), home-cooked ham and eggs (£7.95), curry (£8.95); other dishes such as very tasty local pork from the nearby Marks Hall Estate (£8.75), seafood from Cornwall including fried monkfish medallions with mussels and chorizo (£13) and bass (£14.75); puddings (£4). The restaurant area has an understated barn theme: you'll find stripped brick walls, a manger at one end, and a 'hayloft' part upstairs. The two bar rooms have ordinary pub furnishings, and there's an extra low-ceilinged snug just beside the serving counter. The snug, hayloft, restaurant and bar servery are no smoking. Greene King Abbot, IPA and perhaps Old Speckled Hen are well kept on handpump; unobtrusive piped jazz music. At lunchtime (not Sunday) you can have bar food in part of the restaurant, where the tables are bigger than in the bar. The quiet, neat back garden has lots of picnic-sets under cocktail parasols, and a budgerigar aviary. *(Recommended by Evelyn and Derek Walter, Adrian White, Paul and Ursula Randall, Mrs Margo Finlay, Jörg Kasprowski, Roy and Lindsey Fentiman)*

Greene King ~ Lease Bob and Mandy Greybrook ~ Real ale ~ Bar food (12-2.30, 5.30-9.30; 12-9 Sun) ~ Restaurant ~ (01245) 361030 ~ Children welcome till 8pm ~ Open 12-3, 5.30-11; 12-10.30 Sun

---

LUCKY DIP

Besides the fully inspected pubs, you might like to try these Lucky Dips recommended to us and described by readers (if you do, please send us reports: www.goodguides.co.uk).

ARDLEIGH [TM0429]
☆ *Wooden Fender* [A137 towards Colchester]: Pleasantly refurbished and extended old pub with emphasis on good choice of good value food, friendly service, three well kept real ales, decent wines, beams and log fires, children welcome in dining area; good-sized garden with water feature and play area *(LYM, N R White)*
AYTHORPE RODING [TL5915]
Axe & Compasses [B184]: Enjoyable food, friendly staff and well kept Greene King and other ales, coal fire in unpretentious beamed bar with big compass dividing it from restaurant *(Mrs Margo Finlay, Jörg Kasprowski)*
BATTLESBRIDGE [TQ7894]
☆ *Barge* [Hawk Hill]: White clapboarded local right by waterside antiques and craft centre, low beams and panelled dado, chatty bar on

right, quieter eating areas inc no smoking left, decent reasonably priced food from sandwiches up all day, real ales such as Adnams, Caledonian Deuchars IPA, Greene King Abbot and Marstons Pedigree, chatty licensees and friendly staff, lots of local photographs; piped music, can get crowded at busy times; children welcome, tables out in front, open all day *(BB, Kevin Thorpe, George Atkinson, Tony Hobden, N R White)*
Hawk [Hawk Hill]: Extensive efficiently run Vintage Inn attractively laid out with rugs, settles and oak tables on flagstones, log fire, hanging baskets, farm tools and dried hops; well kept Adnams and Greene King IPA, good choice of wines by the glass, daily papers, three no smoking areas, usual good value food all day from separate servery; piped music, packed wknds with antiques enthusiasts visiting the centre here; open all day, children welcome,

good tables out on front grass *(BB, George Atkinson)*

BILLERICAY [TQ6893]

Duke of York [Southend Rd, South Green]: Pleasant beamed local with good choice of food from sandwiches up in homely old front bar and modern restaurant, well kept Greene King IPA and Abbot and Shepherd Neame Spitfire, long-serving licensees, good service, real fire, longcase clock, local photographs, upholstered settles and wheelback chairs; evenings can get loud and lively; a few roadside picnic-sets *(Ian Phillips, Reg Fowle, Helen Rickwood, R T and J C Moggridge)*

BISHOPS GREEN [TL6317]

Spotted Dog [High Easter rd]: Pretty 18th-c thatched pub, comfortable and welcoming, with well kept Adnams, Greene King IPA and a guest beer, wide blackboard choice of enjoyable food (not Sun evening), good log fire, lots of dalmatian pictures, small dining area, dominoes and cards, games room with darts and pool; picnic-sets in large pleasant garden, quiet hamlet *(Dave Lowe)*

BLACKMORE [TL6001]

Leather Bottle [The Green]: Comfortable furniture on millstone floors, nice décor, five interesting well kept ales such as Porter and Stout, perhaps a bargain guest beer, decent food; dogs warmly welcomed, tables in garden behind *(Eddie Edwards)*

BOREHAM [TL7610]

Cock [Main Rd]: Pleasant beamed central bar with lots of gleaming brass, good value food from sandwiches up, well kept Ridleys IPA and Old Bob, decent wines and coffee; neat family garden *(Ian Phillips)*

Six Bells [Main Rd (B1137)]: Well run dining pub with enjoyable straightforward fresh food in comfortably opened-up bar and neat front restaurant, three or four well kept Greene King ales, courteous service; play area in garden *(Paul and Ursula Randall)*

BRAINTREE [TL7319]

Embassy [Fairfield Rd]: Wetherspoons in former cinema with their usual food and drink, bar where screen used to be, seating in former stalls area with tall stools around high tables at the front, back family area *(Martin Grosberg)*

Green Dragon [London Rd]: Greene King IPA, Abbot and Morlands Original, food inc fresh seafood, daily papers; picnic-sets under cocktail parasols on immaculate lawn *(Ian Phillips)*

BRENTWOOD [TQ6195]

Rose [Chelmsford Rd (A1023), Shenfield]: Reasonably priced food all day, four real ales, daily papers, no smoking dining room; children welcome, picnic-sets on front terrace with attractive flower baskets and tubs *(CMW, JJW)*

BRIGHTLINGSEA [TM0817]

Cherry Tree [Church Rd]: Enjoyable food inc bargain pasta night Weds, well kept Greene King Old Speckled Hen, back room with darts and pool *(Jason Watts)*

CANFIELD END [TL5821]

Lion & Lamb [A120 Bishops Stortford—

Dunmow]: Neat and comfortable, with friendly efficient staff, good atmosphere, wide choice of well presented generous food inc daily fresh fish in open-plan bar and spacious but cosy dining room, well kept Ridleys, decent wines and coffee; piped music; back garden with terrace, barbecue and play area, open all day *(Stephen and Jean Curtis)*

CHELMSFORD [TL7006]

Queens Head [Lower Anchor St]: Lively well run Victorian backstreet local with three well kept Crouch Vale ales and five changing guest beers, late Sept beer festival, summer farm cider, winter log fires, cheap cheerful lunchtime food (not Sun) from separate counter; open all day from noon (11 Sat), terrace tables *(Kay Davy, Dave Lowe, the Didler, Tony Hobden)*

Riverside [Victoria Rd]: Open-plan weatherboarded watermill conversion, low heavy beams, dark corners and some mill gearing, good choice of generous good value food from sandwiches and panini up, well kept Youngs, efficient, neat and cheerful staff, separate restaurant; pleasant waterside terrace, bedrooms *(Paul and Ursula Randall, Ian Phillips, John Saville)*

CHIGNALL ST JAMES [TL6709]

Three Elms: Good fresh food in small open-plan country dining pub with beams and big inglenook fireplace, cheerful relaxed atmosphere, four well kept changing ales, helpful staff *(Mark Hope, Ian and Linda Barnes)*

COGGESHALL [TL8224]

Compasses [Pattiswick, signed off A120 W]: Current friendly licensees (with attached wine business) emphasising the dining side more, with some good enterprising dishes; well kept Mauldons Gold, neatly comfortable spacious beamed bars, partly no smoking barn restaurant; children welcome, plenty of lawn and orchard tables, rolling farmland beyond, has been open all day wknds and summer *(R T and J C Moggridge, Stephen and Jean Curtis, LYM, Reg Fowle, Helen Rickwood, Richard Siebert)*

COLCHESTER [TL9925]

Stockwell Arms [W Stockwell St]: Friendly timber-framed local in the old dutch quarter, well-worn country feel with heavy 14th-c beams and lots of pictures and bric-a-brac, well kept changing ales such as Caledonian Deuchars IPA, Fullers London Pride, Gales Robins Revenge and Nethergate Suffolk County Best, cheap bar lunches from snacks and baguettes to basic hot dishes, bargain Fri fish night and popular Sun lunch; landlord organises local walks *(Pete Baker, Fr Robert Marsh, Dr and Mrs M E Wilson)*

COOPERSALE COMMON [TL4702]

Garnon Bushes: Welcoming beamed country local, formerly two cottages, popular reasonably priced food in bar and small restaurant, well kept Greene King, log fires, brasses, fresh flowers, World War II memorabilia from nearby North Weald airfield; quiet piped music; tables on front terrace *(B J Harding)*

DANBURY [TL7705]

☆ *Griffin* [A414, top of Danbury Hill]: Reliable Chef & Brewer, now completely no smoking, spacious but charmingly divided into small homely and congenial sections, 16th-c beams and some older carved woodwork, roaring log fires, thoughtful friendly service, very wide good value food choice, well kept Adnams Broadside, reasonably priced wines, soft lighting and candles at night; no bookings so get there early, subdued piped classical music; children welcome *(Adrian White, Reg Fowle, Helen Rickwood, Tina and David Woods-Taylor, Robert Turnham)*

DUNMOW [TL6221]

Dunmow Inn [High St]: Open-plan bar, well worn in and friendly, with some armchairs and red plush, dark wood tables and chairs, musical instruments and copper hanging from beams, good value food from panini and chunky sandwiches to fresh fish, Worthington Best; piped local radio *(Paul and Ursula Randall)*

DUTON HILL [TL6026]

☆ *Three Horseshoes* [off B184 Dunmow—Thaxted, 3 miles N of Dunmow]: Traditional village local with friendly licensees, low-priced simple pub food Thurs-Mon (not Sun evening), Archers, Ridleys IPA and one or two guest beers, masses of bottled beers, late spring bank hol beer festival, central fire, aged armchairs by fireplace in homely left-hand parlour, interesting theatrical and 1940s memorabilia, breweriana and enamel signs; darts and pool in small public bar, pleasant views and pond in garden, cl lunchtimes Mon-Weds *(BB, the Didler, Pete Baker, Dave Lowe)*

FEERING [TL8720]

☆ *Sun* [Feering Hill, B1024]: Interesting old pub with 16th-c beams (watch out for the very low one as you enter), plenty of bric-a-brac, woodburners in huge inglenook fireplaces, nice carved bar counter with half a dozen quickly changing well chosen real ales, enjoyable medium-priced food from sandwiches up, quick helpful service, daily papers, board games; well behaved children allowed, tables out on partly covered paved terrace and in attractive garden behind, some wknd barbecues *(LYM, the Didler, Kevin Thorpe, Edmund Coan, Kevin Mayne, Mrs P J Pearce, Eric Robinson, Jacqueline Pratt)*

FELSTED [TL6720]

☆ *Swan* [Station Rd]: Swishly comfortable pub/restaurant with three contemporary dining areas off traditional bar, sofas by central log fire, good gently upmarket food, well kept Ridleys from the nearby brewery, good value wines, huge cappuccinos, cheerful and welcoming young staff, daily papers *(B N F and M Parkin, Mrs Margo Finlay, Jörg Kasprowski)*

FINCHINGFIELD [TL6832]

☆ *Red Lion* [Church Hill – B1053 just E of B1057 crossroads]: Good blackboard choice of sensibly priced food from huffers to some interesting dishes and no-nonsense roast Sun

lunch, generous helpings, well kept Adnams and Ridleys, interesting wine choice, chatty enthusiastic landlord and efficient service, cosy local atmosphere and simple furnishings, Tudor beams, log fire in huge dividing chimney breast, bar billiards, dominoes and cards, small upstairs dining area; attractive garden, three good value bedrooms with own bathrooms, nice spot opp churchyard and 15th-c guildhall, open all day *(Mary O'Sullivan, Craig Turnbull, Pete Baker, N R White)*

FULLER STREET [TL7416]

Square & Compasses [back rd Great Leighs—Hatfield Peverel]: Little country pub, rustic bric-a-brac in L-shaped beamed bar, woodburner and big log fire, Nethergate Suffolk County and Ridleys IPA tapped from the cask, may be decent french regional wines, gentle country views from tables outside; food has been good, but some uncertainty as we go to press – reports on current regime, please *(Hazel Morgan, Bernard Patrick, the Didler, LYM, N R White, Colin and Dot Savill)*

FYFIELD [TL5606]

☆ *Black Bull* [Dunmow Rd (B184, N end)]: 15th-c pub with heavy low beams and standing timbers, comfortably opened-up pubby bar and no smoking country-style dining area with wide range of enjoyable food, well kept ales such as Fullers London Pride and Greene King, open fire, traditional games; quiet piped music; tables out among flower tubs *(R E Dixon, LYM, Roy and Lindsey Fentiman, Anthony Longden)*

GREAT CHESTERFORD [TL5142]

Crown & Thistle [just off M11 junction 9 (A11 exit roundabout); High St]: Busy village pub/restaurant, good value food, well kept beer, range of wines by the glass, decent coffee *(Roy Bromell)*

GREAT EASTON [TL6025]

Swan [2 miles N of Dunmow, off B184 towards Lindsell]: Small and unpretentious old local in attractive village street, two clean and tidy traditional front rooms, cosy and very friendly, country bygones, log fire and sofas, good ordinary food, well kept real ales, good tea and coffee (perhaps with home-made chocolates), back restaurant *(Mrs Margo Finlay, Jörg Kasprowski)*

GREAT HALLINGBURY [TL5119]

Hop Poles [handy for M11 junction 8; A120 towards Dunmow, 1st fork right; Bedlars Green]: Small, clean and well kept village pub in tranquil setting, good value bar food from good baguettes to attractive puddings and good Sun roast, nice ale choice *(Ron Deighton)*

GREAT TEY [TL8925]

Chequers [off A120 Coggeshall—Marks Tey]: Comfortable old pub with friendly new landlord and attentive staff, good value food from sandwiches and baguettes up, attentive service, well kept Greene King IPA and Abbot and a guest beer, darts and pool in public bar, restaurant; children and dogs welcome, fine walled garden, quiet village with plenty of country walks *(Colin and Penny Smith)*

GREAT WALTHAM [TL7013]
Rose & Crown [about ¾ mile from Ash Tree
Corner, old A130/A131]: Small 16th-c pub
back to its old name (had spent a few years as
the Great Waltham Free House), with
particularly well kept Bass, Fullers London
Pride and a guest beer, cheerful friendly
service, good lunchtime bar food; ghost said to
use gents' *(Paul and Ursula Randall)*

HATFIELD HEATH [TL5115]
Thatchers [A1005 towards Bishop's Stortford]:
Neatly refurbished beamed and thatched pub
with well kept Greene King IPA and other ales
from long bar, decent house wines, wide food
choice from good sandwiches up, woodburner,
copper kettles, jugs, brasses, plates and pictures
in L-shaped bar, back dining area; no children
in bar, may be piped music; at end of large
green, tables out under cocktail parasols
(Tina and David Woods-Taylor)

HELIONS BUMPSTEAD [TL6541]
Three Horseshoes [Water Lane]: Long pub
dating from 17th c, gypsy caravan among the
flowers out in front, wide choice of good value
home-made food, well kept Greene King ales,
no smoking restaurant up a step; tables in
attractive garden, charming unspoilt village,
cl Mon lunchtime *(Adele Summers, Alan Black)*

HENHAM [TL5428]
Cock [Church End]: Neat heavily timbered
family pub/restaurant with wide food range
from baguettes up, Adnams and Greene King
IPA, local pictures and shelves of bric-a-brac;
relaxing views from tree-shaded garden,
attractive village *(Michael and Jenny Back)*

HERONGATE [TQ6491]
☆ *Old Dog* [Billericay Rd, off A128
Brentwood—Grays at big sign for Boars
Head]: Long attractive dark-raftered bar
(there's been an inn here for 500 years),
comfortable back lounge, no smoking dining
room, good choice of enjoyable
straightforward home-made bar food and
more upmarket restaurant dishes, up to six
changing well kept ales such as Fullers London
Pride, Greene King Abbot and Ridleys, quick
friendly service even when busy, log-effect gas
fires; pleasant front terrace and neat sheltered
side garden *(R E Dixon, Nick Lawless, LYM)*

HOWE STREET [TL6914]
Green Man [just off A130 N of Chelmsford]:
Spacious beamed and timbered two-bar pub
dating from 14th c, new licensees (they were
popular here before, some five years ago, and
are expanding the restaurant side), generous
good value food, well kept Ridleys,
comfortably plush lounge, nice brass and
prints, log fire; garden with play area *(Paul and
Ursula Randall)*

KIRBY LE SOKEN [TM2221]
Ship [B1034 Thorpe—Walton]: Tastefully
refurbished old pink-washed building with
relaxing atmosphere, well kept Adnams and
Greene King IPA, wide choice of generous
good value food with seasonal veg, good wine
list, pleasant staff; unobtrusive piped music;
children in eating area, rustic tables outside
(Mr and Mrs Staples)

LEIGH-ON-SEA [TQ8385]
☆ *Crooked Billet* [High St]: Homely and friendly
old pub with waterfront views from big bay
windows, well kept Adnams, Bass and a guest
beer, good spring and autumn beer festivals,
sandwiches, ploughman's and salads (not Sun),
log fires, beams and bare boards, local fishing
pictures and bric-a-brac; piped music, live
music nights; open all day, side garden and
terrace, seawall seating over road shared with
Osborne's good shellfish stall; pay-and-display
parking (free Sat/Sun) by fly-over *(John and
Enid Morris, LYM, Ian Phillips, N R White)*

LITTLE BADDOW [TL7708]
Rodney [North Hill, towards Hatfield Peverell]:
Attractive low-beamed country local, former
17th-c farmhouse, nautical connections and
memorabilia, well kept Greene King IPA and
Old Speckled Hen with an interesting guest
beer, enjoyable reasonably priced food from
rolls, sandwiches and baguettes up, small pool
room with unobtrusive piped music; terrace
and good garden with well equipped play area
(Mrs P J Pearce)

LITTLE DUNMOW [TL6521]
☆ *Flitch of Bacon* [off A120 E of Dunmow; The
Street]: Informal country local, simple and
attractive small timbered bar, flowery-
cushioned pews and ochre walls, Greene King
IPA and guest beers such as Mauldons Three
Lions, friendly licensees and delightful pub
labrador, short choice of simple bar food from
baguettes up (not Sun evening, and has been
cl Mon lunchtime), no smoking back eating
area (children welcome here) with french
windows looking out on to terrace; piped
music, no credit cards; a few picnic-sets
outside, peaceful views, bedrooms
*(Ian Phillips, Mrs Margo Finlay,
Jörg Kasprowski, LYM, Terry Buckland)*

LITTLE MAPLESTEAD [TL8334]
Cock [Sudbury Rd (A131)]: Wide choice of
enjoyable reasonably priced food, prompt
service; big garden *(Ron Deighton)*

LITTLE TOTHAM [TL8811]
☆ *Swan* [School Rd]: Fine range of well kept
changing ales such as Adnams, Crouch Vale
and Fullers tapped from the cask, farm ciders,
perry and country wines, low 17th-c beams,
coal fire, dining room extension with enjoyable
local food, bar billiards and darts in tiled
games room; welcoming landlord, music
nights, morris dancers at Jun beer festival;
children welcome, small terrace and picnic-sets
under cocktail parasols on sizeable front lawn,
open all day *(the Didler, Kevin Thorpe, MLR)*

LITTLEY GREEN [TL6917]
Compasses [off A130 and B1417 SE of
Felsted]: Unpretentiously quaint and old-
fashioned country pub with well kept Ridleys
from nearby brewery tapped from cellar casks,
lots of malt whiskies, big huffers, ploughman's
and baked potatoes, no machines; tables in big
back garden, benches out in front *(the Didler)*

LOUGHTON [TQ4296]
Last Post [High Rd]: Wetherspoons post office
conversion, good warming atmosphere,
sensibly priced Courage Best, Greene King

Abbot and Shepherd Neame Spitfire, decent cheap coffee, food all day, no smoking area, old Loughton prints, no music *(Robert Lester)*

MALDON [TL8407]

☆ *Blue Boar* [Silver St; car park round behind]: Quirky cross between coaching inn and antiques or auction showroom, luxurious main lounge with gilt and chenille love-seats, seductive paintings, Canova-look marble figures, dining room with chandeliers, pewter, more paintings and antique refectory table, beams and panelling; separate smallish dark-timbered bar with spectacular raftered upper room (both with interesting antique furnishings and pictures), well kept Adnams tapped from the cask and own-brew Farmers Blue Boar and Pucks Folly, friendly helpful staff; open all day, parking £3 *(Ian Phillips, George Atkinson, LYM, Barry L Sidney, Dave Braisted)*

Jolly Sailor [Church St/The Hythe]: Charming timber-framed quayside pub, three Greene King ales, plenty of fish among other food, up-beat trendy staff; piped music; tables out overlooking Thames barges. Play area and parakeet aviary *(Ian Phillips, John and Enid Morris)*

Queens Head: Good choice of real ales inc Mighty Oak, reasonably priced food, back lounge overlooking river and leading out to quayside terrace *(MLR)*

White Horse [High St]: Unpretentious local with several Shepherd Neame ales, popular lunchtime food, friendly helpful staff; unobtrusive piped music, pool in front bar *(Ian Phillips)*

MARGARETTING [TL6701]

Red Lion [B1002 towards Mountnessing]: Busy but relaxed beamed and timbered local, all tables laid for good choice of reliable generous food inc good fish range, no smoking dining area, well kept Ridleys ales, efficient unrushed service; piped radio; good wheelchair access, pretty in summer, with picnic-sets and play area *(Reg Fowle, Helen Rickwood, John and Enid Morris, Roy and Lindsey Fentiman)*

MARGARETTING TYE [TL6801]

White Hart: Popular with families for its bright and comfortable conservatory-roofed dining room and attractive garden with robust play area, well fenced duck pond and birds and animals to look at; pleasant L-shaped bar, good value unpretentious food from sandwiches up, cheerful friendly service, well kept Adnams Broadside and interesting guest beers from afar *(Reg Fowle, Helen Rickwood, Paul and Ursula Randall, Quentin and Carol Williamson, Mrs P J Pearce)*

MILL GREEN [TL6301]

☆ *Cricketers*: Low beams, lots of interesting cricketing memorabilia, generous and popular fresh bar food, nice restaurant, well kept Greene King IPA, Abbot and a seasonal beer tapped from the cask, decent wines, friendly attentive staff, no smoking area, no music; children very welcome, picturesque setting, plenty of picnic-sets on big front terrace and in extensive tree-shaded garden behind, cl winter

Sun evenings *(Reg Fowle, Helen Rickwood, Evelyn and Derek Walter, David J Bunter, Ian Phillips)*

MISTLEY [TM1131]

Thorn [High St (B1352 E of Manningtree)]: Recently refurbished by new American chef/landlady, entirely no smoking, bar and restaurant specialising in local seasonal produce and seafood, contemporary pictures for sale; children welcome, five well equipped bedrooms with own bathrooms, open all day wknds *(anon)*

NORTH FAMBRIDGE [TQ8596]

☆ *Ferry Boat* [village signed from B1012 E off S Woodham Ferrers; keep on past railway to quay]: Unpretentious 15th-c weatherboarded pub tucked prettily down by the marshes, warmly welcoming chatty landlord, friendly locals, simple traditional furnishings, nautical memorabilia, log fire one end, woodburner the other, good value honest food from sandwiches to Sun lunches, well kept Greene King IPA, Abbot and Ruddles County, traditional games, children in family room and partly no smoking low-beamed dining room; piped music, fruit machine, TV; tables in garden with pond (ducks and carp), six comfortable bedrooms with own bathrooms in barn-like building behind, good breakfast, good lonely walks *(LYM, OPUS, Ian Phillips)*

NOUNSLEY [TL7910]

Sportsmans Arms [off B1019; Sportsman Lane]: Small country local redecorated under new landlady, well kept Adnams Broadside and Greene King IPA, cheerful young staff, enjoyable traditional Sun lunches and bar food, freshly cooked seasonal food in dining extension; piped music, TV and games machine; picnic-sets and swings in big garden *(LYM, Paul and Ursula Randall)*

OLD HARLOW [TL4711]

Marquis of Granby [Market St]: Attractive old tiled building, newly refurbished, with interesting prints and memorabilia, particularly well kept Adnams Broadside, Bass, Shepherd Neame Spitfire and guest beers in no smoking bar area, comfortable seats, friendly staff, usual food from sandwiches and baguettes up, old gas cigar lighter on bar, back pool table; piped music, TV; open all day *(Martin Grosberg)*

ORSETT [TQ6481]

Foxhound [High Rd]: Traditional unsmart local, long-serving chef doing good value straightforward food (not Sun-Tues evenings) with fresh local produce inc rare breed meats, well kept real ales such as Crouch Vale *(Andy and Jill Kassube, Tina and David Woods-Taylor)*

Whitmore Arms [Rectory Rd]: Friendly, cosy and comfortable village pub, Greene King IPA, Abbot and Ruddles Best, enjoyable acceptably priced restaurant food; picnic-sets in small family garden, attractive covered porch *(Mrs J R Sutcliffe, Ian Phillips)*

PELDON [TM0015]

☆ *Rose* [B1025 Colchester—Mersea]: Low 17th-c beams and some venerable bar furnishings contrasting with spacious airy no smoking conservatory, good friendly staff, lots of good affordable wines by the glass, well kept Adnams Best and Broadside, Greene King IPA and a guest beer, enjoyable home-made bar food from sandwiches to local Mersea fish, children's helpings; children very welcome away from bar (high chairs in restaurant), roomy well furnished garden with duck pond, open all day *(Ken Millar, LYM)*

RADWINTER [TL6137]
☆ *Plough* [Sampford Rd (B1053/54 crossroads E of Saffron Walden)]: Quietly placed country pub with enjoyable food inc game, fish and steaks, red plush open-plan black-timbered beamed bar with warm log fire, good friendly service, well kept Greene King IPA and a changing guest beer, neat no smoking dining room extension; children and dogs welcome, very attractive terrace and garden, comfortable bedrooms *(Adele Summers, Alan Black, BB)*

RICKLING GREEN [TL5129]
☆ *Cricketers Arms* [just off B1383 N of Stansted Mountfichet]: Civilised and nicely laid out dining pub with beams, timbers and open fires, good atmosphere and very pleasant service, real ales and decent wines, restaurant with interesting modern british cooking; children welcome in eating areas, tables in sheltered front courtyard, nice position on village cricket green, elegant bedrooms, open all day *(Charles Gysin, LYM)*

ROCHFORD [TQ8790]
Golden Lion [North St (one-way)]: Small white weatherboarded 17th-c local with well kept changing ales such as Adnams, Crouch Vale Brewers Gold, Greene King Abbot, Hidden Brewery Hidden Depths and St Georges Wild Board, low-priced food, dim lighting, hanging hops and pump clips, darts in one side room; TV, juke box, live music Fri; dogs welcome, small terrace, open all day *(Kevin Thorpe, Ian Phillips)*

ROWHEDGE [TM0321]
Anchor [off A134 just S of Colchester; High St]: Lovely lunchtime or summer evening setting, large waterside terrace and picture-window views over marshes and tidal River Colne with its swans, gulls and yachts, attractive flagstoned bar and pine furniture in nicely decorated tiled bistro, enjoyable fresh up-to-date food, real ales inc Greene King IPA and Old Speckled Hen, good house wines; cl Mon *(Roy and Lindsey Fentiman)*

ROXWELL [TL6508]
Hare [Bishops Stortford Rd (A1060)]: Comfortable beamed panelling-effect lounge with farm tools and rustic touches, popular blackboard food with some emphasis on fish, neat attentive staff, Adnams and Courage Directors, light and airy no smoking dining room; piped music may obtrude; children welcome, attractive garden with wendy house and climber *(George Atkinson, Roy and Lindsey Fentiman)*

SOUTH BENFLEET [TQ7786]
Hoy & Helmet [High St]: Rambling 15th-c beamed pub nr church, inglenook and nooks

and crannies, good value standard food inc bargain meal deals, well kept ales inc Adnams Broadside; piped music; tables in pretty garden with terrace, lots of hanging baskets and flowers *(Andy and Jill Kassube)*

STAPLEFORD ABBOTTS [TQ5194]
Royal Oak [Oak Hill Rd/Hale End Rd (B175)]: Well kept beer, reasonably priced food, good atmosphere *(Ron Deighton)*

STISTED [TL7924]
☆ *Dolphin* [A120 E of Braintree, by village turn]: Well kept Ridleys tapped from the cask in heavily beamed and timbered locals' bar on right, popular well priced straightforward food (not Tues or Sun evenings), log fire, bright eating area on left (children allowed here); tables in pretty garden, nice hanging baskets *(the Didler, LYM, Pete Baker)*

STURMER [TL6944]
☆ *Red Lion* [A1017 SE of Haverhill]: Attractive thatched and beamed pub with freshly cooked food inc light lunchtime dishes in bar, dining area, pleasant conservatory and small dining room (both no smoking), well kept real ales, good service, well spaced tables with solid cushioned chairs, big fireplace; level access, large appealing garden *(Adele Summers, Alan Black)*

TENDRING [TM1523]
Cherry Tree [Crow Lane, E of village centre]: Adnams and other well kept ales, enjoyable home-made food *(Robert Turnham)*

THAXTED [TL6130]
Star [Mill End (B184)]: Cheerful old beamed local with well kept Adnams, wide food choice, good service, lots of ancient timbers, quieter room on right *(Dr and Mrs M E Wilson)*
Swan [Bull Ring]: Attractively renovated dark-beamed Tudor pub with Adnams and Greene King, good choice of well presented food, good-sized helpings, light dishes all afternoon, welcoming staff, plenty of well spaced tables in long open bar, restaurant; piped music may obtrude, can be smoky; open all day, bedrooms with own bathrooms (ones at the back are quieter), lovely church and windmill nearby *(David Twitchett, Tim and Ann Newell, David J Bunter, Dr and Mrs M E Wilson)*

TOOT HILL [TL5102]
☆ *Green Man* [off A113 in Stanford Rivers, S of Ongar, or A414 W of Ongar]: Simply furnished country pub in appearance though aiming more at restaurant in style and price (meals rather than bar food), with a long plush dining room alongside the colourful front terrace; very good wine list, well kept ales such as Fullers London Pride, friendly staff; may be piped music, no under-10s, colourful front courtyard and back garden *(LYM, David J Bunter, John and Enid Morris, John Saville)*

WALTHAM ABBEY [TQ4199]
Volunteer [½ mile from M25 junction 26; A121 towards Loughton]: Roomy extensively refurbished family pub popular for its chinese food inc good value lunch special, prompt friendly service, attractive conservatory,

McMullens Country and Mild; piped music; some tables on side terrace, pretty hanging baskets, nice spot by Epping Forest *(BB, John Saville)*

WALTON ON THE NAZE [TM2521]
Queens Head [High St]: Well kept Ridleys, efficient service, good value food, clean modern décor *(Richard Burton)*

WICKFORD [TQ7493]
Duke [High St (just off A129)]: Lively local atmosphere at night, with darts, machines and plenty of chat; bargain lunchtime food, Courage Directors, John Smiths and Tetleys; picnic-sets in neatly kept gardens front and back *(Ian Phillips)*
Quart Pot [Runwell Rd (A132)]: Stylish, elegant and comfortable Ember Inn, light and bright, with Fullers London Pride, Greene King IPA and Marstons Pedigree, decent food choice, no smoking area *(Ian Phillips)*

WOODHAM WALTER [TL8006]
Bell [signed off A414 E of Chelmsford; The Street]: Handsome beamed and timbered 16th-c pub, wide choice of enjoyable pubby food (not Sun/Mon evenings) from ploughman's in good variety up, well kept Adnams Broadside, Greene King IPA and a guest beer, friendly staff, log fire, decorative plates and lots of brass, comfortable alcoves on various levels, small dining area with partly panelled upper gallery; children in eating areas, tables outside front and back *(John Saville, LYM, Tony Hobden)*

☆ *Cats* [back rd to Curling Tye and Maldon, from N end of village]: Relaxed and chatty country cottage, low black beams and timbering in timeless rambling bar with interesting nooks and crannies, roaring log fire each end, shelves of china cats, well kept Adnams, Greene King and beer brewed for them, good doorstep sandwiches, friendly landlord, no children or piped music; pretty garden with farmland views *(LYM, the Didler)*

WRITTLE [TL6807]
Horse & Groom [Roxwell Rd (A1060)]: Useful mock-Tudor Chef & Brewer family dining pub specialising in fresh fish, well kept Adnams, decent wines, polite cheerful staff, spacious bar, big pine tables in good-sized no smoking area, several log fires, evening candles; unobtrusive piped music; tables outside with country views *(Tina and David Woods-Taylor)*
Wheatsheaf [The Green]: Good pubby atmosphere in traditional two-room 19th-c local, well kept Greene King, Mighty Oak and a guest beer, friendly knowledgeable landlord; open all day wknds *(the Didler)*

Post Office address codings confusingly give the impression that some pubs are in Suffolk, when they're really in Essex (which is where we list them).

Gloucestershire

This is a fine county for anyone who likes good pubs. Lovely old stone buildings and scenery coupled with enthusiastic and committed landlords and landladies to make for some memorable outings. There's a lot of money about here, too, which supports a goodly number of very smart dining pubs with excellent food and wine. From the more than 500 Gloucestershire pubs on which we've had reports from readers over the years, and of course our own anonymous inspections, we have now honed down a really fine selection. The wide range of styles is well shown by this year's healthy crop of new main entries: the friendly Cross House at Doynton (good value straightforward food, well kept beer, splendid landlord and warm-hearted family service), the Bull in Fairford (a very well run old Cotswold inn, good all round), the ancient New Inn at Nether Westcote (another welcoming all-rounder), the stylishly modernised Falcon at Poulton (very good imaginative food in this civilised dining pub), and the Snooty Fox in Tetbury (a thriving lively bar in this attractively and comfortably updated town-centre inn). The Falcon is very rewarding for a special meal out, coming straight in with a Food Award. A good many longer-standing main entries too offer first-class food. Indeed, there seems to be a real sense of competition among food-minded Gloucestershire pubs at the moment, which is noticeably raising the stakes. We don't remember a previous year in which so many pubs have newly qualified for our coveted Food Award. Pubs currently earning the warmest praise for their food are the completely no smoking Queens Arms at Ashleworth (immaculately kept by its South African licensees), the friendly Red Hart at Awre (getting all its produce, and its cider, from within a few minutes' drive – one of the new Food Award winners), the Kings Head at Bledington (this charming old place is on top form these days – another to gain a Food Award this year for its treatment of top-class local produce), the attractively laid out Green Dragon near Cowley (doing well under new licensees, whose good modern food earns them a new Food Award too), the hugely enjoyable old Five Mile House at Duntisbourne Abbots (splendid genuine landlord and proper homely cooking), the charmingly reworked White Horse just outside Frampton Mansell (its food too seems to have changed up a gear recently, gaining them a new Food Award), the Inn For All Seasons near Little Barrington (its bar and restaurant opened together this year, great choice on the drinks side), the rather smart Fox at Lower Oddington, the very welcoming Weighbridge near Nailsworth (its two-in-one pies are particularly popular, and they are very kind to children), the rather restaurantly Bell at Sapperton (super carefully sourced food and an amazing wine choice – local beers too), and the Trouble House near Tetbury (restaurant food, and by no means cheap, but good, as are the wines). It's the Five Mile House at Duntisbourne Abbots, perhaps the pubbiest place on this formidable shortlist, which takes the title of Gloucestershire Dining Pub of the Year. Plenty of other pubs here, generally with enjoyable food even if that's not the main attraction, are on really good form too this year. Among them we'd pick out the lovely little unspoilt Red Lion at Ampney St Peter, the waterside Boat at Ashleworth Quay (another unspoilt country pub, no smoking throughout), the genuine and friendly Bear in Bisley (good all round), the bustling and welcoming Red Hart at Blaisdon, the charming Old Spot in Dursley (why can't more town pubs be like this?), the well run Plough at Ford (full of the racing crowd, a proper country pub), the carefully extended old Glasshouse Inn, the relaxed and comfortable White Hart at Littleton-upon-Severn (a favourite all-rounder), the gently quirky Ostrich at Newland (much enjoyed for its homely food and welcome), the lovely little Farriers Arms at Todenham (friendly, with nice food, beer and wine), and the interesting White Hart in Winchcombe (Swedish staff, and just a bit different all round). In the Lucky Dip section at the end of the chapter, current hot prospects are the Old Passage at Arlingham (restaurant rather than pub, but good), Fox at Broadwell, Tunnel House at Coates, Dog and Muffler near Coleford, Plough at Cold Aston, Bull at Hinton Dyrham, Catherine Wheel in Marshfield, Kings Arms at Mickleton, Butchers Arms at Oakridge Lynch, Royal Oaks at Painswick and at Prestbury, Boat at Redbrook, restauranty Swan at Southrop, Queens Head in Stow-on-the-Wold, Gumstool near Tetbury, Fleet at Twyning and Ram at Woodchester. Drinks prices here are close to the national average – sometimes a trifle below. The beautiful little local brewery at Donnington produces bargain beers, and other local names to look out for include Goffs, Wickwar, Uley, Whittingtons, Stanway and Freeminer. Hook Norton, brewed over the border in Oxfordshire, is often the cheapest beer you'll find in pubs here.

ALMONDSBURY ST6084 Map 2
Bowl

1¼ miles from M5 junction 16 (and therefore quite handy for M4 junction 20); from A38 towards Thornbury, turn first left signposted Lower Almondsbury, then first right down Sundays Hill, then at bottom right again into Church Road

There's always quite a crowd of cheerful and chatty customers both inside and outside this popular pub, and being so handy to the motorways, it's an excellent meeting point. The long beamed bar is neatly kept, with terracotta plush-patterned modern settles, dark green cushioned stools and mate's chairs around elm tables, horsebrasses on stripped bare stone walls, and big winter log fire at one end, with a woodburning stove at the other. Up to seven real ales are well kept on handpump: Bass, Bath Gem, Butcombe Bitter, Courage Best, Moles Best and Rucking Mole, and changing guests. Fruit machine and piped music. Reasonably priced bar food includes filled baguettes (from £4.50; chargrilled steak, red onion and blue cheese mayonnaise in baked ciabatta £7.95), ploughman's (from £4.95), thai chicken curry (£7.95), pasta with mushrooms, spinach and parmesan cream sauce (£8.25), steak and kidney pie or roast chicken breast with creamed leeks and cheddar mash (£9.95), scotch rib-eye steak (£13.95), and puddings such as chocolate truffle cake or lemon tart with raspberry coulis (£3.95). They ask to keep your credit card behind the bar. This is a pretty setting with the church next door and lovely flowering tubs, hanging baskets, and window boxes. *(Recommended by Gwen Griffiths, Mr and Mrs J E C Tasker, John and Enid Morris, Meg and Colin Hamilton, Liz and Alun Jones, Mrs Jane Kingsbury, Barry Steele-Perkins, Bob and Margaret Holder, Brian and Ruth Archer, Dr and Mrs A K Clarke, B and M Kendall, Comus and Sarah Elliott)*

Free house ~ Licensee Miss E Alley ~ Real ale ~ Bar food (12-2.30, 6-10) ~ Restaurant ~ (01454) 612757 ~ Children in eating area of bar and restaurant ~ Dogs allowed in bar and bedrooms ~ Open 11.30-3, 5-11; 12-10.30 Sun; closed 25 Dec ~ Bedrooms: £44.50S/£71S

AMPNEY ST PETER SP0801 Map 4
Red Lion 🍺
A417, E of village

As delightful as ever, this totally unspoilt little roadside pub is run by a very friendly long-serving landlord, and it would be hard not to get drawn into easy conversation with both him and the loyal regulars. A central corridor, served by a hatch, gives on to the little right-hand tile-floor public bar. This has just one table, a wall seat, and one long bench facing a small open fire. Behind this bench is an open servery (no counter, just shelves of bottles and – by the corridor hatch – handpumps for the well kept Hook Norton Best and Timothy Taylors Landlord, and perhaps a guest); reasonably priced wine. There are old prints on the wall, and on the other side of the corridor is a small saloon, with panelled wall seats around its single table, old local photographs, another open fire, and a print of Queen Victoria one could believe hasn't moved for a century – rather like the pub itself. There are seats in the side garden. Please note the limited opening hours. *(Recommended by R Huggins, D Irving, E McCall, T McLean, Dr and Mrs A K Clarke, RWC, the Didler, Giles and Annie Francis)*

Free house ~ Licensee John Barnard ~ Real ale ~ No credit cards ~ (01285) 851596 ~ Children and dogs in the tiny games room ~ Open 6-10(10.30 Fri); 12-2, 6(7 Sun)-10 Sat; closed weekday lunchtimes

ASHLEWORTH SO8125 Map 4
Queens Arms 🍽 ♈ 🍺
Village signposted off A417 at Hartpury

Completely no smoking, this is an immaculately kept low-beamed country dining pub. The comfortably laid out and civilised main bar has faintly patterned wallpaper and washed red ochre walls, big oak and mahogany tables and a nice mix of farmhouse and big brocaded dining chairs on a red carpet; at night it is softly lit by fringed wall lamps and candles. Popular bar food includes interesting specials such as mussels in a mild curry cream sauce (£5.50), pressed ox tongue served hot with madeira sauce (£5.75), asparagus and crab tartlet with saffron and chive butter sauce or breast of pigeon on a garlic croûte with bacon and port cream sauce (£6.50), home-made gnocchi with napoletana sauce and pesto (£6.95), belly of pork stuffed with prunes and apples (£13.75), bretonne-style dabs with shrimps, capers and lemon (£13.95), local rabbit casserole (£14.25), lamb shank braised with flageolet beans, garlic and rosemary (£14.50), and puddings like baked chocolate marble cheesecake or raspberry crème brûlée (from £4.50). Well kept Brains Rev James, Donnington BB, and Timothy Taylors Landlord on handpump, a dozen wines by the glass from a thoughtful wine list (including South African choices), and 22 malt whiskies; maybe summer home-made lemonade or winter mulled wine. Piped music, shove-ha'penny, cribbage, dominoes, and winter skittle alley; Bonnie, the little black pub cat, may entertain customers with her ping-pong football antics. Two perfectly clipped mushroom shaped yews dominate the front of the building. There are cast-iron tables and chairs in the sunny courtyard. *(Recommended by Bernard Stradling, RJH, A G Simmonds, Andrew Shore, Maria Williams, John and Christine Lewis, Bob and Margaret Holder, Mark and Sarah Baldwin, Dr G and Mrs J Kelvin, Carl and Jackie Cranmer, Neil and Anita Christopher, Craig Jones, Jim Abbott, Ken Marshall, Jeffrey Barber, Conrad Meehan, Rod Stoneman, Jane Bailey, Pam and Alan Neale, J V Dadswell, Dr A J and Mrs Tompsett)*

Free house ~ Licensees Tony and Gill Burreddu ~ Real ale ~ Bar food (till 10 Fri and Sat) ~ Restaurant ~ (01452) 700395 ~ Well behaved children allowed ~ Open 12-3, 7-11(10.30 Sun); closed Sun evening except bank hol weekends; 25-26 Dec

> Post Office address codings confusingly give the impression that some pubs are in Gloucestershire, when they're really in Warwickshire (which is where we list them).

ASHLEWORTH QUAY SO8125 Map 4

Boat ★ ◨

Ashleworth signposted off A417 N of Gloucester; quay signed from village

For continuous pub ownership, this delightful place, on the bank of the River
Severn, must hold the record – it has been in the same family since it was originally
granted a licence by Charles II. The front suntrap crazy-paved courtyard is bright
with plant tubs in summer, with a couple of picnic-sets under cocktail parasols;
there are more seats and tables under cover at the sides. Inside, the little front
parlour has a built-in settle by a long scrubbed deal table that faces an old-
fashioned open kitchen range with a side bread oven and a couple of elderly fireside
chairs; there are rush mats on the scrubbed flagstones, houseplants in the window,
fresh garden flowers, and old magazines to read. The pub is no smoking
throughout; shove-ha'penny, cribbage, and dominoes in the front room. A pair of
flower-cushioned antique settles face each other in the back room where around
half a dozen swiftly changing beers from breweries such as Archers, Arkells, Bath,
Church End, Hereford, RCH, Slaters, and Wye Valley are tapped from the cask,
along with a full range of Weston's farm ciders. During the week, they usually do
good lunchtime rolls (from £1.50), and sometimes cake (75p). *(Recommended by
Ted George, the Didler, Giles and Annie Francis, R Huggins, D Irving, E McCall, T McLean,
Jim Abbott, Derek and Sylvia Stephenson, Joyce and Geoff Robson, Dr G and Mrs J Kelvin,
Pat and Tony Martin, Conrad Meehan, John Reilly, Annabel Viney, Ken and Jenny Simmonds,
Dr A J and Mrs Tompsett, R T and J C Moggridge, Pete Baker)*

Free house ~ Licensees Ron, Elisabeth and Louise Nicholls ~ Real ale ~ Bar food
(lunchtime only; not Mon and Weds) ~ No credit cards ~ (01452) 700272 ~ Children in
eating area of bar ~ Open 11.30-2.30(3 Sat), 6.30(7 winter)-11; 11.30-3, 7-11 Sun; closed
all day Mon, Weds lunchtime

AWRE SO7108 Map 4 ⌂

Red Hart ⑪ ⛾

Village signposted off A48 S of Newnham

With lots of character, the neat L-shaped bar in this tall 15th-c pub has a deep
glass-covered illuminated well, flagstones, quarry tiles, heavy old beams, stone
fireplaces, and some exposed wattle and daub. Using local suppliers – 90% of their
ingredients come from within a 5-mile radius – the good, interesting food might
include at lunchtime, doorstep sandwiches (from £4), omelettes (from £6.50), local
ham with free-range eggs (£7.95), deep-fried fillet of cod in beer batter (£8.50), and
chicken caesar salad, home-made steak burger topped with smoked bacon,
mushrooms and melted cheese, lancashire hotpot, gloucester old spot sausages with
onion gravy or fresh poached salmon (all £8.95); evening choices such as bass fillet
with asparagus risotto and tomato butter (£10.50), steak in ale pie with a thyme
and rosemary shortcrust pastry top (£10.95), tuna niçoise (£12.50), duck breast
with rösti potatoes, onions and bacon, venison with a redcurrant and port sauce or
loin of lamb en croûte (£13.95), and fillet of beef with celeriac mash and oxtail
broth (£15.95), and puddings like trio of crème brûlée or iced chocolate parfait
with orange syrup and exotic fruit (£4.50) or bite-sized helpings of all their
puddings for two to share (£10.95). Both dining areas are no smoking. Friendly
staff serve well kept Whittingtons Nine Lives, Wickwar BOB, and Wye Valley Butty
Bach and Dorothy Goodbody's Golden Ale on handpump, ten wines by the glass,
and local cider; piped music. Out in front are some picnic-sets. The pub is nicely
placed in an out-of-the-way little farming village between the River Severn and the
Forest of Dean. *(Recommended by Bob and Margaret Holder, Brian McBurnie,
Graham Chamberlain)*

Free house ~ Licensees Marcia Griffiths and Martin Coupe ~ Real ale ~ Bar food (12-3,
7-9.30) ~ Restaurant ~ (01594) 510220 ~ Children welcome ~ Dogs allowed in bar ~
Open 12-3, 6-11; 12-11 Sat; 12-10.30 Sun; opens 6.30 evenings Mon-Sat and 12-3, 7-10.30
Sun in winter; closed last week Jan and first week Feb ~ Bedrooms: £50B/£80B

BARNSLEY SP0705 Map 4

Village Pub 🍽 ♀

B4425 Cirencester—Burford

Despite the emphasis on the good modern cooking, readers have been pleased to find that this smart and rather civilised place is also country-friendly, with dogs in the bar and perhaps horses tethered and waiting patiently in the car park. The low-ceilinged communicating rooms (four of which are no smoking) have oil paintings, plush chairs, stools and window settles around polished candlelit tables, and country magazines and newspapers to read. Using mainly local and organic produce, the enjoyable food might include lunchtime sandwiches, home-made soup (£5), lamb koftas with tomato and cucumber salsa or smoked haddock brandade with poached egg and chives (£6.50), home-made terrine (£6.75), gnocchi with cherry tomatoes and pesto (£10), roast guinea fowl with couscous and crème fraîche (£13.50), barnsley chop with crushed warm minted potato salad (£15), rib-eye steak with béarnaise sauce (£18), and puddings such as honey bavarois with strawberry and cherry compote or warm rice pudding with grape jam (£6); interesting cheeses. Well kept Hook Norton Bitter and Wadworths 6X, with maybe a guest such as Donnington SBA on handpump, local cider and apple juice, and around 14 wines by the glass. The sheltered back courtyard has plenty of good solid wooden furniture under umbrellas, outdoor heaters and its own outside servery. *(Recommended by Bernard Stradling, John Holroyd, John Kane, R Huggins, D Irving, E McCall, T McLean, David Glynne-Jones, A P Seymour, Geoffrey and Penny Hughes, Adrian White, Lynn Nisbet, Sebastian Snow, Derek Thomas, Sheila and Robert Robinson, Iain R Hewitt, A G Marx, Joyce and Geoff Robson, J Crosby, Karen and Graham Oddey, Mr and Mrs Martin Joyce)*

Free house ~ Licensees Tim Haigh and Rupert Pendered ~ Real ale ~ Bar food (12-2.30 (3 Sat and Sun), 7-9.30(10 Fri and Sat)) ~ Restaurant ~ (01285) 740421 ~ Children in eating area of bar ~ Dogs welcome ~ Open 11-3, 6-11; 11-11 Sat; 12-10.30 Sun ~ Bedrooms: £75S/£105S(£115B)

BISLEY SO9006 Map 4

Bear 🍺

Village signposted off A419 just E of Stroud

This is a particularly well run village pub. As well as offering a genuinely warm and friendly welcome to all their customers, the licensees continue to provide good, interestingly filled baguettes and well kept real ales to thirsty walkers, proper home-made meals for those wanting something more substantial, and comfortable bedrooms too. It's an elegantly gothic 16th-c place with a meandering L-shaped bar, a long shiny black built-in settle and a smaller but even sturdier oak settle by the front entrance, and an enormously wide low stone fireplace (not very high – the ochre ceiling's too low for that); the separate no smoking stripped-stone area is used for families. Bass, Flowers IPA, Tetleys, and Wells Bombardier on handpump; darts and table skittles. Besides nicely cooked daily specials such as oxtail casserole, organic salmon fishcakes, slow-roasted lamb rump, and sirloin steak (all £10.95), the bar food might include soup (from £2.95), roasted ratatouille (£4.50), goats cheese and bacon salad (£4.75), lots of filled baguettes (mostly £5.95), and home-made rabbit or steak, kidney and Guinness pies (£9.95). A small front colonnade supports the upper floor of the pub, and the sheltered little flagstoned courtyard made by this has a traditional bench. The garden is across the quiet road, and there's quite a collection of stone mounting-blocks. The steep stone-built village is attractive. *(Recommended by Paul and Shirley White, Brian McBurnie, Nick and Meriel Cox, Tim Gee, Guy Vowles, Neil and Anita Christopher, R Huggins, D Irving, E McCall, T McLean, M Joyner)*

Punch ~ Tenants Simon and Sue Evans ~ Real ale ~ Bar food (not Sun evening) ~ (01452) 770265 ~ Children in family room ~ Dogs welcome ~ Occasional Irish music ~ Open 11.30-3, 6-11; 12-3, 7-10.30 Sun ~ Bedrooms: /£50

BLAISDON SO7017 Map 4

Red Hart ◼

Village signposted off A4136 just SW of junction with A40 W of Gloucester; OS Sheet 162 map reference 703169

Tucked away on the edge of the Forest of Dean, this busy pub is a friendly, welcoming place. The flagstoned main bar has cushioned wall and window seats, traditional pub tables, a big sailing-ship painting above the log fire, and a thoroughly relaxing atmosphere – helped along by well reproduced piped bluesy music, and maybe Spotty the perky jack russell. On the right, there's an attractive beamed two-room no smoking dining area with some interesting prints and bric-a-brac, and on the left, you'll find additional dining space for families. Well kept Burton Bridge Bitter, Hook Norton Best, Otter Head, Tetleys and Timothy Taylors Landlord on handpump (three of these change regularly), and a decent wine list; cribbage, dominoes and piped music. Enjoyable bar food includes home-made soup (£3.75), sandwiches and baguettes (from £3.95), ploughman's or whitebait (£4.75), two sausages and eggs (£5.25), grilled fresh cod or chicken curry (£7.50), rack of ribs (£8), and specials such as salmon and coriander fishcakes (£5.25; main course £7.95), king scallops with a mango and sweet chilli dip (£5.75; main course £10.95), moussaka (£7.95), lemon chicken stir fry with noodles (£9.95), bass with a watercress sauce (£11.95), and wild french duck with wild mushrooms (£12.95). There are some picnic-sets in the garden and a children's play area, and at the back of the building is a large space for barbecues. *(Recommended by Ian Phillips, Mike and Mary Carter, Di and Mike Gillam)*

Free house ~ Licensee Guy Wilkins ~ Real ale ~ Bar food ~ Restaurant ~ (01452) 830477 ~ Children allowed in family room but must be well behaved ~ Dogs allowed in bar ~ Open 12-2.30, 6ish-11; 12-3, 7-10.30 Sun

BLEDINGTON SP2422 Map 4

Kings Head ⊕ ▽ ◼ 🛏

B4450

Friendly and rather smart, this 15th-c inn overlooks the village green where there might be ducks pottering about. Inside, the main bar is full of ancient beams and other atmospheric furnishings (high-backed wooden settles, gateleg or pedestal tables), and there's a warming log fire in the stone inglenook with a big black kettle hanging in it. To the left of the bar a drinking space for locals (popular with a younger crowd in the evening) has benches on the wooden floor, a woodburning stove and darts. Well kept Donnington BB, Hook Norton Best, Wadworths 6X and a couple of guests like Burton Bridge Bitter and Slaters Original on handpump, an excellent wine list with ten by the glass (including champagne), 20 malt whiskies, organic cider and local apple juice. Using as much free-range, organic and local produce as possible, the good popular food might include lunchtime sandwiches or toasted panini (from £4.95), salads like fresh tuna niçoise (£8), and home-made horseradish beefburger (£8.50), as well as soup (£4.50), well liked home-made duck spring roll with sweet chilli sauce (£4.50; main course £9), tunisian aubergine salad with coriander and yoghurt and pitta slices (£5.50), devilled lambs kidneys with mushrooms and fried bread (£5.95; main course £9), gloucester old spot sausages with mustard mash and red onion marmalade (£8.50), steak in ale stew with spring onion and chive mash, cheese and fresh herb fritters and sweet pepper marmalade or chargrilled sirloin steak with pinot noir butter sauce (£9.50), smoked haddock and crayfish pie with salsa verde mash (£9.95), and crab and spinach risotto (£10), with home-made puddings such as orange and chocolate sponge with Cointreau cream sauce, rhubarb and ginger flan or strawberry crème brûlée with home-made shortbread (£4.50); they also do a selection of interesting cheeses (three for £6.50). The dining room is no smoking. There are seats in the back garden. *(Recommended by Derek and Sylvia Stephenson, Tracey and Stephen Groves, Tom Ewing, Clifford Blakemore, John and Jackie Chalcraft, David and Nina Pugsley, Brenda and Rob Fincham, Don and Maureen Medley, Mr and Mrs Martin Joyce,*

Mrs Pamela Fisher, Richard Greaves, Caroline Dunstall, Edmund Coan, Ann and Colin Hunt, Paul and Penny Dawson, Lynn Nisbet, Basil and Jarvis, Pam and David Bailey, Iain R Hewitt, A G Marx, Theocsbrian, M A and C R Starling, Gill Glover)

Free house ~ Licensees Nicola and Archie Orr-Ewing ~ Real ale ~ Bar food ~ Restaurant ~ (01608) 658365 ~ Children in restaurant and family room ~ Dogs allowed in bar ~ Open 11-2.30, 6-11; 12-3, 6.30-10.30 Sun; closed 25 and 26 Dec ~ Bedrooms: /£70S(£125B)

BRIMPSFIELD SO9413 Map 4
Golden Heart ♀

Nettleton Bottom (not shown on road maps, so we list the pub instead under the name of the nearby village); on A417 N of the Brimpsfield turning northbound

This busy pub has a main low-ceilinged bar that is divided into three cosily distinct areas; there's a roaring log fire in the huge stone inglenook fireplace in one, traditional built-in settles and other old-fashioned furnishings throughout, and quite a few brass items, typewriters, exposed stone and wood panelling. A comfortable parlour on the right has another decorative fireplace, and leads into a further room that opens onto the terrace; two areas are no smoking. A fair choice of bar food includes home-made soup (£3.75), doorstep sandwiches (from £3.50), home-made pâté or chilli crayfish salad (£4.95), baked potatoes (from £5.25), ploughman's (from £5.95), omelettes with free-range eggs (£6.95), fish and chips (£7.95), chicken curry (£8.95), mushroom stroganoff (£9.25), bubble and squeak with spicy beef sausages or hungarian goulash (£9.95), steaks (from £10.95), pork steak with creamed apple and calvados (£11.25), and puddings like coconut and lime délice, treacle sponge or rhubarb crumble (£4.25); Sunday roasts. Archers Golden Best and Timothy Taylors Landlord, and a couple of guests such as Marstons Pedigree and Youngs Bitter on handpump, and a decent wine list with helpful notes. From the rustic cask-supported tables on the suntrap terrace, there are pleasant views down over a valley; nearby walks. If you are thinking of staying here, bear in mind that the nearby road is a busy all-night link between the M4 and M5. *(Recommended by A P Seymour, Tony Pope, Karen Bonham, Neil and Anita Christopher, Ian Phillips, R B Gardiner, R Huggins, D Irving, E McCall, T McLean, Mark and Ruth Brock, Mike and Mary Carter, Mr and Mrs I and E Bell, Colin Moore, Guy Vowles)*

Free house ~ Licensee Catherine Stevens ~ Real ale ~ Bar food (12-3, 6-10; 12-10 Sun) ~ (01242) 870261 ~ Children in family room ~ Dogs welcome ~ Open 11-3, 5.30-11(all day during summer hols); 11-11 Sat; 12-10.30 Sun ~ Bedrooms: £35S/£55S

CHEDWORTH SP0511 Map 4
Seven Tuns

Village signposted off A429 NE of Cirencester; then take second signposted right turn and bear left towards church

This year, a new terrace has been constructed here and the skittle alley has been renovated – it also doubles up as a private function room. Across the road there's another little walled raised terrace with a waterwheel and a stream, and there are plenty of tables both here and under cocktail parasols on a side terrace. Inside, a good winter log fire in the big stone fireplace warms the snug little lounge on the right, which has comfortable seats and decent tables, sizeable antique prints, tankards hanging from the beam over the serving bar, and a partly boarded ceiling. Down a couple of steps, the public bar on the left has an open fire, and this opens into a no smoking dining room with another open fire. Well kept Youngs Bitter and Waggle Dance on handpump, 12 wines by the glass, and 16 malt whiskies; darts, shove-ha'penny, dominoes, TV and piped music. There's a short choice of tasty bar food such as lunchtime sandwiches (£4.95), filled baked potatoes (£5.95), and ploughman's (£6.95), as well as soup (£4.50), thai-style duck salad with hoisin and plum sauce (£4.95), home-made smoked haddock and salmon fishcakes with chilli sauce (£5.25; main course £7.95), home-made chicken liver pâté with red onion marmalade (£6.50), home-made burger with bacon and cheese, ham and eggs or sausage and mash (£7.95), fish and chips (£8.95), 10oz sirloin steak (£11.95), and puddings such as chocolate terrine with blackcurrant coulis or home-made lemon and lime tart (£4.50). The famous Roman villa is nearby, and there are nice walks through the valley. *(Recommended by M Thomas, Richard Greaves, Joyce and Geoff Robson, R Huggins, D Irving, E McCall, T McLean, Dennis and Gill Keen, Nick and Meriel Cox, John Reilly, Giles and Annie Francis)*

Youngs ~ Tenant Mr Davenport-Jones ~ Real ale ~ Bar food (12-2.30, 6.30-9.30) ~ (01285) 720242 ~ Children in eating area of bar and restaurant ~ Dogs welcome ~ Open 12-11; 12-10.30 Sun

CHIPPING CAMPDEN SP1539 Map 4
Eight Bells 🍺 🛏️
Church Street (which is one way – entrance off B4035)

This handsome old inn was used, many hundreds of years ago, as a hostel for workmen building the nearby church. It's a pleasant place with heavy oak beams and massive timber supports, stripped stone walls, cushioned pews and solid dark wood furniture on the broad flagstones, daily papers to read, and log fires in up to three restored stone fireplaces. Part of the floor in the no smoking dining room has a glass inlet showing part of the passage from the church by which Roman Catholic priests could escape from the Roundheads. Quite a choice of often ambitious food includes lunchtime toasted ciabatta with various toppings (from £6.50) and three-egg omelettes (£7.25), as well as home-made soup (£4.65), risotto of crispy duck, spinach and porcini mushrooms or warm thai-style beef salad with flat noodles, roasted peanuts and a red chilli and lemongrass dressing (£6.25), home-made smoked salmon, crab and mascarpone ravioli with vodka cream, fresh basil and cherry tomatoes (£6.50), lunchtime main courses like pork and chive sausages with red wine gravy or home-made pies (all £10), evening main courses such as home-made lamb burger with feta salad (£10), bass on vanilla mash, citrus fruits and spinach (£13.50), and seared loin of local venison on a pear tatin topped with berry jam and beetroot crisps and drizzled with chocolate balsamic (£16.75), and puddings such as steamed chocolate pudding drizzled with white chocolate sauce and berry compote or apple, currant and vanilla bean syrup strudel with clotted cream and honey ginger (£4.75). Well kept Adnams Broadside, and Hook Norton Best and Old Hooky on handpump from the fine oak bar counter, quite a few wines, Old Rosie cider and country wines. Piped music, darts, cribbage and dominoes. There's a large terraced garden with plenty of seats, and striking views of the almshouses and church. The pub is handy for the Cotswold Way walk to Bath. *(Recommended by Simon Collett-Jones, Mrs C Lintott, Dr David Cockburn, David J Austin, M Joyner, Ted George, Peter Coxon, Ann and Colin Hunt, Peter and Anne Hollindale, Stephen Buckley, Peter J and Avril Hanson, Chris Smith, Dr G and Mrs J Kelvin, Susan and John Douglas, Russell Grimshaw, Kerry Purcell, Roger Huggins, Tom and Alex McLean, D M Heath, Bob Ellis, George Atkinson)*

Free house ~ Licensee Neil Hargreaves ~ Real ale ~ Bar food (12-2(2.30 Fri and Sat), 6.30-9.30; 12.30-3, 7-9 Sun) ~ Restaurant ~ (01386) 840371 ~ Children in eating area of bar and restaurant ~ Dogs allowed in bar ~ Open 12-3, 5.30-11; 11-11 Fri and Sat; 12-10.30 Sun; closed 25 Dec ~ Bedrooms: £50S/£95S(£85B)

Volunteer 🍺
Lower High Street

This unpretentious village pub has six real ales well kept on handpump: Hook Norton Best, North Cotswold Brewery Genesis and the new Pig Brook, and Stanway Stanney Bitter with a couple of guests like Archers Spring Blond and Wickwar IKB. All the wines on their list are available by the glass. The little bar by ___ has cushioned seats in bay windows, a good log fire piled with big logs in ___ stone fireplace with hops, helmets and horse bits above it, proper old ___irs with sage green plush seats and some similarly covered stools around ___ables, old army (Waterloo and WWI) paintings and bugles on the walls, with old local photographs on the gantry, and quite a few brass spigots dotted about. The public bar (which is popular with a younger crowd) has modern upholstered wing settles, juke box, darts, pool, fruit machine, shove-ha'penny, cribbage and dominoes. Bar food includes soup (£2.95), goats cheese baked on puff pastry with bacon (£4.95), ham and egg or battered cod (£6.95), steak and kidney pie (£6.95), calves liver and bacon with balsamic gravy (£7.95), and 10oz rib-eye pepper steak (£10.75); Sunday roasts. Outside, there are picnic-sets in a small brick-paved ivy courtyard with an arch through to the back garden where there are more seats. *(Recommended by Derek and Sylvia Stephenson, Paul and Margaret Baker, Ted George, Margaret Dickinson, Tracey and Stephen Groves, Tony and Betty Parker, Dr G and Mrs J Kelvin, Peter Coxon, Guy Vowles, Simon Collett-Jones, S Baranowski, E Slavid)*

Free house ~ Licensee Hilary Mary Sinclair ~ Real ale ~ Bar food ~ (01386) 840688 ~ Children in eating area of bar ~ Dogs allowed in bar ~ Open 11.30-2.30(3 Sat), 5(6 Sat)-11; 12-3, 7-10.30 Sun ~ Bedrooms: £40B/£70B

COWLEY SO9714 Map 4
Green Dragon 🍴
Off A435 S of Cheltenham at Elkstone, Cockleford signpost; OS Sheet 163 map reference 970142

New licensees have taken over this attractive stone-fronted dining pub and readers have been quick to voice their enthusiasm.The two bars have a cosy and genuinely old-fashioned feel, big flagstones and wooden boards, beams, two stone fireplaces (welcoming fires in winter), candlelit tables, and a woodburning stove. The furniture and the bar itself in the upper Mouse Bar were made by Robert Thompson, and little mice run over the hand-carved chairs, tables and mantelpiece; the larger Lower Bar (and upstairs restaurant) are no smoking. Good bar food now includes lunchtime sandwiches (from £5.25; not Sunday), tuna niçoise with bread and aïoli (£5.50; generous £11), and asparagus, roquefort and broccoli quiche (£6.50), as well as devilled whitebait with caper, lime and dill mayonnaise (£4.75), goats cheese on puy lentil and mint salad (£6), aubergine and courgette gratin (£9.50), steak and kidney pudding (£10.50), lambs liver with slow roasted sage and red onions (£11.50), corn fed chicken breast with pea, broad bean and mint risotto (£12), roast duck breast with red cabbage and cherries (£13), 10oz sirloin steak with café de paris butter (£14), and puddings (£4.50). Well kept Butcombe Bitter, Courage Directors, Hook Norton Best and Marstons Pedigree on handpump; lots of wines by the glass, a dozen malt whiskies, and Stowford cider. Skittle alley and piped music. Terraces outside overlook Cowley Lake and the River Churn, and the pub is a good centre for the local walks. *(Recommended by R Huggins, D Irving, E McCall, T McLean, C Howard, Jo Rees, Peter and Audrey Dowsett, Tony Pope, Karen Bonham, John Reilly, Mr and Mrs J Brown, Theocsbrian)*

Buccaneer Holdings ~ Managers Sally Wigg and Jonathan Mather ~ Real ale ~ Bar food (12-2.30, 6-10; all day weekends) ~ Restaurant ~ (01242) 870271 ~ Children in eating area of bar and restaurant ~ Dogs allowed in bar and bedrooms ~ Open 11-11; 12-10.30 Sun ~ Bedrooms: £57B/£70B

DIDMARTON ST8187 Map 2
Kings Arms 🍷 🛏
A433 Tetbury road

Close to Westonbirt Arboretum, this busy pub has several knocked-through rooms that work their way around a big central counter: deep terracotta walls above a dark green dado, a pleasant mix of chairs on bare boards, quarry tiles and carpet, hops on beams, and a big stone fireplace. Under the new licensees, bar food includes smoked haddock fishcake with thai green chilli mayonnaise (£4.75; main course £8.95), lunchtime filled rolls (from £4.95), smoked mackerel and trout terrine with horseradish soda bread (£5.95; main course £9.95), risotto of red onion, mint, peas, broad beans, crème fraîche and parmesan (£10.25), red snapper fillet with star anise, braised fennel and a dill and lemon cappuccino (£12.95), fillet of gloucester old spot wrapped in a leek and chicken mousseline with caramelised caper sauce (£14.75), roast rack of lamb with a casserole of kidneys, neck and root vegetables (£14.95), and puddings such as milk chocolate marquise with Horlicks milkshake or sticky toffee pudding with lemon and ginger toffee sauce (from £4.95); it does get very crowded on Sunday lunchtimes. Well kept Butcombe Blonde, Sharps Doom Bar and Uley Bitter on handpump, ten wines by the glass and ten malt whiskies; darts, TV and piped music. There are seats out in the pleasant back garden, and they have self-catering cottages in a converted barn and stable block. More reports please. *(Recommended by Michael Doswell, Di and Mike Gillam, M G Hart, Tom Evans, Simon Collett-Jones, Matthew Shackle, Hugh Roberts, Paul Hopton, Alec and Barbara Jones, Tom and Ruth Rees, Barry and Anne, Stephen Woad, Mr and Mrs W D Borthwick, Richard Stancomb, Mike Pugh, John and Gloria Isaacs, Donald Godden, Sebastian Snow, Andrew Scarr, Dr and Mrs A K Clarke, Malcolm Ward, Richard Wyld, J Crosby, Bernard Stradling)*

Free house ~ Licensee Lizzy Pearce ~ Real ale ~ Bar food ~ Restaurant ~ (01454) 238245 ~ Children welcome ~ Dogs allowed in bar ~ Open 11-3, 6-11; 11-11 Sat; 12-10.30 Sun ~ Bedrooms: £45S/£70S

DOYNTON ST7174 Map 2
Cross House ♦ £
Village signposted with Dyrham off A420 Bristol—Chippenham just E of Wick; High Street

Chattily convivial, this 18th-c village pub owes a lot of its charm to the friendly and helpful landlord, who clearly enjoys keeping his customers in high good humour. The softly lit carpeted bar, with some beams and stripped stone, has simple pub furniture brightened up with cheerful scatter cushions and a good woodburning stove in its big stone fireplace. Two or three steps take you down to a cottagey candlelit dining room with a small no smoking area. Besides good value traditional sandwiches (£2.50), good plain cooking includes soup (£2.95), herrings in madeira sauce (£3.75), smoked mackerel fillet (£3.95), steak and kidney pie (£6.75), pork faggots (£6.95), quite a few vegetarian dishes such as seasonal vegetable cheese bake (£6.95), lamb steak with rosemary and garlic (£7.95), chicken breast in stilton and white wine sauce (£8.50), and sirloin steak with caramelised onion (£8.75), with fresh seasonal vegetables, and traditional puddings (£2.95). Well kept Bass, Courage Best, Fullers London Pride and Greene King Old Speckled Hen on handpump, 17 decent wines by the glass, quick family service, darts, fruit machine, cribbage, dominoes, TV and piped music. There are picnic-sets out by the road. This is good walking country, and Dyrham Park is quite close. *(Recommended by Barry and Anne, Tom and Ruth Rees, Dr and Mrs C W Thomas)*

Unique (Enterprise) ~ Lease André and Liz Large ~ Real ale ~ Bar food (11.30-2, 6-9.15 (10 Sat)) ~ (0117) 937 2261 ~ Children in eating area of bar ~ Dogs allowed in bar ~ Open 11.30-3, 6-11; 12-4, 7-10.30 Sun

DUNTISBOURNE ABBOTS SO9709 Map 4
Five Mile House ⑪ ♦
Off A417 at Duntisbourne Abbots exit sign; then, coming from Gloucester, pass filling station and keep on parallel to main road; coming from Cirencester, pass under main road then turn right at T junction

Gloucestershire Dining Pub of the Year
'I'd really love to get snowed in here', one reader told us wistfully – and it's that sort of place. You'll get a genuinely warm welcome from the cheerful licensee, proper home cooking and well kept real ales. The front room has a companionable bare-boards drinking bar on the right (plenty of friendly banter from the locals), with wall seats around the big table in its bow window and just one other table. On the left is a flagstone hallway tap room snug formed from two ancient high-backed settles by a woodburning stove in a tall carefully exposed old fireplace; newspapers to read. There's a small cellar bar, a back restaurant down steps and a family room

on the far side; cribbage and dominoes. Most eating areas are no smoking. Cooked by the landlord, the enjoyable food at lunchtime includes open sandwiches or filled baked potatoes (from £4.50), ploughman's (from £5.50), free-range egg omelette (£6.95), deep-fried cod and chips or home-cooked smoked ham and eggs (£7.50), and whole local trout with prawn and lemon butter (£8.95); favourites such as home-made soup (£3.75), home-made chicken liver pâté or hot brie with cranberry sauce (£4.95), assorted thai seafood dim sum with prawn crackers and a chilli and ginger dip (£5.45), home-made steak and kidney pie (£9.50), local sausages with bubble and squeak (£10.50), shoulder of lamb with redcurrant and mint or chicken breast stuffed with stilton, wrapped in bacon and served on a mushroom and brandy cream sauce (£10.95), barbary duck breast with a strawberry and port sauce (£12.50), aberdeen angus steaks (£12.75), and home-made puddings like lovely bakewell tart (£4.25). Well kept Donningtons BB, Timothy Taylors Landlord and Youngs Bitter with a local guest such as Archers Village or Wye Valley Butty Bach on handpump (the cellar is temperature-controlled), and an interesting wine list (strong on new world ones). The gardens have nice country views; the country lane was once Ermine Street, the main Roman road from Wales to London. *(Recommended by John Kane, Evelyn and Derek Walter, Ann and Colin Hunt, Paul and Shirley White, R Huggins, D Irving, E McCall, T McLean, Giles and Annie Francis, the Didler, Graham and Helen Eastwood, Kevin Thorpe, Nick and Meriel Cox, Guy Vowles, Dennis Jenkin, Jo Rees, Mr and Mrs I and E Bell, Rod Stoneman, Julie and Bill Ryan, Dr A J and Mrs Tompsett, Gordon Prince, J Crosby)*

Free house ~ Licensees Jo and Jon Carrier ~ Real ale ~ Bar food (12-2.30, 6-9.30) ~ Restaurant ~ (01285) 821432 ~ Children welcome if well behaved ~ Dogs allowed in bar ~ Open 12-3, 6-11; 12-3, 7-10.30 Sun

DURSLEY ST7598 Map 4
Old Spot ⬛ £
By bus station

There's always a cheerful, bustling atmosphere and a good mix of customers in this unassuming town pub – and a choice of up to ten real ales well kept on handpump (and four annual beer festivals). Alongside Uley Old Ric, a typical choice of beers might include Bass, Butcombe Blonde, Everards Original, Otter Bitter, Palmer Tally Ho!, Ringwood Old Thumper and Wychwood Shires; several malt whiskies too. The front door opens into a deep pink little room with stools on shiny quarry tiles along its pine boarded bar counter, and old enamel beer advertisements on the walls and ceiling; there's a profusion of porcine paraphernalia. A little room on the left leading off from here has shove-ha'penny, cribbage and dominoes, and the little dark wood floored room to the right has a stone fireplace. From here a step takes you down to a cosy Victorian tiled snug and (to the right) the no smoking meeting room. Served only at lunchtime, bar food might include doorstep sandwiches (from £2.95), filled baked potatoes (from £3.85), ratatouille bake (£4.25), niçoise salad (£4.75), ploughman's (from £4.75), home-cooked ham with parsley sauce (£5.45), cod and pancetta fishcakes (£5.75), home-made steak in ale pie (£6.25), and braised lamb chump (£6.85). More reports please. *(Recommended by PL, Stan and Susan Fysh, R Huggins, D Irving, E McCall, T McLean)*

Free house ~ Licensee Steve Herbert ~ Real ale ~ Bar food (lunchtime only) ~ (01453) 542870 ~ Children in family room ~ Dogs welcome ~ Various live artists Weds evenings ~ Open 11-11; 12-10.30 Sun

EASTLEACH TURVILLE SP1905 Map 4
Victoria ♀
Village signposted off A361 S of Burford

Although open plan, this low-ceilinged old pub is nicely divided, and rambles cosily around a central bar, with sturdy pub tables of varying sizes, and some attractive seats – particularly those built in beside the log fire in the stripped stone chimney breast. There are some unusual engravings and lithographs of Queen Victoria around the back. Well kept Arkells 2B and a guest such as 3B on handpump, and several wines by the glass; may be unobtrusive piped music. The right-hand area has more of a public bar feel, with darts, shove-ha'penny, cribbage and dominoes. Decent bar food includes moules marinière (£4.50), filled baguettes (from £4.50), warm smoked chicken, bacon and brie salad or gammon and mozzarella (£7.25), steak and mushroom pie (£7.95), calves liver and bacon with red wine sauce (£9.25), organic pork chop with apple and calvados sauce (£9.50), and daily fresh fish (from £10), with home-made puddings such as white chocolate and Baileys mousse (£3.95); the restaurant is no smoking. Service can slow down at peak times. Picnic-sets out in front look down over a steep bank of daffodils at the other stone-built houses and a couple of churches; there are also seats at the back behind the car park. *(Recommended by Michael Cooper, Gaynor Gregory, Richard Greaves, D Reay, Dr A Y Drummond, M Thomas, Lawrence Pearse, R Huggins, D Irving, E McCall, T McLean, Paul and Shirley White, Peter and Audrey Dowsett)*

Arkells ~ Tenants Stephen and Susan Richardson ~ Real ale ~ Bar food ~ Restaurant ~ (01367) 850277 ~ Children in restaurant ~ Dogs allowed in bar ~ Open 12-3, 7-11; 12-4, 7-10.30 Sun

EWEN SU0097 Map 4
Wild Duck ♀
Village signposted from A429 S of Cirencester

Handy for Cirencester, this 16th-c inn looks more like an old manor house in part than a typical pub. The high-beamed main bar has a nice mix of comfortable armchairs and other seats, paintings on the red walls, crimson drapes, a winter open fire and maybe candles on tables. The residents' lounge, which overlooks the garden, has a handsome Elizabethan fireplace and antique furnishings. Besides Duckpond Bitter (brewed especially for the pub), you'll find well kept Archers Golden, Sharps Cornish Coaster, Theakstons Best and Old Peculier and Charles Wells Bombardier on handpump, 28 wines by the glass and several malt whiskies; piped music and shove-ha'penny. Bar food includes soup (£3.95), ploughman's or smoked fish pâté (£6.95), fried chicken livers on walnut and grape salad (£7.50), scampi (£7.95), burger (£8.50), chicken caesar salad (£12.95), bass fillet with a parmesan and herb crust and ratatouille sauce or pork fillet with sweet potato mash and braised red cabbage (£14.95), and steaks (from £14.95). Pleasant in summer, the neatly kept and sheltered garden has wooden tables and seats. Beware, unless you pay in advance for your bar food, or have booked, you will be asked to leave your credit card with them. *(Recommended by R Seifas, R Huggins, D Irving, E McCall, T McLean, Graham Holden, Julie Lee, Gary and Jane Gleghorn, Mr and Mrs G S Ayrton, Pat and Tony Martin, Simon and Amanda Southwell, Keith Rutter, Inga Davis, Dr and Mrs A K Clarke, KC, Paul and Annette Hallett, Ian Phillips, Karen and Graham Oddey)*

Free house ~ Licensees Tina and Dino Mussell ~ Real ale ~ Bar food (12-2, 6.45-10; all day weekends) ~ Restaurant ~ (01285) 770310 ~ Children in restaurant ~ Dogs allowed in bar ~ Open 11-11; 12-10.30 Sun ~ Bedrooms: £70B/£95B

FAIRFORD SP1501 Map 4
Bull ⌂
Market Place

This well run and civilised old hotel has a thriving chatty atmosphere in its sizeable main bar, well used by locals. It's nicely laid out, with beams and timbers, comfortably old-fashioned pubby furnishings including dark pews and settles (we particularly liked sitting at the big table in the bow window overlooking the little market square), and on its ochre walls aircraft pictures and photographs of actors and actresses who have stayed here. There's a coal-effect gas fire. The long bar has well kept Arkells 2B, 3B and Kingsdown on handpump, and friendly service. Up a few stone steps a nice little residents' lounge has some attractive soft leather sofas and armchairs around its big stone fireplace, and fishing prints and plates. The restaurant, in former stables, is charming. A very wide blackboard choice of good value food includes lunchtime baguettes and filled baked potatoes (from £3.25) as well as soup (£2.95), home-made chicken liver pâté (£3.75), bacon and stilton mushrooms (£3.95), cumberland sausage with onion gravy and bubble and squeak or a pie of the day (£7.95), wrapped haddock with bacon on courgette and pepper ragoût (£8.95), gammon and egg, steamed lamb and mint suet pudding or stuffed roast pepper (£9.95), whole trout with garlic and prawn sauce (£10.95), and puddings (£3.75); Sunday roast (£7.95). The village is charming, and the church just along the street has Britain's only intact set of medieval stained-glass windows. *(Recommended by Peter and Audrey Dowsett)*

Arkells ~ Tenants Judy and Mark Dudley ~ Real ale ~ Bar food ~ Restaurant ~ (01285) 712535 ~ Children welcome ~ Dogs allowed in bar ~ Open 11-11; 12-10.30 Sun ~ Bedrooms: £39.50(£49.50B)/£79.50B

FORD SP0829 Map 4 🏠

Plough

B4077 Stow—Alderton

This pretty pub is always busy, but on race meeting evenings it can get packed. It's opposite a well known racehorse trainer's yard and many of the customers are naturally part of the racing crowd – but there are plenty of visitors too. The beamed and stripped-stone bar has racing prints and photos on the walls, old settles and benches around the big tables on its uneven flagstones, oak tables in a snug alcove, four welcoming log fires (two are log-effect gas), and dominoes, cribbage, shove-ha'penny, pool, fruit machine, TV (for the races) and piped music. Very good, well presented bar food includes lunchtime filled baguettes (from £4.95), baked ham and free-range eggs (£8.50), and liver and smoky bacon with onion gravy or steak and mushroom in ale pie (£9.95), with evening dishes such as venison casserole, fresh halibut with shrimp and lemon butter, half a shoulder of lamb with mint and rosemary jus or half a crispy duck with orange and Cointreau sauce (£12.95), and aberdeen angus steak with bacon and chive mash (£14.95); the restaurant is no smoking. They offer breakfasts for travellers on the way to the Gold Cup meeting at Cheltenham, and have traditional asparagus feasts every April to June. Well kept Donnington BB and SBA on handpump, and Addlestone's cider; good efficient service. There are benches in the garden, pretty hanging baskets, and a play area at the back. The Cotswold Farm Park is nearby. *(Recommended by Michael Cooper, Geoff Pidoux, J C Brittain-Long, Patrick Hancock, Roger Braithwaite, Val and Brian Garrod, David J Austin, the Didier, Stephen Woad, Tracey and Stephen Groves, Peter and Margaret Glenister, Iain R Hewitt, A G Marx)*

Donnington ~ Tenant Craig Brown ~ Real ale ~ Bar food (all day weekends) ~ Restaurant ~ (01386) 584215 ~ Children in eating area of bar ~ Dogs allowed in bar ~ Open 11-11; 12-10.30 Sun ~ Bedrooms: £35S/£60S

FRAMPTON MANSELL SO9201 Map 4

White Horse 🍴 ♀

A491 Cirencester—Stroud

Once inside this smart dining pub, the bustling, cheerful atmosphere makes the slightly unpromising exterior and busy road location seem years away. Alongside the pine tables, rush matting and up-to-date décor of the main part, there's a cosy bar area with a large sofa and comfortable chairs for those who want a relaxing drink. Well kept Uley Bitter and a guest such as Arkells Summer Ale or Hook Norton Best on handpump, nine wines by the glass from a well chosen wine list, and quite a few malt whiskies. Using traceable meat and cornish fish and fresh shellfish from their new big external lobster tank, the very good modern cooking might include lunchtime snacks like baguettes filled with smoked cherrywood cheddar and bacon or brie and cranberry (£4.95), home-glazed ham, two eggs and home-made chips (£8.95), and battered cod with tartare sauce (£9.95), as well as river fowey rock oysters with red wine and shallot dressing (£1.95 each), pea and pear soup (£3.95), hot cheese fritters with wholegrain mustard cream sauce (£4.95), fried foie gras, sweet potato pancake, crisp pancetta and muscat butter (£9.50), leek and sun-blush tomato risotto with grilled goats cheese and basil pesto (£10.95), toulouse sausages with spring onion mash and onion gravy (£11.50), roast saddle of rabbit with confit rabbit leg, pancetta and cranberry and port jus (£12.75), fresh lobster (from £14.95), halibut fillet, roasted artichoke, red peppers and a crayfish tail and chive butter (£15.25), and puddings such as individual dark chocolate and coconut iced parfait with chocolate sauce or apple and date strudel with walnut ice-cream (£4.75); popular – if not cheap – Sunday roasts (from £10.50). The landscaped garden is a pleasant place for a meal or a drink. *(Recommended by Tom and Ruth Rees, John and Gloria Isaacs, Keith Rutter, Inga Davis, Evelyn and Derek Walter, Rod Stoneman, Anne Colley, Tim Gee, Dr J J H Gilkes, Paul and Penny Dawson, Andy Barker, Claire Jenkins, Martin and Sue Day)*

Free house ~ Licensees Shaun and Emma Davis ~ Real ale ~ Bar food (12-2.30, 7-9.45; not Sun evening) ~ Restaurant ~ (01285) 760960 ~ Children welcome ~ Dogs welcome ~ Open 11-3, 6-11; 12-4 Sun; closed Sun evening

GLASSHOUSE SO7121 Map 4
Glasshouse Inn ◀

First right turn off A40 going W from junction with A4136; OS Sheet 162 map reference 710213

Especially in fine weather, the neatly kept garden here is just the place for a quiet drink, and there are seats on a tidy fenced lawn (and a yew tree seat) with interesting topiary; lovely hanging baskets in summer, and nearby paths up May Hill with its attractive woodlands. Inside, you'll find a homely mixture of kitchen chairs, settles, old benches, and plain wooden tables on the red quarry tiles and flagstones, warmed by open fires in a cavernous black hearth and a smaller cottagey Victorian fireplace. Also, decorative plates, fish-poaching warnings, hunting and fishing prints, rugby and other memorabilia, and old advertisements on the walls. A new conservatory has a flagstoned floor, timbers in the solid roof, and lots of old prints. Friendly staff serve very well kept Bass and Butcombe alongside a guest such as Hook Norton tapped straight from the cask. The relaxed atmosphere is helped along by the absence of games machines and piped music. Besides generous lunchtime sandwiches (prices have not changed since last year; from £3), and basket meals (from £4.50) or ploughman's (from £5.50), the well liked bar food includes cauliflower cheese and bacon (£6.95), home-cooked ham and eggs, mushroom stroganoff or home-made lasagne (£7.50), steak and kidney with Guinness in two yorkshire puddings or fish pie (£8.50), steaks (from £11), and half a shoulder of lamb with port and redcurrant jelly (£11.50); they don't take bookings. No children inside. *(Recommended by TB, Dr A Y Drummond, Phil and Sally Gorton, Guy Vowles, Mike and Mary Carter, the Didler, Martin and Pauline Jennings, Dr A J and Mrs Tompsett, Lucien Perring)*

Free house ~ Licensee Steve Pugh ~ Real ale ~ Bar food (not Sun) ~ (01452) 830529 ~ Open 11.30-3, 6.30-11; 12-3 Sun; closed Sun evening Jan-Apr

GUITING POWER SP0924 Map 4
Hollow Bottom

Village signposted off B4068 SW of Stow-on-the-Wold (still called A436 on many maps)

There have been quite a few improvements to this friendly 17th-c inn this year. The kitchen has been reworked, a new restaurant area opened, new furniture and carpets installed, and a new cotswold stone garden added. The comfortable beamed bar still has lots of racing memorabilia including racing silks, tunics and photographs (it's owned by a small syndicate that includes Peter Scudamore and Nigel Twiston-Davies), and a winter log fire in an unusual pillar-supported stone fireplace. The public bar has flagstones and stripped stone masonry and racing on TV; newspapers to read, darts, cribbage, dominoes, Spoof and piped music. Well kept Fullers London Pride, Hook Norton and a guest such as Timothy Taylors Landlord on handpump, 15 malt whiskies and seven wines (including champagne) by the glass; the staff are friendly and obliging. As well as specials like fresh fish (from £9.95), mushroom stroganoff in filo pastry (£10.95), trio of pigeon breasts in port and wild berry sauce (£11.95), and strips of wild boar in a dark rum and orange sauce (£13.95), the good food might include home-made soup (£4.25), filled baguettes (from £5.45), pâté (£5.75), filled baked potatoes (from £6.45), ploughman's or home-made burger (£7.95), ham and eggs or cottage pie (£8.50), and steaks (from £14.95); on Sundays they do only a carvery. From the pleasant garden behind are views towards the peaceful sloping fields, and there are decent walks nearby. More reports please. *(Recommended by Michael and Jenny Back, Dr G and Mrs J Kelvin, David A Hammond, Peter B Brown, Tom Bottinga, Ian Arthur, Lynn Nisbet)*

Free house ~ Licensees Hugh Kelly and Charles Pettigrew ~ Real ale ~ Bar food (12-9 (snacks during the afternoon rather than meals) ~ Restaurant ~ (01451) 850392 ~ Children welcome ~ Dogs allowed in bar and bedrooms ~ Occasional live entertainment ~ Open 11-11; 12-10.30 Sun ~ Bedrooms: /£70B

LITTLE BARRINGTON SP2012 Map 4
Inn For All Seasons 🍽 ♟
On the A40 3 miles W of Burford

This year, the bar and no smoking restaurant area have been opened up to give more space and they have some unusual tables and chairs bought from a local antique dealer. The attractively decorated, mellow lounge bar has low beams, stripped stone, flagstones, old prints, leather-upholstered wing armchairs and other comfortable seats, country magazines to read, and a big log fire. From a particularly good wine list there are 20 wines by the glass (from a 120 bin list), 60 malt whiskies, and well kept Sharps Own and Wadworths 6X on handpump with maybe a guest like Wychwood Shire Best on handpump; friendly, kind service. Fish is the speciality here and from quite a choice there might be grilled fresh sardines with garlic, port and parsley butter sauce (£6.25; main course £9.95), flash fried squid with lime and baby spinach salad (£6.50; main course £9.95), grilled fillet of yellow fin tuna on niçoise salad (£12.95), poached wing of skate with baby caper and shallot butter sauce (£11.50), and whole cock crabs (served only in the garden, £16.50); also, light snacks such as soup or sandwiches (£4.25), terrine of the day (£5.50), ploughman's (£6.50), and bubble and squeak topped with crispy bacon and a fried egg (£7.50), and more substantial dishes like sun-dried tomato, olive and basil risotto (£9.50), lemon chicken with tarragon couscous on mushroom sauce (£10.95), oxtail stew (£11.50), and soy, ginger and honey duck with sesame and spring onion noodles (£13.75). Cribbage, TV and piped music. The pleasant garden has tables, a play area and aunt sally, and there are walks straight from the inn. It gets very busy during Cheltenham Gold Cup Week. *(Recommended by Peter and Audrey Dowsett, Peter Neate, Piotr Chodzko-Zajko, Richard and Margaret Peers, Ian Phillips, John Kane, Jim Abbott, Chris and Val Ramstedt, James Woods, Lewis Osborn, Derek Thomas, K Clarkson, B M Eldridge, Les and Barbara Owen, KN-R, Karen and Graham Oddey)*

Free house ~ Licensees Matthew and Heather Sharp ~ Real ale ~ Bar food ~ Restaurant ~ (01451) 844324 ~ Children welcome ~ Dogs allowed in bar and bedrooms ~ Open 11-2.30, 6-11; 12-2.30, 7-10.30 Sun ~ Bedrooms: £56.50B/£97B

LITTLETON-UPON-SEVERN ST5990 Map 2
White Hart 🍺
3½ miles from M48 junction 1; B4461 towards Thornbury, then village signposted

This cosy 17th-c farmhouse is a proper pub with a good mix of customers, and a comfortable, very relaxed atmosphere. The three main rooms have log fires and some fine furnishings such as long cushioned wooden settles, high-backed settles, oak and elm tables, and a loveseat in the big low inglenook fireplace. There are flagstones in the front, huge tiles at the back, and smaller tiles on the left, plus some old pots and pans, and a lovely old White Hart Inn Simonds Ale sign. By the black wooden staircase are some nice little alcove seats, there's a black-panelled big fireplace in the front room, and hops on beams. Similarly furnished, a family room (usually no smoking) has some sentimental engravings, plates on a delft shelf and a couple of high chairs; a back snug has pokerwork seats. Well kept Smiles Best, Youngs Bitter, Special and Waggle Dance, and a seasonal beer on handpump, and several wines by the glass; darts, bar billiards, cribbage and dominoes. Well liked bar food includes lunchtime filled baguettes (from £3.50; sirloin steak £7.95), ploughman's (from £6.50), vegetable or beef curry (from £7.45), ham and egg, battered haddock or sausages of the day (£7.95), steak and kidney pie (£8.95), braised lamb shank with red wine and rosemary jus (£10.95), whole bass with anchovy butter (£13.95), and home-made puddings such as chocolate sponge with chocolate sauce or apple pie (£3.95). Outside, there are picnic-sets on the neat front lawn with interesting cottagey flowerbeds, and by the good big back car park are some attractive shrubs and teak furniture on a small brick terrace; several enjoyable walks from the pub. *(Recommended by Andy and Jill Kassube, Meg and Colin Hamilton, Di and Mike Gillam, R Huggins, D Irving, E McCall, T McLean, W F C Phillips, Pete Devonish, Ian McIntyre)*

Youngs ~ Managers Greg Bailey and Claire Wells ~ Real ale ~ Bar food (12-2(2.30 Sat, Sun), 6.30-9.30(9 Sun)) ~ (01454) 412275 ~ Children in family room ~ Dogs welcome ~ Open 12-2.30, 6-11; 11-11 Sat; 12-10.30 Sun ~ Bedrooms: £55B/£75B

LOWER ODDINGTON SP2326 Map 4
Fox 🍽️ ♀

Signposted off A436 between Stow and Chipping Norton

The Red Room in this smart, popular inn has wine-related paintings on the walls, and the other simply and spotlessly furnished rooms have fresh flowers and flagstones, an inglenook fireplace, hunting scene figures above the mantelpiece, a display cabinet with pewter mugs and stone bottles, and daily newspapers. Served by neat, uniformed staff, the generous helpings of interesting food might include home-made soup (£3.95), red pepper, goats cheese and tapenade tart (£5.75), wild mushroom risotto (£5.75; main course £9.75), chicken liver pâté with cornichons (£5.95), lasagne of roasted red peppers, mozzarella and pesto (£9.50), home-made steak and mushroom pie (£10.95), salmon and leek fishcakes with hollandaise and lemon (£11.50), braised lamb shank (£12.25), barbary duck with port and morello cherries (£13.95), and puddings such as raspberry ripple parfait with raspberry coulis, chocolate brownie or crème brûlée (£4.50); a good wine list with quite a few by the glass, and well kept Adnams Bitter, Hook Norton Best and Greene King Abbot on handpump; excellent service. The terrace has a custom-built awning and outdoor heaters, and the cottagey garden is pretty. A good eight-mile walk starts from here (though a stroll around the pretty village might be less taxing). *(Recommended by C Tilley, Tracey and Stephen Groves, Gary and Jane Gleghorn, Martin and Karen Wake, Gaynor Gregory, A P Seymour, Brian and Pat Wardrobe, Rod Stoneman, John and Gloria Isaacs, Tom McLean, Karen and Graham Oddey)*

Free house ~ Licensees James Cathcart and Ian MacKenzie ~ Real ale ~ Bar food (till 10pm) ~ Restaurant ~ (01451) 870555 ~ Well behaved children in eating area of bar ~ Dogs allowed in bar ~ Open 12-3, 6.30-11; 12-3, 7-10.30 Sun; closed 25 Dec, evenings 26 and 31 Dec, 1 Jan ~ Bedrooms: /£75S(£85B)

MEYSEY HAMPTON SU1199 Map 4
Masons Arms

High Street; just off A417 Cirencester—Lechlade

A new licensee has taken over this 17th-c village pub but happily, not much has changed. There's still a loyal local following but plenty of visitors, too, a pleasantly relaxed atmosphere and a fair choice of real ales. The longish open-plan bar has painted stone walls, carefully stripped beams with some hops, solid part-upholstered built-in wall seats with some matching chairs, good sound tables, a big inglenook log fire at one end with lots of brasses, some farm implements and caps, and perhaps daily newspapers; a few steps up is the no smoking restaurant. Well kept Hook Norton Best and Wickwar Cotswold Way, and a couple of guests such as Archers Silver Train and Dark Star Sunburst on handpump, and 24 malt whiskies; dominoes, cribbage and piped music. Bar food at lunchtime now includes sandwiches (from £1.95; filled baguettes from £3.95), filled baked potatoes or nice salad bowls (from £4.25), and ploughman's (from £5.75); also, home-made soup (£2.85), home-made pâté (£4.65), moules marinière (£5.95; large £7.65), ham and eggs (£5.95), home-made pie of the day (£6.95), pork steak with barbecue sauce and three melted cheeses (£7.65), vegetable and cheese wellington (£8.25), haddock fillet dusted in lemon and cracked pepper with a lemon dressing (£8.65), duck à l'orange (£8.95), and steaks (from £9.85). *(Recommended by Brian McBurnie, Kevin Thorpe, A P Seymour, Roger and Jenny Huggins, R Huggins, D Irving, E McCall, T McLean, Dr and Mrs M E Wilson, Colin McKerrow, Mary Rayner)*

Independent Pub Co ~ Licensee Paul Fallows ~ Real ale ~ Bar food (not winter Sun evening) ~ Restaurant ~ (01285) 850164 ~ Children welcome ~ Dogs allowed in bar ~ Open 11.30-2.45, 6-11; 12-4, 7-10.30 Sun; closed Sun evening in winter ~ Bedrooms: £45S/£70S

MISERDEN SO9308 Map 4
Carpenters Arms

Village signposted off B4070 NE of Stroud; also a pleasant drive off A417 via the Duntisbournes, or off A419 via Sapperton and Edgeworth; OS Sheet 163 map reference 936089

This is the only building in this idyllic Cotswold estate village that is not owned by the Misarden Estate. It's a pleasant place, and the two open-plan bar areas have low beams, nice old wooden tables, seats with the original little brass name plates on the backs, and some cushioned settles and spindlebacks on the bare boards; also, stripped stone walls with some interesting bric-a-brac, and two big log fires. The small no smoking dining room has dark traditional furniture. A sizeable collage (done with Laurie Lee) has lots of illustrations and book covers signed by him. Bar food includes lunchtime sandwiches or filled baguettes (from £4.25), filled baked potatoes (from £4.95), and ploughman's (£6.50), as well as home-made fishcakes, home-cooked honey roast ham with eggs or local lamb burgers (£7.95), fresh beer battered cod (£8.25), and 10-inch stone baked pizzas (£9.95), with specials like cajun chicken (£7.25), rack of barbecued ribs or home-made quiche (£7.95), and lambs liver, sausage and bacon with onion gravy (£8.25). Well kept Greene King IPA, Wadworths 6X and a guest such as Wye Valley Bitter on handpump, several wines by the glass and country wines; darts. There are seats out in the garden; the nearby gardens of Misarden Park are well worth visiting. *(Recommended by Neil and Angela Huxter, Michael Cooper, R Huggins, D Irving, E McCall, T McLean, Brian McBurnie, Gaynor Gregory, Di and Mike Gillam, Mike and Mary Carter, Graham and Helen Eastwood, Neil and Anita Christopher, John Reilly)*

Blenheim Inns ~ Lease Johnny Johnston ~ Real ale ~ Bar food (12-2.30, 7-9.30) ~ Restaurant ~ (01285) 821283 ~ Children welcome ~ Dogs allowed in bar ~ Open 11.30-3, 6.30(6 Sat)-11; 12-3, 6.30-10.30 Sun

NAILSWORTH ST8599 Map 4
Egypt Mill 🍴 🛏

Just off A46; heading N towards Stroud, first right after roundabout, then left

Certainly unusual, this is a stylish conversion of a three-floor stone-built mill still with working waterwheels and the millstream flowing through. The brick-and-stone-floored split-level bar gives good views of the wheels, and there are nice pictures and lots of stripped beams in the comfortable carpeted lounge, along with some hefty yet elegant ironwork from the old mill machinery; piped music. Ideal for summer evenings, the floodlit terrace garden by the millpond is pretty, and there's a little bridge over from the car park. Well liked food includes sandwiches, soup (£3.95), terrine of the day (£4.95), smoked chicken, cranberry and brie pizza (£5.95), crispy thai marinated fish and pawpaw salad (£6.75), steak and kidney pudding (£9.50), liver and bacon (£9.95), haddock and chips (£10.45), nut roast, lentil and vegetable sauce (£13.95), breast of duck, apple and blackberry risotto or saddle of lamb greek style (£14.95), steaks (from £14), and puddings such as dark and white chocolate pyramid filled with Baileys mousse or lemongrass and raspberry crème brûlée (£4.95). It can get quite crowded on fine weekends, but it's spacious enough to feel at its best when busy. Archers, and a changing guest beer on handpump, and several wines by the glass. *(Recommended by Mike and Heather Watson, Fred and Lorraine Gill, Joyce and Maurice Cottrell, Jenny and Brian Seller, John Mitchell, Paul and Shirley White, B R and M F Arnold, Basil and Jarvis, Tim and Suzy Bower, Mr and Mrs W D Borthwick, Alison and Pete)*

Free house ~ Licensee Stephen Webb ~ Real ale ~ (01453) 833449 ~ Children welcome ~ Dogs allowed in bar ~ Occasional live music at weekends ~ Open 11-11; 12-10.30 Sun ~ Bedrooms: £60B/£75B

Weighbridge 🍴 ♀

B4014 towards Tetbury

Even when this pub is busy – which it usually is – the staff remain friendly and welcoming – to all their customers, including children. The relaxed bar has three cosily old-fashioned rooms (one is no smoking) with stripped stone walls, antique settles and country chairs, and window seats. The black-beamed ceiling of the lounge bar is thickly festooned with black ironware – sheepshears, gin traps, lamps, and a large collection of keys, many from the old Longfords Mill opposite the pub. Upstairs is a raftered no smoking hayloft with an engaging mix of rustic tables. Good bar food includes the very popular two-in-one pies which come in a large bowl, and half the bowl contains the filling of your choice while the other is full of home-made cauliflower cheese (or broccoli mornay or root vegetables), and topped with pastry: turkey and trimmings, salmon in a creamy sauce, steak and mushroom, roast root vegetables, pork, bacon and celery in stilton sauce or chicken, ham and leek in a cream and tarragon sauce (from £9.40; you can also have mini versions from £6.90 or straightforward pies from £8). Other dishes include home-made soup (£3.25), filled baguettes (from £3.60; not evenings), filled baked potatoes (from £4), cauliflower cheese (£5.45), cottage pie (£5.95), ploughman's (from £5.95), moussaka (£8.45), scottish smoked salmon and cream cheese cannelloni (£8.95), lamb shank on rosemary and garlic mash or chicken supreme stuffed with ham and cheese and coated in breadcrumbs (£10.95), daily specials, and puddings such as steamed chocolate pudding with chocolate fudge sauce, glazed lemon torte or banana crumble (from £3.95); no noisy games machines or piped music. Well kept Uley Old Spot and Laurie Lee, and Wadworths 6X on handpump, 14 wines (and champagne) by the glass, Weston's cider, and ten malt whiskies. Behind is a sheltered landscaped garden with picnic-sets under umbrellas. Good disabled access and facilities. *(Recommended by Paul and Penny Dawson, Gerald Wilkinson, Mike and Lynn Robinson, Dr and Mrs C W Thomas, Tom and Ruth Rees, Andrew Shore, Maria Williams, Andy Barker, Claire Jenkins, S P Watkin, P A Taylor, John Reilly, R Huggins, D Irving, E McCall, T McLean, John and Jane Hayter)*

Free house ~ Licensee Howard Parker ~ Real ale ~ Bar food (12-9.30) ~ (01453) 832520 ~ Children in family room till 9pm ~ Dogs welcome ~ Open 12-11; 12-10.30 Sun; closed 25 Dec

NETHER WESTCOTE SP2220 Map 4
New Inn

Pub signposted off A424 Burford—Stow

This pretty cottage, in a quiet and appealing village, is a few steps down from the lane, through a small front garden with picnic-sets on the terrace; there's also a good-sized back garden where they still play aunt sally (and where 73 different wild birds have been spotted). In fact it's far from new, being over 300 years old (with some stripped stone and beams showing its age), and pleasantly relaxed inside, with good-natured attentive service, comfortable elbow chairs and cushioned wall seats, a good log fire, a rack of daily papers, and cheerful pictures; the friendly spaniel is called Bob – and in fact the landlord has two rabbits, two pet lambs, a parrot and a large aquarium. Well kept changing real ales on handpump might include Goffs Jouster, Greene King 1799 and Hook Norton Best, farm cider, and decent wines by the glass. The games area has darts, cribbage, dominoes, pool, Jenga and a fruit machine; there may be piped radio. Steps take you down to a small attractive stripped-stone dining room with another log fire; the big blackboard shows interestingly prepared food (using only local suppliers) such as tuscan bean crunch (£7.95) and chicken in orange cream sauce (£11.95), and there's also soup or pâté (£3.95), sandwiches and baguettes (from £3.95), filled baked potatoes (from £4.95), ham and egg (£6.95), ploughman's (£7.95), steak in ale stew (£8.95), liver and bacon (£8.95), pork chop with stilton and apple or vegetarian tagliatelle (£9.95), steaks (from £10.95), and puddings like strawberry jam pudding or spotted dick (£3.50). They have a camp site with showers (and electrics for caravans). *(Recommended by Stuart Turner, Mrs N W Neill)*

Free house ~ Licensee Steve Rix ~ Real ale ~ Bar food (12-2.30, 6-9.30) ~ Restaurant ~ (01993) 830827 ~ Children welcome ~ Dogs welcome ~ Live music Fri evenings ~ Open 11-11; 12-10.30 Sun; 11-2.30, 5-11 in winter

NEWLAND SO5509 Map 4
Ostrich ♀ ◀

Off B4228 in Coleford; or can be reached from the A466 in Redbrook, by the turning off at the England-Wales border – keep bearing right

Run by an exceptionally welcoming landlady (Alfie the dog is very friendly, too), this unspoilt country pub is quite a favourite with many of our readers. The low-ceilinged bar is spacious but cosily traditional, with creaky floors, uneven walls with miners' lamps, window shutters, candles in bottles on the tables, and comfortable furnishings such as cushioned window seats, wall settles and rod-backed country-kitchen chairs; there's a fine big fireplace, newspapers to read and perhaps quiet piped blues. Changing constantly, the eight well kept real ales might include Timothy Taylors Landlord and Wye Valley Butty Bach with guests such as Exmoor Gold, Greene King Abbot, Sharps Doom Bar, Shepherd Neame Spitfire, Wells Bombardier and Youngs Bitter on handpump. Popular home-made bar food includes soup (£4.95), ploughman's with home-made chutney (£6.25), sausages with dauphinoise potato and onion gravy (£6.50), three cheese tart with sun-dried tomatoes and basil (£7), sizzling pork ribs or steak in ale pie (£7.50), and salmon and spinach fishcakes with parsley sauce (£8), or you can eat the restaurant menu in the bar, and choose from dishes such as pigeon and foie gras terrine with sloe and crab apple jelly (£6), fresh egg pasta with wild mushrooms and sun-blush tomatoes in a basil butter cream sauce or slow-roasted spiced belly pork with soy buttered pak choi and egg noodles (£12.50), and chicken breast stuffed with cream cheese, garlic and rosemary in a puff pastry parcel with red pepper salsa (£13.95). There are seats in a walled garden behind and out in front; the church opposite, known as the Cathedral of the Forest, is well worth a visit. *(Recommended by R Huggins, D Irving, E McCall, T McLean, LM, Phil and Heidi Cook, Tim and Ann Newell, Denys Gueroult, Chris and Val Ramstedt, Mike and Mary Carter, David and Pauline Brenner, Jo Rees, Kevin Blake, GSB, V Brogden, Ken and Jenny Simmonds)*

Free house ~ Licensee Kathryn Horton ~ Real ale ~ Bar food (12-2.30, 6.30(6 Sat)-9.30) ~ Restaurant ~ (01594) 833260 ~ Children welcome ~ Dogs welcome ~ Open 12-3, 6.30(6 Sat)-11; 12-4, 6.30-10.30 Sun

NORTH CERNEY SP0208 Map 4 🏠
Bathurst Arms ♀

A435 Cirencester—Cheltenham

On the edge of the little River Churn, this handsome 17th-c inn is nearly always busy. The original beamed and panelled bar has a fireplace at each end (one quite huge and housing an open woodburner), a good mix of old tables and nicely faded chairs, and old-fashioned window seats. There are country tables in an oak-floored room off the bar, as well as winged high-backed settles forming a few booths around other tables; the restaurant is no smoking. Dominoes and piped music. The landlord has devoted a whole wall in the restaurant to display the fine wine list (with around ten wines and champagnes by the glass), and Hook Norton Best and Wickwar Cotswold Way are well kept alongside a guest such as Goffs Tournament on handpump. Well liked, often interesting bar food includes home-made soup (£3.95), sandwiches or fig and peanut salad with crispy smoked bacon, young leaves and mint and raspberry vinaigrette (£4.95), lobster and crab drop scone with asparagus and sweet mustard sauce (£5.25), ploughman's (£5.95), burger on a toasted cheese bap or deep-fried cod fillet in light beer batter with home-made tartare sauce (£7.95), lentil, hazelnut, mushroom and sun-dried tomato cake with a creamy asian fruit sauce (£8.95), chicken stuffed with shallot, apple and cheese wrapped in bacon with a creamy banana sauce and a hint of curry or slowly braised short ribs of beef in port jus (£9.95), and puddings like double chocolate steamed pudding with fudge sauce or blueberry pancakes layered with mascarpone cream and blueberries with maple walnut ice-cream (£4.35). The pleasant garden has picnic-sets sheltered by small trees and shrubs, and there are plenty of surrounding walks. *(Recommended by J Graveling, Alan Strong, Julia and Richard Tredgett, Paul and Shirley White, Peter and Audrey Dowsett, Howard and Lorna Lambert, Guy Vowles, A R Ainslie, Oliver Richardson, Monica Cockburn, Mike Jefferies)*

Free house ~ Licensee James Walker ~ Real ale ~ Bar food ~ Restaurant ~ (01285) 831281 ~ Children in eating area of bar and restaurant ~ Dogs allowed in bar and bedrooms ~ Open 12-3, 6-11; 12-3, 7-10.30 Sun ~ Bedrooms: /£70B

NORTHLEACH SP1114 Map 4

Wheatsheaf ♀ ⇌

West End; the inn is on your left as you come in following the sign off the A429, just SW of its junction with the A40

As well as being a comfortable place to stay, this handsomely proportioned 16th-c stone-built inn is particularly popular on Monday or Tuesday, when all bottles of wine are half price with a meal. The three big-windowed light and airy rooms lining the street all run together. The central bar part has flagstones, the dining area open to it on the right has bare boards, and both have quite high ceilings – so the acoustics can be lively. The room on the left has a less exposed atmosphere which some might prefer. Well kept Hook Norton Best, and Wadworths 6X and JCB on handpump, 14 wines by the glass and a dozen malt whiskies; dominoes and piped music. Besides lunchtime sandwiches, bar food might include sausages and mash (£8), fillet of lemon sole with salsa verde or whole bibury trout with watercress and bacon (£9), and breast of duck with crushed potato and spinach (£11). The restaurant is no smoking. A pretty garden behind the pub is pleasant in fine weather, with picnic-sets on tiers of grass among flowering shrubs. *(Recommended by Martin and Karen Wake, Mayur Shah, Gerald Wilkinson, Ian and Nita Cooper, Peter and Barbara Gardiner, Mr and Mrs D Renwick, Ian Phillips, C Tilley, Ben Seale, Jane Bailey, David G Martin, Keith and Margaret Kettell, Dr and Mrs A K Clarke)*

Punch ~ Lease Caspar and Gavin Harvard-Walls ~ Real ale ~ Bar food (12-3, 7-10) ~ Restaurant ~ (01451) 860244 ~ Children in eating area of bar ~ Dogs allowed in bar ~ Open 12-11; 12-10.30 Sun ~ Bedrooms: £50B/£60B

OLDBURY-ON-SEVERN ST6292 Map 2

Anchor ♀ ▪

Village signposted from B4061

In summer you can eat in the pretty garden here, when the hanging baskets and window boxes are lovely; boules. Inside, the neatly kept lounge has modern beams and stone, a mix of tables including an attractive oval oak gateleg, cushioned window seats, winged seats against the wall, oil paintings by a local artist and a big winter log fire. Well priced for the area, they've Bass, Butcombe Bitter, Theakstons Old Peculier and Wickwar BOB well kept on handpump or tapped from the cask, 75 malt whiskies, and a dozen decent wines by the glass. Diners can eat in the lounge or bar area or in the no smoking dining room at the back of the building (good for larger groups) and the menu is the same in all rooms. Using local produce where possible, bar food might include soup (£3), devilled kidneys and mushrooms on brioche toast (£4.25), ploughman's (£4.50), ciabatta sandwiches (from £4.95), home-cooked honey roast ham with two eggs and bubble and squeak (£6.50), moules marinière or sausages with red onion marmalade (£6.95), vegetable or meaty lasagne (£7.25), home-made steak and kidney pudding (£7.50), roast local duckling with thyme and parsley stuffing or grilled whole lemon sole (£9.50), chargrilled rib-eye steak with green peppercorn sauce (£9.95), and puddings such as treacle tart or white chocolate and raspberry trifle (£3.50). They have wheelchair access and a disabled lavatory. Plenty of walks to the River Severn and along the many footpaths and bridleways, and St Arilda's church nearby is interesting, on its odd little knoll with wild flowers among the gravestones (the primroses and daffodils in spring are lovely). *(Recommended by Tom Evans, James Morrell, Bob and Margaret Holder, R Huggins, D Irving, E McCall, T McLean, Geoff Manning, Andrew Shore, Maria Williams, Charles and Pauline Stride, Dr and Mrs C W Thomas, John and Gloria Isaacs, Mr and Mrs J Brown, Gloria Bax, Barry and Anne)*

Free house ~ Licensees Michael Dowdeswell and Mark Sorrell ~ Real ale ~ Bar food ~ Restaurant ~ (01454) 413331 ~ Children in restaurant ~ Dogs allowed in bar ~ Open 11.30-3, 6.30-11; 11.30-11 Sat; 12-10.30 Sun

POULTON SP1001 Map 4

Falcon

London Road (A417 Fairford—Cirencester)

Good interesting food, changing monthly and relying largely on fresh local produce and fish straight from the West Country, is the main draw in this stylishly decorated pub. Cooked by the landlord, this might include lunchtime, sandwiches on home-made bread (from £3.50), as well as mushroom soup with white truffle cream (£5.95), country pork terrine with cornichons and home-made onion marmalade (£6.50), torbay crab cakes with home-made mayonnaise or cornish mussels with saffron and mustard (£7.50), seared scallops with pea purée, crispy prosciutto and mint vinaigrette (£8.50), mixed herb potato gnocchi with four cheese sauce (£9.95), navarin of cotswold lamb with spring vegetables (£12.95), supreme of free-range chicken with braised pearl barley, crispy bacon and tarragon jus (£13.95), rare breed sirloin steak with watercress butter (£16.95), and puddings such as bramley apple and almond crumble with home-made cinnamon ice-cream or vanilla panna cotta with spiced oranges and home-made shortbread biscuits (£5.95); two-course set lunch (£10) and three-course Sunday lunch (£20). They have kept a proper beige-carpeted bar area on the left, with mixed bar stools, nicely waxed tables, chapel chairs and other more interesting seats, a woodburning stove, a restrained selection of photographs on watery grey-green walls, country magazines sharing a table with an aspidistra, and perhaps a big bunch of lilies on the unobtrusively modern bar counter. This has Hook Norton Best and a guest beer such as West Berkshire Good Old Boy on handpump, good if not cheap wines by the glass, some interesting grown-up soft drinks, and Burts excellent crisps. It opens through into a similarly furnished dining area with flowers on the tables and a log fire in the imposing stone fireplace, with steps up to a further back dining room (and a view into the kitchen). Service is neat and friendly, piped music is sophisticated and unobjectionable, and the lavatories are good – what they call the 'Boys' is very blue. *(Recommended by Adrian White, Fiona Duncan, Keith Rutter, Inga Davis, Rod Stoneman, R Huggins, D Irving, E McCall, T McLean, Barry and Anne Cooper, Michael Dallas, Karen and Graham Oddey)*

Free house ~ Licensee Jeremy Lockley ~ Real ale ~ Bar food (12-2.30-, 7-9; not Sun evening) ~ Restaurant ~ (01285) 850844 ~ Children in eating area of bar and restaurant ~ Dogs allowed in bar ~ Open 11-3, 6-11; 12-3, 6-10.30 Sun

---

Pubs with attractive or unusually big gardens are listed at the back of the book.

SAPPERTON SO9403 Map 4

Bell 🏮 ♀ ◀

Village signposted from A419 Stroud—Cirencester; OS Sheet 163 map reference 948033

There's no doubt that much emphasis in this bustling dining pub is on the imaginative food, but they have reintroduced a snack menu for the many walkers who come in, and keep beers from small local breweries on handpump: Hook Norton Best, Uley Old Spot, Wickwar Cotswold Way and a guest such as Butcombe Bitter. There are three separate, cosy rooms with stripped beams, a nice mix of wooden tables and chairs, country prints and modern art on stripped-stone walls, one or two attractive rugs on the flagstones, roaring log fires and woodburning stoves, fresh flowers, and newspapers and guidebooks to browse; most of the eating tables are no smoking and the front bar is totally no smoking. The menu changes every week and they take great care when sourcing their produce using the best local ingredients, and fish from Brixham or Fairford. As well as bar snacks such as soup (£4.50), spare ribs with celeriac coleslaw (£5.50), a tapas plate (£6.75), and a proper ploughman's with home-made bread and chutney (£6.95), there might be chicken liver parfait with home-made brioche (£5.95), fresh salmon and chive fishcake with light scrambled egg (£6.50), hot cheese fritters with roasted beetroot and a grain mustard cream (£6.25), baked pigeon faggot on sautéed potato with savoy cabbage (£6.50), burger with spiced tomato relish and home-made fries or home-made pasta with mushrooms, herbs and tomato (£11.50), roasted loin of old spot pork and baked mushrooms with a blue cheese and herb crust or free-range chicken with peppers and shallots in a cream sauce with pilau rice (£13.75), chargrilled bacon chop with parsley sauce (£13.95), grilled fillet of wild bass with hollandaise sauce or shank of lamb slowly braised with root vegetables (£15.95), and home-made puddings such as sticky toffee pudding or rhubarb fool with a home-made biscuit (£5.75); a basket of home-made bread and butter and olives comes with every meal. A large and diverse wine list with very helpful notes yields around two dozen by the glass (including champagne by the flute), some interesting aperitifs, and pudding wines, and there are 30 malt whiskies and several armagnacs and cognacs. Harry the springer spaniel is very sociable but must not be fed for health reasons. There are tables out on a small front lawn and in a partly covered and very pretty courtyard, for eating outside. Good surrounding walks, and horses have their own tethering rail (and bucket of water). *(Recommended by Bernard Stradling, Keith Rutter, Inga Davis, R Huggins, D Irving, E McCall, T McLean, Derek Thomas, James Morrell, Mr and Mrs P L Spencer, Mrs N W Neill, Evelyn and Derek Walter, Andy and Jill Kassube, Marianne and Peter Stevens, Paul and Penny Dawson, Mr and Mrs G S Ayrton, Gaynor Gregory, John Kane, Tom and Ruth Rees, A G Marx, B R and M F Arnold, Ken Marshall, Stephen Woad, John Reilly, John Balfour, Andrew Barker, Claire Jenkins, Di and Mike Gillam, Julie and Bill Ryan, Drs M J and P M Cox, Michael Dallas)*

Free house ~ Licensees Paul Davidson and Pat Le Jeune ~ Real ale ~ Bar food ~ Restaurant ~ (01285) 760298 ~ Children allowed but not under 10 in evenings ~ Dogs welcome ~ Open 11-2.30, 6.30-11; 12-3, 7-10.30 Sun; closed 25 Dec and evenings 26 and 31 Dec and 1 Jan

TETBURY ST8993 Map 4

Snooty Fox ♀ 🛏

Market Place; small residents' car park, nearby pay & display; free car park some way down hill

At lunchtime there's a bustling unstuffy atmosphere in this centrally placed inn's high-ceilinged main bar on the left, with lots of chatting ladies clearly enjoying the fine range of 20 wines by the glass – which includes rosé champagne as well as 'ordinary'. They have a fine collection of spirits as well as well kept ales from Butcombe, Moles and Smiles on handpump, an espresso machine, and plenty of cigars; the neat young staff give good service, and there may be unobtrusive piped jazz. This front room – stripped stone, like much of the rest of the ground floor –

has comfortable sturdy leather-armed chairs round the cast-iron tripod tables on its carpet, a big log fireplace flanked by an imposing pair of brass flambeaux, brass ceiling fans, and Ronald Searle pony-club cartoons. Behind is a similar room, with a colourful rug on bare boards and a leather sofa among other seats, and the no smoking restaurant is beyond. On the right a smaller quieter room has leather wing armchairs and sofas, and a couple of imposing portraits. Good bar food includes sandwiches and baguettes (served 12-6, from £4.50) and lunchtime dishes such as soup (£3.50), cauliflower cheese and garlic bread (£5.50), caesar salad with deep-fried anchovies (£5.95), baked leek and bacon tart, rocket and caramelised onion mayonnaise (£6.25), salmon and coriander fishcakes with chive beurre blanc (£7.95), meat pasty with beef gravy or corned beef hash with fried egg (£8.25), and beef battered fish (£8.95), with evening choices like pressed ham hock, lentil and parsley terrine with piccalilli (£5), confit beetroot, aubergine mash and goats cheese salad (£6.25), antipasti misto (£6.95), wild mushroom risotto with focaccia crackers (£9.50), fresh fish with carrot and ginger bisque and caper butter (£13), pork fillet stuffed with smoked cheese and almonds with sweet potato chips and plum sauce (£14.50), and fillet of west country beef with dark pepper sauce (£18); puddings such as walnut treacle tart with butterscotch ice-cream and whisky syrup or dark chocolate mousse with glazed orange segments, basil and mint syrup (£5). They also do cream teas (and a good breakfast for residents). Children are treated well here – clearly looked at more as future customers than as an inconvenience. Outside, a sheltered entryway has teak tables and chairs facing the ancient central covered market. *(Recommended by David A Hammond, Dr and Mrs A K Clarke, Barry and Anne, Colin and Janet Roe, Peter and Audrey Dowsett, Mike and Heather Watson)*

Free house ~ Licensee Marc Gibbons ~ Bar food (12-2, 6-9.30) ~ Restaurant ~ (01666) 502436 ~ Children welcome ~ Dogs allowed in bar ~ Open 11-11; 12-10.30 Sun ~ Bedrooms: £73B/£95B

Trouble House

A433 towards Cirencester, near Cherington turn

There's no doubt that most customers come to this smart but friendly dining pub for a special meal out. Furnishings are mainly close-set stripped pine or oak tables with chapel chairs, some wheelback chairs and the odd library chair, and there are attractive mainly modern country prints on the cream or butter-coloured walls. The rush-matting room on the right is no smoking, and on the left there's a parquet-floored room with a chesterfield by the big stone fireplace, a hop-girt mantelpiece, and more hops hung from one of its two big black beams. In the small saggy-beamed middle room you can commandeer one of the bar stools, where they have well kept Wadworths IPA and Henrys Original on handpump, and a good wine list with helpful notes and 14 wines by the glass; piped music and cribbage. From an ambitious (and expensive) menu, there might be bouillabaisse soup with rouille and croûtons (£4.50 small, £6.50 large), crab and mussel thermidor (£7), foie gras terrine with pickled grapes and monbazillac jelly (£8.25), braised navarin of lamb or confit of smoked streaky bacon with mustard lentils (£15.50), poached lemon sole véronique with scottish cockles (£15.75), rare breed rib-eye steak with béarnaise sauce (£16), roast saddle of local venison with shallot tarte tatin (£16.50), and puddings such as warm chocolate cake or vanilla panna cotta with spiced pineapple (£5.25); attentive service. You can also sit out at picnic-sets on the gravel courtyard behind. *(Recommended by Michael Cooper, Lyn Huxtable, Richard Seers, Joyce and Maurice Cottrell, Mr and Mrs A H Young, Richard Stancomb, Paul Williams, John Kane, Derek Thomas, John and Hazel Williams, Frank Willy, Mary Rayner, Tim and Suzy Bower, Richard Wyld, Michael Dallas, Karen and Graham Oddey)*

Wadworths ~ Tenants Michael and Sarah Bedford ~ Real ale ~ Bar food (not Sun evening or Mon) ~ Restaurant ~ (01666) 502206 ~ Children in restaurant only ~ Dogs welcome ~ Open 11-3, 6.30(7 winter)-11; 12-3 Sun; closed Sun evening, all day Mon; around 2 weeks over Christmas and New Year

TODENHAM SP2436 Map 4

Farriers Arms ♀ ◀

Between A3400 and A429 N of Moreton-in-Marsh

A little off the beaten track, this is a lovely little pub with friendly, courteous staff. There are nice wonky white plastered walls, hops on the beams, fine old polished flagstones by the stone bar counter and a woodburner in a huge inglenook fireplace. A tiny little room off to the side is full of old books and interesting old photographs. Enjoyable bar food includes home-made soup, goats cheese and red onion tart or home-made chicken liver parfait (£5), filled baguettes (from £5.50), home-made lamb burger (£6.50), home-made steak and ale pie (£8), daily specials such as braised steak in ale pie (£9), roast chicken breast on wild mushrooms with madeira sauce or roast vegetable and goats cheese cannelloni with pesto and parmesan glaze (£10), whole grilled lemon sole with tiger prawns (£12), and seared scallops (£13), and puddings such as banoffi pie, Baileys crème brûlée or poached pear in a brandy snap basket (£4); the restaurant is no smoking. Hook Norton Best, and a couple of guests such as Archers Golden or Wye Valley St George's are well kept on handpump, and they've ten wines by the glass; cribbage, dominoes, darts, board games and aunt sally. The pub has fine views over the surrounding countryside from the back garden, and there are a couple of tables with views of the church on a small terrace by the quiet little road. *(Recommended by Lloyd Moon, WAH, Mike and Mary Carter, H O Dickinson, Pat and Roger Fereday, Rod and Chris Pring, Lawrence Pearse, R Huggins, D Irving, E McCall, T McLean, R K Phillips, John Kane, Mr and Mrs P R Thomas, Ian and Nita Cooper)*

Free house ~ Licensees Thomas Young and Charlotte Bishop ~ Real ale ~ Bar food ~ Restaurant ~ (01608) 650901 ~ Children in eating area of bar and restaurant ~ Dogs allowed in bar ~ Open 12-3, 6.30-11; 12-3, 7-10.30 Sun

UPPER ODDINGTON SP2225 Map 4

Horse & Groom ♀

Village signposted from A436 E of Stow-on-the-Wold

Since the present licensees took over, this attractive 16th-c inn has been redecorated throughout and the bedrooms have been refurbished in a cottagey style. The bar has pale polished flagstones, a handsome antique oak box settle among other more modern seats, dark oak beams in the ochre ceiling, stripped stone walls, and an inglenook fireplace. Well kept Hook Norton Best and Wye Valley Butty Bach and Hereford Pale Ale on handpump, and 11 wines by the glass. From a seasonally changing menu backed up by daily specials, the lunchtime choices might include sandwiches (from £5.95; minute steak ciabatta with onion, mushrooms and chips £9.75), wild mushroom risotto (£5.75; main course £10.50), seared tuna niçoise (£6.25; main course £11.50), trio of sausages with chive mash and caramelised onion gravy or home-cooked ham and free-range eggs (£9.50), and beer battered cod with home-made tartare sauce (£10.75); in the evening there might be home-made soup (£4.75), smoked haddock pâté (£5.75), thai spiced crab and salmon fishcakes (£6.50), open tart of chargrilled vegetables (£11), braised lamb shoulder wrapped in leeks with puy lentils (£12.75), and hand cut steaks from Hereford herds (from £16), with home-made puddings like warm chocolate brownie with vanilla bean ice-cream and chocolate sauce, iced praline parfait with orange syrup or banana bavarois with caramel ice-cream and coconut crème anglaise (from £5). Sunday roasts (from £9.75); the restaurant is no smoking. There are seats on the terrace and in the pretty garden where there are grape vines bounded by dry-stone walls and cottages. *(Recommended by Bernard Stradling, Mr and Mrs J Brown, Stuart Turner, Dr and Mrs James Harris, Michael G Butler, Sir Nigel Foulkes, Mr and Mrs Martin Joyce, Gaynor Gregory, Rod Stoneman, Martin and Pauline Jennings, KC, Drs M J and P M Cox, Karen and Graham Oddey)*

Free house ~ Licensees Simon and Sally Jackson ~ Real ale ~ Bar food ~ Restaurant ~ (01451) 830584 ~ Children in eating area of bar and restaurant ~ Open 12-3.30, 5.30-11; 12-11 Sat; 12-10.30 Sun; closed 25 Dec ~ Bedrooms: £64S/£69S(£79B)

WINCHCOMBE SP0228 Map 4
White Hart ♀ 🛏
High Street (B4632)

On Friday and Sunday lunchtimes they do a popular smorgasbord buffet for £14.95 in this interesting place (more café-bar than pub), as the landlady and most of the staff are Swedish. Otherwise, big plates of well prepared food might include a delicious scandinavian seafood platter (£6.95), meatballs in creamy sauce (£8.95), and smorgasbord platter (£10.95), alongside more traditional lunchtime bar snacks such as ploughman's (from £4.95), baguettes (£5.95), and home-made burger (£7.75), and other dishes such as chargrilled steaks (from £10.95), duckling breast with balsamic red wine (£15.25), halibut steak with creamy mash and rich lobster sauce (£15.95), with puddings such as apple and cinnamon cheesecake (£4.95). The main area has mate's chairs, dining chairs and small pine settles around pine tables (candlelit at night), cream walls, and what amounts to a wall of big windows giving on to the village street. The smaller no smoking restaurant has its furniture painted in typical Swedish pale blue-grey with floor matting; the downstairs Stables Bar and pizzeria has old oak beams, stripped stone above the panelled dado, and pews and brightly coloured tables (open weekday evenings from 5pm, except Mon, and all day Saturday and Sunday, from £5.25). Well kept Greene King IPA and Old Speckled Hen, Wadworths 6X and a changing guest such as Whittingtons Cats Whiskers on handpump, and a good choice of wines by the glass – brought to your table unless you're sitting at the big copper-topped counter. There's a good mix of all ages, and an enjoyably relaxed atmosphere; daily papers, laid-back piped music. The back car park is rather small. *(Recommended by Guy Vowles, Roy and Lindsey Fentiman, Mr and Mrs D Renwick, Richard and Jean Phillips, Martin and Pauline Jennings, Neil and Anita Christopher, JMC, Karen and Graham Oddey)*

Enterprise ~ Lease Nicole Burr ~ Real ale ~ Bar food (all day) ~ Restaurant ~ (01242) 602359 ~ Children welcome ~ Dogs allowed in bar and bedrooms ~ May have live music during Cheltenham Races ~ Open 10-11; 11-10.30 Sun; closed 25 Dec ~ Bedrooms: £65S(£75B)/£75S(£85B)

LUCKY DIP

Besides the fully inspected pubs, you might like to try these Lucky Dips recommended to us and described by readers (if you do, please send us reports: www.goodguides.co.uk).

ALDERTON [SP0033]
☆ *Gardeners Arms* [Beckford Rd, off B4077 Tewkesbury—Stow]: Thatched Tudor pub with decent food from filled baps and baked potatoes to bistro dishes and fresh fish, well kept Greene King and guest beers, above-average wines, hospitable landlady and good service, log fire; piped music (turned down on request); dogs and children welcome, tables on sheltered terrace, well kept garden with boules *(LYM, Peter Coxon, Geoff Pidoux, David Eberlin)*

ALDSWORTH [SP1510]
☆ *Sherborne Arms* [B4425 Burford—Cirencester]: Cheerful extended wayside pub with wide choice of quickly served good generous food from baked potatoes and ploughman's up esp fish, friendly service, well kept Greene King IPA, Abbot and Ruddles County, farm cider, log fire, beams, some stripped stone, smallish bar, big dining area and attractive no smoking conservatory; games area with darts, lots of board games, fruit machine, piped music; dogs welcomed kindly, pleasant front garden, lavatory for disabled

(Joyce and Geoff Robson, David Gunn, P and J Shapley, R Huggins, D Irving, E McCall, T McLean, BB, Sheila Brooks, John and Hazel Williams)

AMBERLEY [SO8401]
Black Horse [off A46 Stroud—Nailsworth; Littleworth]: Cheerful local with spectacular views, open fire, interesting murals, conservatory, large no smoking family area on left and games room; has had well kept changing ales such as Archers, farm cider, good wines and attractively priced usual food inc midweek bargains, and been open all day on summer wknds, but changed hands spring 2005 – reports on new regime please; tables on back terrace with barbecue and spit roast area, more on lawn *(LYM)*

ANDOVERSFORD [SP0219]
☆ *Royal Oak* [signed just off A40; Gloucester Rd]: Cosy, attractive and warmly welcoming beamed village pub, lots of stripped stone, nice galleried raised dining room beyond big central open fire, well kept ales inc Hook Norton Best, good reasonably priced food using much local produce inc good value light

meals, prompt obliging service; popular quiz night, tables in garden *(Dr and Mrs James Stewart, Mr and Mrs I and E Bell, BB, Mr and Mrs D Renwick, Derek and Sylvia Stephenson, Brian McBurnie)*

ARLINGHAM [SO7011]

☆ *Old Passage* [Passage Rd]: Upmarket restaurant rather than pub (they do keep a real ale, but you can't really go just for a drink – the serving counter is in the restaurant area), worth the wait for interesting choice of good food esp fish and seafood, friendly helpful staff, nice clean décor; beautiful setting, french windows to pleasant terrace and big garden extending down to River Severn *(BB, Guy Vowles, DM, Rod Stoneman, Dr A Y Drummond, Colin Morgan, Bernard Stradling)*

☆ *Red Lion*: Friendly beamed pub, good value generous fresh food (not Sun evening) from baguettes through familiar standards to unusual dishes, well kept ales such as Caledonian Deuchars IPA, Fullers London Pride and Greene King Ruddles, three ciders, good service, tiled and partly carpeted bar with big fireplace, comfortable button-back seats in no smoking dining lounge on left, steps to small dining room beyond, photographs, paintings (some for sale) and a few rustic implements on uncluttered soft green or terracotta walls, pool room on right, skittle alley; picnic-sets in small courtyard, not far from Severn estuary walks, bedrooms, open all day wknds, cl Tues lunchtime and Mon *(Neil and Anita Christopher, Dr and Mrs C W Thomas, Mrs G P Hall, John and Gloria Isaacs, Dr A Y Drummond)*

AUST [ST5789]

☆ *Boars Head* [½ mile from M48 junction 1, off Avonmouth rd]: Friendly ivy-covered motorway break with wide choice of reasonably priced piping hot food, good helpings and quick service, well kept real ales, good house wines, nice mix of old furnishings in rambling series of linked rooms and alcoves, beams and some stripped stone, huge log fire; piped music; children in partly no smoking eating area away from bar, dogs on lead in bar, pretty sheltered garden *(LYM, Colin Moore, John and Enid Morris, Meg and Colin Hamilton)*

AVENING [ST8898]

Bell [High St]: Comfortable two-bar country local with beams, brasses and stripped stone, good value generous food, well kept Smiles Original, Wickwar BOB and Youngs, courteous service, real fire, one room no smoking *(R Huggins, D Irving, E McCall, T McLean)*

AYLBURTON [SO6101]

Cross [High St]: Decent choice of good food, well kept ales such as Flowers IPA, Greene King Abbot, Tetleys, Wadworths 6X and Worthington, welcoming obliging staff, light and airy open-plan layout with flagstone floors and spruce décor; disabled access and facilities, picnic-sets in pleasant orchard garden *(Ian Phillips)*

BERKELEY [ST6899]

Mariners Arms [Salter St; bottom of main rd through village]: Friendly beamed 15th-c pub, long and low, with well kept Bass, good value home-made food from sandwiches, baps and panini to plenty of hot dishes, interesting photographs, skittle alley; tables outside *(Dr A Y Drummond)*

BIBURY [SP1106]

Catherine Wheel [Arlington; B4425 NE of Cirencester]: Open-plan main bar and smaller back rooms, low beams, stripped stone, good log fires, well kept Adnams and Wadworths 6X, reasonably priced food from sandwiches up, traditional games, no smoking raftered dining room; picnic-sets in attractive and spacious garden with play area, famously beautiful village, handy for country and riverside walks (can be busy in summer); children welcome, picnic-sets out behind, open all day *(Geoff Pidoux, Gloria Bax, LYM, Joyce and Geoff Robson, Geoff and Jen)*

☆ *Swan* [B4425]: Hotel in lovely spot facing River Coln, comfortable and attractive side bar used by locals with well kept Hook Norton Best and Wickwar Cotswold Way, exemplary bar stools, coal fire and long mural of jazz garden party, nice modern adjoining brasserie with enjoyable up-to-date food, good service, smart formal dining room; teak tables out on heated flagstoned terrace, pleasant waterside garden, luxurious bedrooms *(David J Austin, Guy Vowles, R Huggins, D Irving, E McCall, T McLean, BB)*

BIRDLIP [SO9316]

Air Balloon [A417/A436 roundabout]: Much extended and recently comfortably reworked chain dining pub, now all no smoking, standard value food all day, Adnams Best and Caledonian Deuchars IPA, friendly young staff, many levels and alcoves, pubbier front corner with open fire, beams and stripped stone; unobtrusive piped music; tables, some covered, on heated terrace and in garden with play area, open all day *(Mr and Mrs I and E Bell, Mr and Mrs G S Ayrton, Paul and Shirley White, R Huggins, D Irving, E McCall, T McLean, Tim and Ann Newell)*

BLOCKLEY [SP1634]

☆ *Great Western Arms* [Station Rd (B4479)]: Comfortably up-to-date lounge/dining room, cheery landlord, wide choice of quickly served good value home-made pub food from substantial sandwiches and soups up, three well kept Hook Norton ales, no piped music, busy public bar with games room; attractive village, lovely valley view *(Paul and Sue Merrick, B M Eldridge)*

BOURTON-ON-THE-WATER [SP1620]

Duke of Wellington [Sherbourne St]: Large stone-built pub, open-plan carpeted bar with rustic furniture, back dining room, well kept Hook Norton, log fire; garden, bedrooms *(Ted George)*

Kingsbridge Inn [Riverside]: Roomy open-plan pub recently extensively reworked, neat and tidy, with emphasis on enjoyable food (may be a wait for a table in summer), quick friendly service, well kept real ales; pleasant village/river view from terrace tables (Ted George)

Mousetrap [Lansdown, W edge]: Small comfortable stone pub with well kept Hook Norton and Wadworths 6X in long narrow partly beamed bar, good generous food inc imaginative dishes and particularly good steaks in separate attractive kitchen-style dining area, attentive friendly service, welcoming fire; picnic-sets out in front, bedrooms (Lynn Nisbet, Monica Cockburn, Mike Jefferies)

BOX [SO8500]

☆ *Halfway Inn* [edge of Minchinhampton Common, off A46 via Amberley; OS Sheet 162 map ref 856003]: Light and airy open-plan bars with sturdy wooden furnishings on stripped wood floors, good interesting food, charming young friendly staff, well kept Greene King IPA, Smiles and a couple of guest beers, decent wines, woodburner, splendid new lavatories; piped music, fruit machine; children welcome in dining area and no smoking restaurant, tables in landscaped garden, cl Mon, open all day summer (Bernard Stradling, Tom and Ruth Rees, LYM, R Huggins, D Irving, E McCall, T McLean, Michael Doswell)

BROAD CAMPDEN [SP1537]

☆ *Bakers Arms* [off B4081]: Chatty and relaxed traditional pub with inglenook in snug beamed and stripped stone bar, well kept ales such as Donnington BB, Hook Norton Best, Stanway Stanney, Charles Wells Bombardier, traditional games, straightforward bar food (all day in summer) from lunchtime sandwiches and baguettes up, no smoking beamed and stripped stone dining room; no credit cards; children in eating areas, tables out on terrace and garden behind with play area, open all day wknds and summer (DC, Ann and Colin Hunt, Lawrence Pearse, Tracey and Stephen Groves, Peter and Anne Hollindale, Di and Mike Gillam, H O Dickinson, Paul and Shirley White, LYM)

BROADWELL [SP2027]

☆ *Fox* [off A429 2 miles N of Stow-on-the-Wold]: Relaxing pub overlooking broad green in pleasant village, welcoming attentive service, good range of homely food (not Sun evening) from baguettes to popular Sun lunch, good fresh veg, well kept low-priced Donnington BB and SBA, Addlestone's cider, decent wines, good summer lemonade, nice coffee, cosy local feel, stripped stone and flagstones, beams hung with jugs, log fire, darts, dominoes and chess, plain public bar with pool room extension, pleasant separate restaurant; may be piped music; tables out on gravel, good big back family-friendly garden with aunt sally, meadow behind for Caravan Club members (Angus Lyon, David A Hammond, M and J Lindsay, Geoff Calcott, Mrs N W Neill, Alun Evans, Martin and Karen Wake, Roger and Maureen Kenning, BB, Lawrence Pearse, Bob Ellis)

BROCKWEIR [SO5301]

Brockweir Inn [signed just off A466

Chepstow—Monmouth]: Unpretentious local in Wye Valley well placed for walkers (no muddy boots), beams and stripped stonework, quarry tiles, sturdy settles, woodburner, snugger carpeted alcoves with brocaded seats, country décor, well kept Adnams, Bass, Hook Norton Best, Smiles and Worthington BB, Stowford Press cider, friendly landlord, upstairs restaurant, conservatory; pool, machines and piped music in public bar; dogs allowed, children in eating area, small garden with interesting covered terrace; open all day Sat, bedrooms (Bob and Margaret Holder, LYM)

CERNEY WICK [SU0796]

Crown: Roomy modern lounge bar, comfortable conservatory extension, enjoyable reasonably priced popular food inc good Sun roasts, well kept real ales, coal-effect gas fires; unobtrusive piped music, public bar with pool, darts, fruit machine; children welcome, good-sized garden with swings, small motel-style bedroom extension (R Huggins, D Irving, E McCall, T McLean, BB)

CHACELEY [SO8530]

☆ *Old Ferry* [Stock Lane]: Spacious river-view dining-room in remote and rambling country pub down long lane, good choice of reasonably priced food, decent wine list, friendly staff, various different bar areas inc 16th-c core with log fire, restaurant, big games area with pool and juke box; attractive waterside lawns, moorings on Severn; prone to flooding which can close it for long periods (BB, Stuart Fox)

CHARLTON KINGS [SO9620]

Merry Fellow [School Rd/Church St]: Family local with Banks's, Wadworths IPA and 6X and a guest beer, Stowford Press farm cider, good value good food inc good Sun roast; open all day, terrace tables (Mr and Mrs M Clark)

Ryeworth Inn [Ryeworth Rd]: Friendly town pub with Goffs Jouster, Greene King Old Speckled Hen and Hook Norton, decent wines, good value home-made food (Mr and Mrs M Clark)

CHEDWORTH [SP0609]

☆ *Hare & Hounds* [Fosse Cross – A429 N of Cirencester, some way from village]: Good inventive food in rambling stone-built dining pub interestingly furnished with modern touches, soft lighting, cosy corners and little side rooms, two big log fires, small conservatory; well kept Arkells 2B, 3B and Kingsdown, good house wines, cheerful helpful service; children welcome away from bar, disabled facilities, open all day Fri-Sun (LYM, Peter and Audrey Dowsett, Rod Stoneman, R Huggins, D Irving, E McCall, T McLean)

CHELTENHAM [SO9421]

Jolly Brewmaster [Painswick Rd]: Open-plan linked areas around circular serving bar, good range of ales such as Archers, Caledonian Deuchars IPA, Donnington SBA and Hook Norton Best, lunchtime food; can get smoky of an evening (Guy Vowles)

Kemble Brewery [Fairview St]: Small backstreet local with well kept Smiles Best, Timothy Taylors Landlord and Youngs, friendly atmosphere and charming Irish landlady, good value robust lunchtime food; small back garden *(Joe Green, Guy Vowles)*

Restoration [High St]: Long rambling 16th-c pub, much restored, with lots of beams and dim-lit bric-a-brac, simple wooden furniture, good bustling atmosphere, well kept real ales, good coffee, raised dining area with decent food inc two-for-one bargains, friendly young staff; very convenient for the two main shopping arcades *(Klaus and Elizabeth Leist)*

CHIPPING CAMPDEN [SP1539]

☆ *Lygon Arms* [High St]: Comfortable stripped-stone bar with welcoming landlord and helpful staff, very wide choice of enjoyable reasonably priced food till late evening inc interesting dishes, well kept Badger ales, lots of horse pictures, open fires, small back dining room, raftered evening restaurant beyond shady courtyard with tables; children welcome, open all day exc winter wkdys, comfortable well equipped beamed bedrooms, good breakfast *(Gene and Kitty Rankin, Peter Coxon, LYM, Roger Huggins, Tom and Alex McLean)*

CIRENCESTER [SP0103]

Drillmans Arms [Gloucester Rd, Stratton]: Popular old two-room local, warm and relaxing, with low beams, good log fires, well kept Archers and guests such as Moles and Wickwar, reasonable food, lots of wknd bar nibbles, skittle alley doubling as eating area; tables out by small car park *(R Huggins, D Irving, E McCall, T McLean)*

Fleece [Market Pl]: Substantial old hotel, good choice of food in bar from baguettes to scampi and baked potatoes, terrace dining area available from bar or substantial restaurant; bedrooms *(Craig Turnbull, BB)*

☆ *Somewhere Else* [Castle St]: Two simple modern rooms with pale wood café furniture and high stools, well kept Youngs, good wine choice and espresso machine, cheerful staff (wearing shorts even in winter), quickly served up-to-date food from drinks nibbles up, separate games room off with pool, quite a lively pub mood evenings – seems popular for ladies' nights out; piped pop music; lots of tables on heated back terrace *(Joyce and Maurice Cottrell, BB, R Huggins, D Irving, E McCall, T McLean)*

☆ *Twelve Bells* [Lewis Lane]: Cheery backstreet pub with particularly well kept Abbey Bellringer and enterprising choice of five quickly changing beers, forthright hard-working landlord, good generous fresh food inc local produce and some unusual dishes lunchtime and early evening (may be goose around Christmas), small old-fashioned low-ceilinged three-roomed bar, small back dining area with sturdy pine tables and rugs on quarry tiles, good coal fires, pictures for sale, clay pipe collection; can get smoky, piped music may be loud; small sheltered back terrace with fountain *(R Huggins, D Irving, E McCall, T McLean, Ian and Nita Cooper, BB, Phil and Sally Gorton, Mike Pugh, R Michael Richards, Pete Baker, Joyce and Maurice Cottrell)*

Waggon & Horses [London Rd]: Accommodating stone-built pub with comfortably cottagey L-shaped bar, lots of bric-a-brac, well kept ales such as Caledonian Deuchars IPA, Fullers London Pride and Hook Norton, back dining room with enjoyable food lunchtime and evening *(R Huggins, D Irving, E McCall, T McLean)*

Woodbine [Chesterton Lane]: Pleasant stone-built local with compact panelled snug, Shepherd Neame Spitfire and Wychwood Hobgoblin, decent low-priced food, big bar with corner pool and machines *(R Huggins, D Irving, E McCall, T McLean)*

CLEARWELL [SO5708]

Lamb [off B4228; The Cross]: Old settles in cosy snug, larger high-ceilinged divided bar, three well kept ales from small breweries such as Freeminer tapped from the cask; cl Mon/Tues and lunchtimes Weds/Thurs, friendly service *(Pete Baker)*

CLEEVE HILL [SO9826]

Rising Sun [B4632]: Splendid view over Cheltenham to the Malvern Hills from the conservatory, terrace and lawn, esp as the evening lights come on; decent food from panini to bass and salmon, friendly staff, Greene King beers, large carpeted bar with piped radio and big-screen TV one end, lower eating area the other end, restaurant beyond *(Neil and Anita Christopher)*

CLIFFORD'S MESNE [SO6922]

☆ *Yew Tree* [out of Newent, past Falconry Centre]: On slopes of May Hill (NT), large open-plan divided area emphasising good enterprising meals (all day Sun), well kept RCH Pitchfork and Shepherd Neame Spitfire, good house wines; children welcome, tables out on sunny terrace, play area; two bedrooms with own bathrooms *(J E Shackleton, J P Duke)*

COALEY [SO7701]

Fox & Hounds [The Street]: Long bar with reasonably priced food, well kept Clarkes, Uley and interesting guest beers, back skittles alley *(R Huggins, D Irving, E McCall, T McLean)*

COATES [SO9600]

☆ *Tunnel House* [follow Tarleton signs (right then left) from village, pub up rough track on right after rly bridge; OS Sheet 163 map ref 965005]: Rambling country pub with beams and flagstones in idiosyncratic original bar, homely mix of chairs and settees, all sorts of unlikely bric-a-brac and memorabilia, log fire, more conventional pastel-décor eating extension and back conservatory (fills quickly), well kept ales such as Archers, Wickwar Cotswold Way and Wye Valley, Stowford Press cider, enjoyable if not cheap food from sandwiches to interesting blackboard dishes, quick friendly service, amiable ambling black labrador; juke box, smoking allowed throughout; children and dogs welcome (play area and nice walled-in kids' lawn outside, too), impressive views from tables on pleasant terrace, big garden sloping down to former canal (under slow restoration), Sunday barbecues, good walks *(Mike and Mary Carter,*

Mr and Mrs G S Ayrton, Mike and
Lynn Robinson, R Huggins, D Irving,
E McCall, T McLean, Neil and
Anita Christopher, Guy Vowles, John and
Fiona McIlwain, LYM, David A Hammond,
Julia and Richard Tredgett, Theocsbrian)

COLD ASTON [SP1219]

☆ *Plough* [aka Aston Blank; off A436 (B4068) or
A429 SW of Stow-on-the-Wold]: Tiny 17th-c
village pub, low black beams and flagstones,
old-fashioned simple furnishings, friendly
service and locals, log fire, well kept low-priced
Donnington BB, Hook Norton Best and a
guest beer, tables set for good value usual food
from baguettes up; piped music; well behaved
children welcome, picnic-sets under cocktail
parasols on small side terraces, good walks,
has been cl Mon (*R Huggins, D Irving,
E McCall, T McLean, Guy Vowles, LYM,
A G Marx, Lawrence Pearse*)

COLEFORD [SO5813]

☆ *Dog & Muffler* [Joyford, best approached from
Christchurch 5-ways junction B4432/B4428,
by church – B4432 towards Broadwell, then
follow signpost; also signposted from the Berry
Hill post office cross-roads; beyond the hamlet
itself, bear right and keep your eyes skinned]:
Very prettily set 17th-c pub doing well under
new owners, cosy original beamed bar with
log-effect gas fire in big fireplace, beamed and
flagstoned back extension with bright
conservatory restaurant and verandah, good
food from sandwiches and baguettes up, well
kept Sam Smiths and local Freeminers
Speculation, cheerful helpful service; children
welcome, well spaced picnic-sets in large
attractive sheltered garden with lovely views
and good segregated play area, good value
bedrooms, nice walks (*LYM, Mrs Sheela Curtis*)

COLESBOURNE [SO9913]

Colesbourne Inn [A435 Cirencester—
Cheltenham]: 18th-c grey stone gabled
coaching inn reopened 2005 under new
management, beams, partly panelled dark red
walls, log fires, soft lighting, comfortable mix
of settles and softly padded seats, well kept
Wadworths IPA and 6X, good wine list, food
in bar and separate no smoking candlelit
dining room, traditional games; piped music;
dogs welcome, views from attractive back
garden and terrace, nice bedrooms in converted
stable block (*LYM, R Huggins, D Irving,
E McCall, T McLean*)

COLN ST ALDWYNS [SP1405]

☆ *New Inn* [back road Bibury—Fairford; Main
St]: Smart inn in peaceful village, two
attractively furnished main bar rooms with
central log fire, low beams and some stripped
stonework, lighted kitchen range in further
room, well kept ales such as Archers Village,
Hook Norton Best and Wadworths 6X, good
wines by the glass, food (not cheap) inc
lunchtime sandwiches, no smoking restaurant;
provision for children and dogs, plenty of seats
on split-level terrace, bedrooms, open all day
(*Peter and Giff Bennett, Claire George,
David Rule, James Morrell, George and
Gill Peckham, Derek Thomas, LYM,*

A G Marx, Lawrence Pearse, Joyce and
Geoff Robson, Karen and Graham Oddey)

COMPTON ABDALE [SP0616]

☆ *Puesdown Inn* [A40 outside village]: Stylish
and comfortably upmarket, with extensive
series of linked bar areas, leather or brightly
upholstered sofas and armchairs, log fire and
woodburner, big art posters, bare boards,
bright rugs and rafter-effect ceilings, cream and
dark red walls, mainly stripped stone in
extensive no smoking eating areas, wide choice
of good imaginative food using local supplies
from panini up, neat staff, Hook Norton Best
and Old Hooky, decent wines by the glass,
espresso machine, well reproduced piped
music, friendly chocolate labradors; nice
garden behind, bedrooms (*Guy Vowles,
Jo Rees, BB, Ned Kelly*)

COOMBE HILL [SO8926]

Gloucester Old Spot [Elmstone Hardwicke;
A4019 nr M5 junction 10]: Rustic mix of plain
furnishings in four linked areas and adjoining
barn (bargain big evening and wknd meals
here), well kept ales such as Boddingtons and
Timothy Taylors Landlord, good farm ciders,
good value bar lunches, log fire (*Guy Vowles,
Mike and Mary Clark*)

CRANHAM [SO8912]

☆ *Black Horse* [off A46 and B4070 N of Stroud]:
Well worn in 17th-c pub with good log fire
and high-backed wall settles in quarry-tiled
public bar, cosy little lounge, well kept Archers
and other ales such as Wickwar, massively
generous home cooking (not Sun evening) from
good sandwiches and omelettes using their
own free-range eggs to fish and duck, cheaper
small helpings, shove-ha'penny, a couple of
pub dogs, no smoking upstairs dining rooms;
piped music; children welcome (*Pete Baker,
Andrew Shore, Maria Williams, Di and
Mike Gillam, LYM*)

DYMOCK [SO6931]

Beauchamp Arms: Friendly parish-owned pub
with well kept local Whittingtons ales,
interesting range of good value food,
welcoming obliging staff; small pleasant garden
with pond, recently refurbished bedrooms,
handy for Daffodil Trail walkers, cl Mon
lunchtime (*Edna and Ron Holker, Martin and
Pauline Jennings*)

EBRINGTON [SP1840]

Ebrington Arms [off B4035 E of Chipping
Campden or A429 N of Moreton-in-Marsh]:
Well refurbished village pub handy for Hidcote
and Kiftsgate, lively low-beamed bar, stripped
stone, flagstones and inglenooks, attractive
dining room with enjoyable food, well kept
Donnington SBA, Hook Norton Best and
Charles Wells Bombardier, sensible wine range;
no dogs at meal times; children welcome,
picnic-sets on pleasant sheltered terrace, good
play area, bedrooms (*LYM, Barry and
Anne, Therese Flanagan*)

ELKSTONE [SO9610]

☆ *Highwayman* [Beechpike; off northbound
A417 6 miles N of Cirencester]: Rambling and
relaxing 16th-c warren of low beams, stripped
stone, cosy alcoves, antique settles, armchairs

and sofa among more usual furnishings, big log fires, rustic decorations, welcoming staff, well kept Arkells ales, good house wines, wide choice of sensibly priced food, big back eating area; may be quiet piped music; disabled access, good family room, outside play area *(the Didler, Paul and Shirley White, John and Claire Pettifer, LYM)*

FORTHAMPTON [SO8731]

Lower Lode Inn: Brick-built Tudor pub with moorings on River Severn and plenty of waterside tables (prone to winter flooding – hence the stilts for nearby caravan park), flagstones, enormous log fire and traditional seating, enjoyable usual pubby food, friendly helpful landlady, well kept ales such as Donnington, Goffs and Wickwar, back pool room and juke box; children and dogs welcome (swarms with holiday families in summer), good value bedrooms with good breakfast, cl Sun lunchtime and winter Mon to Tues lunchtime *(Gillian and Kenneth Green)*

FOSSEBRIDGE [SP0711]

Fossebridge Inn [A429 Cirencester—Stow-on-the-Wold]: Handsome Georgian inn looking up under new management, much older two-room bar at the back, beams, arches and stripped stone, pleasant old-fashioned furnishings with more modern side area, tasty food from baguettes up here or in dining area, well kept Hook Norton; children welcome, tables out on streamside terrace and spacious lawn, comfortable bedrooms *(LYM, Giles and Annie Francis, Andrew Barker, Claire Jenkins)*

FRAMPTON MANSELL [SO9202]

☆ *Crown* [brown sign to pub off A491 Cirencester—Stroud]: Emphasis on food, with some good unusual dishes from sandwiches up, well kept Courage Best and a guest beer, good choice of wines by the glass, nice atmosphere in heavy-beamed bar with two log fires, stripped stone and rugs on bare boards, friendly attentive staff, daily papers, turkey-carpeted restaurant; piped music; picnic-sets in sunny front garden with terrace and pretty views over village and steep wooded valley, decent bedrooms, good breakfast *(R Huggins, D Irving, E McCall, T McLean, LYM, Gerald Wilkinson, David Whiter)*

FRAMPTON ON SEVERN [SO7407]

Bell [The Green]: Recently refurbished Georgian dining pub by huge village cricket green, well kept real ales inc Bass and interesting guests, decent food, friendly service, log fire and plush seats, steps up to pleasantly decorated family restaurant, separate locals' bar; good small back play area, bedrooms, open all day *(Mrs Ann Gray, Mrs Pamela Fisher, Peter Neate)*

Three Horseshoes [The Green]: Cosy little unpretentious 18th-c pub overlooking splendid green, welcoming landlord, jolly atmosphere, lunchtime sandwiches and great ploughman's, well kept Adnams, Hook Norton Old Hooky and Uley, cracking farm cider, lounge/dining room opened for evening meals *(Mrs R J Gray, Tom Evans)*

FROCESTER [SO7831]

George [Peter St]: Traditional coaching inn owned by a village consortium, good choice of changing well kept ales, welcoming service, decent food choice, big but cosy main room with two log fires, daily papers, smaller no smoking room, large dining room on left; courtyard with boules, huge shuttered bedrooms *(R Huggins, D Irving, E McCall, T McLean)*

GLOUCESTER [SO8318]

☆ *Fountain* [Westgate St/Berkeley St]: Nice passageway entrance to friendly and civilised L-shaped bar, plush seats and built-in wall benches, charming helpful service, well kept ales such as Caledonian Deuchars IPA, Fullers London Pride, Greene King Abbot, Timothy Taylors Landlord and Wickwar BOB, good range of whiskies, attractive prints, handsome stone fireplace (pub dates from 17th c), log-effect gas fire; cheap usual food; tables in pleasant courtyard, good disabled access, handy for cathedral, open all day *(BB, Mike Pugh, Roger and Jenny Huggins, A and B D Craig, B M Eldridge)*

Golden Cross [Southgate St]: Ancient low-beamed pub with alcoves and uneven standing timbers, some bric-a-brac and unusual picture of the pub, decent lunchtime food, mainstream beers; more popular with young people at night *(Kevin Blake)*

New Inn [Northgate St]: Actually one of the city's oldest structures, lovely medieval building with galleried courtyard, restored in recent years as hotel, restaurant and pub, three bars with up to six often local real ales in one, Black Rat farm cider, enjoyable inexpensive lunchtime food inc popular carvery, coffee shop, restaurant; good value bedrooms, open all day (till 1.30 Thurs-Sat) *(the Didler, Klaus and Elizabeth Leist, Theocsbrian)*

Royal Oak [Hucclecote Rd, Hucclecote; quite handy for M5 junction 11A]: Popular open-plan pub with traditional décor, well kept ales inc bargain Flowers, food inc bargain Sun roasts, pleasant staff, no smoking dining area in lounge; live entertainment Fri, Sun quiz night; plenty of picnic-sets on big lawns *(B M Eldridge)*

Union [Westgate St]: Biggish timbered city pub, well furnished, with helpful staff, good value pub food, Fullers London Pride, no smoking area *(Geoff Pidoux)*

GOTHERINGTON [SO9629]

Shutter [off A435 N of Cheltenham; Shutter Lane]: Welcoming pub with good value pub lunches, well kept Adnams, Wadworths 6X and Wickwar Cotswold Way, decent house wines, good service; children welcome, disabled access, garden with good play area, by GWR private railway station, good walks *(Martin and Pauline Jennings, Eric George)*

GREAT BARRINGTON [SP2013]

☆ *Fox* [off A40 Burford—Northleach; pub towards Little Barrington]: 17th-c pub with stripped stone and simple country furnishings in low-ceilinged small bar, well kept Donnington BB and SBA, farm cider, friendly landlord, good choice of promptly served food (all day Sun and summer Sat, not Mon night in winter) from sandwiches to good seasonal pheasant casserole, river-view dining room in former skittle alley, traditional games; juke box, fruit machine, TV; children welcome, pleasant heated terrace by River Windrush (swans and private fishing), orchard with pond, open all day *(LYM, Suzanne Miles, James Woods, Pete Baker, Mrs S Wilkinson, Jim Abbott, the Didler, A G Marx, David Handforth)*

GREAT RISSINGTON [SP1917]

☆ *Lamb* [off A40 W of Burford, via Gt Barrington]: Partly 17th-c, with civilised two-room bar, well kept ales such as Hook Norton Best and Charles Wells Bombardier, decent wines, friendly staff, open fire, enjoyable food (can be a wait), darts, dominoes and cribbage, no smoking olde-worlde candlelit restaurant; may be piped music; children welcome, nice sheltered hillside garden, bedrooms *(LYM, Tom Evans, Mr and Mrs J Brown, David A Hammond, Suzanne Miles, James Woods, Tom Bottinga, Michael and Jenny Back, Guy Vowles, Lawrence Pearse)*

GREET [SP0230]

Harvest Home [Evesham Rd (B4078 by Winchcombe Station bridge)]: Well spaced tables, bay window seats, hop bines on beams, log fires, real ales such as Goffs Jouster, Greene King IPA and Old Speckled Hen, Tetleys and Charles Wells Bombardier, decent house wines, entertaining landlord, friendly attentive service, wide food choice inc good baguettes and wkdy OAP lunches, big beamed pitched-roof barn restaurant (no smoking); sizeable garden, not far from medieval Sudeley Castle and Winchcombe GWR station *(LYM, Dave Braisted, Eric George, B M Eldridge)*

GRETTON [SP0131]

☆ *Royal Oak* [off B4077 E of Tewkesbury]: Appealing upmarket pub with linked bare-boarded or flagstoned rooms, beams hung with tankards, hop bines and chamber-pots, interesting old motor-racing pictures, nice mixed bag of seats and tables, stripped country furnishings in no smoking dining conservatory, enjoyable food, well kept Goffs and a guest ale, decent wines; children and dogs welcome, fine views from flower-filled terrace, big pleasant garden with play area and tennis, GWR private railway runs past, good nearby walks, open all day summer wknds *(Brenda and Rob Fincham, Nick and Meriel Cox, LYM, Pat and Tony Martin, Annabel Viney, Ian and Celia Abbott, Bernard Stradling)*

HARDWICKE [SO7913]

Pilot [Sellars Rd, Sellars Bridge]: Superb canalside location, lock views from restaurant and conservatory, several linked bar areas, carpet and bare boards, well kept Bass and Caledonian Deuchars IPA, usual pub food freshly made from good range of filled rolls and baked potatoes up, efficient friendly service; piped music may obtrude; waterside garden with play area *(Neil and Anita Christopher)*

HAWKESBURY UPTON [ST7786]

☆ *Beaufort Arms* [High St]: Well kept Hook Norton, Wickwar BOB and guest beers, local farm cider, good soft drinks choice, friendly landlord and staff, good value home-made standard food in extended uncluttered no smoking dining lounge on right, darts in stripped-brick bare-boards bar, interesting local and brewery memorabilia, lots of pictures (some for sale), skittle alley; no cards; well behaved children welcome, disabled access and facilities, picnic-sets in pleasant smallish garden, on Cotswold Way *(CMW, JJW, Stan and Susan Fysh, Matthew Shackle, Roger and Jenny Huggins)*

HILLESLEY [ST7689]

Fleece [Hawkesbury Rd/Chapel Lane]: Attractive two-bar village pub with simple traditional furnishings, hearty and tasty food inc very popular Sun lunch, no smoking upper dining bar, well kept real ales, decent wines, friendly newish landlord; small village in lovely countryside nr Cotswold Way, simple bedrooms (own bathrooms planned) *(Brian Kneale)*

HINTON DYRHAM [ST7376]

☆ *Bull* [handy for M4 junction 18; A46 towards Bath, then first right]: Pretty 16th-c stone-built pub, two huge fireplaces, low beams and ancient flagstones, oak settles and pews, stripped stone back area with unusual cushioned cast-iron chairs, family room on the left, enjoyable food from good sandwiches up, well kept Wadworths IPA, 6X and a guest, no smoking restaurant; piped music; dogs and children till 7.30) welcome, plenty of picnic-sets and play equipment in sizeable sheltered upper garden, more on sunny front balcony; cl Mon lunchtime *(John and Joan Nash, Michael Cooper, Brian Root, Michael Doswell, LYM, Barry and Anne, Comus and Sarah Elliott, Nigel Long, Ian Moody, B and M Kendall, Martin and Karen Wake, Joyce and Geoff Robson)*

HORSLEY [ST8497]

☆ *Tipputs* [Tiltups End; A46 2 miles S of Nailsworth]: Spacious and friendly, with well kept Archers Golden and Greene King IPA, Abbot and Ruddles, good wines by the glass, enjoyable food all day from wide range of sandwiches and light dishes to interesting restaurant evening meals, efficient young staff, beams and stripped stone in L-shaped bar, big log fire, guitar duo some nights; lots of room outside, open all day *(Miss M W Hayter, David and Gill Hatton, Michael Doswell)*

KEMBLE [ST9897]

Thames Head [A433 Cirencester—Tetbury]: Stripped stone, timberwork, log fire, intriguing little front alcove (perhaps an ostler's lookout), softly lit cottagey no smoking back area with pews and log-effect gas fire in big fireplace, country-look dining room with another big gas fire, good value wines, Arkells 2B and 3B, helpful staff, skittle alley; TV; children welcome, tables outside, good value four-poster bedrooms, nice walk to nearby low-key source of River Thames *(David Edwards,*

R Huggins, D Irving, E McCall, T McLean, LYM)

KILCOT [SO6925]

Kilcot Inn [B4221, not far from M50 junction 3]: Attractively renovated and extended, with stripped beams, rustic bare brick, log fires, interesting natural modern natural wood furniture, well kept Greene King Old Speckled Hen and local Whittingtons ale, good value blackboard food in bar and no smoking eating area; dogs welcome, garden picnic-sets *(Neil and Jean Spink, Nigel Clifton)*

KILKENNY [SP0018]

☆ *Kilkeney Inn* [A436 W of Andoversford]: Spacious and reliable modernised dining pub with some more adventurous dishes and good puddings, well kept Bass and Hook Norton, good choice of wines by the glass, efficient friendly service, pleasant relaxed surroundings, log fire and comfortably light and airy no smoking conservatory; well behaved children allowed in eating areas, tables outside, attractive Cotswold views, open all day wknds *(LYM, Mrs T A Bizat, Joyce and Geoff Robson, Mr and Mrs J Brown, Guy Vowles, Mike and Mary Carter)*

KINETON [SP0926]

☆ *Halfway House* [signed from B4068 and B4077 W of Stow-on-the-Wold]: Unpretentious country local with helpful friendly licensees, baguettes and sensibly priced traditional hot dishes using local ingredients, well kept cheap Donnington BB and SBA from nearby brewery, decent wines, farm cider, pub games (and juke box), restaurant; no visiting dogs; children allowed lunchtime (can get very busy in school hols), attractive sheltered back garden, tables on narrow front terrace too, simple comfortable bedrooms, good walks *(LYM, A G Marx)*

KINGSCOTE [ST8196]

☆ *Hunters Hall* [A4135 Dursley—Tetbury]: Civilised dining pub with high Tudor beams and stripped stone in individually furnished linked rooms, some sofas and easy chairs, wide choice of food from lunchtime sandwiches (not Sunday) to steak, Greene King Abbot and Ruddles Best and Uley Hogs Head, cheerful if not always speedy service, no smoking area inc restaurant, good log fire in flagstoned back bar with games area, TV and juke box; children and dogs welcome, garden with good play area, bedrooms with own bathrooms, open all day *(R Huggins, D Irving, E McCall, T McLean, Peter and Audrey Dowsett, Meg and Colin Hamilton, Mrs Pat Crabb, Tom and Ruth Rees, Mr and Mrs E Barnes, Neil and Anita Christopher, LYM, Ken Marshall, Steve Godfrey, John and Marion Tyrie, Mr and Mrs M Stratton, Roger Wain-Heapy)*

LECHLADE [SU2199]

New Inn [Market Sq (A361)]: Imposing stone building with vast log fire in big pleasantly plain front lounge, very wide choice of good value generous food from good filled baguettes up, well kept changing ales such as Archers Best, Greene King Morlands Original and

Youngs Special, helpful staff, back restaurant; piped music, end games machine and TV; play area in big garden extending to Thames, good walks, 29 comfortable bedrooms *(Peter and Audrey Dowsett, Dr and Mrs A K Clarke, David Edwards, Ian Phillips)*

LEIGHTERTON [ST8290]

Royal Oak [off A46 S of Nailsworth]: Neatly kept old stone-built pub sensitively refurbished under new management, beams, log fires and mullioned windows, reasonably priced straightforward food from soup and sandwiches to good value roasts, well kept Butcombe, Wickwar BOB and a weekly guest beer, prompt pleasant service; piped music; nice garden, quiet village, good walks, quite handy for Westonbirt Arboretum *(Guy Vowles, Peter and Audrey Dowsett, J L Wedel)*

LONGFORD [SO8320]

Queens Head [Tewkesbury Rd (A38 just N of Gloucester)]: Attractive pub, partly timber-framed, with linked drinking and eating areas inc flagstoned bar and no smoking restaurant area, good value lunches (stop promptly at 2) from baguettes and baked potatoes up, slightly more upmarket evening meals, several well kept ales such as Black Sheep Best and Ringwood Best, pleasant efficient service, log fire *(Gill and Tony Morriss, Dr and Mrs A K Clarke, Tony Pope, Karen Bonham)*

LONGHOPE [SO6720]

Farmers Boy [Boxbush, Ross Rd; A40 outside village]: Unpretentious and busy two-room country pub with friendly licensees, well kept ales such as Boddingtons, Smiles Best and Theakstons, food inc popular two-in-one pies, OAP bargains Thurs, heavy beams, log fire; piped music, separate bar with big-screen TV and electric organ; pleasant garden and terrace, may be cl Mon-Thurs lunchtime in winter *(BB, Mike and Mary Carter)*

MARSHFIELD [ST7773]

☆ *Catherine Wheel* [High St; signed off A420 Bristol—Chippenham]: Stripped stone traditional pub with warm atmosphere, friendly staff, enjoyable food inc imaginative dishes and good choice of Sun roasts, wide range of well kept ales (they plan their own microbrewery), farm cider, decent wines, plates and prints, medley of settles, chairs and stripped tables, open fire in impressive fireplace, cottagey back family bar, charming no smoking Georgian dining room, darts, dominoes, no music or machines; flower-decked back yard, bedrooms, unspoilt village *(Dr and Mrs A K Clarke, LYM, John and Gloria Isaacs, Pamela and Merlyn Horswell, Nigel Long)*

Lord Nelson [A420 Bristol—Chippenham; High St]: Spacious range of sympathetically lightened up beamed rooms with wide choice of quickly served inexpensive food, well kept real ales, open fires, bistro restaurant, games bar with pool and machines; live music Sun afternoon; charming small courtyard, bedrooms in cottage annexe *(Dr and Mrs A K Clarke)*

MAYSHILL [ST6882]
New Inn [Badminton Rd (A432 Coalpit Heath—Yate)]: 17th-c coaching inn with two comfortably carpeted bar rooms leading to restaurant, enjoyable food, well kept ales such as Bass, Bath Gem and Wychwood Hobgoblin; garden with play area *(Roger and Jenny Huggins)*

MICKLETON [SP1543]
☆ *Kings Arms* [B4632 (ex A46)]: Relaxed and civilised open-plan family lounge, wide choice of good locally sourced food from well filled sandwiches up (best to book at wknds), good value OAP lunches, friendly well organised service, well kept Bass and Flowers, lots of good value wines by the glass, farm cider, nice mix of comfortable chairs, soft lighting, interesting homely décor, small log fire, no smoking area, small welcoming locals' bar with darts, dominoes and cribbage; piped music; tables outside, handy for Kiftsgate and Hidcote *(Clive and Fran Dutson, Martin and Pauline Jennings, Mrs B J Edwards, BB, John H Franklin, Andrew Barker, Claire Jenkins)*

MORETON-IN-MARSH [SP2032]
Inn on the Marsh [Stow Rd]: Reasonably priced food from baguettes, fishcakes, burgers and so forth to more restauranty dishes, distinctive unpretentious beamed bar with inglenook woodburner, comfortable armchairs and sofa, lots of pictures particularly ducks, well kept Mansfield and Marstons Bitter and Pedigree, attentive helpful landlord, smartly attractive modern candlelit dining conservatory; bedrooms *(Lynn Nisbet, Monica Cockburn, Mike Jefferies)*

☆ *Redesdale Arms* [High St]: Fine old coaching inn with prettily lit alcoves and big stone fireplace in solidly furnished comfortable panelled bar on right, well kept ales such as Courage Directors and Wye Valley, small but good wine list, cafetière coffee, interesting choice of generous food, good friendly service, log fires, spacious back child-friendly restaurant and dining conservatory, darts in flagstoned public bar; piped music, fruit machine, TV; tables out on heated floodlit courtyard decking, comfortable well equipped bedrooms beyond *(Peter Coxon, BB, Peter Gondris, B M Eldridge)*

Swan [High St]: Good choice of low-priced generous food inc Thurs OAP lunch, well kept Boddingtons and Wadworths 6X, decent wine, neat bright lounge with flowered wallpaper and old photographs, attractive separate dining room, quick friendly service even when coachloads roll in on Tues market day; bare-boards public bar on right (can be smoky) with darts, pool and machines *(Ted George, Mrs M Sands)*

NAILSWORTH [ST8499]
Britannia [Cossack Sq]: Much refurbished large open-plan bar with good range of real ales and good wines by the glass, some emphasis on restaurant side (locally very popular for its choice and quality), friendly efficient service *(Colin Moore)*

NAUNTON [SP1123]
Black Horse [off B4068 W of Stow]: Neat unspoilt black-beamed bar with stripped stone and log fire, straightforward though hardly cheap food from huge baguettes and baked potatoes up (can take a while when busy), pleasant staff, well priced Donnington BB and SBA, darts, cribbage, dominoes, no smoking dining room; piped music; children and dogs welcome, some tables outside, bedrooms with own bathrooms, charming village, fine Cotswold walks *(Martin and Pauline Jennings, Dr G and Mrs J Kelvin, A and B D Craig, Pete Baker, LYM, Monica Cockburn, Mike Jefferies)*

NORTH NIBLEY [ST7596]
New Inn [Waterley Bottom]: New licensees for this peacefully placed pub, well kept Bath Gem Bitter and SPA, Cotleigh Tawny and a guest beer from antique beer engines, short choice of bar food (not Mon/Tues, at least in the past), pleasantly pubby furnishings in partly stripped stone lounge bar, simple public bar with traditional games (and TV); children and dogs welcome, lots of tables on lawn with neat new covered terrace, open all day wknds, has been cl Mon lunchtime *(LYM, Neil and Lorna Mclaughlan)*

NORTHLEACH [SP1114]
☆ *Sherborne Arms* [Market Pl]: Neatly ranked tables stretching back from bare-boards bar on left, cosy lounge on right with wing armchairs and sofas around big stone fireplace, stripped stone restaurant area up a few steps beyond, interesting food using local meats and game, attentive staff, well kept ales such as Banks's Original, Greene King Old Speckled Hen and Shepherd Neame Spitfire, good wines and coffee served in colourful cups; piped pop music may obtrude; one or two picnic-sets out in front, bedrooms *(Claire Lymer, R Huggins, D Irving, E McCall, T McLean, W G Myatt, Gene and Kitty Rankin, BB)*

NYMPSFIELD [SO7900]
☆ *Rose & Crown* [The Cross; signed off B4066 Stroud—Dursley]: Bright well decorated stone-built dining pub under new management, generous food (served through Sun afternoon) from sandwiches, baguettes and baked potatoes to unusual restauranty dishes and things for children, well kept Bath Gem, Otter and Uley, decent wines, local farm cider, helpful friendly staff, daily papers, log fire, pine tables and bare boards in beamed front bar, pews and other seats in large no smoking back dining area; piped music and games machine may obtrude; children and dogs welcome, picnic-sets in side yard and on sheltered lawn with good play area, bedrooms adjacent, handy for Cotswold walks and Woodchester mansion and park (NT) *(Gordon Briggs, BB, Anne Morris, Jason Caulkin, Neil and Anita Christopher)*

OAKRIDGE LYNCH [SO9103]
☆ *Butchers Arms* [off Eastcombe—Bisley rd E of Stroud]: Unpretentious pub under new licensees, with enjoyable food (not Sun evening or Mon) from hot baguettes to steak, well kept

ales such as Archers Best, Greene King IPA and Abbot and Youngs, rambling partly stripped stone bar, three open fires, no smoking dining room; children welcome away from bar, tables on neat lawn overlooking valley, good walks by former Thames & Severn canal (LYM, Nick and Meriel Cox, Brian McBurnie, BB, Mr and Mrs P L Spencer, R Huggins, D Irving, E McCall, T McLean)

OLD DOWN [ST6187]

Fox [off A38 Bristol—Thornbury; Inner Down]: Welcoming low-ceilinged pub popular for enjoyable very varied and well priced food, particularly good vegetarian choice, well kept Bass, Moles and a guest beer (Andy and Jill Kassube, James Morrell)

OLD SODBURY [ST7581]

☆ *Dog* [3 miles from M4 junction 18, via A46 and A432; The Hill]: Two-level bar with open fires, low beams and stripped stone, no smoking room, well kept Marstons Pedigree, Wadworths 6X, Wickwar BOB and a guest beer, extremely wide choice of reasonably priced food from sandwiches up inc plenty of fish; fruit machine, juke box; children in eating area, big garden with barbecues and good play area, bedrooms, open all day (Monica Cockburn, Mike Jefferies, Tom Evans, Mr and Mrs A H Young, Dr and Mrs C W Thomas, Bob Moffatt, Pamela and Merlyn Horswell, Sue and Mike Todd, Fiona McElhone, John Branston, Dr and Mrs A K Clarke, Andy and Yvonne Cunningham, Don and Thelma Anderson, Roy and Lindsey Fentiman, Stan and Susan Fysh, John and Gloria Isaacs, LYM, Paul Humphreys, Donald Godden, Stuart Paulley, Stephen Woad)

PAINSWICK [SO8609]

☆ *Royal Oak* [St Mary's St]: Old-fashioned partly 16th-c three-room town pub with some attractive old or antique seats, plenty of old prints, enjoyable good value food (not Sun) from filled rolls to interesting main dishes, friendly staff, well kept Black Sheep, Hook Norton and Shepherd Neame Spitfire, decent wines, open fire, no smoking lounge and small sun lounge; children in eating area, dogs welcome in public bar, suntrap pretty courtyard (Brian McBurnie, Neil and Anita Christopher, LYM, Eddie Edwards, Margaret and Roy Randle)

PARKEND [SO6208]

Fountain [just off B4234]: Assorted chairs and settles, real fire, old local tools and photographs, wide choice of fresh food inc good range of curries, welcoming efficient service, well kept local Freeminer and interesting guest beers; children and dogs welcome, wheelchair access (CMW, JJW, Pete Baker, Pamela and Merlyn Horswell)

☆ *Woodman* [Folly Rd, Whitecroft]: Roomy and relaxed stripped-stone bar, two open fires, heavy beams, forest and forestry decorations, prints for sale, mix of furnishings inc some modern seats, smaller back bar and dining room, freshly made food (not Sun or Mon evenings) from baguettes and baked potatoes

up inc good vegetarian range, well kept Fullers London Pride, Greene King Old Speckled Hen and Wadworths 6X, decent wines, pleasant service, evening bistro (Thurs-Sat); picnic-sets on front terrace facing green, sheltered back courtyard and garden, bedrooms, good walks in Forest of Dean (BB, Neil and Anita Christopher)

PAXFORD [SP1837]

☆ *Churchill Arms* [B4479, SE of Chipping Campden]: Food that's often really good and imaginative in simply furnished flagstoned bar and bare-boards back extension, assorted old tables and chairs, snug warmed by good log fire, well kept Hook Norton Best and a couple of guest beers, good choice of wines by the glass; service usually friendly and helpful; children welcome, some seats outside (and aunt sally), charming good value bedrooms, good breakfast (John Evans, Dr G and Mrs J Kelvin, John Kane, LYM, Dr R A Smye, Mr and Mrs Martin Joyce, Simon Collett-Jones, Mr and Mrs G S Ayrton, Derek Thomas, Steve Whalley, Mr and Mrs J Tout, Canon Michael Bourdeaux, Michael and Anne Brown)

PRESTBURY [SO9624]

☆ *Plough* [Mill St]: Well preserved thatched village local opp church, cosy and comfortable front lounge with panelling-look wallpaper, service from corner corridor counter in locals' charming and basic flagstoned back taproom (one non-local reader recently celebrated getting a seat in this for the first time in the 40 years he's known the pub), grandfather clock and big log fire, consistently friendly service, well kept Greene King Abbot and Charles Wells Bombardier tapped from the cask, farm cider, perhaps good sandwiches or simple hot dish; outstanding good-sized flower-filled back garden (Di and Mike Gillam, R J Herd, B M Eldridge, Guy Vowles)

☆ *Royal Oak* [The Burgage]: Small comfortable village pub with good generous freshly made restaurant food inc imaginative dishes and delicious puddings, with a simpler lunch menu, good-natured landlord, well kept ales such as Archers Best, Timothy Taylors Landlord and Wadworths 6X, Thatcher's cider and good choice of good value wines, low-beamed bar with green plush settles, cushioned pew and other seats, brasses and fresh flowers, no machines; pleasant garden behind, open all day summer wknds (Joe Green, Mr and Mrs J Brown, Michael Sargent, Mrs C Lintott, Jo Rees, Andrew Barker, Claire Jenkins)

QUEDGELEY [SO8014]

Bumble Bee [Waterwells roundabout, Telford Way]: Vintage Inn with their usual food all day, well kept Bass and Wadworths 6X, log fire and many flagstoned or carpeted separate eating areas (JHBS)

REDBROOK [SO5410]

☆ *Boat* [car park signed on A466 Chepstow—Monmouth, then 100-yard footbridge over Wye; or very narrow steep car access from Penallt in Wales]: Beautifully set laid-back and congenial unsmart Wye-side pub, charming landlord, changing well kept ales such as Archers Gold, Freeminers Honey Dipper, Greene King IPA and Wadworths 6X tapped from casks, good range of country wines and hot drinks, stripped stone walls, flagstone floors and roaring woodburner, inexpensive no-nonsense food inc good value baked potatoes, lots of fresh baguettes and children's dishes (can be delays if busy); live music Tues and Thurs; several cats and dogs; children welcome, rough home-built seats in informal tiered garden with stream spilling down waterfall cliffs into duck pond, open all day *(LYM, R Huggins, D Irving, E McCall, T McLean, Ann and Colin Hunt, Donald Godden, Bob and Margaret Holder, Phil and Heidi Cook, Tim Gorringe, LM, Piotr Chodzko-Zajko)*

RODBOROUGH [SO8404]

Bear [Rodborough Common]: Comfortably cosy and pubby beamed and flagstoned bar in smart hotel, warm welcome, pleasant window seats, good log fire, hops hung around top of golden stone walls, interesting reproductions, Bass and Uley, reasonably priced food (bar and restaurant) inc afternoon tea; children welcome, bedrooms *(BB, Meg and Colin Hamilton, Martin and Karen Wake)*

SAPPERTON [SO9403]

Daneway Inn [Daneway; off A419 Stroud—Cirencester]: Flagstone-floored local in charming quiet wooded countryside, terrace tables and lovely sloping lawn; amazing floor-to-ceiling carved oak dutch fireplace, sporting prints, well kept Wadworths IPA, 6X and JCB, Weston's farm cider, reasonably priced generous simple food from filled baps up (may be a wait in fine weather when it's busy), small no smoking family room, traditional games in inglenook public bar; camping possible, good walks by canal under restoration with tunnel to Coates *(R Huggins, D Irving, E McCall, T McLean, Peter and Audrey Dowsett, LYM, Tim and Suzy Bower)*

SHEEPSCOMBE [SO8910]

☆ *Butchers Arms* [off B4070 NE of Stroud]: Bustling 17th-c pub with log fires, seats in big bay windows, flowery-cushioned chairs and rustic benches, and lots of interesting oddments, well kept Hook Norton Best and a couple of guest beers, good choice of other drinks, new chef doing popular fresh food from lunchtime filled rolls, bagels and wraps up, with wider evening choice, no smoking restaurant, traditional games; children in eating areas, tables outside, terrific views *(Bernard Stradling, LYM, Giles and Annie Francis, Neil and Anita Christopher, John Reilly, Jason Caulkin, Dr A J and Mrs Tompsett)*

SHIPTON MOYNE [ST8989]

Cat & Custard Pot [off B4040 Malmesbury—Bristol; The Street]: Well run pub with enormous choice of good value robust food from sandwiches to steaks, well kept Fullers London Pride, Wadworths 6X and guest beers, Thatcher's cider, neat friendly staff, hunting prints in divided bar/dining room, cosy back snug; picturesque village *(Richard Stancomb, BB, John and Gloria Isaacs)*

SHIPTON OLIFFE [SP0218]

Frogmill [just off A40/A436 S of Andoversford]: 17th-c stone-built coaching inn with large flagstoned bar, no smoking area, friendly service, enjoyable food, well kept Bass, attractive beamed restaurant; tables on streamside terrace with waterwheel, big play area, comfortable bedrooms *(Geoff Pidoux)*

SIDDINGTON [SU0399]

Greyhound [Ashton Rd; village signed from A419 roundabout at Tesco]: Two linked rooms each with a big log fire, former skittle alley converted to restaurant with carvery counter, other food from sandwiches up, well kept Badger Tanglefoot, Wadworths IPA and seasonal beers, public bar with slate floor, darts and cribbage; piped music; garden tables, open all day *(LYM, R Huggins, D Irving, E McCall, T McLean, Paul and Shirley White, Peter and Audrey Dowsett)*

SLAD [SO8707]

☆ *Woolpack* [B4070 Stroud—Birdlip]: Friendly old hillside village local with lovely valley views, several linked rooms with Laurie Lee and other interesting photographs, some of his books for sale, log fire and nice tables, good value food (not Sun evening) from sandwiches and baguettes to enjoyable hot dishes inc generous Sun roast, well kept Bass and Uley ales, local farm ciders and perry, good young staff, games and cards; dogs welcome *(Pete Baker, R Huggins, D Irving, E McCall, T McLean, Eddie Edwards)*

SNOWSHILL [SP0934]

Snowshill Arms: Spruce and airy carpeted bar in honeypot village, stripped stone, neat array of tables, local photographs, friendly service, well kept Donnington BB and SBA, log fire, quickly served straightforward food (fill in your own order form); skittle alley, charming village views from bow windows and from big back garden with little stream and play area, friendly local feel midweek winter and evenings, can be very crowded other lunchtimes – nearby parking may be difficult; children welcome if eating, handy for Snowshill Manor and Cotswold Way walks *(LYM, Dr David Cockburn, Mrs Edna M Jones, Angus Lyon, Martin and Pauline Jennings)*

SOMERFORD KEYNES [SU0195]

Bakers Arms: Pretty stone-built pub, large knocked-together stripped-stone area with lots of pine tables for decent food from baguettes and ciabattas up, well kept real ales, good house wine, two log fires; children welcome, big garden, lovely Cotswold village *(Mark and Ruth Brock)*

SOUTH CERNEY [SU0496]

Royal Oak [High St]: Sympathetically extended ancient local, cheerful landlord, well kept changing ales such as Courage Best, Fullers London Pride, Greene King Old Speckled Hen and Youngs, woodburner, lively atmosphere, big back dining area; pleasant garden behind with big terrace and summer marquee *(R Huggins, D Irving, E McCall, T McLean, Philip Nicholas, Ian Phillips)*

SOUTHROP [SP2003]

☆ *Swan:* Attractive upmarket décor in low-ceilinged front dining lounge with log fire and flagstones, well spaced tables, particularly good generous interesting food at a price, chatty landlord and friendly attentive service, well kept Greene King Abbot and Hook Norton from back bar, good wines, stripped stone skittle alley; children welcome, pretty village esp at daffodil time *(LYM, Dr J J H Gilkes, Gaynor Gregory, R Huggins, D Irving, E McCall, T McLean, Mr and Mrs A H Young, Guy Vowles, A G Marx, Richard Greaves, Karen and Graham Oddey)*

ST BRIAVELS [SO5504]

George [High Street]: Rambling linked black-beamed rooms with old-fashioned seating, toby jugs and antique bottles, big stone open fireplace, very wide bar food choice, Freeminer Bitter, Fullers London Pride, RCH Pitchfork and a couple of guest beers, no smoking restaurant; piped music, service can come under pressure; children and dogs welcome, flagstone terrace over former moat of neighbouring Norman fortress, bedrooms *(Pamela and Merlyn Horswell, Ian Phillips, JHW, Bob and Margaret Holder, Peter and Jean Dowson, Kevin Blake, Colin Morgan, Piotr Chodzko-Zajko, LYM)*

STANTON [SP0734]

☆ *Mount* [off B4632 SW of Broadway; no through road up hill, bear left]: Stunning spot up steep lane from golden-stone village, heavy beams, flagstones and big log fire in original core, horseracing pictures and trappings and plenty of locals, roomy picture-window extensions, one no smoking with cricket memorabilia; well kept Donnington BB and SBA, farm cider, decent bar food (not Sun evening) from super baguettes up, friendly attentive staff; open all day Sat and summer Sun, well behaved children allowed, views to Welsh mountains from large terrace, attractive garden with pets' corner *(K H Frostick, Angus Lyon, Mr and Mrs Colin Roberts, C Howard, John Foord, LYM, Mrs B J Edwards, Ken Marshall, Ian and Celia Abbott, Ann Gray)*

STAVERTON [SO9024]

☆ *House in the Tree* [Haydon (B4063 W of Cheltenham)]: Spick-and-span beamed and partly flagstoned pub, friendly efficient service, Adnams Broadside and Banks's, farm ciders, good value straightforward food on huge plates in main part's rambling linked areas inc no smoking area, Sunday carvery, nice little public bar with high-backed settles by big inglenook log fire (and TV for sports); plenty of tables in garden with good play area and pets' corner *(BB, Roger and Jenny Huggins)*

STOW-ON-THE-WOLD [SP1925]

☆ *Eagle & Child* [attached to Royalist Hotel, Digbeth Street]: Smart dining bar attached to handsome old hotel, woodburner, flagstones, low beams and dark pink walls, nice mix of tables, up-to-date food, well kept Hook

Norton Best, good wine and malt whisky choice; can be smoky; children and dogs welcome, small back courtyard, good bedrooms, open all day *(David Hall, Peter and Jackie Barnett, Sean and Sharon Pines, Ted George, Michael Dandy, Mr and Mrs Martin Joyce, George Atkinson, Peter and Jean Hoare, David J Austin, Mayur Shah, Dr G and Mrs J Kelvin, LYM, Mary Rayner, L Elliott, John and Pat Morris)*

Grapevine [Sheep St]: Substantial hotel with relaxing small front bar, food from generous sandwiches and baguettes to steak and bass, good friendly service, Hook Norton real ale, good choice of wines by the glass, good coffee, restaurant with live vine; pavement tables, bedrooms, open all day *(Michael Dandy, Colin and Janet Roe)*

☆ *Kings Arms* [The Square]: Reasonably priced good food inc lots of fish and real food for children in pleasant bar and charming upstairs dining room overlooking town, good choice of wines by the glass, Greene King Old Speckled Hen and Ruddles County, good coffee (opens early for this), cheerful friendly service, some Mackintosh-style chairs on polished boards, bowed black beams, some panelling and stripped stone, log fire; bedrooms, open all day *(Michael Jones, BB, Pat and Roger Fereday, Mrs Angela Bromley-Martin, Mr and Mrs Martin Joyce, Gary and Jane Gleghorn, Michael and Jeanne Shillington)*

☆ *Queens Head* [The Square]: Traditional unfussy local with good friendly service, heavily beamed and flagstoned back bar with high-backed settles, big log fire, horse prints, lots of tables in civilised softly lit stripped stone front lounge, piped music, good value pub food (not Sun) from sandwiches up inc good home-made pies, well kept Donnington BB and SBA, decent house wines, usual games; dogs and children positively welcome (pub dog lets herself in by opening back door), tables in attractive garden, occasional jazz Sun lunchtime *(Ian and Celia Abbott, the Didler, Gary and Jane Gleghorn, LYM, Paul and Sue Merrick, Tracey and Stephen Groves, Gerry and Rosemary Dobson)*

☆ *Talbot* [The Square]: Light, airy and spacious modern décor, relaxed brasserie/wine bar feel, good reasonably priced continental-feel food, bright friendly service even when busy, three real ales, lots of good value wines by the glass, good coffee, big log fire, plain tables and chairs on wood block floor, modern prints, daily papers; no children inside, may be piped radio, lavatories upstairs; bedrooms nearby, open all day *(Dave and Sue Norgate, BB, Mel Smith)*

STROUD [SO8505]

Golden Fleece [Nelson St, just E of centre]: Cosily unpretentious old terrace local, well kept beer, daily papers, cheerfully musical décor, unobtrusive piped jazz, separate smaller upstairs room *(Dave Irving)*

Lord John [Russell St]: Airy split-level Wetherspoons in former PO sorting office, striking décor with something of a railway theme, tables in alcoves, their usual good value food and wide choice of sensibly priced beers *(G Coates, Dave Irving)*

Prince of Wales [Cashes Green Rd]: Homely neatly kept two-bar local with reasonably priced home-made pub food, efficient friendly service, real ales, small restaurant; attractive small garden *(Gary Bloyce)*

Swan [Swan Lane/Union St]: Recently refurbished, with good value simple pub food inc filled baguettes, well kept beer, friendly prompt service; piped music *(B R and M F Arnold)*

SWINEFORD [ST6969]

Swan [A431, right on the Somerset border]: Converted from three cottages, well kept Bass tapped from the cask and other ales such as Butcombe and Sharps Doom Bar, good local atmosphere, friendly attentive staff, food in neat plain bar with small no smoking dining area and restaurant inc popular good value Sun roasts (booked weeks ahead) *(Michael Doswell)*

TETBURY [ST8993]

Crown [Gumstool Hill]: Large cheerful 17th-c town pub, good value generous bar lunches, well kept ales such as Black Sheep and Hook Norton Best, quick service, long oak-beamed front bar with big log fire and attractive medley of tables, pleasant back no smoking family dining conservatory with lots of plants; may be unobtrusive piped music, no credit cards; picnic-sets on back terrace, comfortable bedrooms *(Peter and Audrey Dowsett, Gordon Prince)*

☆ *Gumstool* [at Calcot Manor Hotel; A4135 W]: Good upmarket dining bar attached to comfortable country hotel, imaginative great-tasting food (small helpings available, and interesting things for children), well kept changing ales such as Butcombe, Fullers London Pride and Sharps Doom Bar, dozens of malt whiskies and fine choice of wines by the glass, good coffees, well organised service, daily papers, stripped pine, flagstones and gingham curtains, leather armchair by big log fire, mainly no smoking restaurant; piped music; children welcome, tables in pleasant garden, comfortable well equipped bedrooms, open all day wknds *(Bernard Stradling, Tom and Ruth Rees, M G Hart, LYM, Andy Barker, Claire Jenkins, Dr and Mrs C W Thomas, Dr and Mrs A K Clarke)*

Royal Oak [Cirencester Rd]: Stone-built former coaching inn with good fires in neat and tidy unspoilt bar, friendly landlord and quick service, Courage, Fullers London Pride and John Smiths, enjoyable reasonably priced food, cosy no smoking dining areas; well equipped bedrooms with own bathrooms, free long-stay car park opp *(Norman and Sheila Davies, Peter and Audrey Dowsett)*

TEWKESBURY [SO8932]

Olde Black Bear [High St]: Well worth a look for the building itself: the county's oldest pub, rambling rooms with heavy low beams (one with leather-clad ceiling), lots of timbers, armchairs in front of open fires, bare wood and ancient tiles, plenty of pictures and bric-a-brac, well kept beers, reasonably priced wines; piped music; children welcome, terrace and play area in riverside garden, open all day *(Paul Williams, John Foord, the Didler, LYM, Gordon Prince)*

TOCKINGTON [ST6186]

Swan: Roomy pub with beams, standing timbers, bric-a-brac on stripped stone walls, log fire, helpful service, reasonably priced food, well kept Bass; piped music; tables in tree-shaded garden, quiet village *(Pamela and Merlyn Horswell, Dr and Mrs A K Clarke)*

TOLLDOWN [ST7577]

☆ *Crown* [a mile from M4 junction 18 – A46 towards Bath]: Well run heavy-beamed pub with simple furnishings and light fresh décor, good value generous interesting food from ciabattas up, well kept Wadworths ales, good house wines, efficient service, good log fire, no smoking area; good disabled access, children in eating area and restaurant, good garden with play area, comfortable bedrooms *(Dr and Mrs A K Clarke, LYM, Mike and Cherry Fann, C L Kauffmann, Howard and Lorna Lambert, Pamela and Merlyn Horswell, Di and Mike Gillam, Mike and Mary Carter)*

TORMARTON [ST7678]

Portcullis [High St]: Quietly friendly old village pub with well kept Butcombe, Otter and local guest beers, good value generous bar food, beams, stonework, prints, brasses and bric-a-brac, log fire (sometimes two), panelled dining room; tables in garden, peaceful village by Cotswold Way *(Bruce Bird)*

TWYNING [SO8737]

☆ *Fleet* [off westbound A38 slip rd from M50 junction 1]: Family holiday pub in superb setting at end of quiet lane though just off motorway, good river views from roomy high-ceilinged bars, interesting boating-theme décor, five well kept real ales, quickly served tasty bar food, woodburner, airy back restaurant area, tearoom and tuck shop; games room with darts and bar billiards (no children in here while games are being played), piped music, fruit machines, entertainment Fri/Sat; disabled access, children welcome, picnic-sets in big waterside garden with two floodlit terraces, rockery cascade and safe enclosed children's area with chipmunk corner; stop on Tewkesbury—Bredon summer boat run, bedrooms, open all day *(LYM, Neil and Anita Christopher, Susan and Nigel Wilson)*

ULEY [ST7998]

Old Crown [The Green]: Rustic 17th-c pub prettily set by village green just off Cotswold Way, long narrow room with settles and pews on bare boards, step up to partitioned-off lounge area, local Uley and several other well kept changing ales, home-made pubby food from sandwiches and baked potatoes up, friendly service, log fire, small games room up spiral stairs with pool, darts etc; dogs on leads welcome (but they have nine cats), live music Tues and Fri; attractive garden behind, bedrooms *(Michael Cooper, R Huggins, D Irving, E McCall, T McLean, Pete Baker, Neil and Anita Christopher)*

UPTON CHEYNEY [ST6969]

Upton Inn [signed off A431 at Bitton]:
Stripped stone with wall hangings, chandeliers
and archways, interesting choice of good
home-made food, friendly helpful service, well
kept beer, decent wines, small smart
restaurant; tables outside, picturesque spot
(Tom and Ruth Rees)

WESTBURY-ON-SEVERN [SO7114]

☆ *Red Lion* [A48, corner Bell Lane]: Substantial
beamed and half-timbered traditional pub on
busy road but by quiet church-side lane to
river, welcoming atmosphere, jovial landlord,
generous interesting home cooking, well kept
ales such as Bass and Fullers London Pride,
decent wine, comfortable bar with button-back
wall seats, velvet curtains, coal stove, big
dining room with old pews; handy for
Westbury Court gardens (NT) *(BB,
B M Eldridge)*

WESTONBIRT [ST8690]

Hare & Hounds [A433 SW of Tetbury]:
Substantial inn with separate entrance for end
turkey-carpeted bar, with high-backed settles,
snacks and good more substantial meals,
Smiles Best and Wadworths 6X, central log-
effect gas fire, sporting prints, games in public
bar on left; small tweedy more central cocktail
bar, pleasant gardens, good value bedrooms,
handy for Arboretum *(BB, Meg and
Colin Hamilton)*

WHITECROFT [SO6005]

Miners Arms [B4234 N of Lydney]:
Remarkable range of well kept ales from
smaller breweries, farm ciders too, in friendly
unpretentious pub, piano in one of two rooms
on either side of bar, lunchtime sandwiches
and limited hot dishes; good gardens front and
back, one with a pleasant little stream, handy
for steam railway *(Pete Baker)*

WHITMINSTER [SO7607]

Fromebridge Mill [Fromebridge Lane (A38 nr
M5 junction 13)]: Large mill-based dining pub
with attractively extended bar and dining
areas, decent reasonably priced food from
sandwiches and baked potatoes up inc popular
good value lunchtime carvery, Greene King
real ales, friendly helpful staff; picnic-sets out
behind with play area, lovely setting
overlooking weir *(Peter Neate)*

WICK [ST7072]

☆ *Rose & Crown* [High St (A420)]: Well run
Chef & Brewer, busy and roomy, with friendly
hands-on service, good relaxed atmosphere,
well kept Courage Best (bargain price), Greene
King Old Speckled Hen, Charles Wells
Bombardier and an unusual guest beer,
interesting wines by the glass, plenty of
character in largely untouched and mainly no
smoking linked 17th-c rooms with low beams,
mixed furnishings and candlelight, very wide
food choice, coal fire in big stone fireplace,
daily papers; good disabled access, picnic-sets
out on terrace, open all day *(Andrew Shore,
Maria Williams, John Cook, Barry and
Anne, Pamela and Merlyn Horswell, BB)*

WILLERSEY [SP1039]

☆ *Bell* [B4632 Cheltenham—Stratford, nr

Broadway]: Attractive stone-built pub, open-
plan and neatly modernised, comfortable front
part impressively set for the carefully prepared
interesting and unpretentious home-made food,
Aston Villa memorabilia and huge collection of
model cars in back area past the big L-shaped
bar counter with its well kept Hook Norton
Best, Tetleys and Wadworths 6X, relaxed
atmosphere, quick friendly helpful service;
darts, Thurs evening chess ladder; overlooks
delightful village's green and duck pond, lots of
tables in big garden, bedrooms in outbuildings
(DC, John Foord, BB)

WINCHCOMBE [SP0228]

☆ *Plaisterers Arms* [Abbey Terr]: Interesting
individually run 18th-c pub with stripped
stonework, beams, Hogarth prints, bric-a-brac
and flame-effect fires, two chatty front bars
both with steps down to dim-lit lower back
dining area with tables in stalls, enterprising
food, well kept Goffs Jouster, Greene King Old
Speckled Hen and Ushers Best; dogs welcome,
good play area in charming garden, long and
narrow, comfortable simple bedrooms with
own bathrooms (tricky stairs), handy for
Sudeley Castle *(BB, Ian and Celia Abbott,
David and Nina Pugsley, Gordon Prince,
Joyce and Geoff Robson)*

WITHINGTON [SP0315]

Mill Inn [off A436 or A40]: Idyllic streamside
setting for mossy-roofed old stone inn, with
tables out in large pretty garden including
some on small island, splendid walks all
around; beams, flagstones, inglenook log fire,
plenty of character with nice nooks and
corners, darts and dominoes, standard food
from baguettes and basket meals up, no
smoking dining room; piped music, keg beer
(but decent wine list); children very welcome,
four old-fashioned bedrooms, good breakfast
*(LYM, Paul and Shirley White, Stuart Lane,
S P Watkin, P A Taylor)*

WOODCHESTER [SO8403]

Old Fleece [Rooksmoor; A46 a mile S of
Stroud – not to be confused with Fleece at
Lightpill a little closer in]: Informal bare-
boards décor in open-plan line of several big-
windowed room areas, largely no smoking,
bar on right, restaurant on left (nice rooms),
wide choice of interesting freshly made bar
food from unusual lunchtime sandwiches up,
well kept Bass, Boddingtons and Greene King
Abbot, good wines, local non-alcoholic
drinks, big log fire, candles, daily papers;
stripped stone or dark salmon pink walls;
children welcome, two roadside terraces,
one with heater *(BB, Stan and Susan Fysh,
Dave Irving)*

☆ *Ram* [Station Rd, South Woodchester]:
Attractively priced well kept ales such as
Butcombe, Otter, Sharps Doom Bar, John
Smiths, Uley Old Spot and Wadworths 6X in
relaxed L-shaped beamed bar with nice mix of
traditional furnishings, stripped stonework,
bare boards, three open fires, darts, friendly
staff, varied food from good value generous
baguettes to steaks and Mon-Thurs lunch
deals, busy front restaurant extension; children

welcome, spectacular views from terrace tables, open all day Sat/Sun *(Stan and Susan Fysh, LYM, Tom and Ruth Rees, Andy Barker, Claire Jenkins, R Huggins, D Irving, E McCall, T McLean, Dave Irving)*

☆ *Royal Oak* [off A46; Church Road, N Woodchester]: Bar on right with homely welcoming atmosphere, scrubbed tables, chapel chairs and big log fire in huge fireplace, popular dining area on left, enjoyable food from baguettes to good Sun roasts, well kept ales such as Bath Spa and Wickwar BOB; big-

screen TV for special events, piped music, some live; children and dogs welcome, open all day *(R Huggins, D Irving, E McCall, T McLean, LYM, Andy Barker, Claire Jenkins, Tim and Suzy Bower)*

WOODMANCOTE [SO9727]

☆ *Apple Tree* [Stockwell Lane]: Interesting choice of good value food in roomy former cider house, now a good family pub, with cheerful courteous staff, real ales, decent wines, restaurant; garden – fine views, secluded setting at foot of hill *(Jo Rees)*

Please keep sending us reports. We rely on readers for news of new discoveries, and particularly for news of changes – however slight – at the fully described pubs. No stamp needed: The Good Pub Guide, FREEPOST TN1569, Wadhurst, E Sussex TN5 7BR or send your report through our web site: www.goodguides.co.uk

Hampshire

New entries in this favoured county are the welcoming and traditional Bull near Bentley (a rewarding respite from the busy A31), the exuberantly decorated Wheatsheaf at Braishfield (fairly priced good food, relaxing atmosphere), the Shoe at Exton (good food here too, and a nice riverside garden), the stylish modern Running Horse at Littleton (such good interesting food that it comes straight in with a Food Award), and the Yew Tree at Lower Wield (another place to gain its Food Award straight off, its friendly new licensees keen to keep it a proper informal country pub). Both the Running Horse and the Yew Tree are sound bets for a special meal out. Among longer-standing entries, other places currently doing really well in the food stakes are the civilised Fox at Bramdean (where the landlord cooks using fresh local ingredients), the cosy, friendly and charmingly decorated Chestnut Horse at Easton (by no means cheap, but very good – and with good value set menus), the warmly welcoming Trooper up above Petersfield, the bustling and well run Plough at Sparsholt, and the nicely individual Wykeham Arms in Winchester. It was the Plough which took our top award here last year – and it's done it again this time. The Plough at Sparsholt, with its interesting carefully made food and friendly helpful service, is Hampshire Dining Pub of the Year. Other pubs here on fine form these days are the Sun at Bentworth (a lovely country pub with great beer choice), the Flower Pots at Cheriton (this simple rustic pub brews its own good beers, and in a county where worthwhile pub food tends to be pricey it earns extra praise for its value-minded food), the unpretentious Royal Oak at Fritham (part of a New Forest farm, warmly welcoming, with good real ales), the well run Peat Spade at Longstock (a sensibly short food choice using local and organic produce), the thriving Half Moon & Spread Eagle at Micheldever (proper local atmosphere yet a warm welcome for visitors, and well liked affordable food), the Brushmakers Arms at Upham (welcoming and easy-going, with a super landlord and fairly priced honest food), and the Black Boy in Winchester (splendidly eccentric décor, well kept local beers, great atmosphere and nice pubby lunchtime food). The Lucky Dip at the end of the chapter is well worth exploring in depth. Pubs we'd particularly recommend here (all inspected and approved by us) are Milbury's at Beauworth, the Bunch of Grapes in Bishop's Waltham, Five Bells at Buriton, Jolly Sailor in Bursledon, Mill Arms at Dunbridge, Hampshire Bowman at Dundridge, East End Arms at East End, George at East Meon, Watership Down at Freefolk, Foresters Arms at Frogham, Bat & Ball at Hambledon, Trout at Itchen Abbas, Royal Oak at Langstone, Jolly Farmer in Locks Heath, Pilgrim in Marchwood, Bucks Head at Meonstoke, White Horse on the downs above Petersfield, Three Tuns in Romsey, Selborne Arms at Selborne, White Lion at Soberton, Jekyll & Hyde at Turgis Green, Red House in Whitchurch and Horse & Groom at Woodgreen. Drinks prices in Hampshire pubs tend to be noticeably higher than the national average. The Flower Pots at Cheriton (brewing its own beer) and Chestnut Horse at Easton (stocking local Itchen Valley beer) were the only main entries here where we found real ale for under £2 a pint. Ringwood and Gales are the main local brewers, and you'll also quite often find Cheriton (from the Flower Pots), Itchen Valley and Hampshire as the cheapest beer a pub stocks.

BANK SU2807 Map 2

Oak 🍺

Signposted just off A35 SW of Lyndhurst

You will need to get here early, as this welcoming place is surprisingly busy given its peaceful New Forest location. On either side of the door in the bay windows of the L-shaped bar are built-in green-cushioned seats, and on the right, two or three little pine-panelled booths with small built-in tables and bench seats. The rest of the bar has more floor space, with candles in individual brass holders on a line of stripped old and blond newer tables set against the wall on bare floorboards, and more at the back; some low beams and joists, fishing rods, spears, a boomerang, and old ski poles on the ceiling, and on the walls are brass platters, heavy knives, stuffed fish and guns. There's also a big fireplace, cushioned milk churns along the bar counter, and little red lanterns among hop bines above the bar; piped music. A good representation of beers from this region includes well kept Butts Barbus Barbus, Hop Back Summer Lightning, Itchen Valley Pure Gold, Ringwood Best, and a guest such as Stonehenge Danish Dynamite, as well as local country wines and cider. Well liked bar food includes good lunchtime doorstep sandwiches (from £4.25) and ploughman's (from £5.25), as well as baked brie with almonds and honey (£3.95), various cured meats with roasted red pepper and pickles (£6.75), pork and herb sausages with rich onion gravy (£7.50), a pie of the day (£7.95), greek salad topped with sliced grilled chicken breast (£8.95), fresh cod in beer batter (£10.95), grilled 12oz rib-eye steak (£12.95), and daily specials such as plaice (from £10), duck breast (£11) and crab and lobster in season (£10–£15). The side garden has picnic-sets and long tables and benches by the big yew trees. *(Recommended by Paul Goldman, Roger and Pauline Pearce, Alan M Pring, Brian and Janet Ainscough, Charles and Pauline Stride, Prof Keith and Mrs Jane Barber, Dr Alan and Mrs Sue Holder, Gordon Stevenson, C J Roebuck, Sue Demont, Tim Barrow, Richard Waller, Pauline Smith)*

Free house ~ Licensee Karen Slowen ~ Real ale ~ Bar food ~ (023) 8028 2350 ~ Children welcome till 6pm ~ Dogs welcome ~ Open 11-11; 12-10.30 Sun; 11-2.30, 6-11 weekdays in winter

BENTLEY SU8044 Map 2

Bull

A31 Alton—Farnham dual carriageway, east of village itself; accessible from both carriageways, but tricky if westbound

It's nice to find such an unexpectedly and genuinely country-pub atmosphere in such a convenient trunk-road stop-off. Inside the tiled white cottage, the main room on the right, restful despite some traffic noise, has soft lighting, witty sayings chalked on low black beams in its maroon ceiling, lots of local photographs on partly stripped brick walls, and pub chairs around neat stripped pub tables. The back room on the left has a good log fire in a huge hearth, a cushioned pew by one long oak-planked table, and in a snug and narrow back alcove another pew built around a nice mahogany table. Good changing blackboard food includes sandwiches (from £4.45), soup (£4.50), ploughman's (£5.50), smoked haddock fishcakes or chicken liver and brandy pâté (£5.95), roasted vegetable and cheese wellington (£10.95), duck breast with mixed berry and Drambuie sauce or grilled calves liver and roasted root vegetables (£13.95), frequently changing daily specials such as chicken and leek pie (£9.25), beef stroganoff (£9.95), and puddings (£4.50); they get their beef and lamb from local farms. Courage Best, Fullers London Pride, Hogs Back TEA and Youngs Best are well kept on handpump, and the friendly staff give free refills of the good coffee. There are plenty of pretty summer flowering tubs and hanging baskets outside, and picnic-sets and a teak table and chairs on the side terrace. *(Recommended by John and Joyce Snell, J P Humphery, Mrs Maricar Jagger, Ian Phillips, Mike Park, William To, Susan Loppert, I D Barnett, Ann and Colin Hunt, Alan M Pring)*

Enterprise ~ Lease Grant Edmead ~ Real ale ~ Bar food (12-2.30, 6.30-9.30; 12-3, 6-8 Sun)

~ Restaurant ~ (01420) 22156 ~ Children in eating area of bar and restaurant ~ Dogs allowed in bar ~ Open 10.30-11; 12-10.30 Sun

BENTWORTH SU6740 Map 2

Sun ◖

Sun Hill; from the A339 coming from Alton the first turning takes you there direct; or in village follow Shalden 2¼, Alton 4¼ signpost

The cheery landlady at this friendly country pub keeps a fine choice of eight changing real ales. With a nice batch of them coming from local brewers, these might include Adnams Best, Cheriton Pots, Fullers London Pride, Hogs Back TEA, Ringwood Best and Old Thumper, Stonehenge Pigswill and Timothy Taylors Landlord on handpump; several malt whiskies. Another strength at this delightful place is the promptly served good home-made bar food, which might include sandwiches or soup (£3.25), creamy garlic mushrooms or pork liver pâté (£3.25), yorkshire pudding with roast beef or pork and leek sausages (£6.50), avocado and stilton bake or fresh tagliatelle with smoked salmon, lemon and dill cream sauce (£7.95), home-made burger with relish, steak and kidney pie or chicken stuffed with walnuts and stilton in a mushroom and port sauce (all £8.95), salmon wrapped in parma ham with pesto (£9.95), well liked cumberland sausage with onion gravy or venison in Guinness with pickled walnuts (£10.95), steaks (from £11.95), and puddings (£3.25). Popular with both locals and visitors, the two little traditional communicating rooms have high-backed antique settles, pews and schoolroom chairs, olde-worlde prints and blacksmith's tools on the walls, and bare boards and scrubbed deal tables on the left; big fireplaces (one with a winter fire) and candles make it especially snug in winter; an arch leads to a brick-floored room with another open fire. There are seats out in front and in the back garden, and pleasant nearby walks. *(Recommended by Martin and Karen Wake, Ann and Colin Hunt, D P and M A Miles, Tony and Wendy Hobden, the Didler, Andrin Cooper, R Lake, Lynn Sharpless, Phyl and Jack Street)*

Free house ~ Licensee Mary Holmes ~ Real ale ~ Bar food (12-2, 7-9.30) ~ (01420) 562338 ~ Children in family room ~ Dogs welcome ~ Open 12-3, 6-11; 12-10.30 Sun

BOLDRE SZ3198 Map 2

Red Lion ★ ♀

Village signposted from A337 N of Lymington

The four spotlessly kept black-beamed rooms at this bustling pub are filled with an array of happy clutter, taking in heavy urns, platters, farm tools, heavy-horse harness, needlework, gin traps, ferocious-looking man traps and rural landscapes. The central room has a profusion of chamber-pots, and an end room has pews, wheelback chairs and tapestried stools, and a dainty collection of old bottles and glasses in the window by the counter. There's a fine old cooking range in the cosy little bar, and two good log fires. Many visitors come here for the generously served enjoyable bar food, which includes sandwiches (£4), ploughman's or panini (£7), filo prawns (£6.60), vegetable risotto (£8.20), breaded plaice or chicken and chorizo pasta (£9.60), steak and Guinness pie (£10.50), chinese-style crispy duck breast with plum and mushroom sauce (£11.80), daily specials such as toad in the hole (£8.80) and saddle of venison wrapped in bacon with port jus (£13.50), and puddings such as mandarin pot or white chocolate and apricot sponge (£4.50). They have an extensive wine list with 14 by the glass, and well kept Bass and Ringwood Best on handpump. In summer, the flowering tubs and hanging baskets outside are charming, and there are tables out in the back garden. No children or dogs inside and most of the pub is no smoking. *(Recommended by David Carr, Phyl and Jack Street, J M G Clarke, Jeff and Wendy Williams, Dr and Mrs A K Clarke, Roger and Pauline Pearce, Glenwys and Alan Lawrence, JDM, KM, D Marsh, Gordon Stevenson, Simon Collett-Jones, Colin Morgan, John and Joan Calvert, JWAC)*

Eldridge Pope ~ Tenant Vince Kemick ~ Real ale ~ Bar food (12-2.30, 6.30-9(9.30 Fri, Sat)) ~ Restaurant ~ (01590) 673177 ~ Open 11-11; 12-10.30 Sun

BRAISHFIELD SU3724 Map 2

Wheatsheaf

Village signposted off A3090 on NW edge of Romsey, pub just S of village on Braishfield Road

A lot of thought must have gone into the rambling layout and idiosyncratic décor here: all sorts of tables from elegant little oak ovals through handsome Regency-style drum tables to sturdy more rustic ones, with a similarly wide variety of chairs, and on the stripped brick or deep pink-painted walls a profusion of things to look at, from Spy caricatures and antique prints through staffordshire dogs and other decorative china to a leg in a fishnet stocking kicking out from the wall and a jokey 'Malteser grader' (a giant copper skimmer). It sounds a bit of a mish-mash, but in fact works well, making for an attractive and relaxed atmosphere – helped along by the way the efficient young staff clearly enjoy their work. Two of the dining areas are no smoking. Enjoyable and interesting food includes rustic breads with oils or soup (£3.95), game terrine or potted shrimps (£6.95), sweet potato and rosemary risotto (£8.95), steak and kidney pudding or mixed vegetable and dolcelatte cottage pie with pine nut mash (£9.95), garlicky roasted cod with mulled wine sauce (£11.95), roast pork in parma ham with black pudding, apple samosa and port gravy or local pheasant casseroled with orange and brandy dumplings (£10.95), daily specials such as scallops with sweet chilli sauce (£7.95) and duck breast with oyster and whisky sauce (£12.95), and puddings such as fresh fig tart with balsamic ice-cream or crème brûlée with lemon and pistachio shortbread (£4.25). They make good use of their own serious and sizeable herb garden, and you may be in luck and visit when their soft fruit cage is cropping. They also do lots of snacks such as olives and nuts, and sell chocolates and sweets. Well kept Hook Norton Old Hooky, Ringwood Best, Timothy Taylors Landlord and a couple of guests such as Caledonian Deuchars IPA and Hook Norton Best, 15 wines by the glass and good coffee; daily papers and several reference books; piped music, TV; disabled access and facilities. Unusually, the chairs, tables and picnic-sets out on the terrace are painted in greek blue. There are woodland walks nearby, and the pub is handy for the Sir Harold Hillier Arboretum. *(Recommended by Geoff Pidoux, Cynthia Norman, Phyl and Jack Street)*

Enterprise ~ Lease Peter and Jenny Jones ~ Real ale ~ Bar food ~ Restaurant ~ (01794) 368372 ~ Children in eating area of bar and restaurant ~ Dogs allowed in bar ~ Open 11-11; 12-10.30 Sun

BRAMDEAN SU6127 Map 2

Fox

A272 Winchester—Petersfield

This comfortable 17th-c weatherboarded dining pub is known for its reliably good bar food, which is cooked, using lots of fresh ingredients, by the landlord himself. Add a pound or two to some of these prices in the evening, and you will need to book: lunchtime sandwiches (from £3.25), soup (£4.50), wild boar pâté (£4.95), scallops fried with bacon (£6.95), cauliflower cheese with bacon (£8.95), steak and kidney pie or chicken breast with almonds in cherry sauce (£10.95), fried skate wing with capers (£11.95), confit of duck with orange gravy (£13.95), baked cod with herb crust and lemon sauce (£14.95), and puddings such as panna cotta with fresh raspberries or sticky toffee pudding (£3.95). The carefully modernised black beamed open-plan bar is civilised and grown up (no children inside), with tall stools with proper backrests around the L-shaped counter, and comfortably cushioned wall pews and wheelback chairs – the fox motif shows in a big painting over the fireplace, and on much of the decorative china. Most of the pub is no smoking. Well kept Greene King Ruddles County on handpump and piped music. At the back of the building is a walled-in terraced area, and a neatly kept spacious lawn spreading among the fruit trees; a play area has a climbing frame and slide. Good surrounding walks. *(Recommended by David Carr, Ann and Colin Hunt, Phyl and Jack Street, Betty Laker, Mike and Heather Watson, R B Gardiner, P F Dakin, Mr and Mrs W Mills, J Stickland, Sue Demont, Tim Barrow)*

Greene King ~ Tenants Ian and Jane Inder ~ Real ale ~ Bar food ~ Restaurant ~
(01962) 771363 ~ Open 11-3, 6-11; 12-3, 7-11 Sun

CHALTON SU7315 Map 2
Red Lion
Village signposted E of A3 Petersfield—Horndean

This has a picture postcard exterior, with deep thatch, black beams, little windows, and overflowing hanging baskets on its wonky white frontage. Known as the county's oldest pub, it was first licensed in 1503. The most characterful part is the heavy-beamed and panelled front bar with high-backed traditional settles and elm tables, and an ancient inglenook fireplace with a frieze of burnished threepenny bits set into its mantelbeam. The lounge and extended dining room have less character, and are no smoking; piped music. Well kept Gales beers are served from three taps, with a guest such as Charles Wells Bombardier on the fourth, alongside ten wines by the glass, and a fine choice of malt whiskies. Bar food includes sandwiches (from £3.65), soup (£3.95), filled baked potatoes (from £4.95), ploughman's (from £5.25), steak baguettes (£6.85), and daily specials such as spinach and ricotta filo strudel or thai fish curry (£8.25), moroccan-style chicken breast (£8.65) and roast half shoulder of lamb (£11.30). The garden is pretty in summer and the farmland views are super. The pub is popular with walkers and riders as it is fairly close to the extensive Queen Elizabeth Country Park, and about half a mile from an Iron Age farm and settlement. The car ferry is only about 20 minutes from here. *(Recommended by Ann and Colin Hunt, Paul and Shirley White, Ian Phillips, Colin Christie, Charles and Pauline Stride, Tony and Wendy Hobden, Kevin Broughton)*

Gales ~ Managers Mick and Mary McGee ~ Real ale ~ Bar food (12-2(2.30 Sun), 6.30-9(9.30 Fri, Sat); not Sun evening) ~ Restaurant ~ (023) 9259 2246 ~ Children in family room ~ Dogs allowed in bar ~ Open 11-3, 6-11; 12-3, 7-10.30 Sun

CHERITON SU5828 Map 2
Flower Pots ★ ◖ £
Pub just off B3046 (main village road) towards Beauworth and Winchester; OS Sheet 185 map reference 581282

This charming village local is enjoyable for its very simple rusticity, and of course, the particularly good own-brew beers from the brewhouse across the car park; well kept Pots Ale, Diggers Gold, Cheriton Best and maybe Village Elder tapped from casks behind the bar. The two straightforward little rooms can attract a lively mix of customers, though the one on the left is a favourite, almost like someone's front room, with pictures of hounds and ploughmen on its striped wallpaper, bunches of flowers, and a horse and foal and other ornaments on the mantelpiece over a small log fire; it can get smoky in here. Behind the servery is disused copper filtering equipment, and lots of hanging gin traps, drag-hooks, scaleyards and other ironwork. The neat extended plain public bar (where there's a covered well) has cribbage and dominoes. Very useful in fine weather (when the pub can fill up quickly), the pretty front and back lawns have some old-fashioned seats, and there's now a summer marquee; maybe summer morris dancers. Bar food from a fairly short straightforward menu includes sandwiches (from £2.80; toasties from £2.90), filled baked potatoes (from £4.40), ploughman's (from £4.80), hotpots such as lamb and apricot, chilli or spicy mixed bean (from £5.80), pork steak, onion and apple sauce bap (£6.30); popular curries on Wednesday evenings; friendly service. The menu and serving times may be restricted at weekend lunchtimes, or when they're busy. The pub is near the site of one of the final battles of the Civil War, and it got its name through once belonging to the retired head gardener of nearby Avington Park. No children inside. *(Recommended by David Carr, Lynn Sharpless, Tracey and Stephen Groves, Val and Alan Green, the Didler, Leigh and Gillian Mellor, Paul and Shirley White, Ann and Colin Hunt, Vincent Howard, Bruce Bird, Michael B Griffith, Stephen C Harvey, Jennifer Banks, Francis Johnston)*

Own brew ~ Licensees Jo and Patricia Bartlett ~ Real ale ~ Bar food (not Sun evening or

bank hol evenings) ~ No credit cards ~ (01962) 771318 ~ Dogs welcome ~ Open
12-2.30, 6-11; 12-3, 7-10.30 Sun ~ Bedrooms: £40S/£60S

EAST TYTHERLEY SU2927 Map 2

Star 🍴

Off B3084 N of Romsey; turn off by railway crossing opposite the Mill Arms at
Dunbridge

Most customers visit this professionaly run inn for a meal – the opening times,
trendy presentation and prices reflect this. The changing menu (vegetables are
extra) might include home-made soup (£3.25), goats cheese fondue with pine nut
and beetroot salad (£6.25), fried foie gras with mango and lime chutney or beef, red
wine and mushroom pie (£9.50), ratatouille lasagne (£11.50), fried skate with
brown butter, capers and crispy parma ham (£15.50), fillet steak (£16), caramelised
duck with puy lentils, spinach and madeira jus (£18.50), and puddings such as pear
and frangipane tart or treacle pudding and custard (from £4.25). You may find the
£10 two-course/£15 three-course menu (Tues-Sat lunchtime, Tues-Thurs evenings)
with things like devilled lambs liver and kidney in a pastry case and sausage and
mash is better value. A lounge area has leather sofas and tub chairs, and the bar has
log fires in attractive fireplaces, horsebrasses and saddlery, and a mix of
comfortable furnishings; there's a lower lounge bar, and a cosily pretty no smoking
restaurant. Ringwood Best and a couple of guests such as Hidden Quest and
Wadworths 6X are well kept on handpump, they've several malt whiskies, and a
thoughtful wine list with around ten by the glass; shove-ha'penny, and a popular
skittle alley for private dining. You can sit out on a smartly furnished terrace, and a
children's play area has equipment made using local reclaimed wood. The well
liked bedrooms overlook the village cricket pitch (which is used every Tuesday and
Saturday through the summer), and breakfasts are highly thought of. Good nearby
walks. *(Recommended by Prof Keith and Mrs Jane Barber, Jeff and Wendy Williams, Phyl and
Jack Street, Prof and Mrs Tony Palmer, Brenda and Rob Fincham, Terry and Linda Moseley,
Trevor Moore, Dr D G Twyman, Richard Haw, Patrick Hall, Julia and Richard Tredgett)*

Free house ~ Licensees Paul and Sarah Bingham ~ Real ale ~ Bar food ~ Restaurant ~
(01794) 340225 ~ Children welcome ~ Dogs allowed in bar ~ Open 11-2.30, 6-11; 12-3
Sun; closed Sun evening, Mon except bank hols ~ Bedrooms: £50S/£70S

EASTON SU5132 Map 2

Chestnut Horse 🍴 ♀

3.6 miles from M3 junction 9: A33 towards Kings Worthy, then B3047 towards Itchen
Abbas; Easton then signposted on right – bear left in village

The friendly welcome from particularly kind and efficient staff, and a cleverly laid
out interior lend a pleasant rural charm to this rather fine upmarket 16th-c dining
pub. Although the interior is all opened together, it keeps the cosy feel of small
separate rooms, with a really snug décor taking in candles and fresh flowers on the
tables, log fires in cottagey fireplaces, comfortable furnishings, black beams and
joists hung with all sorts of jugs, mugs and chamber-pots, and lots of attractive
pictures of wildlife and the local area. The two restaurants are no smoking. Very
good but by no means cheap food from the lunchtime menu includes soup (£4.50),
caesar salad (£4.95), dorset crab cocktail (£8.95), sausage and mash (£10.95),
lasagne or fish and chips (£11.95), duck confit with basil dressing (£13.95) and
10oz aberdeen angus steak (£14.95); Sunday roast is £13.95. The pricier evening
menu might include asparagus, wild mushroom, grilled baby aubergine, rocket and
parmesan and truffle oil risotto (£12.95), roast chicken supreme with port jus
(£15.25) and braised lamb shank with root vegetable mash and cranberry jus
(£16.95). A much more reasonably priced two-course menu is good value, and
a favourite with readers: £10, Mon-Sat lunchtime and Mon-Thurs evenings
6-7.30pm. Well kept Courage Best, Ringwood Best and Chestnut Horse (brewed
for the pub by Itchen Valley) on handpump, ten wines by the glass, and around
60 malt whiskies; fairly unobtrusive piped music. There are good tables out on a

smallish sheltered decked area, with colourful flower tubs and baskets, and plenty of walks in the Itchen Valley from here. *(Recommended by James Price, Matthew Johnson, Ann and Colin Hunt, Vincent Howard, Mrs J A Taylar, A J Atyeo, Phyl and Jack Street, Mike and Heather Watson, Ian Harrison, David Sizer, Dr Alan and Mrs Sue Holder, Lynn Sharpless, Francis Johnston, Martin and Karen Wake, John Evans, Sheila and Robert Robinson, Dr D and Mrs B Woods, Mayur Shah)*

Free house ~ Licensees John and Jocelyn Holland ~ Real ale ~ Bar food (12-2, 6-9.30) ~ Restaurant ~ (01962) 779257 ~ Children welcome ~ Dogs allowed in bar ~ Open 11-11; 12-10.30 Sun; closed Sun evenings in winter

EXTON SU6120 Map 2
Shoe
Village signposted from A32 NE of Bishop's Waltham – brown sign to pub into Beacon Hill Lane

A good choice of really enjoyable food, using local ingredients whenever possible, is the main draw to this attractively placed country pub. It includes sandwiches (from £3.95), ploughman's (from £5.25), ciabattas (from £5.50) and daily specials such as ham and lentil soup (£3.95), salmon and scallop terrine with lime dressing (£5.25), mushroom and potato stroganoff, sausage and mash or lasagne (£7.95), bream fillet with vegetable ribbons and garlic, basil and spring onion sauce (£11.95) and braised lamb shank on leek mash (£13.95), and puddings such as sticky toffee, mango, ginger and melon parfait, apple and blackberry crumble and chocolate and brandy terrine. Bread comes with properly served butter, not messy little packets. Three linked rooms, no smoking except for the one on the left, have a friendly relaxed atmosphere, with comfortable pub furnishings, cricket and country prints, tea lights on tables, and in the right-hand room (which is panelled) a log fire. Well kept Wadworths 6X, Henrys IPA and JCB on handpump; helpful service. Across the quiet lane, there are picnic-sets under a floodlit sycamore, by the River Meon, with abundant ducks, and wild flowers in the next meadow. *(Recommended by Phyl and Jack Street, Diana Brumfit, Dr D and Mrs B Woods, John and Joan Calvert, Matt and Cathy Fawcett, Peter Salmon)*

Wadworths ~ Tenants Mark and Carole Broadbent ~ Real ale ~ Bar food (12-2, 6-9(9.30 Fri, Sat; 8.30 Sun, Mon)) ~ Restaurant ~ (01489) 877526 ~ Children welcome ~ Dogs allowed in bar ~ Open 11-3, 6-11; 12-3, 6-10.30 Sun

FRITHAM SU2314 Map 2
Royal Oak ◀
Village signed from exit roundabout, M27 junction 1; quickest via B3078, then left and straight through village; head for Eyeworth Pond

The appeal of this charming brick and cob thatched pub lies in its simple rural rusticity. In a delightful spot with gentle views across forest and farmland, it is part of a working farm so there are ponies and pigs out on the green, and plenty of livestock nearby. Locals (needless to say it still has a strong local following) and visitors alike are welcomed with genuine interest. Three neatly kept black beamed rooms (one is no smoking) are very simple but full of proper traditional character, with prints and pictures involving local characters on the white walls, restored panelling, antique wheelback, spindleback and other old chairs and stools with colourful seats around solid tables on new oak flooring, and two roaring log fires. The back bar has quite a few books. Well kept Cheriton Pots Ale and Ringwood Best and Fortyniner, along with guests from brewers such as Cheriton and RCH, are tapped straight from the cask; also half a dozen wines by the glass, and they hold a beer festival in September. Simple lunchtime food is limited to home-made soup (£3.50), and ploughman's with home-made pâté, home-cooked pork pie, and home-cooked gammon or cumberland sausage ring (£5). Summer barbecues are put on in the neatly kept big garden, which has a marquee for poor weather; darts, dominoes and pétanque. *(Recommended by Matthew Johnson, Terry and Linda Moseley, Pete Baker, the Didler, Andrea Rampley, Mrs C Lintott, Mr and Mrs John Taylor, Mayur Shah, Mike Turner)*

Free house ~ Licensees Neil and Pauline McCulloch ~ Real ale ~ Bar food (lunchtime only) ~ No credit cards ~ (023) 8081 2606 ~ Children welcome ~ Dogs welcome ~ Open 11-3, 6-11; 11-11 Sat; 12-10.30 Sun

HAMBLEDON SU6414 Map 2
Vine
West Street, just off B2150

Although the emphasis at this country pub is increasingly on its dining aspects (you may need to book), it does still have a pubby feel, with room for a few drinkers and a cheery welcome from the hands-on landlord (not to mention the charming pub dog, Blue, who has his place on the chenille-covered sofa in one bow window). Bar food includes lunchtime sandwiches (from £2.95) and changing specials such as courgette and sweetcorn bake, home-made steak and kidney pie or breaded plaice (all £7.95), fisherman's pie or peppered lamb baked with ginger, coriander and red wine (£8.95) and monkfish poached with smoked salmon, lemon and dill (£11.95). Furnishings and décor include the usual pub tables and chairs plus a winged high-backed settle, a couple of log fires and a woodburning stove, quite a bit of bric-a-brac (signed cricket bats, decorative plates, banknotes, gin traps, a boar's head, snare drums and a sort of shell-based mandolin on the piano), with tankards and copper kettles (and even an accordion) hanging from old brown beams and joists, sporting and country prints, and some interesting watercolours of early 20th-c regimental badges on the cream or dark red walls. The restaurant and one part of the bar are no smoking. Archers Special, Cheriton Village Elder, Gales (called Vine Best here), Ringwood Best and guests like Itchen Valley Godfather are well kept on handpump alongside Addlestone's cider and Gales country wines; shove-ha'penny, dominoes and cribbage. There are tables in a small informal back garden.
(Recommended by Val and Alan Green, Phyl and Jack Street, Charles and Pauline Stride, Ann and Colin Hunt, Ian Phillips, Prof and Mrs Tony Palmer, Paul and Shirley White)

Free house ~ Licensee Peter Lane ~ Real ale ~ Bar food (not Sun evening) ~ Restaurant ~ (023) 9263 2419 ~ Dogs allowed in bar ~ Open 11.30-3, 6-11; 12-4, 7-10.30 Sun

HAWKLEY SU7429 Map 2
Hawkley Inn ◀
Take first right turn off B3006, heading towards Liss ¾ mile from its junction with A3; then after nearly 2 miles take first left turn into Hawkley village – Pococks Lane; OS Sheet 186 map reference 746292

Freshened up by its new landlord, this unpretentious country local is popular with real ale lovers (though dogs, horses, walkers and cyclists are welcome too) as there are usually seven constantly changing beers, well kept and often from small breweries such as Ballards, Hop Back, Itchen Valley, Kings and Ringwood, as well as a couple of local ciders. The opened-up bar and back dining room have a simple décor – big pine tables, dried flowers, and prints on the mellowing walls; parts of the bar can get a bit smoky when it's busy, but there is a no smoking area to the right of the bar – both sides now have a real fire. Bar food might include filled rolls (£3.95), soup (£4.85), ploughman's (£6.25), spaghetti bolognese (£7.50), spinach and ricotta tart (£8.25), cottage pie or cider sausages (£8.95) and steaks (from £11.25); friendly service. The pub is on the Hangers Way Path, and at weekends there are plenty of walkers; tables and a climbing frame in the pleasant garden.
(Recommended by H H Hellin, Ian Phillips, Martin and Karen Wake, Ann and Colin Hunt, Sue Plant, the Didler, JCW, Phil and Sally Gorton, Fr Robert Marsh, Lynn Sharpless, Tony and Wendy Hobden)

Free house ~ Licensee Nick Troth ~ Real ale ~ Bar food (12-2(4 Sat, Sun), 7-9.30; not Sun evening) ~ (01730) 827205 ~ Children welcome until 8pm ~ Dogs welcome ~ Live music alternate Fri or Sats ~ Open 12-3(5 Sat), 5.30-11; 12-5, 7-10.30 Sun

You can send us reports through our web site: www.goodguides.co.uk

LITTLETON SU4532 Map 2

Running Horse ⑪ ♀

Village signposted off B3049 just NW of Winchester; Main Road

Recently reopened after sweeping refurbishment, this is almost incredibly smart for such a remote and rustically placed pub. The stylishly furnished and crisply decorated bar has some deep leather chairs as well as ochre-cushioned metal and wicker ones around matching modern tables on its polished boards, up-to-date lighting, good colour photographs of Hampshire landscapes and townscapes, a potted palm as well as a log fire, and venetian blinds in its bow windows. The neat modern marble and hardwood bar counter (with swish leather, wood and brass bar stools) has well kept Itchen Valley Fagins or Rose and Ringwood Best on handpump, 18 well chosen wines by the glass, and an espresso machine, with staff neatly aproned in the continental style. Linking openly from here, the back no smoking restaurant area has the same sort of elegant modern furniture, on flagstones. The food is inventive and very rewarding, and they bake their own bread and use local produce where possible. The menu changes daily, and might include sandwiches such as pastrami, sauerkraut and gruyère (£6.50), starters such as courgette and mint soup (£4.50) and ragoût of lambs kidneys with bacon and mustard (£6.50), main courses such as pork, pear and ginger sausages, seared bream with pesto mash (£10.95), grilled chicken breast with lemon grass rice, chilli oil and gingered greens (£12.50), roast pigeon (£18), and puddings such as vanilla or honey crème brûlée, lemon posset and blackberry milkshake or chocolate terrine with mango sorbet (£5.50). Good disabled access and facilities; there may be piped pop music. There are green metal tables and chairs out on terraces front and back, with picnic-sets on the back grass by a spreading sycamore. *(Recommended by Mrs J A Taylar, John Moate, John Balfour)*

Free house ~ Licensee Malcolm Osman ~ Real ale ~ Bar food (12-2, 6.30-9.30; 12-4.30 Sun) ~ Restaurant ~ (01962) 880218 ~ Children in eating area of bar and restaurant ~ Dogs allowed in bar ~ Open 11-3, 5.30-11; 12-9 Sun

LONGSTOCK SU3537 Map 2

Peat Spade ♀

Village signposted off A30 on W edge of Stockbridge, and off A3057 Stockbridge—Andover

Local and organic produce feature significantly on the imaginative menu at this well run place. While locals do drop in for a pint and a chat, the emphasis is very much on the good, interesting food; to be sure of a table, it is best to book in advance. Served by helpful, pleasant staff, the sensibly short menu might typically include spring vegetable soup (£4.75), pork rillettes (£5.50), tagliatelle with mussels and chorizo (£8.75), melted goats cheese on sweet potato purée (£10.75), ballotine of chicken and gammon (£13.50), and puddings such as rhubarb and ginger crumble or crème brûlée (£4.50). The roomy and attractive squarish main bar is airy and high-ceilinged, with pretty windows, well chosen furnishings and a nice show of toby jugs and beer mats around its fireplace. A rather elegant no smoking dining room leads off, and there are doors to a big terrace. Well kept Hampshire King Alfreds, Hop Back Best and Ringwood Fortyniner on handpump, and eight wines by the glass from a carefully chosen list. There are teak seats on the terrace, with more in the pleasant little garden, and perhaps free-range chickens, not to mention two cats, Cleo the cocker spaniel and Mollie the dog (who's diabetic and not allowed to be fed). There are plenty of surrounding walks, along the Test Way at the end of the road and in the water meadows around Stockbridge, and Longstock Water Gardens at the end of village. *(Recommended by R T and J C Moggridge, Pat and Robert Watt, Philip and June Caunt, Ann and Colin Hunt, Gaynor Gregory, B and C Perryman, Andrea Rampley, Catherine FitzMaurice, Vincent Howard, Keith and Jean Symons, Betsy and Peter Little, Patrick Hall, T D Soulsby)*

Free house ~ Licensees Bernie Startup and Sarah Hinman ~ Real ale ~ Bar food ~ Restaurant ~ No credit cards ~ (01264) 810612 ~ Children welcome ~ Dogs welcome ~ Open 11-3, 6.30-11; 12-3 Sun; closed Sun evening, all Mon

LOWER WIELD SU6339 Map 2
Yew Tree 🍴 ♀

Turn off A339 NW of Alton at Medstead, Bentworth 1 signpost, then follow village signposts; or off B3046 S of Basingstoke, signposted from Preston Candover

Tucked away on a very quiet narrow lane opposite a cricket field, since its recent reopening under enthusiastic new young licensees this combines good individually cooked food with the informal atmosphere of a relaxed country pub. The small flagstoned bar area on the left has a few military prints above its stripped brick dado, a steadily ticking clock and a crackling log fire – nice for a quiet winter's lunch. Around to the right of the serving counter – which has a couple of stylish wrought-iron bar chairs – it's carpeted, with a few attractive flower pictures, and throughout there is a mix of tables, including some quite small ones for two, and miscellaneous chairs. Using fresh local ingredients, bar food includes a hearty lunchtime soup (£3.50), chunky sandwiches (from £3.25) and ploughman's (£4.95), as well as starters such as cured meats with tapenade and balsamic reduction (£5.95), scallops sautéed in Pernod (£6.95), main courses such as sausages with caramelised onion gravy or spinach and ricotta cannelloni with cashew pesto, cream and parmesan (£7.95), beef, ale, shallot and vegetable casserole (£9.50), medallions of crisply seared gressingham duck with spiced pear (£14.50), fillet steak with red wine, mushroom and madeira reduction (£16.95), and puddings such as prune and white chocolate bread and butter, plum and apple crumble or home-made ice-creams (£3.95). Vegetables are good and seasonal, and nice breads come with good properly served butter; no smoking area. The well chosen wine list, with a dozen or more by the glass, is reasonably priced, and may include Louis Jadot burgundies from a shipper based just along the lane; Cheriton Pots and Morrells Oxford Blue (called Yew Tree Bitter by the pub) are well kept on handpump. Service is friendly and helpful, with a real personal touch. There are solid tables and chunky seats out on the front terrace, with picnic-sets in a sizeable side garden and pleasant views. Nearby walks include one around lovely Rushmoor Pond. *(Recommended by Phyl and Jack Street, Roger Chacksfield)*

Free house ~ Licensees Tim and Libby Manktelow-Gray ~ Real ale ~ Bar food (12-2, 6.30-9(8.30 Sun)) ~ Restaurant ~ (01256) 389224 ~ Children welcome ~ Dogs allowed in bar ~ Open 11-3, 6-11; 12-10.30 Sun; 12-3, 6-10.30 Sun in winter; closed Mon evening

LYMINGTON SZ3295 Map 2
Kings Head 🍷

Quay Hill; pedestrian alley at bottom of High Street, can park down on quay and walk up from Quay Street

Even in daytime they light candles on the tables at this dusky 17th-c pub. Rambling darkly up and down steps and through timber dividers, mainly bare-boarded rooms have tankards hanging from great rough beams, a rug or two here and there, a nice old-fashioned variety of seating at a great mix of tables from an elegant gateleg to a huge chunk of elm, and the local pictures include good classic yacht photographs. A cosy upper corner past the serving counter has a good log fire in a big fireplace, its mantelpiece a shrine to all sorts of drinking paraphernalia from beer tankards to port and champagne cases. Fullers London Pride and Gales HSB and three guests such as Bass Greene King Old Speckled Hen and a seasonal Ringwood ale are well kept on handpump. Enjoyable food includes home-made soup (£3.95), sandwiches (from £4.65), duck salad (£7.95), pasta with smoked chicken and bacon in creamy parmesan sauce (£8.95), home-made steak and mushroom in ale pie (£9.50), and specials such as home-made chicken liver pâté (£5.70), pork and leek sausages with onion gravy (£8.50), seared tuna with sweet chill sauce (£11.50) and fried venison with red wine jus (£11.95). A wall rack holds daily papers; piped pop music. More reports please. *(Recommended by David Carr, Derek Thomas, Mr and Mrs John Taylor)*

Inn Partnership (Pubmaster) ~ Lease Paul Stratton ~ Real ale ~ Bar food (11-2.10(2.30 Sat), 6-10; 12-2.30, 7-10 Sun) ~ (01590) 672709 ~ Children welcome ~ Dogs welcome ~ Open 11-2.30, 6-11; 11-11 Fri, Sat; 12-10.30 Sun

MICHELDEVER SU5138 Map 2
Half Moon & Spread Eagle
Village signposted off A33 N of Winchester; then follow Winchester 7 signpost almost opposite hall

This friendly country local has a cheery thriving atmosphere – it's one of a minority of main entries that still has a pool table, also juke box, darts, fruit machine, cribbage and daily papers. Greene King IPA, Abbot and Old Speckled Hen, and a couple of guests such as Wadworths 6X are well kept on handpump. It's simply decorated, with heavy tables, leather armchairs and good solid seats, and a woodburning stove in the beamed bar; a no smoking area leads off. Well liked bar food, written up on blackboards, includes soup (£3.95), recommended lunchtime baguettes (from £4.50), goats cheese salad with grape marmalade (£5.50), sausage of the week (£6.95), risotto of the week (£7.95), thai green chicken curry (£8.50), pork medallions with cheese sauce (£9.95), grilled lamb steak with tarragon jus (£10.95), veal and bacon pie (£11.50) and puddings such as coffee crème brûlée and bitter chocolate tart with mandarin sorbet (£4.25). There are seats on a sheltered back terrace, and picnic-sets in the recently upgraded garden. This is a good starting point for exploring the Dever Valley, and there are lots of pleasant walks nearby. *(Recommended by Mary Kirman and Tim Jefferson, Phyl and Jack Street, Charles Gysin, Francis Johnston, Ian Phillips, Dr D E Granger, Ann and Colin Hunt, Ian Moody)*

Greene King ~ Tenants Christina Nicholls and Richard Tolfree ~ Real ale ~ Bar food (12-2, 6-9(9.30 Fri, Sat; 8.30 Sun)) ~ Restaurant ~ (01962) 774339 ~ Children welcome ~ Dogs allowed in bar ~ Open 12-3, 6-11(10.30 Sun)

MONXTON SU3144 Map 2
Black Swan ♀
Village signposted off A303 at Andover junction with A343; car park some 25 metres along High Street

Besides ample lunchtime sandwiches (from £4.50) and ploughman's (£6), the daily changing menu at this pretty part-thatched pub could include salmon and scallop terrine with lemon balsamic dressing or stuffed mushrooms with stilton (£5), pork and cranberry sausage with mustard mash and red onion gravy or mushroom and herb risotto (£10), fried calves liver with crispy bacon and redcurrant jus (£12) and braised lamb shank with sweet potato mash and rosemary and honey sauce (£14), and puddings such as white and dark chocolate cheesecake or cappuccino crème brûlée (£4.25). Past a lobby with a settee and easy chairs, a couple of steps take you up to the small mansard-ceiling timbered bar, with the menu boards, a log fire, a table of daily papers and just a few pub tables; well kept Fullers London Pride, Ringwood Best, Timothy Taylors Landlord and a guest such as Black Sheep on handpump, and ten wines by the glass from a large list. Angling off behind here is the main action: a triangular room with floor-to-ceiling windows looking out at picnic-sets in a lovely little sheltered garden by the little slow-flowing Pillhill Brook, and a further good-sized no smoking restaurant, both carpeted, with country-kitchen chairs and tables set for eating. *(Recommended by Phyl and Jack Street, Mandy Barron, Justin le Page, R T and J C Moggridge, S Topham, Gordon Prince)*

Enterprise ~ Lease Mikael Moriniere ~ Real ale ~ Bar food (12-2(2.30 Fri-Sun), 6(7 Sun)-9.30(10 Fri, Sat)) ~ (01264) 710260 ~ Children in restaurant ~ Dogs allowed in bar ~ Open 12-11; 12-10.30 Sun

OVINGTON SU5631 Map 2
Bush
Village signposted from A31 on Winchester side of Alresford

The interior of this family run and picturesquely set little cottage is nicely old-fashioned, with no games machines or piped music. A low-ceilinged bar is furnished with cushioned high-backed settles, elm tables with pews and kitchen chairs, masses of old pictures in heavy gilt frames on the walls, and a roaring fire on one side with an antique solid fuel stove opposite. Three rooms are no smoking. The back garden runs down to the River Itchen, so it's not surprising to find quite a few customers here on a sunny day. Where possible using local ingredients, bar food (which some readers feel is pricey) includes starters such as soup (£4.95), home-made chicken liver pâté (£6.95), king prawns in garlic, chilli and ginger butter (£10.75), and main courses such as hot roast beef baguette (£9.90), french onion tart with goats cheese and olives (£11.50), beef and ale pie (£12.75), skate wing in black butter (£13.60), smoked haddock risotto with poached egg and parsley oil (£13.50), grilled fillet steak on garlic mash with red wine jus (£18.50), and puddings such as banana and peanut butter bread and butter pudding with raspberry jam sauce and plum and port tart (£4.80). Wadworths 6X, IPA, JCB and a guest such as Charles Wells Bombardier are well kept on handpump, with several country wines and malt whiskies; cribbage, dominoes and board games. Efficient, friendly service, and look out for the sociable scottish springer spaniel, Paddy. Please note that if you want to bring children it's best to book, as there are only a few tables set aside for families. *(Recommended by James Price, Peter F Marshall, John and Vivienne Rice, Lynn Sharpless, M A and C R Starling, Michael and Ann Cole, Val and Alan Green, Prof and Mrs Tony Palmer, Lesley and Peter Barrett, Ann and Colin Hunt, Patrick Hall, Dr D J and Mrs S C Walker, CJ Roebuck, Francis Johnston, John Balfour)*

Wadworths ~ Managers Nick and Cathy Young ~ Real ale ~ Bar food (not Sun evening) ~ (01962) 732764 ~ Children in family room ~ Dogs welcome ~ Open 11-3, 6-11; 12-3, 7-10.30 Sun

PETERSFIELD SU7227 Map 2 🏠

Trooper 🍽️ 🍺 🛏️

From B2070 in Petersfield follow Steep signposts past station, but keep on up past Steep, on old coach road; OS Sheet 186 map reference 726273

The charming landlord at this genuinely hospitable bistro-style inn really goes out of his way to make customers feel welcome. A reader who stayed here told us 'Hassan even rang in wishing us a good journey', and another said 'the happiest place we've been in', to quote just two from a string of very contented reader comments. Good food (best to book to be sure of a table) might include soup (£5), baguettes and sandwiches or greenlip mussels with chilli, breadcrumbs and cheddar (£6), curry of the day, sausage and mash or chicken, smoky bacon and mushroom pie (£9), baked mushroom risotto or pasta of the day (£13), roast duck breast with ginger, honey and sesame noodles (£15); separate vegetables are £4. Well kept on handpump, the three or four beers change frequently but tend to be from local or fairly local brewers such as Cheriton, Hogs Back and Hop Back, and they have decent house wines. There's an island bar, blond chairs and a mix of tripod tables on bare boards or red tiles, tall stools by a broad ledge facing big windows that look across to rolling downland fields, old film star photos and paintings by local artists for sale, little persian knick-knacks here and there, quite a few ogival mirrors, big baskets of dried flowers, lit candles all around, fresh flowers, a well tended log fire in the stone fireplace, and carefully chosen piped music; newspapers and magazines to read. The attractive raftered restaurant has french windows to a partly covered sunken terrace, and there are lots of picnic-sets on an upper lawn; the pub is no smoking except for around the bar counter. The horse rail in the car park ('horses only before 8pm') does get used. *(Recommended by Peter Goddard, Dr D and Mrs B Woods, Simon Collett-Jones, John and Glenys Wheeler, Ann and Colin Hunt, Clare and Peter Pearse, Paul Humphreys, Bruce and Penny Wilkie, Tony Radnor, Bruce Bird, Tracey and Stephen Groves, Phyl and Jack Street, Peter Fitton, Mike and Mary Carter, Val and Alan Green)*

Free house ~ Licensee Hassan Matini ~ Real ale ~ Bar food (12-1.45, 7-9) ~ Restaurant ~ (01730) 827293 ~ Children in eating area of bar and restaurant ~ Dogs allowed in bar ~ Open 12-3, 6-11 ~ Bedrooms: £69B/£89B

The knife-and-fork award distinguishes pubs where the food is of exceptional quality.

PORTSMOUTH SZ6299 Map 2

Still & West

Bath Square, Old Portsmouth

In a nice cobbled street, and handy to know about as there isn't another main entry here, this managed pub has wonderful views from here, stretching as far as the Isle of Wight, and the boats and ships fighting the strong tides in the very narrow mouth of Portsmouth harbour seem almost within touching distance. As well as seats on the terrace, the upper deck restaurant (partly no smoking) has fine views from all tables – best to book. The downstairs bar is decorated in nautical style, with paintings of galleons on the ceiling, ship models, old cable, and photographs of famous ships entering the harbour. Gales Best, Butser, HSB and a guest beer are well kept on handpump, alongside a dozen wines by the glass, and two dozen country wines; piped music and fruit machine. Bar food (after 7pm traditionally wrapped cod and chips (£5.95) only) includes soup (£2.95), sandwiches (£4.25), sausage and mash (£5.95), lasagne (£6.95), steak and mushroom pie (£6.95) and cajun chicken (£8.95), with puddings (£3.95). The pub is not far from the Historic Dockyard so can get busy on fine days. Nearby metered parking can be difficult. *(Recommended by David Carr, Ann and Colin Hunt, Mrs Maricar Jagger, Andy and Jill Kassube, Ken Flawn, Susan and John Douglas)*

Gales ~ Manager Tina Blackhall ~ Real ale ~ Bar food (12-9) ~ Restaurant ~ (023) 9282 1567 ~ Children welcome ~ Open 10-11; 11-10.30 Sun

ROTHERWICK SU7156 Map 2

Falcon

4 miles from M3, junction 5; follow Newnham signpost from exit roundabout, then Rotherwick signpost, then turn right at Mattingley, Heckfield signpost; village also signposted from B3349 N of Hook, then brown signs to pub

This quietly placed country pub has a light and fresh open-plan layout, with quite a mixture of dining chairs around an informal variety of tables on its varnished floorboards, big bay windows with sunny window seats, and minimal decoration on its mainly pale mustard-coloured walls; flowers on the tables, and perhaps a big vase of lilies on the terracotta-coloured central bar counter, give colour. A rather more formal no smoking back dining area is round to the right, and on the left are an overstuffed sofa and a couple of ornate easy chairs by one log fire; piped music. Taking examples from the lunchtime snack menu, main menu and the specials board, bar food might include soup (£4), interesting sandwiches (from £3.95), clams in provençale sauce (£5.25), ploughman's (£5.50), roasted fig wrapped in parma ham and stuffed with monkfish and mascarpone (£5.75), niçoise salad (£7.95), sausage and mash or mediterranean filo bundle (£9.95), steak and ale pie (£12.25), poached halibut steak with crab and cream sauce (£12.50) and fried duck breast with gooseberry sauce and noodles (£13.95); Sunday roast (£8.50). They do stick ridgidly to the 2pm food service deadline. Well kept Adnams Best, Brakspears, Fullers London Pride, and a guest such as Shepherd Neame Spitfire on handpump; maybe piped local radio. Terraces at the front and back have sturdy tables and benches, and there are picnic-sets in a sizeable informal back garden which has pasture views; easy walks nearby. *(Recommended by Andy and Yvonne Cunningham, Ian Phillips, R Lake, KC, Martin and Karen Wake, Brian Dawes)*

Unique (Enterprise) ~ Lease Andy Francis ~ Real ale ~ Bar food (12-4 Sun in winter) ~ Restaurant ~ (01256) 762586 ~ Children welcome in restaurant (small children and babies lunchtime only) ~ Dogs allowed in bar ~ Open 11-2.30, 6-11; 12-10.30 Sun; 12-6 Sun in winter

---

'Children welcome' means the pubs says it lets children inside without any special restriction; readers have found that some may impose an evening time limit – please tell us if you find this.

ROWLAND'S CASTLE SU7310 Map 2
Castle Inn
Village signposted off B2148/B2149 N of Havant; Finchdean Road, by junction with Redhill Road and Woodberry Lane

Reasonably priced food, served by smartly dressed staff, draws midday crowds to this nice village pub. The lunchtime snack menu includes filled baguettes (from £3.25), ploughman's (£4.95), beef and ale pie (£6) and lasagne or chicken balti (£6.25). Dishes are only a little pricier in the evening: game pâté (£4.25), smoked duck with roasted grapes (£4.95), salmon with Cointreau and prawn sauce in puff pastry (£7.50) and lamb shank braised in honey and mint (£8.75). There are two appealing little no smoking eating rooms on the left. The front one has rather nice simple mahogany chairs around sturdy scrubbed pine tables, one quite long, rugs on flagstones, a big fireplace, and quite a lot of old local photographs on its ochre walls. The back one is similar, but with bare boards and local watercolour landscapes by Bob Payne for sale. There is a small separate public bar on the right with a good fire and well kept Gales Best, Butser and HSB and a guest such as Greene King IPA on handpump; disabled access and facilities are good, and the garden behind has picnic-sets. *(Recommended by Ann and Colin Hunt, Andy and Jill Kassube, Mrs Jane Kingsbury, Jess and George Cowley, Ian Phillips)*

Gales ~ Tenants Jan and Roger Burrell ~ Real ale ~ Bar food (12-9; not after 2pm on winter Sun) ~ Restaurant ~ (023) 9241 2494 ~ Children in eating area of bar ~ Dogs allowed in bar ~ Open 11-11; 12-10.30 Sun

SOUTHSEA SZ6498 Map 2
Wine Vaults ⬛
Albert Road, opposite Kings Theatre

A great range of ten real ales at this enjoyably basic pub takes in Courage Directors, Fullers London Pride and Hop Back Summer Lightning, with changing guests from brewers of varying size and regions, such as Hidden Brewery, Ruddles, Theakstons and Youngs. It's popular with a good mix of age groups, but despite the crowds, the efficient friendly staff remain unflustered. The straightforward bar has wood-panelled walls, a wood floor, and an easy-going, chatty feel, and the raised back area is no smoking. There are newspapers for you to read, plus pool, chess, draughts, backgammon and a football table; piped music. Handily served all day (but do bear in mind that beer is the forte here), good helpings of reasonably priced bar food includes sandwiches (from £2.45), grilled ones £3.95), filled baked potatoes (from £3.95), steak in ale pie (£5.95), roasted vegetable and goats cheese bruschetta (£7.95), mexican vegetable burrito or various nachos (from £6.25), salads such as cajun chicken, greek or brie and avocado (from £6.50), and puddings (£3.25). There are seats in the little garden, and a wooden gazebo. *(Recommended by David Carr, Ann and Colin Hunt, Mrs Maricar Jagger, the Didler, Michael B Griffith)*

Free house ~ Licensee Mike Hughes ~ Real ale ~ Bar food (12-9.30) ~ Restaurant ~ (023) 9286 4712 ~ Dogs welcome ~ Open 11-11; 12-10.30 Sun

SPARSHOLT SU4331 Map 2
Plough 🍴 🍷
Village signposted off B3049 (Winchester—Stockbridge), a little W of Winchester

Hampshire Dining Pub of the Year

It's pretty much essential to book a table at this well run bustling pub, whatever time you choose to visit. With friendly helpful staff, excellent food and good beer, it's not surprising that it's so popular. Everything is neatly kept, and the main bar has an interesting mix of wooden tables and chairs, with farm tools, scythes and pitchforks attached to the ceiling; two no smoking areas. As well as sandwiches and ploughman's, the interesting bar food, listed on daily changing blackboards, might include pigeon, bacon and mushroom salad (£5.95), chilli and chickpea cakes with avocado salsa (£8.95), wild mushroom, potato and broccoli stroganoff (£9.95), chicken breast filled with roasted pepper mousse on basil cream (£13.95), lamb shank with rosemary jus (£14.95), and tempting puddings such as chocolatey bête noire with crème anglaise and orange and Cointreau crème brûlée (£4.95). Well kept Wadworths IPA, JCB, 6X and perhaps a guest such as Greene King Old Speckled Hen on handpump, and an extensive wine list with plenty by the glass, including champagne and pudding wine. Disabled access and facilities; there's a children's play fort, and plenty of seats on the terrace and lawn. *(Recommended by James Price, John and Joan Calvert, Mandy Barron, Val and Alan Green, Dr and Mrs A K Clarke, Mick Simmons, Phyl and Jack Street, Ann and Colin Hunt, Vincent Howard, Peter F Marshall, Lynn Sharpless, Keith Rutter, Inga Davis, Martin and Karen Wake, Keith and Jean Symons, Peter and Eleanor Kenyon, Peter and Jean Dowson, Patrick Hall, J Stickland, Francis Johnston, T D Soulsby, John Balfour, R Lake)*

Wadworths ~ Tenants R C and K J Crawford ~ Real ale ~ Bar food (12-2, 6-9) ~ Restaurant ~ No credit cards ~ (01962) 776353 ~ Children in eating area of bar ~ Dogs welcome ~ Open 11-3, 6-11; 12-3, 6-10.30 Sun

STEEP SU7425 Map 2
Harrow

Take Midhurst exit from Petersfield bypass, at exit roundabout first left towards Midhurst, then first turning on left opposite garage, and left again at Sheet church; follow over dual carriageway bridge to pub

It seems fitting to start this entry with a tribute to the late Ellen McCutcheon who was born in this old-fashioned pub in 1929, took over the running of it from her mother after the war, and turned it into the special place it still is today – a favourite with many of our readers. Her two daughters have been at the helm since September, and the pub is still the same simple unchanging place it's been for years. The cosy public bar has hops and dried flowers hanging from the beams, built-in wall benches on the tiled floor, stripped pine wallboards, a good log fire in the big inglenook, and wild flowers on the scrubbed deal tables; dominoes and shove-ha'penny. Well kept Cheriton Diggers Gold and Pots, Ringwood Best and maybe a guest such as Ballards Best are tapped straight from casks behind the counter, and they've local wine, apple and pear juice. Good helpings of unfussy home-made bar food include sandwiches, home-made scotch eggs (£3.10), hearty soups such as ham, split pea and vegetable (£4.20), ploughman's, home-made cottage pie, lasagne or quiches (£7.50), and salads (£10.50), with puddings such as treacle tart or seasonal fruit pies (£3.70); staff are polite and friendly, even when under pressure. The big garden is left free-flowering so that goldfinches can collect thistle seeds from the grass. The Petersfield bypass doesn't intrude on this idyll, though you will need to follow the directions above to find it. No children inside. *(Recommended by Phil and Sally Gorton, Ann and Colin Hunt, R B Gardiner, J Stickland, Brenda and Rob Fincham, Lynn Sharpless, Michael B Griffith, the Didler, Charles and Pauline Stride, Irene and Derek Flewin, J L Wedel, Anthony Longden)*

Free house ~ Licensees Claire and Denise McCutcheon ~ Real ale ~ Bar food (not Sun evening) ~ No credit cards ~ (01730) 262685 ~ Dogs welcome ~ Open 12-2.30, 6-11; 11-3, 6-11 Sat; 12-3, 7-10.30 Sun; closed winter Sun evenings

STOCKBRIDGE SU3535 Map 2
Grosvenor

High Street

The high-ceilinged main bar at this handsome Georgian country-town coaching inn has a pleasantly restrained décor entirely in keeping with the distinction of the building itself. Well divided into separate room areas (several are no smoking), it is comfortable and relaxing, with a good log fire. Greene King IPA and Abbot are well kept on handpump, alongside a dozen enjoyable wines by the glass, and decent coffee; piped music. Bar food (surprisingly reasonable given the nice surroundings) includes sandwiches (from £3.95), soup such as sweet roasted pepper and tomato (£3.95), grilled goats cheese on a toasted croûton with roast baby tomatoes (£4.95),

chicken liver and mushroom pâté with red onion marmalade (£5.25), lasagne
(£5.95), sausages and mash with caramelised onions and gravy or steak and ale pie
(£7.95), battered cod (£8.95), and braised lamb shank (£9.95). The impressive oak-
panelled restaurant has some attractive late 19th-c pictures of horserace winners
from the stables of the hotel's then owner, who was Master of the Danebury
Harriers. A back conservatory has more tables. A couple of pavement tables stand
out beside the imposing front portico, with more tables in the good-sized back
garden, prettily laid out with attractive plantings. This is an appealing little town,
with good antiques shops, the National Trust Common Marsh along the River
Test, and downland walks all around. Please tell us about the bedrooms if you stay
here. *(Recommended by Geoffrey Kemp, Dennis Jenkin, Ann and Colin Hunt,
Edward Mirzoeff)*

Greene King ~ Managers Colin and Valerie Holman ~ Real ale ~ Bar food (12-2, 6.30-9) ~
Restaurant ~ (01264) 810606 ~ Children welcome ~ Dogs allowed in bar and bedrooms
~ Open 11-11; 12-10.30 Sun ~ Bedrooms: £85B/£99.50B

Three Cups ♀ ◖
High Street

Readers love the little cottage garden and streamside terrace at this delightful pub.
Inside, there's a settle and hall chair in a small quarry-tiled hallway, an old-
fashioned leather porter's chair by the telephone in an inner lobby, and a snug low-
beamed bar on the right: quite narrow and very dimly lit (candles in bottles on all
the tables at night), with an engaging mix of furnishings on its turkey carpet, from
high-backed settles to a button-back leather sofa, and a variety of mainly oak
tables. The dark red walls are packed with old engravings, fishing gear, one or two
guns and a fair bit of taxidermy, and there are daily papers, and logs blazing in the
woodburning stove. Gales and Ringwood Best and a couple of guests from brewers
like Itchen Valley are well kept, and they have decent wines by the glass; fairly quiet
piped music. Interesting freshly cooked bar food from a changing menu might
include soup (£4.25), lunchtime baguettes such as brie, bacon and roasted peppers
(£6.25), crab and avocado salad (£7.95), mushroom and spinach risotto (£9.95),
venison casserole (£10.50), seared king scallops (£14), bass with coconut and curry
prawns (£14.95), and puddings such as chocolate and honeycomb cheesecake
(£3.95). There is a no smoking restaurant on the left. *(Recommended by James Price,
M A and C R Starling, Dr D G Twyman, Ron Shelton, Edward Mirzoeff, David and
Sheila Pearcey, Dennis Jenkin, Phyl and Jack Street, Ann and Colin Hunt, Mrs Angela Bromley-
Martin, John and Julie Moon, Pam and David Bailey, Dr and Mrs A K Clarke, Alex and
Irene Harvey)*

Free house ~ Licensee Lucia Foster ~ Real ale ~ Bar food (12-2.30, 7-9.30) ~ Restaurant ~
(01264) 810527 ~ Children welcome ~ Dogs allowed in bar ~ Open 12-11(10.30 Sun) ~
Bedrooms: £57.50B/£67.50B

TICHBORNE SU5630 Map 2
Tichborne Arms
Village signed off B3047

New licensees (and their long haired german shepherd Dylan) have no intentions to
alter the course of things at this charmingly old-fashioned country pub. The
comfortable square-panelled room on the right has wheelback chairs and settles
(one very long), a stone fireplace, and latticed windows. On the left is a larger,
livelier, partly panelled room used for eating. Pictures and documents on the walls
recall the bizarre Tichborne Case, in which a mystery man from Australia claimed
fraudulently to be the heir to this estate. Home-made bar food includes sandwiches
(from £3.50), prawn cocktail (£5.50), ploughman's (£5.95), mushroom, leek and
red onion crumble (£8.25), pies such as chicken, tarragon and mushroom, steak, ale
and stilton or fish (from £8.50), lamb shank (£12.50), with puddings such as syrup
sponge or fudge and walnut flan (from £3.50). Well kept Ringwood Best,
Wadworths 6X and a couple of local guests are tapped from the cask, alongside a

decent choice of wines by the glass, country wines and farm cider; sensibly placed darts, bar billiards, shove-ha'penny, cribbage and piped music. Picnic-sets outside in the big well kept garden. You can expect to find quite a few walkers here during the day, as the Wayfarers Walk and Itchen Way pass close by. No children inside. *(Recommended by David Carr, Lynn Sharpless, Ann and Colin Hunt, Michael B Griffith, P Hennessey, R B Gardiner, Mandy and Simon King, the Didler, June and Geoffrey Cox, William Ruxton, Francis Johnston)*

Free house ~ Licensees Nigel and Sarah Burt ~ Real ale ~ Bar food (12-2, 6.30-9.30) ~ (01962) 733760 ~ Dogs welcome ~ Open 11.30-2.30, 6-11; 12-3, 7-10.30 Sun

UPHAM SU5320 Map 2
Brushmakers Arms
Shoe Lane; village signposted from Winchester—Bishops Waltham downs road, and from B2177 (former A333)

Tucked away down a lane (it's best to park by the duck pond), this easy going old village local has a really welcoming atmosphere – probably down to the friendly hospitality of the landlord (and not the pub ghost). Picking up on the pub's name, walls in the L-shaped bar (divided in two by a central brick chimney with a woodburning stove in the raised two-way fireplace) are hung with quite a collection of ethnic-looking brushes. A few beams in the low ceiling add to the cosiness, and there are comfortably cushioned wall settles and chairs, and a variety of tables including some in country-style stripped wood; there's also a little snug, cribbage, fruit machine, shove-ha'penny and sensibly placed darts. Charles Wells Bombardier, Hampshire Brush and Uncle Bob, and Ringwood Best are well kept on handpump. Very well prepared sensibly priced bar food includes lunchtime snacks such as sandwiches (from £3.75), and ham and egg (£5.25), as well as sardines in garlic (£5.50), half a dozen vegetarian dishes (from £7.95), steak and kidney pie or wild rabbit casserole (£8.95), crab salad (£9.95), lamb steak with garlic and red wine or crab and sherry bake (£10.95), and steaks (from £10.95), with home-made puddings (£4.50). The big garden is well stocked with mature shrubs and trees, and there are picnic-sets on a sheltered back terrace among lots of tubs of flowers, with more on the tidy tree-sheltered lawn. Good walks nearby. *(Recommended by Ann and Colin Hunt, Prof and Mrs Tony Palmer, Fr Robert Marsh, Paul and Shirley White, Roy and Lindsey Fentiman, A J Atyeo, Phyl and Jack Street, Dave Braisted)*

Free house ~ Licensee Tony Mottram ~ Real ale ~ Bar food (12-2, 6(7 Sun)-9(9.30 Fri, Sat)) ~ (01489) 860231 ~ Children in eating area of bar ~ Open 11-3, 5.45-11; 11-3.30, 6-11 Sat; 12-3.30, 7-10.30 Sun

WELL SU7646 Map 2
Chequers
Off A287 via Crondall, or A31 via Froyle and Lower Froyle

Cosily low-beamed, with a roaring winter log fire, this friendly place has a good welcome for all. Its panelled walls are hung with 18th-c country-life prints and old sepia photographs of locals enjoying a drink. Alcoves, wooden pews, brocaded stools and a few GWR carriage lamps all add to its character; fruit machine, dominoes, chess and Jenga. Three well kept Badger beers on handpump, and decent wines. Generous helpings of tasty and very reasonably priced bar food include home-made soup (£3.25), sandwiches (from £4.25), duck and orange pâté with tangy fruit and cider chutney (£4.75), warm chicken and bacon salad (£4.95), home-made burger topped with bacon and brie (£6.95), enjoyable steak in ale pie, sausages and mash or wild mushroom and three cheese en croûte (all £7.95), and steaks (from £12.50); the restaurant is no smoking. The vine-covered terrace is a very pleasant place to sit in summer, and the spacious back garden has picnic-sets too. They provide bowls of water and biscuits for dogs. *(Recommended by Andrin Cooper, Paul A Moore, M A and C R Starling, Martin and Karen Wake, Phil and Sally Gorton, Ian Phillips, N R White)*

Badger ~ Managers Sonia Henderson and Tim Llewellyn ~ Real ale ~ Bar food (12-2.30(3.30 Sat, Sun), 6.30-9.30(8.30 Sun)) ~ Restaurant ~ (01256) 862605 ~ Children in restaurant ~ Dogs allowed in bar ~ Open 12-3, 6-11; 12-11 Sat; 12-10.30 Sun

WHERWELL SU3840 Map 2
White Lion
B3420, in village itself

Very neatly kept and well run by a welcoming couple (and their chocolate labrador Harley), the multi-level beamed bar at this 17th-c village pub has delft plates, sparkling brass, fresh flowers, and well kept Bass and Ringwood Best on handpump. The Village bar has an open fire, and there are two dining rooms; piped music. Tasty bar food, at very fair prices, includes soup (£3.80), ploughman's (£5.75), pie or curry of the day (£8.25), alongside blackboard specials such as kidney and sausages in red wine or salmon and asparagus with white wine sauce (£9.25), and fried medallions of pork with sun-dried tomatoes and stilton sauce on mustard mash (£9.50), and puddings (from £3.80); it's a good idea to book for their Sunday roast. Plenty of seats in the courtyard and on the terrace. The village is pleasant to stroll through, and there's a nice walk over the River Test and meadows to Chilbolton. *(Recommended by B J Harding, Leigh and Gillian Mellor, Prof and Mrs Tony Palmer, Mike Gorton, Ann and Colin Hunt, A J Atyeo, Phyl and Jack Street, Lynn Sharpless, OPUS, Mr and Mrs A Silver)*

Punch ~ Lease Adrian and Patsy Stent ~ Real ale ~ Bar food ~ Restaurant ~ (01264) 860317 ~ Children in restaurant ~ Dogs welcome ~ Folk first and third Thurs of month ~ Open 10-2.30(3 Sat), 6-11; 12-3, 7-10.30 Sun; 7-10.30 Weds-Sun evenings in winter ~ Bedrooms: £37.50S/£49.50S

WINCHESTER SU4828 Map 2
Black Boy 🍺
I mile from M3 junction 10 northbound; B3403 towards city then left into Wharf Hill; rather further and less easy from junction 9, and anyway beware no nearby daytime parking – 220 metres from car park on B3403 N, or nice longer walk from town via College Street and College Walk, or via towpath

Readers love the splendidly eccentric décor, fascinating array of knick-knacks and nice old-fashioned feel at this most unusual pub. There are floor to ceiling books in some parts, lots of big clocks, mobiles made of wine bottles or strings of spectacles, some nice modern nature photographs in the lavatories and on the brightly stained walls on the way, and plenty of other things that you'll enjoy tracking down. Furnishings are similarly eclectic. Several different areas run from a bare-boards barn room with an open hayloft (now an evening dining room) down to an orange-painted room with big oriental rugs on red-painted floorboards. Lunchtime bar food includes sandwiches (£4), and home-made hot meals such as sausage and mash with onion gravy, vegetarian pasta, and lamb hotpot (£6-£7.50); evening restaurant meals are more elaborate. The very well kept beers on handpump are more or less local: Cheriton Pots, Hop Back Summer Lightning and Ringwood Best alongside a couple of guests such as Hampshire and Itchen Valley; decent wines, two log fires, and friendly staff. Well chosen and reproduced piped music; table football, shove-ha'penny, cribbage and dominoes; a couple of slate tables out in front, more tables on an attractive secluded terrace with barbecues. Children allowed at parents' liability. *(Recommended by David Carr, Ann and Colin Hunt, Len Beattie, family Buckle, Val and Alan Green)*

Free house ~ Licensee David Nicholson ~ Real ale ~ Bar food (12-2 Weds-Sun) ~ Restaurant ~ (01962) 861754 ~ Dogs welcome ~ Open 11-3, 5-11; 12-3, 7-10.30 Sun

---

If you stay overnight in an inn or hotel, they are allowed to serve you an alcoholic drink at any hour of the day or night.

Wykeham Arms ★ ⑪ ♀

75 Kingsgate Street (Kingsgate Arch and College Street are now closed to traffic; there is access via Canon Street)

It's essential to book a table well ahead at this rather civilised inn, as the food is very popular. Served by neatly uniformed staff, the imaginative lunchtime choice prepared with carefully sourced ingredients, might include tempting sandwiches such as salmon with crème fraîche and watercress (from £4.95), chicken, spinach, apricot and herb roulade with pear and walnut chutney (£5.75), wild mushroom and stilton risotto with truffle oil (£7.50), salmon fishcakes with yoghurt and cucumber dressing (£6.75), beef sandwich topped with duxelles (£7.25), bass fillet on thai vegetable noodles with mango and coriander salsa (£7.50), gammon (£7.95) and 8oz sirloin (£13.75); vegetables are £3.25. The evening menu, served in the restaurant only, is more elaborate and pricier; the eating areas are no smoking. A series of stylish bustling rooms radiating from the central bar has 19th-c oak desks retired from nearby Winchester College, a redundant pew from the same source, kitchen chairs and candlelit deal tables, and the big windows have swagged paisley curtains; all sorts of interesting collections are dotted around. A snug room at the back, known as the Jameson Room (after the late landlord Graeme Jameson), is decorated with a set of Ronald Searle 'Winespeak' prints, a second one is panelled, and all of them have log fires. A fine choice of drinks includes three well kept Gales beers with a guest such as Charles Wells Bombardier on handpump, and 18 wines by the glass from an extensive wine list. There are tables on a covered back terrace (they will serve food at lunchtime only here), with more on a small but sheltered lawn. No children inside. *(Recommended by James Price, David Carr, Vincent Howard, Dr D G Twyman, Mrs Joy Griffiths, Dr D Taub, Lynn Sharpless, Barry and Anne, John and Vivienne Rice, Ann and Colin Hunt, Martin and Karen Wake, the Didler, Brenda and Rob Fincham, M Sharp, Derek Thomas, Edmund Coan, Joan York, John Oates, Denise Walton, Patrick Hall, Di and Mike Gillam, Chris Bell)*

Gales ~ Managers Peter and Kate Miller ~ Real ale ~ Restaurant ~ (01962) 853834 ~ Dogs allowed in bar and bedrooms ~ Open 11-11; 12-10.30 Sun ~ Bedrooms: £57S(£85B)/£95B

LUCKY DIP

Besides the fully inspected pubs, you might like to try these Lucky Dips recommended to us and described by readers (if you do, please send us reports: www.goodguides.co.uk).

ALRESFORD [SU5832]

Bell [West St]: Relaxing refurbished Georgian coaching inn, good choice of good value food, unobtrusively attentive service, several well kept beers, fairly priced wines, extended bar with log fire and daily papers, smallish dining room; tables in attractively renovated back courtyard, comfortable new bedrooms, open all day *(Ron Shelton, Mr and Mrs R W Allan)*
Cricketers [Jacklyns Lane]: Large pub with good value appetising food inc bargain wkdy lunches (book ahead for Sun), well kept real ales, friendly efficient service, cottagey eating area down steps; pleasant garden with covered seating and good play area *(Phyl and Jack Street)*
Globe [bottom of Broad St (B3046)]: Comfortable dining pub in enviable spot with plenty of picnic-sets in garden looking over historic Alresford Pond; priced for its position, with food all day summer wknds, real ales such as Fullers London Pride, Itchen Valley Godfathers, Ringwood Best and Wadworths 6X, good choice of wines by the glass, log fires

each end, unusual pictures; no smoking restaurant (children allowed here and in a less attractive tented area); open all day Sun and summer Sat *(David Carr, Ron Shelton, Ann and Colin Hunt, LYM, Val and Alan Green)*
☆ *Horse & Groom* [Broad St; town signed off A31 bypass]: Warm and welcoming beamed and timbered bar, roomily open-plan but with cosy alcoves, stepped levels and good bow window seats, enjoyable reasonably priced food, well kept ales such as Bass, Fullers London Pride and Wadworths 6X, decent wines by the glass, quick bar service, nice back no smoking restaurant area; decent piped music, open till midnight Sat – popular then with young people; children welcome, small enclosed garden, open all day *(David Carr, Ann and Colin Hunt, LYM, Peter Salmon, Lynn Sharpless)*

ALTON [SU7138]

☆ *French Horn* [The Butts (A339 S of centre, by rly bridge)]: Bright and cheery local with well kept ales from long counter such as Cottage

Merry Hound, Courage Best, Wadworths 6X, Wychwood Hobgoblin and Youngs Bitter and Waggle Dance (beer festival late Nov), good coffee, bar food from sandwiches and baked potatoes up, tankards and whisky-water jugs on beams, old photographs and inglenook log fires, partly stripped brick dining room, efficient hospitable service, generous pub food, sizeable restaurant, motorcyclists not spurned, separate skittle alley; piped pop music; picnic-sets and other tables outside, bedrooms, open all day (Ann and Colin Hunt, E G Parish, Phil and Sally Gorton, BB)

Railway Tavern [Anstey Rd, opp station rd]: Town local owned by fff, with their good beers priced attractively, farm ciders, german beers, occasional guest beers (Jamie Wallis)

ARFORD [SU8336]

☆ *Crown* [off B3002 W of Hindhead]: Unpretentious low-beamed bar with coal and log fires, steps up to homely eating area, good food from sandwiches to hare, buffalo and splendid puddings, well kept Adnams, Fullers London Pride, Greene King Abbot and a guest beer, decent wines by the glass, welcoming service, no smoking restaurant; piped music; children welcome in eating areas, picnic-sets out in peaceful dell by a tiny stream across the road (R B Gardiner, LYM, J D Derry)

ASHMANSWORTH [SU4157]

Plough: Friendly no-frills pub in attractive village, two quarry-tiled rooms knocked together, well kept Archers Village, Best and Golden and a changing guest tapped from the cask, simple home-cooked lunchtime food, good attentive service, log fire, no piped music; seats outside, good walks, handy for Highclere Castle; cl Mon (the Didler)

AXFORD [SU6043]

Crown [B3046 S of Basingstoke]: Three compact linked rooms around central servery, pleasant décor, stripped tables and chapel chairs, small log fire, well kept ales such as Bass, Cheriton Pots, fff Moondance and Altons Pride, several wines by the glass, food (all day summer wknds) from lunchtime ciabattas and baked potatoes up, daily papers; piped music, TV; children and dogs welcome, suntrap terrace and sloping shrub-sheltered garden, open all day summer wknds (Ann and Colin Hunt, LYM)

BASING [SU6653]

Millstone [Bartons Lane, Old Basing (attached to Bartons Mill Restaurant)]: Converted mill in lovely spot by River Loddon, good value dishes of the day, Wadworths and other well kept ales tapped from the cask, quick service even when busy; children welcome, big garden, handy for ruins of Basing House (Nigel Howard)

BEAULIEU [SU3902]

Montagu Arms [almost opp Palace House]: Civilised hotel in attractive surroundings; separate less formal Montys bar/brasserie, open all day, with decent food from nice sandwiches up inc children's helpings, friendly efficient service, Ringwood real ales inc seasonal, good choice of wines by the glass,

lots of malt whiskies, sofas and easy chairs, bare boards, books and panelling, no smoking room; may be piped music; children welcome, dogs allowed in bar area, picnic-sets out on front courtyard, comfortable bedrooms, good spot for walks (LYM, Michael Dandy)

BEAUWORTH [SU5624]

☆ *Milbury's* [off A272 Winchester/Petersfield]: Warmly welcoming licensees in attractive ancient pub, beams, panelling and stripped stone, massive 17th-c treadmill for much older incredibly deep well, log fires in huge fireplaces, well kept ales such as Cheriton Pots, fff and Theakstons Old Peculier, Addlestone's cider, good choice of wines and country wines, decent straightforward bar food, some south african dishes in smart newly done restaurant; piped music; children in eating areas, garden with fine downland views, plenty of walks, bedrooms, open all day (Ann and Colin Hunt, LYM, H H Hellin, the Didler, Guy Vowles, Lynn Sharpless, Paul and Shirley White, Mrs Maricar Jagger)

BIGHTON [SU6134]

Three Horseshoes [off B3046 in Alresford just N of pond; or off A31 in Bishops Sutton]: Old-fashioned country local with very friendly licensees, well kept Gales HSB and BBB and a west country guest beer, decent house wines, Sun bar nibbles, no smoking lounge with woodburner in huge fireplace, dining room, darts and pool in bare-boards stripped-stone back public bar; may be piped music; children welcome, good walks nearby, cl Mon winter lunchtime (Lynn Sharpless, Phil and Sally Gorton, the Didler)

BINSTED [SU7741]

Cedars [off A31 at Bentley, then village signed; The Street]: Friendly and chatty high-ceilinged local with ancient advertisements and blazing fire in airy big-windowed bar, well kept Brakspears, Courage Best, Gales HSB and Marstons Pedigree, good simple home-made traditional food inc very fresh fish and enjoyable Sun lunch, very reasonable prices, pleasant dining room on right with another fire, green baize cards table, darts, corner TV; dogs welcome, big garden with huge further family play garden (Atisa Morgan, Wendy Arnold, BB, Martin and Karen Wake)

BISHOP'S WALTHAM [SU5517]

☆ *Bunch of Grapes* [St Peters St – just along from entrance to central car park]: Neatly kept small local quietly placed in attractive medieval street, smartly updated furnishings and décor yet keeping individuality and unspoilt feel (run by same family for a century), well kept Courage Best and Greene King IPA tapped from the cask, good chatty landlord and regulars; back garden with own serving bar (Phil and Sally Gorton, the Didler, BB, Stephen and Jean Curtis)

White Horse [Beeches Hill, off B3035 NE]: Open-plan pub with central log fire, hop-hung beams and joists, fancy knotwork, candles in bottles, well kept Adnams, Ringwood Best and Shepherd Neame Spitfire, country wines, friendly new mother-and-son licensees doing good range of enjoyable food inc particularly wide vegetarian choice; unobtrusive piped music; picnic-sets on front terrace, open all day *(BB)*

BOTLEY [SU5113]

Bugle [High St]: Attractive beamed Georgian pub with real ales such as Fullers London Pride, Gales BB and Ringwood Best, friendly staff, good value straightforward food from sandwiches to good fish, public bar with darts etc, no smoking restaurant; unobtrusive piped music; tables in flower-filled yard *(Val and Alan Green)*

Railway Inn [Station Hill (A334 nr stn)]: Roomy railway-themed pub with some areas on lower level, well kept ales inc Greene King, decent wines, good menu and specials board inc lots of fresh fish, helpful management, large conservatory (worth booking Sun); Upper Hamble Country Park nearby *(Bruce and Penny Wilkie, Phyl and Jack Street)*

BRAISHFIELD [SU3725]

Newport Inn [Newport Lane – from centre follow Michelmersh, Timsbury signpost]: Plain two-bar brick local, hard-used elderly furnishings, simple huge cheap sandwiches and bargain ploughman's, particularly well kept Gales ales, country wines, down-to-earth long-serving licensees, cribbage; piped music, wknd piano singsongs; informal tree-shaded garden with old furniture, may be geese, ducks or chickens *(Phil and Sally Gorton, the Didler, Lynn Sharpless, BB, Dr and Mrs A K Clarke)*

BRAMBRIDGE [SU4721]

☆ *Dog & Crook* [village signed off M3 junction 12 exit roundabout, via B3335]: Lots of neat tables under hop-hung beams around central bar, emphasis on good food choice from pub standards to some more unusual and restaurantly dishes inc lovely puddings (Sun lunch booked weeks ahead), relaxing atmosphere, quick friendly young staff, well kept Fullers London Pride, Gales HSB and Ringwood Best, country wines, cosy dining room, small smoking area; alloy tables and chairs out on deck and under fairy-lit arbour, grass beyond, walks on Itchen Way nearby *(A and B D Craig, BB, Nicki Watson)*

BRANSGORE [SZ1997]

☆ *Three Tuns* [opposite church, Ringwood Rd, off A35 N of Christchurch]: Pretty 17th-c thatched pub, wide range of above-average imaginative food from ciabattas up, cheerful efficient service, well kept Greene King IPA, Ringwood Fortyniner and Timothy Taylors Landlord, good range of wines and hot drinks, tastefully refurbished olde-worlde bar with stripped brickwork and beamery, comfortable partly no smoking dining area, fresh flowers; dogs allowed, pleasant back lawn with play area and open country views, large flower-decked front terrace; bedrooms *(D Marsh, Phyl and Jack Street, Prof Keith and Mrs Jane Barber)*

BREAMORE [SU1517]

Bat & Ball [Salisbury Rd]: Refurbished village pub with enjoyable good value food, well kept Ringwood, friendly service, two connecting bar areas, attractive restaurant; pleasant side garden, bedrooms, Avon fishing and walks, inc lovely ones up by church and stately Breamore House to Breamore Woods and maze *(Norman and June Williams)*

BROOK [SU2713]

Bell [B3079/B3078, handy for M27 junction 1]: Really a hotel and plush restaurant (with thriving golf club), in same family for over 200 years, but has sociably neatly kept bar with lovely inglenook fire, good choice of well kept ales inc Ringwood and enjoyable bar food from sandwiches to steak, helpful friendly uniformed staff; big garden, delightful village, 25 comfortable bedrooms with own bathrooms *(Carol and Dono Leaman, Phyl and Jack Street, Angela Copeland)*

Green Dragon [B3078 NW of Cadnam]: Big open-plan pub in New Forest, dating from 15th c, wide choice of reliable food, variety of areas with scrubbed pine tables or longer refectory tables, proper bar areas too, quick smiling service, well kept Fullers London Pride, Gales HSB and Ringwood, pool room; pleasant garden with good enclosed play area, picturesque village *(Dick and Madeleine Brown, JWAC)*

BROUGHTON [SU3032]

Tally Ho [High St, opp church; signed off A30 Stockbridge—Salisbury]: Easy relaxed local atmosphere in open-plan largely tiled square bar, two open fires, hunting prints, local landscapes for sale, good sandwiches and reasonably priced home-made hot dishes, well kept ales from fff and Ringwood, good house wines in two glass sizes, darts, no piped music; smoking allowed throughout, no credit cards; children welcome, tables in charming secluded back garden, good walks; has been cl Tues *(Peter Neate, BB, Prof and Mrs Tony Palmer)*

BURGHCLERE [SU4660]

Carpenters Arms [Harts Lane, off A34]: Pleasantly furnished small pub with good country views from attractively laid-out dining conservatory, cheerful helpful landlord, big helpings of bar food from well presented sandwiches to some ambitious dishes, well kept Arkells, decent choice of wines by the glass; unobtrusive piped music; garden tables, handy for Sandham Memorial Chapel (NT) *(Lynn Sharpless)*

BURITON [SU7320]

☆ *Five Bells* [off A3 S of Petersfield]: Appealing pub, spick and span and doing well under current management, enjoyable food from baguettes to imaginative main dishes, well kept Badger beers, good wines by the glass, daily papers, fresh flowers and church candles on numbered tables, low beams and big log fire, some ancient stripped masonry and woodburner on public side; fruit machine, piped music; children in eating areas, tables on informal lawn behind and more on sheltered terraces, pretty village, good walks, self-catering in converted stables *(Wendy Arnold, Ann and Colin Hunt, LYM, Shirley Mackenzie, Tony Phillips, Guy Vowles, Ian Phillips, Phyl and Jack Street)*

BURLEY [SU2202]

☆ *White Buck* [Bisterne Close; ¾ mile E, OS Sheet 195 map ref 223028]: Long comfortable bar in 19th-c mock-Tudor hotel, very wide choice of reasonably priced good generous food, Gales Butser, HSB and GB and Ringwood Best, decent wines and country wines, cheap soft drinks, good coffee, log fire, courteous efficient staff, thriving atmosphere, smart and attractive end dining room with tables out on decking (should book – but no bookings Sun lunchtime); may be quiet piped music; dogs welcome, pleasant front terrace and spacious lawn, lovely setting in New Forest, good value well equipped bedrooms, superb walks towards Burley itself and over Mill Lawn *(BB, John and Joan Calvert, D Marsh)*

BURSLEDON [SU4809]

Fox & Hounds [Hungerford Bottom; two miles from M27 junction 8]: Rambling oak-beamed and partly flagstoned 16th-c Chef & Brewer, log fires, Gales ales, lots of wines, wide choice of enjoyable reasonably priced food from sandwiches up; linked by family conservatory area to ancient back barn with cheerful rustic atmosphere, immense refectory table, lantern-lit side stalls, lots of interesting and authentic farm equipment, wide choice from food bar; children allowed, tables outside *(LYM, Jess and George Cowley)*

☆ *Jolly Sailor* [off A27 towards Bursledon Station, Lands End Rd; handy for M27 junction 8]: Busy Badger dining pub in superb spot overlooking yachting inlet, tastefully refurbished so as to keep much of its old-fashioned nautical character alongside a more up-to-date layout; well presented reasonably priced food (no bookings), four well kept real ales, good wine choice, good friendly service *(Matthew Johnson, Lynn Sharpless, LYM, Charles and Pauline Stride, Jess and George Cowley, the Didler, A and B D Craig, Peter and Audrey Dowsett, Paul and Shirley White, Spider Newth)*

CADNAM [SU3013]

Coach & Horses [Southampton Rd]: Wide choice of good value food from baguettes and baked potatoes to more imaginative dishes, OAP discounts, efficient cheerful service *(D Marsh)*

☆ *Sir John Barleycorn* [Old Romsey Rd; by M27, junction 1]: Picturesque low-slung thatched pub extended from low-beamed and timbered medieval core on left, glossy modern décor and stripped wood flooring now, wide choice of enjoyable up-to-date food, well kept ales inc Ringwood, reasonably priced wines, two roaring log fires, no smoking restaurant end, prompt and friendly young staff; dogs and children welcome, can be very busy; suntrap benches in front and out in garden, eye-catching flowers, open all day *(Phyl and Jack Street, Vince, LYM)*

CANTERTON [SU2613]

☆ *Sir Walter Tyrell* [off A31 W of Cadnam, follow Rufus's Stone sign]: Pretty pub by lovely clearing in New Forest, often with ponies, long divided front bar, long back dining room, wide choice of popular food, good range of real ales inc Ringwood, quick helpful service coping well with big groups; big play area, sheltered terrace, good base for walks *(Michael and Robin Inskip, W W Burke)*

CHARTER ALLEY [SU5957]

White Hart [White Hart Lane, off A340 N of Basingstoke]: Friendly beamed village pub with well kept Butts Jester, Otter, Timothy Taylors Landlord, West Berkshire Maggs Mild and interesting guest beers, continental beers, summer farm cider, decent wines, wide choice of enjoyable reasonably priced food (not Sun/Mon evenings) in dining area, pleasant service, comfortable lounge bar with no smoking area and woodburner in big fireplace, simple public bar with skittle alley; may be unobtrusive piped music; small garden with new terrace *(J V Dadswell, Bruce Bird, Michael and Jeanne Shillington)*

CHAWTON [SU7037]

☆ *Greyfriar* [Winchester Rd]: Neatly kept and popular open-plan pub opp Jane Austen's house, pleasant black-beamed bar with pine tables and other pubby tables and chairs, enjoyable reasonably priced standard bar food (not Sun evening) from well filled home-baked bread sandwiches and baked potatoes up, different menu inc game and aberdeen angus steaks in pine-tabled partly no smoking restaurant area on right, quick friendly service, well kept Fullers ales, good coffee; piped pop music; small garden behind with barbecue, good walks, open all day *(Phyl and Jack Street, Phil and Jane Hodson, R B Gardiner, Roger and Pauline Pearce, BB, Ann and Colin Hunt, B M Eldridge)*

CHILWORTH [SU4118]

Clump [A27 Romsey Rd]: Big busy chain eating place, largely no smoking, with well kept ales such as Wadworths 6X, good choice of wines, two log fires, smart décor with sofas and easy chairs in one part, spacious conservatory; unobtrusive piped music, disabled facilities but steps at entrance; large garden, open all day *(Phyl and Jack Street)*

COLDEN COMMON [SU4821]

Fishers Pond: Big busy Brewers Fayre in style of a converted water mill, vast choice of sensibly priced generous food all day inc children's, real ales such as Greene King Old Speckled Hen and Wadworths 6X, decent coffee, friendly service; terrace tables, pretty wooded lakeside setting with ducks, handy for Marwell Zoo, open all day *(John and Joan Calvert, Phyl and Jack Street, Ann and Colin Hunt)*

CRONDALL [SU7948]

☆ *Hampshire Arms* [village signed off A287 S of Fleet; Pankridge St]: Still has well kept Greene King ales on handpump, and does good sandwiches as well as interesting bar snacks, but since smart new refurbishment best thought of now as mainly good gently upmarket restaurant rather than pub, with almost hotelish décor and furnishings for small bar, comfortable leather armchairs and sofa by splendid log fire, a dozen good wines by the glass, friendly staff; book well ahead wknds, worth booking wkdy evenings too; children welcome, heated tables in back garden *(Mike and Jayne Bastin, Brian and Karen Thomas, BB, Hunter and Christine Wright)*

CROOKHAM [SU7952]

☆ *George & Lobster* [Crondall Rd]: Roomy open-plan dining pub, interesting and tasty range inc seafood in bar and pleasant conservatory restaurant, good wine choice, Courage Best and Directors, comfortable atmosphere *(Francis Johnston)*

CURDRIDGE [SU5314]

Cricketers [Curdridge Lane, off B3035 just under a mile NE of A334 junction]: Open-plan low-ceilinged Victorian village local with banquettes in lounge area, little-changed public part, rather smart dining area, friendly attentive licensees, wide choice of well presented generous food inc sandwiches and good value daily specials, Greene King Abbot and Old Speckled Hen; quiet piped music (live Thurs); tables on front lawn, two friendly dogs, pleasant footpaths *(A and B D Craig, Paul and Shirley White)*

DOGMERSFIELD [SU7852]

☆ *Queens Head* [village signed off A287 and B3016 W of Fleet]: Masses of menu boards and all tables set for eating in well divided dining bar, wide choice of attractively priced food from baguettes to full meals inc seasonal and restaurantry dishes, well kept Adnams, Courage Best and Hogs Back TEA, good choice of wines esp new world, swift friendly service, dark pink walls, some stripped brickwork, a couple of low beams; well reproduced piped pop music, booking advised evenings (two sittings); tree-shaded picnic-sets on front grass, pretty setting, cl Mon *(BB, Ian Phillips)*

DOWNTON [SZ2793]

☆ *Royal Oak* [A337 Lymington—New Milton]: Wide choice of good value food in neat and cheerful partly panelled family pub, half no smoking, with well kept real ales, good wine choice, impeccable friendly service with nice touches such as good-sized napkins, small restaurant; unobtrusive piped music; huge well kept garden with good play area *(John Fairley, D Marsh, L C T Cottrell)*

DUMMER [SU5846]

☆ *Queen* [½ mile from M3 junction 7; take Dummer slip road]: Comfortable pub redecorated and doing well under new landlord, well kept Courage Best, Fullers London Pride and Greene King Old Speckled Hen, decent wines and coffee, good friendly service even on busy Sun lunchtime, beams, lots of softly lit alcoves, log fire, queen and steeplechase prints, no smoking restaurant allowing children; fruit machine, well reproduced piped music, no mobile phones; picnic-sets under cocktail parasols on terrace and in extended back garden, attractive village with ancient church *(Ian Phillips, LYM, P Hennessey, D O Parker, Stephen Allford, Ann and Colin Hunt, R Lake)*

DUNBRIDGE [SU3225]

☆ *Mill Arms* [Barley Hill, just by stn on Portsmouth—Cardiff line]: High-ceilinged open-plan bars rambling around central servery with well kept Hampshire Mottisfont Meddler brewed for the pub, changing ales such as Archers Golden, Ringwood Best and Huffkin and Titanic Majestic, enjoyable reasonably priced blackboard food inc some interesting dishes (fresh herbs from the garden), quietly friendly helpful service, flagstones and bare boards, big pine tables, mix of seating from stripped pews to soft sofas in cosy corner by log fire, magazines and daily papers, some fishing and rustic bric-a-brac, dining area opening into conservatory, separate games room with big-screen TV, late Sept beer festival with live music, refurbished skittle alley; Tues music quiz, Sun general quiz; picnic-sets in pretty two-level garden with wendy house, bedrooms *(John Evans, J Metcalfe, BB, Prof and Mrs Tony Palmer, Dr and Mrs A K Clarke)*

DUNDRIDGE [SU5718]

☆ *Hampshire Bowman* [off B3035 towards Droxford, Swanmore, then right at Bishops W signpost]: Cosy country local, great mix of customers (children, dogs and walkers welcome, usually some classic cars or vintage motorcycles), well kept Ringwood Best and Fortyniner, a changing Cheriton ale, up to three guest beers and farm cider tapped from the cask, decent house wines, country wines, attractively priced home-made food inc some interesting dishes and good value Sun roast, good welcoming service, some colourful paintings; picnic-sets on spacious and attractive lawn (may be archery in next field), peaceful downland walks *(Phil and Sally Gorton, Val and Alan Green, LYM, Ann and Colin Hunt, the Didler, Ron Shelton, Charles and Pauline Stride)*

DURLEY [SU5116]

☆ *Farmers Home* [village signed off B3354 and B2177 SE of Colden Common; Heathen St/Curdridge rd]: Recently extended old village pub, comfortable beamed bar with two-bay dining area and big no smoking restaurant, good choice of generous reasonably priced food inc fresh fish and lovely puddings, well kept ales such as Fullers London Pride and Gales HSB, decent wine, log fire; children welcome, big garden with good neat play area and marquee, nice walks *(Phyl and Jack Street, J Metcalfe)*

Robin Hood [Durley Street, just off B2177 Bishops Waltham—Winchester]: Village pub extensively refurbished under good new management, unusual modern lighting, attractive décor and log fire in smart lounge, bright and roomy new dining area looking over back terrace to fields, good gently upmarket food, cheerful service, well kept Greene King ales with a guest beer, reasonably priced wines, darts in public bar; big pleasant garden with fine view and play area, good walks *(Nigel Braithwaite, Phyl and Jack Street)*

EAST BOLDRE [SU3700]
☆ *Turf Cutters Arms* [Main Rd]: Small dim-lit New Forest country local, warmly welcoming and unpretentious, lots of beams and pictures, sturdy tables, rugs, bare boards and flagstones, log fire, huge helpings of simple local food from sandwiches and basic dishes to quite a lot of game, Gales HSB, Ringwood Best and Wadworths 6X, several dozen malt whiskies, no smoking room, fish tanks, two big friendly dogs; children welcome, garden tables, some good heathland walks, three big old-fashioned bedrooms, simple but comfortable, good breakfast *(BB, Dick and Madeleine Brown, Sue Demont, Tim Barrow)*

EAST END [SZ3696]
☆ *East End Arms* [back road Lymington—Beaulieu, parallel to B3054]: Civilised New Forest country local, stylish and enterprising meals making a nice contrast with the simplicity of its plain and chatty bright bar, log fire, well kept Ringwood Best on handpump and other ales tapped from the cask, good choice of wines by the glass, helpful staff, longish neat candlelit dining lounge with nice pictures; tables in small pleasant garden, popular with families *(BB, Charles and Isabel Cooper, Mary Dibley)*

EAST MEON [SU6822]
☆ *George* [Church St; signed off A272 W of Petersfield, and off A32 in West Meon]: Newly refurbished heavy-beamed rustic pub with inglenook log fires, cosy areas around central bar counter, helpful friendly staff, well kept Badger ales, decent wines, generous reasonably priced traditional food from sandwiches up; soft piped music; children welcome, good outdoor seating arrangements, five small but comfortable bedrooms (book well ahead), good breakfast, pretty village with fine church, good walks *(Ann and Colin Hunt, LYM, Simon Collett-Jones, Paul and Shirley White, Michael and Robin Inskip, Peter Hacker, Neil and Debbie Cook, Mr and Mrs Hubling)*
Izaak Walton [High St]: Friendly two-bar local in delightful village, cheerful helpful service, smart lounge mainly for eaters (good value fresh food inc children's), well kept Wadworths 6X, back family area, darts and pool in public bar; nice table out by front stream, massive back garden; children welcome, open all day Sun, quiz night most Weds *(Ann and Colin Hunt, R T and J C Moggridge)*

EASTON [SU5132]
☆ *Cricketers* [off B3047]: Thriving open-plan local with chatty and welcoming NZ landlord, well kept Otter, Ringwood Best and interesting guest beers, reasonably priced wines, wide choice of good value generous food from sandwiches to piping hot dishes, prompt service, pleasant mix of pub furnishings, darts and shove-ha'penny one end, small bright no smoking restaurant, good wine range; well cared for bedrooms *(Lynn Sharpless, Ann and Colin Hunt, BB, Val and Alan Green, Mr and Mrs R W Allan)*

EMSWORTH [SU7406]
Coal Exchange [Ships Quay, South St]: Friendly bustle in comfortably compact L-shaped Victorian local, low ceilings, lots of locals and yachtsmen, cheerful landlady proud of her well kept Gales ales with a guest such as Jennings, good fresh honest lunchtime food from generous baguettes to nice puddings, popular Sun lunch (open all day then) and Tues curry night, espresso coffee, coal fire each end; tables outside, next to Pay & Display, handy for Wayfarers Walk and Solent Walk *(Andy and Jill Kassube, Ann and Colin Hunt, Val and Alan Green, Minda and Stanley Alexander)*
☆ *Kings Arms* [Havant Rd]: Tidy and relaxing local popular for generous wholesome interesting food cooked by landlady, fresh veg and some organic dishes, good choice of wines, good service, cheerful landlord, well kept Gales ales and a guest beer, good wine choice and coffee, small restaurant area, no mobiles; no children in bar, pleasant garden behind *(Ann and Colin Hunt)*
Lord Raglan [Queen St]: Comfortably worn in Gales local, their ales kept well, wide choice of good value generous promptly served home-made food from sandwiches up, log fire, popular restaurant (must book summer wknds); jovial individualistic landlord enforces his seen-and-not-heard rule for children surprisingly strictly, can be smoky, live music Sun evening; pleasant sea-view garden behind *(Mike Vincent, Andy and Jill Kassube, Irene and Derek Flewin, Tony Hobden, Ann and Colin Hunt, Bruce Bird)*

ENBORNE [SU4264]
Craven Arms [W, towards Hamstead Marshall]: Pleasantly refurbished, with good choice of around five well kept real ales, welcoming service, food from baguettes up; plenty of room in and out, cl Mon *(J V Dadswell)*

EVERSLEY [SU7861]
Golden Pot [B3272]: Interlinked spreading areas inc snug armchairs and sofa by log-effect gas fire, quick cheerful service, well kept Greene King ales, nice wines by the glass, food from baguettes up, pretty no smoking restaurant; they may try to keep your credit card while you eat, piped music, pianist/vocalist Mon night; dogs allowed in bar, picnic-sets outside with masses of colourful flowers, cl winter Sun evening *(Mrs Angela Bromley-Martin, Ian Phillips, LYM, KC, Chris Sexton)*

EVERTON [SZ2994]
☆ *Crown* [Old Christchurch Rd; pub signed just off A337 W of Lymington]: Good interesting food cooked to order (so may be a wait), attractive prices, tiled central bar, two attractive dining rooms with sturdy tables on polished boards off tiled-floor bar, log fires, lots of jugs and china, well kept Gales HSB, Hampshire Strongs Best and Ringwood Best, friendly service; no dogs, picnic-sets on front terrace and back grass, quiet village on edge of New Forest *(Don and Maureen Medley, BB,*

D Marsh, C and R Bromage, Mr and Mrs A Silver)

FACCOMBE [SU3958]

Jack Russell: Light and airy creeper-covered pub under new management, nice setting opp village pond by flint church, decorous pub furnishings in neat bar with a few forestry saws and the like, well kept Greene King IPA and Shepherd Neame Spitfire, good coffee, decent bar food (not Sun evening), darts, sturdy oak tables in carpeted conservatory restaurant; disabled facilities, picnic-sets out on lawn by beech trees, bedrooms spotless and cheerful, good walks with rewarding views *(Phyl and Jack Street, BB)*

FAREHAM [SU5806]

Red Lion [East St]: Long-established hotel with pleasant staff, enjoyable good value food in comfortable bar and restaurant, good layout; bedrooms *(Michael and Robin Inskip)*

White Horse [North Wallington]: Cheerful traditional two-bar local with pictures of old Fareham, well kept ales such as Bass, Oakleaf (from Gosport) and Tetleys, good blackboard choice of well cooked standard food, friendly service, restaurant; piped music; terrace and garden *(Ann and Colin Hunt)*

FARRINGDON [SU7135]

Rose & Crown [off A32 S of Alton; Crows Lane – follow Church, Selborne, Liss signpost]: Roomy pub, clean, bright and comfortable, with log fire, fresh flowers, daily papers, neat back dining room, cheerful efficient service, enjoyable food, several real ales, decent wines and coffee; tables in well kept back garden *(BB, Ann and Colin Hunt)*

Royal Oak [Gosport Rd (A32 S of Alton), Lower Farringdon]: Pleasantly refurbished under hard-working newish young landlady, wide choice of enjoyable food inc fresh fish and other local ingredients, quick friendly service, well kept ales inc Ringwood Best, good coffee, log fire, pictures, brasses, fresh flowers and candles, nice good-sized separate restaurant; well behaved children welcome *(Ann and Colin Hunt)*

FAWLEY [SU4603]

☆ *Jolly Sailor* [Ashlett Creek]: Lively and welcoming plushly modernised waterside pub with good value food inc Sun carvery and good vegetarian choice, changing real ales, prompt service, restaurant, good liner pictures, children welcome; may be piped music; by dinghy club overlooking busy shipping channel (outside, the refinery rather dominates the view), handy for Rothschild rhododendron gardens at Exbury *(LYM, Dr and Mrs A K Clarke)*

FINCHDEAN [SU7312]

George: Cheerful smartly dressed staff, decent food in lounge and neat public bar, Bass and Youngs; good nearby walks, open all day Sun *(Ann and Colin Hunt)*

FLEET [SU8155]

Heron on the Lake [Old Cove Rd]: Welcoming Chef & Brewer, recently done out in pleasant old-fashioned style, lots of beams, nooks and corners, two log fires, candles on tables, good choice of reasonably priced food, polite helpful

service, good coffee; piped classical music mornings, then jazz *(Andy and Yvonne Cunningham, Mrs B Downie, R Lake)*

FREEFOLK [SU4848]

☆ *Watership Down* [Freefolk Priors, N of B3400 – sharp lane uphill at W end of village]: Engaging unpretentious country pub, ancient brick flooring around bar counter with well kept changing ales such as Archers Dark Mild, Butts Barbus Barbus, Itchen Valley Fagins, Titanic UXB and Youngs, friendly staff and chatty atmosphere, popular food from sandwiches to good value Sun roasts, one neat carpeted area with rabbit pictures and well padded wall seating, another with darts, table football, veteran one-arm bandit and other games (TV too), comfortable no smoking conservatory; picnic-sets in big sloping informal garden with sturdy timber play area, more under heaters beside pub, pleasant walks *(Lynn Sharpless, BB)*

FROGHAM [SU1712]

☆ *Foresters Arms* [Abbotswell Rd]: Comfortably refurbished New Forest pub, flagstones and small woodburner, chef/landlord doing enjoyable blackboard food from sandwiches to very popular Sun lunch, reasonable prices, attentive young staff, well kept Wadworths and guest ales, good house wines, compact no smoking dining room; children welcome, pleasant garden and pretty front verandah; small camp site adjacent, nearby ponies and good walks *(John and Joan Calvert, LYM, Phyl and Jack Street)*

FROYLE [SU7542]

Hen & Chicken [loop road just off A31 Alton—Farnham]: Comfortable and friendly 16th-c coaching inn with three attractive linked beamed rooms, inglenook log fire, bar food from sandwiches and ploughman's to venison, children's meals, several Badger ales; children in eating area and restaurant, big garden with picnic-sets and play area, open all day *(Ian Phillips, LYM)*

GOODWORTH CLATFORD [SU3642]

Royal Oak: Smart and comfortable L-shaped bar with friendly efficient service, good food inc interesting dishes as well as the usuals, well kept beer; colourful sheltered dell-like garden, large and neatly kept, good riverside walks nearby *(Phyl and Jack Street)*

GOSPORT [SZ5998]

☆ *Alverbank House* [Stokes Bay Rd, Alverstoke]: Pleasant partly divided hotel lounge, comfortable smallish bar with Ringwood, four well kept guest beers and great choice of malt whiskies, good interesting food (not cheap) inc plenty for vegetarians, cheerful well trained staff; piped music; in woods at end of Stanley Park, over rd from promenade, nice big mature garden with play area and views of Solent and Isle of Wight, bedrooms very well appointed *(Peter and Audrey Dowsett, Val and Alan Green, Phyl and Jack Street, Ann and Colin Hunt, Michael and Jeanne Shillington)*

Anglesey [Crescent Rd, Alverstoke]: Enjoyable food and real ale in friendly unpretentious bar, Jane Austen associations; bedrooms *(Peter and Audrey Dowsett)*

☆ *Clarence* [Clarence Rd/Mumby Rd (A32)]:
Partly 18th-c, incorporating a former chapel
from the Isle of Wight, heavy furnishings, old
books, prints and other pictures, good-sized no
smoking area; wide choice of food in bar and
upstairs restaurant, well kept Oakleaf beers
from over the road (and you can see their own
former microbrewery through glass panels in
bar and minstrel's gallery), log and coal fires,
relaxed atmosphere, Edwardian dining room;
dogs welcome, no games or piped music;
medieval evenings, open all day *(Jess and
George Cowley)*

Jolly Roger [Priory Rd, Hardway]: Harbour-
view pub with four well kept ales inc Greene
King Abbot and Youngs Special, decent house
wines, reasonably priced food, friendly service,
attractive eating area *(Ann and Colin Hunt)*

Queens [Queens Rd]: Bare-boards pub whose
long-serving landlady keeps Ringwood,
Roosters Yankee, Youngs Best and two more
changing strong beers in top condition, quick
service, Sun bar nibbles, perhaps huge filled
rolls and other simple food, three areas off bar
with good log fire in interesting carved
fireplace, sensibly placed darts, quiet pyrenean
mountain dog; family area with TV, quiz night
Thurs; open all day Sat *(Ann and Colin Hunt)*

GREYWELL [SU7151]

Fox & Goose [nr M3 junction 5; A287
towards Odiham then first right to village]:
Two-bar village pub with country-kitchen
furniture, food from sandwiches up (inc cream
teas), Courage Best, Gales HSB and Oakleaf
Bitter; good-sized garden behind, attractive
village, handy for walks by Basingstoke Canal
(Francis Johnston)

HAMBLE [SU4806]

Olde Whyte Harte [High St; 3 miles from M27
junction 8]: Low-beamed bar with blazing
inglenook log fire and yachting memorabilia,
well integrated flagstoned eating area, well
priced fresh food inc plenty of fish, Gales ales,
lots of country wines, decent coffee, no
smoking area; piped music; children in eating
area, some seats outside, handy for nature
reserve *(LYM, Val and Alan Green)*

Victory [High St]: Well kept ales inc Fullers
London Pride and Ringwood Best, good
atmosphere, reasonably priced straightforward
bar food, cheerful welcoming staff; can be
smoky, piped 1960s music *(John E Bailey,
Ann and Colin Hunt)*

HAMBLEDON [SU6716]

☆ *Bat & Ball* [Broadhalfpenny Down; about 2
miles E towards Clanfield]: Extended dining
pub opp the famous first cricket pitch (matches
most summer Sundays), genial landlord and
good friendly service even when crowded, well
kept Gales ales, good wines by the glass,
enjoyable meals inc fresh fish, plenty of cricket
memorabilia, log fires and comfortable modern
furnishings in three linked rooms, panelled
restaurant; children welcome, lovely downs
views and walks *(LYM, Paul and
Shirley White, Peter Salmon, Richard Staveley,
Jess and George Cowley, Mrs Maricar Jagger,
Geoff and Sylvia Donald)*

HATHERDEN [SU3450]

☆ *Old Bell & Crown*: Picturesque old thatched
village pub, roomy inside, with well kept
Wadworths and guest ales, restaurant with no
smoking part, enjoyable food from quick
lunchtime snacks up; pretty garden *(Phyl and
Jack Street)*

HAVANT [SU7106]

☆ *Old House At Home* [South St]: Much
modernised two-bar Tudor pub, low beams
and nice rambling alcovey feel, low-priced
sandwiches, baked potatoes and bargain hot
dishes, three well kept Gales ales, good
welcoming service, smallish no smoking area;
piped music (may be live Sat – very popular
with young people Fri/Sat night); pretty
frontage with splendid hanging baskets, tables
in back garden *(Ann and Colin Hunt, LYM,
Tony Hobden, Mrs Maricar Jagger, Tony and
Wendy Hobden)*

Robin Hood [Homewell]: Neatly refurbished
and relaxing rambling open-plan bar, well kept
real ales, reasonably priced food, good service,
open fire, sensibly placed darts *(Tony Hobden,
Ann and Colin Hunt)*

HAZELEY [SU7459]

☆ *Shoulder of Mutton* [Hazeley Heath]: 18th-c
dining pub with welcoming and helpful family
service, enjoyable bar food from ploughman's
to good pies and steaks (no snacks just meals
on Sun, when many tables are booked), good
log fire in cosy lounge, no smoking area, well
kept Courage Best, Wadworths 6X and a
seasonal ale, decent house wines, amusing
menu, rack of spectacles for the forgetful; may
be quiet piped music; attractive mellow-tiled
building, terrace and garden *(Roger and
Pauline Pearce, R Lake, Ian Phillips,
Doreen and Haydn Maddock, Mr and
Mrs J Brown)*

HECKFIELD [SU7260]

☆ *New Inn* [B3349 Hook—Reading (former
A32)]: Big well run rambling open-plan dining
pub, good welcoming service, enjoyable food
inc good light lunch selection, well kept Badger
and a guest beer, decent wines, attractive
layout with some traditional furniture in
original core, two log fires (good when lit), no
piped music; restaurant; neat tables on pleasant
terrace, bedrooms in comfortable and well
equipped extension *(LYM, T and P)*

HERRIARD [SS6744]

Fur & Feathers [pub signed just off A339
Basingstoke—Alton]: Recently refurbished
open-plan pub, now Fullers (and perhaps less
individual than before), with a guest such as
Everards Tiger, friendly service, decent food
from wraps and baguettes up, stripped pine
tables and chairs on bare boards, log fire;
picnic-sets out in front *(Martin and
Karen Wake, BB, Jill Hurley)*

HOOK [SU7354]

☆ *Crooked Billet* [about a mile towards London]:
Recently well extended and refurbished but
keeping good friendly local feel under same
long-serving licensees, new chef doing wide
choice of enjoyable food inc interesting specials
and plenty of fish, swift friendly service, well

kept Courage Best and Directors and a stream of quickly changing guest beers, good range of soft drinks, homely log fires; soft piped music; children welcome, attractive garden by stream with trout and ducks *(anon)*

HORDLE [SZ2996]

☆ *Mill at Gordleton* [Silver St]: More restaurant-with-rooms than pub, with good if not cheap food in attractive side and back dining bar or out on pretty waterside terraces, but does have a busy public bar; good wines, friendly staff, smart comfortable bedrooms *(John and Joan Calvert)*

HORNDEAN [SU7013]

Ship & Bell [London Rd]: Comfortable and spacious pub/hotel adjoining Gales brewery, full range of their beers kept well, good range of wines, reasonably priced standard food, quick friendly service, cheerfully relaxed bar with deep well and real fire, broad low steps up to comfortable no smoking lounge and dining room, interesting photographs, separate public bar/games room; 14 bedrooms with own bathrooms, nice walk to Catherington church *(Bruce Bird, Ann and Colin Hunt)*

HOUGHTON [SU3432]

Boot [S of Stockbridge]: Country local with good food from top-notch bangers and mash to more unusual dishes in unpretentious bar with blazing log fire or roomy and attractive restaurant on left, Ringwood and other real ales, attentive service, picnic-sets in long garden running down to lovely (unfenced) stretch of River Test, where they have fishing; good walks, and opp Test Way cycle path *(Phyl and Jack Street, Edward Mirzoeff)*

ITCHEN ABBAS [SU5332]

☆ *Trout* [4 miles from M3 junction 9; B3047]: Relaxed country pub with welcoming neatly dressed staff, enjoyable food using some local ingredients from baguettes and bangers and mash to bass on tomato risotto and other up-to-date dishes, simple but smartish décor in quiet no smoking lounge and dining room, well kept Greene King ales, decent wines, chatty separate public bar; tables in sheltered pretty side garden, good river and downland walks nearby, comfortable bedrooms *(Lynn Sharpless, Diana Brumfit, Ann and Colin Hunt, LYM, Jamie Wallis, Stephen Allford)*

KEYHAVEN [SZ3091]

Gun: Busy 17th-c pub looking over boatyard and sea to Isle of Wight, low-beamed bar with lots of nautical memorabilia and plenty of character (less in family rooms); good choice of generous food using local produce, well kept beers tapped from the cask such as Gales HSB, Greene King Old Speckled Hen, Ringwood and Wadworths 6X, well over a hundred malt whiskies, bar billiards; back conservatory, garden with swings and fishpond *(Gordon Stevenson, D Marsh, JWAC)*

LANGSTONE [SU7104]

☆ *Royal Oak* [off A3023 just before Hayling Island bridge; Langstone High St]: Charmingly placed waterside pub, now completely no smoking, overlooking tidal inlet and ancient wadeway to Hayling Island, boats at high tide, wading birds when it goes out; well kept ales such as Flowers Original, Fullers London Pride, Gales HSB and Greene King IPA, good choice of wines by the glass, good pub food inc all-day sandwiches and snacks, plenty of cheerful young staff, spacious recently refurbished flagstoned bar and linked dining areas, log fire; children in eating areas, good coastal paths nearby, open all day *(Ann and Colin Hunt, LYM, Ralph and Jean Whitehouse, Ian Phillips, Jenny Garrett)*

☆ *Ship* [A3023]: Busy waterside 18th-c former grain store, smart and well cared for, plenty of tables on heated terrace by quiet quay, lovely views to Hayling Island from roomy softly lit nautical bar with upper deck dining room, good no smoking areas, quick friendly service, full Gales range kept well, good choice of wines by the generous glass, country wines, log fire, wide range of generous food inc fresh fish and platters for two; children's room, open all day, good coast walks *(Dr D G Twyman, D J and P M Taylor, Geoff Pidoux, Lynn Sharpless, Ian Phillips, Alain and Rose Foote)*

LEE-ON-THE-SOLENT [SU5600]

☆ *Bun Penny* [Manor Way]: Roomy and feeling pleasantly up to date (low beams, flagstones and log fires too), nice choice of good well presented food, well kept Boddingtons, Flowers and Wadworths 6X, good range of wines by the glass, daily papers, friendly attentive staff, conservatory and restaurant; garden, lots of flowers in summer *(Charles and Pauline Stride, Jess and George Cowley, Colette Conlin)*

LINWOOD [SU1910]

☆ *High Corner* [signed from A338 via Moyles Court, and from A31; keep on]: Big rambling pub very popular for its splendid New Forest position up a track, with extensive neatly kept wooded garden and lots for children to do; some character in original upper bar, lots of back extension for the summer crowds, large helpings of good value food from sandwiches to steaks inc Sun carvery (nicely partitioned restaurant open all day Sun), well kept Wadworths beers, decent wine, efficient service, no smoking verandah lounge; interesting family rooms, dogs welcome too, open all day wknds; bedrooms *(LYM, Dave Braisted)*

LITTLE LONDON [SU6359]

Plough [Silchester Rd, off A340 N of Basingstoke]: Cosy unspoilt tucked-away local with tiled floor, low beams, friendly landlord, limited food inc lots of good value baguettes, well kept Ringwood and interesting guest beers, log fire, darts, bar billiards, no piped music; attractive garden, handy for Pamber Forest and Calleva Roman remains *(J V Dadswell)*

LOCKS HEATH [SU5006]

☆ *Jolly Farmer* [2½ miles from M27 junction 9; A27 towards Bursledon, left into Locks Rd, at end T junction right into Warsash Rd then left at hire shop into Fleet End Rd]: Appealing country-style pub with linked softly lit rooms, nice old scrubbed tables (quite close-set) and masses of interesting bric-a-brac and prints, wide choice of enjoyable food from filled baps to steaks and good value very popular two-sitting Sun lunch, good quick friendly service, interesting long-serving landlord, well kept Flowers Original, Gales HSB and Fullers London Pride, decent wines and country wines, coal-effect gas fires, no smoking area; two sheltered terraces (one with a play area and children's lavatories), nice bedrooms *(Michael and Robin Inskip, Peter and Audrey Dowsett, Ann and Colin Hunt, LYM, Roger and Pauline Pearce, Charles and Pauline Stride)*

LONGPARISH [SU4344]

☆ *Plough* [B3048, off A303 just E of Andover]: Comfortable open-plan food pub divided by arches, relaxed friendly atmosphere, pleasant service, enjoyable food from sandwiches up, well kept Gales and Ringwood ales, decent house wines, partly no smoking restaurant; piped music; children in eating areas, tables on terrace and in nice garden, bedrooms *(Neil and Angela Huxter, Dr D E Granger, LYM, Phyl and Jack Street, Mr and Mrs D S Price)*

LOWER FROYLE [SU7643]

☆ *Anchor* [signed off A31]: 14th-c traditional pub with pleasant beamed and carpeted lounge on left, more room on right with big-windowed no smoking eating area, popular with older people lunchtime (esp Weds) for reasonably priced food with wide choice from sandwiches to fish, cheerful family service, well kept Courage Best and Timothy Taylors Landlord, decent malt whiskies; white wrought-iron tables out on grass and by front car park, bedrooms *(R B Gardiner, David Cannings, BB)*

LYMINGTON [SZ3294]

☆ *Fishermans Rest* [All Saints Rd, Woodside]: Wide choice of consistently good interesting food inc very popular Sun lunch, good value, well kept Ringwood ales, decent wines, friendly helpful staff, pleasant atmosphere, plenty of locals at bar; can get busy, wknd booking recommended *(D Marsh, Mr and Mrs A Silver)*
Mayflower [Kings Saltern Rd]: Welcoming service, cosy lounge, larger public bar, enjoyable reasonably priced food, well kept Gales ales; large garden, overlooking Lymington River and marina, open all day *(David Carr)*

LYNDHURST [SU2908]
Stag [High St]: Handsome early 18th-c inn with art deco chandeliers, well kept Greene King IPA and Abbot and good service in plush bar, lunchtime bar food inc dishes from the good smart integral italian restaurant; bedrooms with own bathrooms, open all day *(Brian and Janet Ainscough, Joan and Michel Hooper-Immins)*

MARCHWOOD [SU3810]

☆ *Pilgrim* [Hythe Rd, off A326 at Twiggs Lane]: Picturesque immaculately kept thatched pub with comfortable banquettes in long welcoming L-shaped bar, wide choice of consistently good value home-made food, good long-serving landlord, well kept mainstream beers, english wines, open fires, more expensive restaurant across road; can be crowded, handy for otter and owl park at Longdown; neat garden *(LYM, Phyl and Jack Street, Meg and Colin Hamilton)*

MEDSTEAD [SU6537]

☆ *Castle of Comfort* [signed off A31 at Four Marks; Castle St]: Leisurely village local, homely beamed lounge bar like a rose-tinted memory of the 1960s, well kept ales such as Courage and Wadworths 6X, good basic bar lunches inc soup and sandwiches, toasties and ploughman's, Sun bar nibbles, warmly friendly efficient service, plush chairs, big woodburner and small open fireplace, spartan public bar with darts etc; sunny front verandah, more tables in neat side garden with fairy lights and play tree, nice downland walks to the west *(Phyl and Jack Street, BB, Ron Shelton, Ann and Colin Hunt)*

MEONSTOKE [SU6119]

☆ *Bucks Head* [village signed just off A32 N of Droxford]: Friendly and effective new licensees for partly panelled L-shaped dining lounge looking over road to water meadows, enjoyable sensibly priced food inc popular Sun roasts, well kept Greene King IPA and Old Speckled Hen, log fire, decent wines, plush banquettes, rugs on bare boards and well spaced tables, nice public bar with leather settee by another log fire, darts and juke box; tables and picnic-sets in small garden, lovely village setting with ducks on pretty little River Meon, good walks, comfortable bedrooms with own bathrooms, open all day *(Peter Salmon, Ann and Colin Hunt, BB, Malcolm and Dorothy Hind, Phyl and Jack Street)*

MINLEY [SU8357]
Crown & Cushion [A327, just N of M3 junction 4A]: Attractive small traditional pub with enjoyable fairly priced food from baguettes and ciabattas up, Adnams Broadside, Bass and Tetleys, coal-effect gas fire; big separate raftered and flagstoned rustic 'meade hall' behind, very popular wknds (evenings more a young people's meeting place), with huge log fire; they may not let you run a tab while you eat; children in eating area, heated terrace overlooking own cricket pitch *(LYM, Ian Phillips, Paul Humphreys)*

MINSTEAD [SU2810]

☆ *Trusty Servant* [just off A31, not far from M27 junction 1]: Relaxed 19th-c pub in pretty New Forest hamlet with plenty of easy walks all around, pleasantly informal two-room bar and big airy separate dining room (children allowed here), well kept changing ales such as Fullers London Pride, Ringwood Best and Wadworths 6X, decent house wines and country wines, generous food all day from sandwiches, baguettes and baked potatoes to good game dishes; dogs welcome in bar, good-sized side and back garden, open all day *(D Marsh, Brian and Janet Ainscough, BB, R J Davies, Mrs C Lintott, LYM, Sue Demont, Tim Barrow, Don Manley)*

MORTIMER WEST END [SU6363]
Red Lion [Church Rd; Silchester turn off
Mortimer—Aldermaston rd]: Smart dining pub
under welcoming new licensees, lots of beams,
stripped masonry, timbers and panelling, good
food from generous doorstep sandwiches up,
well kept Badger and other ales, nice wines by
the glass, good log fire; dogs and children
welcome, plenty of seats in pleasant garden
with play area, and on small flower-filled front
terrace, handy for Roman Silchester, open all
day (*LYM, J V Dadswell*)

NEW MILTON [SZ2495]
House Martin [Christchurch Rd (A337)]:
Former Centurian, refurbished as upmarket
dining pub, enjoyable food all day, Badger
beers with a guest such as Ringwood Best,
good service, conservatory; open all day
(*David M Cundy*)

NEWNHAM [SU7054]
Old House At Home [handy for M3 junction
5; A287 then keep on across A30]: Civilised
and welcoming bay-windowed house in
secluded hamlet, perhaps more restaurant than
pub but well worth knowing for its good fresh
food, not cheap but good value and changing
daily, with tempting puddings; friendly
welcome, good wine list, real ales, generous
cafetière coffee, good fire; pleasant walks
nearby (*Mrs Angela McArt, Francis Johnston*)

NEWTOWN [SU6112]
☆ *Travellers Rest* [off A32 N of Wickham]:
Welcoming country pub gently enlarged but
still cosy, obliging service, one chatty local bar,
two further rooms (one no smoking) mainly
for the enjoyable food, well kept Fullers
London Pride, Ringwood Fortyniner and
Youngs, open fires and traditional furnishings;
pretty back garden (*LYM, Richard Waller,
Pauline Smith*)

NORTH GORLEY [SU1611]
☆ *Royal Oak* [Ringwood Rd; village signed off
A338 S of Fordingbridge]: 17th-c thatched pub
by New Forest, neatly refurbished no smoking
lounge on left, busier main bar on right,
attractive bare-boards L-shaped eating area,
partly no smoking, with pine tables and old-
fashioned chairs or booth seating, popular
food (all day in school hols) from lunchtime
sandwiches and baguettes up, well kept Fullers
London Pride, Ringwood Best and a guest
beer, decent wines; piped music, TV, games
machine; children and dogs welcome, neat
sheltered back garden with play area for
children, big duck pond over road, open all
day (*Mark Barker, W W Burke, Peter and
Anne Hollindale, Dr D G Twyman,
Adrian and Christine Smithies, LYM,
Peter Neate*)

NORTH WALTHAM [SU5645]
Fox [signed off A30 SW of Basingstoke; handy
for M3 junction 7]: Foxy décor in comfortable
village pub with log fire in bright elongated
dining area, well kept real ales, welcoming
landlord and well trained staff, good range of
food from sandwiches and baguettes to good
venison and Sun roasts; bar can be rather
smoky; children welcome, garden with

farmland views, pleasant village in nice spot
(walk to Jane Austen's church at Steventon)
(*Phyl and Jack Street, Martin and Karen Wake,
Brian and Pamela Everett, Stephen Allford,
Roger Huxtable*)
Wheatsheaf [visible from M3 and handy for
junction 7, via A30]: Warm and friendly
former Georgian coaching inn, beams and
panelling, oak furniture, three log fires, plenty
of seating inc quiet tucked-away areas, quick
friendly service, good value bar food, well kept
ales, decent wines by the glass, daily papers;
comfortable up-to-date bedroom wing
(*John Fisher, Stephen Allford*)

NORTH WARNBOROUGH [SU7352]
Lord Derby [A287, nr M3 junction 5; Bartley
Heath]: Locally popular for enjoyable
restaurant food with some unusual dishes,
friendly landlord, old-fashioned décor with
hops on beams (*R and M Willes*)

OAKHANGER [SU7635]
Red Lion [off A325 Farnham—Petersfield]:
Traditional village pub with unpretentious
locals' bar and attractive larger dining lounge,
enjoyable food from snacks to more
restauranty dishes, well kept real ales,
thoughtful house wines, decent coffee, friendly
staff, big log fire; garden tables (*Ann and
Colin Hunt*)

ODIHAM [SU7451]
Water Witch [signed off main st]: Olde-worlde
décor in Chef & Brewer with good friendly
staff, reliable food, real ales; lovely hanging
baskets, garden with extensive children's
facilities, very busy wknds (*Andy and
Yvonne Cunningham, Jennifer Banks*)

OTTERBOURNE [SU4623]
Old Forge [Main Rd]: Reliable well run
Vintage Inn, good layout, efficient friendly
staff, Bass and Tetleys, their usual food all day
(*Phyl and Jack Street, Lynn Sharpless*)
White Horse [Main Rd]: Good service and
enjoyable generous varied lunchtime food
under current newish management, pleasant
ambiance and reasonable beer range
(*Sheila and Robert Robinson*)

OVER WALLOP [SU2838]
White Hart: Pretty little thatched pub,
unpretentious and friendly, with several well
kept ales, inexpensive lunchtime home
cooking, open fire; tables on the lawn, good
footpath network (*Patrick Hall*)

OWSLEBURY [SU5123]
Ship [off B2177 Fishers Pond—Lower Upham;
Whites Hill]: Popular family summer pub,
good gardens with play area, toddler zone, pets
corner and lots of space to run around; 17th-c
black oak beams and timbers inside, big central
fireplace, particularly well kept Cheriton Pots
and Greene King ales, good choice of wines by
the glass, cribbage, dominoes and alley skittles,
comfortable dining area and restaurant (both
no smoking) (*James Price, Ann and
Colin Hunt, LYM, Paul and Shirley White,
Phil and Sally Gorton*)

PAMBER END [SU6158]
☆ *Queens College Arms* [Aldermaston Rd (A340
S of Tadley)]: Large roadside pub with good

value well presented food, good wines by the glass, well kept changing real ales, friendly efficient staff, good atmosphere with a faintly elegant feel, roomy restaurant; heated terrace, play area *(Mr and Mrs J Carroll, John Fisher)*

PARK GATE [SU5108]

Talisman [Bridge Rd, Park Gate (A27, a mile from M27 junction 9)]: Busy Badger dining pub, their real ales, generous popular food, beams, oak panels, bare boards and carpets, flame-effect fire, no smoking area; quiet piped music; children welcome, garden *(Jenny and Peter Lowater)*

PETERSFIELD [SU7423]

Good Intent [College St]: Gales full beer range kept well, decent food from sandwiches and ciabattas up (popular with businessmen at lunch), 16th-c core with low oak beams, log fire, well spaced good-sized pine tables with flowers, camera collection, cosy family area; some live music *(Tony and Wendy Hobden, Val and Alan Green)*

☆ *White Horse* [up on old downs rd about halfway between Steep and East Tisted, nr Priors Dean – OS Sheet 186 or 197, map ref 715290]: Charming country pub high and isolated on the downs, rustic 1970s feel in two relaxed and idiosyncratically old-fashioned parlour rooms (candlelit at night); attractive no smoking family dining room, open fires throughout, up to nine real ales, good food (not Sun evening) from sandwiches and baked potatoes to sensibly priced and attractively presented restaurant dishes, quick friendly and helpful service; children welcome, rustic tables out by floodlit pond *(R B Gardiner, Ann and Colin Hunt, LYM, Mrs Maricar Jagger, the Didler, Ann and Stephen Saunders, Brian Dawes, Colin Gooch)*

PHOENIX GREEN [SU7555]

Phoenix [A30 W of Hartley Wintney]: Lots of beams, timber dividers, rugs on bare boards and big end inglenook, decent lunchtime food from sandwiches and baked potatoes up, well kept ales inc Ringwood, decent wines by the glass, friendly staff, back dining room with two flame-effect fires; pleasant outlook from picnic-sets in fair-sized garden *(Martin and Karen Wake)*

PILLEY [SZ3298]

Fleur de Lys [off A337 Brockenhurst—Lymington; Pilley St]: Informal and relaxed country pub with huge inglenook log fire in heavy-beamed no smoking bar, plenty of character, generous food from wide choice of sandwiches and baguettes up to steaks, well kept Ringwood Best and Fortyniner, decent wines and country wines, no smoking family room with children's games; piped music, fruit machine; dogs welcome, fine forest and heathland walks nearby *(David Carr, LYM, Alan M Pring, Charles and Pauline Stride, Matt and Cathy Fawcett)*

PORTCHESTER [SU6204]

Cormorant [next to Portchester Castle]: Big smartly kept open-plan dining pub with solid 1930s feel, friendly helpful staff, reasonably priced generous home-made food all day

(several blackboards), well kept ales such as Fullers London Pride, Gales GB and HSB and Ringwood Best, cafetière coffee, children in large raised back dining area; tables on terrace with lots of flower tubs and baskets, in pleasant close, views over Portsmouth Harbour, plenty of parking, open all day *(Michael and Alison Sandy, Ann and Colin Hunt)*

PORTSMOUTH [SZ6399]

American Bar [White Hart Rd]: Spacious colonial-theme bar with good mix of customers, well kept Courage Directors and a guest beer, reasonably priced all-day bar food from sandwiches and baguettes up, popular restaurant (one room no smoking) with some emphasis on fresh local fish and seafood, good friendly service; garden behind, handy for IOW ferry *(Colin Moore)*

Bridge Tavern [East St, Camber Dock]: Flagstones, bare boards and lots of dark wood, comfortable furnishings, good water views, good simple food from baguettes and baked potatoes up, full range of well kept Gales ales, country wines, smiling service, maritime theme; waterside terrace, nice position *(Mrs Maricar Jagger, Joan and Michel Hooper-Immins, Paul and Shirley White)*

Churchillian [Portsdown Hill Rd, Widley]: Smallish open-plan dining pub, oak, cream and red carpet, big windows with lovely views over Portsmouth and Solent, Bass, Gales GB and HSB and Wadworths 6X, generous popular food; may be piped music; handy for Fort Widley equestrian centre and nature trail *(Val and Alan Green)*

Fountain [London Rd, North End]: Fairly large spick and span bar with family room off, nicely polished brass, interesting pub pictures, mirrors each end, well kept Badger Best and Gales HSB; seats outside *(Ann and Colin Hunt)*

George [Portsdown Hill Rd, Widley]: Friendly unspoilt Georgian local with good choice of well kept ales, decent wines, popular lunchtime food; handy for Portsdown Hill nature reserve, wonderful views of Hayling Island, Portsmouth and Isle of Wight from terrace *(David Carr)*

Old Customs House [Vernon Buildings, Gunwharf Quays]: Good conversion by Gales of handsome Georgian customs house, latterly an admin building for former RN mine clearance and diving school, in bright modern shopping centre by old quays and dockside, now a family dining pub with smoking and no smoking areas divided into small rooms, modern tables and chairs and some armchairs and sofas, quickly served reasonably priced usual food inc children's from central food counter or in upstairs restaurant, five cold real ales; piped music; nearby multistorey car park *(Peter and Audrey Dowsett, David Carr, Tony Hobden, Val and Alan Green, Dr and Mrs M E Wilson)*

Pembroke [Pembroke Rd]: Well run traditional local, well kept ales such as Fullers London Pride, reasonably priced food, good atmosphere;

open all day *(Ann and Colin Hunt)*

Sallyport [High St, Old Portsmouth]:
Comfortable beamed bar with leather
chesterfields, soft lighting, lots of naval prints,
attractively priced usual bar food from
sandwiches and baked potatoes up, decent
coffee, three real ales inc Gales HSB, upstairs
restaurant; bedrooms *(Ann and Colin Hunt,
Neil and Anita Christopher)*

Ship & Castle [The Hard, opp dockyard
entrance]: Long modernised town pub handy
for HMS *Victory* etc, big dining area, well kept
Hampshire Kings Ransom *(Val and
Alan Green)*

Spice Island [Bath Sq]: Vast open-plan
waterside pub, no smoking throughout now,
part dark and panelled in galleon style, part
roomy modern bare-boards style, big windows
overlooking passing ships, well kept ales, food
all day, family room (one of the few in
Portsmouth), bright upstairs restaurant; the
square outside has more harbour-view seats
now *(Mrs Maricar Jagger)*

RINGWOOD [SU1405]

Inn on the Furlong [Meeting House Lane, next
to supermarket]: Long flagstoned bar, stripped
brick and oak timbering, simple décor, full
range of Ringwood beers from nearby brewery
kept well, log fire, daily papers, good friendly
young staff, good value lunchtime food from
low-priced soup and hot-filled sandwiches up,
daytime no smoking area, conservatory dining
extension; quiet piped music; open all day
(cl Sun afternoon), live music Tues, Easter
beer festival *(W W Burke, Terry and
Linda Moseley, Bruce Bird, Sue and
Mike Todd)*

ROCKBOURNE [SU1118]

☆ *Rose & Thistle* [signed off B3078
Fordingbridge—Cranborne]: Attractive 16th-c
thatched pub with fresh home-made food (best
to book Sun lunch), well kept ales such as
Fullers London Pride and Hampshire Strongs
Best, good range of wines, attentive staff,
civilised flagstoned bar with antique settles, old
engravings and cricket prints, good coal fire,
traditional games, log fires in front restaurant
with no smoking area; may be piped classical
music; children and dogs welcome, tables by
thatched dovecote in neat front garden,
charming tranquil spot in lovely village, good
walks *(LYM, Andy Millward)*

ROCKFORD [SU1608]

Alice Lisle: Big well laid-out open-plan family
dining pub attractively placed on green by
New Forest (can get very busy, popular with
older folk wkdy lunchtimes), emphasis on big
conservatory-style eating area, generous
helpings of usual food from sandwiches up,
well kept Gales and guest beers, decent wines;
baby-changing facilities, garden overlooking
lake with peacock and other birds, ponies
wander nearby, play area and summer
children's entertainment, separate adults-only
garden, handy for Moyles Court
(David M Cundy, BB, Mrs Susan Hunter)

ROMSEY [SU3521]

Abbey Hotel [Church St]: Friendly and
comfortable plush and mahogany dining bar
with enterprising food choice from sandwiches,
home-made soup and baked potatoes to rabbit
pie and guinea fowl, fast service, well kept
Courage Best and Directors, risqué Victorian
photographs and postcards; bedrooms, opp
Abbey *(Ron Shelton, Craig Turnbull)*

☆ *Dukes Head* [A3057 out towards Stockbridge]:
Attractive 16th-c dining pub festooned with
flowering baskets in summer, picturesque series
of small linked rooms each with its own
distinct and interesting décor, well kept ales inc
Fullers London Pride and Ringwood, decent
house wines, enjoyable well presented food
from unusual fresh sandwiches up, big log fire,
friendly staff; may be quiet piped music; picnic-
sets out in front, nicer tables on sheltered back
terrace, attractive back garden *(A R Hawkins,
BB, Dr Michael Smith, J V Dadswell,
Geoff Pidoux, David Sizer)*

Old House At Home [Love Lane]: Attractive
16th-c thatched pub surrounded by new
development, appealingly individual and old-
fashioned décor, good freshly made food from
reasonably priced sandwiches up, good friendly
service, well kept Gales ales inc a seasonal one,
small no smoking room; no mobile phones
*(Roger and Pauline Pearce, Gerry and
Rosemary Dobson, A and B D Craig,
Craig Turnbull)*

☆ *Three Tuns* [Middlebridge St (but car park
signed straight off A27 bypass)]: Good
interesting bistro food inc reasonably priced
up-to-date bar lunches in attractively furnished
bow-windowed pub with panelling, flagstones
and some low black beams, starched table
linen, well kept Ringwood ales, good amiable
service; piped music; children allowed at
lunchtime, good tables out on back terrace
*(LYM, Mr and Mrs David Lewis, W W Burke,
Patrick Hall)*

ROPLEY [SU6332]

Chequers [Winchester Rd]: Long bar with log
fire one end, pleasant no smoking dining area
the other, cheerful licensees, reasonably priced
straightforward blackboard food, TV in side
room; handy for Watercress Line station, good
walking on interesting village pathways, open
all day at least wknds *(Ann and Colin Hunt)*

ROTHERWICK [SU7156]

☆ *Coach & Horses* [signed from B3349 N of
Hook; also quite handy for M3 junction 5]:
Individual furnishings and roaring fire in two
comfortably worn in beamed front rooms,
tasty fairly priced generous food from
lunchtime sandwiches to steaks, fresh veg, no
smoking eating areas, inner parquet-floored
serving area with several Badger ales and a
couple of Gribble guests, daily papers, relaxed
friendly atmosphere, helpful staff, entertaining
parrot; tables in back garden, pretty flower
tubs and baskets *(Robin Cordell, LYM,
Mayur Shah)*

ROWLAND'S CASTLE [SU7310]

☆ *Robin Hood* [The Green]: Modern-style bar,
light and airy, with quarry tiles, bare boards
and some carpet, sturdy pine and other tables,
nice contemporary retro artwork, enjoyable

up-to-date food inc plenty of fish on most days, well kept Fullers London Pride and Hook Norton Old Hooky, good wine choice; piped music; disabled access and facilities, picnic-sets on heated front terrace, on green of pleasant village *(BB, John Evans, Ann and Colin Hunt, Jess and George Cowley)*

SELBORNE [SU7433]

☆ *Selborne Arms* [High St]: Character tables, pews and deep settles made from casks on antique boards in appealing bar on left with big log fire, lots of local photographs in no smoking carpeted room on right, well kept ales such as Cheriton Pots, Courage Best, Hampshire Ploughmans Punch, Mighty Oak English Oak and Ringwood Fortyniner, good choice of wines by the glass (three glass sizes), nice coffee, twinkly landlord and pleasant staff, daily papers; good cream teas in back tea room doubling as collectables shop; plenty of tables in garden with arbour, terrace, orchard and good play area, right by walks up Hanger, and handy for Gilbert White museum *(Val and Alan Green, Martin and Karen Wake, Ian Phillips, Michael B Griffith, BB, Ann and Colin Hunt)*

SHALDEN [SU]

Golden Pot [on B3349 Odiham Rd N of Alton]: Extensively refurbished in traditional mode, with log fires, beamery and plenty of pine to keep it light and airy, cheerful friendly staff, well kept Greene King ales, decent choice of wines by the glass, enjoyable straightforward home-made food from good baguettes and well filled wraps up, skittle alley; terrace and garden, open all day *(Martin and Karen Wake)*

SHAWFORD [SU4724]

Bridge Hotel: Large well run beamed Chef & Brewer, several interesting rooms, smart décor, cosy nooks and corners, courteous attentive staff, well kept beers such as Courage Best, Ringwood Fortyniner and John Smiths, decent wines, food all day; pleasant terrace and large garden with play area, downland and Itchen Way walks *(Phyl and Jack Street, Jim and Janet Brown, Lynn Sharpless, Val and Alan Green)*

SHEDFIELD [SU5512]

Wheatsheaf [A334 Wickham—Botley]: Busy and friendly local with well kept ales inc Cheriton tapped from the cask, enjoyable bar lunches, impromptu piano sessions in public bar; garden, handy for Wickham Vineyard *(Val and Alan Green, R Michael Richards)*

SHERBORNE ST JOHN [SU6255]

Swan [Kiln Rd]: Good choice of enjoyable food, good housekeeping; pleasant garden with play area *(John Fisher)*

SILCHESTER [SU6262]

Calleva Arms [The Common]: Spacious cheerful bar on left with interestingly carved bench seats, two smart no smoking dining areas on right, good value food inc speciality ice-creams, Gales and a guest such as Marstons Pedigree, good choice of wines and country wines, games room with pool, no smoking family conservatory; handy for the Roman site,

sizeable attractive garden with boules and big adventure play area *(J V Dadswell)*

SOBERTON [SU6116]

☆ *White Lion* [School Hill; signed off A32 S of Droxford]: Cheerful Georgian-fronted 16th-c village pub in nice spot by green, enjoyable food from good panini to ostrich and buffalo, well kept ales such as Bass, Palmers 200 and one brewed for them by Hampshire, decent house wine, genial licensees, locals and dogs, irregularly shaped bare-boards low-ceilinged bar with built-in wooden wall seats and traditional games, more comfortable lounge, rambling no smoking restaurant; children in eating areas, small sheltered pretty garden with suntrap fairy-lit terrace, open all day, good walks nearby *(Val and Alan Green, LYM)*

SOPLEY [SZ1597]

☆ *Woolpack* [B3347 N of Christchurch]: Pretty thatched pub with rambling candlelit open-plan low-beamed bar, rustic furniture, woodburner and little black kitchen range, friendly helpful staff, enjoyable food from sandwiches and ploughman's to steaks and Sun roasts, well kept Flowers Original, Ringwood Best and Wadworths 6X, good house wine, no smoking conservatory; piped music, bustling Fri/Sat night; open all day, children in eating areas, charming garden, picnic-sets under weeping willows, stream with ducks and footbridges *(LYM, John and Vivienne Rice, Glenwys and Alan Lawrence)*

SOUTHAMPTON [SU4214]

Crown [Highcrown St, Highfield]: Bustling warmly relaxed local, well kept Archers, Flowers Original, Fullers London Pride and Wadworths 6X, substantial bargain lunchtime food from baked potatoes up, helpful staff, open fires; piped music, can be packed with students and academics from nearby Uni; dogs allowed in main bar (giving country feel in the suburbs), heated covered terrace, Sun quiz night, open all day *(Prof Keith and Mrs Jane Barber)*

☆ *Duke of Wellington* [Bugle St (or walk along city wall from Bar Gate)]: Ancient timber-framed building on 13th-c foundations, bare boards, log fire, friendly relaxed atmosphere, really helpful service, well kept reasonably priced ales such as Bass, Ringwood Best, Vale Best and Wadworths IPA and JCB, good choice of wines by the glass, good varied bar food, no smoking back dining room (front bar can get smoky); very handy for Tudor House Museum *(D J and P M Taylor, Val and Alan Green)*

Richmond [Portswood Rd]: Spotless pub with well kept Greene King IPA, Abbot, 1799 and an interesting weekly guest beer, big brass till, liner pictures, may be fresh lunchtime rolls and sandwiches *(Peter and Liz Holmes)*

☆ *White Star* [Oxford St]: Attractive building with smart red-walled bar, banquettes and open fire, comfortable sofas and armchairs in secluded alcoves by south-facing windows, good food from interesting baguettes and up-to-date light dishes to full restaurant menu, smart and pleasant upper dining area, French manager, rather sophisticated friendly aproned staff in black uniforms, Fullers London Pride, good wines by the glass inc ports and sweet wine, lots of cocktails; they may try to keep your credit card while you eat; sunny pavement tables *(Paul A Moore, Val and Alan Green)*

SOUTHSEA [SZ6498]

5th Hampshire Volunteer Arms [Albert Rd]: Popular two-bar backstreet local, three Gales beers and guests such as Greene King Abbot, friendly staff, military memorabilia, good juke box; does not have a no smoking area; open all day *(the Didler, Tony Hobden)*

Diamonds [Norfolk St]: Mainly no smoking, with simple quick suppers such as tapas, well kept changing ales mainly from Oakleaf (Thurs bargains), darts, Weds quiz night *(Mrs Maricar Jagger)*

Eldon Arms [Eldon St/Norfolk St]: Roomy rambling real ale pub with old pictures and advertisements, attractive mirrors, lots of bric-a-brac and bookcases, half a dozen or more changing well kept beers such as Adnams Best and Greene King IPA, friendly service, lunchtime food (not Sat); sensibly placed darts, fruit machine, can get smoky; tables in back garden *(Ann and Colin Hunt, Mrs Maricar Jagger)*

Red White & Blue [Fawcett Rd]: Busy open-plan corner local, well kept Gales ales, food till 5 (not Sun); games nights, jazz Weds, live bands wknd, open all day *(the Didler, Colin Moore)*

Sir Loin of Beef [Highland Rd, Eastney]: Big-windowed pub, simple inside, with up to eight frequently changing well kept ales, tasters offered, reasonably priced bar food, helpful friendly staff, buoyant atmosphere, interesting submarine memorabilia; lacks a no smoking area *(Andy and Jill Kassube, Ann and Colin Hunt, Tony Hobden)*

SOUTHWICK [SU6208]

Golden Lion [High St; just off B2177 on Portsdown Hill]: Welcoming local with large well worn bar and smarter lounge, good value simple food from good baguettes to Sun lunch, well kept Gales, also distinctive Suthwyk ales, brewed by local farm using its own barley which they malt themselves, friendly staff, antique pine, pleasant restaurant; where Eisenhower and Montgomery came before D-Day, picturesque estate village with scenic walks *(Val and Alan Green)*

Red Lion [High St]: Low-beamed village pub, mainly no smoking, with wide choice of generous enjoyable food from good baguettes up inc substantial proper pies, Gales BB and a seasonal beer, decent wines by the glass, friendly prompt service from smart staff; good walks *(Ann and Colin Hunt, Lynn Sharpless)*

ST MARY BOURNE [SU4250]

George: Comfortable dining pub under cordial new licensees, attentive service, pleasant bar eating area and attractively lit restaurant, unusual veg with good Sun carvery; tables outside, attractive village *(Mrs Viv Kington)*

STOCKBRIDGE [SU3535]

☆ *White Hart* [High St; A272/A3057

roundabout]: Roomy and welcoming divided bar, attractive décor with antique prints, oak pews and other seats, enjoyable freshly made food from sandwiches up, quick helpful service, full range of Gales ales kept well, good coffee, decent wines and country wines; disabled access and facilities, children allowed in comfortable beamed restaurant with blazing log fire, tables in garden with terrace, bedrooms, open all day *(Stephen and Jean Curtis, LYM, Fr Robert Marsh, John Balfour, Peter Neate)*

STROUD [SU7223]

Seven Stars [Winchester Rd; set back from A272 Petersfield—Winchester]: Extended flint and brick pub nicely done out in pine and oak, bright and clean with kitchen-style old furniture, flagstones and good log fires, separate counter for ordering wide choice of good value food from good sandwiches to some exotic dishes, friendly efficient young staff, well kept Badger beers and good wine list, large restaurant extension; tables outside, comfortable bedrooms with own bathrooms, good if strenuous walking *(Fr Robert Marsh, Phyl and Jack Street, Val and Alan Green)*

STUBBINGTON [SU5402]

Crofton [Crofton Lane]: Straightforward estate pub, neat and airy, with friendly helpful staff, four well kept ales such as Caledonian Deuchars IPA, good range of food from sandwiches up, simple well mellowed furnishings, large no smoking area on one side *(Stephen C Harvey)*

SUTTON SCOTNEY [SU4639]

Coach & Horses [Oxford Rd, just off A30]: Friendly recently refurbished local, well spaced tables in main area with big open fire, no smoking area off, enjoyable food inc children's; games machine and TV in one area; children welcome, pleasant outdoor area, three bedrooms in adjacent former fire station *(Mr and Mrs S Jones)*

SWANMORE [SU5816]

Hunters [Hillgrove]: Popular and comfortably worn in dining pub, excellent for children, with big plain family room, winding garden with secluded tables (each with a buzzer for when your food's ready) and several substantial play areas for different age groups, plenty under cover and even one for babies; long-serving landlord, well kept Gales HSB, Ringwood Best and Charles Wells Bombardier tapped from the cask, good house wine and country wines, attentive service, lots of boxer pictures, bank notes, carpentry and farm tools, no smoking area; very busy wknds, nice walks N of village *(Val and Alan Green, Phyl and Jack Street)*

New Inn [Chapel Rd]: Village pub with Greene King ales, enjoyable real home cooking inc some adventurous dishes; plenty of local activity, sports TV, some Sat live music (good newish landlord used to be in a band) *(Val and Alan Green)*

SWANWICK [SU5109]

Elm Tree [handy for M27 junction 9]: Comfortably unpretentious and friendly, with two bars and dining area, enjoyable home-made food, helpful staff, Courage Best and Directors and Charles Wells Bombardier; children welcome, tables in garden, handy for Hampshire Wildlife Reserve *(Val and Alan Green, Charles and Pauline Stride)*

SWAY [SZ2898]

Hare & Hounds [Durns Town, just off B3055 SW of Brockenhurst]: Bright and airy comfortable New Forest family dining pub, lots of children, good value enjoyable fresh food, well kept ales inc Ringwood and Wessex, cheerful and enthusiastic young staff, log fires; dogs welcome, picnic-sets and play frame in good-sized neatly kept garden, open all day Sat *(Penny and Peter Keevil, J M G Clarke, Geoff Pidoux, LYM, A D Lealan)*

THRUXTON [SU2945]

George [just off A303]: Bar with nooks and corners, generous enjoyable home-made food (may take a while), Ringwood ales, roomy light and pleasant eating area overlooking garden with terrace and play area; open all day Fri-Sun, cl Tues *(Jennifer Banks, Phyl and Jack Street)*

TIMSBURY [SU3325]

☆ *Bear & Ragged Staff* [A3057 towards Stockbridge; pub marked on OS Sheet 185 map ref 334254]: Useful chain dining pub popular for wide blackboard choice of reasonably priced food all day, good-sized beamed interior, welcoming service, well kept ales such as Ringwood Best and Wadworths 6X, lots of wines by the glass, log fire; children in eating area, tables in extended garden with good play area, handy for Mottisfont, good walks *(Mike and Shelley Woodroffe, Phyl and Jack Street, Dr Michael Smith, LYM, Lynn Sharpless, Mrs T A Bizat)*

Malthouse [A3057 N of village]: Spacious and massively refurbished, with leather sofas and log fire in pleasant lounge area, real ales such as Gales, Ringwood and Wadworths from central bar, conservatory-style dining areas, wide choice of decent blackboard food (best to book wknds), courteous service; good secluded back garden with terrace, pretty fish pond, barbecue house and big well equipped play area, nr fine Norman church, pleasant paths to Michelmersh *(Phyl and Jack Street)*

TITCHFIELD [SU5305]

Coach & Horses [South St]: Cheery new licensees, softly lit partly panelled bar, compact no smoking dining room, reasonably priced generous food, good choice of beers and wines; skittle alley *(Tony Beaulah)*

Fishermans Rest [Mill Lane, off A27 at Titchfield Abbey]: Busy all-day chain pub/restaurant with nice no smoking family area, well kept ales such as Gales HSB, Greene King IPA and Wadworths 6X, cheerful staff, two log fires (not always lit), daily papers, fishing memorabilia, no music or machines; fine riverside position opp Titchfield Abbey, tables out behind overlooking water *(Carol and Dono Leaman, Ann and Colin Hunt, LYM)*

Queens Head [High St; off A27 nr Fareham]: Ancient pub with good value food esp fish

cooked by landlord, four changing well kept ales, good friendly service, interesting small 1930s-feel bar (can be smoky at times) with old local pictures, window seats and central brick fireplace, attractive restaurant; picnic-sets in prettily planted small back yard, bedrooms, pleasant conservation village nr nature reserve and walks to coast *(Ann and Colin Hunt)*

Titchfield Mill [A27, junction with Mill Lane]: Large popular Vintage Inn catering well for families in neatly kept converted watermill, olde-worlde room off main bar, smarter dining room, upstairs gallery, stripped beams and interesting old machinery, well kept Bass and Courage Best, good choice of wines by the glass, freshly squeezed orange juice, attentive cheerful staff; piped music; open all day, sunny terrace by mill stream with two waterwheels – food not served out here *(Ann and Colin Hunt, Phyl and Jack Street, Jess and George Cowley)*

TURGIS GREEN [SU6959]

☆ *Jekyll & Hyde* [A33 Reading—Basingstoke]: Bustling rambling pub with nice mix of furniture and village atmosphere in black-beamed and flagstoned bar, larger stepped-up three-room dining area with good choice of enjoyable reasonably priced food from sandwiches up all day inc breakfast, children's helpings (they are welcome), prompt cheerful service, well kept Badger Best and IPA and Wadworths 6X, some interesting prints, blazing fire; lots of picnic-sets in good sheltered garden (some traffic noise), play area and various games; disabled facilities *(LYM, R C Livesey, D Crook, KC, Martin and Karen Wake, Michael Dandy)*

TWYFORD [SU4824]

Phoenix [High St]: Cheerful open-plan local with lots of prints, bric-a-brac and big end inglenook log fire, wide choice of sensibly priced generous food from sandwiches, ciabattas and baked potatoes to steaks and theme nights, friendly enthusiastic landlord, well kept Greene King and guest beers, decent wines, step up to no smoking dining area, side skittle alley; quiet piped music; children allowed at one end lunchtime, garden *(Lynn Sharpless, Val and Alan Green, David Coleman, Ann and Colin Hunt, Phyl and Jack Street)*

UPPER CLATFORD [SU3543]

Crook & Shears [off A343 S of Andover, via Foundry Rd]: Cosy two-bar 17th-c thatched pub, several homely olde-worlde seating areas, bare boards and panelling, changing real ales such as Bass, Fullers London Pride, Hop Back Crop Circle, Ringwood Fortyniner and Timothy Taylors Landlord, decent food from doorstep sandwiches up, woodburner, small dining room, back skittle alley with own bar; pleasant secluded garden behind *(Phyl and Jack Street, the Didler, N R White)*

UPTON [SU3555]

Crown [N of Hurstbourne Tarrant]: Linked rooms with pine tables and chairs, a pleasant modicum of sporting prints, horse tack and so forth, good log fires, enjoyable fresh food inc interesting evening dishes, good friendly service, well kept Fullers London Pride and Ringwood Best, good coffee, happy bustling atmosphere; may be piped music in public bar; conservatory, small garden and terrace *(BB, Mrs Pat Crabb)*

UPTON GREY [SU6948]
Hoddington Arms [signed off B3349 S of Hook; Bidden Rd]: Friendly and unpretentious open-plan beamed local with dining rooms each end (one no smoking, children allowed), minimal decoration, good reasonably priced food from lunchtime sandwiches to Sun lunch and impressive specials, well kept Greene King ales, good house wines, helpful service; small games room with darts and bar billiards, may be piped music; dogs welcome, good-sized neat garden with terrace and sizeable play area, quiet pretty village *(BB, Martin and Karen Wake, Dr D J and Mrs S C Walker)*

WALHAMPTON [SZ3396]
Towles [B3054 NE of Lymington; aka Walhampton Inn]: Rambling Georgian-style building with emphasis on enjoyable restaurant food inc carvery in raftered former stables and two adjoining areas, Gales and guest ales, pleasant service and atmosphere; good walks nearby inc Solent Way *(Phyl and Jack Street, David M Cundy)*

WEST END [SU4714]
Southampton Arms [Moorgreen Rd, off B3035]: Sizeable and well run city-edge pub with Ringwood ales, enjoyable reasonably priced food, comfortable and cosy bar, attractive conservatory restaurant; good garden *(Phyl and Jack Street)*

WEST MEON [SU6424]
Thomas Lord [High St]: Pleasant layout with sofa by log fire on right, plenty of dining tables, cricket prints and memorabilia inc odd cricket match played by stuffed weasels and stoats, Bass, Greene King Abbot and Ringwood Best, good farm ciders, wines and coffee in great variety, friendly and enthusiastic new licensees putting thought into promising fresh food from good sandwiches up; unobtrusive piped jazz; picnic-sets in sheltered side garden, good walks W of village *(John Branston, BB, Prof and Mrs Tony Palmer)*

WHERWELL [SU3839]
☆ *Mayfly* [Testcombe, outside village; A3057 SE of Andover]: Very popular for its splendid setting – get there early for a table on decking out by River Test; brightly lit red décor with some original fishing pictures, modern pine tables, Gales HSB, Marstons Pedigree, Ringwood Best and Wadworths 6X, decent buffet-style food all day (queuing system can be tiresome at busy lunchtimes – caterer-friendly rather than customer-friendly); piped music; children and dogs welcome, open all day *(B J Harding, Alec and Barbara Jones, Phil and Sally Gorton, Leigh and Gillian Mellor, LYM, Joyce and Geoff Robson, Catherine FitzMaurice, Mrs Ann Gray, Jess and George Cowley, Francis Johnston, Susan and John Douglas)*

WHITCHURCH [SU4648]
☆ *Red House* [London St]: Very popular for

landlord/chef's good choice of generous food from home-baked baguettes through light meals to modern european hot dishes changing daily, in cheerful and chatty compact dining area up a step on right (big mirrored arches making it seem more extensive), sturdy tables on woodstrip flooring, a few big prints, friendly efficient service under on-the-ball landlady, well kept Hampshire Tigers, decent house wines, some very low beams; bar area has good log fire but can be too smoky; children welcome, tables on attractive back terraces with play area and own menu and hatch service *(Irene and Derek Flewin, Lynn Sharpless, Ian and Deborah Carrington, Jennifer Banks, Val and Alan Green, Guy Consterdine, BB)*

WHITSBURY [SU1219]
Cartwheel [off A338 or A354 SW of Salisbury]: Tucked-away local, welcoming and comfortable, with enjoyable straightforward food (not Mon evening), Adnams Broadside, Ringwood Best and guest beers, choice of ciders, pitched high rafters in one part, lower beams elsewhere, snug little room by door, another small side room with darts, pool, other games; piped music, TV, fruit machine; children and dogs welcome, garden with play area *(LYM, Len and Di Bright)*

WICKHAM [SU5711]
Greens [The Square]: Smart no smoking dining pub, enjoyable reasonably priced food from sandwiches and baguettes up, Bass, Fullers London Pride and a guest such as Youngs Special, long-serving licensees and friendly staff, steps down to restaurant; tables out on pleasant lawn overlooking water meadows, cl Mon exc bank hols *(Nick Vernon)*
Kings Head [The Square]: Pretty town pub with pleasant big-windowed open-plan bar, bare board on right and carpeted on left, good solid furnishings and log fire, Gales ales from imposing horseshoe bar counter, good coffee, no smoking restaurant nicely secluded up some steps; tables out on square and in back garden (former coach yard) with play area, attractive village *(Val and Alan Green, Phyl and Jack Street, BB, Ann and Colin Hunt, Richard Waller, Pauline Smith)*

WINCHESTER [SU4728]
Bell [St Cross Rd]: Unpretentious local with friendly helpful landlord, well kept Greene King ales, decent wines by the glass, fresh usual food, liner pictures in comfortable lounge; separate plain public bar with juke box; big pleasant walled garden with swing and slide, handy for St Cross Hospital – lovely water-meadows walk from centre *(David Carr, Lynn Sharpless, Val and Alan Green)*
Hyde Tavern [A333, continuing out of Jewry St]: Cosily old-fashioned and chatty 15th-c two-bar local with hardly a true right angle, welcoming landlady and regulars, particularly well kept Greene King ales, sensible prices *(Phil and Sally Gorton)*
King Alfred [Saxon Rd, Hyde]: Welcoming Victorianised pub with unfussy traditional décor, wood and opaque glass dividers, no

smoking areas, good value food from lunchtime baguettes and baked potatoes to imaginative blackboard dishes and popular Sun lunch, Greene King ales, good wine choice, sensible prices, friendly attentive staff; TV, pool, piped music; large pleasant garden with play area *(Lynn Sharpless)*

Old Gaol House [Jewry St]: Big very popular Wetherspoons with large no smoking area, food all day, good choice of locally brewed beers, low prices, no piped music *(John Oates, Denise Walton, Ann and Colin Hunt)*

Royal Oak [Royal Oak Passage, off upper end of pedestrian part of High St opp St Thomas St]: Notable for the no smoking cellar bar (not always open) whose massive 12th-c beams and Saxon wall give it some claim to be the country's oldest drinking spot; big plain partly no smoking main bar with little areas off (some raised), five or six well kept ales such as Caledonian Deuchars IPA, Greene King IPA and Abbot and Ringwood Fortyniner, good value quickly served food; piped music, games machines, packed with young people Fri/Sat nights *(Val and Alan Green, the Didler, LYM, Ann and Colin Hunt, D J and P M Taylor)*

☆ *Willow Tree* [Durngate Terr]: Warmly welcoming local, landlord/chef doing often unusual and enjoyable food, big perhaps even over-generous helpings, cheerful helpful staff, well kept Greene King beers, good wines, no smoking dining area (could be better ventilated); long and pleasant riverside garden *(Lynn Sharpless, Peter and Eleanor Kenyon, Phil and Sally Gorton)*

WINCHFIELD [SU7753]

Barley Mow [The Hurst]: Friendly two-bar local with light and airy dining extension, generous home-made straightforward food from sandwiches, baguettes and baked potatoes up, well kept ales inc Bass, decent wine; dogs welcome, pleasant seats out by cricket ground, nr Basingstoke canal — lots of good walks *(Ian Phillips)*

WOLVERTON [SU5658]

George & Dragon [Towns End; just N of A339 Newbury—Basingstoke]: Comfortable rambling open-plan pub, beams and standing timbers, log fires, pleasant dining area, wide choice of enjoyable food, range of beers, decent wines, helpful service, no piped music, skittle alley; no children in bar; pleasant large garden with small terrace, bedrooms *(J V Dadswell, Jennifer Banks)*

WOODGREEN [SU1717]

☆ *Horse & Groom* [off A338 N of Fordingbridge]: Nicely set New Forest pub with comfortable linked beamed rooms around servery, nature photographs, log fire in pretty Victorian fireplace, well kept Badger ales, good choice of good value home-cooked food, friendly relaxed landlord; picnic-sets on front terrace and in spreading back garden *(LYM, Dr and Mrs A K Clarke, A and B D Craig, Phyl and Jack Street)*

Herefordshire

This year we welcome back into the main entries a nice country pub, the Butchers Arms at Woolhope, more of a dining pub these days than it used to be, with fresh flowers everywhere. Other pubs doing particularly well here are the welcoming and aptly named Riverside Inn at Aymestrey (good restaurant food and a nice place to stay), the ancient Englands Gate at Bodenham (a warm welcome here too), the Roebuck at Brimfield (new licensees updating its décor and doing good interesting food), the charming Cottage of Content at Carey (moving ahead under new owners), the Pandy at Dorstone (new people here too, food all home-made now), the handsome old Feathers in Ledbury (nicely combining the warmth of a popular local with the style of a comfortable bistro and well run inn), the very rural Three Horseshoes in Little Cowarne (local supplies for its enjoyable food and drink, good bedrooms), the ancient New Inn in Pembridge (good value traditional food, unspoilt bar), the Lough Pool at Sellack (a lovely place to eat out in – first reports on its new licensees indicate that they will keep up its very high reputation), the Stagg at Titley (a top-notch dining pub, adding more bedrooms), the Three Crowns at Ullingswick (good local and organic food, nice for a drink and a chat too), the welcoming and unspoilt Carpenters Arms at Walterstone (a gem), and the Rhydspence at Whitney-on-Wye (a lovely ancient building, good all round). As you can see, good food is a strong point at many of these front-runners – many of them charming buildings in attractive countryside. The one which takes the prize of Herefordshire Dining Pub of the Year is the Stagg at Titley. In the Lucky Dip section at the end of the chapter, pubs to note particularly are the utterly unspoilt Sun in Leintwardine, and the Cliffe Arms at Mathon, Saracens Head at Symonds Yat and Chase at Upper Colwall. Drinks in Herefordshire tend to be cheaper than in most places, with Wye Valley beers brewed at the Barrels pub in Hereford (see Lucky Dip entries) and Hobsons from just over the Shropshire border often standing out as good value here. The Spinning Dog beer brewed and sold at the interesting Victory in Hereford was particularly cheap.

AYMESTREY SO4265 Map 6
Riverside Inn ⑪ ♀ 🛏

A4110, at N end of village, W of Leominster

In a hilly and rewarding area for country walks, with the nearby Mortimer Trail as well as the impressive ramparts of Croft Ambrey hillfort within easy reach, this half-timbered inn stands at an attractive point by a low two-arched bridge spanning the River Lugg, where residents can try fly-fishing. The rambling beamed bar has several cosy areas and the décor is drawn from a pleasant mix of periods and styles, with fine antique oak tables and chairs, stripped pine country kitchen tables, fresh flowers, hops strung from a ceiling wagon-wheel, horse tack and nice pictures; the eating areas are no smoking. Warm log fires in winter, while in summer big overflowing flower pots frame the entrances; piped music. Well kept Woods and Wye Valley on handpump, local farm cider and 20 malt whiskies. The landlord likes to talk to his customers and service is good. Enjoyable bar food includes freshly made baguettes, ploughman's, lasagne, local gammon steak with parsley sauce, sausage with mustard mash and white onion gravy, and locally smoked salmon and prawn salad (£4.25-£9.95), as well as starters such as fillet of herefordshire beef marinated in thyme with balsamic mushrooms or gateaux of cornish crab with chive, lime and tomato dressing (£3.75-£5.25), and main courses like roasted local free-range chicken breast on a white bean and pancetta casserole, beetroot and orange risotto with parmesan or herb crusted local pork tenderloin on caramelised apple and raisin mustard mash with a sage jus (£8.95-£14.95). It does get busy at weekends, so booking would be wise. Picnic-sets make the most of the view, and rustic tables and benches up above in a steep tree-sheltered garden – it has a beautifully sheltered former bowling green, too. *(Recommended by Tim Frith, Richard and Margaret Peers, Peter Cole, John Hale, J E Shackleton, Guy Vowles, Pamela and Merlyn Horswell, Di and Mike Gillam, R M Corlett, Ian Stafford, B P Abrahams, Pam and David Bailey, Brian Wainwright)*

Free house ~ Licensees Richard and Liz Gresko ~ Real ale ~ Bar food (12-2.15, 7-9 Mon-Sat, 12-3.30, 6.30-8.30 Sun) ~ Restaurant ~ (01568) 708440 ~ Children in eating area of bar and restaurant ~ Dogs welcome ~ Open 11-3, 6-11 ~ Bedrooms: £40B/£65B

BODENHAM SO5454 Map 4
Englands Gate
Just off A417 at Bodenham turn-off, about 6 miles S of Leominster

Blazing fires set a welcoming tone as you step inside this handsome black and white 16th-c coaching inn. It has been well opened up inside, rambling around a vast central stone chimneypiece and looks every year of its age, with heavy brown beams and joists in low ochre ceilings, well worn flagstones, sturdy timber props, one or two steps, and lantern-style lighting. One nice corner has a comfortably worn leather settee and high-backed settle with scatter cushions; a cosy partly stripped-stone room has a long stripped table that would be just right for a party of eight; a lighter upper area with flowers on its tables has winged settles painted a cheery yellow or aquamarine. Decent bar food at lunchtime includes sandwiches (from £3.50; baguettes £4.50), mushroom ravioli glazed in parmesan and herbs (£5.95), green thai king prawn curry or spicy cumberland sausage on mustard mash with onion gravy (£6.95) and deep-fried cod in beer batter (£8.50), with evening choices such as soup (£3.50), grilled goats cheese and marinated aubergine (£5.25), fried leg of lamb steaks topped with garlic and herb crumble (£9.75), grilled fillet of salmon with mussels in saffron and dill butter (£10.25), baked breast of chicken with caramelised apple wedges and black pudding (£10.95) and steaks (from £11.50). Well kept Woods Shropshire Lad, Wye Valley Bitter and Butty Bach plus a guest on handpump; friendly staff; piped mellow pop music, and TV; the restaurant is no smoking. There are tables out in an attractive garden. More reports please. *(Recommended by Mike and Mary Carter, Pamela and Merlyn Horswell, Norman Lewis, Mr and Mrs J Tout)*

Free house ~ Licensee Evelyn McNeil ~ Real ale ~ Bar food (12-2.30, 6-9.30; 12-3.30 Sun) ~ Restaurant ~ (01568) 797286 ~ Children welcome until 9pm ~ Dogs allowed in bar ~ Open 11-11; 12-10.30 Sun

BRIMFIELD SO5368 Map 4
Roebuck Inn ⑪ ♀ ⛱
Village signposted just off A49 Shrewsbury—Leominster

Since taking over in 2004 the present licensees have continued to keep the high standards of home-cooked food at this smartly refurbished dining pub near the Shropshire border. The beers are well kept, and the food extremely good; it's also a comfortable place to stay. Each of the three rambling bars has a different but equally civilised atmosphere. The quiet old-fashioned snug (the only place where smoking is permitted) is where you might find locals drinking and playing dominoes and cribbage by an impressive inglenook fireplace. Pale oak panelling in the 15th-c main bar makes for a quietly relaxed atmosphere, and the light and airy Brimfield Bar, given a contemporary look with beige, green and cream colours, has a big bay window and open fire. There's also a brightly decorated cane-furnished dining room. At lunchtime, snacks might include sandwiches (from £4.95), platters with assorted cheeses, home-cooked ham or beef (£7.50), pizzas (£8.50), casserole or faggots, mushy peas and mash (£9). A more elaborate menu includes items such as artichoke filled with field and wild mushrooms, shallots and cream (£6), smoked chicken and raspberry salad (£6.95), seared scallops (£8; £12.50 as a main course), chicken breast wrapped with parma ham on a bed of mediterranean vegetables (£12.95), bass on summer vegetable risotto (£14.50) and fillet steak with oyster mushroom and cognac sauce (£17.50); you can take selected dishes from this menu as part of the excellent value two-course lunchtime menu for £11.50; puddings like chocolate pudding, lemon tart or bread and butter pudding (all £5). In addition to well kept Banks and a couple of guests such as Camerons Strongarm and Hydes Jeckylls Gold, they have an interesting reasonably priced wine list with over 40 wines, and a carefully chosen range of spirits, including single malts and armagnacs. Seats out on the enclosed terrace. *(Recommended by Rod Stoneman, Chris Flynn, Wendy Jones, Ian Phillips, Ian and Joan Blackwell, Tim Field, Carole Thomas, Rodney and Norma Stubington, Pamela and Merlyn Horswell, Dr L Kaufman, Mr and Mrs W Mills, Pam and Alan Neale, Bernard Stradling)*

Union Pub Company ~ Lease David and Jackie Ward ~ Real ale ~ Bar food ~ Restaurant ~ (01584) 711230 ~ Children in eating area of bar ~ Dogs allowed in bar and bedrooms ~ Open 11.30-3, 6.30-11; 12-3, 7-10.30 Sun ~ Bedrooms: £50B/£80B

CAREY SO5631 Map 4
Cottage of Content
Village signposted from good road through Hoarwithy

Home-cooked, freshly done food is the rule at this friendly, tranquil medieval cottage, in a tiny hamlet overlooking sheep pastures. Inside is a pleasant mix of country furnishings – stripped pine, country kitchen chairs, long pews by one big table, and various old-fashioned tables on flagstones and bare boards; plenty of beams and prints. Bar food includes lunchtime snacks such as soup (£3.95), filled baguettes and ciabattas (from £5.25), filled baked potatoes (from £6.50) and ploughman's (from £6.95), plus lasagne (£8.25), grilled supreme of salmon with chorizo sausage £8.75), steak and kidney pie or chicken breast stuffed with brie and bacon (£9.25) and sirloin steak (£11.95); à la carte items, available in the restaurant or bar, change several times a week and might include chicken liver pâté with red onion jam (£5.25), fried bass with saffron and garden herb risotto (£12.25) and fillet of herefordshire beef on celeriac remoulade (£15.50). Well kept Hook Norton Best and Wye Valley Bitter on handpump and in summer they usually have a guest or two such as Whittingtons Nine Lives as well as farm cider; piped music. There are picnic-sets on the flower-filled front terrace, plus a couple of picnic-sets on a back terrace (they are hoping to build a conservatory on this). As we were about to go to press they were about to begin offering accommodation; we would welcome reports from readers who have stayed here. *(Recommended by Christopher J Darwent, Peter B Brown, the Didler, Mike and Mary Carter)*

Free house ~ Licensee Svenia Wolf ~ Real ale ~ Bar food (12-2, 7-9.30) ~ Restaurant ~ (01432) 840242 ~ Dogs allowed in bar ~ Open 11.30-2.30, 6.30-11; 12-3 Sun; closed Mon

DORSTONE SO3141 Map 6
Pandy
Pub signed off B4348 E of Hay-on-Wye

The food here at this striking half-timbered pub – Herefordshire's oldest, dating from 1185 – is now all home made. The neatly kept homely main room (on the right as you go in) has heavy beams in the ochre ceiling, stout timbers, upright chairs on its broad worn flagstones and in its various alcoves, and a vast open fireplace with logs; a side extension has been kept more or less in character. Bar food includes lunchtime baguettes and focaccias with chips (£4.20) and ploughman's (£7.70), as well as soup (£3.95), chicken liver pâté with cumberland sauce (£5.20), confit of duck, steak and ale pie, chicken, broccoli and stilton pie or game pie (£9.50), lamb shank with redcurrant and rosemary gravy (£10.95), and puddings like ginger pudding or white chocolate and lemon cheesecake with summer berry sauce (£3.95); the restaurant is no smoking. Well kept Spinning Dog Herefordshire Old Bull (brewed by the Victory in Hereford) and Wye Valley Butty Bach and Bitter, and quite a few malt whiskies, Gwatkins' farm cider, and decent wines; dominoes, chess, quoits and a winter quiz. The handsome red setter is Apache, and the neat side garden has picnic-sets and a play area. *(Recommended by June and Geoffrey Cox, R T and J C Moggridge, the Didler, Pam and David Bailey, Denys Gueroult, Jacquie and Jim Jones, Roger Thornington, MLR, R Michael Richards, Ryta Lyndley, Sue Demont, Tim Barrow, Dennis and Gill Keen)*

Free house ~ Licensees Bill and Magdalena Gannon ~ Real ale ~ Bar food (12-3, 6-9.30; summer hols 12-10) ~ (01981) 550273 ~ Children welcome until 9pm ~ Dogs welcome ~ Open 12-3, 6-11(all day school summer hols); closed all day Mon winter

HEREFORD SO5139 Map 6
Victory ◖ £
St Owen Street, opposite fire station

There's nothing quite like the astonishing interior of this well worn and idiosyncratic home-brew city pub, with its counter done like a miniature galleon complete with cannon poking out of its top. Down a companionway, the long back room is well decked out as the inside of a man o' war: dark wood, rigging and netting everywhere, benches along sides that curve towards a front fo'c'sle, stanchions and ropes forming an upper crow's nest, and appropriate lamps. The focus is very much on beer: the Spinning Dog brewery based here produces Chase Your Tail, Herefordshire Light Ale, Herefordshire Old Bull, Mutleys Dark, Mutleys Revenge, Mutleys Springer, Mutts Nutts and Pit Stop – they usually have six well kept on handpump at a time plus a couple of guest beers too, and three farmhouse ciders and a perry (also on handpump). With prices unchanged since last year, straightforward bar food (which may not always be available) includes sandwiches (from £2), chilli con carne or chicken curry (£4.50), ploughman's or fish of the day (£5) and 8oz steak (£5.50), with specials such as faggots, mash and peas (£5); they do a curry night on Friday. Service is friendly and informal (they'll show you around the brewery if they're not busy). Juke box (can be very loud), darts, fruit machine, TV, skittle alley, table skittles, cribbage, shove-ha'penny, dominoes and a back pool table; the bar area is no smoking. The garden has a pagoda, climbing plants and some seats. *(Recommended by Gill and Tony Morriss, Paul Davies, Bruce Bird, Ian Phillips, Ian and Liz Rispin)*

Own brew ~ Licensee James Kenyon ~ Real ale ~ Bar food (12-5(10Fri)) ~ Restaurant (Sun only) ~ No credit cards ~ (01432) 342125 ~ Children welcome ~ Dogs welcome ~ Live band Sat and Sun ~ Open 12(11 Sat)-11; 12-10.30 Sun

LEDBURY SO7138 Map 4
Feathers ⑪ ♀ ⇔
High Street, Ledbury, A417

One of Ledbury's numerous half-timbered buildings, this handsome Tudor inn makes a comfortable place for a meal or just a drink. At first sight it's predominantly comfortably hotel-like in character but the Top Bar has plenty of chatty and cheerful locals enjoying a pint quite uninhibited by those enjoying the good food and fine wines at the brasserie tables behind them. There are beams and timbers, hop bines, some country antiques, 19th-c caricatures and fancy fowl prints on the stripped brick chimneybreast (lovely winter fire), and fresh flowers on the tables – some very snug and cosy, in side bays. In summer, abundant pots and hanging baskets adorn the sheltered back terrace. Well kept Bass, Fullers London Pride and Worthington, and a guest such as Timothy Taylors Landlord on handpump; 14 wines by the glass and several malt whiskies. As well as a 'quickies' menu with home-made soup (£3.90) and sandwiches (from £4.50; rare roast beef with green peppercorn mustard £5.50), the enjoyable food includes items like smoked trout fillet with potato salad (£6.95), penne pasta with cream and wild mushrooms (£8.50), rib-eye steak (£10.50), breast of free-range chicken with wild mushroom and tomato jus (£13.75), herefordshire fillet steak (£15.95) and puddings such as bitter chocolate tart with mango and crème fraîche ice-cream, or home-made bread and butter pudding (£4.95). Nice breakfasts, and friendly, helpful staff; the restaurant is no smoking. They do fine afternoon teas in the more formal quiet lounge by the reception area, which has high-sided armchairs and sofas in front of a big log fire, and newspapers to read. *(Recommended by Craig Turnbull, A S and M E Marriott, Joan and Tony Walker, J E Shackleton, Dr and Mrs M W A Haward, Patrick Hancock, David and Nina Pugsley, Pamela and Merlyn Horswell, Annette Tress, Gary Smith, Dr G and Mrs J Kelvin, Peter Cole, Derek Thomas, A D Lealan, J Crosby)*

Free house ~ Licensee David Elliston ~ Real ale ~ Bar food (12-2) ~ Restaurant ~ (01531) 635266 ~ Children welcome ~ Open 11-11; 12-10.30 Sun ~ Bedrooms: £74.50B/£99B

LITTLE COWARNE SO6051 Map 4 🏠

Three Horseshoes ♀ 🛏

Pub signposted off A465 SW of Bromyard; towards Ullingswick

In a captivating rural spot, with lovely views from the tables on the terrace or the neat prettily planted lawn, this friendly bustling place is popular with locals and visitors. There might be a cheerful cribbage match happening, race-goers from Cheltenham reliving their wins, and residents enjoying a good meal before staying overnight in the comfortable bedrooms. The quarry tiled L-shaped middle bar has leather-seated bar stools, upholstered settles and dark brown kitchen chairs around sturdy old tables, old local photographs above the corner log fire, and hop-draped black beams in the dark peach ceiling. Opening off one side is a skylit no smoking sun room with wicker armchairs around more old tables; the other end has a games room with darts, pool, juke box, fruit machine and games machine; also cribbage and dominoes. For the well liked bar food they use local gamekeepers and fishermen, buy local eggs and vegetables (though they grow summer salads, tomatoes and herbs themselves), and make their own chutneys, pickles, jams and sloe gin. Enjoyable bar food includes sandwiches (from £2.25), garlic mushrooms or crab and lime fishcakes (£4.50), local venison and pork terrine with spiced damsons (£4.75), ploughman's (from £5.50), any starter from the blackboard menu, such as devilled kidneys, served with potatoes and vegetables or salad (£6.50), lasagne (£8.95), pheasant breast with cider and rosemary and cream sauce (£9.95), rump steak (£11.95) and roast rack of lamb (£12.95); pudding such as home-made jam roly poly pudding and custard (£3.75); children's menu (£3.95). Popular OAP pie lunch on Thursday. Besides well kept Greene King Old Speckled Hen, Marstons Pedigree and Wye Valley Bitter on handpump, they have decent wines (including local ones, and ten by the glass), and Oliver's local farm ciders from named apple cultivars, and perry; obliging service, and disabled access. A roomy and attractive stripped-stone raftered restaurant extension has a Sunday lunchtime carvery. *(Recommended by Michael Doswell, Mike and Mary Carter, Denys Gueroult, Ian Phillips, Maurice and Della Andrew, A S and M E Marriott, Annette Tress, Gary Smith, Dave Braisted, Theocsbrian, Ian Jones, Neil Kellett, Lucien Perring)*

Free house ~ Licensees Norman and Janet Whittall ~ Real ale ~ Bar food ~ Restaurant ~ (01885) 400276 ~ Children in eating area of bar and restaurant ~ Dogs allowed in bar ~ Open 11-3, 6.30-11; 12-3, 7-10.30 Sun; closed Sun evening ~ Bedrooms: £32.50S/£55S

Post Office address codings confusingly give the impression that some pubs are in Herefordshire when they're really in Gloucestershire or even Wales (which is where we list them).

LUGWARDINE SO5541 Map 4

Crown & Anchor 🍴 ♀

Cotts Lane; just off A438 E of Hereford

Still very much a local and with a pretty garden, this relaxing half-timbered pub has several smallish and charming rooms, a big log fire, newspapers to read, and a bar furnished with an interesting mix of pieces. Well kept Butcombes, Timothy Taylors Landlord, Worthington and a guest such as Marstons Pedigree on handpump, a selection of malt whiskies and nine wines by the glass. As well as a huge choice of good lunchtime sandwiches (from £2.50; hummous and avocado £3, cambozola, cucumber and kiwi £3.30, smoked trout with apple and horseradish £3.70), there might be ploughman's (£6), soup (£3.25), salmon fishcakes (£5.50), cold smoked ham with eggs (£7), poacher's pie with flaked salmon and potato and cheese topping (£8.50), cheese and spinach lasagne (£9), trout or steak and kidney pie (£9.50), chicken madras with fresh chillies (£10) and rib-eye steak (£13); two eating areas are no smoking. The pub is surrounded by newish housing, but in ancient times the Lugg flats round here – some of the oldest Lammas meadows in England – were farmed in strips by local farm tenants, and meetings with the lord of the manor were held in the pub. More reports please. *(Recommended by Ian and Liz Rispin, Denys Gueroult, Andy Trafford, Louise Bayly, Neil and Anita Christopher)*

Enterprise ~ Lease Nick and Julie Squire ~ Real ale ~ Bar food (till 10(9 Sun)) ~ Restaurant ~ (01432) 851303 ~ Children welcome ~ Open 12-11; 12-10.30 Sun; closed 25 Dec, 1 Jan

ORLETON SO4967 Map 6

Boot

Just off B4362 W of Woofferton

Not big by any means, so it quickly gets very full, but this 16th-c pub has welcoming licensees and excellent beer. The traditional-feeling bar has a mix of dining and cushioned carver chairs around a few old tables on the red tiles, one very high-backed settle, hops over the counter, and a warming fire in the big fireplace, with horsebrasses along its bressumer beam. The lounge bar is up a couple of steps, and has green plush banquettes right the way around the walls, mullioned windows, an exposed section of wattle and daub, and standing timbers and heavy wall beams. There's a small and pretty no smoking restaurant on the left. Well kept Hobsons Best and Town Crier and a guest on handpump; cribbage and dominoes. Lunchtime food includes home-made soup (£2.95), sandwiches (from £3.75); ploughman's (£5.50), baguettes (from £5.75), lambs liver, bacon and onion gravy (£7.25) and steak in ale pie or gammon steak with egg (£8.25), with evening choices such as home-made pâté (£3.95), breaded whitebait (£4.25), home-made lasagne (£8.25), home-made chicken and asparagus pie (£8.95), grilled duck breast with a black cherry and port sauce (£9.75), and steaks (from £10.75); specials like grilled black pudding topped with smoked bacon and brie (£4.75), cheese, mushroom and pepper roast (£8.95), tuna steak or lamb fillet (£10.25) and sirloin steak (£11.95). On Sunday they may be serving only hot food. There are seats in the garden under a huge ash tree, a barbecue area, and a fenced-in children's play area. More reports please. *(Recommended by P Hedges, Jonathan Smith, R M Corlett)*

Free house ~ Licensees Philip and Jane Dawson ~ Real ale ~ Bar food ~ Restaurant ~ (01568) 780228 ~ Children welcome ~ Dogs allowed in bar ~ Open 12-3, 6-11; 12-3, 7-10.30 Sun

PEMBRIDGE SO3958 Map 6

New Inn

Market Square (A44)

The recently restored open-sided medieval market hall just outside the front door of this delightful half-timbered pub in its super village looks like something from deepest France, and within sight is the church with its huge detached belfry where you can see all the workings. There's no pub garden as such, but a few tables are set out on the cobblestones by the tiny market place. Inside, three simple but comfortable little beamed rooms in this ancient place ooze antiquity with their oak peg-latch doors and elderly traditional furnishings that include a fine antique curved-back settle on the worn flagstones; the log fire is the substantial sort that people needed long before central heating was reinvented. The homely no smoking lounge has sofas, pine furniture, family photos and books; darts, shove-ha'penny, cribbage, dominoes and quoits in the bar. Well kept Black Sheep, Fullers London Pride and John Roberts XXX, and perhaps a couple of guests such as Fullers London Pride or Hook Norton on handpump, 32 malt whiskies, farm cider, and local wine and apple juice. Readers enjoy the food, which comes in generous helpings. Bar food at lunchtime includes sandwiches (from £3.25), ploughman's (£4.95), creamed kidneys with sherry (£6.95), battered fish and chips, or hot home-baked ham with mustard mash and redcurrant sauce (£7.50) and steak and ale pie (£7.95); evening choices such as cream cheese and spinach lasagne (£7), whole prawns in garlic butter with crusty bread, or trout (£9), fillet of lamb (£10.50) and sirloin steak (£11.50). *(Recommended by Peter and Jean Hoare, Pam and David Bailey, R M Corlett, MLR, JWAC, Denys Gueroult, Anne Morris, Kevin Thomas, Nina Randall, M C and S Jeanes, Martin and Sue Day)*

Free house ~ Licensee Jane Melvin ~ Real ale ~ Bar food ~ Restaurant ~ (01544) 388427 ~ Children in restaurant until 8pm ~ Open 11-3, 6-11; 12-3, 7-10.30 Sun; closed first 4 days of Feb

SELLACK SO5627 Map 4

Lough Pool ★ ⑪ ♀

Back road Hoarwithy—Ross-on-Wye

The new licensees who took over here in April 2005 previously ran the excellent Royal Oak at Cerne Abbas in Dorset, and as we go to press with this chapter in June all the signs are that they are keeping up this attractive black and white timbered cottage's winning ways. It has a strong accent on food, yet firmly remains a traditional pub. The beamed central room has kitchen chairs and cushioned window seats around wooden tables on the mainly flagstoned floor, sporting prints, bunches of dried flowers and fresh hop bines, and a log fire at one end with a woodburner at the other. Other rooms lead off, gently brightened up with attractive individual furnishings and nice touches like the dresser of patterned plates. The same interesting menu – which changes daily – is available in the chatty bar as well as the no smoking restaurant, and might include doorstep sandwiches and ciabattas, starters like cream of parsnip and apple soup (£3.95), haggis fritters with beetroot chutney (£5.95) and goats cheese soufflé with basque pepper stew (£6), brixham crab cakes with salsa (£8.50, and main courses such as shepherd's pie (£9.50, lasagne of wild mushrooms with spinach (£12.75), braised saddle of rabbit in cider, rosemary and tarragon (£12.95), red mullet with crayfish mash (£13.95) and rib-eye steak (£14); puddings might include treacle tart with toffee ice-cream, prune and almond tart, home-made ice-creams or millefeuille of chocolate mousse and sugared pastry (all £5.25). Well kept Wye Valley Bitter and Butty Bach plus a couple of guests such as Adnams Regatta or Fullers London Pride on handpump, a dozen malt whiskies, local farm ciders, perries and apple juices, and a well chosen reasonably priced wine list with a dozen by the glass. Service is good. There are plenty of picnic-sets on its neat front lawned area, and pretty hanging baskets; plenty of bridleways and surrounding walks. More reports on the new regime please. *(Recommended by Mrs R Pearson, Pam and David Bailey, J Crosby, Bernard Stradling)*

Free house ~ Licensees David and Janice Birch ~ Real ale ~ Bar food ~ Restaurant ~ (01989) 730236 ~ Children in eating area of bar and restaurant ~ Dogs allowed in bar ~ Open 11.30-3, 6.30-11; 12-3, 7-10.30 Sun; Sun evening, all day Mon in winter; closed 1 week in Jan

STOCKTON CROSS SO5161 Map 4
Stockton Cross Inn
Kimbolton; A4112, off A49 just N of Leominster

A nice place to stop off for a pint of locally brewed ale, this little black and white timbered pub has a long, heavily beamed bar with a handsome antique settle, and old leather chairs and brocaded stools by the huge log fire in the broad stone fireplace. At the far end is a woodburning stove with heavy cast-iron-framed tables and sturdy dining chairs, and up a step, a small area has more tables. Old-time prints, a couple of épées on one beam and lots of copper and brass complete the picture. Cooked by the landlord and his chef, Neil, the bar food includes soup (£3.95), locally made sausages (to the pub's own recipe) with mash (£6.95), home-made steak and kidney pie (£7.95) and cod and chips (£8.50); plus a more ambitious menu including starters like pancake filled with smoked chicken, bacon and mushrooms in a creamy sauce or prawn, haddock and cheese smokie (both £5.75), several vegetarian options such as pancake filled with ratatouille or stilton and mushroom fusilli (both £8.50), rack of ribs in home-made barbecue sauce (£9.50), chicken pie filled with chicken, mushrooms and onions in tarragon and parsley sauce (£10.95), tagine of lamb with apricots, honey and flaked almonds (£11.50), steaks (from £12.95), wild game casserole (£12.50) and halibut with cream, white wine and prawn sauce (£13.75). Puddings typically include treacle tart, chocolate cake with hot chocolate fudge sauce or bread and butter pudding (£4.50); half the eating area is no smoking; piped music. Well kept Teme Valley This, Wye Valley Butty Bach and a guest such as Wye Valley Hereford Pale Ale on handpump. There are tables out in the pretty garden. More reports please.
(Recommended by John and Lynn Norcliffe, Dr and Mrs C W Thomas, Glenwys and Alan Lawrence, Mike and Mary Carter, Ian and Liz Rispin, Rodney and Norma Stubington)

Free house ~ Licensees Stephen and Julia Walsh ~ Real ale ~ Bar food ~ Restaurant ~ (01568) 612509 ~ Well behaved children welcome ~ Open 12-3, 7-11; closed Sun and Mon evenings

TITLEY SO3360 Map 6 🏠
Stagg 🍴 ♀
B4355 N of Kington

Herefordshire Dining Pub of the Year
Some very impressive food comes out of the kitchen of this justly celebrated dining pub, and the landlord/chef also uses local suppliers wherever possible, so you can be sure of good, fresh often organic ingredients. The pubbier blackboard menu (not available Saturday evening or Sunday lunchtime) has up to ten choices which, besides filled baguettes (from £3.50), could include three-cheese ploughman's, locally smoked salmon salad or smoked chicken and crispy bacon salad (£7.90), and smoked haddock risotto, scallops on parsnip purée or steak sandwich with chips and garlic mushrooms (£8.50). On the more elaborate restaurant menu (which can also be eaten in the bar) you might find starters like soup (£3.70), oxtail terrine (£5.90) and cornish cod on squid risotto (£6.50); main courses might feature herefordshire rump steak (£12.50), gressingham duck breast with spiced rhubarb and cider potato fondant (£14.50), bass fillet with braised fennel and dauphinoise potato (£14.90) and saddle of venison with wild mushrooms (£16.90). Puddings could include chocolate meringue with satsuma cream, three crème brûlées of vanilla, orange and lemon tart with cassis sorbet (£4.90), and there's a choice of around 18 british cheeses, mostly from Herefordshire and Wales. Generally readers leave well satisfied with both the food and the warm welcome. The extensive dining rooms are no smoking. A carefully chosen wine list with ten wines and champagne by the glass, well kept Brains Rev James, Hobsons Best and a guest such as Timothy Taylors Landlord served by air pressure, a fine collection of malt whiskies, and local farm cider, perry and apple juice. The bar, though comfortable and hospitable, is not large, and the atmosphere is civilised rather than lively. The garden has chairs and tables on a terrace. They also have a Georgian vicarage four

minutes away which has no smoking guest accommodation, a two-acre garden with croquet lawn and a vegetable and herb garden for the kitchen; they're planning three double ensuite rooms above the pub. *(Recommended by Chris Flynn, Wendy Jones, Keith and Jean Symons, Guy Vowles, Roy and Lindsey Fentiman, Mr and Mrs J Curtis, RJH, George Atkinson, J E Shackleton, Terry Smith, Christopher J Darwent, Mr and Mrs A H Young, Tony Hall, Melanie Jackson, Mike and Mary Carter, Mark Barker, Tom Halsall)*

Free house ~ Licensees Steve and Nicola Reynolds ~ Real ale ~ Bar food ~ Restaurant ~ (01544) 230221 ~ Children welcome ~ Dogs allowed in bar and bedrooms ~ Open 12-3, 6.30-11; closed Sun evening and Mon (exc bank hol weekends other than May Day bank hol), Tues after bank hol weekends (exc May Day), 1 Jan, first 2 weeks of Nov, 25 and 26 Dec ~ Bedrooms: £60B/£80B

ULLINGSWICK SO5949 Map 4
Three Crowns ⊗ ♀

Village off A465 S of Bromyard (and just S of Stoke Lacy) and signposted off A417 N of A465 roundabout – keep straight on through village and past turn-off to church; pub at Bleak Acre, towards Little Cowarne

With open fires, hops strung along the low beams of its smallish bar, traditional settles, a mix of big old wooden tables with small round ornamental cast-iron-framed ones, and more usual seats, this is a cosily traditional country pub with a leaning towards dining. It makes a nice place to come for a special meal out, and the landlord has recently extended part of it, so that there's enough bar space for it to retain a pubby feel. It has one or two gently sophisticated touches such as candles on tables, and proper napkins; all of the pub is now no smoking; cribbage. Using mostly local and organic products, lunchtime food might include soup (£3.95), salmon fishcakes (£4.95), lambs liver and mash (£8.75) and cod and chips (£9), while from the à la carte menu there might be starters such as fish soup, cheese and spinach soufflé, pressed ham hock and foie gras terrine (all £6), specials such as cumberland sausage with parsley mash (£8.50) or smoked salmon with spinach and tomato (£9.75), main courses like confit of gressingham duck with prune pommes anna and split pea purée, grilled skate with asparagus, nutmeg mash and warm green salsa (all £14.25), and puddings that include lemon tart with bitter chocolate ice-cream, panna cotta with poached rhubarb, and date and pecan nut pudding with ice-cream (all £4.50). Best to book to be sure of a table. They have half a dozen wines by the glass, along with well kept Hobsons Best and maybe Wye Valley Butty Bach on handpump, and local farm ciders on handpump and herefordshire apple juice. Nice summer views from tables out on the attractively planted lawn, and outside heaters for chillier evenings. *(Recommended by Rodney and Norma Stubington, J A Ellis, J E Shackleton, Peter and Jean Hoare, Annette Tress, Gary Smith, Roger White, Sir Nigel Foulkes, Mr and Mrs A H Young, Bernard Stradling)*

Free house ~ Licensee Brent Castle ~ Real ale ~ Bar food (12-2.30, 7-9.30) ~ Restaurant ~ (01432) 820279 ~ Well behaved children in eating area of bar ~ Open 12-2.30, 7-11; closed Mon

UPTON BISHOP SO6527 Map 4
Moody Cow

2 miles from M50 junction 3 westbound (or junction 4 eastbound), via B4221; continue on B4221 to rejoin at next junction

This pub looks as rustic as it sounds, with rough sandstone walls inside that are adorned with cow ornaments and naïve cow paintings, stripped country furniture and floorboards and a welcoming log fire. It is laid out in snug areas that angle in an L around the bar counter. On the far right is a biggish rustic and candlelit restaurant, with hop-draped rafters, and a fireside area with armchairs and sofas. The far left has a second smaller dining area (also no smoking), just five or six tables with antique pine-style tables and chairs; both rooms are no smoking. Home-made and cooked to order, the bar food typically includes sandwiches (from £3.25), soup (£4.50), grilled field mushroom with tomato, pine nut and olive stuffing (£4.95), thai crab fishcakes (£5.95 or £10.95 as a main course), home-made spaghetti with ham and mushrooms in tomato sauce (£8.95), home-made lasagne or carrot and basil tart with pesto and melted mozzarella (£9.95), steak, red wine and onion pie or fish and chips (£10.95), confit of pork with caramelised apple and calvados cream sauce (£13.95) and delicious puddings like bread and butter pudding, sticky toffee pudding or chocolate truffle on a biscuit and hazelnut base (from £4.25); they sell their home-made bread, too. At lunchtime and in early evening you can eat from a fixed-price menu at £9.95 for two courses or £11.95 for three. Hook Norton, Wye Valley Best and a guest such as Bass on handpump; piped music. *(Recommended by Guy Vowles, Lucien Perring, Neil and Anita Christopher, Jo Rees, Chris Flynn, Wendy Jones, LM, Mike and Mary Carter, Bernard Stradling)*

Free house ~ Licensee James Lloyd ~ Real ale ~ Bar food (12-2, 6.30-9.30) ~ Restaurant ~ (01989) 780470 ~ Children in restaurant ~ Dogs allowed in bar ~ Open 12-2.30, 6.30-11; 12-3 Sun; closed Sun evening and Mon

WALTERSTONE SO3425 Map 6
Carpenters Arms
Village signposted off A465 E of Abergavenny, beside Old Pandy Inn; follow village signs, and keep eyes skinned for sign to pub, off to right, by lane-side barn

'If you've never been here before you'll feel like one of the family in no time,' comments one reader of this enchantingly untouched and welcoming little stone cottage on the edge of the Black Mountains. The traditional rooms have ancient settles against stripped stone walls, some pieces of carpet on broad polished flagstones, a roaring log fire in a gleaming black range (complete with pot-iron, hot-water tap, bread oven and salt cupboard), pewter mugs hanging from beams, and the slow tick of a clock. The snug main dining room (which is no smoking) has mahogany tables and oak corner cupboards, with a big vase of flowers on the dresser. Another little dining area has old oak tables and church pews on flagstones; piped music. Reasonably priced and tasty, the home-made food might include sandwiches and rolls (from £2), soup, prawn cocktail or ploughman's (all £4), steak roll (£4.50), home-made dishes such as cod and prawn pie, curry or beef in Guinness pie (all £8), a vegetarian choice, thick lamb cutlets with redcurrant and rosemary sauce (£9), steaks (from £9), and home-made puddings (£4). Well kept Breconshire Golden Valley and Wadworths 6X tapped from the cask; bottled Weston's organic cider. The outside lavatories are cold but in character. *(Recommended by Chris Flynn, Wendy Jones, Alan and Paula McCully, Peter and Jean Hoare, Pamela and Merlyn Horswell, Jacquie and Jim Jones, Peter B Brown, MLR)*

Free house ~ Licensee Vera Watkins ~ Real ale ~ Bar food (12-2.30, 7-9.30) ~ Restaurant ~ (01873) 890353 ~ No credit cards ~ Children welcome ~ Open 12-3, 7-11

WELLINGTON SO4948 Map 6
Wellington 🍺
Village signposted off A49 N of Hereford; pub at far end

It looks a perfectly ordinary Victorian pub from outside, but the publicans have made efforts with the food, and at the back is a pleasant garden with tables, where they have summer barbecues. The carefully refurbished bar has big high-backed dark wooden settles, an open brick fireplace with a log fire in winter and fresh flowers in summer, and historical photographs of the village and antique farm and garden tools around the walls. The charming candlelit restaurant is in the former stables and is no smoking. Well kept Hobsons Best, Wye Valley Butty Bach and a couple of guests such as Charles Wells Bombardier and Timothy Taylors Golden Best on handpump, farm cider and decent wines. Bar food includes soup (£3.75), sausages (made locally to their own recipe; £5.95), scrambled free-range eggs with smoked salmon (£5.95), and steak and mushroom in ale pie or roasted vegetables in filo pastry with a rich tomato sauce (all £6.95); we would like to hear from readers who have tried the more elaborate items from the daily changing menu: this features starters such as crayfish tails with feta cheese (£5.75) and warm salad of smoked pheasant breast (£5.95) and main courses like red onion and balsamic tart with glazed goats cheese (£8.75) or gressingham duck breast with apricot and sweet potato purée (£13.25); Sunday lunchtime carvery (no other food then). Service is friendly; darts and piped music. There are tables out in the attractive garden behind, and summer barbecues. More reports please, especially on the food. *(Recommended by Mike and Mary Carter, Christopher J Darwent, Peter and Jean Hoare)*

Free house ~ Licensees Ross and Philippa Williams ~ Real ale ~ Bar food (not Sun evening) ~ Restaurant ~ (01432) 830367 ~ Children welcome ~ Dogs allowed in bar ~ Open 12-3, 6-11; 12-3, 7-10.30 Sun; closed Mon lunchtime

WEOBLEY SO4052 Map 6
Salutation ♀
Village signposted from A4112 SW of Leominster; and from A44 NW of Hereford (there's also a good back road direct from Hereford – straight out past S side of racecourse)

At the top end of the green in the centre of one of Herefordshire's most perfect-looking black and white villages, this cosy inn has a relaxed, pubby lounge and a more straightforward public bar. The two areas are separated by a few steps and standing timbers and are furnished with brocaded modern winged settles and smaller seats, a couple of big cut-away cask seats, wildlife decorations, and a hop bine over the bar counter; logs burn in a big stone fireplace. More standing timbers separate it from the neat restaurant area, and while the parquet-floored public bar has sensibly placed darts, juke box, TV and fruit machine. Well kept Fullers London Pride, Hook Norton Best Bitter and Wye Valley Butty Bach on handpump, a very good selection of wines and several malt whiskies. Bar food includes lunchtime sandwiches (from £4.25; filled baguettes from £5.50), filled baked potatoes (from £4.25), and omelettes (£5.95), as well as home-made soup (£4.25), home-made lasagne or liver and bacon (£7.95), gammon and egg or steak in ale pie (£8.25), and 10oz rib-eye steak (£11.95); daily specials such as steak and ale pie (£8.95) and baked fillet of cod (£10.95) and very tasty puddings such as brioche and butter pudding, caramelised rice pudding or treacle tart (all £4.50), plus more elaborate restaurant food from a menu that changes every couple of months. The meat is very local and comes from the village butcher (Weobley even has its own slaughter house). On Sundays, they serve a selection of three local roasts and a chef's selection of specials. The restaurant, conservatory and part of the lounge bar are no smoking. There are tables and chairs with parasols on a sheltered back terrace. *(Recommended by Nick and Meriel Cox, Pam and David Bailey, MLR, the Didler, Pat and Roger Fereday, Keith and Jean Symons, Mrs T A Bizat, George Atkinson, Jacquie and Jim Jones, R T and J C Moggridge, A S and M E Marriott)*

Free house ~ Licensee Dr Mike Tai ~ Real ale ~ Bar food (12-2, 7-9.30) ~ Restaurant ~ (01544) 318443 ~ Children welcome until 9.30pm ~ Dogs allowed in bar ~ Open 11-11; 12-10.30 Sun ~ Bedrooms: £52S(£55B)/£78S(£81B)

WHITNEY-ON-WYE SO2747 Map 6
Rhydspence 🛏
A438 Hereford—Brecon

The border with Wales is only the other side of the nearby stream from this charming 14th-c building, originally a manor house, which has a riot of half-timbering on the outside. In the garden, seats and tables make the most of the views over Wye valley. Inside, the rambling, smartly kept rooms have heavy beams and timbers, attractive old-fashioned furnishings, and there's a log fire in the fine big stone fireplace in the central bar. There's a newer bistro-type eating area next to the bar, and this opens into the no smoking family room. The more formal restaurant is also no smoking; nice breakfasts. Good bar food includes home-made soup (£3.85), home-made chicken liver pâté or lunchtime ploughman's (£5.95), leek and brie pancakes (£7.95), fresh cod in lemon batter with home-made tartare sauce (£9.75), steak and kidney pie or a spicy curry (£9.95) and steaks (from £12.50);

popular three-course Sunday lunch for £15.50 (booking strongly advised). Well kept Bass and Robinsons Best on handpump, local Dunkerton's cider on handpump, and a decent wine list; darts, cribbage, dominoes and shove-ha'penny. *(Recommended by Pam and David Bailey, Rodney and Norma Stubington, David and Julie Glover, Andrew Shore, Maria Williams, G W H Kerby)*

Free house ~ Licensee Peter Glover ~ Real ale ~ Bar food ~ Restaurant ~ (01497) 831262 ~ Children in eating area of bar, restaurant and family room ~ Open 11-2.30, 7-11; 12-2, 7-10.30 Sun ~ Bedrooms: £42.50S/£85B

WOOLHOPE SO6135 Map 4
Butchers Arms ◖
Signposted from B4224 in Fownhope; carry straight on past Woolhope village

In seductive countryside and just outside the village itself, this cheery 14th-c country dining pub has a relaxing beer garden with picnic-sets and cheerful flowering tubs and borders looking on to a tiny willow-lined brook. One of the spacious and welcoming bars has very low beams decorated with hops, old-fashioned well worn built-in seats with brocaded cushions, high-backed chairs and stools around wooden tables, and a brick fireplace filled with fresh flowers when it is not in use. Broadly similar though with fewer beams, the other bar has a large built-in settle and another log fire. Tables have fresh flowers; cribbage, dominoes and unobtrusive background music; the restaurant and part of the bar are no smoking. They have five beers well kept on handpump: Hook Norton Hooky, Shepherd Neame Spitfire, Wye Valley Butty Bach and a couple of guests such as Timothy Taylors Landlord and a seasonal Wye Valley ale. Lunchtime bar food includes sandwiches (from £3.95), baguettes (from £5.25) and salads and ploughman's (from £6.95); home-made specials available at lunchtime and in the evening might include soup (£3.95), quiche of the day (£7.25), vegetable lasagne (£8.25), rack of barbecued spare ribs (£11.95) and swordfish with asparagus (£12.50); home-made puddings typically include fruit pie, bread and butter pudding and coffee and belgian chocolate mocha mousse (all £4.50); at quieter times of year they run occasional food nights. To enjoy some of the best of the surroundings, turn left as you come out and take the tiny left-hand road at the end of the car park; this turns into a track and then into a path, and the view from the top of the hill is quite something. *(Recommended by John and Kay Grugeon, Barry Collett, Patrick Hancock, MLR, Mr and Mrs J Tout, Denys Gueroult, R Davis)*

Free house ~ Licensees Cheryl and Martin Baker ~ Real ale ~ Bar food (12-2, 6.30-9) ~ Restaurant ~ (01432) 860281 ~ Children in eating area of bar and restaurant ~ Live jazz or quiz night last Sun in month ~ Open 12-3, 6.30-11(10.30 Sun) ~ Bedrooms: £35/£50

LUCKY DIP

Besides the fully inspected pubs, you might like to try these Lucky Dips recommended to us and described by readers (if you do, please send us reports: www.goodguides.co.uk).

ALLENSMORE [SO4533]
☆ *Three Horseshoes*: Beautifully placed 17th-c timbered pub with attractive flowers and a good deal of character, well kept real ale, enjoyable pub food, warmly friendly licensees *(Donald Walter)*
ALMELEY [SO3351]
Bell [off A480, A4111 or A4112 S of Kington]: Welcoming little two-room pub, well kept Wye Valley ales, pleasant landlord, just a few tables for people eating (good value Sun roast), traditional games, no piped music *(Dave Irving)*
ASTON CREWS [SO6723]
☆ *Penny Farthing*: Partly 15th-c, roomy and

relaxing, with lots of beams, horsebrasses, harness and farm tools, well in bar with skeleton at bottom; good generous competitively priced food from sandwiches up, fish specialities, friendly new landlady, well kept Greene King Abbot and Wadworths 6X, good value wines, easy chairs, log fires, two restaurant areas, one with pretty valley and views of Forest of Dean; subdued piped music; tables in charming garden, bedrooms *(Jo Rees, Alastair Stevenson, Mrs R Lowth, Lucien Perring, BB, Mike and Mary Carter, Kate Glozier, V Gapper)*
BOSBURY [SO6943]
Bell [B4220 N of Ledbury]: Village pub doing

well under welcoming new tenants, good value substantial food, thriving public bar, homely lounge, restaurant *(John Joyce-Townsend)*

BROMYARD [SO6554]

Rose & Lion [New Rd]: Welcoming local tied to Wye Valley brewery, their full range in top condition from central island servery for simple comfortable lounge and games-minded public bar with darts, cards etc; tables out in pleasant courtyard *(Pete Baker)*

BROMYARD DOWNS [SO6755]

☆ *Royal Oak* [just NE of Bromyard; pub signed off A44]: Beautifully placed open-plan low-beamed 18th-c pub with wide views, carpeted bar with lots of pig models, dining room with huge bay window, Hook Norton Best, Weston's farm cider, friendly kind service, wide food range; flagstoned bar with woodburner, pool, juke box and TV, piped music; walkers welcome (good area), picnic-sets on colourful front terrace, swings in orchard *(BB, Annette Tress, Gary Smith, Michael Hyde, Roger and Anne Newbury)*

GOODRICH [SO5719]

Hostelrie: Appealing building with unusual turreted gothic extension, traditional softly lit carpeted bar and lounge, roomy and individual with beams and stripped stone, good value food inc local produce and imaginative dishes, friendly landlord and pleasant service, real ales, good choice of wines, pretty dining room; children welcome, attractive garden, bedrooms, pleasant village nr Goodrich Castle and Wye Valley Walk *(Lawrence Bacon, Jean Scott, Mrs Veronica Mellor)*

HAMPTON BISHOP [SO5538]

Bunch of Carrots: Spaciously refurbished beamed country pub by River Wye, lovely log fires, helpful staff, wide choice of enjoyable food in bars and restaurant inc carvery and salad bar, well kept ales, local farm cider; children and dogs welcome, garden with play area *(Mrs B Sugarman)*

HEREFORD [SO5139]

Barrels [St Owen St]: Plain and cheery two-bar local brewing its own excellent low-priced Wye Valley Hereford and Dorothy Goodbodys ales, barrel-built counter also serving guest beers, farm ciders from Bulmer's, Stowford Press and Weston's, friendly efficient staff, may have sandwiches and pickled eggs, side pool room with games, juke box and TV sports, lots of modern stained glass; piped blues and rock, live music at beer festival end Aug; picnic-sets out on cobbles by brewery, open all day *(Gill and Tony Morriss, Paul Davies, Ian Phillips, the Didler, BB, Joe Green)*

Orange Tree [King St]: Small 17th-c beamed pub nr cathedral, recently restored after fire damage, with enjoyable low-priced food using local produce, Wye Valley beers, comfortable oak-panelled dining area; disabled access, children welcome, terrace tables, open all day *(Anthony Double)*

Spread Eagle [King St]: New management in busy beamed pub down side alley by cathedral, comfortable no smoking front dining area, imaginative bar food choice, young friendly staff, well kept Bass, Fullers London Pride and guest beers; tables in back courtyard *(Gill and Tony Morriss, Anthony Double)*

KINGTON [SO3057]

☆ *Olde Tavern* [Victoria Rd, just off A44 opp B4355 – follow sign to Town Centre, Hospital, Cattle Mkt; pub on right opp Elizabeth Rd, no inn sign but Estd 1767 notice]: Splendidly old-fashioned tap for nearby Dunn Plowman microbrewery, with their ales and guest beers, hatch-served side room opening off small plain parlour and public bar, plenty of dark brown woodwork, big windows, old settles and other antique furniture, china, pewter and curios, welcoming locals, gas fire, no music, machines or food; children welcome, though not a family pub; cl wkdy lunchtimes, outside gents' *(BB, Pete Baker, the Didler)*

Queens Head [Bridge St]: Friendly unassuming Victorian corner local with Bridge Street Four Seasons and Arrow from its back brewery, basic furnishings, darts, juke box *(MLR)*

KINNERSLEY [SO3449]

Kinnersley Arms [off A4112 Hay—Leominster]: One to watch – pleasant country pub redecorated by enthusiastic new licensees, enjoyable food with individual touches inc two-in-one pie and a spiced local lamb pie, good service, separate games bar and restaurant; tables in good-sized garden *(Dave Irving)*

LEDBURY [SO7137]

Prince of Wales [Church Lane; narrow passage from Town Hall]: Pleasantly old-fashioned Banks's pub tucked nicely down charming narrow cobbled alley, low-beamed front bars, long back room, jovial landlord, well kept beers, tasty simple home-made food, low prices; a couple of tables in yard crammed with lovely flower tubs and hanging baskets *(John Wooll)*

LEINTWARDINE [SO4174]

☆ *Sun* [Rosemary Lane, just off A4113]: If you like basic unspoilt pubs, don't miss this one – three bare benches by coal fire in red-tiled front parlour off hallway, well kept local ale such as Hobsons or Woods tapped from the cask in venerable landlady's kitchen, small settee and a couple of chairs by the gas fire in her sitting room for favoured visitors, perhaps wine and some soft drinks, no food exc pickled eggs and crisps *(BB, RWC, Pete Baker, MLR)*

LEOMINSTER [SO4959]

Bell [Etnam St]: Lots of beams and bare boards in several linked rooms, four well kept ales such as a bargain one from local Teme Valley, good value enjoyable simple lunchtime food; tables out in good-sized back area *(MLR)*

Black Horse [South St]: Well run bustling bar, comfortably well worn, with well kept mainly local real ales, good value food (not Sun) inc good sandwiches, traditional games, snug lounge and eating area; children welcome *(BB, MLR)*

Grape Vaults [Broad St]: Compact well preserved two-room pub, friendly and busy, with panelling, etched windows, original dark high-backed settles, veteran tables, coal fire, bottle collection, old local prints and posters, shelves of books in snug; wide range of simple freshly cooked food, well kept Banks's, Marstons and guest beers such as Archers and Freeminers, no machines or music *(MLR)*

MATHON [SO7345]

☆ *Cliffe Arms* [signed off B4220; or reached off A4103 via Cradley]: Pretty black and white heavy-beamed village pub extensively refurbished by new landlord, small slate-floored bar and separate public bar, attractive restaurant behind with 'choir loft', well kept Hobsons, Greene King Old Speckled Hen and Teme Valley T'Other, good wines by the glass, enjoyable fresh bar food such as focaccia and omelettes, good more upmarket restaurant dishes and splendid Sun lunches (till 7), keen young staff; children welcome, comfortable modern furniture in sizeable streamside garden below Malvern Hills, may be cl Sat lunchtime *(Martin and Pauline Jennings, Alan Bowker)*

MONKLAND [SO4557]

Monkland Arms [A44 W of Leominster]: Good-sized roadside pub under new landlady, two or three linked areas set for shortish frequently changing food choice, two Spinning Dog real ales, locals' bar; good garden *(MLR)*

MUCH DEWCHURCH [SO4831]

Black Swan [B4348 Ross—Hay]: Roomy and attractive beamed and timbered pub, partly 14th-c, with warm local atmosphere and log fires in cosy bar and lounge with eating area, reasonably priced food, well kept ales such as Bass, Brains Rev James and Wye Valley, decent wines, friendly staff *(Anthony Double)*

MUCH MARCLE [SO6433]

Scrumpy House [part of Cider Centre]: Good buffet lunches, range of good Weston's farm ciders *(Ron and Sheila Corbett)*

☆ *Slip Tavern* [off A449 SW of Ledbury]: Unpretentious country pub with splendidly colourful gardens overlooking cider orchards (Weston's Cider Centre is close by), well kept Wye Valley ale and local farm cider, usual bar food from generous sandwiches and baguettes to good Sun roasts, friendly prompt service, bar popular with older people at lunchtime, with villagey local evening atmosphere, attractive no smoking conservatory restaurant; folk music first Thurs of month *(Miss M Ruse, Ian and Denise Foster, LYM, John and Kay Grugeon)*

NORTON CANON [SO3748]

Three Horseshoes [A480 Yazor—Eccles Green]: Simple two-bar country pub brewing its own good Shoes ales, inc fearsomely strong Farrier; log fire and old sofas in one room, vintage juke box in the other, and an indoor shooting gallery; may be home-pickled eggs; children welcome, tables in orchard – lovely countryside nr Davies Meadows wildflower reserve; cl lunchtimes exc Weds and wknds *(MLR)*

ORCOP HILL [SO4727]

Fountain [off A466 S of Hereford]: Small village pub with friendly staff and customers, simple cosy bar with daily papers, big helpings of good value straightforward food in back dining room and restaurant, good choice inc

fresh fish specials and cheap lunchtime deals, Marstons Pedigree and John Smiths, good farm cider; darts, piped music; tables in peaceful pretty front garden *(BB, Ian and Denise Foster, Ryta Lyndley)*

ROSS-ON-WYE [SO5924]

Crown & Sceptre [Market Pl]: Friendly open-plan pub in interesting old building, well kept Fullers London Pride, Greene King Abbot and Wye Valley ales, locally sourced food all day, comfortable no smoking area, log fires, back games area (with piped music); very busy wknds; children welcome, tables outside, open all day *(Anthony Double)*

Hope & Anchor [Riverside; coming from A40 W side, 1st left after bridge (Rope Walk)]: Popular pub with big-windowed family extension looking out over gardens to River Wye, plenty of tables out here (and summer ice-cream bar and barbecues), boating-theme slate-floored main bar, steps up to servery with well kept real ales, farm cider, good house wine, friendly prompt service, generous good value food inc good baguettes and good choice for children, Victorian-style upstairs parlour and dining room, cosy touches and good housekeeping; open all day *(LYM, Guy Vowles)*

Kings Arms [Gloucester Rd]: Well run Wetherspoons, tidy and well furnished, with decent sensibly priced food, good staff, real ales such as Greene King Abbot; courtyard tables *(Geoff Pidoux)*

Kings Head [High St]: Comfortably old-fashioned beamed and panelled hotel bar, blazing log fire, lots of old pictures and some cosy armchairs, generous good value pubby food from good sandwiches up, well kept Wye Valley beers, swift friendly service, separate smart restaurant; open all day, bedrooms *(Mr and Mrs A J Edwards, Kevin Blake)*

Mail Rooms [Gloucester Rd]: Light and airy Wetherspoons, open and modern, with relaxing no smoking end, their usual food and attractively priced beers and wines; children in family area till 7, pleasant terrace with tables under big parasols, open all day *(Craig Turnbull, Mike and Mary Carter)*

Royal [Royal Parade]: Good service, enjoyable food and Greene King Abbot in pub/hotel's pleasant bistro bar; fine views from outside decking, bedrooms *(Geoff Pidoux)*

SYMONDS YAT [SO5615]

☆ *Saracens Head* [Symonds Yat E, by ferry, ie over on the Gloucs bank]: Riverside beauty spot next to small ferry, busy basic flagstone public bar popular with canoeists, mountain bikers and hikers (lounge bar for diners only), cheerful efficient staff, good range of well presented nourishing food from unusual sandwiches up, well kept Greene King Old Speckled Hen, Theakstons Best and Old Peculier and Wye Valley, three farm ciders, pine tables, settles and window seats, recently modernised bare-boards restaurant; pool, piped jazz and blues, SkyTV, live music Thurs, and you have to pay for all-day parking – pricey; lots of picnic-sets out on waterside terraces, summer boat trips, super walks, good bedrooms – nice to stay out of season *(John and Lynn Norcliffe, BB, Jim Abbott, Martin and Pauline Jennings, Lawrence Bacon, Jean Scott, Ryta Lyndley, Ian Phillips)*

TARRINGTON [SO6140]

Tarrington Arms [A438 E of Hereford]: Cosy bar (with bellringers at 9 after Fri practice), consistently enjoyable food, well run restaurant *(Neil Kellett)*

UPPER COLWALL [SO7643]

☆ *Chase* [Chase Rd, off B4218 Malvern—Colwall, 1st left after hilltop on bend going W]: Doing well under new management, well kept and described Banks's, Woods and Wye Valley, plenty of tables for wide range of enjoyable good value food from sandwiches to Sun lunch, thriving friendly atmosphere, no smoking room, great views; dogs and walkers welcome, attractive garden, open all day *(Dr D J and Mrs S C Walker, Maurice Ribbans, Andy Trafford, Louise Bayly, John Saul)*

WELLINGTON HEATH [SO7140]

Farmers Arms [off B4214 just N of Ledbury – pub signed right, from top of village; Horse Rd]: Roomy pub smartly modernised under new management, big bowls of citrus fruit, leather sofas, faux fur cushions; enjoyable food inc reasonably priced starters and puddings and good Sun roasts, friendly staff, decent wines; good walking country *(Caroline and Michael Abbey, BB, Ian and Denise Foster, Di and Mike Gillam)*

WESTON-UNDER-PENYARD [SO6323]

☆ *Weston Cross Inn* [A40 E of Ross]: Substantial creeper-covered stone-built pub overlooking picturesque village, good range of well priced home-made food inc good curries and fresh fish, pleasant and roomy beamed dining lounge opening to garden, Bass, Hancocks HB, Tetleys and Whitbreads Best, Stowford Press cider, friendly staff, big TV in separate bar; walkers welcome (they have devised their own walks map), very pretty outside, plenty of picnic-sets on sweeping lawns, play area *(BB, Caroline and Michael Abbey, Guy Vowles, Mike and Mary Carter)*

WHITNEY-ON-WYE [SO2647]

☆ *Boat*: Spacious, quiet and neatly kept redbrick pub with lovely views of river and far beyond from big windows and picnic-sets in pleasant garden; wide blackboard choice of good food, good friendly service, Bass and Robinsons, farm cider, comfortable L-shaped lounge with no smoking dining area, games room with pool; may be piped music; children welcome, bedrooms *(Edward Leetham, CMW, JJW, Dennis and Gill Keen)*

WOOLHOPE [SO6136]

☆ *Crown*: Neatly kept and appealing lounge bar with well kept ales such as Whittingtons Cats Whiskers and Wye Valley Hereford, wide choice of bar food from sandwiches and baked potatoes to good value home-made pies and generous steaks, straightforward comfortable furnishings, friendly service, open fire, darts, timbered divider strung with hop bines, smart no smoking dining area; TV, piped music; children welcome, big garden with outdoor heaters and lighting, open all day Sat *(LYM, Geoff and Teresa Salt, Kevin Blake)*

WOONTON [SO3552]

Lion [A480 SE of Kington]: Nicely placed country pub with good views, new licensees doing enjoyable home-made food from hot beef and other sandwiches up, also dishes (and wines and beers) suitable for vegans, and gluten-free dishes, with a local real ale; has been cl Tues lunchtime and Mon *(MLR)*

The letters and figures after the name of each town are its Ordnance Survey map reference. *Using the Guide* at the beginning of the book explains how it helps you find a pub, in road atlases or large-scale maps as well as in our own maps.

Hertfordshire

Just one new main entry here this year – the community-owned Red Lion at Preston, a classic village-green pub with good drinks and enjoyable food. During the year there has been a fair amount of jostling for position among the county's other top pubs. Ones which stand out as being on particularly good form are the friendly Three Tuns in Ashwell (good atmosphere, enjoyable food), the Gibraltar Castle at Batford (interesting varied food), the child-friendly Woodman at Chapmore End (a nice all-rounder, very much liked for its thoroughly individual approach), and the stylishly rustic Alford Arms at Frithsden (an excellent dining pub). The Alford Arms is outstanding as a place for a special meal out, and is Hertfordshire Dining Pub of the Year – for the fourth year running, which is something of a record. On a more day-to-day plane, the civilised Old Bull in Royston deserves a special mention for keeping the prices of its enjoyable bar meals so pocket-friendly. In the Lucky Dip section at the end of the chapter, places to note particularly this year are the Elephant & Castle at Amwell, Plough at Colney Heath, Horns at Datchworth, Lytton Arms near Knebworth and Plough near St Albans. Hertfordshire drinks prices tend to be somewhat higher than the national average. McMullens is the county's main brewer; smaller local breweries to look out for include Verulam, Green Tye and particularly Tring.

ALDBURY SP9612 Map 4
Valiant Trooper 🍺
Trooper Road (towards Aldbury Common); off B4506 N of Berkhamsted

Nicely positioned for walks through the glorious beech woods of the National Trust's Ashridge Estate, this partly pink-painted pub has an enjoyably unspoilt atmosphere. The first room is beamed and tiled in red and black, and has built-in wall benches, a pew and small dining chairs around the attractive country tables, and a woodburning stove in the inglenook fireplace. The middle bar has spindleback chairs around the tables on its wooden floor, some exposed brickwork – and signs warning you to 'mind the step'. The far room has nice country kitchen chairs around individually chosen tables, and a brick fireplace. Generously served bar food includes filled baked potatoes or open sandwiches (£4.50), ciabattas (£5), ploughman's (£5.50), and home-made daily specials such as soup (£3.50), creamy mushroom carbonara (£8), roast chicken (£9.50) and steak and kidney pie (£10), with puddings such as chocolate and brandy torte (£3.75); children's menu (£3.50). One bar and the restaurant are no smoking. Well kept Fullers London Pride, Timothy Taylor Landlord, Tring Jack o' Legs and one guest such as Morrells Oxford Blue, plus 12 wines by the glass. Dominoes, cribbage and bridge on Monday nights. The enclosed garden has a play house for children. *(Recommended by Colin McKerrow, Brian Root, David and Ruth Shillitoe, Tracey and Stephen Groves, Julia and Richard Tredgett, John and Glenys Wheeler, Susan and John Douglas)*

Free house ~ Licensee Tim O'Gorman ~ Real ale ~ Bar food (12-2.30, 6.30-9.15; not Sun or Mon evenings) ~ Restaurant ~ (01442) 851203 ~ Children in eating area of bar and restaurant ~ Dogs allowed in bar ~ Open 11.30-11; 12-10.30 Sun

ASHWELL TL2639 Map 5
Three Tuns
Off A505 NE of Baldock; High Street

Readers like the friendly atmosphere and tasty food at this graciously old-fashioned flower-decked 18th-c inn. There's an air of Victorian opulence in the cosy lounge with its relaxing chairs, big family tables, lots of pictures, stuffed pheasants and fish, and antiques. The simpler more modern public bar has pool, darts, cribbage, dominoes, a fruit machine, SkyTV. Greene King IPA, Abbot and a guest such as Batemans XXXB are kept under a light blanket pressure and served on handpump, and there's a good choice of wines; piped light classical music. Served by attentive staff, changing home-made bar food might include soup (£4.25), filled baguettes (from £4.25), chicken liver pâté or devilled whitebait (£5.25), ploughman's (from £6.75), vegetarian pasta bake (£7.95), steak and kidney pie (£9.45), grilled salmon fillet (£10.95) and sirloin steak (£14.95); home-made puddings from £4.75; no smoking dining room. The substantial shaded garden has boules, and picnic-sets under apple trees; lavatories are down a steep flight of steps. The village is full of pleasant corners and it's popular with walkers at summer weekends, as the landscape around rolls enough to be rewarding. *(Recommended by Minda and Stanley Alexander, Gordon Neighbour, Jan and Alan Summers, Michael Dandy, Mary Rayner, N R White, Alison and Pete)*

Greene King ~ Tenants Claire and Darrell Stanley ~ Real ale ~ Bar food (12-2.30, 6.30-9.30; all day Sat, Sun) ~ Restaurant ~ (01462) 742107 ~ Children in eating area of bar and restaurant ~ Dogs allowed in bar ~ Open 11-11; 12-10.30 Sun ~ Bedrooms: £39(£59B)/£69B

BATFORD TL1415 Map 5
Gibraltar Castle
Lower Luton Road; B653, S of B652 junction

Liked by readers for its friendly service and tasty food, this roadside pub is stashed with an impressive collection of militaria including rifles, swords, medals, uniforms and bullets (with plenty of captions to read), while the dining area sports a chicken and a witch riding a broomstick and suspended from the ceiling. The long carpeted bar has a pleasant old fireplace, comfortably cushioned wall benches, and a couple of snugly intimate window alcoves, one with a fine old clock; in one area the low beams give way to soaring rafters. Well kept Fullers Chiswick, ESB, London Pride and one or two guest beers on handpump, a good range of malt whiskies and a thoughtful choice of wines by the glass; several board games left on top of the piano, and piped music. The tasty bar food varies according to season and might include lunchtime sandwiches (from £3.95), soup (£3.95), sausage and mash (£7.95), goats cheese, walnut and almond salad or chicken and mushroom pie (£8.95), fisherman's platter (£9.50), rib-eye steak (£12.95), specials such as roeless scallops (£12.95), smoked haddock fillets with smoked salmon and cheese sauce (£13.95), pork loin (£14.95) and lamb wellington (£16.95); home-made puddings (mostly £4.95); booking is recommended for their very popular good value Sunday roast (£9.95). There are tables and chairs on a decked back terrace, a few tables in front by the road, and hanging baskets and tubs dotted around. *(Recommended by MP, John Miles, Pat and Tony Martin, Michael Dandy, John and Joyce Snell, Terry Buckland, B and M Kendall, Angus Johnson, Carol Bolden)*

Fullers ~ Lease Hamish Miller ~ Real ale ~ Bar food (12-2.30(4 Sun), 6-9; not Sun evening) ~ Restaurant ~ (01582) 460005 ~ Children in eating area of bar ~ Dogs welcome ~ Jam session Tues evening ~ Open 11.30-11; 12-10.30 Sun

---

Post Office address codings confusingly give the impression that some pubs are in Hertfordshire, when they're really in Bedfordshire or Cambridgeshire (which is where we list them).

CHAPMORE END TL3216 Map 5

Woodman ◀

Off B158 Wadesmill—Bengeo; 300 yards W of A602 roundabout keep eyes skinned for discreet green sign to pub pointing up otherwise unmarked narrow lane; OS Sheet 166 map reference 328164

There's a refreshing lack of piped music and gimmicks at this charmingly peaceful and relaxed early Victorian local, where you can enjoy a game of boules, chess, backgammon, darts, shove ha'penny or cribbage. Popular with walkers and cyclists, it is tucked away close to the duck pond of a small hamlet. The two little linked rooms have plain seats around stripped pub tables, flooring tiles or broad bare boards, log fires in period fireplaces, cheerful pictures for sale, lots of local notices, and darts on one side, with a piano (and a couple of squeeze boxes) on the other. They have well kept Greene King IPA, Abbot (and a house mix of the two) and usually a guest such as a Greene King seasonal beer or St Austell Triumph tapped from the cask, as well as several malt whiskies. They do a good choice of good value lunchtime sandwiches (from £2.50), warm baguettes (from £3.10), ciabattas (from £3.85), ploughman's (from £4.95), salads (from £5.85), and a couple of daily dishes such as home-made soup, for example spicy parsnip or pea and ham (usually £3). From their very small kitchen they also manage to conjure up a simple Thursday evening meal giving one main dish such as home-made steak and kidney pudding (from £7) and a pudding or home-made ice-cream (from £3) – best to book ahead. Service is friendly and helpful, and in season (when there's an R in the month) they do monthly oyster nights on Wednesdays. There are picnic-sets out in front under a couple of walnut trees; a bigger garden behind has a good fenced play area (there are often toys left around by the publicans' daughters, who generally don't mind other children playing with them) as well as pet rabbits in the garden and a pub cat. The car park has little room but there is usually plenty of on-street parking. (Recommended by Gordon Neighbour, Karen Horton, Ian Arthur, Mike Ridgway, Sarah Miles)

Greene King ~ Tenants Drs Danny Davis and Alex Yates ~ Real ale ~ Bar food (lunchtime and Thurs evening) ~ No credit cards ~ (01920) 463143 ~ Dogs welcome ~ Open 12-2.30, 5-11; 12-11 Sat; 12-10.30 Sun

COTTERED TL3129 Map 5

Bull

A507 W of Buntingford

The owners have recently added an extension and refitted this beautifully placed pub, which now seats around 100. It is surrounded by trees and faces a row of pretty thatched cottages, and its airy low-beamed front lounge is nicely laid out and well looked after, with polished antiques on a stripped wood floor, and a good fire. A second bar has darts and a fruit machine; unobtrusive piped music. They have well kept Greene King IPA and Abbot kept under a light blanket pressure on handpump, and decent wines. At lunchtime thoughtfully presented bar food includes sandwiches (from £3; open toasted sandwiches from £6), home-made burgers (£6.50), ploughman's (from £6), filled baked potatoes (from £6.50), serrano ham and warm goats cheese salad (£6.75, omelette arnold bennett with smoked haddock (£8), steak and kidney pie (£9) and fillet of chicken or salmon (£12). In the evening the menu is slightly longer with some of the same items available for about 50p more, and includes soup (£4.50), fresh crab (£6.75), wild mushroom risotto (£7; £11 as a main course), breast of duck with honey and wholegrain mustard (£12.75), fillet steak (£16.25) and bass on creamed leeks (£16.50); 5% service charge except if dining in the Hunt Bar; friendly and obliging service; no smoking dining area. Benches and tables in the attractive big garden make the best of the setting. You can get tea here on summer Sunday afternoons (3-6). The church has a huge 14th-c wall painting of St Christopher. (Recommended by Adele Summers, Alan Black, Tony Beaulah, Michael Dandy, John Saul, Mrs Margo Finlay, Jörg Kasprowski, W Andrew, Alex and Irene Harvey, Jack and Sandra Clarfelt)

Greene King ~ Lease Darren Perkins ~ Real ale ~ Bar food (12-2, 7-9.30) ~ Restaurant ~ (01763) 281243 ~ Children over 7 in restaurant and eating area of bar ~ Music dinner nights in winter ~ Open 11.30-11; 12-3, 6.30-11 Sat; 12-10.30 Sun; 12-3, 6.30-11 weekdays in winter

FRITHSDEN TL0110 Map 5
Alford Arms ⑪

From Berkhamsted take unmarked road towards Potten End, pass Potten End turn on right, then take next left towards Ashridge College

Hertfordshire Dining Pub of the Year

Hugely popular and fashionably refurbished by thoughtful licensees, this highly praised dining pub is a place for an elegant treat, though be aware that it is often booked up. The interior has simple prints on pale cream walls, with areas picked out in blocks of Victorian green or dark red, and an appealing mix of good furniture from Georgian chairs to old commode stands on bare boards and patterned quarry tiles. It's all pulled together by luxurious richly patterned curtains. Successfully innovative bar food is served by charming staff, and might include starters like sautéed lamb kidneys on toasted brioche (£5.75), home-smoked salmon on herb salad (£6.25) and warm squid, bacon and rocket salad (£6.50), main courses like field mushroom, leek and pine nut steamed pudding (£10.50), beer braised beef stew with herb dumplings or crispy chicken on herb polenta cake with smoked bacon, wild mushroom and red onion (£11.25) and fried bass with roast aubergine and fennel (£13.25), and puddings such as chilled lemon tart with poppy seeds or blackberry crème brûlée (£4.75), rich chocolate and pecan pie with gooseberry and ginger ham (£5) and roast figs in marsala with clotted cream (£5.25); a good wine list features 11 good pudding wines and 15 other wines by the glass. The dining room is now no smoking, but some readers say they would like this ban extended to other eating areas too. Well kept Brakspears, Flowers Original, Marstons Pedigree and Morrells Oxford Blue on handpump; piped jazz. They have plenty of tables out in front. It stands by a village green and surrounded by National Trust woodland. *(Recommended by DB, Edmund Coan, D J and P M Taylor, Bob and Maggie Atherton, Jack and Jill Gilbert, John Hale, Howard Dell, John Picken, Andrew Scarr, Peter and Giff Bennett, Peter and Margaret Glenister, John and Joyce Snell, Annabel Viney, Alex and Irene Harvey, Susan and John Douglas, Tracey and Stephen Groves)*

Enterprise ~ Lease Becky and David Salisbury ~ Real ale ~ Bar food (12-2.30(3 Sun), 7-10) ~ Restaurant ~ (01442) 864480 ~ Children in eating area of bar and restaurant ~ Dogs allowed in bar ~ Open 11-11; 12-10.30 Sun; closed 25, 26 Dec

HERTFORD TL3212 Map 5
White Horse ◆ £

Castle Street

'We only get to Hertfordshire about twice a year but we always head straight for this pub when we get there,' enthuses one reader of this unpretentious town-centre pub. The beer selection is particularly impressive, but the food represents excellent value too. Even though it's a tied house, the choice of real ales can vary from day to day, but you can expect to find beers from brewers such as Beartown, Moorhouses, Woodfordes and Timothy Taylors, alongside the Adnams and Fullers London Pride, Chiswick and ESB – so no need to worry if you can't make it here for their May or August bank holiday beer festivals. They also keep around 20 country wines. Parts of the building are 14th-c, and you can still see Tudor brickwork in the three quietly cosy no smoking rooms upstairs. Downstairs, the two main rooms are small and homely. The one on the left is more basic, with some brewery memorabilia, bare boards, and a few rather well worn tables, stools and chairs; an open fire separates it from the more comfortable right-hand bar, which has a cosily tatty armchair, some old local photographs, beams and timbers, and a red-tiled floor. Service can be quite chatty, and though it's quite a locals' pub, visitors are made to feel welcome; bar billiards, darts, shove-ha'penny, shut the box, cribbage and dominoes. The pub faces the castle, and there are two benches on the street outside. Very inexpensive home-made bar food (lunchtime only plus Monday evenings) includes sandwiches (from £2.40), soup (£2.50), baguettes (from £3.35), baked potatoes (from £3.75), ploughman's (£4.50) and daily specials such as beef and vegetable pie (£4), Moroccan chicken, wild boar casserole, braised lamb shanks armenian style, and sausages and bubble and squeak with onion gravy (all £4.25). On Sunday they do a two-course lunch for £6.50, three courses for £7, and on Monday evenings they do a White Horse Gastronomic Tour, with one exotic dish such as curry for £5; they can do children's portions. More reports please. *(Recommended by Steve Nye, Brian and Rosalie Laverick, Pat and Tony Martin)*

Fullers ~ Lease Nigel Crofts ~ Real ale ~ Bar food (12-2(1-3 Sun); 6-8(Mon only)) ~ (01992) 501950 ~ Well supervised children in upstairs family room until 9pm ~ Dogs welcome ~ Open 12-2.30, 5.30-11; 12-11(10.30 Sun) Fri, Sat

POTTERS CROUCH TL1105 Map 5
Holly Bush 🍺 £

2¼ miles from M25 junction 21A: A405 towards St Albans, then first left, then after a mile turn left (ie away from Chiswell Green), then at T junction turn right into Blunts Lane; can also be reached fairly quickly, with a good map, from M1 exits 6 and 8 (and even M10)

This pretty wisteria-covered white cottagey building is definitely not the kind of place where you'll find fruit machines or piped music. Everything is spotless, and thoughtfully positioned fixtures create the illusion that there are lots of different rooms – some of which you might expect to find in a smart country house. In the evenings, neatly placed candles cast shadows over the mix of darkly gleaming varnished tables, all of which have fresh flowers, and china plates as ashtrays. There are quite a few antique dressers, several with plates on, a number of comfortably cushioned settles, the odd plant, a fox's mask, some antlers, a fine old clock, carefully lit prints and pictures, daily papers, and on the left as you go in a big fireplace. The long, stepped bar counter has particularly well kept Fullers Chiswick, ESB, London Pride and the Fullers seasonal beer on handpump, and the sort of reassuringly old-fashioned till you hardly ever see in this hi-tech age. Service is calm and efficient even when they're busy. Straightforward, freshly prepared bar food from a fairly short menu is served lunchtimes only (not Sunday), and includes sandwiches (from £2.50), burgers (from £3.90), filled baked potatoes (from £4.40), ploughman's (from £5.40), home-made chilli or very good and generously sized platters such as meat or fish, both with salad (from £5.80), apple pie (£2.60) and chocolate fudge cake (£2.70). Behind the pub, the fenced-off garden has a nice lawn, handsome trees, and sturdy picnic-sets – a very pleasant place to sit in summer. No smoking at the bar counters. Though the pub seems to stand alone on a quiet little road, it's only a few minutes from the centre of St Albans. More reports please. *(Recommended by Brian and Rosalie Laverick, Peter and Giff Bennett, John and Joyce Snell)*

Fullers ~ Tenant R S Taylor ~ Real ale ~ Bar food (lunchtime only, not Sun) ~ (01727) 851792 ~ Open 11.30-2.30, 6-11; 12-2.30, 7-10.30 Sun

PRESTON TL1824 Map 5
Red Lion 🍺

Village signposted off B656 S of Hitchin; The Green

Facing the lime trees on a peaceful village green, this is a classic village pub – in more ways than one, as in 1982 this became the first pub in recent times to be acquired by its local community. Now gently smartened up under its quietly friendly and attentive current licensees, it has sturdy well varnished pub furnishings including padded country-kitchen chairs and cast-iron-framed tables on its patterned carpet, a log fire in a brick fireplace, and foxhunting prints in the main room on the left. The somewhat smaller one on the right has steeplechasing ones instead, and some varnished plank panelling. Brocaded bar stools stand on flagstones around the servery, which has well kept Youngs on handpump, and interesting changing ales such as Crouch Vale Brewers Gold, Mighty Oak Mauldon Gold, Hook Norton Old Hooky and Tring Brewery Jack o' Legs. They tap farm cider from the cask, and have eight wines by the glass including an english house wine (Chapel Down) and mulled wine in winter. Enjoyable largely home-made food includes lunchtime sandwiches (£4) and ploughman's (£4.50), soup (£3), grilled goats cheese or pâté (£4), stilton and asparagus quiche or chilli (£5.95), creamy haddock tart (£6.95), steak and kidney pie (£7.95), and specials such as lasagne (£5.95), grilled trout or liver and bacon (£6.95), pheasant in red wine sauce or venison and cranberry casserole (£7.95). You can play dominoes here. A few picnic-sets out on the front grass look across to the green; there are many more, with some shade from a tall ash tree, in the good-sized sheltered garden behind, which is neatly kept, with a colourful herbaceous border. *(Recommended by John and Joyce Snell, Elizabeth Newbery, Steve Nye, Peter and Margaret Glenister)*

Free house ~ Licensee Tim Hunter ~ Real ale ~ Bar food (not Sun or Tues evenings) ~ No credit cards ~ (01462) 459585 ~ Children welcome ~ Dogs welcome ~ Open 12-2.30, 5.30-11; 12-3, 7-11 Sun

ROYSTON TL3540 Map 5
Old Bull £

High Street, off central A10 one-way system – has own car park, or use central car park

Bar service is highly professional, in the best old style, in this fine bow-fronted early Georgian coaching inn. Tucked peacefully away from the traffic, its sunny courtyard is equipped with outdoor heaters, modern tables and chairs and was originally the coachyard in the days when 100 horses were stabled here. The roomy and civilised high-beamed bar, with handsome fireplaces, big pictures and rather fine flooring, has easy chairs, a leather sofa and a table of papers and magazines (and ready-to-pour coffee) at the entrance end with the bar counter, and further in is more set out for eating. Good-value bar food includes sandwiches (from £2.95), soup (£3.50), mixed pepper and mushroom pasta (£4.95), roast beef in yorkshire pudding or chicken curry and rice (£5.95) and home-made puddings such as bread and butter pudding (£4.50). There is a separate more formal no smoking restaurant; Sunday lunches are £7.95 for one course, £9.95 for two and £11.95 for three, with half price for children's portions; children's menu (£4.25); senior citizens' menu (Monday to Friday, £5 for two courses). They have well kept Greene King IPA and Old Speckled Hen plus a guest such as Batemans XXXB on handpump, and decent wines by the glass. The atmosphere is chatty and relaxed; the piped music is fairly unobtrusive; no smoking area in bar; cribbage and dominoes. More reports please. *(Recommended by Conor McGaughey, M R D Foot, Margaret and Roy Randle)*

Greene King ~ Lease Peter Nightingale ~ Real ale ~ Bar food (12-2.30, 6.30-9.30; 12-9 Sat, Sun) ~ Restaurant ~ (01763) 242003 ~ Children in eating area of bar and restaurant ~ Dogs allowed in bar ~ Open 11-11; 12-10.30 Sun ~ Bedrooms: £75S/£90S

SARRATT TQ0499 Map 5
Cock

Church End: a very pretty approach is via North Hill, a lane N off A404, just under a mile W of A405

In front of this cosy cream-painted 17th-c country pub, picnic-sets look out across a quiet lane towards the churchyard, the terrace at the back gives open country views, and a pretty, sheltered lawn has tables under parasols. There's also a children's play area and (at summer weekends) a bouncy castle. The latched front door opens into a carpeted snug with a vaulted ceiling, original bread oven, and a cluster of bar stools. Through an archway, the partly oak-panelled cream-walled lounge has a lovely log fire in an inglenook, pretty Liberty-style curtains, pink plush chairs at dark oak tables, and lots of interesting artefacts and pictures of cocks; piped music, and well kept Badger Best, Sussex, Tanglefoot and a Badger guest; piped music, fruit machine and TV. Straightforward bar food includes soup (£3.95), sandwiches (from £4.25), cod fillet in batter (£8.25) and steak and ale pie (£8.95), plus specials such as chilli con carne (£7.95), vegetable lasagne (£8.95) and bass (£9.95); home-made puddings are £4.75. The no smoking restaurant is in a nicely converted barn. More reports please. *(Recommended by Stan Edwards, Julie Ryan, Tony Radnor, Gill and Keith Croxton, John Saville)*

Badger ~ Tenant Nick Clarke ~ Real ale ~ Bar food (12-2.30, 6-9) ~ Restaurant ~ (01923) 282908 ~ Dogs allowed in bar ~ Open 11-11; 12-10.30 Sun

LUCKY DIP

Besides the fully inspected pubs, you might like to try these Lucky Dips recommended to us and described by readers (if you do, please send us reports: www.goodguides.co.uk).

ALDBURY [SP9612]
☆ *Greyhound* [Stocks Rd; village signed from A4251 Tring—Berkhamsted, and from B4506]: Picturesque village-green pub, roomy and comfortable, with some signs of real age inside, gentle lighting and inglenook log fire, Badger real ales, generous usual bar food (not Sun evening) from lunchtime baguettes and filled baked potatoes to steaks, attentive service, pleasant no smoking conservatory, cribbage and dominoes; not the most retiring clientele, piped music; children and dogs welcome, suntrap gravel courtyard, lovely nearby walks, separate bedroom block, open all day *(LYM, Ian Phillips, Tracey and Stephen Groves)*

AMWELL [TL1613]
☆ *Elephant & Castle* [signed SW from Wheathampstead]: Secluded and spacious floodlit grass garden around low-beamed ancient pub with good blackboard food choice, well kept ales inc a changing guest, amusing landlord and friendly staff, relaxed and welcoming local feel, great inglenook log fire, panelling, stripped brickwork, immensely deep covered well shaft in bar, no piped music; children welcome *(LYM, Jill McLaren)*

ARDELEY [TL3027]
☆ *Jolly Waggoner* [off B1037 NE of Stevenage]: Prettily placed in thatched village, comfortable, relaxed and civilised, with open woodwork, beams, lots of nooks and corners, and pleasant garden and terrace; has been a popular main entry with enjoyable restaurant and bar food, well kept Greene King IPA and Abbot and decent wines, but a new landlady was about to take over as we went to press – reports please *(LYM)*

AYOT GREEN [TL2213]
☆ *Waggoners* [off B197 S of Welwyn]: Friendly pub with low-ceilinged bar, bigger comfortably furnished extension and nicely set out eating area, food from good lunchtime sandwiches to enterprising restaurant dishes, friendly knowledgeable service, six changing real ales; attractive and spacious suntrap back garden with sheltered terrace and play area (some A1(M) noise), dogs must be on a lead, wooded walks nearby, open all day *(BB, John and Joyce Snell, Mr and Mrs John Taylor)*

AYOT ST LAWRENCE [TL1916]
Brocket Arms [off B651 N of St Albans]: Individualistic low-beamed 14th-c pub, simple and old-fashioned, logs blazing in big inglenook, a dozen or so wines by the glass, Greene King and guest ales, traditional games, lunchtime sandwiches and other bar food, may be wider choice in no smoking evening restaurant, leisurely informal service; piped classical music; children welcome, nice suntrap walled garden with outside bar and play area, bedrooms, handy for Shaw's Corner, open all day *(R F Ballinger, Peter Abbott, LYM, Ian Phillips, Eric Robinson, Jacqueline Pratt)*

BARKWAY [TL3834]
Tally Ho [London Rd B1386]: Smart cosy bar with two open fires and some comfortable sofas, three interesting changing ales from small breweries tapped from the cask, good home cooking, friendly staff, candlelit no smoking restaurant area, no music or machines; picnic-sets in good-sized garden *(Kevin Thorpe, D H Burchett, Paul and Marion Watts)*

BATCHWORTH HEATH [TQ1090]
Olde Greene Manne Tidy traditional refurbishment, good seating arrangements, well kept Fullers London Pride; smart terrace *(Tracey and Stephen Groves)*

BELSIZE [TL0300]
Plough Welcoming landlord, central bar, barn-like beamed lounge with open fire, Adnams, Courage Directors and Greene King IPA, enjoyable simple home-made food lunchtimes and wknd evenings; picnic-sets in nice garden *(Andrew Scarr)*

BENINGTON [TL3023]
Bell [Town Lane; just past Post Office, towards Stevenage]: Bustling partly 15th-c pub in very pretty village, generous food from sandwiches up, cheery service, well kept Greene King IPA, Abbot and Morlands Original and a guest beer, hops with fairy lights hanging from low beams, sloping walls, flowers and candles on tables, unusual faded stag-hunt mural over big inglenook fireplace with woodburner, mix of old furnishings, aircraft memorabilia and enamel signs, pleasant no smoking beamed dining room; no children or dogs in bars, piped

music, weekly folk night; big tidy garden with country views, handy for Benington Lordship *(BB, Adele Summers, Alan Black)*

Lordship Arms [Whempstead Rd]: Comfortable and unpretentious, with well kept real ales inc three interesting guest beers, September beer festival, good value simple lunchtime food, welcoming attentive landlord, lots of telephone memorabilia; no credit cards *(Mike Turner, Peter and Betty Ford)*

BISHOP'S STORTFORD [TL4821]

Half Moon [North St]: Well kept changing real ales, Weston's farm cider and lots of country wines, helpful friendly staff, good lunchtime food, lovely old building with no smoking bar and other bare-boards rooms of different sizes and levels, décor tastefully in keeping; piped music; open all day *(Stephen and Jean Curtis)*

BRENT PELHAM [TL4331]

Black Horse Attractive and civilised village pub with beams and log fires, separate bars and restaurant, good choice of food and drink, friendly helpful staff, TV room for children; big garden in tranquil spot, bedrooms, open all day *(Mrs Margo Finlay, Jörg Kasprowski, Ron Deighton)*

BRICKENDON [TL3208]

☆ *Farmers Boy* [S of Hertford]: Enjoyable reasonably priced popular food all day from sandwiches up, helpful cheerful staff, well kept Adnams and Greene King, decent wines, dining area, popular monthly jazz nights first Thurs; picnic-sets in good-sized back garden and over road overlooking green, open all day *(Peter and Margaret Glenister)*

BROOKMANS PARK [TL2504]

Cock o' the North [Great North Rd (A1000, Bell Bar)]: Reliable dining pub with wide choice of consistently good value food, quick friendly service, McMullens real ale, well spaced stripped pine furnishings a contrast with its 1930s roadhouse exterior, pleasant paintings and prints *(Robert F Smith, B and M Kendall, David Hoult)*

CHANDLERS CROSS [TQ0698]

Clarendon Arms [Redhall Lane]: Popular new management in attractively set unpretentious pub, good value generous food all made fresh now inc good lunchtime tapas, cheery service, well kept ales such as Batemans, Courage Best and Fullers London Pride, wide choice of wines by the glass, log fire; children welcome, pleasant verandah, lots of tables and cocktail parasols, handy for woodland and canal walks *(Peter and Giff Bennett, LM, Mike Turner)*

CHIPPERFIELD [TL0401]

Windmill [The Common]: Good choice of home-made food (not Sun evening) and of well kept beers, welcoming helpful service, no smoking dining area; pleasant garden, bedrooms *(Martin and Alison Stainsby)*

CHORLEYWOOD [TQ0395]

☆ *Black Horse* [Dog Kennel Lane, the Common]: Very welcoming to families, walkers and even dogs (basket of dog biscuits on mantelpiece), plenty of good-sized tables under low dark beams in attractively divided traditional room with thick carpet, two massive log fires, good

value usual food (not Mon) from sandwiches to popular Sun lunch, well kept Adnams, Flowers Original, Theakstons Best and Wadworths 6X, decent wines (and tea and coffee), quick friendly service, no music; family area, separate bar with SkyTV; pretty setting, picnic-sets overlooking common *(B Brewer)*

Stag [Long Lane/Heronsgate Rd]: Smartly refurbished and spacious open-plan Edwardian pub with large no smoking eating area extending into conservatory, smiling helpful service, quiet relaxed atmosphere, well kept McMullens ales, decent wines and food, reasonable prices; tables on back lawn, play area, open all day *(Tracey and Stephen Groves, Howard Dell, Keith Callard)*

COLNEY HEATH [TL2006]

☆ *Crooked Billet* [High St]: Charming weatherboarded pub with well kept changing ales such as Grand Union Gold, Slaters Supreme, Tring Mother Haggys and Youngs, lots of unusual bottled beers, series of small rooms with seated alcoves and traditional tiled bar, friendly service, good value home cooking and fresh baguettes; piped music; big garden with play area, barbecues and partly covered terrace *(LYM, Ian Phillips)*

☆ *Plough* [just off back rd N, between A414 St Albans—Hatfield and A1057]: Pleasantly refurbished 18th-c low-beamed local, warm and cosy with good log fire, pleasant chatty atmosphere, good value generous standard food from sandwiches, baguettes and ciabattas up (lunchtime Mon-Sat, and Fri/Sat evening), well kept Greene King IPA and Abbot and Fullers London Pride, friendly efficient staff, small brighter back dining area; white iron tables on pretty front terrace, picnic-sets on sheltered back terrace and lawn *(Monica Cockburn, Mike Jefferies, Brian and Rosalie Laverick, John Cadge)*

DATCHWORTH [TL2717]

☆ *Horns* [Bramfield Rd]: Attractive flower-decked Tudor pub facing small green, low beams and big inglenook one end, high rafters and rugs on patterned bricks the other, attractive décor, good food from proper sandwiches up, quick friendly service, well kept ales such as Fullers London Pride; tables out on crazy-paved terrace among roses *(LYM, Mike Turner)*

ELSTREE [TQ1697]

Battleaxes [Butterfly Lane]: Popular chain family dining pub with wide range of attractively priced food in bar and conservatory, well kept Marstons Pedigree; garden tables *(Stan Edwards, Adele Summers, Alan Black)*

Waggon & Horses [A5183 towards Radlett]: Well kept ales inc Wadworths 6X, good baguettes, cosy personal atmosphere with oak beams, gleaming brassware, blue and white china, fresh flowers and open fire; attractive garden with good views *(Jestyn Phillips)*

FLAMSTEAD [TL0714]

Three Blackbirds [High St, just off A5]: Low-beamed partly Tudor local, much modernised inside but still with old dark wood and

brickwork, pictures, brass, copper, lots of
horse tack, roaring fire, well kept Courage Best
and Shepherd Neame Spitfire from central bar,
good value straightforward food from
substantial baguettes to good Sun roasts,
pleasant service, high-backed settles in no
smoking dining area, darts, pool; piped music,
SkyTV; children's corner, dogs welcome,
picnic-sets on terrace by car park behind,
colourful hanging baskets *(BB, John and
Joyce Snell, Michael Dandy, Mike Turner)*

FLAUNDEN [TL0100]

☆ *Bricklayers Arms* [off A41; Hogpits Bottom]:
Low-beamed and timbered country pub with
attractive décor and nice dining area adjoining
bar/lounge, good pub food from sandwiches
up lunchtime and Mon/Tues evenings,
restaurant meals other evenings, friendly
attentive staff, well kept Fullers London Pride
and Greene King ales, good choice of wines by
the glass, no piped music; children in eating
areas, appealing old-fashioned garden, nearby
walks *(Jarrod and Wendy Hopkinson, LYM,
Alex and Irene Harvey)*

GREEN TYE [TL4418]

Prince of Wales Relaxed and chatty traditional
two-bar village local brewing its own good
Green Tye ales such as Union Jack and
Wheelbarrow, one guest beer, friendly
landlord, usual simple lunchtime food, coal
fire; children and dogs welcome, garden tables,
good walks *(Eric Robinson, Jacqueline Pratt)*

HARPENDEN [TL1413]

☆ *Carpenters Arms* [Cravells Rd]: Cosy, chatty
and welcoming, with friendly efficient staff,
cheap generous uncomplicated home cooking
from good doorstep sandwiches up, well kept
Greene King and guest beers, special-issue
bottled beers, open fire, lovingly collected car
memorabilia inc models and overseas number-
plates; neat well planned terrace garden
*(Monica Cockburn, Mike Jefferies,
Terry Buckland)*

Cross Keys [High St]: Snug and cosy, with
Fullers London Pride and Marstons Pedigree,
lovely flagstones, log fire; garden
(Conor McGaughey, Terry Buckland)

Rose & Groom [Southdown Rd]: Enthusiastic
newish landlord, enjoyable food from good
baguettes up, well kept Fullers London Pride,
good coffee and service, daily papers, smart
modern décor with new furniture on laminate
floor, small bar area with a couple of settees,
airy back conservatory restaurant, games;
piped music; tables outside (busy road)
*(D L Johnson, Michael Dandy,
Terry Buckland)*

Skew Bridge [Southdown Rd]: Popular
commons-edge pub with good range of drinks
and of well cooked food, pleasant service, no
smoking area, no music; children welcome,
nice small garden with TV in wendy house,
attractive hanging baskets *(Jill McLaren)*

HATFIELD [TL2308]

Horse & Groom [Park St, Old Hatfield]:
Friendly old-fashioned town pub with good
value cheap food from sandwiches up, four
well kept ales, dark beams and dado, roaring

fires each end, lots of old local photographs; a
few tables out behind, handy for Hatfield
House *(Dr and Mrs M E Wilson)*

HERTFORD [TL3213]

Hillside [Port Hill, Bengeo (B158)]: No
smoking dining pub with interesting modern
cooking, good house wines, two northern real
ales on electric pump, welcoming service,
stripped beams and brickwork, leather sofas in
pleasant log-fire lounge, quiet décor, side
dining room with chunky scrubbed tables;
shame about the piped music; children
welcome, barn delicatessen, cl Mon, open all
day wknds *(Jack and Sandra Clarfelt)*

☆ *Old Cross Tavern* [St Andrew St]: Particularly
well kept Fullers London Pride, Oakham JHB
and fine choice of up to half a dozen guest
beers, good home-made lunchtime food,
friendly olde-worlde feel with log fire, brass,
china etc (conversion from antiques shop);
dogs welcome, small heated back terrace
(Ian Arthur)

HEXTON [TL1230]

Raven [signed off B655]: Cascades of hanging
baskets on big child-friendly dining pub
matching this mock-Tudor estate village, four
linked largely no smoking areas, plenty of
dining tables, oil paintings (some for sale),
wide range of good value food from baguettes
and baked potatoes up, two children's menus,
well kept ales such as Black Sheep, Fullers
London Pride, Greene King and Timothy
Taylors Landlord, quick friendly service, daily
papers, open fire, pool one end; piped music;
big garden with heated terrace, barbecue, good
play area *(Michael Dandy, Michael and
Alison Sandy, Ian Phillips)*

HIGH WYCH [TL4614]

Rising Sun Cosy unspoilt local, serving hatch
to carpeted lounge with coal or log fire, central
area with Courage Best and good guest beers
tapped from casks behind the counter, friendly
landlord and locals, bare-boards games room
(children allowed) with darts and woodburner;
no food, no mobile phones or pagers, no
music; tables in small garden *(the Didler,
Pete Baker)*

HINXWORTH [TL2340]

☆ *Three Horseshoes* [High St; just off A1(M)]:
Olde-worlde thatched, beamed and timbered
18th-c dining pub, good value enjoyable food,
well kept Greene King IPA and Abbot, decent
wines, good friendly service, pews in extended
red plush bar, woodburner in big brick
inglenook, steps up to no smoking high-
ceilinged dining area, soft lighting; piped
music; children welcome, big attractive garden
with play area *(BB, Geoff and Carol Thorp)*

KIMPTON [TL1718]

Boot [High St (B652)]: Good range of ales and
lagers, warm happy atmosphere, food inc good
Sun lunchtime cheeseboard *(Alan Bigg)*

White Horse [High St]: Pleasantly extended
around low-roofed half-timbered core, amiable
landlord, reasonably good lunchtime food
from sandwiches and baked potatoes to
seafood and fresh fish, McMullens ales, log
fires, separate eating area *(John and*

Joyce Snell, Peter and Margaret Glenister)

KINGS LANGLEY [TL0702]
Saracens Head [High St; handy for M25 junction 20]: Friendly old local with cheap food from proper sandwiches up, well kept Tring Ridgeway, comfortable surroundings *(Comus and Sarah Elliott)*

KNEBWORTH [TL2320]
☆ *Lytton Arms* [Park Lane, Old Knebworth]: Several spotless big-windowed rooms around large central servery, good changing choice of well kept ales from small breweries, two farm ciders, good value food from interesting choice of sandwiches, baguettes and baked potatoes up, friendly service, daily papers, no smoking conservatory; children welcome, picnic-sets on front terrace, back garden with play area, open all day wknds *(Dr P C Rea, John Saville, Bruce Bird, LYM, Peter and Margaret Glenister)*

LITTLE BERKHAMSTED [TL2908]
☆ *Five Horseshoes* [Church Rd]: Attractive and well run largely no smoking Chef & Brewer nr church, 17th-c beams, dark wood and stripped brickwork, two log fires, well kept Courage Best and Directors and two guest beers, decent wines, good generous food choice from sandwiches and baguettes up, quick warmly friendly service even on busy evenings, soft lighting; comfortable restaurant, cosy little upper dining room; garden with picnic-sets, busy in summer, attractive countryside *(Peter and Margaret Glenister, Jeremy King, Mrs E E Sanders, Robert Turnham)*

LONDON COLNEY [TL1803]
Colney Fox [High St/Barnet Rd]: Roomy Vintage Inn with convenient good value food, pleasant décor, quick efficient service even on busy wknds; plenty of tables outside, lots of trees in spacious grounds *(Mike and Jennifer Marsh)*
☆ *Green Dragon* [Waterside; just off main st by bridge at S end]: Roomy and neat, with good value generous straightforward food (not Sun), well kept ales such as Adnams, Fullers London Pride and Shepherd Neame Spitfire, decent wine, cheerful efficient service, lots of ancient timbers, beams and brasses, soft lighting, woodburner, separate dining room; prettily set riverside picnic-sets – would be even nicer without the parked cars *(LYM, Ian Phillips, Stan Edwards)*

MARSWORTH [SP9114]
Anglers Retreat [Startops End]: Unpretentious and convivial, with well kept ales inc Fullers London Pride, Hook Norton and a local brew, reasonably priced tasty food from fresh baguettes to piping hot dishes, very good service even when busy; handy for Tring Reservoirs – special for waterfowl *(C and R Bromage)*

MUCH HADHAM [TL4219]
☆ *Bull* [High St]: Handsome old dining pub recently tastefully refurbished by new licensees, roomy and civilised dining lounge and smaller back dining room, good food changing daily, cheerful service, well kept beers and good choice of wines by the glass inc champagne,

inglenook log fire in unspoilt bar; good-sized garden *(LYM, Charles Gysin)*

NEWGATE STREET [TL3005]
Crown Attractive flower-decked building with colourful garden, cosy inside, with friendly staff and landlord, good varied home-made food esp fresh fish, well kept Greene King IPA and Abbot, good house wine; small well behaved dogs welcome, handy for Northaw Great Wood walks *(Peter and Margaret Glenister, Lucien Perring)*

PERRY GREEN [TL4317]
☆ *Hoops* [off B1004 Widford—Much Hadham]: Village pub opp Henry Moore Foundation (guided tours in summer by appt), stripped brick, terracotta walls, beams, standing timbers and inglenook, friendly attentive staff, enjoyable food from sandwiches to all-day Sun lunch, Fullers London Pride, Greene King IPA and a guest beer, cosy no smoking dining area (children allowed); garden with large new covered terrace, open all day Sun *(LYM, Mrs Margo Finlay, Jörg Kasprowski, Dr P C Rea, George Atkinson, M A and C R Starling)*

PUCKERIDGE [TL3823]
☆ *White Hart* [Braughing Rd]: Rambling 14th-c pub recently decorated in contemporary colours by new licensees, quiet and relaxed informal atmosphere with enjoyable food inc steaks, duck and lots of fresh fish (fish and chips to take away, too), well kept McMullens ales and an occasional guest beer, good freshly ground coffee, log fire; children welcome, big garden now being taken in hand, open all day *(LYM, Mr and Mrs Hill)*

RABLEYHEATH [TL2319]
Robin Hood & Little John [a mile S of Old Knebworth; OS Sheet 153 map ref 235192]: Low-beamed country pub with McMullens Bitter and AK Mild, generous food from sandwiches, baguettes and baked potatoes up, cheerful friendly staff, cosy fires; cricket and rugby TV; picnic-sets in pleasant garden, good walks *(Peter and Margaret Glenister)*

RICKMANSWORTH [TQ0594]
Pennsylvanian [High St]: Wetherspoons with no smoking family area, and all their usual features *(Tony Hobden)*
Rose & Crown [Woodcock Hill/Harefield Rd, off A404 E of Rickmansworth at Batchworth]: Lively, friendly low-beamed pub with emphasis on good choice of restaurant food inc up-to-date dishes, fast friendly service, also comfortable little bar with warm coal fire and well kept ales such as Caledonian Deuchars IPA and Timothy Taylors Landlord; decent-sized garden, wide views from big car park *(anon)*

RUSHDEN [TL3031]
☆ *Moon & Stars* [Mill End; off A507 about a mile W of Cottered]: Good new chef/landlord in cottagey beamed country pub with good food (not Sun evening or Mon) in neatly kept no smoking lounge bar and small dining room (worth booking), inglenook log fire, well kept Greene King ales; pleasant garden, peaceful country setting *(LYM)*

SARRATT [TQ0499]

☆ *Boot* [The Green]: Attractive early 18th-c tiled pub, lively, cheery and unpretentious, with friendly new management, usual pub food inc some innovative sandwiches, well kept Greene King ales, cosy rambling rooms, unusual inglenook fireplace; garden, pleasant spot facing green, handy for Chess Valley walks *(B Brewer, LYM, Ian Phillips, KC)*

ST ALBANS [TL1307]

Blue Anchor [Fishpool St]: Popular dining lounge with good value sandwiches and other bar food (not Sun evening), well kept McMullens ales inc Mild, attractive prices, welcoming landlord, daily papers, small locals' bar with sensibly placed darts, real fire; sizeable garden, handy for Roman remains *(the Didler, Mike and Jennifer Marsh)*

Farmers Boy [London Rd]: Bustling unpretentious bay-windowed pub brewing its own distinctive Verulam IPA, Farmers Joy and a monthly special (ask for a taster), also their own lager and continental bottled beers, lots of old prints on softly lit smoke-effect walls, imposing clock, log fire, back open kitchen serving straightforward food from sandwiches and baked potatoes up all day, helpful staff, two large friendly dogs, no smoking area; SkyTV; open all day, suntrap back terrace with barbecues *(the Didler, Brian and Rosalie Laverick, John Dwane)*

Farriers Arms [Lower Dagnall St]: Plain and welcoming two-bar local where the Campaign for Real Ale started in the early 1970s, well kept McMullens inc Mild and guest beers, bar food wkdys, lots of old pictures of the pub; in no-frills old part *(the Didler, John Kearins, Ian Arthur)*

Garibaldi [Albert St; left turn down Holywell Hill past White Hart – car park left at end]: Fullers local with well kept Chiswick, London Pride and ESB and guest beers, low-priced wholesome lunchtime food (not Mon), good house wines, cheerful staff; may be piped music, occasional live; children welcome, open all day *(the Didler, John Kearins, LYM)*

Lower Red Lion [Fishpool St]: Huge log fire in convivial two-bar local dating from 17th c, relaxing chatty atmosphere, lots of well kept interesting changing ales, imported beers on tap and in bottle, May Day and Aug bank hol beer festivals, home-made food inc Sun lunches, red plush seats and carpet, Weds quiz night; tables in good-sized back garden, pleasant bedrooms, open all day Sat *(the Didler, Steve Nye, John Kearins, John Dwane)*

☆ *Plough* [Tyttenhanger Green, off A414 E]: Friendly village pub popular for its fine range of well kept changing ales, good-humoured licensees, young staff polite and prompt even when it's packed, lovely longcase clock, good log fire, good value straightforward lunchtime food, interesting old beer bottles and mats, back conservatory; big garden with play area *(LYM, the Didler, Monica Cockburn, Mike Jefferies)*

Rose & Crown [St Michaels St]: 16th-c beamed and timbered town pub under new landlord, welcoming service, changing real ales, lunchtime bar food, big log fire, no smoking family room; lots of tables and benches outside, pretty floral and ivy-hung back yard *(LYM, Peter and Giff Bennett)*

☆ *Six Bells* [St Michaels St]: Well kept rambling food pub, welcoming and civilised, with well kept ales such as Adnams, Fullers London Pride and Greene King IPA and Abbot, cheerful helpful service even when bustling with locals, big helpings of fresh food from lunchtime ciabattas and baked potatoes up inc good value pies, wider evening choice, low beams and timbers, log fire, quieter no smoking panelled dining room; children welcome, family room, occasional barbecues in small back garden, very handy for Roman Verulam Museum, open all day Fri-Sun *(LYM, Ian Phillips, Michael and Alison Sandy, Peter and Giff Bennett, Duncan Cloud)*

White Hart Tap [Keyfield; round corner from Garibaldi]: Good white-panelled Victorian pub, friendly and tidy, with four reliably well kept changing ales, good value quickly served fresh lunchtime food and popular Weds night international special; live band Sat, tables outside, open all day *(John Kearins, Derek Field)*

White Lion [Sopwell Lane]: Traditional local doing well under new management, small friendly front bar and roomy linked lounge areas, enjoyable food (not Sun evening or Mon), good choice of well kept ales, darts and other games, live music Tues; big back garden with play area *(John Kearins)*

STEVENAGE [TL2422]

Roebuck [Old London Rd, Broadwater]: Compact bar keeping coaching-inn character in Best Western hotel, well kept Black Sheep and Greene King Abbot, big log fire, limited choice of enjoyable simple restaurant food, sensible prices; 54 comfortable bedrooms *(Mark O'Sullivan)*

TRING [SP9211]

Robin Hood [Brook St (B486)]: Olde-worlde local with good food choice esp fish, several small drinking areas, three well kept Fullers beers, comfortable settles, lots of dark wood, slight nautical theme, dining conservatory with woodburner and diverse prints; piped music; no children or dogs inside, tables on small pleasant back terrace, free public car park nearby *(R E Dixon, Tony Hobden, BB, DM, John Branston)*

WADESMILL [TL3517]

Sow & Pigs [Cambridge Rd, Thundridge (A10 N of Ware)]: Neatly kept and cheerful dining pub, spacious pleasantly rustic beamed dining room off central bar with pig décor, changing real ales, enjoyable food from sandwiches up, log fire; no dogs, children in eating areas, tables outside, open all day *(LYM, Mrs Margo Finlay, Jörg Kasprowski)*

WATER END [TL0410]

Red Lion [Leighton Buzzard Rd (A4146)]: Good no smoking Chef & Brewer extended from 18th-c core into lots of beamed and pillared nooks and corners, their usual food from sandwiches and baked potatoes up, brisk friendly service, real ales such as Courage Directors and Marstons Pedigree from attractive carved bar, wide choice of wines by the glass *(Dennis Jones)*

WATTON-AT-STONE [TL3019]

George & Dragon [High St (B1001)]: Popular country dining pub with interesting mix of antique and modern prints on partly timbered walls, big inglenook fireplace, well kept Greene King IPA and Abbot and a guest beer, decent wines, friendly staff, daily papers, wide food choice (not Sun evening) from sandwiches up; children welcome in eating areas, pretty shrub-screened garden with heaters and boules, open all day wknds *(LYM, Pat and Tony Martin,*

Steve Nye, Mike and Jennifer Marsh, Peter and Margaret Glenister)

WESTON [TL2529]

Cricketers [Damask Green Rd; N of Stevenage]: Light and airy Victorian country pub, good food choice from generous baguettes and other snacks to main meals, well organised pleasant service (ramblers can order ahead), well kept beers inc Rhubarb Ale; lovely big garden *(Mike Turner, Tony Shepherd, Mark Barker)*

WHITWELL [TL1821]

Maidens Head [High St (B651)]: Nice staff in old-fashioned local with usual food from simple sandwiches up, four well kept changing ales tapped from the cask, good coffee, interesting key-ring collection; tables in safe children's garden *(John Branston)*

Isle of Wight

The island's top pubs are the civilised Crab & Lobster at Bembridge (good food, particularly seafood from fresh crab sandwiches up, great sea views from its terrace), the Red Lion at Freshwater (good food here too, and a splendid choice of wines, in this rather adult local), the interesting Seaview Hotel (good all round, as a pub, dining place, or place to stay in), the unspoilt old New Inn at Shalfleet (prime fresh local fish), the charming Crown in the lovely village of Shorwell, and the attractively decorated Spyglass looking out to sea in Ventnor (popular food all day, nightly entertainment). This year, the award of Isle of Wight Dining Pub of the Year goes to the Crab & Lobster at Bembridge, for its nice balance between really good fresh seafood (particularly local crab and lobster) and pubbier dishes. In the Lucky Dip section at the end of the chapter, we'd pick out the Folly outside Cowes, Fishbourne Inn, Buddle at Niton, Volunteer in Ventnor (for its great choice of real ales) and White Horse at Whitwell. Drinks prices on the island are on average higher than the mainland norm; the island's own main local beers, often the cheapest a pub here sells, are Goddards and Ventnor, with Yates also worth looking out for.

ARRETON SZ5486 Map 2
White Lion
A3056 Newport—Sandown

Food is available all day at this warm and welcoming white-painted village local. Besides sandwiches and baguettes (from £3.50) and ploughman's (£5.75), straightforward and mostly home-made dishes include soup (£2.95), chilli con carne (£5.95), lasagne, vegetable curry sausage and mash or haddock and chips (£6.45), pie of the day (£7.25) and steaks (from £9.95), as well as specials that might include indonesian spicy chicken, prawn and rice (£8.95), venison steak with red wine and redcurrant sauce or swordfish steak with garlic prawns (£10.95). There's a no smoking restaurant and family room as well as a no smoking area in the stable room. Fullers London Pride, Timothy Taylors Landlord and a guest such as Badger Best are well kept on handpump. The pleasant beamed lounge bar has partly panelled walls gleaming with brass and horse tack, and cushioned wheelback chairs on the red carpet. There is very quiet piped music, and the public bar has darts, fruit machine and TV. You can sit out in front of the tubs of flowers, and the pleasant garden has a small play area. This pleasant inland village has a manor house and a fine 13th-c church. More reports please. *(Recommended by Ian Phillips)*

Whitbreads ~ Lease Chris and Kate Cole ~ Real ale ~ Bar food (12-9) ~ (01983) 528479 ~ Children in family room ~ Dogs allowed in bar ~ Open 11-11; 12-10.30 Sun

BEMBRIDGE SZ6587 Map 2
Crab & Lobster 🍴
Foreland Fields Road, off Howgate Road (which is off B3395 via Hillgate Road)
Isle of Wight Dining Pub of the Year
Within yards of the shore and prettily adorned with flower baskets in summer, this obscurely located pub has as nautical an air as its name suggests, perched as it is on low cliffs with ships providing the backdrop. Inside it's roomier than you might

expect, and it's done in a civilised, almost parlourish style, with lots of yachting memorabilia and old local photographs. They serve a very good choice of fresh local seafood (as well as non-fishy) specials every day, such as crab cakes (£7.50), spicy baked local crab, lamb steak or grilled salmon fillet (£9.50), seafood tagliatelle or veal escalope (£9.95), crab and lobster platter for two (£22.95) and whole lobster (£23.50; half lobster £12.95). Other very well prepared food includes sandwiches (from £4.25; very good crab ones for £5.50), filled baguettes (from £4.95), soup (from £3.25), assorted pâté (£4.50), baked potatoes (from £4.50), ploughman's (£6.95), home-made lasagne or vegetarian curry (£7.50), mixed grill (£10.50), steak (from £12.95) and puddings such as treacle sponge (£3.75); children's menu (£4.25); the restaurant is no smoking. Well kept Flowers Original, Greene King IPA and a guest such as Goddards Fuggle-Dee-Dum on handpump, decent house wines, about 20 malt whiskies, farm cider, good coffee; piped music (even in the lavatories), darts, dominoes and cribbage. It does get very popular, so best to get there early or late at lunchtime. *(Recommended by Gordon Stevenson, Trevor Moore, John and Glenys Wheeler, Alan Skull, Phil and Heidi Cook, B N F and M Parkin, Alan M Pring, Geoff and Sylvia Donald)*

Whitbreads ~ Lease Richard, Adrian and Pauline Allan ~ Real ale ~ Bar food (12-2.30, 6-9.30) ~ (01983) 872244 ~ Children welcome ~ Dogs allowed in bar ~ Open 11-11; 12-10.30 Sun; 11-3, 6-11 weekdays in winter ~ Bedrooms: £40B/£80B

BONCHURCH SZ5778 Map 2
Bonchurch Inn
Bonchurch Shute; from A3055 E of Ventnor turn down to Old Bonchurch opposite Leconfield Hotel

It's quite a sight as you enter the courtyard of this curious, little-changed place to see the separate bar, restaurant, rooms and kitchens spread around the cobbled courtyard, and all snuggled below a steep, rocky slope. Before it gained its licence in the 1840s the pub used to be stables for the nearby manor house. Tables, a fountain and pergola out here are nicely enclosed, giving the courtyard a slightly continental feel on warm summer days. The furniture-packed Victorian bar has a good chatty atmosphere, and conjures up images of salvaged shipwrecks, with its floor of narrow-planked ship's decking, and seats like the ones that old-fashioned steamers used to have. A separate entrance leads to the very simple no smoking family room (a bit cut off from the congenial atmosphere of the public bar). As well as Scottish Courage Directors and Best tapped from the cask, there are italian wines by the glass, a few bottled french wines, darts, shove-ha'penny, dominoes and cribbage. The welcoming landlord is Italian, and the menu reflects this with several good-value dishes such as spinach cannelloni, tagliatelle carbonara or lasagne (£6.95), spaghetti salmone (£8.50) or seafood risotto (£8.95) as well as standard items such as sandwiches (from £3, toasted 30p extra), soup (£4), grilled plaice (£7.95) and steak (from £10.50); there is a £1 charge for credit cards. The no smoking restaurant is just across the courtyard, and the pub owns a holiday flat for up to six people. *(Recommended by Keith and Jean Symons, David Coleman, Dr D and Mrs B Woods, Geoff and Linda Payne)*

Free house ~ Licensees Ulisse and Gillian Besozzi ~ Real ale ~ Bar food ~ Restaurant ~ (01983) 852611 ~ Children in family room ~ Dogs allowed in bar ~ Open 11-3, 6.30-11; 12-3, 7-10.30 Sun

FRESHWATER SZ3487 Map 2
Red Lion 🍴 ♟

Church Place; from A3055 at E end of village by Freshwater Garage mini-roundabout follow Yarmouth signpost, then take first real right turn signed to Parish Church

In a quiet village street overlooked by the church and virtually on the Freshwater Way footpath that connects Yarmouth with the southern coast at Freshwater Bay, this genuine-feeling local has an atmosphere that visitors without smaller children tend to appreciate. There's a bustling atmosphere in the comfortably furnished open-plan bar, which has open fires, low grey sofas and sturdy country-kitchen style furnishings on mainly flagstoned floors, with bare boards at one end, and lots of local pictures and photographs and china platters on the walls. It's so popular that if you want to eat here it's a good idea to book ahead. Enjoyable bar food includes sandwiches, as well as lunchtime snacks such as baguettes; very well prepared imaginative daily specials are listed on a big blackboard behind the bar, and might include soup such as smoked haddock, leek and potato (£4.20), herring roes on toast (£5.50), stuffed field mushrooms with crab and stilton (£5.75), mushroom and asparagus risotto, sausages and mash or steak and kidney pie (£8.75), half lobster salad or whole lemon sole (£12.95), rib-eye steak (£13.95) and puddings such as rhubarb crumble, chocolate sponge or bread and butter pudding (£4.50). Flowers Original, Fullers London Pride and Wadworths 6X, plus a guest ale such as Goddards are kept under a light blanket pressure and served by handpump, and the good choice of wines includes 16 by the glass. Fines on mobile phone users go to charity (they collect a lot for the RNLI); there's a fruit machine but no music, and smoking is permitted throughout. There are tables on a carefully tended grass and gravel area at the back (some under cover), behind which is the kitchen's herb garden, and a couple of picnic-sets in a quiet square at the front, by the church. *(Recommended by Mrs Maricar Jagger, Keith and Jean Symons, John and Glenys Wheeler, Trevor Moore, Colin and Janet Roe, JDM, KM, Simon Collett-Jones, Gerry and Rosemary Dobson, Ian and Deborah Carrington)*

Enterprise ~ Lease Michael Mence ~ Real ale ~ Bar food (12-2, 6.30(7 Sun)-9) ~ (01983) 754925 ~ Children over 10 ~ Dogs allowed in bar ~ Open 11.30-3, 5.30-11; 11.30-4, 6-11 Sat; 12-3, 7-10.30 Sun

SEAVIEW SZ6291 Map 2
Seaview Hotel 🍴 ♉ 🛏
High Street; off B3330 Ryde—Bembridge

Looking across the Solent to the mainland, this 200-year-old hotel is a civilised place to stay or have a meal. Full of nautical paraphernalia, it has a bustling atmosphere, with reception rooms ranging from pubby to smart dining. The bay-windowed bar at the front has an impressive array of naval and merchant ship photographs, as well as Spy nautical cartoons for *Vanity Fair*, original receipts for Cunard's shipyard payments for the *Queen Mary* and *Queen Elizabeth*, and a line of close-set tables down each side on the turkey carpet. There's a more informal down to earth atmosphere in the simpler back bar, with traditional wooden furnishings on bare boards, lots of seafaring paraphernalia around its softly lit ochre walls, and a log fire. They keep Goddards and a guest on handpump, and have around 20 malt whiskies and a good wine list (the landlord used to be a director of Corney & Barrow, the wine merchants); darts, cribbage, dominoes and shove-ha'penny. Using local ingredients wherever possible and fish fresh from the sea, very good well presented and generously served bar food includes soup (£3.95), hot crab ramekin that's been a long-standing favourite here (£6.25), fried tiger prawns in garlic and lime butter on toast (£6.50), fish pie or roasted tomatoes with couscous and halloumi (£9.50) and sirloin steak (£12.95), plus puddings such as chocolate pudding or poached meringue with crème anglaise and almond praline (£3.95); the restaurant areas are no smoking. Perhaps service could be more attentive at times. Tables on the little terraces on either side of the path to the front door look down to the sea and along the coast, and some of the attractive bedrooms also have a sea view. *(Recommended by Dr Alan and Mrs Sue Holder, JDM, KM, Stephen R Holman, P Price, David Coleman, Michael B Griffith, Simon Collett-Jones, Gerry and Rosemary Dobson)*

Free house ~ Licensee N W T Hayward ~ Real ale ~ Bar food (12-2.30, 7-9.30) ~ Restaurant ~ (01983) 612711 ~ Children welcome ~ Dogs welcome ~ Open 11-11; 12-3, 7-10.30 Sun; closed 24-26 Dec ~ Bedrooms: £72B/£110B

Soup prices usually include a roll and butter.

SHALFLEET SZ4189 Map 2

New Inn 🍴 ♉ ◗

A3054 Newport—Yarmouth

It seems apt that this 18th-c fisherman's haunt, a short stroll from the marshy inlets of the yacht-studded Newtown estuary, should be one of the island's best pubs specialising in fish dishes. Well known for their crab salad (£11.95), lobster salad (£13.95) and seafood platter (£55 for two, £100 for four), they also have a great choice of up to 12 fresh fish dishes a day, with a daily changing menu that typically includes starters like soup (£3.50), crab and prawn cocktail (£4.95) and caramelised onion and goats cheese tartlet (£4.95), and main courses like greek-style lamb steak (£11.50), crab salad, chicken breast with sweet chilli glaze or grilled swordfish steak (£11.95), fish mixed grill (£14.95) and whole grilled local bass (£15.95). There's also a short menu with sandwiches (from £2.95), filled baguettes (from £3.85), ploughman's (from £5.95), sausage and mash (£6.95), home-made lasagne (£7.95), home-made pie (£8.95) and rump steak (from £11.95). You will need to book, and there may be double sittings in summer. The partly panelled flagstoned public bar has yachting photographs and pictures, a boarded ceiling, scrubbed pine tables and a roaring log fire in the big stone hearth, and the carpeted beamed lounge bar has boating pictures and a coal fire. The snug and gallery (with slate floors, bric-a-brac and more scrubbed pine tables) are no smoking. Goddards, Ventnor Golden and a couple of guests such as Bass and Greene King IPA are kept under a light blanket pressure and served by handpump, and they stock around 60 wines; piped music. *(Recommended by Ron and Sheila Corbett, Gordon Stevenson, Brenda and Rob Fincham, Peter and Margaret Glenister, Joan York, Keith and Jean Symons, Vanessa Stilwell, OPUS, David Coleman, Gerry and Rosemary Dobson, B N F and M Parkin, Walter and Susan Rinaldi-Butcher, Mark and Mary Fairman)*

Whitbreads ~ Lease Mr Bullock and Mr McDonald ~ Real ale ~ Bar food (12-2.30, 6-9.30) ~ Restaurant ~ (01983) 531314 ~ Children in eating area of bar ~ Dogs allowed in bar ~ Open 12-3, 6-11(10.30 Sun)

SHORWELL SZ4582 Map 2

Crown

B3323 SW of Newport

A nice chatty atmosphere still predominates in this pub at this gorgeous thatched village, in a fold of the chalk downs. In warmer months the place to sit is the tranquil tree-sheltered garden – which has closely spaced picnic-sets and white garden chairs and tables by a little stream that broadens out into a small trout-filled pool. A decent children's play area blends in comfortably. Inside, four rooms spread pleasantly around a central bar. The beamed two-room lounge has blue and white china in an attractive carved dresser, old country prints on the stripped stone walls, other individual furnishings, and a winter log fire with a fancy tile-work surround. Black pews form bays around tables in a stripped-stone room off to the left, with another log fire; apart from the public bar it's largely no smoking. Bar food includes sandwiches (from £3.25), soup (£3.95), pâté with toast (£4.95), ploughman's or crab cocktail (from £5.25), home-made lasagne (£7.50), fisherman's pie (£7.95), and daily specials such as steak and kidney pie (£8.50), salmon supreme with black-eyed bean salsa or chicken supreme with brandy and apricots (£8.95) and lamb shank with redcurrant gravy (£9.95); puddings (from £3.50) and children's meals. Well kept Boddingtons, Flowers Original and Wadworths 6X, with a guest such as Badger Tanglefoot on handpump; piped music. More reports please. *(Recommended by Simon Collett-Jones)*

Enterprise ~ Lease Mike Grace ~ Real ale ~ Bar food (12-2.30, 6-9.30) ~ (01983) 740293 ~ Children welcome ~ Dogs welcome ~ Open 10-3.30, 6-11; all day bank hol weekends; 12-3, 6-10.30 Sun

---

If we know a pub has a no smoking area, we say so.

VENTNOR SZ5677 Map 2

Spyglass

Esplanade, SW end; road down very steep and twisty, and parking nearby can be difficult – best to use the pay-and-display (free in winter) about 100 yards up the road

A fascinating jumble of seafaring memorabilia fills the quarry-tiled interior of this snug and lively pub, in a sunny position right next to the sea wall and beach. On display are wrecked rudders, ships' wheels, old local advertisements, rope-makers' tools, stuffed seagulls, an Admiral Benbow barometer and an old brass telescope; fruit machine, piped music and nightly entertainment. Usefully served all day, generous helpings of good, very fairly priced bar food are promptly served and include sandwiches (from £3.95, baguettes from £4.95), soup (£4.25), filled baked potatoes (from £5.75), ploughman's (from £6.95), home-made chilli (£7.50), home-made fisherman's pie (£8.50), and sirloin steak (£11.75), with daily specials such as seafood chowder (£5.25), local sausages and mash (£7.50), steak and kidney pie (£7.95), crab tart or seafood stew (£8.95); puddings (£4.25). They have well kept Badger Best, Badger Tanglefoot, Ventnor Golden and about three guests such as Goddards Fuggle-Dee-Dum or St Austell Tribute on handpump. There are strolls westwards along the coast towards the Botanic Garden as well as heftier hikes up on to St Boniface Down and towards the eerie shell of Appuldurcombe House, and the pub owners don't mind muddy boots; no smoking area. *(Recommended by Alan Skull, John and Glenys Wheeler, Ian Phillips, B N F and M Parkin, Geoff and Linda Payne, Mark and Mary Fairman)*

Free house ~ Licensees Neil and Stephanie Gibbs ~ Real ale ~ Bar food (12-9.30(9 Sun)) ~ (01983) 855338 ~ Children welcome ~ Dogs allowed in bar ~ Live entertainment every night ~ Open 10.30-11(10.30 Sun) ~ Bedrooms: /£60B

LUCKY DIP

Besides the fully inspected pubs, you might like to try these Lucky Dips recommended to us and described by readers (if you do, please send us reports: www.goodguides.co.uk).

BEMBRIDGE [SZ6488]
Pilot Boat [Station Rd/Kings Rd]: Enjoyable reasonably priced food, friendly landlord; pleasant terrace *(J Williams)*
BRADING [SZ6087]
Snooty Fox [High St]: Comfortable, well kept and welcoming, with generous and enjoyable usual food (children free with adults eating), well kept ales such as Greene King, decent wines by the glass, old well, lots of farm tools *(Ron and Sheila Corbett)*
CHALE [SZ4877]
☆ *Clarendon (Wight Mouse)* [off A3055/B3399]: Popular high throughput family dining pub rambling around with flagstones here, carpet there, modern-look woody extension around traditional core with log fire, good choice of well kept Badger and other ales from long bar, good value food from snacks up, attentive cheerful service, entertaining quotes chalked up, plenty to keep children occupied, no smoking dining area; extensive outdoor seating, great views out over cliffs, good bedrooms in adjoining hotel *(Joan York, Mrs Maricar Jagger, Alison Cook, LYM, Mark and Mary Fairman)*
COWES [SZ5092]
☆ *Folly* [Folly Lane – which is signposted off A3021 just S of Whippingham]: Splendid estuary setting with big windows and large waterside deck, hearty reasonably priced food

most of the day from sandwiches up, well kept Flowers IPA and Original and Goddards, several wines by the glass, good cheerful music even though busy, opened-out timbered bar with bric-a-brac and old pictures and books, no smoking area; very yachtie-oriented, with wind speed indicator, barometer and chronometer, moorings, showers and breakfast service (call the water taxi on Channel 7); pool, TV and piped music, occasional live; children welcome, garden with summer bouncy castle (very busy then), open all day *(Martin and Karen Wake, LYM, JDM, KM, OPUS, Joan York)*
FISHBOURNE [SZ5592]
☆ *Fishbourne Inn* [from Portsmouth car ferry turn left into Fishbourne Lane no through road]: Warmly welcoming, spacious and neatly kept, with particularly good fresh local fish and seafood, good choice of other food from ploughman's to grills, good service even when packed, real ales such as Bass, Gales and Wadworths 6X, comfortable wall settles in cosy bar, large dining area; attractive well kept outdoor area, nice setting nr ferry terminal and coast path *(Bernard Phelvin, Dr and Mrs A K Clarke, P Price, June and Malcolm Farmer)*
HAVENSTREET [SZ5590]
White Hart [off A3054 Newport—Ryde; Main Rd]: Cosy bar in ancient country pub, tidy and

comfortable, good blackboard choice of reliably good home-made food (worth booking), lots of fresh veg, welcoming service, well kept Badger ales, locomotive prints, interesting beer-bottle collection, no piped music or machines; tables in attractive garden *(Alan Skull, Mrs Christa Sansom)*

HULVERSTONE [SZ3984]

Sun [B3399]: Picture-book thatched pub in charming peaceful setting, cosy bar with flagstones, stripped brickwork and woodburner, friendly helpful staff, well kept real ales, sound food, no piped music or machines; smart tables under cocktail parasols in lovely flower-filled garden with village stocks, terrific sea views *(Sara Nicholls, Andy Moore, Pete and Kate Holford)*

NITON [SZ5075]

☆ *Buddle* [St Catherines Rd, Undercliff; off A3055 just S of village, towards St Catherines Point]: Plenty of character in pretty former smugglers' haunt, heavy black beams, big flagstones, broad stone fireplace, no smoking areas, enjoyable reasonably priced food (freshly made, so may take a while) inc good ploughman's, seafood, griddle dishes and Sun lunches, good welcoming service, family dining room/games annexe, up to half a dozen real ales, friendly dogs; fruit machine; clifftop views from well cared for sloping garden and terraces, good walks; open all day, some live jazz *(Charles and Pauline Stride, Alan Skull, LYM, David Coleman, Mark Flynn, Alan M Pring, Geoff and Linda Payne)*

ROOKLEY [SZ5183]

Chequers [S of village, Chequers Inn Rd/Niton Rd]: Spacious carpeted dining lounge with log fire, big plain no smoking family room, sun lounge and bar looking out over garden and big safely fenced play area, mother-and-baby room, flagstoned locals' bar with pool, darts, other games (and TV), Courage Best and Directors, Gales HSB and two guest beers, usual bar food all day from sandwiches and baked potatoes to steaks, daily papers, downland views; children and dogs welcome, open all day *(LYM, Ian Phillips)*

SANDOWN [SZ5984]

Clancys [Beachfield Rd]: Friendly modern bar/restaurant, bright and spacious, with fair choice of wines, reasonably priced food all freshly made by Antipodean licensees, from snacks and pizzas to evening meals – they do their best to meet special wishes; may be cl winter Sun/Mon evenings *(Colin Moore)*

Fountain [Carter St]: Cheerful local with good lively atmosphere, enjoyable food, live music *(Sam)*

TOTLAND [SZ3285]

High Down [Highdown Lane]: Out-of-the-way pub in great spot at foot of NT Tennyson Down, well kept real ales such as Wychwood Hobgoblin, fresh home-made food using local produce in bar and smart little dining room (former public bar), cheerful service; piped music; dogs and walkers welcome, picnic-sets out in raised paddock area, good value bedrooms *(Paula Lyon, Liz and Brian Barnard)*

VENTNOR [SZ5677]

Richmond [Esplanade]: New pub with excellent sea views, real ales inc Ventnor, fish inc local crab, daily papers, local memorabilia, free Sun bar nibbles *(Liz and John Soden)*

☆ *Volunteer* [Victoria St]: Small 19th-c local with cheerful chatty licensees, half a dozen or more well kept ales such as Courage, Greene King, Ventnor and Yates, reasonable prices, coal fire, darts, the local game of rings, perhaps sandwiches or finger buffet if you order specially, friendly cat called Rosie, no machines or juke box; no children, quiz nights, open all day *(David Ellerington, Jason Reynolds, M Emmerson, Dave Hampton, Jacqueline Hampton)*

WHITWELL [SZ5277]

☆ *White Horse* [High St]: Ancient thatched pub with thriving atmosphere, real ales such as Badger Best, Fullers London Pride, Greene King Abbot and Ventnor Golden, enjoyable food runing up to duck, local pheasant and interesting puddings, cheerful quick service, small eating area in well furnished beamed bar, two large no smoking family dining areas off, country décor, horsebrasses, log fire; picnic-sets out on lawn *(Ian Phillips)*

WROXALL [SZ5479]

Four Seasons [B3327]: Modern pub, clean and comfortable, with enjoyable food and attentive staff, beamery and timber-effect walls, no smoking restaurant *(David Coleman)*

YARMOUTH [SZ3589]

Bugle [The Square]: Old inn with low-ceilinged panelled lounge, lively rather basic bar with nautical memorabilia and counter like galleon stern, enjoyable food from good soup and sandwiches to good fish and seafood choice, decent house wines, Dunkerton's bottled organic cider, cold Greene King Abbot, Wadworths 6X and a beer brewed for them by Yates; restaurant, games room with pool, children very welcome; piped music, little or no nearby parking, can be crowded Sat – get there early; sizeable garden, summer barbecues, bedrooms *(LYM, Colin and Janet Roe, Mrs Maricar Jagger, Joan and Michel Hooper-Immins)*

We mention bottled beers and spirits only if there is something unusual about them – imported Belgian real ales, say, or dozens of malt whiskies; so do please let us know about them in your reports.

Kent

Kent stands out for its large proportion of interesting and attractive pubs that date back several centuries – either kept simple, or sensitively updated to cater for people who want to eat and drink in rather more style. Pubs of all ages on particularly good form here this year include the homely little Unicorn at Bekesbourne (gains a Bargain Award for its good value food, using fresh local ingredients), the Three Chimneys near Biddenden (very good food, good drinks, lovely interior), the friendly and relaxed Wheatsheaf at Bough Beech (good food, beer and wine, lots to look at), the nicely placed and charmingly unspoilt Dove at Dargate (notable food, welcoming licensees), the ancient Windmill in Hollingbourne (this enjoyable dining pub is now all no smoking), the convivial Woodcock tucked away at Iden Green, the remote and unspoilt 17th-c Shipwrights Arms at Oare (nice Kent beers in great surroundings), the well run Bottle House out in the country above Penshurst (splendid atmosphere, great choice of food served all day), the striking gently upmarket Dering Arms at Pluckley (the landlord's fish cooking is good), the welcoming Rose & Crown also at Pluckley (very welcoming, another pub that earns a Bargain Award for its bar food using local produce well), the Rose & Crown in its charming garden at Selling (tasty sensibly priced food), the stylishly updated Chaser at Shipbourne (a civilised new entry this year, nice all round, doing very well particularly on the food side under its current newish landlord), the highly individual Red Lion at Stodmarsh (you won't want to leave – and they do enjoyable generous food), Sankeys in Tunbridge Wells (good seafood, great atmosphere, splendid drinks choice), and the Swan on the Green in West Peckham (generous up-to-date food in appealing airy surroundings, and half a dozen good beers brewed at the pub). Many of these pubs are very rewarding on the food side. For a really special meal out, the Dove at Dargate is Kent Dining Pub of the Year – best to book. In the Lucky Dip section at the end of the chapter, current pubs to note particularly are the Chapter Arms at Chartham Hatch, Star & Eagle in Goudhurst, George & Dragon at Ightham, Plough at Ivy Hatch, Rising Sun at Kemsing, Clarendon at Sandgate, Sportsman in Seasalter, Coastguard at St Margaret's Bay and Padwell Arms at Stone Street. On average, pub drinks prices in Kent tend to be higher than the national norm. Beer from the county's leading brewer Shepherd Neame is often the cheapest on a Kent pub's menu. Two smaller brewers, Goachers (which tends to be temptingly priced) and Larkins, are well worth looking out for, too.

BEKESBOURNE TR1856 Map 3
Unicorn £
Coming from Patrixbourne on A2, turn left up Bekesbourne Hill after passing railway line (and station); coming from Littlebourne on A257, pass Howletts Zoo – Bekesbourne Hill is then first turning on right; turning into pub car park is at bottom end of the little terrace of houses on the left (the pub is the far end of this terrace)

This airy little place has just a few scrubbed old pine tables and bentwood café chairs on worn floorboards, a canary ceiling and walls above a dark green dado, minimal décor, and a handful of bar stools against the neat counter. You can glimpse into the spick-and-span stainless kitchen where (using local produce where possible) the homely licensees produce their enjoyable food. Although only a handful of dishes come in under our bargain award threshold, we felt that overall the food here was such good value that they deserved a new bargain award this year: soup (£2.95), sandwiches and baguettes (from £2.95), avocado and bacon salad (£3.50), grilled sardines (£3.95), cauliflower cheese or vegetable bake (£4.50), sausages and mash (£6.25), steak and ale pie (£8.25), daily specials such as wild mushroom stroganoff or seared pigeon breast with honey and ginger sauce (£9.25), and puddings such as lemon syllabub or waffles (from £2.95). Adnams Broadside and Shepherd Neame Masterbrew are well kept on handpump, with a short but carefully chosen wine list, local cider and apple and pear juice; perhaps piped radio, but no machines – unless you count the veteran penny-in-the-slot bagatelle machine, cribbage and dominoes. There's a piano in one corner, and a little Victorian fireplace. A side terrace, quite prettily planted, has teak tables and benches, and boules. Parking in front is tricky but there is a car park at the back. *(Recommended by Catherine and Rob Dunster, Ron and Sheila Corbett, Fr Robert Marsh, Kevin Thorpe)*

Free house ~ Licensees Clive and Cheryl Barker ~ Real ale ~ Bar food ~ No credit cards ~ (01227) 830210 ~ Children welcome ~ Open 11.30-2.30, 7-11; 12-3, 7-10.30 Sun; closed Sun evening in winter; closed Mon, Tues

BIDDENDEN TQ8538 Map 3
Three Chimneys 🍴 ♀
A262, 1 mile W of village

Although pricey, the imaginative food at this lovely old pub is superbly cooked, and at lunchtime the generously served starters are substantial enough to be a light main course. You will need to get here early, or book, as the food is very popular. Dishes might include soup (£3.95), baked field mushrooms with caramelised red onions and grilled goats cheese (£5.50), ploughman's (£6.50), thai-style crab cakes (£6.95), sautéed lambs liver and bacon with mash and port and red onion gravy (£11.95), duck leg confit with braised puy lentils, chorizo and bacon (£14.95), roast venison and parsnips with braised cabbage and port jus (£18.95), monkfish fillets with tomato and garlic, parma ham and mozzarella (£16.95), and puddings such as strawberry and vanilla crème brûlée (£5.25); friendly service from the knowledgeable staff. Feeling quite pubby, with Adnams Best, Harveys Best, Shepherd Neame Spitfire and a seasonal beer tapped straight from casks racked behind the counter, the series of low-beamed, very traditional little rooms has plain wooden furniture and old settles on flagstones and coir matting, some harness and sporting prints on the stripped brick walls, and good log fires. The simple public bar has darts, dominoes and cribbage. French windows in the civilised candlelit bare-boards restaurant open on to the garden (ploughman's only out here), which has picnic-sets in dappled shade, and a smart terrace area has tables and outdoor heaters. They've a good wine list, with several by the glass, local Biddenden cider and several malt whiskies. Nearby Sissinghurst Gardens are well worth a visit; no muddy boots. *(Recommended by Mrs Sally Kingsbury, Kevin Thorpe, John Hendy , the Didler, Mrs C Lintott, John Evans, Bob and Margaret Holder, Derek Thomas, Brian Wainwright, M Sage, Alan Sadler, Anthony Longden)*

Free house ~ Licensee Craig Smith ~ Real ale ~ Bar food (12-1.50, 6.30-9.30; 12-2.30, 7-9 Sun) ~ Restaurant ~ (01580) 291472 ~ Children in eating area of bar and restaurant ~ Dogs welcome ~ Open 11.30-3, 6-11; 12-3, 7-10.30 Sun

---

Bedroom prices are for high summer. Even then you may get reductions for more than one night, or (outside tourist areas) weekends. Winter special rates are common, and many inns cut bedroom prices if you have a full evening meal.

BOUGH BEECH TQ4846 Map 3
Wheatsheaf ♀ ◀

B2027, S of reservoir

'I wish this pub was in my village', says one reader about this enjoyably bustling pub, with its very friendly welcome and jolly decent food. Full of history, there are masses of interesting things to look at inside, and the older part of the building is thought to have been a hunting lodge belonging to Henry V. The neat central bar and the long front bar (with an attractive old settle carved with wheatsheaves) have unusually high ceilings with lofty oak timbers, a screen of standing timbers and a revealed king post; dominoes and board games. Divided from the central bar by two more rows of standing timbers – one formerly an outside wall to the building – are the snug, and another bar. Other similarly aged features include a piece of 1607 graffiti, 'Foxy Holamby', thought to have been a whimsical local squire. There are quite a few horns and heads, as well as a sword from Fiji, crocodiles, stuffed birds, swordfish spears, and a matapee on the walls and above the massive stone fireplaces. Thoughtful touches include piles of smart magazines, tasty nibbles and chestnuts to roast. It's appealing outside too, with plenty of seats, flowerbeds and fruit trees in the sheltered side and back gardens. Shrubs help divide the garden into various areas, so it doesn't feel too crowded even when it's full. Greene King Old Speckled Hen, Harveys and a guest such as Shepherd Neame Master Brew are well kept on handpump, and they've also three farm ciders, a decent wine list, several malt whiskies, a range of local fruit juices, and mulled wine in the winter. Besides a dozen or so good lunchtime snacks such as spiced chicken and plum sauce on an open sandwich, ploughman's, battered cod or antipasti (£5.95-£7.95), very good food might include soup (£4.95), wild boar pâté (£6.95), steak and kidney pudding (£9.95), thai green curry (£10.95), cod fillet with lemon and herb crust and asparagus and red pepper sauce (£11.95), fried pork fillet with bacon and cream sauce (£12.95), sirloin steak (£15.95), and puddings such as chocolate pudding with chocolate sauce (£4.50); swift and friendly service. *(Recommended by B J Harding, Steve Godfrey, Mrs C Lintott, Derek Harvey-Piper, Alan Sadler, Bob and Margaret Holder, Oliver and Sue Rowell, Vanessa Stilwell, Andrea Rampley, Pete Walker, Richard Smye, M Sage, Mrs Susan Powell, Simon and Amanda Southwell, Ellen Weld, David London, John and Elizabeth Cox, Martin and Sue Day, Sue Demont, Tim Barrow)*

Enterprise ~ Lease Liz and David Currie ~ Real ale ~ Bar food (12-10) ~ (01732) 700254 ~ Children in eating area of bar ~ Dogs welcome ~ folk Weds evenings ~ Open 11-11

BOYDEN GATE TR2265 Map 3
Gate Inn ★ ♀ ◀ £

Off A299 Herne Bay—Ramsgate – follow Chislet, Upstreet signpost opposite Roman Gallery; Chislet also signposted off A28 Canterbury—Margate at Upstreet – after turning right into Chislet main street keep right on to Boyden; the pub gives its address as Marshside, though Boyden Gate seems more usual on maps

The lovely setting of this refreshingly down-to-earth old-fashioned pub is one of the things that makes it special. The sheltered hollyhock flowered garden is bounded by two streams, with tame ducks and geese (they sell bags of food, 10p), and on fine summer evenings, you can hear the contented quacking of a multitude of ducks and geese, coots and moorhens out on the marshes. The comfortably worn interior is properly pubby, with an inglenook log fire serving both the well worn quarry-tiled rooms, flowery-cushioned pews around tables of considerable character, hop bines hanging from the beams and attractively etched windows. Well kept Shepherd Neame Bishops Finger, Master Brew, Spitfire and a seasonal ale are tapped from the cask by the long-standing landlord, and you can also get interesting bottled beers, a fine range of 17 wines by the glass, and country wines; shove-ha'penny, dominoes and cribbage. Straightforward bar food includes sandwiches (from £3), home-made soup (£3.50), lots of different baguettes, baked potatoes and ploughman's (£3.60-£5.50), salads or spicy hotpots (£5.95) and ice-cream sundaes (£2.80). The eating area is no smoking at lunchtime. *(Recommended by*

Bob Richardson, Kevin Thorpe, Andrea Rampley, Bruce Eccles, B and M Kendall, Alan and Paula McCully, Louise English)

Shepherd Neame ~ Tenant Christopher Smith ~ Real ale ~ Bar food (12-2, 6(7 Sun)-8.45) ~ No credit cards ~ (01227) 860498 ~ Well behaved children in eating area of bar and family room ~ Dogs welcome ~ Open 11-2.30(3 Sat), 6-11; 12-4, 7-10.30 Sun

BROOKLAND TQ9724 Map 3

Woolpack £

On A259 from Rye, about a mile before Brookland, take the first right turn signposted Midley where the main road bends sharp left, just after the expanse of Walland Marsh; OS Sheet 189 map reference 977244

This pretty 15th-c white cottage with its low pitched tiled roof has plenty of marshland character. The ancient entrance lobby has an uneven brick floor and black-painted pine-panelled walls. To the right, the simple quarry tiled main bar has basic cushioned plank seats in the massive inglenook fireplace (with a lovely log fire on chilly days), a painted wood-effect bar counter hung with lots of water jugs, some very early ships' timbers (maybe 12th-c) in the low-beamed ceiling, a long elm table with shove-ha'penny carved into one end, other old and newer wall benches, chairs at mixed tables with flowers and candles, and photographs of locals on the walls. To the left of the lobby is a sparsely furnished little room, and an open-plan games room has a central hearth, modern bar counter, and fruit machine; piped music. Fairly priced and well kept Shepherd Neame Master Brew, Spitfire and a seasonal beer on handpump; look out for the two pub cats Liquorice and Charlie Girl. Big helpings of bar food, from a reasonably priced menu, include sandwiches (from £2.75), good soup (£3.50), ploughman's (£5.95), steak pie, battered cod, chilli or stilton and vegetable bake (all £5.95), grilled trout (£8.25), lamb shank (£8.45), sirloin steak (£12.45), and puddings such as apple crumble or cherry pie (£3.75). The big garden has plenty of picnic-sets, well developed shrubs, and pretty hanging baskets; it's all nicely lit up in the evenings. *(Recommended by Andrea Rampley, Paul A Moore, Kevin Thorpe, Conor McGaughey, Christopher Turner, B and M Kendall, V Brogden, Jeremy Woods, Stephen C Harvey, Louise English)*

Shepherd Neame ~ Tenant Barry Morgan ~ Real ale ~ Bar food (12-2, 7-9; 12-9 Sat, Sun) ~ (01797) 344321 ~ Children in family room ~ Dogs welcome ~ Open 11-3, 6-11; 11-11 Sat; 12-10.30 Sun

CHIDDINGSTONE TQ4944 Map 3

Castle Inn ♀

Village signposted from B2027 Tonbridge—Edenbridge

It's worth a wander round this National Trust village, to take in the picturesque cluster of unspoilt Tudor houses, amongst which this cosy rambling old pub (an inn since 1730) fits so beautifully. All this prettiness, and being just round the corner from Chiddingstone Castle, does mean this is something of a tourist destination, so it's maybe best avoided at peak times, when there can be a wait and service can be variable. The handsome, carefully modernised beamed bar has well made settles forming booths around the tables, cushioned sturdy wall benches, an attractive mullioned window seat in one small alcove, and latticed windows (a couple of areas are no smoking); darts, shove-ha'penny, dominoes and cribbage. There are tables in front of the building facing the church, with more in the pretty secluded vine-hung garden. Alongside an impressive wine list they have well kept Larkins Traditional and in winter Porter too (both brewed in the village), along with Harveys Best and a guest on handpump, and a good range of malt whiskies. Lunchtime bar food includes open sandwiches (from £5.25), ploughman's (£7.55) and curry, chilli or pasta of the day (£6.15). The evening bar menu (three courses £17.50), goes up a notch or two, and includes mushroom and mediterranean tart (£6.45), smoked salmon and cream cheese (£6.45), baked salmon with honey and oyster sauce (£11.45), sirloin steak with mushroom and thyme sauce (£12.95) and puddings such as warm pineapple torte or rum and chocolate tart (£5.75). The licensees publish three circular walks from the village. *(Recommended by Andrea Rampley, Roy and Lindsey Fentiman, Mrs B M Hill, B and M Kendall, Mrs C Lintott, Tony and Margaret Cross)*

Free house ~ Licensee Nigel Lucas ~ Real ale ~ Bar food (11-6, 7-9.30) ~ Restaurant ~ (01892) 870247 ~ Children welcome away from public bar ~ Dogs welcome ~ Open 11-11; 12-10.30 Sun

DARGATE TR0761 Map 3
Dove 🍴 🍷
Village signposted from A299

Kent Dining Pub of the Year

It's almost essential to book a table (probably some time in advance), even if you only want to pop in for a snack at this tucked-away, well run dining pub. It is worth the effort though, as the restaurant-style food is terribly good. Lunchtime snacks include sandwiches (£4.25), warm salad of marinated chicken with mint or caramelised pork with stir-fried vegetables (£7.95), served alongside a more elaborate menu that includes dishes such as confit of duck leg with roasted black pudding (£14.95), fried loin of beef with a confit of new potatoes, lardons and mushrooms (£18.99), and grilled bass with a garlic and herb dressing (£19.99); one reader would have preferred an itemised bill. The very friendly landlady ensures a relaxed welcoming atmosphere in the charmingly unspoilt airy rambling rooms, which have flowers on stripped wood tables, photographs of the pub and its licensees throughout the past century on the walls, a good winter log fire, and plenty of seats on the bare boards; piped classical music. Well kept Shepherd Neame Master Brew on handpump. Lovely in fine weather, the sheltered garden has roses, lilacs, peonies and many other flowers, picnic-table sets under pear trees, a dovecote with white doves, a rockery and pool, and a swing. The pub is set down a network of narrow lanes in a quiet hamlet. A bridlepath leads up from the pub (along the quaintly-named Plumpudding Lane) into Blean Wood. *(Recommended by Jonathan Lane, Andrea Rampley, M A and C R Starling, Ian Phillips, Richard Siebert, Philip Denton, Uta and John Owlett, Kevin Thorpe, W Andrew, Clive Flynn)*

Shepherd Neame ~ Tenants Nigel and Bridget Morris ~ Real ale ~ Bar food (not Sun or Tues evening) ~ Restaurant ~ (01227) 751360 ~ Children in eating area of bar ~ Dogs allowed in bar ~ Open 12-3, 6-11.30(7-11 Sun); closed Mon (except bank hols, when they close Tues instead)

DEAL TR3752 Map 3
Kings Head
Beach Street, just off A258 seafront roundabout

You may want to pick your moment to visit this handsome three-storey seaside Georgian inn, that is if you prefer to avoid the lively younger crowd who gather here on Friday and Saturday nights (and may be playing on the games machines in the daytime too). Forming part of a pretty terrace (there are picnic sets out here), the pub is just across the road from the promenade and the sea, and is quite a sight in summer when it's festooned with brightly coloured hanging baskets and window boxes. Four comfortable bar rooms work their way round a central servery, and the walls (partly stripped masonry) are decorated with marine architectural drawings, maritime and local pictures and charts, and other material underlining connections with the Royal and Merchant navies; another area has an interesting collection of cricket memorabilia. There are a couple of warming flame-effect gas fires, and it can get smoky. Well kept real ales might include Fullers London Pride, Harveys Sussex and Shepherd Neame Master Brew on handpump; piped music, TV (which one reader found a bit loud) and darts. Generous helpings of straightforward bar food include sandwiches and filled baguettes (from £2.75), omelettes (from £4), ploughman's (£5.95), dressed crab (£6.95), chicken and leek pie or brie and redcurrant tart (£7.95) and sirloin steak (£9.95); two-course Sunday lunch (£8.95). Beware that traffic wardens here are vigilant during the week: there's pay-and-display (two-hour limit parking opposite, and another (three-hour limit) just a few minutes' walk away. *(Recommended by B J Harding, Michael Dandy, Mike Ridgway, Sarah Miles, Mike and Lynn Robinson, Christopher Turner, Geoff and Molly Betteridge)*

Courage (S & N) ~ Lease Graham Stiles and Shirley Russell ~ Real ale ~ Bar food (11.30-2.30, 6-9) ~ (01304) 368194 ~ Open 10.30-11; 12-10.30 Sun ~ Bedrooms: £45B/£59B

ELHAM TR1743 Map 3
Rose & Crown
High Street

This characterful, partly 16th-c inn has recently been taken over by Shepherd Neame, so we're keeping our fingers crossed. Ancient low beams, uneven floors, and big fires in an inglenook fireplace give a real sense of age, and comfy furnishings an informal atmosphere. A couple of low red plush settees make the most of its open woodburning stove, and a homely couple of armchairs stands by a table with daily newspapers (there's a pile of guide books in another corner); fruit machine. The serving bar, in a smallish area on the right, serves four beers from Shepherd Neame on handpumps, and eight wines by the glass. Over on the left, not much bigger, a pleasant mix of seats and tables shares the space with the settees; it's carpeted throughout. Bar food includes lunchtime ciabattas (not Sunday) such as chargrilled mediterranean vegetables (£6.50) and fried cajun strips (£6.25), with changing specials such as soup (£3.95) and gravadlax (£5.25), roast peppers stuffed with couscous with tomato and coriander sauce (£8.95), liver and bacon (£9.50), steak and kidney pudding or salmon on samphire (£9.95), dressed crab (£11.50), and puddings such as spotted dick or Drambuie trifle (£4.95). Along a passage on the right, decorated with china and bookshelves, is the neat no smoking restaurant, and a flagstoned back terrace has teak tables, chairs and benches. This is a charming village, with a few antiques shops and so forth, in what is perhaps Kent's prettiest valley. *(Recommended by Kevin Thorpe, Peter Heaton, David Barnes, Peter Meister, Catherine and Rob Dunster)*

Shepherd Neame ~ Managers Alison and Patrick Clark ~ Real ale ~ Bar food (12-2, 7-9.30) ~ Restaurant ~ (01303) 840226 ~ Children welcome ~ Dogs welcome ~ Open 11-3, 7-11; 12-11 Sat; 12-10.30 Sun ~ Bedrooms: £55S/£70S

FORDCOMBE TQ5240 Map 3
Chafford Arms
B2188, off A264 W of Langton Green

Creepers and colourful hanging baskets, against a backdrop of carefully tended shrubs and perennials, cascading down the front of this friendly tile-hung old pub give it a gloriously tempting appearance. Inside it's simpler and more spacious than you'd expect, with neatly set apart tables and comfortable seats on a turkey carpet, and minimal décor. Towards the close of the evening, as the dining side winds down, the quite separate public bar, full of sporting memorabilia and trophies, often gets much busier with locals popping in for a drink; darts, cribbage, shove-ha'penny, dominoes, TV and fruit machine. Larkins and Wadworths 6X are well kept on handpump, and they've decent house wines and mulled wine. Straightforward bar food might include sandwiches (from £3.95), home-made soup (£3.75), salads (from £5.95), vegetarian quiche (£6.95), chicken or scampi and chips (£7.45), and grilled trout or gammon and pineapple (£9.45); on Tuesday evenings they do two rib-eye steaks for the price of one, and curry and a pint (£7.50) on Thursday night. Most of the flowers are in front but there's a pleasant sheltered lawn behind with an attractive shrubbery and arbours. If you eat in the garden they will keep your credit card behind the bar. Thankfully, as this is on the Wealdway walking route, the landlord doesn't mind muddy boots, and dogs are welcome too. *(Recommended by Gwyn Jones, Jonathan Shephard, Fr Robert Marsh, Mrs C Lintott, Andrea Rampley, Peter Meister, Angus Johnson, Carol Bolden)*

Enterprise ~ Lease Barrie Leppard ~ Real ale ~ Bar food (not Sun evening in winter and
Mon evenings) ~ Restaurant ~ (01892) 740267 ~ Children in eating area of bar and
restaurant ~ Dogs welcome ~ Jazz third Sun evening of month, folk club fourth Sun of
month ~ Open 11.45-11; 11-11 Sat; 12-10.30 Sun

GROOMBRIDGE TQ5337 Map 3
Crown
B2110

Picnic-sets out in front on a wonky but sunny brick terrace – we even managed an
hour out here on a nice January day – look down over the steep village green, and
just into the lovely grounds of next-door Groombridge Place Gardens. This
characterful tile-hung old smugglers' haunt is prettily set at the end of a row of
picturesque cottages – all with the same colour green front doors. When it got too
chilly outside we went into the snug room on the left and sat at an old table on
worn flagstones by the big brick inglenook with its cosy log fire – arrive early for a
table in here. It can get a little smoky in the low-beamed rooms, which are nicely
ancient feeling, with roughly plastered walls, some squared panelling and timbering,
and a quite a bit of bric-a-brac, from old teapots and pewter tankards to antique
bottles. Walls are decorated with small topographical, game and sporting prints,
and a circular large-scale map with the pub at its centre. The no smoking end room
(normally for eaters) has fairly close-spaced tables with a variety of good solid
chairs, and a log-effect gas fire in a big fireplace. From the long copper-topped bar
counter, they serve Greene King Abbot and IPA, Harveys and Larkins on
handpump; shove-ha'penny, dominoes, cribbage and Scrabble. Served by friendly
staff, straightforward but tasty bar food includes lunchtime soup (£3.95), open
sandwiches (from £5.75), ploughman's (£6.50), sausage and mash (£7.90) and
battered cod (£8.80), while in the evening you might find antipasti (£5.25), steak
and ale pie or fisherman's pie (£7.90), cannelloni with spinach and ricotta with
cheese sauce (£7.95) and 10oz sirloin steak (£14.60). A public footpath across the
road beside the small chapel leads through a field to Groombridge Place Gardens.
*(Recommended by B J Harding, Michael and Ann Cole, Andrea Rampley, Peter Meister,
Liz and Tony Colman, Mrs C Lintott, Tina and David Woods-Taylor, Fr Robert Marsh,
Grahame Brooks)*

Free house ~ Licensee Peter Kilshaw ~ Real ale ~ Bar food (12-3, 7-9; not Sun evening) ~
Restaurant ~ (01892) 864742 ~ Children welcome ~ Dogs allowed in bar ~ Open 11-3,
6-11; 11-11 Sat; 12-10.30 Sun; 11-3, 6-11 Sat, 12-3, 7-10.30 Sun in winter ~ Bedrooms:
£40/£45(£60S)

HAWKHURST TQ7630 Map 3
Queens   .
Rye Road (A268 E)

There's something for almost everyone at this efficiently run wisteria-covered
Georgian fronted inn, whether it's a hearty breakfast (from 8.30am), a pint at the
bar, a tasty meal, a drink listening to live jazz at the weekend, or afternoon tea. The
spreading interior has been sensitively opened up and appealingly decorated in
keeping with its age (it was first recorded as an inn in the 16th c). Light filters in
through lush creepers that threaten to cover the old sash windows above comfy
fireside sofas at the front. Further in, the mood is wine bar-ish: terracotta, sand or
pea-green colourwashes give an airy feel despite the heavy low beams, and there's a
nice mix of old oak tables (pleasantly candlelit at night) on bare boards with plenty
of scattered rugs; piped music. Around to the right, the piano bar is where they
have the live music and serve breakfast and teas; there are newspapers to read.
Friendly staff serve well kept Fullers London Pride and Harveys Best on handpump.
Bar food includes sandwiches and filled baguettes or soup (£4.95), ploughman's
(£5.95), antipasti (£7.25), pizzas (around £9), beer-battered haddock or tagliatelle
with artichoke, peppers, peas and pesto (£9.95), steak and ale pie (£10.95), baked
black bream (£11.95), niçoise salad with grilled tuna (£12.95), 8oz fillet steak

(£16.95), a handful of daily specials, and puddings such as banoffi pie, pear and apple crumble or bread and butter pudding (£4.95); Sunday carvery (£8.95). Two eating rooms are no smoking. There are tables on decking at the front, and more in a side courtyard. *(Recommended by Ann and Colin Hunt, Susan and John Douglas, M Sage, Mayur Shah)*

Enterprise ~ Lease Janelle Tresidder ~ Real ale ~ Bar food (8.30am-9.30(10 Fri, Sat)) ~ Restaurant ~ (01580) 753577 ~ Blues Fri evening, pianist Sat evening, Jazz Sun lunchtime ~ Open 8.30am-11(12 Sat, 10.30 Sun) ~ Bedrooms: £50S/£85S

HOLLINGBOURNE TQ8354 Map 3

Windmill ♀

A mile from M20 junction 8: A20 towards Ashford (away from Maidstone), then left into B2163 – Eyhorne Street village

This welcoming dining pub (it's pretty much set for food throughout) is one more in a slow but steady trickle of places to make the change to no smoking throughout. Tucked up one or two steps towards the back, the island serving bar, with its bar stools, well kept Flowers IPA, Greene King K&B, Shepherd Neame Masterbrew and seven wines by the glass, does give it a pubby core. Under heavy low black beams, several small or smallish mainly carpeted areas link together around this core, sometimes partly separated by glazed or stained-glass panels; the solid pub tables have padded country or library chairs. Soft lighting, black timbers in ochre walls, shelves of books and the good log fire in the huge inglenook fireplace (was that someone's leg we saw dangling down the chimney?) add up to a pleasantly old-world feel. The wide choice of enjoyable food includes good weekday lunchtime sandwiches (from £3.95, sirloin steak £5.95), baguettes or filled baked potatoes (£5.95), liver and bacon or roast red pepper salad (£8.95), steaks (from £8.95) and cajun spiced chicken (£9.95) and daily specials such as knuckle of lamb with wholegrain mustard sauce (£12.75), cod fillet with cheese and parsley sauce (£12.95), and duck confit (£13.95) and puddings such as bread and butter pudding or treacle tart (£4.25); vegetables are fresh and plentiful. The good choice of reasonably priced wines come in two glass sizes. Service is friendly and punctilious, quick even at busy times – and they make young children feel really at home; piped music. A neatly kept sunny little garden has picnic-sets under cocktail parasols, and a play area; the village has a good many handsome buildings. *(Recommended by Peter and Giff Bennett, Alison and Graham Hooper, John Branston)*

Enterprise ~ Lease Graham and Deana Godmon ~ Real ale ~ Bar food (12-2.30, 6-10; 12-10 (9.30 Sun) Sat, Sun) ~ Restaurant ~ (01622) 880280 ~ Children welcome ~ Open 11-3, 6-11; 11-11 Sat; 12-10.30 Sun

HUCKING TQ8458 Map 3

Hook & Hatchet ♀

3½ miles from M2 junction 5; A249 towards Maidstone, then after a mile turn left at Hucking signpost into narrow lane; Church Road

This isolated country pub stands alone on the edge of the Woodland Trust's Hucking Estate, nearly a square mile of woods, farmland and downland now open to the public (free), with plenty of interesting walks – the pub gives away a useful map. Inside, the pub is a haven of civilised comfort. Around a central chimneypiece with fireplaces each side, a variety of well spaced seats spreads over broad polished boards, from a leather armchair and low sofa covered with bright scatter-cushions to pews, cushioned stools and chairs around sturdy tables. There are one or two pictures on the smooth pink walls, varnished joists in the cream ceiling, and comfortable backed seats along the long rather smart bar counter, with its well kept Fullers London Pride, Shepherd Neame Spitfire and a guest on handpump (served in lined glasses); they have a good choice of wines by the glass. One reader found the piped local radio a bit intrusive; dominoes. Bar food includes soup (£3.75), grilled prawns (£6.50), baked stuffed aubergine (£7.50), duck breast with chinese spices and plum sauce (£11.50) and rib-eye steak with wild mushrooms and madeira (£15.95). The softly lit no smoking dining room has high-backed settles forming intimate booths around some of its tables, and another side area is also no smoking. There are tables out on a heated verandah, and lots of picnic-sets in the carefully laid out garden, and a field with plenty of space for children to let off steam in. Two nice touches: the boot-washing tap, and what is certainly the best pub hitching rail for visiting horses that we've seen (they also encourage customers to debox here – with notice). *(Recommended by Rupert Reeves, Philip and Cheryl Hill, David Randall)*

Free house ~ Licensee Christopher Bish ~ Real ale ~ Bar food (12-2.30, 6.30-9.30(9 Mon); not Sun evening) ~ (01622) 880830 ~ Children welcome until 7pm ~ Dogs allowed in bar ~ Open 12-11(10.30 Sun)

IDEN GREEN TQ8031 Map 3
Woodcock

Iden Green is signposted off A268 E of Hawkhurst and B2086 at W edge of Benenden; in village at crossroads by bus shelter follow Standen Street signpost, then fork left just before the orchard down Woodcock Lane (maybe a signpost to pub here) – beware that there is an entirely different Iden Green just 10 miles away near Goudhurst

This friendly little country pub is tucked away down lanes on the edge of Standen Wood. Snugly comfortable, and bustling with cheery locals, the little flagstoned bar has stripped brick walls and very low ceilings bearing down heavily on a couple of big standing timbers. A battered old sofa and armchairs are snugly huddled by a warming woodburning stove, and chunky big old pine tables are tucked snugly into little nooks; darts, TV, shove-ha'penny, and piped local radio. Enthusiastic young staff serve well kept Greene King IPA, Abbot, and Old Speckled Hen, and a changing guest on handpump. Generously served, enjoyable bar food includes baguettes (from £4.50), ploughman's (£5.95), burgers (from £6.95), fish and chips (£7.50), pies or lambs liver (£7.95), and puddings such as home-made crème brûlée (£3.95); you may need to book at weekends when it can get very busy. The partly panelled dining area opens on to a verandah, and there are seats in the pretty side garden. The car park is across the narrow lane. More reports please. *(Recommended by Susan and John Douglas, Ann and Colin Hunt, Fr Robert Marsh, John E Field, Mr and Mrs S Wilson, Nigel and Olga Wikeley, Christopher Turner)*

Greene King ~ Lease Terry & Wendy Peachey ~ Real ale ~ Bar food ~ Restaurant ~ (01580) 240009 ~ Children in eating area of bar ~ Dogs allowed in bar ~ Open 11-11; 12-10.30 Sun

IGHTHAM COMMON TQ5755 Map 3
Harrow 🍴 ♀
Signposted off A25 just W of Ightham; pub sign may be hard to spot

The charming attention to detail at this civilised country inn – daily papers, fresh flowers, and candles on the tables – suggests a thoughtful landlady's touch. Two attractively decorated rooms, both warmed by log fires in winter, have assorted country furniture on nice old brick flooring or black and white squared vinyl, the bigger room is painted a cheerful sunny yellow above dark green dado. A lush grapevine grows around the delightful little antiquated conservatory, which leads off an elegant no smoking dining room laid with white cloths. With plenty of rewarding wines by the glass, there's a decent sensibly priced wine list, and Greene King IPA and Abbot are well kept on handpump. The interesting menu changes constantly, but might include soup (£4.95), crab and ginger spring rolls or pâté (£5.95), sausages and mash (£7.95), tagliatelle with spinach and wild mushrooms or beef and Guinness pie (£9.95), salmon and chive fishcake with lemon butter sauce (£10.95), roast lamb shank with red wine jus (£11.95), and beef sirloin with cracked peppercorn sauce (£13.95), and puddings such as orange and Cointreau tiramisu (£4.50). There are tables and chairs out on a pretty little pergola-enclosed back terrace, and this is handy for Ightham Mote. *(Recommended by Derek Thomas, Andrea Rampley, John Evans, Mrs C Lintott, Susan and John Douglas, M and GR,*

Colin and Stephanie McFie, David Twitchett, Oliver and Sue Rowell, Andy Barker,
Claire Jenkins, M Sage, Catherine and Richard Preston, Comus and Sarah Elliott)

Free house ~ Licensees John Elton and Claire Butler ~ Real ale ~ Bar food (12-2, 6-9) ~ Restaurant ~ (01732) 885912 ~ Children in family room ~ Open 12-3, 6-11; closed Sun evening, and Mon

LANGTON GREEN TQ5538 Map 3

Hare ♀

A264 W of Tunbridge Wells

The front bar (piped music here) of this thriving Edwardian roadside pub is still well liked by drinkers, with the other rooms given over to a pleasantly chatty dining atmosphere. The knocked-through interior has big windows and high ceilings, giving a spaciously civilised feel. Décor, more or less in period with the building, runs from dark-painted dados below light walls, 1930s oak furniture, and turkey carpets on stained wooden floors to old romantic pastels, and a huge collection of chamber-pots hanging from one beam. Interesting old books, pictures and two huge mahogany mirror-backed display cabinets crowd the walls of the big room at the back, which has lots of large tables (one big enough for at least a dozen) on a light brown carpet; from here french windows open onto picnic-sets on a big terrace, and pretty views of the tree-ringed village green; shove-ha'penny, cribbage and dominoes. A good choice of bar food, very handily served all day, might include soup (£3.95), caramelised red onion, artichoke and cheese tart (£5.75), hot roast beef roll (£5.95), smoked salmon with potato and chive salad (£6.95), ploughman's (£7.25), courgette risotto cakes with tomato chutney (£8.95), hake hotpot (£12.95), braised shoulder of lamb with red wine sauce (£13.95) and puddings such as treacle tart (£4.25) and white chocolate mousse and preserved figs (£4.95). Greene King IPA and Abbot are well kept alongside a couple of guests such as Greene King Old Speckled Hen on handpump, they have lots of wines by the glass, and over 50 malt whiskies; no smoking, except in the bar. Parking is limited so get here early, and you may need to book. *(Recommended by M and D J Hill, Gillian Rogers, B J Harding, Oliver and Sue Rowell, Derek Thomas, Mrs C Lintott, Comus and Sarah Elliott, Peter Meister)*

Brunning & Price ~ Tenant Christopher Little ~ Real ale ~ Bar food (12-9.30) ~ (01892) 862419 ~ Children in eating area till 7pm ~ Dogs allowed in bar ~ Open 11-11; 12-10.30 Sun

NEWNHAM TQ9557 Map 3

George

The Street; village signposted from A2 just W of Ospringe, outside Faversham

The lovely interior of this characterfully atmospheric place remains unchanged under its new licensees. A series of spreading open plan rooms has hop-strung beams, rugs on polished floorboards, stripped brickwork, gas-type chandeliers, open fires and candles and lamps on handsome tables, with attractively upholstered mahogany settles. Three Shepherd Neame Master beers are well kept on handpump alongside ten wines by the glass; piped music. Bar food includes lunchtime sandwiches or baguettes (from £3.50), filled baked potatoes (from £5.25) and ploughman's (from £5.75), vegetable curry or steak and kidney pudding (£8.95), with changing specials such as calves liver with smoked bacon and wild mushroom and red wine sauce (£13.95), half shoulder of lamb with mint and coriander gravy or bass fillets with fresh asparagus and hollandaise (£14.95), and home-made puddings such as cherry roly-poly and banoffi pie (£4.35); no smoking restaurant. The spacious sheltered garden has some picnic-sets, and there are pleasant nearby walks. *(Recommended by Jonathan Lane, Philip Denton, Dr Danny Nicol, Fr Robert Marsh, David and Ruth Shillitoe, M Sage, Anthony Barnes, Colin Christie)*

Shepherd Neame ~ Tenants Chris and Marie Annand ~ Real ale ~ Bar food ~ Restaurant ~ (01795) 890237 ~ Children welcome ~ Open 11-3, 6.30-11; 12-3.30, 7-10.30 Sun

OARE TR0163 Map 3

Shipwrights Arms ◖ £

S shore of Oare Creek, E of village; coming from Faversham on the Oare road, turn right into Ham Road opposite Davington School; or off A2 on B2045, go into Oare village, then turn right towards Faversham, and then left into Ham Road opposite Davington School; OS Sheet 178 map reference 016635

This charmingly unspoilt 17th-c fisherman's tavern is the place to go if you want to sample Kent-brewed beers, and tapped straight from the cask at that. As well as two or three kentish guests, they keep one each from Goachers, Hopdaemon and Whitstable Oyster Brewery Company. Stuck nicely out in the middle of nowhere, and 3ft below sea level, the pub is situated in the middle of marshland with lots of birdlife. An interesting approach is to walk from the village through the tangle of boatyard, or you can moor a boat in the creek which runs just below the Saxon Shore Way (up a bank from the front and back gardens of the pub). Three simple little bars are dark and cosy, and separated by standing timbers and wood part-partitions or narrow door arches. A medley of seats runs from tapestry cushioned stools and chairs to black wood-panelled built-in settles forming little booths, pewter tankards over the bar counter, boating jumble and pictures, pottery boating figures, flags or boating pennants on the ceilings, several brick fireplaces, and a good woodburning stove. Look out for the electronic wind gauge above the main door, which takes its reading from the chimney; may be piped local radio; cribbage and dominoes. Reasonably priced bar food includes sandwiches (from £2.95), ploughman's or burger and chips (£5.95), sausage and mash (£6.45), vegetable tikka masala (£6.75), battered cod (£6.95), with puddings such as bread and butter pudding or cherry pancakes (from £3.50); the eating area is no smoking. Parking can be difficult at busy times. *(Recommended by the Didler, Andrea Rampley, Richard Siebert, Keith and Chris O'Neill, Kevin Thorpe, Louise English, B and M Kendall, N R White)*

Free house ~ Licensees Derek and Ruth Cole ~ Real ale ~ Bar food (12-2.30, 7-9; not Sun evening, not Mon) ~ Restaurant ~ (01795) 590088 ~ Children welcome if seated ~ Dogs allowed in bar ~ Open 11(12 Sun)-3(4 Sat), 6-11; closed Mon in winter

PENSHURST TQ5243 Map 3

Bottle House ⑪

Coldharbour Lane, Smarts Hill; leaving Penshurst SW on B2188 turn right at Smarts Hill signpost, then bear right towards Chiddingstone and Cowden; keep straight on

Still doing very well at the moment, this welcoming pub very usefully serves food all day, and even better still, the very extensive range of well cooked dishes means you can't fail to find something you like. Served by friendly attentive staff (who remain unflustered even when it gets busy), the daily changing menu could include soup (£3.95), grilled sardines (£4.95), pork, apple and calvados pâté (£5.25), crispy duck spring rolls with chilli jam (£5.50), ploughman's, cod and chips or brie and tomato filo parcel (£8.95), steak and kidney pie (£10.95), chicken breast stuffed with stilton and wrapped in parma ham (£11.95), beef bourguignon with garlic mash or thai monkfish and king prawn curry (£12.95) and grilled bass with ginger, spring onion and lemon sauce (£13.95). On weekdays, if you eat between 5 and 6.30, you get a 25% discount. Very neatly kept, the low-beamed front bar has a well worn brick floor that extends behind the polished copper-topped bar counter, and big windows look on to a terrace with climbing plants and hanging baskets around picnic-sets under cocktail parasols, and beyond to views of quiet fields and oak trees. The simply decorated red-carpeted main bar has massive hop-covered supporting beams, two large stone pillars with a small brick fireplace (with a stuffed turtle to one side), and old paintings and photographs on mainly plastered walls; quite a collection of china pot lids, with more in the no smoking low-ceilinged dining room. Several cosy little areas lead off the main bar – all can be booked for private parties; one room is covered in sporting pictures right up to the ceiling, and another has pictures of dogs. Harveys and Larkins are well kept on handpump, and they stock local wines; unobtrusive piped music. Good surrounding walks. *(Recommended by Mrs C Lintott, Bob and Margaret Holder, Alan Sadler, Sean and Sharon Pines, Gwyn Jones, Tina and David Woods-Taylor, Mrs G Bolton, Humphry and Angela Crum Ewing, R B Gardiner, Jason Caulkin, Derek and Maggie Washington)*

Free house ~ Licensees Gordon and Val Meer ~ Real ale ~ Bar food (12-9.30 Sun) ~ Restaurant ~ (01892) 870306 ~ Children welcome ~ Dogs allowed in bar ~ Open 11-11; 12-10.30 Sun

PLUCKLEY TQ9243 Map 3

Dering Arms 🍴 ♀

Pluckley Station, which is signposted from B2077; The Grove

Skilfully cooked by the long-standing licensee, the menu at this striking old dutch-gabled stone hunting lodge is sensibly short, with a good share of it given over to fresh fish dishes: soup (£4.25), provençale fish soup or grilled sardines with rosemary butter (£5.25), half a dozen irish oysters (£6), pie of the day (£9.45), leg of lamb steak with peppers, black olives and saffron on couscous (£12.95), whole crab salad, tuna steak with garlic and lemon butter or confit of duck (£14.95), fillet of black bream with marsh samphire and beurre blanc (£14.95), fried scallops with basil spaghetti and saffron sauce (£15.95), and puddings such as white chocolate mousse with orange and Cointreau coulis (£4.85). The stylishly plain high-ceilinged main bar has a solid country feel, with a variety of good wooden furniture on stone floors, a roaring log fire in the great fireplace, country prints and some fishing rods; dominoes, cribbage and shove-ha'penny. The smaller half-panelled back bar has similar dark wood furnishings, and an extension to this area has a woodburning stove, comfortable armchairs and sofas, and a grand piano. The extensive wine list is very good; also well kept Goachers Gold Star and Dering Ale, home-made lemonade, local cider and quite a few malt whiskies. The big simple bedrooms have old ad hoc furnishings and breakfasts are good. Classic car meetings (the landlord has a couple) are held here on the second Sunday of the month, and they have regular special events such as wine tasting evenings, summer garden parties and black tie dinners. *(Recommended by Andrea Rampley, Oliver and Sue Rowell, Anthony Barnes, Pete Walker, Kevin Thorpe, Mrs Sally Kingsbury, Philip and Cheryl Hill, M Sage, Brian and Ruth Archer, Martin and Sue Day, Louise English)*

Free house ~ Licensee James Buss ~ Real ale ~ Bar food (not Sun evening, not Mon) ~ Restaurant ~ (01233) 840371 ~ Children in eating area of bar, restaurant and family room ~ Dogs allowed in bar and bedrooms ~ Open 11.30(11 Sat)-3, 6-11; 12-3, 7-10.30 Sun; closed 25-27 Dec ~ Bedrooms: £35/£45

Rose & Crown £

Mundy Bois – spelled Monday Boys on some maps – off Smarden Road SW of village centre

Not only is the bar menu at this quietly set pub very good value – so much so that this year we've given them a Bargain Award – it's also tasty food, made with some locally sourced produce, and meats from traditional breeds: soup (£3.50), sandwiches (£3.75), ploughman's (£4.50), cauliflower cheese (£4.95), sausage and mash (£5.50), minted lamb burger and chips, cottage or steak and kidney pie (£5.95), cod and chips (£6.95) and mixed grill (£12.50). You can also eat from the pricier and more elaborate restaurant menu in the bar: rack of lamb on mustard mash with rosemary jus (£12.50) and monkfish fillet with white wine, cream and chive sauce (£13.50). The relaxed Village Bar is friendly and welcoming, with a massive inglenook fireplace (favourite spot of Ted the pub labrador) and chesterfield sofas. This leads on to a little pool room; TV and piped music. Shepherd Neame Master Brew, Wadworths 6X and a guest such as Youngs on handpump, and a sensibly priced wine list (country wines too), plenty of malt whiskies, and farm cider; disabled facilities. There are seats in the rather nice garden, which has a good children's play area and terrace. More reports please. *(Recommended by Peter Farres)*

Free house ~ Licensees Peter and Helen Teare ~ Real ale ~ Bar food ~ Restaurant ~
(01233) 840393 ~ Children in eating area of bar and restaurant ~ Dogs allowed in bar ~
Open 11.30-3, 6-11; 11.30-11 Sat; 12-10.30 Sun

SELLING TR0456 Map 3

Rose & Crown ★

Signposted from exit roundabout of M2 junction 7: keep right on through village and
follow Perry Wood signposts; or from A252 just W of junction with A28 at Chilham
follow Shottenden signpost, then right turn signposted Selling, then right signposted
Perry Wood

You will need to book to be sure of a table at this enjoyably welcoming 16th-c pub
– especially if you're going for their very good Sunday roast beef (£8). Other
sensibly priced tasty bar food includes home-made soup (£3.95), filled rolls (from
£4.50), ploughman's or whitebait (£5), chicken, ham and leek pie or spaghetti
bolognese (£6.50), chicken tikka masala, cod and smoked haddock mornay or
chinese crispy chilli beef (£8.75), daily specials such as caribbean chicken or stilton
and asparagus pancake (all £8.75), and lots of puddings displayed in a cold cabinet
down steps in a small family room (£4). Décor is in keeping with the age of the
building, with soft yellow and red walls, a couple of old-fashioned housekeeper's
chairs by the huge log fireplace (filled in summer with a colourful mass of silk
flowers), other comfortably cushioned seats, hop bines strung from the beams, fresh
flowers by each of the sturdy corner timbers of the central servery and, dotted all
round the pub, an interesting collection of corn-dolly work; steps go down to a
comfortably cottagey no smoking restaurant; cribbage, dominoes and piped music.
Adnams Southwold, Goachers Mild and Harveys Best are well kept on handpump,
along with a guest from a local brewer such as Whitstable Bay Brewery, and local
cider. The informal garden behind is charmingly planted with climbers, ramblers
and colourful plants, a fairy-lit pergola has cartwheel-back benches, and there are
plenty of picnic-sets, a neatly kept children's play area, bat and trap, and a small
aviary. The flowering tubs and hanging baskets in front are pretty too, and the
terrace has outdoor heaters. The pub is surrounded by natural woodland, with
good walking. (Recommended by the Didler, Mike and Shelley Woodroffe, Ian Phillips,
M and R Thomas, Alan Cowell, Mr and Mrs J Hale, Michael and Judy Buckley, M Sage,
Dr Danny Nicol, Peter Meister, Simon and Amanda Southwell)

Free house ~ Licensees Richard and Jocelyn Prebble ~ Real ale ~ Bar food (12-2, 7-9.30;
not Sun or Mon evenings) ~ Restaurant ~ (01227) 752214 ~ Children in restaurant and
family room ~ Dogs allowed in bar ~ Open 11-3, 6.30-11; 12-3, 7-10.30 Sun

SHIPBOURNE TQ5952 Map 3

Chaser

Stumble Hill (A227 N of Tonbridge)

While the attractive porticoed exterior of this prettily placed stone and tile hung
country pub appears largely unchanged, the interior has been completely
transformed. Seemingly stretching on and on, several bustling open-plan areas
(resonating with the clatter of stripped wood floors, an open-plan kitchen, customer
chatter and piped pop music) meander into each other, all converging on a large
central island bar counter. Décor is very comfortably relaxed, with frame to frame
pictures on deepest red and cream walls, stripped pine wainscoting, an eclectic mix
of solid old wood tables (with candles) and chairs, shelves of books, and open fires.
A striking school chapel-like restaurant, right at the back, has dark wood panelling
and a high timber vaulted ceiling. French windows open onto a pleasantly enclosed
central courtyard with teak furniture, big green parasols and outdoor heaters, and a
side garden, with the pretty church rising behind, is nicely enclosed by hedges and
shrubs. As well as sandwiches, very generous helpings of quickly served bar food
might include peach, parma ham, mint and mozzarella salad (£5.95), thai crab
cakes with sweet chilli jam or ploughman's (£6.95), sausage and mash (£7.95),
penne with asparagus, mushroom and spinach with basil pesto or steak burger

(£8.95), seared salmon fillet on sweet pepper and fruit couscous with white wine sauce (£13.75), half shoulder of lamb with brioche herb crust and thyme and redcurrant sauce (£13.95), and puddings such as orange tart with vanilla ice-cream or chocolate brownie with white chocolate sauce (£4.95). No smoking except in bar area. Well kept Greene King IPA and Abbot and a couple of guests such as Fullers ESB and Ruddles County and 15 wines by the glass; cribbage, dominoes. There is a small car park at the back, or you can park in the lane opposite by a delightful green; farmer's market Thursday morning. *(Recommended by Uta and John Owlett, Bob and Margaret Holder, Derek Thomas)*

Whiting & Hammond ~ Manager Darren Som⌂on ~ Real ale ~ Bar food (12-9.30(9 Sun)) ~ Restaurant ~ (01732) 810360 ~ Very well behaved children welcome ~ Dogs allowed in bar ~ Open 11-11; 12-10.30 Sun

SMARDEN TQ8842 Map 3

Chequers

Off A20 in Charing, via Pluckley; or off A274 at Standen just under 1 mile N of its junction with A262; The Street

Now under new licensees, this 14th-c inn is in a pretty village, and is handily open all day. A walkway in the attractive landscaped garden leads to a pond with fish and waterfowl, and there's an arbour with climbing plants. A terrace has nice green metal tables and chairs on the york stone. With a pleasantly relaxed atmosphere and chatty locals, the cosily comfortable bar has well kept Greene King IPA and Abbot Harveys Best on handpump; piped music. Well presented bar food includes filled baguettes and panini (from £5), ploughman's (£6.25), scampi or tagliatelle with tomato and basil (£7.95), salads (from £7.95) and chicken curry or crispy duck stir fry (£8.95). There are elegant reproduction tables and chairs in the dining area; more reports please. *(Recommended by Nick Lawless, Comus and Sarah Elliott, Conor McGaughey, Kevin Thorpe, Philip and Cheryl Hill)*

Free house ~ Licensees Mick and Jan Denny ~ Bar food (12-2.30, 6-9.30) ~ Restaurant ~ (01233) 770217 ~ Children in eating area of bar, restaurant and family room ~ Dogs allowed in bar ~ Open 11-11.30; 12-10.30 Sun ~ Bedrooms: £40S/£80S

SNARGATE TQ9928 Map 3

Red Lion ★ ◖

B2080 Appledore—Brenzett

This unique and completely unspoilt village local is one for the pub connoisseur. In the same family for 93 years, it's little changed since 1890, and is a great favourite with readers. Three perfectly simple little rooms still have their original cream tongue and groove wall panelling, a couple of heavy beams in a sagging ceiling, dark pine Victorian farmhouse chairs on bare boards, lots of old photographs and other memorabilia, and a coal fire; outdoor lavatories, of course. One charming little room, with a frosted glass wall through to the bar and a sash window looking out to a cottage garden, has only two dark pine pews beside two long tables, a couple more farmhouse chairs and a nice old piano stacked with books. Cheerful groups of regulars catch up on local news and play toad in the hole, also darts, shove-ha'penny, cribbage, dominoes, nine men's morris and table skittles. Goachers Light and Mild, and a couple of well kept guests from brewers such as Grand Union and Northumberland are tapped straight from casks on a low rack behind an unusual shop-like marble-topped counter (little marks it out as a bar other than a few glasses on two small shelves, some crisps and half a dozen spirits bottles); you can also get Double Vision cider from nearby Staplehurst, and country wines. They don't serve food, but you're welcome to bring your own. *(Recommended by Nick Lawless, Kevin Thorpe, Andrea Rampley, Gwyn Jones, Pete Walker, Pete Taylor, Mrs C Lintott, the Didler, Pete Baker, Phil and Sally Gorton, Peter Meister, Richard Siebert)*

Free house ~ Licensee Mrs Jemison ~ Real ale ~ No credit cards ~ (01797) 344648 ~ Children in family room ~ Dogs allowed in bar ~ Open 12-3, 7-11(10.30 Sun)

STAPLEHURST TQ7847 Map 3

Lord Raglan £

About 1½ miles from town centre towards Maidstone, turn right off A229 into Chart Hill Road opposite Chart Cars; OS Sheet 188 map reference 785472

The cosy interior of this genuinely friendly country inn is quite compact, with a narrow bar – you walk in almost on top of the counter and chatting locals – widening slightly at one end to a small area with a big log fire in winter (though one reader felt a bit chilly). In the other direction it works its way round to an intimate area at the back, with lots of wine bottles lined up on a low shelf. Low beams are covered with masses of hops, and the mixed collection of comfortably worn dark wood furniture on quite well used dark brown carpet tiles and nice old parquet flooring is mostly 1930s. Cheery staff serve well kept Goachers Light and Harveys Best, along with a guest such as Hogs Back TEA on handpump; a good wine list too, and summer farm cider. A handful of very reasonably priced and jolly tasty bar snacks gain them a Bargain Award this year: sandwiches (from £2.75), ploughman's (£3.95) and sausage, egg and chips, macaroni cheese or chilli (£5.95). The main menu is a bit pricier, with smoked venison and pickled walnut (£5.50), penne with tomatoes, peppers, olives and cheese (£7.50), chicken breast with white wine and mushroom sauce (£8.95), grilled lamb chops or guinea fowl breast with red wine sauce (£9.95), grilled dover sole or fillet steak (£16.50), and home-made puddings such as treacle sponge pudding (£3.95). Small french windows lead out to an enticing little high-hedged terraced area with green plastic tables and chairs, and there are wooden picnic-sets in the side orchard; reasonable wheelchair access. More reports please. *(Recommended by Sue Williams, John Hendy, Fr Robert Marsh, John and Joan Calvert, Martin and Sue Day, Louise English)*

Free house ~ Licensees Andrew and Annie Hutchison ~ Real ale ~ Bar food (12-2.30, 7-10; not Sun) ~ (01622) 843747 ~ Children welcome ~ Dogs welcome ~ Open 12-3, 6.30-11; closed Sun

STODMARSH TR2160 Map 3

Red Lion 🏠

High Street; off A257 just E of Canterbury

The relaxed and welcoming atmosphere of this memorable little pub is very much down to the congenial nature of the slightly eccentric landlord – now in his tenth year here. Full of character, several idiosyncratic rooms wrap themselves around the big island bar. You'll find hops all over the place, wine bottles (some empty and some full) crammed along mantelpieces and along one side of the bar, all manner of paintings and pictures, copper kettles and old cooking implements, well used cookery books, big stone bottles and milk churns, trugs and baskets, old tennis racquets and straw hats, a collection of brass instruments in one area with sheet music all over the walls, and some jazz records; a couple of little stall areas have hop sacks draped over the partitioning. There are green-painted, cushioned mate's chairs around a mix of nice pine tables, lit candles in unusual metal candleholders, fresh flowers on every table and big arrangements on the bars, and high bar stools with cheerful chatting locals. The large cats sit snoozily by the big log fire; piped jazz, and bat and trap. Well kept Greene King IPA, Old Speckled Hen, and a seasonal guest are tapped straight from the cask, and they've a good wine list with several by the glass, excellent summer Pimms and winter mulled wine, and cider. Made using plenty of local produce, big helpings of enjoyable dishes from the regularly changing menu might include baguettes (not Sunday lunch or Saturday evening), baby spinach and streaky bacon and avocado salad (£6.25), hot asparagus with pine nuts and butter (£6.75), potted prawns with smoked wild salmon and dill (£7.25), a mixed platter of meat, fish and cheese (£7.95), pies such as chicken, pigeon breast and asparagus or oak-smoked haddock, salmon and cod with sage mash (£10.95), filo pastry parcels with thai vegetables and hoi sin sauce (£11.95), and rabbit, wild pigeon and pheasant casserole (£12.95), with puddings such as bramley apple pie or strawberry and raspberry mousse with mint (£3.95);

they sell eggs and chutneys. There are picnic-sets under umbrellas in the back garden, with pretty flowerbeds, and roaming chickens and ducks. Please note that the bedrooms, though much enjoyed by readers, don't have their own bathrooms. *(Recommended by Kevin Thorpe, Sean and Sharon Pines, Barry and Patricia Wooding, Ian and Lin Gill, Mike and Linda Hudson, Tom and Ruth Rees, Nick Lawless)*

Free house ~ Licensee Robert Whigham ~ Real ale ~ Bar food (not Sun evening) ~ Restaurant ~ (01227) 721339 ~ Children welcome ~ Dogs allowed in bar ~ Live jazz first Weds in month ~ Open 10.30-11; 12-10.30 Sun ~ Bedrooms: /£60

TUNBRIDGE WELLS TQ5639 Map 3 🏠

Beacon ♀ 🍽️

Tea Garden Lane; leaving Tunbridge Wells westwards on A264, this is the left turn-off on Rusthall Common after Nevill Park

A lively social atmosphere (especially at weekends) fills the opened up rooms of this airy modern conversion of a Victorian pub. Regulars sit chatting at the sweeping bar counter, with its ranks of shiny bottles, or on comfortable sofas by the fine wood fireplace. The dining area and spreading bar run freely into each other, with stripped panelling, lovely wood floors and ornately built wall units giving a solidly comfortable feel. Tucked away on the outskirts of the town and built on the side of a hill, the pub has good views across a gentle valley from the pergola-covered raised wooden deck – the perfect place for an early evening or lunchtime drink. A good choice of ten wines by the glass, Harveys Best, Larkins and Timothy Taylors Landlord are well kept on handpump, and served by cheery professional bar staff; TV, piped music. Besides lunchtime sandwiches (from £4.75), enjoyable bar food might include soup (£4.25), Guinness and chive battered haddock and chips (£7.90), pasta with garlic and mushroom cream (£8.25), 8oz rump steak (£8.50), creamy fruity chicken curry (£9), seafood kebabs on prawn and pea couscous with chilli and saffron dressing (£10.25), lamb bourguignon (£11.25), and good puddings (£4.50). The grounds have footpaths between lakes and springs, as well as summer boules and (very rare for a pub these days) even rounders. *(Recommended by Mrs K J Betts, Mrs C Lintott, Peter Meister, Gwyn Jones, Clare and Peter Pearse, B J Harding, V Brogden, Martin and Sue Day)*

Free house ~ Licensee John Cullen ~ Real ale ~ Bar food (12-9.30(5 Sun); 12-5, 6.30-9.30 in winter) ~ Restaurant ~ (01892) 524252 ~ Dogs allowed in bar and bedrooms ~ Folk club alternate Mon evenings ~ Open 11-11; 12-10.30 Sun ~ Bedrooms: £68.50B/£97B

Sankeys 🍴 ♀

Mount Ephraim (A26 just N of junction with A267)

Lunchtime brings local business people and a buoyantly chatty atmosphere to the downstairs flagstoned brasserie bar (no smoking), at this well run family owned establishment. Big mirrors spread the light, and there are stripped brick walls, pews or chairs around closely spaced sturdy tables, and french windows onto a nice suntrap deck with its solid teak tables and chairs under cocktail parasols (monthly spit roast); flat screen TV. Light and airy with big windows and high ceilings, the street level Town Bar tends to attract a younger crowd (it can get smoky), and has comfortably laid out leather sofas round low tables, pews round pubby tables on bare boards, a wine oriented décor, and a big flat screen TV for Sky sports (the landlord is a keen rugby fan, and runner). We love the fresh fish they serve here, particularly the giant cornish cock crab salad (£16.50). Other dishes include seafood soup (£5), mussels cooked in three ways (from £6), queen scallops grilled with garlic (£6.75), haddock and salmon fishcakes in a garlic spinach sauce (£8.50), rib-eye steak (£11.50), poached halibut with green peppercorn sauce (£13.50), paella (£14), and cold puddings; piped music. A great range of drinks includes Harveys Best and Larkins, well kept on handpump, a very good wine list with about eight by the glass, and an astonishing range of 16 imported draught beers. More reports please. *(Recommended by Dr David Cockburn, Mrs C Lintott, Martin and Sue Day, John A Barker)*

Free house ~ Licensee Guy Sankey ~ Real ale ~ Bar food (12-3, 6-10; 12-10 Sat, 1-6 Sun) ~ Restaurant ~ (01892) 511422 ~ Children in eating area of bar ~ Dogs welcome ~ Live bands Sun evening ~ Open 11-11; 12-10.30 Sun

ULCOMBE TQ8550 Map 3
Pepper Box 🍺

Fairbourne Heath; signposted from A20 in Harrietsham, or follow Ulcombe signpost from A20, then turn left at crossroads with sign to pub, then right at next minor crossroads

The homely bar at this cosy old country inn has standing timbers and low beams hung with hops, copper kettles and pans on window sills, some very low-seated windsor chairs, and two leather sofas by the splendid inglenook fireplace with its lovely log fire. A side area, more functionally furnished for eating, extends into a recently refurbished and opened up dining room; piped music. Three very well kept Shepherd Neame beers are tapped from the cask, and they've local apple juice and a dozen wines by the glass; no smoking except in the bar. The tabby tom is called Fred, and there are two more cats, and a couple of collies called Rosie and Molly. Tasty bar food might include soup (£4), fried sardines (£4.50), goats cheese tartlet (£5.50), mushroom stroganoff or fisherman's pie (£10.50), 8oz sirloin or roast supreme of chicken with smoked bacon and avocado sauce or beef stroganoff (£12); extra vegetables (£3.50); no children inside. Views from the hop-covered terrace stretch over a great plateau of rolling arable farmland, and if you're in the garden, with its small pond, shrubs and flowerbeds, you may be lucky enough to catch a glimpse of deer. The name of the pub refers to the pepperbox pistol – an early type of revolver with numerous barrels, and the village church is worth a look. *(Recommended by MLR, Fr Robert Marsh, Howard and Margaret Buchanan, Gordon Stevenson, Leo and Barbara Lionet, Andrea Rampley, Philip and Cheryl Hill, Nigel and Olga Wikeley, Simon and Amanda Southwell, Jan and Alan Summers, Martin and Sue Day, Ian and Nita Cooper)*

Shepherd Neame ~ Tenants Geoff and Sarah Pemble ~ Real ale ~ Bar food (12-2, 7-9.30; not Sun or Mon evenings) ~ Restaurant ~ (01622) 842558 ~ Dogs allowed in bar ~ Open 11-3, 6.30-11; 12-4, 7-10 Sun

WEST PECKHAM TQ6452 Map 3
Swan on the Green 🍺

From A26/A228 heading N, bear left at roundabout onto B2016 (Seven Mile Lane), then second left

Much enjoyed by readers, this tucked-away country pub is doing well on all counts – it's in a lovely spot, the interior is inviting, they brew half a dozen ales, and the food is well prepared. A good mix of customers from suited office workers to friendly locals chatting to the amiable licensee, gather in the bar, which is light, airy, and open-plan, with rush-seated dining chairs and cushioned church settles around an attractive mix of well spaced refectory and other pale oak tables on wood strip floors. Attractive decorations include lovely big bunches of flowers (one placed in the knocked-through brick fireplace), hops on beams, some modern paintings at one end and black and white photographs of locals at the other end; piped classical music and daily papers. Brewed out the back here, Bewick, Fuggles, Ginger Swan, Swan Mild, Portside, Trumpeter and Whooper Pale are well kept on handpump, alongside Biddenden's farm cider. Generously served bar food might include lunchtime filled ciabatta flutes (£5.50) and ploughman's (£6.50), as well as fried chicken livers with caramelised red onions (£6.45), fresh cromer crab or tagliatelle with spinach, chicken and blue cheese (£7.50), warm chicken breast and chargrilled bacon salad (£8.50), baby red mullet with minted couscous (£9.95) and steak (from £12.95), with puddings such as summer fruit pudding with raspberry coulis and clotted cream (£4.25). Their early evening 'beat the clock' special means the bill for your two-course meal is equal to the hour on the clock. Picnic-sets under parasols in front look onto more on the charming cricket green opposite; they take a £10 deposit for a rug if you want to eat outside. The nearby church is partly Saxon. *(Recommended by Andrea Rampley, Simon and Sally Small, Derek Thomas, Mrs C Lintott, Mike Gorton, Richard Houghton, Bob and Margaret Holder, Christopher Turner, Kevin Thorpe, Ian Wilson, Martin and Sue Day, Jan and Alan Summers, Sue Demont, Tim Barrow)*

Own brew ~ Licensee Gordon Milligan ~ Real ale ~ Bar food (not Sun, not Mon evening) ~ Restaurant ~ (01622) 812271 ~ Children welcome ~ Dogs welcome ~ Live entertainment Sun afternoon ~ Open 11-3, 6-11; 11-4, 5-11 Sat; 12-10.30 Sun

---

LUCKY DIP

Besides the fully inspected pubs, you might like to try these Lucky Dips recommended to us and described by readers (if you do, please send us reports: www.goodguides.co.uk).

APPLEDORE [TQ9529]
Black Lion [The Street]: Compact 1930s village pub with welcoming helpful staff, huge range of good value generous food all day esp local fish, three or four changing ales such as Greene King, log fire, partitioned back eating area; tables out by attractive village street *(John Branston, Louise English)*
Railway Hotel [Station Rd (B2080 E)]: Victorian hotel under new management, recently renovated big front bar with some wicker furniture, newly panelled dado, rail memorabilia, open fire, Badger K&B and bar food, daily papers, pool, darts, big back children's room with toys and TV, separate restaurant; fruit machine; good disabled access and facilities, garden tables, 12 bedrooms with own bathrooms in small motel wing *(Kevin Thorpe)*
Swan [The Street]: Recently refurbished in smart comfortable modern style and no smoking throughout, black beams and pastel walls, modern abstract paintings, flowers on stripped wood tables, Shepherd Neame Bitter, wide food choice from sandwiches to steak and (all afternoon) Sun carvery, young uniformed staff; piped pop music, occasional live *(Kevin Thorpe)*

BARFRESTONE [TR2650]
Yew Tree [off A256 N of Dover; or off A2 at Barham]: New tenants in country local tucked behind huge yew tree (and serving as 'shop' for the famous next-door church with its wonderful Norman carvings), four or five well kept ales from small breweries inc a Mild, farm cider, pubby lunchtime food from baguettes and baked potatoes up, evening menu, mix of old pine furniture on bare boards, small carpeted bar area, woodburner, darts and other games in family room with warm red décor; children and dogs welcome; terrace tables, open all day Sat, 11-7 Sun, cl Mon *(Kevin Thorpe, LYM, Richard Pitcher)*

BARHAM [TR2050]
Duke of Cumberland [The Street]: Open-plan country pub with welcoming new licensees, enjoyable straightforward home cooking, three real ales, decent wines, attentive service, bare boards and flagstones, open fire, no smoking back room; bedrooms *(David Barnes, Catherine and Rob Dunster)*

BEARSTED [TQ7956]
Bell [Ware St; by railway bridge, W of centre]: Well kept Boddingtons, Fullers London Pride and Greene King IPA, good range of competitively priced food, prompt friendly helpful service *(Nigel B Thompson)*

BILSINGTON [TR0334]
White Horse: Friendly family-oriented pub under new management, enjoyable food inc new carvery in big separate restaurant area *(Rob)*

BISHOPSBOURNE [TR1852]
☆ *Mermaid* [signed off A2]: Country local kept traditional by welcoming new licensees (former customers), with some careful décor improvements, particularly well kept Shepherd Neame beers inc a seasonal one, simple food such as good filled rolls and baked potatoes, friendly regulars, coal fire, darts and old books in small back public bar, no machines; dogs and walkers welcome, lovely unspoilt Kentish village nr Pilgrims Way and North Downs Way *(Kevin Thorpe, Peter Heaton)*

BRASTED [TQ4654]
White Hart [High St (A25)]: Roomy largely no smoking Vintage Inn, several snug areas taking their mood from the original Battle of Britain bar with signatures and mementoes of Biggin Hill fighter pilots, beams and log fires, helpful staff, well kept Bass and Tetleys, good choice of wine and fresh orange juice; children welcome, big neatly kept garden with well spaced tables and play area; pretty village with several antiques shops *(LYM, Alan Kilpatrick, Conor McGaughey, N R White)*

BRENCHLEY [TQ6841]
Halfway House [Horsmonden Rd]: Recently opened up and attractively refitted in olde-worlde style, mix of rustic and traditional furnishings on bare boards, two log fires, particularly friendly landlord, enjoyable food range (two eating areas as well as main bar), well kept changing ales tapped from the cask with some emphasis on local breweries such as Larkins, Swan Porter (see main entry for Swan on the Green, West Peckham) and the good new Westerham brewery, beer festivals late May and Aug bank hols; picnic-sets and play area in big garden *(Peter Meister, Richard Durrant)*

BRENZETT [TR0027]

Fleur-de-Lys [B2080 towards Snargate]: Good fish menu, not expensive, attentive service, Harveys ale *(David Lowe)*

BRIDGE [TR1854]

Plough & Harrow [High St]: Popular local in 17th-c former maltings, friendly and unpretentious, with well kept Shepherd Neame ales and good wine choice, coal fire and lots of sporting prints in open-plan brick-walled lounge, public bar with bar billiards and open fire, wi-fi internet access, back games room with darts, TV and woodburner; no food, open all day Sat *(Kevin Thorpe, Mike and Lynn Robinson, Craig Turnbull)*

Red Lion [High St]: Cosy and relaxed traditional village pub dating from 16th c, three well kept ales such as Youngs Special, lots of wines by the glass, good genuine home-made food using local produce, friendly staff; dogs welcome, pleasant garden *(Mike and Lynn Robinson)*

☆ *White Horse* [High St]: Good fresh seasonal food using listed local suppliers from bar meals to more elaborate restaurant dishes and good value set lunches Tues-Sat, inventive recipes and presentation, well kept changing ales such as Greene King Abbot, Shepherd Neame Spitfire and Wadworths 6X, fine choice of wines by the glass, cheerful efficient service, thriving atmosphere in comfortable single bar, huge Elizabethan inglenook fireplace, civilised restaurant; dogs welcome, garden tables, attractive village *(Mike and Lynn Robinson, Catherine and Rob Dunster)*

BROADSTAIRS [TR3866]

Brown Jug [Ramsgate Rd]: Long-serving landlady in basic and unchanging old-style two-bar local, Greene King and guest beers, some tapped from the cask, board and quiz games *(the Didler)*

Lord Nelson [Nelson Pl]: Early 19th-c, with lots of Nelson memorabilia in lower bar, smart stripped brick upper area with open fire, Greene King IPA and Abbot and a guest beer; piped radio, TV; tables outside, open all day *(Kevin Thorpe)*

Neptunes Hall [Harbour St]: Friendly early 19th-c two-bar local with attractive bow windows and original shelving and panelling, well kept Shepherd Neame beers, carpeted back lounge with open fire, lunchtime snacks, friendly staff and locals; occasional live folk (daily during Aug folk festival); children and dogs welcome, enclosed terrace, open all day *(the Didler, Kevin Thorpe)*

White Swan [Reading St, St Peters]: Much modernised 17th-c pub with low armchairs and tables in comfortable lounge, pool and darts in public bar area, well kept Adnams and several interesting changing beers, simple bargain food (not Sun lunchtime) from sandwiches or toasties up; dogs welcome *(Kevin Thorpe)*

CANTERBURY [TR1458]

Dolphin [St Radigunds St]: Recently redone as smart dining pub, civilised and friendly, with old and new pictures on warm red walls above stripped dado, books to read, bric-a-brac on delft shelf, well presented food from baguettes to fish specials, Fullers London Pride and Greene King IPA and Abbot, country wines, flagstoned conservatory with fine collection of advertising mirrors; garden behind *(Kevin Thorpe)*

Phoenix [Old Dover Rd]: Unpretentious local with Greene King Abbot, Charles Wells Bombardier and Youngs, good value food all day inc bargain Sun roasts and OAP deals, friendly staff *(Tony Hobden)*

Simple Simons [Church Lane, St Radigunds]: Step down into basic pub in 14th-c building, no smoking front bar with heavy beams, broad floorboards, flagstones and some stripped masonry, two woodburners, dim-lit upstairs banqueting hall, well kept Bass, Theakstons Old Peculier and up to half a dozen guest beers, impressive pump clip collection, low-priced simple food all day inc good value sandwiches and speciality home-made pies; good piped classical music in the daytime, more studenty evening, frequent live jazz or blues; dogs welcome, tables in brick-paved courtyard, open all day *(Conor McGaughey, Kevin Thorpe)*

White Hart [Worthgate Pl, opp tree-shaded square off Castle St]: Three well kept Shepherd Neame real ales, good wines by the glass, enjoyable home-made food, friendly young landlord, good prompt service, side room with open fire and SkyTV; large garden behind – one of very few in the city *(Guy Vowles, Patrick Hancock, Theocsbrian)*

CAPEL [TQ6444]

Dovecote [Alders Rd; SE of Tonbridge]: Beams and some stripped brickwork, pitched-ceiling no smoking dining room, usual food from good sandwiches and baguettes to popular Sun lunch, bargain suppers for two Mon and Thurs, several real ales such as Adnams Broadside and Larkins tapped from the cask, farm cider; lots of picnic-sets in back garden with terrace, doves and play area, pleasant surroundings *(Peter Meister, Alan and Carolin Tidbury, Oliver and Sue Rowell)*

CHARING [TQ9549]

Royal Oak [High St]: Friendly old village pub, reliable generous food, well kept beer *(Stephen and Jean Curtis)*

CHARTHAM HATCH [TR1056]

☆ *Chapter Arms* [New Town St]: Sizeable largely no smoking 18th-c pub overlooking orchards, enjoyable generous food inc good lunchtime salad bar (as much or as little as you want), well kept Shepherd Neame and guest beers, decent wine, friendly service, flowers and candles on tables, heavily hop-hung ceiling with brass instruments and fairy lights, restaurant through doorway decorated in lilac, green and silver; quiet piped music, jazz Mon; nice teak garden furniture, lots of flower tubs etc *(Bruce M Drew, BB, Norman Fox)*

CHIDDINGSTONE CAUSEWAY [TQ5146]

Little Brown Jug [B2027]: Under new landlord, spacious and comfortable, with decent reasonably priced food, Greene King IPA and Abbot; attractive garden with play area, bedrooms *(Gwyn Jones)*

CHILHAM [TR0653]

White Horse [The Square]: Comfortably modernised two-room beamed bar with good log fire, well kept real ales, decent wines, smiling service, back eating area with separate ordering counter for good value food from baguettes and ciabattas up; piped music; a couple of tables out on the corner of Kent's prettiest village square *(Gloria Bax, LYM, Louise English)*

COWDEN [TQ4640]

☆ *Fountain* [off A264 and B2026; High St]: Attractive tile-hung country local in pretty village, steep steps to unpretentious dark-panelled corner bar with Harveys IPA, Best and a seasonal beer, decent wines, friendly licensees, darts and good log fire, mix of tables in adjoining room, sensibly short blackboard choice of good enterprising food from ciabattas to good Sun roast, woodburner in small beamed back dining room with one big table; piped music, may be TV sports; walkers and dogs welcome, annual flower show, cl Mon lunchtime *(Kevin Thorpe, BB, Paul A Moore, Ian Phillips)*

☆ *Queens Arms* [Cowden Pound; junction B2026 with Markbeech rd]: Unspoilt and warmly welcoming two-room country pub like something from the 1930s, with splendid landlady, well kept Adnams, coal fire, darts; dogs welcome, occasional folk music or morris dancers; may be cl wkdy lunchtimes but normally opens 10am *(the Didler, Kevin Thorpe, Pete Baker, RWC, Martin and Sue Day)*

CROCKHAM HILL [TQ4450]

Royal Oak: Cosy village local very popular lunchtime for wide choice of enjoyable good value food from sandwiches and baked potatoes to steaks, particularly friendly and helpful landlord, well kept Shepherd Neame ales, daily papers, comfortable high-backed seats, no music or fruit machines; dogs welcome, small garden, handy for walks *(Gwyn Jones, Gordon Stevenson, N R White, William Ruxton)*

DEAL [TR3752]

☆ *Bohemian* [Beach St]: Relaxed refurbished pub opp pier, comfortable sofas, open fire, wooden floors and modern décor with abstract paintings, fine choice of ales inc Adnams, Caledonian Deuchars IPA, Woodfordes Wherry, continental beers, wide choice of wines, good views from upstairs restaurant; easy wheelchair access, heated back terrace, open all day Fri-Sun, cl Mon in winter *(Peter Meister, Kevin Thorpe)*

Ship: Cosy and neatly kept two-roomed former smugglers' pub, well kept ales such as Fullers ESB, Hook Norton, Hop Back Summer Lightning and Woodfordes Wherry, lots of dark woodwork, stripped brick and local ship and wreck pictures, piano and woodburner; small pretty enclosed garden, open all day *(Hywel Bevan, Kevin Thorpe)*

DENTON [TR2147]

Jackdaw [A260 Canterbury—Folkestone]: Imposing open-plan brick and flint pub with enjoyable family food all day, well kept Shepherd Neame Spitfire, Tetleys Mild, Charles Wells Bombardier and a couple of guest beers, friendly young staff, cream and red décor with RAF memorabilia in front area, large back restaurant; quiet piped music; children welcome, tables in pleasant garden, open all day *(Kevin Thorpe, Eddie Edwards, Mrs Hazel Rainer)*

DOVER [TR3241]

Blakes [Castle St]: Three well kept changing ales from unusual microbreweries, dozens of malt whiskies and good wine choice in small flagstoned cellar bar with paintings for sale on partly panelled brick and flint walls, good low-priced lunchtime food (not Sun) upstairs from soup and sandwiches to sole and salmon; terrace tables, bedrooms, open all day *(Kevin Thorpe)*

DUNGENESS [TR0916]

Pilot [Battery Rd]: Single-storey mid-20th-c pub looking on to shingle beach, two bars and barn family extension, dark plank panelling inc the slightly curved ceiling, wide choice of straightforward food from sandwiches up inc good value fresh fish and chips, well kept Greene King IPA and Abbot, lots of knick-knacks for sale; piped music; picnic-sets in side garden *(Peter Meister, Louise English)*

DUNKS GREEN [TQ6152]

☆ *Kentish Rifleman*: Cosy early 16th-c low-beamed and timbered pub (the big stone-arched vaulted cellar may even be Roman), log fire in well divided dining lounge, friendly staff, welcoming pub dog and good service, well kept changing ales such as Fullers London Pride, Greene King Abbot and Youngs Special, decent wine and coffee, plenty of character, good choice of enjoyable traditional food from soup and sandwiches to Sun roasts, no machines, small public bar welcoming dogs; tables in well designed garden behind, good walks *(Debbie and Neil Hayter, Kevin Thorpe, Annette Tress, Gary Smith, BB, Mrs Catherine Draper, K Gethin, Peter Meister, Carl and Jackie Cranmer, Stephen C Harvey, Louise English)*

EAST STOURMOUTH [TR2662]

Rising Sun [B2046 N of Wingham; The Street]: Much modernised and extended 14th-c pub kept spotless, helpful friendly owners, Shepherd Neame and two guest beers, a dozen wines by the glass, wide food choice running up to chateaubriand steaks, brightly lit tiled central bar with heavy timbers, flowers on nicely laid out stripped pine tables in two large dining areas with panelled dado, modern prints and large art photographs, big bright and airy games room with pool, piano, woodburner, books and plants, warm orange and pastel walls, colourful curtains, small side TV area; quiet piped music; garden tables, play area, bedrooms, open all day wknds *(Kevin Thorpe)*

ELHAM [TR1743]

Kings Arms [St Marys Rd]: Traditional pub

with relaxing attractive lounge bar, good open fire, good value food, unobtrusively attentive friendly service, steps down to big dining area, public bar with games; opp church in square of charming village, attractive sheltered garden *(David Lowe)*

FARNINGHAM [TQ5467]

Chequers [High St/Dartford Rd, just off A20]: One-bar local with good choice of well kept ales such as Fullers ESB, Greene King Abbot and Timothy Taylors Landlord, friendly staff; benches outside, picturesque village *(N R White)*

Pied Bull [High St]: Welcoming and relaxed family-run pub/restaurant with good choice of enjoyable bar food inc fresh seafood and home-made puddings, popular restaurant *(Lisa Brown)*

FAVERSHAM [TR0161]

Albion [Front Brents]: Light and airy waterside pub with solid pine furnishings, local pictures on pale green walls, good plain bar food (not Sun evening) from sandwiches up, well kept Shepherd Neame ales inc seasonal from the nearby brewery, genial staff, flowers and candles on tables; children welcome in restaurant area, disabled lavatories, picnic-sets out on riverside walkway (Saxon Shore long-distance path), open all day summer *(Kevin Thorpe, LYM, Mike and Lynn Robinson, Mike Gorton, Martin and Sue Day, N R White)*

Anchor [Abbey St]: Friendly two-bar local in attractive 17th-c street nr quay and station, several well kept Shepherd Neame ales, good quiet relaxed atmosphere, bare boards, open fires, settles and part-panelling, enjoyable sensibly priced food (not Sun evening or Mon), no smoking candlelit tiled eating area, piano, pub games; may be piped music, some live; a couple of picnic-sets outside, pretty garden, open all day, cl Mon lunchtime *(the Didler, Kevin Thorpe, N R White)*

Bear [Market Pl]: Friendly local dating from 16th c (front rebuilt last century), lounge, snug and public bar off side corridor, well kept Shepherd Neame ales from the nearby brewery, basic good value lunchtime home cooking; tables outside, lively musical following, open all day Sat *(the Didler)*

Crown & Anchor [The Mall]: Friendly open-plan local dating from 19th c, wkdy lunchtime food inc long-serving Hungarian landlord's authentic goulash, Shepherd Neame real ales, games area with darts and pool *(the Didler)*

Sun [West St]: Roomy and rambling old-world 15th-c weatherboarded town pub with good unpretentious atmosphere in small low-ceilinged partly panelled rooms, good value low-priced lunchtime food, well kept Shepherd Neame beers inc seasonal one from nearby brewery, quick pleasant service, smart no smoking restaurant; unobtrusive piped music; wheelchair access possible (small step), tables in pleasant back courtyard, interesting street, newly done bedrooms with own bathrooms, open all day *(Keith and Janet Morris, the Didler)*

FINGLESHAM [TR3353]

Crown [just off A258 Sandwich—Deal; The Street]: Neatly kept low-beamed 16th-c country pub with wide choice of good value food in three dining areas (two no smoking), well kept Greene King, Shepherd Neame and guest beers, good service, daily papers, log fire, attractive décor inc flagstones, inglenook and stripped brickwork; children welcome, lovely garden with play area and barbecues, field for caravans, open all day wknds *(C Welland, Kevin Thorpe)*

FORDWICH [TR1759]

George & Dragon [off A28 at Sturry]: Friendly chain dining pub, well kept real ales; pleasant garden leads down to River Stour, character bedrooms, handy for Stodmarsh nature reserve *(Keith and Chris O'Neill, Mrs Hazel Rainer)*

FOUR ELMS [TQ4748]

Four Elms [B2027/B269 E of Edenbridge]: Large busy open-plan dining pub with wide choice of good value food (not Mon evening) from sandwiches and baguettes to grills, bake their own good breads, rota of well kept ales inc Fullers London Pride, Greene King Abbot and Shepherd Neame Spitfire, decent wine and coffee, cheerful service, several rambling rooms, two big log fires, huge boar's head, family room, no music; tables outside, handy for Chartwell, open all day (Sun afternoon break) *(Alan M Pring, John Evans)*

GOATHURST COMMON [TQ4952]

Woodman: Large mainly no smoking Chef & Brewer, wide blackboard choice of all-day food inc some south african specialities (landlord's from there), decent wine, Courage Directors and guest beers, woodburner, young staff; manicured lawns, delightful walking country *(Tina and David Woods-Taylor)*

GOUDHURST [TQ7237]

☆ *Star & Eagle* [High St]: Striking medieval inn with settles and Jacobean-style seats in attractive heavily beamed open-plan areas, wide choice of good generous freshly made food from crusty ciabattas to restaurant dishes, pleasant efficient service, well kept Adnams (the bar itself seems fairly modern), interesting smuggling-days history; children welcome, tables out behind with pretty views, lovely character bedrooms, well furnished and comfortable, open all day *(R E Dixon, LYM, Craig Turnbull, Leo and Barbara Lionet, Mrs J Ekins-Daukes, Mrs C Lintott, Tina and David Woods-Taylor)*

GRAVESEND [TQ6473]

Crown & Thistle [The Terrace]: Five interesting changing beers from small breweries such as Daleside in small friendly pub, can order in meals from nearby indian/chinese restaurant, brewery pictures, no juke box or machines; no children, occasional live music; open all day *(the Didler)*

HADLOW [TQ6249]

☆ *Rose Revived* [Ashes Lane, off A26]: Attractive 16th-c pub recently refurbished in bistro style, with enjoyable modern food, Fullers London Pride and Harveys Best *(Gerry and Rosemary Dobson)*

Two Brewers [Maidstone Rd]: Taken over and tastefully reworked by Harveys, light and clean, with no smoking lounge and nostalgic décor of stripped pine, replica etched glass screens and old brewing photographs; their ales inc a refreshing one brewed for the pub using only local hops, unpretentious competitively priced food *(Stephen C Harvey)*

HARVEL [TQ6563]

Amazon & Tiger [Harvel Street]: Cosy old two-bar local in pretty village, good value food from bar snacks to three sizes of Sun lunch, friendly service, real ales, restaurant; beautiful walking country *(N R White)*

HEAVERHAM [TQ5758]

Chequers [Watery Lane]: Cottagey old pub with pleasantly pubby main bar and friendly locals' bar, enjoyable food here or in beamed restaurant, well kept Shepherd Neame; children welcome, picnic-sets in big garden *(Gwyn Jones, Martin and Sue Day, N R White)*

HERNHILL [TR0660]

☆ *Red Lion* [A299 via Dargate, or A2 via Boughton Street and Staplestreet]: Pretty Tudor inn by church and attractive village green, densely beamed and flagstoned, log fires, pine tables, no smoking upstairs restaurant, enjoyable food, well kept Fullers London Pride and Shepherd Neame with a guest such as Marstons Pedigree, decent house wines, friendly attentive staff; children welcome, big garden with boules and good play area, bedrooms *(M and R Thomas, LYM, Mrs Margo Finlay, Jörg Kasprowski, N R White)*

HODSOLL STREET [TQ6263]

☆ *Green Man* [off A227 S of Meopham]: Pretty pub by village green, relaxing and no smoking throughout, with well kept Flowers, Fullers London Pride, Youngs and a guest beer, decent wines, bar food from lunchtime sandwiches, wraps and good baguettes up, Tues curries and Weds fish night, popular Sun roast, neat tables in big airy rooms around hop-draped central bar, interesting old local photographs and antique plates, log fire; piped music, Mon quiz night; children and dogs welcome, tables out on lawn, North Downs walks, open all day Fri-Sun *(Annette Tress, Gary Smith, Tony Brace, Gerry and Rosemary Dobson, Paul A Moore, Simon Pyle, LYM)*

HOLLINGBOURNE [TQ8454]

Parkgate [Ashford Rd (A20, nr M20 junction 8 and Leeds Castle)]: Well run chain pub well divided into cosy areas with beams and flagstones, no smoking areas and part just for drinkers, friendly efficient staff, good range of food from cobs and melts up inc some interesting dishes, good wines by the glass, chilled Adnams and Shepherd Neame Spitfire *(John and Elspeth Howell, Val and Alan Green)*

HORSMONDEN [TQ7040]

☆ *Gun & Spitroast* [The Heath]: Happy dining atmosphere in polished 1930s pub on village green, wide choice of sensibly priced food from big filled baguettes to some interesting hot dishes, pretty inglenook dining room with a roasting spit still in use, obliging helpful staff, well kept ales inc Fullers London Pride and Harveys, log fire; dogs and walkers welcome, picnic-sets out behind with play area, comfortable bedrooms in converted coach house *(B and M Kendall)*

HOTHFIELD [TQ9646]

Hop Pickers [Maidstone Rd (A20 NW of Ashford)]: Recent conversion of private house, small bar, eating areas inc no smoking one, Bass and Greene King IPA, good choice of wines by the glass and plenty of food variety; piped music and games; comfortable bedrooms in adjacent Holiday Inn *(Michael Dandy)*

ICKHAM [TR2258]

Duke William [off A257 E of Canterbury; The Street]: Cleanly updated by new licensees, well kept Greene King IPA and Old Speckled Hen, Shepherd Neame and a guest beer, keen staff, reasonably priced standard bar food (not Sun evening or Mon), a few modern pictures, stripped half panelling, branches up in the ceiling, downlighters and blue décor in back bar, more elaborate menu in long no smoking dining room and big well shaded conservatory, pub games; piped music, juke box, live music Sun afternoon; children can eat here, oak furniture and boules in big neat garden, open all day *(Kevin Thorpe, LYM)*

IDE HILL [TQ4851]

Cock [off B2042 SW of Sevenoaks]: Pretty village-green pub with warmly pubby atmosphere, well kept Greene King, wholesome food (not Sun evening) from sandwiches and ploughman's up, fine log fire, bar billiards; piped music, no children; some seats out in front, handy for Chartwell and nearby walks – so gets busy *(LYM, DJH, Bruce M Drew, David H T Dimock)*

IGHTHAM [TQ5956]

☆ *George & Dragon* [A227]: Picturesque early 16th-c black and white timbered dining pub, much modernised inside with sofas among other furnishings in long sociable main bar, heavy-beamed end room, woodburner and open fires, well kept Shepherd Neame Bitter, Spitfire and seasonal ales, decent wines, good choice of fruit juices, short choice of good food from generous snacks (all day till 6.30, not Sun) up, partly no smoking restaurant; children in family/restaurant areas, back terrace, open all day, handy for Ightham Mote (NT), good walks *(LYM, Debbie and Neil Hayter, Susan and John Douglas, Jenny and Brian Seller, Evelyn and Derek Walter, Dave Braisted, Derek Thomas, Martin and Sue Day)*

IVY HATCH [TQ5854]

☆ *Plough* [off A227 N of Tonbridge]: Reopened after refurbishment, friendly helpful new landlord, good food (same good chef but more traditional menu, reasonable prices and the chance of just soup and a roll now, though still not sandwiches), good service, pleasantly informal décor, attractive conservatory and garden *(LYM, Alan Sadler, Bob and Margaret Holder)*

KEMSING [TQ5659]

☆ *Rising Sun* [Cotmans Ash Lane; about a mile N of Heaverham on back rd to Eynsham, OS Sheet 188 map ref 563599]: Think H E Bates – outside a cock may welcome you, and inside are dark and dated beamed bars with red tiles, inglenook fireplaces, well worn brocaded built-in wall benches and stools, chatty locals, perhaps a friendly jack russell and venerable parrot, and darts in one of the end rooms; the service is friendly, the changing beers are well kept, interesting and attractively priced, and the food, in staggering helpings, is a bargain; informal, overgrown garden with picnic-sets and children's play things, good downland walks *(BB, Guy Vowles, B and M Kendall)*

KNOCKHOLT [TQ4658]

Crown [Main Rd]: Cheerful old-fashioned village pub, unchanged for decades, with attractive dark ochre décor, friendly relaxed service, good value food inc sandwiches and sensibly priced home-made hot dishes (popular at lunchtime with older diners), well kept Adnams Bitter and Broadside, walkers with muddy boots welcome in public bar; picnic-sets on lawn with fish pond, colourful flowers, path to North Downs Way *(N R White)*

LAMBERHURST [TQ6736]

Chequers [A21]: Low limed beams and standing timbers in light open-plan main bar, parquet or flagstone floor, big leather sofa on turkey rug, variety of sturdy tables and dining chairs, big inglenook log fire, Shepherd Neame ales, good house wines, daily papers, ambitious food, similar public bar; piped jazz or pop; solid tables on back deck, pretty streamside garden beyond *(BB, Oliver and Sue Rowell)*

Elephants Head [Hook Green; B2169 towards T Wells]: Ancient rambling timber-framed country pub, heavy beams, brick or oak flooring, big inglenook log fire, plush-cushioned pews etc, well kept Harveys ales inc seasonal, pleasant staff, wide food choice – popular wknds for this; darts and fruit machine in small side area, may be quiet piped music; picnic-sets by front green and in big back garden with peaceful view, terrace and good play area, nr Bayham Abbey and Owl House *(Peter Meister, D Travis, LYM)*

LEIGH [TQ5646]

☆ *Plough* [Powder Mill Lane/Leigh Rd, off B2027 NW of Tonbridge]: Attractive Tudor building opened up around big central hearth, good lunches from generous baked potatoes and good steak sandwiches and ciabattas to more adventurous dishes and very popular Sun carvery (often fully booked), well kept Adnams Best, Harveys and Shepherd Neame Spitfire, good wine range; service can slow evenings; pleasant walks *(James Price, Peter Meister, Philip and Ann Board, Gillian Rodgers, BB)*

LITTLEBOURNE [TR2057]

Evenhill [The Hill (A257)]: Smartly upgraded and under new management, with well kept Shepherd Neame and guest ales and open fires in beamed bare-boards Victorian bar, enjoyable bar food all day, restaurant with upper gallery, friendly staff; disabled facilities,

children welcome, garden tables, 16 newly done bedrooms in adjacent block *(Mr and Mrs D Rimell)*

LUDDESDOWN [TQ6667]

☆ *Cock* [Henley Street, N of village – OS Sheet 177 map reference 664672; off A227 in Meopham, or A228 in Cuxton]: Distinctive tucked-away early 18th-c country pub, homely bay-windowed lounge, quarry-tiled bar with pews and other miscellaneous furnishings, lots of old posters, beer mats and bric-a-brac, well kept Adnams Bitter and Broadside, Goachers Mild, Harveys, Shepherd Neame and Youngs, modestly priced generous food (not Sun evening) from sandwiches up, friendly service, traditional games inc bar billiards and three types of darts board, two woodburners; no children allowed in, tables and boules in big secure garden, open all day *(LYM, Kevin Thorpe, N R White)*

MAIDSTONE [TQ7656]

Pilot [Upper Stone St (A229)]: Busy old roadside pub, enjoyable low-priced simple home-made food (not Sun), well kept Harveys ales, chatty landlord, whisky-water jugs hanging from ceiling, darts and pool; live music Sun lunchtime; tables on back terrace, boules *(the Didler)*

Rifle Volunteers [Wyatt St/Church St]: Unspoilt quiet backstreet pub tied to local Goachers, three of their ales inc Mild kept well, good value simple home-made food, chatty long-serving landlord, two gas fires, darts, no machines; tables outside *(the Didler)*

MANSTON [TR3466]

Jolly Farmer [High St]: Open-plan beamed country dining pub with emphasis on good wholesome value from sandwiches, baguettes, baked potatoes and burgers to steaks and so forth, cheerful friendly service, well kept ales such as Flowers, Fullers London Pride, Greene King IPA and Old Speckled Hen and Marstons Pedigree, masses of World War II aircraft prints; picnic-sets under parasols in pleasant garden *(Paul and Ursula Randall)*

MARDEN [TQ7444]

Unicorn [High St (B2079)]: Friendly local with unexpectedly elegant menu and enjoyable food in attractive dining room, lunchtime bar food too, decent wines *(Pat and Graham Williamson)*

MARDEN THORN [TQ7643]

Wild Duck [Pagehurst Lane; off A229 in Staplehurst or B2079 in Marden]: Well worn in country pub with friendly staff, enjoyable food inc good value three-course lunches, well kept Shepherd Neame Spitfire, good-sized dining room *(Richard Durrant, BB, Mark Conn)*

MATFIELD [TQ6642]

Standings Cross [Maidstone Rd]: Welcoming local with beams and panelling, leaded windows, scrubbed tables and darts in small front bar, inexpensive imaginative food, Adnams and Harveys, pleasant helpful service, cosy inglenook fireplace in attractive old back restaurant; walkers and dogs welcome *(Robert Rice)*

MAYPOLE [TR2064]
Prince of Wales [S of Herne Bay]: Open-plan village pub attractively reworked by new owners, comfortable main bar with warm red décor and heavy curtains, Shepherd Neame and Theakstons Best, two open fires, pub games and working 78rpm gramophone, china and old photographs, nicely laid new pine tables and flowers in small back dining area; piped music; children and dogs welcome, garden tables, open all day *(Kevin Thorpe)*

NEW ROMNEY [TR0624]
Ship [High St (A259)]: Tudor former smugglers' pub, wide choice of enjoyable reasonably priced food in attractive restaurant, Shepherd Neame real ales, unpretentious bar with darts, bar billiards and games machines; seven bedrooms *(Mrs S Fairbrother)*

NEWNHAM [TQ9557]
Tapster [Parsonage Farm, Seed Rd]: Long bare-boards bistro/bar, huge log fireplace one end, L-shaped counter the other with Greene King IPA and two guest beers, freshly squeezed orange juice and good wine choice, good enterprising blackboard lunches and evening menu, friendly staff and three playful dogs, candles, flowers and white linen, big pot plants and ferns, broad boards and reclaimed worn brickwork; piped jazz, occasional live music; dogs and children welcome, new picnic-sets in big garden with cider press, bedrooms, open all day in summer, cl Mon in winter *(Kevin Thorpe)*

NORTHBOURNE [TR3352]
Hare & Hounds [off A256 or A258 nr Dover; The Street]: Friendly village local, now completely no smoking, with well kept Fullers London Pride, Harveys BB, Shepherd Neame Bitter and Spitfire and Timothy Taylors Landlord (Aug beer festival), log fires each end, sensibly priced daily-changing blackboard food inc enterprising dishes (they try to cater for special needs); terrace tables, big play area *(Kevin Thorpe)*

OTFORD [TQ5259]
Bull [High St]: Attractively laid out 15th-c Chef & Brewer, their usual huge food choice from sandwiches and baguettes up all day, four real ales, decent wines, several quietly spacious rooms, log fires in two enormous fireplaces, friendly staff; nice garden *(B J Harding, N R White)*

Crown [High St, pond end]: 16th-c two-bar local opp village pond, lounge with sofas, cheerful friendly staff, reasonably priced food inc good Sun lunch, well kept beer; walkers and dogs welcome, good walks nearby *(N R White)*

PAINTER'S FORSTAL [TQ9958]
Alma [signed off A2 at Ospringe]: Charming timbered and weatherboarded village local, homely and tidy, with good value home cooking using local ingredients (not Sun evening or Mon), well kept Shepherd Neame ales, decent wines, cheerful helpful informal service, comfortable largish no smoking dining lounge with country pictures on ochre walls, scrubbed tables and bench seating in small

bare-boards low-ceilinged bar with darts; may be piped classical music; dogs welcome, picnic-sets on lawn, cl Mon *(Kevin Thorpe)*

PEMBURY [TQ6240]
Black Horse [High St]: Attractively refurbished low-beamed local with wide choice of enjoyable food from simple snacks to seafood platter and popular Sun carvery, well kept ales, friendly staff, log fire; neatly kept garden *(Janet Penfold)*

Camden Arms [High St (The Green)]: Family pub with good choice of reasonably priced food *(Oliver and Sue Rowell)*

PENSHURST [TQ4943]
☆ *Rock* [Hoath Corner, Chiddingstone Hoath; OS Sheet 188 map ref 497431]: Two charmingly old-fashioned and simple little beamed rooms with farmers and dogs, stripped brick and timbers, wonky brick floors, woodburner in inglenook, well kept Larkins from the nearby brewery, good house wines, local farm cider, good blackboard food choice (not Sun), friendly staff, ring the bull (with a real bull's head), steps up to small dining room; children and dogs welcome, no mobile phones; front terrace, back garden, beautiful countryside nearby (handy for Eden Valley walk), cl Mon *(Andrea Rampley, Mr and Mrs R P Begg, N R White)*

☆ *Spotted Dog* [Smarts Hill, off B2188 S]: Quaint and neatly kept old tiled pub, half no smoking, with heavy low beams and timbers, antique settles and more straightforward furnishings, rugs and tiles, cosy inglenook log fire, attractive moulded panelling, well kept Harveys Best and Larkins Best and Traditional, enjoyable bar food changing daily, friendly efficient service, no smoking restaurant; may try to keep your credit card while you eat; children welcome till 7pm, tables out in front and on attractive tiered back terrace (with a temporary glimpse of the former renowned view, after some of the neighbouring young view-blocking trees were recently mysteriously felled overnight), open all day summer Thurs-Sun *(Gerry and Rosemary Dobson, Mr and Mrs R Wales, C and R Bromage, LYM, Dr and Mrs T E Hothersall, Mrs C Lintott, Carl and Jackie Cranmer, N R White, Martin and Sue Day)*

PLAXTOL [TQ6054]
Golding Hop [Sheet Hill, ½ mile S of Ightham, between A25 and A227)]: Secluded country local, small and simple dim-lit two-level bar with Adnams, Youngs and a couple of guest beers, four local farm ciders (sometimes even their own), basic good value bar snacks (not Mon/Tues evenings), woodburner, bar billiards; could perhaps sometimes be more welcoming, portable TV for big sports events, game machine; suntrap streamside lawn and well fenced play area over lane, open all day Sat *(B J Harding, Bob and Margaret Holder, Peter Meister, the Didler, LYM, Kevin Thorpe)*

PLUCKLEY [TQ9245]
Black Horse [The Street]: Attractive old house said to be haunted, with bare-boards and flagstones bar, roomy carpeted side and back

dining areas, hops on beams, four log fires inc vast inglenook, plenty of old things to look at, cheery atmosphere, wide food choice from baguettes up (just roasts on Sun), well kept ales inc Fullers London Pride; piped music, big-screen TV, fruit machine; children allowed if eating, picnic-sets in spacious informal garden by tall sycamores, good walks, open all day Fri-Sun *(Conor McGaughey, Dr and Mrs T E Hothersall, BB, Louise English)*

RAMSGATE [TR3865]

Artillery Arms [West Cliff Rd]: Chatty open-plan corner local with well kept Charles Wells Bombardier and four adventurous changing guest ales at sensible prices, bottled belgian beers, two farm ciders, cheap doorstep sandwiches all day, daily papers, straightforward two-level bar with artillery prints, cannons and talking-point stained-glass windows dating from Napoleonic wars, large hat collections (long-established Tues lunchtime funny hat club); juke box (free on Sun) can be intrusive, fruit machine; good wheelchair access, children and dogs welcome, open all day *(Kevin Thorpe)*

Churchill Tavern [Paragon (seafront)]: Big clifftop pub rebuilt in the 1980s with old beams, bare bricks, pews and farm tools, long bar with Fullers London Pride, Ringwood Old Thumper, Charles Wells Bombardier and several changing guest beers, good value food in bar or back restaurant, open fire, pool in games corner; live music downstairs wknds, midweek jazz and quiz nights; children and dogs welcome, harbour, marina and Channel views, open all day *(Kevin Thorpe)*

☆ *Ramsgate Royal Harbour Brewhouse & Bakery* [Harbour Parade]: Lively belgian-style café-bar brewing their own beers (you can look round the back brewery), also six belgian imports on tap, dozens in bottles, and Biddenden farm ciders; table service, bread, pastries and cakes baked all day, ploughman's and simple light meals too, open from 9 for tea and coffee (from 10 for alcohol), regular art shows inc sculptures; open piano, piped music; children welcome, tables out under cocktail parasols *(Kevin Thorpe, Mrs Hazel Rainer)*

ROCHESTER [TQ7468]

Coopers Arms [St Margarets St]: Jettied Tudor building behind cathedral, cosy and quaint inside, bustling local atmosphere, friendly staff, two comfortable bars, generous cheap wkdy bar lunches, well kept Courage Best and Directors; tables in attractive courtyard *(B J Harding)*

ROLVENDEN LAYNE [TQ8530]

☆ *Ewe & Lamb* [Maytham Rd]: Cheerful beamed bar with welcoming local feel, log fire and unusual black-printed wallpaper, friendly service, Adnams, Greene King Old Speckled Hen and Harveys, good house wines, short and interesting choice of good food from sandwiches up, also Sun and midweek carvery, close-set tables in back restaurant *(BB)*

SANDGATE [TR2035]

☆ *Clarendon* [Brewers Hill, off Sandgate—Hythe rd]: Small unpretentious Victorian local, no

smoking sea-view lounge with some pubby memorabilia, right-hand locals' bar, coal fires, well kept Shepherd Neame ales, 15 wines by the glass, 20 malts, sandwiches and a few hot dishes, may be good value crab salad, shove-ha'penny, cribbage, dominoes and backgammon; no credit cards, folk/blues Thurs; well behaved children in no smoking dining area, dogs in bar, a few benches out in front, cl from 5 Sun *(Ian Banham, Alan and Carolin Tidbury, Karina Spero, Ian Phillips, LYM, Paul A Moore, Guy Vowles)*

SANDLING [TQ7558]

Yew Tree [nestling under M20 just N of Maidstone, and about a mile from junction 6; take Bearsted turn off A229 just S of motorway then turn left down Boarley Lane/Grange Lane, then bear right]: Comfortable and peaceful old dining pub with good freshly cooked bargain food, charming décor, friendly efficient staff, well kept Shepherd Neame; pretty village with attractive church *(Gordon Neighbour)*

SANDWICH [TR3358]

George & Dragon [Fisher St]: Fine building attractively opened up keeping old beams and feel of small original rooms, bright efficient service, enjoyable food inc unusual dishes from open-view kitchen, well kept local ales *(Gloria Bax)*

SARRE [TR2564]

☆ *Crown* [Ramsgate Rd (A28)]: Bustling carefully restored pub with good interesting bar lunches and evening restaurant dishes, well kept Shepherd Neame beers, decent house wines, friendly attentive staff, two attractive beamed bars, log fires, pictures of celebrity guests; garden tables, bedrooms, open all day *(Norman Fox)*

SEASALTER [TR0864]

☆ *Sportsman* [Faversham Rd, off B2040]: Good imaginative contemporary cooking (not Sun evening or Mon) in restauranty dining pub in caravan land, just inside the sea wall; three starkly furnished linked rooms (two allowing children), wooden floor, big modern photographs, pine tables, wheelback and basket-weave dining chairs, Shepherd Neame Bitter and Spitfire, well chosen wines, no smoking area; must book to get a table; open all day Sun *(LYM, Basil Wynbergen, Louise English, N R White)*

SELLING [TR0557]

Sondes Arms [by station; Neames Forstal]: Unpretentious open-plan local distinguished by its good freshly made lunchtime food from sandwiches, baguettes and light dishes to flavour-filled main dishes; well kept Shepherd Neame Bitter, obliging friendly service, good prices, darts and pool; unobtrusive piped music; garden with play area *(Paul A Moore)*

SMARDEN [TQ8743]

☆ *Bell* [from Smarden follow lane between church and Chequers, then left at T junction; or from A274 take unsignposted turn E a mile N of B2077 to Smarden]: Pretty rose-covered 17th-c inn with striking chimneys, rambling low-beamed little rooms, dim-lit and snug, nicely creaky old furnishings on ancient brick and flagstones or quarry tiles, warm inglenooks, enjoyable bar food from ciabattas to steaks, Flowers IPA and several Shepherd Neame real ales, local cider, country wines, winter mulled wine, no smoking room; end games area with pool, juke box and TV; picnic-sets in very pleasant mature garden (watch the planes from Headcorn aerodrome), simple bedrooms *(Andrea Rampley, LYM, Kevin Thorpe, the Didler, Peter Meister)*

SOUTHFLEET [TQ5970]

☆ *Wheatsheaf* [High Cross Rd, Westwood; from A2, keep straight on through Southfleet itself, past the Ship]: Unpretentious and welcoming thatched and heavy-beamed Tudor country pub with padded barrel chairs, traditional high-backed settles, dried hops, inglenook log fire, soft lighting, good range of well kept ales, good value food – very popular Sun lunchtime; tables in good-sized garden with floodlit carp pond *(BB, N R White)*

ST MARGARET'S BAY [TR3744]

☆ *Coastguard* [The Bay]: Tremendous views to France from cheery and lively nautical-theme seaside pub, enjoyable food inc exceptional cheese choice and plenty of fresh fish, children's helpings of most things, three well kept changing real ales from small breweries, dozens of malt whiskies; children and dogs welcome, lots of tables on balcony with pretty hanging baskets and other plants, more down by beach below NT cliff and nr Pines Garden, open all day *(Kevin Thorpe, John Hendy, David and Ruth Shillitoe)*

ST MARY IN THE MARSH [TR0627]

Star [opp church]: Relaxed and remote down-to-earth pub, Tudor but very much modernised; friendly family service, well kept Shepherd Neame beers, good simple reasonably priced food from sandwiches to Sun lunch, huge log fireplace, pool, darts and quiz teams, amiable pub labrador; tables in nice garden, good value attractive beamed bedrooms with Romney Marsh views, lovely setting opposite ancient church *(Michael and Jenny Back, David Lowe)*

ST NICHOLAS AT WADE [TR2666]

Bell [just off A299; The Street]: Thriving olde-worlde 16th-c village pub, four beamed rooms, big log fires, well kept Adnams Broadside and Greene King IPA and Old Speckled Hen, good value generous unfussy food from baguettes to fresh fish and good Sun roasts in bar and restaurant, friendly staff, games and juke box in big back room; children and dogs welcome, open all day wknds *(Kevin Thorpe, Norman Fox, Paul and Ursula Randall)*

STONE STREET [TQ5655]

☆ *Padwell Arms* [off A25 E of Sevenoaks, on Seal—Plaxtol by-road; OS Sheet 188 map ref 569551]: Neatly kept orchard-view country local, red plush banquettes and airy back dining extension, wide choice of generous home-made food inc children's dishes and popular Sun roast, sensible prices, efficient friendly service, well kept changing real ales,

nice wines, good coffee, log fire and darts; long tables on front terrace (lovely flowering baskets and window boxes), more in pleasant back garden, plenty of shade, good walks *(BB, Fr Robert Marsh, Geoff Pidoux, Lynn Sharpless, the Didler, B and M Kendall, Debbie and Neil Hayter, Martin and Sue Day, Oliver and Sue Rowell)*

☆ *Snail*: Well run restaurant rather than pub, wide choice of good reasonably priced food at big oak farmhouse tables, good wines and well kept Harveys, ad lib coffee, friendly staff and relaxed atmosphere, pleasant brasserie layout with some stripped stone; attractive rambling garden *(BB, Melanie Ginger)*

STOWTING [TR1241]

☆ *Tiger* [off B2068 N of M20 junction 11]: Partly 17th-c country pub owned by village consortium, consistently good well presented food using fresh local produce, entertaining landlord, good staff and friendly atmosphere, good choice of well kept ales such as Everards, Fullers, Marstons Pedigree and Shepherd Neame Spitfire, attractive unpretentious furniture, rugs on bare boards, candles and good log fire, book and games shelf, back dining room; well behaved children allowed, garden tables with occasional barbecues and hitching rail, good jazz Mon (cl Mon lunchtime), open all day wknds *(LYM, Kevin Thorpe, Clive W Greaves)*

TENTERDEN [TQ8833]

Eight Bells [High St]: Pleasant old inn popular with older people for lunch, enjoyable food with nice veg, well kept ales, young helpful and patient staff, restful traditional long bare-boards bar, central courtyard glazed in as further no smoking eating area; easy wheelchair access, good value old-world beamed bedrooms, tasty breakfast *(Mike and Heather Watson, Peter Meister)*

William Caxton [West Cross; top of High St]: Cosy and friendly 15th-c local, heavy beams and bare boards, huge inglenook log fire, woodburner in smaller back bar, wide blackboard choice of enjoyable reasonably priced food made by licensees, well kept Shepherd Neame beers inc seasonal, pleasant small dining room; piped music; children welcome, tables in attractive front area, open all day, bedrooms *(Conor McGaughey, Kevin Thorpe, Peter Meister, the Didler)*

TILMANSTONE [TR3051]

Plough & Harrow [Dover Rd (A256)]: Small country pub with friendly staff, sensibly priced food all day (chef will try to meet your wishes), Shepherd Neame Bitter and Spitfire, log fire all year, extensive pig collection, lots of mirrors, posters and bank notes, bar billiards, steps down to no smoking conservatory restaurant; piped music, fruit machine; dogs welcome (no children in bar), pretty hillside garden, bedrooms, open all day *(Ian Phillips, Kevin Thorpe)*

TOYS HILL [TQ47521]

Fox & Hounds [off A25 in Brasted, via Brasted Chart and The Chart]: Emphasis now on good if not cheap changing choice of enjoyable food (not Sun evening), smart staff, extensive wine list and carpeted dining extension; tiled partly no smoking bar area with log fire, Greene King IPA and Abbot, books and guides to read; piped music, occasional live; disabled access, garden tables, open all day summer *(Kevin Thorpe, LYM, Kevin Flack, A D McDowall, Mrs Susan Powell)*

TUDELEY [TQ6145]
Poacher [Hartlake Rd]: Open-plan family dining pub, light and airy, with enjoyable straightforward food and well kept ales such as Marstons Pedigree, Oxenhope Old Tosser and Youngs Special *(Peter Meister)*

UNDER RIVER [TQ5551]
☆ *White Rock* [SE of Sevenoaks, off B245]: Pretty village pub, beams, bare boards and stripped brickwork, well kept Fullers London Pride, Harveys and a guest beer, enjoyable food from bar snacks to Sun lunch, good service, pool in larger public bar, back dining extension; quiet piped music; children welcome, picnic-sets on big back lawn, handy for Greensand Way (walkers asked to use side door) *(Peter Meister, Debbie and Neil Hayter, Martin and Sue Day, N R White)*

UPNOR [TQ7570]
Kings Arms [High St]: Old pub with three linked areas, enjoyable food, friendly service and well kept ales such as Fullers London Pride and Timothy Taylors Landlord; no no smoking area; delightful riverside village nr Upnor Castle, good walks *(Gerry and Rosemary Dobson, A and B D Craig, Ian and Nita Cooper)*

WEST FARLEIGH [TQ7152]
Tickled Trout [B2010 SW of Maidstone]: Pleasant dining pub with massive choice of decent food from the simple to the esoteric inc good fish, steak bargains for two, cheerful staff; colourful flowers and hanging baskets outside, Medway views (esp from big garden with play area), path down to river with good walks *(LYM, Janet Penfold)*

WEST MALLING [TQ6857]
Farmhouse [High St]: Former Bear tastefully reworked as pub and brasserie, pleasant atmosphere and good cross-section of customers, good beer choice on draught and in bottle, enjoyable food *(Derek Thomas)*
Lobster Pot [Swan St]: Open fire in quiet local's carpeted main bar with old posters, nets and lobster pots, step up to pleasant small panelled dining room, Adnams and five other changing ales usually inc Larkins, coffees in variety, enjoyable pub food (not Mon) from sandwiches up; darts and piped local radio down in small dark-panelled public bar, Mon

quiz night, some live music, upstairs skittle alley; open all day *(Kevin Thorpe)*

WESTBERE [TR1862]
Old Yew Tree [just off A18 Canterbury—Margate]: New restaurateur licensees in interesting very heavily beamed early 14th-c pub, good cooking from bar food to restaurant meals, Shepherd Neame Bitter and two changing beers from small breweries, cosy atmosphere, friendly staff; tables in garden behind *(Kevin Thorpe)*

WHITSTABLE [TR1167]
East Quay Shellfish Bar [East Quay]: Converted waterside oyster grading buildings, now a family-oriented place with big open fish tank and other amusements downstairs (which is no smoking); food from baguettes up, lots of shellfish and fish, Whitstable IPA tapped from the cask, various Whitstable bottled beers; open 12-5 wknds, perhaps longer hours in season *(Gerry and Rosemary Dobson)*

WICKHAMBREAUX [TR2258]
Rose [The Green]: Dating from 14th c, across green from church and watermill; three small rooms, stripped brick, beams and panelling, log fire in big fireplace, good value home-cooked food from fine sandwich choice, baked potatoes and baguettes to stews and Sun roasts, quick service, Greene King IPA and two guest beers such as Adnams and Wadworths 6X, bottled belgians, shove-ha'penny, piano (occasional live music); dogs on leads and children welcome (chocolate for sale), garden with summer barbecues, hanging baskets, open all day *(Kevin Thorpe)*

WORMSHILL [TQ8757]
Blacksmiths Arms [handy for M20 junction 8]: Attractive 18th-c low-beamed pub with big log fire, candles, old prints and well worn tiles in small bar area, smarter furnishings in upper no smoking room mainly for eating, flame-effect fire in stripped brick carpeted restaurant, good range of changing real ales, Stowford Press cider, nice choice of chip-free food from baguettes to some quite expensive main dishes; no children, cl Sun evening and Mon *(Kevin Thorpe, Philip and Cheryl Hill)*

YALDING [TQ6950]
☆ *Walnut Tree* [B2010 SW of Maidstone]: Pleasant brightly lit bar on several levels with lots of old beams, inglenook and interesting pictures, friendly efficient staff, reasonably priced food from good baguettes to fresh fish, bargain OAP wkdy lunch, wide restaurant choice, well kept Harveys and Wadworths 6X; piped music not over-intrusive, live music Sun evening; bedrooms, attractive village, handy for Organic Garden *(S and T Roberts)*

Please tell us if any Lucky Dips deserve to be upgraded to a main entry – and why.
No stamp needed: The Good Pub Guide, FREEPOST TN1569,
Wadhurst, E Sussex TN5 7BR.

Lancashire
(with Greater Manchester and Merseyside)

Classic town pubs, with several rooms, often Victorian or Edwardian décor, and sometimes even table drinks service, still flourish abundantly here. Splendid examples include the Philharmonic Dining Rooms in Liverpool and Britons Protection in Manchester, with the Lucky Dip section at the end of the chapter offering many more suggestions. Town or country, the archetypal Lancashire pub is particularly convivial and chatty, and scores over most other parts of Britain in its pricing. Drinks are notably cheap here, with a good chance still of finding beer for well under £2 a pint, especially in one of the many pubs brewing their own – the Church Inn at Uppermill was outstandingly cheap. Two local breweries, Holts and Hydes, have a splendid policy of low or very low pricing, and other local breweries, including the two big regional firms of Robinsons and Thwaites, generally offer good value. There are many smaller local breweries well worth looking out for, such as Moorhouses, Phoenix, Cains, Lees, Bowland, Bazens and Boggart Hole Clough. Generous food, often including some regional dishes, also tends to be priced attractively here. This is true both at the bargain end of the scale (and it's worth noting that an increasing number of town pubs here are now serving simple low-priced food right through the day till early evening), and among the rather smarter and foodier places. Even if some of these seem a little pricey by local standards, they offer real value compared with similar quality down south. Foody pubs currently on fine form here are the inviting Bay Horse at Bay Horse (very good food, super presentation), the Eagle & Child at Bispham Green (high praise for its food, good drinks too, and great atmosphere), the friendly Dog & Partridge up at Chipping (back in the *Guide* after a break, with careful cooking at good value prices), the Derby Arms at Longridge (a classic country pub with long views and good fish specials), the contemporary-look White Hart at Lydgate (interesting upmarket food, great choice of wines by the glass), the Oddfellows Arms in Mellor (new French landlord getting off to a good start, some interesting cooking, and it's now completely no smoking), the beautifully placed and welcoming Parkers Arms at Newton (a very broad range from cheerful snacks to more elaborate and costly things, good wines too), the Black Bull at Rimington (a remarkable collection of railway memorabilia as well as its good food), the restauranty Spread Eagle at Sawley, the airy and attractive Lunesdale Arms up at Tunstall (particularly good local meat among other enjoyable dishes), the lovely Inn at Whitewell (following the recent sad death of that great innkeeper Richard Bowman, it's now in the hands of his son Charles), and the cottagey New Inn at Yealand Conyers (enjoyable food all day – the specials are often exceptional here). From this impressive list of places that might suit a special meal out, it's the Eagle & Child at Bispham Green, on splendid form these days, that for the second year running secures the title of Lancashire Dining Pub of the Year. Among pubs of strong appeal in other ways here, ones currently doing particularly well include the Fox & Hounds at Barnston (a nice all-rounder, with some interesting and individual features), the nicely placed

Black Dog at Belmont (bargain food, drink and bedroom accommodation), the White House on Blackstone Edge (terrific views, bargain food), the Cartford at Little Eccleston (great atmosphere, splendid beers including ones brewed at the pub, good value bedrooms), the Marble Arch in Manchester (good beers including its own distinctive brews, good value pubby food), and the Dressers Arms at Wheelton (great service, fine choice of beers including their own brew, generous cheap food). The Lucky Dip section has plenty of stars, too: ones shining particularly brightly these days are the Rose & Crown in Edgworth, Fence Gate at Fence, Three Fishes at Great Mitton, Hest Bank Hotel, Sun in Lancaster, Peveril of the Peak in Manchester, Wheatsheaf at Raby, Royal Oak at Riley Green, Arden Arms in Stockport and Old Sparrow Hawk at Wheatley Lane.

BARNSTON SJ2783 Map 7
Fox & Hounds ♥ ▮ £
3 miles from M53 junction 3: A552 towards Woodchurch, then left on A551

This neat, chatty pub is full of interesting assembled bits and pieces. Tucked away opposite the serving counter is a charming old quarry-tiled corner with an antique kitchen range, copper kettles, built-in pine kitchen cupboards, and lots of earthenware or enamelled food bins. With its own entrance at the other end of the pub, a small locals' bar is worth a peek for its highly traditional layout – as well as a collection of hundreds of metal ashtrays on its delft shelf; beside it is a snug where children are allowed. The main part of the roomy bay-windowed lounge bar has red plush button-back built-in banquettes and plush-cushioned captain's chairs around the solid tables on its green turkey carpet, and plenty of old local prints on its cream walls below a delft shelf of china, with a collection of police and other headgear; TV, darts and dominoes. Arrive early if you want to eat the enjoyable, good-value lunchtime bar food, which includes open sandwiches (from £2.75), home-made soup (£2.95), filled baked potatoes (from £3.75), quiche or various platters such as greek salad (from £4.95), ploughman's (£6.50), with changing specials such as curry or chilli (£5.50), lasagne (£5.75), fish and chips (£5.95), hot pie of the day (£6.25), salmon and broccoli fishcakes (£6.25), roasts (£6.95) and duck breast (£7.75); during food times, the lounge and snug are no smoking. Marstons Pedigree, Theakstons Best and Old Peculier, and Websters Yorkshire are swiftly served by the well groomed staff, along with a couple of guests such as Weetwood Eastgate on handpump; 50 whiskies and 11 wines by the glass. There are some picnic-sets under cocktail parasols in the yard behind, below a dairy farm. *(Recommended by Charles and Pauline Stride, Mrs P J Carroll, Paul Boot, Mike and Linda Hudson, Pat and Tony Martin, Steve Whalley, Maurice and Gill McMahon)*

Free house ~ Licensee Ralph Leech ~ Real ale ~ Bar food (lunchtime) ~ (0151) 648 1323 ~ Children in family room ~ Dogs allowed in bar ~ Open 11-11; 12-10.30 Sun

BAY HORSE SD4952 Map 7
Bay Horse ⊕
1¼ miles from M6 junction 33: A6 southwards, then off on left

Arrive early or book to be sure of a table for the imaginative, locally sourced food at this inviting dining pub (note they don't accept lunchtime bookings for parties of fewer than eight). Beamed and comfortable, its red-walled bar is attractively decorated, with a good log fire, cushioned wall banquettes in bays, a friendly cat, and gentle lighting including table lamps on window sills; the atmosphere is warm and cosy. As well as a decent, fairly priced wine list (ten wines by the glass; fruit wines too), friendly staff serve well kept Moorhouses Pendle Witches Brew and Thwaites Lancaster Bomber, plus a guest such as Black Sheep or Robinsons on handpump; they also have around 25 malts. There are usually fresh flowers on the counter, and may be piped music (which can be obtrusive). The main emphasis though is on the food, with a series of small no smoking dining areas rambling around – the feel of a civilised country restaurant, with a red décor, another log fire, candle-flame-effect lights and nice tables, including one or two good-sized ones having an intimate corner to themselves. As well as lunchtime sandwiches (from £4.25) they now do a lunch menu that includes starters such as soup, caesar salad with smoked duck and anchovies and terrine of ham hock and local chicken (all £4), and main courses like poached fillet of naturally smoked haddock on mash, lancashire hotpot or roast corn-fed chicken with potato purée (all £10); delicious (but not cheap) evening dishes might include local shrimps potted with brandy and chives (£6.75 – may also be available in pots to buy and take away), lamb shank slow-cooked in ale and thyme (£14.95), and fillet of bass (£17.50); puddings include warm treacle and walnut tart with toffee ice-cream and crème brûlée (£4.75). It's peacefully set, and there are tables out in the garden behind (peaceful, though the railway is not far off). *(Recommended by Mrs P J Carroll, Sarah and Peter Gooderham, Tony and Maggie Harwood, Gwyn and Anne Wake, A C English, J S Burn, Matt and Vicky Wharton, John Kane, Pat and Sam Roberts, Jo Lilley, Simon Calvert, Revd D Glover, Christine and Neil Townend, Mike and Linda Hudson, Jane Bailey, Peter and Jean Walker)*

Mitchells ~ Tenant Craig Wilkinson ~ Real ale ~ Bar food (12-2(3 Sun), 7-9.15; not Sun evening, not Mon) ~ Restaurant ~ (01524) 791204 ~ Children in restaurant ~ Open 12-3(2 Sat), 6.30-11; 12-4, 8-10.30 Sun

BELMONT SD6716 Map 7
Black Dog £ 🛏️
A675

You can eat and drink very well at this characterful 18th-c farmhouse for remarkably low prices (and the homely bedrooms are reasonable too): the Holts Bitter is just £1.51 a pint – they also have Mild and often a guest from the Holts range, all well kept on handpump – and most of the main courses are under £6. Cosy and atmospheric, the original cheery and traditional small rooms around the bar are packed with antiques and bric-a-brac, from railwaymen's lamps, bedpans and chamber-pots to landscape paintings. There are also service bells for the sturdy built-in curved seats, rush-seated mahogany chairs, and coal fires, and a plush turquoise banquette in the bay opposite the bar. Two rooms (one very small) off the main bar are no smoking, and the games room has a fruit machine; piped music. Outside, two long benches on the sheltered sunny side of the pub give delightful views of the moors above the nearby trees and houses. Enjoyably straightforward, generously served bar food includes soup (£2.36), garlic mushroom in stilton (£3.50), cottage pie (£5.40), battered cod (£5.85), steak and ale pie (£5.95), chicken and black pudding stack (£6.10); puddings (£2.75); until 6pm you can also get sandwiches (from £3.10) and baked potatoes (from £3). They also do a Sunday lunch (£5.75). It tends to fill up quickly; they don't take bookings on Sunday, so get there early for a table. A track leads from the village up Winter Hill and (from the lane to Rivington) on to Anglezarke Moor, and there are paths from the dam of the nearby Belmont Reservoir. *(Recommended by Peter Abbott, Pam and John Smith, Len Beattie, Peter Heaton, MLR, Pat and Tony Martin, Norma and Noel Thomas)*

Holts ~ Manager Victor Dewbrey ~ Real ale ~ Bar food (12-2, 6-8.30 Mon-Thurs (not Tues evening); 12-8.30 Fri-Sat; 12-7 Sun) ~ (01204) 811218 ~ Children in no smoking areas ~ Open 12-11(10.30 Sun) ~ Bedrooms: /£42S

> Post Office address codings confusingly give the impression that some pubs are in Lancashire when they're really in Yorkshire (which is where we list them).

BISPHAM GREEN SD4813 Map 7

Eagle & Child 🍴 ♟ 🍺

Maltkiln Lane (Parbold—Croston road, off B5246)

Lancashire Dining Pub of the Year

You can try your hand at bowls or croquet on the neat green outside this brick pub, but beware that the crowns deceive even the most experienced players. The friendly former landlady came back out of retirement to run the pub, assisted by a really good Scots bar manager, and it continues to earn high praise from readers for its food and drink. Well divided by stubs of walls, the largely open-plan bar is appealingly simple and civilised. Attractively understated old furnishings include a mix of small oak chairs around tables in corners, an oak coffer, several handsomely carved antique oak settles (the finest apparently made partly from a 16th-c wedding bed-head), and old hunting prints and engravings. There's coir matting in the snug, and oriental rugs on flagstones in front of the fine old stone fireplaces; unobtrusive piped music, and most of the pub is no smoking. You'll find quite an emphasis on the well cooked food, and besides snacks (not Saturday evening) such as sandwiches with chips and salad (from £4.25), fish and chips or steak and ale pie (£8), the friendly and helpful staff serve interesting daily changing specials such as asparagus and garden pea risotto (£8.50), sautéed lambs liver with bacon mash (£9), rump steak (£10.50) and bass with oriental vegetables (£12.50); puddings might include butterscotch tart or lychee and lemon grass brûlée (£4). A good range of well kept beers includes Moorhouses Black Cat and Thwaites, with four changing guest ales from brewers such as Archers, Hanbys and Phoenix, and they also have changing farm cider, decent wines, some country wines and around 40 malt whiskies. The pub holds a popular beer festival in May over the first bank holiday weekend. A nice wild garden has crested newts and nesting moorhens; the pub's dogs are called Harry and Doris. *(Recommended by Revd D Glover, A P Seymour, John and Claire Pettifer, Brian Kneale, P R Morgan, Mrs H Turner, Johnny Cohen, Mandy and Simon King, Mrs P J Carroll, Yvonne and Mike Meadley, Pat and Roger Fereday, Steve Whalley, Paul Humphreys, Mike Tucker, MLR, Jack Clark, Margaret and Jeff Graham)*

Free house ~ Licensees Monica Evans and David Anderson ~ Real ale ~ Bar food (12-2, 6-8.30(9 Fri, Sat); 12-8.30 Sun) ~ (01257) 462297 ~ Children in eating area of bar ~ Dogs allowed in bar ~ Open 12-3, 5.30-11; 12-10.30 Sun

BLACKSTONE EDGE SD9716 Map 7

White House £

A58 Ripponden—Littleborough, just W of B6138

For walkers along the Pennine Way, this isolated 17th-c pub, on the moors and 400 metres (1,300ft) above sea level, makes an ideal stopping point, providing welcome shelter from the elements. In decent conditions, the far-ranging view over the spectacularly empty scenery from the no smoking Moorland Room is quite something. Inside the atmosphere is cheery, and the cosily bustling main bar has a turkey carpet in front of a blazing coal fire, and a large-scale map of the area. The snug Pennine Room opens off here, with brightly coloured antimacassars on its small soft settees; there's also a dining extension. A spacious room on the left has comfortable seating, and a big horseshoe window has impressive moorland views; fruit machine. Theakstons Best is promptly served by the friendly staff along with three guests from brewers such as Black Sheep, Moorhouses and Timothy Taylors; also a fair selection of bottled belgian beers and malt whiskies. The reasonably priced unpretentious menu includes tasty bar food such as soup (£2), sandwiches (from £3), cumberland sausage with egg or beef curry (£4.95), steak and kidney pie (£5.25), salmon (£6.95), halibut or lamb henry (£8.95), with puddings such as home-made apple pie (from £2.50). Muddy boots can be left in the porch. Blackstone Edge itself is a breezy moorland ridge easily reached from the pub, and close by is what's often cited as one of Britain's best-preserved sections of Roman road. *(Recommended by MLR, Len Beattie, Mr and Mrs John Taylor, Dennis Jones)*

Free house ~ Licensee Neville Marney ~ Real ale ~ Bar food (12-2, 6.30-9.30; 12-9.30 Sun)
~ (01706) 378456 ~ Children welcome ~ Open 12-3, 6.30-11; 12-11 Sun

BURY SD8115 Map 7
Lord Raglan ✦

2 miles off M66 northbound, junction 1; A56 S then left in Walmersley, up long cobbled
lane to Mount Pleasant, Nangreaves; if coming from N, stay on A56 S instead of joining
M66, and turn left in Walmersley as above

The own-brew beers are a big attraction at this 18th-c pub (run by the same family
for nearly half a century) on the moors above Bury. On handpump alongside a
seasonal guest are well kept Leyden Balaclava, Black Pudding, Crowning Glory,
Forever Bury, Light Brigade, Nanny Flyer, Raglan Steve and Sebastopol, and they
hold a beer festival in June. They've also 20 malt whiskies and interesting foreign
bottled beers; TV, dominoes and piped music. All sorts of bric-a-brac is dotted
around the snugly welcoming neatly kept beamed front bar, with lots of pewter,
brass and interesting antique clocks, and there's a mix of spindleback chairs and old
wooden settles. The back room has a huge open fire, china on a high delft shelf and
welsh dresser, and windows giving a splendid view down the valley. A plainer but
more spacious dining room on the left is panelled in light wood. Available in the
bar or the restaurant, tasty dishes include open sandwiches (from around £2.95),
baked potatoes (£4.50), chilli con carne or cumberland sausage and egg (£5.25), red
thai vegetable curry or chicken balti (£7.25), poached salmon fillet or fried plaice
(£8.25), chicken chasseur (£8.50), and steaks (from £9.25), with puddings such as
sticky toffee pudding (£3.25); children's meals (£2.75). More reports please.
(Recommended by Steve Whalley, Graham Patterson, Mary Kirman and Tim Jefferson)

Own brew ~ Licensee Brendan Leyden ~ Real ale ~ Bar food ~ Restaurant ~
(0161) 764 6680 ~ Children in eating area of bar and restaurant ~ Dogs allowed in bar ~
Open 12-2.30, 7(5 Fri)-11; 12-11(10.30 Sun) Sat

CHIPPING SD6243 Map 7
Dog & Partridge ♀

Hesketh Lane; crossroads Chipping—Longridge with Inglewhite—Clitheroe

In very attractive countryside between Longridge and Wolf Fell, this is a very
comfortable, snugly genteel dining pub dating in part back to 1515, though it has
been much modernised and extended since, with the eating space now spreading
over into a nearby stable. The comfortable main lounge has small armchairs around
fairly close-set low tables on a blue patterned carpet, brown-painted beams, a good
winter log fire, and multicoloured lanterns; the pub has piped music. Served by
friendly and well trained staff, the enjoyable lunchtime bar food (not Sunday)
includes home-made soup (£3.20), sandwiches (from £4.50), duck and orange pâté
(£4.90), around four vegetarian dishes such as curried nut roast or broccoli and
stilton pancakes (£8.75), home-made steak and kidney pie with shortcrust pastry or
roast chicken with stuffing (£9), roast duckling with apple sauce and stuffing
(£12.50) and grilled sirloin steak with mushrooms (£13.75), as well as daily
lunchtime and evening specials like very good hot potted shrimps (£4.80), battered
haddock (£9) or roast pheasant (£10.50) and puddings such as home-made fruit pie
or raspberry shortcake (£4). They have well kept Tetleys Bitter and Mild with a
weekly changing guest such as Black Sheep Bitter on handpump. Smart casual dress
is preferred in the restaurant – open evenings and Sunday lunchtime; dining areas
are no smoking, and you may need to book. *(Recommended by J F M and M West,
Norma and Noel Thomas, Maurice and Della Andrew)*

Free house ~ Licensee Peter Barr ~ Real ale ~ Bar food (12-1.45, 7-9; not Sun) ~
Restaurant (7-9 Mon-Sat; 11.45-8.30 Sun) ~ (01995) 61201 ~ Children welcome ~
Open 11.45-3, 6.45-11; 11.45-10.30 Sun

Pubs with outstanding views are listed at the back of the book.

GOOSNARGH SD5839 Map 7 🏠

Horns ♀ 🛏

Pub signed from village, about 2 miles towards Chipping below Beacon Fell

Older than its mock-Tudor façade suggests, this welcoming civilised former coaching inn, in rolling country beneath the Pennines, is valued by many readers as a place to eat. Besides sandwiches (from £4.50), and ploughman's (£5.95), nicely presented dishes include soup (£4.25), home-made duck liver pâté (£4.75), creamy garlic shrimps (£4.95), grilled plaice (£8.50), home-made steak and kidney pie (£8.95), roast local pheasant (£9.50) and roast duckling with apple sauce (£10.25), with specials such as tomato and lancashire cheese salad or black pudding from Bury with hot mustard sauce (£5.25), battered cod with mushy peas (£8.95) and roast baby leg of lamb with cranberry (£9.50); home-made puddings (£4.95). The neatly kept snug rooms have colourful flower displays and winter log fires, and a relaxing atmosphere; beyond the lobby, the pleasant front bar opens into attractively decorated middle rooms. The dining rooms and bedrooms are no smoking; piped music. They don't keep real ales, but there's an extensive wine list with quite a few by the glass, and a fine choice of malt whiskies. *(Recommended by Nikki Wild, Dr and Mrs T E Hothersall, Ken Richards, Edward Mirzoeff, Margaret Dickinson, Rev D E and Mrs J A Shapland, Dr A McCormick)*

Free house ~ Licensee Mark Woods ~ Bar food (not lunchtime Sun, Mon, or Sat evening) ~ Restaurant ~ (01772) 865230 ~ Children in eating area of bar and restaurant ~ Open 11.30-3, 6.30-11; 12-3, 6.30-10.30 Sun; closed Mon lunchtime ~ Bedrooms: £59B/£79B

LITTLE ECCLESTON SD4139 Map 7

Cartford 🍽 £ 🛏

Cartford Lane, off A586 Garstang—Blackpool, by toll bridge

The tidal River Wyre flows beneath a toll bridge within yards of this pub, which has gained a deserved reputation for its interesting and very well kept real ales. Aside from a couple from Hart (their own good microbrewery behind the pub, with brewery tours by arrangement), you'll find Boddingtons, Fullers London Pride and up to five changing ales from interesting brewers such as Boggart Hole Clough, Jennings and Salopian; also decent house wines and several malt whiskies. The rambling interior has oak beams, dried flowers, a log fire and an unusual layout on four different levels, with uncoordinated seating areas; pool, darts, fruit machine, dominoes and piped music. Two levels are largely set for dining (the upstairs part is no smoking). Straightforward low-priced bar food includes soup (£2.60), sandwiches (from £3.55), steak and mushroom pie (£5.55), battered haddock (£5.25), and 12oz sirloin steak (£9.95), with specials. There are tables out in a garden (not by the water), with a play area; the pub has fishing rights along 1½ miles of the river. *(Recommended by Keith and Chris O'Neill, Tony and Maggie Harwood, Dr and Mrs A K Clarke, Steve Whalley, Pam and John Smith, David Green, MLR, Maurice and Gill McMahon)*

Own brew ~ Licensee Andrew Mellodew ~ Real ale ~ Bar food (12-2, 6.30-9.30; 12-9 Sun) ~ (01995) 670166 ~ Children welcome ~ Dogs welcome ~ Open 12(11.30 Sat)-3, 6.30-11; 12-10.30 Sun ~ Bedrooms: £36.95B/£48.95B

LIVERPOOL SJ4395 Map 7

Baltic Fleet 🍽 £

Wapping

Just across the water from Albert Dock, this strikingly maritime own-brew pub is gradually becoming more of a local as the area is being developed and more people move in. The owner is now focusing on the brewery in the basement, and has recently let the pub itself to a new licensee, who continues to sell an interesting range of reasonably priced beer and has expanded the range of food on offer. Seven beers well kept on handpump include the own-brew regulars Cornhill Pils, Tabley Mild, Wapping Bitter, Mild and Summer Ale alongside guests from brewers such as

Tigertops on handpump; also several wines by the glass and Saxon's farm cider. The triangular end-of-terrace building has big arched windows and a bright green, burgundy and white painted exterior. An abundance of interior woodwork and stout mahogany board floors adds to its nautical feel, as do the interesting old mersey shipping prints. There's also a good mix of old school furniture and dark wood tables; piped music. Very reasonably priced bar food on the blackboard typically includes soup (£2.95), gravadlax (£3.95), steak pie or black pudding with caramelised apples and mash (£4.50), scandinavian meatballs with spicy tomato sauce (£4.50), fillet of trout with crayfish sauce (£6.95) and desserts like chocolate walnut brownie or sticky toffee pudding (£2.95); very popular two-course Sunday lunch, with roasts, fish and a vegetarian choice (£9.95); the more expensive upstairs restaurant has some of these as well as other dishes. The back of the bar area and part of the restaurant are no smoking. *(Recommended by Patrick Hancock, the Didler, Paul Davies, MLR, Eric Robinson, Jacqueline Pratt, Jack Clark)*

Own brew ~ Licensee Simon Holt ~ Real ale ~ Bar food (12-2.30, 6-9.30) ~ Restaurant ~ (0151) 709 3116 ~ Children in eating area of bar and restaurant ~ Open 12-11(10.30 Sun)

Philharmonic Dining Rooms ★ ◗

36 Hope Street; corner of Hardman Street

The astonishing period details of this magnificent late marble-fronted Victorian building, once a favourite haunt of John Lennon, extend right down to the sanitary arrangements: don't miss the original 1890s Adamant gents' lavatory (all pink marble and glinting mosaics); ladies are allowed a look if they ask first. It's also well worth a visit here for the beer: they have up to ten changing guest ales well kept on handpump, with usually a Cains beer and others such as Batemans, Caledonian and Humpty Dumptys Broadlands. The heart of the building is a mosaic-faced serving counter, from which heavily carved and polished mahogany partitions radiate under the intricate plasterwork high ceiling. The echoing main hall is decorated with stained glass including contemporary portraits of Boer War heroes Baden-Powell and Lord Roberts, rich panelling, a huge mosaic floor, and copper panels of musicians in an alcove above the fireplace. More stained glass in one of the little lounges declares 'Music is the universal language of mankind', and backs this up with illustrations of musical instruments; there are two plushly comfortable sitting rooms; two side rooms are called Brahms and Liszt (the latter and the bar counter are no smoking). Straightforward lunchtime food (which can be eaten only in the table-service grand lounge dining room) could include soup (£2.95), baked potatoes (from £4.25), sandwiches (from £4.25, hot sandwiches from £4.95), ploughman's (£5.95), steak pie or fish and chips (£6.50) and puddings (from £2.75); they also have evening restaurant food. The pub attracts a pleasant mix of customers, with theatre-goers, students, locals and tourists making up the contented bustle; fruit machine and mellow piped jazz or blues. No children inside. *(Recommended by the Didler, Dorsan Baker, Patrick Hancock, Peter F Marshall, Eric Robinson, Jacqueline Pratt, Joe Green)*

Mitchells & Butlers ~ Manager Marie-Louise Wong ~ Real ale ~ Bar food (12-3) ~ Restaurant ~ (0151) 707 2837 ~ Open 12-11(10.30 Sun); closed August bank hol

LONGRIDGE SD6039 Map 7
Derby Arms ♀

Chipping Road, Thornley; 1½ miles N of Longridge on back road to Chipping

This long-established stone-built country pub has a reassuring feeling of continuity over many years. The same welcoming family has run the pub for over 20 years (and the current licensee's great-grandmother was married from here in 1898). In the main bar it's very much hunting and fishing, with old photographs commemorating notable catches, some nicely mounted bait above the comfortable red plush seats, and a stuffed pheasant that seems to be flying in through the wall. To the right is a smaller room with sporting trophies and mementoes, and a regimental tie collection, while off to the left are a couple of no smoking dining areas. The gents' has dozens of riddles on the wall; you can buy a sheet of them in the bar (the money goes to charity). Along with a good range of wines including several half-bottles and a dozen or so by the glass (they're particularly strong on south african), you'll find well kept Black Sheep and Marstons Pedigree on handpump. Enjoyable bar food might include sandwiches (from £3.95), soup (£3.30), ploughman's (£4.95), ham, egg and chips, spicy chicken satay or vegetarian hotpot (£7.95), seafood pasta or steak and kidney pudding (£8.95), chargrilled lamb chops (£10.95), and 10oz sirloin steak (£12.95), plus local game in season and several fish specials such as fresh dressed crab (£7.25, or £9.95 as a main course) and fresh monkfish in beer batter (£7.95 or £14.95); puddings such as bread and butter pudding or sherry trifle (£3.75); potatoes and vegetables come in separate dishes. A few tables out in front, and another two behind the car park have fine views across to the Forest of Bowland. Note that they sometimes close earlier than midnight during the week. *(Recommended by Peter and Jean Walker, Norma and Noel Thomas, Jim and Maggie Cowell, Revd D Glover, Jo Lilley, Simon Calvert, Maurice and Gill McMahon)*

Inn Partnership (Pubmaster) ~ Lease Mrs G M Walne ~ Real ale ~ Bar food (12-2.15, 6.15-9.30(10 Fri, 10.15 Sat); 12-9.15 Sun) ~ Restaurant ~ (01772) 782623 ~ Children in restaurant ~ Live jazz some nights ~ Open 12-3, 6-12; 12-12 Sat; 12-11.30 Sun

LYDGATE SD9704 Map 7 🏠
White Hart ⑪ ♀ ⇐

Stockport Road; Lydgate not marked on some maps so not to be confused with the one near Todmorden; take A669 Oldham—Saddleworth, and after almost 2½ miles turn right at brow of hill onto A6050, Stockport Road

Happy chat from clearly satisfied diners fills the warmly elegant brasserie, the biggest of the main rooms at this upmarket stone-built inn overlooking Saddleworth Moor. Its reputation continues as one of the finest places to eat in the area, and though it feels a little like a smart restaurant with rooms, it's very much a proper pub too, with a good few locals clustered round the bar, or in the two simpler rooms at the end. Many of the building's older features remain, but the overall style is more contemporary than traditional, so beams and exposed stonework are blended skilfully with deep red or purple walls, punctuated with a mix of modern paintings, black and white photos, and stylised local scenes; most rooms have a fireplace, and fresh flowers; all dining areas are no smoking. The thoughtfully prepared meals are pricier than in most pubs around here, but the quality is consistently high; a typical menu might include soup (£4.95), open sandwiches (from £6.25), starters like terrine of spiced pork with pickled red cabbage (£6.50), ravioli of chicken and wild mushroom with mushroom butter and hazelnut salad (£6.95) or a platter of six oysters (£7.50), followed perhaps by griddled sweet potatoes with curried leek risotto (£13.75), fillet of haddock in beer batter with fried potatoes, minted peas and caper beurre blanc (£14.75) and pot-roast rump of lamb or roast maize-fed chicken breast with wild garlic butter, thyme hash brown and wilted greens (£16.25); among the puddings might be apple strudel (£5) or steamed chocolate pudding (£5.50). They do a two-course lunch for £12.50 (£14.75 Sun), and a fish menu on Tuesday evenings. Well kept Lees Bitter, Tetleys, Timothy Taylors Landlord and a changing guest on handpump; the wine list includes around 15 by the glass. Good service from smartly dressed staff. There are picnic sets on the lawn behind. Bedrooms are comfortable, with free internet access. They have plenty of special events based around themed menus, including wine and beer tastings and even a brass band contest. The lavatories are unusually smart. *(Recommended by Revd D Glover, John and Sylvia Harrop, Mrs P J Carroll, Keith Moss)*

Free house ~ Licensee Charles Brierley ~ Real ale ~ Bar food (12-2.30, 6-9.30 Mon-Sat; 1-7.30 Sun) ~ Restaurant ~ (01457) 872566 ~ Well behaved children welcome ~ Open 12-11(10.30 Sun) ~ Bedrooms: £85B/£110B

Waterside pubs are listed at the back of the book.

LYTHAM SD3627 Map 7

Taps ■ £

A584 S of Blackpool; Henry Street – in centre, one street in from West Beach

Eight very well kept real ales make this cheerful seaside pub deservedly popular, but even when it's full to capacity – which is often – the service remains efficient and friendly. With a good mix of visitors, the Victorian-style bare-boarded bar has a sociable unassuming feel, plenty of stained-glass decoration in the windows, depictions of fish and gulls reflecting the pub's proximity to the beach (a couple of minutes' walk away), captain's chairs in bays around the sides, open fires, and a coal-effect gas fire between two built-in bookcases at one end. There's also an expanding collection of rugby memorabilia with old photographs and portraits of rugby stars on the walls; shove-ha'penny, dominoes, a quiz machine and a fruit machine. A view-in cellar lets you admire the beers, and alongside Boddingtons, regularly changing guests on handpump might include Batemans Spring Breeze, Coach House Honeypot, Phoenix Double Gold, Taps (brewed for the pub by Titanic) Best and Dark, and Woods Best and Bomber County; they also usually serve some country wines and a farm cider. There are seat belts on the bar and headrests in the gents' to help keep you out of harm's way if you have one too many. Served only at lunchtime, a few cheap, straightforward bar snacks include sandwiches (from £2.25; soup and a hot roast sandwich from £3.95), filled baked potatoes or burgers (from £2.50), and chilli or curry (£3.95). There are a few seats and a heated canopied area outside. Parking is difficult near the pub so it's probably best to park at the West Beach car park on the seafront (free on Sunday), and walk. *(Recommended by Dr and Mrs A K Clarke, Steve Whalley, Ken Richards, Jo Lilley, Simon Calvert, Pat and Tony Martin, Pam and John Smith)*

Greene King ~ Manager Ian Rigg ~ Real ale ~ Bar food (12-2.30, not Sun) ~ No credit cards ~ (01253) 736226 ~ Children welcome until 8pm ~ Open 11-11; 12-10.30 Sun

MANCHESTER SJ7796 Map 7

Britons Protection ♀ £

Great Bridgewater Street, corner of Lower Mosley Street

On various evenings this bustling city pub hosts a range of events, including poetry readings, storytelling, silent film shows and acoustic gigs. The rather plush little front bar has a fine chequered tile floor, some glossy brown and russet wall tiles, solid woodwork and elaborate plastering. A tiled passage lined with battle murals depicting the Peterloo Massacre of 1819, which took place a few hundred yards away, leads to two cosy inner lounges, one served by hatch, with attractive brass and etched glass wall lamps, a mirror above the coal-effect gas fire in the simple art nouveau fireplace, and again good solidly comfortable furnishings. As something of a tribute to Manchester's notorious climate, the massive bar counter has a pair of heating pipes as its footrail. Although it's busy at lunchtime, it's usually quiet and relaxed in the evenings; the atmosphere is welcoming, and the staff are friendly, though it's not really a place for children. As well as around 235 malt whiskies and bourbons, they have Jennings, Robinsons, Tetleys and two changing guests such as Coach House Ostlers and Popplethwaites superbly kept on handpump, and good wines too. Straightforward bar food includes home-made soup (£1.85), sandwiches (from £2), ploughman's (£4), ham and egg (£4.50, leek and mushroom crumble or various pies (£4.95) and home-made daily specials (from £4.75); piped music. There are tables out on the garden behind. The pub is handy for Bridgewater Hall (and it is well known to many orchestral players), and the GMEX centre. *(Recommended by the Didler, Peter F Marshall, Stephen Buckley, Patrick Hancock, Russell Lewin, Pam and John Smith, Dennis Jones, Stephen and Jean Curtis)*

Punch ~ Lease Peter Barnett ~ Real ale ~ Bar food (11(12 Sat)-2.30; not Sun) ~ (0161) 236 5895 ~ Old time music hall first Tues of month, monthly film shows, storytelling nights and poetry readings; acoustic gigs at various times ~ Open 11(12 Sat)-11; 11-10.30 Sun

Dukes 92 £

Castle Street, below the bottom end of Deansgate

Walk past the re-creation of Manchester's Roman fort, under a soaring railway arch and you reach this most evocative place, a converted stable block among old rejuvenated warehouses by the Rochdale Canal. It has tables out by the canal basin which opens into the bottom lock of the canal. Inside, black wrought-iron work contrasts boldly with whitewashed bare plaster walls, the handsome bar is granite-topped, and an elegant spiral staircase leads to an upper room and balcony. Down in the main room the fine mix of furnishings is mainly rather Edwardian in mood, with one particularly massive table, elegantly comfortable chaises-longues and deep armchairs. They have Moorhouses and Timothy Taylors well kept on handpump and do an excellent range of over three dozen cheeses and several pâtés with a generous helping of granary bread (£5.50, served till 8.30). Other good value bar food includes soup (£2.95), toasties (from £3.25), filled baked potatoes or open sandwiches (from £3.95), salads (from £5.95) and three weekly specials like fish and chips or chicken curry (£5.95) as well as stone-baked pizzas (from £5.95). They've decent wines, a wide choice of malt whiskies, and the belgian wheat beer Hoegaarden on tap; piped jazz. The gallery has temporary exhibitions of local artwork. *(Recommended by John Fiander, Brian and Anna Marsden, Russell Lewin, Stephen Buckley, Mrs Hazel Rainer)*

Free house ~ Licensee James Ramsbottom ~ Real ale ~ Bar food (12-3(6 Fri-Sun)) ~ Restaurant ~ (0161) 839 8646 ~ Children in eating area of bar and restaurant ~ Dogs allowed in bar ~ Open 11.30-11(12 Fri-Sat); 12-10.30 Sun

Marble Arch ◀ £

Rochdale Road (A664), Ancoats; corner of Gould Street, just E of Victoria Station

The striking interior of this Victorian alehouse is beautifully preserved, and readers also enjoy it for its outstanding range of real ales (including the pub's own brew), very good value food and welcoming atmosphere. The pub has a magnificently restored lightly barrel-vaulted high ceiling, and extensive marble and tiling – the frieze advertising various spirits, and the chimneybreast above the carved wooden mantelpiece, particularly stand out. Seating is a cheerful mix of pews, wing-back chairs, cushioned settles and deep armchairs, around a mix of tables, and all the walls are stripped back to the glazed brick; there's a collection of breweriana, and a cabinet has a display of pump clips; a separate back room for eating is no smoking. The sloping mosaic floor in the bar can be a bit disconcerting after a few pints; fruit machine, pinball and a juke box. From windows at the back, you can look out over the brewery (tours by arrangement) where they produce the distinctive Lagonda IPA, Manchester Bitter, Marble Bitter, Marble Ginger Ale as well as a seasonal brew and they also have four guest ales such as Bazens Riverside and Phoenix Pale Moonlight; farm cider. They do soup or haddock goujons (£2.95), generously filled sandwiches (£4.50), curry or potato gnocchi with baby artichokes and tomatoes (£5.95), lemon sole or steak and ale pie (£6.95) and seared fillet of beef or roasted lamb rump (£7.95). There's a little garden. The Laurel and Hardy Preservation Society meet here on the third Wednesday of the month and show old films. *(Recommended by G Coates, Revd D Glover, the Didler, Peter F Marshall, Pat and Tony Martin, Miss Schofield, Mr Robinson)*

Own brew ~ Licensee John Evason ~ Real ale ~ Bar food (12-7.30(5.30 Sun)) ~ (0161) 832 5914 ~ Well behaved children in eating area of bar ~ Dogs allowed in bar ~ Open 11.30-11; 12-11(10.30 Sun) Sat

---

Cribbage is a card game using a block of wood with holes for matchsticks or special pins to score with; regulars in cribbage pubs are usually happy to teach strangers how to play.

MELLOR SJ9888 Map 7
Oddfellows Arms

Heading out of Marple on the A626 towards Glossop, Mellor is the next road after the B6102, signposted off on the right at Marple Bridge; keep on for nearly 2 miles up Longhurst Lane and into Moor End Road

This pleasant old pub has recently gained a new French owner, and early reports show that while its atmosphere is as buoyant as ever, its food if anything is even more of an attraction now. It's refreshingly devoid of piped music and games machines, and is now completely no smoking; get here early to be sure of a table. A wide choice of dishes might include soup (£3.25), field mushrooms grilled with mozzarella, parmesan and pesto (£4.95), black pudding salad (£4.95 or £7.50 as a main course), thai spiced prawns (£5.50), club sandwich with chicken, bacon, egg, avocado, peppers, served with chips (£6.25), sausage and champ (£7.95), fish and chips (£9.25), proper cassoulet of duck, pork, ham and haricot beans (£10.95), and specials such as roasted figs stuffed with blue cheese and wrapped in parma ham (£5.95), roast of the day (£8.95) or red mullet (£12.95). The pleasant low-ceilinged flagstoned bar has nice open fires; there's a small no smoking restaurant upstairs. Served with or without a sparkler, Adnams Southwold, Marstons Best, Phoenix Arizona and a weekly changing guest such as Cottage Best are well kept on handpump. There are a few tables out by the road. It can be tricky to secure a parking space when they're busy. *(Recommended by Mrs P J Carroll, Maurice and Della Andrew, Brian and Anna Marsden, Michael Butler, Jo Lilley, Simon Calvert, Roger Yates)*

Free house ~ Licensee Olivier Berton ~ Real ale ~ Bar food (12-2, 6.30-9.30; not Sun evening) ~ Restaurant ~ (0161) 449 7826 ~ Children welcome ~ Dogs allowed in bar ~ Open 12-3, 5.30-11(7-10.30 Sun); closed Mon

NEWTON SD6950 Map 7
Parkers Arms ♀

B6478 7 miles N of Clitheroe

An enchanting feature of this cream and green pub is the view from the garden and restaurant, towards the Hodder valley and the distant fells, with scarcely another building in sight. You get the feeling the welcoming staff enjoy the place as much as the customers. It's comfortably furnished, with red plush button-back banquettes, a mix of chairs and tables, stuffed animals, prints, and an open fire; piped music, cribbage, dominoes. Beyond an arch is a similar area with sensibly placed darts, a log fire, fruit machine and TV; it can get smoky. Well kept Flowers IPA and Tetleys on handpump along with a couple of guests such as Copper Dragon, with a good range of malt whiskies and around 50 wines (ten by the glass). Predominantly home-made bar food includes lunchtime sandwiches (from £3.65), basket meals such as scampi or battered haddock (£4.95), and leek, ham and chicken crumble (£7.50), kleftiko (£10.95), and dover sole with prawn mornay sauce (£16.95), with puddings such as white chocolate and raspberry cheesecake or fruit crumble (£3.75); the charming restaurant is no smoking. They keep lots of pets – pygmy goats, rabbits, guinea pigs, hens, pheasants, parrots and two playful black labradors. *(Recommended by Norma and Noel Thomas, David Barnes, Martin Knowles, Tony and Ann Bennett-Hughes, Melanie Lawrenson)*

Enterprise ~ Lease Barbara Clayton ~ Real ale ~ Bar food (12-2.30, 6-9; 12-9 Sat-Sun) ~ Restaurant ~ (01200) 446236 ~ Children welcome until 9pm ~ Open 11-3, 5-11; 11-11 Sat; 12-10.30 Sun ~ Bedrooms: /£50S

RIBCHESTER SD6435 Map 7

White Bull 🛏

Church Street; turn off B6245 at sharp corner by Black Bull

Not many pubs can boast a Roman bathhouse in view from the garden, but this one can – Ribchester itself is a Roman settlement with a small Roman museum – and the 18th-c pub porch actually incorporates tuscan pillars of Roman origin brought from a nearby building. A new licensee took over the running of this dining pub late in 2004, and feedback from readers has so far been favourable. It has a spacious main bar with comfortable old settles, Victorian advertisements and various prints, and a stuffed fox in two halves that looks as if it's jumping through the wall. Most areas are set out for eating during the day, and food, from a reasonably priced menu, includes home-made soup (£2.95), sandwiches (from £3.50), duck spring rolls with sweet chilli and hoisin sauce (£3.50), beef and ale pie (£6.50), local sausage and mash (£7), salmon fillet (£7.95), chicken breast with black pudding and mustard mash (£8.50), duck breast with fruit salsa plum sauce (£9.25) and 10oz rib-eye steak (£9.50); seven or eight daily specials might include king scallops in saffron beurre blanc (£4.75), swordfish niçoise salad (£8.25) and braised shoulder of lamb (£8.95); puddings, some home-made, include bread and butter pudding, and sticky toffee pudding (£3). The two dining areas are no smoking; TV, fruit machine, dominoes and piped music. Boddingtons, Charles Wells Bombardier and Greene King Abbot are well kept on handpump, and they've decent wines and Hoegaarden on tap. In summer you can sit out in the pleasant garden behind. More reports on the new regime please. *(Recommended by Len Beattie, Yvonne and Mike Meadley, J Conti-Ramsden, Rex and Mary Hepburn, Abi Benson, Roy and Lindsey Fentiman, Keith and Chris O'Neill, Martin and Sue Day)*

Enterprise ~ Lease Jason Keen ~ Real ale ~ Bar food (12-9) ~ Restaurant ~ (01254) 878303 ~ Children welcome ~ Dogs allowed in bar ~ Open 12-11(10.30 Sun); closed 3-5 Mon-Sat in winter ~ Bedrooms: £35B/£50B

RIMINGTON SD8045 Map 7

Black Bull

Off A59 NW of Clitheroe, at Chatburn; or off A682 S of Gisburn

You can see a faithful model of this stone-built pub inside the extraordinary little museum crammed into a room at the back: ask the landlady to open it up for you (entry is by donation; her husband set up the collection, which is now run by local volunteers) and you'll encounter the fascinating array of model trains, planes, cars and ships. It really is worth it; anyone with even the slightest interest in models of historic vehicles will be enthralled. Further exhibits are dotted around the airy, rather elegant rooms of the pub proper – including a model Mississippi paddle steamer near the loos – but the very good, well presented food stands out as the main attraction, with a real emphasis on fresh, local ingredients. From a printed menu are soup (£3.50), sandwiches (from £3.95), parcel of oak smoked salmon (£5.95), linguini with sautéed wild mushrooms, roast garlic and a tarragon and white wine cream sauce (£8.50), roast of the day (£7.95) and game casserole (£8.95), and there's a changing à la carte board with items like fried chicken breast in cranberry sauce (£8.95) and rack of local lamb (£12.95), plus around six fresh fish specials like grilled hake (£7.95) or lemon sole (£11.95); puddings change regularly too, and might include raspberry pavlova or apple and sultana strudel (£4.50). The big, old-fashioned and civilised main bar has a model locomotive in a glass case beside an attractively tiled fireplace, a plane hanging from the ceiling, various platform signs on the walls, and comfortable banquettes and window seats; a central area with leatherette chairs leads through to a quietly refined dining room, with an exhibition of wildlife art on the walls; piped music; the restaurant and snug area are no smoking. It may all sound rather unpubby, but in the evenings it does feel very much like a village local, just as happy serving local lads a pint. Theakstons Best and a guest such as Caledonian Deuchars are served on handpump under a light blanket pressure; good welcoming service. *(Recommended by*

Mrs P J Carroll, Yvonne and Mike Meadley, John and Sylvia Harrop, Steve Whalley)

Free house ~ Licensee Mrs Barbara Blades ~ Real ale ~ Bar food (12-2.30, 7-9.30; not Sun evening) ~ Restaurant ~ (01200) 445220 ~ Children in restaurant ~ Open 12-3, 7-11(10.30 Sun); closed Mon inc bank hols

SAWLEY SD7746 Map 7

Spread Eagle 🍴 ♀

Village signposted just off A59 NE of Clitheroe

A few steps away from this popular dining pub stand ruins of a 12th-c cistercian abbey, and you might want to make a pilgrimage here for the wine list, which now has 140 bottles (11 wines by the glass), or to sample one of their 50 whiskies. The light and airy continental-feeling main bar has comfortable banquette seating, plenty of paintings and prints and lovely photographs of local views on the walls, a roaring winter coal fire, and well kept Black Sheep, and Sawleys Drunken Duck (brewed for the pub by local microbrewery Bowland), on handpump; piped music. The short lunchtime bar menu might include soup (£3.25), filled rolls (from £3.95), grilled black pudding medallion (£4.95), and duck leg confit salad or grilled goats cheese niçoise (£5.50). In the no smoking restaurant, which overlooks the River Ribble, you can choose from dishes such as roasted vegetable plate (£9.25), fried fillet of salmon with broad bean gnocchi (£9.95), grilled duck breast with chunks of poached pineapple, spring onions and aniseed sauce (£11.25) and fillet steak with peppercorn sauce (£16.50); two-course lunch menu (£9.50 Tuesday to Friday, £12.50 at weekends). They have various theme and gourmet evenings and you get swift service from the smartly dressed and attentive staff. The pub is very handy for the Forest of Bowland, an upland with terrific scope for hefty walks. *(Recommended by Adrian White, R A K Crabtree, Mrs R A Cartwright, Mrs P J Carroll, Norma and Noel Thomas, Jo Lilley, Simon Calvert, John and Sylvia Harrop, Maurice and Gill McMahon, Paul Edwards)*

Free house ~ Licensees Nigel and Ysanne Williams ~ Real ale ~ Bar food (lunchtime Tues-Sat only) ~ Restaurant ~ (01200) 441202 ~ Children in eating area of bar and restaurant ~ Open 12-3, 6-11; 12-3 Sun; closed all day Mon

STALYBRIDGE SJ9698 Map 7

Station Buffet 🍺 £

The Station, Rassbottom Street

You might blink in disbelief as you get off the train here, on the main line from Manchester to Huddersfield, and wander into the buffet, to be greeted by this nicely unsmart Victorian survival. The bar has a welcoming fire below an etched-glass mirror, newspapers and magazines to read, and old photographs of the station in its heyday and other railway memorabilia; there's a little conservatory. An extension along the platform leads into what was the ladies' waiting room and part of the station-master's quarters, with original ornate ceilings and a dining/function room with Victorian-style wallpaper; dominoes, cribbage, draughts; one room is no smoking. On a sunny day you can sit out on the platform. They serve a marvellous range of up to 20 interesting guest ales a week (and are continually being approached by microbreweries to stock their latest brew) and usually have around half a dozen alongside well kept Bass and Boddingtons on handpump. You can also get farm cider, and belgian and other foreign bottled beers; beer festivals are held in early May and late November. They do cheap old-fashioned snacks such as tasty black peas (50p) and sandwiches (from £1.95), and three or four daily specials such as home-made pie with peas (£2.50), bacon casserole (£3.20) and all day breakfast (£3.25); freshly made coffee and tea by the pot. More reports please. *(Recommended by Dennis Jones, MLR, John Fiander, the Didler)*

Free house ~ Licensees John Hesketh and Sylvia Wood ~ Real ale ~ Bar food (all day) ~ No credit cards ~ (0161) 303 0007 ~ Children welcome ~ Dogs welcome ~ Folk music Sat evenings, quiz Mon night ~ Open 11-11; 12-10.30 Sun

TUNSTALL SD6173 Map 7
Lunesdale Arms ♀
A683 S of Kirkby Lonsdale

Great care goes into the food at this bustling dining pub, and they make the most of local organic produce, including meat from local farms, and very tasty home-baked bread. Enjoyable dishes might include lunchtime soup (£3.75), open sandwiches (from £4), welsh rarebit (£5.50), and steak and kidney pie (£9), with evening dishes such as chicken liver parfait (£4.25), spicy butterbean bobotie with home-made bread (£7.50), kedgeree or corn-fed chicken breast with tarragon sauce (£10.50), lamb rump with onion mash (£10.95) and sirloin steak with gremolata sauce (£11.90), as well as delicious puddings such as lemony lancaster tart or cappuccino crème brûlée (£4.25); Sunday lunch (from £8.50). They do smaller helpings of some main courses. The bright atmosphere is helped along by bare boards and lively acoustics, and shades of blue and yellow. On yellow walls the big unframed oil paintings (some for sale) are often of bluebells, some of the pews and armchairs have blue and/or yellow upholstery, and the blinds for most of the big windows are also blue and yellow. On one side of the central bar part, a white-walled area (where the pictures are framed) has a good mix of stripped and sealed solid dining tables, and sofas around a lower table with daily papers, by a woodburning stove which has a couple of orchids on the stone mantelpiece. At the other end, an airy games section has pool, table football and TV, and a snugger little flagstoned back part has another woodburning stove; dominoes. Besides well kept Black Sheep and a guest such as Copper Dragons Golden Pippin on handpump, they have a good range of sensibly priced wines by the glass (in a choice of sizes), and summer Pimms; piped music. This pretty village in the Lune Valley has a church with Brontë associations. *(Recommended by Malcolm Taylor, Jo Lilley, Simon Calvert, John and Sylvia Harrop, R T and J C Moggridge, Karen Eliot)*

Free house ~ Licensee Emma Gillibrand ~ Real ale ~ Bar food (12-2(2.30 Sat-Sun), 6-9) ~ Restaurant ~ (01524) 274203 ~ Children welcome ~ Dogs allowed in bar ~ Live piano music most Thurs nights ~ Open 12-3(3.30 Sat-Sun), 6-11(10.30 Sun); closed Mon (exc bank hols), 25-26 Dec

UPPERMILL SD9905 Map 7
Church Inn ◀ £
From the main street (A607), look out for the sign for Saddleworth Church, and turn off up this steep narrow lane – keep on up!

All alone on a steep moorland slope, this highly individual own-brew pub has quite a menagerie of animals roaming around its garden – rabbits, chicken, dogs, ducks, geese, horses and a couple of peacocks, and there's an increasing army of rescued cats. The fairly priced own-brewed Saddleworth beers are a big draw (with prices from a staggeringly modest £1.20 a pint), and Ayrtons, Hopsmacker, Saddleworth More, St Georges, Shaftbender and seasonal ales (including some named after their children and which appear around their birthdays), as well as guests like Thwaites Lancaster Bomber and Original are well kept on handpump; continental wheat beer and dark lager on tap too. The big unspoilt L-shaped main bar has high beams and some stripped stone; one window at the end of the bar counter looks down over the valley, and there's also a valley view from the quieter no smoking dining room. The comfortable furnishings include settles and pews as well as a good individual mix of chairs, and there are lots of attractive prints, staffordshire and other china on a high delft shelf, jugs, brasses and so forth; TV (only when there's soccer on) and unobtrusive piped music. The horse-collar on the wall is worn by the winner of their annual gurning (face-pulling) championship (part of the lively Rush Cart Festival, usually held over the August bank holiday), and handbells here are the church bellringers' practice set. Children and dogs are made to feel very welcome, though one reader found the food service slow. Reasonably priced bar food such as soup (£1.75), sandwiches (from £2.95), ploughman's (£3.25), steak and ale pie (£5.75), roast beef (£5.95), jumbo cod (£7.75) and puddings such as banoffi pie or apple crumble (£2.25); children's meals (£3). *(Recommended by the Didler, Mrs P J Carröll, MLR, John Fiander)*

Own brew ~ Licensee Julian Taylor ~ Real ale ~ Bar food (12-2.30, 5.30-9; 12-9 Sat-Sun) ~ Restaurant ~ (01457) 820902 ~ Dogs on leads welcome in bar ~ Live bands some Sat nights in conservatory ~ Open 12-11(10.30 Sun)

WHEELTON SD6021 Map 7
Dressers Arms 🍺 £

2.1 miles from M61 junction 8; A674 towards Blackburn, then in Wheelton fork right into Briers Brow; 3.6 miles from M65 junction 3, also via A674

Generous portions of very reasonably priced bar food and an interesting range of beers make this pub in a converted row of cottages a popular choice. It's much bigger than it looks from the outside, with a series of genuinely atmospheric, low-beamed little rooms that remain darkly cosy even on the sunniest of days, full of old oak and traditional features, including a handsome old woodburning stove in the flagstoned main bar. Candles on tables add to the welcoming feel, and there are newspapers and magazines; two areas are no smoking (including one side of the bar); piped music, juke box, pool table, fruit machine and TV. They usually keep eight real ales on at once, such as their own Big Franks (now brewed off the site) as well as the more familiar Boddingtons, Tetleys and Timothy Taylors Landlord, plus four guests such as Cwmbrans Double Hop, Fullers London Pride, Ridleys Prospect and Robinsons Unicorn; also around 20 malt whiskies, and some well chosen wines. Served all day at weekends, the good locally sourced bar food includes soup (£2.50), sandwiches (from £2.50) and hot filled baguettes (from £5.50), several vegetarian dishes such as vegetable curry or cheese and broccoli bake (£5.75), steak and kidney pie or paella (£5.95), deep-fried king prawns in filo pastry (£6.25), liver and onions or sausage and mash (£6.50) and blackboard specials such as lamb chops (£6.95), ham hock (£8.95) or fillet steak (£12.95); Sunday roasts (£8.95) and straightforward children's meals (£3.75, including an ice-cream). On the first floor is a cantonese restaurant. Lots of picnic-sets on a terrace in front of the pub, as well as a large umbrella with lighting and heaters; they have a very big car park, across the road. The licensees are great pet-lovers and welcome dogs. *(Recommended by Andy and Jill Kassube, MLR, Richard Houghton, Yvonne and Mike Meadley, R M Corlett, Mike and Linda Hudson, Jo Lilley, Simon Calvert)*

Own brew ~ Licensees Steve and Trudie Turner ~ Real ale ~ Bar food (12-3, 5-9; 12-9 weekends and bank hols) ~ Restaurant ~ (01254) 830041 ~ Children in family room ~ Dogs welcome ~ Quiz night on Tues ~ Open 11-11; 12-10.30 Sun

WHITEWELL SD6546 Map 7
Inn at Whitewell ★★ 🍴 🍷 🛏

Most easily reached by B6246 from Whalley; road through Dunsop Bridge from B6478 is also good

The delightful location in the Hodder valley with the backdrop of the moors of the Forest of Bowland might itself tempt you to stay at this inn, where they have recently added six bedrooms and a new restaurant that projects out over the river. The newly created riverside bar and adjacent terrace also make the most of the view. Impressively furnished, the old-fashioned pubby main bar has antique settles, oak gateleg tables, sonorous clocks, old cricketing and sporting prints, roaring log fires (the lounge has a very attractive stone fireplace), and heavy curtains on sturdy wooden rails; one area has a selection of newspapers and magazines, local maps and guide books, there's a piano for anyone who wants to play, and even an art gallery. In the early evening, there's a cheerful bustle but once the visitors have gone, the atmosphere is tranquil and relaxing. Their good wine list contains around 180 wines (including a highly recommended claret), and they've well kept beers from Bowland Brewery, Copper Dragon and Timothy Taylors on handpump. Besides lunchtime sandwiches (from £4.25), delicious, well presented food from the mostly traditional bar menu includes home-made soup (£3.50), fried chicken livers with a salad of flat mushrooms, roast onions and crispy bacon (£5.80), cumberland sausages and champ (£8.20), fish pie (£9.25) and goosnargh chicken breast with stilton potato cake, roast pears and warm cumberland sauce (£11.50), with specials such as fried chicken livers with grilled chorizo and black pudding (£5.80), lamb fillet with champ potatoes and red wine jus (£6.25) and main courses like fried salmon with chorizo and pepper tapas with basil pesto or roast goosnargh duck (£11.50), and chargrilled sirloin steak with wild mushroom ragoût and red wine jus (£12.50), with mouthwatering home-made puddings (£4.20) and farmhouse cheeses (from £3.80); the staff are courteous and friendly. The dining room and one of the two bars are no smoking. You can get coffee and cream teas all day; they sell jars of home-made jam. As this is such a popular place to stay, you now have to book quite a long way ahead to secure a room. There's plenty of fell walking, they own several miles of trout, salmon and sea trout fishing on the Hodder, and with notice they'll even arrange shooting; they're happy to do picnic hampers for guests. *(Recommended by J S Burn, Jo Lilley, Simon Calvert, Revd D Glover, Mrs P J Carroll, Oliver and Sue Rowell, Louise English, Len Beattie, Brenda and Rob Fincham, Karen Eliot, Air Commodore and Mrs A Curry, Steve Kirby, Peter and Jean Walker, Simon Cleasby)*

Free house ~ Licensee Charles Bowman ~ Real ale ~ Bar food (12-2, 7.30-9.30) ~ Restaurant ~ (01200) 448222 ~ Children welcome ~ Dogs welcome ~ Open 11-3, 6-12; 12-3, 6-11 Sun ~ Bedrooms: £70B/£96B

YEALAND CONYERS SD5074 Map 7
New Inn
3 miles from M6 junction 35; village signposted off A6

With very nicely cooked food served all day this village pub is a useful place to stop at, whether you're on the nearby M6 or visiting the rich wildlife site at at Leighton Moss RSPB reserve, a huge area of reedbeds. Inside the 17th-c ivy-covered building, the simply furnished little beamed bar on the left has a cosy village atmosphere, with its log fire in the big stone fireplace, and cribbage and dominoes. On the right, two communicating no smoking cottagey dining rooms have dark blue furniture, shiny beams and an attractive kitchen range. Well kept Robinsons Hartleys XB, one of their seasonal ales and another such as Cumbria Way on handpump, around 30 malt whiskies, winter mulled wine and perhaps summer home-made lemonade; piped music. There's a bustling atmosphere with plenty of locals and visitors. The same menu runs through the dining rooms and bar, and dishes might include soup (£3.15), sandwiches (from £3.85), filled baked potatoes (from £3.95), cajun potato skins (£4.75), mussels (£4.95), cumberland sausage with garlic and mustard mash or spicy mexican bean chilli tortilla (£8.95) and rib-eye steak (£14.75), with more imaginative good specials such as fillet of halibut with garden herb cream sauce, roast guinea fowl with bacon and apricot stuffing, and an enterprising vegetarian dish of the day (from £9.95 to £12.95). A sheltered lawn at the side has picnic-sets among roses and flowering shrubs. *(Recommended by Jo Lilley, Simon Calvert, Richard Greaves, Patrick and Phillipa Vickery, Simon J Barber, Malcolm and Jane MacDonald, Peter Abbott, Jim Abbott, Alan Wilcock, Christine Davidson, Dr D J and Mrs S C Walker, Mr and Mrs A Dewhurst, Michael Doswell, Mrs Phoebe A Kemp, Maurice and Gill McMahon, Paul and Margaret Baker)*

Robinsons ~ Tenants Bill Tully and Charlotte Pinder ~ Real ale ~ Bar food (11.30(12 Sun)-9.30) ~ Restaurant ~ (01524) 732938 ~ Children welcome ~ Dogs allowed in bar ~ Open 11.30-11; 12-10.30 Sun

---

Stars after the name of a pub show exceptional character and appeal. They don't mean extra comfort. And they are nothing to do with food quality, for which there's a separate knife-and-fork symbol. Even quite a basic pub can win stars, if it's individual enough.

LUCKY DIP

Besides the fully inspected pubs, you might like to try these Lucky Dips recommended to us and described by readers (if you do, please send us reports: www.goodguides.co.uk).

AFFETSIDE [SD7513]
Pack Horse [Watling St]: Attractive neatly kept moorland local on Roman road, particularly well kept Hydes ale, big helpings of good value lunchtime bar food, snug pool room, restaurant early evenings (not Sun); good walking country, open all day wknds *(Peter Abbott, David R Brown, Norma and Noel Thomas)*

ALTHAM [SD7732]
Walton Arms [Burnley Rd (A678)]: Attractive and relaxed, with wide range of good reasonably priced food from filled rolls and dim sum up, early evening bargains, well kept Jennings, good wine choice, friendly efficient service, oak furniture in no smoking flagstoned dining room *(Mark Butler, John and Sylvia Harrop)*

ASHTON-UNDER-LYNE [SJ9399]
Caledonia [Warrington St]: Welcoming open-plan town pub with wide choice of good value food (not Sun or Mon evenings) inc sandwiches, baked potatoes and popular pies and hotpot, some more expensive early evening dishes, well kept Robinsons inc Hatters Mild, several distinct areas inc raised no smoking section; bedrooms, open all day (cl Sun afternoon) *(Pete Baker, Dennis Jones)*
Oddfellows Arms [Alderley St, just off Kings Road]: Small, friendly and unpretentious, with several areas around single bar, log fires, well kept Robinsons, traditional games *(Pete Baker)*

ASPULL [SD6006]
Kirkless Hall Inn [Top Lock]: Good reasonably-priced chef-served food, no smoking lounge, two guest beers, canal memorabilia; quiet piped music; tables out by top lock of 21-lock Wigan flight on Leeds—Liverpool Canal *(Bill Sykes)*

BIRKENHEAD [SJ3289]
Crown [Conway St]: Interestingly tiled three-room alehouse with Cains, John Smiths and several guest beers, Weston's farm cider, good value generous food all day till 6; open all day *(the Didler)*
Dispensary [Chester St]: Well kept Cains and guest beers, good value lunchtime food, handsome glass ceiling; handy for ferry, open all day *(the Didler)*
Stork [Price St]: Friendly early 19th-c pub with tiled façade, four rooms around island bar, polished original mosaic floor, old dock and ferry photographs, several well kept real ales (early evening bargains), decent food wkdy lunchtime and early evening, no smoking area; open all day (not Sun) *(the Didler)*

BLACKO [SD8541]
☆ *Moorcock* [A682 towards Gisburn]: Beautifully placed moorland dining pub, roomy and comfortably old-fashioned, with big picture windows for breathtaking views, tables set close for the huge range of popular and often

enterprising food inc lamb from their own flock and excellent beef, very friendly helpful staff, decent wine, Thwaites Bitter and Mild under top pressure; tables in hillside garden with various animals, open all day for food Sun, children and dogs welcome, bedrooms *(Norma and Noel Thomas, LYM, Margaret Dickinson)*

BLACKPOOL [SD3136]
Ramsden Arms [Talbot Rd, opp Blackpool North station]: Large friendly local with several panelled areas, masses of old prints and mainly beer-related bric-a-brac, helpful staff, well kept ales such as Blackpool, Boddingtons, Jennings and Tetleys, perhaps one at bargain price, over 40 whiskies, may be lunchtime food, no smoking area; CD juke box, pool and games; good value bedrooms *(Dr and Mrs A K Clarke, the Didler, John Dwane, Abi Benson)*

BOLTON [SD7109]
Dog & Partridge [Manor St/Bank St]: Unpretentious backstreet pub with well kept Thwaites Bitter and Lancaster Bomber, friendly young landlord, pool; popular alternative rock music nights, also comedy and quiz nights *(Michael Gallagher)*
Howcroft [Pool St]: Friendly local serving as tap for Bank Top ales, also guest beers, lots of small screened-off rooms around central servery with fine glass and woodwork, cosy snug with coal fire, good value lunches in lounge, plenty of pub games; bowling green, occasional folk nights, open all day *(the Didler)*
Olde Man & Scythe [Churchgate]: Interesting timbered local, largely 17th-c with cellar dating from 12th c, lively long low-beamed and flagstoned drinking area, two quieter bare-boards rooms popular for bargain lunchtime food (not Sun) from sandwiches up, well kept ales such as Boddingtons, Fullers London Pride, Greene King Old Speckled Hen and cheap Holts, two or more farm ciders, swift cheerful service, darts and chess, sign language evenings; juke box, quiz nights, Fri night singalongs; delightful back terrace, handy for shopping area, open all day *(Steve Whalley, Andy Hazeldine)*

BRINDLE [SD5924]
☆ *Cavendish Arms* [3 miles from M6 junction 29; A6 towards Whittle-le-Woods then left on B5256 (Sandy Lane)]: Extended old village pub, hard-working new licensees, good value lunchtime food and italian evening menu, well kept Banks's and a guest beer, several quaint little snugs, interesting stained-glass partitions, decorative china and heraldic plasterwork, comfortable seats; children welcome, picnic-sets on terrace with newly restored rockery and on small lawn, tranquil little village with handsome stone church opposite, open all day wknds *(Dr D J and Mrs S C Walker, LYM, Graham Patterson)*

BURNLEY [SD8728]

Ram [Cliviger (A646 S)]: Olde-worlde Vintage Inn with well kept ales such as John Smiths, lots of wines by the glass, good value food all day (they make an effort with their specials), pleasant reconditioned pine furniture, blazing coal fire, quick service; tables and chairs outside, beautiful setting looking across to moors, open all day *(Steve Whalley, Roy and Lindsey Fentiman)*

BURTON-IN-KENDAL [SD5376]

Kings Arms [Main St]: Village pub with wide range of good value substantial food inc local dishes in bar or no smoking dining room, good atmosphere, five or six real ales, separate locals' area with pool and TV; comfortable bedrooms *(Simon Cleasby)*

BURY [SD8313]

Trackside [East Lancs Railway Station, Bolton St]: Busy station bar by East Lancs steam railway, good range of well kept real ales and bottled imports, bargain wkdy lunches (from breakfast time till 5 wknds); open all day *(the Didler)*

CHEADLE [SU8586]

Griffin [Wilmslow Rd (B5358, corner Finney Lane)]: Large 1960s local, lively and friendly, good value straightforward lunchtime food inc popular Sun lunches, well kept low-priced Holts, huge divided main bar, games-oriented public bar *(Pete Baker)*

Old Star [High St (A560)]: Traditional mock-Tudor town local very popular lunchtimes for good straightforward bargain food, well kept Hydes, comfortable lounge, friendly little public bar, quaint and unspoilt, with darts, cards and dominoes; quiz nights, live music Sat *(Pete Baker)*

CHIPPING [SD6243]

☆ *Sun* [Windy St]: Charming stone-built country local with three small snug rooms, lots of dark oak panelling, hearty simple food inc pies and local cheeses, well kept Boddingtons and a guest such as Coniston Bluebird or Timothy Taylors Landlord (an underground stream cools the cellar), quick friendly service, coal fire, papers and magazines, interesting local photographs and ironstone china, games room with pool and darts; very busy wknds, tables in courtyard with kiosk for families, opp church in attractive village, good walks *(BB, Dennis Jones)*

CHURCHTOWN [SD3618]

Bold Arms [off A565 from Preston, taking B5244 in Southport; Botanic Rd]: Substantial coaching inn handy for the Botanic Gardens, lots of panelling and several separate rooms (children allowed in one), good value food from sandwiches up, well kept ales inc one or two guest beers, plenty of atmosphere; tables outside in picturesque surroundings *(MLR)*

☆ *Punch Bowl* [Church St, off A586 Garstang—St Michaels-on-Wyre]: Good choice of consistently good food, generous and reasonably priced, in busy and attractive mock-Tudor beamed pub/restaurant with two small quaint and old-fashioned bar rooms, panelling,

stained glass, lots of stuffed animals, billiards room, attractive no smoking back dining room, friendly staff, well kept Tetleys, good fires; disabled facilities, lovely village *(Graham and Doreen Holden)*

CLAUGHTON [SD5666]

Fenwick Arms [A683 Kirkby Lonsdale—Lancaster]: Black and white pub popular for its food, with well kept Black Sheep and Boddingtons and good range of wines; piped music may obtrude *(Jo Lilley, Simon Calvert)*

CLITHEROE [SD6642]

Craven Heifer [Chipping Rd, Chaigley, off B6243 W]: Well run country dining pub with fine views, large dining room, bar area with comfortable armchairs, sofas and big log fire, wide range of enjoyable food cooked to order, well kept ales such as Moorhouses Premier, impressive wine list *(Dennis Jones)*

COLNE [SD8939]

Admiral Lord Rodney [Mill Green]: Welcoming chatty local with half a dozen real ales from interesting small breweries, bar food (not Mon), no TV or machines *(Tony Hobden)*

Hare & Hounds [Skipton Old Rd, Foulridge]: Good value food inc some unusual dishes, good service, relaxed unhurried atmosphere, Timothy Taylors ales, small no smoking restaurant; handy for canal and walks around lower reservoir *(Stuart Paulley)*

COMPSTALL [SJ9690]

Andrew Arms [George St (B6104)]: Welcoming landlord with remarkable memory for a name or a face, surprisingly good menu for such a small pub, bargain lunch Mon, Robinsons real ale, growing bric-a-brac collection, back dining room; handy for Etherow Country Park *(Dennis Jones)*

CONDER GREEN [SD4556]

Stork [just off A588]: Fine spot where River Conder joins the Lune estuary among bleak marshes, cheery bustle and good fire in rambling dark-panelled rooms, generous popular standard food inc all-day sandwiches and light snacks, young staff, mainstream real ales; pub games inc pool, juke box or piped music; children welcome, handy for Glasson Dock, comfortable bedrooms, open all day *(Mike and Linda Hudson, Dave Braisted, Margaret Dickinson, LYM, A and B D Craig)*

COWAN BRIDGE [SD6277]

☆ *Whoop Hall* [off A65 towards Kirkby Lonsdale]: Spacious, airy and comfortable linked areas with wide choice of interesting quick food all day from 8am from popular buttery, friendly proficient service, well kept real ales, decent wines, pleasant back eating area; children welcome, tables in garden well off road with play area, well appointed bedrooms *(LYM, Margaret Dickinson)*

CRANK [SJ5099]

Red Cat [Red Cat Lane]: Friendly pub/restaurant with good if not cheap food cooked carefully and interestingly using very fresh local produce, in front lounge and nicely decorated dining room – must book; well kept beer, notable wine list with good value bin ends *(Ruth McNeil)*

CROSTON [SD4818]

Crown [Station Rd]: Lively beamed village pub with enthusiastic young licensees, emphasis on competitively priced home cooking inc OAP bargain lunches, well kept Thwaites; children welcome *(Jim and Maggie Cowell)*

Wheatsheaf [Town Rd]: Convivial and chatty, nice décor, hops and fresh flowers, 19th-c local photographs, stripped boards and quarry tiles, alcoves, generous interesting food all day inc home-baked bread and lunchtime and early evening bargains, good friendly service, well kept weekly changing beers, no smoking area; unobtrusive piped music; open all day *(Margaret Dickinson, Brian Kneale)*

DOBCROSS [SD9906]

☆ *Swan* [The Square]: Some emphasis on enjoyable varied well priced home-made food inc children's in low-beamed pub with three interesting areas (one no smoking) off small central bar, guest beers and full Jennings range kept well, attentive young staff, partitioned alcoves, flagstones and traditional settles, friendly atmosphere; Thurs folk night; tables outside, attractive village below moors *(Pete Baker, John Fiander, Bill Sykes, Richard Houghton)*

DOWNHAM [SD7844]

Assheton Arms [off A59 NE of Chlitheroe, via Chatburn]: Exceptionally pretty village makes this pub popular at wknds; wide range of good generous food, friendly staff, Castle Eden and Moorhouses Premier, 18 wines by the glass, rambling partly no smoking beamed bar with nice furniture and massive stone fireplace; piped music; children and dogs welcome, picnic-sets outside, open all day Sun *(Len Beattie, John Kane, Yvonne and Mike Meadley, Norma and Noel Thomas, GLD, LYM, Louise English, Betty and Cyril Higgs, Mrs P J Carroll)*

ECCLES [SJ7798]

Grapes [Liverpool Rd, Peel Green; A57 ½ mile from M63 junction 2]: Well restored Edwardian local with superb glass, tiling and mosaic floor, lots of mahogany, eye-catching staircase, cheap Holts Bitter and Mild, fairly quiet roomy lounge and smoke room, pool in classic billiards room, vault with Manchester darts, drinking corridor; tables outside, open all day *(Pete Baker, the Didler)*

Lamb [Regent St (A57)]: Handsomely preserved Edwardian three-room local, splendid etched windows, fine woodwork and furnishings, extravagantly tiled stairway, admirable trophies in display case; cheap well kept Holts Bitter and Mild, bargain lunchtime sandwiches, full-size snooker table in original billiards room; popular with older people, open all day *(the Didler)*

Royal Oak [Barton Lane]: Large unspoilt Edwardian pub on busy corner, several rooms off corridor, handsome tilework and fittings, cheap Holts Bitter and Mild, good licensees, pool; children allowed in former back billiards room (may be organ singalongs), open all day *(GLD, the Didler)*

Stanley Arms [Eliza Ann St/Liverpool Rd (A57), Patricroft]: Busy mid-Victorian corner local with cheap Holts Bitter and Mild, lunchtime filled rolls, popular front bar, hatch serving drinking corridor to small back rooms, *(the Didler)*

White Lion [Liverpool Rd, Patricroft, a mile from M63 junction 2]: Welcoming unchanging Edwardian local, clean, tidy and popular with older people, with great value Holts Bitter and Mild, games in lively traditional public bar, smoke room (wknd pianist) and quiet lounge off tiled side drinking corridor *(the Didler, Pete Baker)*

ECCLESTON [SD5117]

☆ *Original Farmers Arms* [Towngate (B5250, off A581 Chorley—Southport)]: Long low-beamed pub/restaurant, wide choice of consistently good generous food all day, wkdy bargains and some unusual twists to familiar themes, tempting puddings cabinets as you go in, cheery décor, well kept changing ales such as Boddingtons, Caledonian Deuchars IPA, Ringwood Fortyniner and Timothy Taylors Landlord, friendly helpful service from smartly uniformed staff, darts; piped music and machines (can be noisy), parking can be tight when busy; good value bedrooms some with own bathroom, open all day *(BB, T and P, Margaret Dickinson, Norma and Noel Thomas, W W Burke)*

EDENFIELD [SD7919]

Original Coach & Horses [Market St]: Locally popular pub for freshly made pubby food from ploughman's and plenty of other salads to steaks, nicely priced dishes for smaller appetites, helpful friendly staff, decent wines, tasteful new extension *(Rachel and Ross Gavin)*

EDGWORTH [SD7316]

Black Bull [Bolton Rd, Turton]: Reliable three-room dining pub in moorside village, good value food from sandwiches and baguettes to bistro dishes (all day wknds), Weds night steak bargains for two, friendly staff, five well kept changing ales, open fire, hill and reservoir views from light and airy restaurant extension, lovely summer floral displays; Tues quiz night, live music Thurs, good walks *(Norma and Noel Thomas, Michael and Marion Buchanan, Mr and Mrs A Silver)*

☆ *Rose & Crown* [Bury Rd]: Very friendly service and good home-made food (all day wknds) from sandwiches, baguettes and baked potatoes up inc carefully sourced meat, plenty of vegetarian dishes, Sun carvery and impressive bargain wkdy lunches and suppers, cosy bars and flagstoned two-room dining area (one no smoking), well kept real ales, reasonably priced wines; children welcome, good value bedrooms with own bathrooms *(Michael and Marion Buchanan, Rachel and Ross Gavin, Greg Yerbury)*

ENTWISTLE [SD7217]

Strawbury Duck [signed off Edgworth—Blackburn rd; by station]: Tucked-away traditional beamed and flagstoned country pub, Victorian pictures, some bare stone, good choice of well kept northern ales, generous bar food all day, friendly service; pool, fruit machine, TV and piped music; children welcome, tables outside, good for Pennine walks, open all day *(MLR, Greg Yerbury, Michael and Marion Buchanan, Steve Whalley, Mike and Linda Hudson, LYM, Yvonne and Mike Meadley, Miss Schofield, Mr Robinson)*

EUXTON [SD5518]

Euxton Mills [A49 S, 3 miles from M6 junction 28]: Neatly kept roomy pub with wide choice of good value food from good sandwiches to daily roasts, popular wkdy lunchtime OAP deals, friendly service, three real ales inc Burtonwood and Everards *(R A Watson)*

FENCE [SD8337]

☆ *Bay Horse* [Wheatley Lane Rd]: Small and spotless country dining pub with good imaginative wide-ranging food served with professional flair, well kept Marstons Pedigree and Theakstons Best, good wine range, friendly licensees, restaurant, separate locals' tap room with darts, table football and pool; cl Mon *(Peter Abbott, Jim Abbott, Margaret Dickinson)*

☆ *Fence Gate* [just off A6068]: Good-natured tastefully redecorated bar with enjoyable competitively priced fresh food inc their own speciality sausages, good steak sandwich, more elaborate dishes and some lunchtime bargains, also good contemporary brasserie with topiary, well kept Moorhouses and other ales, bright pleasant young staff; children welcome *(Peter Abbott, Graham Patterson, D J Newth)*

FLEETWOOD [SD3247]

☆ *North Euston* [Esplanade, nr tram terminus]: Big architecturally interesting Victorian railway hotel dominating the seafront, extensive pubby bar giving great sea and hill views; good choice of well kept changing ales, decent lunchtime food from sandwiches up, consistently good service from smart staff, lots of separate-seeming areas inc large no smoking family room (till 7), café-bar and two restaurants; live music Sat; seats outside, comfortable bedrooms, open all day (Sun afternoon break) *(BB, Yvonne and Mike Meadley, Margaret Dickinson, Keith and Chris O'Neill)*

GARSTANG [SD4943]

Bradbeer Bar [Garstang Country Hotel & Golf Club; B6430 S]: Relaxed and spacious bar overlooking golfing greens, good value imaginative food, helpful well trained staff, huge woodburner; tables outside, bedrooms *(Margaret Dickinson)*

Royal Oak [Market Pl]: Typical small-town inn in same family for nearly 50 years, cosy yet roomy and comfortably refurbished, with attractive panelling, several eating areas inc charming snug, generous consistently above-average food (all day Sun) inc imaginative specials, small helpings for children or OAPs, pleasant staff, Robinsons real ales, good value coffee, restaurant, spotless housekeeping; disabled access, comfortable bedrooms, open all day Sun *(Margaret Dickinson)*

☆ *Th'Owd Tithebarn* [off Church St]: Rustic barn with big flagstoned terrace overlooking

Lancaster Canal, Victorian country life theme with very long refectory table, antique kitchen range, masses of farm tools, stuffed animals and birds, flagstones and high rafters, simple food all day from filled baguettes up, Flowers IPA and Tetleys, lots of country wines, quieter parlour welcoming children; piped music in main bar may be loud, can get very busy; open all day summer *(LYM, Abi Benson, Bill Sykes)*

GLASSON [SD4456]

Dalton Arms [Ten Row, Glasson Dock]: Traditional pub with chatty newish landlady, enjoyable standard food at bargain prices, well kept Thwaites Bitter and Lancaster Bomber, amiable staff *(Pete Yearsley)*

GOOSNARGH [SD5536]

Bushells Arms [4 miles from M6 junction 32; turn right off A6 in Broughton, then left to Goosnargh in Whittingham]: Spotless straightforwardly refurbished pub with well kept real ale, decent food in big dining area *(LYM, Peter and Jean Walker)*

☆ *Grapes* [Church Lane]: Well kept changing ales inc some rare brews, massive helpings of food (not Mon evening) from huge doorstep sandwiches to good Sun roast and interesting up-to-date dishes, helpful welcoming staff, two low-beamed areas separated by big coal fire, lots of brass around this, collection of whisky-water jugs and old telephones, separate games room with darts and pool; tables outside, bowling green *(MLR, Tony and Ann Bennett-Hughes)*

☆ *Stags Head* [B5269]: Lots of separate mainly old-world areas rambling around a central servery, plenty of nice features (even proper old-fashioned radiators), good value generous fresh food inc imaginative dishes, children's helpings, good service, Flowers IPA, popular restaurant (may be fully booked); well reproduced contemporary chart music, live music Fri inc frequent tribute nights; tables out in pleasant pergola with lawn *(Margaret Dickinson, BB)*

GREASBY [SJ2587]

Greave Dunning [Greasby Rd (off B5139)]: Comfortably extended pub popular for civilised lunches inc light dishes, with quiet alcoves in flagstoned bar, lofty main lounge with upper gallery, good helpful staff, well kept real ales, decent wines; can get lively evenings *(Mrs P J Carroll, LYM, E G Parish)*

GREAT MITTON [SD7138]

Aspinall Arms [B6246 NW of Whalley]: Roomy dual bars with red plush wall banquettes, comfortable chairs, settees and bar stools, well kept local ales, enjoyable food from good cold or hot sandwiches to generous fresh fish and steaks, friendly chatty landlord, coal fire, papers, books and magazines to read, no music or machines, small separate dining room on right; piped music may obtrude; children welcome away from bar, nice surroundings, picnic-sets on flagstoned terrace and in big garden with play area and planned barbecue area just above River Ribble, bedrooms, usefully opens earlier than most pubs around here *(Dr and Mrs T E Hothersall,*

BB, Steve Whalley, Rona Murdoch, Dennis Jones)

☆ *Three Fishes* [Mitton Rd]: Reopened by owners of Northcote Manor Hotel (other side of Whalley) after thorough-going traditional refurbishment, no smoking throughout, roomy and spruce with flagstones and three log fires, good food inc regional specialities with a modern twist and using named local produce suppliers in bar and dining room, good unrushed attentive service, well kept ales such as Moorhouses Pride of Pendle and Thwaites Lancaster Bomber, farm cider, good value wines, log fires *(Nigel Stevenson, Alyson and Andrew Jackson)*

GREENFIELD [SD9904]

King William IV [Chew Valley Rd (A669)]: Welcoming chatty village local, good low-priced home-made food till 7 in small eating area, separate but not cut off (best to book), well kept Bass, Lees, Tetleys and perhaps a guest beer; children and dogs welcome, no pool or darts, tables on front terrace *(Pete Baker)*

Railway Hotel [Shaw Hall Bank Rd, opp station]: Popular for live music most nights inc Fri open mike night; well kept ales such as Timothy Taylors Landlord, Charles Wells Bombardier and guest beers, good value pizzas, chilli etc lunchtimes and early evening, games bar with darts, cards, pool; simple bedrooms *(Pete Baker)*

GRIMSARGH [SD5934]

Plough [Preston Rd (B6243 Preston—Longridge)]: Well kept Courage-related and guest beers, good variety of food from sandwiches to popular fish, curry and steaks, proficient service, appealing country décor with plenty of variety from tiles, flagstones and bare boards to carpeting *(Jim and Maggie Cowell, Margaret Dickinson)*

HALE [SJ7686]

Railway [Ashley Rd, Hale (B5163)]: Two appealingly homely rooms (one no smoking) off popular lounge, well kept Robinsons real ales, decent home-made wkdy lunches, lively public bar with darts, dominoes, cards and friendly locals; open all day *(Pete Baker)*

HALTON [SD4964]

White Lion: Good atmosphere, good range of food from lots of tapas to traditional pies and roasts, well kept Jennings Cumberland, Everards Beacon and guest beers; open all day Sun, cl Mon lunchtime and Tues *(Andy and Jill Kassube)*

HAMBLETON [SD3742]

Shovels Inn [Green Meadow Lane]: Old-fashioned pub with old-fashioned food from sandwiches up, mature attentive staff, Boddingtons, Fullers London Pride and Worthington *(Margaret Dickinson)*

HAWKSHAW [SD7515]

☆ *Red Lion* [Ramsbottom Rd]: Good value generous fresh local food, well above average, in pub/hotel's roomy and attractive bar and separate well run restaurant, well kept ales such as Bank Top, Jennings and Phoenix, enthusiastic friendly licensees, cheerful efficient

staff; comfortable bedrooms, quiet spot by River Irwell *(Brian Wainwright, Peter Abbott, Norma and Noel Thomas, Mark Butler, John and Sylvia Harrop)*

HEATON WITH OXCLIFFE [SD4461]

Golden Ball [shd be signed Overton off B5273 Lancaster—Heysham]: Charming old pub isolated by River Lune, road sometimes cut off at high tide; three cosy little low-beamed traditional rooms with hatch service and antique settles; very friendly staff, reasonably priced pub food from sandwiches and baguettes up, warm fires, evening restaurant; children welcome, tables outside *(LYM, David Carr)*

HESKIN GREEN [SD5214]

☆ *Farmers Arms* [Wood Lane (B5250, N of M6 junction 27)]: Cheerful country pub with wide choice of good value home cooking inc nicely cooked veg and good vegetarian choice in two-level dining area, friendly helpful staff, good range of well kept ales, heavy black beams, sparkling brasses and china, public bar with darts; piped music (even outside), SkyTV; picnic-sets on big lawn, good play area, pets from pigs to peacocks, more tables front and side, comfortable pretty bedrooms, open all day wknds *(Jim and Maggie Cowell, BB)*

HEST BANK [SD4666]

☆ *Hest Bank Hotel* [Hest Bank Lane; off A6 just N of Lancaster]: Picturesque three-bar coaching inn, comfortably worn in and welcoming to families, with wide range of good freshly made generous food all day from sandwiches, local potted shrimps and interesting salads to mixed grill and fresh local fish, bargain set menus and special food nights, well kept Boddingtons, Cains, Timothy Taylors Landlord and a monthly changing guest beer, decent wines, friendly and helpful young staff, separate restaurant area, lively history, Weds quiz night; plenty of garden tables by Lancaster canal, attractive setting close to Morecambe Bay *(Margaret Dickinson, Dr and Mrs S Donald, Jo Lilley, Simon Calvert, Stephen Gibbs, Rowena Lord, BB, Bill Sykes, E G Parish)*

HEYSHAM [SD4161]

Royal [Main St]: Early 16th-c quaint and low-beamed two-bar pub doing well under new management, good range of changing real ales, well priced wines, decent food; dogs allowed (not at meal times), tables out in front and good-sized sheltered garden, pretty village with great views from interesting church *(Margaret Dickinson, Tony and Maggie Harwood)*

HOLDEN [SD7749]

☆ *Copy Nook* [the one up by Bolton by Bowland]: Spick-and-span roomy dining pub with helpful staff, wide choice of good popular reasonably priced food, particularly beef, lamb and fish, and specials inc plenty of game, well kept Marstons Pedigree and Tetleys, three dining rooms off main bar; piped music; children welcome, six bedrooms with own bathrooms *(Steve Whalley, BB, Norma and Noel Thomas, Mr and Mrs R B Berry)*

HURST GREEN [SD6837]

Shireburn Arms [Whalley Rd]: Quiet comfortable 17th-c hotel in idyllic setting with good reasonably priced food, Thwaites and other ales, armchairs and log fire in beamed lounge bar, light and airy restaurant, separate tea room; panoramic Ribble valley views from lovely neatly kept back garden and terrace, safe low-key play area, pretty Tolkien walk from here, bedrooms *(Margaret Dickinson)*

HYDE [SJ9595]

Sportsman [Mottram Rd]: Restored Victorian pub popular for its fine range of well kept real ales; plenty of atmosphere, welcoming licensees, open fires, memorabilia; children and dogs welcome *(Greg Banks, the Didler)*

LANCASTER [SD4761]

Blue Anchor [Market St]: Lots of atmosphere in several friendly nautical-theme linked areas inc roofed-in former back courtyard, four well kept ales from central bar, straightforward inexpensive bar food inc two-for-one lunchtime bargains, upstairs restaurant *(MLR)*

☆ *Sun* [Church St]: Ancient pub opened up, extended and restored to show old fireplaces and well, wide range of changing real ales and bottled beers, friendly service, reasonably priced healthy lunchtime food, good sandwiches and light dishes all day, open for imaginative breakfasts too; tables on new terrace, nine bedrooms with own bathrooms, open all day *(Jo Lilley, Simon Calvert, Mike Pugh)*

☆ *Water Witch* [parking in Aldcliffe Rd behind Royal Lancaster Infirmary, off A6]: Cheerful and attractive conversion of 18th-c canalside barge-horse stabling, flagstones, stripped stone, rafters and pitch-pine panelling, fine changing beer choice, lots of bottled beers, dozens of wines by the glass and good spirits range from mirrored bar, enjoyable stylishly cooked local food inc good cheese board, upstairs restaurant; children in eating areas, tables outside, open all day *(Jo Lilley, Simon Calvert, Claire Moore, LYM)*

LATHOM [SD4511]

☆ *Ship* [off A5209 E of Burscough; Wheat Lane]: Big pub tucked below embankment at junction of Leeds & Liverpool and Rufford Branch canals, several separate beamed rooms, some interesting canal memorabilia and naval pictures and crests, up to nine reliably well kept changing ales inc smaller breweries such as Moorhouses and Phoenix, some parts set for the unpretentious food from lunchtime sandwiches up (small helpings for children), prompt service even when busy; games room with pool, big-screen sports TV; children welcome, tables outside, open all day *(BB, Jim and Maggie Cowell, Steve Kirby, MLR, Bill Sykes, Steve Whalley)*

LIVERPOOL [SJ4395]

☆ *Cains Brewery Tap* [Stanhope St]: Well restored Victorian pub with Cains full beer range kept well at attractive prices, guest beers from other small breweries, friendly efficient staff, good well priced wkdy food till 6 (2 Sat), nicely understated décor, wooden floors, plush raised side snug, interesting old prints and breweriana, handsome bar, flame-effect gas fire, newspapers, cosy relaxing atmosphere; popular exceptional value brewery tour ending here with buffet and singing; sports TV, open all day *(Patrick Hancock, the Didler)*

Carnarvon Castle [Tarleton St]: Long and narrow, with one main bar and comfortable back lounge, well kept Cains Bitter and Mild and a guest or two, lunchtime bar snacks, cabinet of Dinky toys and other eclectic collections, no music; open all day, cl Sun evening, Mon/Tues lunchtime (opens 8pm then) *(the Didler, Patrick Hancock, Joe Green)*

☆ *Cracke* [Rice St]: Friendly backstreet local, bare boards and pews, lots of posters for local events and pictures of local buildings, unusual Beatles diorama in largest room, very cheap food till 6, also Thurs curry night, well kept Phoenix Bitter and Wobbly Bob, Timothy Taylors Landlord and guest beers, imported wheat beers; juke box and TV, popular mainly with young people; open all day, sizeable garden *(Patrick Hancock, the Didler, MLR, Eric Robinson, Jacqueline Pratt)*

Crown [Lime St]: Well preserved art nouveau showpiece with fine tiled fireplace and copper bar front, plush banquettes, splendid ceiling in airy corner bar, smaller back room with another good fireplace, impressive staircase sweeping up under splendid cupola to handsome area with ornate windows, usual food inc some massive yet low-priced dishes, bargain real ales from small breweries such as Coach House and Hampshire *(Joe Green)*

☆ *Dispensary* [Renshaw St]: Small chatty local-feeling central pub with well kept Cains ales and two guest beers, lots of bottled imports, friendly staff (may let you have tasters), good value wkdy food 12-7, polished panelling, marvellous etched windows, bare boards, comfortable raised back bar, Victorian medicine bottles and instruments; open all day *(Peter F Marshall, the Didler, Patrick Hancock)*

☆ *Doctor Duncan* [St Johns Lane]: Neatly kept classic Victorian pub with particularly attentive staff, full Cains range and two guest beers kept well, belgian beers on tap, convivial atmosphere, enjoyable food from sandwiches to economical main dishes till 7 (Tues curry night), pleasant helpful service, daily papers and magazines, several rooms inc impressive back area with pillared and vaulted tiled ceiling, no smoking family room; may be piped music, busy wknds; open all day *(Patrick Hancock, Andrew York, Peter F Marshall, the Didler, Mark Harrington)*

Globe [Cases St, opp station]: Chatty comfortably carpeted local, pleasant staff, well kept Cains, Tetleys and two guest beers, good port, lunchtime filled baps, cosy snug, tiny quiet sloping-floor back lounge, lots of prints of old Liverpool; may be piped 1960s music; open all day *(the Didler, Patrick Hancock, Joe Green)*

Grapes [Mathew St]: Lively and friendly, with well kept Cains, Tetleys and guest beers, good value lunchtime bar food, open-plan but pleasantly well worn cottagey décor (flagstones, old range, wall settles, no two chairs the same, gas-effect lamps); open all day, can get crowded Fri/Sat, cl Sun *(Patrick Hancock, the Didler)*

Lion [Moorfields, off Tithebarn St]: Ornate Victorian alehouse, sparkling etched glass and serving hatches in central bar, unusual wallpaper, big mirrors, panelling and tilework, two small back lounges one with fine glass dome, friendly atmosphere and landlord interested in the history, well kept Lees and changing guest beers such as Caledonian Deuchars IPA, lunchtime food from sandwiches and baguettes up (good value cheese choice and monster pork pies), may be free bar nibbles, coal fire; open all day *(Pete Baker, Patrick Hancock, the Didler, Paul Davies)*

Ma Boyles [Tower Gardens, off Water St]: Much modernised backstreet local with good value bar food (all day Sat) from dim sum and pies to oysters from Galway, well kept Hydes and guest beers, quieter downstairs bar; jazz Weds, open all day, cl Sat night and Sun *(the Didler, Joe Green)*

Midland [Ranelagh St]: Neatly kept Victorian local with original décor, ornate lounge, long corner bar, nice etched glass, mirrors and chandeliers; keg beers *(the Didler)*

Peter Kavanaghs [Egerton St, off Catherine St]: Well kept Cains, Greene King Abbot and guest beers in backstreet 19th-c local with plenty of character, interesting small rooms (two with old-world murals) and bric-a-brac; open all day *(Patrick Hancock, the Didler)*

Poste House [Cumberland St]: Small comfortable early 19th-c backstreet local surrounded by huge redevelopment, well kept Cains Bitter and Mild and guest beers, good wkdy lunches, friendly licensees, daily papers, room upstairs; open all day *(the Didler, Joe Green)*

Roscoe Head [Roscoe St]: Three tiny unspoilt rooms, spotlessly kept, chatty and civilised, with well kept Carlsberg Burton, Jennings Cumberland, Tetleys Mild and Bitter and guest beers, good value wkdy home-made lunches, amusing cartoons, tie collection, cribbage school Weds, Tues quiz night; open all day *(Patrick Hancock, the Didler, Joe Green)*

Ship & Mitre [Dale St]: Friendly gaslit local popular with university people, up to a dozen well kept changing unusual real ales served in over-sized lined glasses, imported beers, two farm ciders, good-humoured service, good value basic food lunchtime and Fri evening, pool, occasional beer festivals, Thurs quiz night; piped music; open all day, cl Sun lunchtime *(Paul Davies, Andrew York, the Didler, Joe Green)*

Swan [Wood St]: Well kept Cains, Phoenix Wobbly Bob, guest beers and Weston's farm cider in recently refurbished bare-boards pub with good value cobs and home-cooked wkdy lunches, friendly staff, comfortable loft in second upstairs bar (open at busy times); good loud 1970s rock juke box; open all day *(Patrick Hancock, the Didler)*

Vines [Lime St]: Comfortable and friendly, with Victorian mahogany and mosaic tilework, handsome high-ceilinged room on right with stained glass; keg beer, can get very busy; open all day *(the Didler)*

White Star [Rainford Gdns, off Matthew St]: Welcoming traditional local with well kept Bass and several changing guest beers, good service, lots of woodwork, boxing prints, White Star shipping line and Beatles memorabilia, big-screen sports TV in comfortable back lounge; open all day *(Patrick Hancock, the Didler)*

LONGRIDGE [SD6137]

Corporation Arms [Lower Rd (B6243)]: 18th-c pub recently refurbished by newish licensees, traditional food with modern touches, three changing guest beers, plenty of malt whiskies, three small linked rooms and restaurant; comfortable bedrooms with own bathrooms *(Graham and Doreen Holden)*

LONGTON [SD4525]

Dolphin [Marsh Lane, towards Longton Marsh]: Busy family pub with good cheap food served 12-8 from sandwiches and baked potatoes to Sun roasts, pleasant speedy service, well kept Boddingtons and several guest beers, occasional beer festivals; lots of tables out behind with good play area *(Phil Berrill, Jim and Maggie Cowell)*

LYDIATE [SD3604]

Scotch Piper [Southport Rd]: Medieval thatched pub with heavy black beams, flagstones and thick stone walls, well kept Banks's and Marstons ales, darts in middle room off corridor, carpeted back snug, three coal fires, no food, music or machines; picnic-sets in large garden with aviary, hens, donkey and abundant flower baskets, open all day wknds *(the Didler)*

LYTHAM [SD3427]

Fairhaven [Marine Drive]: Neatly kept extended modern pub with wide choice of generous fresh food from sandwiches and baguettes up, popular Fri thai night, Boddingtons, Marstons Pedigree and Theakstons, obliging staff; handy for beach and Fairhaven Lake *(Tina and Griff)*

MANCHESTER [SJ8284]

☆ *Ape & Apple* [John Dalton St]: Big friendly open-plan pub with low-priced Holts kept well, bargain hearty bar food, comfortable seats in bare-boards bar with nice lighting and lots of old prints and posters, armchairs in upstairs lounge; piped music, TV area, games machines; good mix on busy wknd evenings (unusually for city centre, over-25s won't feel out of place), quieter lunchtime or midweek; unusual brick cube garden, bedrooms, open all day *(the Didler)*

Bar Centro [Tib St]: Continental-style two-floor café-bar, relaxed at lunchtime with well kept Hydes and a couple of local guest beers, continental draught beers, farm cider, up-to-date food, daily papers, local paintings for sale, nice woodwork; popular with young people evenings – frequent live music and DJs, small

dance floor; open all day (till 1am Thurs-Sat)
(the Didler)

Bar Fringe [Swan St]: Convivial continental café-style bare-boards bar specialising in beers from the low countries, also three well kept changing ales from local small breweries, farm cider, friendly staff, enjoyable food till 7, daily papers, shelves of empty beer bottles, cartoons, posters and bank notes, polished motorcycle hung above door, games inc pinball, good music; tables out behind, open all day
(the Didler, Martin Grosberg)

Beer House [Angel St, off Rochdale Rd]: Lively bare-boards open-plan pub thriving under newish landlord, ten or so well kept real ales, several belgian beers each served in its proper glass, farm ciders, perry and country wines, robust cheap bar food lunchtime and early evening, darts, up-to-date CD juke box, games machine, more comfortable upstairs bar with bar billiards, table football and SkyTV, ceilidh band Tues; tables out in small area behind, open all day *(the Didler, G Coates)*

Bridge St Tavern [Bridge St]: Long narrow panelled room with two fine tiled and ironwork fireplaces (surely that can't be an original Lucien Freud above one of them), two real ales, similar upstairs room for diners – some emphasis on the food side *(Dennis Jones)*

Bulls Head [London Rd, below Piccadilly Stn]: Traditional city pub, friendly staff, well kept Banks's, Marstons Pedigree and guest beers, enjoyable food wkdys, all-day breakfast and Sun roast lunch, lots of wood, nice pictures, gas fire, popular Tues quiz night *(G Coates, the Didler)*

Castle [Oldham St, about 200 yards from Piccadilly, on right]: Unspoilt traditional front bar, small snug, full Robinsons range kept well from fine bank of handpumps, games in well worn back room, nice tilework outside; no food, children allowed till 7, blues Thurs, open all day (cl Sun afternoon) *(Patrick Hancock, the Didler)*

Circus [Portland St]: Two tiny rooms, back one panelled with leatherette banquettes, very well kept Tetleys from minute corridor bar (or may be table drinks service), friendly landlord, celebrity photographs, no music or machines; often looks closed but normally open all day (you may have to knock) *(the Didler, Patrick Hancock)*

City Arms [Kennedy St, off St Peters Sq]: Five or six well kept beers changing often (awe-inspiring pump-clip collection), belgian bottled beers, occasional beer festivals, busy for cheap bar lunches inc sandwiches and baked potatoes, quiet evenings; coal fires, bare boards and banquettes, prints and panelling, handsome tiled façade and corridor; good piped music, TV, games machine; wheelchair access but steps down to back lounge, open all day (cl Sat lunchtime, Sun) *(the Didler, Dennis Jones)*

Coach & Horses [Old Bury Rd, Whitefield; A665 nr Besses o' the Barn Stn]: Early 19th-c coaching inn keeping several separate rooms, popular and friendly, with well kept Holts,

table service, darts, cards; open all day
(the Didler)

Crescent [The Crescent (A6), Salford – opp Salford Univ]: Three 18th-c houses converted into beer house in 19th, unusual layout and homely unsmart décor, buoyant local atmosphere (popular with students and university staff), up to eight changing real ales, farm ciders, lots of foreign bottled beers, good value food (not Sat/Mon evenings or Sun), friendly staff, open fire, pool room, juke box; small enclosed outside area, open all day
(the Didler)

Eagle [Collier St, Salford (keep on Greengate after it leaves B6182)]: Old-fashioned basic backstreet local, well kept low-priced Holts Bitter and Mild, friendly service, cheap filled rolls, bar servery to tap and passage with two smoke rooms, old Salford pictures; sports TV; open all day *(the Didler)*

Egerton Arms [Gore St, Salford; A6 by station]: Several rooms, chandeliers, art nouveau lamps, well kept low-priced Holts Bitter and Mild, guest beers such as Boddingtons and Marstons; open all day *(the Didler)*

Grey Horse [Portland St, nr Piccadilly]: Small traditional Hydes local, welcoming and busy, with timbering, pictures and plates, well kept Bitter and Mild, some unusual malt whiskies; can bring in good sandwiches from next door; no juke box or machines, open all day
(the Didler, G D K Fraser, Patrick Hancock)

Hare & Hounds [Shudehill, behind Arndale]: Traditional layout and décor, long narrow bar linking front snug and comfortable back lounge (with TV), notable tilework, panelling and stained glass, well kept Holts, Lees and Tetleys, sandwiches, friendly staff; games and machine, piano singalongs Weds and Sun, upstairs Fri folk club; open all day *(Pete Baker, the Didler)*

Jolly Angler [Ducie St]: Plain backstreet local, long a favourite, small and friendly, with well kept Hydes Bitter and a seasonal beer, coal or peat fire; darts, pool and sports TV, informal folk nights Thurs and Sun; open all day Sat *(the Didler, BB, Pete Baker)*

Kings Arms [Bloom St, Salford]: Big busy and friendly local redone a few years ago with plain tables, bare boards and flagstones contrasting with opulent maroon and purple décor and stained glass, good changing range of well kept ales usually inc Caledonian Deuchars IPA and local Bazens, lunchtime food; juke box may obtrude, live jazz upstairs Weds, occasional theatre nights; open all day (cl Sun evening) *(the Didler, Martin Grosberg)*

Lass o' Gowrie [36 Charles St; off Oxford St at BBC]: Lively tiled Victorian pub with big-windowed long bar, stripped brickwork, hop pockets draped from the ceiling, and long a main entry for its lively atmosphere, good range of real ales (at one time it brewed its own) and bargain food, with a proper no smoking room; we do not yet know how it will turn out after 2005 takeover by Greene King, and new tenants – reports please
(LYM)

☆ **Mark Addy** [Stanley St, off New Bailey St, Salford]: Unusual converted waiting rooms for boat passengers, barrel-vaulted red sandstone bays with wide glassed-in brick arches, cast-iron pillars and flagstones, bargain food inc good cheese choice, well kept real ale, quite a few wines, fast friendly service; flower-filled waterside courtyard, ducks on the cleaned-up River Irwell *(David Carr, LYM, Dennis Jones)*

Metropolitan [Lapwing Lane, Didsbury]: Huge welcoming dining pub, enjoyable generous food from wholesome bar lunches to some interesting evening dishes, popular Sun lunch, well kept ales such as Burtonwood, Caledonian Deuchars IPA and Timothy Taylors Landlord, impressive décor with separate areas and unspoilt airy feel, open fires, gabled roof; tables out on heated decking, outside summer bar *(Chris Howarth, Barry Lavin)*

Moon Under Water [Deansgate]: Britain's biggest pub, Wetherspoons cinema conversion with entertainer stills, very long, two no smoking areas; half a dozen well kept ales inc bargain pints from very long bar counter, bustling atmosphere (very busy evenings, when upper gallery with two more bars open), well trained staff, popular food all day inc deals for two, opens 10.30 for coffee *(Steve Whalley)*

☆ **Mr Thomas Chop House** [Cross St]: Long Victorian city pub, bare boards, panelling and original gas lamp fittings in front bar with stools at wall and window shelves, back tiled eating area, period features inc wrought-iron gates, good popular traditional english lunchtime food with innovative touches, well kept Boddingtons (the new higher strength one), Timothy Taylors Landlord and a guest such as Archers, decent wines, no smoking area; open all day *(Mr and Mrs Colin Roberts, the Didler, Revd D Glover, Susie Symes, Roger Huggins, Tom and Alex McLean)*

Old Monkey [Portland St]: Holts showpiece recently built in traditional style, etched glass and mosaic tiling, interesting memorabilia, bargain generous tasty food, well kept cheap Bitter and Dark Mild, quick friendly service even when busy, upstairs lounge, wide mix of customers *(John Fiander, the Didler, Patrick Hancock)*

☆ **Peveril of the Peak** [Gt Bridgewater St]: Three very welcoming traditional rooms around central servery, lots of mahogany, mirrors and stained or frosted glass, splendidly lurid art nouveau green external tilework; busy lunchtime but friendly and homely evenings, with cheap basic lunchtime food (not Sun), family service, log fire, well kept Boddingtons, Marstons Pedigree, Charles Wells Bombardier and guest beers, sturdy furnishings on bare boards, interesting pictures, pub games inc pool, table football, Tues folk night; TV; pavement tables, children welcome, cl wknd lunchtimes *(Patrick Hancock, the Didler, Stephen Buckley, LYM, Dennis Jones, Jack Clark, Stephen and Jean Curtis)*

Plough [Hyde Rd (A57), Gorton]: Classic tiling, windows and gantry in unspoilt local, wooden benches in large public bar, two quieter back lounges, small pool room and lots of pub games, well kept Robinsons; TV; open all day *(the Didler)*

☆ **Queens** [Honey St, Cheetham; off Red Bank, nr Victoria Stn]: Well preserved tiled façade, well kept changing beers from small breweries, lots of belgian imports, farm ciders, simple enjoyable food (all day wknds), coal fire, bar billiards, board games; children welcome, unexpected views of Manchester across the industrialised Irk Valley and its railway lines from large back garden with good play area, open all day *(the Didler)*

☆ **Rain Bar** [Gt Bridgewater St]: Appealing umbrella works conversion, lots of woodwork and flagstones, full range of Lees beers kept well, 16 wines by the glass, good value food all day from 9am wknd breakfast through panini and light meals to fish and chips etc, relaxed atmosphere, brisk pleasant service, daily papers, coal fire in small snug, large upstairs café-bar too; piped music may be loud; no under-21s or scruffs evenings, good back terrace overlooking spruced-up Rochdale Canal, handy for Bridgwater Hall, open all day *(Andy and Jill Kassube, Patrick Hancock, the Didler, Dennis Jones)*

Sams Chop House [Back Pool Fold, Chapel Walks]: Small pleasant dining pub, offshoot from Mr Thomas Chop House, with thriving atmosphere, well kept beers, good wine choice, formal waiters *(Revd D Glover, Peter F Marshall, John Fiander, Jo Lilley, Simon Calvert)*

☆ **Sinclairs** [2 Cathedral Gates, off Exchange Sq]: Reconstructed low-beamed and timbered 18th-c pub repositioned here in the recent redevelopment, cheap food, bargain Sam Smiths Bitter and Stout, friendly helpful staff, great atmosphere, upstairs bar with snugs and Jacobean fireplace; plastic glasses for the tables out by ultra-modern Exchange Sq *(Revd D Glover, LYM, the Didler)*

Smithfield [Swan St]: Open-plan family-run local with well kept Phoenix and lots of interesting changing guest beers, some in jugs from the cellar, frequent beer festivals, enjoyable bargain food from sandwiches up from open kitchen servery, daily papers, friendly staff and landlady; pool on front dais, games machine, juke box, sports TV in back lounge/eating area; good value bedrooms in nearby building, open all day *(the Didler, BB)*

Vine [Kennedy St]: Well kept real ale, brisk cheerful service, lots of brass and old photographs, cheap generous food in popular basement food bar *(Dennis Jones)*

White House [Gt Ancoats St]: Friendly local with long-serving licensees, well kept cheap Holts and two or three interesting guest beers, film star pictures in big lounge, public bar with darts and pool; cl Tues evening, opens 8 other evenings *(the Didler)*

White Lion [Liverpool Rd, Castlefield]: Busy but friendly Victorian pub, lots of dark wood, tables for eating up one side of three-sided bar, home-made food all day inc good hot beef sandwiches and children's helpings, changing ales inc Phoenix and Timothy Taylors Landlord, decent house wine, good tea, friendly service, real fire, lots of prints and Man Utd pictures, shelves of bottles and jugs; big-screen sports TV, nostalgic discos Fri-Sun; disabled access, children welcome, tables out among excavated foundations of Roman city overlooking fort gate, handy for Museum of Science and Industry and Royal Exchange Theatre, open all day *(the Didler, G Coates)*

MARPLE [SJ9389]

Hare & Hounds [Dooley Lane (A627 W)]: Attractive old Hydes pub with their usual beers and reasonably priced standard food, welcoming staff, pleasant relaxing atmosphere, tasteful modern extension; Weds quiz night *(Dennis Jones)*

Railway [Stockport Rd]: Bright bustling pub with well kept Robinsons ales, good value lunchtime food (children allowed then) from toasties to Sun roasts; handy for Middlewood Way, open all day *(Dennis Jones)*

MARPLE BRIDGE [SJ9690]

Spring Gardens [Compstall Rd]: Well kept Boddingtons and other ales, enjoyable freshly made food at low prices, friendly atmosphere and staff; big garden with play area and animals *(Dennis Jones)*

MAWDESLEY [SD5016]

☆ *Robin Hood* [Blue Stone Lane (Croston—Eccleston road, N of village – keep going)]: Popular open-plan dining pub with button-back wall banquettes, reproduction Victorian prints, decorative plates, stained-glass seat dividers, some stripped stone; wide choice of good value generous home cooking (all day wknds) from sandwiches and baguettes up, cheap children's helpings, OAP bargain lunches, friendly staff coping well with the bustle, well kept Boddingtons, Timothy Taylors Landlord and four interesting guest ales, decent wines, children's room, small pretty upstairs evening restaurant; may be piped music, fruit machine; picnic-sets on neat side terrace, good fenced play area, open all day *(Margaret Dickinson, Ian and Sue Wells, Yvonne and Mike Meadley)*

MELLOR [SJ9888]

Devonshire Arms [Longhurst Lane; this is the Mellor nr Marple, S of Manchester]: Appealing layout of separate rooms, Victorian fireplaces throughout, well kept Robinsons Best and Mild, enjoyable food; picnic-sets out in front and in attractively reworked back garden *(LYM, R Yates)*

MERE BROW [SD4118]

Legh Arms [B5246, off A565 W of Southport]: Popular for good choice of enjoyable food (best to book), pleasant atmosphere, friendly service; children welcome, garden tables *(Tom Halsall)*

MERECLOUGH [SD8730]

☆ *Kettledrum* [off A646 Burnley—Halifax]: Friendly and cosy country local with young licensees doing wide choice of good value genuine home cooking, well kept ales such as Black Sheep and Theakstons, good service, fine views, partly no smoking gaslit upstairs dining

room; children welcome, tables outside *(LYM, Len Beattie)*

MOTTRAM [SJ9894]

☆ *Waggon* [off A57 M'ter—Barnsley; at central traffic lights turn opp B6174 into Broadbottom Rd]: Generous reliable food served very promptly all day in comfortable open-plan local, sensible prices, well kept Robinsons Best and Best Mild on electric pump, friendly waitresses, big central fire; good wheelchair access, picnic-sets and good play area outside *(BB, Mr and Mrs R B Berry)*

OLDHAM [SD9204]

Ashton Arms [Clegg St]: Comfortable open-plan pub, sofas in one corner, good open fire, four or five real ales from mainly local microbreweries, bar food till 6, friendly regulars; TV for cricket; open all day *(Martin Grosberg)*

☆ *Roebuck* [Roebuck Low, Strinesdale, off A62 NE]: Welcoming unpretentious moorland pub, a local byword for wide choice of good generous home-made food; well kept Wadworths 6X, decent wines, helpful staff, log fire in front lounge, central bar, back restaurant (often booked up even midweek), great hillside views day and night *(Matt and Vicky Wharton, Mrs P J Carroll)*

PARBOLD [SD4911]

Wayfarer [A5209/Alder Lane]: Civilised pub with enjoyable bar meals, good service and atmosphere; children welcome *(Brian Kneale)*

PAYTHORNE [SD8351]

Buck: Welcoming country pub, busy in season (nr big caravan park), generous reasonably priced home-made food largely using local produce, two local real ales, real fire, no smoking area; outside seating *(Dudley and Moira Cockroft)*

PLEASINGTON [SD6426]

Butlers Arms [Pleasington Lane/Victoria Rd]: Substantial Georgian pub redone in rustic Victorian style, well kept Fullers London Pride, Wychwood Three Shires and two guest beers, friendly young staff, usual food (all day Sun); children welcome, views from bowling green behind *(Steve Whalley)*

POULTON-LE-FYLDE [SD3439]

River Wyre [Breck Rd]: Spreading pub with eating and drinking areas, scrubbed pine tables on bare boards, fish specialities and other food, changing real ales, good choice of wines by the bottle *(Tracey and Stephen Groves)*

Thatched House [Ball St/Breck Rd]: Compact unpretentious town pub with well preserved 1920s décor in older building, interesting changing real ales, friendly staff, no piped music; open all day *(Tracey and Stephen Groves)*

PRESTON [SD5330]

Black Horse [Friargate]: Friendly traditional pub in pedestrian street, full Robinsons ale range kept well, inexpensive lunchtime food, unusual ornate curved and mosaic-tiled Victorian main bar, panelling, stained glass and old local photographs, two quiet cosy enclosed snugs off, mirrored back area, upstairs 1920s-style bar, good juke box;

no children, open all day, cl Sun evening
*(the Didler, Pete Baker, Jim and
Maggie Cowell)*
New Britannia [Heatley St, just off Friargate]:
Enthusiastic landlady, half a dozen or more
real ales from small breweries such as Pictish,
bargain simple lunches, lively friendly
atmosphere *(Pam and John Smith)*

RABY [SJ3179]
☆ *Wheatsheaf* [off A540 S of Heswall; Raby
Mere Rd]: Attractive thatched and timbered
pub with unspoilt homely furnishings in chatty
rambling bar inc high-backed settles making a
snug around fine old fireplace, splendid choice
of well kept ales and of malt whiskies, polite
attentive service, spacious evening restaurant
(not Sun/Mon) and no smoking conservatory;
they may try to keep your credit card while
you eat; children and dogs allowed, picnic-sets
on terrace and in pleasant back garden, pretty
village *(Mrs B M Hill, MLR,
Roger Thornington, LYM, Paul Humphreys,
Mr and Mrs M Stratton, Dr Phil Putwain,
Theocsbrian)*

RILEY GREEN [SD6225]
☆ *Royal Oak* [A675/A6061]: Cosy low-beamed
three-room former coaching inn, good food inc
notable steak muffins, well kept Thwaites (full
range) from long back bar, friendly efficient
service, ancient stripped stone, open fires, seats
from high-backed settles to red plush
armchairs, lots of nooks and crannies, turkey
carpet, soft lighting, impressive woodwork,
fresh flowers, interesting model steam engines
and plenty of bric-a-brac, two comfortable
dining rooms; can be packed Fri night and
wknds; tables outside, short walk from Leeds
& Liverpool Canal, footpath to Hoghton
Tower, open all day Sun *(Peter Abbott,
Norma and Noel Thomas, BB)*

RINGLEY [SD7605]
Horseshoe [Fold Rd, Stoneclough; right off
A667 at sign for Kidds Garden Centre]: Good
imaginative food, wider choice evenings
(special dishes with advance notice), friendly
landlord, well kept Thwaites, three areas off
main bar, open fire, interesting local pictures;
well behaved children lunchtime, pleasant back
garden *(Norma and Noel Thomas)*

ROBY MILL [SD5107]
Fox [not far from M6 junction 26; off A577 at
Up Holland]: Nicely placed big traditional
two-roomed black and white village pub, well
kept Marstons Pedigree and Timothy Taylors
Landlord, wide range of good value food in
bar and restaurant, tasteful old-world décor,
friendly staff *(Jack Clark)*

ROCHDALE [SD8814]
Healey [Shawclough Rd (B6377 NW of
centre)]: Unspoilt old stone-built pub with old
film star photographs in main bar, separate no
smoking lounge, well kept Robinsons;
attractive good-sized garden with boules; open
all day from noon wknds (from 3 wkdys)
(Pete Baker)

SALESBURY [SD6732]
Bonny Inn [B6245 Ribchester—Wilpshire]:
Good reasonably priced home-made bar meals,

imaginatively served, in pleasant neatly kept
pub with friendly landlord and back picture-
window views *(Ken and Josephine Bunyan)*

SALTERFORTH [SD8845]
Anchor [Salterforth Lane]: Friendly local by
Leeds & Liverpool Canal, four well kept real
ales, good range of generous reasonably priced
food, dining area, pool room off big public
bar; garden with play area
(Malcolm M Stewart, Nick and Lynne Carter)

SAMLESBURY [SD6229]
Nabs Head Hotel [Nabs Head Lane]: Neatly
kept bay-windowed pub, light and airy, with
good value straightforward home-made food
inc popular Sun lunch, hard-working friendly
staff, well kept Thwaites ales, charming décor;
no credit cards; peaceful country hamlet,
handy for Samlesbury Hall
(Margaret Dickinson, Steve Whalley)

SILVERDALE [SD4574]
Silverdale Hotel [Shore Rd]: Good value
generous food, well kept Bass and a quickly
changing guest beer, four dining areas inc large
conservatory and two no smoking rooms,
spacious pool room; children welcome, plenty
of picnic-sets in good-sized attractive garden,
bedrooms, beautiful setting *(John Foord)*
Woodlands [Woodlands Dr]: Interestingly
decorated Victorian hotel with good evening
atmosphere, up to four well kept quickly
changing real ales at appealing prices, cheap
rolls wknds *(Simon Cleasby)*

SIMISTER [SD8305]
Same Yet [Simister Lane]: Recently opened up
and refurbished Lees dining pub, their real ales
kept well, good range of enjoyable attractively
priced food, no smoking in small room off bar
or light and airy restaurant with Pennine views
(Gerry and Rosemary Dobson)

SIMONSTONE [SD7735]
☆ *Higher Trapp Hotel* [Sabden rd, off School
Lane]: Attractive bar with relaxing views,
tempting food in bar and restaurant (all day
Sun), well kept ales, attentive staff, no smoking
areas, big conservatory; children welcome,
lovely garden, comfortable bedrooms
(Margaret Dickinson)

SLAIDBURN [SD7152]
☆ *Hark to Bounty* [B6478 N of Clitheroe]:
Friendly old stone-built inn in charming Forest
of Bowland village, neat rather modern décor
in line of linked rooms, wide choice of good
value generous food (lots of tables) inc
children's and old-fashioned puddings, good
hospitable service, three well kept real ales,
decent wines and whiskies, comfortable chairs
by open fire, games room with darts, pool and
machines one end, well appointed restaurant
the other; bedrooms, open all day, pleasant
garden behind, good walks *(LYM,
Clive Gibson, Len Beattie, Dennis Jones)*

SLYNE [SD4765]
Slyne Lodge [Main Rd]: Popular well run
hotel, interesting décor, good value pubby
food, well kept Jennings ales, friendly helpful
staff, open fire, welcoming bar, conservatory,
imaginative mediterranean-style dining room;
terrace tables, ten reasonably priced bedrooms

with own bathrooms in former stables *(Andy and Jill Kassube, A C English)*

STANDISH [SD5711]

Crown [not far from M6 junction 27; Platt Lane]: Recently refurbished traditional country pub with open fire in comfortable panelled bar, wide range of well kept real ales (even a daily beers list), enjoyable food inc grills priced and chosen by weight from chiller, early-eater deals, airy dining extension and pleasant conservatory; children allowed away from bar *(Miss Schofield, Mr Robinson)*

STANSFIELD MOOR [SD9227]

☆ *Sportsmans Arms* [Kebcote; old packhorse rd Burnley—Hebden Bridge – actually just over the W Yorks border]: Remote old moorland farm building, a pub since 1920, beams, some dark panelling, stone-mullioned windows, sofas as well as tables and chairs, welcoming fire, country bric-a-brac, enjoyable food (esp steaks and inventive wknd dishes) freshly cooked by landlord using local supplies, well kept ales such as Black Sheep, Halifax and Thwaites, plenty of malt whiskies, decent wines; separate room with darts, pool, games machine; walkers and dogs welcome; open all day Sun, otherwise opens 7 *(LYM, Len Beattie)*

STOCKPORT [SJ8889]

Alexandra [Northgate Rd]: Large backstreet local, reputedly haunted, with preserved Victorian interior, well kept Robinsons Best and Mild; pool room *(the Didler)*

☆ *Arden Arms* [Millgate St, behind Asda]: Good inventive freshly made lunchtime food and well kept Robinsons in welcoming pub with fast cheerful service, well preserved traditional horseshoe bar, old-fashioned tiny snug through servery, two coal fires, longcase clocks, well restored tiling and panelling; tables out in courtyard sheltered by the original stables, open all day *(the Didler, Patrick Hancock, Dennis Jones, Pete Baker, John C Gould)*

Armoury [Shaw Heath]: Comfortable lounge, small unspoilt locals' bar, Robinsons Best and Hatters Mild, perhaps Old Tom from a cask on the bar, lunchtime family room upstairs; open all day *(the Didler)*

Blossoms [Buxton Rd (A6)]: Busy main-road Victorian local, very friendly, with well kept Robinsons Best and Hatters Mild, perhaps Old Tom tapped from the cask, lunchtime food, three rooms off corridor inc pool room with pin table and attractive back lounge with handsome fireplace; open all day wknds *(the Didler)*

Crown [Heaton Lane, Heaton Norris]: Partly open-plan Victorian local under arch of vast viaduct, three cosy lounge areas (one no smoking) off gaslit bar, stylish décor, huge range of well kept ales, farm cider, good value lunchtime bar food, pool, darts; TV, frequent live music; tables in cobbled courtyard, open all day Fri/Sat *(the Didler, Patrick Hancock)*

Hinds Head [Heaton Chapel]: Traditional mock-Tudor pub with comfortable banquettes and lots of tables, generous reasonably priced food, four changing real ales, conservatory restaurant; big garden *(Dennis Jones)*

Navigation [Manchester Rd (B6167, former A626)]: Unpretentious pub with half a dozen or so well kept ales from local Beartown Brewery and a guest beer, several farm ciders tapped from cellar casks, continental imports, friendly landlady and staff; open all day *(the Didler)*

Nursery [Green Lane, Heaton Norris; off A6]: Friendly efficient service, enjoyable straightforward lunchtime food from servery on right with visible kitchen, popular set Sun lunch, big bays of banquettes in panelled front lounge, brocaded wall banquettes in back one, cheap well kept Hydes Bitter and Mild, separate games-oriented public bar, all very neat and clean; children welcome if eating, on narrow cobbled lane at E end of N part of Green Lane, immaculate bowling green behind, open all day wknds *(the Didler, BB, Pete Baker)*

Olde Woolpack [Brinksway, just off M60 junction 1 – junction A560/A5145]: Well kept Theakstons and interesting changing guest beers, good value home-made food, friendly landlord, traditional three-room layout with drinking corridor; open all day Fri-Sun *(the Didler)*

Porters Railway [Avenue St (just off M63 junction 13, via A560)]: Porters ales and three guest beers kept well, lots of foreign beers, farm cider, masses of whiskies and country wines, decent straightforward home-made food (not Sun), bargain prices throughout, friendly staff, bright and airy L-shaped bar with old Stockport prints and memorabilia, bar billiards; may be piped local radio; tables out behind, open all day *(Richard Houghton, the Didler, Dennis Jones)*

Queens Head [Little Underbank (can be reached by steps from St Petersgate)]: Long narrow late Victorian local with delightful separate snug and back dining area, good friendly bustle, reasonable bar food, well kept low-priced Sam Smiths, daily papers, bench seating and bare boards, rare brass cordials fountain and old spirit lamps, old posters and adverts; no smoking area, some live jazz, open all day; famous narrow gents' upstairs *(the Didler, Patrick Hancock)*

☆ *Red Bull* [Middle Hillgate]: Steps up to friendly well run local, impressive beamed and flagstoned bar with dark panelling, substantial settles and seats, open fires, lots of pictures, mirrors and brassware, traditional island servery with well kept Robinsons Best and Best Mild from nearby brewery, good value home-cooked bar lunches (not Sun); quiet at lunchtime, can get crowded evening, open all day (cl Sun afternoon) *(the Didler, LYM, David Hoult)*

Swan With Two Necks [Princes St]: Traditional panelled local, comfortable panelled bar, back skylit lounge and drinking corridor, Robinsons Mild and Bitter, friendly licensee and locals, enjoyable lunchtime food; handy for shops, open all day, cl Sun *(Patrick Hancock, the Didler)*

Tiviot [Tiviot Dale (E end of main shopping

centre)]: Little altered for decades, friendly and unspoilt, with four rooms off central bar inc good games-oriented public bar, lots of old local and steam locomotive photographs, simple inexpensive wkdy lunchtime food, well kept Robinsons; open all day (not Sun evening) *(Pete Baker)*

TATHAM [SD6169]

Tatham Bridge Inn [B6480, off A683 Lancaster—Kirkby Lonsdale]: Cosy old pub with comfortable opened-up low-beamed bar, well kept ales inc Dent and Jennings Cumberland, friendly landlord, enjoyable food from sandwiches up, dining room along corridor; bedrooms *(Dr and Mrs P Truelove, Tony and Maggie Harwood)*

THURSTASTON [SJ2484]

Cottage Loaf [A540]: Comfortable, with well kept Cains and a guest such as Wadworths 6X, enjoyable food inc starters and light dishes, good uniformed staff, open fires *(E G Parish, Martin and Alison Stainsby)*

TYLDESLEY [SJ6999]

Cart & Horses [Manchester Rd, Astley]: Late Victorian local, largely open-plan, with good value Holts ale, welcoming service, good value straightforward food lunchtime and early evening inc good Sun lunch, friendly traditional public bar with darts and cards; small garden *(Pete Baker)*

Mort Arms [Elliott St]: Two-room 1930s pub, etched glass and polished panelling, comfortable lounge with old local photographs, well kept low-priced Holts Bitter and Mild, friendly landlord, TV horseracing Sat; open all day *(the Didler)*

WADDINGTON [SD7243]

Waddington Arms [Clitheroe Rd]: Enjoyable food (all day wknds) using fresh local produce from sandwiches to regional dishes and more up-to-date things, four or more well kept ales, flagstones and bare boards, woodburner in big 17th-c inglenook, red-walled room off with leather sofa and motor-racing pictures, neat dining extension; children welcome, six comfortable chintzy bedrooms – where the church bells either will or won't lull you to sleep *(anon)*

WEST KIRBY [SJ2186]

White Lion [A540 Chester rd]: Interesting small 17th-c sandstone pub, several small beamed areas on different levels, well kept Courage Directors, John Smiths, Theakstons and a guest beer, friendly staff, good value simple bar lunches inc wide choice of sandwiches, coal stove; no children, attractive secluded back garden *(MLR)*

WHEATLEY LANE [SD8338]

☆ *Old Sparrow Hawk* [Wheatley Lane Rd]: Good fresh food with some distinctive cooking,

good sandwiches too, in comfortable and civilised country dining pub with attractive layout, dark oak panelling, stripped stonework and interesting furnishings, buoyant relaxed atmosphere, friendly well trained staff, good wines, well kept ales (a pleasant place for an early evening drink); children welcome in eating areas, tables out on roomy terrace with views to the moors beyond Nelson and Colne *(Michael and Deirdre Ellis, LYM)*

WHEELTON [SD5921]

Top Lock [Copthurst Lane]: Jaunty barge-like pub in picturesque spot on Leeds & Liverpool Canal, friendly hard-working staff, canal-related décor, half a dozen well kept ales such as Cains and Coniston Bluebird, wide range of food inc authentic indian dishes *(David Wright)*

WOODFORD [SJ8882]

Davenport Arms [A5102 Wilmslow-Poynton]: Down-to-earth convivial country pub with small rooms, coal fires, well kept Robinsons Best and Best Mild, good house wines, popular reasonably priced home cooking, good games room, no smoking room; children allowed in back no smoking snug, tables on front terrace and in attractive back garden with play area *(Dave Braisted)*

WREA GREEN [SD3931]

☆ *Grapes* [Station Rd]: Busy Chef & Brewer with good layout of cosy olde-worlde linked areas, enjoyable fresh food (may be a wait) from good sandwiches to some imaginative specials, well kept Theakstons, Timothy Taylors Landlord and Charles Wells Bombardier, good choice of wines by the glass, open fire and candles; tables out overlooking village green, picturesque church *(Spider Newth, Brian Kneale, Dr and Mrs A K Clarke, Tracey and Stephen Groves)*

WRIGHTINGTON [SD5011]

Rigbye Arms [3 miles from M6 junction 27; off A5209 via Robin Hood Lane and left into High Moor Lane]: 16th-c moorland inn with good value generous food from straightforward favourites to some interesting specials, good fresh veg, well kept ales inc Greene King Old Speckled Hen and Timothy Taylors Landlord, decent wines, nice relaxed atmosphere, pleasant country setting *(Nick Holding, P R Morgan, Norma and Noel Thomas, Jack Clark)*

WRIGHTINGTON BAR [SD5313]

☆ *Mulberry Tree*: More classy restaurant than pub now, light, airy and stylish, with plenty of tables, good generous if not cheap imaginatively served food (best to book Sun lunch), attentive friendly service *(Brenda and Stuart Naylor, Karen Eliot)*

Leicestershire and Rutland

Three new entries here this year are the comfortable and chatty Sugar Loaf at Ab Kettleby (a good all-rounder with enjoyable generous food), the Three Horse Shoes at Breedon on the Hill (splendidly reworked by its new owners as an attractive dining pub, already well in the running for a Food Award), and the friendly family-run Griffin at Swithland (another appealing all-rounder, its fine choice of well kept ales earning it a Beer Award). Other pubs currently attracting great attention here are the entirely no smoking Exeter Arms at Barrowden (imaginative food, brewing its own good beers), the well run Olive Branch at Clipsham (lovely food and marvellous drinks in attractive civilised surroundings – a great favourite), the Nevill Arms at Medbourne (friendly long-serving licensees, good food and drink, nice bedrooms), the Cow & Plough in Oadby (an interesting place with lots to see, surprisingly modern food and good beers), the friendly New Inn at Peggs Green (much enjoyed by people who like their pubs thoroughly unspoilt and unpretentious), the bustling and cheerful Stilton Cheese at Somerby (good beers and wines, and, with three chefs in the family, properly home-made food), the Three Crowns there (a good value thriving local with bargain OAP lunches), the Red Lion at Stathern (super imaginative food, an excellent choice of drinks – as more readers discover this, we expect it to become one of the top favourites), the Jackson Stops at Stretton (another splendid place for a good stylish meal, with a charming little old-fashioned bar too), and the Finches Arms above Rutland Water at Upper Hambleton (a new bar serving the terrace to make the most of the views, and very good modern food – good bedrooms too). From among all these, the Olive Branch at Clipsham again stands out as Leicestershire and Rutland Dining Pub of the Year – as it has been since it first entered the Guide four years ago. In the Lucky Dip section at the end of the chapter, we'd particularly pick out the Blue Ball at Braunston, Old Barn at Glooston, Swan in the Rushes in Loughborough, Old Red Lion in Market Bosworth, Royal Horseshoes at Waltham on the Wolds, Wheatsheaf on the edge of Woodhouse Eaves and restauranty Hammer & Pincers at Wymeswold. Drinks prices in the area have been held fairly static this last year, and are now a shade below the national average. The area's main brewer is Everards of Leicester. Beers from two good well priced smaller brewers often found here are Grainstore (from the pub of that name in Oakham) and Oakham (not actually from there, but from Peterborough over in Cambridgeshire).

Although we don't normally mention what might be called office matters, one oddity here struck us as being worth a note this year. Almost always, pubs are very happy to give us the factual information, about prices, opening times and so forth, that we ask them for. After all, they know that a mention in this bestselling guide (not just to pubs, but in all travel fields) is a big boost to their business. The odd thing was that this year we found that getting information out of quite a few pubs in just this area was like getting blood out of a stone. Your guess as to why this should be is as good as ours!

AB KETTLEBY SK7519 Map 7

Sugar Loaf

Nottingham Road (A606 NW of Melton)

This well run country pub, open-plan, largely no smoking and comfortably modernised, has a relaxed and chatty atmosphere. The substantial carved bar counter, with well cushioned stools, has well kept Bass, Belvoir Beaver, Fullers London Pride, Grainstore Gold and Shepherd Neame Spitfire on handpump, and good solid pale wood tables and chairs on the discreetly patterned carpet spread from here into a pleasant conservatory. There are good big black and white photographs of Shipstones brewery dray horses and a variety of country prints on the ragged canary walls. As well as all-day snacks such as filled baked potatoes (from £4.45), filled baguettes with home-made chips (from £4.75), and burgers and ploughman's (from £4.95), there might be lunchtime choices like home-made soup (£3.75), home-made pâté (£5.45), sausage and mash with red wine gravy (£6.75), and lasagne or beef in ale pie (£7.95), and evening meals such as black pudding with horseradish sauce (£5.45), prawns topped with shredded parma ham and a light lemon dressing (£5.95), vegetable and mozzarella timbale (£7.95), breast of chicken with garlic mushrooms and smoked bacon sauce (£8.95), fillet of salmon with orange and ginger (£10.95), and steaks (from £13.75). The food comes in hearty helpings on big plates, and service is quick and friendly. A bare-boards end area with a coal-effect gas fire has darts, cribbage, dominoes, a quiet juke box and fruit machine. There are a few picnic-sets out by the road and car park. *(Recommended by Phil and Jane Hodson)*

Free house ~ Licensees Josephine and Dennis Donovan ~ Real ale ~ Bar food (all day) ~ Restaurant ~ (01664) 822473 ~ Children welcome ~ Open 11-11; 12-10.30 Sun

BARROWDEN SK9400 Map 4

Exeter Arms 🍽 ◀

Main Street, just off A47 Uppingham—Peterborough

Whether you drop into this peaceful 17th-c no smoking coaching inn for a pint of their own-brewed beer or an imaginative meal, you can be sure of a warm welcome from the new licensees. The long open-plan bar – painted a cheery yellow – stretches away either side of a long central counter, and is quite straightforwardly furnished with wheelback chairs at tables at either end of the bar, on bare boards or blue patterned carpet; there's quite a collection of pump clips, beer mats and brewery posters. In an old free-standing barn behind, the pub brews its own Blencowe beers. Served from up to six handpumps, these might include Beach Boys, Danny Boys, Fun Boy Four and Boys with Attitude as well as a couple of guests; also about ten wines by the well filled glass. Cribbage, dominoes, shove-ha'penny, piped music, and boules. Well liked bar food might include home-made soup or sandwiches (£3.95), pheasant terrine, grilled goats cheese with pear and pine nuts or smoked salmon salad (£5), gammon steak in creamy mustard sauce (£9.50), fillet of salmon with citrus and herb cream sauce (£10.50), confit duck legs (£11.50), half a crispy duck with cumberland sauce (£12.50) and puddings such as syrup tart or banana and chocolate cheesecake (£4). There are picnic-sets on a narrow terrace overlooking the pretty village green and ducks on the pond, with broader views stretching away beyond, and more well spaced picnic-sets in a big informal grassy garden at the back. *(Recommended by John Wooll, Jim Farmer, Mrs Daphne White, Michael Doswell, Dorsan Baker, the Didler, David Barnes, Barry Collett, Colin McKerrow, Keith Widdowson, Di and Mike Gillam, Mike and Sue Loseby)*

Own brew ~ Licensees Martin and Sharon Allsopp ~ Real ale ~ Bar food (not Sun evening, Mon) ~ Restaurant ~ (01572) 747247 ~ Children welcome away from the bar till 7.30pm ~ Folk club alternate Mon ~ Open 12-2.30(3 Sat), 6-11; 12-3, 7-10.30 Sun; closed Mon lunchtime ~ Bedrooms: £35S/£70S

BELMESTHORPE TF0410 Map 8
Blue Bell
Village signposted off A16 just E of Stamford

On two levels, this pleasant place was originally three cottages. From the first little beamed cottagey room, which has gleaming brass platters, pews and settles, and an open fire in a huge stone inglenook you peer down into the bar counter. From here a slope winds down round the counter to a dining area, or you can go through to the games room. The enjoyable menu (they tell us prices have not changed since last year) includes soup (£3.45), sandwiches (£3.50), filled ciabattas (from £5.95), home-made lincolnshire sausages and mash (£6.25), scampi and chips or gammon (£7.95), 12oz sirloin (£11), as well as daily specials such as chicken curry (£7.95) and puddings such as treacle sponge with custard or banoffi pie (£3.45). The restaurant is no smoking. Well kept Bass and Hop Back Summer Lightning with guests such as Greene King Abbot, Hop Back Summer Lightning and two changing guest beers on handpump, and a good choice of wines by the glass; darts, piped classical radio, pool. There are plenty of picnic-sets in the garden. More reports please. *(Recommended by Ray and Winifred Halliday, Paul and Annette Hallett)*

Free house ~ Licensees Lee Thompson and Angeline Hennessy ~ Real ale ~ Bar food (12-2, 6.30-9; not Sun evenings) ~ Restaurant ~ (01780) 763859 ~ Children welcome ~ Open 12-2.30, 6-11; 12-10.30 Sun

BREEDON ON THE HILL SK4022 Map 7
Three Horse Shoes
Main Street (A453)

Newly taken over by a landlord whose good interesting food and civilised style made the Nags Head in Castle Donington a popular main entry, this 18th-c building opposite a quaint little conical village lock-up has been transformed into a good stylish dining pub, with a cheerful chatty atmosphere. The main two-room eating area on the right is no smoking, with big quite close-set tables on rush matting, colourful modern country prints and antique engravings on canary walls, and some inset shelves of bric-a-brac. Good popular blackboard food, using local produce and suppliers, includes home-made soup (£4.50), interesting sandwiches (from £4.95), cajun chicken salad with tzatziki dressing £5.95), grilled goats cheese with cranberry dressing or chicken liver parfait (£5.95), seared scallops with balsamic vinegar or beef stir fry (£6.95), leek and potato bake with cheese sauce (£10.95), chicken breast with stilton sauce (£14.95), monkfish with stir-fried oriental vegetables (£15.50), lamb shank with mustard mash (£16.50), and puddings such as chocolate whisky trifle or an excellent treacle oat tart with custard (£4.50). Even at lunchtime there are lighted candles in elegant modern holders. A central bar area, with simple pubby tables on its worn flooring tiles, a log fire and a few more attractive pictures, has well kept Caledonian Deuchars IPA, Courage Directors, Marstons Pedigree and Theakstons XB on handpump, 30 malt whiskies, and good house wines. Beyond here on the left is a step up to a further eating room, with maroon walls, dark pews and cherry-stained tables. No children inside. *(Recommended by Ian and Jane Irving)*

Free house ~ Licensees Ian Davison, Jennie Ison, Stuart Marson ~ Real ale ~ Bar food (12-2, 5.30-9; not Sun) ~ Restaurant ~ (01332) 695129 ~ Dogs allowed in bar ~ Open 11.30-2.30, 5.30-11; 12-2.30, 7-10.30 Sun

---

Bedroom prices normally include full English breakfast, VAT and any inclusive service charge that we know of. Prices before the '/' are for single rooms, after for two people in double or twin (B includes a private bath, S a private shower).

CLIPSHAM SK9616 Map 8

Olive Branch ★ ⑪ ♀ ◀

Take B668/Stretton exit off A1 N of Stamford; Clipsham signposted E from exit roundabout

Leicestershire and Rutland Dining Pub of the Year

This is a particularly well run and civilised pub with friendly, efficient staff, as one reader found out when, despite there being no electricity on his visit, everything ran without a hitch and he had an excellent lunch by candlelight. The various smallish attractive rambling room areas have dark joists and beams, there's a cosy log fire in the stone inglenook fireplace, an interesting mix of pictures (some by local artists), country furniture, and books (many bought at antique fairs by one of the partners – ask if you see something you like, as much is for sale). Two rooms are no smoking. There's quite an emphasis on the imaginative food so it's worth booking in advance: sandwiches, home-made soup (from £3.95), pork and stilton pie with their own piccalilli (half a pie £4.50; whole pie £8), smoked mackerel pâté with melba toast (£5.50), rigatoni pasta, rocket, pine nuts, olive oil and parmesan (£5.50; large £9.75), baked goats cheese with sweet pepper mousse (£5.75), crab ravioli with stir-fried vegetables and shellfish bisque (£7.50), local sausages with mustard mash and sauerkraut (£9.75), super fish and chips with tomato sauce (£9.95), chargrilled gammon with bubble and squeak rösti, poached egg and mustard sauce (£11.50), poached sea trout with asparagus (£12.50), calves liver with chargrilled baby artichokes and tapenade jus (£13.75), roast loin of lamb with saffron and garlic mash (£14.50), and puddings such as caramelised lemon tart with raspberry coulis, chocolate fondant with pistachio ice-cream or praline parfait with tropical fruit salad (from £5.75); interesting cheeses, good coffee, and lovely petit fours. Three-course Sunday lunch (£18.50). Well kept Grainstore Olive Oil and guests such as Burton Bridge Stairway to Heaven and Marstons Pedigree on handpump, an enticing wine list, a fine choice of malt whiskies, armagnacs and cognacs, and 14 different british and continental bottled beers. Shove-ha'penny and maybe unobtrusive piped music. Lovely in summer, there are picnic-sets out on a heated terrace, with more on the neat lawn sheltered in the L of its two low buildings. A new private dining room will be open by the time this edition is published. *(Recommended by Tony and Betty Parker, Sally Anne and Peter Goodale, Dorsan Baker, Phil and Jane Hodson, Roy Bromell, Michael Rodgers, John Saul, Nazeer Chowdhury, Barry Collett, Peter Fitton, Tina and David Woods-Taylor, Les and Barbara Owen, Mike and Sue Loseby, Derek and Sylvia Stephenson, Jeff and Wendy Williams, Brian Wainwright)*

Free house ~ Licensees Sean Hope, Ben Jones and Marcus Welford ~ Real ale ~ Bar food ~ Restaurant ~ (01780) 410355 ~ Children in eating area of bar and restaurant ~ Dogs allowed in bar ~ Open 12-3, 6-11; 12-11(10.30 Sun) Sat; closed 25 Dec, 1 Jan

COTTESMORE SK9013 Map 7

Sun ♀

B668 NE of Oakham

New licensees have taken over this 17th-c thatched and stone-built village pub since our last edition. There are stripped pine furnishings, a winter log fire in the stone inglenook, pictures on the walls, and well kept Adnams Best, Everards Tiger, and a couple of guest beers on handpump. Decent bar food now includes lunchtime sandwiches (£3.25; filled baguettes £4.25), cottage pie (£4.95), and ham and egg (£5.95), as well as soup (£3.25), pâté or haddock and spring onion fishcakes (£3.95), broccoli and cream cheese bake (£6.25), steak and kidney pudding (£7.50), three or four fresh fish dishes (from £7.95), daily specials such as chicken wellington (£8.95) or fillet steak in a creamy pepper sauce (£11.95), and puddings like treacle sponge (£3.25); one dining area is no smoking. There are seats out on the terrace. More reports please. *(Recommended by Jim Auld, Patrick Hancock, Ken and Barbara Turner, Barry Collett)*

Everards ~ Tenants Mr and Mrs Sardinha ~ Real ale ~ Bar food ~ Restaurant ~
(01572) 812321 ~ Children in eating area of bar ~ Dogs allowed in bar ~ Open
11.30-2.30, 5-11; 12-11 Sat; 12-10.30 Sun

EMPINGHAM SK9408 Map 4
White Horse
Main Street; A606 Stamford—Oakham

Being so close to Europe's largest man-made lake, Rutland Water, and open all day,
makes this big bustling old dining pub a very handy place for a drink or meal. The
open-plan carpeted lounge bar has a big log fire below an unusual free-standing
chimney-funnel, and lots of fresh flowers, while outside are some rustic tables
among urns of flowers. Bar food includes sandwiches and baguettes, home-made
soup (£3.45), garlic mushrooms or cream cheese, walnut and celery pâté (£4.95),
greek-style salad (£8.25), ploughman's (£8.45), steak, mushroom and ale pie or
spicy vegetable crumble (£8.75), daily changing fishcakes or home-made lasagne
(£9.25), 10oz sirloin steak with creamy stilton and bacon sauce (£14.95), and daily
specials such as wild boar and apple sausages with onion gravy in a big yorkshire
pudding (£9.25), roast pheasant breast with smoked bacon and red wine jus
(£9.95), and local trout fillets (£9.50). The bistro and the Orange Room are no
smoking; TV, fruit machine and piped music. Well kept Adnams Best and Greene
King Abbot and Ruddles Best on handpump, and quite a few wines by the glass.
Bedrooms are in a converted stable block, and in case any of their residents manage
to catch anything, they offer freezing facilities. They have a wheelchair for disabled
visitors and a ramp makes access easy. (Recommended by Jim Auld, Glenwys and
Alan Lawrence, Duncan Cloud, David and Brenda Tew, P S Hoyle, Barry Collett, Brian and
Ruth Archer, Paul and Annette Hallett, Martin and Sue Day, Bob)

Enterprise ~ Lease Ian and Sarah Sharp ~ Real ale ~ Bar food (12-2.15, 7-9.30; all day Sun)
~ (01780) 460221 ~ Children in eating area of bar and restaurant ~ Dogs allowed in
bedrooms ~ Open 11-11; 12-10.30 Sun ~ Bedrooms: £50B/£65B

EXTON SK9211 Map 7
Fox & Hounds
Signposted off A606 Stamford—Oakham

This year, the Italian licensees at this handsome old country coaching inn have
upgraded the bedrooms and redecorated the public bar. The comfortable high-
ceilinged lounge bar is quietly civilised and has some dark red plush easy chairs as
well as wheelback seats around lots of pine tables, maps and hunting prints on the
walls, fresh flowers, and a winter log fire in a large stone fireplace. There's a gentle
Italian lean to the good well presented bar food, and wine list (with a good range
by the glass). Well liked bar food includes sandwiches or ciabatta (from £4.95; soup
and a sandwich from £7.45), and ploughman's (£8.25), as well as home-made
chicken liver pâté or grilled halloumi cheese on salad leaves (£4.25), lots of pizzas
(from £6.25), home-made lasagne or vegetarian pasta (£7.95), farm sausages and
onion gravy (£8.25), lambs liver and bacon (£9.25), gressingham duck breast with
fruit of the forest sauce (£10.95), rack of lamb with apricots and rosemary
(£11.25), and puddings (from £3.50); the restaurant and lounge are no smoking.
Well kept Archers Best Bitter, Grainstore Ten Fifty, and Greene King IPA on
handpump; darts, dominoes, cribbage and piped music. Seats among large rose
beds on the pleasant well kept back lawn look out over paddocks, and the tranquil
village green with its tall trees out in front is most attractive. More reports please.
(Recommended by Roy Bromell, Derek and Sylvia Stephenson, Jim Auld, Patrick Hancock,
Barry Collett, Jeff and Wendy Williams)

Free house ~ Licensees Valter and Sandra Floris ~ Real ale ~ Bar food (not Sun evening) ~
Restaurant ~ (01572) 812403 ~ Children welcome ~ Dogs allowed in bar ~ Open 11-3,
6-11; 12-3, 7-10.30 Sun ~ Bedrooms: £40B/£50(£60B)

LYDDINGTON SP8797 Map 4
Old White Hart 🍴
Village signposted off A6003 N of Corby

Handy after a visit to Bede House, this welcoming and civilised old inn is just the place to head for, and the staff are courteous and attentive. The softly lit low-ceilinged bar (the only place you can smoke) has just three close-set tables in front of its glass-shielded roaring log fire, and heavy bowed beams. The bar opens into an attractive restaurant, and on the other side is another tiled-floor room with some stripped stone, lots of horse pictures, cushioned wall seats and mate's chairs, and a woodburning stove. Most people come here for the particularly good food which might include filled panini, grilled sardines on tomato toast with pesto dressing (£5.95), spinach, plum tomato and pine nut risotto (£9.95), and deep-fried haddock (£10.95), with puddings like white chocolate cheesecake with cherries or bread and butter pudding with crème anglaise. Well kept Greene King IPA, Abbot and a guest such as Fullers London Pride on handpump; shove-ha'penny, cribbage and dominoes, and 12 floodlit boules pitches. The pretty walled garden is very pleasant, and if you sit outside on Thursday evening you'll probably hear the church bell-ringers. This is a picturesque village with good nearby walks. *(Recommended by Rona Murdoch, Christopher Beadle, Mr and Mrs G S Ayrton, Mr and Mrs S Wilson, Barry Collett, Phil and Jane Hodson, Les and Barbara Owen, Paul and Annette Hallett, Tracey and Stephen Groves, Mike and Sue Loseby, Duncan Cloud)*

Free house ~ Licensee Stuart East ~ Real ale ~ Bar food (not Sun evening) ~ Restaurant ~ (01572) 821703 ~ Children welcome ~ Open 12-3, 6.30-11; 12-3, 7-10.30 Sun ~ Bedrooms: £55B/£80B

MARKET OVERTON SK8816 Map 7
Black Bull
Village signposted off B668 in Cottesmore

Handy for exploring Rutland Water, this old thatched stone-built pub has a new licensee this year. The low black-beamed bar has plush stools and cushioned spindleback chairs around dark wood pub tables, maybe flowers on the sills of its little curtained windows, and Bass, Fullers London Pride, Greene King IPA and a guest like Caledonian Deuchars IPA on handpump. Bar food such as home-made soup (£3.95), deep-fried whitebait (£4.50), lunchtime baguettes (from £4.95), beer-battered haddock (£7.25), pasta of the day, chicken curry or ham and egg (£7.50), and steak and kidney pudding (£7.95); the dining room is no smoking. They serve well kept Greene King IPA, Morlands Original and a guest such as Greene King Triumph on handpump; piped music, TV, fruit machine, dominoes and cribbage. More reports on the new regime please. *(Recommended by Glenwys and Alan Lawrence, Robert Turnham, Glenys and John Roberts, Patrick Hancock, Stuart Orton, Barry Collett)*

London and Edinburgh Inns ~ Manager Ron Graham ~ Real ale ~ Bar food ~ Restaurant ~ (01572) 767677 ~ Children in eating area of bar and restaurant ~ Dogs allowed in bar ~ Open 12-3, 6-11; 12-3, 6-10.30 Sun ~ Bedrooms: £40S/£50S

MEDBOURNE SP7993 Map 4
Nevill Arms ★ 🍴 £ 🛏
B664 Market Harborough—Uppingham

This is an attractive building, with handsome stonework, imposing latticed and mullioned windows, and a large studded oak door – you get to it by a footbridge over the little duck-filled River Welland. The inviting main bar has a buoyant atmosphere and a good mix of drinkers and diners, two log fires in stone fireplaces at either end, chairs and small wall settles around its tables, and a lofty dark-joisted ceiling; a second smaller room has dark furniture and another open fire; piped music. Much needed at busy times, a spacious back room by the former coachyard has pews around more tables, its own bar, and some toys to amuse children.

Popular traditional bar food includes sandwiches (from £2.75; hot bacon and brie baguette £4.50), home-made soup (£2.95), filled baked potatoes (from £3.95), ploughman's (£4.25), jumbo sausage and chips (£5.50), battered cod (£5.95), and daily specials such as yorkshire pudding filled with beef, lamb casserole, spinach and mushroom filo, and pork in apricot and celery (all £6.50); friendly service. Well kept Adnams Bitter, Fullers London Pride, Greene King Abbot and two changing guests like Hook Norton Bitter or Timothy Taylors Landlord on handpump, and about two dozen country wines; darts, shove-ha'penny, cribbage, dominoes and carpet bowls. Look out for Truffles the cat and the inquisitive great dane, Bertie. There are seats outside by the dovecote that overlook the village green. The church over the bridge is worth a visit. The bedrooms are in two neighbouring cottages, and the first-class breakfasts are served in the pub's sunny conservatory. *(Recommended by David and Ruth Hollands, Brian and Jacky Wilson, Patrick Hancock, John Wooll, David Field, Rod and Chris Pring, Derek and Sylvia Stephenson, the Didler, Jim Farmer, CMW, JJW, Mr and Mrs Neil Draper, G Coates, Paul Humphreys, R T and J C Moggridge, Barry Collett, George Atkinson, Mike and Sue Loseby)*

Free house ~ Licensees Nicholas and Elaine Hall ~ Real ale ~ Bar food (12-2, 7-9.45) ~ (01858) 565288 ~ Children welcome ~ Dogs allowed in bar ~ Open 12-2.30(3 Sat), 6-11; 12-3, 7-10.30 Sun; closed evenings 25 and 31 Dec ~ Bedrooms: £45B/£60B

MOWSLEY SP6488 Map 4
Staff of Life ♀
Village signposted off A5199 S of Leicester; Main Street

From the outside, this high-gabled early 20th-c house looks almost more like a fairly substantial private house than a pub. This year, the conservatory has been replaced with a new no smoking restaurant resembling a country barn, and the back garden has been landscaped and has a large pergola and teak furniture (no children here). The roomy bar is quite traditional, with a panelled ceiling, and comfortable seating including some high-backed settles on flagstones; it does get its fair share of locals dropping in for a pint of well kept Greene King IPA, and Langton Stuff of Life and maybe Inclined Plain on handpump but most customers are here to enjoy the popular food. At lunchtime, this might include home-made soup (£3.50), filled baguettes and ciabattas (£4.25), pâté with red onion marmalade (£4.30), ploughman's (from £4.95), and daily specials such as a pie of the day (£6.95), home-made fillet steak burgers (£7.95), honey-roasted belly pork in black pudding mash (£8.95), and king black tiger prawns (£10.95); from a much more extensive menu, there are evening choices such as foie gras and chicken liver pâté with purple plum chutney or wild mushroom tart on baby leeks with balsamic onions (£4.95), pigeon breasts roasted with cranberries (£5.95), pasta shells in a tomato pesto with pine nuts, spinach and mozzarella (£8.75), chicken breast filled with crab mousse and a wild mushroom and madeira sauce and tiger prawns (£10.95), rib-eye steak (£13.95), and specials like potted smoked salmon with sour cream and pesto oil or garlic field mushroom with stilton on toasted brioche (£4.95), lamb kleftiko (£12.95), and beef wellington (£15.75). The puddings are rather individual: choux swans filled with white chocolate mousse floating on a rich chocolate sauce, baked alaska with passion fruit dressing or cheesecake such as mint and honeycomb (£4.50); two-course Sunday lunch (£9.95). Up to 15 good wines by the glass. More reports please. *(Recommended by John Coatsworth, Michael Ward, P Tailyour, Duncan Cloud, Les and Barbara Owen, Gerry and Rosemary Dobson)*

Free house ~ Licensee Spencer Farrell ~ Real ale ~ Bar food (12-2.30, 6.30-9.30; 12-3 Sun) ~ Restaurant ~ (0116) 240 2359 ~ Children in restaurant if eating ~ Jazz Weds evening ~ Open 12-3, 6-11; 12-10.30 Sun; closed Mon lunchtime except bank hols

NEWTON BURGOLAND SK3708 Map 4

Belper Arms

Village signposted off B4116 S of Ashby or B586 W of Ibstock

The bustling bar is the place to head for in this roadside place. Although very opened up, many ancient interior features reflect the various stages in its development (heavy beams, changing floor levels and separate areas with varying floor and wall materials) and give it an enjoyably intimate feel. Parts are said to date back to the 13th c, and much of the exposed brickwork certainly looks at least three or four hundred years old. A big freestanding central chimney has a fire one side and a range on the other, with groups of captain's chairs. There are lots of interesting bits and pieces dotted around, from a suit of old chain mail, to a collection of pewter teapots, some good antique furniture and the story of the pub ghost (Five to Four Fred) which is framed on the wall. They hold a beer festival during the August bank holiday, but usually have well kept Bass, Black Sheep, Hook Norton Best, Marstons Pedigree, and Theakstons Old Peculier on handpump; nine wines by the glass. Pleasant piped music and dominoes. Tasty bar food includes soup (£3.50), baguettes or ciabattas (from £4.95), curry of the day (£7.95), mediterranean vegetable lasagne (£8.25), gammon steak with grilled tomato, mushrooms and a fried egg (£8.50), and sirloin steak (£11.75), with specials such as salmon fillet or fish and chips (£8.95), and puddings (from £3.50); three-course Sunday lunch (£11.50). The restaurant is very big, and service can slow down when they get busy. A rambling garden has boules, cricket nets and children's play area, and works its way round the pub to teak tables and chairs on a terrace, and a steam-engine-shaped barbecue; there's a good campsite here too. (Recommended by Tony Rose, Daphne Slater, Rona Murdoch, Trevor and Sheila Sharman, Joyce and Maurice Cottrell, the Didler, Joan and Tony Walker, Ian and Jane Irving, Derek and Sylvia Stephenson, Mark Butler, Duncan Cloud, Michael Butler)

Mercury Taverns ~ Manager Guy Wallis ~ Real ale ~ Bar food (12-2.30, 7-9.30; all day Sun) ~ Restaurant ~ (01530) 270530 ~ Children in eating area of bar and restaurant ~ Dogs allowed in bar ~ Open 12-3, 6-11; all day Fri-Sun

OADBY SK6200 Map 4

Cow & Plough 🍺

Gartree Road (B667 N of centre)

The two dark back rooms known as the Vaults are the best part of this interesting old place. These are packed with an extraordinary and ever-expanding collection of old brewery memorabilia lovingly assembled by the landlord. Almost every item has a story behind it, from the enamel signs and mirrors advertising long-forgotten brews, through the aged brass cash register, to the furnishings and fittings salvaged from pubs and even churches (there's some splendid stained glass behind the counter). The pub first opened about 15 years ago with just these cosily individual rooms, but it soon tripled in size when an extensive long, light, flagstoned conservatory was added to the front; it too has its share of brewery signs and the like, as well as plenty of plants and fresh flowers, a piano, beams liberally covered with hops, and a real mix of traditionally pubby tables and chairs, with lots of green leatherette sofas and small round cast-iron tables. One section has descriptions of all Leicester's pubs. Named after the pub jack russell Billy, a star feature here is the Steamin' Billy beers which are brewed for the landlord under licence by Grainstore: Billy Grand Prix Mild, Skydiver and Steamin Billy Bitter, as well as Fullers London Pride, Holdens Bitter and Timothy Taylors Golden Best on handpump or tapped from the cask. Six ciders and lots of country wines. Using local and organic ingredients, the freshly prepared modern food might include lunchtime sandwiches (from £3.95), home-made soup (£3.95), vodka and saffron steamed mussels (£4.25), beer battered cod goujons with mushy peas (£7.95), proper ploughman's with home-made pickles (£8.25), sausages and mash (£8.95), baked stuffed aubergine with walnuts and stilton on harissa spiced couscous or chargrilled fresh tuna steak marinated in fresh ginger, lemon and sweet indonesian soy with a mild coconut curried jasmine rice (£10.95), and pot-roasted guinea fowl with smoked bacon and an onion confit (£11.25). Apart from the Vaults, the whole pub is no smoking; darts, TV, shove-ha'penny, table skittles, bar billiards, cribbage and dominoes. There are picnic-sets outside. *(Recommended by Jim Farmer, Rona Murdoch, Bernie Adams, the Didler, David Field, Barry Collett, John Fiander)*

Free house ~ Licensee Barry Lount ~ Real ale ~ Bar food (12-3, 6-9 (not Mon evening); 12-5 Sun) ~ Restaurant ~ (0116) 272 0852 ~ Children in eating area of bar and restaurant ~ Dogs welcome ~ Live jazz Weds lunchtime ~ Open 12-3, 5-11; 12-11 Sat; 12-10.30 Sun

OAKHAM SK8508 Map 4

Grainstore ♩

Station Road, off A606

Within staggering distance from the station, this converted three-storey Victorian grain warehouse is particularly popular for its own-brewed beers. Laid back or lively, depending on the time of day, the interior is plain and functional, with wide well worn bare floorboards, bare ceiling boards above massive joists (and noises of the workings above) which are supported by red metal pillars, a long brick-built bar counter with cast-iron bar stools, tall cask tables and simple elm chairs. Their fine ales (Grainstore Cooking, Gold, Rutland Panther, Steamin' Billy and Triple B) are served traditionally at the left end of the bar counter, and through swan necks with sparklers on the right; the friendly staff are happy to give you samples. Bar food includes sandwiches, baguettes, baked potatoes or burgers (from £3.95), all-day breakfast (£4.95), gnocchi in tomato and olive sauce (£5.95), ploughman's (from £5.95), and a mexican taster platter for two (£9.95). In summer they open huge glass doors on to a terrace stacked with barrels, and with picnic-sets; sporting events on TV, fruit machine, bar billiards, cribbage, dominoes, darts, giant Jenga and bottle-walking. Disabled access. You can tour the brewery by arrangement, and they do take-aways. *(Recommended by Peter and Jean Hoare, the Didler, David Field, John and Wendy Allin, Ian Stafford, Barry Collett, Derek and Sylvia Stephenson, Di and Mike Gillam, J M Tansey, Tracey and Stephen Groves, Mike and Sue Loseby)*

Own brew ~ Licensee Tony Davis ~ Real ale ~ Bar food (11.30-3; not evenings or Sun) ~ (01572) 770065 ~ Children welcome ~ Dogs allowed in bar ~ Live jazz monthly Sun afternoon and blues and rock monthly Sun evening ~ Open 11-11; 12-10.30 Sun

PEGGS GREEN SK4117 Map 7

New Inn £

Signposted off A512 Ashby—Shepshed at roundabout, then Newbold sign down Zion Hill

Very laid back and friendly and with plenty of regulars around the old-fashioned booth bar, this unspoilt little pub is in the second generation of the same very welcoming Irish family, who like to think of it as an extension of their home. The two cosy tiled front rooms have an incredible collection of old bric-a-brac (it'll keep you busy for ages) which covers almost every inch of the walls and ceilings. The little room on the left, a bit like a kitchen parlour, has china on the mantelpiece above a warm coal fire, lots of prints and photographs and little collections of this and that, three old cast-iron tables, wooden stools and a small stripped kitchen table. The room to the right has quite nice stripped panelling, and masses of bric-a-brac. The small back lounge, with a stripped wooden floor, has a really interesting and quite touching display of old local photographs including some colliery ones. They serve filled baps all day (from £1.40), but otherwise, note the limited food serving times. The short and very good value menu could include faggots and peas (£3.95), corned beef hash or two smoked haddock fillets (£4.50) with one or two specials such as stew and soda bread or steak, Guinness and mushroom pie (£4.95). Well kept Bass, Marstons Pedigree and a weekly guest such as Caledonian Deuchars IPA or Greene King Old Speckled Hen on handpump; piped music, cribbage and dominoes. There are tables out in the attractive cottage garden. *(Recommended by Derek and Sylvia Stephenson, George Atkinson, the Didler, B and M Kendall, Rona Murdoch, John Fiander, Robin and Tricia Walker)*

Enterprise ~ Lease Maria Christina Kell ~ Real ale ~ Bar food (12-2; 6-8 Mon; not Tues-Sat evenings; not Sun) ~ No credit cards ~ (01530) 222293 ~ Children in eating area of bar but must be well behaved ~ Dogs allowed in bar ~ Open 12-2.30, 5.30-11; 12-3, 6.30-11 (7-10.30 Sun) Sat

SOMERBY SK7710 Map 7

Stilton Cheese ♀ ◀

High Street; off A606 Oakham—Melton Mowbray, via Cold Overton, or Leesthorpe and Pickwell; can also be reached direct from Oakham via Knossington

There's a bustling, cheerful atmosphere in this 17th-c pub and even when very busy, the friendly staff make time for a chat. The hop-strung beamed bar/lounge has dark carpets lots of country prints on its stripped stone walls, a collection of copper pots, a stuffed badger and plenty of restful seats. Five handpumps serve well kept and thoughtfully sourced ales from brewers such as Acorn, B&T, Belvoir, Blackpool, Brewsters, Clarks, Cottage, Nethergate and Newby Wyke, and they've 14 wines by the glass, cider on handpump, and over 25 malt whiskies; shove-ha'penny, cribbage and dominoes. With three chefs in the family, it's not surprising that the food is so good and popular: sandwiches (from £2.25), home-made soup (£2.65), ploughman's (£5.25), home-made lasagne or macaroni cheese (£6.25), steaks (from £9.75), and daily specials with starters like warm salad with bacon, mushrooms and stilton, grilled fresh sardines with garlic butter or home-made duck liver and raisin pâté (£2.65-£4.95), main courses that include wild mushroom risotto, liver, bacon and onion gravy, home-made pies, local trout with prawn and tarragon butter, and duck breast with orange and ginger (£6.50-£11.25), and puddings such as ginger and walnut treacle tart, sherry trifle, and chocolate sponge with chocolate sauce (£3.25). The restaurant is no smoking. There are seats and outdoor heaters on the terrace. *(Recommended by Rona Murdoch, Phil and Jane Hodson, Annette and John Derbyshire, Duncan Cloud, Jim Farmer, G Coates, George Tucker, CMW, JJW)*

Free house ~ Licensees Carol and Jeff Evans ~ Real ale ~ Bar food (12-2, 6-9) ~ Restaurant ~ (01664) 454394 ~ Children in eating area of bar ~ Dogs allowed in bedrooms ~ Open 12-3, 6-11(7-10.30 Sun) ~ Bedrooms: £30/£40

Three Crowns ◀ £

Off A606 Oakham—Melton Mowbray, via Cold Overton, or Leesthorpe and Pickwell; can also be reached direct from Oakham via Knossington; High Street

A good mix of customers is attracted to this well run, bustling pub for the good beers, bargain lunches and live weekend music. There's been some redecoration to the comfortable main bar which now has a happy mix of old-fashioned dining chairs around dark oak tables, and a good log fire in the big stone fireplace; brick arches separate this room from the (also newly decorated) no smoking dining room. There's a friendly, welcoming atmosphere and well kept Bass, Greene King IPA and Parish Bitter on handpump. Well liked and good value straightforward bar food includes soup (£2.25), sandwiches (from £2.95), garlic mushrooms (£3.75), ploughman's or home-made vegetable curry (£4.95), and home-made steak and Parish ale pie (£5.95), with puddings such as fruit pies (£2.50); they do an OAP two-course lunch (on Monday, Wednesday and Thursday, £4.50), a bargain two-course Sunday lunch menu (£5.95), and on Tuesday and Friday you can get two meals for £6. Fuit machine, darts, TV and piped music; they hold a beer festival in May. An enclosed garden has benches and white plastic tables. *(Recommended by Duncan Cloud, O K Smyth, Phil and Jane Hodson, Barry Collett)*

Free house ~ Licensees Wendy and Mick Farmer ~ Real ale ~ Bar food (12-2, 7(6 Fri)-9; 12-2, 5-7.30 Sun) ~ Restaurant ~ (01664) 454777 ~ Children welcome ~ Dogs allowed in bar ~ Live bands first Sat in month ~ Open 12-2.30, 6.30(5.30 Fri)-11; 12-10.30 Sun ~ Bedrooms: /£40S

STATHERN SK7731 Map 7
Red Lion ⊗ ♀ ◖

Off A52 W of Grantham via the brown-signed Belvoir road (keep on towards Harby – Stathern signposted on left); or off A606 Nottingham—Melton Mowbray via Long Clawson and Harby

Rather civilised and very popular, this friendly dining pub does place much emphasis on the imaginative food but still offers a warm welcome to those wanting just a drink and a chat. The splendid range of drinks takes in well kept Grainstore Olive Oil and changing guest beers such as Black Sheep Special, Marstons Pedigree and Wells Bombardier on handpump, draught belgian beer and continental bottled beers, several ciders, a varied wine list with around a dozen by the glass, and winter mulled wine and summer home-made lemonade. Bar food ingredients are sourced locally, they smoke their own meats, make their own preserves and pickles, and have a kitchen shop where you can buy produce and fully prepared dishes: home-made soup (£3.95), smoked chicken caesar or gnocchi, watercress, crispy parma ham and smoked cheese sauce (£5.95, main course £11.25), aubergine, tomato and chickpea bake with grilled halloumi or fish and chips with tartare sauce (£9.50), lincolnshire sausages with onion gravy (£9.75), chicken breast with pommes anna, asparagus and morel mushroom sauce (£13.25), calves liver, celeriac mash, spinach and crispy bacon (£13.95), baked halibut, tomato fondue, herb crust and lemon sauce (£14.50), and puddings such as glazed blood orange tart with chocolate sorbet, banana fritters with maple syrup, and vanilla crème brûlée with mixed berry compote (from £5.25). There's a relaxed country pub feel to the yellow room on the right, a relaxing lounge with sofas, a fireplace and a big table with books, paper and magazines; it leads off the smaller, more traditional flagstoned bar, with terracotta walls, another fireplace with a pile of logs beside it, and lots of beams and hops. Dotted around are various oddities picked up by one of the licensees on visits to Newark Antiques Fair: some unusual lambing chairs for example, and a collection of wooden spoons. A little room with tables set for eating leads to the long, narrow main dining room in what was once the pub's skittle alley, and out to a nicely arranged suntrap garden, with good hardwood furnishings spread over its lawn and terrace, and an unusually big play area behind the car park, with swings, climbing frames and so on. This is under the same ownership as the Olive Branch in Clipsham. *(Recommended by Peter F Marshall, Anthony Rickards Collinson, Mr and Mrs R P Begg, Alan and Jill Bull, Tony and Betty Parker, David Edwards, Ian Stafford, Nazeer Chowdhury, Mr and Mrs Richard Osborne, Les and Barbara Owen)*

Free house ~ Licensees Sean Hope, Ben Jones, Marcus Welford ~ Real ale ~ Bar food (not Sun evening) ~ Restaurant ~ (01949) 860868 ~ Children in eating area of bar and restaurant ~ Dogs allowed in bar ~ Open 12-3, 6-11; 12-11 Sat; 12-5.30 Sun

STRETTON SK9415 Map 8
Jackson Stops ⊗ ♀

Rookery Road; a mile or less off A1, at B668 (Oakham) exit; follow village sign, turning off Clipsham road into Manor Road, pub on left

Once a farmhouse but a pub since 1903, this thatched place has an appealing and homely country bar – though many customers are here to enjoy the good interesting food. Down on the left, that small friendly room with black beams and some timbering in its ochre walls has just a couple of bar stools, a cushioned stripped wall pew and an elderly settle on its worn tile and brick floor, with a coal fire in the corner, and well kept Oakham JHB and Timothy Taylors Landlord on handpump. The main room, on the right, is airy and light, carpeted in dark blue, its stone walls mainly painted canary, and its half dozen well spaced stripped tables nicely mixing ancient and modern, with linen napkins in rings, big steel platters and lit candles in brass sticks. This has another smokeless coal fire in its stone corner fireplace, and a couple of striking modern oils alongside a few tastefully disposed farm tools. Right along past the bar is a second dining room, older in style, with stripped stone walls, tiled floor and an old open cooking range. Three dining rooms are no smoking.

Attractively presented, the menu might include minestrone with dark truffle oil (£4.50), pressed ham hock and mustard terrine with poached egg and hollandaise or filo baked camembert with rocket and pine salad (£5.50), deep-fried crab cake with sweet chilli sauce (£6.50), chicken parmigiana with pasta and tomato sauce (£10.95), roasted beetroot risotto with grilled goats cheese (£11.95), calves liver with pea purée and crisp onions (£12.95), whole lemon sole with nut brown butter (£13.50), half a roast duck with sautéed savoy cabbage and orange jus (£13.95), and puddings like pear tarte tatin or hot chocolate fondant with white chocolate ice-cream (from £4.50). The thoughtful wine range includes around ten good wines by the glass, several enterprising half-bottles of pudding wine, and late-bottled vintage port by the glass. The unobtrusive piped music in the main dining room doesn't disturb the chatty and relaxed atmosphere. Service is efficient and attentive without being intrusive, and the lavatories are exemplary. As you might guess from the inn-sign, this used to be called the White Horse; it got its present name years ago from an estate agent's sign, when it was waiting for a buyer. More reports please. *(Recommended by Mrs Margo Finlay, Jörg Kasprowski, M Raworth, Bernie Adams, Heather Couper)*

Free house ~ Licensee James Trevor ~ Real ale ~ Bar food (till 10pm; not Sun evening or Mon) ~ Restaurant ~ (01780) 410237 ~ Children in restaurant ~ Dogs allowed in bar ~ Open 12-2.30, 6.30-11; 12-3 Sun; closed Sun evening, Mon; 27 Dec-3 Jan

Ram Jam Inn ♀ 🛏

Just off A1: heading N, look out for warning signs some 8 miles N of Stamford, turning off at big inn sign through service station close to B668; heading S, look out for B668 Oakham turn-off, inn well signed on left ¼ mile after roundabout

Although this is not a pub, it does serve real ales, food all day, and is extremely handy if you're on the A1. As you go in, the first part of the big stylish open-plan bar/dining area has terracotta-coloured walls decorated in one place with a spread of old breadboards, big ceramic tiles on the floor, bentwood chairs and café tables, and sofas in a cosy panelled alcove with daily papers and a standard lamp. The bar on the left here has Fullers London Pride and John Smiths on handpump, good house wines with about ten by the glass, freshly squeezed orange juice and excellent fresh-ground coffee; faint piped music. This area spreads on back to a no smoking oak-boarded part with old prints and maps, more bentwood chairs, dining chairs, and (by a woodburning stove) another sofa and some wicker armchairs. On the right is a more formal dining layout, also no smoking, with big solid tables and attractive mediterranean photoprints by Georges Meris. Swiftly served by the friendly staff, enjoyable food might include light meals such as soup with home-made bread (£3.50), chicken liver pâté (£3.75), ciabatta or doorstep sandwiches (£4.95), steak burger (£7.95), tomato and basil pasta (£8.95), and local sausages and mash (£9.95), and more elaborate dishes like goats cheese and red onion relish in a filo tartlet with spinach and watercress salad and a sweet pepper coulis (£8.95), poached salmon on tagliatelle with roasted ratatouille and a garlic and coriander dressing (£11.25), chicken and wild mushroom risotto (£11.95), chargrilled rib-eye steak with peppercorn sauce (£12.95), and puddings such as smooth chocolate marquise or raspberry crème chantilly and shortbread millefeuille (£4.95). *(Recommended by Paul and Ursula Randall, Stuart Paulley, John Coatsworth, Eithne Dandy)*

Free house ~ Licensee Trevor Smith ~ Real ale ~ Bar food (12-9.30) ~ Restaurant ~ (01780) 410776 ~ Children welcome ~ Open 10-11; 12-10.30 Sun ~ Bedrooms: £62B/£72B

Bedroom prices normally include full English breakfast, VAT and any inclusive service charge that we know of. Prices before the '/' are for single rooms, after for two people in double or twin (B includes a private bath, S a private shower). If there is no '/', the prices are only for twin or double rooms (as far as we know there are no singles).

SWITHLAND SK5413 Map 7

Griffin

Main Street; between A6 and B5330, between Loughborough and Leicester

In a small, tucked away village, this attractive stone-built pub is a family run and friendly place. The communicating rooms have beams, some panelling, and a happy mix of wooden tables and chairs and bar stools. Part of one bar and all of the restaurant are no smoking. There's a fine choice of half a dozen real ales well kept on handpump – Everards Beacon, Original and Tiger with guests like Adnams Southwold, Badger Tanglefoot and Gales HSB – quite a few malt whiskies, and a good wine list. Popular bar food includes soup (£2.95), filled baguettes (from £3.25; steak and stilton £5.60), ploughman's (from £5.25), pie of the day (£7.75), trio of local sausages with onion gravy or lambs liver and bacon with redcurrant and onion sauce (£7.95), wild mushroom risotto (£8.50), medallions of pork tenderloin with apple mash (£9.25), steaks (from £10.95), and daily specials like chicken liver pâté (£4.25), battered haddock or grilled gammon with pineapple (£7.25), roast mediterranean vegetables with goats cheese (£8.95), barnsley chop with mint and onion gravy (£9.50), and puddings such as treacle sponge or double mint and chocolate terrine (£3.75); they hope to open a tea and gift shop which will be open all day, and have speciality afternoons and evenings like opera nights, live jazz, Gilbert & Sullivan nights and so forth. Piped music and skittle alley. This is a nice setting, handy for Bradgate Country Park, and walks in Swithland woods.
(Recommended by Duncan Cloud, Brian and Ruth Archer, Phil and Jane Hodson, Pete Baker)

Everards ~ Tenant John Cooledge ~ Real ale ~ Bar food (12-2.30, 6-9(9.30 Fri/Sat); 12-4.30 Sun; not Sun evening) ~ Restaurant ~ (01509) 890535 ~ Well behaved children welcome ~ Dogs welcome ~ Open 11-11(5-11 Mon); 12-10.30 Sun; closed Mon lunchtime

THORPE LANGTON SP7492 Map 4

Bakers Arms 🍴

Village signposted off B6047 N of Market Harborough

As the opening hours at this well run, civilised, tucked away pub are somewhat limited, it is pretty essential to book a table in advance. Emphasis is very much on the imaginative food – it's definitely the place for a special meal out rather than a quick drink. Dishes could include home-made soup (£4.50), mediterranean vegetable tartlet with goats cheese and pesto dressing (£5.50), fried scallops with black pudding and orange sauce (£7.95), baked avocado with confit of red onions and brie (£10.95), pork fillet filled with mozzarella and sage served with tomato jus (£11.95), stuffed chicken wrapped in parma ham (£12.95), calves liver with shallot and red wine jus (£14.95), halibut on mustard tagliatelle (£15.95) and puddings such as sticky toffee pudding or vanilla brûlée with orange in Cointreau and orange tuile biscuit (£4.50). Stylishly simple old-fashioned furnishings in the knocked-through cottagey beamed interior include stripped pine tables and oriental rugs on bare boards, and nice black and white photographs; no games or piped music. They've a good wine list (also not cheap) with around five by the glass, well kept Langton Brewery Bakers Dozen on handpump, and in winter they do mulled wine too; the staff are friendly and attentive. There are picnic-sets in the garden.
(Recommended by Duncan Cloud, Laura and Stuart Ballantyne, Gerry and Rosemary Dobson, Mike and Sue Loseby, P Tailyour)

Free house ~ Licensee Kate Hubbard ~ Real ale ~ Restaurant ~ (01858) 545201 ~ Children over 12 in restaurant only ~ Open 6.30-11; 12-2.30, 6.30-11 Sat; 12-2.30 Sun; closed Sun evening, Mon, lunchtime Tues-Fri

UPPER HAMBLETON SK9007 Map 4

Finches Arms 🍴 ♀ 🛏️

Village signposted from A606 on E edge of Oakham

In fine weather, there's now a bar that serves the suntrap hillside terrace here, so you can enjoy the lovely views over Rutland Water without going inside. If it is cold, you can ask for a window table in the no smoking modern restaurant (redecorated this year) which also looks over the water. Served by efficient staff, the very good, attractively presented food might include soup (£2.95), aubergine caviar gateau, parmesan crackling and roasted cashew nut cream (£4.25), stilton, bacon and new potato cake with a port sauce (£4.95), lunchtime panini (from £5.95), local sausages and mash with red onion gravy (£7.95), smoked haddock and spinach parmentier (£8.95), fried gressingham duck with orange, cranberry and chilli sauce (£13.95), egg noodles with asparagus, broccoli, spinach, feta and courgettes (£9.95), lamb confit on grain mustard mash and bacon julienne (£10.95), delicious fillet of beef with foie gras sauce (£15.95), and puddings such as warm almond tart with praline parfait or raspberry mousse on a light vanilla sponge (£3.95). There's stylish cane furniture on wooden floors, well kept Oakham JHB, Timothy Taylors Landlord and a guest like Archers Swindon Strong Bitter on handpump, eight wines and three champagnes by the glass, Sheppy's cider and several malt whiskies; piped music and dominoes. The bedrooms are in the process of being upgraded. *(Recommended by Derek and Sylvia Stephenson, David Field, Robert Turnham, Bob and Maggie Atherton, Colin McKerrow, Dr Brian and Mrs Anne Hamilton, Paul Humphreys, Tony and Margaret Cross, Phil and Jane Hodson, Di and Mike Gillam, Robert F Smith, Mike and Sue Loseby)*

Free house ~ Licensees Celia and Colin Crawford ~ Real ale ~ Bar food (12.-2.30, 6.30-9.30; 12-8 Sun) ~ Restaurant ~ (01572) 756575 ~ Children welcome ~ Open 11-11; 12-10.30 Sun ~ Bedrooms: £65B/£75B

WING SK8903 Map 4

Kings Arms 🍴 ♀ 🛏️

Village signposted off A6003 S of Oakham; Top Street

As well as being a comfortable place to stay, this 17th-c inn is popular for its very good food and well kept real ales. The charming bar has a traditional feel, beams, some stripped stone and a flagstone floor, pine tables, old local photographs and a collection of tankards and old-fashioned whisky measuring pots. Two large log fires, one in a copper-canopied central hearth, make it cosy in winter; they've also a snug. Friendly, helpful staff serve well kept Grainstore Cooking, Marstons Pedigree and Timothy Taylors Landlord with a guest such as Castle Rock Harvest Pale on handpump, and nine wines by the glass; piped music. The restaurant is no smoking. As well as lunchtime ciabatta sandwiches (from £4.50), bar food might include steamed mussels in either Pernod and parsley or oriental with coconut (£5.50; main course £10), ham and free-range eggs or trio of local sausages with pepper Boursin mash and rich cumberland gravy (£8.50), wild mushrooms, herbs and cream cheese in a crispy spring roll with cold tomato gazpacho (£9.50), steak and kidney in ale pie with beer gravy or fresh cod in beer batter (£12), aberdeen angus rib-eye steak (£15), daily specials like cream of vine ripened tomato soup with basil pesto and a herb croûte (£4), lime and ginger cured salmon and sweet chilli, soy seared tiger prawns (£6.50; main course £11), and venison haunch ragoût or rack of lamb chops with lamb jus and sweet orange, chilli and chicory marmalade (£14.50), and puddings such as sticky toffee pudding or crème brûlée with fresh fruit (from £5); Sunday roasts (from £9.50). Outside are colourful hanging baskets in summer, and the sunny yew-sheltered garden has seats and a small play area. There's a medieval turf maze just up the road. *(Recommended by Jim Farmer, Alan and Jill Bull, Dave Braisted, Ken Marshall, Duncan Cloud, Anthony Barnes, Philip and June Caunt, Anthony R Locke, Colin McKerrow, Derek and Sylvia Stephenson, Sally and Dave Bates, Jackie Coaker, Barry Collett, Di and Mike Gillam, Robert F Smith)*

Free house ~ Licensee David Goss ~ Real ale ~ Bar food (12-2, 6-9) ~ Restaurant ~
(01572) 737634 ~ No children in eating areas after 8pm ~ Open 12-3, 6-11; 12-3, 6-10.30
Sun ~ Bedrooms: £65S/£75S

LUCKY DIP

Besides the fully inspected pubs, you might like to try these Lucky Dips recommended to
us and described by readers (if you do, please send us reports: www.goodguides.co.uk).

BARROW UPON SOAR [SK5717]

Hunting Lodge [South St]: Pleasantly
renovated stone-built inn with individual
character, veneered panels and hunting
pictures, good value varied food inc bargain
lunches, well kept Greene King Old Speckled
Hen, Highgate Davenports, Marstons Pedigree
and Timothy Taylors Landlord, friendly staff,
no smoking back restaurant; children welcome,
big garden with swings, boules and barbecues,
six spotless and comfortable bedrooms
*(Comus and Sarah Elliott, Phil and
Jane Hodson, Brian and Ruth Archer)*

☆ *Navigation* [off South St (B5328)]: Extended
split-level pub based on former barge-horse
stabling, good warm atmosphere, good value
freshly made standard food (may be limited
winter) inc good baguettes and Sun roast, well
kept changing ales such as local Belvoir,
Marstons Pedigree and Timothy Taylors
Landlord, keen friendly licensees, daily papers,
central open fire, unusual bar top made from
old pennies, old local photographs, darts,
skittle alley, family room; piped music, SkyTV,
games machine; lovely canal view from small
back terrace with moorings, open all day
*(Comus and Sarah Elliott, Rona Murdoch,
Gwyn and Anne Wake, Brian and
Ruth Archer, Duncan Cloud)*

BILLESDON [SK7102]

New Greyhound [Market Pl]: Friendly old
local with three real ales and good soft drinks
choice, good cheap filled cobs (and perhaps
free bar nibbles), L-shaped lounge; bar with
TV, separate games room with pool and
machines, no dogs; children welcome *(CMW,
JJW)*

BLABY [SP5697]

Bakers Arms [quite handy for M1 junction 21;
The Green]: Tucked-away recently thatched
and refurbished pub with lots of low beams,
nooks and crannies in linked rooms, wide
choice of enjoyable reasonably priced home-
made food from sandwiches and baguettes up,
efficient friendly local staff, real ales; tables in
big landscaped garden *(J M Tansey)*

BOTCHESTON [SK4805]

Greyhound [Main St, off B5380 E of Desford]:
Beamed village pub now with two light and
airy no smoking dining rooms, pine tables,
good freshly made food inc lunchtime special
deals, popular Mon pie and wine night, Thurs
italian night, Sun carvery roasts, friendly
service, well kept Burtonwood; garden with
play area *(Stan and Dot Garner, R J Harwood,
Rod Weston, Barbara Barber)*

BRANSTON [SK8129]

☆ *Wheel* [Main St]: Good food (not Sun/Mon
evenings) in 18th-c village pub's cosy and
comfortable beamed bar and small neatly set
dining room, chef happy to alter his recipes to
suit, plenty of fresh veg, log fires, friendly
atmosphere, well kept Adnams and a changing
guest beer from central servery, good short
reasonably priced wine choice; attractive
garden, next to church, splendid countryside nr
Belvoir castle, cl Mon/Tues lunchtimes *(Mr and
Mrs R P Begg, R and M Tait, BB)*

BRAUNSTON [SK8306]

☆ *Blue Ball* [off A606 in Oakham; Cedar St]:
Pretty thatched and beamed dining pub in
attractive village, welcoming staff, wide choice
of good interesting food at sensible prices inc
children's helpings, good range of well kept
ales and wines, country pine in spotless linked
rooms inc no smoking room and small
conservatory, lovely open fire, dominoes,
shove-ha'penny; children welcome, open all
day Sun *(P Tailyour, R V Peel, LYM,
Roy Bromell, Barry Collett)*

☆ *Old Plough* [off A606 in Oakham; Church St]:
Welcoming black-beamed pub, comfortably
opened up, with log fire, well kept Grainstore
and guest ales, enjoyable food, friendly staff,
appealing back dining conservatory (children
allowed); tables in sheltered garden
*(Phil and Jane Hodson, LYM, Barry Collett,
Duncan Cloud)*

BRUNTINGTHORPE [SP6089]

☆ *Joiners Arms* [Church Walk/Cross St]: More
bistro restaurant than pub, largely no smoking,
with good imaginative up-to-date food and
popular Sun lunches in three beamed areas of
open-plan dining lounge, Greene King IPA
from small bar counter, short choice of decent
wines, lots of china and brasses, friendly staff;
cl Sun evening and Mon *(Gerry and
Rosemary Dobson, Mike and Brenda Roberts)*

CASTLE DONINGTON [SK4426]

Nags Head [Diseworth Rd/Hill Top; A453, S
end]: Low-beamed pub under new
management, well kept Banks's and related
beers, enjoyable food from low-priced
lunchtime baguettes and filled baked potatoes
to more elaborate and expensive dishes,
quarry-tiled bar opening into intimate little
dining room one side, larger and airier dining
area with open-view kitchen on the other side
*(LYM, Michael Dandy, Brian and
Ruth Archer, J Crosby, Phil and Jane Hodson)*

COLEORTON [SK4117]

George [Loughborough Rd]: Attractive bar

with stripped brick and timber, friendly landlord and staff, well kept changing guest beers such as Marstons Pedigree, Ridleys Rumpus and Timothy Taylors Landlord, good choice of well presented food inc light dishes; unobtrusive piped music; large garden behind with play area *(Tim and Rosemary Wells)*

CROXTON KERRIAL [SK8329]

Peacock [A607 SW of Grantham]: Much modernised 17th-c former coaching inn, good plain cooking running up to aberdeen angus steaks, consistently well kept real ales inc local Belvoir Star, decent wines, efficient friendly service, chunky stripped tables and partly wrought-iron chairs in big open-plan bare-boards bar, separate small simple dining room and garden room, hops on beams, log fire partitioned off at one end, some bric-a-brac (resident ghost shifts the ashtrays around overnight); well behaved children welcome, picnic-sets in inner courtyard and pleasant sloping garden with views, bedroom block with own bathrooms *(John Wooll, Phil and Jane Hodson, BB)*

DESFORD [SK4803]

Lancaster [Station Rd]: Large pub with emphasis on enjoyable food from sandwiches and baguettes to steaks and bass, well kept Everards ales with a guest such as Adnams, no smoking restaurant with big conservatory marquee extension *(Gerry and Rosemary Dobson)*

EAST LANGTON [SP7292]

☆ *Bell* [off B6047; Main St]: Recently redecorated, with log fire and good atmosphere in long stripped-stone beamed bar, no smoking dining room, Langton Caudle Bitter and Inclined Plain brewed behind the pub, also Greene King IPA and Abbot, daily changing bar food (not winter Sun evening) from sandwiches and baguettes up inc some modern dishes; piped music; children and dogs welcome, replanted garden with outdoor heater, attractive village in peaceful countryside, bedrooms, cl winter Mon *(LYM, P Tailyour, David Field, Brian and Ruth Archer, R V Peel, Duncan Cloud, John Saville, Mrs L Aquilina, G Coates)*

GLOOSTON [SP7595]

☆ *Old Barn* [off B6047 in Tur Langton]: Pleasant 16th-c village pub with beams, stripped kitchen tables, country chairs and log fire, well kept changing ales inc Batemans XB and one brewed for the pub, flexible helpful service, enjoyable food inc good value Tues-Fri lunch and innovative evening menu, no smoking dining area (well behaved children allowed); tables out in front, bedrooms with compact shower cabinets, good breakfast, cl Mon lunchtime *(David Field, LYM, Rona Murdoch, Duncan Cloud, Jim Farmer, O K Smyth, Les and Barbara Owen)*

GREAT BOWDEN [SP7488]

☆ *Red Lion* [off A6 N of Mkt Harboro; Main St]: Attractive red-walled bar now with two fireplaces, sofas and a central group of tables, well kept ales such as Greene King IPA and Jennings Cumberland (Nov beer festival), well

chosen wines, friendly staff, enjoyable food, cosy dining room; piped music, TV; children and dogs welcome, tables in big garden, bedrooms, open all day wknds *(Rona Murdoch, Duncan Cloud, LYM, Jeff and Wendy Williams)*

GREAT GLEN [SP6597]

Old Greyhound [A6 Leicester—Mkt Harboro]: Enjoyable food, Adnams Broadside and Greene King Abbot, friendly service *(David Field, Duncan Cloud)*

Yews [A6]: Roomy Chef & Brewer, softly lit and relaxing series of areas, largely no smoking, wide range of enjoyable food, good wine choice, Greene King Old Speckled Hen, Marstons Pedigree and a guest beer, coal fires; piped music; good disabled access and facilities, big attractive garden with terrace, open all day *(P Tailyour, BB)*

GREETHAM [SK9214]

Plough [B668 Stretton—Cottesmore]: Tied to Grainstore of Oakham, with their beers kept well, enjoyable and interesting home-made food from baguettes up, friendly licensees, staff and locals, coal-effect gas fire dividing cosy lounge from eating area, lots of prints, pub games; tables out behind (with quoits), open all day Fri-Sun *(P S Hoyle)*

☆ *Wheatsheaf* [B668 Stretton—Cottesmore]: Neat and comfortable L-shaped communicating rooms, wide choice of good value generous food served till 11 pm through crusty baguettes through bargain wkdy lunches and specials to lots of chargrills, well kept John Smiths and Tetleys or Worthington, cheerful staff, blazing stove in stone fireplace, dining room with local artwork for sale, darts and pool in end room; soft piped music; dogs welcome, wheelchair access, picnic-sets out on front lawn and in tidy garden by back car park beside pretty little stream, popular annexe bedrooms *(Michael and Jenny Back, BB, David and Brenda Tew)*

GUMLEY [SP6890]

☆ *Bell* [NW of Market Harboro; Main St]: Cheerful neatly kept beamed village pub with traditional country décor, attractively priced straightforward bar food (not Mon evening) from sandwiches to steaks inc popular OAP bargains and good value Sun lunch, well kept Bass, Batemans XB, Greene King IPA and a guest beer, good soft drinks choice, open fire, darts and cribbage, small no smoking dining room (children over 5 allowed here), interesting cricket memorabilia in lobby; pretty terrace garden (not for children or dogs), cl Sun evening *(G Coates, George Atkinson, Jim Farmer, Lloyd Moon, Gerry and Rosemary Dobson, BB, DC, P Tailyour, John Fiander, LYM, Barry Collett)*

HALLATON [SP7896]

☆ *Bewicke Arms* [off B6047 or B664]: Old thatched pub with sensibly priced food from sandwiches to steak, inventive specials, well kept beers such as Flowers IPA and Grainstore Cooking, friendly landlady, log fires, pine furnishings, orange paintwork, some interesting memorabilia about the ancient local

Easter Monday inter-village bottle-kicking match; darts, shove-ha'penny, piped music; children in eating areas, stables tearoom across yard, big terrace overlooking paddock and lake, pretty spot, open all day Sun *(Pat and Roger Fereday, Mike Huysinga, Patrick Hancock, LYM, Jim Farmer, Duncan Cloud)*

HATHERN [SK5021]

Dew Drop [Loughborough Rd (A6)]: Friendly traditional two-room local with well kept Hardys & Hansons, plenty of malt whiskies, darts and dominoes; tables outside *(the Didler)*

HOBY [SK6717]

Blue Bell [Main St]: Attractive three-room thatched pub well restored after fire damage, good choice of realistically priced food from lunchtime sandwiches and baguettes through pubby favourites to the welcoming French landlord/chef's evening specialities, well kept Everards, comfortable modern furniture, separate dining area; pleasant garden with play area *(Michael and Anne Brown, Phil and Jane Hodson)*

HOSE [SK7329]

☆ *Black Horse* [Bolton Lane]: Down-to-earth beamed and quarry-tiled Tynemill pub with panelled restaurant and growing emphasis on good value blackboard food inc interesting dishes; well kept Castle Rock and several other ales, friendly landlord, coal fire, darts; pretty village, nice countryside *(the Didler, R M Taylor)*

Rose & Crown [Bolton Lane]: Unpretentious Vale of Belvoir local with up to eight real ales from far and wide, simple food from baguettes up, no smoking areas in lounge and dining room (children allowed); piped music; tables on fairy-lit back terrace, fenced family area *(the Didler, David Glynne-Jones, LYM, R M Taylor)*

HOUGHTON ON THE HILL [SK6703]

Old Black Horse [Main St (just off A47 Leicester—Uppingham)]: Hospitable and comfortable, with good value home-made food (no hot food Mon lunchtime), welcoming helpful staff, well kept Everards and a guest beer, good sensibly priced wines by the glass, partly no smoking bare-boards dining area with lots of panelling; big attractive garden with boules *(P Tailyour, Rona Murdoch)*

HUNCOTE [SP5197]

Red Lion [Main St]: Lively and friendly two-bar local with well kept Everards and a guest beer, no smoking dining area; piped music *(Rona Murdoch)*

ILLSTON ON THE HILL [SP7099]

☆ *Fox & Goose* [Main St, off B6047 Mkt Harboro—Melton]: Welcoming and idiosyncratic unspoilt chatty two-bar local, plain but comfortable and convivial, with interesting pictures and assorted oddments, well kept Everards ales and a guest beer, table lamps, good coal fire; no food, but bedrooms sometimes available *(LYM, Bernie Adams, the Didler)*

KEGWORTH [SK4826]

Britannia [London Rd]: Good friendly service, well kept Hardys & Hansons, cheap food all day *(M J Winterton, the Didler)*

Cap & Stocking [handy for M1 junction 24, via A6; Borough St]: Friendly new licensees for interestingly old-fashioned three-room pub, brown paint, etched glass, coal fires, big cases of stuffed birds and locally caught fish, Bass and Greene King IPA, back room with windows to secluded garden, may be food; piped music, no credit cards; children welcome *(Ian Phillips, the Didler, Brian and Ruth Archer, Mrs Hazel Rainer, Mike Turner, Pete Baker, LYM)*

Red Lion [a mile from M1 junction 24, via A6 towards Loughborough; High St]: New licensees keeping up this village local's reputation for the quality and gravity range of its changing real ales (up to five, usually inc a Mild), four brightly lit traditional rooms around small servery, limited choice of good wholesome food (not Sun), assorted furnishings, coal and flame-effect fires, delft shelf of beer bottles, daily papers, darts and cards, no smoking room; picnic-sets in small back yard, garden with play area, well equipped bedrooms with own bathrooms, open all day *(Pete Baker, BB, the Didler, G Coates, M J Winterton)*

KIBWORTH BEAUCHAMP [SP6893]

Coach & Horses [A6 S of Leicester]: Popualr turkey-carpeted local with friendly efficient staff, wide choice of good honest home-made food (mainly roasts on Sun), well kept beers such as Bass and Wadworths 6X, heartening log fire in huge end inglenook, china and pewter mugs on beams, relaxing candlelit restaurant *(Jim Farmer, Rona Murdoch, Duncan Cloud, BB)*

KILBY [SP6295]

Dog & Gun [Main St, off A5199 S of Leicester]: Much-extended pub particularly popular with older people for its wide choice of enjoyable food from good baguettes up; friendly helpful service, well kept Bass, Greene King Abbot, Marstons Pedigree and Websters (also the name of the lovely white cat), good wine choice, coal fire, attractive side restaurant with grandfather clock; attractive garden with terrace and pergola *(Michael and Jenny Back)*

KNOSSINGTON [SK8008]

Fox & Hounds [off A606 W of Oakham; Somerby Rd]: Small beamed country pub with good interesting food inc good value lunches, welcoming unhurried atmosphere, small popular restaurant (best to book), well kept Courage with guests such as Bass and Boddingtons, decent wines, lots of malt whiskies, coal fire in comfortable lounge with rather random décor, darts and pool room; summer barbecues in big garden *(Barry Collett, Duncan Cloud)*

LEICESTER [SK5804]

Ale Wagon [Rutland St/Charles St]: Basic two-room 1930s interior, good range of changing ales, Weston's perry; open all day, handy for station *(the Didler)*

Black Horse [Braunstone Gate/Foxon St]: Unspoilt late 19th-c two-room corner local with Everards Beacon and Tiger and a guest beer (may be two at the end of the week), traditional layout (with outside lavatories), darts and dominoes, character back lounge; popular with students in term-time *(Pete Baker, G Coates)*

Criterion [Millstone Lane]: Under same ownership as Swan & Rushes, with good value pizzas and tapas and well kept beers (good choice of different guest ales, dozens of imports), rather wine-bar-like carpeted main room with close-set tables, dark wood and burgundy décor, relaxed room on left with games, decent wines by the glass; food served normal times Mon-Thurs, till 11 Fri, 2-11.30 Sat, not Sun; reasonable wheelchair access (small front step) *(G Coates)*

Gateway [The Gateway]: Tynemill pub in old hosiery factory (ladies' underwear on show), bare boards except in no smoking area, up to five well kept and interesting changing ales (may be fewer outside term time) from long bar counter on left, imported beers and good reasonably priced range of other drinks, sensibly priced freshly made food all day till 8 (6 Sun) inc Sun carvery and good vegetarian/vegan range, friendly knowledgeable service; piped music (may be turned down if loud), drop-down big-screen sports TV, some live music; good disabled access and facilities, open all day *(CMW, JJW, the Didler, G Coates, J M Tansey)*

☆ *Globe* [Silver St]: Well refurbished early 18th-c town pub, lots of woodwork in four old-fashioned uncluttered areas off central bar, charming more peaceful upstairs dining room, wrought-iron gas lamps, well kept Everards ales, nicely priced honest food 12-7, keen young landlord and knowledgeable friendly staff, children allowed in some parts; piped pop music (not in snug), very popular with young people wknd evenings – doorman then; open all day *(CMW, JJW, J M Tansey, the Didler, LYM)*

Swan & Rushes [Oxford St/Infirmary Sq]: Well kept Oakham JHB and changing guest beers, several imported beers on tap and many dozens in bottle, farm cider, beer festivals, enjoyable food inc frequent continental theme nights; open all day *(J M Tansey, the Didler)*

LEIRE [SP5290]

White Horse [Main St]: Open-plan dining pub kept spotless, wide-ranging good food from ciabattas and interesting snacks up, good Spanish landlord and welcoming staff, Greene King Abbot and Tetleys, small bars and dining room; children welcome, has been open all day wknds *(P Tailyour, Michael J Caley)*

LITTLE BOWDEN [SP7386]

☆ *Cherry Tree* [Church Walk; edge of Mkt Harboro, nr Sainsburys]: Attractive low-beamed thatched and timbered pub with friendly jovial landlord and hard-working family, well kept Everards Beacon, Tiger and Old Original, good value food (not Sun evening) from filled baked potatoes up, two sitting rooms, lots of prints, no smoking dining room on left, Royal Naval Assoc

room, back bar with darts and table skittles; children welcome, front garden with picnic-sets and play area, heated child-free back one, open all day Fri-Sun, nr 12th-c church *(Rona Murdoch)*

LITTLETHORPE [SP5497]

Plough [not far from M1 junction 21; Station Rd, off B4114]: Partly thatched 16th-c local, local pictures, lots of brass, bric-a-brac and china in roomy beamed lounge with comfortable wall banquettes, smoke room with darts and copper-topped tables, Everards full beer range kept well, food inc fortnightly curry Mon and bargain OAP lunches; children and dogs welcome, picnic-sets outside, open all day Sat *(Rona Murdoch)*

LOUGHBOROUGH [SK5319]

Albion [canal bank, about ¼ mile from Loughborough Wharf]: Down-to-earth canalside local with emphasis on well kept changing ales, friendly owners, cheap straightforward home-made food, coal fire, darts room; children welcome, occasional barbecues, budgerigar aviary in pleasant big courtyard *(the Didler)*

☆ *Swan in the Rushes* [A6]: Cheery down-to-earth bare-boards town local with good range of well kept ales tapped from the cask, plenty of foreign bottled beers, good value straightforward home-made food (not Sat/Sun evenings), daily papers, traditional games, open fire, three smallish high-ceilinged rooms; children in eating areas, tables outside, open all day *(Pete Baker, the Didler, Les Baldwin, Theocsbrian, Sue Demont, Tim Barrow, LYM, BB, Brian and Ruth Archer)*

LUTTERWORTH [SP5484]

Unicorn [Church St, off A426; handy for M1 junction 20]: Welcoming town pub, banquettes in lounge and back restaurant, bargain food from sandwiches up inc children's dishes and popular OAP bargain lunches, Sat night steak special, nice log fire, well kept Bass, Greene King IPA and Robinsons, more basic bar with traditional games inc hood skittles; sports TV, no credit cards *(P Tailyour, Pete Baker)*

MARKET BOSWORTH [SK4003]

Black Horse [Market Pl]: 18th-c, with several beamed rooms, wide choice of enjoyable plentiful food, cheerful helpful service, well kept Adnams and Greene King, good house wines and coffee, cosy local bustle, log fire, comfortable restaurant; tables outside – nice setting next to almshouses in attractive village not far from Bosworth Field *(Joan and Tony Walker, R T and J C Moggridge, Richard Waller, Pauline Smith)*

☆ *Old Red Lion* [Park St; from centre follow Leicester and Hinckley signs]: Cheerful and civilised black-beamed split-level pub with sensibly priced food from sandwiches and baked potatoes up inc proper steak and kidney pie, plushly tidy L-shaped bar with well kept ales such as Banks's Bitter and Mild, Marstons Pedigree and Theakstons XB and Old Peculier, prompt efficient service even when busy; may be piped music; children welcome, tables and play area in sheltered courtyard, bedrooms, attractive village *(LYM, Pete Baker, Peter King, C J Fletcher)*

MARKET HARBOROUGH [SP7387]

Angel [High St]: Former coaching inn with nice lunchtime food in quiet smoke-free atmosphere, efficient friendly service, good range of beers; bedrooms *(Ian and Jane Irving)*
Sugar Loaf [High St]: Popular Wetherspoons, smaller than many, with pleasant atmosphere, good choice of real ales, good value food all day, no smoking dining area, no piped music; children allowed, open all day *(P Tailyour, CMW, JJW)*
☆ *Three Swans* [High St]: Comfortable and handsome coaching inn renovated as Best Western conference hotel, beams and old local prints in plush and peaceful panelled front bar, comfortable no smoking flagstoned back dining lounge and fine courtyard conservatory (also no smoking, opened Thurs/Fri evening as separate good value bistro) in more modern part, friendly helpful staff, wide range of good value bar lunches from sandwiches up, some bar food early evenings, well kept Courage Directors and a guest beer such as Websters, decent wines, good coffee, more formal upstairs restaurant; piped music; attractive suntrap courtyard, good bedroom extension *(Gerry and Rosemary Dobson, George Atkinson, David and Ruth Hollands)*

MELTON MOWBRAY [SK7519]

Anne of Cleves [Burton St, by St Mary's Church]: Unpretentious pub in building of great potential – lovely ancient monks' chantry attached to parish church, chunky tables and character chairs and settles on flagstones, heavy Tudor beams and latticed mullioned windows, tapestries on burnt orange walls; well kept Everards Tiger and Original and a guest beer, nice coffee, quick neat service, popular unpretentious food, small end dining room and no smoking room; piped music, no under-7s; tables in pretty little walled garden with flagstoned terrace, open all day, Sun afternoon closure *(Duncan Cloud, BB)*
Crown [Burton St]: Handy central pub with Everards and a couple of guest beers, friendly outgoing landlord, good mix of customers, quiet lounge on right; garden behind *(Rona Murdoch)*

MOUNTSORREL [SK5815]

Waterside [Sileby Rd]: Comfortable modern split-level lounge and dining area overlooking busy lock on the Soar, well kept Everards ales, good range of bar food from filled baps to Sun roast (to order, so may be a wait); piped music, games machine; children welcome, disabled access and facilities, picnic-sets outside *(Bernie Adams, B M Eldridge)*

NETHER BROUGHTON [SK6925]

Red House [A606 N of Melton Mowbray]: Substantial and elegant extended Georgian house, mainly a hotel and restaurant, also enjoyable sensibly priced bar food from sandwiches and local cheeses to steaks in separate ex-stabling bar with open kitchen; garden picnic-sets, eight well equipped

bedrooms *(BB, Phil and Jane Hodson)*

OADBY [SP6399]

Grange Farm [Florence Wragg Way, just off A6]: Attractive early 19th-c farmhouse sympathetically converted to roomy Vintage Inn, log fires, old local photographs, daily papers, wide food range from lunchtime sandwiches to steak, bass and Sun roast, friendly staff, good wine choice, well kept ales, good mix of customers, no smoking area; picnic-sets out in front *(Mr and Mrs D Moir, Les and Barbara Owen)*

OAKHAM [SK8508]

Wheatsheaf [Northgate]: Attractive three-room 17th-c local nr church, well kept Everards and guest ales, enjoyable lunchtime pub food, friendly attentive service, comfortable furnishings, open fire, plenty of bric-a-brac, no music, back family room/conservatory; pretty suntrap back courtyard *(Barry Collett)*

OLD DALBY [SK6723]

☆ *Crown* [by school in village centre turn into Longcliff Hill; Debdale Hill]: Three or four intimate little farmhouse rooms up and down steps, black beams, one or two antique oak settles among other seats, hunting and other rustic prints, open fires, well kept Belvoir, Courage Directors, Charles Wells Bombardier and guest beers from a homely servery, popular fresh locally sourcd food (not Sun evening) from sandwiches and ciabattas up, no smoking snug, relaxed dining room, friendly cat, darts and cribbage; children and dogs welcome, nice tables in attractive garden with terrace, sheltered sloping lawn and boules, cl Mon lunchtime *(Tom Evans, Barry and Anne, the Didler, LYM, G Coates, P T Sewell)*

PACKINGTON [SK3614]

Bull & Lion [High St]: Quietly placed country pub, unpretentious and relaxed, under friendly new licensees, with well kept Marstons Pedigree and a guest such as Shepherd Neame Bishops Finger (occasional beer festivals), wide food range from sandwiches to steaks, venison and buffalo, character beamed lounge with old photographs, pretty end restaurant, panelled bar with TV and pub games; open all day Sat *(Rona Murdoch)*

QUORNDON [SK5616]

White Hart [High St (A6)]: One of very few pubs which are Grade I listed, modernised but keeping original character, with real ales such as Caledonian Deuchars IPA, Greene King IPA, Timothy Taylors Landlord and Wadworths 6X, home-made food, log fires, Victorian family dining room with handsome stove; big-screen sports TV; tables out behind with boules *(Rona Murdoch)*

ROTHLEY [SK5812]

Woodmans Stroke [Church St]: Popular pub with lots of rugby and cricket memorabilia in two small areas, usual beers; picnic-sets outside, open all day *(anon)*

RYHALL [TF0310]

Millstone [Bridge St]: Comfortably plush village local with congenial licensees, good generous fresh food from baguettes to choice

of Sun roasts, well kept Mansfield and
Marstons ales, good short wine choice, lots of
malt whiskies, proper coffee, small no smoking
restaurant, separate bar with pool and juke
box; well behaved children welcome
*(Martin and Helen Ball, Susan Pennant Jones,
Tim and Rosemary Wells)*

SADDINGTON [SP6591]
Queens Head [S of Leicester between A5199
(ex A50) and A6; Main St]: Reasonably priced
food (not Sun evening) from baguettes to
steaks and a fair amount of fish, well kept
Everards ales and a couple of guest beers,
decent wines, quick polite service, daily papers,
lots of knick-knacks and plastic plants; no
under-5s, steps from area to area; country
views from dining conservatory and tables in
long sloping garden *(LYM, George Atkinson,
Gerry and Rosemary Dobson)*

SALTBY [SK8426]
Nags Head [Back St]: Small beamed and stone-
built old pub, very welcoming, with good
choice of enjoyable low-priced home cooking
using local supplies, three changing well kept
ales (landlord won't stock more than he knows
he can sell while still in top condition),
separate dining room; cl Mon lunchtime
(R and M Tait, R M Taylor, Orson Carte)

SCALFORD [SK7624]
Kings Arms [King St]: Hospitable country inn
doing well under current Yorkshire landlord,
good attractively priced food inc enjoyable Sun
lunch, well kept real ale, buoyant local
atmosphere, small intimate eating area; two
comfortable bedrooms with own bathrooms
(Phil and Jane Hodson)

SEAGRAVE [SK6117]
White Horse [off A46 N of Leicester; Church
St]: Welcoming staff and regulars in nice old
unpretentious white-painted village local, well
kept Greene King Abbot, cheerful bar (dogs
welcome), more formal dining lounge on right;
piped music *(Rona Murdoch)*

SEATON [SP9098]
George & Dragon [Church Lane, off B672
Caldecott—S Luffenham]: Generous
attractively priced food from sandwiches and
baguettes to hot dishes cooked to order,
warmly welcoming helpful landlord, quick
service, well kept ales such as Adnams
Broadside, Greene King IPA, Marstons
Pedigree and Wychwood Hobgoblin, good
wine choice, pine furniture, two bars, one no
smoking with wide variety of sports
memorabilia; piped jazz; tables outside,
unspoilt village, good views of famous viaduct
*(Jim Farmer, David Barnes, Gerry and
Rosemary Dobson)*

SHACKERSTONE [SK3706]
☆ *Rising Sun* [Church Rd, nr Bridge 52, Ashby
Canal]: Relaxed olde-worlde canal-side pub,
good enterprising food in panelled lounge
bar and converted barn restaurant, good
value house wine, well kept changing ales;
tables outside, nr steam railway centre
(Neil Kellett)

SHAWELL [SP5480]
White Swan [Main St; village signed down

declassified rd (ex A427) off A5/A426
roundabout – turn right in village; not far from
M6 junct 1]: Attractive 17th-c beamed and
panelled pub, open fire and nice touches,
engaging landlord, well kept Greene King IPA,
Abbot and Ruddles County, good house wines,
helpful service even when busy, decent food inc
Thurs/Fri fish specials and good Sun lunch, no
smoking restaurant; tables out in front,
bedrooms, cl Sun evening, Mon, and lunchtime
exc Sun *(Anthony Barnes, Gerry and
Rosemary Dobson)*

SHEPSHED [SK4719]
Pied Bull [handy for M1 junction 23; Belton
St]: Nicely thatched two-bar local with
enjoyable home-made food, friendly staff,
Banks's-related and guest ales from central bar,
log fire in open-plan beamed lounge, back
restaurant; children welcome, large garden
behind *(Brian and Ruth Archer)*

SIBSON [SK3500]
Cock [A444 N of Nuneaton; Twycross Rd]:
Ancient picturesque black and white timbered
building, low doorways, heavy black beams
and genuine latticed windows, immense
inglenook, three no smoking areas, good
service, well kept Bass, Hook Norton Best and
a guest such as Greene King Old Speckled Hen,
a dozen wines by the glass, popular bar food
till 10pm; piped music, games machine;
children welcome, tables in courtyard and
small garden, handy for Bosworth Field
*(Joan and Tony Walker, W and P J Elderkin,
Leigh and Gillian Mellor, John and
Wendy Allin, LYM, Kevin Blake)*

STAPLETON [SP4398]
Nags Head [A447 N of Hinckley]: Two
smallish congenial rooms served by same bar,
all no smoking at lunchtime (very popular
then), friendly helpful service, enjoyable
bargain food from sandwiches and baguettes
to popular Sun lunch (worth booking), wider
evening choice though still straightforward,
Everards Tiger and Marstons Bitter and
Pedigree, no music, restaurant; good-sized
garden with play area *(Stuart Turner, Stan and
Dot Garner)*

THORPE SATCHVILLE [SK7311]
Fox [Main St (B6047)]: 1930s tap for nearby
John o' Gaunt brewery, three or four well kept
ales, good choice of wholesome traditional
food in two carpeted bars (one with pool and
darts) and no smoking back lounge/dining area
with open fire, friendly landlord and helpful
staff, children's books and games; quiet piped
music; picnic-sets in front and in back garden
with play area, small budgerigar aviary *(CMW,
JJW, Phil and Jane Hodson, G Coates)*

THURCASTON [SK5611]
Wheatsheaf [Leicester Rd]: Cosy and clean
open-plan village pub, well kept ales such as
Adnams, Marstons Pedigree and Wadworths
6X, enjoyable home-made food from
sandwiches to fish caught by the landlord,
friendly staff, no smoking plush-seat beamed
lounge with log fire, another in bar; tables on
prettily planted terrace, well appointed skittle
alley *(Phil and Jane Hodson)*

TILTON ON THE HILL [SK7405]

Rose & Crown [B6047]: Friendly old place with reasonably priced appetising fresh food from good snack choice to restaurant meals, well kept ales such as Adnams Broadside and Charles Wells Bombardier, farm cider, long recently refurbished lounge with assorted tables (some with window seats) and log fire in huge hearth, no smoking restaurant; unobtrusive piped traditional jazz, live Thurs; garden tables, open all day wknds *(Rona Murdoch)*

TUR LANGTON [SP7194]

Crown [off B6047; Main St (follow Kibworth signpost from centre)]: Attractive pub with decent food from bangers and mash to more upmarket and modern dishes, friendly service, well kept Caledonian Deuchars IPA, Courage Directors and Greene King IPA, flagstoned bar with central log fire, side room with pool, back no smoking restaurant with own bar; terrace tables *(LYM, Gerry and Rosemary Dobson)*

UPPINGHAM [SP8699]

Crown: Town hotel with well worn in large pubby open-plan bar (can be smoky), Everards real ales, friendly if not speedy service, good range of reasonably priced food, back restaurant; piped radio may obtrude *(anon)*

Falcon [High St East/Market Sq]: Civilised and relaxing coaching inn with plenty of character in oak-panelled bar and comfortable lounge, light and airy, with skylights and big windows over market sq, pleasant light lunches inc sandwiches and rolls, afternoon teas, friendly attentive well trained staff, well kept Greene King IPA, Abbot and Old Speckled Hen, good coffee, nice open fire, daily papers and magazines; bedrooms, back barrier-exit car park *(P Tailyour, George Atkinson)*

Vaults [Market Pl]: Attractive family-run pub next to church, reasonably priced fresh filling food (can take a while) inc good pies, helpful staff, well kept Marstons ales, comfortable banquettes, pleasant upstairs dining room; piped music; some tables out overlooking picturesque square, bedrooms *(P Tailyour, Barry Collett, Mr and Mrs Bentley-Davies)*

WALTHAM ON THE WOLDS [SK8024]

☆ *Royal Horseshoes* [Melton Rd (A607)]: Attractive thatched stone-built inn, sturdily furnished and comfortable, with enjoyable food, friendly staff, three well kept real ales, good wines and fair range of malts, spotless housekeeping, three open fires, interesting aquarium (with albino frog) in no smoking dining lounge; subtle piped music; children welcome in eating area, tables outside, bedrooms *(LYM, Phil and Jane Hodson)*

WALTON ON THE WOLDS [SK5919]

Anchor [Loughborough Rd]: Long rambling open-plan beamed pub with sofas as well as chairs and tables, good range of reasonably priced food (not Sun eve, Mon) inc wkdy OAP lunches, well kept Timothy Taylors Landlord, welcoming staff and regulars, daily papers, darts, no smoking end; quiet piped music; tables on front lawn with awning, nice village *(Rona Murdoch)*

WHITWICK [SK4614]

Bulls Head [Warren Hills Rd, former B587 towards Copt Oak; handy for M1 junction 22]: Cosy L-shaped plush beamed bar with splendid views over Charnwood Forest – highest pub in Leics; generous enjoyable food using good ingredients, friendly efficient service; children welcome, big garden *(Brian and Ruth Archer)*

Three Horseshoes [Leicester Rd]: Friendly and utterly unpretentious community local, bar and tiny smoke room, well kept Bass, M&B Mild and Marstons Pedigree, darts, dominoes and cards, no food; outdoor lavatories *(the Didler, Pete Baker)*

WIGSTON [SP6098]

Horse & Trumpet [Bull Head St]: Friendly and spotless bare-boards pub with well kept Everards beers and dual personality – older people at lunchtime after its good value generous lunchtime food (very popular on pensions day), lively local evening atmosphere (can get smoky then); skittle alley *(J M Tansey, Rona Murdoch)*

William Wygston [Leicester Rd]: Roomy Wetherspoons, bright and airy, with their usual well presented food, six well kept good value real ales, obliging young staff, accessible books – not exactly riveting except for specialists *(Veronica Brown)*

WOODHOUSE EAVES [SK5314]

☆ *Wheatsheaf* [Brand Hill; beyond Main St, off B591 S of Loughborough]: Busy open-plan beamed country pub with light and airy upstairs dining area, good home-made food from sandwiches up inc interesting specials, changing ales such as Adnams, Hook Norton Best and Timothy Taylors Landlord, good house wines, friendly helpful staff, log fire, motor-racing memorabilia; no motor-cyclists or children; dogs welcome, floodlit and heated terrace tables *(David Field, Comus and Sarah Elliott, David Glynne-Jones, LYM, the Didler, Les and Barbara Owen, Brian and Ruth Archer)*

WYMESWOLD [SK6023]

☆ *Hammer & Pincers* [East Rd (A6006)]: New licensees doing good bar and restaurant food (not Sun evening or Mon-Tues) in smart restauranty dining pub, small entrance bar with black leather settees and armchairs around low tables, shallow steps up to dark-carpeted linked eating areas with chunky modern pine furniture, contemporary lighting and big abstract artworks, decent wines, neat polite staff; piped music; picnic-sets on sheltered well landscaped back terrace, sturdy play area behind; cl Mon *(Roger and Maureen Kenning, CMW, JJW, BB)*

Three Crowns [45 Far St]: Snug and chatty 18th-c village pub with welcoming new landlord, good value standard food, four or five well kept ales, good soft drinks choice, attentive service, pleasant character furnishings in beamed bar and lounge with steps up to cosy no smoking area, darts; games machine, quiz nights; picnic-sets out on decking

(the Didler, CMW, JJW, Roger and
Maureen Kenning)
WYMONDHAM [SK8518]
Berkeley Arms [Main St]: Attractive old stone
building with friendly helpful landlord,
enjoyable fresh food from crusty bread
sandwiches up, nice prices, good choice of
beers such as Adnams, Marstons Pedigree and
Tetleys, good coffee, appealingly pubby
uncluttered décor with pine furniture, two cosy
bars and restaurant; well spaced picnic-sets in
pleasant garden, nice village *(Michael Doswell)*

If a pub tries to make you leave a credit card behind the bar, be on your guard. The
credit card firms and banks which issue them condemn this practice. After all, the
publican who asks you to do this is in effect saying: 'I don't trust you'. Have you any
more reason to trust his staff? If your card is used fraudulently while you have let it be
kept out of your sight, the card company could say you've been negligent yourself – and
refuse to make good your losses. So say that they can 'swipe' your card instead, but
must hand it back to you. Please let us know if a pub does try to keep your card.

Lincolnshire

Pubs on the top of their form here this year are the friendly Welby Arms at Allington (a popular all-rounder), the attractive and comfortably cottagey Blue Bell at Belchford (its good imaginative food now earning it a Food Award), the ancient Wheatsheaf at Dry Doddington (doing extremely well since its recent reopening by excellent licensees, nice food in a warmly inviting atmosphere), the distinguished old George of Stamford (great all round, and an exceptional building), and the Chequers at Woolsthorpe (splendid choice of drinks, good food with particularly imaginative evening choices). The Blue Bell and the Chequers are both sound choices for a special meal out, and do good bar food as well as more restauranty dishes. The George of Stamford gives even more sense of a special occasion with its restaurant meals, and so yet again takes the title of Lincolnshire Dining Pub of the Year. It's worth underlining that, throughout the county, there's also some bargain food to be found, with even entirely unpretentious pubs caring about their cooking. And this year we've noticed quite a lot of Lincolnshire pubs using meat from local farms to good effect. In the Lucky Dip section at the end of the chapter, pubs to note particularly are the Chequers at Gedney Dyke, Bell at Halton Holegate, Willoughby Arms at Little Bytham, White Swan at Scotter, Cross Keys at Stow and restauranty Farmers Arms at Welton Hill. The Batemans Brewery visitor centre in Wainfleet also deserves a special mention, as a good alternative for lunchtime bar snacks, and as an entertaining place to visit in its own right. Family-run Batemans is the main local brewer, and its beers are usually particularly good value (in general, Lincolnshire drinks prices tend to be pretty close to the national average). Other smaller local breweries to look out for include Tom Woods (Highwood), Newby Wyke and Oldershaws.

ALLINGTON SK8540 Map 7
Welby Arms ♀ ◧ ⇌
The Green; off A1 N of Grantham, or A52 W of Grantham

Handy for the A1, this is a bustling place with friendly, attentive licensees. The large bar area is divided by a stone archway and has black beams and joists, log fires (one in an attractive arched brick fireplace), red velvet curtains and comfortable burgundy button-back wall banquettes and stools. The civilised back no smoking dining lounge (where they prefer you to eat) looks out on to tables in a sheltered walled courtyard with pretty hanging baskets in summer. A back courtyard formed by the restaurant extension and the bedroom block beyond has tables, with more picnic-sets out on the front lawn. A good choice of well kept real ales (served through a sparkler) might include Bass, John Smiths, Timothy Taylors Landlord and three guests such as Adnams Regatta, Jennings Cumberland, and Shepherd Neame Spitfire on handpump, 11 wines by the glass, and 20 malt whiskies; dominoes, cribbage and piped music. Bar food is popular: soup (£3.25), wholemeal hoagies or filled baguettes (from £3.95; hot sirloin steak and stilton £4.95), home-made chicken liver pâté or garlic mushrooms (£4.25), chicken pasta, steak and mushroom in ale pie or home-made lasagne (all £7.95), chargrilled steaks (from £10.95), and specials like pork and black pudding sausage or fresh grimsby haddock with mushy peas (£7.95), lambs liver and onions (£8.95), and lamb shank or poached plaice with prawn sauce (£10.95). Best to book to be sure of a table.

(Recommended by Michael and Jenny Back, June and Ken Brooks, MJVK, Joyce and Geoff Robson, Alan and Jill Bull, P J Holt, JMC, Kevin Thorpe, Patrick Hancock, the Didler, F J Robinson, Darly Graton, Graeme Gulibert, John and Sylvia Harrop, W and P J Elderkin, Duncan Cloud, P W Taylor, Andy and Jill Kassube, Jonathan Tong, Martin and Sue Day)

Free house ~ Licensees Matt Rose and Anna Cavanagh ~ Real ale ~ Bar food ~ (01400) 281361 ~ Well behaved children in dining area at lunchtime, must be over 7 in evening ~ Open 12-2.30(3 Sat), 6-11; 12-4, 6-10.30 Sun ~ Bedrooms: £48S/£60S

BARNOLDBY LE BECK TA2303 Map 8
Ship ♀
Village signposted off A18 Louth—Grimsby

There's certainly plenty to look at in this pleasant little pub, and the amazing collection of Edwardian and Victorian bric-a-brac includes stand-up telephones, violins, a horn gramophone, bowler and top hats, old racquets, crops and hockey sticks, a lace dress, and grandmotherly plants in ornate china bowls. Heavy dark-ringed drapes swathe the windows, comfortable dark green plush wall benches have lots of pretty propped-up cushions, and there are heavily stuffed green plush Victorian-looking chairs on a green fleur de lys carpet. Many of the tables are booked for dining, and enjoyable food could include home-made soup (£3.95), sandwiches or filled baguettes (from £3.95), chicken liver parfait with redcurrant jus (£4.95), fresh crêpe of salmon, prawns and white fish in a light mornay sauce (£5.25), vegetable bourguignon with savoury dumplings (£8.50), beef in ale pie (£8.95), cajun-style salmon (£10.95), steaks (from £11.95), pork loin cutlets finished with reduced apples and stilton and lightly grilled (£12.50), chicken breast with a smoky bacon, onion and mushroom jus (£12.95), daily specials such as scallops (£6.50), stilton bake (£7.95), chicken balti (£9.95), and dover sole (£17.95), and puddings like hot chocolate and brandy fudge cake (£4.25). The restaurant is no smoking. Well kept Black Sheep and Timothy Taylors Landlord on handpump, and several wines by the glass; piped music. Out behind are a few picnic-sets under pink cocktail parasols and hanging baskets in a fenced-off suntrap area. *(Recommended by Kay and Alistair Butler, Alan Cole, Kirstie Bruce, James Browne, Derek and Sylvia Stephenson, Keith Rutter, Inga Davis, Kevin Blake)*

Inn Business ~ Lease Michele Hancock ~ Real ale ~ Bar food (12-2, 7-9.30; 12.30-2.30, 7-9.30 Sun) ~ Restaurant ~ (01472) 822308 ~ Children in eating area of bar and restaurant ~ Open 12-3, 6-11(10.30 Sun)

BELCHFORD TF2975 Map 8
Blue Bell ⑪
Village signposted off A153 Horncastle—Louth (and can be reached by the good Bluestone Heath Road off A16 just under 1½ miles N of the A1104 roundabout); Main Road

This cottagey 18th-c place is very much a dining pub with emphasis on its imaginative modern food. The cosy and comfortable bar has a relaxing pastel décor, some armchairs and settees, as well as more upright chairs around the good solid tables, and well kept Black Sheep, Shepherd Neame Spitfire, and Wells Bombardier on handpump; the eating area of the bar and attractive restaurant are no smoking. From an interesting menu, there might be soup (£2.95), chicken liver parfait with home-made onion marmalade and melba toast (£4.75), thai-style salmon and prawn fishcakes with mustard mayonnaise (£5.50), green lip mussel and saffron velouté with a ribbon of smoked halibut (£5.95), tandoori marinated vegetable ravioli with home-made pasta on a mint raita and a coconut masala sauce (£10.50), roast breast of guinea fowl wrapped in bacon stuffed with plum and ginger on braised fennel with orange and honey (£11.95), soy marinated bass stuffed with orange, coriander, spring onion and chilli baked in a bag with wilted pak choi (£12.95), fried wild boar steak on a thyme, chilli and shallot jam with black pudding and seared apple finished with a scrumpy cider and wholegrain mustard sauce or cumin roasted lamb rump on basil and mint ratatouille with roast garlic jus (£13.50), and beef fillet on a field mushroom stuffed with wild mushroom duxelle topped with a horseradish cream and brandy jus (£17.50). Decent wines by the glass, and friendly, prompt service. The neat garden behind, with a terrace, has picnic-sets, and the pub is well placed for Wolds walks, and the Viking Way. More reports please. *(Recommended by John Wall, Gordon B Thornton, Bill and Sheila McLardy, Derek and Sylvia Stephenson)*

Free house ~ Licensees Darren and Shona Jackson ~ Real ale ~ Bar food (12-2, 6.30-9) ~ Restaurant ~ (01507) 533602 ~ Children in eating area of bar and restaurant ~ Open 11.30-2.30, 6.30-11; 12-4 Sun; closed Sun evening and Mon

BILLINGBOROUGH TF1134 Map 8

Fortescue Arms

B1177, off A52 Grantham—Boston

In a nice village, this friendly pub has several linked turkey-carpeted rooms. There are low beams, pleasant mainly Victorian prints, and big log fires in two see-through fireplaces that give a cosily old-fashioned feel. Also, bay window seats, fresh flowers and pot plants, brass and copper, a stuffed badger and pheasant, with various quiz books in one place, and attractive dining rooms at each end, one with stripped stone walls, flagstones and another open fire; the restaurant is no smoking. Unusually, a long red and black tiled corridor runs right the way along behind the serving bar, making it an island. Well kept Batemans XXXB, Ind Coope Burton, and Tetley Imperial on handpump, around 70 malt whiskies, and decent wines. Bar food includes spare ribs (£6.75), steak and mushroom pie (£6.95), baked fish (£7.95), and thai curry or fish pie (£8.75). The car park is more like the gravelled drive of a country house; on one side are picnic-sets on a lawn under apple trees, and on the other a sheltered courtyard with flowers planted in tubs and a manger. More reports please. *(Recommended by anon)*

Free house ~ Licensees John and Sharon Cottingham ~ Real ale ~ Bar food (not Mon exc bank hols) ~ Restaurant ~ (01529) 240228 ~ Children in restaurant ~ Open 12-3, 6-11; 12-3, 7-10.30 Sun; closed Mon exc bank hols

CONINGSBY TF2458 Map 8 🏠

Lea Gate Inn 🍺

Leagate Road (B1192 southwards, off A153 E)

This 16th-c inn once stood by one of the perilous tracks through the marshes before the fens were drained, and outside the door you can still see the small iron gantry that used to hold a lamp to guide travellers safely through the mist. Inside, there are three separate cosy, softly lit areas linked together around the corner bar counter, with heavy black beams supporting ochre ceiling boards. It's attractively furnished, with a cabinet holding a collection of ancient bottles, a variety of tables and chairs, including antique oak settles with hunting-print cushions, and two great high-backed settles making a snug around the biggest of the fireplaces. Another fireplace has an interesting cast-iron fireback depicting the Last Supper. Well liked bar food includes home-made soup (£2.70), lunchtime sandwiches (£2.95), garlic mushrooms (£3.25), mushroom stroganoff (£7.25), steak and kidney pie (£7.95), chicken breast with cider, apples, bacon and herbs (£9), chargrilled pork steak with stilton and creamy wholegrain mustard sauce or lamb rump with rosemary and madeira jus (£9.95), and beef wellington (£11.95). The restaurant is no smoking. Well kept Marstons Pedigree and Theakstons XB with a guest such as Archers on handpump; piped music. The appealing garden has tables and an enclosed play area. Bedrooms are in a newish block. *(Recommended by M C and S Jeanes, Richard Cole, the Didler, Bill and Sheila McLardy, C A Hall, Maurice and Gill McMahon)*

Free house ~ Licensee Mark Dennison ~ Real ale ~ Bar food ~ Restaurant ~ (01526) 342370 ~ Children welcome ~ Open 11.30-3, 6.30(6 Sat)-11; 12-3, 6-10.30 Sun ~ Bedrooms: £52.50B/£70B

DRY DODDINGTON SK8546 Map 8

Wheatsheaf

1½ miles off A1 N of Grantham; Main Street

This largely 16th-c village pub has been transformed by its new licensees – new to the pub, though far from new to the *Guide*, as the Dyers won warm praise from many readers at their former Lincolnshire pub. A lot of work has gone into smartening up the outside, in its fresh ochre colourwash on what looks like new rendering, and crisp new roof tiles. Inside is spotless, the front bar basically two rooms, with a log fire, a variety of settles and chairs, and tables in the windows facing across to the green and the lovely 14th-c church with its crooked tower. The serving bar on the right has well kept Belvoir Beaver Bitter, Doddingtons Delight, Highwood Tom Wood's Best Bitter, and Timothy Taylors Landlord on handpump, good hot drinks, and a nice choice of wines by the glass; you may smoke in only one part of the bar. A slight slope takes you back down to the comfortable and thickly carpeted smallish dining room with a relaxing red and cream décor. This part, once a cow byre, is even more ancient, perhaps 13th-c. Enjoyable food cooked by the landlady and largely using local supplies includes light lunchtime choices such as filled baguettes (from £4.50), a good mixed salad platter of cheeses, ham and pâté (£6.95), and honey and mustard roasted ham and egg (£6.95), as well as home-made soup (£3.95), chicken liver pâté with orange marmalade or roasted peppers topped with melted goats cheese and drizzled with pesto dressing (£4.95), english asparagus with parma ham and parmesan (£5.45), mediterranean-style haddock with ratatouille and mozzarella cheese topping (£10.95), roasted breast of duck with morello cherry and brandy sauce (£13.95), rack of english lamb with redcurrant and rosemary jus (£14.95), steaks (from £14.95), daily specials like lincolnshire sausages with bubble and squeak and onion gravy (£7.95), steak, mushroom and ale pie or fresh grimsby haddock (£8.95), and spinach, brie and aubergine bake (£9.95); two-course Sunday lunch (£10.95). Under a landlord who clearly enjoys getting to know his customers, service is friendly and efficient; with no piped music, the atmosphere is buoyant and cheerful. Disabled access at the side; smart new lavatories. The front terrace has neat dark green tables under cocktail parasols, among tubs of flowers. *(Recommended by Michael and Jenny Back, Keith Wright)*

Free house ~ Licensees Bob and Josie Dyer ~ Real ale ~ Bar food (12-2, 6-9.30 (not Sun evening)) ~ Restaurant ~ (01400) 281458 ~ Children in eating area of bar ~ Open 12-2.30, 5.30-11; 12-4, 7-10.30 Sun

GRANTHAM SK9135 Map 8

Angel & Royal 🛏

High Street

The elaborately carved stone façade here dates from the 14th c, when it had already been offering hospitality to kings and commoners alike for a couple of centuries, as a Commandery and Hospice of the Knights Templar. The restored gilded crown and angel over the entrance arch is thought to commemorate a visit by Edward III, and he and his queen Philippa may be among the other carved effigies which still watch over the street just as they did when it was the Great North Road. Through this arch, head to the left and up to the ancient Angel Bar, to see its formidable inglenook fireplace, and the charming little medieval oriel window seat jutting out over the road. A second high-beamed bar on the right has another massive inglenook. Downstairs, a stylish bistro/bar with elegant modern tables and comfortable chairs on its pale oak boards, and a décor neatly combining clean lines and up-to-date pastels with some ancient stripped stonework, serves a wide choice of good modern food: home-made chicken liver pâté or home-made soup (£3.95), fishcakes with mango and lime salsa (£3.95; large £6.60), kedgeree (£4.50; large £7.50), stuffed mushrooms with welsh rarebit (£7.25), deep fried haddock (£7.95), caramelised pork fillet with sweet and sour sauce or roast leg of lamb (£8.25), sirloin steak (12.95), and puddings like sticky toffee jam sponge or baked chocolate tart with a cherry and kirsch compote (£4.95); sandwiches (from £3.45). There is a grand-manner upstairs weekend restaurant, in the gorgeous room where Richard III may well have signed the order for the death of his treacherous cousin the Duke of Buckingham, on 19 October 1483. The bedrooms are in a more modern back extension, alongside the narrow flagstoned inner coachway, and they have good parking. More reports please. *(Recommended by W W Burke, Phil and Jane Hodson)*

Free house ~ Licensee Diane Edwards ~ Real ale ~ Bar food ~ Restaurant ~ (01476) 565816 ~ Children in eating area of bar ~ Open 11.30-2.30, 6-11; 12-2.30, 7-10.30 Sun ~ Bedrooms: £85B/£110B

GRIMSTHORPE TF0422 Map 8

Black Horse

A151 W of Bourne

There's a quietly composed eating-out mood in the neat rooms of this handsome grey-stone coaching inn. A cosy window seat and a nice round oak table stand on oak flooring just as you go in. The narrowish room then stretches away past the oak-timbered bar counter and bar stools down one side, and a row of tables, some of which are quite intimate in their own little booths, down the other. We have been unable to contact the pub either by post or by phone so we are keeping our fingers crossed that things have not changed here. They have offered bar as well as more elaborate restaurant meals, and have kept three changing real ales from brewers such as Black Dog, Charles Wells and Newby Wyke on handpump. More news please. *(Recommended by John Wooll, Roger Thornington, MJB, Alan and Jill Bull, Gordon Neighbour, Paul and Annette Hallett, Derek and Sylvia Stephenson)*

Free house ~ Licensee Shaun Gilder ~ Real ale ~ Bar food (12-2, 6-9; 12-4 Sun) ~ Restaurant ~ (01778) 591247 ~ Children welcome ~ Open 12-2, 6-11; 12-4 Sun; closed Sun evening ~ Bedrooms: £45B/£55B

LINCOLN SK9771 Map 8

Victoria ■ £

Union Road

Up a steep back street behind the castle, this basic early Victorian local is popular for its fine choice of up to nine real ales. Along with Batemans XB, Castle Rock Harvest Pale and Timothy Taylors Landlord, friendly staff serve five or six guests from brewers such as Badger, Brains, Batemans, Everards, Fullers, Oakham and Oldershaws, as well as foreign draught and bottled beers, around 20 country wines, a farm cider on tap, and cheap soft drinks. They hold beer festivals in the last week in June and the first week in December. With a good mix of ages, the simply furnished little tiled front lounge has a coal fire and pictures of Queen Victoria; it's especially bustling at lunchtime and later on in the evening. Readers recommend the sausages and mash, and other good value lunchtime food, from a short menu, includes filled cobs (from £1.40, big bacon ones £3.10), all-day breakfast and basic home-made hot dishes such as beef stew, chilli, curry or ploughman's (from £4.50); the lounge is no smoking at lunchtime. Children are welcome in the restaurant which is open only on Sunday lunchtimes (Sunday roast £5.50). You can sit in the small conservatory or out in the gravelled side garden, which has good views of the castle. *(Recommended by Derek and Sylvia Stephenson, Rona Murdoch, Patrick Hancock, the Didler, David Carr, Geoff and Kaye Newton, Mike and Linda Hudson)*

Tynemill ~ Manager Neil Renshaw ~ Real ale ~ Bar food (12(11 Sat)-2.30; 12-2 Sun) ~ Restaurant (Sun) ~ (01522) 536048 ~ Dogs allowed after 3pm ~ Open 11-11; 12-10.30 Sun

Wig & Mitre ★ ♀

Steep Hill; just below cathedral

No matter what time it is, you can pop into this bustling café-style pub and get something to eat as they serve food from 8am till midnight. Spreading over a couple of floors, the building itself dates from the 14th c, and has plenty of period features. The big-windowed beamed downstairs bar has exposed stone walls, pews and gothic furniture on oak floorboards, and comfortable sofas in a carpeted back area. Upstairs, the calmer dining room is light and airy, with views of the castle walls and cathedral, shelves of old books, and an open fire. The walls are hung with antique prints and caricatures of lawyers and clerics, and there are plenty of newspapers and periodicals lying about – even templates to tempt you to a game of noughts and crosses. The food works its way up from the breakfast menu (full english £8.50) to a choice of caviar (from £38). Other dishes might include soup (£4.50), sandwiches (from £5.50), smoked haddock fishcakes with beurre blanc (£5.95; large £10.50), parma ham and celeriac remoulade with potato truffle dressing (£6.95), baked goats cheese and thyme soufflé (£7.45), moulded vegetable risotto with poached egg and red pepper sauce (£10.50), confit of pork belly on champ mash with thyme jus (£13.75), roasted duck with parsnip purée and balsamic jus (£14.50), skate wing on saffron scented potatoes with wilted spinach (£14.75), daily specials such as goats cheese and pickled walnut parfait (£6.95), game terrine with spicy chutney (£7.25), home-made lasagne (£8.50), roast breast of chicken with vegetable risotto (£12.95), and puddings like chocolate, fruit and nut parfait with coffee ice-cream or crêpe suzette (£4.95). They have 35 wines by the glass, lots of liqueurs and spirits and well kept Batemans XB and Black Sheep Bitter on handpump. *(Recommended by Mrs Brenda Calver, David Carr, Patrick Hancock, Richard Jennings, Christopher Beadle, Kay and Alistair Butler, Peter and Eleanor Kenyon, Keith and Chris O'Neill, Barry Collett, Anthony Barnes)*

Free house ~ Licensees Valerie Hope, Toby Hope ~ Real ale ~ Bar food (8am-12pm) ~ Restaurant ~ (01522) 535190 ~ Children in eating area of bar and restaurant ~ Dogs allowed in bar ~ Open 8am-12pm

NEWTON TF0436 Map 8

Red Lion

Signposted from A52 E of Grantham; pub itself also discreetly signed off A52

Comfortable and civilised, this friendly pub has old-fashioned seating, partly stripped stone walls covered with old farming tools, and various stuffed birds and animals. As well as a popular daily cold carvery (£8.50, £10.50 for a big plate; they do a hot carvery on Friday and Saturday evenings and Sunday lunchtimes), bar food might include soup (£2.95), battered haddock (£7.50), courgette bake or steak and kidney pie (£7.95), fillet steak (£14.95), and daily specials such as chicken fillet in white wine sauce (£9.95) and rib-eye steak (£11.95), and home-made puddings like lemon meringue pie; the dining room is no smoking. Well kept Batemans XB, Greene King Ruddles County, and Timothy Taylors Landlord on handpump; piped music and fruit machine. A neat, sheltered back garden has some seats on the grass and on the terrace. According to local tradition this village is the highest point between Grantham and the Urals. More reports please. *(Recommended by MJB, Gene and Kitty Rankin)*

Free house ~ Licensee Mr Blessett ~ Real ale ~ Bar food ~ Restaurant ~ (01529) 497256 ~ Well behaved children over 5 in restaurant ~ Open 12-3, 7(6 Sat)-11; 12-3, 7-10.30 Sun

---

'Children welcome' means the pub says it lets children inside without any special restriction. If it allows them in, but to restricted areas such as an eating area or family room, we specify this. Some pubs may impose an evening time limit. We do not mention limits after 9pm as we assume children are home by then.

ROTHWELL TF1499 Map 8
Blacksmiths Arms
Off B1225 S of Caistor

Handily open all day at weekends, this long white-painted pub is a refreshing oasis in this part of the world. The pleasant bar is divided by a couple of arches and has a relaxed atmosphere, a warm central coal fire, attractive wildlife prints, heavy beams and comfortable chairs and tables. The spacious restaurant is no smoking. At lunchtime, bar food might include filled baked potatoes (from £3.75), sandwiches (from £3.95), burgers (from £4.50), omelettes (from £4.75), ploughman's (£4.95), and full english breakfast (£5.50); there's also home-made soup (£3.50), whitebait (£4.50), sausage and mash with onion gravy (£6.25; large £7.25), stir-fried vegetables with noodles or fresh haddock in light batter (£7.25), home-made steak in ale pie (£7.95; large £8.95), home-made moussaka (£8.25), chicken italian (£9.50), steaks (from £11.95), and puddings (£3.50); Sunday roasts (£7.25). There's also an early bird weekday menu between 5 and 7pm (£7.95 for a meal and a drink). Five well kept real ales on handpump such as Batemans XB, Greene King Abbot, and Tom Woods Shepherds Delight with a couple of guests like Archers Little Rascal or Daleside Special, and 20 malt whiskies; piped music, fruit machine, darts and dominoes. There are plenty of tables outside. Take care coming out of the car park: it's a blind bend. More reports please. *(Recommended by James Browne)*

Free house ~ Licensees Rick and Julie Sandham ~ Real ale ~ Bar food (12-2, 5-9.30; 12-9.30(9 Sun)Sat) ~ Restaurant ~ (01472) 371300 ~ Children in restaurant ~ Open 11.30-3, 5-11; 11.30-11 Sat; 12-10.30 Sun

SOUTH WITHAM SK9219 Map 8
Blue Cow 🍺
Village signposted just off A1 Stamford—Grantham (with brown sign for pub)

If you are lucky, you might get a little tour around the small brewery next door to this old stone-walled country pub – and the friendly landlord could even sell you some of their own-brewed beer to take home: Thirlwells Best and Witham Wobbler on handpump. The two appealing individual bars are separated by a big central open-plan counter. One dark-beamed room has bentwood chairs at big indonesian hardwood tables, wickerwork and panelling, and prettily curtained windows. The second room has big black standing timbers and beams, partly stripped stone walls, shiny flagstones and a dark blue flowery carpet; piped music, TV, cribbage, and dominoes. Just inside the entrance lobby you pass an endearing little water feature on floodlit steps that go down to the cellar. Bar food such as sandwiches, soup (£3.50), and chicken curry or vegetable pancake (£7.75). The garden has tables on a pleasant terrace. *(Recommended by David Edwards, the Didler, Anne Harries, Stuart Paulley, Phil and Jane Hodson, Kevin Thorpe, Keith and Chris O'Neill)*

Own brew ~ Licensees Dick and Julia Thirlwell ~ Real ale ~ Bar food (12-2.30, 6-9.30) ~ Restaurant ~ (01572) 768432 ~ Children in eating area of bar, restaurant and family room ~ Dogs allowed in bar and bedrooms ~ Open 12-11 ~ Bedrooms: £40S/£45S(£55B)

STAMFORD TF0207 Map 8
George of Stamford ★ 🍽 ♀ 🛏
High Street, St Martins (B1081 S of centre, not the quite different central pedestrianised High Street)

Lincolnshire Dining Pub of the Year

Readers love this place. It must be one of the best preserved old coaching inns in England and although it oozes atmosphere, it is still very much in touch with the 21st c. It was built in 1597 for Lord Burghley (though there are visible parts of a much older former Norman pilgrims' hospice, and a crypt under the cocktail bar that may be 1,000 years old), and during the 18th and 19th c was the hub of 20 coach trips a day each way from London and York (two of the front rooms are still named after these destinations). The atmosphere is smartly relaxed, and there are plenty of comfortably conversing customers enjoying a break from the busy A1, meeting friends for a drink or a meal or staying in the lovely bedrooms. Seats in its beautifully furnished rooms range through leather, cane and antique wicker to soft settees and easy chairs, while the central lounge has sturdy timbers, broad flagstones, heavy beams, and massive stonework. The other front room making up the surprisingly pubby bar is the York Bar, where you can get snacks such as soup (£4.65), sandwiches (from £4.95; open toastie £5.45; triple decker £6.50), crostini of button mushrooms in a wine cream sauce (£5.95), and chicken liver pâté with cumberland sauce or ploughman's (£6.45). Our Food Award, though, is for the delicious (but not cheap) more elaborate meals served in the oak-panelled restaurant (jacket and tie) and less formal Garden Lounge restaurant (which has well spaced furniture on herringbone glazed bricks around a central tropical grove). Made using high quality ingredients, food in the Garden Lounge takes on a continental tilt (one of the licensees is Italian). Besides a cold buffet (£13.45), the menu includes several pasta dishes such as linguini with rocket and parmesan (£9.55) or pasta strips with salmon and fresh peas in a saffron cream (£11.55), and shellfish such as oysters (£7.25 for six), and dressed crab (£12.95), as well as caesar salad (£7.25), hot smoked salmon fishcakes with spring onion and coriander (£8.75; main course £12.45), eggs benedict with parma ham (£8.95), home-made beefburger or moroccan lamb (£12.55), baked cod on a sweetcorn pancake with tomato and onion sauce (£13.95), and puddings (£5.25); they do afternoon tea (£13.50). Well kept Adnams Broadside, Fullers London Pride, and Greene King Ruddles County on handpump, an excellent choice of wines (many of which are italian and good value, with about 18 by the glass), freshly squeezed orange juice, and malt whiskies. The staff are professional, with waiter drinks service in the charming cobbled courtyard at the back, which has comfortable chairs and tables among attractive plant tubs and colourful hanging baskets on the ancient stone buildings. There's also a neatly kept walled garden, with a sunken lawn where croquet is often played. *(Recommended by M Sharp, Gordon Neighbour, Roy Bromell, Martin and Anne Muers, the Didler, David Glynne-Jones, W W Burke, Bob and Maggie Atherton, J F M and M West, Dr M A Turner, A J Bowen, Ian Phillips, Tina and David Woods-Taylor, Di and Mike Gillam, Grahame Brooks, Mike and Sue Loseby, Tracey and Stephen Groves, Richard Waller, Pauline Smith)*

Free house ~ Licensees Chris Pitman and Ivo Vannocci ~ Real ale ~ Bar food (11-11) ~ Restaurant ~ (01780) 750750 ~ Children welcome ~ Dogs allowed in bar and bedrooms ~ Occasional jazz Fri evenings in garden lounge restaurant ~ Open 11-11; 12-11 Sun ~ Bedrooms: £78B/£115B

SURFLEET TF2528 Map 8
Mermaid
Just off A16 N of Spalding, on B1356 at bridge

There's been quite a bit of refurbishment here over the last year and by the time this edition is published, they hope to have opened up ensuite bedrooms. A small central glass-backed bar counter (complete with original Babycham décor) serves two high-ceilinged rooms, which have huge netted sash windows, green patterned carpets, red Anaglypta dado, navigation lanterns and horse tack on cream textured walls, and a mixture of banquettes and stools; cribbage and dominoes. Two steps down, the no smoking restaurant is decorated in a similar style. Besides lunchtime snacks such as sandwiches (from £2.50; baguettes from £3.25), hamburgers (from £2.75), omelettes (from £2.95), and ham and egg (£4.95), the well liked food might include home-made soup (£2.75), cottage pie (£6.95), home-made lasagne or steak in ale pie (£7.25), cod in beer batter (£7.50), lincolnshire sausage and herby mash with red onion gravy (£7.95), calves liver and bacon or wild mushroom and goats cheese tagliatelle (£8.25), chicken breast stuffed with spinach and leek mousse with a white wine sauce (£8.50), steaks (from £10.95), and daily specials like braised lamb shank or duo of cod and salmon with a cream and prawn sauce (£8.95), and braised ham hock with plum sauce (£10.50). Well kept Adnams Broadside, Greene King IPA and maybe Everards Tiger on handpump, and quite a few malt whiskies.

The pretty garden has lots of seats and a terrace with thatched parasols, and its own bar; a children's play area is safely walled from the River Glen which runs beside the pub. *(Recommended by Michael and Jenny Back, Roy Bromell, J M Tansey, Gordon Neighbour)*

Free house ~ Licensee Chris Bustance ~ Real ale ~ Bar food (12-2.30(3 Sun), 6-9.30 (9 Sun)) ~ Restaurant ~ (01775) 680275 ~ Children welcome ~ Open 12-11; 12-10.30 Sun

WOOLSTHORPE SK8435 Map 8

Chequers ♀

The one near Belvoir, signposted off A52 or A607 W of Grantham

The heavy-beamed main bar in this 17th-c coaching inn has two big tables, one a massive oak construction, a comfortable mix of seating including some handsome leather chairs and leather banquettes, and a huge boar's head above a good log fire in the big brick fireplace. Among cartoons on the wall are some of the illustrated claret bottle labels from the series commissioned from famous artists, initiated by the late Baron Philippe de Rothschild. The lounge on the right has a deep red colour scheme, leather sofas and big plasma TV, and on the left there are more leather seats in a dining area housed in what was once the village bakery; piped music. A corridor leads off to the light and airy main restaurant with contemporary pictures (a smaller restaurant is no smoking), and there's now a second bar. Well kept Hardys & Hansons Kimberley Bitter and Olde Trip, and guests like Brewster's Marquis and a seasonal ale on handpump, over 20 wines by the glass, over 20 champagnes, and 50 malt whiskies. High quality food includes lunchtime soup (£4.25), sandwiches (from £4.25; mozzarella and parma ham toastie £5.25), goats cheese and fig tatin (£5.25), ploughman's (£7.95), sausages and mash (£8.95), fish and chips with home-made tartare sauce (£9.50), chicken breast with stilton and bacon (£10.95), and fillet of brill with saffron risotto and roast pepper and tomato (£13.95), with evening choices such as wild mushroom, artichoke and black olive salad with parmesan (£5.50), tempura tiger prawns with chilli mayonnaise (£7.25), wild mushroom and artichoke risotto (£9.95), fried bass fillet with red cabbage sauerkraut, confit tomato and brown butter (£13.95), roast rack of lamb with aubergine, chorizo and apricot ragoût (£14.95), and chargrilled sirloin steak with horseradish potato gateau and red wine jus (£15.95); puddings such as chocolate and banana almond tart or bread and butter pudding with crème anglaise (from £4.70). There are nice teak tables, chairs and benches outside, and beyond some picnic-sets on the edge of the pub's cricket field; boules too, and views of Belvoir Castle. *(Recommended by Toppo Todhunter, W W Burke, Pat and Sam Roberts, Mrs E A Macdonald)*

Free house ~ Licensee Justin Chad ~ Real ale ~ Bar food (12-2.30, 7-9.30; 12-4, 6.30-8.30 Sun; not winter Sun evening) ~ Restaurant ~ (01476) 870701 ~ Children in eating area of bar and restaurant ~ Dogs allowed in bar and bedrooms ~ Open 12-3, 5.30-11; 12-10.30 Sun; 12-7 Sun in winter ~ Bedrooms: £49B/£59B

LUCKY DIP

Besides the fully inspected pubs, you might like to try these Lucky Dips recommended to us and described by readers (if you do, please send us reports: www.goodguides.co.uk).

ALFORD [TF4576]
Anchor [East St]: Red banquettes in homely 19th-c pub's long bar, enjoyable straightforward food inc wkdy lunchtime bargains, a changing real ale such as Dixons Desert Rat, no piped music; lots of flowers outside *(Ian and Nita Cooper)*
ASWARBY [TF0639]
☆ *Tally Ho* [A15 S of Sleaford (but N of village

turn-off)]: 17th-c beamed pub in nice spot, two log fires, country prints and candles on tables in big-windowed front bar redecorated in pastel yellow, enjoyable food from baguettes to steaks, friendly helpful service, well kept Bass, Batemans XB and a guest beer, good house wines, daily papers, pine-furnished restaurant; piped music; children and dogs welcome, tables out behind among fruit trees

(LYM, Bob and Marilyn Baylis, R and M Tait)

AUBOURN [SK9262]

Royal Oak: Partly 16th-c, recently refurbished but keeping its character, with well kept Adnams Broadside, Batemans XB, Greene King Abbot and a couple of guests such as Timothy Taylors Landlord, generous straightforward food inc fresh fish from Grimsby, friendly service, open fire, interesting aviation prints, extended dining room, darts; tables out in nice small front garden and bigger back one *(Lee Mansell)*

BARKSTON [SK9341]

Stag [Church St]: Beamed pub with well kept Everards Tiger and Beacon and a guest beer, cheerful helpful staff, good home-made food in left-hand dining bar with mixed tables and chairs, good wine choice, pool, darts and TV in second bar, small back conservatory; picnic-sets out in front and in back garden, pleasant village *(Mick and Moira Brummell)*

BOSTON [TF3445]

Ball House [Wainfleet Rd (A52 NE)]: Generous good value fresh food using local produce, bargain Sun lunch, well kept Batemans; colourful flower garden *(C and G Fraser)*

Coach & Horses [Main Ridge]: Friendly traditional one-bar pub with well kept Batemans XB, good coal fire, pool and darts *(the Didler)*

Mill [Spilsby Rd (A16)]: Roadside pub with enjoyable reasonably priced food from lunchtime sandwiches and baguettes to steaks and fish, separate evening and wknd menu, plush dining rooms (one no smoking), helpful service, Batemans XB and a guest beer such as Bass, bar counter covered in old pennies; quiet piped music; seats out in front *(Michael and Jenny Back)*

BOURNE [TF0920]

Smiths [North St]: Large extensively renovated shop conversion spreading through various bar areas and levels, pleasant décor with soft lighting, cosy corners and log fires, well kept Fullers London Pride, Oakham JHB and two guest beers, food all home-made using local supplies (part no smoking at lunchtime); discreet piped music; children welcome, large terrace with barbecues, open all day *(Martin and Helen Ball, the Didler)*

BRANDY WHARF [TF0196]

☆ *Cider Centre* [B1205 SE of Scunthorpe (off A15 about 16 miles N of Lincoln)]: Entirely no smoking, with huge range of ciders – up to 15 on draught, eight tapped from casks, many more in bottles and other smallish containers, also country wines and meads; simple main bar, dimly lit lounge bar with lots of cider memorabilia and jokey bric-a-brac, reasonably priced straightforward food (all day Sun); piped music, and housekeeping could be perked up; children in eating area, simple glazed verandah, tables and play area in meadows or by river with moorings and slipway, open all day wknds *(A C English, Keith and Chris O'Neill, the Didler, Stuart Paulley, Stuart Brown, David and Brenda Tew, A J Bowen, LYM)*

BRANT BROUGHTON [SK9154]

Generous Briton [just off A17 Leadenham—Newark; High St]: Neat and welcoming family-run two-bar pub, good choice of enjoyable sensibly priced food; pretty village *(Bill and Sheila McLardy)*

CLEETHORPES [TA3008]

No 2 Refreshment Room [Station Approach]: Clean and comfortable single-room platform bar with well kept M&B Mild, Worthington and a small-brewery guest beer, friendly service, no food; tables out under heaters, open all day *(Alan Cole, Kirstie Bruce, the Didler)*

☆ *Willys* [Highcliff Rd; south promenade]: Open-plan bistro-style seafront pub with panoramic Humber views, café tables, tiled floor and painted brick walls; visibly brews its own good beers, also well kept Batemans and guest beers, range of belgian beers, popular beer festival Nov, good value lunchtime home cooking inc Thurs curry night, friendly staff, nice mix of customers from young and trendy to weather-beaten fishermen; quiet juke box; a few tables out on the prom, open all day *(the Didler)*

COLEBY [SK9760]

Bell [village signed off A607 S of Lincoln, turn right and right into Far Lane at church]: Friendly dining pub with wide choice of home-made bar food all day (not Mon) inc some unusual regional dishes, well kept ales, three linked low-beamed rooms each with a log fire, restaurant; picnic-sets outside, handy for Viking Way walks, good value bedrooms, open all day (cl afternoon Jan/Feb) *(LYM, Peter and Eleanor Kenyon)*

DYKE [TF1022]

Wishing Well [village signed off A15 N of Bourne; Main St]: Long heavily beamed stripped stone front bar with huge fireplace, well kept Everards Tiger, Greene King Abbot and three guest beers, reasonably priced straightforward bar food from sandwiches to steaks, big no smoking restaurant, darts, pool, TV and so forth in public bar, small conservatory; children welcome, garden with tables and play area, bedrooms *(LYM, Derek and Sylvia Stephenson)*

FROGNALL [TF1610]

Goat [B1525, off A16 NE of Mkt Deeping]: Log fires, low 17th-c beams, stripped stone, interesting well kept ales such as Archers, Elgoods, Lees Moonraker and Orkney Dark Island, enjoyable food from lunchtime sandwiches up, cheerful service, two dining rooms (one no smoking where children welcome); may be piped music; good wheelchair access, big garden with terrace and play equipment, separate area for under-5s *(Michael and Jenny Back)*

GAINSBOROUGH [SK8189]

Eight Jolly Brewers [Ship Court, Silver St]: Bustling unpretentious pub with beams, bare bricks and brewery posters, up to eight well kept well priced changing ales and plans for their own microbrewery, farm cider, quieter bar upstairs, simple lunchtime food (not Sun), friendly staff and locals; folk club, open all day Fri-Sun *(the Didler)*

GEDNEY [TF4024]

Old Black Lion [Main Rd]: Straightforward country pub with good welcoming service and well cooked plentiful food, real ale such as Adnams, good house wines; bedrooms *(anon)*

☆ **GEDNEY DYKE** [TF4125]

☆ *Chequers* [off A17 Holbeach—Kings Lynn]: Fenland pub well worth knowing for the landlady's good food, from sandwiches with home-baked bread and chutney to gloucester old spot chop, guinea fowl and good fresh fish, friendly and obliging if not always speedy service, simple bar with open fire, no smoking dining conservatory, good wines by the glass, well kept Adnams and Greene King Abbot; piped music; children welcome, garden picnic-sets, cl Mon *(Sally Anne and Peter Goodale, John Wooll, Bill and Marian de Bass, Alan and Sue Folwell, Roger and Maureen Kenning, LYM, Grahame Brooks, Mark and Mary Fairman, Ken Marshall)*

GRANTHAM [SK9135]

☆ *Beehive* [Castlegate]: Hive of bees in the good-sized back garden's lime tree has been this unpretentious pub's unique inn sign for a couple of centuries or more – same strain of bees all that time; well kept ales from the nearby Newby Wyke microbrewery, simple cheap food from sandwiches up (all day, not Sun evening), friendly service, coal fire, back room with games, juke box and TV; children welcome till 7.30, open all day *(the Didler, LYM, Steve Kirby)*

☆ *Blue Pig* [Vine St]: Pretty jettied Tudor pub, low beams, panelling, stripped stone and flagstones, lots of pig ornaments, friendly bustle, helpful staff, interesting well kept changing ales, good simple lunchtime food, open fire, daily papers, lots of prints and bric-a-brac; piped music, juke box, games machines, no children or dogs; tables out behind, open all day *(the Didler, BB)*

Muddle Go Nowhere [Barrowby Road (A52, nr A1)]: Large comfortable family pub with inside as well as outside play areas, lots of beams, woodwork and bare brick, country décor with range fireplaces, no smoking area, good value generous food inc Sun roasts, well kept mainstream ales, distinct no smoking area, friendly if not always speedy service; disabled facilities, picnic-sets outside, open all day *(R C Vincent)*

GREATFORD [TF0811]

Hare & Hounds: Large beamed bar, smaller dining room, well kept ales such as Adnams Broadside, Oakham and Charles Wells Bombardier, wide choice of enjoyable fresh food inc bargain lunch; picnic-sets in small back garden, attractive village *(LYM, Barry Collett)*

HALTON HOLEGATE [TF4165]

☆ *Bell* [B1195 E of Spilsby]: Unchanging pretty village local, simple but comfortable and consistently friendly, with wide choice of very generous home-made food cooked by landlord inc Sun lunches and outstanding fish and chips, tempting prices, well kept Batemans XB and Highwood Tom Woods Best or Bomber

County, Lancaster bomber pictures, pub games, and Samson their nice old golden labrador; children in back eating area with tropical fish tank and restaurant *(Michael and Jenny Back, LYM, the Didler, Ian and Nita Cooper)*

HOUGH-ON-THE-HILL [SK9246]

☆ *Brownlow Arms* [High Rd]: 16th-c building more smart restaurant-with-rooms than pub, but does have well kept Marstons Bitter and Pedigree and Timothy Taylors Landlord in relaxing lounge bar with sofas and comfortable chairs; very good interesting food inc notable Sun lunch (two sittings), friendly efficient service; no children; good value pretty bedrooms, good breakfast, peaceful picturesque village, cl Sun evening, Mon and lunchtimes exc Sun *(W W Burke, John and Ann Menzies)*

INGHAM [SK9483]

Inn on the Green [The Green]: Wide choice of quickly served good fresh home-made food from good sandwich range to steaks and venison in well modernised pub, warmly welcoming, with well kept changing ales such as Black Sheep, Fullers London Pride and Timothy Taylors Landlord, great wine choice, lots of brass and copper in spacious beamed lounge bar, good fire, locals' bar, downstairs and upstairs dining rooms; children welcome *(Keith and Chris O'Neill, Mrs Brenda Calver)*

LEADENHAM [SK9552]

☆ *George* [off A17 Newark—Sleaford; High St]: Solid old coaching inn in village now peaceful since the bypass, with neat and pleasant two-room bar, well kept ales such as Oldershaws, good choice of wines by the glass, remarkable range of whiskies, good smart restaurant; side games room, may be piped music; picnic-sets out under heated pergola, good value bedrooms, good breakfast *(DC, LYM, Phil and Jane Hodson, Kevin Blake)*

LINCOLN [SK9872]

Golden Eagle [High St]: Cheerfully busy Tynemill two-bar town pub, up to half a dozen well kept and attractively priced changing ales, good choice of country wines, cheap soft drinks, good value lunchtime food; tables outside, open all day *(the Didler)*

Morning Star [Greetwellgate]: Friendly well scrubbed local handy for cathedral, enjoyable cheap lunches esp Fri specials, well kept reasonably priced Bass, Greene King Abbot and Ruddles, Charles Wells Bombardier and guest beers, coal fire, aircraft paintings, sofas in no smoking lounge; piano night Sat, quiz Tues; nice outside area, open all day exc Sun *(the Didler, Pete Baker, Patrick Hancock)*

Pyewipe [Saxilby Rd; off A57 just S of bypass]: Much extended 18th-c waterside pub popular for its position by Roman Fossdyke Canal (pleasant walk out from centre), friendly attentive staff, wide range of good food inc good fish choice, well kept ales such as Timothy Taylors Landlord; pleasant tables outside, comfortable reasonably priced bedrooms *(Mrs Brenda Calver, Kay and Alistair Butler)*

Sippers [Melville St, opp bus station]: Two-bar pub popular at lunchtime for good value food inc good Sun lunch, Hop Back real ales with others such as John Smiths and Marstons Pedigree *(the Didler)*

☆ *Strugglers* [Westgate]: Cosily refurbished well run local with particularly well kept ales such as Bass, Black Sheep, Fullers London Pride, Greene King and Timothy Taylors Landlord, above-average home-made food, coal-effect fire in small back snug; heaters and canopy for terrace tables (no under-18s inside), open all day *(the Didler, Patrick Hancock, John Cross)*

LITTLE BYTHAM [TF0118]

☆ *Willoughby Arms* [Station Rd, S of village]: Good Newby Wyke beers from back microbrewery kept at perfect temperature, interesting guest beers, Weston's farm cider, frequent beer festivals, reasonably priced substantial food from sandwiches up, friendly staff and local atmosphere, daily papers, simple bar with wall banquettes, stripped tables and coal fire, pleasant no smoking end dining room, airy games room with pool and sports TV; piped music, live Fri/Sat; good disabled access, children welcome, picnic-sets in pleasant good-sized back garden with quiet country views, bedrooms, open all day wknds *(the Didler, Kevin Thorpe, BB, David and Brenda Tew, Bill and Sheila McLardy, G Coates)*

LITTLE CAWTHORPE [TF3583]

Royal Oak [off A157 E of A16 roundabout S of Louth; Watery Lane]: Comfortable beamed and carpeted pub reached over a ford (pub nicknamed the Splash), with wide choice of enjoyable food (not Sun evening) inc Tues and Sun carvery using meats from local farms, Greene King beers, evening restaurant; picnic-sets under cocktail parasols out on lawn, six neatly comfortable bedrooms with own bathrooms, open all day *(anon)*

LITTLE STEEPING [TF4363]

Eaves: Pleasant family-run country pub with enjoyable food (not Mon or wkdys), plenty for vegetarians, welcoming service *(anon)*

LONG BENNINGTON [SK8344]

☆ *Reindeer* [just off A1 N of Grantham]: Thriving atmosphere in old inn with welcoming landlady, good choice of enjoyable home-made food in bar and more formal dining lounge, cut-price small helpings, well kept real ales, good wines *(Mr and Mrs J Hutton)*

LOUTH [TF3387]

Olde Whyte Swanne [Eastgate]: Low 16th-c beams, coal or log fires in comfortable and relaxed front bar and dining room, good choice of enjoyable food all day using local produce, helpful friendly staff, well kept ales such as Black Sheep, Caledonian, Greene King and Theakstons; children welcome, open all day, bedrooms *(the Didler, Peter and Sandra Cullen, Ian and Nita Cooper)*

Wheatsheaf [Westgate]: Cheerful early 17th-c low-beamed pub, coal fires in all three bars, well kept changing real ales and a late May beer festival, decent lunchtime food (not

Sun), old photographs; tables outside *(the Didler)*

MESSINGHAM [SE8905]

Bird in the Barley [Northfield Rd (A159 S of Scunthorpe)]: Large U-shaped pub with central bar, decent well presented food (not Sun evening or Mon), reasonable prices, farmland views; cl Mon lunchtime *(Kay and Alistair Butler)*

Hurn [High St (A159 S of Scunthorpe)]: Welcoming, with decent food such as fish and chips and meat pies with proper pastry, John Smiths and a couple of guest beers such as Highwood or Greene King *(Derek and Sylvia Stephenson)*

MOULTON CHAPEL [TF2918]

Jolly Farmer [Roman Rd]: Good value usual food (not Mon) in brightly lit pub with lots of old farming photographs and china models in dining rooms, airy no smoking dining conservatory, well kept ales, friendly helpful staff; piped music; children welcome, tables outside with play area *(anon)*

NORTH KELSEY [TA0401]

Butchers Arms [Middle St; off B1434 S of Brigg]: Busy village local, opened up but not too modern, low ceilings, flagstones, bare boards, dim lighting, with five well kept Tom Woods Highwood beers (brewed by owner on his farm), good value cold lunches, enthusiastic cheerful service, woodburner; pub games, no juke box, tables outside, opens 4 wkdys, open all day wknds *(the Didler)*

OSBOURNBY [TF0638]

Whichcote Arms [London Rd (A15)]: Unassuming old pub with log fire and nice prints in eating area off small bar, good food inc interesting snacks, welcoming atmosphere and quietly friendly landlord, separate dining room; bedrooms *(R and M Tait, Bill and Sheila McLardy)*

REDBOURNE [SK9799]

Red Lion [Main Rd]: Pleasant traditional pub recently comfortably restored by newish owners, flagstones, panelling, open fires and lots of duck ornamentation, affordable home-made pub food with some more individual dishes, friendly helpful staff, well kept ales such as Greene King and no smoking garden room restaurant; dogs welcome, garden with terrace, comfortable bedrooms, good breakfast, open all day *(Michael Weston)*

SCAMPTON [SK9579]

Dambusters [High St]: Beams, hops and masses of interesting Dambusters and other World War II memorabilia, reasonably priced simple food (not Sun/Mon evenings), pleasant nostalgic atmosphere, well kept Greene King IPA, Abbot and Ruddles and guest beers, log fire, adjoining post office; very near Red Arrows runway viewpoint *(Keith and Chris O'Neill)*

SCOTTER [SE8800]

☆ *White Swan* [The Green]: Well kept pub comfortably laid out for dining, varied well prepared generous food inc fish board and bargain three-course special, well kept Black Sheep, John Smiths, Websters and interesting changing guest beers, several levels inc snug panelled area by one fireplace, friendly landlady and neat cheerful staff, big-windowed restaurant looking over lawn with picnic-table sets to duck-filled River Eau (best to book wknds); piped music, steps up to entrance; 14 comfortable bedrooms in modern extension, open all day Fri-Sun *(BB, Paul and Ursula Randall, Kay and Alistair Butler)*

SKEGNESS [TF5660]

☆ *Vine* [Vine Rd, off Drummond Rd, Seacroft]: Unspoilt small hotel based on late 18th-c country house, unpretentious well run bar with friendly staff, welcoming fire and well kept Batemans XB, Mild and XXB, good value food using local produce, imposing antique seats and grandfather clock in turkey-carpeted hall, inner oak-panelled room, restaurant; tables on big back sheltered lawn with swings, good reasonably priced bedrooms, peaceful suburban setting not far from beach and bird-watching *(the Didler, BB, Brian and Ruth Archer, Maurice and Gill McMahon, Ian and Nita Cooper)*

SOUTH FERRIBY [SE9921]

Hope & Anchor [Sluice Rd (A1077)]: Recently refurbished, big front room and back dining area with wide views over confluence of rivers Ancholme and Humber, popular all-day carvery, plenty of beers; good disabled access and facilities *(Kay and Alistair Butler)*

SOUTH HYKEHAM [SK9871]

Lincoln Brewsters [Gateway Park, Roman Way; just off A1434/A46 SW of Lincoln]: Popular new family pub, good choice of well prepared food at sensible prices, usual beers and lagers; wheelchair access *(Michael Tack)*

SOUTH ORMSBY [TF3675]

☆ *Massingberd Arms* [off A16 S of Louth]: Small village pub with welcoming and obliging landlord, well kept John Smiths Magnet and a couple of interesting guest beers, short choice of enjoyable fresh food inc game and Sun lunch, restaurant Thurs-Sun evenings; dogs welcome, pleasant garden, good Wolds walks, cl Mon lunchtime *(the Didler, Ian and Nita Cooper)*

SOUTH THORESBY [TF4077]

☆ *Vine* [about a mile off A16 N of Ulceby Cross]: Two-room village inn with small local pub part – tiny passageway servery, steps up to three-table lounge, separate pool room; wide choice of quickly served food, prompt welcoming service, well kept Batemans XB, good value wines, nicely panelled no smoking dining room; bedrooms, tables in pleasant back garden *(the Didler, R M Corlett, David and Ruth Hollands, Ian and Nita Cooper)*

SPALDING [TF2422]

White Horse [Churchgate]: Attractive two-bar 17th-c thatched pub next to High Bridge over River Welland, lively and friendly, notable for the splendidly low price of its well kept Sam Smiths; usual pub food inc good value all-day Sun lunch in no smoking dining room; open all day *(John Honnor)*

STAMFORD [TF0306]

☆ *Bull & Swan* [High St, St Martins]: Good

traditional atmosphere, with warmly welcoming licensees, enjoyable food, well kept real ales, three low-beamed connecting rooms, gleaming copper and brass, log-effect gas fires; children welcome, tables out in former back coachyard, friendly service; bedrooms *(Josephine Messinger, LYM)*

☆ *Crown* [All Saints Pl]: Good pubby feel in large rambling stone-built hotel's panelled country bar, well kept ales such as Adnams Best, Black Sheep and Timothy Taylors Landlord, decent wines and coffee, polite friendly staff, good reasonably priced seasonal country cooking using local produce and meat from their own farm in two civilised no smoking dining rooms; dogs welcome, comfortable quiet bedrooms, open all day *(the Didler, Mr and Mrs B Jeffery, Ben and Helen Ingram)*

Green Man [Scotgate]: Well kept Theakstons and half a dozen more changing guest beers, belgian beers and two farm ciders, friendly staff, good value lunchtime food, sturdy scrubbed pale wood tables on flagstones, log fire, steps up to back room with good bottle collection and TV; garden tables, comfortable bedrooms sharing bathroom, open all day *(the Didler, G Coates, Tracey and Stephen Groves)*

STOW [SK8881]

☆ *Cross Keys* [B1241 NW of Lincoln]: Long-serving licensees keeping up high standards in pleasantly modernised and extended largely no smoking dining pub nr Saxon minster church (which is in desperate need of repair), prettily presented fresh food inc lots of interesting blackboard specials and good puddings, well kept Greene King Old Speckled Hen, Highgate Cromwell and Theakstons Best and Old Peculier, good range of wines, quick friendly service, big woodburner; may be piped music, cl Mon lunchtime *(Michael and Jenny Back, David and Ruth Hollands, Mrs Brenda Calver, BB)*

SURFLEET SEAS END [TF2729]

Ship [Reservoir Rd; off A16 N of Spalding]: Riverside pub reopened after complete rebuilding, flagstoned hall with broad steps up to big-windowed largely no smoking dining room overlooking river (as does its balcony), woodburner in good-sized bar with well spaced tables in big open bays, well kept ales, home-made food using local supplies *(anon)*

TATTERSHALL THORPE [TF2159]

Blue Bell [Thorpe Rd; B1192 Coningsby–Woodhall Spa]: Attentive new licensees working hard in attractive very low-beamed pub said to date from 13th c (and used by the Dambusters), good choice of reasonably priced bar food in bargain pie, well kept real ales, plenty of character, small dining room; tables in garden, impressive lavatera bushes, bedrooms *(Derek Smith, the Didler, Bill and Sheila McLardy)*

TETFORD [TF3374]

☆ *White Hart* [East Rd, off A158 E of Horncastle]: Interesting early 16th-c pub with good choice of above-average food inc good local beef, well kept Adnams, Fullers London Pride, Greene King and guest beers, Stowford Press cider, old-fashioned curved-back settles, slabby elm tables, red tiled floor and log fire in pleasant quiet inglenook bar, no smoking snug, basic games room; unobtrusive piped music; tables on sheltered back lawn, simple bedrooms, pretty countryside, cl Mon lunchtime *(LYM, the Didler, R M Corlett)*

WAINFLEET [TF5058]

☆ *Batemans Brewery* [Mill Lane, off A52 via B1195]: Not exactly a pub, but very pubby circular bar in brewery's ivy-covered windmill tower with Batemans ales in top condition, czech and belgian beers on tap, ground-floor dining area with unpretentious lunchtime food such as local sausages and pork pies, games room with plenty of old pub games (more of these outside), lots of brewery memorabilia and plenty for families to enjoy; entertaining brewery tours at 2.30, brewery shop (helpful service), tables out on terrace and grass, opens 11.30-3.30 *(Gordon Neighbour)*

WELLINGORE [SK9856]

Marquis of Granby [off A607 Lincoln—Grantham; High St]: Attractive and neatly kept old pub with pleasant service, good value imaginative food, well kept changing ales, comfortable button-back banquettes, log fire, nice quiet dining room; bedrooms, tiny pretty village on Lincolnshire's 'ridge' *(Bill and Sheila McLardy)*

WELTON HILL [TF0481]

☆ *Farmers Arms* [A46 Lincoln—Market Rasen]: Well run comfortable no smoking dining pub with hearty helpings of good freshly made food from baguettes to popular Sun lunch, emphasis on top-notch local produce, good house wines (wine-theme décor), Boddingtons, Castle Rock Gold and Theakstons Mild, prompt service from helpful friendly licensees and neat staff, panelling and some stripped brickwork, houseplants and fresh flowers; disabled access, very shallow steps to upper dining room *(Mrs Brenda Calver, P W Baldwin)*

WEST DEEPING [TF1009]

Red Lion [King St]: Long low-beamed bar with plenty of tables, very popular lunchtime for wide choice of generous food from good baguettes and baked potatoes up, friendly service, well kept Everards and other ales such as Hop Back, Dent or John Smiths, good coffee, roaring coal fire, stripped stone, brassware and pictures, fish tank at no smoking end; piped music; disabled access (best by front door), tables in back garden with attractive play area, open all day *(Michael and Jenny Back)*

WHAPLODE ST CATHERINE [TF3419]

Blue Bell [Cranesgate S – 3 miles down a country lane]: Welcoming village pub brewing its own ales such as Old Session and Old Honesty, enjoyable food in bar and well appointing dining room inc locally popular Sun carvery (worth booking ahead), good wine choice, log fire in lounge, pool in side room; cl wkdy lunchtimes *(anon)*

WILLOUGHBY [TF4771]

Willoughby Arms [Church Lane]: Wide choice of enjoyable wholesome generous food, well kept changing ales, welcoming licensees, flagstoned bar with bric-a-brac on beams, pleasant restaurant; tables outside, quiet village, cl Mon lunchtime *(C Bramley)*

WOODHALL SPA [TF1962]

Abbey Lodge [B1192 towards Coningsby]: Family-run roadside inn with bustling discreetly decorated bar, Victorian and older furnishings, World War II RAF pictures, friendly staff, good straightforward reasonably priced bar food from sandwiches up, Marstons Pedigree; children over 10 in restaurant, may be piped Radio 1; cl Sun *(John Branston, LYM, Maurice and Gill McMahon)*

Village Limits [Stixwould Rd]: Good choice of enjoyable food inc good seafood, a well kept real ale and friendly service in smallish bar with plush banquettes and aeroplane prints; nine bedrooms in separate back motel block *(P S Hoyle)*

Norfolk

There is some super freshly made food to be found in Norfolk pubs these days, though often it's far from cheap. And there's no shortage of really friendly places, many of them near lovely walks or beaches. Pubs which stand out for the current warmth of readers' praise for them are the Kings Head at Bawburgh (new to this edition – it was in the *Guide* a few years ago, but now it's been totally reworked, with an excellent new chef who brings it straight in with a Food Award and a Wine Award), the friendly Lord Nelson at Burnham Thorpe (really interesting Nelson memorabilia in this nice pub with good food), the Walpole Arms at Itteringham (good all round, this year adding a Food Award and Wine Award to its Beer Award), the ancient and surprisingly homely Adam & Eve in Norwich (an exemplary town pub, very well run), the Rose & Crown at Snettisham (a favourite these days, good all round, with quite a few good new developments), the Old Ram at Tivetshall St Mary (really well run, keeping plenty of character and personal attention while dealing well with a great many customers), the Three Horseshoes at Warham (very much enjoyed by people who value genuine unspoilt individuality above all), the Fur & Feather at Woodbastwick (a rewarding country pub next to Woodfordes brewery, with all their beers kept well), and the pretty early Tudor Green Dragon in Wymondham (another newcomer to the *Guide*, lively and friendly, with good value food). Several of these are very good for a special meal out, as are the White Horse at Brancaster Staithe, Hoste Arms in Burnham Market, Ratcatchers at Cawston, Saracens Head at Erpingham and Crown at Wells-next-the-Sea. Under its enthusiastic and imaginative chef, it's the Kings Head at Bawburgh which takes the title of Norfolk Dining Pub of the Year. Pubs and inns in the Lucky Dip section at the end of the chapter which are showing particularly well these days are the Chequers at Binham, Buckinghamshire Arms at Blickling, Crown at Colkirk, Feathers near Dersingham, Kings Head at Great Bircham (very smart now), Rose & Crown at Harpley, Victoria at Holkham (another smart place, yet very welcoming to all), Dun Cow at Salthouse, Goat at Skeyton, Chequers at Thompson, Bowling Green in Wells-next-the-Sea and Bell at Wiveton. Drinks prices here average out rather above the national norm. Woodfordes, the most popular local beer, quite often shows as the cheapest beer stocked by a pub (though in fact we found Adnams, from over the Suffolk border, taking the cheapest-beer slot even more commonly in Norfolk pubs). There are quite a few good smaller Norfolk breweries that you might come across, such as Wolf, Reepham and Iceni.

BAWBURGH TG1508 Map 5
Kings Head 🍴 ♀
Pub signposted down Harts Lane off B1108, which leads off A47 just W of Norwich
Norfolk Dining Pub of the Year
A major refurbishment over the last year in this cosy old pub has created a no smoking bar and a smoking bar, a new no smoking restaurant area, a private dining area and conference room. There are wooden floors, leather sofas and seats,

a mix of nice old wooden tables and wooden or leather dining chairs, low beams and some standing timbers, a warming log fire in a large knocked-through canopied fireplace, and a woodburner in the attractive inglenook in the end room. Extremely good modern food might at lunchtime include sandwiches on toasted ciabatta with home-made coleslaw (£4.95), rustic pork, pistachio and apricot terrine with toasts and home-made pickles (£7), ploughman's with home-made pickles and chutney or potted prawns with café de paris butter and toasted soda bread (£7.50), portobello mushrooms on toast with a free-range egg, parmesan and wild mushroom oil (£7.95), smoked eel, scrambled eggs and watercress on rye bread (£8.50), ham and free-range eggs (£9.50), deep-fried cod with hand-cut chips and home-made tartare sauce (£10.50), and Guinness and beef stew with dumplings (£12.50); evening choices such as griddled squid, judia bean, sun-blush tomato salad, mint, rocket and bergamia oil (£7.50), beef carpaccio with spiced aubergine spread, courgettes, rocket, parmesan and mushroom oil (£8), wild mushroom and leek risotto (£10.50), moroccan marinated chicken breast with spicy aubergine ragoût, couscous, yoghurt and preserved lemon or wing of skate, nut butter, brown shrimps, and capers (£13.50), calves liver, fava bean, pancetta, italian sausage, chianti and oregano ragoût, soft sage polenta and braised little gem (£14.50), and grilled entrecote steak with glazed béarnaise and peppercorn butter (£18.50). Super puddings like hot chocolate fondant, sweet mascarpone and griottine cherries or hot plums and frangipane on sweet brioche and home-made vanilla ice-cream (£5.50). Well kept Adnams Bitter, Woodfordes Wherry and a guest such as Courage Directors on handpump and 16 wines by the glass; piped music. There are seats outside in the garden. *(Recommended by Bruce and Penny Wilkie, Tina and David Woods-Taylor, Ken Millar, Gerry and Rosemary Dobson, Peter and Jean Dowson, Chris and Diana Aylott)*

Free house ~ Licensee Anton Wimmer ~ Real ale ~ Bar food (12-2(2.30 Sun), 6.30-9.30; not Sun or Mon evenings) ~ Restaurant ~ (01603) 744977 ~ Children welcome ~ Open 11.30-11; 12-10.30 Sun; closed 25 Dec evening

BLAKENEY TG0243 Map 8

Kings Arms 🍺

West Gate Street

Just a stroll from the harbour, this bustling place has friendly licensees who have been here for over 30 years. The three simply furnished, knocked-through pubby rooms have a good mix of locals and visitors, low ceilings, some interesting photographs of the licensees' theatrical careers, other pictures including work by local artists, and what must be the smallest cartoon gallery in England – in a former telephone kiosk. Look out for the brass plaque on the wall that marks a flood level. Two small rooms are no smoking, as is the airy garden room; darts, fruit machine, shove-ha'penny, table skittles, cribbage and dominoes. Well kept Greene King Old Speckled Hen, Marstons Pedigree, and guests like Adnams Bitter, Websters Yorkshire and Woodfordes Old Wherry on handpump; good efficient service. Reasonably priced, well liked bar food includes sandwiches, soup (£2.95), filled baked potatoes (from £4.75), rough pork and garlic pâté (£5.25), local mussels (winter only £6.50), cream cheese and broccoli bake (£6.75), home-made lasagne or battered haddock (£7.50), ham and egg (£7.95), and steaks (£12.95). Lots of tables and chairs in the large garden; good nearby walks. *(Recommended by Geoff and Pat Bell, Keith and Chris O'Neill, Robert Turnham, Esther and John Sprinkle, MDN, Dr and Mrs R G J Telfer, Sue and Graham Fergy, Moira and John Cole, Keith and Janet Morris)*

Free house ~ Licensees John Howard, Marjorie Davies, and Nick Davies ~ Real ale ~ Bar food (12-9.30(9 Sun) ~ (01263) 740341 ~ Children welcome ~ Dogs welcome ~ Open 11-11; 12-10.30 Sun ~ Bedrooms: /£65S

People named as recommenders after the main entries have told us that the pub should be included. But they have not written the report – we have, after anonymous on-the-spot inspection.

White Horse

Off A149 W of Sheringham; High Street

Many people head for the big back no smoking dining conservatory at the back of this busy little hotel. The long main bar is predominantly green with a venetian red ceiling, and restrained but attractive décor, including watercolours by a local artist. The bar is the only place you can smoke throughout the pub. Well kept Adnams Bitter and Broadside, and Woodfordes Nelsons Revenge and Wherry on handpump, and a dozen wines by the glass. Enjoyable bar food includes lunchtime sandwiches or filled ciabattas (from £3.95), home-made cockle chowder (£4.45), deep-fried soft herring roes on toasted potato bread (£4.95), smoked prawns with chilli dip or fresh local crab with aïoli (£5.95), pasta with griddled vegetables and tomato dressing (£7.95), wild boar sausages with crispy onions and mustard sauce (£8.50), braised ham hock in cream sauce with fettuccine (£8.95), moroccan spiced maize-fed chicken with pickled lemon, black olives and herby couscous (£9.95), specials such as warm salad of pigeon breast with bacon and pine nuts (£5.95), and roasted whole black bream with onion and dill sauce (£13.95), and puddings like rich chocolate mousse or vanilla crème brûlée (£4.95). There are tables in a suntrap courtyard and a pleasant paved garden. *(Recommended by Mike and Heather Watson, Minda and Stanley Alexander, Chris and Louise Taylor, Tracey and Stephen Groves, M A and C R Starling, M Thomas, J F M and M West, Mike and Shelley Woodroffe, Peter and Pat Frogley)*

Free house ~ Licensees Dan Goff and Simon Scillitoe ~ Real ale ~ Bar food ~ Restaurant ~ (01263) 740574 ~ Children in restaurant and family room ~ Open 11-3, 6-11; 12-3, 6-10.30 Sun; closed second and third weeks in Jan ~ Bedrooms: £40B/£60B

BRANCASTER STAITHE TF7743 Map 8

White Horse 🍴 ♟ 🛏

A149 E of Hunstanton

There's quite an emphasis on the successful hotel and restaurant side here, but the bar is a good place for a drink and a chat (and popular with both visitors and locals), and does offer lunchtime food. It's all more or less open-plan. In the front bar there are good local photographs on the left, with bar billiards and maybe piped music, and on the right is a quieter group of cushioned wicker armchairs and sofas by a table with daily papers, and local landscapes for sale. This runs into the no smoking back restaurant with well spaced furnishings in unvarnished country-style wood, and some light-hearted seasidey decorations; through the big glass windows you can look over the sun deck to the wide views of the tidal marshes and Scolt Head Island beyond. Well kept Adnams Bitter, Fullers London Pride, Woodfordes Wherry, and a guest beer on handpump from the handsome counter, 15 malt whiskies and about a dozen wines by the glass from an extensive and thoughtful wine list. The lunch menu can be eaten in the bar, restaurant or outside: sandwiches, soup (£3.95), poached smoked haddock fishcake with spinach and herb cream sauce (£5.25; main course £10.95), caesar salad (£6.50; main course £8.50), dressed cromer crab with lime crème fraîche (£6.95; main course £9.50), spiced griddled chicken with guacamole dressed cos and corn bread (£6.95; main course £9.50), home-made linguini with spinach and wild mushrooms (£9.50), and local pork and leek sausage with onion gravy (£10.50). In the evening, there might be griddled sardines with tomato salsa (£5.25), crispy duck salad with sweet plum dressing (£5.50), tuna niçoise (£5.95), half a dozen local rock oysters grilled with parmesan and cream (£7.95), herb pancake with ratatouille (£9.25), pork fillet with roast garlic, thyme and cocotte potatoes (£11.25), roast fillet of cod with colcannon and red wine jus or poached fillet of lemon sole with hand-dived scallops and sorrel sauce (£12.95), and roast fillet of beef with wild mushroom fricassee (£17). Service can get stretched at peak times. The coast path runs along the bottom of the garden. *(Recommended by John Wooll, M Thomas, Tracey and Stephen Groves, Philip and Susan Philcox, MDN, Steve Nye, Mr and Mrs P L Spencer, D H Burchett, Dr David Cockburn, Simon Rodway, Graham and Julie Newsom, George Atkinson, Giles and Annie Francis, Charles Gysin, DavidField, Dr Ian S Morley,*

Louise English, Simon Jones, J L Nash, Hazel Morgan, Bernard Patrick, Peter and Liz Holmes, Mike and Sue Loseby, Peter Rozée, Adele Summers, Alan Black)

Free house ~ Licensees Cliff Nye and Kevin Nobes ~ Real ale ~ Bar food (lunchtime only) ~ Restaurant ~ (01485) 210262 ~ Children in eating area of bar and restaurant ~ Dogs allowed in bar ~ Open 11-11; 12-10.30 Sun ~ Bedrooms: £75B/£110B

BURNHAM MARKET TF8342 Map 8

Hoste Arms 🕮 ⅄ 🛏
The Green (B1155)

Many people do come to this civilised and smart 17th-c inn for a meal or to stay in the comfortable bedrooms, but the bar still retains the atmosphere of a village pub and there's a nice mix of customers from gentry and shoppers to farmers and fishermen. This panelled bar is on the right and has a series of watercolours showing scenes from local walks, there's a bow-windowed bar on the left, a nice sitting room, a little art gallery in the staircase area, and massive log fires. The lovely walled garden has plenty of seats (you can enjoy full restaurant service here), or you can eat in the airy no smoking conservatory with its comfortable sofas; one restaurant is no smoking, another is partly no smoking, and the lounge has a separate no smoking area. Imaginative food includes lunchtime sandwiches (from £3.75), home-made soup (£4.25), duck rillette, poached egg, caper, gherkin and thyme dressing or sun-dried tomato and salmon fishcake, marinated aubergine and sun-blushed tomato salad (£5.95; main course £10.95), chicken caesar salad (£6.95; main course £10.95), local oysters (from £7.20), seared scallops, apple fritters, sultana and grape seed emulsion (£7.95), burger with crispy bacon, cheddar, tomato and sweetcorn relish with home-cut chips (£9.25), honey glazed ham hock with mango and chilli mash and lime jus (£9.50), leek cannelloni, tomato ragoût and gruyère cheese glaze (£9.95), fried thick cut calves liver with sweet pickled cabbage and shallots, mash and crispy parma ham (£14.50), and fried bass with brown shrimp paella, chilli, garlic and saffron butter (£15.75). From a bin end wine list of 300, they offer 25 by the glass as well as 25 malt whiskies, and 18 cognacs and armagnacs. Well kept Adnams Southwold, Greene King Abbot and Woodfordes Nelsons Revenge and Wherry on handpump. A big awning covers a sizeable eating area in the garden. *(Recommended by Simon Cottrell, MDN, Roy Bromell, Simon Rodway, DF, NF, Mike and Heather Watson, David Cosham, John and Claire Pettifer, George Atkinson, Sally Anne and Peter Goodale, Michael Sargent, Giles and Annie Francis, Chris and Susie Cammack, Eric Robinson, Jacqueline Pratt, Minda and Stanley Alexander, Pete Devonish, Ian McIntyre, Roy and Gay Hoing, Jack Shonfield)*

Free house ~ Licensees Paul Whittome and Emma Tagg ~ Real ale ~ Bar food ~ Restaurant ~ (01328) 738777 ~ Children in restaurant ~ Dogs allowed in bar and bedrooms ~ Open 11-11; 12-10.30 Sun ~ Bedrooms: £82S/£114B

BURNHAM THORPE TF8541 Map 8

Lord Nelson 🍺
Village signposted from B1155 and B1355, near Burnham Market

Dating back to 1637, this warmly friendly pub was frequented by Nelson – who was also born in this sleepy village, so it's no surprise to find lots of pictures and memorabilia of him lining the walls. The little bar has well waxed antique settles on the worn red flooring tiles and smoke ovens in the original fireplace, and an eating room has flagstones, an open fire, and more pictures of Nelson; there are two no smoking rooms. Well kept Greene King IPA and Abbot, Woodfordes Nelsons Revenge, and a summer guest such as Greene King Old Speckled Hen tapped from the cask in a back stillroom, and 13 wines by the glass. They also have secret rum-based recipes called Nelson's Blood and Lady Hamilton's Nip; Nelson's Blood was first concocted in the 18th c and is passed down from landlord to landlord by word of mouth. Enjoyable daily changing bar food at lunchtime includes home-made soup (£4.50), chicken liver parfait with onion marmalade (£5.50), sandwiches (from £5.75; minute steak with roast onions £6.95), local mussels (£5.95), plate of cold meats with roast shallots and roasted artichokes (£6.95), seafood crumble or steak in ale pie (£10.95), calves liver with a whisky and grain mustard sauce (£14.95), grilled rib-eye steak (£16.95), and puddings like sticky toffee pudding with butterscotch sauce (£5.50); two-course evening menu (£17.95) and three courses (£23.95). Sunday roast (£9.95; child £4.95); the eating areas are no smoking. Shove-ha'penny, cribbage and dominoes. There's a good-sized play area in the very big garden, and they are kind to children. *(Recommended by R E Dixon, Roy Bromell, the Didler, Esther and John Sprinkle, O K Smyth, H O Dickinson, D and J Allen, Maggie and Carl Van Baars, David Boult , Eric Robinson, Jacqueline Pratt, Barry Collett, Philip and Susan Philcox, Geoff and Carol Thorp, Anthony Longden)*

Greene King ~ Lease David Thorley ~ Real ale ~ Bar food (not Sun evening or Mon in winter) ~ Restaurant ~ (01328) 738241 ~ Children in eating area of bar and in restaurant but must be over 12 in evening restaurant ~ Dogs allowed in bar ~ Live bands Thurs mid-Sept-June ~ Open 11-3, 6-11; open all day cricket/bank hol days; 12-3, 6.30-10.30 Sun; 12-2.30, 6-11 in winter; closed Mon Oct-June (except school hols and bank hol Mon)

CAWSTON TG1422 Map 8
Ratcatchers 🍴 ♉

Eastgate, S of village – on B1149 from Norwich turn left towards Haveringland at crossroads ½ mile before the B1145 Cawston turn

Run by friendly people, this well run dining pub is particularly popular on Sundays when it is open all day. The L-shaped beamed bar has an open fire, nice old chairs, and a fine mix of walnut, beech, elm and oak tables; there's a quieter and cosier candlelit dining room on the right, and a conservatory (both of these rooms are no smoking). Popular bar food includes lunchtime sandwiches (not Sunday), bacon, mushrooms and cambozola cheese cooked in a pot with a puff pastry lid (£5.20), filled baked potatoes (from £6.25), ploughman's (£7.25), sausage and mash (£8.95), red thai vegetable curry (£9.25), home-made steak and kidney pie (£9.95), garlic chicken (£11.50), steaks (from £13.25), and daily specials such as pigeon breast with caramelised red onion marmalade (£9.45) or chicken and crab with a sweet pepper, leek and cream sauce (£10.95). Well kept Greene King IPA, Hancocks HB and Woodfordes Nelson's Revenge or Wherry on handpump, and 20 malt whiskies; cribbage and piped music. The terrace has heaters for outdoor dining in cooler weather. *(Recommended by David Barnes, John Wooll, Mike and Lynn Robinson, Dr and Mrs R G J Telfer, Ian Phillips, Anthony Barnes, Glenys and John Roberts, Mike and Chris Higgins, Barry Collett, Comus and Sarah Elliott, Philip and Susan Philcox, M and G R, Roy and Gay Hoing)*

Free house ~ Licensees Peter and Denise McCarter ~ Real ale ~ Bar food (12-2, 6-10; all day Sun) ~ Restaurant ~ (01603) 871430 ~ Children welcome ~ Open 12-3, 6-11; 12-11 Sun; closed 26 Dec

ERPINGHAM TG1732 Map 8
Saracens Head 🍴 ♉ 🛏

At Wolterton – not shown on many maps; Erpingham signed off A140 N of Aylsham; keep on through Calthorpe, then where road bends right take the straight-ahead turn-off signposted Wolterton

Mr Dawson-Smith has been at the helm of this gently civilised dining pub for 16 years now. The two-room bar is simple and stylish, with high ceilings, terracotta walls, and red and white striped curtains at its tall windows – all lending a feeling of space, though it's not actually large. There's a mix of seats from built-in leather wall settles to wicker fireside chairs as well as log fires and flowers, and the windows look out on to a charming old-fashioned gravel stableyard with picnic-sets. A pretty little five-table parlour on the right, in cheerful nursery colours, has another big log fire. Well kept Adnams Bitter and Woodfordes Wherry on handpump, an interesting wine list, local apple juice, and decent malt whiskies; the atmosphere is enjoyably relaxed. To be sure of a table, you'd be best to book and from the daily changing menu there might be local mussels with cider and cream, fricassee of wild and common mushrooms, soused bass with balsamic and crème fraîche or red onion and goats cheese tart (from £5.25), main courses like fried scallops with bacon and white wine, medallions of venison with red fruit jus, local pheasant with calvados and cream or baked cromer crab with mushrooms and sherry (from £10.75), and puddings such as brown bread and butter pudding, orange and Cointreau cheesecake or treacle tart (£4.50); there's also a two-course weekday lunch (£7.95). The Shed next door (run by Mr Dawson-Smith's daughter Rachel) is a workshop and showcase for furniture and interior pieces. *(Recommended by John Wooll, David Twitchett, Wombat, Maggie and Carl Van Baars, M and GR, DF, NF, Anthony Barnes, Minda and Stanley Alexander, Philippe and Frances Gayton, Jeff and Wendy Williams, Alan and Jill Bull, Philip and Susan Philcox, Pete Devonish, Ian McIntyre)*

Free house ~ Licensee Robert Dawson-Smith ~ Real ale ~ Bar food ~ Restaurant ~ (01263) 768909 ~ Children in eating area of bar and restaurant ~ Dogs allowed in bedrooms ~ Open 11.30-3.30, 6-11; 12-3.30, 7-10.30 Sun; closed 25 Dec and evening 26 Dec ~ Bedrooms: £45B/£85B

ITTERINGHAM TG1430 Map 8
Walpole Arms 🍴 ♈ 🍺
Village signposted off B1354 NW of Aylsham

This is a popular and friendly dining pub where you must arrive early or pre-book a table. The biggish open-plan bar has exposed beams, stripped brick walls, little windows and a mix of dining tables. Well kept Adnams Bitter and Broadside and a beer named for the pub brewed for them by Wolf; 12 wines by the glass and Aspel cider. There's a snack menu with occasional sandwiches, ham and eggs (£6.75), ploughman's (£6.95), lambs liver, bacon and garlic and rosemary mash (£9), and smoked haddock, leek and potato cake with soft boiled egg and crème fraîche (£9.25), as well as cream of jerusalem artichoke soup with rocket and lemon oil (£5.50), spanish cured meats with pickles, olives and tomato bread (£5.75), cromer crab with pickled ginger, chilli and soy with japanese-style pickled vegetables (£6.25), saffron risotto with piquillo pepper, basil, parmesan and rocket (£9.25), pork and prune sausages with split pea purée and rösti potato (£10.50), fillet of black bream with puy lentil, grapefruit and tomato salad (£13.25), confit of duck leg with baby fig jus (£13.95), braised lamb shank (£14.25), and puddings like gingerbread, caramelised banana with cinnamon ice-cream, cream cheese, chestnut and honey parcels with spiced apple purée or pavlova of pineapple and pomegranate (from £5). The attractive restaurant is no smoking; piped music. Behind the pub is a two-acre landscaped garden and there are seats on the vine-covered terrace. *(Recommended by David Twitchett, Wombat, O K Smyth, John Wooll, Terry and Linda Moseley, Chris and Jan Harper, Anthony Barnes, Helen and Ian Jobson, Dr John Reynolds, Mike and Shelley Woodroffe, Pete Devonish, Ian McIntyre)*

Free house ~ Licensee Richard Bryan ~ Real ale ~ Bar food (not Sun evening, not Mon or Tues evenings for 4 weeks Jan/Feb) ~ Restaurant ~ (01263) 587258 ~ Children welcome ~ Dogs allowed in bar ~ Open 12-3, 6-11; 12-3, 7-10.30 Sun

LARLING TL9889 Map 5
Angel 🍺 🛏
If coming along A11, take B1111 turn-off and follow pub signs

Run by a super chatty landlord and his friendly staff, this neatly kept pub has been in the same family since 1913; they still have the original visitors' books with guests from 1897 to 1909. The comfortable 1930s-style lounge on the right has cushioned wheelback chairs, a nice long cushioned and panelled corner settle, some good solid tables for eating and some lower ones, squared panelling, a collection of whisky-water jugs on the delft shelf over the big brick fireplace which houses a big woodburner, a couple of copper kettles, and some hunting prints. The dining room and breakfast room are no smoking. There's quite a choice of popular food: soup (£3.25), home-made pâté (£4.25), open sandwiches (from £4.25), creamy mushroom pot (£4.95), omelettes (from £4.95), ploughman's (from £6.25), burgers (from £6.25), broccoli and cream cheese bake (£7.25), ham and egg or chicken korma (£7.50), fish crumble (£7.95), lamb chops with mint sauce (£8.95), steaks (from £11.95), specials such as fresh cod in beer batter or sweet and sour pork (£7.95), home-made steak and kidney pie (£8.25), and puddings like sticky apricot and cinnamon pudding or filled crêpes (£3.95). Well kept Adnams Bitter with guests from Iceni, Orkney, RCH, Timothy Taylors, and Wolf on handpump, and around 100 malt whiskies. The quarry-tiled black-beamed public bar has a good local atmosphere, with darts, dominoes, cribbage, juke box and fruit machine, and piped music. A neat grass area behind the car park has picnic-sets around a big fairy-lit apple tree, and a safely fenced play area. Peter Beale's old-fashioned rose nursery is nearby. *(Recommended by Dave Braisted, Ian Phillips, Catherine Pitt, John Saville, Stuart and Alison Ballantyne, Simon Pyle)*

Free house ~ Licensee Andrew Stammers ~ Real ale ~ Bar food (till 10 Fri and Sat) ~ Restaurant ~ (01953) 717963 ~ Children welcome ~ Open 11-11; 12-10.30 Sun ~ Bedrooms: £35B/£60B

NORWICH TG2308 Map 5
Adam & Eve ♀ £
Bishopgate; follow Palace Street from Tombland, N of cathedral

Even though this does get packed, service remains friendly and courteous, and in good weather there are plenty of outside seats amongst the colourful tubs and hanging baskets. It's full of history and is thought to date back to at least 1249 (when it was used by workmen building the cathedral), and even has a Saxon well beneath the lower bar floor, though the striking dutch gables were added in the 14th and 15th c. The little old-fashioned bars have a good mix of customers, and antique high-backed settles (one handsomely carved), cushioned benches built into partly panelled walls, and tiled or parquet floors; the snug is no smoking, and lower bar is no smoking until 7pm. Good value, tasty bar food includes sandwiches or filled baguettes (from £3.15; lunchtime only and not Sunday), soup (£3.45; cheese and ale soup £4.45), spicy spinach and feta goujons with a honey and ginger dip (£5.45), elizabethan pork, home-made chilli or ploughman's (£5.95), ham and egg (£6.25), daily specials like liver and bacon (£6.95) or large yorkshire pudding filled with beef in Guinness (£7.25), and early evening specials such as mushroom stroganoff, haddock fillet with chips, 4oz rump steak or chicken kiev (£4.50 each or £8 for two people; not Saturday). Well kept Adnams Bitter, Greene King IPA, Theakstons Old Peculier and Wells Bombardier on handpump, over 60 malt whiskies, around a dozen decent wines by the glass, and Aspall's cider; piped music. *(Recommended by John Wooll, the Didler, Pat and Clive Sherriff, Fred and Lorraine Gill, Tina and David Woods-Taylor, Meg and Colin Hamilton, Richard Jennings, John Saville, N R White, MJVK)*

Unique (Enterprise) ~ Lease Rita McCluskey ~ Real ale ~ Bar food (12-7; 12-2.30 Sun) ~ (01603) 667423 ~ Children in snug until 7pm ~ Open 11-11; 12-10.30 Sun; closed 25-26 Dec, 1 Jan

Fat Cat ◀
West End Street

A beer drinker's paradise, this classic town pub has around 25 quickly changing real ales. About half of their beers are on handpump, while the rest are tapped from the cask in a stillroom behind the bar – big windows reveal all: Adnams Bitter, Caledonian 80/-, Enville Ginger, Fullers ESB and an organic one, Honeydew, Greene King Abbot, Harviestoun Bitter & Twisted, Hop Back Summer Lightning, Kelham Island Pale Rider, North Yorkshire Flying Herbert, Oakham Bishops Farewell, RCH Old Slug Porter, a beer named for the pub from Reepham, Salopian Lemon Dream, Timothy Taylors Landlord, Tipperary Carlo Red Ale and Dwan Black Pearl Stout, Titanic White Star, and Woodfordes Norfolk Nog. You'll also find six draught belgian beers (two of them fruit), draught lagers from Germany and the Czech Republic, up to 15 bottled belgian beers, 15 country wines, and local farm cider. Open all day, with a good mix of customers, and a lively bustling atmosphere at busy times, with tranquil lulls in the middle of the afternoon. The no-nonsense furnishings include plain scrubbed pine tables and simple solid seats, lots of brewery memorabilia, bric-a-brac and stained-glass. Bar food consists of a dozen or so rolls (60p) and good pies (£1.60) at lunchtime (not Sunday). There are tables outside. More reports please. *(Recommended by Dr David Cockburn, Catherine Pitt, the Didler)*

Free house ~ Licensee Colin Keatley ~ Real ale ~ Bar food (available until sold out; not Sun) ~ No credit cards ~ (01603) 624364 ~ Children allowed in conservatory ~ Dogs allowed in bar ~ Open 12(11 Sat)-11; 12-10.30 Sun; closed evening 25 Dec, 31 Dec

RINGSTEAD TF7040 Map 8

Gin Trap

Village signposted off A149 near Hunstanton; OS Sheet 132 map reference 707403

There's quite an emphasis on dining in this attractive white painted pub and to be sure of a table, it is best to book. The neat bar has beams, a woodburning stove, captain's chairs and cast-iron-framed tables, and well kept Adnams Bitter, Woodfordes Wherry, and perhaps Greene King Old Speckled Hen on handpump, and eight wines by the glass. The small no smoking dining room is candlelit in the evening, and the top bar is also no smoking. Bar food includes sandwiches or granary baps (from £4.50), ploughman's (from £7.50), bangers and mash with red wine sauce (£8.25), burger (£8.50), steak and kidney pie (£8.75), and fresh cod in beer batter (£9.75); more elaborate choices such as local oysters with lemon and shallot vinegar (£1.40 each), soup (£4.25), risotto of aged pecorino with broad beans and garlic crisps (£5.50; main course £7.75), grilled marinated fresh sardines with spicy couscous (£5.75), seared tuna loin with aubergine relish, lemon oil and confit tomatoes (£11.25), calves liver and bacon (£14.50), glazed shank of lamb with port wine sauce (£15.25), and puddings such as orange and Grand Marnier panna cotta with cracked pepper tuiles, sticky toffee pudding or hot chocolate fondant (from £5.25). Outside, a handsome spreading chestnut tree shelters the car park, and the neatly kept back garden has seats on the grass or small paved area, and pretty flowering tubs. There's an art gallery next door, and self-catering accommodation. The Peddar's Way is close by. *(Recommended by Peter F Beever, Mike and Shelley Woodroffe, Tracey and Stephen Groves, David Green, O K Smyth, John Dwane, Keith and Avril Stringer, David Barnes, Ian Arthur, Chris and Susie Cammack, Ben and Helen Ingram, Roy and Gay Hoing, Ian and Nita Cooper)*

Free house ~ Licensee Margaret Greer ~ Real ale ~ Bar food (12-2, 6-9) ~ Restaurant ~ (01485) 525264 ~ Children welcome ~ Dogs allowed in bar ~ Open 11.30-2.30(3 Sat), 6-11; 12-3, 6-10.30 Sun; 11-2.30, 6-11(10.30 Sun) in winter ~ Bedrooms: /£70S(£80B)

SNETTISHAM TF6834 Map 8 🏠

Rose & Crown 🍽 ♀ 🛏

Village signposted from A149 King's Lynn—Hunstanton just N of Sandringham; coming in on the B1440 from the roundabout just N of village, take first left turn into Old Church Road

Never people to rest on their laurels, the hard-working licensees of this pretty white cottage continue to make improvements. The Cellar Bar is to have comfortable upholstered chairs and new tables which would give a rather more sophisticated feel, the Garden Room is to be completely redecorated and refurbished which will provide better seating arrangements for breakfasts and be more intimate for evening diners (while retaining the lovely relaxed feel that appeals to families and larger groups), and – as well as the continuation of the upgrading of the bedrooms – five new bedrooms are to be added, two downstairs for people with mobility problems. The lavatories are now very smart and there is one for disabled customers. This is a place that our readers really love, particularly as they seem to cleverly pull off that rare trick of being both a genuine pub and fine restaurant. There are two bars (the only places you can smoke), each with a separate character: an old-fashioned beamed front bar with black settles on its tiled floor, and a great log fire, and a back bar with another big log fire and the landlord's sporting trophies and old sports equipment. Using local seasonal suppliers and produce, the super menu is the same throughout but changes every lunchtime and evening: home-made soup (£4.50), sweet potato and pecorino ravioli, tomato salsa (£5.50; main course £8.95), asian-style terrine of duck, chilli and peanut dressing (£5.75), fishcake with lemon and tarragon aïoli or confit duck, toasted brioche terrine, rocket and orange salad (£5.95), chargrilled burger with red onion relish and cheese (£8.75), spinach and ricotta cannelloni with roast beetroot and tomato confit (£8.95), tossed king prawn linguini, lime and chilli bisque (£9.75), crispy fried mackerel, goats cheese pasty and basil pesto (£10.95), griddled corn-fed chicken breast with chorizo and pearl barley risotto (£11.50), whole rump of lamb, mint mash and borlotti bean jus (£13.95), and puddings such as white chocolate cheesecake with cranberry salsa, chocolate fudge brownie or vanilla panna cotta with shortbread biscuit and orange salsa (£4.95). Well kept Adnams Bitter and Broadside, Bass, Fullers London Pride and Greene King IPA on handpump, 20 wines by the glass, organic fruit juices, and farm cider. The colourful enclosed garden has smart café-style aluminium and blue chairs with matching blue tables, cream parasols and an outdoor heater; pretty herbaceous borders, flowering shrubs, and two spectacular willow trees, and a wooden fort for children. *(Recommended by John Wooll, Peter Rozée, Terry and Linda Moseley, Esther and John Sprinkle, David Eberlin, Maggie and Carl Van Baars, Pat and Roger Fereday, DF, NF, David Field, Tracey and Stephen Groves, Dr Ian S Morley, J Jennings, Simon Jones, Keith and MargaretKettell, A G Marx, Ryta Lyndley, Hazel Morgan, Bernard Patrick, Barry and Patricia Wooding, Comus and Sarah Elliott)*

Free house ~ Licensee Anthony Goodrich ~ Real ale ~ Bar food (12-2(till 2.30 wknds and summer holidays), 6.30-9(9.30 Fri, Sat)) ~ Restaurant ~ (01485) 541382 ~ Children in family room ~ Dogs welcome ~ Open 11-11; 12-10.30 Sun ~ Bedrooms: £60B/£90B

STANHOE TF8036 Map 8
Crown
B1155 towards Burnham Market

Popular locally, this little open-plan country place is clean and bright inside with aircraft pictures on the white walls that give a clue to the welcoming and attentive landlord's background – he's ex-RAF. There are upholstered wall seats and wheelback chairs around dark tables on the carpet, a central log fire, and beams and joists overhead – one beam densely studded with coins. Gas masks, guns and various military headgear hang behind the bar, which often has a big bunch of flowers and dispenses well kept Elgoods Cambridge and Greyhound on handpump, and decent house wines and coffee; piped music. A sensibly short choice of bar food includes sandwiches (from £3.90), sausages, chips and beans (£6.50), poached salmon, lamb chops or steak and kidney pie (£7.20), and puddings such as treacle sponge (£4). Service is friendly, and the atmosphere is good-hearted and relaxed. There are tables on a side lawn with a couple of apple trees, and a bigger lawn behind with room for caravans; fancy breeds of chicken may be running free. *(Recommended by John Wooll, Tracey and Stephen Groves, John Beeken)*

Elgoods ~ Tenants Page and Sarah Clowser ~ Bar food (not Sun evening) ~ Restaurant ~ No credit cards ~ (01485) 518330 ~ Well behaved children welcome ~ Dogs allowed in bar ~ Open 12-3.30, 6-11; 12-3.30, 7-10.30 Sun

STIFFKEY TF9743 Map 8
Red Lion
A149 Wells—Blakeney

The oldest parts of the simple bars here have a few beams, aged flooring tiles or bare floorboards, and big open fires; there's also a mix of pews, small settles and a couple of stripped high-backed settles, a nice old long deal table among quite a few others, and oil-type or lantern wall lamps. Well kept Woodfordes Nelsons Revenge and Wherry and a couple of guests on handpump, ten wines by the glass, and 30

malt whiskies; dominoes and cribbage. Bar food includes sandwiches, crab soup
(£4.50), herring roes on toast (£4.95), crab fishcakes with sweet and sour relish
(£7.95), and sausages and mash (£8.50). A back gravel terrace has proper tables
and seats, with more on grass further up beyond; there are some pleasant walks
nearby. More reports please. *(Recommended by John Wooll, P Price, M Thomas,
David Cosham, Ken Arthur, the Didler, Mr and Mrs I and E Bell, Pat and Clive Sherriff,
Dr B and Mrs P B Baker, Michael and Marilyn Switzer, R C Vincent, Dr John Reynolds,
A G Marx, Dave Aldridge, Charles Gysin)*

Free house ~ Licensee Andrew Waddison ~ Real ale ~ Bar food ~ Restaurant ~
(01328) 830552 ~ Children welcome ~ Dogs welcome ~ Open 11-11; 12-10.30 Sun

STOW BARDOLPH TF6205 Map 5
Hare Arms ♀
Just off A10 N of Downham Market

There's a proper traditional village pub atmosphere in this neatly kept creeper-
covered pub, and the friendly licensees have now been here for 29 years. The
bustling bar has bric-a-brac, old advertising signs, fresh flowers, plenty of tables
around its central servery, and a good log fire. This bar opens into a spacious
heated and well planted no smoking conservatory; the restaurant is also no
smoking. Tasty bar food includes lunchtime sandwiches (from £3; crayfish tails
with lemon crème fraîche £5.50), filled baked potatoes (from £4.75), and
ploughman's (from £7.25), as well as home-made curry (£8), home-made lasagne
(£8.75), large salads (from £8.75), and daily specials such as sausages with red
onion and cider gravy on apple mash (£7.50), asparagus, pea and rocket risotto
with tomato and basil dressing or chicken breast wrapped in oak-smoked bacon
with a dijon mustard and honey sauce (£8.75), queen scallops with garlic butter or
cajun spiced salmon fillet with red onion and mint yoghurt dip (£9.50), and slow-
cooked lamb shank (£9.75). From the more elaborate restaurant menu they offer a
four-course set menu (£22.50). Well kept Greene King IPA, Abbot and Old
Speckled Hen, and a guest such as Batemans XXXB or Marstons Pedigree on
handpump, a decent range of wines and quite a few malt whiskies; fruit machine.
There are plenty of seats in the large garden behind, and in the pretty front garden
too, and chickens and peacocks roam freely. The local church contains an effigy of
Lady Sarah Hare, who is reputed to have died as a consequence of sewing on a
Sunday and pricking her finger. *(Recommended by John Wooll, Stephen and Jean Curtis,
Tracey and Stephen Groves, Eric Robinson, Jacqueline Pratt)*

Greene King ~ Tenants David and Trish McManus ~ Real ale ~ Bar food (12-2, 7-10) ~
Restaurant ~ (01366) 382229 ~ Children in family room and conservatory ~ Open
10.30-2.30, 6-11; 12-2.30, 7-10.30 Sun; closed 25-26 Dec

SWANTON MORLEY TG0117 Map 8
Darbys ♣
B1147 NE of Dereham

There's always a good mix of both regulars and visitors in this creeper-covered
local, which isn't surprising given that they have eight real ales on handpump:
Adnams Best and Broadside, Badger Tanglefoot, Ringwood Old Thumper,
Theakstons Mild and Old Peculier, Thwaites Thoroughbred and Woodfordes
Wherry. The long bare-boarded country-style bar has a comfortable lived-in feel,
with lots of gin traps and farming memorabilia, a good log fire (with the original
bread oven alongside), tractor seats with folded sacks lining the long, attractive
serving counter, and maybe fresh flowers on the big stripped pine tables. A step up
through a little doorway by the fireplace takes you through to the no smoking
dining room. The children's room (also no smoking) has a toy box and a glassed-
over well, floodlit from inside; piped music. They tell us the enjoyable bar food
(and prices) have not changed: filled baguettes and baked potatoes (from £4), thai
fishcakes with chilli dipping sauce (£5.50), shrimp and salmon salad (£5.95),
ploughman's (£6.50), beer battered haddock (£7.50), curries (from £7.50),

mushroom and vegetable pesto bake (£8.95), pork steak stacked with bacon, pineapple and melted mozzarella (£9.25), steak and mushroom pudding (£10.85), baked whole bass with lemon grass and ginger (£10.95), and steaks (from £11.65). The garden has a really good play area; the two dogs are called Boots and Dylan. B&B is available in carefully converted farm buildings a few minutes away, and there's plenty to do if you're staying, as the family also own the adjoining 720-acre estate, and can arrange clay pigeon shooting, golf, fishing, nature trails and craft instruction. *(Recommended by Ian Phillips, Dr and Mrs R G J Telfer, Michael and Jenny Back, Pat and Tony Martin, MDN, Philippe and Frances Gayton, J G and P D Holdsworth, Stuart and Alison Ballantyne, Comus and Sarah Elliott)*

Free house ~ Licensees John Carrick and Louise Battle ~ Real ale ~ Bar food (12-2.15, 6.30-9.45) ~ Restaurant ~ (01362) 637647 ~ Children welcome ~ Dogs allowed in bar ~ Open 11.30-3, 6-11; 11.30-11 Sat; 12-10.30 Sun

TERRINGTON ST JOHN TF5314 Map 8
Woolpack
Village signposted off A47 W of King's Lynn

'Bustling and boisterous' is how several readers describe this cheerfully run and airy roadside pub. The rooms are decorated with the landlady's bright modern ceramics and cheerful contemporary prints, and the bar has red plush banquettes and matching or wheelback chairs around its dark pub tables, a patterned red carpet, and terracotta pink walls; the large back no smoking dining room (which looks out on to the garden) has comfortable green seating, and an art deco décor punctuated by Mondrian prints. The reliably good value food, with friendly efficient waitresses, also underpins the pub's popularity. As well as hot and cold filled baps, ciabattas, and sandwiches, there might be home-made soup (£2.95), chicken liver pâté (£3.95), vegetarian lasagne (£6.95), honey and mustard home-cooked ham with eggs or steak and kidney suet pudding (£6.95), seafood medley (£7.95), salmon in lemon butter sauce (£8.50), lambs liver and smoked bacon or chicken and bacon tower with creamy peppercorn sauce (£8.95), steaks (from £11.95), and the famous pudding trolley with all manner of home-made cheesecake, crumbles, gateaux and tarts (£3.95). Well kept Greene King IPA, Shepherd Neame Spitfire and Wells Eagle on handpump; fruit machine and piped music; good disabled access. There are picnic-sets on neat grass by a herb garden and the car park (which has recycling bins including Planet Aid clothes and shoes). *(Recommended by John Wooll, Michael and Jenny Back, Sally Anne and Peter Goodale, Chris and Susie Cammack, Richard and Margaret McPhee, Dr John Reynolds)*

Free house ~ Licensees Lucille and Barry Carter ~ Bar food ~ Restaurant ~ (01945) 881097 ~ Children in eating area of bar and restaurant ~ Open 11.30-2.30, 6.30-11; 12-7 Sun; closed evenings 25 and 26 Dec

THORNHAM TF7343 Map 8
Lifeboat 🛏
Turn off A149 by Kings Head, then take first left turn

A new licensee has taken over this bustling old white-painted stone pub, but as we went to press, there were few changes. The main Smugglers bar is lit with antique paraffin lamps suspended among an array of traps and yokes on its great oak-beamed ceiling. It's cosily furnished with low settles, window seats, pews, carved oak tables and rugs on the tiled floor, and there are also masses of guns, swords, black metal mattocks, reed-slashers and other antique farm tools. A couple of little rooms lead off here, and in all in all there are five open fires. No games machines or piped music, though they still play the ancient game of 'pennies' which was outlawed in the late 1700s, and dominoes. Up some steps from the no smoking conservatory is a sunny terrace with picnic-sets, and further back is a children's playground with fort and slide. Bar food now includes home-made soup (£3.95), mushrooms in a stilton and garlic cream sauce (£5.15), chicken liver pâté (£5.25), mediterranean salad (£5.25; main course £9.25), filled baguettes (from £5.40), ploughman's (£6.50), chargrilled burger with bacon and cheese, spinach and mozzarella lasagne or cromer crab salad (£8.95), beer-battered fish with home-made tartare sauce or liver and bacon (£9.50), hickory pork ribs (£9.95), steaks (from £13.95), and daily specials such as grilled sardines on tomato and red onion salad (£5.25), home-made beef pie (£9.25), and duck breast with apricot and walnut stuffing with bilberry gravy (£13.75). The restaurant is no smoking. Well kept Adnams, Greene King IPA and Abbot, and Woodfordes Wherry on handpump, and several wines by the glass. The inn faces half a mile of coastal sea flats, and there are lots of lovely surrounding walks. Most of the bedrooms have sea views. More reports on the new regime please. *(Recommended by Mark, Amanda, Luke and Jake Sheard, Mike Ridgway, Sarah Miles, A J Murray, David Eberlin, DF, NF, O K Smyth, Ian Arthur, John Wooll, Giles and Annie Francis, Pam and David Bailey, John and Marion Tyrie, Terry and Linda Moseley, David Cosham, the Didler, Esther and John Sprinkle, Gordon Neighbour, Stephen and Jean Curtis, David Field, Louise English, J Jennings, Eric Robinson, Jacqueline Pratt, Simon Jones, Keith and Margaret Kettell, Keith and Janet Morris, W K Wood, Hazel Morgan, Bernard Patrick, Alk, Alison and Pete, Chris Mawson, Mike and Sue Loseby)*

Free house ~ Licensee Tracey Racey ~ Real ale ~ Bar food (12-2.30, 6(6.30 in winter)-9.30) ~ Restaurant ~ (01485) 512236 ~ Children welcome ~ Dogs allowed in bar and bedrooms ~ Open 11-11; 12-10.30 Sun ~ Bedrooms: £66B/£92B

TIVETSHALL ST MARY TM1686 Map 5

Old Ram ♀ ⇌

A140 15 miles S of Norwich, outside village

As well as serving food all day from 7.30am, this well run and warmly friendly pub is a very nice place to stay, too. The spacious country-style main room has lots of stripped beams and standing timbers, antique craftsmen's tools on the ceiling, a huge log fire in the brick hearth, a turkey rug on rosy brick floors, and a longcase clock. It's ringed by smaller side areas, and one dining room has striking navy walls and ceiling, swagged curtains and an open woodburning stove; this leads to a second comfortable dining room and gallery. Good, enjoyable bar food from a wide menu might include soup (£3.95), sandwiches (from £4.95; soup and a sandwich £6.50; until 6pm), goats cheese and vine tomato tartlet (£4.95), roast baby back pork ribs in barbecue sauce or niçoise salad (£5.50), filled baked potatoes (£5.95), chargrilled burger (from £7.50), sausages and mash with onion gravy (£8.95), chicken curry (£9.50), goats cheese, aubergine and vegetable stack (£9.95), grilled skate with black butter (£11.95), well hung aberdeen angus steaks (from £15.50), daily specials such as prosciutto with fresh brazilian figs (£4.95), fresh crab and crayfish tails with sweet chilli and cucumber sauce (£5.95), saddle of venison with cumberland sauce (£14.95), and wild halibut with chilli, ginger, coriander and lime yoghurt dressing (£15.95), and home-made puddings like bread and butter pudding with crème anglaise, crème brûlée or cheesecake (£4.25). OAP two-course lunch (£7.95). All dining rooms are no smoking; courteous and attentive service. Unobtrusive fruit machine, TV, cribbage, dominoes and piped music. Well kept Adnams, Woodfordes Wherry and a couple of guests like Bass or Timothy Taylors Landlord on handpump, 28 wines by the glass, fresh orange, apple, pineapple and carrot juice, milkshakes, and 20 malt whiskies. The sheltered flower-filled terrace of this much extended pub is very civilised, with outdoor heaters and big green parasols. *(Recommended by Martin and Pauline Jennings, Ken Millar, Bill and Marian de Bass, Michael Sargent, Alan and Jill Bull)*

Free house ~ Licensee John Trafford ~ Real ale ~ Bar food (all day) ~ Restaurant ~ (01379) 676794 ~ Children in eating area of bar and in restaurant but under-7s must leave by 8pm ~ Dogs welcome ~ Open 11-11; 12-10.30 Sun; closed 25-26 Dec ~ Bedrooms: £60.50B/£83B

Post Office address codings confusingly give the impression that some pubs are in Norfolk when they're really in Suffolk (which is where we list them).

UPPER SHERINGHAM TG1441 Map 8

Red Lion

B1157; village signposted off A148 Cromer—Holt, and the A149 just W of Sheringham

This traditional-looking flint cottage has a bustling, chatty atmosphere, and the two modest but charming little bars have stripped high-backed settles and country-kitchen chairs on the red tiles or bare boards, terracotta painted walls, a big woodburning stove, and newspapers to read; the red-walled snug is no smoking. It's best to book to be sure of a table if you are hoping to eat: home-made soup (£3.50), sandwiches (from £4.50), home-made pâté or stilton-stuffed mushrooms (£4.75), lambs liver in port and orange gravy (£7.95), vegetarian lasagne (£8.50), lots of fresh fish dishes (from £8.50), steak in ale pie (£8.75), chicken fillet in stilton and asparagus sauce (£9.25), and puddings (from £4.50); the dining area gets very busy at weekends during the holiday season. Well kept Greene King IPA and Woodfordes Wherry on handpump, with around 12 malt whiskies and decent wines; dominoes and card games. As we went to press, there were planning problems over proposed extensions, alternatively a move to a nearby site; we hope for a speedy resolution. *(Recommended by John Wooll, Geoff and Pat Bell, Dr David Cockburn, George Atkinson, David and Julie Glover, Dr and Mrs R G J Telfer, Bruce and Penny Wilkie, Philip and Susan Philcox, W K Wood)*

Free house ~ Licensee Sue Prew ~ Real ale ~ Bar food (12-2, 6.30-9) ~ No credit cards ~ (01263) 825408 ~ Children in family room ~ Dogs welcome ~ Open 11.30-11; 12-10 Sun; more restricted in winter, best to phone winter; closed winter Sun evenings

WARHAM TF9441 Map 8

Three Horseshoes ★ 🍽 🛏

Warham All Saints; village signposted from A149 Wells-next-the-Sea—Blakeney, and from B1105 S of Wells

One of our long-standing readers feels that no visit to north Norfolk is complete without a visit here – and indeed, this year we have given it a star for its character and genuine individuality that is so refreshingly different in an age of so much calculated uniformity. It's genuinely unspoilt and old-fashioned, and the simple interior with its gas lighting looks little changed since the 1920s; parts of the building date back to the 1720s. There are stripped deal or mahogany tables (one marked for shove-ha'penny) on a stone floor, red leatherette settles built around the partly panelled walls of the public bar, royalist photographs, and open fires in Victorian fireplaces. An antique American Mills one-arm bandit is still in working order (it takes 5p pieces), there's a big longcase clock with a clear piping strike, and a twister on the ceiling to point out who gets the next round; darts, cribbage, shove-ha'penny and dominoes. Most people choose from the specials board: samphire and crab soup (£3.50), rabbit liver and pork pâté (£4.80), neck of lamb hotpot, grilled local herrings or savoury mince pie (£7.50), mushroom, nut and wine pie or cider pork (£8.20), and syrup and coconut tart or apple and blackberry pie (£3.25), and the menu also offers lunchtime sandwiches (not at weekends), filled baked potatoes (from £4.20), ploughman's (£6.80), cheese and vegetable pie (£7.50), and steak and kidney pudding (£8.50). They don't take bookings, so it's a good idea to arrive early at busy times; the eating area of the bar is no smoking. Greene King IPA, Woodfordes Wherry and a weekly guest well kept on handpump or tapped from the cask, country wines, local summer cider, and home-made lemonade. One of the outbuildings houses a wind-up gramophone museum – opened on request. There's a courtyard garden with flower tubs and a well, and a garden. *(Recommended by the Didler, Giles and Annie Francis, Anthony Longden, John Beeken, P Price, Pam and David Bailey, Barry Collett, Philip and Susan Philcox)*

Free house ~ Licensee Iain Salmon ~ Real ale ~ Bar food (12-1.45, 6-8.30) ~ No credit cards ~ (01328) 710547 ~ Children in eating area of bar; no children in bedrooms ~ Dogs welcome ~ Open 11.30-2.30, 6-11; 12-2.30, 6-10.30 Sun ~ Bedrooms: £26/£56(£60S)

WELLS-NEXT-THE-SEA TF9143 Map 8 🏠

Crown 🍴 🍷 🛏️

The Buttlands

This is a smart 16th-c coaching inn with quite an emphasis on the imaginative food
and comfortable bedrooms, but the beamed bar is a friendly place with an informal
mix of furnishings on the stripped wooden floor, local photographs on the red
walls, a good selection of newspapers to read in front of the open fire, and well
kept Adnams Bitter, Woodfordes Wherry and a guest on handpump; 15 wines by
the glass. The sunny no smoking conservatory with wicker chairs on the tiled floor,
beams, and modern art is where families with well behaved children can sit, and
there's a pretty no smoking restaurant; piped music. Good modern dishes in the bar
might include soup (£3.95), chicken liver parfait with onion marmalade and melba
toast (£5.10), spiced pear and stilton bruschetta (£5.25; main course £8.95), grilled
squid with crisp pancetta and guacamole (£5.50), filled bloomers with home-made
crisps (from £5.80), minted lamb burger with cucumber yoghurt (£8.75), aubergine
and courgette stack stuffed with goats cheese and walnut (£8.95), haddock goujons
in beer batter with hand-cut sweet potato chips and tartare sauce (£9.95), rare tuna
with caramelised onion mash and red pepper pesto (£10.20), roast chicken breast
with coconut braised rice (£10.45), thai watermelon and fish curry with coriander
yoghurt (£10.75), and puddings such as honey and thyme crème brûlée with
gingerbread biscuit, chocolate brownie and pistachio meringue with passion fruit
cream (from £4.50). You can sit outside on the sheltered sun deck. *(Recommended by
R E Dixon, MDN, Terry and Linda Moseley, Fred and Lorraine Gill, A D Cross, Alan and
Sue Folwell, Mike and Heather Watson, Louise English, Keith and Chris O'Neill, Eric Robinson,
Jacqueline Pratt)*

Free house ~ Licensees Chris and Jo Coubrough ~ Real ale ~ Bar food (12-2.30, 6.30-9.30)
~ Restaurant ~ (01328) 710209 ~ Children in eating area of bar and restaurant ~ Dogs
allowed in bar ~ Live music every other Sun afternoon ~ Open 11-11; 12-10.30 Sun ~
Bedrooms: £100B/£120B

WEST BECKHAM TG1339 Map 8

Wheatsheaf 🍺

Off A148 Holt—Cromer; Church Road

Pleasantly traditional, even homely, this flint-walled village pub is a friendly place.
There are beams and cottagey doors, a roaring log fire in one part with a smaller
coal one in another, comfortable chairs and banquettes, and perhaps, the enormous
black cat. A fine range of up to seven real ales is well kept on handpump or tapped
from the cask: Greene King IPA, Woodfordes Wherry, Nelsons Revenge, Norfolk
Nog and Headcracker, and guests like Archers Spirit of St George and Wadworths
IPA. Wine is served by the glass or carafe. At lunchtime, the well liked food might
include sandwiches or filled baguettes (from £3.50), filled baked potatoes (from
£4.25), ciabattas (£5.95), ploughman's (from £5.75), ham and egg (£6.95),
mediterranean pasta bake (£7.50), liver and bacon with rosemary gravy or cod in
home-made beer batter (£7.95), and steak and kidney pudding (£8.95), with evening
choices like home-made chicken liver pâté with red onion marmalade (£4.50), local
mussels in white wine and cream (£4.75), salmon fishcakes with a sour cream dip
(£5.10), mixed fish lasagne (£7.95), venison and cranberry casserole topped with
home-made scones (£8.95), and sirloin steak (£11.95); weekly changing specials such
as crab, cream cheese and spring onion tart (£4.25), thai-style prawns in filo pastry
with chilli dip (£5.95), chicken breast layered with sweetcorn fritters with a
mushroom and tarragon cream sauce (£9.50), chargrilled lamb steak with garlic
roasted new potatoes and redcurrant gravy (£10.95) and puddings like chocolate
crème brûlée or poached pears in cider and cinnamon (£3.75). The two dining
rooms are no smoking. Darts, pool, cribbage, dominoes, fruit machine, juke box, TV
and piped music. There are tables out in the partly terraced front garden, and an
area for children with swings, some elusive rabbits, and chickens. *(Recommended by
Derek Field, Tracey and Stephen Groves, O K Smyth, R E Perry)*

Free house ~ Licensees Clare and Daniel Mercer ~ Real ale ~ Bar food (not Sun evening)
~ Restaurant ~ (01263) 822110 ~ Children in eating area of bar and restaurant ~ Dogs
allowed in bar ~ Open 11.30-3, 6.30-11; 12-3, 7-10.30 Sun; 12-2.30, 6.30-11 in winter

WINTERTON-ON-SEA TG4919 Map 8
Fishermans Return 🍺 🛏
From B1159 turn into village at church on bend, then turn right into The Lane

Not far from a sandy beach and much older than most of the expanded holiday
village, this is a friendly and attractive little pub. It is spotlessly kept, and the cosily
white-painted no smoking lounge bar has a roaring log fire, neat brass-studded red
leatherette seats, and vases of fresh flowers. The panelled public bar has low
ceilings and a glossily varnished nautical air (good fire in here too), and the family
room, dining room and small bar are no smoking. It's been well run by the same
hospitable licensees for over 30 years, and the staff are friendly and courteous. The
short choice of tasty bar food includes toasties (from £2.50), filled baked potatoes
(from £3.75), ploughman's (£5.50), fish pie (£5.75), chilli con carne or vegetarian
omelette (£7.50), and sirloin steak (£11.75), and there are regularly changing
specials such as local griddled smoked salmon (£6.25), chicken and broccoli lasagne
or stuffed red and green peppers (£8.25), and beef in ale pie or loin of pork stuffed
with apricots and pine nuts (£8.75). Well kept Adnams Bitter and Broadside and
Woodfordes Wherry and Norfolk Nog with guests like Greene King IPA and
Woodfordes Great Eastern, Mardlers, and Nelsons Revenge on handpump, 12
wines by the glass, several malt whiskies and farm cider; darts, piped music,
dominoes, cribbage, pool, fruit machine, juke box and piped music. In fine weather
you can sit on the attractive wrought-iron and wooden benches on a pretty front
terrace with lovely views, or in the sheltered garden. *(Recommended by Anthony Barnes,
Comus and Sarah Elliott, Peter Meister, Quentin and Carol Williamson, Maggie and
Carl Van Baars, K Christensen, Nick Lawless)*

Free house ~ Licensees John and Kate Findlay ~ Real ale ~ Bar food ~ (01493) 393305 ~
Children in family room ~ Dogs welcome ~ Open 11-2.30, 6-11; 11-11 Sat; 12.10.30 Sun
~ Bedrooms: £50B/£70B

WOODBASTWICK TG3315 Map 8
Fur & Feather 🍺
Off B1140 E of Norwich

With the Woodfordes brewery next door, it's not surprising that this friendly and
carefully converted thatched cottage is so popular. They keep all eight of their beers
on handpump or tapped from the cask – Woodfordes Admiral's Reserve, Great
Eastern, Mardlers, Nelsons Revenge, Norfolk Nog, Headcracker, Wherry, and a
beer named for the pub. You can also visit the brewery shop. The style and
atmosphere are not what you'd expect of a brewery tap as it's set out more like a
dining pub and the décor is modern. Bar food includes home-made soup (£3.50),
sandwiches or filled baguettes (from £3.75), filled baked potatoes (£5.50), meaty or
vegetarian burgers (from £7.50), home-baked ham and eggs (£7.75), mussels and
chips (£8.50), pie of the day or home-made steak and kidney pudding (£9), duck
stir fry (£9.75), and puddings such as home-made bread and butter pudding (£4);
nine wines by the glass. You can smoke only in one small area of the bar; piped
music. The pub forms part of a very attractive estate village and has tables out in a
very pleasant garden. *(Recommended by Adele Summers, Alan Black, Esther and
John Sprinkle, Dave Braisted, Neil and Angela Huxter, Keith and Chris O'Neill, Chris Pelley,
Philip and Susan Philcox, the Didler, Stephen and Jean Curtis, Gerry and Rosemary Dobson,
B N F and M Parkin, N R White, Pete Devonish, Ian McIntyre)*

Woodfordes ~ Tenants Tim and Penny Ridley ~ Real ale ~ Bar food (12-2, 6-9) ~
Restaurant ~ (01603) 720003 ~ Children in eating area of bar and restaurant ~
Open 11.30-11; 12-10.30 Sun; 11.30-3, 6-11 winter

WYMONDHAM TG1101 Map 5

Green Dragon
Church Street

Very picturesque, the heavily timbered black and white façade of this 14th-c inn is jettied out above the pavement. If you look closely, you can see some scorching from a fire which swept through the town in 1615, destroying most of the other buildings. Inside, the cosy beamed and timbered back bar has old tools and horse tack above the big log fire in a rather fine Tudor fireplace, traditional settles among more up-to-date seats around the cast-iron-framed tables on its uneven floor, and some interesting pictures. There's a story that the latticed windows were originally recycled from a sailing ship, and one could imagine the same of the low doorways. The atmosphere is thriving and buoyant, they have well kept Adnams Bitter and Broadside and a guest such as Greene King Old Speckled Hen on handpump, and service is friendly and relaxed; there may be piped music. The good-sized carpeted front dining area, with very heavy black beams and more timbering, is no smoking, as is the breakfast room. Bar food includes light lunches such as home-made soup (£3.25, well liked seafood chowder £4.95), filled baps or sandwiches (from £3.25), aberdeen angus burger with home-made chips or mixed cheese ploughman's (£4.95), and ham and free-range eggs (£5.95), as well as chicken liver pâté (£3.95), mushrooms topped with port and stilton sauce (£4.25), lasagne or mushroom stroganoff (£7.95), duck, orange and apricot or steak and kidney in ale pies (£8.95), chicken in bacon, cognac and cream (£9.50), slow-cooked lamb in rosemary and garlic (£9.95), steaks (from £10.95), and puddings (£3.50); they do a bargain two-course weekday lunch (£5.95). The huge nearby abbey church, its nave a scaled-down version of Norwich cathedral and its roof filled with carved angels, is well worth a look, with really helpful and informative volunteer guides. *(Recommended by Geoff and Pat Bell, Anthony Rogers, Michael B Griffith, Gerry and Rosemary Dobson, the Didler)*

Punch ~ Tenants Jimmy and Elaine Lowe ~ Bar food ~ Restaurant ~ (01953) 607907 ~ Children in restaurant ~ Dogs allowed in bedrooms ~ Landlord plays the accordion occasionally ~ Open 11-11; 12-10.30 Sun; 11-2.30, 6.30-11 weekdays in winter ~ Bedrooms: £35(£39B)/£55(£59B)

LUCKY DIP

Besides the fully inspected pubs, you might like to try these Lucky Dips recommended to us and described by readers (if you do, please send us reports: www.goodguides.co.uk).

AYLMERTON [TG1840]
Roman Camp [Holt Rd (A148)]: Comfortable panelled bar with cosy armchair sitting room off and neat and stylish dining room, well kept Adnams, Timothy Taylors Landlord and Charles Wells Bombardier, good food, helpful staff; picnic-sets in attractive sheltered garden behind, well equipped bedrooms with own bathrooms *(Mike and Shelley Woodroffe)*
BARFORD [TG1107]
Cock [B1108 7 miles W of Norwich]: Attractive and relaxed, brewing its own good Blue Moon ales, a couple of well kept local guest beers too, good interesting food (freshly made, so may take a time) from large lunchtime sandwiches to plenty of fish, friendly helpful service, shove-ha'penny, newly extended no smoking restaurant; occasional jazz *(Chris Pelley, Rachel Abbott, Gerry and Rosemary Dobson)*
BEACHAMWELL [TF7505]
☆ *Great Danes Head* [off A1122 Swaffham—

Downham Mkt]: Cosy and friendly open-plan dark-beamed pub facing green of small village, good plentiful food using local produce, helpful licensees, Woodfordes Wherry and Norfolk Nog, good house wine, big log fire, freshly refitted bar, recently extended no smoking restaurant with pre-meal sofas; children and dogs welcome *(BB, Paul and Penny Rampton)*
BINHAM [TF9839]
☆ *Chequers* [B1388 SW of Blakeney]: 17th-c, with prompt cheerful service, four frequently changing interesting and well kept real ales, unusual bottled beers, decent house wines, reasonably priced food using local produce, long low-beamed bar, inglenook, sturdy plush seats, splendid coal fires each end, some nice old local prints, small no smoking dining area; picnic-sets out in front and on grass behind, interesting village with huge priory church, two bedrooms, open all day *(John Knighton, BB, John Dwane, George Atkinson, Tracey and*

Stephen Groves, Steve Nye, Richard Lewis)

BLICKLING [TG1728]

☆ *Buckinghamshire Arms* [B1354 NW of Aylsham]: Handsome Jacobean inn by gates to Blickling Hall (NT), neat pews around stripped pine tables in lounge, banquettes in small front snug, enjoyable food from baguettes and baked potatoes up, friendly efficient service, well kept Adnams Best and Broadside and Woodfordes Wherry, local cider, good range of wines; well behaved children in restaurant, lots of tables out on big lawn with summer food servery, bedrooms with own bathrooms, may open all day in summer *(John Wooll, LYM, Mike and Shelley Woodroffe, Dr and Mrs R G J Telfer)*

BRANCASTER STAITHE [TF7944]

☆ *Jolly Sailors* [Main Road (A149)]: Three appealingly old-fashioned simply furnished beamed rooms, log fire, well kept Woodfordes Wherry and good Brancaster beers brewed at the pub, decent wines and help-yourself coffee, popular food (all day in summer) from baguettes up, no smoking restaurant; piped music, fruit machine, TV; children in eating areas, sheltered tables in nice garden with terrace and smallish play area (best for younger children), open all day *(Esther and John Sprinkle, Neil and Angela Huxter, Mr and Mrs P L Spencer, George Atkinson, LYM, Tracey and Stephen Groves, Philip and Susan Philcox)*

BRISLEY [TF9521]

Bell [B1145; The Green]: 16th-c pub in good spot on edge of sheep-grazed common (England's biggest), olde-worlde long beamed bar with massive log fireplace and some stripped brick, charming staff, well kept Fullers London Pride, Tetleys and a beer brewed locally for them, wide choice of home-made food inc local fresh fish, separate restaurant; tables out on green; children and dogs welcome; bedrooms *(Ian Phillips)*

BURNHAM MARKET [TF8342]

Lord Nelson [Creake Rd]: Newish licensees doing wide range of generous traditional bar food from good baguettes up, some Nelson memorabilia, well kept ales inc Greene King IPA, good choice of wines, games in public bar, small unpretentious no smoking restaurant; four attractive bedrooms, two in former outbuilding *(John Wooll, LYM, A D Cross, Michael and Marilyn Switzer)*

BURSTON [TM1383]

Crown [Mill Rd]: Friendly two-bar country local with good relaxed atmosphere, lots of old woodwork, simple fresh home cooking, well kept ales, small restaurant *(Sue Austin)*

BUXTON [TG2322]

Old Crown [Crown Rd]: Doing well under hard-working new management, enjoyable reasonably priced food, well kept ales such as Adnams and Woodfordes Wherry *(Jill and Roger Hambling)*

CASTLE ACRE [TF8115]

☆ *Ostrich* [Stocks Green]: Unpretentious relaxed pub prettily placed overlooking the tree-lined green, very long-serving landlord and barmaid, individual mix of utilitarian furnishings and

fittings with some ancient beams, masonry and huge inglenook fireplace, well kept Greene King ales, cheap food with vegetarian emphasis, dominoes, cribbage; piped music, fruit machine; jazz 2nd and 3rd Weds of month, folk last Weds; children welcome, picnic-sets in sheltered informal garden with doves and aviary, cheap plain bedrooms sharing shower (good breakfast), attractive village with castle and monastery remains, may be open all day at least summer Sats *(John Wooll, Charles Gysin, LYM)*

CLEY NEXT THE SEA [TG0443]

☆ *Three Swallows* [off A149; Newgate Green]: Cheery take-us-as-you-find-us local on quiet lane facing green, emphasis on the straightforward bar food (all day wknds) from sandwiches up, banquettes around long high leathered tables, log fire, steps up to another small family eating area, second log fire in no smoking stripped pine dining room on left, well kept Adnams and Greene King IPA and Abbot from unusual richly carved bar, decent wines, nice photographs, dominoes, cribbage; children and dogs welcome, big garden with budgerigar aviary, surprisingly grandiose fountain, wooden climbing frame; handy for the salt marshes, open all day wknds and summer *(Geoff and Pat Bell, John Dwane, Pat and Tony Martin, Barry Collett, LYM)*

COLKIRK [TF9226]

☆ *Crown* [off B1146 S of Fakenham; Crown Rd]: Unpretentious two-bar pub with solid country furniture, rugs and flooring tiles, open fires, lots of wines by the glass, well kept Greene King ales, good coffee, charming efficient service, wide choice of popular bar food, no smoking dining room, darts, cribbage; fruit machine; good disabled access; children and dogs allowed, picnic-sets in garden with suntrap terrace *(Mark, Amanda, Luke and Jake Sheard, Maggie and Carl Van Baars, John Beeken, Mike and Shelley Woodroffe, LYM, George Atkinson, Adrian White, John Wooll, R C Vincent, Peter Rozée)*

COLTON [TG1009]

☆ *Ugly Bug* [well signed once off A47]: Extensive country pub with quietly old-fashioned quite smart layout, built-in banquettes, turkey carpet, red velvet curtains, old enamel advertisements, good value food in bar and no smoking restaurant, wider evening choice, well kept changing ales such as Nethergate and Woodfordes Wherry, sensible choice of wines, good service; piped music; children in conservatory with bar billiards, terrace and big garden with koi carp in pretty lake; two comfortable bedrooms *(BB, Gerry and Rosemary Dobson)*

DENVER SLUICE [TF6101]

☆ *Jenyns Arms* [signed via B1507 off A1122 Downham Mkt bypass]: Extensive well laid out pub in fine spot by spectacular hydraulic sluices controlling Great Ouse, extensive generous food (not Sun eve) from good sandwiches up, friendly helpful staff cope well with coach parties, well kept ales such as

Adnams and Greene King IPA and Old Speckled Hen, light and airy games area; piped music; children welcome, tables out by water, self-catering (BB, Keith and Janet Morris, Bill and Sheila McLardy)

DERSINGHAM [TF6930]

☆ *Feathers* [B1440 towards Sandringham]: Solid Jacobean sandstone inn with two relaxed modernised dark-panelled bars, well kept Adnams, Bass and Black Sheep, log fires, wide choice of generous bar food from sandwiches to interesting specials, restaurant (not Sun evening), separate games room; children welcome and well catered for, large family garden with elaborate play area inc wendy house and outsize snakes and ladders, attractive secluded adults' garden with pond, comfortable well furnished bedrooms (Mike Ridgway, Sarah Miles, LYM, MDN, Esther and John Sprinkle, John Wooll)

DILHAM [TG3325]

Cross Keys [off A149 S of N Walsham]: Traditional village pub, friendly and comfortable, with real ales inc Adnams Broadside, generous fresh pubby food inc good puddings; dogs welcome, colourful garden overlooking bowling green (Georgina Winnington)

DRAYTON [TG1713]

Red Lion [Fakenham Rd (A1067 NW of Norwich)]: Country Carvery chain pub with wide choice of bar food and enjoyable carvery (three roasts), service efficient even when very busy (R C Vincent)

EAST BARSHAM [TF9133]

White Horse [B1105 3 miles N of Fakenham]: Attractive extended pub, big log fire in long beamed main bar, steps to other areas, well kept ales such as Adnams Bitter and Broadside and Charles Wells Bombardier, decent wine, good coffee, friendly attentive staff, wide choice of enjoyable meals inc OAP lunches and good value steak nights, two small attractive dining rooms; piped music, darts; children welcome, well kept bedrooms – a pleasant quiet place to stay (Mike Marsh, Susan and Nigel Wilson, R C Vincent)

EAST RUSTON [TG3428]

Butchers Arms [back rd Horning—Happisburgh, N of Stalham]: Comfortable village pub, friendly and well run, with generous enjoyable food inc bargain lunchtime dish of the day, well kept real ales, lots of golf talk, two dining rooms; attractive garden, pretty hanging baskets (Alan M Pring, M J Bourke)

FAKENHAM [TF9129]

Globe [Oak St]: New pub, entirely no smoking, in former wine merchants, clean and stylish décor, comfortable sofas and bar on one side, simply furnished dining area the other, Courage Directors and John Smiths, several wines by the glass, pleasant service, reasonably priced usual food; children welcome, open all day (John Wooll)

GREAT BIRCHAM [TF7632]

☆ *Kings Head* [B1155, S end of village (called and signed Bircham locally)]: Reopened after stylish makeover, comfortable sofas in log-fire bar, light and airy modern dining room, much stainless steel, glass and plain dark wood, leather-walled back area, very good if pricey up-to-date meals inc simple interesting lunches but not bar snacks, friendly efficient young staff, sumptuous lavatories; tables and chairs out front and back with rustic view, comfortable bedrooms, good breakfast (LYM, John Wooll)

GREAT CRESSINGHAM [TF8401]

Windmill [village signed off A1065 S of Swaffham; Water End]: Lots of interesting pictures and bric-a-brac in extensive series of rambling linked rooms with plenty of cosy corners and no smoking areas, bar food from sandwiches to steak, well kept Adnams Bitter and Broadside, Greene King IPA, Windy Miller Quixote (brewed for the pub) and a couple of interesting guest beers, decent sensibly priced wines, 25 malt whiskies, well lit pool room, pub games; faint piped music, big sports TV in side snug; children and dogs welcome, picnic-sets and good play area in big garden, well screened caravan site (Esther and John Sprinkle, LYM)

HAPPISBURGH [TG3831]

Hill House [by village church]: Cheery heavy-beamed village pub with plush seats, woodburner in big inglenook, open fire other end, well kept changing ales such as Adnams, Greene King, O'Hanlons Royal Oak and Shepherd Neame Spitfire, reasonably priced usual bar food from sandwiches up, darts and bar billiards, Sherlock Holmes memorabilia, separate no smoking restaurant; tables outside front and back, bedrooms, pleasant setting (Esther and John Sprinkle, BB, John Beeken)

HARLESTON [TM2483]

☆ *Swan* [The Thoroughfare (narrow main st on one-way circuit, look out for narrow coach entry)]: Nicely worn in 16th-c coaching inn, two linked lounge rooms with ancient timbers and log fire in big fireplace, snacks or meals here or in timbered restaurant (only carvery Sat night/Sun lunchtime, only bar snacks Sun evening), Adnams real ales, short choice of wines by the glass, welcoming service and atmosphere, old tools and cooking utensils, public bar with pool and SkyTV; quiet piped radio; good value Georgian bedrooms – the plumbing's a bit more modern (KC)

HARPLEY [TF7825]

☆ *Rose & Crown* [off A148 Fakenham—Kings Lynn; Nethergate St]: Village pub freshened up and doing well under new management, simple old wooden tables and contemporary local art, thriving atmosphere, roaring log fire, enjoyable decently priced home-made food (not Mon), good friendly service, no smoking dining room on left; tables in attractive garden with play equipment (John Wooll, R C Vincent, BB)

HETHERSETT [TG1504]

Queens Head [Norwich Rd (B1172)]: Large family-oriented pub with Adnams Bitter and Broadside and Greene King IPA, good value wines, back dining extension (Gerry and Rosemary Dobson)

HILLINGTON [TF7125]
Ffolkes Arms [Lynn Rd (A148)]: Roomy and relaxed food-oriented pub, handy for Sandringham, with sensible prices, well kept Adnams and Marstons Pedigree, pub ginger cat with own chair by window; garden behind, reasonably priced bedroom block *(Comus and Sarah Elliott)*

HOLKHAM [TF8943]
☆ *Victoria* [A149 near Holkham Hall]: Charmingly furnished small hotel with sprawling sofas, interesting pictures and good eclectic décor, welcoming bar enjoyed by locals for its four well kept ales such as Buffys, Earl Soham and Woodfordes Wherry, splendid wine choice, log fire, good upmarket restaurant; children and dogs welcome, picnic-sets in pretty garden with pleasant terraces, apple trees and small play area, eight luxurious bedrooms – handy for coastal nature reserves, beach and Holkham Hall *(John Wooll, M Thomas, J F M and M West, TW, MW, Keith and Chris O'Neill, Esther and John Sprinkle, Tracey and Stephen Groves, Neil and Angela Huxter, Minda and Stanley Alexander, LYM, Eric Robinson, Jacqueline Pratt)*

HOLME NEXT THE SEA [TF7043]
White Horse [Kirkgate St]: Attractive traditional pub with good value generous food inc notable fish and chips as well as more adventurous dishes, well kept ales inc Flowers, small separate restaurant; big garden *(Michael and Marilyn Switzer)*

HOLT [TG0738]
Feathers [Market Pl]: Relaxed and unsmart town hotel, bustling locals' bar comfortably extended around original panelled area with open fire, attractive entrance/reception area with antiques, helpful friendly staff, good value promptly served generous food, well kept Greene King IPA and Abbot, decent wines, good coffee, calm dining room; piped music, can get smoky, busy on Sat market day; dogs welcome *(Geoff and Pat Bell, BB, Christine and Neil Townend, O K Smyth)*
Kings Head [High St/Bull St]: Cheerful rambling pub recently refreshed by simpler furnishings and no smoking conservatory, promptly served reasonably priced food all day (may be afternoon closure winter wkdys), four real ales inc Adnams and Woodfordes, fair choice of wines, pleasant staff; children welcome, some tables outside *(Susan and Nigel Wilson, Keith and Janet Morris)*

HONINGHAM [TG1011]
Olde Buck [just off A47]: Ancient pub with four busy beamed rooms, some emphasis on massive food choice from huge sandwiches and lunchtime bargains to adventurous dishes and popular Sun lunch, well kept Greene King IPA, reasonably priced wines, relaxing candlelit atmosphere, no smoking area *(Mr and Mrs P L Spencer, Gerry and Rosemary Dobson, Chris and Diana Aylott)*

HORNING [TG3417]
Swan [Lower St]: Popular Brewers Fayre by paddle-boat cruiser stop, worth knowing for its views of Broads, with reliable food and pleasant efficient service; picnic-sets on splendid riverside terrace, bedrooms, open all day *(Quentin and Carol Williamson, Ian and Nita Cooper)*

HORSEY [TG4622]
Nelson Head [off B1159; The Street]: Two cheerily unpretentious rooms, shiny bric-a-brac, small local pictures for sale, good log fire, well kept Woodfordes Wherry and Nelsons Revenge, usual bar food from baguettes to steak, no smoking family room, cribbage, dominoes, shove-ha'penny; piped music, no credit cards, charge even for tap water; children and dogs allowed, picnic-sets in garden, good coast walks *(M J Williams, Gordon Neighbour, K Christensen, Peter Gibbs, LYM, B N F and M Parkin, Mike and Shelley Woodroffe, Mrs Margo Finlay, Jörg Kasprowski)*

INGHAM [TG3926]
Swan: Olde-worlde low-beamed thatched inn with interesting corners in compact rambling rooms on two levels, scrubbed tables and fishing boat photographs, jolly atmosphere, enormous helpings of good food from baguettes and standard pubby things to more elaborate dishes, five well kept ales inc Woodfordes Wherry and Nelsons Revenge, friendly staff, small family room; small enclosed garden and courtyard, bedrooms in detached block *(Sue Rowland, Paul Mallett, Roger and Anne Newbury)*

KING'S LYNN [TF6118]
Freebridge Farm [Clenchwarton Rd, West Lynn]: Chain family dining pub with reasonably priced food in pleasant surroundings, good choice of wines by the glass, well equipped indoor and outdoor play areas; bedrooms in adjoining Travel Inn *(R C Vincent)*
Lloyds No 1 [King St/Tuesday Market Pl]: Spacious neatly kept good value Wetherspoons, two-for-one food bargains, good beer choice, decent wines, friendly helpful service; children welcome till 7, attractive back garden down to river, pleasant bedrooms, good value breakfast *(John Wooll, R C Vincent, Hazel Morgan, Bernard Patrick)*
Wenns [Saturday Market Pl]: Up-to-date town pub with Greene King ales, decent wines, wide choice of reasonably priced simple food from baguettes and baked potatoes up, efficient friendly service *(John Wooll)*

LETHERINGSETT [TG0638]
Kings Head [Holt Rd (A148)]: A boon for young families, with plenty of tables and lots of amusements for children on extensive lawn, summer brass or jazz bands, well worn bar with sepia prints of Norfolk life, prominent Union flags, good local range of well kept beers such as Adnams, Greene King IPA and Abbot and Woodfordes Wherry, plain family food all day from sandwiches up, even children's vegetarian dishes, log fire, small lounge, games room; piped music; dogs welcome, open all day *(R C Vincent, Adrian White, Tracey and Stephen Groves,*

Esther and John Sprinkle, LYM, David Cosham)

LITTLE FRANSHAM [TF8911]

Canary & Linnet [Maid Rd (A47 Swaffham—Dereham)]: 16th-c former blacksmith's cottage with good value food (not Sun evening) in beamed bar and no smoking back restaurant, well kept Greene King IPA and guests such as Adnams Broadside and Woodfordes Wherry, decent wines, inglenook woodburner, pictures and brasses; pretty cottage garden *(anon)*

MORSTON [TG0043]

Anchor [The Street]: Several pleasantly old-fashioned rooms, Greene King real ales, decent wines, food from sandwiches and rolls to quite a lot of fresh fish, daily papers, local prints and photographs *(John Wooll, Roy and Gay Hoing)*

NEATISHEAD [TG3421]

White Horse [The Street]: Warm and welcoming multi-roomed pub popular with boaters (free mooring nearby), lots of old pictures of Broads, welcoming family service, well kept Adnams and Tetleys, popular basic food *(B N F and M Parkin)*

NORTH CREAKE [TF8538]

☆ *Jolly Farmers* [Burnham Rd]: Two small bars, relaxed and friendly, with good log fire in one, woodburner in the other, well kept Adnams Bitter and Broadside, good wines by the glass, tasty gently upmarket food freshly made from local produce, reasonable prices, good service, two pleasant dining areas allowing children; tables in sheltered garden, charming village, cl Sun evening, all Mon, Tues lunchtime *(Mike and Shelley Woodroffe, Hugh and Anne Pinnock)*

NORTH ELMHAM [TF9820]

Kings Head [B1110/B1145 N of E Dereham]: Cordial prompt service, wide choice of good value straightforward home-made food inc popular Sun carvery, log-fire lounge with coaching prints, good-sized no smoking dining area, games room; quiet piped music; children welcome, garden with play area, big character old-fashioned bedrooms, good breakfast, pleasant walks *(R C Vincent)*

NORWICH [TG2207]

Eagle [Newmarket Rd]: Attractively refurbished, comfortable and welcoming, with wide choice of good food cooked to order (so takes a while), well kept Adnams, Greene King and a guest beer, friendly staff; pleasant lawned garden and play area *(Anthony Barnes, M J Bourke)*

Garden House [Pembroke Rd]: Cheerful backstreet pub with plenty of atmosphere, well kept beer, good freshly made food inc local fish and mezze-style smaller dishes, friendly staff coping well with the bustle; barbecues in good-sized attractive garden *(Sue Demont, Tim Barrow)*

Rose [Rupert St/Trinity St]: Pleasantly spacious main bar, good choice of real ales and of wines by the glass, dining area with plentiful freshly cooked food inc interesting variations on standard menu; tables outside *(Anthony Barnes)*

Wig & Pen [St Martins Palace Plain]: Friendly beamed bar opp cathedral close, lawyer and judge prints, roaring stove with horsebrasses on overmantel, prompt generous bar food, good range of real ales, good value wines by the glass, staff who take an interest; piped music *(Anthony Barnes)*

OLD BUCKENHAM [TM0691]

☆ *Gamekeeper* [The Green]: Pretty 16th-c pub, good atmosphere with blazing log fire, church candles and dried hops, tasty seasonal food in cosy bar or larger dining room, Sun lunch 12-5, welcoming attentive service, well kept ales such as Adnams, local Wolf and one brewed for the pub, good wine list, no machines; children welcome *(TW, MW, Simon and Mandy King)*

POTTER HEIGHAM [TG4119]

Falgate [A1062 Ludham Rd]: Very wide choice of well priced food, massive helpings, well kept Adnams, Greene King, John Smiths and Tetleys, friendly service, restaurant; may be piped music; handy for the river, popular with boaters *(David and Julie Glover, Ian and Nita Cooper)*

RANWORTH [TG3514]

Maltsters [signed from B1140 Norwich—Acle]: Included for its position across quiet lane from Ranworth Broad, superb nature trail nearby, ferry to wildlife centre; rather nautical décor, basic food, friendly helpful service, well kept Woodfordes *(LYM, Eostre Caswell)*

REEDHAM [TG4001]

Ferry Inn [B1140 Beccles—Acle, beside ferry]: Popular with boaters (refundable mooring and showers if you eat here), with well spaced tables out by the River Yare, long front bar with big picture windows, comfortable banquettes and some robust rustic tables carved from slabs of tree-trunk, secluded back bar with antique rifles, copper and brass, and a fine log fire, well kept Adnams, Fullers London Pride and Woodfordes Wherry, quite a few malt whiskies, country wines, cheerful staff, no smoking restaurant and family room; piped music *(LYM, Comus and Sarah Elliott)*

REEPHAM [TG0922]

Kings Arms [Market Pl]: Local feel in 17th-c coaching inn, pleasant décor with several areas, stripped brickwork, open fire and farm tools, well kept ales such as Adnams, Reepham and Woodfordes Wherry, three open fires, wide choice of reasonably priced food from sandwiches and well filled baked potatoes up, cheerful willing service, games area one end, steps to restaurant; tables out in sunny courtyard, bedrooms *(MDN)*

☆ *Old Brewery House* [Market Sq]: Georgian hotel with big log fire in no smoking high-ceilinged panelled bar overlooking old-fashioned town square, lots of farming and fishing bric-a-brac, well kept Adnams, Greene King Abbot and a guest beer, friendly staff, good value food, carpeted lounge, no smoking conservatory; piped music; children and dogs welcome, tables on front terrace and back garden with pond and fountain, bedrooms with own bathrooms, open all day

(John Wooll, the Didler, LYM, Dr and Mrs R G J Telfer)

RUSHALL [TM1982]

Half Moon [The Street]: Spotless extended 16th-c coaching inn with generous good value food inc plenty of fish and big puddings, well kept Adnams and Woodfordes, good friendly service, beamed and flagstoned bar, large modern back no smoking dining room (best to book at night), dolls and bric-a-brac for sale; bedrooms in adjacent modern chalets *(David Barnes, Ian and Nita Cooper)*

SALTHOUSE [TG0743]

☆ *Dun Cow* [A149 Blakeney—Sheringham]: Airy pub overlooking salt marshes, enjoyable generous usual food all day from sandwiches and baked potatoes to local crab and fish, polite friendly staff, well kept ales inc Adnams Broadside, decent wines, open fires, stripped beams and cob walls in big barn-like main bar, no smoking family bar and games room with pool; piped radio, blues nights; big attractive walled garden with sheltered courtyard, figs and apples, separate sea-view family garden with play area, good walks and bird-watching, bedrooms *(John Wooll, Rodney and Norma Stubington, Esther and John Sprinkle, BB, George Atkinson, Tracey and Stephen Groves)*

SHERINGHAM [TG1543]

Lobster [High St]: Sizeable pub almost on seafront, seafaring décor in tidy lounge bar with old sewing-machine treadle tables and warm fire, well kept Adnams and Greene King ales, farm cider, summer beer festival, decent wines, good value quickly served bar meals and no smoking restaurant with good seafood specials, pleasant staff, no piped music; dogs on leads allowed, two courtyards with summer hog roasts *(Chris and Louise Taylor, Catherine Pitt, Keith and Janet Morris)*

Two Lifeboats [promenade]: Sea view from comfortable lounge, reasonably priced bedrooms and from terrace tables, no smoking restaurant and cosier rooms behind, big helpings of good food from crab sandwich up, well kept Greene King IPA and Abbot, quick friendly young staff *(Michael Tack)*

Wyndham Arms [Wyndham St]: Comfortable low-beamed lounge bar with big no smoking area and real fire, good fresh straightforward home-cooked food inc good range of local fish, sensible prices, well kept ales inc Adnams and Woodfordes, cheap house wine, quick friendly service, no smoking restaurant; pool and piped music in busy public bar; courtyard picnic-sets, open all day *(Geoff and Pat Bell)*

SKEYTON [TG2524]

☆ *Goat* [off A140 N of Aylsham; Long Rd]: Convivial extended thatched and low-beamed pub with good reasonably priced food inc exotic dishes in bar and attractive restaurant (best to book Sat evening), well kept Adnams and Woodfordes ales, good value wines, first-rate service by good-humoured licensees and enthusiastic cheerful staff, log-effect gas fire; pleasant terrace and good-sized garden *(Dr and Mrs R G J Telfer, Chris and Jan Harper, Philip and Susan Philcox)*

SMALLBURGH [TG3324]

Crown: 15th-c thatched and beamed village inn with reliable fresh country cooking from immaculate kitchen in bar and small popular dining room, welcoming landlord, prompt service, well kept Greene King ales with a guest beer, daily papers; no dogs or children inside; tables outside, bedrooms *(Marguerite Pointer, M and GR, Shaun and Diane, P B Morgan)*

SOUTH CREAKE [TF8635]

Ostrich [B1355 Burnham Mkt—Fakenham]: Popular local with bold rather smart décor, high-backed settles in main bar, leather sofas and interesting books off to the left, cheerful informal atmosphere, well kept Woodfordes Wherry and an interesting guest beer, good wine choice, friendly hard-working owners; piped music; children welcome, bedrooms with self catering *(John Wooll, Tracey and Stephen Groves)*

SOUTH LOPHAM [TM0481]

White Horse [A1066 Diss—Thetford]: Cheerful beamed pub with good choice of enjoyable home-made food from good sandwiches to bargain OAP roast lunch with plenty of choices, good staff (holiday visitors treated like regulars), well kept Adnams, Greene King IPA and Marstons Pedigree; tables in big garden, bedrooms, handy for Bressingham Gardens *(G P V Creagh, Gerry and Rosemary Dobson)*

SOUTH WOOTTON [TF6422]

Farmers Arms [part of Knights Hill Hotel, Grimston Rd (off A148/A149)]: Olde-worlde conversion of barn and stables, good value tasty food all day in bar and restaurant, puddings cabinet, good changing choice of real ales, good wines, abundant coffee, friendly prompt service; children welcome, health club, comfortable motel bedrooms, open all day *(MDN, John Wooll, R C Vincent)*

SUTTON [TG3823]

Sutton Staithe [signed off A149]: In unspoilt part of the Broads, linked areas with little alcoves, welcoming service, well kept Adnams ales, good value simple lunchtime food and wider choice of home-made evening dishes, traditional puddings and children's dishes, bargain prices, popular carvery, games area with pool; tables on front terrace, play area, good nearby moorings, bedrooms *(Jonathan and Gillian Shread, BB)*

THOMPSON [TL9296]

☆ *Chequers* [Griston Rd, off A1075 S of Watton]: Long, low and picturesque 16th-c thatched dining pub with good interesting food inc local game and lots of fresh fish in partly no smoking series of olde-worlde quaint rooms, well kept Adnams, Fullers London Pride and Woodfordes, good modestly priced wine list, friendly service and atmosphere, low beams, inglenooks, some stripped brickwork, antique tools and traps; dogs allowed in bar, tables in good-sized garden with play area, good bedroom block *(R C Livesey, LYM)*

TRUNCH [TG2834]
Crown [Front St]: Small cheery village local with wide choice of low-priced pubby food (not Mon/Tues) from sandwiches and baguettes to steaks, well kept Batemans and other ales, pleasant service, small dining room *(Alan M Pring, Richard Durrant)*

WALCOTT [TG3532]
Lighthouse [Coast Rd, nr church (B1159 S of village)]: Wide range of generous fresh family food from sandwiches, baguettes and burgers up, Adnams and other well kept changing ales, friendly caring staff; children in partly no smoking dining room and family room with toys; tables on covered terrace, summer barbecues with children's entertainer/disco Tues and Thurs evening, good walks nearby *(Alan M Pring)*

WALSINGHAM [TF9336]
Black Lion [Friday Market Pl]: Dates from 14th c, comfortable and welcoming, with three panelled rooms, cast-iron stove in one, open fire in another, various alcoves and small restaurant; well kept beers, wide choice of good value bar food, Greene King IPA and Abbot, decent wines, prompt service; good bedrooms *(Hazel Morgan, Bernard Patrick)*

WELLS-NEXT-THE-SEA [TF9143]
Ark Royal [Freeman St]: Chatty bar with fire each end and large intricate model of the *Ark Royal*, Greene King ales, generous reasonably priced usual food, daily papers; quiz nights *(John Wooll)*
☆ *Bowling Green* [Church St]: Attractively refurbished and welcoming L-shaped bar, hearty traditional food at raised dining end (freshly made so may be a wait), friendly helpful landladies, well kept Greene King IPA and Abbot and Woodfordes Wherry and Nelsons Revenge, two woodburners, panelling, flagstone and brick floor, simple furnishings; tables out on back terrace *(Mike and Shelley Woodroffe, John Beeken, Michael and Marilyn Switzer, John Wooll)*
Edinburgh [Station Rd/Church St]: Friendly unpretentious local giving good value, with well kept Bass and Hancocks in long bar, reasonably priced bar food inc lovely home-made puddings, sizeable restaurant; piped music may obtrude; bedrooms *(John Beeken)*

WEST ACRE [TF7815]
Stag [Low Rd]: Pleasant village pub in attractive spot, limited choice of good value home cooking using local produce from good value baguettes up, good choice of well kept changing ales, particularly cheerful and welcoming service *(Mrs V A Varley, A R Clemow, Dr and Mrs R G J Telfer)*

WESTON LONGVILLE [TG1115]
Parson Woodforde [signed off A1067 Norwich—Bawdswell in Morton]: Clean and spacious beamed pub with well kept Adnams and a guest beer, Aspall's farm cider, enjoyable food from sandwiches to some interesting main dishes, hard-working landlord and cheerful staff, lots of alcoves, two huge fireplaces, big restaurant; tables on terrace, flower-filled back garden *(David Twitchett, Anthony Barnes)*

WEYBOURNE [TG1043]
Maltings: Cosy and comfortably old-fashioned hotel, small bar (dogs very welcome) with well kept Wolf beers and friendly helpful staff, relaxing lounges, good restaurant food – not cheap but good value; bedrooms *(David Cosham)*
Ship [The Street (A149 W of Sheringham)]: Big comfortable bar, two no smoking dining rooms, wide food choice (not Sun evening) from plenty of sandwiches and baked potatoes up, well kept ales such as Adnams Broadside and Winters Tempest, decent wines by the glass, pleasant staff; unobtrusive piped music; garden tables and tearoom, cl Mon *(Keith and Janet Morris)*

WIGGENHALL ST GERMANS [TF5914]
Crown & Anchor [Lynn Rd]: By River Great Ouse, with Greene King real ales, decent wine, enjoyable food inc bargain OAP lunches, helpful staff, log fire and lots of photographs in panelled lounge, darts in public bar, no smoking dining room; cl Mon lunchtime in winter *(John Wooll)*

WIGHTON [TF9439]
Carpenters Arms [High St]: 17th-c flint pub under new licensees, good modern cooking, well kept Adnams ales with Marstons Pedigree, Woodfordes Wherry and another guest beer, long room with central stove; tables in large charming garden *(Ian Arthur)*

WIVETON [TG0342]
☆ *Bell* [Blakeney Rd]: Warmly welcoming open-plan dining pub, Danish landlord cooking wide choice of enjoyable food for bar and restaurant inc some danish dishes and interesting specials, well kept Adnams Broadside and Woodfordes, good wines, helpful service, no music or machines; large warmly carpeted no smoking conservatory, picnic-sets on lawn and garden behind, has been cl Mon lunchtime *(Pamela Goodwyn, BB, Tracey and Stephen Groves)*

WORTWELL [TM2784]
Bell [High Rd]: Several well kept real ales, enjoyable food, cheerful landlord and staff, separate bar area popular with young locals, restaurant *(Stewart Orr)*

YAXHAM [TG0110]
Yaxham Mill [Norwich Rd (B1135)]: Converted tower mill with Adnams Broadside and Woodfordes Wherry in comfortable and attractive simple bar, pleasant restaurant, decent food, helpful willing staff; comfortable bedrooms with own bathrooms, good breakfast *(Ian Phillips)*

Pubs with particularly interesting histories, or in unusually interesting buildings, are listed at the back of the book.

Northamptonshire

This year's foremost Northamptonshire pubs are the Great Western Arms near Aynho (plain outside, elegant and individual inside, with good food especially fish), the charming and traditional Queens Head at Bulwick (thriving under new licensees, doing good food and splendid on the drinks side – gaining a Wine Award this year), the good value Red Lion at Crick, the upmarket Falcon at Fotheringhay (very good food, and now entirely no smoking), the George at Great Oxendon (popular new chef/landlord settling in well), the cheerful George at Kilsby (it's the hands-on landlady who makes this special), the smart and friendly Snooty Fox at Lowick (back in the main entries, under a good new landlord, after a gap of quite a few years), the chatty old Ship at Oundle (a good proper pub), and the well run Star at Sulgrave (appealing surroundings, plenty of character). The Falcon at Fotheringhay, very rewarding for a special meal out, is Northamptonshire Dining Pub of the Year. Pubs currently showing particularly well in the Lucky Dip section at the end of the chapter are the George & Dragon at Chacombe, Bulls Head at Clipston, Royal Oaks at Duddington and at Eydon, Fox & Hounds at Great Brington, Dusty Fox at Harlestone, Old Saracens Head at Little Brington (these last three pubs are within a very few minutes' drive of each other), Stags Head at Maidwell, Malt Shovel in Northampton, Mill just outside Oundle and Boat at Stoke Bruerne. Drinks prices here tend to be slightly above the national average; two good local breweries to look out for are Frog Island and Potbelly.

AYNHO SP5133 Map 4

Great Western Arms

Just off B4031 W, towards Deddington; Aynho Wharf, Station Road

It may not be much to look at from outside, but this friendly and efficiently run pub – sandwiched between the railway and the Oxford Canal – has attracted much praise for its elegant atmosphere and food. It strikes some people as 'Cotswoldy', yet keeping its own character – and still a relaxing place to drop into for a quiet drink. A rambling series of linked areas has good solid country tables and regional chairs on broad flagstones, and the golden stripped stone of some walling tones well with the warm cream and deep red plasterwork elsewhere. A good log fire warms cosy seats in two of the areas. There are candles and fresh flowers throughout, daily papers and glossy magazines, and a collection of interesting GWR memorabilia including lots of steam locomotive photographs which it had been feared might be dispersed when the pub was redeveloped; the dining area on the right is rather elegant. Numerous seafood and fish dishes feature amongst the freshly made food, which might include lunchtime sandwiches, soup or fish soup (£5.50), fried sardines (£5.85), whitebait (£5.95), sausage and mash (£7.95), steak and kidney pie or various pasta dishes (£8.95), kedgeree (£9.95), honey and rosemary marinaded rack of lamb (£13.95), as well as blackboard specials such as moules marinière (£5.95), cullen skink stack (£10.95), game pie (£10.95) and crab salad (£11.95). All dining areas are no smoking and they have occasional piped music. They have well kept Hook Norton Best, Generation and the current Hook Norton seasonal ale or a beer from a brewer such as Adnams on handpump, and good wines by the glass; service is welcoming and attentive. Opening out of the main bar, the former stable courtyard behind has white cast-iron tables and chairs; there are moorings and a marina nearby. *(Recommended by Susan and John Douglas, Graham Lynch-Watson, Michael Jones, Alan Crompton, Meg and Colin Hamilton, Ian Phillips, Eric George, John Saul, Iain R Hewitt, Stuart Turner)*

Hook Norton ~ Lease Frank Baldwin ~ Real ale ~ Bar food (12-2.30, 6.30-9.30) ~ Restaurant ~ (01869) 338288 ~ Children welcome ~ Dogs allowed in bar ~ Open 12-3, 6(6.30 Sat)-11; 12-3, 6.30-10.30 Sun; closed Sun evening in winter

BADBY SP5559 Map 4

Windmill

Village signposted off A361 Daventry—Banbury

This old thatched inn has a pleasant terrace by the green of the attractive ironstone village. Past Oscar, the large pub dog asleep in the corridor, two beamed and flagstoned bars have a nice country feel with an unusual woodburning stove in an enormous tiled inglenook fireplace, simple country furnishings in good solid wood, and cricketing and rugby pictures. There's also a comfortably cosy lounge. The modern-feeling, brightly lit carpeted restaurant is no smoking. Bar food is popular so it is worth booking: in addition to lunchtime sandwiches (from £2.75; triple-decker sandwiches £7.25), they typically have soup of the day (£3.25), potato skins with yoghurt and mint or salsa dip (£3.95), smoked duck breast on salad leaves with honey and mustard dressing (£5.50), steak and kidney pie or broccoli, parsnip and sweet potato crunch with cheese sauce (£8.95), venison casserole with game sausages and herb and mint suet dumplings (£9.95), cajun chicken supreme (£10.95), poached salmon with dill mayonnaise (£11.25), fillet steak topped with melted roquefort cheese (£16.95), and puddings (£3.50). Flowers Original, Timothy Taylor Landlord, Wadworths 6X plus guests such as Bass, Fullers London Pride and Shepherd Neame Spitfire are kept under a light blanket pressure and served on handpump, and good fairly priced wines by the bottle; quiet piped music. A pleasant path leads south through Badby Wood, carpeted with bluebells in spring, to a landscaped lake near Fawsley Hall. *(Recommended by Jo Lilley, Simon Calvert, Charles and Pauline Stride, George Atkinson, Dr Martin Owton, Mike and Mary Carter, Catherine and Rob Dunster, Suzanne Miles, Les and Barbara Owen)*

Free house ~ Licensees John Freestone and Carol Sutton ~ Real ale ~ Bar food (12-2(2.30 Sun), 6.30-9.30) ~ Restaurant ~ (01327) 702363 ~ Children in eating area of bar and restaurant ~ Dogs welcome ~ Open 11.30-3, 5.30-11; 12-11 Sat, Sun ~ Bedrooms: £59.50B/£72.50B

BULWICK SP9694 Map 4

Queens Head ♀

Just off A43 Kettering—Duddington

Bellringers pop in to this delightfully traditional village local after their Wednesday practice, and the darts and dominoes teams are very much active. In a 600-year-old cottage row, it has been a pub since 1647 and the friendly licensees have injected their enthusiasm for country life, food and real ale since taking over in 2004. A big draw is the changing choice of good fresh food which is cooked fresh to order, using local produce where possible. The menu runs from pubby lunchtime snacks such as soup (from £3.25), filled baguettes (from £4.95), ploughman's (£7.50) and lincolnshire sausages and mash (£7.95) to more elaborate dishes from monthly changing menus and blackboard specials, such as roast aubergine, slow-roasted tomatoes, melted mozzarella, aubergine caviar and coriander pesto (£4.95), shredded duck confit with mango and cucumber salad (£5.25), trout fillet with black olives, cherry tomatoes and lemon oil (£10.25), risotto of butternut squash with grilled goats cheese and basil butter (£10.95), local roast venison with bacon and spinach roll and redcurrant jus (£13.50) and rib-eye steak with sausage and savoy cabbage parcel and brandy and peppercorn sauce (£13.95). The civilised dining area is no smoking. The ancient two-room stone floored bar has beams, and a small fire in a stone hearth at each end; darts, shove-ha'penny and dominoes;

piped music. Shepherd Neame Spitfire and two or three interesting guests from brewers such as Belvoir, Church End, Newby Wyke, the very local Rockingham ales and Thwaites are well kept and served from a stone bar counter by efficient staff. A good wine list includes interesting bin-ends, with nine wines by the glass; over 20 malt whiskies. There can be few more pleasant experiences than a summer evening on the garden terrace (with its own well) listening to swallows and martins, sheep in the adjacent field and bells ringing in the nearby church. This is an attractive bypassed village in an area where you may be lucky enough to see red kites. *(Recommended by Cecil and Alison Chapman, Anthony Barnes, Dr Carola Haigh, Fred and Lorraine Gill, William Salaman, Ian Stafford)*

Free house ~ Licensee Geoff Smith ~ Real ale ~ Bar food (12-2.30(3.30 Sun), 6-9.30(10 Fri, Sat); not Sun evening) ~ Restaurant ~ (01780) 450272 ~ Children in restaurant ~ Dogs allowed in bar ~ Open 12-3, 6-11.30; 12-4, 7-11 Sun; closed all day Mon

CRICK SP5872 Map 4
Red Lion 🍷 £
1 mile from M1 junction 18; A428

Readers continue to be impressed at the extremely reasonable prices of food at this stone and thatched pub. Its cosy low-ceilinged bar is relaxed and welcoming, with lots of comfortable seating, some rare old horsebrasses, pictures of the pub in the days before it was surrounded by industrial estates, and a tiny log stove in a big inglenook. At lunchtime you can have sandwiches (from £1.80), ploughman's (from £3.20), and straightforward hearty main courses such as chicken and mushroom pie, leek and smoky bacon bake, plaice or vegetable pancake rolls (all £4.20); they do a similarly bargain-price Sunday roast (£4.75). Prices go up a little in the evening when they offer a wider range of dishes that might include wild mushroom lasagne (£6.50), stuffed salmon fillet (£7.25), roast duck (£12) and steaks (from £10); puddings such as lemon meringue pie (from £2.20). The snug is no smoking. Four well kept beers on handpump include Greene King Old Speckled Hen, Marstons Pedigree, Websters and a guest such as St Austell Tinners. There are a few picnic-sets under cocktail parasols on grass by the car park, and in summer you can eat on the terrace in the old coachyard, which is sheltered by a Perspex roof; lots of pretty hanging baskets. *(Recommended by Ian and Nita Cooper, R Johnson, Rita and Keith Pollard, Patrick Hancock, Ian Phillips, Ian and Denise Foster, George Atkinson, Ted George, David and Ruth Shillitoe, Karen Eliot, Mrs M Wheatley, Mrs Hazel Rainer)*

Wellington ~ Lease Tom and Paul Marks ~ Real ale ~ Bar food (12-2, 6.30-9; not Sun evening) ~ (01788) 822342 ~ Children under 14 welcome lunchtimes only ~ Dogs welcome ~ Open 11-2.30, 6.15-11; 11-3, 7-10.30 Sun

EAST HADDON SP6668 Map 4
Red Lion 🍷
High Street; village signposted off A428 (turn right in village) and off A50 N of Northampton

Full of interesting old objets, this rather smart substantially-built golden stone hotel has a neat lounge bar with antique furniture, including panelled oak settles, library chairs and a mix of oak, mahogany and cast-iron-framed tables. Little kegs, pewter, brass pots, swords and so forth are hung sparingly on a couple of beams, and there's attractive white-painted panelling with recessed china cabinets and old prints. Though a meal here might be a little more expensive than elsewhere, the good food, generous helpings and excellent service make it worth that little bit extra. Bar food includes soup (£4), sandwiches (from £4; not Saturday evening or Sunday lunchtime), chicken liver parfait (£7), pie of the day, vegetarian lasagne or fish and chips (£10), cordon bleu of chicken or cold salmon fillet (£11) and sirloin steak (£14). The pretty no smoking restaurant overlooking the garden has a more elaborate menu. They serve very well kept Adnams Broadside, Charles Wells Bombardier and Eagle, and a guest such as St Austell Tribute on handpump, and decent wines including about ten by the glass; piped music. The walled side garden is pretty, with lilac, fruit trees, roses and neat flowerbeds, and leads back to the bigger lawn, which has well spaced picnic-sets. A small side terrace has more tables under cocktail parasols, and a big copper beech shades the gravel car park. *(Recommended by Gerry and Rosemary Dobson, Eric Robinson, Jacqueline Pratt, Michael Dandy, John Saville)*

Charles Wells ~ Lease Ian Kennedy ~ Real ale ~ Bar food (12-2, 7-9.30, not Sun evening) ~ Restaurant ~ (01604) 770223 ~ Children in eating area of bar and restaurant ~ Open 11-2.30, 6-11; 12-2.30, 7-10.30 Sun ~ Bedrooms: £60B/£75B

FARTHINGSTONE SP6155 Map 4

Kings Arms 🍺

Off A5 SE of Daventry; village signposted from Litchborough on former B4525 (now declassified)

The publicans at this gargoyle-embellished stone 18th-c country pub take pains to source foods for their originality of style, methods of rearing, smoking or organic farming methods, and they grow their own salad vegetables and herbs too. Some visitors come specially to see the gardens, where there's always something new and often wacky; in summer the hanging baskets are at their best, and the tranquil terrace is charmingly decorated with flower and herb pots and plant-filled painted tractor tyres. Inside, there's plenty of character in the timelessly intimate flagstoned bar which has a huge log fire, comfortable homely sofas and armchairs near the entrance, whisky-water jugs hanging from oak beams, and lots of pictures and decorative plates on the walls. A games room at the far end has darts, dominoes, cribbage, table skittles and board games. Youngs is well kept on handpump alongside a couple of guests such as Black Sheep and Thwaites, the short wine list is quite decent, and they have a few country wines; the outside gents' has an interesting newspaper-influenced décor. Listed on a blackboard, dishes feature loch fyne fish, interesting british cheeses, home-made chutneys and regional meat; the choice typically includes sandwiches (from £3.25), winter and autumn soup (£3.95), baguettes (from £4.60), cheese platter (£6.20), roast smoked salmon and salad or a ploughman's of british cheeses, cumberland ham and scottish smoked mussels all on one plate (£6.45), filled yorkshire puddings with steak and kidney or game casserole (£6.55), argyll venison with salad (£6.75) and a scottish fish platter (£6.95). They also retail a range of carefully selected food items, such as cheese, cured meat, sausages, fish and olives. It's worth ringing ahead to check the limited opening and food serving times noted below as the licensees are sometimes away. The village is picturesque, and there are good walks including the Knightley Way. More reports please. *(Recommended by Catherine and Rob Dunster, Pete Baker, David Hoult)*

Free house ~ Licensees Paul and Denise Egerton ~ Real ale ~ Bar food (12-2 Sat, Sun lunchtime only) ~ No credit cards ~ (01327) 361604 ~ Children welcome ~ Dogs welcome ~ Open 7-11; 12-3, 7(9 Sun)-11 Sat; closed weekday lunchtimes and Mon, Weds evenings

FOTHERINGHAY TL0593 Map 5

Falcon ★ 🍴 🍷

Village signposted off A605 on Peterborough side of Oundle

Northamptonshire Dining Pub of the Year

Visitors to this civilised, relaxed pub – which is now entirely no smoking – lavish praise on the very well presented, inventive food from the seasonally changing bar menu. It's good value, particularly the two-course lunch menu (£12.50, not Sunday), and bar food might include tasty home-made crisps (£1.50), soup (£4.95), chicken liver parfait with brioche and red onion jam (£5), grilled mackerel or chicken, mushroom and leek pie (£9.50), open steak sandwich with chips (£10.75), and puddings such as home-made sherry trifle or sticky toffee pudding (£5.50). The buzz of contented conversation fills the neatly kept little bar, which has cushioned slatback armchairs and bucket chairs, good winter log fires in a stone fireplace, and fresh flower arrangements. The conservatory restaurant is pretty, and if the weather's nice the attractively planted garden is particularly enjoyable. A very good range of drinks includes well kept Adnams and Greene King IPA on handpump, alongside a guest such as City of Cambridge Hobson's Choice, good wines with 17 by the glass, organic cordials and fresh orange juice. Locals gather in the much smaller tap bar, where you can enjoy a game of dominoes or darts. The vast church behind is worth a visit, and the ruins of Fotheringhay Castle, where Mary Queen of Scots was executed, are not far away. *(Recommended by Dr Brian and Mrs Anne Hamilton, Sarah Flynn, Oliver and Sue Rowell, Sally Anne and Peter Goodale, Alan Sutton, Philip and Susan Philcox, John Saul, Derek Stafford, Arnold Bennett, Michael Sargent, Fred and Lorraine Gill, O K Smyth, Howard and Margaret Buchanan, Sue and Keith Campbell, Les and Barbara Owen, Paul and Annette Hallett, Mike and Sue Loseby)*

Free house ~ Licensees Ray Smikle and John Hoskins ~ Real ale ~ Bar food (12-2.15, 6.30-9) ~ Restaurant ~ (01832) 226254 ~ Children welcome ~ Dogs allowed in bar ~ Open 11.30-3, 6-11; 12-3, 6-10.30 Sun

GREAT OXENDON SP7383 Map 4

George ♀ ⇌

A508 S of Market Harborough

'We've been coming for 30 years and it's never been better', reports one reader of this elegant and thoughtfully furnished 16th-c dining pub. The bar is cosy and clubby, with rather luxurious dark wallpaper, panelled dark brown dado, green leatherette bucket chairs around little tables, daily papers on poles and a big log fire; the turkey-carpeted conservatory overlooks a shrub-sheltered garden. There may be piped easy-listening music; the conservatory and restaurant are no smoking. The entrance lobby has easy chairs and a former inn-sign, while the lavatories are entertainingly decked out with rather stylish naughty pictures. They put quite an emphasis on the food (you might want to book): soup (£4.25), pork and leek sausages and mash (£9.25), home-made steak, pigeon and Guinness pie (£9.95), grilled haddock or honey-roast lamb shank (£10.95) and puddings such as lemon tart or warm chocolate fondant (£4.50). The evening menu is slightly more elaborate with dishes such as goan fish curry (£11.25) and confit of barbary duck leg (£11.95). Well kept Adnams, Bass and perhaps a guest such as Greene King Old Speckled Hen on handpump, a dozen wines by the glass and around 15 malts. *(Recommended by David and Ruth Hollands, Anthony Barnes, Jeff and Wendy Williams, Rod and Chris Pring, Mike and Mary Carter, Jim Farmer, Sheila and Peter Brown, Catherine and Rob Dunster, Duncan Cloud, Gerry and Rosemary Dobson, K M Crook)*

Free house ~ Licensee David Dudley ~ Real ale ~ Bar food (12-2, 7-10) ~ Restaurant ~ (01858) 465205 ~ Children welcome ~ Dogs allowed in bedrooms ~ Open 11.30-3, 6.30(7 Sat)-11; 12-3 Sun; closed Sun evenings ~ Bedrooms: £57.50B/£60B

HARRINGWORTH SP9298 Map 4

White Swan ⇌

Seaton Road; village SE of Uppingham, signposted from A6003, A47 and A43

Not far from the majestic 82-arch Victorian railway viaduct spanning the River Welland, this eye-catching Tudor inn has a Cotswoldy look with its limestone walls and imposing central gable. There's plenty of exposed stone inside the pub too. The neatly kept central bar area has good solid tables, a hand-crafted oak counter with a mirror base and an attractive swan carving, pictures relating to the World War II Spanhoe airfield nearby and a collection of old village photographs (in which many of the present buildings are still recognisable). An open fire divides the bar and dining area, and three guests such as Badger Tanglefoot, Brewsters Daffys Elixir and Marstons Pedigree are well kept on handpump; quiz machine, piped music, darts, cribbage and dominoes. The roomy lounge/eating area has comfortable settles, while a quieter no smoking dining room has a collection of old jugs, craft tools, dried flower arrangements and locally painted watercolours; darts, cribbage, dominoes. Bar food includes soup, sandwiches and hot baguettes (from £3.25), black pudding with stilton sauce or chicken liver and black olive pâté (£3.95), wild mushroom pasta (£7.95), steak and Guinness pie or haddock mornay (£8.45) and home-made puddings such as treacle tart or bread and butter pudding (£4.25). There are tables out on a little terrace, and Rockingham race track is just four miles away. *(Recommended by Dr B and Mrs P B Baker, Fred and Lorraine Gill, Jim Farmer, George Atkinson, Mike and Sue Loseby)*

Free house ~ Licensee Martin Bott ~ Real ale ~ Bar food ~ Restaurant ~ (01572) 747543 ~ Children welcome ~ Open 11.30-2.30, 6.30-11; 12-5 Sun ~ Bedrooms: £45S/£65S

KILSBY SP5671 Map 4
George

2½ miles from M1 junction 18: A428 towards Daventry, left on to A5 – look out for pub off at roundabout

The landlady here maintains a particularly cheerful, buzzy atmosphere, making this a welcoming and relaxing stopping point from the nearby M1 and A5. Among the wholesome and reasonably priced bar food, the lighter lunch menu includes soup (£3), sandwiches (from £3), local sausages, egg and chips (£3.90), filled baguettes (from £4), ploughman's (£5.95), home-made meat or vegetable lasagne (£6.90) and steak and kidney pudding (£7.90); the evening menu typically features home-made chicken liver pâté or deep-fried breaded brie wedges (£4.90), steak (from £7.90), salmon fillet (£7.90) and lamb shank (£8.90); specials might include deep-fried strips of squid (£4.90), turkey breast cubes in cream, sherry with onion and sweet peppers and rice (£7.50) and beef and ale pie (£7.90). It's best to book if you go for Sunday lunch (£6.95). A high-ceilinged bar on the right, with plush banquettes, dark panelling, a coal-effect gas stove and a big bay window, opens on the left into a cheerful and attractive no smoking dining area with solidly comfortable furnishings. A long brightly decorated back public bar has a juke box, darts, a good pool table, fruit machine, table football and a large-screen TV. Well kept Fullers London Pride, Greene King IPA and Abbot and a guest such as York Stonewall on handpump, a splendid range of malt whiskies in generous measures, and decent wines in big glasses; no smoking at the bars. There are wood and metal picnic-sets out in the back garden, by the car park. *(Recommended by Ian and Nita Cooper, Ted George, George Atkinson, CMW, JJW, B and M Kendall, Catherine and Rob Dunster, Neil and Brenda Skidmore, Ian Phillips, David and Ruth Shillitoe, Karen Eliot)*

Punch ~ Lease Maggie Chandler ~ Real ale ~ Bar food (12-2, 6.30-9; 12-4 Sun) ~ Restaurant ~ (01788) 822229 ~ Children in restaurant ~ Dogs allowed in bar ~ Live music first Sat in month ~ Open 11.30-3, 5.30(6 Sat)-11; 12-10.30 Sun ~ Bedrooms: £35/£50

LOWICK SP9780 Map 4
Snooty Fox

Signed off A6116 Corby—Raunds

Since the present owners took over this imposing 16th-c inn back in 2003 they have added a glass partition which allows you to see into the new kitchen and rotisserie, and they've also created two smart no smoking dining rooms. It has handsomely moulded dark oak beams, stripped stone walls and a formidable monumentally carved bar counter. On wintry days a log fire roars away in the huge stone fireplace in the atmospheric lounge. Good bar food might include sandwiches (from £4.95; £1 extra with fat chips), fishcake with spinach, roast lamb on home-made broad pitta bread or shepherd's pie (£8.95) and oxtail and kidney pudding with mash (£9.25). They also do a good value set lunch (£9.95 for two courses), and a rotisserie and grill menu with items such as salmon gravadlax with horseradish crème fraîche (£6.95), seared tuna (£13.95) and pork belly with savoy cabbage and mash (£13.95). Well kept ales include Greene King Abbot and IPA, plus specials such as Greene King Old Speckled Hen and Pottons Village Bike are kept on handpump under a light blanket pressure; piped music; the restaurant is no smoking. The softly floodlit picnic-sets on the grass in front are very inviting on a warm evening. *(Recommended by Judith and Oliver Stobart, Michael and Jenny Back, K C Watson, Jeff and Wendy Williams, Emma Handley)*

Free house ~ Licensees Clive Dixon and David Hennigan ~ Real ale ~ Bar food (12-2, 6-9.30) ~ Restaurant ~ (01832) 733434 ~ Children welcome ~ Dogs allowed in bar ~ Open 12-3, 6-11; 12-11(10.30 Sun) Sat; closed 24-26 Dec

NETHER HEYFORD SP6558 Map 4

Olde Sun 🍺 £

1¾ miles from M1 junction 16: village signposted left off A45 westbound – Middle Street

Outside this unpretentious 18th-c golden stone pub, blue-painted grain kibblers and other antiquated hand-operated farm machines, some with plants in their hoppers, stand beside a fairy-lit front terrace with picnic-sets. The enjoyable collections of bygones and bric-a-brac continue inside: nooks and crannies in the several small linked rooms are packed with all sorts of curios, from gleaming brassware (one fireplace is a grotto of large brass animals), to colourful relief plates, 1930s cigarette cards, railway memorabilia and advertising signs, World War II posters and rope fancywork. There are beams and low ceilings (one painted with a fine sunburst), partly glazed dividing panels, steps between some areas, rugs on parquet, red tiles or flagstones, a big inglenook log fire – and up on the left a room with full-sized hood skittles, a fruit machine, darts, TV, cribbage, dominoes and sports TV. Furnishings are mostly properly pubby; piped music. Well kept Banks's, Greene King Ruddles, Marstons Pedigree and a weekend guest such as Everards are served on handpump from two counters. The old cash till is stuck at one and a ha'penny; OK, so your pint and meal won't be that cheap, but the prices here are very reasonable. Quite a lot of the cooking is done by the landlord himself, and the bar food includes lunchtime sandwiches (£3.50), soup (£2.95), hot steak roll, peppered pork or chicken chasseur (all £4.50) and ploughman's (£5.25). In the evening, food is served by waitresses at one end of the pub and in the restaurant only, and the menu is a little pricier: home-made steak pie (£9.25), battered cod (£9.50), spinach and ricotta cannelloni with goats cheese (£9.75) and steak (from £11.50); Sunday lunch (£7.95 for one course); children's meals (£3.95); the dining areas are no smoking. *(Recommended by Gerry and Rosemary Dobson, Val and Alan Green, Leigh and Gillian Mellor, June and Ken Brooks, Jo Lilley, Simon Calvert, Catherine and Rob Dunster, George Atkinson, Ann Price, Kevin Blake)*

Free house ~ Licensee James Allen ~ Real ale ~ Bar food (12-2.30, 6.45-9.30; not Mon evening or Sun) ~ Restaurant ~ (01327) 340164 ~ Children welcome ~ Open 12-3, 6-11; 12-11 Sat; 12-10.30 Sun

OUNDLE TL0388 Map 5

Ship

West Street

A genuinely friendly, chatty atmosphere pervades this bustling down-to-earth local, home to a companionable black and white pub cat called Midnight. The heavily beamed lounge bar (watch your head if you are tall) is made up of three areas that lead off the central corridor, one of them no smoking at lunchtime. Up by the street there's a mix of leather and other seats, with sturdy tables and a log fire in a stone inglenook, and down one end a charming little panelled snug has button-back leather seats built in around it. The wood-floored public side has a TV, fruit machine and a juke box. Kept under a light blanket pressure on handpump are rotated guest beers from brewers such as Church End and Newby Wyke, alongside Bass and Oakham JHB; a good range of malt whiskies. Enjoyable bar food in generous helpings is home-made where possible, and might include soup (£3.75), vegetarian lasagne (£6), beef lasagne, haddock, chicken breast with mushroom sauce or pork curry (all £7) or rib-eye steak (£10.95); Sunday lunch is £7.95 for one course, or £11 for two. The wooden tables and chairs out on the series of small sunny but sheltered terraces are lit at night. *(Recommended by B N F and M Parkin, George Atkinson, the Didler, Richard Waller, Pauline Smith)*

Free house ~ Licensees Andrew and Robert Langridge ~ Real ale ~ Bar food (12-9) ~

(01832) 273918 ~ Children welcome ~ Dogs welcome ~ Jazz last Sun in month ~
Open 11-11; 12-10.30 Sun ~ Bedrooms: £35(£40S)/£70S

SULGRAVE SP5545 Map 4

Star 🍺

E of Banbury, signposted off B4525; Manor Road

Originally a farmhouse, this 17th-c creeper-covered place tends towards the
upmarket but has kept much of its old rustic character, with no piped music to
spoil the peace and period feel. Furnishings include small pews, cushioned window
seats and wall benches, kitchen chairs and cast-iron-framed tables, with polished
flagstones in an area by the big inglenook fireplace, and red carpet elsewhere. Look
out for the stuffed back end of a fox, seeming to leap into the wall. Framed
newspaper front pages record memorable events such as Kennedy's assassination
and the death of Churchill; alley skittles (by arrangement), Jenga, cribbage and
dominoes. Well kept Hook Norton Hooky, Old Hooky, a Hook Norton seasonal
beer and a monthly changing guest such as Adnams on handpump; piped music.
The lunch menu features items such as celeriac and potato soup (£4.25), duck and
chicken liver terrine, onion marmalade and toast (£5.75), sausages and mash
(£6.95), smoked haddock fishcakes (£8.95), corn-fed chicken with broccoli and
bacon and mash (£9.95) and rump steak or gressingham duck (£12.50); the evening
menu has many of the same items plus for example fillet of beef with potato, truffle
and chive mash (£17.50), plus specials such as buttered asparagus (£5.50), lamb
shank (£7.95) or bass with prawn mousseline (£12.95). Puddings might include
treacle tart with jersey cream or chocolate brownie (£3.95); no smoking back
dining room. In summer you can eat outside under a vine-covered trellis. There are
benches at the front, and in the back garden. On bank holiday Monday evenings
they often run a pub quiz with a meal for participants (phone to check first). The
pub is a short walk from Sulgrave Manor, the ancestral home of George
Washington, and is handy for Silverstone. *(Recommended by Michael Jones,
Michael Sargent, Theocsbrian, Mick Furn, Iain R Hewitt, George Atkinson)*

Hook Norton ~ Tenants Jamie and Charlotte King ~ Real ale ~ Bar food (12-2, 6.30-9;
12.30-2.30 Sun; not Mon) ~ Restaurant ~ (01295) 760389 ~ Children in restaurant ~
Dogs allowed in bar and bedrooms ~ Open 11-2.30, 6-11; 12-5 Sun; closed Mon in winter,
Sun evening, Dec 26 ~ Bedrooms: £35S/£75S

WADENHOE TL0083 Map 5

Kings Head 🍺

Church Street; village signposted (in small print) off A605 S of Oundle

In a pretty village of up-and-down lanes and thatched stone cottages, this stone-
built 16th-c country inn has an idyllic setting by a big wooded meadow next to the
River Nene, with views of the church, and if you're arriving by boat there's no
charge for mooring here if you are using the pub. Picnic-sets among the willows
and aspens on the sloping grass make pleasant vantage points. Because of its setting
it does get very busy on summer days. The lunch menu includes filled rolls with
salad (from £4.25), soup (£4.50), home-baked ham with chips and salad (£5.75)
and scampi (£7.50); good value specials (daytime and weekday evenings) might
include grilled sardines, cod with prawn and parsley crème, steak and kidney
braised in ale and chicken liver and brandy pâté with salad and bread (all £6.50);
more expensive evening specials available all week feature eight or nine dishes,
including four fish options, such as sausage and mash (£9.50), venison breast, with
red cabbage and kidney and merlot sauce (£10.50), smoked haddock grilled with
red onion (£10.75), shark steak with tomato and Pernod jus (£10.95) and rib-eye
steak (£14). There's an uncluttered simplicity to the very welcoming partly stripped-
stone main bar, which has pleasant old worn quarry-tiles, solid pale pine furniture
with a couple of cushioned wall seats, and a leather-upholstered chair by the
woodburning stove in the fine inglenook. The bare-boarded public bar has similar
furnishings and another fire; steps lead down to a games room with dominoes and

table skittles, and there's yet more of the pale pine furniture in an attractive little beamed dining room. Adnams Bitter and Broadside and a guest like Marstons Pedigree or Ringwood are kept on handpump under a light blanket pressure; pleasant service; no piped music; the restaurant and lounge bar are no smoking. Well equipped bedrooms look out over the garden. *(Recommended by Michael Tack, Ben and Helen Ingram, Mr and Mrs W E Cross, Dave and Jen Harley)*

Freehouse ~ Licensee Richard Spolton ~ Real ale ~ Bar food (not Mon evening) ~ Restaurant ~ (01832) 720024 ~ Children welcome ~ Dogs allowed in bar ~ Open 12-2(4 Sat), 6.30-11; 12-4 Sun; closed Sun evening and Tues ~ Bedrooms: £35B/£50B

WOODNEWTON TL0394 Map 5

White Swan £

Main Street; back roads N of Oundle, easily reached from A1/A47 (via Nassington) and A605 (via Fotheringhay)

Batemans brew for this nicely unpretentious village pub a special beer named Coco's Wisdom in honour of two great comics (Coco the Clown and Norman Wisdom) with local connections, and it's well kept on handpump alongside Adnams Bitter, Bass, Fullers London Pride and a changing guest from brewers such as Black Sheep; they've also Aspell's farm cider. The enthusiastic licensees have lived in the village for over 20 years, and have run this pub since 2004. They inject a genuinely friendly welcome that brings the fairly simple but spacious beamed bar and restaurant to life. The licensees are not here to make a killing but to provide a good village pub, so you'll find that with most dishes priced under our Bargain Award price limit the bar food is particularly good value: soup (£3.50), smoked mackerel with horseradish and rocket (£4.25), wild mushroom stroganoff (£5.75), pie of the day, scampi or battered cod (£5.95), curry of the day or chilli (£6.95), up to eight daily specials such as duck with raspberry sauce (£9.95), and home-made puddings including their speciality cheesecakes which come in unusual but tempting flavours including Cointreau and white chocolate (£3.50). The restaurant and part of the bar are no smoking; piped music. The back lawn has tables and a boules pitch (league matches Tuesday evenings). More reports please. *(Recommended by Oliver and Sue Rowell, Peter and Pat Frogley, Ben and Helen Ingram)*

Free house ~ Licensees Jenny Chalkley and Andrew Downing ~ Real ale ~ Bar food (not Sun evenings) ~ Restaurant ~ (01780) 470381 ~ Children in eating area of bar and restaurant ~ Open 12-2.30, 6-11; 12-11 Sat; 12-10.30 Sun; closed all day Mon and Tues lunchtime

---

LUCKY DIP

Besides the fully inspected pubs, you might like to try these Lucky Dips recommended to us and described by readers (if you do, please send us reports: www.goodguides.co.uk).

ABTHORPE [SP6446]
New Inn [signed from A43 at 1st roundabout S of A5; Silver St]: Tucked-away partly thatched real country local, rambling dim-lit bars, beams, stripped stone, inglenook log fire, masses of pictures and old family photographs, attractively priced home cooking from sandwiches to Sun lunch, well kept Hook Norton, good choice of malt whiskies, hospitable landlord; nice big garden with goldfish, rabbits and aviary, quiet village *(BB, Mick Furn)*

ARTHINGWORTH [SP7581]
Bulls Head [Kelmarsh Rd; just above A14 by A508 junction]: Much extended village pub, once a farmhouse, with open fires in big beamed L-shaped bar, separate front no smoking dining room, enjoyable straightforward family food from sandwiches to steaks, well kept changing ales such as Adnams, Arkells, Everards Tiger and Charles Wells Eagle, reasonable prices, quick cheery service; open all day Sun and summer *(Gerry and Rosemary Dobson, Ian and Nita Cooper)*

ASHBY ST LEDGERS [SP5768]
Olde Coach House [off A361]: Interesting rambling old place with plenty of individuality and atmosphere, that's been popular with readers, but closed for the months before this edition went to press; news please *(LYM)*

ASHLEY [SP7990]
George [Main St]: Friendly local in picturesque village pub, huge beam in left-hand dining

lounge with comfortable settles and tables, homely bar with chatty local atmosphere, darts, dominoes and team photographs, well kept changing ales, decent food cooked by landlord inc popular Sun lunch and gourmet evenings; TV *(Rona Murdoch)*

ASHTON [TL0588]

Chequered Skipper [the one NE of Oundle, signed from A427/A605 island]: Handsomely rebuilt thatched pub on chestnut-tree green of elegant estate village, helpful and friendly young staff, changing ales such as Adnams, Newby Wyke Bear Island, Oakham JHB and Tetleys, reasonably priced food (not Mon) from baked potatoes and ciabattas to restauranty main courses, light and airy open-plan layout with tables left and right *(Oliver and Sue Rowell, Michael and Jenny Back)*

Old Crown [the one off A508 S of M1 junction 15]: 18th-c beamed stone-built dining pub under new management, enjoyable generous food from good value baguettes up, Charles Wells real ales, good wines, roomy no smoking area; tables out on lawn *(Alan Sutton, Gerry and Rosemary Dobson)*

AYNHO [SP5133]

☆ *Cartwright Arms* [Croughton Rd]: Small busy stone-built coaching inn, neatly modernised beamed lounge and bar, some dark stripped stone, leather sofas by log fire in big fireplace, well kept Greene King Abbot and Ruddles, helpful friendly staff, daily papers, enjoyable home-made bar food, games room with pool, reasonably priced restaurant and conservatory; a few tables in pretty corner of former coachyard, comfortable attractive bedrooms, nice village *(BB, Ian Phillips)*

BARNWELL [TL0484]

☆ *Montagu Arms* [off A605 S of Oundle, then fork right at Thurning, Hemington sign]: Attractive unspoilt stone-built pub in pleasant streamside village, two bars with low beams, flagstones or tile and brick floors, not smart but warm, cosy and welcoming; good interesting food running up to swordfish, hearty helpings, well kept Adnams Bitter and Broadside, Flowers IPA and a guest beer, decent wines, helpful cheerful staff, log fire, neat back dining room; games room off yard, big garden with good well equipped play area, barbecue and camping, open all day wknds *(BB, Oliver and Sue Rowell, David Treherne-Pollock)*

BRACKLEY HATCH [SP6441]

☆ *Green Man* [A43 NE of Brackley (tricky exit)]: Spacious Chef & Brewer dining pub on busy dual carriageway nr Silverstone, comfortable old-look beamed lounge area and conservatory, big no smoking family restaurant, wide range of reliable food all day from baguettes and baked potatoes to steaks and mixed seafood grill, fresh veg, relaxed atmosphere, quick, friendly and helpful service, Courage Directors, Theakstons Old Peculier and Charles Wells Bombardier, good wines and coffee, log fires; piped music, games; tables on lawn, bedrooms in Premier Lodge behind,

open all day *(Phil and Jane Hodson, BB, R C Vincent, Andy and Yvonne Cunningham, Michael Dandy, R T and J C Moggridge, George Atkinson)*

BRAFIELD-ON-THE-GREEN [SP8258]

Red Lion [A428 5 miles from Northampton towards Bedford]: Comfortable modern bistro-style Chef & Brewer, up-to-date brasserie food from fancy sandwiches and ciabattas up in two main rooms (one no smoking), small drinking area with a couple of settees, Fullers London Pride, Greene King Old Speckled Hen and Charles Wells Bombardier, good choice of wines by the glass, courteous attentive service; garden tables front and back, open all day *(Gerry and Rosemary Dobson, Michael Dandy, Bruce and Sharon Eden)*

BRAUNSTON [SP5465]

Admiral Nelson [Dark Lane, Little Braunston, overlooking Lock 3 just N of Grand Union Canal tunnel]: Warmly welcoming 18th-c ex-farmhouse in peaceful setting by Grand Union Canal Lock 3 and hump bridge; cosy tiled-floor part by bar, longer dining end and back restaurant, enjoyable food with interesting as well as basic dishes, well kept Greene King IPA and Abbot and a guest such as Shepherd Neame Spitfire, good cheery service, daily papers, games room with table skittles; lots of picnic-sets in pleasant waterside garden over bridge, bedroom overlooking lock, towpath walks *(Ted George, George Atkinson, Ian Phillips)*

BRIXWORTH [SP7470]

Coach & Horses [Harborough Rd, just off A508 N of Northampton]: Cosy and unpretentious 17th-c stone-built inn with friendly helpful staff, generous and enjoyable if not cheap food from wide choice of good sandwiches to fresh fish, seasonal game and popular Sun lunches, well kept ales such as Adnams, Banks's Original and Marstons Pedigree, decent house wines, friendly helpful service, beams and lots of pictures, small no smoking restaurant; piped music; children welcome, attractive village with famous Saxon church *(Mrs M Wheatley, Gerry and Rosemary Dobson, George Atkinson, Mr and Mrs Bentley-Davies)*

BUCKBY WHARF [SP6066]

New Inn [A5 N of Weedon]: Picnic-sets out on terrace by busy Grand Union Canal lock, several rooms radiating from central servery, inc small dining room with nice fire, lively cockatiel and parakeet, decent sensibly priced food from baguettes and baked potatoes up, two well kept Frog Island ales and others such as Boddingtons, Greene King or Everards, table skittles; forthright landlord, big-screen TVs, live music Sat, quiz Sun; open all day *(LYM, George Atkinson, Ian Phillips)*

CHACOMBE [SP4943]

☆ *George & Dragon* [handy for M40 junction 11, via A361; Silver St]: Beams, flagstones, log fire in massive fireplace and even an old well, wide range of enjoyable food from baguettes and baked potatoes up, good friendly service, Everards real ales, no smoking area in restaurant; darts, dominoes, TV and piped music; children in eating areas, bedrooms, pretty village with interesting church, open all day *(Susie Symes, Gordon Prince, Derek Tynan, Klaus and Elizabeth Leist, Roger and Anne Newbury, Jean and Douglas Troup, Chris Glasson, Mick Furn, B M Eldridge, Les and Barbara Owen)*

CHAPEL BRAMPTON [SP7266]
Brampton Halt [Pitsford Rd, off A5199 N of Northampton]: Major refurbishment and extension, opening as we go to press with this edition, of what has been a pleasant pub based on former stationmaster's house on Northampton & Lamport Railway (possibly wknd train rides), which had Victorian-style décor, lots of railway memorabilia, a high-raftered dining area and small sun lounge – likely to be altogether bigger now, and the location has always been a nice quiet one, with Nene Valley Way walks; reports please *(LYM)*
Spencer Arms [Northampton Rd]: Largely no smoking beamed Chef & Brewer family dining pub, plenty of stripped tables in long timber-divided L-shaped bar, huge blackboard food choice, pleasant service, Greene King Old Speckled Hen and Theakstons Bitter and Old Peculier, two log fires; piped music *(Gill and Keith Croxton, Eithne Dandy, Simon J A Powis, Gerry and Rosemary Dobson)*
Windhover [A5199/Pitsford Rd]: Roomy well done Vintage Inn, largely no smoking, with Bass and Tetleys, good choice of wines and soft drinks, food all day inc lunchtime sandwiches, log fire; piped music; picnic-sets on terrace, pleasant Brampton Valley Way walks *(Michael Tack, Simon J A Powis)*

CHELVESTON [SP9969]
Star & Garter: Friendly local with good value food, well kept beers and decent wine by the glass; pool, juke box, dogs (and bikers) welcome *(Ryta Lyndley)*

CLIPSTON [SP7181]
☆ *Bulls Head* [B4036 S of Market Harboro]: Relaxing dim-lit village pub with friendly and helpful landlord, enjoyable good value food, Everards real ales and perhaps a guest beer, hundreds of whiskies, good wine choice, log fire and heavy beams – some coins in the cracks put there by World War II airmen who never made it back for their next drink; unobtrusive piped music; children welcome in no smoking areas, terrace tables, comfortable bedrooms *(Catherine and Rob Dunster, LYM, Mike and Mary Carter, Mary and Bill Kemp, Martin and Sue Day, K M Crook)*

COSGROVE [SP7843]
☆ *Navigation* [Castlethorpe Rd]: Lovely canalside setting, bustling rambling open-plan bar up steps with chesterfield and armchairs around open fire, lots of canal prints and memorabilia, friendly helpful service, Greene King IPA and Old Speckled Hen and two guest beers, sandwiches, baguettes and enjoyable meals cooked to order (so may be a wait at busy times), no smoking restaurant; can be very busy wknds and school hols; children

welcome, lots of tables out by water, moorings *(Tony Hobden, BB, Ann Price, Gerry and Rosemary Dobson)*

DENFORD [SP9976]
Cock [High St, S of Thrapston]: Neatly kept Elizabethan pub, cosy L-shaped bar with log fire, bare boards, dark beams and plank ceilings, woodburner in long restaurant (not Sun-Tues nights), wide choice of good value freshly made food, five well kept ales, good soft drinks choice, chatty landlord, attentive service, darts, hood skittles; may be piped music, games machine; picnic-sets in garden, River Nene walks nearby *(CMW, JJW)*

DUDDINGTON [SK9800]
☆ *Royal Oak* [A43 just S of A47]: Attractive stone hotel, spotless and comfortable, with good log fire, fresh flowers, theatrical photographs and programmes and plush banquettes in bar areas, no smoking family section, dining room with gleaming brass shell cases and other memorabilia from nearby World War II airfield, wide choice of good value hearty food, very welcoming efficient staff, well kept ales such as Robinsons Enigma and Timothy Taylors Landlord; quiet piped music; nice garden and terrace, six good bedrooms, pleasant village *(Tim and Rosemary Wells, George Atkinson, John Wooll)*

EYDON [SP5450]
☆ *Royal Oak* [Lime Ave; village signed off A361 Daventry—Banbury, and from B4525]: Extended late 17th-c pub with several tastefully done rooms, stripped stone and assorted old furnishings on polished flagstones, thriving informal atmosphere, good meals (not Sun evening or Mon), Greene King IPA and Hook Norton Best, friendly young South African staff, nice inglenook log fire, daily papers, games room with darts, hood skittles and TV; piped music; children and dogs welcome, tables out in partly covered back courtyard, picnic-sets on front terrace, attractive surroundings *(George Atkinson, LYM, Sue and Keith Campbell, Mick Furn)*

FARTHINGHOE [SP5339]
Fox [just off A422 Brackley—Banbury; Baker St]: Friendly village local, beams and stripped stone, floors part tiled and part carpet, enjoyable food from good sandwiches and baguettes to some interesting dishes, cheery service, Charles Wells ales, woodburner; picnic-sets in garden *(Arnold Bennett, George Atkinson)*

GAYTON [SP7054]
Queen Victoria [High St]: Spotless and comfortable village pub, four areas off central bar (two no smoking), light panelling, beams, lots of pictures, books and shelves of china, inglenook woodburner, wide choice of decent food from baguettes up, Charles Wells Eagle and Bombardier and guests such as Everards Tiger and Wadworths 6X, good wine choice, attentive friendly staff, daily papers, pool; piped music, games machines, Tues quiz night *(Gerry and Rosemary Dobson, LYM, Tony Hobden, CMW, JJW)*

GREAT ADDINGTON [SP9575]
Hare & Hounds [Main St]: Small friendly
L-shaped pub with simple well presented food,
cheerful landlord, very friendly staff, Charles
Wells Eagle and Bombardier with a guest beer;
plenty of tables outside *(Anthony Barnes)*

GREAT BRINGTON [SP6664]
☆ *Fox & Hounds/Althorp Coaching Inn* [off
A428 NW of Northampton, nr Althorp Hall]:
Charming thatched stone-built pub with fine
log fires in quaint low-beamed flagstoned bar,
lots of atmosphere and bric-a-brac, fresh
flowers throughout, well kept Fullers London
Pride, Greene King and lots of interesting
changing beers, decent wines, friendly relaxed
staff, good choice of enjoyable home-made
food inc local game from separate bar and
restaurant menus, two small no smoking
dining rooms, one in basement; children and
dogs welcome, tables in attractive courtyard
and side garden with play area, nice setting,
open all day wknds and summer *(Trevor and
Judy Pearson, Gerry and Rosemary Dobson,
LYM, George Atkinson, Ted George, Sue and
Keith Campbell, Tim and Ann Newell)*

GREAT HOUGHTON [SP7959]
Old Cherry Tree [Cherry Tree Lane; a No
Through Road off A428 just before the White
Hart]: Recently rethatched and refurbished,
stripped stone, low beams and panelling, old
fireplace and open fire in snug, no smoking
area, good range of bar food from baguettes
up, Charles Wells real ales, upstairs restaurant
with separate menu and good speciality nights
(Sue and Keith Campbell)
White Hart [off A428 Northampton—
Bedford; High St]: Pleasantly unpretentious
stone and thatch pub with four linked areas,
enjoyable fresh food, four or five real ales,
good choice of wines and soft drinks, friendly
helpful staff; quiet piped music, two TVs,
games machine, quite a few steps; attractive
garden with terrace *(CMW, JJW)*

HACKLETON [SP8054]
White Hart [B526 SE of Northampton]:
Comfortably traditional 18th-c country pub
with no smoking dining area down corridor,
stripped stone, beamery and brickwork,
illuminated well, brasses and artefacts, soft
lighting, fresh flowers, interesting generous
fresh food inc local produce and early evening
bargains, well kept Fullers London Pride and
Greene King ales, plenty of wines and soft
drinks, good coffee, split-level flagstoned bar
with flame-effect fire, pool and hood skittles;
quiz Sun; children welcome, garden with
picnic-sets and goal posts, open all day *(CMW,
JJW, Mike Becker, Reg Falkner)*

HARLESTONE [SP7064]
☆ *Dusty Fox* [A428, Lower Harlestone]:
Attractive and relaxed Vintage Inn, small front
bar and lounge, tasteful old-world furnishings,
hops on beams, local photographs, mainly no
smoking light and airy dining area and
conservatory-style barn; enjoyable food all day
from separate servery inc good sandwiches,
well kept Bass and Tetleys Imperial, good wine
and soft drinks choice, prompt friendly

attentive service, two log fires, no piped music;
children welcome, tables in nice garden, open
all day, handy for Harlestone Firs walks
*(Mr and Mrs Bentley-Davies, CMW, JJW,
Ted George, George Atkinson,
Michael Dandy)*

HINTON-IN-THE-HEDGES [SP5536]
Crewe Arms [off A43 W of Brackley]: 17th-c
pub bought by local villager and reopened late
2004 after refurbishment, roomy alcovey bars
and modern restaurant extension, well kept
Hook Norton and a guest beer, enjoyable food
evenings and all day Sun, games room with
pool; some picnic-sets outside, cl Sun evening
and lunchtimes exc Sun *(anon)*

KINGS SUTTON [SP4936]
Butchers Arms [Whittall St]: Well run village
pub recently renovated by Hook Norton, their
full beer range kept well, decent reasonably
priced food, restaurant; TV; tables outside with
aunt sally, in neat sandstone village easily
spotted by spire *(Mick Furn, Giles and
Annie Francis)*

LAMPORT [SP7574]
Lamport Swan: Imposing stone building with
good views, reopened under new ownership
after major reworking as modern pub/bistro,
good-sized front bar with well kept Courage
Directors and Greene King IPA and good
choice of wines by the glass, emphasis on large
no smoking wood-floored side restaurant with
big flame-effect fire one end, some pubby as
well as more bistroish dishes, prompt service
by abundant attentive staff *(Gerry and
Rosemary Dobson)*

LITTLE BRINGTON [SP6663]
☆ *Old Saracens Head* [4½ miles from M1
junction 16, first right off A45 to Daventry;
also signed off A428; Main St]: No smoking
throughout, roomy U-shaped lounge with good
log fire, flagstones, chesterfields and lots of old
prints, book-lined eating room off and
extended restaurant, enjoyable food from soup
or baguettes to full meals with plenty of choice
and interesting dishes, well kept Fullers
London Pride, Greene King IPA and Timothy
Taylors Landlord, good soft drinks range;
piped music; tables in neat back garden, handy
for Althorp House and Holdenby House
*(George Atkinson, BB, Gerry and
Rosemary Dobson, CMW, JJW)*

LITTLE HARROWDEN [SP8671]
☆ *Lamb* [Orlingbury Rd/Kings Lane – off A509
or A43 S of Kettering]: Newly decorated
17th-c pub under eager-to-please new landlord,
three-level no smoking lounge/dining room
with log fire, brasses on beams and fresh
flowers, wide choice of reasonably priced
enjoyable food (freshly made, so may be a
wait), well kept Charles Wells Eagle and
Bombardier and a guest beer, good coffee;
quiet piped radio, public bar with darts, hood
skittles and machines, Sun quiz night; children
welcome, small terrace and garden, delightful
village *(CMW, JJW)*

MAIDWELL [SP7477]
☆ *Stags Head* [A508 Northampton—Mkt
Harboro]: Wide choice of good value fresh

food in three largely no smoking areas, attractively light and airy, off small, spotless and comfortable beamed front bar with log fire and well chosen pictures, well kept Greene King IPA and guests such as Adnams or Fullers London Pride, good choice of wines and soft drinks, friendly attentive staff; piped music; disabled facilities, tables on terrace (dogs on leads allowed here) by back lawn with paddock beyond, bedrooms, not far from splendid Palladian Kelmarsh Hall in its parkland *(Gerry and Rosemary Dobson, George Atkinson, P Tailyour, Mrs M Wheatley, CMW, JJW)*

MARSTON ST LAWRENCE [SP5342]
Marston Inn [off A422 Banbury—Brackley]: Small, cosy and welcoming end-of-terrace local perking up under new landlord, cottagey lounge with well kept Hook Norton ales, enjoyable food inc sausage specialities; pleasant garden with aunt sally and play area *(LYM, Mick Furn)*

MIDDLETON CHENEY [SP5041]
New Inn [Main Rd, off A422 E of M40 junction 11]: Good choice of well kept ales in former 17th-c turnpike inn, popular food, welcoming service, growing bottle collection in bar and outer barn, no smoking back restaurant, mid-July beer festival; dogs welcome, good-sized neatly kept garden with aunt sally, open all day Sat *(Mick Furn, Chris Glasson)*

MOULTON [SP7866]
Telegraph [West St]: Friendly village pub with very reasonable prices, straightforward food in front bar, well kept Greene King Old Speckled Hen, Shepherd Neame Spitfire and a guest beer, pleasant service, locals' back bar with TV *(M Warren, Gerry and Rosemary Dobson)*

NASSINGTON [TL0696]
☆ *Black Horse* [Fotheringhay Rd – 2½ miles S of A1/A47 interchange W of Peterboro]: Civilised olde-worlde 17th-c beamed and panelled dining pub in nice village, wide range of good value food inc danish dishes, even a danish menu (Danish landlord), well kept real ales, good varied wine list, quick attentive service, splendid big stone fireplace, easy chairs and small settees in two rooms linked by bar servery; attractive garden, open all day summer wknds *(LYM, Paul Humphreys)*

NEWNHAM [SP5759]
Romer Arms [The Green]: Pine panelling, mix of flagstones, quarry tiles and carpet, log fire, light and airy back dining conservatory, cheerful attentive licensees, reliably good generous home cooking (not Mon) inc some unusual dishes, Tues-Sat lunchtime bargains, popular Sun lunch (no snacks then), Greene King Old Speckled Hen and Charles Wells Eagle, good soft drinks choice, public bar with darts and pool; piped music, opens noon or so, picnic-sets in enclosed back garden looking over fields, small attractive village *(CMW, JJW, George Atkinson)*

NORTHAMPTON [SP7560]
Fish [Fish St]: Large bare-boards pub in

pedestrian area, half a dozen well kept ales inc unusual ones, farm cider, popular food till 6; piped music, games machines; disabled access, bedrooms, open all day *(Richard Waller, Pauline Smith)*

King William IV [Green End, Kingsthorpe]: Friendly open-plan village pub, cheery obliging landlord, Fullers London Pride and Greene King IPA and Abbot; lots of seats and picnic-sets in pleasant secluded garden behind, can get very busy on summer wknds *(George Atkinson)*

☆ *Malt Shovel* [Bridge St (approach rd from M1 junction 15); best parking in Morrisons opp back entrance]: Very popular for its interesting choice of up to a dozen or so well kept changing ales inc local Frog Island Natterjack, also Rich's farm cider, belgian bottled beers, over 50 malt whiskies, country wines, good soft drinks choice, occasional beer festivals, daily papers, breweriana inc some from Carlsberg Brewery opposite, open fire, darts, cheap pubby lunchtime food (not Sun); quiet piped music sometimes (live Weds); picnic-sets on small back terrace, back disabled access *(CMW, JJW, the Didler, Tony Hobden, Tony and Wendy Hobden, John Kearins, Andy Lickfold, Mick Furn)*

OUNDLE [TL0386]
☆ *Mill* [Barnwell Rd, S (just off A605 bypass)]: Converted mill's main attraction is great setting on the River Nene, with picnic-sets under cocktail parasols on front terrace and side grass; stripped-stone bar (may be cl wkdy lunchtimes in winter), huge choice of good value food from baguettes up in no smoking upstairs low-beamed Trattoria, top-floor no smoking granary restaurant (not always open), also stripped stone with lots of beams, cheerful efficient staff, well kept Theakstons and a couple of interesting guest beers; children welcome *(LYM, Jane Walker, Paul Humphreys, Suzanne Miles, Catherine and Rob Dunster, George Atkinson)*

PITSFORD [SP7567]
☆ *Griffin* [off A508 N of Northampton]: Enthusiastic young chef/landlord doing enjoyable sensibly priced lunchtime bar food from baguettes up with wider restaurant choice, all freshly made, neat beamed bar, no smoking back lounge with steps up to small eating area and to pleasant evening restaurant extension (also no smoking), helpful efficient staff, well kept Fullers London Pride, Greene King IPA and Abbot and Youngs Special, reasonably priced wines, pictures and old advertisements; pretty village nr Pitsford Water/Brixworth Country Park *(Gerry and Rosemary Dobson, George Atkinson)*

PYTCHLEY [SP8574]
Overstone Arms [Stringers Hill/Isham Rd]: Small bar and long countrified dining room, good range of enjoyable food (freshly made so can take a while), well kept real ales, pleasant attentive service; children welcome if eating, big orchard garden and another smaller enclosed one, attractive countryside *(Mrs M Wheatley)*

RAVENSTHORPE [SP6670]

☆ *Chequers* [Chequers Lane]: Refurbished and extended beamed local with wide range of good value generous food from baguettes and baked potatoes to steaks, well kept Greene King IPA, Fullers London Pride and three changing guest beers, good soft drinks choice, friendly attentive staff, open fire, lots of bric-a-brac, no smoking dining room, games room, may have free-range eggs for sale; TV, games machine, quiet piped music; children welcome, open all day Sat, small secluded garden behind with terrace and play area *(CMW, JJW, Gerry and Rosemary Dobson, Michael Tack, George Atkinson)*

ROADE [SP7551]

Cock [just off A508 S of M1 junction 15]: Friendly family-run village pub with enjoyable well presented reasonably priced bar food (not Sun/Mon evenings), Marstons Pedigree, Theakstons and guest beers, good soft drinks choice, cheerful staff, plates, horsebrasses, flame-effect gas fire, pine tables on flagstones in no smoking stripped brick dining area on right; piped music, games machine, TV; children in lounge bar, dogs on leads allowed in garden, open all day *(Alan Ruddle, CMW, JJW)*

RUSHDEN [SP9566]

Station Bar: Not a pub, but part of station HQ of Rushden Historical Transport Society (non-members can sign in), restored in 1940s/60s style, with good changing choice of interesting real ales, friendly staff, filled rolls (perhaps hot dishes too), gas lighting, enamelled advertisements, old-fangled furnishings; authentic waiting room with piano, also museum and summer trains; cl wkdy lunchtimes *(the Didler)*

SIBBERTOFT [SP6782]

Red Lion [Welland Rise, off A4303 or A508 SW of Mkt Harboro]: Reworked under new licensees, with modern tables on tiles of bistro-style beamed dining room, good if not cheap food (veg charged extra) inc excellent puddings, splendid wine list, prompt attentive service, comfortable partly panelled bar with well kept Everards and changing guest beers such as Adnams, Archers, Batemans or Youngs; covered terrace tables *(Gerry and Rosemary Dobson, George Atkinson)*

SILVERSTONE [SP6644]

White Horse [Stocks Hill/High St]: Friendly staff and nicely presented good value food in traditional former 16th-c coaching inn; tables out on terrace and garden *(S and D Moir)*

SLIPTON [SP9579]

☆ *Samuel Pepys* [Slipton Lane – pub well signed locally]: Lovely 16th-c low-beamed country pub, long airy bar with informal eating area, some stripped stone, neat no smoking restaurant and dining conservatory, wide choice of good food using fresh local supplies, from sandwiches and ciabattas up, friendly service, prompt and helpful, five well kept changing ales such as Adnams, Hook Norton Best, Oakham JHB and local Potbelly Streaky and Shannon, decent wines, good tea and

coffee, colourful jars of preserves as part of décor; good disabled access, provision for children, country views from garden with play area *(Michael and Jenny Back, Judith and Oliver Stobart, Mark Butler)*

STAVERTON [SP5461]

☆ *Countryman* [Daventry Rd (A425)]: Recently refurbished beamed pub, spotless and well run, with carpeted no smoking side and back dining areas, very popular reasonably priced food from sandwiches and baguettes to lots of fish, good puddings range, smaller bar with games area, Fullers London Pride and Tetleys, attentive cheery staff; should book Sun lunch and Fri/Sat night; some tables outside and in small garden *(George Atkinson)*

STOKE BRUERNE [SP7449]

☆ *Boat* [3½ miles from M1 junction 15 – A508 towards Stony Stratford then signed on right; Bridge Rd]: Appealing two-part old-world flagstoned bar in picturesque canalside spot by beautifully restored lock, though main focus is modernised central-pillared back lounge without the views (children allowed in this bit); well kept ales such as Adnams, Banks's, Marstons Pedigree and a guest such as Mansfield Mild or Thwaites, wide food range from baguettes and baked potatoes up, prompt friendly service, comfortable no smoking restaurant and all-day tearooms; tables out by towpath opp British Waterways Museum and shop, canal boat trips, bar open all day summer Sats *(W W Burke, Tony Hobden, R C Vincent, LYM, Doreen and Haydn Maddock, Keith and Janet Morris, George Atkinson)*

Navigation: Large clean family-friendly canalside pub, several levels and cosy corners, sturdy wood furniture, reasonably priced generous usual food from sandwiches up inc Sun lunch till 5, well kept Marstons Pedigree, decent wines, quick friendly young staff; nice tables out overlooking water, big play area, open all day *(Michael Tack)*

SUDBOROUGH [SP9682]

Vane Arms [off A6116; Main St]: Traditional thatched pub with stripped stonework, cosy plush lounge, inglenook fires, well kept Everards ales, pleasant staff, good value coffee, enjoyably home-made food from fresh lunchtime sandwiches up, small no smoking area, upstairs restaurant; bedrooms in purpose-built block, pretty village, cl Mon *(LYM, B M Eldridge)*

SUTTON BASSETT [SP7790]

Queens Head [B664; village signed off A6 Mkt Harboro bypass]: Welcoming beamed village pub overlooking Welland Valley, Adnams, Timothy Taylors Landlord and a guest beer, beer festival end June, enjoyable reasonably priced home cooking, upstairs restaurant; children welcome, some seats out beyond car park, open all day Sat and summer *(Dr B and Mrs P B Baker)*

THORPE MANDEVILLE [SP5344]

Three Conies [off B4525 E of Banbury]: Attractive 17th-c stone-built pub with unspoilt two-room bar, beams, some stripped masonry, flagstones and bare boards, log fires each end, mix of old dining tables, enjoyable honest food from good value sandwiches up, well kept Hook Norton Best and First Light, friendly chef/landlord and wife, large family dining room; piped music; tables out in front and on lawn *(LYM, Ted George, George Atkinson, Mick Furn)*

THORPE WATERVILLE [TL0281]

Fox [A605 Thrapston—Oundle]: Extended old stone-built pub with helpful and obliging hard-working landlord, wide range of decent food inc some unusual dishes, well kept Charles Wells ales with a guest beer from central bar, several wines by the glass, log-effect fire, lots of fox pictures, light and airy no smoking dining area; piped music, children allowed, no dogs, small garden with play area *(John Wooll, Martin Grosberg)*

TOWCESTER [SP6948]

Plough [Watling St E]: Well kept Charles Wells Eagle and Bombardier and decent food from simple basic snacks to good steaks in three linked areas, helpful landlady, cheerful efficient service, darts in back lounge section; piped radio may obtrude; terrace tables among flowers and hanging baskets *(Joe Green, Pete Baker, CMW, JJW)*

☆ *Red Lion* [Foster's Booth (A5 3m N)]: Attractive 16th-c former posting inn with friendly hard-working licensees, Fullers London Pride and a guest such as Wychwood Hobgoblin, good value blackboard food from good sandwiches and baked potatoes up, dark wood furniture in carpeted lounge bar with big inglenook fireplace, beams and bric-a-brac, copper and brass, another fire in chatty quarry-tiled public bar, daily papers, carpeted games room with hood skittles and darts, restaurant; TV, lacks a no smoking area; garden picnic-sets *(CMW, JJW, George Atkinson)*

WEEDON [SP6359]

Crossroads [3 miles from M1 junction 16; A45 towards Daventry; High St, on A5 junction]: Plush and spacious Chef & Brewer, enjoyable sensibly priced food in well divided beamed bar and dining area, friendly staff, real ales such as Timothy Taylors Landlord, good coffee and log fires, no smoking areas; piped jazz or classical music; picnic-sets in attractive gardens down to river, comfortable Premier Lodge bedroom block *(LYM, George Atkinson)*

Heart of England [A45, handy for M1 junction 16; High St]: Much refurbished and enlarged around 18th-c beamed core, decent reasonably priced food, Marstons Pedigree, friendly hard-working staff, busy lounge bar with small areas off, large airy partly no smoking panelled restaurant and conservatory; unobtrusive piped music; big garden leading down to Grand Union Canal moorings, good value pine-furnished bedrooms

(George Atkinson)

WELFORD [SP6480]

Wharf [pub just over Leics border]: Castellated folly by two marinas, Banks's, Marstons Pedigree and three changing guest beers in compact locals' bar, enjoyable fresh standard food using local supplies, pleasant dining section; waterside garden *(John Moore)*

WESTON [SP5846]

Crown [the one N of Brackley; Helmdon Rd]: No-frills three-room local in handsome 17th-c stone-built ex-farmhouse, log fire, beams, flagstones and bare boards, prompt friendly family service, three or four well kept ales, good coffee, enjoyable reasonably priced home-made food (not Sun evening), unusual long room (former skittle alley) with cubicle seating; pool room, darts alcove, no smoking room; children welcome, bedrooms, attractive village handy for NT Canons Ashby and Sulgrave, cl Mon lunchtime and winter Sun evening *(Keith and Janet Morris)*

WOODFORD [SP9677]

Dukes Arms [High St]: Family-run 18th-c pub opp village green, three real ales, enjoyable food inc some less common dishes, no smoking beamed dining lounge with fresh flowers, bar with hood skittles, pool and games machine; piped music; children welcome, garden with small play area, may be barbecue Sat evening, walks nearby *(CMW, JJW)*

YARDLEY HASTINGS [SP8656]

☆ *Red Lion* [High St, just off A428 Bedford—Northampton]: Pretty thatched stone-built local with good value food (not Sun/Mon evenings) from sandwiches up, wider evening choice, well kept Charles Wells Eagle and Bombardier, good range of soft drinks, friendly staff (and cat), cosy lounge with beams and stripped stone, lots of pictures, plates and interesting brass and copper, step up to tiled-floor bar with games and small no smoking carpeted dining area; quiet piped music, no dogs; tables in nicely planted sloping garden, and in front *(CMW, JJW, Michael Dandy, BB)*

Rose & Crown [just off A428 Bedford—Northampton]: Spacious and friendly 18th-c pub in pretty village, flagstones, beams, stripped stonework and quiet corners, lots of pictures and brasses, step up to big comfortable no smoking family dining room, wide choice of enjoyable fresh food, Charles Wells and guest ales, good soft drinks choice, helpful staff; quiet piped music; picnic-sets in small courtyard and good-sized garden *(CMW, JJW)*

YELVERTOFT [SP5975]

Knightley Arms [High St]: Comfortable family pub with well kept real ales, good value fresh food, good coffee, lounge divided by log fire, solid wooden furnishings, pictures and bric-a-brac, neat dining area; children welcome, large garden *(C Luck)*

Northumbria
(County Durham, Northumberland and Tyneside)

The North East has a fine range of good pubs, right across the spectrum from highly traditional to very up-to-date, from no-nonsense hearty food at bargain prices (especially in the cities) to top-notch creative cooking, from remarkable buildings in grand landscapes to simple taverns made special by the warmth of the welcome. If there is one common factor, it is this sheer friendliness, and the good feeling that comes from landlords and landladies who really care. Throughout, there's a great deal of true individual character. Places that have been shining brightly in recent months are the County in Aycliffe (everything spot on at this welcoming and civilised dining pub with its talented chef/landlord), the Manor House Inn at Carterway Heads (a favourite all round, with good drink, delicious food and comfortable bedrooms), the cheerful Dipton Mill Inn at Diptonmill (great local cheeses and splendid drinks including its own Hexhamshire beers), the Victoria in Durham (an unspoilt period piece), the well run and stylish Queens Head at Great Whittington (imaginative food in a civilised atmosphere), the Feathers at Hedley on the Hill (this properly pubby place gains a Beer Award this year, to join its Food Award), the comfortable Apple at Lucker (this new main entry, thriving under newish licensees, makes a good break from the A1), the friendly and interesting Keelman in Newburn (brews its own excellent Big Lamp beers, and now wins a Place to Stay Award), the classic well preserved Crown Posada in Newcastle (welcoming and chatty, with good beers), the bustling Cook & Barker Arms at Newton-on-the-Moor (good value food), the very well run Rose & Crown prettily placed at Romaldkirk (great attention to detail in this fine all-rounder), and the highly nautical Olde Ship in Seahouses (good beer, nice bedrooms, character in abundance). For a special meal out, four of these stand out: the County, the Manor House Inn, the Feathers and the Rose & Crown. The Manor House Inn at Carterway Heads, giving so much pleasure to so many readers this year, is Northumbria Dining Pub of the Year. Pubs to note particularly in the Lucky Dip section at the end of the chapter, all of them potential main entries, are the Red Lion in Alnmouth, Foxtons in Berwick-upon-Tweed, General Havelock at Haydon Bridge, Crown & Anchor on Holy Island, Magnesia Bank in North Shields, Travellers Rest at Slaley, Hermitage in Warkworth and Boathouse in Wylam. Drinks tend to cost a few pence less in this area than the national norm, with plenty of good interesting local breweries. We found Big Lamp, Hadrian & Border, Wylam and Hexhamshire each supplying more than one of the main entries with its cheapest beer – though it was a 'foreign' beer, Black Sheep from Yorkshire, which most often turned up as a pub's cheapest beer here.

ALLENHEADS NY8545 Map 10 🏠

Allenheads Inn £ 🛏

Just off B6295

Every last inch of this quirky pub is crammed with an amazing collection of bric-a-brac and interesting collectables. In any of the loosely themed rooms you might find stuffed animals, mangles, old radios, typewriters, long-silenced musical instruments, an engine-room telegraph, brass and copper bygones, a plastic lobster, local photographs, aeroplane propellers, brooms, birdcages and even shoes – the list is endless, and it's all very neatly kept. The games room (with darts, pool and dominoes) has perhaps the most effervescent collection, and the car club discs and number plates on the panelling echo the efforts by members of a classic car club to try to persuade their vehicles to wend their way up here. Tables outside are flanked by more hardware – the sort of machinery that wouldn't fit inside. The licensee couple are friendly and welcoming and the pub feels at the heart of the village community, with cheery locals popping in for the Black Sheep and Greene King Abbot, which are well kept on handpump along with a couple of guests from brewers such as Durham and Mordue; decent coffee, real fire, TV, and piped music. Enjoyable hearty food from the straightforward pubby menu includes toasted sandwiches (from £1.90), soup (£2.30), pizzas (from £4.25), vegetable curry (£4.90), sausage casserole (£5), scampi or chicken pie (£5.95), sirloin steak (£8.50), and puddings such as rice pudding or fudge cake (£2.50); children's meals (£3.50). The music room and the dining room are no smoking. The pub is on the Sustrans C2C cycle route; it's particularly peaceful here in winter. They do good breakfasts. *(Recommended by Paul Davies, Steve and Liz Tilley, The Popplewells, Colin Wakeling, A G Taylor, Tracey and Stephen Groves, Jane and David Hill, M J Winterton)*

Free house ~ Licensees Stephen and Sue Wardle ~ Real ale ~ Bar food (12-2.30, 7-9) ~ Restaurant ~ (01434) 685200 ~ Children in pool, music and dining rooms ~ Dogs allowed in bar ~ Open 12-11(10.30 Sun) ~ Bedrooms: £28B/£49B

ANICK NY9665 Map 10

Rat 🍷

Village signposted NE of A69/A695 Hexham junction

A coal fire blazes invitingly in the blackened kitchen range at this unspoilt country pub, and soft lighting gently illuminates lots of interesting knick-knacks: antique floral chamber-pots hanging from the beams, china and glassware, maps and posters, framed sets of cigarette cards, and quite a lot of Laurel and Hardy memorabilia, from figurines to a signed photograph. Furnishings keep up the cosily relaxed traditional mood, with brocaded chairs around old-fashioned pub tables; piped music, daily papers and magazines. Besides the two small eating areas, the no smoking conservatory has pleasant valley views. From a changing blackboard menu, generous helpings of tasty pubby food might include soup (£2.90), open sandwiches (from £3.25), ploughman's (£4.50), lamb in mint gravy or their popular burger (£6.50), beef and ale pie or burger (£7.25), chicken breast with white wine and mushroom sauce (£9.95), and tuna steak (£11.95), with enjoyable puddings such as apple and raspberry crumble pie (£3.50); Sunday carvery (£6.95). Timothy Taylor Landlord is well kept alongside guests such as Caledonian IPA, John Smiths and Mordue Radgie Gadgie. Service is friendly, and the landlord is happy to chat about the beers. Parking is limited. Tables out on the terrace and in the charming garden (with dovecote, statues and flowers), have lovely views of the North Tyne valley. *(Recommended by Pat and Stewart Gordon, John Foord, Mike and Lynn Robinson, Paul Davies, Andy and Jill Kassube, Gerry Miller, Ann and Stephen Saunders, Tim and Suzy Bower)*

Free house ~ Licensees Joan and Donald D'Adamo ~ Real ale ~ Bar food ~ Restaurant ~ (01434) 602814 ~ Children welcome ~ Open 11-3, 6-11; 12-3 Sun; closed Sun evening

---

It's against the law for bar staff to smoke while handling food or drink.

AYCLIFFE NZ2722 Map 10

County 🍴 ♀ 🍺

The Green, Aycliffe village; just off A1(M) junction 59, by A167

'Everything is right', one reader says about this very welcoming, stylish place. Right enough anyway to attract such bright lights as Jacques Chirac and Tony Blair. Minimalist décor and blond wood floors are light and modern, and furnishings in the extended bar and no smoking bistro are definitely geared to dining. With a talented chef/landlord at the helm, food (prepared using mostly local produce) is tremendously good, and the civilised atmosphere is delightfully welcoming – service is superbly attentive. Pubby bar food (served at lunchtime and in the early evening only) includes soup (£3.95), open sandwiches (£5.45), smoked salmon and scrambled egg toasted muffin (£5.95), lambs liver and bacon with mash, scampi or cajun-spiced chicken with salsa (£8.95). Otherwise you can also eat from the more elaborate (and pricier) bistro menu, which might include smoked rabbit and leek terrine with red onion marmalade (£7.95), provençale vegetables and goats cheese lasagne (£10.95), halibut fillet with herb pasta, baby spinach and white mushroom, saffron and white wine velouté (£15.95), venison medallions with celeriac purée, roast carrots and artichoke and thyme and rosemary sauce (£17.95), good puddings such as chocolate torte, and the cheeseboard is well worth a look. The children's menu is good value, and the Sunday roast is recommended. Dishes are freshly cooked, so there might be a bit of a wait, and booking is a good idea. As well as a good choice of wines by the glass, they've well kept Charles Wells Bombardier and Mordue Geordie Pride, alongside a couple of guests such as Cameron Strong Arm and Hambleton Old Raby; piped music. The green opposite is pretty. (Recommended by Philip and June Caunt, Christine and Phil Young, Peter and Jean Hoare, John and Sylvia Harrop, Judith and Edward Pearson, M A Borthwick)

Free house ~ Licensee Andrew Brown ~ Real ale ~ Bar food (12-2, 6-9.15(6.45-9.15 Sat)) ~ Restaurant ~ (01325) 312273 ~ Children in eating area of bar and restaurant ~ Open 12-3, 5.30(6.30 Sat)-11; closed Sun

BLANCHLAND NY9750 Map 10

Lord Crewe Arms 🛏

B6306 S of Hexham

The tremendous age of this fine old hotel is evident everywhere, and is reason enough for a visit. Dating back to the 13th c, when the Premonstratensians built this remote village robustly enough to resist most border raiding parties, it's still separated from the rest of the world by several miles of moors, rabbits and sheep. It was originally part of the monastery guest-house, and then became home to several distinguished families after the dissolution in 1536. The ancient feeling bar is housed in an unusual long and narrow stone barrel-vaulted crypt, its curving walls being up to eight feet thick in some places. Plush stools are lined along the bar counter on ancient flagstones, and next to a narrow drinks shelf down the opposite wall; darts. Upstairs, the Derwent Room has low beams, old settles, and sepia photographs on its walls, and the Hilyard Room has a massive 13th-c fireplace once used as a hiding place by the Jacobite Tom Forster (part of the family who had owned the building before it was sold in 1704 to the formidable Lord Crewe, Bishop of Durham). The bar and restaurant are no smoking. Bar food includes soup (£2.75), filled rolls (from £3.50), ploughman's (from £5.25), cumberland sausage with black pudding, apple sauce and mash or smoked salmon, prawn and tuna salad (£6.85), a handful of daily specials such as pasta with parma ham, garlic, mushrooms and cream (£6.50), duck breast with port wine and redcurrant sauce (£8.25), and puddings (£3.50). Well kept Wylam Gold Tankard and maybe a guest such as Black Sheep on handpump. The lovely walled garden was formerly the cloisters. (Recommended by Dr and Mrs T E Hothersall, Paul Davies, Michael Butler, Tracey and Stephen Groves, Norma and Noel Thomas, Comus and Sarah Elliott, M J Winterton)

Free house ~ Licensees A Todd, Peter Gingell and Ian Press, Lindsey Sands ~ Real ale ~ Bar food ~ Restaurant ~ (01434) 675251 ~ Children welcome ~ Dogs allowed in bar and bedrooms ~ Open 11-11.30; 12-10.30 Sun ~ Bedrooms: £80B/£120B

CARTERWAY HEADS NZ0552 Map 10

Manor House Inn ⑪ ♀ 🍺 🛏

A68 just N of B6278, near Derwent Reservoir

Northumbria Dining Pub of the Year

Doing very well on all counts, this bustling slate-roofed stone house is superbly run by welcoming licensees, and continues to impress readers with its very good food, and as a comfortable place to stay (breakfasts are good too). The delicious food, using local ingredients where possible, is served in generous helpings, and might include soup (£2.95), sandwiches (from £3.45), stilton and red onion tartlets (£4.25), sausage and mash (£5.75), pasta of the day (£8.15), stir-fried chicken (£9.95), daily specials such as chicken breast in parma ham with cassoulet of beans (£11.50) or fried scallops with chilli jam (£12.95) and highly praised puddings such as ginger cheesecake and sticky toffee pudding; smiling service by the helpful young staff. The locals' bar has an original boarded ceiling, pine tables, chairs and stools, old oak pews, and a mahogany counter. Picture windows in the comfortable lounge bar (with woodburning stove) and from the partly no smoking restaurant give fine views over moorland pastures, and rustic tables in the garden have the same views; darts, dominoes, TV and piped music (only in the bar). They've around 70 malt whiskies, farm cider and decent wines (with about eight by the glass), along with well kept Charles Wells Bombardier, Courage Directors, Theakstons Best and a guest from a local brewer such as Wylam on handpump. You can buy local produce, as well as chutneys, puddings and ice-cream made in the kitchens from their own little deli. *(Recommended by Mike and Linda Hudson, John Foord, Jeff and Wendy Williams, Michael Doswell, Michael E Bridgstock, Kay and Alistair Butler, Tracey and Stephen Groves, Prof and Mrs Tony Palmer, J C Poley, Alex and Claire Pearse, Andy and Jill Kassube, Christine and Keith Whale, Liz and Brian Barnard, M J Winterton)*

Free house ~ Licensees Moira and Chris Brown ~ Real ale ~ Bar food (12-9.30(9 Sun)) ~ Restaurant ~ (01207) 255268 ~ Children welcome away from bar ~ Dogs allowed in bar and bedrooms ~ Open 11-11; 12-10.30 Sun ~ Bedrooms: £38S/£60S

CORBRIDGE NY9868 Map 10

Errington Arms

About 3 miles N of town; B6318, just off A68 roundabout

Run by a father-and-son team, this friendly 18th-c stone-built inn has been attractively reworked as a good dining pub (you may need to book). It has a relaxed atmosphere, and a nice mix of mainly pine candlelit tables under oak beams, on stripped boards here, and quarry tiles there, with a log fire, some plank panelling, some ochre paintwork, and some stripped stonework; there is a modicum of bric-a-brac, on window sills and so forth; no smoking restaurant. From a sensibly short menu and cooked to order, big helpings of food include lunchtime snacks such as good sandwiches (from £3.50), ploughman's or cumberland sausage and onion mash (£4.95), and spaghetti bolognese (£5.95), with a wide range of other enjoyable dishes such as soup (£3.50), steak and ale pie (£7.50), wild boar and pheasant pie (£7.95), roasted duck with leeks (£12.95), various steaks (from £12.95), steaks (£13.95) and loin of lamb with mushroom and chive risotto with red wine jus (£14.50), and puddings such as blackberry crumble and banoffi pie (£3.95); on Sundays they concentrate mainly on roasts. Two or three real ales on handpump are Black Sheep and Jennings Cumberland, and possibly a guest from a brewer like Greene King, and they make good coffee; piped music. Out on the front terrace are some sturdy metal and teak tables under canvas parasols. *(Recommended by Mr and Mrs Broadhurst, Dr and Mrs S Donald, Michael Doswell)*

Punch ~ Lease Nicholas Shotton ~ Real ale ~ Bar food (12-2.30(3 Sun), 6-9.30) ~ Restaurant ~ (01434) 672250 ~ Children welcome ~ Open 11-11; 12-3 Sun; closed Sun evening, Mon (exc bank hols)

COTHERSTONE NZ0119 Map 10

Fox & Hounds 🏠

B6277 – incidentally a good quiet route to Scotland, through interesting scenery

With a good winter log fire, the simple but cheery beamed bar at this 200-year-old country inn has comfortable furnishings such as thickly cushioned wall seats, and local photographs and country pictures on the walls in its various alcoves and recesses. Don't be surprised by the unusual lavatory attendant – an african grey parrot called Reva. Using some local ingredients, bar food could include lunchtime sandwiches (maybe cotherstone cheese and home-made chutney), tasty soup such as carrot and parsnip (£3.40), warm bacon, cotherstone cheese and apple salad (£6.20), pork, sage and apple pie (£6.80), roast mediterranaean vegetable crêpe baked with wensleydale cheese (£8.25), battered haddock (£8.95), chicken breast with red wine and mushroom jus (£9.90) and fried pork tenderloin with mustard and cream sauce (£10.80); efficient service from the friendly staff. Both of the dining rooms are no smoking, and you may need to book. They've ten wines by the glass, 12 malt whiskies from smaller distilleries, and Black Sheep Best and a Jennings beer are well kept on handpump. *(Recommended by R M Corlett, Michael Doswell, Derek and Sylvia Stephenson, Peter and Jan Humphreys, Pat and Tony Martin, Mike and Sue Loseby, I A Herdman, M J Winterton)*

Free house ~ Licensees Nichola and Ian Swinburn ~ Real ale ~ Bar food (12-2, 7-9(8.30 Sun)) ~ Restaurant ~ (01833) 650241 ~ Children in restaurant ~ Open 12-2.30, 6.45-11 (10.30 Sun) ~ Bedrooms: £47.50B/£75B

DIPTONMILL NY9261 Map 10

Dipton Mill Inn 🍺 £ 🍷

Just S of Hexham; off B6306 at Slaley, Blanchland and Dye House, Whitley Chapel signposts (and HGV route sign); not to be confused with the Dipton in Durham

The cheery landlord at this appealing little two-roomed pub is a brewer in the family-owned Hexhamshire Brewery, and Hexhamshire Shire Bitter, Devils Water, Devils Elbow, Old Humbug and Whapweasel are all well kept on handpump; also 18 wines by the glass (in two different sizes), two dozen malt whiskies, and Weston's Old Rosie cider. Ideal with your pint, try one of their excellent ploughman's (from £4.75), with one of the great range of a dozen northumbrian cheeses they keep (or you can have cheese after your meal). Other straightforward but tasty bar food might include sandwiches (from £1.70), salads (from £5.25), ratatouille with couscous or tagliatelle with creamy basil sauce (£5), haddock baked with tomatoes and steak and kidney or turkey, bacon and mushroom pie (£6.20), and chicken breast in sherry sauce (£7), with puddings such as fruit crumble or creamy lemon tart (from £1.80). The pub is tucked away in a peaceful wooded valley hamlet and surrounded by steep hills, with plenty of easy-walking footpaths nearby. In fine weather it's pleasant to sit out on the sunken crazy-paved terrace by the restored mill stream, or in the attractively planted garden with its aviary. The neatly kept, snug bar has dark ply panelling, low ceilings, red furnishings, a dark red carpet and two welcoming open fires. The back games room has darts, shove-ha'penny and dominoes. *(Recommended by Mr and Mrs Maurice Thompson, Stephen Woad, Paul Davies, Mart Lawton, Tracey and Stephen Groves, Mike and Lynn Robinson, Gerry Miller, Dr D J and Mrs S C Walker, Comus and Sarah Elliott)*

Own brew ~ Licensee Geoff Brooker ~ Real ale ~ Bar food (12-2, 6.30-8.30) ~ No credit cards ~ (01434) 606577 ~ Children welcome ~ Open 12-2.30, 6-11; 12-3 Sun; closed Sun evening

---

Looking for a pub with a really special garden, or in lovely countryside, or with an outstanding view, or right by the water? They are listed separately, at the back of the book.

DURHAM NZ2 2 Map 10
Victoria 🏨

Hallgarth Street (A 77, near Dunelm House)

Delightfully unspo t, this immaculately kept little brick-built local retains its original layout, an attracts an eclectic bunch of cheery bantering locals. Served by the characterfully iendly landlord, one big attraction is the five interesting and well kept real ales which might typically include Big Lamp, Durham Magus, Hexhamshire Dev Water, Jarrow Swinging Gibbet and Mordue Geordie Pride on handpump; also g d cheap house wines, around 50 malts and a great collection of 36 irish whiskeys. uilt in the closing years of Queen Victoria's reign (and little altered since), the ab celebrates her life with lots of period prints and engravings, and staffordshire urines of her and the Prince Consort. The very traditional layout means thre little rooms lead off a central bar, with typically Victorian décor: mahogany, ched and cut glass and mirrors, colourful William Morris wallpaper over a h panelled dado, some maroon plush seats in little booths, some worn leather te wall seats, long narrow drinkers' tables, handsome iron and tile fireplaces for t coal fires, a piano, and some photographs and articles showing a very proper prid in the pub. They've dominoes, a fruit machine, a veteran space invaders game, a T vial Pursuit machine and a TV; at lunchtime they do toasties (from £1). The go value bedrooms are simple but pleasant; a hearty breakfast (good vegetarian e too) is served in the upstairs dining room. *(Recommended by Pete Baker, Patrick P acock, the Didler, Steve Barrett, Tracey and Stephen Groves, Earl and Chris Pick, Peter Cle nson)*

Free house ~ Licens e Michael Webster ~ Real ale ~ (0191) 386 5269 ~ Children in restaurant ~ Dogs w lcome ~ Open 11.45-3, 6-11; 12-2, 7-10.30 Sun ~ Bedrooms: £40B/£58B

EGLINGHAM N J1019 Map 10
Tankervill Arms

B6346 Alnwick—W oler

A cheerful country tmosphere fills the pleasant rooms of this long stone pub, and with a coal fire at ch end it's especially warm and cosy in winter. It's quite traditional with bl k joists, some walls stripped to bare stone and hung with brassware, and plu banquettes and captain's chairs around cast-iron-framed tables on the turke carpet. Well presented, enjoyable bar food might include a choice of soups (£ 5), sandwiches (£4.50), leek risotto with smoked salmon (£6.50), scampi or ast courgette and mozzarella tart on tomato salad (£9), roast stuffed aubergine .50), steak and ale pie (£9.75), duck breast with thyme sauce or roast cod on m terranean vegetables (£12), and puddings such as apricot bread and butter puddin r mango cheesecake (£3.95). Well kept on handpump, they serve two or three al ales such as Black Sheep and Mordue Workie Ticket, as well as a decent selectio of wines and malt whiskies. The bar is no smoking; dominoes, darts and piped m ic. It's in an attractive village, and picnic sets in the pleasant garden have fine v ws. *(Recommended by Michael Doswell, GSB, Jenny and Peter Lowater)*

Free house ~ Licens J E Blackmore ~ Real ale ~ Bar food (from 6pm in summer) ~ Restaurant ~ (0166 578444 ~ Children welcome ~ Open 12-2, 6-11; 12-3, 6-10.30 Sun; 7pm evening openin n winter; closed lunchtime Mon-Weds Jan-March

GREAT WHIT NGTON NZ0171 Map 10
Queens H ad 🍽

Village signposted A68 and B6018 just N of Corbridge

The imaginative m u, cooked using local meat and fish fresh from the quay, is the main attraction at is well run and civilised dining pub. Besides lunchtime sandwiches, imagi tive bistro food (which you can eat in the bar) is beautifully presented, and mi include soup (£4.50), fried king scallops with bacon and green bean salad (£7.95 oast gammon with dijon mash and mustard sauce (£12.95), fried chicken breast on herb rösti with roast garlic jus (£13.95) and bass fillet on roast mediterranean vegetables or roast duck breast with caramelised apple and ginger and calvados sauce (£15.95). They do a good value two-course lunch (£11.50). Staff are attentive and well trained, paying attention to the details, and all the dining areas are no smoking. Modern furnishings alongside some handsome carved oak settles and log fires give its two fairly simple beamed rooms a stylishly comfortable feel. The room nearest the bar counter has a mural over its fireplace; perhaps unobtrusive piped music. Black Sheep and Queens Head (brewed for them by Hambleton) are very well kept on handpump, and they've 30 malt whiskies, and an extensive wine list. The small front lawn has half a dozen picnic-sets, and this attractive old building is in a smart stone-built village, surrounded by partly wooded countryside. They may close for a week's holiday during the summer. *(Recommended by Stephen Woad, Michael Doswell, John Foord, JWAC, Alex and Claire Pearse, R Macfarlane, Lawrence Pearse)*

Free house ~ Licensee Ian Scott ~ Real ale ~ Bar food ~ Restaurant ~ (01434) 672267 ~ Children in eating area of bar ~ Open 12-2.30(3 Sun), 6-11; closed Sun evening, Mon

GRETA BRIDGE NZ0813 Map 10 ☗
Morritt Arms 🍴 � 🛏
Hotel signposted off A66 W of Scotch Corner

Forming part of a rambling country house hotel, the charmingly pubby bar here is named after Charles Dickens, who stayed here in 1838 on his way to start his research for *Nicholas Nickleby*. Well worth a visit in its own right, a very jolly larger-than-life Dickensian mural runs round the walls of the bar. It was painted in 1946 by J V Gilroy – more famous for his old Guinness advertisements, six of which are displayed on the walls here too. Big windsor armchairs and sturdy oak settles cluster around traditional cast-iron-framed tables, big windows look out on the extensive lawn, and there are nice open fires. There's a proper old shove-ha'penny board, with raisable brass rails to check the lie of the coins, cribbage and dominoes, and a TV for major sporting events. The attractively laid out garden has some seats, with teak tables in a pretty side area looking along to the graceful old bridge by the stately gates to Rokeby Park, and swings, a slide and a wendy house at the far end. Black Sheep, Timothy Taylors Landlord and Jennings Cumberland are well kept on handpump, and they've quite a few malt whiskies, and an extensive wine list; good service from the pleasant and professional staff. Freshly prepared and beautifully presented bar food includes soup (£2.95), sandwiches (from £4), chicken liver parfait with apricot and pear chutney (£5.50), steak and kidney pie (£8.95), wild mushroom and leek risotto (£9.95), cod, chips and mushy peas (£11.50), and sirloin steak (£15); they bake their own bread (which you can buy to take away). With a more elaborate menu, the no smoking bistro has wood floors and wrought iron, and is densely hung with paintings and prints (for sale) by local artists. *(Recommended by C A Hall, Derek and Sylvia Stephenson, Kay and Alistair Butler, Janet and Peter Race, Michael Doswell, David and Ruth Shillitoe, Mrs Jane Kingsbury, David and Jean Hall)*

Free house ~ Licensees Peter Phillips and Barbara Johnson ~ Real ale ~ Bar food (12-9.30) ~ Restaurant ~ (01833) 627232 ~ Children welcome ~ Dogs welcome ~ Open 11-11 (10.30 Sun) ~ Bedrooms: £65B/£90B

HALTWHISTLE NY7166 Map 10
Milecastle Inn
Military Road; B6318 NE – OS Sheet 86 map reference 715660

This cosily welcoming 17th-c dining pub is popular for its good value and rather tasty food, which is served in generous helpings – just right after a bracing walk in this famously bleak and scenic part of the county: good sandwiches (£3.50), as well as soup (£3), breaded garlic mushrooms (£3.95), battered haddock (£7.25), vegetable lasagne (£7.75), various much enjoyed home-made pies (£7.95), sirloin steak (£12.95), and daily specials such as venison in orange and brandy sauce or fish pie. It's worth getting here early for a table. The snug little rooms of the beamed bar are decorated with brasses, horsey and local landscape prints and attractive fresh flowers, and have two winter log fires; at lunchtime the small comfortable no smoking restaurant is used as an overflow. Friendly hard-working staff serve well kept Big Lamb and Prince Bishop, and they have a fair collection of malt whiskies, and a good wine list; piped music. The tables and benches out in a pleasantly sheltered big walled garden with a dovecote and rather stunning views are popular in summer, and there's a large car park. Being on the old Roman road from Newcastle, the pub is very handy for Hadrian's Wall. *(Recommended by Brenda Peery, R F Ballinger, Kay and Alistair Butler, Michael Doswell, Alex and Claire Pearse, Ray and Winifred Halliday, Jane Massam, Molly Crozier, Christine and Neil Townend, Melanie Christie, Gerry Miller, Dr D J and Mrs S C Walker, Mark and Ruth Brock)*

Free house ~ Licensees Clare and Kevin Hind ~ Real ale ~ Bar food (12-9; 12-3, 6-9 Oct-March) ~ Restaurant ~ No credit cards ~ (01434) 321372 ~ Children in eating area of bar and restaurant ~ Open 12-11(10.30 Sun); 12-3, 6-9 Oct-March

HEDLEY ON THE HILL NZ0759 Map 10
Feathers
Village signposted from New Ridley, which is signposted from B6309 N of Consett; OS Sheet 88 map reference 078592

Quality is the byword at this attractive old stone inn. They're not open as often as other pubs (see below), but when they are, they get things just right (it's a good idea to book). With such a friendly welcome and comfortable pubby atmosphere it's not surprising that locals pop in for a drink, with others coming from further afield for the beautifully prepared and sensibly priced food. A short but very appealing weekly changing menu might typically include celeriac, tomato and lentil soup (£3.50), salmon, prawn and dill pâté (£4.50), greek salad (£4.75), cannellini bean cakes with chilli and tomato salsa (£7.95), cumberland sausage with creamy cider and mustard sauce (£7.95), smoked haddock and spinach filled pancakes (£10.95), braised beef with shallots, wine, brandy and mushrooms (£10.95), and puddings such as ginger pudding with butterscotch sauce or very tasty chocolate fudge (£4.50). Three well kept turkey-carpeted traditional bars have an appealingly pubby atmosphere, with beams, open fires, stripped stonework, solid brown leatherette settles and old black and white photographs of local places and farm and country workers. Mordue Workie Ticket is well kept alongside three guests from brewers such as Big Lamp, Charles Wells and Harviestoun; also decent wines and around 30 malt whiskies. Shove-ha'penny, table skittles, cribbage and dominoes. They hold a mini beer festival at Easter with over two dozen real ales and a barrel race on Easter Monday. Picnic-sets in front are a nice place to sit and watch the world drift by. They accept only debit cards. *(Recommended by Jenny and Brian Seller, Paul Davies, Mr and Mrs W R Bolton, GSB, Mr and Mrs Pattison, Alex and Claire Pearse, Dr Richard Higgins, Keith Cohen)*

Free house ~ Licensee Marina Atkinson ~ Real ale ~ Bar food (not Mon except bank hols) ~ No credit cards ~ (01661) 843607 ~ Children in family room and lounge ~ Open 6-11; 12-3, 6-11(7-10.30 Sun) Sat; closed weekday lunchtimes except bank hols

LANGLEY ON TYNE NY8160 Map 10
Carts Bog Inn
A686 S, junction B6305

Handy if you're passing, the welcoming neatly kept main black-beamed bar at this isolated moorside pub has a blazing log fire in the central stone fireplace, local photographs and horsebrasses, and windsor chairs and comfortably cushioned wall settles around the tables. It rambles about, with flagstones here, carpet there, and mainly white walls with some stripped stone. A side lounge (once a cow byre) with more wall banquettes has pool; piped music; quoits pitch. Reasonably priced straightforward bar food, in generous helpings, includes sandwiches (from £2.50), soup (£3.50), baked avocado with stilton (£6.50), steak and ale casserole or beer-battered haddock (£7.50), thai lamb (£8), sirloin steak (£10), weekend specials such as seared salmon fillet with mediterranean vegetables (£9), and tasty puddings such as chocolate fudge cake and apple crumble (£3.50); quick amiable service even when busy. The no smoking restaurant has good views over the silvery dry-stone walls of high hilly sheep pastures, as do tables in the garden. Well kept Yates, and a couple of guests such as Greene King IPA and Jennings Cumberland on handpump, and they've around 30 malt whiskies. *(Recommended by Adam and Joan Bunting, Brian Brooks, Mart Lawton, Dr Graham Thorpe)*

Free house ~ Licensee Richard Bainbridge ~ Real ale ~ Bar food (12-2, 6.30-9) ~ Restaurant ~ (01434) 684338 ~ Children in restaurant ~ Dogs allowed in bar ~ Open 12-2.30, 5-11; 12-11(10.30 Sun) Sat; closed Mon lunchtime

LUCKER NU1631 Map 10

Apple

Village (and pub) well signposted off A1 N of Morpeth

Attractively refurbished a few years ago, this substantial village pub on the Duke of Northumberland's estate is kept spotless by its friendly newish licensees. The welcoming bar area has some walls stripped to show massive neatly dressed blocks of stone masonry, others painted a restful ochre, and some sturdy padded seats-for-two among other more usual pubby furnishings such as dark country-kitchen chairs and padded banquettes. The large brick-and-stone fireplace has a woodburning stove. Decoration is restrained, and the overall impression is of spacious civilised relaxation. The roomy and big-windowed side dining area on the left is fresh and airy, with flowers on the tables. The enjoyable food is given an uplift by quite a few individual touches, and vegetables are carefully cooked: soup (£3.25), sandwiches (from £3.95), ploughman's, chicken and bacon salad or cumberland sausage and mash (£5.95), pie of the day (£6.95), fish and seafood platter, artichoke, leek and potato bake (£8.95) and puddings such as vanilla cheesecake with black cherries or sticky toffee pudding (£3.85). The no smoking restaurant menu serves more ambitious dishes (evenings only). The short well chosen wine list is sensibly priced, with decent wines by the glass; it would be nice if they installed a cask-conditioned ale; piped music, darts and dominoes. The campsite behind the pub is completely separate. *(Recommended by Joan York, Michael Doswell, Bill and Sheila McLardy, R J Herd, C A Hall, Mr and Mrs D W Mitchell)*

Free house ~ Licensees Jane and Bob Graham ~ Bar food (12-2, 7-9; not Fri-Mon evenings) ~ Restaurant ~ (01668) 213450 ~ Children welcome ~ Dogs allowed in bar ~ Open 12-3, 6.30-11; 12-10.30(12-3, 7-10.30 winter) Sun; closed Mon lunchtime

NEWBURN NZ1665 Map 10

Keelman 🍺 £ 🛏

Grange Road: follow Riverside Country Park brown signs off A6085 (the riverside road off A1 on Newcastle's W fringes)

Built originally in 1854 as a pumping station, and converted in 1996, this unusual and rather distinguished-looking granite pub is the tap for the good Big Lamp Brewery, on the same site. The bar counter's impressive array of eight handpumps usually dispenses the full range, in top condition and at attractive prices, and if you're confused about which one to go for, the neatly dressed staff will happily let you sample a couple first – but beware of the aptly named Blackout, at 11%, it's very strong. With an easy-going atmosphere and attracting a good mix of customers, the high-ceilinged bar has lofty arched windows, making it light and airy, and it's not too crowded with tables (access for wheelchairs is easy). There are more tables in an upper gallery, and the modern all-glass no smoking conservatory dining area (pleasant at sunset) contrasts stylishly with the original old building. Service is first-class, and the hands-on landlord is quick to help out when needed, and the whole place is kept spick and span. Reasonably priced and served in generous helpings, straightforward food includes sandwiches (from £3.70), baked potatoes (from £3.75), beef and ale pie or large fish and chips (£6.15), grilled trout

(£6.25), and 10oz sirloin steak or a big mixed grill (£9.95), with puddings such as apple pie and custard (£3.40); they do an early evening special on weekdays from 5 till 7 (£4.50 for a selection of their main courses). Piped music and fruit machine. There are plenty of picnic-sets, tables and benches out on the terraces, among flower tubs and beds of shrubs. This is a great base for walks along the Tyne, with six up-to-date bedrooms in an adjoining block. *(Recommended by John Foord, Roger and Kathleen Lucas, Michael Doswell, Alex and Claire Pearse, Andy and Jill Kassube, Liz and Brian Barnard)*

Own brew ~ Licensee George Story ~ Real ale ~ Bar food (12-9) ~ Restaurant ~ (0191) 267 0772 ~ Children in eating area of bar and restaurant ~ Open 11-11; 12-10.30 Sun ~ Bedrooms: £44S/£62S

NEWCASTLE UPON TYNE NZ2563 Map 10
Crown Posada 🍺
The Side; off Dean Street, between and below the two high central bridges (A6125 and A6127)

This marvellously old-fashioned little gem is a favourite with many readers. Quite apart from being a very friendly place to come for a drink, this unspoilt pub (the second oldest in the city) is architecturally fascinating, and well worth a special visit if you're in town. A golden crown and magnificent pre-raphaelite stained-glass windows add grandeur to an already imposing carved stone façade, while inside highlights include the elaborate coffered ceiling, stained glass in the counter screens, a line of gilt mirrors each with a tulip lamp on a curly brass mount matching the great ceiling candelabra, and Victorian flowered wallpaper above brown dado. Fat low level heating pipes make a popular footrest when the east wind brings the rain off the North Sea. It's a very long and narrow room, making quite a bottleneck by the serving counter; beyond that, a long soft green built-in leather wall seat is flanked by narrow tables. There's a fruit machine, and an old record player in a wooden cabinet provides mellow background music when the place is quiet; dominoes. From half a dozen handpumps, Bass and Jennings and Timothy Taylors Landlord are kept in top condition alongside continually changing guests from brewers such as Durham, Jarrow and Mordue. The atmosphere is easy-going and chatty, and a good time to visit is during the week when regulars sit reading the papers in the front snug; at the weekend it's usually packed, but even then you'll get a warm welcome from the barmen. They don't do food, but at lunchtime you can get a sandwich with a packet of crisps for £1.50. It's only a few minutes' stroll to the castle. *(Recommended by Mike and Lynn Robinson, the Didler, Pete Baker, Tracey and Stephen Groves, Tim and Ann Newell, Andy and Jill Kassube, Tony and Wendy Hobden, R T and J C Moggridge, Eric Robinson, Jacqueline Pratt)*

Free house ~ Licensee Derek Raisbeck ~ Real ale ~ No credit cards ~ (0191) 232 1269 ~ Open 11-11; 7-10.30 Sun; closed Sun lunchtime

Head of Steam @ The Cluny 🍺 £
Lime Street (which runs between A193 and A186 E of centre)

Something a little different, this unusual pub shares an impressively refurbished early 19th-c former bonded whisky warehouse with several dozen artists and craftsmen who have studios here. Its back area functions as an interesting gallery for changing exhibitions of their paintings, sculptures and pottery, and for work by visiting artists. The friendly L-shaped bar is trendy and gently bohemian-feeling despite its minimalist décor, with slightly scuffed bare boards, some chrome seating and overhead spotlights. Around seven well kept real ales (though one reader was disappointed to find quite a few off), with quite a few from local brewers such as Adnams, Durham, Hadrian & Border, Jarrow, Mordue and Wylam; also rotating continental and american beers on tap, lots of bottled world beers, a good range of soft drinks, and a fine row of rums, malts and vodkas, not to mention banana smoothies £2. Simple bar food, served by cheerful staff, includes soup, sandwiches or toasties (£3), ploughman's, burgers, beef or spinach, chickpea and mushroom chilli (£4.50), daily specials, with puddings such as fudge cake (£2.50); Sunday roast (£6.50); it's all home-made so there may be a wait. A raised area looking down on the river (with much redevelopment work afoot) has comfortable seating including settees, with daily papers and local arts magazines. A separate room has a stage for live bands and comedy nights; disabled access and facilities, fruit machine and well reproduced piped music. To get here – opposite the Ship on Lime Street look out for a cobbled bank leading down to the Ouseburn, by the Byker city farm, and stretching down here, the pub (known to everyone locally as the Cluny) is below the clutch of bridges. *(Recommended by Russell Lewin, Mike and Lynn Robinson, Tracey and Stephen Groves)*

Head of Steam ~ Lease Dave Campbell ~ Real ale ~ Bar food (12-9) ~ (0191) 230 4475 ~ Children welcome ~ Live bands most nights ~ Open 12-1(12.30 Sun)

NEWFIELD NZ2033 Map 10
Fox & Hounds ♀

Turn off A688 at 'Willington, Newfield' signpost, or off A690 in Willington, into aptly named Long Lane; Newfield signposted off this, then turn left at Queens Head into Stonebank Terrace

Useful if you are in the area and want a good value snack lunch, this is quite restaurranty, though it still keeps a comfortable pub layout with a serving bar in the dining room, and a cosy carpeted ante-room with a three-piece suite in brown velour by an old cream-coloured kitchen stove in a high stone fireplace (good fires in winter). The comfortable and gently lit no smoking dining area has a polished wood-strip floor, with candles and flowers on the neatly laid tables all around its sides, big brass platters on its dark pink timbered walls, and mugs, tankards and whisky-water jugs hanging from beams skeined with fairy-lights. Big windows look down over steeply rolling countryside. The light lunch menu includes soup (£3.25), green thai chicken curry, mushroom and peanut butter stroganoff, sausage with borlotti beans, red onion and grenadine gravy and mash and lamb tagine with couscous (all £5.95). The much more elaborate à la carte menu includes queen scallops with lime and ginger (£4.75), salmon, pancetta, leek and sweet potato cake with steam ginger and chilli dip (£5.50), roast halibut steak with prawns, pecans and leek sauce (£12.95), duck breast with brandy and orange sauce (£14.95), and puddings such as tiramisu ice-cream profiteroles with warm chocolate sauce or rhubarb, ginger and marsala syllabub (£3.75); Sunday roast (£6.45). Saturday night gets fully booked well ahead. The house wines are good, but unfortunately no real ale; friendly service. More reports please. *(Recommended by M Lochore)*

Free house ~ Licensees William Thompson and Raymond Henry ~ Bar food (12-1.30, 7-8.30; not Mon, or Sun evening) ~ Restaurant ~ (01388) 662787 ~ Children over 12 weekdays midweek early evening and lunchtimes only ~ Open 12-3, 7-11; closed Mon

NEWTON-BY-THE-SEA NU2424 Map 10
Ship

Village signposted off B1339 N of Alnwick; Low Newton – paid parking 200 metres up road on right, just before village (none in village)

Run by a characterful landlady (who escaped up here several years ago) this rather special place is tucked charmingly into the top corner of a National Trust courtyard of low white-painted stone cottages, and looks down over a sloping grassy square to the broad beach, and beyond to off-shore rocks packed with seabirds and sometimes seals. It's essential to book in the evening, and we recommend a phone call before your visit as the opening times can vary, particularly in winter. Brilliantly simple cooking lets the marvellous quality of the fresh local, and quite often organic, ingredients shine through. A short lunchtime menu (when it's likely you'll be in the company of local walkers and their dogs) includes delicious local crab sandwiches (£3.50), warm goats cheese ciabatta (£4.50), free-range ham stottie (£5.50) and ploughman's with local unpasteurised cheese (£6.75). In the evening, when the atmosphere shifts a gear gently, the menu might include crab salad

(£8.50), venison rump steak with red wine and peppercorn sauce (£10.50), grilled wild sea trout (£11.50), scallops (£14.50), or local lobster (from £18), with puddings such as fruit crumble, sticky toffee pudding or good local ice-creams (£3.75). The plainly furnished bare-boards bar on the right has nautical charts on its dark pink walls, beams and hop bines. Another simple room on the left has some bright modern pictures on stripped-stone walls, and a woodburning stove in its stone fireplace. It's very quiet here in winter when they have just one or two local real ales. By contrast, they really only just cope when queues build up on hot summer days, and the beer range extends to two or three guests from brewers such as Durham, Hadrian & Border and Wylam; also decent wines, an espresso machine (colourful coffee cups, good hot chocolate), and good soft drinks. Out in the corner of the square are some tables among pots of flowers, with picnic-sets over on the grass. There's no nearby parking. *(Recommended by Joan York, Michael Doswell, Tracey and Stephen Groves, John Knighton, A C English, Tim and Suzy Bower, Comus and Sarah Elliott, Mike and Sue Loseby)*

Free house ~ Licensee Christine Forsyth ~ Real ale ~ Bar food (12-2.30, 7-8, not Sun and Mon evening) ~ No credit cards ~ (01665) 576262 ~ Children welcome ~ Dogs allowed in bar ~ Open 11-11; 12-10.30 Sun; 12-3, 8-11, and maybe closed Mon-Tues evening in winter

NEWTON-ON-THE-MOOR NU1605 Map 10
Cook & Barker Arms 🍴 🛏
Village signposted from A1 Alnwick—Felton

Very much a popular dining pub, this welcoming stone inn has an incredibly cheerful atmosphere, good food and a great choice of wines. Though most people are here for the generously served food, the relaxed and unfussy long beamed bar feels buoyantly pubby, with stripped stone and partly panelled walls, brocade-seated settles around oak-topped tables, brasses, a highly polished oak servery, and a lovely fire at one end with a coal-effect gas fire at the other. A no smoking eating area has an old settle, scrubbed pine furniture, and french windows leading on to the terrace; the top bar area is also no smoking; piped music. The well cooked changing bar menu could include broccoli and stilton soup (£3.25), parma ham and melon (£4.25), steak and onion pie or stir-fried vegetables with noodles, ginger and black bean sauce (£6.95), crab risotto with tiger prawns, parsley and cream (£7.95), mixed grill (£9.75), grilled halibut (£12.95) and puddings (£3.95), and there's a more elaborate restaurant menu. Four well kept ales on handpump rotate between Bass, Clarks Classic Brunette, Black Sheep, Fullers London Pride, Marstons Pedigree and Timothy Taylors Landlord; their extensive wine list includes a dozen by the glass, and they've also local bottled beer, and quite a few malt whiskies. *(Recommended by Joan York, Mrs J Ekins-Daukes, Prof and Mrs Tony Palmer, Michael and Margaret Slater, John and Sylvia Harrop, C A Hall, Keith and Margaret Kettell, Mike Green, Michael Doswell, Richard Cole, Clare and Peter Pearse, Tony Baldwin, Dr and Mrs R G J Telfer, Comus and Sarah Elliott)*

Free house ~ Licensee Phil Farmer ~ Real ale ~ Bar food (12-2, 6-9) ~ Restaurant ~ (01665) 575234 ~ Children welcome ~ Open 11-11; 12-10.30 Sun ~ Bedrooms: £45B/£70B

RENNINGTON NU2119 Map 10
Masons Arms 🛏
Stamford Cott; B1340 NE of Alnwick

The pleasantly modernised and comfortable beamed lounge bar at this immaculately cared for pub has wheelback and mate's chairs around solid wood tables on a patterned carpet, plush bar stools, and plenty of pictures (some may be for sale), photographs and brass. Under friendly new licensees, reasonably priced popular bar food (some home-made) includes soup (£2.95), craster kipper pâté or spicy chicken wings (£4.75), fried haddock (£6.95), curry of the day (£7.50), game casserole (£7.95), roast duck with orange sauce (£9.95), steak (from £12.95), daily specials such as fried camembert (£4.75) or steak and kidney pie (£7.50), and puddings such as berry crumble (£3.65). The no smoking dining rooms have pine panelling and wrought-iron wall lights. Hadrian & Border Gladiator and Secret Kingdom and possibly a guest are well kept on handpump; piped classical music. There are sturdy rustic tables on the little front lavender surrounded terrace, and picnic-sets at the back. Bedrooms are in an adjacent stable block and annexe. *(Recommended by S and N McLean, Joan York, D Digby, Richard Cole, Christine and Malcolm Ingram, Adam and Joan Bunting, Derek Stafford, Michael Doswell, Prof and Mrs Tony Palmer, Tony Baldwin, Alex and Claire Pearse, Michael J Caley, D S and J M Jackson)*

Free house ~ Licensees Bob and Alison Culverwell ~ Real ale ~ Bar food (12-2, 6.30-9) ~ Restaurant ~ (01665) 577275 ~ Children welcome ~ Dogs allowed in bedrooms ~ Open 12-11(10.30 Sun); 12-2.30, 6.30-11(10.30 Sun) winter ~ Bedrooms: £55B/£65B

ROMALDKIRK NY9922 Map 10
Rose & Crown ★ ⑪ ♀ 🛏
Just off B6277

In quite a special league, this handsome 18th-c country coaching inn is run with keen attention to detail, resulting in a charming environment, notably welcoming service and superbly cooked food (you do need to book). From a changing menu, and served by attentive professional staff, imaginative dishes might include lunchtime goats cheese ciabatta with sweet and sour red onions (£4.75) and ploughman's (£6.95), also baked cheddar and spinach soufflé (£4.75), seared tuna niçoise salad (£6.25), steak, kidney and mushroom pie (£9.75), coq au vin with leek risotto (£10.50), fried pigeon with vegetable rösti, onion confit and juniper berry sauce (£10.95), halibut baked with cotherstone cheese, cream and red onion marmalade (£12.95), and puddings such as baked vanilla cheesecake with stewed blackcurrants, dark rum and chocolate tart, or north country cheeses (£3.75). The enthusiastic licensees even make their own marmalades, jams, chutneys and bread. The emphasis when it comes to décor is on civilised comfort. The traditional cosy beamed bar has old-fashioned seats facing a warming log fire, a Jacobean oak settle, lots of brass and copper, a grandfather clock, and gin traps, old farm tools, and black and white pictures of Romaldkirk on the walls. Black Sheep and Theakstons Best are well kept on handpump alongside about a dozen wines, all of which you can have by the glass, and organic cordials. The smart brasserie-style Crown Room (bar food is served in here) has large cartoons of French waiters on dark red walls, a grey carpet and smart high-back chairs. The hall has farm tools, wine maps and other interesting prints, along with a photograph (taken by a customer) of the Hale Bopp comet over Romaldkirk church. There's also an oak-panelled restaurant. Lovely in summer, tables outside look out over the village green, still with its original stocks and water pump. The village is close to the excellent Bowes Museum and the High Force waterfall, and has an interesting old church. *(Recommended by Pat and Stewart Gordon, Lynda and Trevor Smith, Brian Brooks, Mike Green, Tony Baldwin, Jack Clark, Mike Turner, Mike and Sue Loseby)*

Free house ~ Licensees Christopher and Alison Davy ~ Real ale ~ Bar food (12-1.45, 6.30-9.30) ~ Restaurant ~ (01833) 650213 ~ Children welcome, must be over 6 in restaurant ~ Dogs welcome ~ Open 11-3, 5.30-11; 12-3, 7-10.30 Sun; closed 24-26 Dec ~ Bedrooms: £75B/£126B

SEAHOUSES NU2232 Map 10
Olde Ship ★ 🍺 🛏
Just off B1340, towards harbour

A rich sense of nautical history fills the atmospheric rooms of this friendly stone harbour-top hotel, not least as it's been in the same family for nearly 100 years – far back enough for the current licensees' ancestors to have been involved when this was an important fishing port. With its fascinating (and ever growing) collection of seafaring memorabilia, the entire bar is a tribute to the sea and seafarers – even the floor is scrubbed ship's decking and, if it's working, an anemometer takes wind speed readings from the top of the chimney. Besides lots of other shiny brass fittings, ship's instruments and equipment, and a knotted anchor made by local fishermen, there are sea pictures and model ships, including fine ones of the North Sunderland lifeboat, and Seahouses' lifeboat the *Grace Darling*. There's also a model of the *Forfarshire*, the paddle steamer that Grace Darling went to rescue in 1838 (you can read more of the story in the pub), and even the ship's nameboard. The bar is gently lit by stained-glass sea picture windows, and it has an open fire in winter. One clear glass window looks out across the harbour to the Farne Islands, and as dusk falls you can watch the Longstones lighthouse shine across the fading evening sky. The low-beamed Cabin Room is no smoking; piped music, dominoes, putting and quoits. Five well kept ales on handpump – Bass, Black Sheep, Courage Directors, Greene King Old Speckled Hen and Theakstons Best – rise to eight in summer months with guests such as Greene King Ruddles County, Hadrian & Border Farne Island and Hydes Fine and Dandy; also around 30 malt whiskies and a good choice of wines. Very tasty bar food, from a changing menu, could include a well liked crab soup (£3.75), chicken and mushroom casserole, fried plaice, smoked fish chowder or lamb curry (£8), with puddings such as chocolate trifle or steamed lemon pudding (£4.50). The pub is not really suitable for children though there is a little family room, and along with walkers, they are welcome on the battlemented side terrace (you'll even find fishing memorabilia out here). This and a sun lounge look out on the harbour. You can book boat trips to the Farne Islands Bird Sanctuary at the harbour, and there are bracing coastal walks, particularly to Bamburgh, Grace Darling's birthplace. *(Recommended by Joan York, Michael Doswell, Dr and Mrs T E Hothersall, Michael and Hilary Stiffin, Adam and Joan Bunting, the Didler, Alan Cole, Kirstie Bruce, Comus and Sarah Elliott, Brian and Janet Ainscough, Ian and Nita Cooper, Mike and Lynn Robinson, Mark Walker, Dr and Mrs R G J Telfer, Peter D La Farge, Andrew Storey, Keith and Chris O'Neill, Karen and Graham Oddey, D Lorking)*

Free house ~ Licensees Alan and Jean Glen ~ Real ale ~ Bar food ~ Restaurant ~ (01665) 720200 ~ Children in family room ~ Open 11-11; 12-10.30 Sun ~ Bedrooms: £50S/£100B

STANNERSBURN NY7286 Map 10 🏠

Pheasant

Kielder Water road signposted off B6320 in Bellingham

This homely old village pub is cosily spotless, with gleaming brass and wood, and a friendly welcome. The low beamed comfortable traditional lounge (no smoking) has ranks of old local photographs on stripped stone and panelling, red patterned carpets, and upholstered stools ranged along the counter. A separate public bar is similar but simpler, and opens into a further cosy seating area with beams and panelling. The evening sees a good mix of visitors and locals, when the small no smoking dining room can get quite crowded. Building up from one in winter, to four in the summer months, real ales might be from brewers such as Marstons, Timothy Taylor and Wylam, and they've just over 30 malt whiskies, and a decent reasonably priced wine list. Home-made bar food could include lunchtime sandwiches (from £2.50) and ploughman's (£6.25), also red onion and goats cheese tart (£4.75), garlic chicken breast salad (£6.95), and game and mushroom pie or roast lamb with redcurrant jus (£7.25). In the evening (when prices for the same dishes go up by a couple of pounds), you can also choose from a handful of more elaborate dishes such as grilled bass with lemon and parsley butter (£11.50) or confit of duck breast with port and raspberry glaze (£12.50). Puddings might be treacle sponge or lemon and lime cheesecake (£3.50); roast Sunday lunch (£7.25); piped music, dominoes. In a peaceful valley, with quiet forests all around, this is very handy for Kielder Water, just down the road, and the streamside garden is pleasant in summer, with picnic-sets, and a pony paddock behind. *(Recommended by Pat and Stewart Gordon, Richard and Karen Holt, David and Elizabeth Briggs, Prof and Mrs Tony Palmer, Jean and Douglas Troup, R Macfarlane, Ann and Stephen Saunders, Mark and Ruth Brock)*

Free house ~ Licensees Walter and Robin Kershaw ~ Real ale ~ Bar food ~ Restaurant ~ (01434) 240382 ~ Children welcome ~ Dogs allowed in bedrooms ~ Open 12-3, 6.30-11(7-10.30 Sun); closed Mon, Tues Nov-Mar ~ Bedrooms: £40S/£70S

STANNINGTON NZ2279 Map 10

Ridley Arms

Village signposted just off A1 S of Morpeth

Just off the A1, and very handily serving food all day, this big and more or less open-plan extended dining pub is cleverly laid out in a way that gives the feel of several separate relaxing areas, each slightly different in mood and style from its neighbours; even when it's busy it doesn't feel crowded. The front is a proper bar area, with darts and a fruit machine, and stools along the counter. The beamed dining areas, largely no smoking, lead back from here, with a second bar counter, comfortable armchairs and upright chairs around shiny dark wood tables on polished boards or carpet, with portraits and cartoons on cream, panelled or stripped stone walls, careful lighting and some horsey statuettes. Black Sheep and Timothy Taylors Landlord are well kept along with four guests from brewers such as Charles Wells, Jennings and Mordue on handpump, and they've ten wines by the glass. Generously served tasty bar food such as soup (£3.50), sandwiches (£3.95), chilli mussels (£4.50), asparagus and new potato tart (£4.75), sausage and mash or fried haddock (£7.95), parma ham wrapped chicken (£9.50), 10oz sirloin (£13), daily specials, and puddings such as lemon meringue pie or toffee nut tart (£4.50); Sunday lunch (£7.50). Disabled access is good; unobtrusive piped music, and dominoes. There are tables outside on a terrace. *(Recommended by Val and Alan Green, John Foord, Dr Peter D Smart, Adam and Joan Bunting, Gerry Miller, Comus and Sarah Elliott, Mr and Mrs D S Price, Keith Cohen)*

Sir John Fitzgerald ~ Managers Lynn and Gary Reilly ~ Real ale ~ Bar food (12-9.30(9 Sun)) ~ (01670) 789216 ~ Children in eating area of bar ~ Dogs welcome ~ Open 11.30-11; 12-10.30 Sun

THROPTON NU0302 Map 10

Three Wheat Heads

B6341

Popular with older folk going for a meal out, this comfortable stone-built 17th-c village hotel has a fairly sedate dining atmosphere. The carpeted bar on the right and the pleasant and roomy flock-wallpapered dining area have wheelback chairs around neat rows of dark tables, heavily cushioned brocaded seats, good coal fires (one in a fine tall stone fireplace) and comfortable bar stools with backrests. Bar food includes soup (£2.95), fried brie or chicken satay (£3.95), battered cod (£6.95), vegetable curry (£7.50), steak and mushroom pie (£8.25), chicken breast stuffed with roquefort (£8.95), and gateaux and cheesecakes (£3.75); the restaurant is no smoking. Friendly staff serve well kept Marstons Pedigree and Theakstons and possibly a guest such as Black Sheep on handpump; darts, dominoes, cribbage, TV and piped music. An attractive garden has lovely views towards the Simonside Hills, a play area and a dovecote. More reports please. *(Recommended by June and Ken Brooks, Dr and Mrs T E Hothersall, Keith and Margaret Kettell, Derek Stafford, Stuart Orton, Dave Braisted, D Lorking)*

Punch ~ Lease Danny and Elke Scullion ~ Real ale ~ Bar food (12-2.30, 6-9.15) ~ Restaurant ~ (01669) 620262 ~ Children welcome ~ Dogs allowed in bar ~ Open 11-3, 6-11; 11(12 Sun)-11 Sat ~ Bedrooms: £42B/£65B

If a service charge is mentioned prominently on a menu or accommodation terms, you must pay it if service was satisfactory. If service is really bad you are legally entitled to refuse to pay some or all of the service charge as compensation for not getting the service you might reasonably have expected.

WELDON BRIDGE NZ1399 Map 10

Anglers Arms 🛏

B6344, just off A697; village signposted with Rothbury off A1 N of Morpeth

Make sure you're hungry if you eat at this substantial hotel – the enjoyable bar food comes in huge helpings: dishes might include soup (£3.25), black pudding with cheese sauce and poached egg (£4.95), sandwiches (from £5.95), cod and chips or steak and ale pie (£7.95), spinach and ricotta cannelloni (£8.25), steak sandwich or lime and coriander chicken (£8.95), blackened cajun salmon (£9.95) and puddings such as white chocolate crème brûlée or banana split (£4.45). Nicely lit and comfortable, the traditional turkey-carpeted bar is divided into two parts: cream walls on the right, and oak panelling and some shiny black beams hung with copper pans on the left, with a grandfather clock and sofa by the coal fire, staffordshire cats and other antique ornaments on its mantelpiece, old fishing and other country prints, some in heavy gilt frames, a profusion of other fishing memorabilia, and some taxidermy. Some of the tables are lower than you'd expect for eating, but their chairs have short legs to match – different, and rather engaging. The no smoking side restaurant in a former railway dining car is more formal but light and airy, with crisp white linen and a pink carpet. Timothy Taylors Landlord is well kept on handpump alongside a couple of guests such as Everards Tiger and Greene King Old Speckled Hen, also decent wines and an espresso machine. There are tables in the attractive garden with a good play area; they have rights to fishing on a mile of the River Coquet just across the road. *(Recommended by Dr and Mrs S Donald, Anne Evans, John and Sylvia Harrop, H Bramwell, Mart Lawton, David and Heather Stephenson, Dr and Mrs R G J Telfer)*

Free house ~ Licensee John Young ~ Real ale ~ Bar food (12-2, 6-9.30) ~ Restaurant ~ (01665) 570271 ~ Children welcome ~ Dogs allowed in bedrooms ~ Open 11-11; 12-10.30 Sun ~ Bedrooms: £37.50S/£60S

LUCKY DIP

Besides the fully inspected pubs, you might like to try these Lucky Dips recommended to us and described by readers (if you do, please send us reports: www.goodguides.co.uk).

ACOMB [NY9366]
Miners Arms [Main St]: Charming small 18th-c country pub with well kept Durham Magus, Jennings Cumberland, Yates and a guest beer, good value simple home cooking by landlady (not wkdy lunchtimes) from sandwiches to good value Sun lunch, comfortable settles, huge fire in stone fireplace, children in dining room; small garden behind, has been open all day Sun and summer *(Len Beattie, Andy and Jill Kassube, Gerry Miller)*
ALNMOUTH [NU2511]
Hope & Anchor [Northumberland St]: Recently reopened, with friendly helpful young staff, manageable choice of food inc some enterprising dishes, well kept beer, pleasant dining room; dogs welcome, good value bedrooms *(B Christie, Bill and Sheila McLardy)*
☆ *Red Lion* [Northumberland St]: Relaxed and informal 16th-c inn, four well kept ales inc local Hadrian & Border, good choice of mainly new world wines by the glass, good value food from wholesome generous lunchtime sandwiches, crusty baguettes and panini to evening meals in pleasant gallery restaurant, daily fresh fish and Tues-Thurs

tapas, log fire in nicely old-fashioned panelled bar full of theatre bills and memorabilia; shame about the piped pop music; children and dogs welcome, neat garden by alley with raised deck looking over Aln estuary, comfortable bedrooms, generous breakfast, quietly appealing coastal village, open all day Sun, cl Mon in winter *(Bill and Sheila McLardy, Michael Doswell, Dr Roger Smith, Judy Nicholson, Comus and Sarah Elliott)*
☆ *Saddle* [Northumberland St (B1338)]: Unpretentious and hospitable stone-built hotel rambling through several areas inc spacious dining area, wide choice of good attractively priced pubby food inc particularly good cheeseboard, popular Sun lunch, choice of helpings size, pleasant efficient service even when busy, well kept ales such as Greene King Old Speckled Hen and Theakstons Best, games room with ping pong as well as pool etc, no smoking restaurant; unobtrusive piped music; children welcome, open all day Sat, tables outside, comfortable bedrooms, attractive beaches, good coastal walks *(Bill and Sheila McLardy, LYM, Dr Peter D Smart)*
BAMBURGH [NU1834]
Lord Crewe Arms [Front St]: Small hotel prettily set in charming coastal village

dominated by Norman castle, log fire and dark furniture inc some settles in two carpeted bar rooms, Bass and a guest beer such as Fullers London Pride, good choice of wines by the glass, short choice of lunchtime bar food comprising sandwiches, baguettes and a few light and main dishes, good food in separate modern restaurant; short walk from splendid sandy beach, comfortable bedrooms, good breakfast esp kippers *(Michael Dandy, LYM)*

☆ *Victoria* [Front St]: Substantial hotel with lots of mirrors and pictures in two-part peaceful panelled bar, enjoyable quickly prepared bar food all day from sandwiches up, two well kept rotating ales from Black Sheep and/or Mordue, decent wines by the glass, caring young staff, good menu in stylish more upmarket no smoking brasserie, young children's playroom; comfortable bedrooms (popular with coach parties), lovely setting, open all day *(Michael Dandy, Comus and Sarah Elliott)*

BEADNELL [NU2229]

New Beadnell Towers: Doing well under new owners, with good atmosphere and food, and reasonable prices; comfortable bedrooms – dogs welcome in hotel *(Aubrey and Janet Gibson)*

BEAMISH [NZ2153]

Beamish Mary [off A693 signed No Place and Cooperative Villas, S of museum]: Friendly down-to-earth pub, quiet lunchtime, with 1960s-feel mix of furnishings, bric-a-brac, 1920s/30s memorabilia and Aga, Durham NUM banner in games room, attentive helpful staff, up to seven well kept changing ales, interesting choice of good value very generous bar food, good Sun lunch (best to book), coal fire, annual beer festival; piped music, children allowed until evening, live music most nights in converted stables concert room; bedrooms *(Richard Houghton, Mark Walker)*

☆ *Shepherd & Shepherdess*: Very useful for its position nr outstanding open-air heritage museum, efficient friendly staff, good range of quick fairly priced straightforward food, well kept ales, decent wines, coal fires, tables around walls of spacious lounge; piped music; children welcome, tables and play area with glass-fibre monsters out among trees, open all day *(LYM, Mark Walker)*

☆ *Sun* [far side of Beamish Open Air Museum – paid entry]: Turn-of-the-century pub moved from Bishop Auckland as part of the lively and excellent museum; very basic real period feel at quieter times, with costumed barmaid, well kept Theakstons, good cold snacks, big coal fire *(LYM, Keith and Chris O'Neill)*

BELSAY [NZ1277]

☆ *Highlander* [A696 S of village]: Comfortable and roomy country dining pub, generous good value food from good lunchtime sandwiches up in extensively refurbished side bar and open-plan dining area, nice plain wood tables, plenty of nooks and corners for character, reasonable prices, welcoming helpful service, well kept Black Sheep, Hadrian & Border and Timothy Taylors ales, good log fires, separate

locals' bar; unobtrusive piped music; open all day, handy for Belsay Hall and Gardens *(Comus and Sarah Elliott)*

BERWICK-UPON-TWEED [NT9952]

☆ *Barrels* [Bridge St]: Convivial pub with unconventional mix of styles – thorough-going nautical décor in bar, car memorabilia, Beatles pictures and interesting pine furniture inc old school desks in lounge; well kept ales such as Black Sheep and Fullers London Pride, good malt whisky choice, lunchtime filled rolls, imaginative evening food (perhaps not Mon) from snacks and tapas to main dishes, friendly accommodating staff; live music downstairs, good juke box; open all day *(David Field, Michael Butler)*

☆ *Foxtons* [Hide Hill]: More chatty and comfortable two-level wine bar than pub, with lively side bistro, but does have three or four well kept ales such as Caledonian Deuchars IPA and 80/- and Timothy Taylors Landlord, wide choice of good imaginative food, good range of wines, whiskies and coffees, impressive friendly service; busy, so worth booking evenings, cl Sun *(Joe Green, John and Sylvia Harrop, David Field, Ian and Nita Cooper, Michael Butler, Comus and Sarah Elliott)*

☆ *Rob Roy* [Dock View Rd/Dock Rd, Spittal (Tweedmouth)]: Quiet and cosy seaview restaurant (rather than pub, though they do bar meals too) with good fresh local fish and outstanding speciality fish soup, dark fishing-theme rustic bar with roaring fire and polished wood floor, pleasant dining room, friendly chatty landlord; keg beers but decent wines and good fresh coffee; bedrooms, may be cl wkdy lunchtimes out of season *(Michael Butler)*

BIRTLEY [NZ2856]

Mill House [Blackfell; handy for A1 southbound, just S of Angel, off A1231 Sunderland/Washington slip rd]: Popular and busy extended dining pub with enjoyable food all day, compact bar area, two changing real ales, decent house wines, no smoking dining room with olde-barn décor, alcoved eating areas and conservatory *(Gerry and Rosemary Dobson)*

Moulders Arms [Peareth Terr]: Busy pleasantly refurbished local by church in old part of village, small public bar, no smoking raised back area in comfortable lounge allowing children, friendly helpful staff, good value substantial plain cooking (till 10 evenings) from lunchtime sandwiches up, well kept changing mainstream ales; garden *(Mark Walker, Gerry and Rosemary Dobson)*

BISHOPTON [NZ3621]

Talbot [The Green]: Wide choice of popular food from good value sandwiches with chips and salad up, friendly efficient service, long modern bar with teak furniture and banquettes, wartime memorabilia, compact dining rooms each end *(Peter Hacker)*

BOWES [NY9913]

☆ *Ancient Unicorn*: Substantial stone inn with some 17th-c parts and interesting *Nicholas*

Nickleby connection, obliging chatty licensees who look after their real ales carefully (spring beer festival), good value generous food from sandwiches to steak, pleasant atmosphere in spacious and comfortable open-plan bar with small but earnest open fire, coffee shop; good-sized clean bedrooms in converted stables block around big cobbled courtyard *(Ian Thurman, LYM, Jack Clark)*

CHATTON [NU0528]

☆ *Percy Arms* [B6348 E of Wooller]: Stone-built inn with neat lounge bar extending through arch, well kept beers and plenty of malt whiskies, enjoyable food in bar and attractive panelled dining room from lunchtime baguettes up, cheerful efficient staff, public bar with games; piped music; children in good family area and dining room, picnic-sets on small front lawn, bedrooms (12 miles of private fishing) *(Joan York, D Digby, Mark and Cath Caley, R J Herd, LYM, Bob Ellis, Prof and Mrs Tony Palmer)*

CHESTER-LE-STREET [NZ2652]

Plough [High Flatts, NW of centre]: Country inn with friendly local atmosphere, Wadworths 6X and guest beers, panoramic views of Angel of the North and Penshaw Monument *(Mr and Mrs Maurice Thompson)*

CONSETT [NZ1151]

Grey Horse [Sherburn Terr]: Well run two-bar beamed 19th-c pub brewing its own Derwent Rose beers in former back stables, inc Red Dust, Steel Town and The Works recalling the former steel works here; also a guest beer, dozens of malt whiskies, occasional beer festivals, very friendly licensees, cheap basic food such as doorstep sandwiches, good toasties and all-day breakfast, good range of customers, pool; pavement tables, open all day *(Richard Houghton, Andy and Jill Kassube)*

CORBRIDGE [NY9964]

Angel [Newcastle Rd]: Small 17th-c hotel with good fresh food (not cheap by northern standards) from sandwiches to stylish restaurant meals, large bar and adjoining plush panelled lounge, well kept Black Sheep and two local guest beers, good wines and coffees, friendly service; bedrooms, nr lovely bridge over River Tyne *(LYM, Andy and Jill Kassube, Michael Doswell)*

Black Bull [Middle St]: Roomy unpretentious pub, old-fashioned and low-ceilinged, with comfortable mix of seating inc traditional settles in stone-floored bar, four changing well kept ales, good attractively priced wine choice, friendly atmosphere, brisk service, roaring fire, several linked no smoking eating areas with usual food all day from sandwiches up inc reasonably priced light lunches; open all day *(Gerry Miller, Peter and Eleanor Kenyon)*

☆ *Robin Hood* [East Wallhouses, Military Rd (B6318 5 miles NE)]: Unpretentious pub with generous food inc good steak baguettes (choice widest in good-sized candlelit back restaurant), Theakstons Best and two other real ales, beamed lounge with blazing fires, lots of bric-a-brac and interesting carved settles, great views from bay window, quick friendly service even when busy, daily papers, piped music *(Gerry Miller)*

Wheatsheaf [Watling St/St Helens St]: Big refurbished stone-built village hotel, popular esp with older lunchers for wide choice of generous food (all day summer wknds) from sandwiches to seasonal game and tender Sun roasts, quick service by cheerful helpful staff, well kept Jennings Cumberland and Marstons Pedigree, good choice of wines and malt whiskies, pleasant Victorian décor in no smoking dining lounge and big warm conservatory restaurant with distant hill views; pub games, piped music, some picnic-sets outside; bedrooms *(John Foord, LYM)*

CRAWCROOK [NZ1363]

Rising Sun [Bank Top]: Roomy and well refurbished, bright and welcoming, with huge choice of hearty popular food (all day Fri-Sun) inc good panini and proper pies, well kept quickly changing real ales from good small breweries, cheerful staff, long bar with steps up to lounge, pool room, dining area and conservatory; neatly kept garden, open all day *(John Foord)*

DUNSTAN [NU2419]

☆ *Cottage* [off B1339 Alnmouth—Embleton]: Big family dining pub with low beams and lots of dark wood, some stripped brickwork, banquettes and dimpled copper tables, generous reasonably priced lunches and evening meals, all-day sandwiches and snacks inc good local kippers, well kept Belhaven, Wylam and a guest beer, young staff who do their best, no smoking conservatory, medieval-theme restaurant, games area; children welcome, tables out on flowery terrace and lawn, good adventure play area *(Prof and Mrs Tony Palmer, LYM, Mike and Lynn Robinson, Tony Baldwin, Revd John E Cooper)*

DURHAM [NZ2642]

Colpitts [Colpitts Terr/Hawthorn Terr]: Basic friendly two-bar local with particularly cheap Sam Smiths, sandwiches, open fires, pool; TV and machines, folk music most nights; perhaps the country's smallest beer garden in yard, open all day *(Patrick Hancock, the Didler)*

Court Inn [Court Lane]: Good generous home-made food all day from sandwiches to steaks and late-evening bargains in unpretentious traditional town pub's extensive no smoking stripped brick eating area, real ales such as Hancocks HB and Worthington 1744, no mobile phones; bustling in term-time with students and teachers, piped pop music; seats outside, open all day *(Pete Baker, BB)*

☆ *Dun Cow* [Old Elvet]: Very welcoming and unspoilt traditional town pub in pretty 16th-c black and white timbered cottage, tiny chatty front bar with wall benches, corridor linking it to long narrow back lounge with banquettes, machines etc (can be packed with students), particularly well kept Castle Eden and other ales such as Boddingtons, good value lunchtime soup and sandwiches etc, friendly staff; piped music; children welcome, open all day Mon-Sat, Sun too in summer *(LYM,*

Pete Baker, the Didler, Patrick Hancock, Tracey and Stephen Groves)

Old Elm Tree [Crossgate]: Big busy pub on steep hill opp castle, two-room main bar and small lounge, prompt cheerful service, open fires, several well kept ales, farm cider; TV, machines, juke box, Tues folk night; small back terrace, open all day wknds *(the Didler)*

Shakespeare [Saddler St]: Unchanging pub with signed actor photographs in busy basic front bar, charming panelled snug and neatly refurbished back room, friendly staff, simple cheap bar snacks, lots of malt whiskies, well kept McEwans 80/- with guest beers such as Hydes and Theakstons Best, pub and board games; children welcome, open all day – convenient for castle, cathedral and river *(LYM, Tracey and Stephen Groves)*

Swan & Three Cygnets [Elvet Bridge]: Comfortably refurbished Victorian pub in good bridge-end spot high above river, city views from big windows and picnic-sets out on terrace, friendly service, bargain lunchtime food from hot filled baguettes up, cheap well kept Sam Smiths OB; open all day *(Mike and Lynn Robinson, BB, Nick Holding)*

EBCHESTER [NZ1055]

☆ **Derwent Walk** [Ebchester Hill (B6309 outside)]: Friendly pub by the Gateshead—Consett walk for which it's named, wide range of reliably enjoyable home-made food from interesting sandwiches through speciality cobblers and interesting dishes of the day to steaks, full Jennings range kept well and a guest beer, good wine range, good log fire and appealing old photographs in character bar, conservatory with fine Derwent Valley views; walkers welcome, pleasant heated terrace *(Michael Doswell, Andy and Jill Kassube)*

ELWICK [NZ4532]

McOrville [¼ mile off A19 W of Hartlepool]: Open-plan L-shaped bar with carved panelling, friendly young licensees (he does the cooking – a frequently changing enjoyable choice), Black Sheep and Timothy Taylors Landlord *(JHBS)*

EMBLETON [NU2322]

☆ **Sportsman**: Large bar and dining room in well sited pub/hotel with stunning views to Dunstanburgh Castle, well kept Hadrian & Border real ales, good individual evening cooking mainly using local produce, fish and game at reasonable prices, good value lunchtime baguettes, small well chosen wine list, friendly cheerful service; frequent wknd live music; lots of terrace tables, bedrooms, not far from beach *(Michael Doswell, Mr and Mrs J Hale)*

FELTON [NU1800]

☆ **Northumberland Arms** [village signed off A1 N of Morpeth]: Attractive pub with beams, stripped stone and good coal fires in roomy and comfortable open-plan bar, nice mix of furnishings inc big blue settees, elegant small end restaurant; good range of food, well kept Bass and Black Sheep Best, good coffee and wines, pleasant atmosphere, laid-back service; well reproduced piped music, esp in conservatory pool room, monthly live music

1st Weds; five bedrooms, steps down to bench by River Coquet, open all day *(John Oddey, BB, Mike and Lynn Robinson)*

GATESHEAD [NZ2758]

Lambton Arms [Rockcliffe Way, Eighton Banks]: Comfortably updated no smoking pub with good range of good value food in bar and restaurant (should book wknds), well kept Greene King IPA, Abbot and Old Speckled Hen, good reasonably priced wine choice, pleasant friendly service; children welcome, open all day *(Christine and Phil Young, Gerry and Rosemary Dobson)*

Three Tuns [Sheriffs Highway (B1296)]: Good music pub with live bands most nights, well kept beers inc three or four changing guest ales *(Mark Goddard)*

HALTWHISTLE [NY7566]

Twice Brewed [B6318 NE]: Busy pub handy for the wall, well kept local ales such as High House Auld Hemp and Redburn Summus, good value food from baguettes and burgers through hearty main dishes to nice proper puddings, cheerful staff; open all day, tables outside *(Andy and Jill Kassube)*

HARTLEPOOL [NZ5233]

Harbour of Refuge [Croft Terrace, The Headland]: Well worn in two-bar pub and restaurant overlooking harbour entrance, panoramic coastal views and interesting local port photographs, good local fish as well as traditional lunchtime pub food (can be a bit slow with large groups), low prices, coal fire; keg beers; open all day Fri/Sat *(John Cook)*

HAYDON BRIDGE [NY8364]

☆ **General Havelock** [A69]: Civilised and individually furnished dining pub, same great care going into interesting baguettes as into imaginative hot dishes using fresh local ingredients from open-view kitchen, well kept changing local ales, good wines by the glass and coffee, efficient service and relaxing atmosphere, open fires, more upmarket evening set menus in smart Tyne-view stripped stone restaurant; children welcome, tables on terrace *(Andy and Jill Kassube, LYM, Michael Doswell)*

HOLWICK [NY9126]

Strathmore Arms [back rd up Teesdale from Middleton]: Quiet and cosy unspoilt country pub in beautiful scenery just off Pennine Way, welcoming landlord, good home cooking at attractive prices, well kept ales such as Youngs Waggle Dance, log fire, darts, piano; bedrooms and camp site, open all day *(Mr and Mrs Maurice Thompson)*

HOLY ISLAND [NU1241]

☆ **Crown & Anchor**: Comfortable pub/restaurant with emphasis on enjoyable interesting food from good fresh ciabattas up, small cheerful bar, well kept Caledonian Deuchars IPA, good wines by the glass and fresh coffee, friendly efficient young staff, pleasant pink and beige décor with interesting rope fancy-work, spotless bright modern back dining room; three bedrooms *(Michael Doswell, Val and Alan Green, Mrs Ann Gray)*

Ship [Marygate; causeway passable only at low

tide, check times (01289) 330733]: Nicely set summer pub, spotless bar with no smoking bare-boards eating area off and some seaside decorations, straightforward pub food from filled stotties up, well kept Hadrian & Border Blessed and Theakstons in summer, good choice of whiskies; no dogs, even in garden; three comfortable Victorian-décor bedrooms, may close for a while Jan/Feb *(Michael Dandy, Val and Alan Green, Anne Evans, Mr and Mrs Staples)*

HORSLEY [NZ0966]

Lion & Lamb [B6528, just off A69 Newcastle—Hexham]: New chef doing good food (not Sun evening) from sandwiches to interesting dishes at reasonable prices, up to eight well kept changing ales inc local ones, cafetière coffee, attentive well trained staff, two main rooms, small smart restaurant, no smoking area, stripped stone, flagstones, panelling, untreated tables and chairs; views of Tyne from attractive garden with roomy terrace and particularly good adventure play area, open all day *(John Oddey, Gerry Miller, John Foord)*

HUMSHAUGH [NY9171]

Crown: Quiet old village pub with enjoyable generous home cooking, cheerful bar, comfortable separate dining room, welcoming staff, decent wines; dogs allowed exc at busy times, bedrooms *(John Oddey)*

LAMESLEY [NZ2557]

Ravensworth Arms [minor rd S of Gateshead western bypass, A1, Team Valley junction]: Largely no smoking stone-built Chef & Brewer, stripped brick and recycled timber dividers, reasonably priced popular fresh food from sandwiches and baked potatoes to steak, fish and game, cheerful helpful staff, good wine choice, three or four real ales; piped music, can be busy evenings; children welcome, play area and picnic-table sets outside, 13 bedrooms, open all day *(Mark Walker)*

LONGBENTON [NZ2768]

Benton Ale House [Front St]: Small, friendly and comfortable, with ales such as Adnams, Banks's, Batemans XXB, Camerons Strongarm and Marstons Pedigree in lined glasses, good cheap simple lunchtime food from hot and cold sandwiches up, friendly staff, TV alcove, back room with pool, juke box and machines; good disabled facilities, open all day *(Mike and Lynn Robinson)*

LOWICK [NU0139]

☆ *Black Bull* [Main St (B6353, off A1 S of Berwick-upon-Tweed)]: Good warmly welcoming service in nicely decorated country pub, good choice of plentiful good value food from good soup and sandwiches up (take-aways too), well kept Belhaven 60/- and 70/- and Theakstons, comfortable main bar, small back bar, big back dining room; children welcome, three attractive bedrooms, on edge of small pretty village *(Michael and Hilary Stiffin, Mr and Mrs Staples, Bill and Sheila McLardy)*

MIDDLESTONE [NZ2531]

Ship [Low Rd]: Half a dozen well kept and interesting often local real ales at competitive prices, welcoming licensees and warm friendly

atmosphere, good fire, great view, beer festivals and lots of other events; piped music; cl wkdy lunchtimes, open all day Fri-Sun *(Ann and Brian Denton, Nigel Sharman, G Jackson)*

MITFORD [NZ1785]

Plough [just off A1 Morpeth bypass]: Roomy and welcoming open-plan family-friendly pub in small village, has had several successive management changes but current friendly landlord/chef looks set to stay, doing enjoyable food from substantial hot sandwiches to a hefty mixed grill all home-made and largely locally sourced (he puts his heart into the puddings), well kept Theakstons Best and a weekly guest, cafetière coffee with home-made shortbread, comfortable bay-window banquettes, lacy tablecloths in dining end; small play area *(Christopher and Jo Barton, Michael Doswell)*

☆ **MORPETH** [NZ1985]

☆ *Sun* [High Church]: Large open-plan pub with emphasis on food using fresh local ingredients from good generous baguettes, wraps and baked potatoes through traditional pubby things to enterprising contemporary cooking, well kept Caledonian Deuchars IPA and a guest such as Adnams Broadside, decent wines, smiling efficient service even when busy, good-sized partly stripped stone beamed dining area, more basic bar (which can be smoky) with pool beyond; piped music *(Michael Doswell)*

NETHERTON [NT9807]

Star [off B6341 at Thropton, or A697 via Whittingham]: Unchanging local in superb remote countryside, neat and spartan, with many original features, well kept Castle Eden tapped from cellar casks and served from hatch in small entrance lobby, large high-ceilinged room with panelled wall benches, charming landlady and welcoming regulars; no food, music or children; usually open evenings and Sun lunchtime *(the Didler, RWC)*

NEWCASTLE UPON TYNE [NZ2464]

Bacchus [High Bridge East, between Pilgrim St and Grey St]: Chic new look with large comfortable lounge area, relaxed atmosphere, good modern food from interesting doorstep sandwiches and ciabattas through unusual light dishes to more substantial things all at keen prices, well kept changing ales such as Hook Norton Old Hooky, Mordue Workie Ticket, Stones and Timothy Taylors Landlord; open all day *(Michael Doswell, Andy and Jill Kassube)*

Bodega [Westgate Rd]: Majestic Edwardian drinking hall, colourful walls and ceiling, snug front cubicles, spacious tiled back area with a handsome rug under two magnificent original stained-glass domes (has been a mosque); well kept Big Lamp Prince Bishop, Durham Magus, Mordue Geordie Pride (sold here as No 9) and three guest beers tapped from the cask, friendly service, lunchtime food, table football; juke box or piped music, machines, big screen TV, busy evenings; open all day, next to Tyne Theatre *(the Didler, Tracey and Stephen Groves, Kevin Blake)*

☆ **Bridge Hotel** [Castle Sq, next to high level bridge]: Big cheery high-ceilinged room divided into several areas leaving plenty of space by the bar with replica slatted snob screens, particularly well kept Black Sheep, Caledonian Deuchars IPA, Durham, Mordue Workie Ticket and three guest beers, decent lunchtime food and Sun afternoon teas, magnificent fireplace, great views of river and bridges from raised back no smoking area; sports TV, piped music, fruit machines, very long-standing Mon folk club upstairs; tables on flagstoned back terrace overlooking section of old town wall, open all day *(LYM, John Foord, Mike and Lynn Robinson, Kevin Blake, the Didler)*

☆ **Cooperage** [The Close, Quayside]: Ancient building in good waterfront setting, great atmosphere in stripped stone bar and cosy beamed lounge, good choice of well kept ales, hearty fresh sensibly priced lunchtime food, lively evenings with upstairs night club; pool, juke box; disabled facilities, cl Sun lunchtime *(LYM, the Didler)*

Cumberland Arms [Byker Buildings]: Friendly traditional local with particularly well kept Wylam ales (tapped straight from the cask if you wish), basic sandwich-type food, obliging staff; live music most nights, cl lunchtime *(R T and J C Moggridge)*

Fitzgeralds [Grey St]: Handsomely refurbished Victorian pub in elegant street on fringe of Bigg Market, lots of levels and alcoves (two short sets of steps between entrance, main area and lavatories), discreet lighting, red mahogany and polished brass, Black Sheep, Mordue Workie Ticket and two guest beers, wide range of good value lunchtime food (not Sun) inc freshly baked baguettes; can get very busy wknds, piped music, machines; open all day, cl Sun lunchtime *(Kevin Blake)*

Hotspur [Percy St]: Cheerful smallish Victorian pub with big front windows and decorated mirrors, good spread of customers (not just the youth market), well kept Courage Directors, McEwans 80/-, Theakstons Best and Old Peculier and three guest beers, farm cider, lots of bottled belgian beers, good value wine, sandwiches and hot snacks all day; piped music, machines, big-screen sports TV, can get packed, esp pre-match, upstairs ladies'; open all day *(John Foord, GSB)*

Lloyds No 1 [Keel Row, The Gate, Newgate St]: Good service even when fairly packed, decent well priced food inc two-for-one offers, well kept ales; large courtyard *(Tim and Ann Newell)*

Newcastle Arms [St Andrews St]: Open-plan pub on fringe of chinatown, well kept Black Sheep, Fullers London Pride or ESB and guest beers, occasional mini beer festivals, friendly staff, decent food till 6 inc sandwiches, interesting old local photographs; piped music, big-screen sports TV, can get very busy esp on match days; open all day *(Mike and Lynn Robinson)*

Tyne [Maling St]: Busy pub at end of quayside walk by confluence of Ouseburn and Tyne, plastered with band posters and prints –

frequent live music upstairs; Black Sheep, Durham Magus, a Mordue beer and a guest, exotic hot or cold sandwiches all day, interesting free CD juke box; fruit machine, sports TV, stairs up to lavatories; fairy-lit garden (loudspeakers out here too) under an arch of Glasshouse Bridge, barbecues, open all day *(Mike and Lynn Robinson, Gerry Miller)*

NORTH HYLTON [NZ3557]

☆ **Shipwrights** [Ferryboat Lane; N bank of River Wear almost under the A19 bridge]: Welcoming pubby feel in cosy bar and eating area of small riverside hotel, great log fire, chamber-pots and copper pans hanging from beams, good value pubby food from hot filled baps to Sun roasts, well kept ales such as Jennings Cumberland, Marstons Pedigree and Wadworths 6X, good friendly service; bedrooms *(Andy and Jill Kassube)*

NORTH SHIELDS [NZ3470]

☆ **Magnesia Bank** [Camden St]: Lively well run refurbished Victorian pub, roomy bar with raised eating areas, half a dozen or more well kept ales inc Black Sheep, Durham, Jarrow and Mordue in lined glasses, good wines and coffee, vast choice of cheerful home-made lunchtime food from cheap toasties to local lamb and fish, super puddings, good value all-day breakfast from 8.30am, attentive friendly uniformed staff and approachable chef, intriguing mix of customers, open fire, no smoking side restaurant (same menu); quiet piped pop music, TV, machines, upstairs comedy nights, live music Thurs and Sun; children welcome, tables outside, open all day *(Mike and Lynn Robinson, John and Gloria Isaacs, Kevin Thorpe, D J Etheridge, Mr and Mrs M Brandrith)*

PONTELAND [NZ1871]

Badger [Street Houses; A696 SE, by garden centre]: Well done Vintage Inn, more character than most pubs in the area, relaxing rooms and alcoves, old furnishings and olde-worlde décor, flagstones, carpet or bare wood, timbered ceilings, stripped stone, brick and timbering, real fires, Bass, Tetleys and Fullers London Pride, good choice of wines by the glass and good hot drinks, friendly attentive uniformed staff; quiet piped music, all-day food *(Michael Doswell, BB, A H C Rainier)*

RENNINGTON [NU2118]

☆ **Horseshoes**: Neat and comfortable flagstone pub, very popular locally, with sociable and helpful landlord, well kept Bass and Hadrian & Border Gladiator, simple bar with lots of horsebrasses, enjoyable hearty fresh food inc two-course lunch deals and good local meat and smoked fish, efficient service, spotless compact restaurant with blue and white china; children welcome, tables outside, attractive quiet village nr coast *(Robert M Warner, G Dobson, Michael Doswell)*

ROCHESTER [NY8497]

Redesdale Arms [A68 3 miles W of Otterburn]: Neatly rebuilt borders hotel with friendly landlord and attentive young staff, decent traditional food inc local organic lamb and fresh veg, changing ales such as Fullers,

Timothy Taylors Landlord or Theakstons, good wine choice; good bedrooms (A Rellie, Martin Sandilands, D Lorking)

ROTHBURY [NU0501]

☆ *Newcastle Hotel*: Small solid Victorian hotel in imposing spot at end of green, comfortably refurbished lounge with separate dining area, second bar, friendly service and entertaining locals, good plentiful carefully prepared food from filled baguettes to substantial Sun lunch, cheap high teas 3.30-5.30 Apr-Oct, toasties only winter Sun pm, Caledonian Deuchars IPA and Greene King Abbot and Old Speckled Hen, no smoking upstairs dining room; piped music; good value comfortable bedrooms with own bathrooms, pretty village with river walks, handy for Cragside (NT), open all day (Patrick Hancock, Mrs M Granville-Edge, Alex and Claire Pearse)

Queens Head: Cheery chatty bar with welcoming attentive service, good value food from massive sandwiches and good chips up, Bass, Greene King IPA and Worthington; bedrooms (Mr and Mrs Staples)

SEDGEFIELD [NZ3528]

Dun Cow [Front St]: Large two-bar village inn with comfortable dining room, wide changing food choice from well filled sandwiches to game, fresh whitby fish and unusual puddings, prompt friendly service, Castle Eden and good range of guest beers, whiskies in great variety; children welcome; good bedrooms sharing bathrooms (Peter Hacker, T and P)

SHINCLIFFE [NZ2940]

Seven Stars [High St N (A177 S of Durham)]: 18th-c village pub with coal fire in largely no smoking lounge bar, food from sandwiches up in bar or no smoking candlelit dining room, well kept ales inc Black Sheep, quick pleasant service; piped music; dogs welcome, children in eating areas, some tables outside, simple bedrooms with own bathrooms, open all day (LYM, Charles and Pauline Stride, Comus and Sarah Elliott)

SLALEY [NY9757]

Rose & Crown: Early 18th-c village pub newly tied to Jennings with their beers kept well, good value home-made standard food from sandwiches to restaurant meals, welcoming service, comfortable dark-beamed lounge hung with lots of mugs and jugs, public bar with darts etc; tables in small neat garden, quiet village with views behind, bedrooms attractive and well equipped (Andy and Jill Kassube)

☆ *Travellers Rest* [B6306 S of Hexham (and N of village)]: Attractive stone-built country pub, spaciously opened up inside, with farmhouse-style décor, beams, flagstones and polished wood floors, comfortable high-backed settles forming discrete areas; enjoyable food (not Sun evening) from well filled baguettes and simple hot dishes (12-5) to more inventive and enterprising mealtime dishes in bar and pretty dining room, good children's menu, friendly staff, five well kept ales such as Black Sheep, Greene King, Mordue and Wylam Whistlestop, decent wines; dogs welcome, tables outside with well equipped adventure play area behind,

three good value bedrooms, open all day (Andy and Jill Kassube, Mr and Mrs C Walker, Dr D J and Mrs S C Walker)

SOUTH SHIELDS [NZ3567]

Alum Ale House [Ferry St (B1344)]: Stylish and relaxed 18th-c pub handy for ferry, big bars with polished boards, coal fire in old inglenook range, pictures and newspaper cuttings, well kept Banks's, Camerons, Marstons and guest beers, tea and coffee, good beer festivals, good value basic lunchtime bar food from filled stotties up; piped music, machines, some live music; children welcome, open all day (Mike and Lynn Robinson, Andy and Jill Kassube)

Steamboat [Mill Dam/Coronation St]: Masses of interesting nautical bric-a-brac esp in split-level back room, friendly landlord, well kept Black Sheep, Timothy Taylors Landlord and local guest beers such as Jarrow, Mordue and Whitby, bargain stotties, pool in central area; usually open all day, nr river and market place (Andy and Jill Kassube, Mike and Lynn Robinson)

ST JOHN'S CHAPEL [NY8838]

Blue Bell [Hood St]: Particularly friendly and relaxing, cosy and clean, with real fires, well kept Theakstons, darts, dominoes, pool and juke box; Sun quiz night (Jane Massam, Molly Crozier)

STAMFORDHAM [NZ0772]

Bay Horse [off B6309]: Friendly and chatty licensees eager to please in comfortable long beamed bar, wide attractively priced food choice from fresh lunchtime baguettes with chips through homely hot dishes such as mince and dumplings to fish and grills, good veg and thoughtful children's dishes, three well kept ales, good coffee; dogs welcome, doubles as shop and post office, at end of green in attractive village (Mike and Lynn Robinson, Bill and Sheila McLardy, Michael Doswell)

STOCKTON-ON-TEES [NZ4217]

☆ *Masham* [Hartburn village, southern outskirts]: Four small rooms each with its own character, from black and gold flock wallpaper to panelling, with showy chandeliers; well kept Black Sheep Special, a guest such as Timothy Taylors Landlord and very good whisky collection, good cheap baps, sandwiches and hot meals (not Sat/Sun evenings) inc succulent Sun roasts, keen dominoes players, occasional live music; attractive garden with aviary and play area backing on to paddock, open all day, nr end of Castle Eden walkway (Simon Woodward, JHBS)

Sun [Knowles St]: Friendly town local specialising in particularly well kept Bass, well served at tempting price, quick service even when busy; folk night Mon, open all day (the Didler)

SUNDERLAND [NZ3857]

Darwin Bar [Tavistock Ropery, Websters Bank, Deptford]: Bar in large converted industrial building (complex also includes popular brasserie and italian restaurant), tap for Darwin brewery a mile or two away, their beers kept well in cellar visible through glass

wall, inc new brews on trial or launch
(Steven Proudfoot)

THROPTON [NU0302]

☆ *Cross Keys* [B6341]: Attractive little three-room village local, hearty pub food from good value baguettes to plenty of North Shields fish, well kept Bass, hard-working young licensees, open fires in cosy beamed main lounge, small modern back restaurant, darts; satellite TV; nice steeply terraced garden looking over village to the Cheviots, open all day at least in summer *(LYM, Michael Doswell)*

WALDRIDGE [NZ2550]

Inn on the Green [off B6532 Durham—Stanley, and signed from Chester-le-Street centre]: Upmarket dining pub recently smartly reworked with deep sofas and armchairs in bar, comfortable banquettes at well spaced tables in adjoining dining room, modern décor in shades of brown with indoor shrubs and illuminated objets, good imaginative contemporary cooking, Charles Wells Bombardier and Worthington, good coffee, friendly unpretentious service; by Waldridge Fell, one of the last surviving low-level moors, cl Mon *(Michael Doswell)*

WARDEN [NY9166]

Boatside [½ mile N of A69]: Extended dining pub with good range of fresh bar food from soup and good sandwiches to steaks, friendly attentive service, well kept Jennings and Wadworths 6X, interesting bric-a-brac and World War II memorabilia, warm pastel décor, restaurant and smaller dining room; small neat enclosed garden, attractive spot by Tyne bridge *(Bruce Field, Mart Lawton, Dr D J and Mrs S C Walker)*

WARENFORD [NU1429]

☆ *Warenford Lodge* [off A1 3 or 4 miles S of Belford]: Good meals using fresh local ingredients in slightly quirky place with simple 1960s décor, stripped stone, steps up to comfortable extension, warm fires, friendly if sometimes far from speedy service, decent wines, malt whiskies, farm-pressed fruit juices and teas (keg beer); children in eating areas, cl Mon, Tues-Fri lunchtimes, and also in winter Sun evening and Tues *(Joan York, BB, Sam and John Pallett, LYM, Comus and Sarah Elliott)*

WARKWORTH [NU2406]

☆ *Hermitage* [Castle St]: Rambling local with interesting quaint décor, old range for heating, well kept Jennings and John Smiths, enjoyable generous food from sandwiches to fresh local fish, quick service even when busy, dry-humoured landlord and staff, dining area and small plush upstairs restaurant; TV or piped music; bedrooms, tables out in front, attractive setting *(BB, John Cook)*

Warkworth House [Bridge St]: Hotel not pub, but unusual in having a proper bar with darts, bar billiards and a real ale (Greene King Old Speckled Hen); friendly atmosphere, comfortable sofas, helpful staff, good choice of spirits, enjoyable food, decent wines and

coffee; dogs welcome; bedrooms comfortable, open all day *(Comus and Sarah Elliott)*

WEST AUCKLAND [NZ1926]

Manor House [Front St]: Handsome and substantial stone-built hotel with good bar lunches inc popular Sun roast, real ale such as Black Sheep and Courage Directors, and a log fire (and beehive bread oven) in the attractive bar's massive stone fireplace, separate brasserie and restauran; comfortable bedrooms *(Andy and Jill Kassube)*

WEST MOOR [NZ2770]

George Stephenson [Great Lime Rd; northern outskirts of Newcastle]: Nicely refurbished, with friendly staff, good choice of well kept interesting changing northern ales such as Durham, Northumberland and Wylam, frequent bargains; good busy live music nights Weds, Thurs and Sat; dogs welcome, nice garden beside Stephenson's railway track, open all day *(Mike and Lynn Robinson)*

WHITFIELD [NY7857]

Elks Head [off A686 SW of Haydon Bridge]: Straightforward open-plan pub, light and spacious, with some stripped stone, friendly obliging service, good value food from generous thick-cut sandwiches up, real ales, good coffee, games area and piano; occasional live entertainment; children welcome, picnic-sets in small pretty front garden with quoits, bedrooms, lovely scenic area *(Michael Doswell)*

WHITLEY BAY [NZ3473]

Briardene [The Links]: Spotless brightly decorated and very well furnished two-room seaside pub with well kept Timothy Taylors Landlord and other interesting changing ales, frequent mini beer festivals, good value hearty food, friendly efficient staff; seats outside with play area, open all day *(Andy and Jill Kassube)*

WINSTON [NZ1416]

Bridgewater Arms [B6274, just off A67 Darlington—Barnard Castle]: Attractively converted Victorian school house, fine snugs, pictures of old station and school plays, interesting food inc early evening bargains, changing real ales such as Greene King Abbot and Timothy Taylors Landlord *(Andrew York)*

WYLAM [NZ1265]

☆ *Boathouse* [Station Rd; across Tyne from village, handy for Newcastle—Carlisle rail line]: Increasingly popular riverside pub, convivial and well run, tap for local Wylam with their ales kept well and other northern beers on nine handpumps, keen prices with one cut-price bargain, good choice of malt whiskies, good cheap fresh filled buns and simple wknd hot dishes inc popular Sun lunch, clean bright low-beamed lounge bar with roaring woodburner; poor disabled access, loud band nights; children and dogs welcome, small garden, open all day *(Mr and Mrs Maurice Thompson, John Foord, G Coates, Richard Houghton, Michael Doswell, Mike and Lynn Robinson, Tony and Wendy Hobden)*

Nottinghamshire

Two new entries here are well worth a special mention: the Muskham Inn at North Muskham, barely a stone's throw from the A1 and a splendidly relaxing refuge from it, with good food; and the immaculately kept Chequers by the canal at Ranby, an appealing and individual all-rounder. Other pubs earning warm praise these days are the chatty Victoria in Beeston (exceptional changing beer range, great choice of other drinks, and good value interesting food), the civilised Caunton Beck in Caunton (very good if not cheap food all day from 8 in the morning), the spotless and welcoming Waggon & Horses in Halam (its imaginative cooking gains it a Food Award this year, and it has good value weekday lunchtime and early evening meal deals), and the homely Dovecote at Laxton (friendly young staff, sensibly priced generous food, comfortable bedrooms). Since their arrival in late 2003, the tenants of the Waggon & Horses in Halam have steered its food into the big time; it is Nottinghamshire Dining Pub of the Year. Nottingham itself is packed with pubs serving good beer and bargain food, and many of these have tremendous character. The half dozen we describe fully as main entries are all most interesting, and the Lucky Dip section at the end of the chapter includes another 18 – we'd single out the Lion. Elsewhere, Lucky Dip pubs to note particularly are the Horse & Plough in Bingham, Nelson & Railway in Kimberley, Beehive at Maplebeck, Square & Compass at Normanton on Trent, Red Lion at Thurgarton and Stratford Haven in West Bridgford. Drinks prices in the county are generally far lower than the national average. Local brews such as Hardys & Hansons and, particularly, Castle Rock (the house beers for the good small local Tynemill pub group) hit the price/quality target spot on. Pubs brewing their own also give outstanding beer value here.

BEESTON SK5338 Map 7
Victoria ⑪ ♀ ◥

Dovecote Lane, backing on to railway station

Thriving happily, this converted railway hotel is run with real passion and commitment by former Tynemill director, chef Neil Kelso. Down to earth but welcoming, it stocks a hugely impressive choice of drinks, and serves enjoyable very fairly priced food. Three unpretentious downstairs rooms have kept their original long narrow layout, and have simple solid traditional furnishings, very unfussy décor, stained-glass windows, stripped woodwork and floorboards (woodblock in some rooms), newspapers to read, and a chatty atmosphere. Service remains quick and polite even during very busy peak times; dominoes, cribbage and maybe piped music. The lounge and bar back on to the railway station, and a covered heated area outside has tables overlooking the platform, with trains passing just a few feet away. They run through as many as 500 different beers each year, widely sourced changing guests coming from a great range of brewers such as Brakspear, Buffys, Oakham, Ossett, St Peter and Wentworth, and well kept alongside the house beers – Castle Rock Harvest, Hemlock and Ryland and Everards Tiger. The full pump complement is a dozen. They've also continental draught beers, farm ciders, over 100 malt whiskies, 20 irish whiskeys, and even over two dozen wines by the glass. A lively time to visit is during their two-week beer and music festival at the end of

July. Bar food is listed on a daily changing blackboard, and might include filled rolls (from £1.80), sausage and mash, and half a dozen vegetarian dishes such as penang vegetable curry or penne with goats cheese, tomato and rocket pesto (£6.95), beef bourguignon or roast pork catalan (£8.95), a spanish platter (£13.95 for two), puddings such as chocolate mousse or almond tart (from £2.95), and a good cheese board (£4.95). The much loved wolfhound lurcher cross pub dog is called Fritz. Parking is limited and readers have warned us about active parking wardens in the area. *(Recommended by David Eberlin, C J Fletcher, Simon and Mandy King, John and Wendy Allin, Andy and Ali, the Didler, Peter and Eleanor Kenyon, R M Taylor, Kevin Blake, Brian and Ruth Archer, R Brackenbury, Mark and Mary Fairman)*

Free house ~ Licensees Neil Kelso and Graham Smith ~ Real ale ~ Bar food (12-8.45(7.45 Sun)) ~ (0115) 925 4049 ~ Children in dining areas till 8pm ~ Dogs allowed in bar ~ Live music Sun and jazz Mon evenings Sept-May ~ Open 11-11; 12-10.30 Sun

CAUNTON SK7460 Map 7
Caunton Beck 🍴 ♀
Main Street; village signposted off A616 Newark—Ollerton

Most readers feel the beautifully presented and very good food at this delightfully civilised dining pub is worth the slightly higher than normal outlay, but if you do balk at the prices, their set menu is more reasonable (two courses £11, not Saturday evening or Sunday lunchtime). Something is served at most times of the day, starting with a hearty english breakfast (£7.95) first thing, then later going onto delicious sandwiches (from £5.95), and a fairly elaborate quarterly changing menu (with a handful of daily specials) such as soup (£4.75), garlic and rosemary sardines with pancetta and toasted pine nuts (£5.95), potted shrimps (£6.95), sausage and mash (£9.50), mushroom and tarragon ravioli with soft poached egg and gruyère (£11.50), seared bass fillet with tomato, olive and basil compote (£14.50) and fillet steak with béarnaise sauce (£17.95) and puddings such as honeycomb and caramel crème brûlée or honey and whisky jelly with red berry compote (£4.75); no smoking restaurant. The building itself is almost new, but as it was reconstructed using original timbers and reclaimed oak, around the skeleton of the old Hole Arms, it seems old. Scrubbed pine tables, clever lighting, an open fire and country-kitchen chairs, low beams and rag-finished paintwork in a spacious interior make for a relaxed atmosphere. With lots of flowers and plants in summer, the terrace is a nice place to sit when the weather is fine. About half the wines (around 30) on the very good wine list are available by the glass, and they've well kept Batemans XB, Marstons Pedigree and a guest such as Maypole Lions Pride on handpump; also espresso coffee. Service is pleasant and attentive; daily papers and magazines, no music. *(Recommended by Adrian White, Richard Marjoram, R F Ballinger, Blaise Vyner, Michael Doswell, Joyce and Geoff Robson, David and Ruth Hollands, Ray and Winifred Halliday, Derek and Sylvia Stephenson, Stephen Woad, R Brackenbury, Alison and Pete, Gerry and Rosemary Dobson, Steve Harvey)*

Free house ~ Licensees Julie Allwood and Toby Hope ~ Real ale ~ Bar food (8am-10.30pm) ~ Restaurant ~ (01636) 636793 ~ Children in eating area of bar and restaurant ~ Dogs allowed in bar ~ Open 8am-12 midnight

CAYTHORPE SK6845 Map 7
Black Horse 🍺
Turn off A6097 450 metres SE of roundabout junction with A612, NE of Nottingham; into Gunthorpe Road, then right into Caythorpe Road and keep on

Quaint and old-fashioned, this lovely little 300-year-old country local has been run by the same family for many years, and gives the impression that it exists in a different era. The timelessly uncluttered carpeted bar has just five tables, with brocaded wall banquettes and settles, a few bar stools hosting cheerful evening regulars, a warm woodburning stove, decorative plates on a delft shelf and a few horsebrasses on the ceiling joists. The landlady herself serves the tasty Caythorpe Dover Beck which is brewed here and is well kept alongside two or three changing guest beers such as Adnams and Greene King Morland Original. Off the front corridor is a partly panelled inner room with a wall bench running right the way around three unusual long copper-topped tables, and quite a few old local photographs; down on the left an end room has just one huge round table; darts and dominoes. Simple, but very enjoyable reasonably priced food from a shortish list includes soup (£2.25), prawn cocktail or cod roe on toast (£3.25), king prawns in chilli sauce (£3.50), fried cod, haddock or plaice (£7.50), seafood salad (£8.75), fillet steak (£13), daily specials such as cottage pie (£7), and puddings such as banana ice-cream cake and treacle sponge (from £2.75). Booking is essential. The entire pub is no smoking at lunchtime (except on Sunday). There are some plastic tables outside, and the River Trent is fairly close, for waterside walks. *(Recommended by R and M Tait, Derek and Sylvia Stephenson, the Didler, W M Paton, R Brackenbury)*

Own brew ~ Licensee Sharron Andrews ~ Real ale ~ Bar food (12-1.45, 7-8.30; not Sat evening, or Sun) ~ Restaurant ~ No credit cards ~ (0115) 966 3520 ~ Dogs allowed in bar ~ Open 12-2.30, 5(6 Sat)-11; 12-5, 7(8 in winter)-10.30 Sun; closed Mon exc bank hols when they close Tues lunchtime instead

ELKESLEY SK6975 Map 7
Robin Hood
High Street; village well signposted just off A1 Newark—Blyth

This fairly low key pub is a handy stop if you're on the A1 – though the right turn if you're heading north can be tricky. The neatly kept roomy carpeted dining room and lounge area are cheery with a pleasant mix of dark wood furniture; TV and dominoes. Changing bar food might include baked egg, spinach and cheese (£6), ham hock terrine with plum and apple chutney (£6.50), chicken curry or red onion and goats cheese filo tart (£10.50), sausage and mash (£11), and puddings such as cherry pie or Baileys crème brûlée (£4.50). The set menu (two-course £11, three-course £14, not Friday-Sunday) is good value. One bar and the dining room are no smoking. Marstons Pedigree is well kept on handpump. The garden (which is moderately well screened from the A1) has picnic-sets and a play area.
(Recommended by Edward and Deanna Pearce, Richard Cole, Brian Brooks, Martin and Jane Bailey, MJVK, Joyce and Geoff Robson, A J Bowen, Kevin Thorpe, Derek and Sylvia Stephenson, Mike and Linda Hudson, R T and J C Moggridge, Ian Phillips, Mr and Mrs J E C Tasker, MJB, Dr and Mrs R G J Telfer, Irene and Ray Atkin)

Enterprise ~ Lease Alan Draper ~ Real ale ~ Bar food ~ Restaurant ~ (01777) 838259 ~ Children welcome ~ Dogs allowed in bar ~ Open 11.30-2.30, 6.30-11; closed Sun evening, Mon lunchtime

HALAM SK6754 Map 7
Waggon & Horses 🍽
Off A612 in Southwell centre, via Halam Road
Nottinghamshire Dining Pub of the Year

Unanimously good reader reports for the consistently well prepared food, and a good value two-course offer (£11.50, lunchtimes and 6pm to 7pm Monday-Thursday), at this welcoming heavily oak-beamed dining pub earn it a new Food Award this year. Served by cheery staff, the often quite inventive menu includes lunchtime rolls or baked potatoes with unusual fillings such as ham, stilton and apricot (from £3.95) and ploughman's (£6.50), as well as starters such as cauliflower cheese soup with crispy bacon (£3.75), chunky hungarian fish soup (£7.50), seared red mullet with sweet potato, chorizo and bean salad (£6), and main courses such as spinach and beetroot tart with grilled halloumi and parsley and walnut pesto (£10), seared calves liver with sage jus (£11), cod stuffed with sun-dried tomato butter with minted pea purée (£12) and rib-eye steak with stilton, mushroom and port sauce (£12.50) and a couple of daily specials such as tuna steak with red pepper coulis and baked aubergine (£14). Spotlessly kept, the bright and cheery open-plan area has a pleasant dining atmosphere (though drinkers are welcome), and is well divided into smallish sections (an appealing black iron screen dividing off the no smoking part is made up of tiny african-style figures of people and animals). Good sturdy high-back rush-seat dining chairs are set around a mix of solid mainly stripped tables, there are various wall seats, smaller chairs and the odd stout settle too, with lots of pictures ranging from kitten prints to Spy cricketer caricatures on walls painted cream, brick red and coffee; candles throughout give a pleasant night-time glow. Three Thwaites beers are well kept on handpump; piped jazz (which was a bit loud for one reader). Out past a piano and grandfather clock in the lobby are a few roadside picnic-sets by the pretty window boxes. *(Recommended by David Glynne-Jones, W M Paton, Phil and Jane Hodson, Colin Fisher, Derek and Sylvia Stephenson, CMW, JJW, Michael Doswell, R Brackenbury)*

Thwaites ~ Tenants Rebecca and William White ~ Real ale ~ Bar food (12-2.30(3 Sun), 6-9.30; not Sun evening) ~ Restaurant ~ (01636) 813109/816228 ~ Children welcome ~ Dogs welcome ~ Open 12-2.30, 5.30-11; 12-11 Sat; 12-10.30 Sun

LAXTON SK7267 Map 7
Dovecote 🛏
Signposted off A6075 E of Ollerton

Readers really enjoy this very welcoming redbrick free house, which manages to maintain a pubby atmosphere, despite the popularity of the food (you may need to book). Served by very friendly and courteous staff, fairly priced dishes come in big helpings and might include soup (£3.25), sandwiches (from £3.75), grilled goats cheese salad (£4.50), garlic prawns (£5.95), steak and kidney pie (£6.99), mushroom stroganoff (£8.50) and scampi (£8.25), with specials such as chicken and mushroom cream pie (£7.99), battered cod (£8.99), bass stuffed with prawns (£9.99) and pork medallions in mushroom and brandy cream (£10.99). The puddings, such as cheesecake (£3.50) are made by Aunty Mary, the landlord's aunt, who lives in the village. The central lounge has dark wheelback chairs and tables on wooden floors, and a coal-effect gas fire. This opens through a small bay (the former entrance) into a carpeted no smoking dining area. Around the other side, another little lounge leads through to a pool room with darts, fruit machine, pool, dominoes and piped music. They have well kept Marstons Pedigree and a couple of guests from brewers such as Charles Wells and Wychwood on handpump and around ten wines by the glass. There are wooden tables and chairs on a small front terrace by a sloping garden, which has a disused white dovecote. It's handy for the A1, and as well as the two bedrooms, they have a site and facilities for six caravans. The pub stands next to three huge medieval open fields as Laxton is one of the few places in the country still farmed using the traditional open field system. Every year in the third week of June the grass is auctioned for haymaking, and anyone who lives in the parish is entitled to a bid – and a drink. You can find out more at the visitor centre behind the pub. *(Recommended by Mr and Mrs D W Mitchell, Richard Cole, Patrick Hancock, W and P J Elderkin, Keith and Chris O'Neill, Ian Phillips, Comus and Sarah Elliott, T and P)*

Free house ~ Licensees Stephen and Betty Shepherd ~ Real ale ~ Bar food (12-2, 6.30(7 Sun)-9) ~ Restaurant ~ (01777) 871586 ~ Children welcome ~ Dogs allowed in bar ~ Open 11.30-3, 6.30(6 Sat)-11(7-10.30 Sun) ~ Bedrooms: £35B/£50B

MORTON SK7251 Map 7
Full Moon
Pub and village signposted off Bleasby—Fiskerton back road, SE of Southwell

This friendly dining pub is tucked away in a remote hamlet not far from the River Trent. L-shaped and beamed, the main part (partly no smoking) has pink plush seats and cushioned black settles around a variety of pub tables, with wheelback chairs in the side dining area, and a couple of fireplaces. Fresh flowers and the very long run of Christmas plates on the walls add a spot of colour; look out for the two sociable pub cats. Charles Wells Bombardier, Greene King Ruddles (which they call Full Moon), Shepherd Neame Spitfire and a changing guest are well kept on handpump, and service is friendly; piped music that one reader felt was a little loud.

Lots of effort has gone into the garden which comprises a peaceful back terrace with picnic-sets, with more on a sizeable lawn, and some sturdy play equipment. Enjoyable food includes soup (£2.95), home-made pâté with cumberland sauce (£4.25), caesar salad (£7.95), steak and kidney pie (£8.25), parsnip and chestnut bake or grilled sea bream (£9.95), mixed grill (£12.25) and puddings such as lemon brûlée or treacle sponge pudding (£3.95); two-course OAP bargain lunch (£6.50). *(Recommended by the Didler, David Glynne-Jones, Patrick Hancock, Derek and Sylvia Stephenson, Ian and Nita Cooper, Paul and Margaret Baker, Eric Robinson, Jacqueline Pratt, R Brackenbury, Phil and Jane Hodson)*

Free house ~ Licensees Clive and Kim Wisdom ~ Real ale ~ Bar food (12-2(2.30 Sun), 6.30(7 Sun)-9.30(10 Fri, Sat);) ~ Restaurant ~ (01636) 830251 ~ Children welcome ~ Open 11-3, 6-11; 12-3, 7-10.30 Sun

NORTH MUSKHAM SK7958 Map 7
Muskham Inn
Just off A1 4 miles N of Newark; take Ollerton Newark B6325 exit, pub is on exit roundabout

This has recently developed into a very handy and civilised retreat from the A1; it looks as if funds for the conversion may have been somewhat limited, but they have squeezed a lot of appeal out of what may have been a fairly tight budget. Lots of soft dark leather settees crowd around low tables in the bar, which has a log fire, tabloids to read, and fresh flowers on the tables, though little decoration on its red walls. Big windows look up to the traffic spinning silently by; there may be laid-back piped music. The modern bar counter has well kept Timothy Taylors Landlord and Charles Wells Bombardier on handpump, a good choice of wines by the glass, and a full range of good coffees and teas; service is polite, and they have Scrabble and other board games. Behind here is a spacious dining area, with a relaxed country décor, and comfortably cushioned wicker seats around well spaced tables on the tiled floor. They take care over their ingredients (aberdeen angus beef and corn-fed chickens on GM-free rations, for instance, and free-range eggs), and with careful cooking the results are good. The bar menu includes club sandwich (£7), venison sausages with garlic crushed potato, chicken breast and penne in honey, wholegrain and cream sauce or lemon and lime battered haddock (£8), and daily specials such as watercress and spring onion soup (£4), mackerel baked in tomato, garlic and chorizo (£10) and cod fillet wrapped in parma ham with horseradish cream (£13). There are tables out on a sheltered terrace behind, under cover. We have not yet had reports from anyone staying in the well equipped modern bedrooms, which are in a separate block. *(Recommended by Derek and Sylvia Stephenson)*

Punch ~ Tenant Rebecca Drew ~ Real ale ~ Bar food (12-2, 6-9; not Mon-Weds evening) ~ Restaurant ~ (01636) 704010 ~ Children in restaurant ~ Open 12-11(10.30 Sun); 5-11 Tues; closed Tues lunchtime ~ Bedrooms: £50B/£60B

NOTTINGHAM SK5640 Map 7
Bell 🍺 £
Angel Row, off Market Square

Dwarfed by the office tower next door, this 500-year-old building is reputed to have formed part of a Carmelite friary. Its venerable age is clearly evident throughout – some of the original timbers have been uncovered, and in the front Tudor bar you can see patches of 300-year-old wallpaper (protected by glass). This room is perhaps the brightest, with french windows opening (in summer) to tables on the pavement, and bright blue walls. The room with the most historical feel is the very pubby and sometimes quite smoky low-beamed Elizabethan Bar, with its half-panelled walls, maple parquet floor and comfortable high-backed armchairs. Upstairs, at the back of the heavily panelled Belfry (usually open only at lunchtime, when it functions as a family restaurant), you can see the rafters of the 15th-c crownpost roof, and you can look down on the busy street at the front. The cellars, about ten metres down in the sandstone rock, were dug by Norman monks (tours 7.30pm Tues). Eight real ales include Hardys & Hansons, Kimberley Bitter, Mild, Olde Trip, William Clark (brewed for the pub) and one of their seasonal brews, and three or four guests from thoughtfully sourced brewers such as Burton Bridge, RCH and Tring. These are well kept alongside about 11 wines by the glass, quite a few malt whiskies and a farm cider; fruit machine and piped music. Reasonably priced straightforward bar food includes soup (£1.90), burgers (from £1.99), ploughman's (£3.99), steak and kidney pudding (£4.99), red pepper and mushroom lasagne or cod in parsley sauce (£5.99), 8oz rump steak (£7.99) and puddings such as jam roly-poly (£2.99) and lots of ice-cream sundaes (£3.79). *(Recommended by Doug Christian, Geoff Pidoux, Patrick Hancock, the Didler, Ian and Nita Cooper, David Carr, R M Taylor, Martin and Sue Day)*

Hardys & Hansons ~ Manager Brian Rigby ~ Real ale ~ Bar food (11-9.30; 12-6 Sun) ~ Restaurant ~ (0115) 947 5241 ~ Children over 8 if eating ~ Dogs allowed in bar ~ Live jazz Sun-Tues, rock Weds, covers band Thurs, new bands Sun evening ~ Open 10.30-11; 12-10.30 Sun

Fellows Morton & Clayton 🍺 £

Canal Street (part of inner ring road)

The large decked terrace overlooking the water at the back of this former canal warehouse is a great place for a summer evening drink. Inside, there's a buzzy town atmosphere in the softly lit downstairs bar, which has dark red plush seats built into alcoves on shiny blond wood floors, lots of exposed brickwork, glossy dark green high ceiling, more tables on a raised carpeted area, and a rack of daily newspapers; a sympathetic extension provides extra seating. From a big window in the quarry-tiled, no smoking glassed-in area at the back you can see the little brewery where they brew the tasty Samuel Fellows and Post Haste, which are served alongside Castle Eden, Deuchars IPA, Fullers London Pride, Timothy Taylor Landlord and a couple of guests such as Charles Wells Bombardier and Mallard Duck Slayer. Popular reasonably priced bar food might include soup (£2.75), seasonal pâté (£3.50), mushroom stroganoff (£5.25), fish and chips (£5.95), beef burger in focaccia (£6.50), sausage and mash or steak and kidney pie (£6.95), 10oz sirloin (£9.95) and daily specials. At lunchtime it's popular with local workers, while in the evenings (when it can get smoky) you'll find a younger set; very audible piped pop music, fruit machine, big TVs; service is prompt and friendly. *(Recommended by C J Fletcher, Patrick Hancock, the Didler, David Carr)*

Own brew ~ Licensees Les Howard and Keely Willans ~ Real ale ~ Bar food (11.30-9; 12-6 Sun; not Sun evening) ~ Restaurant ~ (0115) 950 6795 ~ Children in restaurant ~ Live music Friday ~ Open 11-11(12 Fri, Sat); 12-10.30 Sun

Lincolnshire Poacher 🍺 £

Mansfield Road; up hill from Victoria Centre

The very impressive range of drinks alone at this popular two room pub would be reason enough for a visit, but it's also worth seeking out for the simple but very good value tasty food, and cheery bustling atmosphere. The traditional big wood-floored front bar has wall settles, plain wooden tables and breweriana, and opens on to a plain but lively room on the left, with a corridor that takes you down to the chatty panelled no smoking back snug, with newspapers, cribbage, dominoes, cards and backgammon; piped music. A conservatory overlooks tables on a large terrace behind. It can get very busy in the evening, when it's popular with a younger crowd. A dozen real ales include Batemans XB and XXXB, and the splendid local Castle Rock Poachers Gold and Harvest Pale, which are well kept alongside guests from a wide range of brewers such as Burton Bridge, Butcombe, Enville, Ossett, Robinsons, Pictish and White Horse, five continental draught beers, and around 30 continental bottled beers, good farm cider, around 80 malt whiskies and ten irish ones, and very good value soft drinks. Bar food includes greek platter (£5.50), mushroom stroganoff or vegetable sag curry (£5.75) and sausage and mash, lambs kidneys in red wine or cajun chicken gumbo (£6.25), and delicious treacle pudding. *(Recommended by the Didler, Patrick Hancock, Doug Christian, David Carr, R M Taylor, Bruce Bird, Eric Robinson, Jacqueline Pratt, R Brackenbury)*

Tynemill ~ Manager David Whitaker ~ Real ale ~ Bar food (12-3(4 Sun); 5-8(7 Sat); not Sun evening) ~ (0115) 941 1584 ~ Children in conservatory till 8pm ~ Dogs allowed in bar ~ Open 11-11; 12-10.30 Sun

Olde Trip to Jerusalem ★ ▉ £

Brewhouse Yard; from inner ring road follow The North, A6005 Long Eaton signpost until you are in Castle Boulevard, then almost at once turn right into Castle Road; pub is up on the left

The name of this ancient place is a reference to the 12th-c crusaders who used to meet at this site on their way to the Holy Land, and pub collectors of today make their own crusades to come here. Some say this is the oldest pub in the country (it does feel suitably well worn). Whether or not that's true, it's probably quite unlike any other you'll visit. Parts are darkly built into caverns burrowed into the sandstone rock below the castle, and the siting of the current building is attributed to the days when a brewhouse was established here to supply the needs of the castle above. The panelled walls of the unusual upstairs bar (thought to have served as cellarage for that earlier medieval brewhouse) soar narrowly into a dark cleft above; also mainly carved from the rock, the downstairs bar has leatherette-cushioned settles built into dark panelling, tables on flagstones and snug banquettes built into low-ceilinged rock alcoves; there's also a no smoking parlour/snug, and two more caves open to visitors. If you prefer not to visit with the crowds it's best to go early evening or on a winter lunchtime, but staff do cope efficiently with the busy mix of tourists, conversational locals and students (it can be smoky). They keep their real ales in top condition, and you'll find Hardys & Hansons Kimberley Best and Mild and Olde Trip, alongside guests such as Bath Spa on handpump. Attractively priced straightforward bar food includes soup (£1.90), burgers (from £1.99), sandwiches (from £2.99), tortilla wraps (from £3.50), steak and kidney pudding (£4.99), lasagne (£5.90), red pepper and mushroom lasagne (£5.99), and rump steak (£7.99). They've ring the bull and a fruit machine, and there are some seats in a small courtyard. The museum next door is interesting. *(Recommended by Hugh Roberts, John and Wendy Allin, Bernie Adams, Geoff Pidoux, Mike and Mary Carter, Doug Christian, the Didler, Patrick Hancock, Geoff and Kaye Newton, Mike and Linda Hudson, David Carr, R M Taylor, Anthony Barnes, Kevin Blake, Stephen Buckley, Colin Gooch, A P Seymour)*

Hardys & Hansons ~ Manager Karen Ratcliffe ~ Real ale ~ Bar food (11(12 Sun)-6) ~ (0115) 9473171 ~ Children allowed until 7pm ~ Storytelling last Thurs in the month ~ Open 11-11; 12-10.30 Sun

Pit & Pendulum

Victoria Street

Pseudo gothic reigns at this big theatrical theme bar. Dark and dramatic, it's lit by heavy chandeliers and (electronically) flaring torches, with flashes of colour from an overhead tangle of Frankenstein-laboratory glass tubing and wiring. Dark seating runs from gothic thrones to spooky red-padded side booths with a heavy bat's-wing hint, tables are inset with ancient documents and arcane jewellery – even the cups and saucers have a spider's web design (the coffee is good). There is plenty of ghoulish carving and creeping ivy, and old horror movies run in silence on the TV above the bar counter – where a tortuous web of piping replaces the usual beer taps. Good wheelchair ramps add cleverly to the design, with their curves and heavy black balusters, and the disabled lavatory is through a false bookcase. Downstairs (and that is indeed a shackled skeleton looming through the distorted glass) there's more of the same, with clearly separated areas, and some more conventional seating; well reproduced piped music, fruit machine and friendly staff. Bar food includes dough balls with garlic butter (£2.75), grilled goats cheese

(£3.95), duck stir fry (£4.95), monster double burger (£5.75), grilled salmon and pesto mash (£7.45), 8oz rump (£7.95) and puddings (from £2.75); more reports please. *(Recommended by David Carr)*

Scottish Courage ~ Tenant Ian Povey ~ Bar food (11-9(8 Fri, Sat)) ~ (0115) 950 6383 ~ Open 11-11; 12-10.30 Sun

Vat & Fiddle 🍺

Queens Bridge Road, alongside Sheriffs Way (near multistorey car park)

It's worth popping in at this plain little brick pub to try the very well kept Castle Rock beers (the pub is right next to the brewery), which are served alongside half a dozen interesting guests from brewers such as, Big Lamp, Black Sheep, Exmoor, Newby Wyke, Oakham and Shepherd Neame; occasional beer festivals. They also have around 70 malt whiskies, farm cider, a good range of continental bottled beers and several polish vodkas; good value soft drinks too. Down to earth, chatty and relaxed, with more genuine character perhaps than other Nottingham main entries, the fairly functional open-plan interior has quite a strong 1930s feel, with cream and navy walls and ceiling, varnished pine tables and bentwood stools and chairs on parquet and terrazzo flooring, patterned blue curtains, and some brewery memorabilia. An interesting display of photographs depicts demolished pubs in a nearby area. Also magazines and newspapers to read, piped music some of the time, and a fruit machine. Chilli (£3.75) is served at lunchtime, and rolls (from £1.60) are available until they run out. There are picnic-sets out in front by the road; the train and bus stations are both just a short walk away. *(Recommended by Tony and Wendy Hobden, Patrick Hancock, the Didler, C J Fletcher, David Carr, R M Taylor)*

Tynemill ~ Manager Sarah Houghton ~ Real ale ~ Bar food (12-3; not evenings) ~ (0115) 985 0611 ~ Children in eating area of bar till 8pm ~ Dogs allowed in bar ~ Open 11-11; 12-10.30 Sun

RANBY SK6580 Map 7

Chequers

Ranby signposted off A620 Retford—Worksop, just E of A1

The hands-on newish landlord is making the most of this extensive open-plan pub by the Chesterfield Canal. The main area opens into three neatly kept more or less self-contained carpeted side bays, each with an appealingly homely feel – particularly the front one on the right, which is like a pleasantly kitsch parlour with its deeply cushioned sofa and wing armchairs, dolls, nice lamps and coal-effect fire in an attractive panelled surround. Other furnishings are more orthodox, good and solid in a pleasant variety of styles, and the walls are coloured and textured. Generous attractively priced lunchtime food includes sandwiches or soup (from £3.95), ham and egg (£5.95), scampi or poached salmon with hollandaise (£6.95), and in the evening, food goes up a gear to maybe include coconut salmon (£7.95), duck with red onion marmalade, sirloin steak or red snapper fillet with lime dressing (£9.95) and puddings such as chocolate and toffee mousse or pistachio cheesecake (£3.95). They have well kept Wadworths 6X on handpump, and Burts good crisps; there may be piped music. The ladies' has all sorts of hand creams and such. There are tables on a small neat terrace behind, where you may well see a colourful narrowboat mooring; there is some noise out here from the A1 traffic beyond. *(Recommended by P Jeffries, Anne and Paul Horscraft)*

Enterprise ~ Lease Christopher Jessop ~ Real ale ~ Bar food (12-2.30, 6-9; 12-9.30 Sat; 12-8 Sun) ~ Restaurant ~ (01777) 703329 ~ Children in restaurant if eating ~ Open 11.30-3, 5.30-11; 12-11(10.30 Sun) Sat; closed Mon in autumn and winter

---

We checked prices with the pubs as we went to press in summer 2005. They should hold until around spring 2006 – when our experience suggests that you can expect an increase of around 10p in the £.

WALKERINGHAM SK7792 Map 7

Three Horse Shoes £

High Street; just off A161, off A631 W of Gainsborough

A new licensee has taken over this white painted pub, and sadly its magnificent floral displays have gone, but as this area is a bit of a desert for good pubs we've decided to leave it in for a year and keep our fingers crossed. Inside is simple with old-fashioned décor (red carpets and dark wood wheelbacks), piped music and darts, and Adnams, Charles Wells Bombardier and maybe a guest in summer on handpump. Very cheap bar food includes sandwiches or baguettes (£3.50), soup (£2.95), lasagne, battered haddock, fish or steak pie and roast of the day (all £4.95), and home-made puddings such as sticky toffee pudding (£2.95). *(Recommended by Stephen Woad, CMW, JJW)*

Free house ~ Licensee Andy Womack ~ Real ale ~ Bar food (12-2, 6.30-9; 12-3, 6-8 Sun; not Mon) ~ Restaurant ~ (01427) 890959 ~ Children welcome ~ Dogs allowed in bar ~ Open 12-2.30, 6-11; 12-4, 6-10.30 Sun; closed Mon lunchtime

LUCKY DIP

Besides the fully inspected pubs, you might like to try these Lucky Dips recommended to us and described by readers (if you do, please send us reports: www.goodguides.co.uk).

ASKHAM [SK7375]
Duke William [Town St]: Pleasant 18th-c beamed village pub, three real ales and good choice of other drinks, wide choice of reasonably priced food, prints for sale, farm tools and flat irons in no smoking dining room, back room with woodburner (and piano, TV and games machine), friendly playful pub dog; a couple of picnic-sets outside *(CMW, JJW)*

AWSWORTH [SK4844]
Gate [Main St, via A6096 off A610 Nuthall—Eastwood bypass]: Friendly old traditional local with Hardys & Hansons Best and Mild, coal fire in lounge, small pool room; nr site of once-famous railway viaduct – photographs in passage *(the Didler)*

BAGTHORPE [SK4751]
Dixies Arms [2 miles from M1 junction 27; A608 towards Eastwood, then first right on to B600 via Sandhill Rd, then first left into School Rd; Lower Bagthorpe]: Character 18th-c beamed and tiled-floor local, well kept Greene King Abbot, Theakstons Best and a guest beer, entrance bar with tiny snug next to counter, small part-panelled parlour with fine fireplace, longer narrow room with toby jugs and darts, wknd folk music, Sun quiz night; unobtrusive fruit machine, rarely used juke box; big garden with play area and football pitch, own pigeon, gun and morris dancing clubs; open 2-11, all day wknds *(the Didler, Derek and Sylvia Stephenson)*

BALDERTON [SK8251]
Chesters [Worthington Rd]: Wide choice of enjoyable food in bar and recently refurbished restaurant *(Sharon Smith)*

BARNBY IN THE WILLOWS [SK8552]
Willow Tree [Front St; off A17 E of Newark]: Extended 18th-c village pub with original features in open-plan L-shaped beamed bar,

friendly chatty licensees, reasonably priced freshly cooked food evenings and wknds in bar and restaurant, three real ales, good soft drinks choice, log fires throughout, games room; piped music; children welcome, courtyard tables, seven bedrooms *(CMW, JJW)*

BEESTON [SK5236]
Crown [Church St]: Popular local with well kept Hardys & Hansons, small bar with traditional settles, settles in larger panelled room, comfortable lounge; open all day *(the Didler)*

BINGHAM [SK7039]
Crown [Market Pl]: Recently done up in current bar style, with comfortable chairs and sofa in bar, dining room with appealing menu, good sandwiches, Adnams, Bass and Timothy Taylors Landlord; big-screen sports TV *(Hugh Roberts)*
☆ *Horse & Plough* [off A52; Long Acre]: Low beams, flagstones and stripped brick, prints and old brewery memorabilia, comfortable open-plan seating inc pews, great value generous lunchtime baguettes, melts, baked potatoes and three or four hot bar dishes (may be limited Sat), well kept Caledonian Deuchars IPA, Charles Wells Bombardier and four guest beers inc a Mild (tasters offered), good wine choice, popular upstairs grill room (Tues-Sat, and Sun lunch – bargain steaks Tues/Weds) with polished boards, hand-painted murals and open kitchen; piped music, can be smoky; open all day *(Andrew Crawford, the Didler, Hugh Roberts, BB)*

BLEASBY [SK7149]
Waggon & Horses [Gypsy Lane]: Comfortable banquettes in country pub's carpeted lounge, coal fire in character bar, Banks's and Marstons Pedigree, good value fresh lunchtime food from snacks up, Fri fish and chips night, chatty landlord; piped music; back lobby with

play area and comfortable chairs to watch over it, tables outside, small camping area behind *(the Didler)*

BLIDWORTH [SK5855]

Bird in Hand [signed off A617 Mansfield—Newark; Main St]: Victorian local with wide choice of enjoyable reasonably priced food, two well kept Banks's related ales, comfortable U-shaped bar/lounge; piped music, TV, juke box; big garden with terrace picnic-sets and fine view over Sherwood Forest *(CMW, JJW)*

Black Bull [signed off A617 Mansfield—Newark; Main St (B6020)]: Mock-Tudor two-bar village pub doing well under new landlord, cosy lounge with candlelit tables, pictures and plates, enjoyable food inc occasional theme nights, John Smiths and a guest beer; handy for Sherwood Forest walks *(Kevin Blake)*

BLYTH [SK6287]

☆ *Charnwood Hotel* [Sheffield Rd (A634 W, handy for A1)]: A Best Western hotel, not a pub, but a good friendly and civilised alternative, with decent home-made bar food all day, Greene King Ruddles County, Marstons Pedigree and Theakstons Cool Cask and Old Peculier, helpful staff, well spaced comfortable chairs and airy pastel décor in linked bar areas, new conservatory overlooking spreading lawn and pond, formal restaurant; good bedrooms, open all day *(BB)*

CHILWELL [SK5135]

Cadland [High Rd]: Comfortably relaxed well divided open-plan pub with well kept Bass and guest beers, good value popular food all day, open fires, friendly staff; Mar beer festival, Tues/Sun quiz nights; open all day *(the Didler)*

CODDINGTON [SK8354]

Inn on the Green [off A17 just E of Newark]: Well kept Fullers London Pride, Marstons Pedigree and a guest beer, enjoyable food in restaurant *(Brian Douglas)*

COLSTON BASSETT [SK7033]

☆ *Martins Arms*: Smart and restaurant country dining pub with formal uniformed service, good upmarket food (not winter Sun evenings) at a price, antiques and warm log fires in Jacobean fireplaces in comfortable bar, no smoking snug, seven well kept ales, good range of wines, malt whiskies and cognacs, elegant restaurant (children welcome here and in family room); they may try to keep your credit card while you eat outside; antiques shop in their converted stables, sizeable attractive garden (summer croquet) backing on to parkland *(Annette and John Derbyshire, Ian and Nita Cooper, Tony and Betty Parker, the Didler, Hugh Roberts, Derek and Sylvia Stephenson, R Brackenbury, LYM)*

COSSALL [SK4843]

Gardeners [Awsworth Lane]: Neat open-plan local with cheap well kept Hardys & Hansons Bitter, Mild and seasonal beers, good value lunchtime food, end games area with pool and sports TV, quiz nights *(the Didler)*

COTGRAVE [SK6435]

Rose & Crown [Main Rd, off A46 SE of Nottingham]: Welcoming and comfortable, with consistently good value food all day inc

midweek and early evening bargains, also more elaborate evening dishes, four well kept changing ales, good soft drinks choice, log fires, no smoking area; children welcome, garden picnic-sets *(Sally and Dave Bates, CMW, JJW)*

DRAKEHOLES [SK7090]

White Swan [off A631 Bawtry—Gainsborough]: Dining pub with spacious linked rooms, lots of pictures, civilised plush lounge bar, attractively airy brasserie-style restaurant with good range of light dishes from sandwiches to extensive lunchtime carvery, friendly efficient staff, well kept Barnsley and Timothy Taylors Landlord; piped music; children in eating area, neat landscaped gardens with pretty view above Chesterfield Canal, open all day, quiet bedrooms, good breakfast *(LYM, Tony Hobden)*

EAST MARKHAM [SK7473]

Queens [off A57; High St]: Friendly and chatty Edwardian village local, lounge and dining area one end, games the other, four real ales and good food choice *(CMW, JJW)*

EASTWOOD [SK4846]

Foresters Arms [Main St, Newthorpe]: Relaxed and friendly open-plan local, Hardys & Hansons real ales, darts, dominoes, open fire, old local photographs, wknd organ singalong; TV; nice garden, occasional barbecues *(the Didler)*

EGMANTON [SX7368]

Old Plough [Tuxford Rd]: Chef/patrons doing good food, great atmosphere *(Ross Martin)*

ELSTON [SK7647]

Chequers [Toad Lane]: Several levels, beams, banquettes and tables and chairs, enjoyable food inc bargain meal deals, three real ales, good soft drinks choice, prompt service, log fire, darts, quiz night; quiet piped music, TV, games machine, lacks a no smoking area *(CMW, JJW)*

EVERTON [SK6991]

Blacksmiths Arms [Church St]: L-shaped bar with no smoking dining area down step opening into well heated conservatory, real ales such as Barnsley and Marstons Pedigree, friendly chatty staff, wide food choice inc bargain family Sun lunches, separate restaurant menu, pool in games room; quiet piped music; dogs welcome, smallish garden with play area, open all day wknds *(Tony Hobden)*

FARNSFIELD [SK6456]

Plough [E end]: Attractive L-shaped beamed lounge, good value lunchtime and (not wknds) early evening food inc good Sun roasts, well kept Mansfield beers with a guest Mild, good fireplace; may be quiet piped music, darts, pool, TV and video games, Mon quiz night; garden with play area, open all day wknds *(Gerry and Rosemary Dobson, CMW, JJW, Kevin Blake)*

GRANBY [SK7436]

Marquis of Granby [Dragon St]: 18th-c pub with two cosy rooms, beams and flagstones, enthusiastic landlord and welcoming staff, seven or more quickly changing guest beers from chunky yew bar counter inc local

Brewsters and Mallard, usually a Mild and a Stout, regular beer festivals, hundreds of pump clips, books to read, enjoyable fresh food from open kitchen, entertaining theme nights; can be somewhat smoky; wheelchair access, cl Mon-Weds lunchtimes, open all day wknds, lovely village *(the Didler, R M Taylor, Phil and Jane Hodson)*

GRINGLEY ON THE HILL [SK7390]
Blue Bell [High St, just off A361 Bawtry—Gainsboro]: Friendly village local with well kept ales such as Adnams, Caledonian Deuchars IPA, John Smiths and Charles Wells Bombardier, reasonably priced blackboard food, small pleasant dining room, games room with pool and TV; children and dogs welcome, open all day wknds, cl wkdy lunchtimes *(Tony Hobden)*

HOVERINGHAM [SK6946]
Reindeer [Main St]: Comfortable low-beamed Tynemill pub, friendly and unpretentious, with well kept changing real ales inc Castle Rock, decent fairly priced food, coal fires in bar and lounge, back restaurant; hatch for back cricket pitch *(the Didler)*

KIMBERLEY [SK4944]
☆ *Nelson & Railway* [Station Rd; handy for M1 junction 26 via A610]: Cheery and chatty two-room beamed Victorian pub with mix of Edwardian-looking furniture, brewery prints and railway signs, particularly well kept Hardys & Hansons ales from brewery opposite, simple low-priced food from sandwiches and hot rolls up, no smoking area, traditional games inc alley and table skittles; piped music, fruit machine, juke box; dogs allowed in bar, children in restaurant, tables and swings in good-sized cottagey garden, bedrooms, open all day *(Patrick Hancock, Pete Baker, Geoff and Angela Jaques, Ian Stafford, the Didler, Roy Branson, LYM, Dr D and Mrs B Woods, Dr Alan and Mrs Sue Holder)*
Stag [Nottingham Rd]: Friendly 16th-c traditional local run by devoted landlady, two cosy rooms, small central counter and corridor, low beams, dark panelling and settles, well kept Adnams, Boddingtons, Marstons Pedigree, Timothy Taylors Landlord, a Mild and another guest beer, May bank hol beer festival, vintage working penny slot machines and Shipstones brewery photographs; attractive back garden with play area, cl wkdy lunchtime (opens 5; 1.30 Sat, 12 Sun) *(the Didler)*

KIRKBY IN ASHFIELD [SK5056]
Countryman [Park Lane (B6018 S)]: Thriving traditional pub with good value generous bar food (not Sun, Mon evening), well kept Bass, Theakstons and usually guest beers, decorative plates, mining memorabilia and attractive bas relief shooting murals in cottagey beamed lounge bar, public bar with pool, live bands wknds; popular with walkers, play area, open all day *(the Didler)*

KIRTON [SK6868]
Fox [Main St (A6075 Ollerton—Tuxford)]: Much bigger inside than you'd have guessed,

various areas, Hardys & Hansons Bitter and Olde Trip, food all day, separate conservatory pool area; car park tack shop *(Ian Phillips)*

LINBY [SK5351]
Horse & Groom [Main St]: Friendly staff, four well kept local ales and wide choice of decent straightforward food (not Sun-Thurs evenings) in unpretentious pub with no piped music or mobile phones; big play area, attractive village nr Newstead Abbey *(CMW, JJW, the Didler)*

LOWDHAM [SK6746]
Magna Charta [Southwell Rd]: Attractive Hardys & Hansons pub with emphasis on good range of enjoyable standard food from sandwiches, wraps and baked potatoes to steaks, friendly efficient staff, well kept beers, plenty of tables, different linked areas inc no smoking ones; special children's lavatory, garden *(Gerry and Rosemary Dobson)*

MANSFIELD [SK5260]
Nell Gwynne [A38 W of centre]: Former gentlemen's club with the look of a private house, two well kept usually quite strong changing ales, welcoming landlord, homely lounge with log-effect gas fire, old colliery plates and mementos of old Mansfield pubs, games room; sports TV, 1960s piped music, nearby parking can be difficult; cl Mon-Thurs lunchtimes *(the Didler, Derek and Sylvia Stephenson)*
Railway Inn [Station St; best approached by viaduct from nr market pl]: Friendly traditional pub with long-serving licensee, well kept attractively priced Batemans XB and a guest beer, bargain home-made lunches, divided main bar and separate room; handy for Robin Hood Line station, normally open all day, cl Sun evening; talk of redevelopment plans – news please *(Pete Baker, the Didler)*

MANSFIELD WOODHOUSE [SK5463]
Greyhound [High St]: Quietly friendly two-room village local with Banks's Mansfield, Courage Directors, Everards Home, Theakstons Mild and a guest beer, darts, dominoes and pool; quiz nights Mon and Weds *(the Didler)*

MAPLEBECK [SK7160]
☆ *Beehive* [signed down pretty country lanes from A616 Newark—Ollerton and from A617 Newark—Mansfield]: Cosy and unspoiled beamed country tavern in nice spot, chatty landlady, tiny front bar, slightly bigger side room, traditional furnishings, coal or log fire, free antique juke box, well kept local Maypole and guest ales; tables on small terrace with flower tubs and grassy bank running down to little stream, play area with swings, barbecues; no food, may be cl wkdy winter lunchtimes, very busy wknds and bank hols *(LYM, the Didler)*

NEWARK [SK7953]
Castle [Castle Gate]: Newly refurbished, with bare-boards front room, long panelled and carpeted back room, old wooden furniture, lots of mirrors and old prints, witty quotes on bold-coloured walls, two interesting guest beers, several wines by the glass, simple food (plans for adjacent bar/restaurant); piped music

(David and Ruth Hollands, Kevin Blake)

Castle & Falcon [London Rd]: Former coaching inn with local atmosphere, John Smiths and guest beers, two bars and family conservatory, spacious games area with darts and pool; skittle alley, evening opening 7 *(David Carr, the Didler)*

☆ **Fox & Crown** [Appleton Gate]: Well run open-plan Tynemill pub, chatty and relaxed, with several well kept Castle Rock ales and guests such as Archers, Everards Tiger, Hook Norton Best and Oldershaws from central servery, Stowford Press cider, lots of whiskies, vodkas and other spirits, good coffee and decent wines by the glass, attractively priced fresh food from filled rolls, baguettes, panini and baked potatoes up, several side areas inc no smoking ones (children allowed); piped pop music may be loudish; good wheelchair access, occasional Thurs live music, open all day *(the Didler, David and Ruth Hollands, BB)*

Mail Coach [London Rd, nr Beaumond Cross]: Friendly open-plan Georgian local, three candlelit separate areas, lots of chicken pictures, hot coal fires and comfortable chairs, well kept Boddingtons, Flowers IPA and Original and two or more local guest beers, pleasant staff, lunchtime food (not Mon); May beer festival, pub games, frequent live music Thurs, upstairs ladies'; tables on back terrace *(the Didler, Di and Mike Gillam)*

Old Malt Shovel [North Gate]: Welcoming and comfortably opened-up, with enjoyable food from doorstep sandwiches to restaurant dishes, well kept Adnams Broadside, Caledonian Deuchars IPA, Timothy Taylors Landlord, Charles Wells Bombardier, Worthington 1744 and guest beers, open fire, choice of teas, lots of books and bottles on shelves, cheerfully laid-back atmosphere and service; pub games, skittle alley, wheelchair access, terrace tables *(the Didler)*

NEWSTEAD [SK5252]

Station Hotel [Station Rd]: Busy basic red-brick village local opp station on Robin Hood rail line, bargain well kept Barnsley Bitter and Robinsons Old Tom Mild, fine old railway photographs; no food Sun *(the Didler)*

NORMANTON ON SOAR [SK5123]

Plough [village signed from A6006]: Large pleasantly refurbished pub by canalised River Soar, Banks's-related ales in good-sized bar area, enjoyable well priced food in spacious no smoking dining room, good friendly service; good-sized waterside garden, own moorings *(Gerry and Rosemary Dobson, Mrs C Stafford)*

NORMANTON ON TRENT [SK7969]

☆ **Square & Compass** [East Gate; signed off B1164 S of Tuxford]: Opened-up low-beamed pub under new landlady, good choice of enjoyable generous food (all day wknds) at tempting prices, quick chatty attentive service, well kept Adnams and local ales, good wine range, local photographs for sale; children welcome in eating areas, small play area out behind, bedrooms with own bathrooms *(LYM, D Jordan, Phil and Jane Hodson)*

NOTTINGHAM [SK5739]

Bunkers Hill [Hockley, next to Ice Stadium]: High-beamed former bank recently stylishly reworked, with smart new floor and attractive servery, espresso machine and good wine choice as well as half a dozen well kept ales such as Mallard Duck & Dive and Nottingham Rock, enjoyable up-to-date food (not Sun evening), live music upstairs Fri; pleasant terrace tables, open all day – till 1am Fri/Sat *(the Didler, Richard Houghton)*

Canal House [Canal St]: Big conversion of wharf building, bridge over indoors canal spur complete with narrowboat, lots of bare brick and varnished wood, huge joists on studded steel beams, long bar recently emphasising lagers (at least a couple of real ales too), good choice of house wines (two glass sizes), lots of standing room; good upstairs restaurant and second bar, masses of solid tables out on attractive waterside terrace; piped music (live Sun), popular with young people at night; open all day – till midnight Thurs, 1am Fri/Sat *(the Didler, BB)*

Cock & Hoop [Lace Market Hotel, High Pavement]: Comfortable no smoking split-level pub attached to hotel, good range of beers inc Fullers London Pride, Greene King Abbot and one brewed by Nottingham for the pub, panelling and old-fashioned pewter bar top, small elegant cellar lounge; bedrooms in hotel part, open all day – till 1am Thurs, 2 Fri/Sat *(the Didler)*

Coopers Arms [Porchester Rd, Thornywood]: Solid Victorian local with three unspoilt rooms, Theakstons real ales, small family room in skittle alley; cl Weds lunchtime *(the Didler)*

Elwes Arms [Oakdale Rd, Carlton]: Comfortable and attractive, with huge range of home-cooked food, good beer range; unobtrusive piped music; nice garden *(Kevin Blake)*

Falcon [Canning Circus/Alfreton Rd]: Two small friendly rooms with old pictures and flame-effect fire in attractive fireplace, particularly well kept Adnams Bitter and Broadside and a guest beer, good choice of wines, enjoyable fresh food inc some interesting specials in bar and pleasant upstairs restaurant; terrace tables and barbecues, open all day *(the Didler, Patrick Hancock)*

Fox & Crown [Church St/Lincoln St, Old Basford]: Unpretentious open-plan local with window to back microbrewery producing its own splendid Alcazar beer range, brewery tours Sat, guest beers, good continental bottle choice; enjoyable fresh food from sandwiches to wide choice of early evening pizzas, helpful staff and Canadian landlord; good piped music, games machines, Tues quiz night, frequent beer festivals, big-screen sports TV; disabled access possible (lavatories difficult), tables out behind, open all day *(the Didler, R M Taylor)*

Gladstone [Loscoe Rd, Carrington]: Thriving two-room local, four or five well kept ales inc a changing guest, cosy comfortable lounge with reading matter, basic bar with darts and sports

TV; upstairs folk club Weds, quiz Thurs; cl wkdy lunchtimes, open all day wknds *(the Didler, R Brackenbury)*

Globe [London Rd]: Light and airy roadside pub with attractively priced fresh food all day, six well kept real ales mainly from local breweries, farm cider, coal fire; handy for cricket or football matches, open all day *(the Didler, Des and Jen Clarke, R M Taylor)*

Horse & Groom [Radford Rd, New Basford]: Unpretentious and well run partly open-plan pub by former Shipstones brewery, still with their name and other memorabilia, friendly atmosphere, eight well kept changing ales, good value fresh food from sandwiches to Sun lunches, daily papers, nice snug, wknd live music; open all day *(the Didler, R M Taylor, Kevin Blake)*

Keanes Head [St Marys Gate]: Comfortable new addition to Tynemill group, entirely no smoking, lots of real ales inc Adnams, Batemans XB and Castle Rock, good foreign beer and wine choice, enjoyable fresh food till late (morning breakfast too), friendly staff, open all day *(the Didler)*

☆ *Lion* [Lower Mosley St, New Basford]: Three or four Batemans ales and half a dozen interesting changing guest beers kept well in one of city's deepest cellars (glass viewing panel – and can be visited at quiet times), Broadstone farm cider, ten wines by the glass, wide choice of good value wholesome home-made food inc doorstep sandwiches and children's helpings; open plan but the feel of separate areas, bare bricks and polished dark oak boards, coal or log fires, daily papers; live music Fri/Sat, jazz Sun lunchtimes; well behaved children welcome, pleasant terrace with summer barbecues, open all day *(Andrew Crawford, the Didler, R M Taylor, Brian and Ruth Archer, Kevin Blake, Andy Lickfold)*

News House [Canal St]: Friendly two-room Tynemill pub with attractive blue exterior tiling, eight well kept changing ales inc bargain Castle Rock, belgian and czech imports on tap, Weston's Old Rosie farm cider, good wine choice, lots of flavoured vodkas, enjoyable fresh food inc Sun lunch, mix of bare boards and carpet, one room filled with local newspaper front pages spanning years of events and personalities; sports TV; open all day *(the Didler)*

Old Moot Hall [Carlton Rd, Sneinton]: Nine well kept and priced ales inc novelties from small breweries, czech Budvar on tap, foreign bottled beers, farm cider, good wine choice, enjoyable wholesome food from fresh cobs up, polished boards, nice pictures, wooden furniture, coal-effect gas fire, upstairs bar with pool; big-screen sports TV, Sun quiz night; open all day *(the Didler, Kevin Blake)*

☆ *Plough* [St Peters St, Radford]: Unpretentious two-room 19th-c local drawing real ale enthusiasts more widely with the interesting Nottingham ales brewed on site, also a guest beer and farm ciders, good bargain food inc fresh rolls and popular Sun lunch (live jazz

then), bargain curries Tues evening, two coal fires, traditional fittings and nice windows, bar billiards and other traditional games (competitions Weds), Thurs irish music night (may be free chilli); Sun barbecues, open all day Thurs-Sun *(the Didler, R M Taylor)*

Punchbowl [Porchester Rd, Mapperley]: Comfortable suburban pub with good choice of food and of real ales inc Fullers London Pride and a changing guest beer, surprising range of wines by the glass *(R Brackenbury)*

☆ *Salutation* [Hounds Gate/Maid Marion Way]: Good range of well kept changing ales and lots of bottled beers, ancient lower back part with beams, flagstones and cosy corners inc two small quiet rooms and a no smoking area, plusher modern front lounge, helpful staff, speedily served enjoyable plain food till 7; piped music, games machine, can get busy and noisy – but a haven in the centre, increasingly dominated by designer bars; open all day *(Geoff Pidoux, BB, R M Taylor)*

☆ *Sir John Borlase Warren* [Ilkeston Rd/Canning Circus (A52 towards Derby)]: Several attractively individual linked rooms with comfortable settees, interesting Victorian decorations, enjoyable lunchtime food, friendly staff, several real ales, no smoking eating area; children welcome (not Fri/Sat evenings), tables in nicely lit back garden with barbecues *(BB, R Brackenbury)*

RADCLIFFE ON TRENT [SK6439]

Black Lion [A52]: Good choice of good value food all day from filled rolls to full meals, well kept Courage Directors, Everards Home and three quickly changing guest beers, farm cider, good soft drinks choice, big comfortable lounge, half no smoking, with small TVs, games machine and coal fire, friendly bar with pool and big-screen sports TV; Weds jazz upstairs twice a month, beer festivals; big enclosed garden, barbecues and play area, open all day *(David Glynne-Jones, CMW, JJW, the Didler)*

RETFORD [SK6980]

☆ *Market Hotel* [off West Carr Rd, Ordsall; follow Leisure Centre signs from A620, then just after industrial estate sign keep eyes skinned for pub sign on left]: In same family for over 40 years, with eight well chosen and kept changing ales (up to 40 in autumn beer festival), comfortable plush banquettes, generous good value straightforward food (not Sun evening) from sandwiches and rolls up, popular Sun carvery lunch, friendly helpful service; children welcome till early evening, very busy Fri/Sat night, jazz 3rd Sun in month; tables outside, bedrooms, open all day Sat *(LYM, Tony Hobden)*

Turks Head [Grove St]: Cosy oak-panelled town pub with three distinct areas, good value food (not Sun evening), Adnams and Banks's, real fire, games room with traditional games as well as pool *(Tony Hobden)*

RUDDINGTON [SK5733]

Victoria [off A60 S of Nottingham; Wilford Rd]: Pleasant village local with reasonably priced food (not wknds exc Sun lunchtime) from interesting baguettes to enjoyable sizzle dishes, well kept Bass and two guest beers such as Adnams, friendly and enthusiastic young licensees *(Derek and Sylvia Stephenson, CMW, JJW)*

☆ **Pilgrim Fathers** [Great North Rd (A638 S of Bawtry)]: Neatly kept beamed pub with good freshly made food, well kept Greene King Abbot, friendly and unobtrusively efficient service, leather wing armchair and nicely panelled window seat among other furnishings in comfortable carpeted main bar, small homely end dining area, simpler separate public bar, lots of games such as shove-ha'penny and bagatelle, sizeable conservatory; unobtrusive piped music, games machine; dogs welcome, garden tables *(Dave and Liz Cubbon, BB)*

SELSTON [SK4553]

Horse & Jockey [handy for M1 junctions 27/28; Church Lane]: Three carefully refurbished main rooms on three levels, cosy snug off lower bar area, low beams, flagstones and coal fire in cast-iron range, well kept Bass, Greene King Abbot, Timothy Taylors Landlord and other ales on handpump or in jugs direct from the cellar, bargain home-made bar lunches (not wknds) inc good fresh cobs and roasts, darts, bar billiards and pool in top room; open all day Sat *(the Didler)*

SOUTH LEVERTON [SK7881]

Plough [Town St]: Tiny pub doubling as morning post office, basic trestle tables and benches, real fire, Greene King Ruddles Best and a guest beer, traditional games, tables outside; open 2-11 (all day Sat, 12-4, 7-10.30 Sun) *(the Didler)*

SOUTHWELL [SK6953]

Bramley Apple [Church St (A612)]: Good value enjoyable food (not Sun evening) from simple lunch choice to more elaborate evening dishes, well kept Springhead and changing guest ales, farm cider, friendly attentive service, light and airy long bar with front room off; may be live music wknds, open all day Sat/Sun *(the Didler, W W Burke, BB, Richard Jennings)*
Old Coaching House [Easthorpe]: Up to six changing well kept ales inc a Mild, summer farm cider, welcoming service, three roaring coal or log fires, bar billiards, shove-ha'penny and other traditional games, beams, old-world alcoves; terrace tables, cl wkdy lunchtimes, open all day wknds, handy for Minster and Workhouse *(Joan and Tony Walker, Dr Brian and Mrs Anne Hamilton; the Didler)*

THURGARTON [SK6949]

☆ **Red Lion** [Southwell Rd (A612)]: Cheery 16th-c inn with consistently good freshly cooked food (all day wknds and bank hols) inc fresh fish and some adventurous dishes in brightly decorated split-level beamed bars and restaurant, lots of nooks and crannies, comfortable banquettes and other seating, smart friendly service, well kept ales such as Black Sheep, Hook Norton and Mansfield, flame-effect fire, big windows to attractive

good-sized two-level back garden with well spaced picnic-sets (dogs on leads allowed here); unobtrusive fruit machine, steepish walk back up to car park; children welcome, comfortable bedrooms *(David Glynne-Jones, Derek and Sylvia Stephenson, Phil and Jane Hodson, David and Ruth Hollands, BB)*

UNDERWOOD [SK4751]

☆ **Red Lion** [Church Lane; off B600, nr M1 junction 27]: Character 17th-c split-level beamed village pub, spacious open-plan quarry-tiled bar with open fire, some cushioned settles, pictures and plates on dressers, reliable sensibly priced family food inc OAP lunches and good fresh fish, well kept ales such as Fullers London Pride, Marstons Pedigree and Rudgate, good friendly service, penny arcade machine, no piped music; children welcome, picnic-sets and large adventure playground in big garden with terrace and barbecues, attractive setting, open all day wknds *(the Didler, Derek and Sylvia Stephenson, Kevin Blake)*

UPTON [SK7354]

☆ **French Horn** [A612]: Neatly comfortable open-plan dining pub with wall banquettes and glossy tables, wide choice of good interesting generous food (all day Sun), lunchtime sandwiches, baguettes and baked potatoes too, friendly service, well kept Charles Wells Bombardier; piped music, children welcome, picnic-sets in big sloping back paddock, open all day *(Phil and Jane Hodson, LYM, Andy and Ali)*

WALKERINGHAM [SK7692]

Brickmakers Arms [Fountain Hill Rd, off B1403]: Pub gradually expanded into hotel and restaurant too, enjoyable bargain-priced food from good bacon butties up, plenty of choice for children, well kept beer, helpful staff; 16 bedrooms *(W W Burke, Anne and Paul Horscraft)*

WATNALL CHAWORTH [SK5046]

☆ **Queens Head** [3 miles from M1 junction 26: A610 towards Nottingham, left on B600, then keep right; Main Rd]: Cosy and tastefully extended three-room old pub with great fish and chips and wide range of other good value food (all day summer), well kept ales such as Greene King IPA, St Austell and Theakstons, efficient friendly service; intimate snug, dining area, beams and stripped pine, coal fire; fruit machine, piped music; picnic-sets in spacious and attractive back garden with big play area, open all day Fri/Sat *(the Didler, Derek and Sylvia Stephenson)*
Royal Oak [Main Rd; B600 N of Kimberley]: Friendly nicely restored beamed village local with interesting plates and pictures, well kept Hardys & Hansons, guest beers and beer festivals, fresh cobs, woodburner, back games room and pool room, upstairs lounge open Fri-Sun; sports TV, occasional live 60s nights in back cabin; open all day *(the Didler)*

WEST BRIDGFORD [SK5838]

Southbank [Trent Bridge]: Bright well run sports bar with polished wood floors, sofas, real ales such as Boddingtons, Fullers London

Pride, Timothy Taylors Landlord and local Mallard and Nottingham, wide choice of lagers and soft drinks, coffee, good all day food choice from baguettes and light dishes to mixed grills, Mon curry night, friendly efficient staff; several big screens and lots of other sports TVs; big garden overlooking river, handy for cricket ground and Notts Forest FC, open all day till midnight (10.30 Sun) *(the Didler)*

☆ *Stratford Haven* [Stratford Rd, Trent Bridge]: Busy and chatty Tynemill pub, bare-boards front bar and feel of several separate areas inc airy skylit and carpeted yellow-walled back part with relaxed local atmosphere, well kept Castle Rock ales and good choice of changing guest beers, exotic bottled beers, farm ciders, ample whiskies and wines, good value simple home-made food all day, daily papers; some live music, can get crowded; handy for cricket ground and Nottingham Forest FC, tables outside, open all day *(John and Wendy Allin, Andrew Crawford, the Didler, BB, R M Taylor, Derek and Sylvia Stephenson)*

Test Match [Gordon Sq, West Bridgford]: Handsome art deco décor with revolving door, high ceiling and sweeping staircase up to lounge, unpretentious furnishings, big cricketing prints, some signed bats, full range of Hardys & Hansons beers kept particularly well, friendly staff, bar food, no smoking room, separate sports and games bar; live music Sun; disabled access and facilities, tables outside *(Sarah Cunningham)*

WEST LEAKE [SK5226]

☆ *Star* [Melton Lane, off A6006]: Comfortable oak-panelled lounge with good central log fire, pewter mugs, china, pictures, attractive table lamps and side eating area, traditional beamed and quarry-tiled country bar on left with wall settles, plenty of character and traditional games, good value home-made food (not Sun/Mon evenings) from substantial baps to cheap steaks, well kept Bass and up to three changing guest beers, several malt whiskies, good coffee, jovial landlord, helpful service, no piped music or machines; children in eating area, picnic-sets on front terrace (quiet spot)

and in garden with play area, bedrooms *(LYM, the Didler, Brian and Ruth Archer)*

WEST STOCKWITH [SK7894]

Waterfront [Canal Lane; opp marina, off A161]: Extended two-bar pub in excellent waterside spot on basin between River Trent and Chesterfield Canal, big dining area with wide choice of good value food, well kept Caledonian Deuchars IPA and Tetleys, crowded summer evenings with jolly boating types; may be piped music, TV, fruit machine; garden with barbecues, caravan park behind, open all day wknds *(Tony Hobden)*

WIDMERPOOL [SK6429]

☆ *Pullman* [1st left off A606 coming towards Nottingham from A46 junction; Kinoulton Lane]: Thriving family dining pub in well converted and extended station building, abundant locomotive and train paintings, friendly helpful service, generous good food inc fish and carvery nights, two well kept ales, good wine choice; piped pop music; tables and picnic-sets outside *(John and Sylvia Harrop, CMW, JJW, Phil and Jane Hodson)*

WORKSOP [SK5879]

Mallard [Station, Carlton Rd]: Friendly local feel in idiosyncratic station building, quickly changing beers from small breweries, wide range of foreign bottled beers, coal fire, traditional games; beer festivals, wheelchair access, seats outside, parking in station pay-and-display, open all day Sat, cl wkdy lunchtimes and Sun evening *(the Didler)*

Regency [Carlton Rd]: Comfortable and civilised, with armchairs, Marstons Burton, John Smiths Magnet and a guest beer, straightforward food at bargain prices, no smoking dining room; bedrooms *(Tony Hobden)*

WYSALL [SK6027]

Plough [Keyworth Rd; off A60 at Costock, or A6006 at Wymeswold]: Welcoming and attractive 17th-c beamed country local, well kept changing ales, enjoyable food, two rooms on either side of central bar with nice mix of furnishings, soft lighting, big log fire; french doors to pretty terrace with flower tubs and baskets *(Brian and Ruth Archer)*

Real ale may be served from handpumps, electric pumps (not just the on-off switches used for keg beer) or – common in Scotland – tall taps called founts (pronounced 'fonts') where a separate pump pushes the beer up under air pressure. The landlord can adjust the force of the flow – a tight spigot gives the good creamy head that Yorkshire lads like.

Oxfordshire

A rewarding crop of new main entries here consists of the individualistic Shepherds Crook at Crowell (good beers and food especially fresh fish in unpretentious surroundings), the pretty thatched Half Moon at Cuxham (almost a good French country restaurant masquerading as a quintessential English pub – it comes straight in with a Food Award), the White Hart at Fyfield (doing well under its current management, with imaginative food in a remarkable medieval building), the nicely unspoilt Dog & Duck at Highmoor (lots of character, and the newish landlord is pulling people in for enjoyable food at lower prices than the county norm), the Blue Boar at Longworth (popular food and a thriving cheerful atmosphere in this picturesque thatched village local), and the nicely done out Red Lion at Tetsworth (open all day, with plenty of pub games and a welcome for anyone just dropping in for a chat and a drink, while the enterprising licensees are really getting things moving on the food side). Other pubs on fine form here are the Chequers in Chipping Norton (warm praise for food, beer, service and atmosphere – it wins a Star this year for its all-round appeal), the Chequers at Churchill (its interesting food earns a Food Award this year, and the licensees add a good dash of special warmth), the stylish Eyston Arms in East Hendred (its food is liked a lot), the Merrymouth at Fifield (praise for the food here too, particularly the fish, and also the service), the Falkland Arms beautifully placed in Great Tew (good beer in a lovely old pub), the Gate Hangs High near Hook Norton (a nice all-rounder), the Turf Tavern tucked down its ancient alley in Oxford (lots of character, great choice of beers), the Home Sweet Home at Roke (warm approval for the new décor, as well as the food and service), and the Trout at Tadpole Bridge (very good imaginative food, good atmosphere and comfortable bedrooms, in an enviable spot). Good food figures prominently in the appeal of quite a few of these top Oxfordshire pubs. The one which takes the award of Oxfordshire Dining Pub of the Year is one of this year's new entrants: the Half Moon at Cuxham. In the Lucky Dip section at the end of the chapter pubs to catch the eye are the Lord Nelson at Brightwell Baldwin, Tite at Chadlington, Crown at Church Enstone, Red Lion at Cropredy, Bat & Ball at Cuddesdon, Bear & Ragged Staff in Cumnor, Unicorn in Deddington, Trout at Godstow, Catherine Wheel in Goring, Bell at Langford, Bell at Shenington, Baskerville Arms at Shiplake, Talk House at Stanton St John, and Cherry Tree at Stoke Row and restaurant Crooked Billet there. Drinks tend to cost distinctly more here than the national norm. The two main local breweries are Hook Norton and Brakspears; Brakspears is now brewed on the new Wychwood brewery site in Witney (using equipment salvaged when the original Brakspears site in Marlow was sold). Of the two, Hook Norton tends to be cheaper, and is the beer we most commonly found pubs here selling as their cheapest. Loddon is another newer smaller brewery whose beers are worth looking out for.

ALVESCOT SP2704 Map 4
Plough
B4020 Carterton—Clanfield, SW of Witney

They've added a tropical fish tank and a cocktail menu, but otherwise it's business as usual at this well run partly 17th-c village pub, popular for its properly pubby atmosphere and wide range of food. The neatly kept carpeted bar has a collection of aircraft prints and a large poster of Concorde's last flight, as well as plenty of cottagey pictures, china ornaments and house plants, a big antique case of stuffed birds of prey, sundry bric-a-brac, and a good log fire. Comfortable seating includes cushioned settles, a nice armchair, and of course the bar stools bagged by cheerful regulars in the early evening. Snug and intimate at night, the dining area has an extensive choice of dishes such as soup (£3.35), warm crusty rolls (from £3.20), filled baked potatoes (from £3.50), ploughman's (from £4.80), combination starters for two people (from £5.25), spinach and ricotta cannelloni, ham and eggs, chicken kiev or liver and bacon casserole (all £6.95), steak and kidney suet pudding (£7.25), salmon steak with watercress sauce (£7.75), a full rack of barbecue ribs (£9.75), steaks (from £10.25), half a roast duck with orange and Cointreau sauce (£11.25), half lamb shoulder with minted gravy (£11.75), and daily specials such as seafood platter (£6.95) or honey and mustard chicken breast (£7.25). At lunchtimes (except Sun), they offer two meals for £10. Well kept Wadworths IPA, 6X and a seasonal beer on handpump, and hot chocolate with marshmallows; welcoming, reliable service. A proper public bar (now the only place where smoking is allowed) has pool and a fruit machine; darts, TV, bar billiards, alley skittles and piped music. They have two friendly dogs, Bruno and Rocky. Two picnic-sets stand out in front below particularly colourful hanging baskets by the quiet village road, with more behind under trees, by a bird table and play area; aunt sally. *(Recommended by KN-R, Peter and Audrey Dowsett, Marjorie and David Lamb, Ian Phillips, Karen and Graham Oddey)*

Wadworths ~ Tenant Kevin Robert Keeling ~ Real ale ~ Bar food (12-2, 6.30-9 (7-8.30 Sun)) ~ Restaurant ~ (01993) 842281 ~ Children in eating area until 8.30pm ~ Dogs allowed in bar ~ Open 11-3, 6-11; 12-3, 7-10.30 Sun

BANBURY SP4540 Map 4
Reindeer £
Parsons Street, off Market Place

Friendly and characterful, this pubby place has a particularly interesting history, its handsomely proportioned Globe Room used by Cromwell as his base during the Battle of Edgehill in 1642. Quite a sight, it still has some wonderfully carved 17th-c dark oak panelling. The warmly welcoming front bar has heavy 16th-c beams, very broad polished oak floorboards, a magnificent carved overmantel for one of the two roaring log fires, and traditional solid furnishings. Served only at lunchtime, straightforward bar food in generous helpings might include soup (£2.50), sandwiches (from £2.80), well liked omelettes or good filled baked potatoes (from £4), all day breakfast (£4.20), bubble and squeak (£4.95), and changing daily specials. The five well kept beers on handpump usually include the full range of Hook Norton ales and a guest like Everards Tiger, and they also have country wines, several whiskies, and even snuffs and clay pipes for the more adventurous; skittle alley, cribbage, dominoes and piped music. A smaller back room up steps is no smoking at lunchtime. The little back courtyard has tables and benches under parasols, aunt sally and pretty flowering baskets. No under-21s (but see below). *(Recommended by George Atkinson, Arnold Bennett, Geoff Pidoux, Ian Phillips, Mrs P J Pearce, the Didler, Klaus and Elizabeth Leist, Tony and Wendy Hobden, Iain R Hewitt, David Green, Ted George, Bob)*

Hook Norton ~ Tenants Mr and Mrs Puddifoot ~ Real ale ~ Bar food (11-2.30) ~ (01295) 264031 ~ Children in family room ~ Dogs allowed in bar ~ Open 11-11; 12-3 Sun

Our web site (www.goodguides.co.uk) now includes postcodes for pubs.

BURFORD SP2512 Map 4

Lamb ♀ ◀ ⊨

Village signposted off A40 W of Oxford; Sheep Street (B4425, off A361)

This civilised 500-year-old stone-built inn changed hands again in the spring, but the manager and chef remain the same. Perhaps more of a hotel these days, it wasn't quite so universally praised by readers last year as it has been in the past (several feel prices are now too high), but it remains a bustling and characterful place to meet, particularly in summer when the garden is an attractive spot for afternoon tea. Recently refurbished, the roomy beamed main lounge is charmingly traditional, with distinguished old seats including a chintzy high winged settle, ancient cushioned wooden armchairs, and seats built into its stone-mullioned windows, bunches of flowers on polished oak and elm tables, oriental rugs on the wide flagstones and polished oak floorboards, and a winter log fire under its fine mantelpiece. The pictures are quite striking, they have shelves of plates and other antique decorations, one corner has a writing desk, and a grandfather clock. The public bar has high-backed settles and old chairs on flagstones in front of its fire, and well kept Brakspears and Hook Norton Best; there's also an extensive wine list with quite a few by the glass, and a good range of soft drinks. Bar food might include soup (£4.95), open cold rare roast beef sandwich with horseradish and potato salad or crab and sweetcorn risotto (£9.50), chargrilled pork T-bone steak with cheddar cheese and leek mash (£13.50), and half a grilled lobster with garlic butter and mango and chilli sauce (£14.40); children's helpings (£5.50), and Sunday roasts (£12.50). The restaurant is no smoking. A pretty terrace with teak furniture leads down to small neatly kept lawns surrounded by flowers, flowering shrubs and small trees, and the garden itself is a real suntrap, enclosed as it is by the warm stone of the surrounding buildings. More reports on the new regime please. *(Recommended by R Huggins, D Irving, E McCall, T McLean, the Didler, Mr and Mrs Martin Joyce, Karen and Graham Oddey, A P Seymour, Ian Phillips)*

Free house ~ Licensee Gavin Thomson ~ Real ale ~ Bar food (12-3, 6.30-9.30) ~ Restaurant ~ (01993) 823155 ~ Children welcome ~ Dogs welcome ~ Open 11-11; 12-10.30 Sun ~ Bedrooms: £115B/£145B

CAULCOTT SP5024 Map 4

Horse & Groom ◀

Lower Heyford Road (B4030)

Everyone talks to everyone at this creeper-covered, partly thatched cottage, and even though the friendly licensees are often rushed off their feet, visitors this year say they always have a smile on their face and work hard to please. It's a good lunch stop en route to the Cotswolds, so there's always a good mix of visitors as well as the very loyal local following. It's not a huge place and an L-shaped red-carpeted room angles around the servery, with plush-cushioned settles, chairs and stools around a few dark tables at the low-ceilinged bar end, framed racehorse cigarette cards, and a blazing fire in the big inglenook, with masses of pump clips under its long bressumer beam; shove-ha'penny, cribbage, dominoes. The far end, up a shallow step, is set for dining (and is no smoking; best to book), with lots of decorative jugs hanging on black joists, and some decorative plates. There are some lovely watercolours and original drawings dotted around, including a charming one of Harvey the west highland terrier who greets everyone on arrival; look out too for the nice old poster of the auction of the pub in 1899. Three quickly changing interesting guest beers like Archers Hop Bouquet, Brakspears and Cottage Jack and the Dragon are well kept alongside Hook Norton Best on handpump; decent house wines. They serve a good selection of O'Hagan speciality sausages, with flavours such as chorizo, pork and red wine, somerset scrumpy, creole, and drunken duck (all £7.50); also, sandwiches and toasties (from £3.40), home-made soup (£3.95), filled baked potatoes (from £3.90), ham and egg (£6.25), daily specials such as a pint of prawns (£7.95), chicken breast (£8.75), steaks (from £10.95), and beef wellington (£13.95), with puddings (£4.25). Food service does slow down at peak times. There is a small side sun lounge, with picnic-sets under cocktail parasols on a neat side lawn. *(Recommended by David Twitchett, E A and D C T Frewer, Simon Collett-Jones, Barbara and Peter Kelly, Peter and Jean Hoare, David Barnes, Dick and Madeleine Brown, Tracey and Stephen Groves, Kevin Blake, Susan and Nigel Wilson, Mrs Hazel Rainer, Sue Demont, Tim Barrow)*

Free house ~ Licensees Chris and Celestine Roche ~ Real ale ~ Bar food (not 25 Dec) ~ Restaurant ~ (01869) 343257 ~ Children in restaurant lunchtime only ~ Open 11-3, 6-11; 12-3, 7-10.30 Sun

CHECKENDON SU6684 Map 2
Black Horse

Village signposted off A4074 Reading—Wallingford; coming from that direction, go straight through village towards Stoke Row, then turn left (the second turn left after the village church); OS Sheet 175 map reference 666841

Simple and unpretentious (some may even say basic), this classic country local survives in all its unspoilt glory because the same family have now been in charge for a hundred years. There's a refreshingly relaxed atmosphere in the back still room, where three changing West Berkshire beers are tapped from the cask. The room with the bar counter has some tent pegs ranged above the fireplace, a reminder that they used to be made here; a homely side room has some splendidly unfashionable 1950s-look armchairs, and there's another room beyond that. They keep pickled eggs and usually do very simple filled rolls (from £2), served, says one reader, 'as if we were part of the family dropping by for lunch'. There are seats out on a verandah and in the garden. Popular with walkers and cyclists, the pub is tucked away in very attractive walking country. *(Recommended by the Didler, Dick and Madeleine Brown, Richard Greaves, Pete Baker, Susan and John Douglas)*

Free house ~ Licensees Margaret and Martin Morgan ~ Real ale ~ No credit cards ~ (01491) 680418 ~ Children allowed but must be well behaved ~ Open 12-2(2.30 Sat), 7-11; 12-3, 7-10.30 Sun; closed evening 25 Dec

CHIPPING NORTON SP3127 Map 4
Chequers ★ ♀ ◗

Goddards Lane

Nothing seems too much trouble at this smashing place, which this year has earned lots of well deserved praise from readers. Unpretentious, bustling and friendly, it's run by a landlord who really cares about his customers. The three softly lit beamed rooms have no frills, but are clean and comfortable, with low ochre ceilings, plenty of character, and blazing log fires. Friendly efficient staff serve very well kept Fullers Chiswick, London Pride, ESB and seasonal brews from handpump – unusual to have the full Fullers range around here – and they have good house wines (with 18 by the glass, including champagne), espresso and cappuccino coffee. Good bar food at lunchtime includes sandwiches (from £3.25), soup with garlic bread (£3.95), smoked haddock kedgeree or red onion tart topped with crispy duck garnished with sweetened plum tomatoes (£4.95), ploughman's (£5.95), home-cooked honey and cider roast ham with free-range egg (£7.95), thai curry or braised leek and wild mushroom filo tart with red lentil purée (£8.95), chicken stir fry (£9.25), shellfish with noodles (£10.75), and chargrilled 10oz rib-eye steak (£10.95); in the evening they may add main courses like baked cod wrapped in parma ham on sun-dried tomato and pine nut couscous with roasted pepper coulis, or duck breast with pesto risotto and raspberry and ginger jus (£10.95), with specials like roast pheasant with marrow and apple chutney and madeira sauce (£10.50), and whole lemon sole grilled with lemon butter (£10.95). The no smoking restaurant at the back was converted from an old barn adjacent to the courtyard. It's very handy for the town's Victorian theatre. *(Recommended by the Didler, Brian and Rosalie Laverick, Richard Greaves, Mrs N W Neill, Simon Collett-Jones, Mrs Joy Griffiths, Alan Sadler, Chris Glasson, Rod Stoneman, A G Marx, J Iorwerth Davies, Peter Bailey, Tracey and Stephen Groves)*

Fullers ~ Tenants Josh and Kay Reid ~ Real ale ~ Bar food (12-2.30, 6-9; 12-5 Sun; not Sun evening) ~ Restaurant ~ (01608) 644717 ~ Children in restaurant if over 12 ~ Dogs allowed in bar ~ Open 11-11; 12-10.30 Sun; closed 25 Dec

CHURCHILL SP2824 Map 4

Chequers 🍴

B4450 Chipping Norton—Stow (and village signposted off A361 Chipping Norton—Burford); Church Road

The success of this dramatically refurbished 18th-c village pub is chiefly down to its delightfully friendly licensees, whose welcome is regarded by some as the best in the business. It says much for the impression they leave on visitors that when they were away for several months last year readers did notice, and while still praising the food and service a few couldn't help feeling there was something missing. It's been stylishly transformed into a light and airy open-plan dining pub, with an unexpectedly big extension at the back; a little like a church with its soaring rafters, it fits in so well that some customers have been surprised to learn that the beams aren't original (and in fact are brand new). At one end is an unusual dresser with lots of wine bottles. The front bar has a more traditional feel, with a light stone flagstoned floor, a couple of old timbers, modern oak furnishings, some exposed stone walls around a big inglenook (with a good winter log fire), and country prints on the pale yellow walls; newspapers are laid out on a table. There's some emphasis on the very popular and attractively presented bar food, promptly served by attentive staff; a typical menu might include lunchtime sandwiches (£5), soup (£3.50), wild boar terrine (£5.50), spinach and goats cheese pie (£9), wild mushroom tortellini (£9.50), poached salmon supreme with coriander mash and prawn and chive butter sauce (£11.50), baked pork fillet with black pudding and caramelised apple on bubble and squeak (£12.50), whisky-marinated venison (£13), specials such as braised ox tongue charcuterie (£9.50) or grilled bass with poached leeks (£12.50), and on Sundays a choice of roasts (from £8.50). Helpings are big, and they'll bring delicious fresh bread to your table. On Thursday nights they do half a crispy duck on a bed of mash with pink peppercorn sauce and spring onions (£13.50). Well kept Hook Norton Best and a changing guest like Adnams Broadside on handpump, farm cider, and a good wine list. Though there's lots of space it can get busy; it may be worth booking. A couple of readers have again felt that the acoustics, what with hard walls and floors and high ceilings, are a bit too lively; it's quieter in a cosy but easily missed area upstairs which, like the restaurant, is no smoking. The pub's outside is cotswold stone at its most golden, and the village church opposite is impressive. (*Recommended by John Kane, P and J Shapley, David Glynne-Jones, Christopher White, Stuart Turner, Richard Greaves, Matthew Shackle, Martin and Pauline Jennings, Colin Wood, Mr and Mrs J Brown, John and Fiona McIlwain, Colin McKerrow, Sue Watkin, Gordon Doolan, Hunter and Christine Wright*)

Free house ~ Licensees Peter and Assumpta Golding ~ Real ale ~ Bar food (12-2 (3 Sat), 7-9.30; no food 25 Dec) ~ Restaurant ~ (01608) 659393 ~ Children welcome ~ Irish music once every sixth Weds evening; quiz nights ~ Open 11-11; 12-10.30 Sun

CLIFTON SP4831 Map 4 🏠

Duke of Cumberlands Head ♀ 🛏

B4031 Deddington—Aynho

The thatched roof of this small, peaceful pub is particularly impressive at the back, where it seems in places to run almost to the ground. A short walk from the canal, it's a popular place, especially on Sunday lunchtimes. The low-beamed turkey-carpeted lounge has a good log fire in a vast stone fireplace, attractive paintings by the landlord's mother of lilies and rhododendrons grown by her on the west coast of Scotland, and mainly sturdy kitchen tables, with a few more through in the little yellow-painted no smoking dining room, which has some stripped stone – none of the walls or ceilings is straight. The well liked bar food might include tomato and basil soup (£3.50), herrings marinated in dill and madeira (£4.50), fresh grilled sardines (£5.50), cottage pie or breaded scampi (£9; small helping £6), chicken korma, mushroom stroganoff or spanish garlic beef (all £10; small helping £7), lamb shanks in red wine (£11), and steaks (from £14); two-course Sunday lunch (£15). Good-natured service, with well kept Black Sheep and Hook Norton Best on handpump, alongside a guest such as Adnams Southwold. Plenty of wines to choose from and more than 30 malt whiskies too. Picnic-sets out on the grass behind. The pub can be hard to spot if they've forgotten to light the sign. *(Recommended by Val and Alan Green, Trevor and Judy Pearson, Hugh Spottiswoode, Gerry and Rosemary Dobson, Mrs J Groom, Richard Marjoram, Sir Nigel Foulkes, Phoebe and Duncan Thomas, William Ruxton, Peter Shapland, Ian Phillips, A G Marx, Michael Dandy, Mark O'Sullivan)*

Free house ~ Licensee Nick Huntington ~ Real ale ~ Bar food (12-2, 6.30-9(9.30 Fri/Sat); not Mon lunchtime) ~ Restaurant ~ (01869) 338534 ~ Children welcome ~ Dogs welcome ~ Open 12-2.30(3 Sat), 6.30-10.30(11 Sat); 12-3, 6.30-10 Sun; closed Mon lunchtime, plus Sun evenings Oct-Apr ~ Bedrooms: £50S(£50B)/£65B

CROWELL SU7499 Map 4
Shepherds Crook 🍺

B4009, 2 miles from M40 junction 6

The straight-talking landlord of this characterful village pub used to be a fish merchant, so the menu is dominated by fish, delivered overnight from Brixham. For some that's the main draw, but for others it's the excellent range of very well kept real ales, with the emphasis very much on beers from regional breweries (a typical choice might be Bathams, Loddon Hoppit, Springwood Charlies Angel, Timothy Taylors Landlord, and Youngs). And for others the appeal is simply finding the kind of traditional pub where the licensees aren't afraid to have opinions, and don't mind drawing others into the debate. On our last visit the day's hot topic was the relative merits of dishwashers, but you're as likely to find discussions on anything from vegetarians (not hugely in favour here) to horseracing and cricket. The bar is unpretentious (but not scruffy), and cheerfully pubby, with beams and exposed brickwork, stone-flagged floors, books on shelves and in a case, and a big fire in a brick fireplace; standing timbers divide it from a partly no smoking dining area with high wooden rafters, sporting prints, and chunky tables. Cooked to order, and relying on local produce wherever possible (they grow their own vegetables), the choice of food is chalked up on blackboards, and might include sandwiches, tasty black and white pudding flamed in calvados (£4.50), half a dozen oysters (£5.50), sausages and mash (£8.95), steak and kidney pie (£9.50), and changing fish specials like skate, turbot, and king prawns, with a choice of five diifferent kinds of fish and chips (from £8.50); friendly service. Like the beer, the wines are sourced from smaller producers, with some from the Lebanon. The golden retriever is called Compton. No music or machines, but a discreet TV; dominoes, cribbage. There are a few tables in front on the common, and decent walks nearby. *(Recommended by David Oakley, Torrens Lyster, Tracey and Stephen Groves)*

Free house ~ Licensees Steve and Elizabeth Scowen ~ Real ale ~ Bar food (12-2.30, 7-9.30; 12-3, 7-9 Sun) ~ Restaurant ~ (01844) 351431 ~ Well behaved children welcome ~ Dogs allowed in bar ~ Open 11.30-3, 5-11; 11.30-11 Sat; 12-10.30 Sun

CUXHAM SU6695 Map 4
Half Moon 🍴

4 miles from M40 junction 6; S on B4009, then right on to B480 at Watlington

Oxfordshire Dining Pub of the Year

Painstakingly restored after it was gutted by a fire several years back, this beautiful 16th-c thatched house may look like the quintessential English pub, but under its French landlord it's taken on something of the air of a smart gallic restaurant. The food is excellent, relying on fresh produce carefully sourced both locally and from further afield (many ingredients are collected on weekly trips to France), and though many of the dishes don't come cheap, the lunchtime bar menu includes several meals at surprisingly reasonable prices. A typical choice might include home-made soup (£5.50), a choice of ploughman's, some with french cheeses (from £7.50), moules marinière (£7.50), warm chicken liver salad (£7.95), a very good beef bourguignon (£8.50), and more elaborate dishes like breast of duck with five berries sauce (£18) and scallops with foie gras, white wine and coriander (£21.50); all meals come with delicious home-made bread. On our visit we had the place to ourselves but if the staff were disappointed they hid it well: service was friendly and attentive, and the atmosphere – though perhaps a touch formal for some tastes – relaxed and civilised. Most tables are set for eating, and though the biggest rooms are the two main eating areas (both no smoking), there's also a small red and black-tiled bar, with oak benches and tables, stripped beams and a brick fireplace; traditional brasses sit comfortably among the champagne bottles, and there are vineyard boxes stacked around the whitewashed walls. Brakspears on handpump; the wines and piped music are both mostly french. Behind is a good-sized garden, where they plan to grow their own vegetables. There's a minimum charge for credit cards. *(Recommended by R K Phillips, Ruth Kitching)*

Brakspears ~ Tenant Alain Madoni ~ Real ale ~ Bar food (12-2.30) ~ Restaurant ~ (01491) 614151 ~ Children in restaurant ~ Open 12-2.30, 5.30-11; 12-10 Sun

EAST HENDRED SU4588 Map 2
Eyston Arms
Village signposted off A417 E of Wantage; High Street

Stylishly reburbished in a modern country style, this nicely set old place is predominantly a dining pub, but there are good sized tables for drinkers too and you'll be just as welcome if you don't plan to eat. Attractively laid out and furnished, the several separate seeming areas have neat new tables and chairs, stripped timbers, flagstoned floors, and particularly low ceilings and beams; there's an attractive inglenook (with logs blazing in winter), some cushioned wall-seats, and a piano. The bar counter has olives to pick at, and even on a sunny day the candles may be lit. The food can be very good indeed, including lunchtime baguettes such as brie, bacon and cranberry and goats cheese with sun-blushed tomatoes and rocket (£5.95), their speciality grilled king prawns (£5.75 starter, £12.95 main), warm tart of the day (£7.50), sausages with mash and onion gravy (£7.95), sweet potato rösti with smoked salmon and crème fraîche (£8.95), local lamb steaks (£11.50), twice baked four cheese soufflé (£11.95), breast of free-range chicken with a white wine, pancetta and crème fraîche sauce (£12.95), plenty of fresh fish, and good steaks – their beef is hung for three weeks for fuller flavour. A two-course set lunch is £12.95, three courses £14.95. An area is no smoking – though some readers feel this is too small to be effective. Well kept Adnams and Wadworths 6X on handpump, good wines, friendly helpful service; maybe piped easy-listening music, cribbage, chess, dominoes. A couple of outside tables overlook the pretty village lane. *(Recommended by Dick and Madeleine Brown, Paul Butler, Peter Brown, Dr D Scott, Susan and John Douglas, Terry Miller)*

Free house ~ Licensee George Dailey ~ Real ale ~ Bar food (12-2.15, 7-9.30) ~ Restaurant ~ (01235) 833320 ~ Children in eating area of bar and restaurant ~ Dogs allowed in bar ~ Open 11-3, 6-11; 12-3, 7-11 Sun; closed 25 Dec

FIFIELD SP2318 Map 4 🏠
Merrymouth
A424 Burford—Stow

Dating back to the 13th c, this family-run country inn is well liked for its food (their fish dishes drawing particular praise this year), but also wins praise for its welcoming, thoughtful service. The simple but comfortably furnished L-shaped bar has nice bay-window seats, flagstones, horsebrasses and antique bottles hanging from low beams, some walls stripped back to the old masonry, and an open fire in winter. Except for five tables in the bar, the pub is no smoking; piped classical music. Enjoyable bar food might include home-made soup (£3.95), lunchtime baguettes (from £5.50), smoked mackerel pâté (£4.75), creamy leek and prawn tart

(£5.25), cold home-baked ham (£7.75), sausages with onion gravy (£7.95), chicken
pieces with bacon, mushrooms, cheese and cream (£8.95), steaks (from £10.95),
and rack of lamb with port and redcurrant sauce (£11.95), with daily specials such
as pasta with smoked cheese and tomato sauce (£7.50), steak and kidney pie
(£8.50), and hake with a cheese and herb crust (£10.95), and home-made puddings
like bread pudding with whisky sauce (£4.25). Well kept Brakspears and White
Horse Bitter on handpump, and decent wines. There are tables on a terrace and in
the back garden (there may be a little noise from fast traffic on the road). The
quaint bedrooms are well cared for. The Domesday Book mentions an inn on this
site, and its name comes from the Murimuth family, who once owned the village.
*(Recommended by Neil and Angela Huxter, Suzanne Miles, Tom Bottinga, Colin McKerrow,
Gill and Keith Croxton, B Brewer, Martin and Pauline Jennings, B and F A Hannam, KN-R)*

Free house ~ Licensees Andrew and Timothy Flaherty ~ Real ale ~ Bar food (12-2(2.30 Sat
and Sun), 6.30-9) ~ Restaurant ~ (01993) 831652 ~ Children in eating area of bar and
restaurant ~ Dogs welcome ~ Open 12-3, 6-11; 12-3, 7-10.30 Sun ~ Bedrooms:
£45S/£65B

FYFIELD SU4298 Map 4

White Hart 🍴 ♀ 📖

Off A420 Oxford—Faringdon

Originally built for Sir John Golafre in about 1450 to house priests who would
pray for his soul, this civilised and impressive place is well worth wandering
around. The bustling main room is a grand hall with soaring eaves, huge stone-
flanked window embrasures, and an attractive carpeted upper gallery. A nice
contrast is the cosy low-ceilinged side bar, which has an inglenook fireplace with a
huge black urn hanging over the grate, and a framed history of the pub on the wall.
The restaurant is no smoking. Imaginative food at lunchtime includes home-made
soup (£4.95), ciabatta sandwiches or ham hock terrine with apricot chutney
(£5.50), home-made fishcake with lemon mayonnaise (£5.95), local sausages with
onion marmalade or wild mushroom risotto (£8.95), bacon and cheese burger or
beer battered cod with home-made tartare sauce (£9.50), and niçoise salad with
fresh seared tuna (£10.25); in the evening there might be salad of shredded confit of
duck with fresh cherries (£6.25), seared red mullet with oriental salad and sweet
chilli sauce (£6.50), tagliatelle with chargrilled mediterranean vegetables (£9.95),
rolled pork tenderloin with sage mash and apple scrumpy compote or baked bass
with chorizo and red pepper coulis (£15.25) and braised ballantine of lamb with
dauphinoise potatoes and port wine jus (£15.50), with puddings such as warm
chocolate with chocolate sauce, lovely panna cotta with fruit coulis or raspberry
crème brûlée (£4.95). Well kept White Horse Bitter and guests like Beartown Ursa
Major, Castle Rock Harvest Pale, and Titanic Anchor on handpump, and a good
wine list; piped music. There are elegant metal seats around tables under smart
umbrellas on the really big terrace, and flower-edged lawns. *(Recommended by
Ian Phillips, Geoffrey Tyack, Clive and Kathryn Brimsom, Jeremy Woods, A P Seymour,
Mark and Ruth Brock)*

Free house ~ Licensee Ian Rogers ~ Real ale ~ Bar food ~ Restaurant ~ (01865) 390585
~ Children welcome ~ Open 12-3, 6-11; 12-11 Sat; 12-10.30 Sun

GREAT TEW SP3929 Map 4 🏠

Falkland Arms 📖

Off B4022 about 5 miles E of Chipping Norton; The Green

Like the other untouched golden-stone cottages in this charming village, this
picturesque thatched inn really is extraordinarily attractive, but what's especially
nice is that there's plenty more to recommend it too – not least its excellent choice
of beers. The only downside is that the pub is hardly an undiscovered gem, and it
can get extremely busy. Unspoilt and welcoming, the partly panelled bar has high-
backed settles and a diversity of stools around plain stripped tables on flagstones
and bare boards, one, two and three-handled mugs hanging from the beam-and-

board ceiling, dim converted oil lamps, shutters for the stone-mullioned latticed windows, and a fine inglenook fireplace with a blazing fire in winter. Along with well kept Wadworths IPA, 6X and a seasonal ale such as Summersault, they serve up to four guests like Highgate Fox's Nob, St Peters Golden Ale, Shardlow Whistlestop, and Titanic English Glory on handpump, and hold an annual summer beer festival. The counter is decorated with tobacco jars and different varieties of snuff which you can buy, and you'll also find 60 malt whiskies, 16 country wines, and farm cider; darts, cribbage and dominoes. Lunchtime bar food includes soup (£3.95), filled baguettes (from £4.25), ploughman's (from £5.95), and changing daily specials like beef and ale pie, smoked haddock chowder and mushroom and herb stroganoff (from £6.95); in the evenings bar snacks are limited to their hand-reared pork pies, but the restaurant does more sophisticated meals such as slow-cooked lamb shank with rosemary and garlic gravy (you'll need to book). The dining room is no smoking. You have to go out into the lane and then back in again to use the lavatories. There are tables out in front of the pub, and picnic-sets under cocktail parasols in the garden behind. Dogs must be on a lead. Small good value bedrooms (no under-14s). *(Recommended by the Didler, Patrick Hancock, Brenda and Rob Fincham, Guy Vowles, John and Gloria Isaacs, Angus Lyon, Mrs P Sarson, Dr David Cockburn, Geoff Pidoux, Keith Jacob, Bob Ellis, Michael Dandy, Tracey and Stephen Groves, Kevin Blake, DP and RA Pascoe, M J Winterton, Andy Trafford, Louise Bayly, A P Seymour)*

Wadworths ~ Managers Paul Barlow-Heal and S J Courage ~ Real ale ~ Bar food (12-2, 7-8; not Sun evening) ~ Restaurant ~ (01608) 683653 ~ Children in restaurant lunchtimes only ~ Dogs allowed in bar ~ Live folk Sun night, other live music last Fri/Sat of month ~ Open 11.30-2.30, 6-11; all day in summer hols Sat; 12-3, 7-10.30 (all day summer hols) Sun ~ Bedrooms: £50S/£75S(£110B)

HENLEY SU7882 Map 2

Anchor 🍷

Friday Street; coming in over bridge, first left towards A4155 then next right

It's quite a surprise to find such an old-fashioned, homely local in this smart little town. Recently redecorated and spruced up, it nevertheless still has a nicely lived-in and slightly cluttered feel to its two traditionally furnished main rooms. The beams in the dark ochre ceiling are thickly hung with chamber-pots, steins, whisky-water jugs, copperware and so forth, and there are interesting pictures: mainly local river photographs in the left room, a mix of antique sporting, ship and comical prints on the right, which has a piano and TV; shove-ha'penny, backgammon, cribbage, dominoes and winter darts. Throw rugs, scatter cushions, chintz curtains, some venerable wall boarding and dim lighting add to the cottagey feel. A simply furnished back dining room has lots of rowing photographs, and a cage with a chatty cockatiel; behind is a charming informal terrace surrounded by lush vegetation and hanging vines. Besides an impressive choice of lunchtime sandwiches (from £3.50), generously served bar food includes baked potatoes (from £5), baguettes, ciabattas or ploughman's (£5), salads (£7), fish pie, thai green curry, and changing specials such as winter stews and hotpots, steak and kidney pie, somerset chicken and liver and bacon (all £8); they may also have some fresh fish specials. The landlady is helpful and friendly. Well kept Brakspears Bitter and Special with a seasonal ale on handpump, and a good range of malt whiskies and New World wines by the glass. Ruger the friendly chocolate labrador is much in evidence. *(Recommended by Mike and Sue Richardson, David Edwards, Jim Abbott, the Didler, Barry and Anne, Tracey and Stephen Groves)*

Brakspears ~ Tenant G A Ion-Savage ~ Real ale ~ Bar food (not Sun or Mon evenings) ~ (01491) 574753 ~ Well behaved children in restaurant until 8pm ~ Open 11-11; 12-10.30 Sun; closed evening 25 Dec

HIGHMOOR SU7084 Map 2

Dog & Duck
Off A4130 Henley—Oxford; B481

Cosy and cottagey, this unspoilt country pub is doing very well under its newish landlord, and on our winter inspection was packed with people enjoying the good, hearty home-made food. Our favourite part is the tiny beamed bar on the left, with space for barely three tables, a piano and a coal fire; warmly characterful, it's the kind of place where you can't help striking up conversations with whoever else is in the room. Slightly bigger, though still not huge, is the flagstoned dining room on the right, with hatch service, several house plants and lighted candles, an eclectic mix of old prints and pictures, and a few tables squeezed round the edge of the room; a room leading off here (popular with families) is no smoking. Blackboards list the range of lunchtime baguettes (from £3.75), ploughman's (£4.25), and changing hot dishes like home-made broccoli and stilton soup (£4.25), crab and herb pancakes (£6.75), gnocchi with bacon, cream and parmesan, sautéed liver and bacon or leek and gruyère tart (£7.25), steak and kidney pie (£7.75), chicken breast with chorizo and tomato salsa (£8.75), and venison steak with black pudding (£12.75). Well kept Brakspears Bitter and Special, helpful service from friendly staff; piped music, cribbage, dominoes. The long garden has some play equipment at the end. Dr Crippen stayed here while attempting to escape to America. There are plenty of walks in the surrounding woods. *(Recommended by the Didler, Roger Yates)*

Brakspears ~ Tenant Simon Rudd ~ Real ale ~ Bar food ~ (01491) 641261 ~ Children welcome ~ Dogs welcome ~ Occasional folk nights, Weds night quiz ~ Open 11.30-3, 6-11; 12-3, 7-10.30 Sun; closed winter Sun evenings

Rising Sun
Witheridge Hill, signposted off B481; OS Sheet 175 map reference 697841

There's been another change of licensee at this pretty black and white pub, and the new landlord has lots of plans for jazz and other entertainments; in the meantime, early reports are promising, and it remains an attractive, quiet spot. There are seats around a few simple tables in a smallish carpeted area on the right, by the bar, with some bar stools too, and a log-effect stove in a big brick inglenook fireplace. The main area spreading back from here has shiny bare boards and a swathe of carpeting, with well spaced tables and attractive pictures on the walls; piped music, dominoes and cribbage. The new lunchtime menu includes sandwiches, baguettes or ciabattas (£4.75), home-made soup (£3.95), ploughman's (£4.75), cheese, leek and wine pancakes (£6.95), sausage and mash (£7.50), beef and ale pie (£7.95), herbed chicken breast with tagliatelle in a creamy mushroom sauce (£11.95), and sirloin steak with peppercorn or stilton sauce (£14.50); they have dairy and gluten-free options too. Well kept Brakspears Bitter, Special and seasonal beers on handpump, and 14 wines by the glass; hospitable, welcoming service. In fine weather the terrace is a pleasant place to sit and there are also tables on the grass among the trees. More reports please. *(Recommended by Bob and Margaret Holder, Julia and Richard Tredgett, P Tailyour, Philip and June Caunt, Tracey and Stephen Groves, Jeremy Woods, John Roots)*

Brakspears ~ Tenant Alan Quinn ~ Real ale ~ Bar food ~ Restaurant ~ (01491) 641455 ~ Children welcome ~ Dogs allowed in bar ~ Open 12-3, 6-11; 12-11 Sat; 12-10.30 Sun

---

The Post Office makes it virtually impossible for people to come to grips with British geography, by using a system of post towns which are often across the county boundary from the places they serve. So the postal address of a pub often puts it in the wrong county. We use the correct county – the one the pub is actually in. Lots of pubs which the Post Office alleges are in Oxfordshire are actually in Berkshire, Buckinghamshire, Gloucestershire or Warwickshire.

HOOK NORTON SP3533 Map 4 🏠
Gate Hangs High 🍽 ♀ 🍺

Banbury Road; a mile N of village towards Sibford, at Banbury—Rollright crossroads

Despite its nicely tucked-away location this cheery country pub gets surprisingly busy, though if you arrive early enough you can sometimes have it almost to yourself. It's a nice all-rounder, popular for food, drink and well ordered service, with the wide choice of bar food typically including sandwiches (£4 – some unusual ones like black pudding and mango), pork crackling with apple sauce (£3.50), black pudding and bacon rösti with a poached egg (£5.95), steak and ale pie (£9.95), braised rabbit in cider and mustard (£11.50), winter jugged hare (£12.95), and pork fillet with mushrooms, cream and sherry or whole bass, tomato and mozzarella (£12.95). They have a good children's menu (from £3.50), excellent home-made puddings, and a two-course weekday set menu (£10.95; 3 courses £12.95). You'll need to book for Saturday evening and Sunday lunch, in the slightly chintzy no smoking side dining extension. The bar has joists in the long, low ceiling, a brick bar counter, stools and assorted chairs on the carpet, baby oil lamps on each table, a gleaming copper hood over the hearth in the inglenook fireplace, and hops over the bar counter. Well kept Hook Norton Best, Old Hooky and maybe a guest like Adnams on handpump, bottled beers and decent wines; piped music and dominoes. There's a pretty courtyard garden, and seats on a broad lawn behind, with holly and apple trees, and fine views; the flower tubs and wall baskets are very colourful. The new bedrooms are in converted barns; we've yet to hear from anyone who's stayed here. *(Recommended by Trevor and Judy Pearson, Stuart Turner, Alan Scaife, Des and Jen Clarke, Sir Nigel Foulkes, David J Austin, Michael Dandy, Simon Jones, Iain R Hewitt, Pam and David Bailey)*

Hook Norton ~ Tenant Stephen Coots-Williams ~ Real ale ~ Bar food (12.30-2.30, 6-10; all day Sat and Sun) ~ Restaurant ~ (01608) 737387 ~ Children in eating area of bar and restaurant ~ Dogs allowed in bar ~ Open 12-3, 6-11; 12-11 Sat; 12-10.30 Sun ~ Bedrooms: £40B/£60B

Sun 🍺 🛏

High Street 🏠

Facing the church in a prime site in a pretty village, this bustling place has tables on the street in front (as well as on a back terrace) that give a pleasantly continental feel on summer evenings. Inside, the flagstoned front bar has a relaxed local atmosphere, a huge log fire, hop-strung beams, well kept Hook Norton Best, Mild, Old Hooky and seasonal ales on handpump, and seven wines by the glass; dominoes, cribbage and alley skittles. Behind the central servery a cosy newly carpeted room with comfortable banquettes and other seats leads into the attractive no smoking restaurant. Bar food includes various ciabattas or filled baked potatoes (£5.95), home-made soup (£3.50), scallops and king prawns in a creamy tarragon and white wine sauce (£5.50), black pudding with creamed potatoes and onion cream gravy (£5.95), red onion and brie cannelloni (£9.25), confit of duck leg on caramelised red cabbage with juniper berries and red wine sauce (£9.75), pan-fried calves liver or glazed bacon hock (£10.50), marinated shoulder of lamb in rosemary and garlic on artichoke mash or whole grilled plaice with parsley and caper dressing (£10.95), and daily specials like lemon and pepper chicken fillet on caesar salad (£8.25) and tempura battered skate wing with home-made tartare dressing (£8.50); they do a popular Sunday lunch (two courses £12.95, three courses £15). Good wheelchair access and disabled facilities. *(Recommended by Darren and Jane Staniforth, Gill and Tony Morriss, George Atkinson, Tim and Ann Newell, Brian Wainwright, Pete Baker, Pam and David Bailey, Michael Dandy, Simon Jones)*

Hook Norton ~ Tenant Stuart Rust ~ Bar food ~ Restaurant ~ (01608) 737570 ~ Children in eating area of bar and restaurant ~ Dogs allowed in bar ~ Open 11-3, 6-11; 12-3, 7-10.30 Sun ~ Bedrooms: £40S/£60S(£60B)

KELMSCOTT SU2499 Map 4

Plough 🛏

NW of Faringdon, off B4449 between A417 or A4095

Very handy for the Thames and the former summer home of William Morris, this pretty little inn has ancient flagstones and stripped stone walls in its small traditional beamed front bar, along with a good log fire, and the relaxed chatty feel of a real village pub. Most of the bar food is served in a choice of small and large helpings, from a menu that takes in a good choice of substantial sandwiches, home-made soup (£4.50/£6.50), devilled kidneys (£4.95/£6.95), roast ham and eggs (£5.50/£7.50), ploughman's (£5.50/£9.50), mussels or pan-flashed red mullet on grilled bruschetta with cherry tomato salsa (£6.50/£8.50), crispy duck with noodles and ginger or grilled seafood skewers with lemon and thyme rice (£7.50/£9.50), and various changing pies (£8.50). The pleasant dining area has attractively plain and solid furnishings. Well kept Archers Best, Hobgoblin Wychwood, Hook Norton Best and Timothy Taylors Landlord on handpump, and Black Rat farm cider; piped music, pool, TV and darts. The garden is pretty, with seats among plantings of unusual flowers and aunt sally, and there are picnic-sets under cocktail parasols out in front. The Oxfordshire Cycleway runs close by. More reports please. *(Recommended by Geoff Pidoux, Tony and Wendy Hobden, R Huggins, D Irving, E McCall, T McLean, Paul Butler, Ann and Colin Hunt, Karen and Graham Oddey, A P Seymour)*

Free house ~ Licensee Martin Platt ~ Real ale ~ Bar food (12-2.30, 7-9; all day weekends) ~ Restaurant ~ (01367) 253543 ~ Children welcome ~ Dogs allowed in bar ~ Live entertainment Sat evening ~ Open 11-11.30; 12-11 Sun ~ Bedrooms: £45S/£75B

LEWKNOR SU7198 Map 4

Olde Leathern Bottel

Under a mile from M40 junction 6; just off B4009 towards Watlington

A useful break from the M40, this pleasant country pub has heavy beams and low ceilings in its two bar rooms (both no smoking), as well as rustic furnishings, open fires, and an understated décor of old beer taps and the like; the family room is separated only by standing timbers, so you won't feel segregated from the rest of the pub. Bar food includes lunchtime filled baguettes or ploughman's (from £4.95), ham and eggs (£5.95), and daily specials like chicken and bacon caesar salad (£6.95), stir-fried beef in black bean sauce, roasted duck breast with plum sauce), and wok-fried king prawns (£9.95), with home-made puddings such as apple and mincemeat pie (£2.95). Well kept Brakspears Bitter and Special on handpump, and a dozen wines by the glass. The attractive sizeable garden has plenty of picnic-sets under parasols, and a children's play area. More reports please. *(Recommended by Howard Dell, Tracey and Stephen Groves, Alec and Joan Laurence, Ian Phillips, Mrs B M Hill, Dr D J and Mrs S C Walker, Brian Wainwright)*

Brakspears ~ Tenant L S Gordon ~ Real ale ~ Bar food (12-2, 7-9.30) ~ Restaurant ~ (01844) 351482 ~ Children in restaurant and family room ~ Dogs welcome ~ Open 11-2.30(3 Sat), 6-11; 12-3, 7-10.30 Sun

LONGWORTH SU3899 Map 4

Blue Boar

Off A420/A415; Tucks Lane

This 17th-c thatched stone local was a delight when we visited on a bitterly cold winter lunchtime. We'd expected it to be as deserted as the other pubs we'd seen that day, but instead it was thriving, the three low-beamed, characterful little rooms packed with people enjoying its genuinely welcoming atmosphere and wide choice of decent food. From the outside it's pretty much the classic image of an English country pub, and inside too it's warmly traditional, with well worn fixtures and furnishings, and two blazing log fires, one beside a fine old settle. Brasses, hops and assorted knick-knacks like skis and an old clocking-in machine line the ceilings and walls, there are fresh flowers on the bar and scrubbed wooden tables, and faded rugs on the tiled floor; benches are firmly wooden rather than upholstered. The main eating area is the red-painted room at the end (it's no smoking in here), with plenty of blackboards listing things like lunchtime sandwiches (from £3.95), soup (£4.25), antipasti (£5.95), standard dishes like steak and kidney pie (£6.95) and burgers (£7.50), a good range of vegetarian meals, and more interesting changing specials like seared scallops with a rocket and balsamic salad; meals are promptly served, in good-sized helpings. Well kept Brakspears, Greene King Ruddles Best and Hook Norton Best and Old Hooky on handpump, up to 20 malt whiskies, and a wide choice of wines, several by the glass. Though the piped music wasn't quiet, it was easily drowned out by the buzz of conversation. The licensee has been here for 27 years, though his friendly young team are generally more in evidence. There are tables in front, and more in a pleasant garden behind. The Thames is a short walk away. *(Recommended by M Grieve)*

Free house ~ Licensee Paul Dailey ~ Real ale ~ Bar food (12-2, 7-10; 12-2.30 Sat; 12-3 Sun) ~ Restaurant ~ 01865 820494 ~ Children welcome in restaurant at lunchtimes ~ Dogs allowed in bar ~ Open 12-3(3.30 Sat), 6-11; 12-10.30 Sun; closed 25 Dec, evening of 1 Jan

OXFORD SP5106 Map 4

Rose & Crown

North Parade Avenue; very narrow, so best to park in a nearby street

What could be a fairly ordinary neighbourhood pub is given a great deal of atmosphere and originality by its licensees. Bearded and sharp-witted Mr Hall and his wife have been running this congenial and chatty place in their distinctive way for quite some time now; while he keeps his Adnams Bitter and Broadside, and Hook Norton Old Hooky (on handpump) particularly well, produces almost a work of art in the five minutes or so that he takes to pour a pint of Guinness, and keeps around 25 malt whiskies and a large choice of wines, she looks after the kitchen. This produces traditional lunchtime food, straightforward but much enjoyed, such as sandwiches (from £3.45), tortilla wraps (£4.25), baked potatoes (from £4.25), ploughman's (£5.75), gammon and egg (£6.75), whole trout or 10oz rump steak (£8.45), daily specials like cottage pie or warm chicken salad (from £5.95), and puddings like sticky toffee or apple pie (£3.95). The front door opens into little more than a passage by the bar counter, with a piano in the small room on the left (Mr Hall enjoys people playing if they're good – but is quick to give his opinion if not). The panelled back room, with traditional pub furnishings and decorated with pennants, hockey sticks and the like, is slightly bigger, and you'll find reference books for crossword buffs; one room is no smoking. There's a blessed freedom from mobile phones (though not always from smoke), as well as from piped music and machines – and not too many undergraduates, though graduate students from St Anthony's like it. The pleasant walled back yard (no children – except at weekend lunchtimes) can be completely covered with a huge awning, and was one of the first places in Britain to have belgian-style outdoor heaters, well over ten years ago; at the far end is a little overflow eating room. The lavatories are pretty basic. No children inside. *(Recommended by Geoff Pidoux, Torrens Lyster, Robert Lorimer, Chris Glasson)*

Punch ~ Tenants Andrew and Debbie Hall ~ Real ale ~ Bar food (12-2.15(3.15 Sun), 6-9; not 25, 26 or 31 Dec) ~ No credit cards ~ (01865) 510551 ~ children in courtyard weekend lunchtimes only ~ Open 10-2.40, 5-11; 12-10.30 Sun; closed 25 and 26 Dec

---

We mention bottled beers and spirits only if there is something unusual about them – imported Belgian real ales, say, or dozens of malt whiskies; so do please let us know about them in your reports.

Turf Tavern 🍺

Tavern Bath Place; via St Helen's Passage, between Holywell Street and New College Lane

Hidden behind the high stone walls of some of the city's oldest buildings, this is arguably Oxford's most characterful pub, and considering how tricky it can be to find, it's extraordinary how busy it usually is. Though students are a major part of the mix, its two dark-beamed and low ceilinged little bars pack in quite a range of customers, and there are many more who whatever the time of year prefer to sit outside in the three attractive walled-in flagstoned or gravelled courtyards (one has its own bar); in winter, they have coal braziers, so you can roast chestnuts or toast marshmallows, and there are canopies with lights and heaters. Up to 11 real ales are well kept on handpump, typically including brews like Adnams Broadside, Batemans Combined Harvest, Beartown Ginger Bear, Butcombe Gold, Caledonian Deuchars IPA and Golden Promise Organic Ale, Everards Perfick, Greene King Abbot and IPA, Highgate Old Ale and White Horse Bitter; they have regular beer festivals. Also Hoegaarden on tap, Weston's Old Rosie cider, and in winter mulled wine. Straightforward bar food includes baguettes (from £3.75), caesar salad (£4.95), sausage and mash (£5.75), steak and ale pie (£7.25), fish and chips (£7.45), with puddings such as apple and blackberry crumble (£3.25); the top food area is no smoking. Service is generally friendly and knowledgeable, but can be strteched at busy times (as are the lavatories). *(Recommended by the Didler, Derek and Sylvia Stephenson, Kevin Blake, R E Perry, A G Marx, Ann and Colin Hunt, Chris Glasson, Michael and Alison Sandy)*

Greene King ~ Manager Darren Kent ~ Real ale ~ Bar food (12-7.30) ~ (01865) 243235 ~ Children in eating area of bar ~ Dogs welcome ~ Live music Thurs evenings ~ Open 11-11; 12-10.30 Sun

RAMSDEN SP3515 Map 4

Royal Oak 🍷 🍺 🛏

Village signposted off B4022 Witney—Charlbury

Opposite the church, this unpretentious inn is a proper village pub, with no music or machines, and a relaxed, genial atmosphere. The basic furnishings are comfortable, with fresh flowers, bookcases with old and new copies of *Country Life* and, when the weather gets cold, a cheerful log fire. Well kept Hook Norton Best and guests like Arkells Moonlight and Butts Barbus Barbus on handpump, and a splendid choice of wines from Languedoc and Roussillon (many by the glass); several armagnacs and farm cider. There's quite an emphasis on the food, sourced mostly from local suppliers, which might include lunchtime ploughman's (£5.50), club sandwich (£6.25), and sausages and mash (£6.95), as well as home-made soup (£3.50), a vegetarian dish of the day, a pie of the week (£7.95), home-made burgers (from £7.95), mediterranean-style lamb casserole (£11.50), steamed steak and mushroom suet pudding (£11.95), sirloin steak (£12.95), daily specials, and puddings (£4.25); they do a three-course Sunday lunch (£15.50), and on Thursdays have steak, pudding and a glass of wine for £13.95. The dining room is no smoking. There are tables and chairs out in front and on the terrace behind the restaurant (folding back doors give easy access); outdoor heaters. The bedrooms are in separate cottages; breakfasts are well liked. Though most of the reports we've received this year have been enthusiastic, a few suggest that on occasion the service – and even the food – may not reach their normally high standards. *(Recommended by John Hale, B Edgar, Pat and Graham Williamson, David Barnes, Peter Green, Michael Jones, Dennis Dort, Comus and Sarah Elliott, Pierre Boyer, Chris Wood, Mr and Mrs Billy Rideout, Keith and Maureen Trainer, Paul Duthrie, Rainer Zimmer, Ann and Colin Hunt, Nigel and Sue Foster, John Cook)*

Free house ~ Licensee Jon Oldham ~ Real ale ~ Bar food (12-2, 7-10) ~ Restaurant ~ (01993) 868213 ~ Children in restaurant ~ Dogs allowed in bar ~ Open 11.30-3, 6.30-11; 12-3, 7-10.30 Sun; closed 25 Dec ~ Bedrooms: £40S/£60S

ROKE SU6293 Map 2

Home Sweet Home

Village signposted off B4009 Benson—Watlington

The new look of this smart old favourite works well, in places creating a more sleek and modern feel, and yet somehow making other parts seem more ancient. There are two warmly welcoming smallish bar rooms with a pleasantly relaxed atmosphere, a particularly striking big log fire, heavy stripped beams, and traditional furniture, and on the right, a carpeted room with low settees and armchairs that leads through to the no smoking restaurant. Good well-presented bar food includes soup (£4.50), lunchtime filled baguettes, potato, stilton and chive brûlée (£4.95), sweet pepper, tomato and mozzarella pancake (£7.95), beef and ale pie or pork, honey and mustard sausages with spring onion mash (£8.25), pork tenderloin on a bed of black pudding or chicken supreme filled with brie with a creamy smoked bacon and chive sauce (£10.95), calves liver and bacon (£12.50), fillet steak (£13.95), and puddings like gooseberry and ginger cheesecake (£4.50). They have occasional curry or fish nights, and in winter now use the fire for spit roasts every Wednesday, Friday and Sunday. Well kept Adnams Best, Fullers London Pride and Loddon Brewery Hoppit on handpump; there's a family connection to the Loddon Brewery, who this year sponsored the pub's first beer festival. Also, ten wines by the glass (champagne as well), and several malt whiskies; friendly service, no music or machines. There are lots of flowers around tables out by the well and a low-walled front garden. The landlord runs another popular main entry, the Horns at Crazies Hill in Berkshire. *(Recommended by Tracey and Stephen Groves, Doreen and Haydn Maddock, Geoff and Teresa Salt, Margaret and Roy Randle, Heather Couper, Susan and John Douglas, Roy and Gay Hoing)*

Free house ~ Licensee Andy Hearn ~ Real ale ~ Bar food (12-2, 6.45-9.30; not Sun evening) ~ Restaurant ~ (01491) 838249 ~ Children in restaurant ~ Dogs allowed in bar ~ Open 11.30-2.30, 6.30(6 Sat)-11; 12-4 Sun; closed Sun evening; 25 and 26 Dec

SIBFORD GOWER SP3537 Map 4

Bishop Blaize

Village signposted just off B4035 W of Banbury; Burdrop

Named for the patron saint of wool combers, this stone-built old local has some interesting features in its unspoilt bar, but it's the setting and attractively planted gardens that really impress. Tables on the spacious sloping lawn and lower terrace offer splendid views down over the sheep-strewn hillside and across the surrounding fields – on a clear day stretching into Gloucestershire and Warwickshire; swings in one corner. Inside, the heavily beamed partly tiled bar has big windows overlooking the garden, some panelling, cosy and comfortable country furnishings, a few framed cartoons, and leaflets advertising local concerts and events. There's an unusual curved wooden counter, opposite which is a very snug inglenook, once used for wakes, but now squeezing in a couple of tiny tables and chairs by an ancient stove; piped music, darts, cribbage, dominoes. Well kept Vale Best and a couple of guests like Jennings Golden Host, Theakstons Best or Vale Special on handpump, and several wines by the glass; piped music and darts. Friendly staff serve straightforward bar food such as sandwiches (£2.95), soup (£2.95), deep-fried camembert with cranberry jelly (£3.95), ham, egg and chips or haddock and chips (£6.45), chicken curry (£7.25), home-made steak and kidney or chicken and leek pies (£7.45), and fillet steak (£11.95); on Mondays fish or sausage and chips are just £3.25. There's a level entrance onto the lawn and into the pub with a ramp onto a small terrace. Occasional summer morris dancers, and good nearby walks. *(Recommended by George Atkinson, Arnold Bennett, K H Fröstick, Stuart Turner, Simon Jones, Chris Glasson)*

Free house ~ Licensees Sam and Sheila Merchant ~ Real ale ~ Bar food (not Sun evenings) ~ (01295) 780323 ~ Open 12-2.30, 6-11.30; 12-3, 7-10.30 Sun

STANTON ST JOHN SP5709 Map 4

Star

Pub signposted off B4027, in Middle Lane; village is signposted off A40 heading E of Oxford (heading W, you have to go to the Oxford ring-road roundabout and take unclassified road signposted to Stanton St John, Forest Hill etc)

This pleasant old pub is appealingly arranged over two levels, with the oldest parts two characterful little low-beamed rooms, one with ancient brick flooring tiles, and the other quite close-set tables. Up some stairs is an attractive extension on a level with the car park, with old-fashioned dining chairs, an interesting mix of dark oak and elm tables, rugs on flagstones, pairs of bookshelves on each side of an attractive inglenook fireplace (good blazing fires in winter), shelves of good pewter, terracotta-coloured walls with a portrait in oils, and a stuffed ermine. Decent bar food includes sandwiches (£3.25, soup and sandwich £5.75), chicken liver pâté (£4.95), ploughman's (from £4.95), venison pie or battered haddock (£7.95), moussaka (£8.25), red thai chicken curry (£9.25), and lamb shank in redcurrant and rosemary (£11.95), with puddings such as spotted dick or banoffi pie (£3.75). Well kept Wadworths IPA and 6X on handpump; attentive service. The rather straightforward family room and conservatory are no smoking; piped music (rather loud at times), darts, shove-ha'penny and dominoes. The walled garden has seats among the rockeries and children's play equipment. *(Recommended by CMW, JJW, Geoff Pidoux, Gordon Tong, Matthew Shackle, Mr and Mrs John Taylor, Simon Collett-Jones, KC, Roy and Gay Hoing)*

Wadworths ~ Tenant Michael Urwin ~ Real ale ~ Bar food (not Sun evening) ~ (01865) 351277 ~ Children in family room ~ Dogs welcome ~ Open 11-2.30, 6.30-11; 12-2.30, 7-10.30 Sun

STEEPLE ASTON SP4725 Map 4

Red Lion ♀

Off A4260 12 miles N of Oxford

The suntrap front terrace of this rather civilised little stone pub has lovely flowers and shrubs and is a fine place to relax in summer. Inside, the comfortable partly panelled bar is welcoming and pubby, with beams, an antique settle and other good furnishings, well kept Hook Norton Best and a couple of changing guests on handpump – typically Hook Norton's seasonal brew, and White Horse Bitter. Also, a carefully chosen wine list, quite a few whiskies, single estate cognacs, and farm cider. Bar snacks (also served on the terrace) include nachos (£3.95), half-pound cheeseburger (£6.95; a gourmet version with a bottle of champagne is £39.50), and caesar salad (£7.95), with evening dishes like cumberland sausage with leek and cheddar mash (£7.95), roast red pepper and butternut risotto (£5.25 starter, £9.50 main), steak and ale pie (£9.50), roast bass with garlic, white wine, rosemary and lemon (£12.50), various steaks (from £12.95), and herb-crusted rack of lamb with a port, redcurrant mint jus (£14.50). The dining areas are no smoking; piped music in nicely extended 18th c restaurant. More reports please. *(Recommended by Bruce and Penny Wilkie, J A Ellis, Mrs Jill Silversides, Barry Brown)*

Free house ~ Licensee Neil Protheroe ~ Real ale ~ Bar food (not Sun evening, not Mon except bank hols) ~ Restaurant ~ (01869) 340225 ~ Children in eating area of bar and restaurant ~ Dogs allowed in bar ~ Open 12-3, 6-11; 12-3, 7-10.30 Sun; closed Mon lunchtime, 1 Jan

---

Bedroom prices normally include full English breakfast, VAT and any inclusive service charge that we know of. Prices before the '/' are for single rooms, after for two people in double or twin (B includes a private bath, S a private shower). If there is no '/', the prices are only for twin or double rooms (as far as we know there are no singles). If there is no B or S, as far as we know no rooms have private facilities.

SWALCLIFFE SP3737 Map 4

Stags Head ♀

Bakers Lane, just off B4035

A new landlord arrived at this picturesque thatched pub not long before we went to press. The main draw for visitors has long been the series of neatly terraced gardens, lovely in summer, with palm trees, a small fountain, several tables under a pergola, and a sensibly segregated play area. Inside, the low-beamed bar has a big woodburning stove at one end, a standard lamp beside it, and high-backed wooden pews and cushioned seats along the stone walls. Lots of little jugs hang from the ceiling, and the paintings of local scenes – by the landlord – are for sale. A lighter room has lots more tables and a tiled fireplace, along with newspapers to read, plenty of books, and lists of various local events and activities; at night all the tables have candles. Half the pub is no smoking. Bar food now includes filled baguettes (£4.95), soup (£3.95), chicken liver parfait with redcurrant jelly and melba toast (£4.50), local sausages and mash (£7.95), roast salmon, pesto mash and tarragon sauce or burger topped with stilton and parma ham (£8.95), duck breast with olive mash and Cointreau sauce (£9.95), fillet steaks (from £11.95), and specials like moroccan lamb (£7.95); children's menu. Black Sheep, Hook Norton Old Hooky and a weekly changing guest like Adnams Southwold on handpump, farm cider, and several wines by the glass; cribbage, dominoes, Wednesday evening bridge. A letting bedroom has its own kitchenette. More reports please. *(Recommended by Andrew Kerr, Clive and Fran Dutson, Graham and Christina Page, Jeff Lynn, Kevin Blake, Stuart Turner, Iain R Hewitt, Simon Jones, Dr H Marcovitch)*

Free house ~ Licensee Stephen Kingsford ~ Real ale ~ Bar food (12-2, 7(6 Sat)-9.30; 12-3 Sun; not Sun evening, Mon) ~ Restaurant ~ (01295) 780232 ~ Children welcome ~ Dogs welcome ~ Open 12-2.30(11-3 Sat), 6-11; 12-3, 7-10.30 Sun; closed Mon ~ Bedrooms: £40S/£60S

SWINBROOK SP2811 Map 4

Swan

Back Road a mile N of A40, 2 miles E of Burford

This 17th-c country pub benefits from its delightful setting, in a lovely spot close to the River Windrush and its bridge; old-fashioned benches by the fuchsia hedge are the best place to take in the view. The tiny interior is cosy, peaceful and dimly lit, with simple antique furnishings and a woodburning stove in the flagstoned tap room and the back bar; darts, dominoes and cribbage. Well kept Archers Village Bitter, Greene King IPA, Wadworths 6X and Wychwood Hobgoblin on handpump, a choice of good coffees, and herbal teas. Tasty bar food at lunchtime includes home-made soup (£3.95), filled baguettes (from £5.95), goats cheese salad (£7.50), pasta with seafood or with sun-dried tomatoes and parmesan (£7.95), home-made steak and kidney pie (£8.95), and chicken filled with brie, wrapped in bacon and topped with pesto sauce (£10.95); in the evening, there might be wild mushrooms in garlic butter (£4.95), pork tenderloin with apricot, sage and cashew nut pâté and stem ginger jus (£11.95), barbary duck breast on parsnip and potato mash or salmon fillet with a champagne, shrimp and chive sauce (£12.95), and puddings such as home-made apple crumble (£4.25). *(Recommended by Klaus and Elizabeth Leist, Michael and Ann Cole, David Handforth, Carol Mills, R Huggins, D Irving, E McCall, T McLean, Comus and Sarah Elliott, Stuart Turner, Iain R Hewitt, Karen and Graham Oddey)*

Free house ~ Licensee Andrew Morris ~ Real ale ~ Bar food (not Sun evening) ~ (01993) 822165 ~ Well behaved children welcome away from bar ~ Dogs allowed in bar ~ Open 11.30-3, 6.30-11; 12-3, 7-10.30 Sun; closed 25 Dec

---

We accept no free drinks, meals or payment for inclusion. We take no advertising, and are not sponsored by the brewing industry – or by anyone else. So all reports are independent.

TADPOLE BRIDGE SP3300 Map 4 ⌂

Trout ⑪ ♀ 🛏️

Back road Bampton—Buckland, 4 miles NE of Faringdon

The food at this bustling, comfortably upmarket inn has again won lots of enthusiastic praise from readers this year; inventive and well prepared, it draws the crowds at weekends (when booking is pretty much essential), but you may find things quieter during the week. The emphasis is very much on the meals, but drinkers drop in too, and it's also a nice place to stay with some rooms overlooking the Thames (one suite has its own terrace and overlooks both the garden and river). As well as filled baguettes, the attractively presented dishes might include sautéed king scallops with lamb sweetbreads and black pudding (a delicious dish) or tomato and black olive risotto with roasted vegetables (£8.95), roast breast of duck with mustard galette, fig tatin and apple jus (£14.95), pan-fried loin of local venison with potato and butter bean cake and pear chutney (£15.95), and daily specials including several fish dishes such as whole devilled cornish crab (£12.95), pan-fried fillet of red mullet with carrots escabeche and lightly curried cauliflower purée (£13.95) and roast fillet of monkfish wrapped in prosciutto with mussel and leek risotto (£14.95). Their well hung beef is normally charollais or aberdeen angus, and they do use a lot of good local produce – some from Mr Green's father's nearby farm. The L-shaped bar has plenty of seats and some rugs on flagstones, a modern wooden bar counter with terracotta wall behind, some stripped stone, a woodburning stove, and a large stuffed trout; the restaurant is no smoking, and it's all appealingly candlelit in the evenings. Friendly and efficient staff serve well kept White Horse Bitter, Youngs, and one or two guests like Butts Jester or Chubbs Lunchtime Bitter, as well as a dozen wines by the glass, home-made sloe gin, cherry plum brandy and elderflower cordial; darts, dominoes, cribbage, backgammon and piped music. The well kept garden is a lovely place to sit in summer, with small fruit trees, attractive hanging baskets and flower troughs. Breakfasts are good. They sell day tickets for fishing on a two-mile stretch. *(Recommended by Bob and Margaret Holder, David and Ruth Hollands, Derek and Sylvia Stephenson, Martin and Karen Wake, Mrs June Wilmers, David and Hazel Lee, D R Ellis, Robert Southgate, T and P, Mary Rayner, Susan Loppert, Norman and Sarah Keeping, Keith and Maureen Trainer, Ian Phillips, Mrs C Hamilton, David Ellis, Tony and Tracy Constance, Mrs Phoebe A Kemp, Karen and Graham Oddey, A P Seymour, Charles Artley, Jane Skerrett)*

Free house ~ Licensee Chris Green ~ Real ale ~ Bar food (not Sun evening) ~ Restaurant ~ (01367) 870382 ~ Children welcome ~ Dogs welcome ~ Open 11.30-3, 7-11; 12-3 Sun; closed Sun evening; 25, 26 and 31 Dec, 1 Jan, and first week Feb ~ Bedrooms: £55B/£80B

TETSWORTH SP6801 Map 4

Red Lion

2.7 miles from M40 junction 7 northbound (a bit further from junction 6 southbound); A40 S

In a nice setting overlooking the big village green, this stylishly reworked pub has become very attractive and comfortable under its current rather enterprising licensees, who've managed to make it an appealing destination for gently upmarket food while still pleasing the locals coming just for a drink. Several spacious areas ramble around the central bar counter, with its big stuffed lion's head; we particularly liked the way each of the tables has its own individual pub game, from backgammon and nine men's morris to miniature table football. All is light, modern and softly sophisticated, with pale wooden floors, a mix of wooden and upholstered seats (including some sofas), a log fire, salmon coloured walls, fresh flowers, and plenty of candles, especially in the evening. On the right hand side is a self-playing baby grand piano, in evidence every lunchtime (at night the music is piped). An attractive new no smoking dining area at the back is something of a cross between a conservatory and a smart library, many of the books reflecting the licensees' background in film and TV; they hope to introduce Saturday book sales.

It opens onto a garden terrace. Good freshly prepared food might include soup (£4.75), starters like seared scallop and herb risotto (£5.75) or tiger prawn, mango and rocket tartlet (£6.50), and main courses such as beer-battered cod (£9.50), calves liver with caramelised shallots, thyme scented mash and rosemary lamb jus (£9.75), truffled exotic mushroom gateau (£10.50), poached guinea fowl with roasted butternut squash (£13.75), grilled red snapper on ratatouille with grilled pancetta (£14.25), and local fillet of beef with horseradish potato rösti (£16.95); they do a choice of Sunday roasts (when the menu may be more limited), children's helpings, and a set lunch menu (two courses £11.95, three courses £15.95). On Monday evenings they have themed suppers for £5 (it gets very busy then, and food may sell out fast), and as we went to press were planning to start having free tapas on Wednesday evenings. The well kept beers usually include two from Greene King and a guest like Hook Norton Old Hooky; they have a wide range of wines, and plenty of coffees. Service is helpful and friendly. A red lion is clearly visible on the pink-washed exterior, but is harder to spot on the sign across the road, where it appears as a tattoo on the body of a naked nymphette. *(Recommended by Torrens Lyster, Susan and John Douglas)*

Free house ~ Licensees Bluey and Stewart Richards ~ Real ale ~ Bar food ~ Restaurant ~ (01844) 281274 ~ Children in restaurant ~ Live jazz Tues ~ Open 11-11; 12-10.30 Sun

---

LUCKY DIP

Besides the fully inspected pubs, you might like to try these Lucky Dips recommended to us and described by readers (if you do, please send us reports: www.goodguides.co.uk).

ADDERBURY [SP4735]
Plough [Aynho Rd]: Recently refurbished medieval thatched pub, attractive furnishings, friendly cottage atmosphere and log fire in small L-shaped bar, enjoyable bar lunches from wide choice of sandwiches and baguettes to half a dozen cheap home-made pub hot dishes, helpful staff, well kept Gales HSB and Charles Wells Eagle and Bombardier, larger separate restaurant with broad menu; TV, games *(Colin Gooch, Michael Dandy)*
☆ *Red Lion* [The Green; off A4260 S of Banbury]: Congenial pub with three linked bar rooms, big inglenook log fire, panelling, high stripped beams and stonework, old books and Victorian and Edwardian pictures, well kept Greene King ales, good wine range, quick friendly service, daily papers, popular pubby food from baguettes, ciabattas and baked potatoes to steak, games area on left; piped music; children in eating area, picnic-sets out on well kept terrace, comfortable bedrooms, open all day summer *(John and Claire Pettifer, Meg and Colin Hamilton, Geoff Pidoux, LYM, E A and D C T Frewer, Michael Dandy)*
ASHBURY [SU2685]
☆ *Rose & Crown* [B4507/B4000; High St]: Relaxing, roomy and comfortable open-plan beamed bar with helpful service from two friendly families, decent blackboard food in charming roomy restaurant and bar with highly polished woodwork, traditional pictures, chesterfields, deep armchairs and pews, raised section with further oak tables and chairs, well kept Arkells 2B and 3B, good range of wines by the glass and other drinks, separate public bar with pool and juke box; tables out in front, lovely view down pretty

village street of thatched cottages, 11 bedrooms – handy for Ridgeway *(Marjorie and David Lamb, BB, Gerald Wilkinson)*
ASTHALL [SP2811]
☆ *Maytime* [off A40 at W end of Witney bypass, then 1st left]: Comfortably genteel dining pub with very wide food choice from sandwiches and snacks up (just set lunch on Sun), slightly raised plush dining lounge neatly set with tables, airy conservatory restaurant with family area, two changing real ales, good wine range, welcoming landlord and prompt service, interesting pictures, small bar with flagstones and log fire; piped music; in tiny hamlet, nice views of Asthall Manor and water meadows from garden, attractive walks, quiet comfortable bedrooms around charming back courtyard *(BB, Mike Vince, E A and D C T Frewer)*
ASTON TIRROLD [SU5586]
Chequers [Fullers Rd, just off A417 Streatley—Wantage]: New French chef's notable cooking now drawing enthusiastic customers to this village pub; best to book *(B H and J I Andrews)*
BALSCOTE [SP3841]
Butchers Arms [signed off A422 W of Banbury; Shutford Rd]: Chatty open-plan village local, homely and basic, with friendly welcome, good value big lunchtime baguettes, well kept Hook Norton ales, darts, cards and dominoes at public end *(Gill and Tony Morriss)*
BAMPTON [SP3103]
Morris Clown [High St]: Folies Bergère-style murals in former coaching inn with three well kept cheap sensibly priced changing ales, farm cider, darts, bar billiards; garden with old

mangle collection, aunt sally, morris dancing late spring bank hol; open all day wknds, cl wkday lunchtimes (the Didler, Mark Hammick)

BARNARD GATE [SP4010]

Boot [off A40 E of Witney]: Stone-tiled dining pub with stout standing timbers and stub walls with latticed glass, huge log fire, solid country tables and chairs on bare boards, attractive décor inc masses of celebrity footwear, well kept Brakspears and Hook Norton Best, decent wines, usual food from sandwiches up; children welcome, tables out in front, open all day wknds (Ian Phillips, LYM)

BECKLEY [SP5611]

☆ *Abingdon Arms* [signed off B4027; High St]: Interesting old pub in unspoilt village, floodlit terrace, extensive pretty garden dropping away into orchard with superb views over RSPB Otmoor reserve; enjoyable food from sandwiches to nicely presented main dishes inc some imaginative things, friendly staff, well kept Brakspears, bare boards, lots of beams and stripped stone, two real fires, a variety of seating inc pews, board games, separate dining room; good walks (LYM, Geoff Pidoux, Dr and Mrs R Booth, Canon Michael Bourdeaux)

BESSELS LEIGH [SP4501]

Greyhound: Roomy no smoking family dining pub, comfortable and cheerful, with varied good value food from baguettes to Sun carvery inc some imaginative dishes, well kept beers, decent wines, friendly helpful staff, open fires, children's room with toys; piped music; open all day, play area outside (Geoff Pidoux, Colin and Janet Roe, Peter and Audrey Dowsett)

BINFIELD HEATH [SU7478]

☆ *Bottle & Glass* [off A4155 at Shiplake; between village and Harpsden]: Lovely thatched black and white timbered Tudor cottage doing well under new tenants, emphasis on enjoyable good value food from sandwiches up, bleached pine tables, low beams and flagstones, fine fireplace, black squared panelling, three well kept Brakspears ales, decent wines, no smoking dining area, shove-ha'penny, dominoes; no children or dogs inside; big attractive garden with tables under little thatched roofs (Wombat, D J and P M Taylor, Anthony Longden, LYM, the Didler, Paul Humphreys, Susan and John Douglas, Rebecca Knight)

BLADON [SP4414]

White House [Park St (A4095)]: Relaxed and cheerful pub opp church where Churchill is buried, good value traditional home-made food all day inc low-priced Sun roast, Greene King IPA and Abbot or Old Speckled Hen, good young lively staff, endearing mix of old tables and chairs in long bar with individual old-fashioned décor and ceiling bric-a-brac, rocking chair by good log fire, no smoking area; darts, weekly quiz, occasional live music; tables outside (those round the side are quieter), aunt sally, handy for back gate of Blenheim Park (beautiful right-of-way walk) (Mark Percy, Lesley Mayoh, Geoff Pidoux,

E A and D C T Frewer, Gill and Keith Croxton)

BLETCHINGDON [SP5017]

Blacks Head [Station Rd; B4027 N of Oxford]: Cosy neatly kept stripped-stone lounge with woodburner, enjoyable traditional food such as shepherd's pie or rabbit and pigeon pie here and in extended upmarket dining area with conservatory, well kept Greene King ales, welcoming local atmosphere, games room; pleasant garden, good value simple bedrooms (Geoff Pidoux, E A and D C T Frewer)

BLOXHAM [SP4335]

☆ *Elephant & Castle* [off A361, fairly handy for M40 junction 1; Humber St]: Unchanging pub in imposing Cotswold village, with striking 17th-c stone fireplace in simple but elegant bare-boards public bar, big winter log fire in comfortable lounge, well kept Hook Norton ales, farm cider (guests in summer), around 30 malt whiskies, decent coffee, promptly served lunchtime food at very low prices, friendly service, traditional games inc antique shove-ha'penny board; children welcome, sunny flower-filled courtyard and garden, may be wknd barbecues, open all day Sun (George Atkinson, LYM)

☆ *Joiners Arms* [off A361; Old Bridge Rd]: Good welcoming service, beamed woodblock-floor bar, above-average food inc interesting blackboard dishes here or in smart restaurant down steps, well kept real ales, good choice of wines, open fires; fire-door disabled access from car park (BB, Stuart Turner)

BOARS HILL [SP4901]

Fox [between A34 and B4017; Fox Lane]: Well run and attractive Chef & Brewer in pretty wooded countryside, comfortable and spacious, with interesting rambling rooms on different levels, huge log fireplaces, wide choice of reasonably priced food, well kept ales, decent wine, polite service, day's paper framed in gents'; may be soft piped classical music or jazz; children welcome, pleasant raised verandah, charming big sloping garden with play area, open all day (Geoff Pidoux, Andrew Scarr, Peter and Anne Hollindale)

BODICOTE [SP4537]

☆ *Plough* [Goose Lane/High St; off A4260 S of Banbury]: Well worn 14th-c pub in same family for many decades, usually brewing its own cheap ales such as Bodicote Bitter, No 9, Porter and Life Sentence, guests such as Greene King IPA and Worthington, country wines, friendly landlord, wide choice of well cooked straightforward food from good value sandwiches and baguettes to steaks and Sun roast; low heavy beams, stripped stone, hops, pictures and brasses, no music, small open fire; darts, TV and fruit machine in public bar, no credit cards; children and dogs welcome (pub retriever called Daisy), twice-yearly beer festivals (the Didler, BB, Pete Baker)

BRIGHTWELL BALDWIN [SU6594]

☆ *Lord Nelson* [off B480 Chalgrove—Watlington, or B4009 Benson—Watlington]: Civilised and friendly dining pub with snug armchair area too, dining chairs around candlelit linen-set tables, wide range of enjoyable food esp duck and game, helpful friendly service and spotless housekeeping, real ales and decent house wines, good log fires, plenty of Nelson memorabilia, no smoking part; front verandah, back terrace and attractive garden *(LYM, Geoff and Teresa Salt, Peter and Giff Bennett)*

BRITWELL SALOME [SU6793]

☆ *Goose* [B4009 Watlington—Benson]: Restaurant country pub with sensibly short choice of good fresh interesting home-made food using local produce in two small back dining rooms, good sandwiches in the small bar too (well used by locals), reasonably priced wines, good coffee, efficient young staff, nice atmosphere; garden tables *(Paul Butler, Geoff and Teresa Salt, Bob and Judy Smitherman)*

BUCKLAND [SU3497]

Lamb [off A420 NE of Faringdon]: Smart gently old-fashioned 18th-c stone-built dining pub with enjoyable food (not Mon) from popular lunchtime favourites to grander and more expensive evening menus, Hook Norton Best, good choice of wines by the glass, formal no smoking restaurant; piped music; children welcome, pleasant tree-shaded garden, good walks nearby, comfortable bedrooms, cl Sun evening and over Christmas/New Year *(the Didler, John Hale, Philip and June Caunt, LYM, David Ellis, Di and Mike Gillam, Mary Rayner, Sue Demont, Tim Barrow, Richard Wyld, J Crosby, A P Seymour, Ian Phillips)*

BUCKNELL [SP5525]

Trigger Pond [handy for M40 junction 10; Bicester Rd]: Welcoming stone-built pub opp the pond, good range of popular food (must book Sun lunch), nice atmosphere, full Wadworths beer range kept well; pleasant terrace and garden *(Marjorie and David Lamb, E A and D C T Frewer)*

BURFORD [SP2512]

Angel [Witney St]: Long heavy-beamed dining pub in attractive ancient building, good brasserie food *(David and Ruth Hollands, Geoff Pidoux, LYM, Rod Stoneman)*

Cotswold Arms [High St]: Cosy bar with welcoming log fire, enjoyable food from baguettes and ploughman's to steak and bass, larger back dining area, beautiful stonework, pleasant efficient service, Courage Best and Theakstons; music nights Weds and Fri; tables out in front and in back garden *(Geoff Pidoux, Michael Dandy)*

☆ *Golden Pheasant* [High St]: Small early 18th-c hotel with settees and armchairs among more usual lounge bar furnishings in cosy front bar, enjoyable imaginative food from interesting sandwiches to wide choice of restaurant dishes, well kept Greene King IPA and Old Speckled Hen, daily papers, stuffed pheasant above fire, back dining room down some steps; occasional live music; pleasant back terrace, comfortable bedrooms, open all day *(R Huggins, D Irving, E McCall, T McLean, David and Ruth Hollands, BB, Mrs Pat Crabb, Michael Dandy)*

☆ *Mermaid* [High St]: Handsome jettied Tudor dining pub with attractive long narrow bar, beams, flagstones, panelling and stripped stone, log fire, well kept Greene King ales, lots of wines by the glass, decent good value food from lunchtime baguettes up, efficient service, bay seating around row of dining tables on the left, further airy back dining room and no smoking upstairs restaurant; piped music, fruit machine; children in eating areas, picnic-sets under cocktail parasols outside, open all day *(Geoff Pidoux, Peter and Audrey Dowsett, Jim Abbott, Paul and Shirley White, Comus and Sarah Elliott, LYM, Mike and Mary Carter, Michael Dandy, Karen and Graham Oddey)*

Old Bull [High St]: Handsome building well reconstructed in the 1980s with beams, panelling and big fireplaces, then smartly refurbished in wine bar/bistro style, settees and open fire, steps down to no smoking eating area, restaurant behind, Greene King ales, decent wines, wide choice of usual food from sandwiches and baked potatoes up; piped music; children welcome, open all day, tables out in front or back through old coach entry, comfortable bedrooms *(LYM, Jim Abbott, Geoff Pidoux, Michael Dandy)*

☆ *Royal Oak* [Witney St]: Relaxed and homely 17th-c stripped stone local with long-serving friendly landlord, Greene King Old Speckled Hen and Wadworths 6X from central bar, wide range of generous food using local produce, efficient service, over a thousand beer mugs and steins hanging from beams, antlers over good big fire, some settles, pine tables and chairs on flagstone floor, more in back dining room, bar billiards; tables out on reworked terrace, sensibly priced bedrooms off garden behind *(R Huggins, D Irving, E McCall, T McLean, Geoff Pidoux, E A and D C T Frewer, Martin and Pauline Jennings, Ted George)*

CHADLINGTON [SP3222]

☆ *Tite* [off A361 S of Chipping Norton, and B4437 W of Charlbury; Mill End, slightly out of village – at garage turn towards Churchill, then left at playground]: Food-oriented traditional local with good home-made food from sandwiches to lovely puddings, some unusual dishes, vine-covered back restaurant evenings and Sun lunchtime, well kept Youngs, a guest stout and a beer such as Butcombe, good house wines, farm perry or cider, cheerful long-serving traditional landlord, good service, big log fire in huge fireplace, settles, wooden chairs, prints, rack of guide books, daily papers and magazines; piped classical music – and they have the uproarious village pantomime here; children welcome, superb garden full of shrubs, some quite unusual, with stream running under pub, good walks nearby, cl Mon *(BB, Guy Vowles, Richard Greaves, Stuart Turner)*

CHARLBURY [SP3519]

☆ *Bell* [Church St]: Attractive civilised two-room bar in small olde-worlde 17th-c hotel, flagstones, stripped stonework and huge inglenook log fire, welcoming service, short choice of good interesting bar lunches (not Sun) from sandwiches up (veg charged extra), well kept Greene King IPA, Morlands Original and Old Speckled Hen, good value wines, wide choice of malt whiskies, pleasant restaurant; children welcome in eating area, dogs in bar, comfortable quiet bedrooms, good breakfast *(LYM, Geoff Pidoux, George Atkinson, Diana Campbell)*

Rose & Crown [Market St]: Town pub with strong following for its good range of particularly well kept beers inc guests, real pubby feel (no food, and can get a bit smoky); tables out behind *(Colin Critch)*

CHARNEY BASSETT [SU3794]

☆ *Chequers*: Buoyant atmosphere in 18th-c village-green beamed local, spacious and rambling, with good-sized dining room and separate bar, enjoyable home-made food from sandwiches up (may be snacks only, Sat lunchtime), well kept real ales (good value pitchers), decent wines, good friendly unrushed service, daily papers; pool, piped music; mall garden, children welcome, has been cl Mon *(BB, D Marsh)*

CHESTERTON [SP5521]

Red Cow [The Green]: Comfortably updated softly lit traditional local with beams, brasses, old photographs, two log fires, lunchtime food from baguettes and ciabattas to good value hot dishes, well kept Greene King ales, good coffee, small dining area; picnic-sets out under cocktail parasols *(Marjorie and David Lamb, E A and D C T Frewer)*

CHISLEHAMPTON [SU5998]

Coach & Horses [B480 Oxford—Watlington, opp B4015 to Abingdon]: Extended former 16th-c coaching inn with two beamed bars, homely but civilised, and sizeable restaurant (polished oak tables and wall banquettes); good choice of well prepared food from baguettes and good ploughman's to game specials, friendly obliging service, well kept ales inc Flowers and Hook Norton, big log fire; piped music; well kept terraced gardens overlooking fields by River Thame, some tables out in front, motel-style bedrooms in separate block in back courtyard *(Mr and Mrs Jenkins, BB, D and M T Ayres-Regan)*

CHRISTMAS COMMON [SU7193]

☆ *Fox & Hounds* [off B480/B481]: Upmarket Chilterns dining pub in lovely countryside, two compact beamed rooms simply but comfortably furnished, bow windows, red and black tiles and big inglenook, snug little back room, extension front barn restaurant, well kept Brakspears ales, proper coffee, friendly trendy staff; children and dogs welcome, rustic benches and tables outside, has been open all day in summer *(Heather Couper, LYM, Richard Greaves, the Didler, Derek Harvey-Piper, Susan and John Douglas)*

CHURCH ENSTONE [SP3724]

☆ *Crown* [Mill Lane; from A44 take B4030 turn-off at Enstone]: Popular and attractive old pub, smart and uncluttered, with congenial bar, beams, stripped stone and sisal matting, log

fire in brass-fitted stone fireplace, good enterprising fresh food (not Mon night) from tasty lunchtime baguettes up, good-sized light modern dining area and roomy conservatory, friendly staff, well kept Hook Norton Best, Shepherd Neame Spitfire and Wadworths 6X, decent wines by the glass, plenty of atmosphere; may be piped music, may be cl Mon lunchtime; garden tables *(Mr and Mrs J Curtis, Guy Vowles, Chris Glasson, J A Ellis, Stuart Turner, Geoff Pidoux, Richard Marjoram, LYM)*

CLIFTON HAMPDEN [SU5495]

☆ *Barley Mow* [towards Long Wittenham, S of A415]: Interesting and welcoming thatched Chef & Brewer dining pub, plenty of atmosphere with very low ancient beams and nice dark corners, oak-panelled family room, well kept ales such as Adnams Broadside and Charles Wells Bombardier, good choice of wines by the glass, efficient friendly young staff, log fire, decent food all day from sandwiches up, restaurant; piped music; tables on pleasant terrace and in well tended waterside garden, short stroll from the Thames; open all day *(Rob and Catherine Dunster, Chris Glasson, LYM, D J and P M Taylor, B M Eldridge, Mel Smith)*

COTHILL [SU4699]

Merry Miller: Large neatly kept and comfortably olde-worlde pub/restaurant based on 17th-c granary, stripped stone and flagstones, wide food choice from sandwiches up, friendly efficient staff, well kept ales, good choice of wines, log fires; disabled access *(Dr Alan and Mrs Sue Holder)*

CRAWLEY [SP3412]

Crawley Inn [Foxburrow Lane, off B4022 just NW of Witney]: Large well worn stone-built pub with three areas, well kept real ales inc a guest such as Goffs Camelot, log fire, minimal very mixed furnishings *(Guy Vowles)*

☆ *Lamb* [Steep Hill; just NW of Witney]: Comfortably extended 17th-c stone-built pub, several areas off unspoilt old beamed bar, no smoking family area and restaurant, good value varied food, good house wines, well kept real ales inc a seasonal one, quick service, friendly licensees, log fire in big fireplace, cricketing décor; may be quiet piped music; views from tables on terraced lawn behind, pretty village, good walks *(Guy Vowles)*

CROPREDY [SP4646]

Brasenose [Station Rd]: Straightforward village inn nr Oxford Canal, well kept Caledonian Deuchars IPA and Hook Norton, new licensees doing wide choice of reasonably priced food (not Sun evening or Mon), long bar with woodburner, darts and big pool table, flowers in no smoking dining room; piped music may be loud; good welcome for walkers and dogs, bedrooms, open all day Fri-Sun *(Chris Glasson, BB, Martin and Alison Stainsby, CMW, JJW)*

☆ *Red Lion* [off A423 N of Banbury]: Rambling old thatched stone-built pub charmingly placed opp pretty village's churchyard, low beams, inglenook log fire, high-backed settles, brass, plates and pictures; friendly staff, well kept changing ales such as Greene King Old Speckled Hen, new chef using local ingredients in enjoyable food from sandwiches and baguettes up (two rooms set for eating, children allowed in restaurant part), games room; piped music, limited parking, picnic-sets under cocktail parasols on back terrace by car park *(John Saville, Meg and Colin Hamilton, LYM, Charles and Pauline Stride, Simon Jones)*

CROWMARSH GIFFORD [SU6189]
Queens Head [The Street (A4130)]: Friendly old pub incorporating good value thai restaurant, reasonably priced Fullers ales, good service; garden tables *(DHV)*

CUDDESDON [SP5902]
☆ *Bat & Ball* [S of Wheatley; High St]: Civilised pub full of all sorts of interesting cricketing memorabilia, low beams, some flagstones, well liked food from baguettes to elaborate dishes (evening concentration on this, big no smoking dining extension), Banks's LBW, Marstons Pedigree and a guest beer, decent wines, neat and attentive young staff; cribbage, dominoes, piped music; children welcome, pleasant back terrace with good views, aunt sally, comfortable annexe bedrooms (some small), open all day *(Penny and Peter Keevil, Richard Marjoram, Pam and John Smith, Sean and Sharon Pines, LYM, Mel Smith, A P Seymour)*

CUMNOR [SP4503]
☆ *Bear & Ragged Staff* [signed from A420; Appleton Rd]: Busy comfortably rambling dining pub with interesting furnishings and kitsch bric-a-brac in five dim-lit partly flagstoned small rooms and separate restaurant, good choice of enjoyable food inc popular Sun roasts and enterprising vegetarian dishes, well kept real ales from varying breweries (there's a proper drinking area), efficient friendly largely South African staff, two big log fires, no smoking area; children in eating areas, open all day Sun in summer *(LYM, Sue Demont, Tim Barrow, Geoff Pidoux, Alan and Carolin Tidbury)*

CURBRIDGE [SP3208]
Lord Kitchener [Lew Rd (A4095 towards Bampton)]: Bustling easy-going atmosphere, good value food inc generous Sun lunch and two-for-one meal deals in neat, light and roomy no smoking dining extension, old local photographs, big log fire, well kept real ales, quick efficient service by chirpy NZ family; piped music; garden with play area, open all day *(Peter and Audrey Dowsett, Richard Marjoram, Marjorie and David Lamb)*

DEDDINGTON [SP4631]
☆ *Deddington Arms* [off A4260 (B4031) Banbury—Oxford; Horse Fair]: Welcoming beamed and timbered hotel with mullioned windows and good log fire in cosy bar, sizeable more modern back eating area allowing children, enjoyable food from good sandwiches and light dishes up, well kept ales such as Caledonian Deuchars IPA, Greene King IPA and Wadworths 6X, good choice of wines by the glass, friendly attentive young staff, updated décor with much ochre paintwork,

smart restaurant; unobtrusive piped music; open all day, comfortable chalet bedrooms around courtyard, good breakfast, attractive village with lots of antiques shops *(LYM, M Sharp, Hugh Spottiswoode, Trevor and Judy Pearson, George Atkinson, Michael Dandy, E A and D C T Frewer)*
Red Lion [Market Pl]: Recently refurbished as smart bar and bistro (and back to this name after a spell as the Forge), modern décor with new tables on bare boards, Brakspears and Fullers London Pride, good choice of wines by the glass, good inexpensive coffee, reasonably priced food from lunchtime sandwiches and baked potatoes up, friendly staff; piped music may be loudish, games; courtyard tables *(Michael Dandy)*
☆ *Unicorn* [Market Pl]: Cheerful 17th-c inn run by helpful hands-on mother and daughter, good value generous food (not Sun evening) from sandwiches and baked potatoes up in freshly decorated clean-cut L-shaped bar and beamed dining areas off, well kept Hook Norton and Fullers London Pride, good choice of wines by the glass, proper coffee, quick courteous young staff, inglenook fireplace, no smoking areas; dogs welcome in bar, cobbled courtyard leading to lovely walled back garden, open all day (from 9 Sat for farmers' market), good bedrooms *(BB, Michael Dandy, Richard Tosswill, George Atkinson)*

DENCHWORTH [SU3891]
Fox [off A338 or A417 N of Wantage; Hyde Rd]: Picturesque old thatched village pub with friendly attentive staff, reasonably priced food with strong local emphasis, Greene King IPA, Abbot and Morlands Original, good house wines and coffee, two good log fires and plush seats in low-ceilinged connecting areas, old prints and paintings, airy no smoking dining extension; pleasant sheltered garden, peaceful village *(BB, Dick and Madeleine Brown)*

DORCHESTER [SU5794]
☆ *Fleur de Lys* [High St]: Carefully preserved coaching inn opp abbey, dating from 16th c, comfortably traditional two-level interior, wide choice of good value home cooking, all fresh, well kept Greene King ales, good hands-on licensees and friendly helpful staff, interesting old photographs of the pub; unobtrusive piped music; children very welcome, picnic-sets on front terrace and in back garden *(R Michael Richards, B M Eldridge)*

DRAYTON [SU4794]
Red Lion [B4017 S of Abingdon]: Simple and unpretentious, with bargain food from sandwiches and home-made bar meals to popular lunchtime carvery, good friendly service, Greene King Morlands, games room *(R C Vincent)*
Roebuck [Stratford Rd (A422 W of Banbury)]: Comfortable 16th-c creeper-covered pub with good choice of realistically priced food, welcoming family service, well kept Hook Norton ales *(Mr and Mrs P Tonsley)*

DUCKLINGTON [SP3507]
☆ *Bell* [off A415, a mile SE of Witney; Standlake Rd]: Pretty thatched local near village duck

pond, wide choice of generous good value home-made food (not Sun eve) inc particularly good sandwiches, well kept Greene King ales, good house wines, friendly service; big stripped stone and flagstoned bar with scrubbed tables, log fires, glass-covered well, old local photographs, farm tools, hatch-served public bar, roomy and attractive well laid out back restaurant, its beams festooned with bells; cards and dominoes, no piped music; folk night 1st Sun of month, events such as morris dancing or raft races; small garden behind with play area, colourful hanging baskets, nine bedrooms *(BB, Peter and Audrey Dowsett, Pete Baker, Comus and Sarah Elliott)*

Strickland Arms [off A415 SE of Witney; Witney Rd]: Cosy low-beamed village pub well liked by locals, some exposed stonework, traditional food, well kept Adnams and Wadworths 6X, regular themed menu or music nights, compact no smoking restaurant, TV in bar but no music or machines; pretty terraced back garden with seats, skittles and aunt sally *(Geoff Pidoux, Mr and Mrs P Lally, Comus and Sarah Elliott, BB)*

DUNS TEW [SP4528]

☆ *White Horse* [off A4260 N of Kidlington]: Unspoilt 16th-c beamed pub with welcoming attentive licensees, enjoyable food in main area with stripped bricks and stonework, rugs on flagstones, oak timbers and panelling, enormous inglenook, settles and homely candlelit stripped tables, well kept Hook Norton Best and Wadworths 6X, decent wine list, two cosy side areas; disabled access, bedrooms in former stables, attractive village *(Neil and Jenny Dury, LYM, George Atkinson)*

ENSLOW [SP4818]

Rock of Gibraltar [A4095 about 1½ miles SW of Kirtlington]: Tall pub with three well kept changing ales such as Hook Norton, well prepared reasonably priced food, friendly service, beams, stripped stone, bright narrowboat paintwork, modern dining extension overlooking canal, upper conservatory with even better view; popular Thurs folk night; lots of picnic-sets under cocktail parasols in pretty waterside garden *(Pete Baker)*

EWELME [SU6491]

Shepherds Hut [off B4009 about 5 miles SW of M40 junction 6; High St]: Cosy and relaxed beamed local with good choice of fresh food inc some unusual specials, well kept Greene King ales, decent coffee, small restaurant; children welcome, small pleasant garden with barbecues *(Marjorie and David Lamb, Susan Loppert)*

FARINGDON [SU2895]

☆ *Bell* [Market Pl]: Appealing and unchanging old inn with 17th-c carved oak chimney-piece for inglenook fireplace, red leather settles, interesting faded mural in inner bar, well kept Wadworths ales, wide choice of enjoyable generous food inc interesting dishes and plenty of fish in bar and restaurant, friendly staff and customers; children and dogs allowed, tables out among flowers in heated cobbled back

coachyard, character beamed bedrooms *(LYM, Tom and Ruth Rees, Dr and Mrs A K Clarke)*

FERNHAM [SU2991]

☆ *Woodman* [B4508, off A420 SW of Oxford]: Heavily beamed 17th-c country pub now reopened (it closed in 2001 for conversion to a private house), great log fire in rambling bar with lots of character, well kept ales tapped from the cask, good food (not Sun) in thriving pubby atmosphere, no piped music; children welcome *(LYM, Peter and Audrey Dowsett, Tony and Tracy Constance)*

FILKINS [SP2304]

☆ *Five Alls* [signed off A361 Lechlade—Burford]: Big 18th-c Cotswold stone pub under friendly new licensees, relaxed local atmosphere, well priced home-made food, well kept Brakspears, decent house wines, beams, flagstones, stripped stone and good log fire, settees, armchairs and rugs on polished boards, good-sized eating areas; unobtrusive piped music; plenty of tables on terrace and neat lawns, five attractive well-equipped bedrooms, nice village *(BB, B M Eldridge, M A and C R Starling, Karen and Graham Oddey)*

FINSTOCK [SP3616]

Crown [School Rd]: Good choice of enjoyable food and drink, friendly service *(Alan and Anita Thomas)*

Plough [just off B4022 N of Witney; High St]: Rambling thatched and low-beamed village local, long divided bar with armchair by open woodburner in massive stone inglenook, entertaining pub dogs, well kept ales such as Adnams, Brakspears and Hook Norton, small choice of decent wines, enjoyable simple food from generous sandwiches up, pleasant service, crates of lending books, separate games area with bar billiards, stripped-stone dining room; children in eating areas, dogs allowed in public bar; sizeable garden with old-fashioned roses and aunt sally, good walks, good value bedroom with own bathroom *(LYM, Susan Loppert, Chris Glasson)*

FRINGFORD [SP6028]

Butchers Arms [off A421 N of Bicester]: Bustling village pub with darts and TV in L-shaped bar, generous blackboard food, three real ales, good soft drinks choice, separate smaller dining room; tables outside *(CMW, JJW)*

GODSTOW [SP4809]

☆ *Trout* [off A34 Oxford bypass northbound, via Wytham, or A40/A44 roundabout via Wolvercote]: Olde-worlde Vintage Inn in genuinely medieval creeper-covered building, several linked rooms (all but one no smoking), log fires in three huge hearths, hop-hung beams, carvings and shiny ancient flagstones, attractive pictures and country bric-a-brac, decent food all day inc good lunchtime sandwiches, well kept Adnams and Bass, good choice of wines by the glass, friendly young well trained staff; can be very busy – especially on Sun – with long queue at order counter, quiet piped music; charming in summer with lovely flagstoned heated terrace (dogs allowed out here) by a stream full of greedily plump perch, long restored footbridge to island owned by pub with ducks and peacocks, abbey ruins opp; in winter they may serve mulled wine and hand out blankets for roasting chestnuts out here *(Geoff Pidoux, LYM, Peter and Audrey Dowsett, George Atkinson, Paul and Shirley White, P and J Shapley, A Rees, Martin and Karen Wake, Andy Trafford, Louise Bayly)*

GORING [SU6080]

☆ *Catherine Wheel* [Station Rd]: Smart and well run, with friendly landlord and good informal atmosphere in two neat and cosily traditional bar areas, especially the more individual lower room with its low beams and big smouldering inglenook fireplace; good choice of well priced home-made food inc popular pies and pasta, Tues steak nights, well kept Brakspears and Hook Norton ales, Stowford Press cider, decent wine; back restaurant (children welcome here), notable door to gents'; nice courtyard and garden behind, handy for Thames Path, attractive village, open all day *(Andy and Jill Kassube, Rob Winstanley, the Didler, BB)*
John Barleycorn [Manor Rd]: Pleasantly unpretentious low-beamed cottagey local with prints in cosy little lounge bar, attractive adjoining eating area, well kept Brakspears, good service, pool in end room; children welcome, clean and stylish bedrooms *(Rob Winstanley, the Didler, Jeremy Woods)*

HAILEY [SU6485]

☆ *King William IV* [the Hailey nr Ipsden, off A4074 or A4130 SE of Wallingford]: Attractive 16th-c pub in charming peaceful countryside, some concentration on wide choice of good generous mainly traditional food, friendly landlord and helpful staff, thriving atmosphere, full Brakspears range kept well, beams, bare bricks and tiled floor (carpet in middle room), big inglenook log fire, clean fresh décor and well kept traditional furnishings, extended dining room; outstanding views from pub and tables on front terrace *(the Didler, LYM, Barry Collett)*

HANWELL [SP4343]

Moon & Sixpence: Warmly welcoming dining pub, wide choice of above-average food in comfortable bar and dining area (often booked up), efficient service, well kept real ales, decent wines by the glass; small terrace, pretty location *(Zac Webster)*

HENLEY [SU7682]

Angel on the Bridge [Thameside, by the bridge]: Prime spot by Thames, new furniture in small front bar with open fire, back bar and adjacent bistro restaurant with settles, food from sandwiches and usual pubby lunchtime dishes to more elaborate evening menu, Brakspears beer, good choice of wines by the glass; no no smoking area, parking limited; nice waterside terrace (plastic glasses for this) *(Michael Dandy)*

☆ *Three Tuns* [Market Pl]: Heavy-beamed front bar with old-fashioned seating inc traditional settles, coal-effect gas fire, well kept Brakspears and decent wines; back dining area crisply

rustic with cream-painted panelling and neat table linen, fresh imaginative food, friendly young staff; may be piped music; tables in small attractive back courtyard *(LYM, Jim Abbott, the Didler, Michael Dandy)*

HOOK NORTON [SP3533]

☆ *Pear Tree* [Scotland End]: Pleasant village pub under new tenant, full Hook Norton beer range kept well from nearby brewery, country wines, usual bar food (not Sun evening) from sandwiches and baked potatoes up, partly no smoking chatty knocked-together bar area with country-kitchen furniture, good log fire, daily papers and magazines; TV; children and dogs welcome, sizeable attractive garden with outdoor chess, wendy house and play area, bedrooms, now open all day *(Robert Gomme, Michael Dandy, LYM)*

ISLIP [SP5214]

Red Lion [High St (B4027)]: Relaxed linked areas with short choice of enjoyable food from fresh generous sandwiches up, changing ales such as Adnams, Caledonian Deuchars IPA and Fullers London Pride, quick friendly service, conservatory; disabled facilities, good garden with play area *(E A and D C T Frewer, Marjorie and David Lamb)*

KINGSTON BAGPUIZE [SU4098]

Hinds Head [Witney Rd]: Spotless and welcoming two-room country pub, relaxed and unpretentious, with good range of attractive good value meals (freshly made so may be a wait) in beamed bar and no smoking restaurant from toasties and baguettes up, three well kept Greene King ales, good soft drinks choice, two labradors; piped music, Sun quiz night; dogs welcome, plenty of picnic-sets in good-sized pretty garden with two water features and play area *(Ian Phillips, Marjorie and David Lamb, CMW, JJW)*

KINGSTON BLOUNT [SU7399]

☆ *Cherry Tree* [Park Lane (B4009)]: Cheery and brightly modernised brick Brakspears local, stripped down and brought up to date by young licensees, with leather sofas and welcoming brasserie feel in light, contemporary bar, and extensive choice of imaginative food (plenty of fish) in busy back dining room, friendly service, relaxed chatty atmosphere; may be piped jazz/easy listening music; children welcome *(Heather Couper, BB)*

KINGSTON LISLE [SU3287]

Blowing Stone [signed off B4507 W of Wantage]: Friendly pub/restaurant with good choice of meals and snacks, West Berkshire real ale, daily papers, log fire, comfortable lounge, cheerful modernised bar and attractive dining conservatory; children welcome, tables out in lovely garden with goldfish pond, pretty bedrooms, handy for Uffington Castle hill fort and the downs *(LYM, C and E Henry)*

KIRTLINGTON [SP4919]

Oxford Arms [Troy Lane, Kirtlington]: Oak-beamed dining pub with enjoyable food from proper sandwiches to traditional english main dishes, charming young staff, well kept Hook Norton Best and two other ales from central bar with small standing area, leather settees and open fire one end, no smoking dining area with fresh wood furniture the other; small sunny back garden *(Phoebe and Duncan Thomas, E A and D C T Frewer, C Cottrell-Dormer)*

LANGFORD [SP2402]

☆ *Bell* [off A361 N of Lechlade]: Country dining pub doing well under enthusiastic newish young owners, good interesting generous food, efficient friendly service, decent wines, proper coffee and well kept Hook Norton Best and Marstons Pedigree, two quaint rooms off tiny bar, big inglenook log fire, pleasantly low-key simple décor and furnishings, warm atmosphere *(Mrs Linda Ferstendik, Barry and Anne Cooper, Karen and Graham Oddey)*

LEAFIELD [SP3215]

☆ *Navy Oak* [Lower End]: Elegantly refurbished under friendly new licensees, with roomy dining areas and stylish relaxing bar with grandfather clock, exposed stonework, dark wooden tables, magazines to read, and brown leather sofas around big fireplace; short choice of good food from enthusiastic chef/landlord, well kept Hook Norton beers; piped easy listening music; children welcome away from bar *(Siobhan Daly, BB)*

LITTLE COXWELL [SU2893]

Eagle [just off A420 SW of Faringdon – then turn right into No Through Road signed to pub and village]: Pleasantly refurbished airy bar, comfortable sofa and armchairs among other furnishings on polished boards, friendly service, well kept Archers and Bass, well chosen wines, enjoyable generous food from good sandwiches to good value Sun lunch in bar and attractive no smoking restaurant; dogs welcome in bar; ten bedrooms with own bathrooms, charming thatched village *(Peter and Jean Hoare)*

LITTLEWORTH [SU3196]

Snooty Fox [A420 NE of Faringdon]: Straightforward pub with good value carefully prepared food, friendly efficient service, good wines, well kept ales, big log fire, small no smoking restaurant; garden with play area and apple trees *(Tom and Ruth Rees)*

LOWER ASSENDON [SU7484]

Golden Ball [B480]: Attractive and welcoming 16th-c beamed pub, cosily rustic traditional interior, good usual food, exemplary service, well kept Brakspears, good choice of house wines, log fire; children welcome, nice big garden behind, vietnamese pot-bellied pig called Rosie *(Heather Couper, Charles van der Lande, Mr and Mrs G Swire)*

LOWER HEYFORD [SP4824]

Bell [Market Sq]: Charming creeper-clad building in small village square of thatched cottages, uncluttered refurbished rooms around central beamed bar, cheerful helpful staff, good range of generous enjoyable food freshly cooked to order inc some interesting dishes, well kept Adnams Broadside, Bass and Greene King Abbot; disabled access and facilities, bedrooms, nearby walks by Oxford Canal *(Meg and Colin Hamilton, K H Frostick)*

MAIDENSGROVE [SU7288]

☆ *Five Horseshoes* [off B480 and B481, W of village]: Friendly rambling country dining pub on lovely common high in the Chilterns beechwoods, low ceiling covered in world banknotes, log fire, enjoyable if not cheap bar food, well kept Brakspears ales, good wines by the glass, restaurant and airy no smoking dining conservatory; children and dogs welcome, plenty of tables outside, good walks, open all day summer wknds, cl winter Sun evening *(Jim Abbott, Alistair Forsyth, Brian Root, Bob and Maggie Atherton, Michael Porter, Paul Hopton, Martin and Karen Wake, Tracey and Stephen Groves, LYM, Jeremy Woods, Anthony Longden, Roy and Gay Hoing)*

MIDDLETON STONEY [SP5323]

☆ *Jersey Arms* [Ardley Rd (B430/B4030)]: Small 19th-c stone-built hotel with nicely countrified bow-windowed bar, beams, oak flooring and some stripped stone, attractive tables, sofa and daily papers, good inglenook log fire, interesting if not cheap home-made fresh food from well filled baguettes up, friendly owner and staff, efficient service, good range of wines and spirits, good coffee, Flowers IPA or Wadworths 6X, attractive largely no smoking two-level dining room; piped music, popular for business lunches, car park across road; tables in courtyard and garden, comfortable bedrooms *(BB, Simon J Barber, E A and D C T Frewer, Michael Dandy, Mr and Mrs Bentley-Davies)*

MINSTER LOVELL [SP3111]

Old Swan [just N of B4047 Witney—Burford]: Interesting old building with variety of secluded seating areas, deep armchairs and rugs on flagstones, well kept Hook Norton ales, log fire, enjoyable lunchtime snacks and light meals, carvery restaurant; piped music, and more an adjunct to the adjacent Old Mill Conference Centre than an individual pub; tables in lovely garden, bedrooms, idyllic village *(LYM, Sean and Sharon Pines, E A and D C T Frewer)*

White Hart [B4047 Witney—Burford, opposite B4477 village turn-off]: 17th-c former coaching inn under new management, roomy and simple, with well updated period furniture and fittings, well kept Brakspears, Fullers London Pride and White Horse, reasonably priced food from sandwiches, grilled panini and baked potatoes to pubby hot dishes, good log fire, motorcycle models, area for smokers, big separate restaurant; quiet piped music; dogs welcome one end, open all day *(Comus and Sarah Elliott, Dick and Madeleine Brown)*

MURCOTT [SP5815]

Nut Tree [off B4027 NE of Oxford]: Charming open-plan beamed and thatched medieval building, enjoyable food from substantial lunchtime sandwiches up, more elaborate evening dishes, well kept ales inc Hook Norton, decent wines, friendly young smartly dressed staff, log fire, small back conservatory-style no smoking restaurant; pretty garden with terrace, pond and aunt sally *(Mr and Mrs R P Welch, LYM, Richard Greaves)*

NEWBRIDGE [SP4001]

Maybush [A415 7 miles S of Witney]: Low-beamed dining pub in lovely Thames-side setting, wide food choice, well kept Greene King Morlands, new restaurant area; children truly welcome, good moorings, pretty and neatly kept waterside garden with new terrace *(Peter and Giff Bennett, LYM, Comus and Sarah Elliott, A P Seymour)*

☆ *Rose Revived* [A415 7 miles S of Witney]: Roomy recently refurbished pub well worth knowing for its lovely big lawn by the upper Thames, prettily lit at night (good overnight mooring free); wide range of fairly priced food all day, quick cheerful service, well kept Greene King ales, good coffee, log fires; some live music; children welcome, comfortable bedrooms *(LYM, Comus and Sarah Elliott, Ann and Colin Hunt)*

NORTH LEIGH [SP3813]

Woodman [New Yatt Rd]: Roomy stone-built village local with interesting choice of inexpensive freshly prepared food inc good curries, real ales such as Hook Norton Best, Greene King IPA and Wadworths 6X, Easter and bank hol beer festivals, decent wines, proper coffee, attentive staff, daily papers; darts, TV; big garden with attractive terrace, comfortable bedrooms, open all day Sun *(C and R Bromage, Stuart Turner, Guy Vowles)*

NUFFIELD [SU6787]

Crown [A4130/B481]: Neatly kept beamed lounge bar with country furniture and inglenook log fire, friendly helpful staff, enjoyable inexpensive food from sandwiches up, well kept Brakspears ales; children in small family room, pleasant garden with tables outside front and back, good walks *(LYM, E A and D C T Frewer, John Roots)*

OXFORD [SP5106]

Eagle & Child [St Giles]: Pleasant panelled front bar, compact mid-bars full of actors' and Tolkien/C S Lewis memorabilia, tasteful stripped-brick modern back dining extension with no smoking conservatory, varied food, well kept mainstream real ales, newspapers, events posters; piped music, busy at lunchtime; open all day *(BB, Chris Glasson, Richie V, Ned Kelly, Ann and Colin Hunt)*

☆ *Kings Arms* [Holywell St]: Bustling take-us-as-you-find-us 16th-c pub with cosy comfortably worn in side and back rooms, daily papers, relaxed atmosphere, well kept Youngs and a guest beer such as Black Sheep, 20 wines by the glass; children in eating area, a few tables outside, open all day *(Derek and Sylvia Stephenson, the Didler, Paul Hopton, Arnold Bennett, Colin and Janet Roe, Tim and Ann Newell, Kevin Blake, LYM, Simon Jones, Ann and Colin Hunt)*

Lamb & Flag [St Giles/Banbury Rd]: Old pub owned by nearby college and recently attractively refurbished, modern in front with big windows over street, more atmosphere in back rooms with exposed stonework and

panelled ceilings, well kept changing ales such as Skinners Betty Stogs, good value well served food, cheerful service; can be packed with students *(Richard Greaves)*

Marlborough House [Western Rd, just off Abingdon Rd S of Folly Bridge]: Small friendly side-street local, well kept Adnams Bitter and Broadside, Caledonian Deuchars IPA and Greene King IPA, inexpensive lunchtime snacks such as filled rolls, charming little snug off corridor, simple main bar with darts and juke box *(Pete Baker)*

Watermans Arms [South St, Osney]: Tidy and unpretentious riverside pub nr Osney Lock, well kept Greene King ales, good value generous home cooking, tables outside *(Alan Kilpatrick)*

Wharf House [Butterwyke Pl/Speedwell St]: Half a dozen or so well kept changing real ales in bare-boards early Victorian local with knowledgeable, friendly and helpful landlord, two farm ciders, masses of bottled german and belgian beers with their proper glasses, rickety old tables and chairs, darts, cards, elderly bull terrier; occasional vinyl records played, old TV brought out for sports, some impromptu singing; open all day Sat *(Pete Baker)*

☆ *White Horse* [Broad St]: Bustling and studenty, squeezed between bits of Blackwells bookshop; single small narrow bar with snug one-table raised back alcove, mellow oak beams and timbers, ochre ceiling, beautiful view of the Clarendon building and Sheldonian, good lunchtime food (the few tables reserved for this), interesting changing range of beers, Addlestone's cider, friendly licensees *(Giles and Annie Francis, BB)*

Woodstock Arms [Woodstock Rd]: Obliging service in friendly neat local with well kept Greene King IPA and plentiful cheap pub food, separate games bar; seats outside front and back *(R T and J C Moggridge)*

PISHILL [SU7389]

☆ *Crown* [B480 Nettlebed—Watlington]: Wisteria-covered ancient building, tidy and highly polished, with black beams and timbers, good log fires and candlelight, wholesome home-made food from good baguettes up inc carefully chosen ingredients and local venison, well kept Brakspears ales; children welcome in no smoking restaurant, pleasant bedroom in separate cottage, picnic-sets on attractive side lawn, pretty country setting – lots of walks *(the Didler, LYM, Tracey and Stephen Groves, Susan and John Douglas, Paul Humphreys, Peter Abbott)*

PLAY HATCH [SU7476]

Crown: Rambling olde-worlde heavily beamed 16th-c dining pub, spacious, civilised and good for families, two bars and several rooms inc barn restaurant and big, modern no smoking conservatory, well kept Brakspears ales tapped from the cask, extensive choice of decent wines, log fires, smartly dressed young antipodean staff; piped music; big pleasant garden with play area *(A P Seymour, John Baish, BB, Julia and Richard Tredgett, Mr and Mrs D J Pickles)*

RADCOT [SU2899]
Swan [A4095 2½ miles N of Faringdon]:
Welcoming Thames-side pub with enjoyable
food from generous baguettes up, friendly
landlord, log fire, Greene King ales, lots of
stuffed fish; children in eating area; piped
music; pleasant waterside garden, summer boat
trips (lift to bring wheelchairs aboard), four
good value bedrooms *(LYM, Alan Kilpatrick,
A P Seymour)*

ROTHERFIELD GREYS [SU7282]
Maltsters Arms: Old Brakspears pub with
helpful and friendly landlord, enjoyable piping
hot food, well kept ales, lovely country views
(John A Barker, Roy and Gay Hoing)

SHENINGTON [SP3742]
☆ *Bell* [off A422 NW of Banbury]: 17th-c two-
room village pub with emphasis on landlady's
consistently good reasonably priced home
cooking, good sandwiches too, low-priced
Hook Norton Best, good wine choice, informal
service, relaxed atmosphere, heavy beams,
some flagstones, stripped stone and pine
panelling, coal fire, friendly dogs, cribbage,
dominoes; children in eating areas, tables out
in front, small attractive back garden,
bedrooms, good surrounding walks, cl Mon
lunchtime *(Amanda Newcomb, LYM,
Sir Nigel Foulkes, Hugh Spottiswoode,
John Kane, K H Frostick, Michael and
Jeanne Shillington)*

SHIPLAKE [SU7779]
☆ *Baskerville Arms* [Station Rd]: Former long-
term licensees of Five Horseshoes,
Maidensgrove (till 2000) have now taken over
this relaxed and comfortable brick dining pub,
doing good, popular food with interesting
individual touches inc good value lunches,
extensive wine list, Fullers London Pride,
Timothy Taylors Landlord and a beer from
local Loddon, friendly service, sporting prints
and substantial houseplants around the orange
rooms, lit candles on every table; unobtrusive
piped classical music; attractive garden with
barbecues Thurs evening and Sun lunchtime,
comfortable bedrooms *(BB)*

SHIPTON-UNDER-WYCHWOOD
[SP2717]
Lamb [off A361 to Burford]: Cheerful and
stylish dining pub, not cheap, with enjoyable
food from light dishes to daily fresh Brixham
fish, charming service, Greene King ales and
perhaps a guest beer, some stripped stone and
log fire, exotic flower displays and elegant
candle holders, no smoking restaurant in
Elizabethan core; piped music, jazz Sun night;
children and dogs welcome, tables outside, five
attractive bedrooms (some over bar which can
stay lively till late), good breakfast
*(Arnold Bennett, LYM, G and R Cartey,
M and GR, R Huggins, D Irving, E McCall,
T McLean, Derek Stafford)*
☆ *Shaven Crown* [High St (A361)]: Memorable
ancient building with magnificent lofty
medieval rafters and imposing double stairway
in hotel part's hall; separate back beamed bar
with more modern décor and booth seating,
enjoyable food, well kept Hook Norton,

several wines by the glass and traditional
games, no smoking restaurant; piped music;
children and dogs welcome, peaceful courtyard
with outside heaters, bowling green
*(A P Seymour, LYM, Chris Glasson,
Howard and Margaret Buchanan,
Mrs Phoebe A Kemp)*

SHRIVENHAM [SU2488]
☆ *Prince of Wales* [High St; off A420 or B4000
NE of Swindon]: Convivial 17th-c stone-built
local with spotless low-beamed lounge,
pictures, lots of brasses, log fire and candles,
wholesome generous food (not Sun evening)
inc Sun roasts, enthusiastic young licensees,
well kept ales inc Wadworths and Charles
Wells Bombardier, good soft drinks choice,
small dining area, side bar with darts, board
games and machines; may be quiet piped
music, no dogs; children welcome, picnic-sets
and heaters in secluded back garden
(A P Seymour, CMW, JJW)

SHUTFORD [SP3840]
☆ *George & Dragon* [Church Lane]: Ancient
stone-built pub with pleasant staff, good
reasonably priced home-made food with
interesting flexible menu and Sun lunches, well
kept Hook Norton Best and good changing
guest beers, fine choice of wines by the glass,
comfortable flagstoned L-shaped bar with
impressive fireplace, and oak-panelled beamed
dining room; children and dogs welcome, small
garden, pretty village, cl Mon, open all day Sun
*(BB, Graham Pearson, Mrs E Widdowson,
Chris Glasson)*

SIBFORD GOWER [SP3537]
Wykham Arms [signed off B4035 Banbury—
Shipston on Stour; Temple Mill Rd]: Pretty
and cottagey thatched and flagstoned dining
pub, largely no smoking, with comfortable
open-plan low-beamed stripped-stone lounge,
nice pictures, table made from glass-topped
well, inglenook tap room, friendly efficient
staff, well kept real ales, good house wines and
coffee; children welcome; country views from
big well planted garden, lovely manor house
opp; has been cl Mon lunchtime
(Chris Glasson, LYM, Iain R Hewitt)

SOUTH LEIGH [SP3908]
Mason Arms [3 miles S of A40 Witney—
Eynsham; Station Rd]: Restaurant rather than
pub really, with enjoyable traditional food,
two big log fires, good interesting wines, well
kept beer, welcoming service, pictures on
dusky red walls, candlelight and flagstones,
sturdy antique furnishings; tables outside, cl
Mon *(LYM, Stuart Turner)*

SOUTH MORETON [SU5588]
☆ *Crown* [off A4130 or A417 E of Didcot;
High St]: Rambling old open-plan village
pub, relaxed and convivial, with friendly
licensees, well kept Badger Tanglefoot,
Wadworths 6X and a guest beer, decent wines
and coffee, wide range of good fresh home-
made food from sandwiches up (OAP
discounts), good service; piped music, Mon
quiz night; children allowed, small garden
*(Dick and Madeleine Brown, Marjorie and
David Lamb)*

SOUTH NEWINGTON [SP4033]

☆ *Duck on the Pond*: Thriving dining pub doing well after recent refurbishment, wide choice of generously served food from wraps, melts and other light dishes to steak and mixed grill, four changing ales inc Bass, Hook Norton and Loddon Hoppit, good service from smartly dressed young staff, some stripped stonework and flagstones, step up to linked eating areas with fresh flowers and lit candles, separate smoking area; piped pop music may be rather loud; lots of tables out on terrace and lawn; open all day *(Ted George, Stuart Turner, BB)*

SPARSHOLT [SU3487]

☆ *Star* [Watery Lane]: Comfortable 16th-c country pub, friendly and compact, with short choice of good freshly made straightforward food at sensible prices, two well kept real ales, daily papers, log fire, attractive pictures, horse-racing talk; may be subdued piped music; back garden, pretty village – snowdrops fill churchyard in spring *(Marjorie and David Lamb, G S R Cox)*

STANDLAKE [SP3902]

Bell [High St]: New licensees (again) doing wide choice of enjoyable food inc Fri fresh fish specials in friendly refurbished bar and no smoking back restaurant, well kept Greene King IPA, Morlands Original and Abbot, convivial atmosphere; children (and dogs) truly welcome, with games and drawing things *(anon)*

Black Horse [High St]: Good Sun carvery and huge choice of other food from sandwiches hot or cold to imaginative blackboard dishes, several real ales, three large rooms (one no smoking for families), chatty landlady and friendly efficient service, no piped music *(Bob Ellis)*

STANFORD IN THE VALE [SU3393]

Horse & Jockey [Faringdon Rd]: Popular local in racehorse country, good drawings and paintings of horses and jockeys, Batemans XXB and Greene King Morlands Original and Tanners Jack, usual food, woodburner; dogs welcome *(Ian Phillips)*

STANTON ST JOHN [SP5709]

☆ *Talk House* [Wheatley Rd (B4027 just outside)]: Peacefully placed 17th-c pub taken gently up market by new licensees, serious food, well kept Hook Norton Best, Wadworths 6X and a guest beer, intelligent friendly service, Oxford academia prints on partly stripped stone walls, lots of oak beams, flagstones and tiles, simple but solid rustic furnishings, pleasant area by log fire; children welcome in restaurant, tables in sheltered courtyard, comfortable bedrooms, has been open all day in summer *(LYM, Heather Couper)*

STEVENTON [SU4791]

Cherry Tree [B4017 (High St); village signed off A34 S of Abingdon via A4130]: Gently refurbished 18th-c pub with good choice of generous quickly served well priced food from good sandwiches up in rambling bar and expanded dining area, well kept Wadworths IPA, JCB and 6X and a guest beer such as Butcombe, decent wines, friendly service, open-

plan beamed areas around island bar, flagstones and bare boards, mix of furniture inc heavily carved settles and brocaded dining chairs, dark green walls, open fires and old prints, no smoking area; they may try to make you leave a credit card at the bar if you eat; disabled facilities, tables out on repaved terrace, open all day Fri-Sun, three new bedrooms *(W W Burke, BB, Marjorie and David Lamb, Dick and Madeleine Brown)*

☆ *North Star* [Stocks Lane, The Causeway, central westward turn off B4017]: Carefully restored old-fangled village pub with tiled entrance corridor, main area with ancient high-backed settles around central table, Greene King Morlands Original on handpump and two guest ales tapped from the cask in small tap room off (no bar counter), hatch service to side room with plain seating, a couple of tables and good coal fire, simple lunchtime food, mainly inexpensive sandwiches, ploughman's and hot-filled baguettes, friendly staff and three-legged cat; sports TV; tables on side grass, front gateway through living yew tree *(Giles and Annie Francis, LYM, the Didler, Pete Baker)*

STOKE LYNE [SP5628]

☆ *Peyton Arms* [from minor road off B4110 N of Bicester fork left into village]: Largely unspoilt stone-built pub cleaned up by new licensees (planning food using veg from pub garden), well kept Hook Norton beers (full range) tapped from casks behind small corner bar in sparsely decorated front snug, tiled floor, inglenook log fire, hops on beam, bigger refurbished games room with darts and pool, charity book store, good lavatories; well behaved children and dogs welcome, pleasant garden with aunt sally; cl Mon-Thurs *(Jeremy Morrison, Pete Baker, the Didler, Conor McGaughey, Mick Furn, CMW, JJW)*

STOKE ROW [SU6884]

☆ *Cherry Tree* [off B481 at Highmoor]: Pretty tiled cottage reopened 2004 under new licensees after careful gentrification in restrained modern white-walled style with plenty of woodwork and keeping its heavy low beams and some flagstones, enjoyable food in roomy no smoking eating areas, friendly staff, good choice of wines by the glass, well kept Brakspears and a belgian beer on tap; picnic-sets out on pleasant green, four well done bedrooms in new block, breakfast a treat *(BB, Julie Woolmer, Jim Cooper, P Price, Roy and Gay Hoing, Karen and Graham Oddey)*

☆ *Crooked Billet* [Nottwood Lane, off B491 N of Reading – OS Sheet 175 map ref 684844]: Good restaurant, not pub (so not eligible for the main entries), but a *Guide* favourite, keeping its rustic pub layout with heavy beams, flagstones, antique pubby furnishings and great inglenook log fire as well as crimsonly Victorian dining room; wide choice of well cooked interesting meals inc good value lunch (you can have just a starter), friendly helpful service, well kept Brakspears tapped from the cask (no bar counter), good wines, relaxed homely atmosphere – like a french country restaurant; children truly welcome, occasional live music, big garden by Chilterns beechwoods *(Mr and Mrs Bentley-Davies, Heather Couper, Penny and Peter Keevil, LYM, the Didler, Gerald Hughes, Paul Humphreys, Mrs E A Macdonald, Karen and Graham Oddey, Bob and Judy Smitherman)*

Grouse & Claret [off B481 S of Nettlebed; towards Kingwood Common]: This attractive and highly individual dining pub, a main entry in the last edition, was closed as we went to press, with plans for conversion to a private house *(LYM)*

STONESFIELD [SP3917]

Blacks Head [Church St]: Good pub for walkers, with no smoking section, book share scheme and real ale *(Colin Critch)*

STRATTON AUDLEY [SP6026]

Red Lion [off A421 NE of Bicester; Church St]: Thatched local with quick friendly service, well priced generous food inc notable burgers and more restaurant dishes, good atmosphere, three real ales and good soft drinks choice, big inglenook log fire, stripped stone and low beams, antique sale posters, old varnished wooden furniture; children and dogs welcome, pavement tables, more on heated terrace in small colourful garden, pretty village *(Paul and Jane Walker, E A and D C T Frewer, CMW, JJW)*

SUNNINGWELL [SP4900]

☆ *Flowing Well* [just N of Abingdon]: Relaxed and convivial, with good plentiful enterprising food from baguettes to restaurant dishes (children's menu), well kept Greene King Abbot and Morlands and Wadworths 6X, good wine choice inc many organic ones, plus organic coffees and juices, remarkable collection of rare rums; refurbished in a simple, laid-back style, with plenty of space, big no smoking area, pool; TV, gentle live jazz and blues nights (at other times piped jazz can be loud); garden with small well and picnic-sets under cocktail parasols *(Derek Goldrei, Geoff Pidoux, BB)*

SWERFORD [SP3731]

☆ *Masons Arms* [A361 Banbury—Chipping Norton]: Tastefully refurbished dining pub with helpful young South African staff, enjoyable food from reasonably priced sandwiches and baguettes through good local ham and eggs to some ambitious main dishes, well kept Hook Norton Best, decent wines, brightly modernised bar with rugs on pale boards and comfortable blue armchairs around big tables, steps down to plank-walled room with chunky tables, roomy back candlelit dining room; great views from this and from small terrace and neat lawn *(John and Sue Woodward, LYM, Arnold Bennett, Robert Gomme, Chris Glasson, Iain R Hewitt)*

SYDENHAM [SP7201]

☆ *Crown* [off B4445 Chinnor—Thame]: Relaxed low-beamed village local popular for good home-made food inc Fri/Sat fresh fish and nice puddings, welcoming attentive service, well kept Greene King beers, above-average wines, open fires in long narrow bar; may be quiet

piped music, dominoes, darts, quiz and dress-up theme nights; children welcome, small garden with roses and climbing frame, views of lovely church, picturesque village *(Jestyn Phillips, BB)*

TACKLEY [SP4720]

Gardeners Arms [Medcroft Rd, off A4260]: Comfortable 17th-c beamed village pub with genial and helpful landlord, enjoyable usual food inc Weds OAP bargains, three well kept Greene King ales, coal-effect gas fire in inglenook, prints, brasses, old photographs and cigarette cards; separate public bar with darts, TV and fruit machine, piped music, bookable skittle alley; picnic-sets on sunny terrace, handy for Rousham House *(Michael Tack, Marjorie and David Lamb, Sue Demont, Tim Barrow)*

TETSWORTH [SP6802]

Swan [A40, not far from M40 junction 7]: Lively and welcoming bar doubling as restaurant and afternoon teashop for antiques centre in other parts of this rambling 15th-c coaching inn, appropriate furnishings, gilt-framed paintings and masses of character, good upmarket food, pleasant atmosphere and helpful service, good log fire in massive fireplace; keg beer *(B H and J I Andrews, Susan and John Douglas)*

THAME [SP7005]

Swan [Upper High St]: Civilised heavily beamed 16th-c coaching inn, a popular main entry for its individual even slightly quirky style, with a comfortable mix of furnishings and of good bric-a-brac; it's also had well kept Hook Norton Best, Shepherd Neame Spitfire, Timothy Taylors Landlord and a seasonal Archers ale, quite a few wines by the glass and enjoyable food from sandwiches and baguettes to home-made hot dishes (the upstairs restaurant has a medieval ceiling); children and dogs have been welcome, bedrooms, open all day; recently sold, so there may well be changes – news please *(LYM)*

THRUPP [SP4815]

☆ *Boat* [off A4260 just N of Kidlington]: Stone-built pub particularly popular in summer for its attractive position by Oxford Canal, nice safely fenced garden behind with plenty of tables, some in shade; good value decent food from good baguettes up, well kept Greene King ales, decent wine, coal fire, old canal pictures and artefacts, bare boards and stripped pine, restaurant, no piped music; good folk night 2nd Sun *(Geoff Pidoux, Sue Demont, Tim Barrow, Pete Baker)*

WANTAGE [SU3988]

Lamb [Mill St, past square and Bell; down hill then bend to left]: Low beams, timbers and soft lighting, attractive and comfortable furnishings with cosy corners and no smoking part, unpretentious atmosphere, well kept Greene King ales, wide choice of generous good value blackboard food from baked potatoes to steak, duck and salmon, quick smiling service, log fire; disabled access and facilities, garden with some covered tables and good play area *(LYM)*

WARBOROUGH [SU5993]

Cricketers Arms [Thame Rd (off A329)]: Neat local under friendly new licensees, pleasant décor, good value fresh food (booking recommended on Sun), well kept Greene King IPA and Abbot, proper bar and dining area, good service; tables outside *(Margaret and Roy Randle, Marjorie and David Lamb)*

☆ *Six Bells* [The Green S; just E of A329, 4 miles N of Wallingford]: Low-ceilinged thatched 16th-c pub facing cricket green, attractive country furnishings in linked areas off bar, well kept Brakspears and a guest beer, decent wines, friendly efficient service, enjoyable food, big log fire, beams and stripped stone, fresh flowers, antique photographs and pictures; tables in back orchard *(LYM, Barry Collett, Martin and Karen Wake)*

WATLINGTON [SU6894]

Chequers [3 miles from M40 junction 6, via B4009; Love Lane]: Attractive rambling bar with very wide choice of good value food from sandwiches to steaks and popular Sun lunch, well kept Brakspears PA, SB and a seasonal beer, good atmosphere, character seating and a few good antique oak tables, low beams and candles, steps down to further eating area, vine-hung conservatory (children allowed here); picnic-sets in pretty garden, nice walks nearby *(Alistair Forsyth, LYM, Wombat, Colin Wood)*

WEST HENDRED [SU4489]

☆ *Hare* [A417 Reading Rd, outside village]: Civilised and welcoming open-plan pub, low-ceilinged main bar with bare boards and big terracotta tiles, partly divided by timber studding, pleasantly individual seating, comfortable parquet-floor no smoking dining area, enjoyable traditional food, well kept Greene King IPA, Abbot and Morlands Original, decent wines, efficient friendly service; piped music; colonnaded verandah, picnic-sets in side garden *(LYM, Mark and Ruth Brock)*

WHEATLEY [SP5905]

Railway: Popular Fullers pub with their beers kept well, lively atmosphere, decent bar food; piped music *(Mark O'Sullivan)*

WITNEY [SP3509]

Angel [Market Sq]: Wide choice of bargain food from good sandwiches up inc OAP specials in comfortably bustling 17th-c town local, extended but unchanging, well kept ales such as Courage Best, Hook Norton Best and Charles Wells Bombardier, daily papers, welcoming softly lit homely surroundings and hot coal fire, quick friendly service even when packed; pool room, coffee bar; can get smoky, parking nearby can be difficult *(Peter and Audrey Dowsett, Ian Phillips, Derek Allpass)*

☆ *Three Horseshoes* [Corn St, junction with Holloway Rd]: Warmly welcoming and attractive 16th-c stone-built pub, heavy beams, flagstones, log fires, well polished and comfortable old furniture, consistently good home-made food from filled baguettes, ciabattas and other pubby lunchtime food to more imaginative restauranty dishes, well kept Greene King Abbot and Morlands Original

and a guest beer, decent house wines, separate dining room *(Patrick Hancock, LYM, Comus and Sarah Elliott, Ian Phillips, KN-R)*

WOLVERCOTE [SP5009]

Plough [First Turn/Wolvercote Green]: Lots of comfortably well worn-in pubby linked areas, warm and friendly, with bustling atmosphere, armchairs and Victorian-style carpeted bays in main lounge, well kept real ales, decent wines, varied inexpensive food in flagstoned ex-stables dining room and library (children allowed here), traditional snug, woodburner; may try to keep your credit card while you eat; picnic-sets on front terrace looking over rough meadow to canal and woods *(BB, Alan and Carolin Tidbury)*

WOODSTOCK [SP4416]

Bear [Park St]: Handsome old inn with relaxing heavy-beamed bar on right, cosy alcoves, tastefully casual mix of antique oak, mahogany and leather furniture, paintings and sporting trophies, blazing inglenook log fire, well kept but pricey Bass and Greene King Old Speckled Hen, bar lunches inc good fresh sandwiches, helpful staff, good bedrooms *(BB, Mr and Mrs J Hutton)*

Kings Arms [Market St/Park Lane]: Enjoyable food, pleasant furnishings and friendly helpful staff in roomy pub/hotel with several different areas and something of a brasserie feel, good value wines and well kept Theakstons; bedrooms *(Geoff Pidoux, Guy Vowles)*

Woodstock Arms [Market St]: 16th-c heavy-beamed stripped-stone local with long narrow bar, separate dining area, good value straightforward home-made food inc good vegetarian choice, prompt service by young friendly staff, warm lively atmosphere, well kept Greene King IPA, Abbot and Old Speckled Hen, decent wines, log-effect gas fires in splendid stone fireplaces; tables out in yard, bedrooms *(R Huggins, D Irving, E McCall, T McLean, Geoff Pidoux, Chris Glasson)*

WOOLSTONE [SU2987]

☆ *White Horse* [village signed off B4507]: Plushly refurbished partly thatched 16th-c pub with steep Victorian gables, two big open fires in spacious beamed and part-panelled room with quite a variety of décor styles, wide choice of decent quickly served bar food, friendly relaxed staff and black labrador, well kept Arkells, decent wines, lots of whiskies, good coffee, log fire, evening dining; quiet piped music, no visiting dogs; children allowed in eating area, sheltered garden, four charming good value bedrooms, big breakfast, secluded interesting village handy for White Horse and Ridgeway walkers *(BB, Darly Graton, Graeme Gulibert, Mary Rayner)*

WOOTTON [SP4320]

☆ *Killingworth Castle* [Glympton Rd; B4027 N of Woodstock]: Striking three-storey 17th-c coaching inn, lively local atmosphere, pleasant service, well kept Greene King ales, decent house wines, wide choice of generous food, long narrow main bar with pine furnishings, parquet floor, candles, lots of brasses and log fire with books above it, daily papers, bar billiards, darts and shove ha'penny in smaller games end, attractive garden; soft piped music, frequent live music nights; bedrooms *(Stuart Turner, Pete Baker, Simon Collett-Jones, R Huggins, D Irving, E McCall, T McLean, BB)*

☆ Kings Head [off B4027 N of Woodstock; Chapel Hill]: 17th-c cotswold stone house, completely no smoking and better thought of as upmarket and rather formal restaurant-with-rooms than as pub, with good food (best to book), armchairs, sofas and old oak settles and chairs in tasteful hotelish beamed lounge bar with log fire, well kept Greene King Ruddles County and Hook Norton Old Hooky, good wines; children not welcome, immaculate bedrooms, good breakfast, cl Sun evening and Mon *(Geoff Pidoux, Simon Collett-Jones, DRH and KLH, Sir Nigel Foulkes, Di and Mike Gillam, LYM, Colin and Bernardine Perry, Janet Gladstone)*

WYTHAM [SP4708]
White Hart [off A34 Oxford ring rd]: More restaurant than pub, enjoyable modern rather pricey food all day, several eating areas inc informal relaxed red-walled no smoking area allowing children, log fire in gently updated bar with settles, handsome panelling and flagstones, friendly calm young staff, well kept Fullers London Pride and Hook Norton, good value house wines; open all day, pretty garden with big tables and solid fuel stove in covered eating area, may be summer barbecues, unspoilt preserved village *(LYM, Di and Mike Gillam, Brenda and Stuart Naylor)*

YARNTON [SP4812]
Turnpike [A44 N of Oxford]: Large Vintage Inn pub/restaurant with good atmosphere in spacious low-ceilinged bar areas, wide range of promptly served food all day, well kept Bass, helpful staff, log fire *(Nigel and Sue Foster, Geoff Pidoux)*

A very few pubs try to make you leave a credit card at the bar, as a sort of deposit if you order food. They are not entitled to do this. The credit card firms and banks which issue them warn you not to let them out of your sight. If someone behind the counter used your card fraudulently, the card company or bank could in theory hold you liable, because of your negligence in letting a stranger hang on to your card. Suggest instead that if they feel the need for security, they 'swipe' your card and give it back to you. And do name and shame the pub to us.

Shropshire

This is a good value county for pubs, with both drinks and food prices tending to be rather lower than most areas, an interesting choice of good local beers, food that's often a big plus, and plenty of real character. Pubs and inns attracting special praise recently are the Castle Hotel in Bishop's Castle with its warmly welcoming bar, the cheerful Six Bells there (brewing its own good beer), the Clive/Cookhouse at Bromfield (good food, and its new bedrooms earn it a Place to Stay Award this year), the attractively decorated and welcoming Burlton Inn (good imaginative food), the interestingly furnished Crown at Hopton Wafers (good all round, with most enjoyable food in its bar, and more elaborate restaurant meals), the stylishly reworked Inn at Grinshill (a new entry – good bar, bistro and restaurant food), the Malthouse in Ironbridge (much enjoyed for its food, décor and atmosphere), the Church Inn in Ludlow (another thriving all-rounder, using local produce to good effect – and in these days of proliferating CCTVs the only pub we know to have a camera obscura instead), the George & Dragon in Much Wenlock (back in the *Guide* on fine form, after a few years' absence), the food-oriented Sun at Norbury, the newly extended Bottle & Glass at Picklescott (its food side thriving), and the unusual Armoury in Shrewsbury (good food and drinks in this elegantly converted historic warehouse). It is the Crown at Hopton Wafers which takes the title of Shropshire Dining Pub of the Year. In the Lucky Dip section at the end of the chapter, pubs to note particularly are the Railwaymans Arms in Bridgnorth, restauranty Pheasant in Broseley, Coalbrookdale Inn, Sun at Corfton, Station Hotel in Marshbrook and Stiperstones Inn. As we have said, beer prices are lower than the national average here. Hobsons is the main local beer, and often the cheapest stocked by pubs here; Woods is also easy to find, and other local beers to look out for include Salopian, Six Bells, John Roberts and Hanby.

BISHOP'S CASTLE SO3289 Map 6

Castle Hotel 🖛

Market Square, just off B4385

There's a good deal of creaky charm about this splendid early 18th-c stone coaching inn, and the warm welcome from staff makes it a very pleasant place to stay and explore this part of the county. Neatly kept and attractively furnished, the clubby little beamed and panelled bar, glazed off from the entrance, has a good coal fire, old hunting prints and sturdy leather chairs on its muted carpet. It opens into a much bigger room, with maroon plush wall seats and stools, big Victorian engravings, and another coal fire in an attractive cast-iron fireplace. The lighting in both rooms is gentle and relaxing, and the pub tables have unusually elaborate cast-iron frames; shove-ha'penny, dominoes, cribbage, board games and no piped music. Hobsons Best and Mild, local Six Bells Big Nevs and Duck and Dive are well kept on handpump, they've decent wines, and over 30 malt whiskies. Made with good quality ingredients, a short choice of enjoyable bar food might include lunchtime baguettes (£5.25), battered haddock (£6.25), and steak and kidney pie (£7.45), with other dishes such as soup (£3.50), pork and duck terrine (£5.95), cheese, leek and mushroom sausages with sun-dried tomato sauce (£8.95), salmon poached in white wine with tarragon and cream (£9.25), beef and ale pie (£9.45), and good steaks (from £11.95), with puddings such as raspberry cheesecake (£4.25). The handsome no smoking panelled dining room is open in the evening and on Sunday lunchtime. The old-fashioned bedrooms are spacious, and they do good breakfasts. It is especially lovely in summer, when the pub is festooned with pretty hanging baskets, and there are picnic-sets in the back garden, which has terraces with green chairs on either side of a large formal raised fish pond, pergolas and climbing plants, and stone walls; it looks out over the town rooftops to the surrounding gentle countryside. A new extension links the garden to the bars, with access for the disabled, via a lower courtyard with a miniature waterfall. *(Recommended by John Wooll, Steve Whalley, Greta and Christopher Wells, Kevin Thorpe, the Didler, Tony and Maggie Harwood, Pat Bradbury, John and Gloria Isaacs, Reg Fowle, Helen Rickwood, David Field, Paul and Gloria Howell)*

Free house ~ Licensees David and Nicky Simpson ~ Real ale ~ Bar food (12-1.30, 6.30-8.45) ~ (01588) 638403 ~ Children in restaurant ~ Dogs welcome ~ Open 12-2.30, 6-11; 12-2.30, 7-10.30 Sun ~ Bedrooms: £40B/£70S

Six Bells 🍺

Church Street

The own-brew beer in this cheerfully chatty former coaching inn is a big attraction: Big Nevs is most people's favourite, and you'll also find Marathon, Cloud Nine and Duck & Dive – you can arrange a tour of the brewery, and they have a beer festival on the second full weekend in July. They also keep a wide range of country wines. The pub consists of just two simple no-frills rooms. One bar is really quite small, with an assortment of well worn furniture and old local photographs and prints. The second, bigger room has bare boards, some stripped stone, a roaring woodburner in the inglenook, plenty of sociable locals on the benches around plain tables, darts and lots of board games (you may find people absorbed in Scrabble here in winter). The service is very friendly. As we went to press, we heard that the food is going to a new caterer, who will make the menu cheaper and more pubby, with all main course items under £10 apart from steaks; the dining area is no smoking. It can be packed here on the weekend. *(Recommended by Tracey and Stephen Groves, Steve Whalley, the Didler, Kevin Thorpe, Tony and Maggie Harwood, Glenwys and Alan Lawrence, Guy Vowles, David Field, MLR, Paul and Gloria Howell)*

Own brew ~ Licensee Neville Richards ~ Real ale ~ Bar food (12-2(2.30 Sun), 6.30-9; not Sun evening or Mon) ~ Restaurant ~ No credit cards ~ (01588) 630144 ~ Children welcome if well behaved ~ Open 12-2.30, 5-11; 12-11(10.30 Sun) Sat; closed Mon lunchtime

Three Tuns 🍺

Salop Street

Full of friendly conversation and undisturbed by piped music, this sociable pub has no-frills beamed rooms that are very simply furnished with low-backed settles and heavy walnut tables, and newspapers left for customers to read. The four-storied Victorian John Roberts brewhouse across the yard supplies the well kept beers: you'll find John Roberts XXX, Clerics Cure, Three 8 and a John Roberts seasonal brew served from old-fashioned handpumps by the friendly staff. They always have a farm cider or perry on too. They do carry-out kegs, and the brewery (now a separate business) sells beer by the barrel; a popular annual beer festival takes place in July. Tasty home-made bar food might include sandwiches from (£3.75), vegetable lasagne or vegetable risotto (£7.95), beef pie or wild boar sausage and mash (£8.95) and puddings (£3.50). There's a small garden, and they have self-contained rooms to let. The outside gents' is now suitable for disabled people, and they're adding an inside loo. *(Recommended by Steve Whalley, John Fiander, Pat and Tony Martin, Kevin Thorpe, the Didler, Tracey and Stephen Groves, R and H Fraser, Guy Vowles, MLR, Paul and Gloria Howell, JMM)*

John Roberts ~ Tenant Mick Leadbetter ~ Real ale ~ Bar food (12-2.30, 7.9.30 Weds-Sun; not Mon, Tues) ~ Restaurant ~ (01588) 638797 ~ Children welcome ~ Dogs allowed in bar ~ Live music every weekend ~ Open 12-11(10.30 Sun) ~ Bedrooms: /£60B

BRIDGES SO3996 Map 6
Horseshoe ◀

Near Ratlinghope, below the W flank of the Long Mynd

Walking groups find their way to this remote pub in splendid country in the Shropshire hills, and the TV series *The Green, Green Grass* was recently filmed here, using locals as extras; the interior has been redone, with light oak beams, log burners and lots of rustic bygones. The down-to-earth yet comfortable bar has interesting windows, lots of farm implements, pub mirrors and musical instruments, and well kept Adnams Bitter, Horseshoe Brew brewed specially for the pub by Bass, and Timothy Taylor Landlord on handpump, and they've also Old Rosie farm cider. A small no smoking dining room leads off from here; cribbage, darts and dominoes, Scrabble (Monday evenings) and occasional, discreet piped music. Home-made bar food such as sandwiches (from £2.20), soup (£2.95), farmhouse sausage and mash (£5.75), meat lasagne or a vegetable special such as spinach and mascarpone lasagne (£6.25), home-made steak and kidney pie (£6.95), cod and home-made chips (£8.25), and a huge 24oz rump steak (£11.75), with puddings such as apple pie or bread and butter pudding (£2.95); children's menu (£2.50). On Wednesday evenings they have a 'feast for a fiver', with themed food such as curry or mexican for just £5. Tables are placed out by the little River Onny; the Long Mynd rises up behind. They have plans to turn the outbuildings into bedrooms and maybe a restaurant. *(Recommended by Dave Braisted, Ian Phillips, Reg Fowle, Helen Rickwood)*

Free house ~ Licensees Bob and Maureen Macauley ~ Real ale ~ Bar food (12-2.45, 6-8.45; 12-8.45 Sat; 12-6.45 Sun) ~ Restaurant ~ (01588) 650260 ~ Children welcome if well behaved ~ Dogs allowed in bar ~ Open 12-11(10.30 Sun)

BROMFIELD SO4877 Map 6
Clive/Cookhouse ♀ ⇔

A49 2 miles NW of Ludlow

Once home to Clive of India, this handsome and immaculately kept Georgian brick house is known in full as the Clive Restaurant with Rooms and Cookhouse Café Bar, and it scores well for both food and accommodation. Inside it's an interesting contemporary take on the traditional inn. The front section has been brightly modernised in minimalist city style, but the back part is more traditional – though still with a modern edge. During the day the focus is on the dining room, café-bar in style, with modern light wood tables, and a big open kitchen behind the end stainless steel counter. A door leads through into the bar, sparse but neat and welcoming, with round glass tables and metal chairs running down to a sleek, space-age bar counter with fresh flowers, newspapers and spotlights. Then it's down a step to the Clive Arms Bar, where traditional features like the huge brick fireplace, exposed stonework, and soaring beams and rafters are appealingly juxtaposed with wicker chairs, worn sofas and new glass tables. The restaurant and café bar are no smoking; piped jazz, daily papers. Besides sandwiches, good bar food includes soup (£4.25), goats cheese, spinach and lentil terrine with rocket salad (£5.95), smoked haddock rarebit (£6.95), cassoulet of wild mushrooms, provençale vegetables and salad (£8.95), venison sausages and mash, peppered fillet of salmon or a Cookhouse platter, with tuna, artichoke, air-dried ham, egg, anchovy and pâté on dressed leaves (£9.95) and fillet steak (£13.95). They do two courses for £12.50 and a more expensive restaurant menu. The good wine list includes ten by the glass, and Hobsons Best is well kept on handpump; they also have a range of coffees and teas. An attractive secluded terrace has tables under cocktail parasols and a fish pond. They have 15 stylishly modern, good-sized no smoking bedrooms, and breakfast is excellent. *(Recommended by George Atkinson,*

John Whitehead, Therese Flanagan, Mike and Mary Carter, Bruce and Sharon Eden, Jo Lilley, Simon Calvert, Michael Sargent)

Free house ~ Licensee Paul Brooks ~ Real ale ~ Bar food (12-3, 6-9.30) ~ Restaurant ~ (01584) 856565 ~ Children in eating area of bar and restaurant ~ Open 11-11; 12-10.30 Sun; closed 25-26 Dec ~ Bedrooms: £50B/£70B

BURLTON SJ4626 Map 6
Burlton Inn ⊕ ◫ ⇔
A528 Shrewsbury—Ellesmere, near junction with B4397

As soon as you step into this extremely welcoming and attractively refurbished old pub everything seems meticulously arranged and well cared for, from the pretty flower displays in the brick fireplace or beside the neatly curtained windows, to the piles of interior design magazines in the corner. There are a few sporting prints, spurs and brasses on the walls, open fires in winter and dominoes and cribbage. The food here continues to deserve high praise, and besides interesting specials such as seafood pancake or tartlet of filo pastry, pear, walnut and gorgonzola (£9.95), locally made sausages and mash (£10.50) and cider chicken tagliatelle (£10.95), an enticing choice of home-made bar food could include soup (£3.50), filled ciabattas, rolls or baked potatoes (from £5.50), tandoori chicken skewer (£5.95), steak, kidney and beer pie (£9.95), tarragon and mustard chicken (£12.95) and teriyaki-marinated fresh tuna fillet (£13.50). There may be two set-time evening sittings in the restaurant, part of which is no smoking. French windows lead from the new garden dining room to the pleasant terrace, with its smart wooden furniture; the snug has comfortable seats, great for sinking into with a drink. Eleven wines by the glass are available; along with well kept Banks's, you'll find three continually changing guests from brewers such as Adnams, Greene King and Cottage. They have facilities for the disabled. There are tables on a small lawn behind, with more on a strip of grass beyond the car park. *(Recommended by Roger Thornington, Howard and Lorna Lambert, M Thomas, J S Burn, Ray and Winifred Halliday, H Wardlaw, John and Caroline, Stan Edwards, Derek and Sylvia Stephenson, Mr and Mrs F Carroll, Neil Kellett, Tony and Caroline Elwood, Rosemary Cladingbowl, John and Jane Hayter)*

Free house ~ Licensee Gerald Bean ~ Real ale ~ Bar food (12-2, 6.30-9.45(7-9.30 Sun)) ~ Restaurant ~ (01939) 270284 ~ Children in eating area of bar and restaurant ~ Open 11-3, 6-11; 12-3.30, 7-10.30 Sun; closed bank hol Mon lunchtimes; 25-26 Dec and 1 Jan ~ Bedrooms: £50B/£80B

CARDINGTON SO5095 Map 4
Royal Oak
Village signposted off B4371 Church Stretton—Much Wenlock, pub behind church; also reached via narrow lanes from A49

In a delightful rural setting in a landscape that wavers between lowland and upland, this friendly ancient place is bright in summer with flowers and hanging baskets, and tables in the front courtyard make the most of the view. Inside, the rambling, low-beamed bar has a roaring winter log fire, cauldron, black kettle and pewter jugs in its vast inglenook fireplace, the old standing timbers of a knocked-through wall, and red and green tapestry seats solidly capped in elm; darts, dominoes and occasional live music. A comfortable no smoking dining area has exposed old beams and studwork. The welcoming and efficient waitresses help create a relaxed atmosphere. Big helpings of tasty good value bar food include soup (£2.50), garlic mushrooms (£3), baguettes (from £3.25), filled baked potatoes (from £3.50), ploughman's (from £4.50), chicken tikka masala or spinach and mascarpone lasagne (£7.50), grilled trout or home-made fidget pie filled with gammon in spiced cider and apples (£8), and steaks (from £9.95); children's meals (£3); they also have specials such as thai fishcakes (£4.50), apricot stuffed lamb (£9.50) and bass in lime and coriander sauce (£10.95). Hobsons, Timothy Taylors and a couple of guests such as Wye Valley Butty Bach and Six Bells Duck Dive are well kept on handpump. A mile or so away to the west – from the track past Willstone (ask for directions at the pub) – you can walk up Caer Caradoc Hill, which has great views. *(Recommended by Gloria Bax, Derek and Sylvia Stephenson, John Whitehead, George and Gill Peckham, J S Burn, Jim and Maggie Cowell, Alison and Graham Hooper, A H Gordon Clark, MLR, TOH, A G Roby, David and Gilly Wilkins, Nigel Long)*

Free house ~ Licensees Steve Oldham and Eira Williams ~ Real ale ~ Bar food ~ Restaurant ~ (01694) 771266 ~ Children in eating area of bar and restaurant ~ Dogs allowed in bar ~ Open 12-3, 7-11(10.30 Sun); closed Mon except bank hols

GRINSHILL SJ5223 Map 7

Inn at Grinshill

Off A49 N of Shrewsbury

In the last couple of years the licensees here have attractively revamped this early Georgian inn, built of brick and locally quarried sandstone (which graces Grinshill and Clive, the next village); in summer the local cricket team comes in here after the match. At the front is the 19th-c bar (still called the Elephant and Castle bar, after the pub's former name), leading into the informal family area at the rear. Across the hall is the main no smoking restaurant, with a view straight into the kitchen and with doors into the rear garden, laid out with tables and chairs. Home-made food available in the bar areas or in the restaurant includes soup (£4), wild mushroom risotto (£6), smoked salmon platter (£7), thai chicken curry, breaded lamb cutlets or cold poached salmon with wasabi coleslaw (£12), fish specials available Thursday to Saturday like whole red mullet (£12) and puddings such as summer pudding or steamed ginger sponge in chocolate orange sauce (all £4.50); children's portions (£6.50); the restaurant also has a more elaborate menu during the evenings from Thursday to Saturday. At lunchtime and before 7.30 during weekdays you can take advantage of the 'lunchtime and early bird menu', with three courses for £9.95, and four choices of each course. Greene King Ruddles, Hanbys Drawell and Theakston XB plus a guest such as Hop Back Summer Lightning are well kept on handpump; TV, piped music, dominoes, and an evening pianist on Friday. Ask at the bar for directions to the top of the hill of Grinshill, not at all high but with an astonishingly far-ranging view. In spring 2005 they added soundproofed rooms with wide-screen TV and broadband access, and we would be interested to receive reports from readers who stay here. *(Recommended by John and Jenny Pullin, Noel Grundy, Mr and Mrs P Lally, J S Burn, M Joyner, TOH, Geoffrey Parker)*

Free house ~ Licensees Kevin and Victoria Brazier ~ Real ale ~ Bar food (12-2.30, 6.30-9.30) ~ Restaurant ~ (01939) 220410 ~ Children in family room ~ Dogs allowed in bar ~ Open 11-3, 6-11; 12-3 Sun; closed Sun evening ~ Bedrooms: £85B/£120B

HOPTON WAFERS SO6476 Map 6

Crown 🍽 ♀ 🛏

A4117 Kidderminster—Ludlow

Shropshire Dining Pub of the Year

A stream running beside the garden makes this creeper-covered 16th-c inn at the foot of Titterstone Clee Hill an inviting place to sit outside in summer, with tubs of bright flowers and a duck pond, and pleasant terrace areas with tables under cocktail parasols. Friendly and attentive staff make it an enjoyable place to eat at or stay in. The emphasis is on the good, freshly prepared food, and the changing menu might include soup (£3.50), chicken liver pâté (£4.50), local sausages and mash (£7.95), home-made pie (£8.75), steaks (from £11.75), with blackboard specials (including good fresh fish dishes) such as crab and mussel chowder (£4.50), pork and stilton sausages with apricot gravy (£7.95), salmon and asparagus fishcakes (£8.95) and roast duck breast (£12.25), with mouthwatering home-made puddings (£4.25); they do smaller helpings of some dishes for children. Neatly kept with an understated atmosphere, the cosy cream-painted beamed bar has a large inglenook fireplace, dark wood furniture, oil paintings and fresh flowers. The restaurant (with a more elaborate menu) has another impressive inglenook and pretty table settings, and is no smoking; piped music. Hobsons Best and Timothy Taylors Landlord are well kept alongside a guest such as Black Sheep on handpump, and they've ten wines by the glass, and 30 malt whiskies. *(Recommended by Gerry and Rosemary Dobson, Ian Phillips, Prof Keith and Mrs Jane Barber, A P Seymour, Dave Braisted, Paul and Margaret Baker, Mike and Mary Carter, Janet and Peter Race, Jo Lilley, Simon Calvert, Peter Fitton, Comus and Sarah Elliott, Andy Sinden, Louise Harrington, Lynda and Trevor Smith)*

Free house ~ Licensee Howard Hill-Lines ~ Real ale ~ Bar food (12-2.30, 6.30-9.30) ~ Restaurant ~ (01299) 270372 ~ Children in eating area of bar ~ Open 12-3, 6-11; 11-11 Sat-Sun; 12-3, 6-11(10.30 Sun)Sat in winter ~ Bedrooms: £49.50B/£85B

IRONBRIDGE SJ6704 Map 6 🏠
Malthouse ♀ ⊯
The Wharfage (bottom road alongside Severn)

The buzzy, vibrant atmosphere and spotless interior make this 18th-c former malthouse stand out, and the beer and food are good too. The spacious bar is broken up by pine beams and iron pillars, and has lots of scrubbed light wooden tables with candles; piped music. Appropriately informal, the bar menu includes dishes such as pesto and parmesan pasta (£3.75), minute steak and blue cheese baguette (£5.50), ham and cheddar ploughman's platter (£5.95), egg noodles with various flavours (from £6.50), mild and creamy chicken curry (£7.50), cheeseburger or poached salmon salad (£7.95), and sirloin steak (£9.95), with puddings such as chocolate cake with Baileys (£3.50); they have a good children's menu (£4.95). The atmosphere is quite different in the recently refurbished restaurant (along with the eating area of the bar it's no smoking), which has a much more elaborate menu. Fullers Hock and Scottish Courage Best and Directors are well kept on handpump, and they've a wide choice of wines including several by the glass; flexible and friendly service. There are a few tables outside in front (beware, they retain your credit card if you eat in the bar). *(Recommended by Michael and Alison Sandy, Kevin Thomas, Nina Randall, M Joyner, Pamela and Merlyn Horswell, Bob)*

Malthouse Pubs Ironbridge Ltd ~ Lease Alex and Andrea Nicoll ~ Real ale ~ Bar food (12-2, 6-9.30 (all day summer weekends)) ~ Restaurant ~ (01952) 433712 ~ Children welcome ~ Live jazz and world music two evenings a week ~ Open 11-11; 12-10.30 Sun; 11-3, 5-11 weekdays in winter ~ Bedrooms: /£79B

LUDLOW SO5174 Map 4
Church Inn 🍺
Church Street, behind Butter Cross

Right in the middle of one of England's most satisfying country towns, this much-liked old inn makes an ideal stopping point, and they've recently installed a camera obscura here and upstairs lounge that make the most of the views. They serve eight well kept real ales including Hobsons Mild and Town Crier, Hook Norton Old Hooky, Ringwood Old Thumper, Weetwood Eastgate, Wye Valley Bitter and a couple of swiftly changing guests on handpump; also 14 malt whiskies and country wines. In summer you can get three different types of Pimms, while in winter there's mulled wine and hot toddy, and they do a roaring trade in tea and coffee too. Appealingly decorated, with comfortable banquettes in cosy alcoves off the island bar, and pews and stripped stonework from the church (part of the bar is a pulpit), the interior is divided into three areas; hops hang from the heavy beams, daily papers and piped music. There are displays of old photographic equipment, plants on windowsills, and church prints in the no smoking side room; a long central area with a fine stone fireplace (good winter fires) leads to lavatories. The more basic side bar has old black and white photos of the town. The civilised no smoking upstairs lounge has vaulted ceilings and long windows overlooking the church, display cases of glass, china and old bottles, and musical instruments on the walls, along with a mix of new and old pictures. Service is friendly and relaxed, the pub is popular with locals (the landlord is the town's former mayor), and there's a cheerful atmosphere. Enjoyable sensible food (they make good use of local suppliers) could include lunchtime snacks such as sandwiches (from £3.50, baguettes from £3.95), filled baked potatoes (£4.95) and ploughman's (£7.95), with other dishes such as soup (£3.50), garlic mushrooms with melted brie (£3.75), vegetable casserole with dumplings (£6.25), mixed fish platter or chicken tikka (£6.95) and rack of lamb with garlic and rosemary (£8.25), with a short choice of puddings such as bread and butter pudding (£3.75); children's meals (£3.25). The restaurant is no smoking. The bedrooms are simple but comfortable; good breakfasts. Car parking is some way off. *(Recommended by John Whitehead, Kerry Law, Simon Smith, Mark Rogers, MLR, Chris Flynn, Wendy Jones, Kevin Thorpe, Tracey and Stephen Groves, Christopher J Darwent, Ian Phillips, Pam and John Smith, Joe Green, J C Poley, Reg Fowle, Helen Rickwood, Jo Lilley, Simon Calvert, Gwyn and Anne Wake, Di and Mike Gillam, Richard Waller, Pauline Smith, Paul and Gloria Howell, JMM)*

Free house ~ Licensee Graham Willson-Lloyd ~ Real ale ~ Bar food (12-2(3 Sat, 3.30 Sun), 6.30-9) ~ Restaurant ~ (01584) 872174 ~ Children welcome ~ Dogs welcome ~ Singer/guitarist second Weds in month ~ Open 11-11; 12-10.30 Sun ~ Bedrooms: £70S/£70S(£80B)

Unicorn

Corve Street – the quiet bottom end, beyond where it leaves the main road to Shrewsbury

At the bottom of the town, this prettily placed white-fronted 17th-c inn adjoins a row of black and white cottages and the atmosphere is appealing as soon as you walk through the door. The solidly beamed and partly panelled bar with its huge log fire in a big stone fireplace gives a real feel of age, and there's often a pleasant mix of locals and visitors, maybe some playing dominoes. Four real ales such as Fullers London Pride and Wye Valley Bitter, and a couple of guests such as Hancocks HB and Robinsons Union are well kept on handpump, and they have several malt whiskies; it can get smoky. Generously served food (available in the bar or restaurant) could include home-made soup (£3.25), sandwiches (from £3.40), garlic mushrooms (£4.50), beer-battered cod (£7.75), greek-style lamb (£7.95), gammon and egg (£8.25), bass (£12.75), lamb shrewsbury or fish of the day (£13.50), chateaubriand medley for two (£32.95) and seafood medley for two (£34.95), with tasty puddings such as treacle sponge or ginger nut, sherry and almond gateau (£3.75). The timbered candlelit dining areas are no smoking. Parking in this picturesque town may be tricky. Tables on the terrace shelter pleasantly among willow trees by the modest River Corve. *(Recommended by Chris Flynn, Wendy Jones, Mark Rogers, Joe Green, Dr John Henderson, Dr Graham Thorpe, Jo Lilley, Simon Calvert, A G Roby, TOH, Paul and Gloria Howell, Andy Hazeldine)*

Free house ~ Licensees Mike and Rita Knox ~ Real ale ~ Bar food (12-2.15, 6(7 Sun)-9.15) ~ Restaurant ~ (01584) 873555 ~ Well behaved children in eating area of bar and restaurant ~ Dogs welcome ~ Irish live music night third Fri of month ~ Open 12-3, 6-11; 12-3.30, 6.30-10.30 Sun

MUCH WENLOCK SO6299 Map 4

George & Dragon 🍺

High Street (A458)

Open all day, this is a pleasant and atmospheric place to enjoy one of five real ales that include Greene King Abbot and PA, Hobsons Town Crier, Timothy Taylors Landlord and a guest, all well kept on handpump; they also have country wines and farmhouse cider. The cosy rooms house an impressive array of pub paraphernalia, including old brewery and cigarette advertisements, bottle labels and beer trays, and George-and-the-Dragon pictures, as well as around 500 jugs hanging from the beams. Furnishings such as antique settles are among more conventional seats, and there are a couple of attractive Victorian fireplaces (with coal-effect gas fires). At the back is the no smoking restaurant. The pub is popular with locals, and the pleasant atmosphere is helped along by the courteous landlord. The enjoyable bar food could include soup (£4.25), sandwiches (from £4.25), ploughman's (£5.95), leek and mushroom bake, thai curry or tasty local faggots and onion gravy (£6.50), salmon fillet (£9.95), dover or lemon sole (£11.95-£15.95), rack of lamb (£12.95) and roast crispy duck (£13.95), with puddings such as apple crumble (£4.25); they do a Sunday roast (£7.25) and occasionally have live music. *(Recommended by Michael and Alison Sandy, Sarah and Peter Gooderham, David and Sally Cullen, Mr and Mrs J R Shrimpton, Reg Fowle, Helen Rickwood, Pete Baker, Mr and Mrs A B Moore, Paul and Gloria Howell)*

Punch ~ Lease Milton Monk ~ Real ale ~ Bar food (12-2, 6-9) ~ Restaurant ~ (01952) 727077 ~ Children in eating area of bar and restaurant ~ Occasional live music ~ Open 12-11(10.30 Sun); 12-3, 6-11(10.30 Sun) winter

Talbot 🛏

High Street (A458)

Dating back to 1360, this inn was once part of Wenlock Abbey, the ruins of which still stand nearby. The several neatly kept areas have low ceilings, and comfortable red tapestry button-back wall banquettes around their tables. The walls are decorated with prints of fish and brewery memorabilia, and there are art deco-style lamps and gleaming brasses. Bass and Woods Shropshire Lad are well kept alongside a guest like Charles Wells Bombardier on handpump, and they've several malt whiskies, and half a dozen wines by the glass; quiet piped music. The lunchtime menu has standard bar food such as soup (£3.60), sandwiches (from £3.20, baguettes from £4.25), filled baked potatoes (from £4.50), thai fishcakes or lasagne (£7.50), and sirloin steak (£10.95), and there is a more elaborate (and not as cheap) evening menu; the dining area is no smoking. It also has a little courtyard with green metal and wood garden furniture and pretty flower tubs. There's a cheap car park close by. *(Recommended by Margaret Dickinson, Blaise Vyner, Brian and Jacky Wilson, Tracey and Stephen Groves, John Oates, Denise Walton, Kevin Thorpe, Jim and Maggie Cowell, John Whitehead, Derek and Sylvia Stephenson, M Joyner, Mrs Catherine Draper, A G Roby)*

Free house ~ Licensees Mark and Maggie Tennant ~ Real ale ~ Bar food (12-2.30, 7-9.15) ~ Restaurant ~ (01952) 727077 ~ Children welcome ~ Open 11-3, 6-11; 11-11 Sat; 12-4, 7-11 Sun; 11-3, 6-11 Sat winter ~ Bedrooms: £40B/£80B

NORBURY SO3692 Map 6

Sun 🛏

Off A488 or A489 NE of Bishop's Castle; OS Sheet 137 map reference 363928

Worth seeking for its food and its lovely location, this admirably well run dining pub is in a peaceful village amid splendid walking country; the dramatically craggy Stiperstones ridge can be reached from here. A proper tiled-floor bar has settees and Victorian tables and chairs, cushioned stone seats along the wall by the gas stove, and a few mysterious implements (the kind that it's fun to guess about) on its neat white walls; shove-ha'penny and dominoes. Wye Valley Bitter and maybe a guest such as Woods are kept on handpump under a light blanket pressure, and they have several malts and decent house wines. The restaurant side has a charming lounge with button-back leather wing chairs, easy chairs and a chesterfield on its deep-pile green carpet. The log fire, nice lighting, comfortable seats, willow-pattern china on the dark oak dresser, fresh flowers, candles and magazines quickly make you feel at home; service is friendly. The elegantly furnished no smoking dining room serves a shortish choice of good food. The blackboard bar menu (also fairly short) might typically include baguettes (from £3.95), cumberland sausage (£7.50), smoked trout or scampi (£8.50) and rump steak (£10.75); they also have an evening restaurant menu. There are tables outside by a pond. *(Recommended by David Field, Kevin Thorpe, Reg Fowle, Helen Rickwood, Paul Davies, Brian and Jacky Wilson)*

Free house ~ Licensee Carol Cahan ~ Real ale ~ Bar food (7-9; 12-2 Sun, and summer Sats) ~ Restaurant ~ (01588) 650680 ~ Children welcome in eating area and in restaurant; over-12s only in restaurant in evening ~ Dogs allowed in bar ~ Open 7-11(10.30 winter); 12-2, 7-11 Sat; 12-3 Sun; closed Sat lunchtime in winter, Sun evening and Mon (exc for residents) ~ Bedrooms: /£70S

NORTON SJ7200 Map 4

Hundred House ♀

A442 Telford—Bridgnorth

Sensitively refurbished, this pleasantly chatty old place stands by the bowling green. Inside bunches of fresh flowers brighten the tables and counter in the neatly kept bar, and there are hops and huge bunches of dried flowers and herbs hanging from beams; there's a good chatty atmosphere. Handsome fireplaces have log fires or working coalbrookdale ranges (one has a great Jacobean arch with fine old black cooking pots), and a variety of interesting chairs and settles with some long colourful patchwork leather cushions set out around sewing-machine tables. Steps lead up past a little balustrade to a partly panelled eating area, where the stripped brickwork looks older than that elsewhere. The main dining room and one other room are no smoking; piped music. Davenports Bitter, Heritage Bitter and Mild (the last two brewed especially for them by a small brewery) are well kept on handpump alongside a guest such as Highgates Saddlers, and they've also an extensive wine list with house wines by the carafe, half carafe and big or small glass. Bar food includes soup (£3.95), greek salad (£5.95, or £9.95 as a main course), lasagne (£7.95), speciality sausage and mash, steak and kidney pie or thai chicken curry (£8.95), 10oz rib-eye steak (£12.95), specials such as fried sardines stuffed with garlic and mushroom with sweet chilli sauce (£13.95) and puddings such as raspberry crème brûlée (£5.95). You must book for the restaurant, though you can eat from its (not cheap) menu in the bar for items such as breast of gressingham duck or roast rack of lamb (£17.95). Some readers have reported service to be slow at times. The gardens have old-fashioned roses, trees, herbaceous plants, and a big working herb garden that supplies the kitchen – you can buy bags of their herbs for £1 and the money goes to charity. *(Recommended by Oliver and Sue Rowell, John H Franklin, A P Seymour, Lynda and Trevor Smith, Patrick and Phillipa Vickery, Simon Jones, Pamela and Merlyn Horswell, Rosemary Cladingbowl, A Darroch Harkness)*

Free house ~ Licensees Henry, Sylvia, Stuart and David Phillips ~ Real ale ~ Bar food (12-2.30) ~ Restaurant ~ (01952) 730353 ~ Children welcome ~ Dogs allowed in bedrooms ~ Open 11-3, 5.30-11(7-10.30 Sun); closed 25-26 Dec evenings ~ Bedrooms: £69B/£99B

PICKLESCOTT SO4399 Map 6

Bottle & Glass

Village signposted off A49 N of Church Stretton

The fire keeps going all year in the small beamed and quarry-tiled candlelit bar of this 16th-c pub, which has two cats, Hello and Cookie. The licensees have recently added a lounge, dining area and library area (for dining or sitting in), each with its own open fire. There are a few picnic-sets in front (they're hoping to create more of a terrace soon) and the pub has a lovely position 1,000 feet above sea level and near the Long Mynd. The jovial old-school landlord has celebrated his 40th year in the trade, and his 30th as a licensee; he works hard to make sure everyone is happy, and on our visit effortlessly ran the bar while striking up conversations with various customers, many of whom were soon chatting to each other as if they were old friends (ask him to tell you about the antics of the resident ghost of the former landlord, Victor). Very good home-made bar food (promptly served, in hearty helpings) might include lunchtime baps (£4.50) and ploughman's (£4.50) as well as soup (£3.50), stilton, pork and celery pâté (£4.25), sausage and mash (£8.50), steak, kidney and Guinness pie or fish pie (£8.95) and rosemary and garlic crusted rack of lamb with red wine, honey and redcurrant sauce (£14). Well kept Hobsons, Woods Shropshire Lad and a changing guest beer such as Wadsworth 6X on handpump; unobtrusive piped music. Around half the pub is no smoking. Disabled access and loo. *(Recommended by Sean Mulholland, J C Brittain-Long, Pete Yearsley, Ken Marshall)*

Free house ~ Licensees Paul and Jo Stretton-Downes ~ Real ale ~ Bar food (12-2, 7-9; not

Sun evening) ~ Restaurant ~ (01694) 751345 ~ Children over 10 welcome except in bars ~ Dogs allowed in bar ~ Open 12-2.30, 6-11(7-10.30 Sun)

SHREWSBURY SJ4912 Map 6

Armoury ⑪ ♀ ◖

Victoria Quay, Victoria Avenue

In an 18th-c former warehouse, this friendly, lively and efficiently run open-plan pub attracts lots of people in the evenings and at weekends, and there may be queues. Long runs of big arched windows in the uniform red brick frontages have views across the broad river at the back, and there are interspersed hanging baskets and smart coach lights at the front. Spacious and light, the appealing open-plan interior has a mix of wood tables and chairs on expanses of stripped wood floors, a dominating display of floor-to-ceiling books on two huge walls, a grand stone fireplace at one end, and masses of old prints mounted edge to edge on the stripped brick walls. Colonial-style fans whirr away on the ceilings, which are supported by occasional green-painted standing timbers, and glass cabinets display collections of explosives and shells. The long bar counter has a terrific choice of drinks, and besides well kept Boddingtons, a seasonal brew from Salopian and Woods Shropshire Lad, they've up to five changing guest beers from brewers such as Archers, Northumberland and Oakham on handpump. If beer is not your thing, you can also choose from a tempting wine list (with 16 by the glass), around 50 malt whiskies, a dozen different gins, lots of rums and vodkas, a variety of brandies, and some unusual liqueurs. Superbly cooked bar food, from an interesting menu, includes tasty soup (£3.95), sandwiches with imaginative fillings (from £4.25), peppered chicken strips with rosemary and baby leaf salad (£6.95), local sausages and mash (£7.95), ploughman's or vegetable stew with rice (£8.95), braised shoulder of shropshire lamb (£12.95) with puddings such as rhubarb and apple crumble and sticky toffee pudding (from £3.95). Tables at one end are laid out for eating, and part of the eating area is no smoking. The pub doesn't have its own parking, but there are plenty of places nearby. (Recommended by Simon and Mandy King, Steve Whalley, Derek and Sylvia Stephenson, M Joyner, Ian Phillips, Tracey and Stephen Groves, Paul and Gloria Howell, Joe Green)

Brunning & Price ~ Manager Andy Barker ~ Real ale ~ Bar food (12-9.30(9 Sun)) ~ (01743) 340525 ~ Children in eating area of bar ~ Open 12-11(10.30 Sun); closed 24 Dec evening, 25-26 Dec

WENTNOR SO3893 Map 6

Crown ⇚

Village and pub signposted (not very clearly) off A489 a few miles NW of junction with A49

Seats on the back lawn give charming views over the Long Mynd from this 16th-c country inn. Much of the main bar area is laid for eating; one end has a snug area with pictures and fixed seating, and there are good log fires. Hobsons Best and Mild, and a couple of changing guests such as Salopian Shropshire Gold and Woods Shropshire Lad are well kept on handpump, and they have decent wines, along with a good choice of malt whiskies; piped music, dominoes and cribbage. Tasty bar food such as sandwiches (from £3.75), soup (£2.95), smoked salmon and dill quiche (£5.50), chicken with leek and stilton sauce or cod (£6.95), salads or scampi (£7.25), home-made pie such as venison or minced lamb (£7.95), roast duck (£12.95) and home-made puddings such as lemon cheesecake or chocolate and ginger truffle slice (£3.50); pleasant service. The cosy beamed restaurant is no smoking. The location and the good value pretty bedrooms make this a nice place for a night's stay. There's plenty of space for parking. (Recommended by Ian Phillips, Kevin Thorpe, Reg Fowle, Helen Rickwood, TOH, Philip and Susan Philcox, Steve Whalley)

Free house ~ Licensees Mike and Chris Brown ~ Real ale ~ Bar food (12-2, 6-9; all day weekends) ~ Restaurant ~ (01588) 650613 ~ Children in eating area of bar and restaurant ~ Open 12-3, 6-11; 12-11 Sat; 12-10.30 Sun ~ Bedrooms: £35B/£60B

WISTANSTOW SO4385 Map 6
Plough ⬛

Village signposted off A49 and A489 N of Craven Arms

It's worth making a pilgrimage to this corner of Shropshire to find this pleasant pub right next to Woods brewery. Woods Parish, Plough Special, Shropshire Lad and seasonal ales are very well kept on handpump (you can buy bottles of Woods beer to take away) as well as Weston's cider. Straightforward bar food on the lunchtime menu might include soup (£3.50), fresh baguettes (£5.75), home-made pies such as steak and kidney (£7), vegetable lasagne (£7.25), Woods beer-battered cod (£7.50) and sirloin steak (£10.95); in the evening the food, served in both the bar and restaurant, is more elaborate and may feature crab and chilli linguini (£10.50), shropshire lamb chops with shrewsbury sauce (£11.25) and fillet steak rossini (£14.95); puddings are all home-made (£4). The pub is simply furnished with high rafters and cream walls, and a russet turkey carpet, oak or mahogany tables and chairs and welsh dressers to give the modernised bar a more homely feel. The games area has darts, pool and dominoes; piped music. There are some tables under cocktail parasols outside, and the licensee is planning to add a conservatory and another bar. *(Recommended by Stan Edwards, John Evans, MLR, J C Poley, Tracey and Stephen Groves, John Whitehead, A G Roby, TOH, Paul and Gloria Howell)*

Woods ~ Lease Richard Sys ~ Real ale ~ Bar food (12-2.30, 6-9(6.30-9 Sun)) ~ Restaurant ~ (01588) 673251 ~ Children welcome until 9pm ~ Dogs allowed in bar ~ Open 12-3, 6-11; 12-3, 6.30-10.30 Sun; closed Mon (exc bank hols)

LUCKY DIP

Besides the fully inspected pubs, you might like to try these Lucky Dips recommended to us and described by readers (if you do, please send us reports: www.goodguides.co.uk).

ALBRIGHTON [SJ4918]
Old Bush [High St]: Banks's and Marstons Pedigree, decent limited bar food, wider reasonably priced restaurant choice *(Francis Johnston)*
ALL STRETTON [SO4595]
Yew Tree [Shrewsbury Rd (B4370)]: Comfortable neatly kept pub with houseplants and lots of interesting watercolours, well kept Hobsons Best and Wye Valley Butty Bach, good log fire, pleasant licensee, bookable dining room (not always open), lively public bar with darts, pub cats; children welcome, small village handy for Long Mynd, cl Tues *(Margaret Dickinson, Reg Fowle, Helen Rickwood, TOH)*
ATCHAM [SJ5409]
☆ *Mytton & Mermaid*: Comfortable and friendly, with good food from panini to guinea fowl in bar and relaxed easy-going restaurant, well kept Greene King Ruddles and Woods Shropshire Lad, good wine choice, helpful staff, some theme nights; pleasant Severn-view bedrooms, nice setting opp entrance to Attingham Park (NT) *(Joan and Tony Walker, Mr and Mrs F Carroll, Francis Johnston)*
BRIDGNORTH [SO7193]
Bear [Northgate (B4373)]: Former coaching inn with well kept ales such as Hop Back Summer Lightning and Timothy Taylors Landlord, attractively priced pubby lunchtime food (not Sun) from sandwiches up, decent wines by the glass, helpful licensees, two

unpretentious bars with wall banquettes and a mix of other furnishings; french windows to small sheltered lawn with picnic-sets, bedrooms *(Gill and Tony Morriss, LYM)*
Bell & Talbot [Salop St (former A458 towards Shrewsbury)]: Charming early 19th-c stone building with log fires each end of L-shaped main room, record sleeves, guitars and other instruments covering ceiling, well kept Holdens and other local beers, smaller room off and interesting back conservatory, no machines; well chosen piped music, live bands wknds; cl wkdy lunchtimes *(Gill and Tony Morriss, Paul and Gloria Howell)*
Friars [St Marys St, Central Ct (down passage from High Street)]: Peaceful town pub in quaint location off courtyard, three well kept beers, reasonably priced simple food, good coffee; piped music; bedrooms *(Richard Waller, Pauline Smith)*
Halfway House [Cleobury Rd (B4363 S)]: Heavily black-beamed bar with settles, wheelback chairs and big fireplace, some interesting ancient wall decoration, friendly staff and good pubby atmosphere, good value pubby food with some imaginative dishes in dining lounge and pleasant back conservatory with views, well kept local ales such as Woods Shropshire Lad, good wines by the glass, several dozen malt whiskies; limited disabled access; garden with barbecue, good walks, good value comfortable bedrooms – they organise activity holidays *(Martin and Pauline Jennings, Janice Towers)*

☆ *Railwaymans Arms* [Severn Valley Station, Hollybush Rd (off A458 towards Stourbridge)]: Well kept Bathams, Hobsons and interesting changing guest beers at a good price in chatty old-fashioned converted waiting-room at Severn Valley steam railway terminus, bustling on summer days; coal fire, station nameplates, superb mirror over fireplace, tables out on platform; may be simple summer snacks and good baguettes, children welcome, wheelchair access; the train to Kidderminster (another bar there) has an all-day bar and bookable Sun lunches *(Gill and Tony Morriss, Tracey and Stephen Groves, the Didler, LYM, Richard Waller, Pauline Smith, Paul and Gloria Howell)*

BROOME [SO4081]

☆ *Engine & Tender*: Homely bar with well kept Woods from art deco servery, railway memorabilia and other bric-a-brac, cosy corners with tables for eating, also quite extensive restaurant with interesting collection of pottery inc teapots and shelves of jugs, good freshly made food (not Mon) inc generous Sun roast and good puddings, good value wines, cheerful helpful unhurried service, lushly planted conservatory, games room with pool and glassed-over well; caravan site with hook-up points and showers, nice countryside *(Mrs J Wood, Michael Hyde)*

BROSELEY [SJ6701]

Duke of York [Hockley Rd]: Friendly pub with popular bar, enjoyable food in quiet restaurant *(Tony Brace)*

☆ *Pheasant* [Church St]: Appealing beamed and timbered dining pub smartly done up in shabby-chic style, small choice of good imaginative restaurant food inc seasonal game, welcoming individualistic licensees, good wines (no list, just what they have at the moment), real ales, small friendly tiled-floor bar with gleaming copperware, two rooms with sturdy built-in seats, big stripped tables on oak boards, large oil paintings, log fire, fresh flowers, candles and gas lamps; tasteful bedrooms, good breakfast; cl lunchtimes exc Sun, also Sun/Mon evenings *(John and Lynn Norcliffe, Robert J Fisk-Moore)*

BUCKNELL [SO3574]

☆ *Baron of Beef* [Chapel Lawn Rd; just off B4367 Knighton Rd]: Smartly decorated dining pub with good bar food inc enterprising dishes, largish upstairs restaurant with own bar and popular wknd carvery, big log fire in front bar, back lounge with fresh flowers, interesting prints, rustic memorabilia inc grindstone and cider press, well kept Greene King IPA, Hobsons and Woods, farm cider, decent house wines; views from big garden with play area *(Reg Fowle, Helen Rickwood)*

BURWARTON [SO6185]

☆ *Boyne Arms* [B4364 Bridgnorth—Ludlow]: Imposing Georgian coaching inn with imaginative generous good value food, friendly helpful staff, changing well kept ales such as Bass and local Hobsons and Woods, cheerfully unassuming local atmosphere, restaurant, public bar with pool; tables in large garden

with good timber adventure playground *(DC, Robin and Tricia Walker, Paul and Gloria Howell)*

CHURCH ASTON [SJ7317]

Last [A518 Newport—Wellington, outside village]: Pleasant staff, wide range of enjoyable traditional food *(D Travis)*

CLEOBURY MORTIMER [SO6775]

Royal Fountain [Church St]: Friendly pub with well kept real ale, home-made food using some local produce, sensibly short wine list; garden tables *(Joe Green)*

Talbot [Talbot Sq]: Unpretentious old pub with plentiful enjoyable food at bargain prices inc popular family Sun lunch, well kept Hobsons Town Crier *(Joe Green)*

CLUN [SO3081]

☆ *Sun* [High St]: Beamed and timbered Tudor pub with some sturdy antique furnishings, modern paintings and older prints, enormous open fire in lively flagstoned public bar with darts, cards and dominoes, good value generous blackboard food in larger carpeted lounge bar, well kept Banks's Bitter and Original and Hobsons Best, charming landlady; children allowed in eating area, tables in sheltered well planted back garden with terrace, lovely village, nice bedrooms, cl Weds lunchtime *(the Didler, BB, Kevin Thorpe)*

☆ *White Horse* [Market Sq]: Well laid out, friendly and neatly kept low-beamed local with inglenook and open woodburner, helpful service, good value food, half a dozen well kept and well priced changing ales such as Hobsons, Salopian, Six Bells and Wye Valley, Weston's farm cider, good coffee, books and pub games near front, pool table and games machine far end; children welcome, pavement tables in front, small back garden, bedrooms, open all day *(Gill and Tony Morriss, Martin Lewis, Tracey and Stephen Groves, Ian and Joan Blackwell, Nigel Long)*

COALBROOKDALE [SJ6704]

☆ *Coalbrookdale Inn* [Wellington Rd, opp Museum of Iron]: Handsome dark brick 18th-c pub doing well under welcoming new management, simple bustling tiled-floor bar with local pictures, six well kept quickly changing ales from square counter, good value often imaginative food using local meats, cheeses etc in bar and separate refurbished restaurant, good log fire, farm ciders, country wines, cheerful mix of people, piano, naughty beach murals in lavatories; bar can be smoky, long flight of steps to entrance; dogs welcome, a few tables outside, opens noon *(Michael and Alison Sandy, BB, the Didler, Richard Tosswill, Fred and Lorraine Gill, M Joyner)*

COALPORT [SJ6903]

☆ *Boat* [Ferry Rd, Jackfield; nr Mawes Craft Centre]: Long but cosy 18th-c quarry-tiled bar, coal fire in lovely range, reasonably priced good food inc meat, game and cheeses and good value Sun lunch, welcoming service, well kept Banks's Bitter and Mild and related beers, Weston's farm cider, darts, restaurant extension planned; summer barbecues on big tree-shaded lawn, in delightful if floodable part of Severn Gorge, footbridge making it handy for Coalport China Museum *(Michael and Alison Sandy, BB, G A and G V M A Taylor, the Didler, Fred and Lorraine Gill)*

COCKSHUTT [SJ4329]

Leaking Tap [A528 Ellesmere—Shrewsbury]: Friendly new licensees doing enjoyable typical pub food inc good Sun lunch *(Mr and Mrs J Carroll)*

CORFTON [SO4985]

☆ *Sun* [B4368 Much Wenlock—Craven Arms]: Unpretentious two-bar country local with its own well kept Corvedale ales from brewery behind (takeaways and tours available), a guest beer too, particularly friendly chatty landlord, ample sensibly priced food using local produce from generous baguettes to bargain Sun lunch, lots of breweriana, dining room with no smoking area and covered well, public bar with internet access as well as darts and pool, tourist information; piped music; particularly good disabled access throughout, tables on terrace and in good-sized garden with good play area *(BB, John Whitehead, Kevin Thorpe, Michael and Jenny Back, MLR, Gwyn and Anne Wake, Paul and Gloria Howell)*

CRESSAGE [SJ5904]

☆ *Riverside* [A458 NW, nr Cound]: Spacious pub/hotel, light and airy, with lovely views of Severn from roomy conservatory and tables in big terraced garden, pleasant mix of furnishings inside, relaxed atmosphere, enjoyable food from lunchtime baguettes to salmon and steak, reasonable prices, interesting wine choice, two or three real ales such as Salopian Shropshire Gold; old-fashioned inexpensive bedrooms, open all day wknds *(Michael and Alison Sandy, Mrs Susan Pritchard, LYM, Mike and Mary Carter)*

DORRINGTON [SJ4703]

Bridge Inn [A49 N]: Streamside pub with settees and armchairs as well as plenty of tables and chairs in roomy lounge bar, well spaced tables in conservatory restaurant, enjoyable wholesome food inc bar snacks and bargain lunches inc popular three-course Sun lunch; caravan spaces in paddock behind *(TOH)*

ELLESMERE [SJ3934]

☆ *Black Lion* [Scotland St; back car park on A495]: Good value simple cheap substantial food all day inc popular OAP bargains (also for children), pleasantly relaxed and well run beamed bar with interesting décor and some nice unusual features such as the traditional wood-and-glass screen along its tiled entrance corridor, quiet and comfortable roomy dining room, prompt polite service, well kept Marstons Bitter, restaurant; piped music; bedrooms, handy car park, not far from canal wharf *(Peter and Audrey Dowsett, Pamela and Merlyn Horswell, BB)*

FRODESLEY [SJ5101]

Swan [just off A49 S of Dorrington]: Restaurantly pub with interesting varied bistro menu inc light brasserie dishes, good aberdeen angus chargrills and Sun lunch, elegant dining room with two log fires, small bar; tables

outside, cl lunchtime Mon–Weds *(Nigel Long)*

HALFWAY HOUSE [SJ3411]

Seven Stars [A458 Shrewsbury—Welshpool]: Spotless and unspoilt small bar with two high-backed settles by the gas fire, well kept ales such as Banks's or Marstons Pedigree tapped from casks in the friendly licensee's kitchen area, no food or music *(the Didler, RWC)*

HAMPTON LOADE [SO7486]

River & Rail: Welcoming pub with wide choice of enjoyable fresh food, attentive family service, real ale, modern surroundings; plenty of seating outside overlooking River Severn and steam railway *(Dr and Mrs James Stewart, Juliet Browning)*

HEATHTON [SO8192]

☆ *Old Gate* [off B4176 W of Wombourn]: 17th-c, very popular for fresh well prepared food from lunchtime baguettes (not Sun, no food Sun evening) to traditional favourites and some interesting specials; plenty of tables packed into the two small main rooms, two open fires, reddish décor (reflecting landlord's enthusiasm for Manchester United), friendly service, well kept Enville, Greene King Abbot, Olde Swan Entire and perhaps a guest beer, farm cider, wines from their own burgundy vineyard, golden retriever called Cromwell; children very welcome, colourful garden with picnic-sets and play equipment, cl Mon *(LYM, TOH)*

HINSTOCK [SJ6927]

Falcon [just off A41 9 miles N of Newport; Wood Lane]: Friendly service, four well kept ales, enjoyable and interesting reasonably priced food in bar and restaurant from generous open sandwiches up, decent wines and malt whiskies *(Bill and Celia Witts)*

HODNET [SJ6128]

☆ *Bear* [Drayton Rd (A53)]: Relaxing refuge from the busy road, small beamed quarry-tiled bar with log fire and Courage Directors, Theakstons Best and Youngs Special, broad arch to rambling open-plan carpeted main area with blond seats and tables set for the good range of reasonably priced well presented food from sandwiches up, well filled puddings cabinet, snug end alcoves with heavy 16th-c beams and timbers, friendly helpful staff, decent wines; may be faint piped radio; children welcome (high chairs and child-size cutlery), six good value bedrooms, opp Hodnet Hall gardens and handy for Hawkstone Park, open all day *(Anthony Barnes, BB, Francis Johnston)*

IRONBRIDGE [SJ6703]

Bird in Hand [Waterloo St (B4373 towards Broseley)]: Plush banquettes and well spaced tables, wide choice of enjoyable promptly served food from baked potatoes and interesting starters to good steaks, friendly helpful licensees, two well kept changing ales, brasses, mirrors and prints; steps up from road, tables on terrace and lawn in lovely spot above wooded gorge, comfortable bedrooms *(Michael and Alison Sandy)*

Golden Ball [Newbridge Rd/Wesley Rd, off Madeley Hill]: Smart and interesting partly

Elizabethan local at the top of the town, good views and atmosphere, helpful landlord and friendly staff, three well kept changing ales such as Timothy Taylors Landlord, good blackboard choice of good value substantial food from sandwiches and baguettes to Sun roasts in low-beamed bar or neat back restaurant (very busy Fri/Sat night), real fire; TV corner; children welcome, sheltered picnic-sets with more out in front, pleasant terraced walk down to river, comfortable bedrooms, open all day wknds *(Michael and Alison Sandy, Richard Tosswill, John Dwane)*

Horse & Jockey [Jockey Bank, off Madeley rd]: Cosy and welcoming, with emphasis on sensibly priced home-cooking inc real steak and kidney pie and good steaks, thriving atmosphere, well kept ales such as Marstons and Robinsons; open during meal times only, best to book evenings *(Michael and Alison Sandy, Richard Tosswill)*

Robin Hood [Waterloo St]: Popular Severn-side pub now owned by Holdens, their ales kept well, five comfortable and attractive linked rooms with various alcoves inc barrel-vaulted dining room, lots of gleaming brass and old clocks, wide choice of usual food served noon till 6 from sandwiches to Sun carvery, helpful staff; attractive seating area out in front, nice setting handy for museums, bedrooms, good breakfast *(Michael and Alison Sandy, Richard Waller, Pauline Smith, John Dwane)*

Swan [Wharfage]: Friendly ex-warehouse under same management as neighbouring Malthouse, more traditional and informal in style, with stripped wood and lots of alcoves, well kept ales and a continental beer on tap, attractively served sensibly priced bistro-type food, separate restaurant; tables outside *(M Joyner, Fred and Lorraine Gill)*

LEEBOTWOOD [SO4798]

Pound [A49 Church Stretton—Shrewsbury]: Modernised thatched 16th-c pub reopened under new management, banquettes and log-effect gas fire in busy but roomy carpeted main bar, big comfortable no smoking restaurant area with partly no smoking smaller bar acting as overflow, well kept Greene King Abbot, decent wines; well reproduced piped music; garden tables *(BB, Reg Fowle, Helen Rickwood)*

LEINTWARDINE [SO4175]

Jolly Frog [Toddings; A4113 out towards Ludlow]: Distinctive yellow-green pub/bistro with emphasis on good imaginative food esp fish, sensible prices and early evening bargains, cosy informal atmosphere, mix of table sizes (high chairs for small children), log fire, a beer brewed for them, good wine list, relaxed friendly and informative service, quirky décor, no smoking restaurant; may be unobtrusive piped jazz *(Rodney and Norma Stubington, Peter and Jean Hoare)*

LITTLE STRETTON [SO4491]

Green Dragon [village well signed off A49]: Well kept Bass, Wadworths 6X, Woods Shropshire Lad and quickly changing guest beers, reasonably priced food from baguettes up, cheap house wine, children in eating area and restaurant; tables outside, handy for Cardingmill Valley (NT) and Long Mynd *(G S R Cox, LYM, TOH)*

LONGVILLE [SO5393]

☆ *Longville Arms* [B4371 Church Stretton—Much Wenlock]: Two neat and spacious bars with beams, stripped stone and some oak panelling, warm friendly atmosphere, reasonably priced bar food from baguettes to steak, well kept ales such as Courage Directors, Theakstons Best and Woods Pot of Gold, large no smoking restaurant, adult games room with juke box, darts and pool; piped music; disabled facilities, children and dogs welcome, terraced side garden with good play area, lovely countryside, bedrooms, open all day wknds *(John Whitehead, Reg Fowle, Helen Rickwood, LYM, TOH)*

LUDLOW [SO5174]

Charlton Arms [Ludford Bridge]: Former coaching inn in great spot overlooking River Teme and the town, now taken over by landlord of the Church Inn (see main entries) and being extensively refurbished as this edition went to press – very promising, though during the works the operation was very restricted, with just sandwiches and well kept beers such as Ringwood Old Thumper; waterside garden, bedrooms (may be traffic noise), open all day *(Paul and Gloria Howell, Joe Green)*

Feathers [Bull Ring]: Superb timbered building, striking inside too with Jacobean panelling and carving, fine period furnishings, pleasant service; for a snack or drink you'll probably be diverted to a less distinguished side café-bar (good sandwiches and other decent bar food, Woods real ale); good parking, lift to comfortable bedrooms, not cheap *(Dr and Mrs A K Clarke, LYM, the Didler, Francis Johnston)*

Wheatsheaf [Lower Broad St]: Traditional 17th-c beamed pub spectacularly built into medieval town gate, spotless housekeeping, generous food using good local produce, well kept ales inc Woods Shropshire Lad, choice of farm cider, good value wines, restaurant; attractive bedrooms, warm and comfortable *(Joe Green)*

MARKET DRAYTON [SJ6832]

Four Alls Inn [Four Alls (A529, 2 miles S towards Woodseaves)]: Pub/restaurant based on 16th-c inn comfortably extended with motel and conference facilities, several low-beamed areas around longish bar with Enville Amadora, Charles Wells Bombardier and Woods Shropshire Lad, plenty of helpful cheerful staff, wide choice of reasonably priced food all day from sandwiches, baguettes and baked potatoes to full meals, carvery counter, decent wines and fresh coffee and tea, large free-standing open fire, daily papers, simple décor and dark wood furnishings; piped music, fruit machine; bedrooms, handy for Shropshire Union Canal, open all day *(Paul and Ursula Randall)*

MARSHBROOK [SO4489]

☆ *Station Hotel* [Marshbrook Industrial Estate signed over level crossing by B4370/A49, S of Church Stretton]: Quiet at lunchtime, lively in the evening, solidly refurbished and comfortably traditional on right, contemporary café-bar/restaurant on left; relaxed friendly atmosphere, well kept Boddingtons, Flowers Original and Salopian Shropshire Gold from bar's high-gloss counter, prompt attentive service, log fire, some stripped stone; good value food counter in extensive glass-fronted eating areas, good choice from warm baguettes through interesting light dishes to restaurant meals (worth booking), elegant metal-framed furniture on limestone flooring; piped music (Gloria Bax, BB, John Whitehead, TOH, Julian and Linda Cooke)

MARTON [SJ2802]

Sun [B4386 NE of Chirbury]: Good well presented food in good-sized helpings (but veg extra), attentive friendly service; new dining room extension (P Bottomley)

NEENTON [SO6387]

Pheasant [B4364 Bridgnorth—Ludlow]: Charming village pub with quick friendly service by hard-working licensees, well kept real ale, short choice of good reasonably priced food, open fires in panelled lounge, plenty of regulars; restaurant (DC, Theo, Anne and Jane Gaskin)

NESSCLIFFE [SJ3819]

☆ *Old Three Pigeons* [off A5 Shrewsbury—Oswestry (now bypassed)]: 16th-c pub with quaint and appealing dining area, wide blackboard choice of enjoyable reasonably priced meals (freshly made so may be quite a wait) inc bargains for two, plenty of fish and good puddings, quick service, well kept Moles real ale, good choice of wines by the glass, warm log fires, brown sofas and close mix of tables in two bar areas; children welcome, some tables outside, opp Kynaston Cave, good cliff walks (Miss J E Edwards, Malcolm Avery, David Gordon, LYM, Mike and Jayne Bastin, William Ruxton, TOH)

NORTON IN HALES [SJ7038]

Hinds Head [Main Rd]: Comfortably extended three-room country pub with good food choice, not cheap but good cooking, from bar snacks to restaurant meals, friendly attentive service, four real ales inc Timothy Taylors Landlord, open fire, conservatory; disabled access, beautiful village setting by church (Margaret and Allen Marsden, Les and Barbara Owen)

PORTH-Y-WAEN [SJ2623]

☆ *Lime Kiln* [A495, between village and junction with A483, S of Oswestry]: Neatly opened up pub with welcoming new landlord, neatly kept stripped pine bar with pews and big pine tables, enjoyable food inc popular Sun lunch, well kept Banks's, Marstons Pedigree and a guest beer, good value wines; children in eating areas, picnic-sets out in side garden with boules and terraced lawn, open all day wknds (LYM, Mr and Mrs Peter Longland)

QUATFORD [SO7390]

Danery [A442 Kidderminster—Bridgnorth, a bit N of Shatterford]: Bustling old-fashioned pub with good fresh food at reasonable prices, several rooms off central bar, open fires, friendly service, real ales, small restaurant (same menu) (J H Bushell)

SHIFNAL [SJ74508]

White Hart [High St]: Consistently good value friendly timbered 17th-c pub, quaint and old-fashioned, separate bar and lounge, comfortable but without frills, half a dozen or more interesting changing well kept ales such as Bathams, Black Sheep and Enville, wide range of sandwiches, promptly served reasonably priced home-made hot dishes, welcoming staff; couple of steep steps at front door (Pamela and Merlyn Horswell)

SHREWSBURY [SJ4812]

Bellstone [Bellstone]: Minimalist modern bar/restaurant with different rooms each with its own atmosphere, good value food inc good ciabattas, friendly service, good wine list, a couple of real ales; courtyard tables (Howard and Lorna Lambert, M Joyner)

Coach & Horses [Swan Hill/Cross Hill]: Welcoming unspoilt Victorian local, panelled throughout, with main bar, cosy little side room and back dining room, good value food inc daily roasts and some unusual dishes, well kept Bass, Goodalls Gold (brewed for pub by Salopian) and a guest beer, relaxed atmosphere, prompt helpful service even when busy, interesting prints; pretty flower boxes outside (Pete Baker, Jeff and Sue Evans, the Didler, Joe Green)

Lion [follow City Centre signposts across the English Bridge]: Grand largely 18th-c coaching inn with cosy oak-panelled bar and sedate series of high-ceilinged rooms opening off, civilised service, real ale, reasonably priced bar lunches inc succulent sandwiches, tea or coffee and cakes other times; children welcome, bedrooms comfortable (LYM, Francis Johnston)

☆ *Loggerheads* [Church St]: Small old-fashioned pub, panelled back smoke room with flagstones, scrubbed-top tables, high-backed settles and real fire, three other rooms with lots of prints, flagstones and bare boards, quaint linking corridor and hatch service of Banks's Bitter and Mild, related beers and a guest beer, friendly and meticulously professional bar staff, bargain lunchtime food (not Sun) inc doorstep sandwiches, baked potatoes and good steak pie with great chips; darts, dominoes, poetry society, occasional live music; open all day (the Didler, Martin Grosberg, Pete Baker, Joe Green)

☆ *Three Fishes* [Fish St]: Timbered and heavily beamed 16th-c pub much enjoyed for its no smoking policy (no mobiles either), well kept Caledonian Deuchars IPA, Fullers London Pride, Timothy Taylors Landlord and guest beers, good value wines, simple hearty bar food (not Sun evening) from baguettes and filled baked potatoes up, friendly service; open all day Fri/Sat (M Joyner, LYM, the Didler, Stan Edwards, Martin Grosberg, Jeff and Sue Evans, Hugh Roberts, Paul and

Gloria Howell, Joe Green)
STIPERSTONES [SJ3600]
☆ *Stiperstones Inn* [signed off A488 S of
Minsterley; OS Sheet 126 map ref 364005]:
Simple bargain fresh food all day just right for
hungry walkers in welcoming no-frills pub
with well kept Six Bells or Woods Parish, small
modernised lounge bar, comfortable leatherette
wall banquettes, lots of brassware on ply-
panelled walls, decent wine, real fire, darts in
plainer public bar, restaurant; may be
unobtrusive piped music; tables outside, clean
basic cheap bedrooms (small dogs welcome),
good breakfast, good walking – they sell maps
(*Edward Leetham, BB, Guy Vowles, John and
Gloria Isaacs*)
STREET DINAS [SJ3338]
Greyhound [B5069 St Martin's—Oswestry]:
Comfortable bar profusely decorated with
pictures, mining memorabilia, hundreds of
whisky miniatures and beer bottles, masses of
chamber-pots hanging from beams, Banks's
Best, Greene King Abbot, Thwaites and
Websters, welcoming, ebullient and efficient
landlord, good value food from good
sandwiches and baguettes to full meals, dining
room, back games room and end TV; tables in
individualistic garden with water features,
Reliant Robin as a sort of sculpture, busy
dovecote (*Michael and Jenny Back*)
TELFORD [SJ6707]
Station Inn [Station Rd]: Cosy traditional pub
with Courage Directors and Woods Craven
and Shropshire Lad, decent wines, enjoyable
up-to-date food using local produce; tables in
back garden, cl Mon (*Tony and Pam Gale*)
UPPER AFFCOT [SO4486]
Travellers Rest [A49 S of Church Stretton]:
Agreeable olde-worlde conversion, spacious
and well furnished, with enjoyable standard
food at bargain prices, Bass, Hobsons and
other ales, decent wine, friendly efficient
service, no smoking roadside dining room,
light conservatory extension; children and dogs
welcome, four ground-floor bedrooms with
own bathrooms (*Dr and Mrs M E Wilson*)
WALL UNDER HEYWOOD [SO5092]
Plough [B4371]: Roomy and comfortable bars
and restaurant extension redecorated for genial
new Scots landlord and wife, enjoyable food in
manageable helpings, well kept real ales;
garden tables (*John Whitehead, TOH*)
WENLOCK EDGE [SO5796]
Wenlock Edge Inn [B4371 Much Wenlock—
Church Stretton]: Charmingly placed country
dining pub, pleasant two-room bar (dogs
allowed) with open fire and inglenook
woodburner, more modern no smoking dining
extension, welcoming service, reasonably
priced home-made food from baguettes up,
well kept local Hobsons Best and Town Crier;
children welcome in eating areas, tables out on
terraces front and back, cosy attractive
bedrooms, lots of walks; may be cl winter
wkdy lunchtimes (*Gloria Bax, David Field,
LYM, M Thomas, Rodney and
Norma Stubington*)

WHITCHURCH [SJ5441]
☆ *Old Town Hall Vaults* [St Marys St]: Simple
18th-c pub, birthplace of Sir Edward German
(so there may be piped light classics), central
bar serving small lounge and separate public
bar, good value straightforward food, a real
ale, good coffee, small no smoking dining
room, welcoming staff (*Stuart Paulley*)
White Bear [High St]: Busy friendly pub with
enjoyable bar meals, real ales, quick service;
tables in small courtyard (*Peter and
Audrey Dowsett*)
☆ *Willey Moor Lock* [signed off A49 just under
2m N]: Large pub in picturesque spot by
Llangollen Canal, linked rooms with low
beams, countless teapots, two log fires,
cheerful chatty atmosphere, half a dozen well
kept changing ales from small breweries,
around 30 malt whiskies, good value quickly
served simple food from sandwiches and baked
potatoes up; fruit machine, piped music,
several dogs and cats; children welcome away
from bar, terrace tables, garden with big play
area (*LYM, Gwyn and Anne Wake, MLR*)
WHITTINGTON [SJ3532]
Narrowboat [Welsh Frankton, A495
Ellesmere—Oswestry]: Spacious and
welcoming waterside pub with chandlery,
water and overnight mooring, simple bar with
good range of reasonably priced food (can also
be eaten in restaurant part, which
predominates), real ales; tables out on grass by
lively Llangollen Canal (*Peter and
Audrey Dowsett*)
WHIXALL [SJ5136]
Waggoners [Platt Lane]: Three linked
traditional rooms, some emphasis on popular
food inc Sun lunch, good atmosphere, friendly
service, well kept ales; piped music; tables in
garden, short walk from Llangollen Canal with
overnight moorings (*Peter and Audrey Dowsett*)
WOOFFERTON [SO5168]
Salwey Arms [A49 Ludlow—Leominster]:
Pleasantly old-fashioned panelled bar with
woodworking tools, cases of masonic medals
and open fire (not always lit), no smoking
family room with old kitchen range, standard
food, well kept ales such as Wye Valley
(*Martin Lewis, Neil and Anita Christopher*)
WOORE [SJ7342]
Swan [London Rd (A51)]: Neat convivial bar,
popular food from simple bar lunches to full
meals, real ales, good value wines, smart
friendly service (*Les and Barbara Owen*)
YORTON [SJ5023]
Railway: Same family for over 60 years,
friendly and chatty mother and daughter,
unchanging atmosphere, simple tiled bar with
hot coal fire, newly cushioned settles and a
modicum of railway memorabilia, big back
lounge (not always open) with fishing trophies,
well kept Woods Bitter and Shropshire Lad
and other ales, mainly local, such as Archers,
Goldthorn, Holdens, Salopian or Slaters,
simple sandwiches if you ask, darts and
dominoes – no piped music or machines; seats
out in yard (*the Didler, Martin Grosberg*)

Somerset

In this chapter we include Bristol, as well as Bath. Many of the better Somerset pubs seem rather less geared to holiday-makers and more to their local regulars than in other parts of the West Country. This gives them a sturdily genuine feeling – perhaps not smart, and sometimes they could do with a bit of redecoration, but the down-to-earth qualities that really count are all in place. That's by no means to say that you can't find smart places here. Indeed, the area's top pubs span a splendid range, from simple to sophisticated, often with very good food. Places currently on top form include the Red Lion at Babcary (a new entry, warmly welcoming and quite stylishly reworked, coming straight in with a Food Award), the bustling Old Green Tree in Bath (a favourite town pub with particularly well kept beers), the Bear & Swan in Chew Magna (interesting modern food in this civilised up-to-date take on a country pub), the Crown at Churchill (a bastion of tradition, much enjoyed for its proper home cooking and splendid real ales), the neatly kept Ring o' Roses at Holcombe (enjoyable bar lunches, rewarding evening restaurant), the George in Ilminster (particularly well run, with a nice small bar and good fairly priced food), the cosy little Pilgrims Rest tucked away at Lovington (now entirely no smoking, with super cooking by the landlord – by no means cheap, though there is a good value fixed-price lunch), the welcoming Bird in Hand at North Curry (a nice all-rounder), the busy and unassuming Halfway House at Pitney (great for beers, three good fires), the Windmill in Portishead (this high-throughput family-oriented place has surprising virtues), the cheerily warm-hearted and thriving Rose & Crown at Stoke St Gregory, and the well run Crown in Wells (a popular meeting place all day, and it gains a Place to Stay Award this year). Several of these stand out for their good food, but it's the new entrant, the Red Lion at Babcary, which takes the crown as Somerset Dining Pub of the Year. The Lucky Dip section at the end of the chapter is full of interest this year. Pubs we'd particularly pick out (the great majority of them now inspected and approved by us) are the Ring o' Bells at Ashcott, Coeur de Lion and Hop Pole in Bath, Woolpack at Beckington, Queens Arms at Bleadon, White Horse at Bradford-on-Tone, Adam & Eve in Bristol, Strode Arms at Cranmore, Helyar Arms at East Coker, Faulkland Inn, Lord Poulett Arms at Hinton St George, Old Crown at Kelston, Kings Arms at Litton, Hope & Anchor at Midford, Phelips Arms in Montacute, Plume of Feathers at Rickford, Vobster Inn, Cotley Inn at Wambrook, Fox & Badger at Wellow, Fountain in Wells, Holman Clavel near Widcombe and Stags Head at Yarlington. Drinks prices here average out almost bang on the national norm. Butcombe is the good local beer which we most often found pubs here stocking as their cheapest. Cotleigh, Exmoor and RCH also featured commonly at sensible prices, and other good local brews you may easily come across here are Abbey, Bath and Cottage. Otter and Teignworthy, both from Devon, are also often offered at attractive prices here, particularly over in the west.

APPLEY ST0721 Map 1
Globe 🍴

Hamlet signposted from the network of back roads between A361 and A38, W of B3187 and W of Milverton and Wellington; OS Sheet 181 map reference 072215

This 500-year-old pub is a pleasant and friendly place for both a drink or a meal. The simple beamed front room has a built-in settle and bare wood tables on the brick floor, and another room has a GWR bench and 1930s railway posters; there's a further room with easy chairs and other more traditional ones, open fires, and a collection of model cars, art deco items and *Titanic* pictures; skittle alley. A brick entry corridor leads to a serving hatch from where Cotleigh Tawny and Sharps Will's Resolve are well kept on handpump; Heck's farm cider. Tasty bar food includes sandwiches, home-made soup (£3.25), chicken liver pâté (£5.50), seafood pancake (£7.95), vegetable pasta topped with stilton (£8.50), chicken curry (£9.50), home-made steak and kidney in ale pie (£8.95), steaks (from £10.50), duckling with madeira sauce (£11.95), daily specials such as chicken, bacon and leeks in a creamy sauce topped with puff pastry (£8.95) and grilled fillet of cod on tagliatelle with tomato, basil, cream and white wine sauce (£10.95), and puddings like home-made treacle tart or hot banana pancake with a rum and caramel sauce (from £4.25); Sunday roast (£6.50). The restaurant and one room in the bar are no smoking. Seats, climbing frame and swings outside in the garden; the path opposite leads eventually to the River Tone. *(Recommended by Bob and Margaret Holder, Richard and Anne Ansell, the Didler, Paul Hopton, Brian and Anita Randall, Michael Rowse, John and Fiona McIlwain)*

Free house ~ Licensees Andrew and Liz Burt ~ Real ale ~ Bar food ~ Restaurant ~ (01823) 672327 ~ Children in eating area of bar and restaurant ~ Open 11-3, 6.30-11; 12-3, 7-10.30 Sun; closed Mon except bank hols

ASHILL ST3116 Map 1
Square & Compass

Windmill Hill; off A358 between Ilminster and Taunton; up Wood Road for 1 mile behind Stewley Cross service station; OS Sheet 193 map reference 310166

The sweeping views from this nicely remote simple pub over the rolling pastures around Neroche Forest can be enjoyed from the upholstered window seats in the little bar; there are other seats and an open winter fire – and perhaps the pub cats Daisy and Lilly. Well kept Bass, Exmoor Ale, St Austell HSD and Windmill Hill Bitter on handpump; skittle alley. Bar food includes sandwiches, soup (£3.50), cauliflower cheese topped with mushrooms (£6.50), lasagne (£6.95), steak in ale pie (£7.95), pork steak with cider, apple and leek sauce or braised venison in a rich red wine and garlic sauce (£9.95), breast of chicken in a creamy stilton and bacon sauce (£10.95), and seared tuna steak with stir-fried vegetables and noodles in a black bean sauce (£11.95). Piped classical music at lunchtimes. There's a terrace outside and a garden with picnic-sets, and a children's play area. *(Recommended by Kevin Thorpe, R T and J C Moggridge, John and Fiona McIlwain, Pat and Tony Martin)*

Free house ~ Licensees Chris, Janet and Beth Slow ~ Real ale ~ Bar food (not Tues, Weds or Thurs lunchtimes) ~ (01823) 480467 ~ Children welcome ~ Dogs welcome ~ Monthly live music in separate barn ~ Open 12-3, 6.30-11; 12-2.30, 7-10.30 Sun; closed Tues, Weds and Thurs lunchtimes

AXBRIDGE ST4255 Map 1
Lamb

The Square; off A371 Cheddar—Winscombe

There's always a good mix of regulars and shoppers in this ancient place as it's right on the market square. The big rambling bar is full of heavy beams and timbers, cushioned wall seats and small settles, an open fire in one great stone fireplace, and a collection of tools and utensils including an unusual foot-operated grinder in another. Well kept Butcombe Bitter and Gold, and a couple of guests like

Hook Norton Bitter or Marstons Pedigree on handpump from a bar counter built largely of bottles, and local cider; shove-ha'penny, cribbage, dominoes, table skittles and skittle alley. Reasonably priced bar food includes lunchtime sandwiches and filled baguettes (from £3), as well as home-made soup (£2.75), chicken liver pâté with fruit chutney (£4.25), deep-fried brie with redcurrant jelly (£4.50), filled baked potatoes (from £4.75), home-cooked ham and eggs (£6.25), home-made leek and potato bake (£6.50), home-made curry or tasty beef in ale pie (£7.45), steaks (from £8.95), daily specials such as home-made fishcakes or pork in cider casserole (£7.25), lamb shank in rosemary and redcurrant sauce (£9.25), and duck cassoulet (£9.50). OAP two-course lunch (Tuesday and Thursday, £6.25), and Sunday roast (£5.50). Nearly half the pub is no smoking. Although the sheltered back garden is not big, it's prettily planted with rock plants, shrubs and trees. The National Trust's medieval King John's Hunting Lodge is opposite. *(Recommended by Francis Johnston, Tom Evans, Frank Willy, P M Wilkins, J Coote, Dr A J and Mrs Tompsett, Steve Kirby)*

Butcombe ~ Manager Alan Currie ~ Real ale ~ Bar food (not Sun evening) ~ (01934) 732253 ~ Children in eating area of bar ~ Dogs allowed in bar ~ Open 11.30-3, 6-11; 11.30-11 Sat; 12-10.30 Sun

BABCARY ST5628 Map 2
Red Lion ⊕ ♀
Off A37 about 5 miles south of Shepton Mallet
Somerset Dining Pub of the Year

In a sleepy village, this golden stone thatched pub is run by an enthusiastic and personable young landlord and his wife. A huge amount of effort has gone into the refurbishment yet they have managed to keep a smashing, relaxed and proper pubby atmosphere much enjoyed by both locals and visitors. Several distinct areas work their way around the bar. To the left of the entrance is a longish room with dark pink walls, a squashy leather sofa and two housekeeper's chairs by a low table and a woodburning stove, just a few well spaced tables and captain's chairs including a big one in a bay window with built-in seats. There are elegant rustic wall lights, some clay pipes in a cabinet, and local papers to read; board games and gardening magazines too. Leading off here with lovely dark flagstones is a public bar area with a panelled dado, a high-backed old settle and more straightforward chairs; darts, dominoes, cribbage, shove-ha'penny and table skittles. The good-sized smart no smoking dining room has a large stone lion's head on a plinth above the open fire (with a huge stack of logs to one side), a big rug on polished bare boards, and properly set tables. It all adds up to a feeling of unhurried well-being. Extremely good food using local produce includes at lunchtime delicious soups with a warm fresh loaf on its own little breadboard (£3.95), sandwiches (from £4.95), roasted red pepper, goats cheese pastry tart and shaved fennel salad (£5.25), crispy pork belly, preserved lemon noodles and honey soy dressing (£5.50), salad of baby cos, prosciutto, croûtons, parmesan and caesar dressing (£5.95), ploughman's with elderflower chutney (£6.75), ham, poached duck egg, fried hen egg and chips (£6.95), beef burger with tomato relish (£7.95), and linguini, confit of cherry tomato, butternut squash, rocket and lemon dill sauce (£9.25), with evening choices such as chicken liver parfait with grape compote and toasted brioche (£5.50), warm duck pancakes, spring onions and hoisin dipping sauce (£5.75), roasted wild garlic, toasted almonds, salami and mascarpone risotto (£9.50), chicken breast with tagliatelle, red pepper, artichokes and pesto crème fraîche (£10.75), 10oz rib-eye steak with béarnaise sauce (£12.25), and herb crusted rack of lamb, colcannon, cracked pepper pumpkin and coffee jus (£13.95); fish dishes are listed on a specials board, and for children they will gladly prepare any dish in smaller helpings. Well kept O'Hanlon's Yellowhammer and Teignworthy Old Moggie and Reel Ale on handpump or tapped from the cask, 7 good wines by the glass, summer smoothies and iced tea, and a proper bloody mary. There's a long informal garden with picnic tables and a play area with slide for children. They plan to open bedrooms next year. *(Recommended by Michael Doswell, Jane Legate, Clare West, Guy Vowles)*

Free house ~ Licensee Charles Garrard ~ Real ale ~ Bar food (12-2.30, 7-9.30) ~
Restaurant ~ (01458) 223230 ~ Children welcome ~ Dogs allowed in bar ~ Open
12-2.30(3 Sat), 6-11; 12-3 Sun; closed Sun evening

BATCOMBE ST6838 Map 2
Three Horseshoes 🍴 🍷
Village signposted off A359 Bruton—Frome

New licensees again for this honey-coloured stone dining pub, but the same chef is
staying on, and the friendly new people are hoping to change very little. The longish
narrow main room has beams, local pictures on the lightly ragged dark pink walls,
built-in cushioned window seats and solid chairs around a nice mix of old tables,
and a woodburning stove at one end with a big open fire at the other; at the back
on the left, the snug has dark panelled walls, tiled floors and old pictures. The no
smoking, stripped-stone dining room is pretty. Good, interesting bar food might
include thai fishcake with sweet chilli dressing (£4.95), chicken liver salad with
bacon lardons or warm tartlet of local brie with avocado and sunblush tomato
salsa (£5.25), sandwiches (from £5.25), wild mushroom risotto with tomato coulis
(£7.95), wild boar sausage on black pudding with red wine jus or roast salmon
niçoise (£8.95), fish pie or coq au vin (£9.95), chicken caesar salad (£9.95), filo
parcel of chickpea, spinach and ricotta with a neapolitan sauce (£11.95), duck
breast with puy lentil mash (£13.95), rib-eye steak with a julienne of roasted
peppers (£14.75), and puddings such as white and dark chocolate rum cappuccino
mousse, pears poached in red wine with honey jasmine ice-cream or Galliano and
brioche bread and butter pudding with apricots and pears (£4.50). Well kept
Butcombe Bitter and a beer they brew for the pub, Bats in the Belfry, on
handpump, and eight wines by two sizes of glass. The back terrace has picnic-sets,
with more on the grass, outdoor heaters, and a pond with koi carp. The pub is on a
quiet village lane by the church which has a very striking tower. (*Recommended by Mr
and Mrs R B Berry, Roger Wain-Heapy, Peter Craske, Mr and Mrs Peter Llewellyn, Julian and
Jennifer Clapham, Susan and Nigel Wilson*)

Free house ~ Licensees Bob Wood and Shirley Greaves ~ Real ale ~ Bar food ~
Restaurant ~ (01749) 850359 ~ Children in eating area of bar and in restaurant but must
be over 8 in evening ~ Dogs allowed in bar ~ Open 12-3, 6.30-11; 12-3, 7-10.30 Sun

BATH ST7464 Map 2
Old Green Tree 🍺
12 Green Street

'Excellent' is a word used by lots of our readers to describe this smashing little pub.
It's always busy but keeps a friendly, relaxed atmosphere – and of course a fine
range of real ales. On handpump, these might include Hop Back Summer
Lightning, RCH Pitchfork, Stonehenge Spire Ale, Wickwar Brand Oak Bitter and
Mr Perretts Traditional Stout, and a beer named for the pub. Also, a dozen wines
by the glass from a nice little list with helpful notes, 35 malt whiskies, winter hot
toddies, a proper Pimms, and good coffee. The three little oak-panelled and low
wood-and-plaster ceilinged rooms include a comfortable lounge on the left as you
go in, its walls decorated with wartime aircraft pictures in winter and local artists'
work during spring and summer, and a no smoking back bar; the big skylight
lightens things up attractively. Popular lunchtime bar food includes soup and
sandwiches (from £4), bangers and mash with cider or beer and onion sauce
(£6.50), and daily specials such as enjoyable rare roast beef platter, mushroom and
leek risotto, curry of the day, and smoked trout and asparagus (all £6.50); if you
get there when the pub opens, you should be able to bag a table. Chess, cribbage,
dominoes, backgammon, shut the box and Jenga. The gents', though good, are
down steep steps. No children. (*Recommended by Malcolm Ward, Pete Baker, Dr and
Mrs A K Clarke, John and Gloria Isaacs, Emma Hughes, R Huggins, D Irving, E McCall,
T McLean, David Carr, Patrick Hancock, the Didler, Dr and Mrs M E Wilson, Mike Pugh,
Michael Butler, Mary Rayner, Gaynor Gregory, Susan and Nigel Wilson*)

Free house ~ Licensees Nick Luke and Tim Bethune ~ Real ale ~ Bar food (lunchtime until 3) ~ No credit cards ~ Dogs allowed in bar ~ Open 11-11; 12-10.30 Sun; closed 25 and 26 Dec

Star ◖

23 Vineyards; The Paragon (A4), junction with Guinea Lane

As the brewery tap for Abbey Ales, this honest old pub keeps Abbey Bellringer very well on handpump – plus Bass, Batemans XXXB, Kelham Pale Rider and Timothy Taylors Landlord. It is set in a quiet street of undeniably handsome if well worn stone terraces, and the four (well, more like three and a half) small linked rooms are served from a single bar, separated by sombre panelling with glass inserts. They are furnished with traditional leatherette wall benches and the like – even one hard bench that the regulars call Death Row – and the lighting's dim, and not rudely interrupted by too much daylight. With no machines or music, chat's the thing here – or perhaps cribbage, dominoes and shove-ha'penny. Filled rolls only (from £1.60; served throughout opening hours during the week), and Sunday lunchtime bar nibbles; friendly staff and customers. No children inside. *(Recommended by Andy and Jill Kassube, R Huggins, D Irving, E McCall, T McLean, Pete Baker, the Didler, Patrick Hancock, Di and Mike Gillam, David Carr, Dr and Mrs M E Wilson, N R White, Rob Stevenson)*

Punch ~ Lease Paul Waters and Alan Morgan ~ Real ale ~ Bar food (see text) ~ No credit cards ~ (01225) 425072 ~ Dogs welcome ~ Open 12-2.30, 5.30-11; 12-11 Sat; 12-10.30 Sun

CATCOTT ST3939 Map 1

Crown ◖

Village signposted off A39 W of Street; at T junction turn left, then at war memorial turn off northwards into Brook Lane and keep on

The pubby little room to the left of the main door is the place to head for in this tucked away former cider house. There are built-in brocade-cushioned settles, a church pew and red leatherette stools around just four rustic pine tables, a tall black-painted brick fireplace with dried flowers and a large cauldron, and working horse plaques; around the corner is a small alcove with a really big pine table on its stripped stone floor. Most of the pub is taken up with the roomy, more straightforward dining area with lots of wheelback chairs around tables, and paintings on silk of local views by a local artist on the cream walls. Bar food includes soup (£3.25), chicken liver pâté (£3.50), sandwiches (from £3.50), ploughman's or filled baked potatoes (from £4.95), vegetable lasagne (£6.95), steak and kidney pie or ham and egg (£7.95), trout with almonds (£8.95), steaks (from £10.95), daily specials like salmon mousse (£3.95), deep-fried brie fritters (£3.95), pork tenderloin in brandy and cherry sauce (£9.95), and lamb in mint and honey sauce (£13.95), and puddings such as warm ginger pudding with ginger toffee sauce (£3.95); all dining areas are no smoking. Well kept Butcombe Bitter, Timothy Taylors Landlord and a guest like Charles Wells Bombardier on handpump, nine wines by the glass, and piped old-fashioned pop music; skittle alley. The original part of the pub is white-painted stone with black shutters and is pretty with window boxes and tubs. Out behind are picnic-sets and a play area for children with wooden equipment. More reports please. *(Recommended by Peter Craske, KC, Colin and Janet Roe)*

Free house ~ Licensees C R D Johnston and D Lee ~ Real ale ~ Bar food (12-2, 6-9) ~ (01278) 722288 ~ Children welcome ~ Open 11.30-2.30, 6-11; 12-3, 7-10.30 Sun; closed 25 Dec ~ Bedrooms: £30S/£60S

Half pints: by law, a pub should not charge more for half a pint than half the price of a full pint, unless it shows that half-pint price on its price list.

CHEW MAGNA ST5763 Map 2
Bear & Swan ⑪ ♀
B3130 (South Parade), off A37 S of Bristol

The interesting food here is so popular that you must book in advance to be sure of a table. The pub has an appealingly up-to-date feel, which comes as something of a surprise in such an austerely traditional-looking building. It's entirely open-plan, and includes an L-shaped no smoking restaurant end on the left, beyond a piano, with stripped stone walls, dark dining tables, a woodburning stove, bare boards and an oriental rug. The other half, also bare boards with the odd oriental rug, has various sizes of pine tables, pews and raffia-seat dining chairs. In this part a relaxed and civilised mix of customers runs from young men chatting on the bar stools through smart lunching mums sipping champagne to older people reading the racing form. Décor is minimal, really just plants in the windows with their heavy dark blue curtains, and some china above the huge bressumer beam over a splendid log fire; a wide-screen TV may be on with its sound turned down; cribbage. Changing every day, with a manageably short blackboard choice, the good food might include filled baguettes (lunchtime only, not Sunday; from £4.25), home-made soup (£3.50), goats cheese, aubergine and ham roulade with spiced apricot chutney (£6), tiger prawn and chorizo bruschetta (£6.50), gammon and egg (£7.95), pork loin with smoked paprika sauce and mustard mash (£8), steak and kidney pie (£8.50), wild mushroom risotto (£8.95), bass with a prawn spring roll and soy and sesame oil dressing (£14), and puddings such as summer pudding or pecan tart (from £4). The long bar counter has well kept Bath Gem, Butcombe Bitter and Courage Best on handpump, and 18 wines by the glass. The car park is small, and street parking needs care (this road is rather a lorry rat-run). *(Recommended by Michael Doswell, Jacqueline Healy, JCW, Mr and Mrs Johnson-Poensgen, Dr Diana Terry, Tim O'Keefe, Gaynor Gregory, Ken Marshall, Julian and Jennifer Clapham)*

Free house ~ Licensees Nigel and Caroline Pushman ~ Real ale ~ Bar food (not Sun evening) ~ Restaurant ~ (01275) 331100 ~ Children welcome ~ Dogs allowed in bar ~ Open 11-11; 12-10.30 Sun ~ Bedrooms: £50S/£80S

CHISELBOROUGH ST4614 Map 1
Cat Head
Take the slip road off A303 at Crewkerne A356 junction

In summer, the attractive gardens behind this neatly kept and friendly country pub are very pretty, and there are plenty of picnic-sets and colourful plants; nice views over the peaceful village, too. The spotless, traditional flagstoned rooms have light wooden tables and chairs, some high-backed cushioned settles, flowers and plants, a woodburning stove, and curtains around the small mullioned windows. A carpeted area to the right is no smoking. The pub often gets busy in the evenings (particularly at weekends), but at lunchtime you may have its peaceful charms almost to yourself. Popular food at lunchtime might include soup (£3.80), peppered smoked mackerel pâté (£4.70), ploughman's (£4.80), grilled goats cheese and pine nut salad (£4.90), baked haddock and prawn mornay (£6.30), steak and kidney pie (£7.80), and roast lamb shank with red onion gravy (£8.30), with evening choices such as lambs kidneys in madeira sauce (£4.80), baked cornish crab and scallops (£6.10), pigeon breasts with port and wild mushroom sauce (£10.20), roast rack of lamb with a port and redcurrant sauce (£12.80), and fillet steak with a green peppercorn sauce or half a crispy duck with scrumpy sauce (£13.80); daily specials like chicken breast in cider, cream and mushrooms (£7.20), braised oxtail in Guinness (£7.80), grilled whole lemon sole with parsley butter (£11.90), and seasonal game. Well kept Fullers London Pride, Otter Bitter and Ringwood Best Bitter on handpump, a good wine list, and Thatcher's cider; soft piped music, darts, alley skittles, shove-ha'penny, cribbage and dominoes. *(Recommended by M Carr, Mary Ellen Cummings, Michael Hasslacher, Brenda and Tony Morgan, J V Dadswell, Mrs A P Lee, Marianne and Peter Stevens, Guy Vowles, Mary Stokes, Rev D E and Mrs J A Shapland, Norman and Sarah Keeping, Richard Wyld, Geoff and Sylvia Donald)*

Enterprise ~ Lease Duncan and Avril Gordon ~ Real ale ~ Bar food ~ Restaurant ~
(01935) 881231 ~ Children in eating area of bar ~ Open 12-3, 6(7 Sun)-11

CHURCHILL ST4560 Map 1
Crown 🍺 £

The Batch; in village, turn off A368 into Skinners Lane at Nelson Arms, then bear right

Particularly at weekends, this unspoilt little cottage is extremely busy. There's been
some tidying up this year, but nothing that will alarm its enthusiastic supporters
who love the untouched interior. The small and local stone-floored and cross-
beamed room on the right has a wooden window seat, an unusually sturdy settle,
and built-in wall benches; the left-hand room has a slate floor, and some steps past
the log fire in a big stone fireplace lead to more sitting space. Up to ten real ales are
tapped from the cask: Bass, Church End Stout Coffin, Hop Back GFB, Newmans
Wolvers Ale, Palmers IPA, RCH Hewish and PG Steam, and Sharps Special.
Straightforward lunchtime bar food includes sandwiches (from £3.40), good soup
(£3.50), filled baked potatoes (from £3.95), ploughman's (from £5.25), salads
(from £6.80), home-made daily specials like cauliflower cheese or chilli (£4.50),
broccoli and cheese bake (£4.95), and beef casserole (£5.95), and puddings such as
well liked treacle pudding or hot chocolate fudge cake (£3). Outside lavatories.
There are garden tables on the front and a smallish back lawn, and hill views; the
Mendip Morris Men come in summer. Good walks nearby. *(Recommended by
Michael Doswell, Alan and Paula McCully, Stan and Susan Fysh, Dr and Mrs A K Clarke,
the Didler, Jacqueline Healy, Tom Evans, Andrea and Guy Bradley, P M Wilkins, J Coote,
Geoff and Carol Thorp, John and Gloria Isaacs, John Urquhart)*

Free house ~ Licensee Tim Rogers ~ Real ale ~ Bar food (12-2.30(3 weekends); not
evenings) ~ No credit cards ~ (01934) 852995 ~ Children welcome ~ Dogs welcome ~
Open 11.30-11; 12-10.30 Sun

CLAPTON-IN-GORDANO ST4773 Map 1
Black Horse

**4 miles from M5 junction 19; A369 towards Portishead, then B3124 towards Clevedon;
in N Weston opposite school turn left signposted Clapton, then in village take second
right, maybe signed Clevedon, Clapton Wick**

In summer, the flower-decked building and little flagstoned garden in front of this
unspoilt and interesting old place are exceptionally pretty; there are some old rustic
tables and benches, with more to one side of the car park. The partly flagstoned
and partly red-tiled main room has winged settles and built-in wall benches around
narrow, dark wooden tables, window seats, a big log fire with stirrups and bits on
the mantelbeam, and amusing cartoons and photographs of the pub. A window in
an inner snug is still barred from the days when this room was the petty-sessions
gaol; high-backed settles – one a marvellous carved and canopied creature, another
with an art nouveau copper insert reading East, West, Hame's Best – lots of mugs
hanging from its black beams, and plenty of little prints and photographs. There's
also a simply furnished room (which is the only place families are allowed; several
this year were disappointed to be so cut off from the jolliness of the rest of the pub);
piped music, darts, cribbage and dominoes. Straightforward bar food (lunchtime
only) includes filled hot and cold baguettes (from £4.25), ploughman's (£5.25), and
a few hot dishes like soup (£3.25), and leek and macaroni cheese or chilli con carne
(from £5.50). Well kept Bass, Butcombe Bitter, Courage Best, Shepherd Neame
Spitfire and Websters Green Label on handpump or tapped from the cask. Paths
from the pub lead up Naish Hill or along to Cadbury Camp. *(Recommended by
Tom Evans, Ian Phillips, the Didler, Gaynor Gregory, Susan and John Douglas, Gloria Bax)*

Inntrepreneur ~ Tenant Nicholas Evans ~ Real ale ~ Bar food (not evenings, not Sun) ~
No credit cards ~ (01275) 842105 ~ Children in very plain family room only ~ Dogs
welcome ~ Live music Mon evening ~ Open 11-2.30, 5-11; 11-11 Sat; 12-10.30 Sun

COMPTON MARTIN ST5457 Map 2

Ring o' Bells 🍺

A368 Bath—Weston

In an attractive position, this is a bustling country pub with a friendly welcome from the landlord and his staff. The cosy, traditional front part of the bar has rugs on the flagstones and inglenook seats right by the log fire, and up a step is a spacious carpeted back part with largely stripped stone walls and pine tables; the lounge is partly no smoking. Bar food includes sandwiches (from £2.50), home-made soup (£3.25), filled baked potatoes (from £4.25), ham and eggs (small £4.25; large £4.95), omelettes (from £4.95), ploughman's (from £5.50), broccoli, mushroom and almond tagliatelle (£6.75), beef in ale or lasagne (£6.95), and steaks (from £10.50). Well kept Butcombe Bitter, Blond, and Gold on handpump; darts, table skittles, cribbage and dominoes in the public bar. The family room is no smoking, and has blackboards and chalks, a Brio track and a rocking horse. The big garden has swings, a slide and a climbing frame. Blagdon Lake and Chew Valley Lake are not far away, and the pub is overlooked by the Mendip Hills. *(Recommended by Tom Evans, Brian McBurnie, Basil and Jarvis, P M Wilkins, J Coote, Geoff and Carol Thorp, Gaynor Gregory)*

Butcombe ~ Manager Roger Owen ~ Real ale ~ Bar food ~ Restaurant ~ (01761) 221284 ~ Children in family room ~ Dogs allowed in bar ~ Open 11.30-3, 6.30-11; 12-3, 7-10.30 Sun

CONGRESBURY ST4464 Map 1

White Hart

Wrington Road, which is off A370 Bristol—Weston just E of village – keep on

This is a pleasant country pub, and the L-shaped carpeted main bar has a few heavy black beams in the bowed ceiling of its longer leg, country-kitchen chairs around good-sized tables, and a big stone inglenook fireplace at each end, with woodburning stoves and lots of copper pans. The short leg of the L is more cottagey, with wooden games and other bric-a-brac above yet another fireplace and on a delft shelf, lace and old-gold brocaded curtains and brocaded wall seats. A roomy family Parlour Bar, open to the main bar, is similar in mood, though with lighter-coloured country-style furniture, some stripped stone and shiny black panelling, and big bright airy conservatory windows on one side; the restaurant is no smoking. Tasty bar food includes home-made soup (£4.25), deep-fried cheese with cranberry sauce (£4.50), ham and eggs (£6.25), cauliflower cheese (£6.50), stilton, leek and walnut pie (£7.75), home-made lasagne (£7.75), home-made steak pie (£8.25), chicken in stilton (£9.25), and puddings such as home-made fruit crumbles (£3.75); they are happy to help with dietary requirements such as gluten or dairy-free dishes. Well kept Badger Fursty Ferret, Gold and Tanglefoot on handpump; piped music, shove-ha'penny, cribbage, dominoes and table skittles. There are picnic-sets under an arbour on the terrace behind, and a children's play area in the large garden; the hills you see are the Mendips. *(Recommended by J H Bescoby, Susan and John Douglas, Bob and Margaret Holder, Colin Morgan)*

Badger ~ Tenants Paul Merrick and Rebecca North ~ Real ale ~ Bar food (12-2, 6-9.30; all day in summer) ~ Restaurant ~ (01934) 833303 ~ Children in family room ~ Dogs welcome ~ Open 11.30-2.30, 6-11; 12-10.30 Sun; 12-3, 7-10.30 Sun in winter; closed 25 Dec

---

Anyone claiming to arrange or prevent inclusion of a pub in the *Guide* is a fraud. Pubs are included only if recommended by genuine readers and if our own anonymous inspection confirms that they are suitable.

CROWCOMBE ST1336 Map 1 🏠

Carew Arms 🍺 ⇖

Village (and pub) signposted just off A358 Taunton—Minehead

There's quite often something happening in this 17th-c beamed inn, from regular Sunday lunchtime jazz to special food events. It's a friendly place, and the front bar has long benches and a couple of old long deal tables on its dark flagstones, a high-backed antique settle by the woodburning stove in its huge brick inglenook fireplace, and a thoroughly non-PC collection of hunting trophies to remind you that this is the Quantocks. A back room behind the bar is a carpeted and gently updated version of the front one, and on the right are a library and residents' lounge. The smart dining room has doors to one side leading to an outside terrace where you can eat in fine weather. Well kept Exmoor Ale and either Fox, Gold or Hart on handpump, eight wines by the glass, Lane's strong farm cider and a dozen malt whiskies. Dominoes, cribbage, darts, skittle alley, fruit machine and piped music (only in the Garden Room); several dogs. Enjoyable bar food includes sandwiches, soup (£4.50), fried mushrooms and grilled bacon (£5), king scallops in hot garlic butter (£7.95; main course £14.95), garlic roasted vegetables with red pepper jus (£8.50), steak in ale pie (£9.50), chicken breast with bubble and squeak or salmon with basil and tomato cream (£10), grilled lamb cutlets with braised onions (£11), halibut fillets with brown shrimps (£12), and steaks (from £12). Picnic-sets out on the back grass look over rolling wooded pasture, and the attractive village at the foot of the hills has a fine old church and church house. *(Recommended by June and Peter Shamash, Jeremy Whitehorn, the Didler, Dennis and Gill Keen, David R Brown, Hugh Roberts, Bob and Margaret Holder, Henry and Fiona Dryden, Bob and Marilyn Baylis, P M Wilkins, J Coote)*

Free house ~ Licensees Simon and Reg Ambrose ~ Real ale ~ Bar food ~ Restaurant ~ (01984) 618631 ~ Children welcome ~ Dogs allowed in bar ~ Live jazz twice a month in summer, monthly Sun in winter, lunchtimes ~ Open 11-3.30, 5-11; 11-11 Sat; 12-10.30 Sun ~ Bedrooms: £45B/£72B

DOULTING ST6445 Map 2

Waggon & Horses ⦿

Doulting Beacon, 2 miles N of Doulting; eastwards turn off A37 on Mendip ridge N of Shepton Mallet, just S of A367 junction; pub is also signed from A37 at Beacon Hill crossroads and from the A361 at Doulting and Cranmore crossroads

Although things have obviously changed under the new licensees, many readers are happy with the way this bustling pub is going. The rambling bar has studded red leatherette seats and other chairs, a homely mix of tables including antiques, and well kept Butcombe Bitter, Greene King IPA and Wadworths 6X on handpump, and quite a few wines by the glass. Half the pub is no smoking. Bar food now includes sandwiches, and daily specials such as soup (£3.90), salad of grilled goats cheese with roasted peppers and pine nuts (£4.90), thai-style crab cakes with chilli dip or a baked whole camembert with cranberry sauce (£6.50), vegetable lasagne (£8.50), sausages with onion gravy (£9.90), lamb stew (£10.90), venison steak with stilton sauce (£12.90), grilled cod fillet with béarnaise sauce (£13.90), and puddings such as treacle tart or brioche and butter pudding (£4.50). The big walled garden (with summer barbecues) is lovely: elderly tables and chairs stand on informal terracing, with picnic-sets out on the grass, and perennials and flowering shrubs intersperse themselves in a pretty and pleasantly informal way. There's a wildlife pond, and a climber for children. More reports on the new regime, please. *(Recommended by Colin and Janet Roe, John Urquhart, Adam and Joan Bunting, MRSM, Mrs Pat Crabb, Richard Fendick, Susan and Nigel Wilson)*

InnSpired ~ Tenants Simon Cooke and Clare Wilson ~ Real ale ~ Bar food (11.30-2.30, 6.30-10) ~ Restaurant ~ (01749) 880302 ~ Children tolerated but must be well behaved and quiet ~ Dogs welcome ~ Jazz first Fri of month, quiz second Fri, local band third Fri, and blues fourth Fri ~ Open 11.30-3, 6-11; 12-3, 7-10.30 Sun

EAST LYNG ST3328 Map 1

Rose & Crown

A361 about 4 miles W of Othery

In warm weather, most customers head for the pretty back garden here (largely hedged off from the car park) where there are lots of seats and lovely rural views. Inside, there's an open-plan beamed lounge bar with a winter log fire (or a big embroidered fire screen) in the stone fireplace, a corner cabinet of glass, china and silver, a court cabinet, a bow window seat by an oak drop-leaf table, copies of *Country Life*, and impressive large dried flower arrangements. Well liked and reasonably priced bar food includes sandwiches (from £2.50), soup (£3.25), ploughman's (from £5.25), ham and egg (£5.50), omelettes (from £6), steaks (from £10.75), roast duckling with orange sauce (£13.75), daily specials such as mushroom and red pepper stroganoff, beef curry, pasta and tuna bake or pork chop with mustard sauce (all £7), and puddings like treacle tart, caramel, nut and chocolate pie or fresh fruit crumble (£3.65); the dining room is no smoking. Well kept Butcombe Bitter and Gold and Palmers 200 on handpump; skittle alley and piped music. *(Recommended by Ian Phillips, D P and M A Miles, Bob and Margaret Holder, Mrs A P Lee, Comus and Sarah Elliott, M G Hart, George Atkinson)*

Free house ~ Real ale ~ Bar food ~ (01823) 698235 ~ Children in restaurant ~ Open 11-2.30, 6.30-11; 12-3, 6.30-10.30 Sun ~ Bedrooms: £34S/£56S

EXFORD SS8538 Map 1

White Horse 🛏

B3224

Though the old coach road climbs from here up over Exmoor, the attractive village itself is sheltered – pretty in summer, with the river running past this large three-storey creepered place with its half-timbered top storey. The more or less open-plan bar has windsor and other country kitchen chairs, a high-backed antique settle, scrubbed deal tables, hunting prints, photographs above the stripped pine dado, and a good winter log fire. Well kept Exmoor Ale, Fox, Gold and Hound Dog, and Greene King Old Speckled Hen on handpump, and over 150 malt whiskies. Straightforward bar food includes sandwiches (from £2.25; filled baguettes from £3.50), home-made soup (£2.95), filled baked potatoes (from £3.25), cornish pasty (£4.65), breaded haddock (£4.75), smoked ham and egg (£4.95), steak in ale pie (£6.45), local trout (£8.25), steaks (from £8.95), and home-made puddings (£3.50); three-course Sunday lunch (£10.95). The restaurant and eating area of the bar are no smoking. The village green with children's play equipment is next to the pub. *(Recommended by A and B D Craig, Patrick Hancock, Bob and Margaret Holder, P and J Shapley, Anne and Paul Horscraft, Lloyd Moon, Lynda and Trevor Smith, Dr and Mrs A K Clarke, Rod and Chris Pring, Phil and Sally Gorton, Klaus and Elizabeth Leist)*

Free house ~ Licensees Peter and Linda Hendrie ~ Real ale ~ Bar food (12-2.30, 6-9.30) ~ Restaurant ~ (01643) 831229 ~ Children welcome ~ Dogs allowed in bar and bedrooms ~ Open 11-11; 12-10.30 Sun ~ Bedrooms: £30B/£60B

FAULKLAND ST7354 Map 2

Tuckers Grave ★ £

A366 E of village

For some people, this basic but warmly friendly cider house – still claiming the title of Smallest Pub in the *Guide* – is one of their all-time favourite pubs. Nothing has changed for many years, and the flagstoned entry opens into a teeny unspoilt room with casks of well kept Bass and Butcombe Bitter on tap and Thatcher's Cheddar Valley cider in an alcove on the left. Two old cream-painted high-backed settles face each other across a single table on the right, and a side room has shove-ha'penny. There's a skittle alley and tables and chairs on the back lawn; winter fires and maybe newspapers to read. Food is limited to sandwiches and ploughman's at lunchtime. There's an attractive back garden. *(Recommended by Pete Baker,*

Roger Huggins, Tom and Alex McLean, MLR, the Didler, Dr and Mrs A K Clarke, Ian Phillips, Mike Ridgway, Sarah Miles)

Free house ~ Licensees Ivan and Glenda Swift ~ Real ale ~ Bar food ~ No credit cards ~ (01373) 834230 ~ Children welcome ~ Open 11.30-3, 6-11; 12-3, 7-10.30 Sun; closed 25 Dec

HOLCOMBE ST6649 Map 2

Ring o' Roses 🍴 🛏️

Village signposted off A367 by War Memorial in Stratton-on-the-Fosse, S of Radstock

Well run by friendly, helpful licensees, this is a quietly placed, extensively modernised country pub. The bar has flagstones, two woodburning stoves, some orthodox cushioned captain's chairs around cast-iron-framed pub tables, and a handsome counter facing attractively cushioned window seats; behind is a gently lit parlourish area with sofas and cushioned chairs around low tables. There are more easy chairs in a pleasant panelled lounge on the right, and a good-sized dining area is nicely divided by balustrades and so forth, and has blue and white plates and some modern prints on the walls. Bar food is served lunchtimes only and includes home-made soup (£3.50), sandwiches (£5.95), duck liver pâté (£4.25), grilled goats cheese salad with warm cranberry jam (£4.50), strips of lambs liver with onion gravy and crispy bacon (£6.50), battered cod (£6.95), home-cured gammon steak and egg (£7.50), roasted vegetable risotto (£8.25), and rump steak (£9.95); the evening restaurant menu is more elaborate, and the restaurant is no smoking. Otter Ale and Bitter on handpump, several wines by the glass, daily papers, and piped music. There are peaceful farmland views from picnic-sets on a terrace and on the lawn around the side and back, with nice shrub plantings and a small rockery. The chocolate labrador is called Sam. *(Recommended by John A Barker, Michael Doswell, Doreen and Haydn Maddock, Ian Phillips, Malcolm Ward, Steve and Liz Tilley, Bruce and Sharon Eden, Vince Lewington)*

Free house ~ Licensee Richard Rushton ~ Real ale ~ Bar food ~ Restaurant ~ (01761) 232478 ~ Children welcome ~ Dogs allowed in bar and bedrooms ~ Open 11.30-11; 11.30-2.30, 7-11 Sat; 12-2.30, 7-10.30 Sun; closed 26 Dec ~ Bedrooms: /£85B

HUISH EPISCOPI ST4326 Map 1

Rose & Crown

Off A372 E of Langport

Mrs Pittard's family have been running this very unspoilt thatched pub for well over 135 years, and now Mrs Pittard's son and two daughters are involved in the business. Known locally as 'Eli's' after the friendly landlady's father, this is like a real step back in time, with a determinedly unpretentious atmosphere and character. There's no bar as such – to get a drink, you just walk into the central flagstoned still room and choose from the casks of well kept Teignworthy Reel Ale or guests such as Glastonbury Mystery Tor, Otter Bright, and Palmers 200; also, several farm ciders (and local cider brandy). This servery is the only thoroughfare between the casual little front parlours with their unusual pointed-arch windows; genuinely friendly locals. Food is home-made, simple and cheap and uses local produce (and some home-grown fruit): generously filled sandwiches (from £2.30), home-made soup (£2.90), filled baked potatoes (from £3.70), ploughman's (from £4.70), stilton and broccoli tart (£6.25), chicken breast in a creamy white wine and tarragon sauce (£6.50), steak in ale pie (£6.75), and puddings such as sticky toffee pudding (£2.95); good helpful service. Shove-ha'penny, dominoes and cribbage, and a much more orthodox big back extension family room has pool, darts, fruit machine and juke box; skittle alley and popular quiz nights. One room is no smoking. There are tables in a garden, and a second enclosed garden with a children's play area. The welsh collie is called Bonny. Summer morris men, good nearby walks, and the site of the Battle of Langport (1645) is close by.

(Recommended by Dr and Mrs A K Clarke, Nick and Lynne Carter, OPUS, Pete Baker, MLR, the Didler, Steve and Liz Tilley, Lucy Osborn, Bruce Horsefield, Philip Kingsbury)

Free house ~ Licensee Mrs Eileen Pittard ~ Real ale ~ Bar food (12-2, 5.30-7.30; not Sun evening) ~ No credit cards ~ (01458) 250494 ~ Children welcome ~ Dogs welcome ~ Folk singers every third Sat and Irish night fourth Thurs in month Sept-May ~ Open 11.30-2.30, 5.30-11; 11.30-11 Fri and Sat; 12-10.30 Sun

ILMINSTER ST3614 Map 1

George 🍴 ♀

North Street, opposite central butter market

With good food at sensible prices, smiling service and a streak of real individuality, it's not surprising that this little dining pub is so popular; booking is essential to be sure of a table. The neat and relaxed tiled-floor bar is small and very civilised, just a short row of tables along the wall, each with a lit candle, vase of flowers and cushioned dining chairs, a rug at one end, and on the canary wall above the creamy yellow-painted panelled dado a series of big late Victorian prints showing the Beaufort Hunt in action. The lighting is gentle, the piped music unobtrusive, and on the bar counter a fine carving of a family of ducks. Well kept Otter Bitter and St Austell Tribute on handpump, and seven good wines by the glass. A neat blackboard lists a changing choice of food which might include broccoli and crispy bacon soup or mixed salami with dill pickles (£4.50), sandwiches (from £4.75), ploughman's (£5.50), filled baked potatoes (from £6), home-baked ham with eggs and sauté potatoes (£6.25), sausages with bubble and squeak and onion gravy or spinach crêpe with cheese sauce topping (£7.25), steak and kidney pie (£7.75), cod loin steak with parsley butter or fried barnsley chop with rosemary and redcurrant sauce (£8.25), steaks (from £9.25), and puddings such as fresh rhubarb sponge pudding, treacle tart or blackcurrant bakewell (£4.50). The no smoking main dining area, furnished similarly to the bar (and with plenty more ducks), is curtained off at the back. Prudes should perhaps avoid looking at the antique french cartoons in the gents. *(Recommended by Douglas Allen, Theo, Anne and Jane Gaskin)*

Free house ~ Licensee Dora Phelps ~ Real ale ~ Bar food (12-2.30, 7-9.30; no evening food Mon, Weds, Thurs, Sat or Sun; Sun lunch first Sun of month only) ~ Restaurant ~ (01460) 55515 ~ Children in eating area of bar ~ Dogs allowed in bar ~ Open 11.30-3, 7-11; 12-3 Sun; closed Sun evening

KINGSDON ST5126 Map 2

Kingsdon Inn

At Podimore roundabout junction of A303, A372 and A37 take A372, then turn right on to B3151, right into village, and right again opposite post office

Handy for the Lytes Cary (National Trust) and the Fleet Air Arm Museum, this pretty thatched cottage has new licensees this year. There are four charmingly decorated, low-ceilinged rooms. On the right are some very nice old stripped pine tables with attractive cushioned farmhouse chairs, more seats in what was a small inglenook fireplace, a few low sagging beams, and an open woodburning stove; down three steps through balustrading to a light, airy room with cushions on stripped pine built-in wall seats, more stripped pine tables, and a winter open fire. Another similarly decorated room has more tables and another fireplace. They tell us that the bar food and prices have not changed at all: home-made soup (£3.60), ploughman's (£4.80), home-made fishcakes with pepper and chilli mayonnaise (£5.20), smoked haddock and prawn mornay, cottage pie, sausages with onion gravy and lambs liver, bacon and onions (all £6.90), mushroom parcel with wild mushroom sauce (£8.90), wild rabbit in a dijon mustard and white wine sauce (£10.90), half a roast duck in scrumpy cider sauce (£13.40), rack of lamb with port and redcurrant sauce (£13.90), and daily specials. Two areas are no smoking. Well kept Butcombe Bitter, Cotleigh Barn Owl and Otter Bitter on handpump, and several wines by the glass. Picnic-sets on the grass. More reports on the new regime please. *(Recommended by Mike and Heather Watson, Robert Coates, J D O Carter, J Stickland, R T and J C Moggridge, Julie Walton, OPUS, Pat and Robert Watt, Mrs Angela McArt,*

M G Hart, Liz and Tony Colman, Sylvia and Tony Birbeck, Mike Gorton, Clare West, Mrs Ann Webb, Lucy Osborn, Bruce Horsefield, Simon Jones, Charles Gysin, Stuart Paulley, John and Angela Main, Malcolm Ward, Mr and Mrs A Silver, John and Jane Hayter)

Free house ~ Licensees Bob and Carol Horler ~ Real ale ~ Bar food ~ Restaurant ~ (01935) 840543 ~ Children must be well behaved ~ Dogs allowed in bar ~ Open 11-3, 6-11; 12-3, 7-10.30 Sun

LANGLEY MARSH ST0729 Map 1
Three Horseshoes 🍺
Village signposted off B3227 from Wiveliscombe

Tucked away in the Somerset hills, this red sandstone pub is a traditional local. The back bar has low modern settles and polished wooden tables, dark red wallpaper, planes hanging from the ceiling, bank notes papering the wall behind the bar counter, a piano and a local stone fireplace. Well kept Harveys Bitter, Otter Bitter, Palmers IPA and Youngs Bitter tapped from the cask, and farm cider. Bar food includes sandwiches, baguette-style pizzas (from £5.50), steak and kidney pie (£7.75), fish pie (£8.75), steaks (from £9.75), daily specials such as cheese, leek and mushroom stuffed squash (£7.75), baked gilt-head bream with garlic, rosemary and wine (£10.25), honey-roast guinea fowl with smoked bacon and orange (£10.50), locally farmed venison steak with wild mushrooms, brandy and crème fraîche (£11.25), and puddings like chocolate and brandy torte or fruity bread and butter pudding with whisky and marmalade sauce (from £3.25). The no smoking dining area has antique settles, tables and benches; dominoes, cribbage, shove-ha'penny, table skittles, separate skittle alley, and piped music. Part of the bar area is no smoking. You can sit on rustic seats on the verandah or in the sloping back garden, with a fully equipped children's play area; in fine weather there are usually vintage cars outside. They offer self-catering (and maybe bed and breakfast if they are not already booked up). More reports please. *(Recommended by Richard and Anne Ansell, Lyn Huxtable, Richard Seers, Mrs Romey Heaton, the Didler, J Stickland, Brian Monaghan, P M Wilkins, J Coote)*

Free house ~ Licensee John Hopkins ~ Real ale ~ Bar food (12-1.45, 7-9; not winter Mon) ~ (01984) 623763 ~ No children under 8 inside ~ Occasional folk music ~ Open 12-2.30, 7-11; closed winter Mon; 2 weeks early July

LOVINGTON ST5930 Map 2
Pilgrims Rest 🍴 ♀
B3153 Castle Cary—Keinton Mandeville

Now totally no smoking, this quietly placed and civilised country bar/bistro places much emphasis on the particularly good food cooked by the landlord. There's a chatty, relaxed feel, a few bar stools by a corner counter, nice wines by the glass and well kept Cottage Champflower on handpump, from the nearby brewery. A cosy little dark green inner area has sunny modern country and city prints, a couple of shelves of books and china, a cushioned pew, a couple of settees and an old leather easy chair by the big fireplace. With flagstones throughout, this runs into the compact eating area, with candles on tables and some stripped stone; piped music. Using local produce and daily fresh fish, the menu might include lunchtime anchovy soldiers (£5), sandwiches on home-made bread (from £5; smoked salmon with mascarpone and horseradish £7), good cheeses with biscuits or a hunk of their own bread (£7), and hearty fish soup (£8), as well as mushroom tart or potted smoked chicken (£5), tiger prawns in tempura batter with a soy and lime dipping sauce (£6), courgette, tomato and baby red peppers stuffed with vegetable risotto and baked with a piquant tomato sauce (£14), beef stroganoff (£15), free-range chicken under a parmesan crust in a gruyère and tarragon sauce or lemon sole flambéed with a dash of Noilly Prat (£16), rack of lamb with a rich redcurrant and rosemary gravy (£17), and puddings such as sticky toffee pudding, chocolate mousse or crème brûlée (£5). Perhaps better value is the two-course (£12) or three-course (£16) fixed lunch menu; there is also a separate, more formal carpeted dining room. The landlady's service is efficient and friendly, and there's a rack of daily papers. The enclosed garden has tables, chairs and umbrellas on a decked terrace. The car park exit has its own traffic lights – on your way out line your car up carefully or you may wait for ever for them to change. *(Recommended by Brenda and Stuart Naylor, B and M Kendall, OPUS, Anne Westcott, John and Diana Head, Paul and Annette Hallett, Julian and Jennifer Clapham)*

Free house ~ Licensees Sally and Jools Mitchison ~ Real ale ~ Bar food (see opening hours) ~ Restaurant ~ (01963) 240597 ~ Children welcome ~ Dogs allowed in bar ~ Open 12-2.30, 7-11; closed Sun evening, Mon, Tues lunchtime

LUXBOROUGH SS9837 Map 1 ⌂

Royal Oak 🍺

Kingsbridge; S of Dunster on minor roads into Brendon Hills – OS Sheet 181 map reference 983378

The refurbishment programme continues in this busy 14th-c country inn – they hope eventually to put in french windows which will lead to the pretty courtyard garden. The atmospheric bar rooms have beams and inglenooks, good log fires, flagstones in the front public bar, a fishing theme in one room, and a real medley of furniture; the three characterful dining rooms are no smoking. Well kept Cotleigh Tawny, Exmoor Gold and Palmers IPA and 200 on handpump, local farm ciders and several malt whiskies. Lunchtime bar food includes filled baguettes or rustic herb bread (from £4.50), shellfish bisque (£4.95), ploughman's (£5.75), lamb koftas with mint yoghurt (£5.95), thai-style beef curry (£7.25), and specials such as grilled rib-eye steak with stilton sauce (£12.95), and seared cornish scallops with coriander pesto or baked supreme of chicken with a creamy leek and smoked bacon sauce (£13.95); in the evening, there might be deep-fried parcels of red pepper, feta and basil with a coarse pesto dressing (£6.25), salad of avocado and crab with a pink grapefruit dressing (£6.95), spinach and shi-itake mushroom crêpe (£10.50), a pot of cornish mussels (£12.25), and roast rack of local lamb with a ratatouille filled plum tomato and basil jus (£14.95). Shove-ha'penny, darts, dominoes, cribbage and board games. Tables outside, and lots of good surrounding walks. *(Recommended by Brian Root, the Didler, Terry and Dot Mitchell, Jay Smith, John Yardley, Peter and Jane Mawle, Patrick Hancock, Richard and Anne Ansell, MLR, Andrea Rampley, Kev and Gaye Griffiths, Mrs Ann Webb, P M Wilkins, J Coote, John and Gloria Isaacs)*

Free house ~ Licensees James and Sian Waller and Sue Hinds ~ Real ale ~ Bar food ~ Restaurant ~ (01984) 640319 ~ Children in restaurant and family room only ~ Dogs allowed in bar and bedrooms ~ Open 12-2.30, 6-11; 12-2.30, 7-10.30 Sun; closed 25 Dec ~ Bedrooms: £55B/£60(£65B)

MELLS ST7249 Map 2

Talbot 🍺

W of Frome; off A362 W of Buckland Dinham, or A361 via Nunney and Whatley

The attractive main room in this interesting pub has stripped pews, mate's and wheelback chairs, fresh flowers and candles in bottles on the mix of tables, and sporting and riding pictures on the walls, which are partly stripped above a broad panelled dado, and partly rough terracotta-colour. A small corridor leads to a nice little reception with an open fire, and on to restaurant rooms with solid oak tables, high-backed settles and wheelback chairs on a rough pine floor; shove-ha'penny, darts, cribbage and dominoes can be played in the beautifully restored barn bar. Well kept Butcombe and Fullers London Pride tapped from the cask. Taken in the no smoking restaurant, the lunchtime food might include home-made soup (£4.50), chicken liver parfait with spiced apple chutney (£5.50), tagliatelle with wild mushrooms and asparagus in a tarragon cream sauce (£6.25; main course £11.95), ploughman's (£7.50), ham and free-range eggs (£8.65), cottage pie (£8.95), and confit leg of barbary duck with peppercorn sauce (£10.50), with evening choices such as layered pork and chicken terrine with apricot and orange compote (£4.95), individual mozzarella and tomato tartlet drizzled with pesto

(£7.30), steaks (from £12.95), steak, Guinness and mushroom pie (£13.60), calves liver with garlic mash and roast onion gravy (£13.95), and fish dishes like scallops with coriander and garlic butter (£7.95; main course £15.90), plaice fillets in home-made batter (£11.95), and whole brixham lemon sole (£15.95). There are seats in the cobbled courtyard and a vine-covered pergola. The village was purchased by the Horner family of the 'Little Jack Horner' nursery rhyme and the direct descendants still live in the manor house next door. *(Recommended by Gaynor Gregory, Clive and Geraldine Barber, Neil and Angela Huxter, David Hoult)*

Free house ~ Licensee Roger Stanley Elliott ~ Real ale ~ Bar food ~ Restaurant ~ (01373) 812254 ~ Children in eating area of bar and restaurant ~ Dogs allowed in bar and bedrooms ~ Open 12-2.30(3 Sat), 6.30-11; 12-3(3.30), 7-10.30 Sun ~ Bedrooms: /£85B

NORTH CURRY ST3225 Map 1
Bird in Hand
Queens Square; off A378 (or A358) E of Taunton

You can be sure of a warm welcome from the friendly landlord in this well run village pub. The bustling but cosy main bar has some nice old pews, settles, benches and old yew tables on the flagstones, original beams and timbers, some locally woven willow work, and a cheerful atmosphere; cricketing memorabilia, and a log fire in the inglenook fireplace. From an interesting menu, the well liked meals might include sandwiches (from £2.95), baked garlic field mushrooms topped with grilled goats cheese (£5.25), ploughman's (£5.50), moules marinière (£6.50), aubergine and courgette in tomato sauce in a filo parcel (£7.75), hot and sour strips of beef in sweet chilli noodles or thai seafood kebabs (£7.95), steak and kidney pie (winter only, £8.25), barramundi with tomato, coriander and chilli salsa (£13.95), and home-made puddings such as ginger and lemon crunch pie with stem ginger ice-cream or summer pudding (£4.50); Sunday roast lunch. More formal dining is available in the separate, newly redecorated no smoking restaurant area. Well kept Otter Ale and a couple of guests like Butcombe Gold and Fullers London Pride on handpump, Rich's farm cider, and eight wines by the glass; good service. Piped music and fruit machine. *(Recommended by Roger Wain-Heapy, Michael Butler, John and Gloria Isaacs, Ian Phillips, Dr Martin Owton, Stephen and Jean Curtis)*

Free house ~ Licensee James Mogg ~ Real ale ~ Bar food ~ Restaurant ~ (01823) 490248 ~ Children in eating area of bar and restaurant ~ Dogs allowed in bar ~ Open 12-3, 6-11; 12-4, 7-11 Sat; 12-3, 7-10.30 Sun

NORTON ST PHILIP ST7755 Map 2
George 🛏
A366

This remarkable old building has been a pub for nearly 600 years, and was originally built to house merchants buying wool and cloth from the rich sheep-farming Hinton Priory at the great August cloth market. The central Norton Room, which was the original bar, has really heavy beams, an oak panelled settle and solid dining chairs on the narrow strip wooden floor, a variety of 18th-c pictures, an open fire in the handsome stone fireplace, and a low wooden bar counter. Well kept Wadworths IPA, 6X and a seasonal guest on handpump, and pleasant service. As you enter the building, there's a room on the right with high dark beams, squared dark half-panelling, a broad carved stone fireplace with an old iron fireback and pewter plates on the mantelpiece, a big mullioned window with leaded lights, and a round oak 17th-c table reputed to have been used by the Duke of Monmouth who stayed here before the Battle of Sedgemoor – after their defeat, his men were imprisoned in what is now the Monmouth Bar. The Charterhouse Bar is mostly used by those enjoying a drink before a meal: a wonderful pitched ceiling with trusses and timbering, heraldic shields and standards, jousting lances, and swords on the walls, a fine old stone fireplace, high backed cushioned heraldic-fabric dining chairs on the big rug over the wood plank floor, and an oak dresser with some pewter. You can eat in the bar from the lighter menu or from the more elaborate restaurant one: pasta in a tomato and basil sauce, a cold meat or cheese platter with pickles, ham and egg, chicken curry or fish pie (all £7.50), as well as home-made soup (£3.95), celery and stilton tartlet (£5.45), chicken liver parfait (£5.95), mixed nut and red lentil roast (£9.95), home-made steak and mushroom in ale pie (£10.95), fillet of local trout with toasted almonds (£11.95), and half a duck with sage and onion stuffing or rib-eye steak marinated in Tabasco and chilli (£13.95). The no smoking dining room (a restored barn with original oak ceiling beams, a pleasant if haphazard mix of early 19th-c portraits and hunting prints, and the same mix of vaguely old-looking furnishings) has a good relaxing, chatty atmosphere. The bedrooms are very atmospheric and comfortable – some reached by an external Norman stone stair-turret, and some across the cobbled and flagstoned courtyard and up into a fine half-timbered upper gallery (where there's a lovely 18th-c carved oak settle). A stroll over the meadow behind the pub (past the picnic-sets on the narrow grass pub garden) leads to an attractive churchyard around the medieval church whose bells struck Pepys (here on 12 June 1668) as 'mighty tuneable'. *(Recommended by Klaus and Elizabeth Leist, the Didler, Dr and Mrs A K Clarke, W K Wood, Ian Phillips, Michael Hasslacher, H W Roberts, Mark and Mary Fairman)*

Wadworths ~ Managers David and Tania Satchel ~ Real ale ~ Bar food ~ Restaurant ~ (01373) 834224 ~ Well behaved children welcome ~ Dogs allowed in bar ~ Open 10.30-2.30, 5.30-11; 10.30-11 Sat; 12-3, 7-10.30 Sun; closed evenings 25 Dec and 1 Jan ~ Bedrooms: £60B/£80B

OAKE ST1526 Map 1
Royal Oak
Hillcommon, N; B3227 W of Taunton; if coming from Taunton, ignore signpost on left for Oake and go 200 yards, pub is on left directly off B3227

This pub's not easy to find, but persevere; there's always a good bustle in this neatly kept country place and plenty of weekday customers keen to enjoy the popular food. The spacious bar has several separate-seeming areas around the central servery; on the left is a little tiled fireplace, with a big woodburning stove on the other side. The windows have smart curtains, there are plenty of fresh flowers, and lots of brasses on the beams and walls. At the back is a long dining area which leads out to a pleasant sheltered garden. Tables are candlelit in the evenings. Most of the pub is no smoking. Well kept Cotleigh Tawny, Exmoor Gold and RCH Pitchfork on handpump and several wines by the glass; cheerful service. At lunchtime, bar food includes sandwiches (from £3.95; filled baguettes from £4.25), filled baked potatoes (from £4.95), ploughman's (£5.95), four-egg omelette (from £6.95), and home-made curry or lasagne (£7.95), with evening choices such as home-made soup (£3.95), brandied chicken liver pâté (£4.95), king prawns in filo pastry (£5.50), steak and mushroom in ale pie (£7.95), good sausages with spring onion crushed potato (£8.75), cajun chicken on onion and lime marmalade (£9.75), steaks (from £9.95), and lots of home-made daily specials such as pork tenderloin in cider, apple, honey and cream or breast of chicken stuffed with fresh asparagus, wrapped in bacon with a rich shallot and red wine sauce (£12.95), seared red snapper with tomato and shallot salsa (£13.50), and venison steak with a madeira and juniper sauce (£13.95). There's a lunchtime carvery on Sunday, Tuesday and Thursday (£7.50; OAP £6.25 including a free pudding). Skittle alley in winter, and piped music. *(Recommended by Bob and Margaret Holder, John and Fiona McIlwain, Sheila Brooks, Theo, Anne and Jane Gaskin)*

Free house ~ Licensees John and Judy Phripp ~ Real ale ~ Bar food (11-3, 6.30-9.30) ~ (01823) 400295 ~ Children in restaurant ~ Open 11-2.30(3 Sat), 6-11; 12-3, 6.30-10.30 Sun; closed 25 Dec

---

If we don't specify bar meal times for a main entry, these are normally 12-2 and 7-9; we do show times if they are markedly different.

PITNEY ST4428 Map I
Halfway House 🍺
Just off B3153 W of Somerton

It's always so friendly in this old-fashioned and busy pub with a good mix of people chatting at communal tables and enjoying the fantastic range of up to ten real ales. The three rooms all have roaring log fires and a homely feel underlined by a profusion of books, maps and newspapers; it can get a bit smoky. As well as regular ales tapped from the cask such as Branscombe Vale Branoc, Butcombe Bitter, Hop Back Crop Circle and Summer Lightning, and Teignworthy Reel Ale, there are four changing guests. They also have 20 or so bottled beers from Belgium and other countries, Wilkins's farm cider, and quite a few malt whiskies; cribbage and dominoes. Good simple filling food includes sandwiches (from £2.95; smoked salmon and cream cheese £3.95), soup (£3.50), filled baked potatoes (from £3.45), and a fine ploughman's with home-made pickle (£5.50). In the evening they do about half a dozen home-made curries (from £7.95). There are tables outside. *(Recommended by Brian Pearson, Bruce Bird, Sarah and Anthony Bussy, Alan and Paula McCully, Andrea Rampley, the Didler, Guy Vowles, OPUS, Mrs Ann Webb, Lucy Osborn, Bruce Horsefield, Theo, Anne and Jane Gaskin)*

Free house ~ Licensee Julian Lichfield ~ Real ale ~ Bar food (not Sun) ~ (01458) 252513 ~ Children welcome ~ Dogs welcome ~ Open 11.30-3, 5.30-11; 12-3, 7-10.30 Sun

PORTISHEAD ST4777 Map I
Windmill 🍺
3.7 miles from M5 junction 19; A369 into town, then follow 'Sea Front' sign off left and into Nore Road

Sometimes, this place is so popular that the car park fills up and you have to park in a nearby field. It is by no means a traditional village pub and started life as a golf clubhouse but re-opened as a three-level all-day family dining pub. One of its big pluses is that in fine weather there's a marvellous view over the Bristol Channel to Newport and Cardiff (with the bridges on the right), from the wall of picture windows on the top and bottom floors. The bottom floor is a simple easy-going no smoking family area, the top one a shade more elegant with its turkey carpet, muted green and cream wallpaper and dark panelled dado. The middle floor, set back from here, is quieter and (with its black-painted ceiling boards) more softly lit. A third of the building is no smoking; fruit machine. To eat, you find a numbered table, present yourself at the order desk (by a slimline pudding show-cabinet), pay for your order, and return to the table with a tin (well, stainless steel) tray of cutlery, condiments and sauce packets. It works well: the good value generous food then comes quickly, and might include home-made soup (£3.25), grilled goats cheese with chilli jam (£3.45), sandwiches (from £3.50), filled baked potatoes (from £3.95), ploughman's (£4.95), chicken, ham and leek suet pudding (£6.95), spinach and red pepper lasagne (£7.50), home-made steak and mushroom in ale pie (£7.75), daily specials such as faggots (£6.95), lambs liver (£7.25), home-made curry (£7.75), and lamb shank (£8.95); there are dishes for smaller appetites (from £3.25) and early bird offers. Unexpectedly, they have six quickly changing real ales on handpump, such as Bass, Butcombe Gold, Courage Best, RCH Pitchfork and two guest beers. Out on the seaward side are picnic-sets on three tiers of lantern-lit terrace. *(Recommended by P Price, Stan and Susan Fysh, Comus and Sarah Elliott, Ian Phillips, J H Bescoby, Tom Evans, Emma Kingdon, Dr and Mrs A K Clarke, John A Barker, B and M Kendall)*

Free house ~ Licensee J S Churchill ~ Real ale ~ Bar food (all day) ~ (01275) 843677 ~ Children in eating area of bar and family room ~ Dogs allowed in bar ~ Open 11-11; 12-10.30 Sun

---

Though we don't usually mention it in the text, most pubs will now make coffee or tea – always worth asking.

SHEPTON MONTAGUE ST6731 Map 2
Montague Inn
Village signposted just off A359 Bruton—Castle Cary

A new licensee has taken over this busy little country pub. The rooms are simply but tastefully furnished with stripped wooden tables, kitchen chairs and a log fire in the attractive inglenook fireplace, and there's a restaurant with french windows overlooking the gardens. At lunchtime, bar food now includes sandwiches, soup (£3.95), and ham and eggs, ploughman's, hot and sour pickled tiger prawns, vegetarian tarte de provence, and seared scallops and smoky bacon (all £6.95); evening choices such as steaks (from £12), half a roast guinea fowl or pork tenderloin (£13), duck with raspberries (£14), and puddings (from £4). Well kept Greene King Abbot and IPA tapped from the cask, and quite a few wines by the glass. The pretty back garden and terrace have good views. More reports on the new regime please. *(Recommended by Katharine Cowherd, John Close, Colin and Janet Roe, Des and Olga Hall, Clare West, David and Ruth Hollands, Fergus Dowding, Edward Mirzoeff, OPUS, Glen and Nola Armstrong)*

Free house ~ Licensee Sean O'Callaghan ~ Bar food (not Sun evening, Mon) ~ Restaurant ~ (01749) 813213 ~ Children welcome ~ Open 11.30-3(3.30 Sat), 5.30-11; 12-4, 7-10 Sun; closed Mon ~ Bedrooms: /£65S

STANTON WICK ST6162 Map 2
Carpenters Arms 🍽 ♀ 🛏
Village signposted off A368, just W of junction with A37 S of Bristol

Most customers come to this neatly kept and attractive, low tile-roofed inn to enjoy the good, very popular food. At lunchtimes during the week (best to book then) it is full of diners mostly of retirement age and the helpful and friendly landlord offers a warm welcome to all. The no smoking Coopers Parlour is on the right and has one or two beams, seats around heavy tables, and attractive curtains and plants in the windows; on the angle between here and the bar area there's a fat woodburning stove in an opened-through corner fireplace. The bar has wood-backed built-in wall seats and some leather-cushioned stools, stripped-stone walls, and a big log fire. There's also a snug inner room (lightened by mirrors in arched 'windows') and a newly refurbished no smoking restaurant which has leather sofas and easy chairs in a comfortable lounge area. From the menu, there might be home-made soup (£3.95), caesar salad with anchovy dressing (£4.95), sandwiches (from £4.95), salmon, cod and chive fishcake with provençale sauce (£5.50), chicken liver and wild mushroom pâté with spiced pear chutney (£5.95), spaghetti tossed with cherry tomatoes, black olives, garlic and parmesan (£8.95), steak, mushroom and ale pie (£9.95), fillet of cod in pesto batter with tomato mayonnaise (£10.95), lambs liver and crispy bacon on sage mash with red wine jus or thai chicken curry (£11.95), pork tenderloin on caramelised apple and shallot with honey mustard dressing (£12.95), steaks (from £14.95), and puddings such as chocolate and Baileys tart, honey, vanilla crème brûlée or raisin and apple crumble (£4.75); there are also daily specials. They may ask you to leave your credit card behind the bar. Well kept Butcombe Bitter, Courage Best, and Wadworths 6X on handpump, ten wines by the glass and a dozen malt whiskies; fruit machine and TV. The inn is set in peaceful countryside with pretty flowerbeds, lovely hanging baskets and tubs, and picnic-sets on the front terrace. *(Recommended by Richard and Judy Winn, Dr and Mrs T E Hothersall, Mr and Mrs R J Weller, David and Wendy Puttock, Mr and Mrs Johnson-Poensgen, John Mitchell, Julia and Richard Tredgett, Dr and Mrs A K Clarke, M G Hart, Ian Phillips, John and Fiona McIlwain, P M Wilkins, J Coote, Alan and Paula McCully, Barry and Anne, MRSM)*

Buccaneer Holdings ~ Manager Simon Pledge ~ Real ale ~ Bar food (12-2.30, 7-10) ~ Restaurant ~ (01761) 490202 ~ Children in eating area of bar and restaurant ~ Dogs allowed in bar ~ Pianist Fri and Sat evenings ~ Open 11-11; 12-10.30 Sun ~ Bedrooms: £64.50B/£89.50B

STOKE ST GREGORY ST3527 Map 1 🏠

Rose & Crown 🍺 ♀

Woodhill; follow North Curry signpost off A378 by junction with A358 – keep on to Stoke, bearing right in centre, passing church and follow lane for ½ mile

Unsmart but cheerful and friendly, this bustling country pub is still a thriving family business. The cosy bar is decorated in a pleasant stable theme: dark wooden loose-box partitions for some of the interestingly angled nooks and alcoves, lots of brasses and bits on the low beams and joists, stripped stonework, a wonky floor, and appropriate pictures including a highland pony carrying a stag; many of the wildlife paintings on the walls are the work of the landlady, and there's an 18th-c glass-covered well in one corner. The two rooms of the dining area lead off here with lots of country prints and paintings of hunting scenes, animals and birds on the walls, more horsebrasses, jugs and mugs hanging from the ceiling joists, and candles in bottles on all tables. At lunchtime, the popular food includes good sandwiches on home-made granary bread (from £3.75; chorizo, egg mayonnaise and watercress £4.25), ploughman's (from £4.75), home-cooked ham and eggs (£5.50), home-made beefburger topped with stilton or salmon fishcakes (£7.50), large salads (from £7.50), lambs liver and bacon (£8.50), a big bowl of moules marinière (£9.50), and tandoori chicken (£10.50); evening choices such as home-made soup (£3.50), goats cheese and walnut salad with apple vinaigrette (£5.25), crab cakes with sweet chilli (£6.50), stir-fried vegetables and rice (£8.50), steaks (from £12.50), half a crispy duck with orange and brandy sauce (£13.50), skate wings in parsley butter (£14.50), and home-made puddings like milk chocolate and Baileys mousse, apple and blackberry crumble or baked lemon and lime tart with blackcurrant coulis (from £3.75); helpful, polite service. The restaurants are no smoking. Well kept Exmoor Ale, Fox and Gold, and a guest such as Archers Village Bitter on handpump, and decent wines; piped music and fruit machine. Under cocktail parasols by an apple tree on the sheltered front terrace are some picnic-sets. The pub is in an interesting village in the Somerset Levels with willow beds still supplying the two basket works. *(Recommended by Mrs A P Lee, Bob and Margaret Holder, Mr and Mrs Colin Roberts, Michael Rowse, P and J Shapley, Ian Phillips, Liz and Alun Jones, Michael Doswell, Rev D E and Mrs J A Shapland, DRH and KLH, Ken Marshall, Mrs Ann Webb, P M Wilkins, J Coote, Michael Hasslacher, Theo, Anne and Jane Gaskin, Mr and Mrs P Dix, Geoff and Sylvia Donald)*

Free/house ~ Licensees Stephen, Sally, Richard and Leonie Browning ~ Real ale ~ Bar food ~ Restaurant ~ (01823) 490296 ~ Children welcome ~ Dogs allowed in bar ~ Open 11-3, 6.30(6 Sat)-11; 12-3, 7-11 Sun; closed evening 25 Dec ~ Bedrooms: £36.50(£46.50B)/£53(£73B)

TRISCOMBE ST1535 Map 1

Blue Ball 🍺 ♀

Village signposted off A358 Crowcombe—Bagborough; turn off opposite sign to youth hostel; OS Sheet 181 map reference 155355

This smart inn is on the first floor of a lovely 15th-c thatched stone-built former coaching stables. The long, low building slopes gently down on three levels, each with its own fire, and cleverly divided into seating by hand-cut beech partitions. Well kept Cotleigh Tawny, and guests such as Exmoor Gold, St Austell HSD and Tribute, and Sharps Doom Bar on handpump, and eight house wines by the glass. From the lunchtime menu, the good, popular food includes soup (£4.50), filled rolls (£4.95), ploughman's (£6.95), hickory home-smoked chicken salad with mango salsa (£5.95), cod in beer batter (£8.50), pigeon breast with wholegrain mustard mash and honey cranberries (£13.50), vine-ripened tomato tarte tatin with goats cheese and pesto (£9.95), and rack of lamb with tarragon and bean cassoulet and port sauce (£14.95), with evening dishes such as leek, potato and crayfish terrine with lemon and chive crème fraîche (£6.95), seared hand-dived scallops with black pudding and chorizo dressing (£7.95), duck breast and confit leg with orange butter sauce and onion marmalade (£14.50), and fillet steak with confit leek and madeira sauce (£16.95); puddings like italian lemon tart, sticky toffee pudding with butterscotch sauce, and cappuccino crème brûlée (£4.75). All dining areas are no smoking. They have two friendly springer spaniels and two pure white cats. The decking at the top of the woodside, terraced garden makes the most of the views. *(Recommended by Jay Smith, Gaynor Gregory, Anne and Paul Horscraft, Basil and Sylvia Walden, Canon Michael Bourdeaux, Peter and Giff Bennett, P M Wilkins, J Coote, Trevor and Diane Waite, Pete Devonish, Ian McIntyre, John and Jane Hayter, Mrs J L Wyatt, Rod and Chris Pring)*

Free house ~ Licensees Sharon Murdoch and Peter Alcroft ~ Real ale ~ Bar food (12-1.45, 7-9; not Sun evening or Mon) ~ Restaurant ~ (01984) 618242 ~ Children in eating area of bar and restaurant ~ Dogs allowed in bar ~ Open 12-3, 7-11; 12-3, 7-10.30 Sun; closed Mon ~ Bedrooms: £40B/£60B

WELLS ST5545 Map 2
City Arms ◗
High Street

The pub has been completely refurbished this year, and now has a first floor terrace in the cobbled courtyard serving food. The main bar has been extended and operates as a café bar/patisserie during the day and as a bistro at night, and they have opened a second kitchen to cope with demand. They keep six real ales on handpump: Butcombe Bitter, Gold and Blond, Greene King Abbot, Moles Rucking Mole, Sharps Doom Bar and Wadworths IPA. Also, 15 wines by the glass, 30 malt whiskies, and four draught ciders. The restaurant and main bar are no smoking. Bar food includes sandwiches and filled baked potatoes (from £2.25), home-made soup (£2.95), home-made chicken liver pâté with home-made bread (£3.95), vegetable tagine with couscous or smoked haddock and spinach in a creamy sauce (£4.95; ample helping £6.95), ham and egg or sausage and mash (£6.95), hot chicken curry (£7.95), poached salmon with hollandaise (£8.75), steaks (from £9.95), and home-made puddings like bread and butter pudding or treacle and orange tart (£3.95); piped music, cribbage and dominoes. More reports please. *(Recommended by David Carr, Hugh Roberts, Richard and Margaret Peers, Mr Williams, Dr and Mrs A K Clarke, Joyce and Maurice Cottrell, OPUS, Henry and Fiona Dryden)*

Free house ~ Licensee Jim Hardy ~ Real ale ~ Bar food (all day until 10(9 Sun) ~ Restaurant ~ (01749) 673916 ~ Children welcome ~ Dogs allowed in bar ~ Open 9-11; 9-10.30 Sun

Crown 🛏
Market Place

In the Market Place and overlooked by the cathedral, this former coaching inn is an ideal meeting place. The various bar areas have a very clean, contemporary feel, with the walls painted white or blue, light wooden flooring, and plenty of matching chairs and cushioned wall benches; up a step is a comfortable area with a sofa and newspapers. A sunny back room (where children tend to go) has an exposed stone fireplace, GWR prints, and a couple of fruit machines and TV; it opens on to a small courtyard with a few tables. Reliable bar food at lunchtime includes soup (£3.75), sandwiches and panini (from £3.75), ploughman's or crispy battered cod (£5.75), chilli, lasagne or honey roast ham and egg (£5.95), and puddings such as warm almond tart with praline ice-cream or glazed lemon tart with raspberry coulis (£4.75); early evening extras such as roast supreme of chicken stuffed with asparagus and wrapped in pancetta on creamy sweetcorn mash or chargrilled vegetable and goats cheese strudel (£10.95), salmon and prawns in garlic and herb butter (£12.95), and rib-eye steak (£14.95). Well kept Bass and Butcombe Bitter and Blond on handpump, and 11 wines by the glass. The restaurant and part of the Penn Bar are no smoking; piped music, fruit machine and TV. William Penn is said to have preached from a window here in 1685. This is a nice place to stay. *(Recommended by Rob Bowran, David Carr, Mrs C Peters, Henry and Fiona Dryden, Minda and Stanley Alexander, Michael H Legge)*

Free house ~ Licensee Adrian Lawrence ~ Real ale ~ Bar food (all day) ~ Restaurant ~
(01749) 673457 ~ Children welcome ~ Dogs allowed in bedrooms ~ Open 11-11;
12-10.30 Sun ~ Bedrooms: £55S/£85B

WITHYPOOL SS8435 Map 1

Royal Oak 🏠
Village signposted off B3233

R D Blackmore stayed in this country village inn while writing *Lorna Doone*. It has
new owners and new licensees this year so we are keeping our fingers crossed that
not too much will change. The beamed lounge bar has a fine raised log fireplace,
comfortably cushioned wall seating and slat-backed chairs, sporting trophies and
paintings, and various copper and brass ornaments on its walls. The locals' bar has
some old oak tables, and plenty of character. Bar food now includes sandwiches,
home-made soup (£3.95), home-made chicken liver pâté (£5.95), dressed crab
(£10.25), grilled salmon supreme with hollandaise or home-made beef, mushroom
and ale pie (£10.95), monkfish with wild mushrooms and a white wine, cream and
cheese sauce or lamb shank in rosemary, redcurrant and red wine gravy (£13.95),
fried breast of duck with cherry sauce (£14.95), fillet steak slices in stilton, cider
and cream (£15.95), and home-made puddings (from £4.50). The dining room is no
smoking. Well kept Exmoor Ale and a guest like Courage Best or Exmoor Gold on
handpump, and several wines by the glass. There are wooden benches on the
terrace, and just up the road, some grand views from Winsford Hill. The River
Barle runs through the village itself, with pretty bridleways following it through a
wooded combe further upstream. *(Recommended by Andrea Rampley, Patrick and
Phillipa Vickery, Jay Smith, Bob and Margaret Holder, Brian and Anita Randall, P R Morley,
C S McVeigh, S Topham, Alex Mason, Phil and Sally Gorton, Duncan Cloud, Bob and
Marilyn Baylis, Paul Humphreys)*

Coast & Country Inns ~ Manager Rita Redway ~ Real ale ~ Bar food (12-2, 6.30-9) ~
(01643) 831506 ~ Children in eating area of bar and restaurant ~ Dogs allowed in bar and
bedrooms ~ Open 11-11; 12-10.30 Sun; closed 25 Dec ~ Bedrooms: £65B/£110B

WOOKEY ST5145 Map 2

Burcott 🍺
B3139 W of Wells

Welcoming and old-fashioned, this is a neatly kept little roadside pub liked by both
locals and visitors. There are two simply furnished small front bar rooms that are
connected but different in character – they hope to refurbish them over the next
year: a square corner bar counter in the lounge, fresh flowers at either end of the
mantelpiece above the tiny stone fireplace, Parker-Knollish brocaded chairs around
a couple of tables, and high bar stools. The other bar has beams (some willow
pattern plates on one), a solid settle by the window and a high backed old pine
settle by one wall, cushioned mate's chairs and fresh flowers on the mix of nice old
pine tables, old-fashioned oil-type wall lamps, and a hunting horn on the bressumer
above the fireplace. A little no smoking room on the right has darts, shove-
ha'penny, cribbage and dominoes, neat built-in wall seats, and small framed
advertisements for Schweppes, Coke, Jennings and Oakhill, and there's a roomy
back no smoking restaurant with black joists, stripped stone walls and sea-green
check tablecloths; piped music. Good, proper home cooking includes chicken liver
pâté or salmon and dill fishcake (£3.95), sandwiches or filled baked potatoes (from
£4.25), ploughman's (£5.25), honey roast ham and eggs (£6.45), tasty lasagne or
vegetable and cashew nut bake (£6.95), steak in ale pie (£7.45), apricot chicken
breast (£9.75), steamed salmon in lemon, garlic and thyme (£10.45), steaks (from
£11.45), and daily specials. Well kept Branscombe Vale Draymans, Hop Back
Summer Lightning and RCH Pitchfork on handpump, and several wines by the
glass. The window boxes and tubs in front of the building are pretty in summer,
and the sizeable garden is well spread and has picnic-sets, plenty of small trees and
shrubs, and views of the Mendip Hills; there's a paddock beyond. They are hoping

to convert the stables into four self-catering units. *(Recommended by Phil and Sally Gorton, Tom Evans, Alan and Paula McCully, P M Wilkins, J Coote)*

Free house ~ Licensees Ian and Anne Stead ~ Real ale ~ Bar food (12-2, 6.30-9.30; not Sun or Mon evenings) ~ Restaurant ~ (01749) 673874 ~ Children in straightforward family room ~ Open 11.30-2.30, 6-11; 12-3, 6(7 Sun)-11 Sat; closed 25 and 26 Dec, 1 Jan

LUCKY DIP

Besides the fully inspected pubs, you might like to try these Lucky Dips recommended to us and described by readers (if you do, please send us reports: www.goodguides.co.uk).

ASHCOTT [ST4436]
☆ *Pipers* [A39/A361, SE of village]: Reliable dining pub with large welcoming beamed lounge, good range of well kept mainstream and other ales, Addlestone's cider, wide choice of enjoyable reasonably priced food from sandwiches to steaks inc children's, prompt helpful friendly service, woodburner, leather armchairs, pictures for sale and potted plants, prettily set no smoking beamed dining area; unobtrusive piped music; pleasant roadside garden *(Dr and Mrs C W Thomas)*
☆ *Ring o' Bells* [High St; follow Church and Village Hall signs off A39 W of Street]: Neatly kept comfortably modernised local, steps up and down making snug areas (at least for the able-bodied), well kept local Moor Merlins Magic and two interesting guest beers, Wilkins's farm cider, wide choice of good value wholesome home-made food from good sandwiches and rolls to unusual dishes and sturdy puddings, separate no smoking stripy pink dining room, decent wines, chatty landlord and helpful service, inglenook woodburner; piped pop music, fruit machines, skittle alley; attractively planted back garden with play area, camping *(S J and B S Highmore, BB)*
AXBRIDGE [ST4354]
Oak House [The Square]: Good bar area though more restaurant than pub, good food, local Wolvershill real ale *(Hugh Roberts)*
BARRINGTON [ST3918]
Royal Oak: Welcoming and roomy old stone pub opp church in pretty village, handy for Barrington Court, with popular food inc generous lunchtime carvery, friendly prompt attentive service *(P and D Carpenter)*
BATH [ST7564]
Ale House [York St]: Relaxed and unassuming city-centre local with big windows to street, well kept Courage, Fullers London Pride and Charles Wells Bombardier, flame-effect fire, bargain lunchtime food from baked potatoes up in rambling cellar bar, more seating upstairs, Bath RFC memorabilia *(Colin and Peggy Wilshire, Dr and Mrs A K Clarke, Michael and Alison Sandy, Ian Phillips)*
Barley Mow [Bathwick St]: Bigger than it looks, with reasonably priced fresh food, good wine choice, Bass, Butcombe and Fullers London Pride, friendly atmosphere, lounge area with sofas, board games and shove-

ha'penny; small courtyard *(Michael Mutton)*
Bell [Walcot St]: Split-level real ale pub, long and narrow, with eight well kept regular ales and interesting guest beers, dark ceiling, lots of pump clips and gig notices, good value baguettes, bar billiards; calm at lunchtime, packed and lively with loud piped music evenings, frequent live music *(R Huggins, D Irving, E McCall, T McLean, Dr and Mrs A K Clarke, Pete Baker, Rob Stevenson)*
Boaters [Argyle St, by Pulteney Bridge]: Good spot near river and weir, main bar upstairs, neat cellar bar mainly for younger people, well kept Bass and Courage, enterprising filled rolls, friendly staff; no children inside; tables in good-sized floodlit courtyard *(Dr and Mrs A K Clarke)*
Boathouse [Newbridge Rd]: Large riverside establishment nr Kennet & Avon marina on outskirts, rugs on wooden floor, apple-theme and riverside decorations, good value food from filled ciabattas to steaks and restaurant dishes, efficient courteous service, decent house wines, Greene King IPA and Old Speckled Hen; children very welcome, wicker furniture and potted plants in conservatory on lower level, picnic-sets out in neat garden with labelled herbs and steps up to waterside balcony *(Dr and Mrs A K Clarke, Betsy and Peter Little)*
☆ *Coeur de Lion* [Northumberland Pl; off High St by W H Smith]: Tiny single-room pub, perhaps Bath's prettiest, simple, cosy and friendly, with well kept ales such as Adnams and Jennings, candles and log-effect gas fire, good mulled wine at Christmas, lunchtime filled rolls in summer; may be piped music, stairs to lavatories; open all day, tables out in charming flower-filled flagstoned pedestrian alley *(Patrick Hancock, LYM, Mike Pugh, Dr and Mrs A K Clarke, the Didler, R Huggins, D Irving, E McCall, T McLean, Dr and Mrs M E Wilson)*
☆ *Cross Keys* [Midford Rd (B3110)]: Pleasant dining lounge with smarter end restaurant (best to book, high chairs for children), good cheap food cooked to order from good sandwiches (home-baked bread), home-made pies and sausages up inc popular pies and great choice of puddings, real ales such as Everards, friendly service, locals' bar; big garden with prettily populated aviary – great attraction for children *(Meg and Colin Hamilton, Francis Johnston)*

☆ *George* [Bathampton, E of Bath centre, off A36 or (via toll bridge) off A4; Mill Lane]: Big well reworked and extended Chef & Brewer dining pub with good-sized bar opening through arches into pleasantly rambling beamed no smoking rooms with soft lighting, candles on nice mix of tables, rugs on polished boards, dark panelling, period portraits and plates, three log fires, wide blackboard food choice all day at good range of prices from baguettes to duck and fresh fish, well kept Courage Best and Directors, Greene King Old Speckled Hen and Wadworths 6X, good range of wines by the glass, efficient young uniformed staff; may be quiet piped jazz; children welcome, picnic-sets on enclosed terrace and out on grass (shorter menu for outside) *(Chris and Ann Coy, Dr and Mrs A K Clarke, James Morrell, Dr and Mrs M E Wilson, Meg and Colin Hamilton, Betsy and Peter Little)*

☆ *Hop Pole* [Albion Buildings, Upper Bristol Rd]: Bustling Bath Ales pub, their beers and a guest kept well, farm cider, decent wines by the glass and good soft drinks, good if not cheap food Tues-Sun lunchtimes from sandwiches through modern recipes using good fresh ingredients to juicy steak in bar and former skittle alley restaurant, traditional settles and other pub furniture on bare boards in four tastefully reworked linked areas inc no smoking area, lots of black woodwork and ochre walls, no juke box or pool; children welcome while food served, attractive two-level back courtyard with boules, terrace tables, fairy-lit vine arbour and summer houses with heaters, opp Victoria Park with its great play area, open all day Fri-Sun *(OPUS, Mark O'Sullivan, Pamela and Merlyn Horswell, Colin and Peggy Wilshire, BB, Ian Phillips, Michael Doswell)*

Olde Farmhouse [Lansdown Rd]: On hill overlooking Bath, well kept Abbey Bellringer from neighbouring microbrewery, Butcombe and Wadworths, real fire, perhaps filled cobs, L-shaped parquet-floor bar with wall seats, panelling, stained-glass lamps and bar gantry, big jazz pictures; juke box, big-screen TV; jazz some evenings, open all day *(David Carr, the Didler, Rob Stevenson)*

Pig & Fiddle [Saracen St]: Lively pub with several well kept sensibly priced real ales inc Abbey and Bath, two big open fires, clocks set to different time zones, bare boards and cheery red and yellow walls and ceiling, good value home-made food, steps up to darker bustling servery and little dining area, takeaways too, games area and several TVs; lots of students at night, good piped trendy pop music then; picnic-sets on big heated front terrace *(Dr and Mrs A K Clarke, BB, Dr and Mrs M E Wilson, the Didler)*

Pulteney Arms [Daniel St/Sutton St]: Small old-fashioned pub with well kept Butcombe, Fullers London Pride, Wadworths 6X and Youngs from casks behind capacious three-sided bar counter, food inc good big chip baps, daily papers, old furniture on wooden floors, jug collection, books, lots of rugby posters and Bath RFC memorabilia; unobtrusive piped music, TV; pavement tables *(Dr and Mrs A K Clarke, Pete Baker, Patrick Hancock, Michael Dandy)*

Raven [Queen St]: Reworked (after a spell as Hatchets) in civilised lighter style, small and friendly, with four changing ales such as Abbey Bellringer, Archers, Badger Tanglefoot and Wickwar Cotswold Way, cheerful helpful staff, good lunchtime food choice inc speciality pies and sausages, open fire, charity bookshelves, some stripped stone, no smoking room upstairs *(Terry Buckland, Dr and Mrs M E Wilson)*

Richmond Arms [Richmond Pl, off Lansdown Rd]: Relaxed informal atmosphere in small 18th-c house converted into two-room pub off the tourist track, bright smiling service, good imaginative food, good wine choice, well kept Bass and Butcombe, bare boards, pine tables and chairs, attractive pastel décor, some aboriginal artefacts and pictures; children welcome, tables in enclosed pretty front garden *(Bernard Stradling, David Carr)*

Ring o' Bells [Widcombe Parade]: Small warmly welcoming pub/bistro, good fresh and individual sensibly priced food in relaxed surroundings, well kept Fullers London Pride and foreign beers on tap, good coffee; worth the walk – don't expect to park nearby *(Michael Doswell, Roger Wain-Heapy)*

Salamander [John St]: Traditional town-centre pub tied to Bath Ales, their full range and guest beers kept well, friendly if not always speedy service, bare boards, black woodwork and dark ochre walls, popular bar lunches from sandwiches up, two rooms downstairs, no smoking open-kitchen upstairs restaurant, decent wines, daily papers, no pool, juke box or machines *(Dr and Mrs M E Wilson, Guy Vowles, Dr and Mrs A K Clarke, James Morrell, BB)*

BECKINGTON [ST8051]

☆ *Woolpack* [off A36 Bath—Warminster]: Well refurbished old inn with imaginative and well prepared if not cheap food from well filled ciabattas up (nice to have linen napkins even with snacks), well kept Greene King Abbot and John Smiths, decent wines, charming helpful staff, big log fire and chunky candlelit tables in flagstoned bar, attractive smarter no smoking oak-panelled dining room and conservatory; children welcome, comfortable period bedrooms with own bathrooms (but avoid the attic), open all day *(Guy Vowles, LYM, M and D J Hill, Michael Butler, Henry and Fiona Dryden)*

BISHOP'S WOOD [ST2512]

Candlelight [off A303/B3170 S of Taunton]: Roomy and busy yet cosy, wide choice of popular reasonably priced food from sandwiches to bargain wkdy lunches, pleasant dining room, cheerful staff, spotless housekeeping, Butcombe and Cottage or Otter, warm fire, no smoking areas *(Bob and Margaret Holder, Dr and Mrs M E Wilson)*

BLACKFORD [ST4147]

☆ *Sexeys Arms* [B3139 W of Wedmore]: Pleasant village pub dating from 1400s, cosy beamed lounge with big fireplace, basic tiled floor public bar, enjoyable meals all cooked to order in two sizes of helpings, cheerful service, evening restaurant; unobtrusive piped music; garden picnic-sets, cl Mon at least in winter (when wkdy hours are a bit restricted) *(P M Wilkins, J Coote)*

BLAGDON [ST5058]

☆ *New Inn* [off A368; Park Lane]: No smoking, old-fashioned beamed pub with some comfortable antique settles among more modern furnishings, two inglenook log fires, enjoyable well priced food from filled rolls up (even Sun evening), proper landlord and efficient friendly service, well kept Butcombe and Wadworths IPA and 6X; piped music, no mobile phones, children or dogs; nice views from tables outside looking down to Blagdon Lake and beyond *(LYM, Stuart Paulley, Michael and Judy Buckley, Ian and Rose Lock)*

BLEADON [ST3457]

☆ *Queens Arms* [just off A370 S of Weston; Celtic Way]: 16th-c pub with attractive linked areas, winged settles, woodburners and old hunting prints, no smoking stripped-stone back bar area and flagstoned restaurant, well kept Butcombe and several changing ales tapped from the cask, bar food from sandwiches and baked potatoes to steaks, duck and bass, skittle alley; has suffered management changes but seems on good convivial form in recent months; piped music, TV, no children; some seats outside, open all day Fri-Sun *(Grahame Brooks, LYM, M G Hart, Dr and Mrs C W Thomas, P M Wilkins, J Coote, John Coote, Comus and Sarah Elliott, Tom Evans)*

BRADFORD-ON-TONE [ST1722]

☆ *White Horse* [fairly nr M5 junction 26, off A38 towards Taunton]: Neatly kept and comfortable stone-built local in quiet village, wide choice of enjoyable reasonably priced food in straightforward bar eating area and cheerfully decorated dining room, good service, well kept Badger Tanglefoot and Cotleigh Tawny, decent wines, armchairs by ornate woodburner, hunting cartoons, bar billiards; piped music; back garden with fairy-lit arbour and picnic-sets on lawn, skittle alley *(Nick and Lynne Carter, Frank Willy, BB, Christine and Neil Townend, Peter and Jean Hoare, Bob and Margaret Holder)*

BRADLEY GREEN [ST2438]

Malt Shovel [off A39 W of Bridgwater, nr Cannington]: Friendly staff in beamed pub with elm tables, simple seating and woodburner, little beamed snug, no smoking restaurant and family room, well kept Butcombe and guest beers, wines by the glass, decent bar food with children's helpings, traditional games and sizeable skittle alley; piped music; children in eating areas, picnic-sets in garden *(Bruce Bird, Hugh Roberts, LYM, Mr and Mrs G Sadie)*

BRISTOL [ST5672]

☆ *Adam & Eve* [Hope Chapel Hill, Hotwells]: Backstreet pub transformed by new chef doing good inexpensive creative food changing daily, with all sorts of interesting recipes and organic ingredients; organic wines and juices too, belgian beers, good country-pub atmosphere, friendly staff, log fire, dark bare boards, café chairs and wall settles, quaint nooks and corners; gentle piped music, not much parking nearby *(Gaynor Gregory, BB)*

Bag o' Nails [St Georges Rd, Hotwells]: Popular real ale pub with half a dozen or so well kept changing ales, lots of bottled beers, Nov beer festival, lunchtime rolls, long bare-boards panelled bar lined with benches and some small tables, soft gas lighting, inglenook seat by gas fire, glazed portholes into cellar, old local pictures; piped music *(the Didler, Ian and Nita Cooper, Simon and Amanda Southwell, Catherine Pitt)*

☆ *Brewery Tap* [Upper Maudlin St/Colston St]: Well kept sensibly priced Smiles ales in chatty and relaxed unpretentious pub, interesting décor, panelling and bare boards, log fire in no smoking half, good value simple lunches, unusual continental bottled beers, no piped music; tables on good-sized heated terrace, open all day *(Dr and Mrs A K Clarke, Simon and Amanda Southwell, Stan and Susan Fysh, Joan and Michel Hooper-Immins, the Didler, Bob and Margaret Holder, Rob Stevenson)*

Bridge Inn [Passage St]: Neat little one-bar city pub nr floating harbour, good friendly service, lots of film stills and posters, well kept Bath and guest ales, popular lunchtime snacks; well reproduced piped music; open all day *(the Didler)*

☆ *Commercial Rooms* [Corn St]: Impressive Wetherspoons in former merchants' club, big hall with lofty domed ceiling and snug cubicles along one side, gas lighting, comfortable quieter no smoking room with ornate balcony; wide changing choice of good real ales, their sensibly priced food all day, friendly chatty bustle, wind indicator; good location, very busy wknd evenings, side wheelchair access *(Ian and Nita Cooper, Dr and Mrs A K Clarke, Alan and Paula McCully, the Didler, Rob Stevenson)*

Cornubia [Temple St]: 18th-c backstreet pub popular for well kept real ales and bottled beer choice, farm cider, good value home-cooked food inc Sun roasts, small woody seating areas in oranges, browns and reds; benches outside *(Mike Pugh, Simon and Amanda Southwell, the Didler, Rob Stevenson)*

Highbury Vaults [St Michaels Hill, Cotham]: Friendly series of small partly panelled rooms with old-fashioned furniture and prints, well kept Youngs, cheap bar food (not Sat/Sun evenings), bar billiards, dominoes, cribbage; busy with Uni students and teachers, steep steps to lavatories; children welcome, attractive back terrace with heated arbour, open all day *(Simon and Amanda Southwell, Ian Phillips, LYM, the Didler)*

Hope & Anchor [Jacobs Wells Rd, Clifton]: Bare-boards 18th-c pub with large shared pine tables, well kept changing ales from small breweries, two belgian beers, fast pleasant service, reliable substantial cheap food inc lots of sandwiches, interesting dishes and sumptuous ploughman's – very popular lunchtime; piped music, occasional live, can get crowded late evening; disabled access, summer evening barbecues in good-sized tiered back garden with interesting niches *(Simon and Amanda Southwell, David Carr, Donald Godden, Catherine Pitt)*

☆ *Kings Head* [Victoria St]: Narrow 17th-c pub with big front window and splendid mirrored bar back, corridor to cosy panelled back snug with serving hatch, well kept Bass, Courage Best and Smiles, toby jugs on joists, old-fashioned local prints and photographs, interesting gas pressure gauge, friendly relaxed atmosphere, generous reasonably priced food inc filling toasties and good yorkshire puddings wkdy lunchtimes; no credit cards, lacks a no smoking section; pavement tables, cl Sat lunchtime, open all day Weds-Fri *(Dr and Mrs A K Clarke, Pete Baker, Di and Mike Gillam, the Didler, BB, Susan and Nigel Wilson, Meg and Colin Hamilton)*

Knights Templar [The Square]: Roomy new glass and stainless steel Wetherspoons very handy for Temple Meads station, decent usual food and well kept beers; tables outside *(Giles and Annie Francis, Rob Stevenson)*

Old Fish Market [Baldwin St]: Imposing red and cream brick building converted to roomy and airy pub, good mural showing it in 1790s along one wall, lots of wood inc rather ornate counter, parquet floor, relaxed friendly atmosphere, good value lunchtime food from sandwiches through home-baked pies to Sun lunch, well kept Fullers London Pride, ESB and seasonal and guest beers, good coffee, daily papers; quiet piped music, unobtrusive sports TV *(Simon and Amanda Southwell, Dr and Mrs A K Clarke, Richard Pierce)*

Ostrich [Lower Guinea St, Bathurst Basin – follow General Hospital sign from inner ring rd]: Unassuming three-room pub in good dockside position, with plenty of waterside seating, Courage Best and Directors and Wadworths 6X, good value usual food from adventurous baguettes up inc wkdy bargains, small dining area down a few steps; quiet piped music *(Michael and Alison Sandy)*

Penny Farthing [Whiteladies Rd, Clifton]: Bright panelled ex-bank with half a dozen or more real ales such as Adnams Broadside, Badger Tanglefoot, Bass, Butcombe and Wadworths IPA and 6X racked behind bar, late Victorian bric-a-brac inc penny-farthing (and photographs of them), armchairs opp bar, lots of table seating, very reasonably priced home-made food lunchtime and evening, friendly helpful staff; can get very busy evenings, with doorman; pavement tables *(Emma Kingdon, the Didler)*

Robin Hood [St Michaels Hill]: Friendly local with well kept Wadworths beers, cheap lunchtime food from baguettes and baked potatoes up, rock star photographs especially Elvis; small pleasant heated outside area *(Simon and Amanda Southwell)*

Wellington [Gloucester Rd, Horfield (A38)]: Lively Bath Ales local with their beers and guest ales kept well, separate no smoking room off large horseshoe bar, food served (we've had no reports on this yet); jazz and blues nights; plenty of tables outside, open all day Sun, and Fri/Sat in summer *(R Huggins, D Irving, E McCall, T McLean, Rob Stevenson)*

White Lion [Quay Head, Colston Ave]: Small simple bare-boards bar with very friendly licensees, well kept Wickwar and interesting guest ales, wide choice of sandwiches, log fire; a couple of tables out by road, garden with wrought-iron furniture *(Simon and Amanda Southwell, BB)*

BRUTON [ST6835]

Royal Oak [Coombe St]: Cosy open-plan beamed pub, comfortable old settles, good range of well kept changing ales, good value food *(B M Eldridge)*

BUCKLAND DINHAM [ST7551]

☆ *Bell* [High St]: Good atmosphere in 16th-c pub with narrow beamed main bar, pine furnishings inc booth settles, interesting décor, woodburner in huge inglenook; wide choice of generous good value food, helpful service, well kept ales Butcombe Bitter and Gold and Fullers London Pride, quite a few malt whiskies, children allowed in partly no smoking two-level dining room; cribbage, dominoes, piped music; dogs welcome, sheltered garden with side terraces *(LYM, Ian Phillips, Jenny Garrett)*

CANNINGTON [ST2539]

Rose & Crown [High St]: Character beer pub with tiled floor, big fireplace and lots of bric-a-brac inc clocks all stopped at ten to eight; Caledonian Deuchars IPA and other well kept changing ales *(Phil and Sally Gorton)*

CASTLE CARY [ST6333]

Brookhouse [N of centre]: Stone-built pub with well priced pubby food from sandwiches to popular Sun roasts, Butcombe, Gribble Fursty Ferret and Sharps Doom Bar, skittle alley; pleasant garden *(Ian Phillips)*

George [just off A371 Shepton Mallet—Wincanton; Market Pl]: Thatched country-town hotel, quiet and civilised, with big inglenook in small front bar, inner no smoking lounge off main central reception area, decent food from sandwiches and filled baked potatoes up, well kept Greene King ales, decent house wines, no smoking restaurant; children welcome, 16 bedrooms, open all day *(LYM, Phil and Sally Gorton)*

CHARLTON ADAM [ST5328]

Fox & Hounds [Broadway Rd, just off A37 about 3 m N of Ilchester]: Big neatly kept pub with prompt friendly service, good value home-made food, three welcoming labradors *(G J C Moss)*

CHEDDAR [ST4653]

☆ *Gardeners Arms* [Silver St]: New licensees in comfortably modernised pub tucked quietly away in the old part of the town, Bass, Butcombe and Courage Best, attractive no smoking two-room beamed dining area – we have not yet had reports on the food here, from ciabattas and baguettes up, which was good under the previous landlord, and included some things served all day; children and dogs welcome, picnic-sets with playthings and a wendy house in back garden, open all day; news please *(LYM)*

Riverside [Cliff St]: Stone-built pub with good helpings of enjoyable well presented food in separate restaurant, reasonable prices, bar food and decent children's dishes too, efficient staff; garden with play area, open all day *(E Clark)*

CHEW MAGNA [ST5763]

Pelican [S Parade]: Quiet and unostentatious villagey pub, Bass, Butcombe and Marstons Pedigree, usual current pub food, some small helpings available, warm woodburner enjoyed by dozing cat *(Ian Phillips)*

☆ *Pony & Trap* [Knowle Hill, New Town; back rd to Bishop Sutton]: Small gently refurbished tucked-away pub with comfortable layout, flagstones and antiques, relaxing atmosphere, good variety of food inc plenty of puddings, quick friendly service, well kept Butcombe and Ushers, good coffee, daily papers, children's room, downstairs restaurant – good views at the back; quiet piped music; good walks, delightfully rural hillside setting near Chew Valley Lake *(Meg and Colin Hamilton)*

CHURCHINGFORD [ST2112]

York [Honiton Rd (old coach rd across Blackdown Hills)]: Attractive old creeper-covered inn with cheery young landlord, wide food choice (steaks have been praised), two Greene King ales and Otter, dark beams and panelled dado, leather sofas as well as wheelback chairs around the tables in central area with big log fireplace, lighter tables in dining area on right, public bar with pool and TV on left; a couple of tables out in front, bedrooms with own bathrooms *(Dr and Mrs M E Wilson)*

CLEVEDON [ST4071]

Old Inn [Walton Rd (B3124 on outskirts)]: Neatly refurbished and extended by new licensees, well kept changing ales, bargain filled rolls *(Tom Evans)*

☆ *Salthouse* [Salthouse Rd, above Marine Lake]: Recently reopened after major nautical-theme refurbishment, large bar in enviable position looking across bay towards pier, simple furnishings, well kept Bass, Sharps Doom Bar and Shepherd Neame Spitfire, enjoyable reasonably priced food (can take a while when they're busy) esp fish and seafood in dining room, proficient service; stunning sea and pier views from picnic-sets on large front terrace, open all day *(Alan and Paula McCully, Steve Whalley, Tom and Ruth Rees)*

COMBE FLOREY [ST1531]

Farmers Arms [off A358 Taunton—Williton, just N of main village turn-off]: Neatly rebuilt and very popular dining pub, picturesquely thatched and beamed, well kept Bass, Exmoor and a couple of other real ales, cheerful staff, good log fire; plenty of tables outside *(Bob and Margaret Holder, BB)*

COMBE HAY [ST7359]

☆ *Wheatsheaf* [off A367 or B3110 S of Bath]: Pleasantly old-fashioned low-beamed rooms, rustic furnishing and décor, big log fire, friendly attentive service, enjoyable generous food, well kept Courage Best, Greene King Old Speckled Hen and John Smiths tapped from the cask, spiced hot winter drinks; children in eating areas, tables on spacious terraced lawn overlooking church and steep valley, dovecotes built into the walls, plenty of good nearby walks, open all day in summer *(Dr and Mrs A K Clarke, Brian and Bett Cox, Rev Michael Vockins, LYM, Mark and Heather Williamson, Mr and Mrs W D Borthwick, Basil and Jarvis)*

COMPTON DUNDON [ST4832]

Castlebrook Inn [Castlebrook]: Cheerful two-bar village local with super flagstone floors, blazing fire, well kept local beer, big back family restaurant; tables on lawn behind *(Steve and Liz Tilley)*

CONGRESBURY [ST4363]

Old Inn [Pauls Causeway, down Broad St opp The Cross]: Low-beamed and flagstoned local, pleasant décor with pretty curtains in deep-set windows, huge fireplaces, one with ancient stove opening to both bar and no smoking dining area, reasonably priced pubby food, well kept Bass and Youngs tapped from the cask; tables in back garden, open all day *(Alan and Paula McCully)*

CORSTON [ST6764]

Wheatsheaf [A39 towards Marksbury]: Small no smoking bar off main one, log fire in each, friendly staff, huge helpings of good value pub food from lunchtime sandwiches, baguettes and baked potatoes up, well kept Butcombe, farm cider, stripped pine, bare boards, local prints on stripped stone walls *(Basil and Jarvis, Nigel Long)*

CORTON DENHAM [ST6322]

Queens Arms: Attractive old stone-built inn in tucked-away village nr Cadbury Castle, keen young staff, good enterprising food using fresh local supplies, fine wines by the glass, well kept beer, low tables in comfortable smallish main bar with flagstones and woodburner, pleasant dining room; may be quiet piped music; children, dogs and muddy boots welcome, tables under cocktail parasols on colourful heated back terrace, five comfortable recently refurbished bedrooms with own bathrooms and good views *(OPUS)*

COSSINGTON [ST3640]

Red Tile [Middle Rd]: Welcoming local with enjoyable generous food, helpful service, good choice of west country real ales, cosy fire; children and dogs welcome, garden with big adventure play area *(Jackie and Alan Moody)*

CRANMORE [ST6643]

☆ *Strode Arms* [off A361 Frome—Shepton Mallet]: Largely no smoking dining pub back on form under new chef/landlord and his wife, good choice of enjoyable food from substantial bar snacks up, named local meat suppliers, imaginative puddings, pleasant relaxed atmosphere and friendly staff, well kept Wadworths real ales, good reasonably priced wine range, attractive country furnishings in linked rooms of former farmhouse, log fire; piped music; children in restaurant, tables on front terrace and in back garden, handy for East Somerset Railway (*Annie Barratt, LYM, Sylvia and Tony Birbeck, Mrs Pat Crabb, Gaynor Gregory*)

CROSCOMBE [ST5844]

☆ *George* [Long St]: Relaxed village pub with enjoyable home-made food freshly made by landlady from sandwiches up, good seasonal veg, friendly efficient Canadian landlord and young staff, three real ales and two or three local farm ciders, good short choice of sensibly priced wines, log fire, chatty locals, darts, unusual table games, back skittle alley, stylish and attractive no smoking dining room with local artwork or photographs; attractive garden behind (*David Barnes, Phil and Sally Gorton, Sylvia and Tony Birbeck*)

CROSS [ST4254]

New Inn [A38 Bristol—Bridgwater, junction A371]: Roadside pub worth knowing for good choice of changing ales; fine views, usual pub food, upstairs games room (*Hugh Roberts*)

White Hart [not far from A38; Old Coach Rd]: Attractive and relaxing old two-bar local, beams, pillars and big log fires, generous bar food inc good fish and chips, good service, nice wines and well kept beer (*Henry and Fiona Dryden*)

DITCHEAT [ST6236]

☆ *Manor House* [signed off A37 and A371 S of Shepton Mallet]: Pretty village inn under new ownership, keen young manager and staff, well kept Butcombe and two guest beers, enjoyable home-made food from bar snacks to both hearty and more sophisticated main dishes, open fires, unusual arched doorways linking big flagstoned bar to comfortably relaxed lounge and restaurant, skittle alley; children welcome, bedrooms being upgraded, tables on back grass (*BB, Michael Sargent, P M Wilkins, J Coote*)

DOULTING [ST6443]

☆ *Poachers Pocket* [Chelynch Rd, off A361]: Cheerful and popular modernised black-beamed local, log fire in stripped-stone end wall, lots of stripped pine, gundog pictures, plentiful good value food from sandwiches through good specials to Sun roasts, welcoming quick service, well kept Butcombe, Wadworths 6X and a guest beer, local farm cider (a spring cider festival, as well as an autumn beer one), pub games, friendly cat and dog; children in eating area and large family room/skittle alley, back garden with country views (*Susan and Nigel Wilson, LYM*)

DRAYCOTT [ST4750]

Strawberry Special [off A371; Station Rd]: Vibrant village local with high-backed settles, huge open fire, good choice of beers, very welcoming landlord and American landlady (*Ken Flawn*)

DULVERTON [SS9127]

Woods [Bank Sq]: Friendly staff, well kept Cotleigh Tawny, Exmoor Fox and Otter Head, enjoyable reasonably priced food inc interesting vegetarian dishes and log fire in new conversion of beamed former bakery and café (*Len Clark*)

DUNSTER [SS9943]

☆ *Luttrell Arms* [High St; A396]: Small hotel in 15th-c timber-framed abbey building, high beams hung with bottles, clogs and horseshoes, stag's head and rifles on walls above old settles and more modern furniture, big log fires, good cheerful service, fairly priced bar food from sandwiches and baguettes (home-made bread) to interesting hot dishes, small helpings available, well kept Bass and Exmoor Fox, good wines in three glass sizes; ancient glazed partition dividing off small galleried and flagstoned courtyard, upstairs access to quiet attractive garden with Civil War cannon emplacements and great views, comfortable bedrooms; we had been thinking of making this a main entry, but (a bad sign) their PR people were too unhelpful when it came to fact-checking time – so if you think it should be one, please give us plenty of detail on prices, opening times etc! (*A and B D Craig, R Michael Richards, H O Dickinson, BB, Dr D J and Mrs S C Walker, Gordon Stevenson, Michael Rowse, S Topham*)

EAST COKER [ST5412]

☆ *Helyar Arms* [off A37 or A30 SW of Yeovil; Moor Lane]: Good fresh well presented food with inventive treatment of local produce in spotless and roomy open-plan low-beamed lounge and old-fashioned high-raftered dining room, good welcoming service, well kept real ales, local farm cider, reasonably priced wines, woodburner, lots of brass and pictures, dark-stained traditional furnishings, world map with pushpins for visitors; may be piped classical music; no dogs, comfortable bedrooms with own bathrooms, attractive setting (*Mary Ellen Cummings, John and Diana Head, Charles Gysin*)

EAST HARPTREE [ST5453]

Castle of Comfort [B3134, SW]: Mendips coaching inn, tree-trunk supporting beams in ancient bar, well kept Bass, Butcombe and a guest beer, enjoyable food inc good Sun roasts from named local farms, interesting vegetarian menu; big garden with play area (*Rob Stevenson*)

EAST LAMBROOK [ST4218]

Rose & Crown: Attractive stone-built pub sympathetically extended from compact 17th-c core with log fire, appealing atmosphere, enjoyable inexpensive food, real ales, restaurant extension showing old well through central glass floor panel (*Guy Consterdine*)

EAST WOODLANDS [ST7944]

☆ *Horse & Groom* [off A361/B3092 junction]: Small country pub with pews and settles in flagstoned bar, woodburner in comfortable lounge, big no smoking dining conservatory, reasonably priced bar food, well kept Archers Golden, Branscombe Vale Branoc and Butcombe Bitter tapped from the cask, traditional games; dogs welcome away from restaurant, children in eating areas, picnic-sets in nice front garden with more seats behind, handy for Longleat (*LYM, Dr and Mrs M E Wilson, Jack Taylor, the Didler,*

Martin and Karen Wake, Mr and Mrs A H Young)

ENMORE [ST2434]

Tynte Arms: Warm and welcoming, with pleasant staff, good value food, well kept real ales, attractive rooms, low beams and open fires *(Bob and Margaret Holder, B M Eldridge)*

EXEBRIDGE [SS9324]

☆ *Anchor* [B3222 S of Dulverton; pub itself actually over the river, in Devon]: Comfortable child-friendly pub in idyllic Exmoor-edge spot, some attractive furnishings, oak panelling and pictures, huge good value blackboard food choice, good friendly service, three well kept ales such as Exmoor and Wadworths 6X, local farm cider, above-average wines, woodburner, family eating area and no smoking restaurant; smaller back games bar, skittle alley; open all day at least in summer, nice big riverside garden with plenty of tables and play area, comfortable bedrooms, good breakfast, fishing rights (nets for sale) *(LYM, Keith and Jackie Middleton)*

EXFORD [SS8538]

Crown [The Green (B3224)]: Attractive Exmoor inn for sale as we went to press; two-room bar with hunting décor, old local photographs and big stone fireplace, Exmoor Ale and Gold and a guest beer, Thatcher's farm cider, ambitious bar food, restaurant; piped music, TV; children and dogs welcome, charming waterside garden behind, smaller terraced side garden overlooking village and green, bedrooms, open all day wknds *(Geoff and Teresa, S Topham, Lynda and Trevor Smith, Bob and Margaret Holder, LYM)*

FAILAND [ST5171]

Failand Inn [B3128 Bristol—Clevedon]: Simply furnished old coaching inn with tasty reasonably priced popular food, cheerful efficient service, well kept ales, comfortable dining extension; may be piped music *(Tom Evans, Richard and Judy Winn, A D Lealan)*

FAULKLAND [ST7354]

☆ *Faulkland Inn*: L-shaped country local with good value food from interesting hot or cold filled sandwiches to wider evening choice inc modern starter/light dishes and good carefully cooked fresh fish, friendly well trained staff, Butcombe Bitter and Gold and Otter or Palmers Dorset Gold, decent wines, contemporary colours alongside beams, flagstones and some stripped stone, dining area on left, games area in public end; piped music; children welcome, picnic-sets on small back lawn, four good value bedrooms, pretty village *(Jack Taylor, BB, Ian Phillips)*

FRESHFORD [ST7960]

☆ *Inn at Freshford* [off A36 or B3108]: Comfortable modernised stone-built beamed pub with plenty of atmosphere, well kept Butcombe, Courage Best, Wadworths 6X and a guest beer, popular bar food from sandwiches, baguettes and filled baked potatoes up, no smoking restaurant; piped music, some live; children and dogs welcome,

picnic-sets in pretty garden, nearby walks *(Meg and Colin Hamilton, Roger Wain-Heapy, LYM, Susan and Nigel Wilson)*

FROME [ST7748]

Griffin [Milk St]: Unpretentious and civilised, very much a one-man operation, good beer brewed by the friendly landlord in the back room, open fire, bare boards, easy-going mixed crowd; occasional live music, cl lunchtime *(B M Eldridge)*

GLASTONBURY [ST4938]

King Arthur: Newly refurbished, with farm ciders as well as real ales, good company and atmosphere *(David Ellerington)*
Who'd A Thought It [Northload St]: Friendly and helpful new licensees, well kept Palmers IPA and 200, good choice of wines by the glass, usual food from toasties up, daily papers, attractive décor with high-backed curved settle, coal fire, pine panelling, stripped brick, beams and flagstones, nicely quirky oddments, no smoking dining area; children and dogs welcome, bedrooms being refurbished as this edition went to press, open all day *(LYM, Ian Phillips, Virginia Williams)*

HALSE [ST1428]

New Inn [off B3227 Taunton—Bampton]: 17th-c traditional inn with good range of well kept real ales, local farm ciders, enjoyable generous home cooking, friendly family service, woodburner in big inglenook, no smoking candlelit dining room, separate games area and skittle alley, no piped music; tables in garden, homely bedrooms with own bathrooms and good breakfast, lovely village *(P M Wilkins, J Coote)*

HASELBURY PLUCKNETT [ST4511]

Haselbury Mill [Merriott Rd; off A30 E of Crewkerne towards Merriott, away from village]: Very modernised country dining place in quiet spot, big picture windows looking over duck pond, good inexpensive food inc carvery and OAP bargains, well spaced tables in comfortable light and airy dining lounge, snug low-ceilinged bar on right; tables out on informal lawn by pretty stream, open all day exc Sun afternoon (and may be taken up with weddings Sat), bedrooms *(Bob and Margaret Holder, BB)*

HILLFARRANCE [ST1624]

Anchor: Comfortable modernised pub with lots of flower tubs outside, well presented usual food in eating areas off attractive two-part bar, pleasant atmosphere, well kept Butcombe and Exmoor, friendly prompt service, family room; garden with play area, bedrooms, caravan site, holiday apartments *(Bob and Margaret Holder)*

HINTON CHARTERHOUSE [ST7758]

Rose & Crown [B3110 about 4 miles S of Bath]: Roomy partly divided pub with well kept Bass, Butcombe and Smiles tapped from casks, wide choice of good value generous home-made food inc plenty of fish, nice panelling, ornate stone fireplace, rugby memorabilia, restaurant, skittle alley; open all day Sat *(Meg and Colin Hamilton, BB, P M Wilkins, J Coote)*

☆ *Stag* [B3110 S of Bath; High St]: Attractively furnished bustling ancient pub very popular for good sensibly priced home-made food in cosy log-fire bar and stripped-stone no smoking dining area, well kept ales such as Bass and Butcombe, smiling helpful service (but can slow – it gets very busy), no piped music; provision for children, tables outside, has been open all day (*Dr and Mrs M E Wilson, LYM, Meg and Colin Hamilton*)

HINTON ST GEORGE [ST4212]

☆ *Lord Poulett Arms* [off A30 or A356 NW of Crewkerne; High St]: 17th-c pub with quietly attractive antique furnishings, lots of cosy nooks and open fires, some emphasis on enjoyable upmarket food, friendly relaxed service; also small plain public bar with well kept Butcombe, guest beers tapped from the cask, farm cider, good value wines, skittle alley with darts; children welcome, good disabled access, tables in prettily planted back garden, rare very old fives court, attractive stone village with good walks, four bedrooms, cl Mon lunchtime (*LYM, OPUS, David Howell, Fergus Dowding*)

HOLFORD [ST1541]

Plough [A39]: Busy village pub popular for enjoyable food inc good value Sun roasts and good steaks, well kept real ale, good friendly service; wonderful walks in Quantocks (*Mike Vince, Paul Humphreys*)

HORFIELD [ST5976]

Wellington [off A38 Gloucester Rd]: Friendly and roomy 1920s pub done up in traditional unpretentious style by Bath Ales, their real ales kept well, comfortable bar seating, no smoking room, enjoyable simple fresh food inc generous Sun roasts; very busy on home match days for Bristol RFC or Bristol Rovers; open all day Sun (*Barry and Anne*)

HORSINGTON [ST7023]

Half Moon [signed off A357 S of Wincanton]: 18th-c beamed pub with light and airy knocked-through bars, stripped stone and oak floors, inglenook log fires, proper village atmosphere, tasty sensibly priced home-made food from ploughman's with local cheeses to steak, well kept Badger Tanglefoot, Palmers Tally Ho and Ringwood Best, decent wines, friendly prompt service, evening restaurant; good disabled access and facilities, attractive sloping front garden, big back garden with play area, comfortable chalet bedrooms (*Chris and Ann Coy, LYM, B M Eldridge*)

HUNTWORTH [ST3134]

Boat & Anchor [just off M5 junction 24; local rd off exit roundabout, then turn right towards narrow canal bridge]: Enjoyable food inc consistently good steaks, good house wines, lovely canalside garden, simple bedrooms (*Andy Sinden, Louise Harrington*)

ILCHESTER [ST5222]

Dolphin [High St]: Two neatly renovated high-ceilinged bars with dark wood and lighter prints, sound pub food, Wadworths real ales, friendly service; dogs welcome (*B Phenin*)

KELSTON [ST7067]

☆ *Old Crown* [Bitton Rd; A431 W of Bath]: Four small convivial traditional rooms with beams and polished flagstones, carved settles and cask tables, logs burning in ancient open range, two more coal-effect fires, well kept ales such as Bath Gem, Butcombe Gold and Blonde and Wadworths 6X tapped from the cask, Thatcher's cider, well priced wines, friendly barmaids, cheap wholesome bar food (not Sun or Mon evenings) inc good salads, small restaurant (not Sun), no machines or music; dogs welcome (biscuit tub behind bar), children in eating areas, open all day wknds, picnic-sets under apple trees in sunny sheltered back garden (*Roger Wain-Heapy, Dr and Mrs A K Clarke, Barry and Anne, LYM, Michael Doswell, Dr and Mrs M E Wilson, P M Wilkins, J Coote*)

KEWSTOKE [ST3263]

Commodore [Beach Rd]: Hotel at end of Sand Bay, beach and dune walks, attractive beamed bar with no smoking part and nautical bric-a-brac, neat dark tables, welcoming service, Courage and John Smiths from small counter, reasonably priced food, two for one lunches popular with older people (younger customers evenings); bedrooms (*Dr and Mrs C W Thomas*)

KEYNSHAM [ST6568]

☆ *Lock-Keeper* [A4175]: Bustling and popular, in lovely spot on Avon island with terrace and big shady garden by lock, marina and weir; full Youngs range kept well, appealing well priced food from baguettes and baked potatoes to more upmarket dishes, friendly helpful young staff, small room by bar, arches to unpretentious main divided room with rust and dark blue décor, black beams and bare boards, barrel-vaulted lower area; boules (*Dr and Mrs A K Clarke, Michael Doswell*)

KILMERSDON [ST6952]

Jolliffe Arms: Attractive setting, reasonably priced home-made food inc enjoyable light lunches, well kept beer, good wines by the glass, friendly service (*Jenny Garrett*)

KILVE [ST1442]

☆ *Hood Arms* [A39 E of Williton]: Friendly attentive service, enjoyable good value bar food cooked to order (no sandwiches), well kept ales such as Exmoor, cosy little plush lounge, woodburner in bar, no smoking restaurant, skittle alley, tables on sheltered back terrace by pleasant children's garden, nice bedrooms – back are quietest (*Bob and Margaret Holder, LYM*)

LITTON [ST5954]

☆ *Kings Arms* [B3114, NW of Chewton Mendip on A39 Bath—Wells]: Great character in interesting partly 15th-c pub rambling more extensively than you'd have thought, low heavy beams and timbers, polished flagstones, nice old-fashioned settles, huge fireplace with plenty of copper and brass, appealing food from sandwiches to more upmarket hot dishes, well kept Greene King IPA and Ruddles County, large family room; picnic-sets in neat sloping streamside gardens with good play

area, open all day Sun (cl 3-5 wkdys)
(Chris and Ann Coy, LYM)

LONG ASHTON [ST5370]

Miners Rest [Providence Lane]: Basic friendly pub, comfortable and unpretentious, with good farm cider and well kept beer *(Gaynor Gregory)*

LYDFORD ON FOSSE [ST5630]

Cross Keys [just off A37]: Interesting pub with enjoyable good value straightforward meals, welcoming service, well kept Wadworths 6X and a guest such as Glastonbury Lady of the Lake, milk shakes too *(Joan and Michel Hooper-Immins)*

MARSTON MAGNA [ST5922]

Red Lion [Rimpton Rd]: Current licensees building strong local reputation for enjoyable varied food in pub with relaxed wine bar feel, real ales inc Salisbury, good wines, pleasant staff; good garden *(OPUS)*

MERRIOTT [ST4412]

Swan [Lower St]: Enjoyable hearty home-made food with good fresh veg, log fire snugged in by high-backed settles, Beryl Cook prints *(Marianne and Peter Stevens)*

MIDFORD [ST7660]

☆ *Hope & Anchor* [Bath Rd (B3110)]: Good attractively presented interesting food from light dishes to mouthwatering more elaborate things and imaginative puddings in civilised bar and heavy-beamed and flagstoned restaurant end, well kept Bath Gem, Butcombe Gold and a guest such as Sharps Cornish Coaster, good house wines, proper coffee, efficient service, candles and soft lighting, log fire; teak tables on sheltered back terrace, picnic-sets on next level up, pretty walks along canals and River Frome *(Roger Wain-Heapy, M G Hart, Gaynor Gregory, BB, Michael Doswell, Andy Lickfold)*

MIDSOMER NORTON [ST6654]

White Hart [The Island]: Chatty Victorian local with several rooms, Bass and Butcombe tapped from the cask, old local mining photographs and memorabilia, enjoyable bar snacks; open all day *(Dr and Mrs A K Clarke, the Didler)*

MILBORNE PORT [ST6718]

Queens Head [A30 E of Sherborne]: Friendly helpful staff, quick service, wide range of enjoyable food inc bargain nights, good range of well kept ales such as Butcombe, Greene King Old Speckled Hen and Wadworths 6X, farm ciders, decent wines, neat beamed lounge, restaurant and no smoking conservatory, games in public bar, skittle alley, live music nights; provision for children and quiet dogs, reasonable disabled access, tables in sheltered courtyard and garden with play area, three cosy good value bedrooms *(LYM, Dennis Jenkin)*

MINEHEAD [SS9646]

Queens Head [Holloway St]: Attractive bay-windowed stone building, mainly open-plan, with no smoking at central bar which has well kept ales inc Exmoor Gold and Hart, alcove seating, raised family dining area on left, pleasant décor with old local photographs,

thriving atmosphere, friendly professional service, generous and enjoyable usual food such as sandwiches, baguettes, baked potatoes, cottage pie and fish and chips, back pool room; may be quiet piped music, nearby parking difficult *(R Michael Richards, Martin Grosberg)*

MONKSILVER [ST0737]

☆ *Notley Arms* [B3188]: Pleasant beamed country pub smartened up a bit under current licensees, generous food from sandwiches and filled pitta breads to locally reared sirloin steak and some exotic dishes, well kept Exmoor, Smiles Best and Wadworths 6X, farm cider, country wines, cribbage, dominoes and alley skittles, bright no smoking family room with play things; dogs welcome, immaculate charming streamside garden *(P and J Shapley, the Didler, LYM, Karen Eliot)*

MONKTON HEATHFIELD [ST2526]

Merry Monk: Lots of space for the popular food, good young staff, two real ales *(Bob and Margaret Holder)*

MONTACUTE [ST4916]

☆ *Kings Arms* [Bishopston]: Extended partly 16th-c hotel with simple modern tables and chairs in small stripped stone bar, log fire between it and no smoking restaurant, some emphasis on enjoyable reasonably priced food from panini and interesting light dishes up, well kept Greene King IPA and Ruddles with a guest such as Highgate Black Pig, good wines by the glass and coffee, magazines and daily papers; children welcome, pleasant garden behind, comfortable bedrooms with own bathrooms *(Peter B Brown, Mary Ellen Cummings, LYM, Dennis Jenkin, Klaus and Elizabeth Leist)*

☆ *Phelips Arms* [The Borough; off A3088 W of Yeovil]: Good choice of interesting fresh food from filled crusty rolls to elaborate restauranty main dishes in roomy and airily refurbished open-plan bar and smart yet relaxed restaurant, attentive landlord and friendly efficient service even when busy, well kept Palmers ales, farm cider, good coffee and carefully chosen wines, nice fireplace; children and dogs welcome, skittle alley, tables in attractive garden behind, comfortable bedrooms, pretty square next to Montacute House *(Mrs J Duke, Pam and Alan Neale, Mary Ellen Cummings, Aubrey and Janet Gibson, Mr and Mrs D J Fugler, Brian and Bett Cox, BB, John A Barker)*

MUDFORD [ST5719]

Half Moon [A359 N of Yeovil]: Enjoyable generous food, well kept ales inc RCH Pitchfork, welcoming service, large dining area with stripped pine tables; good value bedrooms *(Guy Vowles, M Payne)*

NAILSEA [ST4670]

Blue Flame [West End]: Small well worn 19th-c unspoilt farmers' local, two rooms with mixed furnishings, well kept Bass, RCH and guest beers such as Abbey and Bath, Thatcher's farm cider, filled rolls and doorstep sandwiches, coal fire; folk and Thurs cards and pasty nights, pub games and cards, children's room, sizeable informal garden with barbecue, open all day Sun in summer *(Phil and Sally Gorton, the Didler)*

NEWTON ST LOE [ST7064]

☆ *Globe*: Roomy and popular, attractively split into smaller areas by dark wood partitions, pillars and timbers giving secluded feel, good atmosphere, friendly service, enjoyable food all day, well kept beer, large no smoking area *(Dr and Mrs A K Clarke, Dr and Mrs M E Wilson)*

NORTH PERROTT [ST4709]

Manor Arms [A3066 W of Crewkerne; Middle St]: Attractive 16th-c inn on pretty village green, concentrating on restaurant and bedroom side, with imaginative freshly made meals rather than snacks, small but good wine choice, good coffee, friendly staff; long tidily restored bar, beams and mellow stripped stone, log fire and plenty of character, does have well kept Butcombe but more hotel feel than pub; simple comfortable bedrooms, good breakfast, pleasant garden with adventure play area *(B M Eldridge)*

NORTON FITZWARREN [ST1925]

Cross Keys [A358 roundabout NW of Taunton]: Good Chef & Brewer in extended 19th-c stone building, big chalkboard of enjoyable well prepared food inc good hot baguettes, friendly cheerful staff, Courage Best and Directors, Theakstons XB and a guest beer, generous coffee, good wine choice, logs blazing in big hearth *(Jane McConaghie, Ian Phillips, Bob and Margaret Holder)*

NORTON ST PHILIP [ST7755]

☆ *Fleur de Lys* [High St]: Unspoilt chatty local atmosphere in 13th-c stone cottages joined centuries ago, steps and pillars giving cosy feel of separate rooms in the beamed and flagstoned areas around the central servery, well kept Butcombe and Wadworths beers, friendly landlord, good value home-made food from baguettes through sausages and mash etc to steak, huge fireplace; car park can be awkward; children very welcome, skittle alley *(Dr and Mrs A K Clarke, BB, the Didler, Ian Phillips)*

NUNNEY [ST7345]

George [Church St; signed off A361 Shepton Mallet—Frome]: Rambling much modernised open-plan bar with panelling and stripped stone, log fire, helpful service, well kept changing ales such as Black Sheep, sound food in bar and restaurant; piped music, pool; rare gallows inn-sign spanning road, in quaint village with stream and ruined castle; no dogs, children allowed in side room, comfortable bedrooms *(BB, Howard C R Shaw, Susan and Nigel Wilson)*

PANBOROUGH [ST4745]

Panborough Inn [B3139 Wedmore—Wells]: Large well run 17th-c dining pub, welcoming bar staff, wide range of generous food, several attractive rooms, inglenook, beams, gleaming brass and copper, fresh and dried flowers, well kept real ale, Fri music night; skittle alley, quiet views from tables on front terrace *(BB, Tom Evans)*

PITMINSTER [ST2219]

Queens Arms [off B3170 S of Taunton (or reached direct); nr church]: Cosily renovated village pub doing well under current landlord, skilled chef doing good choice of reasonably priced food (can take a while at busy times), well kept ales inc Cotleigh and Otter, interesting wines, log fires, simple wooden bar furniture, pleasant dining room; no music, dogs allowed, bedrooms with own bathrooms *(Colin and Alma Gent, Bob and Margaret Holder)*

PORLOCK WEIR [SS8547]

Ship [separate from but run in tandem with neighbouring Anchor Hotel]: Prettily restored old inn in wonderful spot by peaceful harbour (so can get packed), with tables in terraced rose garden and good walks (but no views to speak of from bars); nets and chalked beams in touristy Mariners Bar, three well kept ales, Taunton cider, good soft drinks choice, huge log fire, usual food; piped music, big-screen TV, young staff, little free parking but pay & display opposite, back family room; children and dogs welcome, attractive bedrooms *(Heather Couper, LYM, H O Dickinson, J Stickland, Geoff and Teresa)*

PORTBURY [ST4975]

Priory [Station Rd, ½mile from A369 (just S of M5 junction 19)]: Reliable much extended Vintage Inn dining pub, several beamed rooms, some no smoking, with nice mix of solid furnishings in alcoves, wide choice of nicely presented usual food all day till 10, well kept Bass, good range of house wines, pleasant efficient service; piped music; bedrooms, open all day *(James Morrell, DAV, Dr and Mrs C W Thomas, Dr A J and Mrs Tompsett)*

PORTISHEAD [ST4475]

Ship [the one on Down Rd (coast rd to Walton in Gordano)]: Quiet and relaxing modern pub, limited bargain lunchtime food (pleasant Edwardian-style dining room), changing ales such as Bass, Butcombe and Sharps Doom Bar, lots of Royal Navy memorabilia, superb views across to Newport and Cardiff esp at sunset *(Ian Phillips, Stan and Susan Fysh, Tom Evans)*

PRIDDY [ST5450]

Hunters Lodge [from Wells on A39 pass hill with TV mast on left, then next left]: Welcoming and unchanging walkers' and potholers' inn above ice-age cavern, in same family for generations, well kept Butcombe and Exmoor tapped from casks behind the bar, Weston's farm cider, good plain food inc bread and local cheese, low prices, log fire, flagstones; garden picnic-sets, bedrooms *(LYM, Gaynor Gregory)*

New Inn [off B3135; The Green]: Bustling low-beamed pub, modernised but still traditional, with friendly staff, well kept real ales, good local cider and house wines, good value food inc interesting dishes and tasty local cheeses, warm log fire, spacious conservatory, skittle alley; bedrooms comfortable and homely, tables out facing quiet village green with famous hurdles *(Julia and Richard Tredgett)*

Queen Victoria [village signed off B3135; Pelting Drove]: Relaxed character country pub with stripped stone, flagstones and three good log fires (one open on two sides), interesting bric-a-brac, collected furnishings inc miscellaneous tables and old pews, welcoming licensees, well kept Butcombe Bitter and Gold and Wadworths 6X tapped from the cask, organic beers, farm ciders and perries, good coffee, basic low-priced food such as filled rolls, ploughman's and cottage pie; good garden for children over road, cl lunchtime Oct-Apr exc hols *(Phil and Sally Gorton)*

PRISTON [ST6960]

Ring o' Bells: Two small friendly rooms, generous basic pub food (not Mon/Tues or Thurs), well kept Greene King beers; tables outside, pretty village *(Nigel Long)*

PURITON [ST3141]

Puriton Inn [just off M5 junction 23; Puriton Hill]: Friendly character pub, dark, clean and tidy, with ample straightforward food, well kept beer, warmly welcoming service even when busy; good disabled access, large garden *(Dr and Mrs A K Clarke, Brian and Rosalie Laverick, Brian Dawes)*

RICKFORD [ST4859]

☆ *Plume of Feathers* [very sharp turn off A368]: Unspoilt cottagey and partly flagstoned pub with enjoyable simple home-made food from baked potatoes up, relaxed atmosphere, four well kept ales inc Butcombe and Wychwood Hobgoblin, friendly family service, table skittles, log fires and tongue and groove panelling; wknd parking unlikely; rustic tables on narrow front terrace, pretty streamside hamlet *(John Urquhart, BB, Stan and Susan Fysh, M G Hart, Richard Wyld, Dr M E Williams)*

RODE [ST8053]

☆ *Bell* [Frome Rd (A361)]: Comfortable, spotless and roomy, with nicely balanced choice of good value generous food from well filled baguettes up, curry nights and other food themes, well kept Courage Best and three Butcombe beers, friendly landlady and obliging service, good atmosphere, roomy sparely decorated bar on left with a couple of armchairs as well as pleasantly practical furnishings, step up to good-sized pool room, smaller bar on right leading to busy no smoking restaurant; dogs welcome, tables in good-sized side and back garden *(Dr and Mrs M E Wilson, John and Joan Nash, Ted George)*

Mill: Pleasantly refurbished watermill in lovely setting, freshly made food from unpretentious things to up-to-date main dishes, friendly helpful staff, smart layout, upstairs no smoking area, children's room with impressive games; some wknd live music; garden and decks overlooking river *(Dr and Mrs M E Wilson)*

ROWBERROW [ST4458]

☆ *Swan* [off A38 S of A368 junction]: Biggish dining pub with olde-worlde beamery and so forth (most atmosphere in bar part), popular food from lunchtime sandwiches, baguettes and baked potatoes to steaks, well kept Bass

and Butcombe Bitter, Blond and Gold, good choice of wines by the glass, Thatcher's cider, good log fires; dogs welcome, no children *(Gaynor Gregory, Comus and Sarah Elliott, MRSM, Alan and Paula McCully, Bob and Margaret Holder, Hugh Roberts, LYM, John and Fiona McIlwain, P M Wilkins, J Coote)*

RUDGE [ST8251]

☆ *Full Moon* [off A36 Bath—Warminster]: Black-beamed 17th-c inn doing well under current management, well kept Butcombe and other ales, local ciders, good service, good value food, nice mix of furnishings in cottagey front bars, inglenook fireplace, flagstoned tap room, back no smoking restaurant extension, traditional games and skittle alley; children welcome, pretty gardens with plenty of seats, comfortable bedrooms, self-catering cottages, open all day *(Mr and Mrs A H Young, Dr and Mrs A K Clarke, Mike Gorton, LYM, Derek and Brenda Lamont)*

RUMWELL [ST1923]

Rumwell Inn [A38 Taunton—Wellington, just past Stonegallows]: Good comfortable atmosphere, old beams and cosy corners, lots of tables in several areas, quietly friendly attentive staff, wide range of good value pubby food inc lots of fish and local meat and other produce, children's dishes, well kept changing ales such as Flowers IPA, espresso machine, roaring log fire, restaurant (best to book), family room; garden tables, handy for Sheppy's Cider *(Nigel Howard, Francis Johnston, J and F Gowers)*

SALTFORD [ST6867]

Bird in Hand [High St]: Lively local, comfortable and friendly, with lots of bird pictures, popular locally for good value fresh food from mini-ploughman's to daily roast, huge omelettes and whitby fish, attractive conservatory dining area, quick service even when quite a queue for food, small family area, good range of beers such as Abbey Bellringer, Bass and Courage Bitter; live entertainment; picnic-sets down towards river, handy for Bristol—Bath railway path *(Meg and Colin Hamilton)*

SHURTON [ST2044]

Shurton Inn: Friendly neatly kept local in farming village, enjoyable and keenly priced homely food, good beer choice *(Glen and Nola Armstrong)*

SIDCOT [ST4256]

Sidcot Hotel [Bridgwater Rd (A38)]: Newly refurbished Brewers Fayre, decent choice of wines and other drinks, good staff, promptly served food *(Mick and Moira Brummell)*

SOUTH CADBURY [ST6325]

Camelot [Chapel Rd]: Newly refurbished and extended in modern rural style, interesting food and beer, skittle alley, plenty of locals; just below Cadbury Castle *(Pat and Robert Watt, OPUS)*

SOUTH CHERITON [ST6924]

White Horse: Small attractive pub doing well under new licensees, friendly atmosphere, small choice of well cooked nicely served food, small individual dining areas, family room with games *(J C Burgis)*

SPARKFORD [ST6026]

☆ *Sparkford Inn* [just W of Wincanton; High St]: Rambling layout of softly lit low-beamed rooms (inc no smoking restaurant) with pleasant mix of furnishings, popular lunchtime carvery alongside other usual bar food from good value sandwiches up, good puddings choice, Boddingtons and Courage Directors; queuing system for drinks then food usually fast but can come under strain when busy, with young staff; children and dogs welcome, tables and decent bar area outside, bedrooms with own bath or shower, open all day *(B J Harding, Guy Consterdine, Peter Salmon, LYM, Richard and Anne Ansell, Reg Fowle, Helen Rickwood, Sarah and Anthony Bussy, B and M Kendall, Michael Rowse, Dr and Mrs M E Wilson, Clive and Vivienne Locks, June and Robin Savage, Mr and Mrs D S Price, Ian and Nita Cooper)*

STAR [ST4358]

Star [A38 NE of Winscombe]: Cheerful newly refurbished roadside pub with two-for-one food bargains 12-6 in back carvery and extended eating area, well kept Marstons Pedigree, good log fire in huge inglenook fireplace, abundant fresh flowers; country views from picnic-sets in field behind, open all day *(Alan and Paula McCully)*

STOGUMBER [ST0937]

☆ *White Horse* [off A358 at Crowcombe]: Pleasant village pub with good value food from good sandwiches to proper Sun roasts, well kept Cotleigh Tawny, Greene King Old Speckled Hen and Marstons Pedigree, welcoming service, long neat bar, old village photographs with more recent ones for comparison, good log fires, no smoking dining area, games room and skittle alley; children welcome away from bar, quiet garden, bedrooms, open all day wknds and summer *(LYM, Dr D J and Mrs S C Walker, Peter F Marshall, Bob and Margaret Holder)*

STOKE ST MARY [ST2622]

Half Moon [from M5 junction 25 take A358 towards Ilminster, 1st right, right in Henlade]: Roomy much-modernised village pub, five neat open-plan main areas, wide choice of enjoyable food from sandwiches to steaks, one no smoking restaurant, pleasant staff, well kept real ales inc Butcombe, nice coffee, quite a few malt whiskies, pleasant local atmosphere; bar billiards, may be piped music; children welcome, picnic-sets in well tended garden *(Bob and Margaret Holder, LYM)*

TARR [SS8632]

Tarr Farm [Tarr Steps – rather narrow rd off B3223; OS Sheet 181 map ref 868322]: Beautifully set for river walks, lovely views from gardens front and back, cosy inside with four smallish rooms, huge slabby tables, cosy leather settees and armchairs, well kept Exmoor and other ales, nice wines, good soft drinks choice, good value food from sandwiches to fresh fish and Sun roast, good

cream teas (log fires in tea room), charming evening restaurant, no piped music; dogs welcome lunchtime, nice bedrooms (no children staying under 10), self catering too, open all day *(CMW, JJW, Peter Abbott)*

TAUNTON [ST2525]

☆ *Hankridge Arms* [Hankridge Way, Deane Gate (nr Sainsbury); just off M5 junction 25 – A358 towards city, then right at roundabout, right at next roundabout]: 16th-c former farm reworked as well appointed old-style dining pub in modern shopping complex, buoyant atmosphere and quick friendly service, generous food from interesting soups, sandwiches and baguettes through sensibly priced pubby things to restaurant dishes, largely no smoking dining room, Badger Best, K&B and Tanglefoot, decent wines, big log fire; piped music, can be hard for older people to get to when surrounding shops busy; plenty of tables in pleasant outside area *(Pamela and Merlyn Horswell, Dr and Mrs A K Clarke, Gill and Keith Croxton)*

Masons Arms [Magdalene St]: This appealing pub, a main entry in the last edition, has closed following the landlord's retirement *(LYM)*

THURLOXTON [ST2730]

Maypole [A38 Taunton—Bridgwater, between M5 junctions 24 and 25]: Attractively refurbished beamed pub with several traditional areas, well kept if not cheap real ales, log fire, biggish no smoking area, wide food choice; soft piped music, no dogs, skittle alley; enclosed garden with play area, lovely flowers, peaceful village *(Bob and Margaret Holder)*

TIMBERSCOMBE [SS9542]

Lion [Church St]: Newly refurbished Exmoor-edge former coaching inn dating from 15th c, home-made food from good fresh baguettes up, welcoming attentive service, well kept Exmoor and a guest such as St Austell tapped from the cask, three rooms off comfortable flagstoned main bar, good log fire, simple furnishings; dogs welcome, bedrooms *(Jenny and Peter Lowater, Michael Rowse)*

TRUDOXHILL [ST7443]

☆ *White Hart* [off A361 SW of Frome]: Welcoming new landlord with innovative menu ideas, enjoyable food from good open sandwiches and baguettes up, well kept changing ales, Thatcher's farm cider, interesting sensibly priced wine choice, mainly table seating with a couple of easy chairs by one of the two log fires, beams and stripped stone; no dogs, children in eating area, picnic-sets in flower-filled sheltered side garden *(the Didler, LYM, Hugh Roberts, MRSM, Pat and Robert Watt)*

UPTON NOBLE [ST7139]

Lamb [Church St; off A359 SW of Frome]: Friendly 17th-c village local with wide blackboard choice of good unfussy home-made food from Yorkshire chef/landlord, efficient staff, well kept Butcombe, Flowers and Fullers London Pride, comfortable lounge bar, beams, stripped stone, brasses and ornaments, lovely view from no smoking restaurant; darts, pool etc in public bar, two dogs; big garden, nice location, cl Mon lunchtime, perhaps other wkdy lunchtimes *(Michael Doswell, Susan and Nigel Wilson)*

VOBSTER [ST7049]

☆ *Vobster Inn* [Lower Vobster]: Roomy old stone-built dining pub particularly popular with older people (children welcomed too), relaxed atmosphere, good food choice from smart sandwiches and range of local cheeses to fish fresh daily from Cornwall in three comfortable open-plan areas, friendly licensees from Australia, helpful young staff, well kept Fullers London Pride, good new world wines by the glass (plenty of room if you just want a drink); tables on side lawn with boules, peaceful views, adventure playground behind *(J Burke, BB, Sylvia and Tony Birbeck, Gaynor Gregory)*

WAMBROOK [ST2907]

☆ *Cotley Inn* [off A30 W of Chard; don't follow the small signs to Cotley itself]: Smartly unpretentious stone-built pub, good food from reasonably priced light dishes to fish and steaks, friendly efficient staff, Otter and Wadworths 6X, nice ambiance, simple flagstoned entrance bar opening on one side into small plush bar, several open fires, popular two-room no smoking dining area (best to book, children allowed here); pool, piped music, skittle alley; seats and play area in nice garden, well refurbished bedrooms, quiet spot with plenty of surrounding walks *(LYM, Bob and Margaret Holder, Mike and Jenny Beacon, Mr and Mrs W Mills)*

WANSTROW [ST7141]

Pub [Station Rd (A359)]: Attractive interior, enjoyable homely food, six well kept ales inc local Blindmans, friendly owners; charming little floral courtyard *(Andrew Liyyatt)*

WATCHET [ST0643]

Star [Mill Lane (B3191)]: Old low-beamed cottagey pub nr seafront, wooden furniture, cheerful efficient service, good log fire, straightforward reasonably priced food, four well kept ales; picnic-sets out in front and in garden *(CMW, JJW)*

WATERROW [ST0525]

Rock [A361 Wiveliscombe—Bampton]: Keen new young licensees trying an enterprising choice of food inc some elaborate dishes and fresh brixham fish, well kept ales such as Cotleigh Tawny and Exmoor Gold, log fire in neat smallish bar exposing the rock it's built on, couple of steps up to dining room; good well equipped bedrooms, charming setting in small valley village *(Bob and Margaret Holder, Michael Rowse)*

WEDMORE [ST4347]

New Inn [Combe Batch]: Welcoming traditional town pub, wide choice of enjoyable bargain food, well kept Butts, good wines by the glass *(Tom Evans)*

WELLOW [ST7358]

☆ *Fox & Badger* [signed off A367 SW of Bath]: Cheery bustle in flagstoned lounge with snug alcoves, small winged settles, woodburner in massive hearth, flowers on tables, well kept

Badger, Bass and Butcombe ales, Thatcher's farm cider, wide range of good value bar food, warmly welcoming service, family dining room; games and piped music in cosy bareboards public bar; children and dogs welcome (pub sealyham and springer spaniel), picnic-sets in covered courtyard with barbecues, open all day Fri-Sun *(Roger and Jenny Huggins, LYM, Ian Phillips)*

WELLS [ST5545]

☆ *Fountain* [St Thomas St]: Comfortable dining pub dating from 16th c, consistently good wholesome sensibly priced food from filled baguettes to fresh fish and interesting dishes in homely downstairs bar with roaring log fire, or popular more formal restaurant up steep stairs (worth booking wknd, good Sun lunch); welcoming attentive staff, well kept ales such as Butcombe, Courage Best and Greene King IPA, good choice of wines, good coffee, daily papers and magazines; can get very full wknd lunchtimes, may be piped music; children welcome, right by cathedral and moated Bishop's Palace *(John Coatsworth, Gaynor Gregory, Terry Buckland, Henry and Fiona Dryden, Douglas and Ann Hare)*

WEST BUCKLAND [ST1621]

Blackbird [A38 N of village, 3 miles E of Wellington and handy for M5 junction 26]: Clean, quiet and homely partly 16th-c inn, good value home-cooked food from sandwiches to Sun lunch, two well kept real ales, friendly service, skittle alley, large restaurant; pleasant garden, well equipped bedrooms *(Bob and Margaret Holder)*

WEST CAMEL [ST5724]

Walnut Tree [off A303 W of Wincanton; Fore St]: Extended upmarket dining pub/hotel, comfortable grey plush banquettes and red plush cushioned wicker chairs, good choice of enjoyable home-made brasserie and restaurant food (not Sun evening or Mon lunchtime) esp fresh fish and puddings, friendly efficient uniformed staff, well kept Bass and Butcombe; neatly kept garden, good bedrooms, pretty village *(A Thorpe)*

WEST CHINNOCK [ST4613]

Muddled Man [Lower St]: Particularly friendly unassuming local with attractively priced straightforward food using good local meat (ham ploughman's hotly tipped), interesting choice of well kept local ales, farm cider, unobtrusive small pool area off simple single bar; attractive rustic village, open all day Fri-Sun, cl winter Mon lunchtime *(Guy Vowles, Pete Baker)*

WEST HATCH [ST2719]

Farmers Arms [W of village, at Slough Green; from A358 head for RSPCA centre and keep past]: Spacious and friendly 16th-c beamed dining pub with good enterprising up-to-date food, two well kept Otter ales tapped from the cask, open fires, bleached wood furniture, unassumingly modern décor, no smoking restaurant; children welcome, garden with nice herb garden, small terrace and play area *(Bob and Margaret Holder)*

WEST HUNTSPILL [ST3044]

☆ *Crossways* [A38 (between M5 exits 22 and 23)]: Friendly and comfortably worn in, with several seating areas inc a family room, interesting decorations, beams and log fires, enjoyable sensibly priced food, good choice of well kept real ales and local farm cider, decent wines, quick attentive service, no piped music; skittle alley and pub games, picnic-sets among fruit trees in sizeable informal garden *(Dr J R Long, Rona Murdoch, LYM, Tom Evans)*

WESTBURY-SUB-MENDIP [ST5048]

Westbury Inn: Pleasant mellow interior with some character, dozens of old local photographs, pretty dining room, enjoyable reasonably priced food from good sandwiches up, well kept Bass and guest beers, local farm cider, warmly welcoming licensees; dogs welcome, enclosed garden behind *(Bob and Marilyn Baylis)*

WESTON-IN-GORDANO [ST4474]

White Hart [B3124 Portishead—Clevedon, between M5 junctions 19 and 20]: Friendly neatly kept roadside pub with lots of old photographs and bric-a-brac in lower room, large pleasant dining area, reasonably priced straightforward food cooked to order (so may be a wait), agreable staff, well kept Courage and John Smiths; Gordano valley views from fine back lawn with play area, open all day *(Mrs M E Hutchison, Alan and Paula McCully)*

WESTON-SUPER-MARE [ST3562]

Golden Lion [High St, Whorle]: Very popular wkdy lunchtimes for its bargain deals for two in two helpings sizes, enjoyable food, good value wines, well kept beers, friendly helpful staff *(Ken Flawn)*

Queens Head [Bleadon Hill]: Pleasant unspoilt pub with good honest home cooking, friendly staff, well kept Cotleigh Tawny *(Michael Rowse)*

Woolpack [St Georges, just off M5, junction 21]: Neatly kept olde-worlde 17th-c coaching inn with good varied well priced food inc some sophisticated dishes, chargrills and lots of fresh fish, pleasant window seats and library-theme area, several well kept changing beers such as Greene King Old Speckled Hen and Palmers, good house wines, small but attractive restaurant, conservatory; starters mean starters (must be followed by main courses), they stick rather too rigidly to the menu (and the food service cut-off times), and forbid children and dirty workmen; skittle alley *(Alan and Paula McCully, Comus and Sarah Elliott, Stan and Susan Fysh)*

WHEDDON CROSS [SS9238]

Rest & Be Thankful [A396/B3224, S of Minehead]: Spotless comfortably modern two-room bar with wide range of generous home-cooked food from good fresh sandwiches up (can be a wait if busy), well kept ales such as Exmoor and Greene King Old Speckled Hen, good soft drinks choice, two good log fires, huge jug collection, no smoking restaurant, games area with pool and darts, skittle alley; piped music, no dogs; tables out in courtyard,

public lavatory for the disabled, bedrooms with own bathrooms *(LYM, CMW, JJW)*

WIDCOMBE [ST2216]

☆ *Holman Clavel* [Culmhead, by ridge rd W of B3170 2 miles S of Corfe]: Simple but comfortable old-fashioned deep-country local dating from 14th c and named after the massive holly chimney-beam over its huge log fire; good home cooking, friendly informal staff, well kept Butcombe Bitter and Gold and Fullers London Pride, colourful wine list, nice atmosphere with fresh local produce for sale; dogs welcome, handy for Blackdown Hills *(BB, Lee and Liz Potter, Michael Rowse)*

WINCANTON [ST7128]

George [Mill St]: Handsome newly renovated Georgian building, comfortable and relaxed, with sofas and log fires, good choice of well kept real ales and of wines, fresh food; lovely large garden, cl Mon *(B M Eldridge)*

WINSCOMBE [ST4257]

Woodborough [Sandford Rd]: Extensively refurbished as big beamed dining pub, smart and comfortable, with separate drinking areas, good range of above-average food inc local produce and good veg, well kept Butcombe and Wadworths 6X *(Bob and Margaret Holder, Stan and Susan Fysh)*

WINSFORD [SS9034]

☆ *Royal Oak* [off A396 about 10 miles S of Dunster]: Rather smart and prettily placed thatched Exmoor inn with talk of a possible sale, attractively furnished lounge bar with big bay-window seat looking across towards village green and foot and packhorse bridges over River Winn, more eating space in second bar, several pretty and comfortable lounges, three no smoking rooms, bar and restaurant food, Brakspears and Butcombe tapped from the cask; children and dogs welcome, good bedrooms *(LYM, Peter Abbott, Jay Smith, Peter and Giff Bennett, David and Sheila Pearcey)*

WINSHAM [ST3706]

Bell [Church St]: Well kept and friendly, with good beer; cl Mon lunchtime *(Alain and Rose Foote)*

WITHAM FRIARY [ST7440]

Seymour Arms [signed from B3092 S of Frome]: Well worn in unspoilt flagstoned local, two simple rooms off hatch-service corridor, one with darts, the other with central table skittles; well kept Bass and Ushers Best, Rich's local farm cider, open fire, cards and dominoes – no juke box or machines; can be smoky; good-sized attractive garden by main rail line *(the Didler, Edward Mirzoeff, Pete Baker)*

WOOKEY [ST5145]

Ring o' Bells [High St]: Welcoming village local with big log fire each end, well kept Butcombe and Smiles, generous sensibly priced food, dark wood tables and settles, separate dining room; may be piped music *(Alan and Paula McCully)*

WOOKEY HOLE [ST5347]

Wookey Hole Inn: Usefully placed family pub with unusual cool and trendy décor, relaxed atmosphere, four changing real ales and several belgian beers, enjoyable and innovative realistically priced food, nice staff; jazz Sun lunchtime, pleasant garden, comfortable bedrooms *(Christopher Stott, P M Wilkins, J Coote)*

WOOLVERTON [ST7954]

Red Lion [set back from A36 N of village]: Roomy refurbished pub, beams, panelling, flagstones and lots of stripped wood, candles and good log fire, well kept Wadworths IPA and 6X, decent wines by the glass, generous enjoyable food from popular filled baked potatoes and good value children's meals to more upmarket dishes, friendly staff; piped music; open all day, plenty of tables outside *(Chris and Ann Coy, LYM, Michael Butler)*

WRANTAGE [ST3022]

Canal Inn [A378 E of M5 junction 25]: Welcoming unpretentious three-room pub with friendly and helpful young licensees, enjoyable food all freshly made in bar and dining room, well kept real ales, farm cider, log fires; surcharge for credit cards; garden with play area *(A J and C D Stodgell, David Clark)*

WRAXALL [ST4971]

Old Barn [just off Bristol Rd (B3130)]: Rustic gabled barn conversion with scrubbed tables, school benches and soft sofas under oak rafters, stripped boards, flagstones and festoons of dried flowers; welcoming atmosphere, wide choice of good home-made food, five well kept beers inc Bass and local brews tapped from the cask, friendly service; two TV screens, Sun quiz night; garden with good play area and barbecues on cobbled terrace *(Richard Houghton, the Didler)*

WRINGTON [ST4662]

Golden Lion [Broad St]: Small comfortable village coaching inn with well kept Bass, Bath Gem and Butcombe, Stowford Press cider, good hands-on landlord, plenty of regulars, lunchtime rolls, log fire in big fireplace, pool room, occasional Sat piano sing-songs, late May beer festival; small pretty back courtyard with wknd barbecues, open all day *(John A Barker, Alan and Paula McCully, Peter Darling)*

Plough [2½ miles off A370 Bristol—Weston, from bottom of Rhodiate Hill]: Large friendly beamed pub rambling around central servery with well kept Smiles and Youngs and interesting wine list, quarts of cocktails, popular good value food (all day Sun) inc tapas, traditional pubby décor, step up to long no smoking dining area, two coal or log fires; two TVs, fruit machine and cash machine; lots of picnic-sets out on sloping grass, more under cover on heated terrace, open all day *(BB, Bob and Margaret Holder, John A Barker, Alan and Paula McCully, Ken Marshall, P M Wilkins, J Coote)*

YARLINGTON [ST6529]

☆ *Stags Head* [Pound Lane]: Interesting old flagstoned and low-ceilinged country pub tucked away in rustic hamlet, well kept Bass and Otter from small central locals' bar, woodburner, chapel chairs and mixed pine tables on left, carpeted room on right with big log fire, modern landscape prints and a collection of old seats and tables, good upscale cooking using fresh fish and local produce and game, decent wines; picnic-sets in sheltered back garden with small flagstoned back terrace and barbecue; cl Sun evening and Mon *(Richard Wyld, BB, Mary Kirman and Tim Jefferson)*

Staffordshire

In the county's pubs, the big selling point is sheer value. Throughout both the main entries and the Lucky Dip entries at the end of the chapter, attractive prices for both food and drink score points again and again. Drinks prices are among the lowest in the country, and while pub food prices elsewhere are now often climbing towards restaurant levels, that is not the case here. Staffordshire food prices tend to be most appealing. The food on offer, even in the county's best pubs, is normally honest and straightforward no-nonsense cooking rather than haute cuisine (especially given the bargain pricing, this in itself seems to be a plus point to many readers here). If you are in search of something a bit more special, you have to look harder, but at every level the prices here are very fair. For quality food, the appealing Holly Bush at Salt (now serving it all day) takes great care over the ingredients for its traditional English cooking; and the new Italian landlord who has freshened up the ancient Goats Head in Abbots Bromley is doing some interesting specials alongside more familiar dishes. Staffordshire Dining Pub of the Year is the Boat near Lichfield, with imaginative food served from its open kitchen in rather smart modern surroundings. Other particularly well liked pubs here are the George at Alstonefield, a cheerful and most enjoyable Peak District all-rounder, and the Burton Bridge Inn in Burton upon Trent, brewing its own good beers at alluring prices. Good new licensees in the Greyhound at Warslow and the Olde Royal Oak at Wetton both promise well. The Yew Tree at Cauldon is in a class of its own for sheer individuality, a good-humoured well worn pub full of remarkable collections, with very cheap drinks. Top pubs in the Lucky Dip section (all five now inspected and approved by us) are the Queens at Freehay near Cheadle, George in Eccleshall, Cat at Enville, Whittington Inn at Kinver and Olde Dog & Partridge in Tutbury. As we have said, beer prices here are low. The main regional brewer is Marstons in Burton upon Trent (part of the Wolverhampton & Dudley group which now owns several other breweries such as Banks's, Burtonwood and Jennings). Other smaller Staffordshire brewers to look out for include Burton Bridge, Old Cottage and Tower (all also in Burton), and Blythe, Enville, Eccleshall, Leek and Titanic.

ABBOTS BROMLEY SK0824 Map 7
Goats Head
Market Place

An enthusiastic new Italian licensee has injected a burst of energy into this black and white timbered pub. The interior has been opened and freshened up with cream paint on the walls and panelling, and now that most of the carpets have gone there are nice oak and stone floors. Furniture runs from the odd traditional oak settle to comfy leather sofas, and a big inglenook has a warm fire. Daily specials might include asparagus in parma ham with hollandaise sauce or kofta meatballs with minted yoghurt (£4.95), langoustines in garlic (£5.95), rabbit and hare casserole (£8.95) and sea bass (£11.95), while the more traditional bar menu includes soup or sandwiches (£3.95), steak and kidney pie or spaghetti bolognese (£6.95) and fish pie (£7.95), with puddings such as lemon meringue or apple pie (£3.95). Greene King Abbot, Marstons Pedigree and a guest such as Greene King Old Speckled Hen are well kept on handpump, and you can have any of the wines on their good wine list (Tanners of Shrewsbury) by the glass; piped music. Picnic-sets and teak tables out on a neat sheltered lawn look up to the church tower behind – this is a charmingly unspoilt village, famous for its annual horn dance; more reports please. *(Recommended by David J Austin)*

Punch ~ Tenant Silvio Scarpello ~ Real ale ~ Bar food (12-9.30) ~ Restaurant ~ (01283) 840254 ~ Children welcome away from bar ~ Open 11-11; 12-10.30 Sun

ALSTONEFIELD SK1355 Map 7
George
Village signposted from A515 Ashbourne—Buxton

All sorts of people, from sightseers and campers, to cyclists and walkers (though no muddy boots) enjoy the charming simplicity and cheery local atmosphere at this stone-built Peak District pub. It's in a peaceful farming hamlet by the green, and in fine weather it's a real pleasure to sit out on the stone seats beneath the inn-sign and watch the world go by, or in the big sheltered stableyard behind the pub which has picnic-sets by a pretty rockery. For a longer stay you can arrange with the landlord to camp on the croft. The unchanging straightforward low-beamed bar has pewter tankards hanging by the copper-topped bar counter (well kept Burtonwood Bitter and Marstons Pedigree on handpump), a collection of old Peak District photographs and pictures, a roaring coal fire on chilly days, darts, cribbage and dominoes. The spacious no smoking family/dining room has plenty of tables and wheelback chairs. Tasty no nonsense home-made food is good value and includes sandwiches (from £2.40), soup (£2.75), ploughman's (from £5.20), meat and potato pie (£6.40) lasagne (£7.10), fillet steak (£11.95), a couple of daily specials, and delicious home-made puddings such as fudge and walnut pie and meringue glaze (£2.95); you order food from the friendly staff at the kitchen door. *(Recommended by Pauline and Terry James, Paul Robinshaw, Colin Buckle, the Didler, P Price, W W Burke, Nigel Long, Michael B Griffith, Geoff and Linda Payne)*

Union Pub Company ~ Tenants Richard and Sue Grandjean ~ Real ale ~ Bar food ~ (01335) 310205 ~ Children in family room ~ Open 11-3, 6-11; 11-11 Sat; 12-10.30 Sun

BURTON UPON TRENT SK2423 Map 7
Burton Bridge Inn 🍺 £
Bridge Street (A50)

Happily, this straightforward bustling old brick local, with its genuinely friendly atmosphere, continues in the same cheery down-to-earth way from one year to the next. It's the tap for Burton Bridge Brewery (out in the long old-fashioned yard at the back) which produces the Bitter, Festival, Golden Delicious, Gold Medal and Porter that are well kept and served on handpump here, alongside a guest such as Timothy Taylors Landlord. They also keep around 25 whiskies and over a dozen country wines. The simple little front area leads into an adjacent bar, separated from a no smoking oak-panelled lounge by the serving counter. The bar has wooden pews, plain walls hung with notices, awards and brewery memorabilia, and the lounge has oak beams, a flame-effect fire and old oak tables and chairs. Simple but hearty bar snacks include filled cobs, including roast beef and pork cobs (from £2.20), filled yorkshire pudding (from £3.40) and ploughman's (£3.60); the panelled upstairs dining room is open only at lunchtime. A blue-brick patio overlooks the brewery. *(Recommended by the Didler, C J Fletcher, Pete Baker, P Price, Dr and Mrs A K Clarke, Patrick Hancock, Theo, Anne and Jane Gaskin)*

Own brew ~ Licensees Kevin and Jan McDonald ~ Real ale ~ Bar food (lunchtime only, not Sun) ~ No credit cards ~ (01283) 536596 ~ Children welcome ~ Dogs welcome ~ Open 11.30-2.15, 5-11; 12-2, 7-10.30 Sun; closed bank hol Mon lunchtime

CAULDON SK0749 Map 7

Yew Tree ★★ £

Village signposted from A523 and A52 about 8 miles W of Ashbourne

This idiosyncratic place cradles a veritable museum's-worth of curiosities all lovingly collected by the charming landlord himself. The most impressive pieces are perhaps the working polyphons and symphonions – 19th-c developments of the musical box, often taller than a person, each with quite a repertoire of tunes and elaborate sound-effects; take plenty of 2p pieces to work them. But there are also two pairs of Queen Victoria's stockings, ancient guns and pistols, several penny-farthings, an old sit-and-stride boneshaker, a rocking horse, swordfish blades, a little 800BC greek vase, and even a fine marquetry cabinet crammed with notable early staffordshire pottery. Soggily sprung sofas mingle with 18th-c settles, plenty of little wooden tables and a four-person oak church choir seat with carved heads which came from St Mary's church in Stafford; above the bar is an odd iron dog-carrier (don't ask how it works!). As well as all this there's an expanding choir of fine tuneful longcase clocks in the gallery just above the entrance, a collection of six pianolas (one of which is played most nights) with an excellent repertoire of piano rolls, a working vintage valve radio set, a crank-handle telephone, a sinuous medieval wind instrument made of leather, and a Jacobean four-poster which was once owned by Josiah Wedgwood and still has his original wig hook on the headboard. Clearly it would be almost an overwhelming task to keep all that sprucely clean. The drinks here are very reasonably priced (so no wonder it's popular with locals), and you'll find well kept Bass, Burton Bridge and Grays Dark Mild on handpump or tapped from the cask, along with about a dozen interesting malt whiskies; piped music (probably Radio 2), darts, shove-ha'penny, table skittles, dominoes and cribbage. Simple good value tasty snacks include hot pork pies (from 70p), meat and potato pies, chicken and mushroom or steak pies (85p), hot big filled baps and sandwiches (from £1.50), quiche, smoked mackerel or ham salad (£3.50), and home-made puddings (£1.50). When you arrive here don't be put off by the plain exterior, or the fact that the pub is tucked unpromisingly between enormous cement works and quarries and almost hidden by a towering yew tree. (*Recommended by David J Austin, W W Burke, the Didler, Rona Murdoch, Patrick Hancock, Mr and Mrs John Taylor, MLR, Mike and Mary Carter, Simon Cleasby*)

Free house ~ Licensee Alan East ~ Real ale ~ Bar food (12-2(3 Sat, Sun), 7-9) ~ No credit cards ~ (01538) 308348 ~ Children in polyphon room ~ Dogs welcome ~ Folk music first Tues in month ~ Open 10-3, 6-11; 12-3, 7-10.30 Sun

LICHFIELD SK0705 Map 4

Boat ⑪

2.7 miles from M6 Toll, junction T6: B5011 S, then left on A5, then at Muckley Corner roundabout head SW on A461 Walsall Road

Staffordshire Dining Pub of the Year

This tightly run modern pub is popular for its very well prepared very fairly priced imaginative food, which might include soup (£2.95), crayfish terrine with lemon dressing (£4.50), smoked duck salad with pine nuts and watercress (£4.95), mackerel fillet on chive mash with mustard sauce (£7.95), filo parcel of goats cheese with walnut and watercress (£7.50), pork fillet on sweet potato mash with crispy parma ham (£9.25), rack of lamb with a cassoulet of mixed beans (£11.25), fillet steak with wild mushroom sauce (£14.50), and puddings such as warm chocolate tart or toffee banana crumble (£3.95). Well lit from above by a big skylight, the first area as you enter is the most contemporary, with bright plastic flooring, views straight into the kitchen, striking photoprints, blue and russet café furniture and potted palms, all of which is dominated by huge floor-to-ceiling food blackboards. A dining area to the left has views on to the canal (currently undergoing restoration), and to the right the solid light wood bar counter has three constantly changing thoughtfully sourced real ales from brewers such as Blythe, Hook Norton and Olde Swan (which you may know as Ma Pardoe, from Netherton) on handpump, and around ten wines by the glass. Further round to the right a plainer area has sturdy modern pale pine furniture on russet pink carpets and prints on white walls; faint piped music. It's all immaculately kept, staff are cheerful and terribly attentive, and the restaurant and part of the bar are no smoking. A landscaped area outside is paved with a central raised decking area. There is good wheelchair access throughout. *(Recommended by Karen Eliot, Tony and Maggie Harwood, Brenda and Rob Fincham, Colin Fisher, Brian and Jacky Wilson, Simon and Mandy King, Roy and Lindsey Fentiman, Peter Robinson, Ian and Jane Irving, P Burns, Arthus, Bren and Val Speed, Jo Lilley, Simon Calvert, Neil Kellett)*

Free house ~ Licensee Ann Holden ~ Real ale ~ Bar food (12-2.30, 6.30-9.30; 12-8.30 Sun) ~ Restaurant ~ (01543) 361692 ~ Children in restaurant ~ Dogs allowed in bar ~ Open 12-3, 6-11; 12-11 Sun

SALT SJ9527 Map 7
Holly Bush
Village signposted off A51 S of Stone (and A518 NE of Stafford)

The charming deep thatched, flower bedecked exterior of this lovely white-painted 14th-c house won't disappoint. Inside, the oldest part has a heavy beamed and planked ceiling (some of the beams are attractively carved), a salt cupboard built in by the coal fire, and other nice old-fashioned touches such as an antique pair of clothesbrushes hanging by the door, attractive sporting prints and watercolours, and an ancient pair of riding boots on the mantelpiece. Several cosy areas spread off from the standing-room serving section, with comfortable settees as well as more orthodox seats. A modern back extension blends in well, with beams, stripped brickwork and a small coal fire. About half the pub is no smoking. Adnams, Marstons Pedigree and a guest such as Jennings Sneck Lifter are well kept on handpump, and served by really cheerful staff. The environmentally conscious landlord enjoys sourcing fresh local ingredients to use in a menu that features traditional english dishes. Served in generous helpings, and very reasonably priced, there might be soup (£2.10), staffordshire blue stuffed pears or warm watercress, potato and bacon salad (£3.25), battered cod (£6.95), steak and kidney pudding or chicken breast in red wine with raisins and apricots (£7.95), braised venison with celery and chestnuts (£8.25), mixed grill or lamb and barley stew (£8.50), puddings such as crumbles (from £3.25), and a british cheeseboard (£4.25); arrive early for a table if you want to eat. The back is beautifully tended, with rustic picnic-sets on a big lawn, and they may have traditional jazz and a hog roast in summer and a fireworks display on 5 November. One reader was asked for his credit card as security, but they seem to be flexible on this. *(Recommended by Michael and Jenny Back, Dr and Mrs T E Hothersall, Alan and Paula McCully, Roy and Lindsey Fentiman, Karen Eliot, Roger Braithwaite, Bob and Laura Brock, Alec and Joan Laurence, Richard and Anne Ansell, Ian and Ruth Laurence, Dave Braisted, Maurice and Gill McMahon)*

Free house ~ Licensees Geoffrey and Joseph Holland ~ Real ale ~ Bar food (12-9.30) ~ (01889) 508234 ~ Children in eating area of bar ~ Open 12-11

STOURTON SO8485 Map 4
Fox
A458 W of junction with A449, towards Enville

A big stretch of sloping grass at this lonely roadside pub has well spaced picnic-sets, and is surrounded by woodland. It's also well placed for Kinver Country Park walks and the Staffordshire Way. Several cosily small areas ramble back from the small serving bar by the entrance, with its well kept Bathams Best and Enville on handpump (and a noticeboard of hand-written travel offers). Tables are mostly sturdy and varnished, with pews, settles and comfortable library or dining chairs; there is green carpet here, dark blue there, bare boards beyond, with a good positive colour scheme picked up nicely by the curtains, and some framed exotic menus and well chosen prints (jazz and golf both feature). The woodburning stoves may be opened to give a cheery blaze on cold days. They put out big bunches of flowers, and the lighting (mainly low voltage spots) has been done very carefully, giving an intimate bistro feel in the areas round on the right, but the warm atmosphere is largely down to the welcoming family who've been running it for over 30 years. Apart from possible free evening nibbles on the counter, bar food includes tomato and basil pasta (£6.75), mediterranean risotto (£9.25), battered cod or fish pie (£9.50), steak and stout pie (£9.95) and 8oz sirloin steak (£7.95); it's a good idea to book if you want to go to one of their fortnightly fish evenings; no smoking dining areas including a smart conservatory which has neat bentwood furniture and proper tablecloths; piped music. *(Recommended by Chris Glasson, Theo, Anne and Jane Gaskin)*

Free house ~ Licensee Stefan Caron ~ Real ale ~ Bar food (12-2.30, 7-9.30; not Sun evening) ~ Restaurant ~ (01384) 872614 ~ Children welcome ~ Open 11-3, 4.30-11; 11(12 Sun)-11 Sat

WARSLOW SK0858 Map 7
Greyhound 🛏️
B5053 S of Buxton

Enthusiastic new licensees are set to stay at this very welcoming slate and stone-built pub – good news as it's been through a few unsettling changes recently. Straightforward but cosily comfortable inside, the beamed bar has long cushioned antique oak settles (some quite elegant), houseplants in the windows, cheerful fires and a no smoking eating area. Hearty food includes a very big bowl of soup (£3.95), the hungry hiker: a soup, sandwiches and chips (£5), ploughman's (£5.95), leek and potato bake with cheese (£6.95), home-made pies or 10oz gammon and two eggs (£8.95), and puddings such as apple pie or spotted dick (£2.95). In summer, Batemans XXXB and Black Sheep will be joined by a couple of well kept guests such as Bath Spa and Timothy Taylors Landlord; TV, fruit machine, pool, darts, dominoes and piped music. The side garden has picnic-sets under ash trees, with rustic seats out in front where window boxes blaze with colour in summer, and is surrounded by pretty countryside. Bedrooms are basic but good value and the pub is handy for the Manifold Valley, Dovedale and Alton Towers. *(Recommended by David Field, Mr and Mrs A Campbell, Michael Butler, Ian and Gill Everett)*

Free house ~ Licensees Ian and Lorna Bateman ~ Real ale ~ Bar food (12-3, 6.30-8.30 (8 Sat); not Sun evening) ~ Restaurant ~ (01298) 84249 ~ Children welcome ~ Dogs welcome ~ Soft rock most Sats ~ Open 12-3(4 Sat), 6-11; 12-5, 7-10.30 Sun ~ Bedrooms: £25/£30

WETTON SK1055 Map 7
Olde Royal Oak
Village signposted off Hulme End—Alstonefield road, between B5054 and A515

New licensees have changed very little at this aged white-painted and shuttered stone-built village house, which nestles in the heart of lovely National Trust countryside. Wetton Mill and the Manifold Valley are nearby, and a croft behind the pub takes caravans and tents. Not surprisingly the pub is popular with walkers. There's a good convivial atmosphere in the bar, which has black beams with white ceiling boards above, small dining chairs around rustic tables, an oak corner cupboard, and a coal fire in the stone fireplace. The bar extends into a more modern-feeling area, which in turn leads to a carpeted sun lounge looking out over the small garden; piped music, darts, TV, shove-ha'penny, cribbage and dominoes. The family room is no smoking. You can choose from more than 30 whiskies, and they've well kept Adnams and Greene King Abbot and a guest such as Ridleys Tolly Original on handpump. Reasonably priced bar food includes baps (from £2.95), battered cod or mediterranean vegetable bake (£6.45), gammon or chicken tikka (£6.95), steaks (from £9.45) and puddings such as treacle sponge or strawberry ice-cream sundae (£2.95); Sunday roasts (£6.50). More reports please. *(Recommended by W W Burke, the Didler, Peter and Jackie Barnett, Nigel Long, Brian and Anna Marsden, Ken Richards)*

Free house ~ Licensees Brian and Janet Morley ~ Real ale ~ Bar food (not Tues) ~
(01335) 310287 ~ Children in family room ~ Open 12-3, 7-11(10.30 Sun); closed Tues
lunchtime and Weds lunchtime in winter ~ Bedrooms: /£55S

LUCKY DIP

Besides the fully inspected pubs, you might like to try these Lucky Dips recommended to
us and described by readers (if you do, please send us reports: www.goodguides.co.uk).

ABBOTS BROMLEY [SK0824]
Coach & Horses [High St]: Comfortable
Tudor village pub with decent standard food in
refurbished beamed bar and restaurant, well
kept real ales, friendly helpful staff; pleasant
garden, good value bedrooms *(David J Austin,
John Wooll)*

ACTON TRUSSELL [SJ9318]
Moat House [signed from A449 just S of
Stafford; handy for M6 junction 13]: Busy
timbered food place by Staffs & Worcs Canal,
partly dating from 1320 but now with 50-
room hotel attached; comfortable oak-beamed
bar with big open fireplace and armchairs, nice
décor, smart customers and lots of efficient
young staff, enjoyable bar food (only
restaurant meals Sun lunchtime), good wine list
(keg beers), no smoking restaurant; fruit
machine, piped music; children welcome, open
all day wknds, attractive grounds with picnic-
sets overlooking charming duck pond
*(Pauline and Terry James, Roz Lowrie,
Derek and Heather Manning, LYM, Paul and
Gloria Howell)*

ALREWAS [SK1715]
☆ *George & Dragon* [off A38; Main St]: Three
friendly low-beamed linked rooms with well
kept Banks's, Marstons Pedigree and Thwaites
Lancaster Bomber, good value generous simple
food (not Sun) inc fresh veg and children's
dishes, efficient staff, attractive paintings; piped
music; pleasant partly covered garden with
good play area, children welcome in eating
area; opens 5 wkdys *(LYM, Francis Johnston,
John Tavernor)*
William IV [William IV Rd, off main st]:
Friendly and comfortable, with well kept
Marstons Pedigree and monthly guest beers,
enjoyable reasonably priced honest food (all
day Fri-Sun), two for one lunchtime bargains
(not Sun), good service, no smoking lounge
with raised eating area (busy wknds, best to
book then); music nights, sports TV; tables in
garden with aviary and chipmunks, short walk
from Grand Trunk Canal *(Bob and
Laura Brock, C J Fletcher, John and
Yvonne Davies)*

ALSTONEFIELD [SK1255]
☆ *Watts Russell Arms* [Hopedale]: Cheerful light
and airy beamed pub handy for Dovedale and
the Manifold (can get busy wknds), well kept
Black Sheep, Timothy Taylors Landlord and
an occasional guest beer, decent range of soft
drinks, low-priced straightforward food from
sandwiches up, traditional games; children
welcome, picnic-sets under parasols on
sheltered tiered terrace and in garden, cl Mon

and winter Sun evening *(Dave Braisted,
the Didler, Peter and Jackie Barnett,
W W Burke, LYM)*

AMINGTON [SK2204]
Gate [Tamworth Rd, by Coventry Canal
bridge 69]: Pleasantly decorated canalside local
with limited but imaginative food in lounge bar
(and restaurant), also separate bar, Marstons
ales, good value house wines, good-sized
family room, good service; moorings
(Neil Kellett)

ANSLOW [SK2024]
☆ *Burnt Gate* [Hopley Rd]: Pleasant largely no
smoking country pub, comfortable lounge with
well kept Bass and Marstons Pedigree, good
fresh home-made food with imaginative
touches and local produce, friendly efficient
staff, popular Sun lunch in separate restaurant
*(Paul Baxter, C J Fletcher, John and
Yvonne Davies)*

ARMITAGE [SK0716]
☆ *Plum Pudding* [Rugeley Rd (A513)]: Canalside
pub and brasserie with modern warm colour
scheme, good contemporary food inc good
value set menu, sandwiches and light dishes
too, well kept Bass, Greene King Old Speckled
Hen and Marstons Pedigree, decent wines
(choice of large or giant glasses), friendly
efficient service; waterside terrace *(Alan Cole,
Kirstie Bruce, John Rushton, Bren and
Val Speed)*

BLITHBURY [SK0819]
Bull & Spectacles [Uttoxeter Rd (B5014 S of
Abbots Bromley)]: Wide choice of food inc
bargain lunchtime Hot Table – half a dozen or
so generous main dishes with help-yourself veg,
and small choice of puddings; good friendly
service *(David Green)*

BRADLEY [SJ8717]
Red Lion [off A518 W of Stafford; Smithy
Lane]: Friendly old-world 16th-c village pub,
well kept Bass and good guest beers, good
varied sensibly priced food inc OAP midweek
bargains and good Sun lunch, decent wine
choice, no smoking dining room
(John Tavernor)

BRAMSHALL [SK0633]
Old Bramshall Inn: Attractive welcoming
country pub, three real ales, enjoyable food,
good friendly service *(John Tavernor)*

BRANSTON [SK2221]
Bridge Inn [off A5121 just SW of Burton;
Tatenhill Lane, by Trent & Mersey Canal
Bridge 34]: Cosy low-beamed canalside pub
with new Italian landlord doing good
reasonably priced pizzas and pastas, well kept
Marstons Pedigree on handpump now, friendly

staff and atmosphere, warm log fire; tables in waterside garden, good moorings, basic supplies for boaters and caravanners *(Paul Baxter, C J Fletcher, B M Eldridge)*

BRETBY [SK2423]

Stanhope Arms [Ashby Rd E (A511 Burton—Swadlincote)]: Friendly Brewers Fayre with warm atmosphere, plenty of small areas, well kept national beers, good range of salads, steaks and grills; good disabled facilities, pleasant garden, bedrooms *(B M Eldridge)*

BREWOOD [SJ8808]

Bridge Inn [High Green; by Shrops Union Canal Bridge 14]: Friendly and comfortable two-bar pub with generous usual food at bargain prices (very popular wknds), Burtonwood and two guest beers, separate dining room *(Susan and Erik Falck-Therkelsen, Keith and Maureen Trainer)*

BURSTON [SJ9330]

Greyhound [just off A51 Sandon—Stone]: Traditional pub, largely no smoking, extended from 17th-c core, with spacious dining areas behind rambling bar, three well kept ales such as Bass, Tetleys Imperial and Titanic, wide choice of enjoyable food (all day wknds), quick friendly service *(Ian and Sue Wells, John Tavernor)*

BURTON UPON TRENT [SK2523]

Burton Bar [part of Bass Museum, Horninglow St]: Reconstructed Edwardian bar, comfortable, with well kept unusual local ales; the brewing museum is an interesting outing *(Tony and Maggie Harwood, Tony and Wendy Hobden)*

Coopers Tavern [Cross St]: Tynemill pub with nice traditional layout, well kept locally brewed Bass, Marstons Pedigree and Worthington 1744, also Castle Rock Burton Gold and a guest beer, tapped from casks in counterless back room (the tables in this room are casks, too), cheap nourishing lunchtime food (not Sun) from hot filled cobs to imaginative things like ostrich burgers, homely no smoking front parlour with piano, coal fire and small family area; impromptu folk nights Tues *(LYM, Patrick Hancock, Pete Baker, C J Fletcher, the Didler)*

Derby Inn [Derby Rd]: Unspoilt friendly local with well kept Marstons Pedigree, long-serving landlord, local produce for sale wknd, brewery glasses collection in cosy panelled lounge, lots of steam railway memorabilia in long narrow bar; sports TV; open all day Fri/Sat *(the Didler, C J Fletcher)*

Devonshire Arms [Station St]: Tied to Burton Bridge, with a good range of their ales and of continental bottled beers, also country wines, decent food (all day Fri/Sat, not Sun), lots of snug corners – some no smoking; pleasant back terrace with water feature, open all day Fri/Sat *(Patrick Hancock, C J Fletcher, the Didler)*

Old Cottage Tavern [Rangemoor St/Byrkley St]: Tied to local small brewery Old Cottage, three of their good beers and guest beer, good value food (not Sun evening) inc bargain specials, solid fuel stove, four rooms inc no

smoking room, games room and compact back restaurant; open all day *(the Didler, C J Fletcher)*

Thomas Sykes [Anglesey Rd]: Closed as we go to press while neighbouring site is redeveloped as flats, but due to reopen under same landlord by the time this new edition is published, and we do hope it will stay out of developers' hands; former brewery stables and waggon shed, two friendly rooms with mugs, jugs and bric-a-brac on high rafters, stable fittings, breweriana and pump clips, wood benches, cobbled floors, well kept Bass, Marstons Pedigree, Tower and guest beers tapped from the cask, good cheap filled cobs, small snug; outside gents'; seats out in yard, children welcome till 8ish, open all day Fri *(C J Fletcher, Richard Houghton, the Didler)*

BUTTERTON [SK0756]

Black Lion [off B5053]: Traditional 18th-c low-beamed stone-built inn in Peak District conservation village, logs blazing in inner room's kitchen range, some banquette seating, enjoyable bar food from filled rolls up, half a dozen well kept ales such as Thwaites Lancaster Bomber, reasonable prices, traditional games and pool room; piped music; children in eating areas, tables on terrace, tidy bedrooms, cl Mon and Tues lunchtimes *(the Didler, LYM, David and Thelma Taylor, Peter F Marshall)*

CANNOCK WOOD [SK0412]

Park Gate [Park Gate Rd, S side of Cannock Chase]: Good atmosphere in extended brick pub under new management, cushioned chairs and pews, lots of woodwork, attractively priced food (not Sat evening) from sandwiches and baguettes up, well kept Banks's Mild, Marstons Pedigree and Worthington, woodburner, extensive restaurant and conservatory; plenty of picnic-sets and play area outside, by Castle Ring Iron Age fort, good Cannock Chase walks *(Anton Mans)*

CHEADLE [SK0342]

☆ *Queens at Freehay* [Counslow Rd, SE]: Good mainly familiar food in dining pub which caters well for children, arch to neat and airy no smoking area from comfortable lounge, well kept Bass and Worthington, swift attentive service *(LYM, Jean and Douglas Troup, John Tavernor, Martin and Alison Stainsby)*

CHEDDLETON [SJ9751]

☆ *Boat* [Basford Bridge Lane, off A520]: Cheerful local with neat long bar, low plank ceilings, particularly well kept Marstons Bitter and Pedigree, good value generous simple food, interesting pictures, attractive dining room with polished floor, black-leaded range and brass fittings; handy for flint mill, steam museum and country park; children welcome, fairy-lit heated tables out overlooking canal *(LYM, Martin and Alison Stainsby)*

CODSALL [SJ8603]

Codsall Station [Chapel Lane/Station Rd]: Pub in simply restored listed waiting room and ticket office (station still used by trains) with added conservatory, good range of Holdens beers kept well inc one brewed for the pub, lots of railway memorabilia, good value basic food (not Sun) from sandwiches and baked potatoes up; open all day wknds *(Blaise Vyner, the Didler)*

CONSALL [SK0049]

☆ *Black Lion* [Consall Forge, OS Sheet 118 map ref 000491; best approach from Nature Park, off A522, using car park ½ mile past Nature Centre]: Traditional take-us-as-you-find-us tavern tucked away in rustic old-fashioned canalside settlement by restored steam railway station, enjoyable generous unpretentious food freshly cooked by landlord inc good fish choice, good coal fire, well kept Marstons Best and Pedigree; piped music, no muddy boots; busy wknds, good walking area *(LYM, L Elliott, Paul Robinshaw, Colin Buckle, the Didler, Ian and Ruth Laurence)*

CRESSWELL [SJ9739]

☆ *Izaak Walton* [off A50 Stoke—Uttoxeter; Cresswell Lane]: Wide food choice all day from sandwiches and filled rolls to steaks and mixed grill in attractive country inn with prints and panelling, several small rooms and larger upstairs area, well kept ales such as Adnams Best, Bass and Fullers London Pride, good wines by the glass, attentive welcoming service; well behaved children welcome, disabled facilities (but some steps), attractive back garden, open all day *(Rob and Catherine Dunster, LYM, John Tavernor)*

DILHORNE [SJ9743]

Charlie Bassetts [New Rd]: Small recently refurbished traditional pub, well laid out, with enjoyable well priced bar and restaurant food, welcoming family service and atmosphere; attractive family service *(Mark Heath)*

ECCLESHALL [SJ8329]

☆ *George* [A519/B5026]: Several good Slaters beers brewed here by the licensees' son, beams, flagstones, coal fire in splendid central inglenook, cosy alcoves, well worn in unassuming furnishings, good wines by the glass, farm cider, quick friendly and cheerful service, good value generous food from lunchtime sandwiches, baguettes and baked potatoes up in recently refurbished brightly lit bistro restaurant (all day wknds), reasonable prices; may be piped music; children in eating areas, dogs welcome, open all day *(Stan and Hazel Allen, PL, LYM, Patrick Hancock, Dr and Mrs A K Clarke, Alec and Joan Laurence, John Tavernor, Paul and Ursula Randall, David Howell, Robert Garner, Derek and Sylvia Stephenson)*

ENVILLE [SO8286]

☆ *Cat* [A458 W of Stourbridge]: 17th-c, with heavy beams, timbers and log fire in two appealingly old-fashioned rooms on one side of servery, plush banquettes on the other, well kept local Enville Ale, White and seasonal Phoenix, two or three interesting changing guests (landlord helpful with the choice), mulled wine, quickly served generous food from imaginative sandwiches to unusual specials, popular upstairs restaurant, tabby cat and quiet collie; nice yard with picnic-sets,

popular with walkers (on Staffordshire Way) – and now after a 300-year ban is open on Sun too *(BB, Lynda and Trevor Smith, the Didler, Paul and Gloria Howell)*

ETRURIA [SJ8747]

☆ *Plough* [Etruria Rd (off A53 opp Festival site)]: Small two-room pub, very friendly licensees and staff, five well kept Robinsons beers, nice atmosphere and décor, coal fires, huge choice of good value food served till late esp steaks and fine range of sandwiches hot or cold, will do anything on request; busy lunchtime and wknds *(Robert Garner)*

HARDINGS WOOD [SJ8354]

☆ *Blue Bell*: Traditional boaters' tavern between Macclesfield and Trent & Mersey canals, welcoming and unpretentious, up to half a dozen well kept quickly changing ales from small breweries, imports on tap and lots of foreign bottled beers, farm cider, helpful staff, filled rolls, busy front bar, quieter back room; impromptu Sun folk nights; dogs welcome, cl Mon, also wkdy lunchtimes *(Sue Holland, Dave Webster, the Didler)*

HARTSHILL [SJ8745]

Jolly Potters [Hartshill Rd (A52)]: Welcoming and gently updated local popular for its particularly well kept Bass, central bar, corridor to public bar (with TV) and three small homely lounges *(the Didler, Pete Baker)*

HIGH OFFLEY [SJ7725]

Anchor [off A519 Eccleshall—Newport; towards High Lea, by Shrops Union Canal, Bridge 42; Peggs Lane]: Real boaters' pub, little changed in the century or more this family have run it, two small simple rooms behind partition, well kept Marstons Pedigree and Wadworths 6X in jugs from cellar, Weston's farm ciders, may be lunchtime toasties; on Shrops Union Canal, outbuilding with small shop and semi-open lavatories, lovely garden with great hanging baskets, caravan/campsite; occasional wknd singalongs, cl Mon-Thurs winter *(the Didler, Ian and Ruth Laurence, Nick and Lynne Carter)*

HOAR CROSS [SK1323]

☆ *Meynell Ingram Arms* [Abbots Bromley Rd, off A515 Yoxall—Sudbury]: Newly extended beamed country dining pub, neat minimalist décor keeping old-fashioned touches inc log fires in no smoking main lounge and in public side, separate little front snug; enjoyable and inventive if not cheap bar food from sandwiches to formal restaurant meals, plenty of local produce, well kept Marstons Pedigree and Timothy Taylors Landlord, good wine choice, friendly helpful young staff; courtyard tables, attractive spot in summer *(Tony and Maggie Harwood, Jackie Faker, Pete Baker, David Martin, Ian Tolfts)*

HOPWAS [SK1704]

Tame Otter [A51 Tamworth—Lichfield]: Cosily rustic Vintage Inn with lots of beams, nooks and alcoves, three log fires, easy chairs, settles, dining chairs, old photographs and canalia, friendly well trained staff, reasonably priced food all day, good choice of wines, well kept Bass; huge car park *(DC, Colin Gooch)*

HULME END [SK1059]

☆ *Manifold* [B5054 Warslow—Hartington]: Attractive 18th-c country pub nr river, well kept ales such as Marstons Pedigree and Whim Hartington, wide choice of generous sensibly priced food using local produce, good sandwiches, helpful service, neat comfortable lounge bar, log-effect gas fires, separate light and airy dining room; children and cyclists welcome, disabled facilities, tables outside, camp site, bedrooms in converted stone smithy off secluded back courtyard *(BB, B M Eldridge)*

KINGSTONE [SK0428]

Blythe Inn [The Blythe, towards Stowe-by-Chartley]: Friendly licensees and staff, enjoyable fresh food (not Sun evening) in neat carpeted bar and large pleasant restaurant, carvery Fri/Sat evening and Sun lunch, well kept ales such as Bass, Marstons Pedigree, Worthington and guest beers, open fire; coach parties welcome; picnic-sets on terrace, open all day *(George and Fran Mellor)*

KINVER [SO8483]

Plough & Harrow [High St (village signed off A449 or A458 W of Stourbridge); aka the Steps]: Old split-level local tied to Bathams with their Best, Mild and XXX kept very well, good choice of ciders and malt whiskies, cheap plain bar food (filled rolls even Sun lunchtime), low prices, film star pictures; proper public bar with darts, dominoes etc, lounge with nostalgic juke box, SkyTV sports and fruit machine, folk nights 1st and 3rd Weds; children allowed in some parts, tables in back courtyard, open all day wknds *(Pete Baker, the Didler, Paul and Gloria Howell)*

☆ *Whittington Inn* [A449 between Kidderminster and Wall Heath, by Staffs & Worcs Canal]: Striking black and white timbered Tudor house, genuine Dick Whittington connection, interesting old-fashioned bar, roaring fire, lots of panelling, little nooks and corners, low doorways, passages and wall paintings, conservatory, good value food all day, well kept Banks's, Marstons Pedigree and a guest beer, attentive staff; attractive garden, open all day *(Gill and Tony Morriss, LYM)*

LEEK [SJ9856]

Red Lion [Market Pl]: Large unpretentious town-centre pub with well kept Hydes, good choice of wines by the glass, cheap tasty food, friendly efficient young staff; nice room upstairs with lots of panelling and sofas *(John Wooll, Bob Richardson)*

☆ *Swan* [St Edward St]: Bustling old three-room pub popular for cheap lunchtime food from sandwiches and baguettes up, quick helpful service even when busy, well kept changing ales such as Bass, Fullers London Pride and Jennings Snecklifter, occasional beer festivals, lots of malt whiskies, choice of coffees, several rooms around central servery inc no smoking lounge; downstairs wine bar, folk club, seats in courtyard *(Rona Murdoch, the Didler)*

☆ *Three Horseshoes* [A53 NNE, on Blackshaw Moor]: Friendly family-run inn with emphasis on reliable generous food from sandwiches to roasts inc wild boar, brasserie, and candlelit beamed restaurant – Sat dinner-dance; lots of nooks and crannies, open fire, no smoking area, good service, well kept Courage Directors, Greene King Old Speckled Hen and Theakstons XB, sensible prices, children's area; no dogs, bedrooms *(Dr D J and Mrs S C Walker)*

☆ *Wilkes Head* [St Edward St]: Convivial three-room local dating from 18th c (still has back coaching stables), tied to Whim with their ales and a guest beer kept well, good choice of whiskies, farm cider, friendly chatty landlord, welcoming regulars and dogs, lunchtime rolls, home-made stilton for sale, pub games, gas fire, lots of pumpclips; juke box in back room, Mon music night; children allowed in one room (but not really a family pub), fair disabled access, tables outside, open all day *(the Didler, John Wooll, Pete Baker)*

LICHFIELD [SK1010]

Hedgehog [Stafford Rd (A51)]: Large Vintage Inn with lots of tables and plenty of nooks and corners, good choice of well prepared food, Marstons Pedigree, friendly attentive staff; children welcome, picnic-sets outside, bedrooms *(Tony and Maggie Harwood, Colin Gooch)*

LONGNOR [SK0965]

Olde Cheshire Cheese: Welcoming 14th-c building, a pub for 250 years, well kept Robinsons, traditional main bar and two attractive dining rooms with their own separate bar; hikers welcome, bedrooms *(Derek and Heather Manning, Theocsbrian)*

MEERBROOK [SJ9960]

Lazy Trout: Two small comfortable bars, dining room, wide choice of good value food, decent wine list, interesting well kept guest beers, friendly staff; plenty of tables in pleasant garden behind, attractive setting *(Mr and Mrs John Taylor)*

MILWICH [SJ9533]

Red Lion [Dayhills; B5027 towards Stone]: Old-fashioned bar at end of working farmhouse, old settle and log fire, Bass and one or two guest beers tapped from the cask, friendly welcome, darts, dominoes and cribbage; cl lunchtimes exc Sun *(the Didler)*

OAKAMOOR [SK0645]

Olde Star [Star Road (B5417 NE, towards A52)]: Good-sized cosy low-beamed 16th-c pub with inviting coal fire, lots of brassware, friendly staff, four real ales, good tea and coffee, generous fairly priced food inc good home-made puddings; quite handy for Alton Towers *(Matt Waite)*

PENKRIDGE [SJ9214]

Boat [Penkridge Lock, Cannock Rd (B5012), by Staffs & Worcs Canal, Bridge 86]: Comfortably old-fashioned pub by canal (not very scenic here, but quite busy with boaters), pleasant layout, good value generous food (not Sun) from sandwiches up, well kept ales; piped music; picnic-sets outside *(Colin Gooch)*

Horse & Jockey [Market St]: Traditional local with good value pubby food, well kept

Banks's, Marstons Pedigree and guest beers *(Robert Garner)*

Littleton Arms [St Michaels Sq/A449 – M6 detour between junctions 12 and 13]: Substantial Vintage Inn done out in olde-worlde style, particularly well kept Bass, John Smiths and Tetleys, good value food all day, quick helpful service from friendly young staff; children welcome, open all day *(Roy and Lindsey Fentiman, Gerry and Rosemary Dobson, Ian and Ruth Laurence)*

☆ *Star* [Market Pl]: Charming open-plan local with lots of low black beams and button-back red plush, well kept Banks's ales, limited lunchtime bar food from chip butties to cheap main dishes, friendly prompt service, open fires; piped music, sports TV; open all day, terrace tables *(Colin Gooch, BB, Ian and Ruth Laurence)*

RUSHTON SPENCER [SJ9362]
Royal Oak [A523 Leek—Macclesfield]: Welcoming new landlord's wife doing enjoyable home-made food for lounge bar and no smoking restaurant, well kept Burtonwood ales, decent wines, log fires, pleasant décor *(Brenda Pauline, Pam Haines)*

SHARESHILL [SJ9406]
Elms [Church Rd]: Two-bar local with Highgate and other ales such as Greene King Old Speckled Hen, Hook Norton Old Hooky and Hop Back Summer Lightning, good value food, welcoming staff and regulars *(Nigel Simkin)*

STAFFORD [SJ9222]
Picture House [Bridge St/Lichfield St]: Grade II listed art deco cinema well converted by Wetherspoons keeping ornate ceiling plasterwork and stained-glass name sign, bar on stage with well kept Courage Directors, Marstons Pedigree, Theakstons Best and XB, Wadworths 6X and guests such as Lichfield Steeplejack, farm cider, seating in stalls, circle and upper circle, no smoking areas, good choice of food all day, lively atmosphere, friendly efficient staff (and Peter Cushing mannequin in preserved ticket box), film posters; good disabled facilities, spacious terrace overlooking river, open all day *(John Tavernor)*

Shire Horse [1 mile from M6 junction 14 via A34 – junction A34/A513]: Welcoming staff, attractive wide-ranging choice of food served quickly even when very busy *(Christine and Neil Townend)*

Stafford Arms [Railway St; turn right at main entrance outside station, 100 yards down]: Open-plan pub reopened after spotless modern updating with clever wall lighting and new no smoking area up a couple of steps, big solid tables and nautical décor, four well kept Titanic ales, farm cider; open all day exc Sun afternoon *(Peter F Marshall, John Tavernor, Martin Grosberg, Paul and Gloria Howell)*

STANLEY [SJ9352]
Travellers Rest: Reliable food inc bargain Sun lunch, well kept Marstons Pedigree, friendly service – smart without being fussy *(anon)*

SWINSCOE [SK1348]
Dog & Partridge [A52 3 miles W of Ashbourne; Town End Lane]: 17th-c beamed and stone-built coaching inn, smart and friendly, with enjoyable home-made food, well kept Whim Hartington, efficient service, superb views from dining room's new conservatory extension; comfortable adjoining motel accommodation *(Paul and Margaret Baker)*

TAMWORTH [SK2004]
Tweedale Arms [Albert Rd/Victoria Rd]: Substantial building with modern airy atmosphere, daily papers, restaurant with good steaks and attentive service; games machines *(Colin Gooch)*

TATENHILL [SK2021]
☆ *Horseshoe* [off A38 W of Burton; Main St]: Cheerfully civilised tiled-floor bar, cosy no smoking side snug with woodburner, two-level restaurant and back family area, enjoyable food (all day Sat) from sandwiches to steaks and more ambitious dishes, proper children's food, well kept Marstons ales, good wine range, quick polite service; pleasant garden, good play area with pets corner *(LYM, C J Fletcher)*

TEAN [SK0138]
Dog & Partridge [Uttoxeter Rd]: Good imaginative food, very reasonably priced, in pleasant conservatory restaurant; live music Fri *(Mrs C Stafford)*

THORNCLIFFE [SK0158]
Red Lion: Comfortable and attractively homely 17th-c pub with good choice of enjoyable fresh food from sandwiches up, Thurs steak night, all-day Sun roasts, hard-working young licensees, good atmosphere, log fires, wide range of wines and beers, no smoking dining room, games area with pool; children welcome *(Pauline and Terry James, Howson and Janet Adams, Brenda Pauline, Pam Haines)*

TRYSULL [SO8594]
Bell [Bell Rd]: Extended red brick village pub, softly lit lounge with lots of table lamps, big grandfather clock, inglenook fire and good chatty atmosphere, many original features in cosy bar with brasses and locomotive number-plates, Holdens Bitter, Special and Golden Glow, Bathams Best and a guest beer, interesting bar food from sandwiches up at fair prices, evening restaurant Weds-Sat; open all day wknds *(Gill and Tony Morriss, the Didler, Paul and Gloria Howell)*

TUTBURY [SK2128]
☆ *Olde Dog & Partridge* [High St; off A50 N of Burton]: Good Chef & Brewer in handsome Tudor inn, rambling extensively bedecked with heavy beams, timbers, various small rooms, nooks and corners, their usual food with good blackboard specials, well kept ales such as Mansfield, Marstons Pedigree, Ridleys and Charles Wells Bombardier, prompt cheerful service, good log fire, thriving atmosphere; comfortable well equipped bedrooms, open all day *(LYM, Dennis Jones, Michael J Caley, Francis Johnston)*

WATERFALL [SK0851]
Red Lion: Warmly friendly traditional stone-built pub in quiet Peak village, good log fires in two linked rooms, decent range of enjoyable food, well kept Bass; children welcome, tables in attractive area outside, great views, good walking country *(B M Eldridge)*

WATERHOUSES [SK0850]
George [Leek Rd (A523)]: Large three-room 1930s roadside dining pub, good sensibly priced fresh generous bar food from sandwiches up, restaurant specialising in fish, nice puddings, Greene King IPA and Marstons, locals' bar, play area; particularly friendly, if not full of character; children welcome, handy for manifold cycle trail, local bike hire *(Elaine Wintle, Lorna Duval)*

Olde Crown [Leek Rd]: Attractive pub dating from 17th c, friendly staff and welcoming atmosphere, good range of well kept ales, good value food; reasonably priced comfortable bedrooms *(B M Eldridge)*

WHITTINGTON [SK1608]
Dog [the one nr Lichfield; Main St]: Traditional family-run pub very popular lunchtime for wide choice of good value food from sandwiches to steaks, well kept Adnams, Marstons Pedigree and Timothy Taylors Landlord, friendly efficient service, lots of beams and brassware, no smoking area; bedrooms *(Ian and Jane Irving, Colin Gooch)*

YOXALL [SK1420]
Foresters [Wood Lane]: Recently refurbished under new management, friendly proficient service, enjoyable good value food freshly cooked from local ingredients, help for special diets *(Mrs Margaret Stinton)*

Golden Cup [Main St (A515)]: Well furnished village inn dating from early 18th c, attentive staff, reasonably priced home-made food from sandwiches up (they don't like just two of you sitting at tables for four), well kept Marstons Pedigree and a guest beer, no smoking lounge bar, games in public bar; waterside garden, good value bedrooms with own bathrooms, open all day wknds *(Tony and Maggie Harwood, John and Yvonne Davies, Robin and Tricia Walker)*

'Children welcome' means the pub says it lets children inside without any special restriction. If it allows them in, but to restricted areas such as an eating area or family room, we specify this. Places with separate restaurants often let children use them; hotels usually let them into public areas such as lounges. Some pubs impose an evening time limit – let us know if you find this.

Suffolk

The Suffolk pubs which stand out these days for the amount of sheer pleasure that they have been giving readers are the relaxed and welcoming Queens Head at Bramfield (lovingly prepared food using local and organic ingredients), the Crown at Buxhall (again, really good food, with a thriving atmosphere and welcoming chatty licensees), the immaculately kept Crown at Great Glemham (some emphasis on food, much enjoyed by families), the Angel in Lavenham (a favourite, excellent all round), the timeless good value Kings Head at Laxfield, the interesting old Crown at Snape (gaining a Food Award this year), St Peters Brewery at South Elmham (this gorgeous building with its attached microbrewery makes a most appealing and unusual 'pub'), the rather smart Crown in Southwold (very good food, beer and wines), the hugely convivial Lord Nelson there (a new entry this year), and the charming old Bell by the sea at nearby Walberswick (a great range of Adnams ales, and a nice place to stay in). The Crown at Snape, on great form these days, takes the title of Suffolk Dining Pub of the Year. It's worth noting that several of the main entries here have now ruled out smoking in any part of the pub, and many others are now largely no smoking. It's not just the foody places, either: the thoroughly unpretentious Victoria at Earl Soham, one of those which is now entirely no smoking, is renowned chiefly for its good beers from the good nearby Earl Soham microbrewery. In general, Suffolk drinks prices tend to be rather higher than the national average. Greene King, the dominant regional brewer, is available throughout, and Adnams is also easily obtainable (and to many beer lovers is the true taste of Suffolk). Besides Earl Soham and St Peters, other good local ales to look out for are Mauldons and Nethergate. Pubs in the Lucky Dip section at the end of the chapter that have been drawing warm praise recently are the Cock at Brent Eleigh, George at Cavendish, Peacock at Chelsworth, restauranty Fox & Goose at Fressingfield, Angel in Halesworth, Fat Cat in Ipswich, Plough & Sail at Snape and Duke of Marlborough at Somersham.

BRAMFIELD TM4073 Map 5

Queens Head 🍴

The Street; A144 S of Halesworth

Despite some emphasis on the well prepared food, the comfortably relaxed atmosphere at this bustling pub still attracts regulars for a drink at the bar. Clearly, real loving care goes into the food preparation. They make their own preserves (which you can buy) and bread, and many of the ingredients they use come from small local organic farms. As well as good filled baguettes, and a lunchtime one-pot-meal (£4.95), daily changing specials might include cream of spinach and coconut soup (£3.75), grilled goats cheese with roast beetroot and smoked duck breast (£5.95), steak, kidney and ale pie (£8.95), seafood crumble or filo parcel with spinach, goats cheese, pine nuts and olives or cod fillet with crispy cheese and garlic topping (£10.95), rib-eye steak with mustard and cream sauce (£14.95), memorable puddings such as chocolate and brandy pot or lemon tart (£4.25), home-made ice-cream (£2.95) and a great cheese platter (£4.50); service is really friendly. They've well kept Adnams Bitter and Broadside, and a good wine list, including lots of organic ones and half a dozen wines by the glass, home-made elderflower cordial, and organic apple juices and cider. The high-raftered lounge bar has scrubbed pine tables, a good log fire in its impressive fireplace, and a sprinkling of farm tools on the walls; a separate no smoking side bar has light wood furnishings (one half of the pub is no smoking). There are seats in the pretty garden, a dome-shaped bower made of willow, and a family of bantams. They hold various special events such as wine tasting and Spanish evenings, and they do a popular paupers evening (£12.95 for three courses) from time to time; the church next door is rather lovely. *(Recommended by John Wooll, A J Murray, Fred and Lorraine Gill, Comus and Sarah Elliott, Tina and David Woods-Taylor, J F M and M West, Rob Winstanley, David Treherne-Pollock, Pat and Tony Hinkins, MJVK, TW, MW, Richard and Margaret McPhee, Clive and Vivienne Locks, M and GR, Neil Powell)*

Adnams ~ Tenants Mark and Amanda Corcoran ~ Real ale ~ Bar food (12-2, 6.30-10(7-9 Sun)) ~ (01986) 784214 ~ Children in eating area of bar ~ Dogs welcome ~ Open 11.45-2.30, 6.30-11; 12-3, 7-10.30 Sun

BROME TM1376 Map 5
Cornwallis ♀ 🛏

Rectory Road; after turning off A140 S of Diss into B1077, take first left turn

At the heart of this civilised 19th-c country house hotel is a well appointed beamed and timbered 16th-c bar. From here, a step up from the tiled-floor serving area takes you through heavy timber uprights to a stylishly comfortable carpeted area. This is attractively furnished with a good mix of old and antique tables, some oak settles alongside cushioned library chairs, a glazed-over well, and a handsome woodburning stove. They've an extensive carefully chosen wine list with over a dozen by the glass, a local cider and organic juices, and Adnams, St Peters Best and a guest such as Greene King IPA on handpump. They set themselves quite a challenge with the rather complicated bar food, which might include starters such as soup (£5), smoked eel on wilted baby spinach and watercress with samphire and asparagus (£6), lamb carpaccio with roquefort, pickled walnuts and baby gem lettuce (£9) and main courses such as honey roast quail stuffed with black pudding mousseline and flamed in apricot brandy, with creamed pak choi (£12), roast monkfish wrapped in baby spinach on sweet mash with cockles in white wine cream (£15) and puddings such as sticky dark chocolate and pecan tart with caramel sorbet or steamed marmalade sponge with whiskey custard (from £5). A nicely planted Victorian-style side conservatory has coffee-lounge cane furniture, and there's an elegant no smoking restaurant; piped music and board games. The 20 acres of ground and tree-lined drive here are quite splendid; in summer they have jazz and blues concerts, and archery and balloon launches out on the lawn. *(Recommended by Dr and Mrs R G J Telfer, David Twitchett, Sean and Sharon Pines, Adrian White, M A and C R Starling, Charles Gysin, TW, MW, Simon Cottrell, Peter and Jean Dowson, Richard and Margaret McPhee)*

Swallow Group ~ Managers Peter Bartlett and Paul Beard ~ Real ale ~ Bar food (12-2.30, 6-9) ~ Restaurant ~ (01379) 870326 ~ Children welcome ~ Open 11-11; 12-10.30 Sun ~ Bedrooms: £95B/£115B

BURY ST EDMUNDS TL8564 Map 5
Nutshell

The Traverse, central pedestrian link off Abbeygate Street

This tiny little bare-boards local dates from the 17th c and has been selling beer since 1873, though a precursor is said to have been first licensed by Charles II (and there are tales of a tunnel to the abbey). Its timeless interior contains a short wooden bench along its shop-front corner windows, one cut-down sewing-machine table, an elbow rest running along its rather battered counter; well kept Greene King IPA and a guest on handpump are served by the talkative landlord. Rather bizarrely, a mummified cat, which was found walled up here (something our ancestors did quite commonly to ward off evil spirits) hangs from the dark brown ceiling, along with stacks of other bric-a-brac – from bits of a skeleton through vintage bank notes, cigarette packets and military and other badges to spears and a great metal halberd; piped music, cribbage and dominoes. The modern curved inn sign is appealing. More reports please. *(Recommended by the Didler)*

Greene King ~ Tenant Martin Baylis ~ Real ale ~ No credit cards ~ (01284) 764867 ~ Dogs welcome ~ Open 11(12 in winter)-11

Old Cannon

Cannon Street, just off A134/A1101 roundabout N end of town

Looking more like a stylish private town house than a pub, this solidly built, square-cut early Victorian yellow brick place makes a pleasant change from the usual pub style. For a start, there are clear indications in the bar on the right that this has special interest for the beer lover: two gleaming stainless steel brewing kettles, often gently burbling, that produce the pub's own good reasonably priced Old Cannon Best, Gunners Daughter, in winter their Black Pig Porter, and in summer their refreshing and light-tasting (but by no means weak) Blonde Bombshell. They also have a couple of guest beers from brewers such as Adnams and Nethergates on handpump, good wines by the glass, a farm cider and continental beers. This room has miscellaneous chairs around a few tables on dark bare boards, dark red or ochre walls, one with a big mirror, and plenty of standing space; a fanciful touch is that where you'd expect a ceiling there is instead a sort of floorless upper room complete with radiator, table and chairs. On the left, another dark red-walled and bare-boards room has neat slat-backed dining chairs around tables, and opens at the back into the neat kitchen, which produces enjoyable, fairly priced and generously served lunchtime bar food such as home-made soup (£3.95), sandwiches (from £4.25, baguettes from £4.95), toad in the hole, ham, egg and chips, venison burger, moroccan lamb curry, roast mushrooms and peppers with penne in spinach, ricotta and asparagus cream sauce or cod and chips (all £7.50), with puddings such as lime and chocolate cheesecake or cappuccino mousse (£3.75); the menu for the smarter no smoking evening restaurant is more elaborate. Service is quick, friendly and attentive, and the sociable licensees get a good buoyant atmosphere going; it can get pretty busy on Friday and Saturday nights; piped music. Behind, through the old side coach arch, is a good-sized cobbled courtyard neatly set with planters and hanging baskets, with rather stylish metal tables and chairs in bays at the back. We have so far had only secondhand recommendations for the bedrooms in a separate building across this courtyard, but these suggest that as more reports come in this is likely to qualify for one of our Place to Stay Awards. *(Recommended by MLR, C W Dix, Clare Phillips, Mike and Mary Carter)*

Free house ~ Licensee Carole Locker ~ Real ale ~ Bar food (lunchtime only) ~ Restaurant ~ (01284) 768769 ~ Dogs allowed in bar ~ Open 12-3, 5-11(7-10.30 Sun); closed Mon lunchtime ~ Bedrooms: £49S/£58S

BUXHALL TM0057 Map 5
Crown

Village signposted off B1115 W of Stowmarket; fork right by post office at Gt Finborough, turn left at Buxhall village sign, then second right into Mill Road, then right at T junction

Once again this buzzing 17th-c timber framed country pub earns a good batch of enthusiastic reader reports. Given the quality of the imaginative food, it's not surprising that this is so popular, and to be sure of a table, you must book. Skilfully cooked with fresh seasonal ingredients, monthly changing dishes might include curried sweet potato and spinach soup (£4.25), fried lambs kidneys on herb croûte with tarragon sauce (£5.75), sausage and mash (£8.50), battered haddock or fried spaghetti with toasted pine nuts and garlic butter (£8.95), wild mushroom risotto with grilled goats cheese (£9.95), lamb shank in oyster sauce with braised lentils and pak choi (£12.50) and fried duck breast with blackberry sauce (£14.95); they also do lunchtime bar snacks such as chips with cheese and anchovy fillets (all £2.95), and sandwiches (from £3.75); Sunday roast (£8.50). Good service from the chatty licensees and friendly staff. All the wines on their carefully chosen wine list are available by the glass, they've well kept Greene King IPA, Mauldons Bitter, Tindalls Best and Woodfordes Wherry on handpump, and over 25 whiskies. The intimate little bar on the left has an open fire in a big inglenook, a couple of small round tables on a tiled floor, and low hop-hung beams. Standing timbers separate it from another area with pews and candles, and flowers in summer on beech tables with leather chairs, and there's a further light and airy room which they call the Mill Restaurant (no smoking); piped music, cribbage, dominoes. Plenty of seats and solid wood tables under parasols on the heated terrace, and they've a pretty garden, with nice views over gently rolling countryside. A large enclosed side garden has wooden decking and raised flowerbeds. *(Recommended by M and GR, Mike and Mary Carter, Pamela Goodwyn, Derek Field, C W Dix, MDN, Mr and Mrs M Hayes, Dom Bradshaw, Adele Summers, J F M and M West)*

Greene King ~ Lease Trevor Golton ~ Real ale ~ Bar food (12-2, 6.30-9.30; not Sun evening) ~ Restaurant ~ (01449) 736521 ~ Well behaved children in restaurant ~ Dogs allowed in bar ~ Open 12-3, 6.30-11; closed Sun evening, Mon

CHELMONDISTON TM2038 Map 5
Butt & Oyster

Pin Mill – signposted from B1456 SE of Ipswich

Unchanging from year to year, this staunchly simple old bargeman's pub is popular with visitors; in summer you can sit outside on the suntrap terrace watching ships coming down the River Orwell from Ipswich and lines of moored black sailing barges. In winter you can enjoy the same view through bay windows. Pleasantly worn and unfussy, the half-panelled timeless little smoke room has model sailing ships around the walls and high-backed and other old-fashioned settles on the tiled floor; ferocious beady-eyed fish made by a local artist stare at you from the walls. Generous helpings of reasonably priced food include soup (£3.65), deep-fried camembert (£4.95), burgers (from £4), vegetable crumble (£7.25), greek-style lamb or chilled poached salmon (£7.95), and steaks (from £8.95); they also serve sandwiches at lunchtime (till 6pm at weekends). As space is limited, you might need to arrive early on the weekend to get a seat. Adnams Best and Broadside and Greene King IPA are well kept on handpump or tapped from the cask, and there are decent wines; shove-ha'penny, cribbage and dominoes. The annual Thames Barge Race (end June/beginning July) is fun. *(Recommended by Mrs A Chapman, Pat and Clive Sherriff, David Stokes, Pamela Goodwyn, the Didler, JDM, KM, Peter and Jean Dowson)*

Punch ~ Lease Steve Lomas ~ Real ale ~ Bar food ~ Restaurant ~ (01473) 780764 ~ Children in eating area of bar and restaurant ~ Dogs allowed in bar ~ Open 11-11; 12-10.30 Sun

COTTON TM0467 Map 5
Trowel & Hammer ♀

Mill Road; take B1113 N of Stowmarket, then turn right into Blacksmiths Lane just N of Bacton

The new landlady at this civilised, thatched pub has introduced a changing tapas menu which is very usefully served all day: maybe olives, tiger prawns, salmon rolls in raspberry and champagne sauce (all £4.75). The bar menu also changes every day, but a typical choice might include home-made soup (£3.25), home-made creamy salmon mousse (£5.75), roast beef with yorkshire pudding or fried chicken breast with thyme and garlic cream sauce (£8.95), red snapper on creamy thai noodles (£9.95), home-made steak and ale pie (£8.95), venison and apricot sausages on spring onion mash with cranberry gravy or grilled lemon sole with lemon and parsley butter (£10.95), and braised lamb shank with rosemary gravy (£11.95); no smoking dining room. Although there is quite a lot of emphasis on the food, there's a nice informal atmosphere, and they serve well kept Adnams, Greene

King IPA and Abbot, and a guest, usually from Adnams or Nethergate on handpump or tapped from the cask; also lots of unusual spirits, and an interesting wine list. The spreading series of quiet rooms has fresh flowers, lots of beamery and timber baulks, a big log fire (as well as an ornate woodburning stove at the back), and plenty of wheelbacks and one or two older chairs and settles around a variety of tables. The staff are pleasant and friendly, though service may slow down at busy times; pool, fruit machine and a juke box. The back garden is pretty with lots of roses and hollyhocks, neat climbers on trellises, picnic-sets, and even a swimming pool and croquet. *(Recommended by Alan Cole, Kirstie Bruce, Dom Bradshaw, Mrs A Chapman, Ian and Nita Cooper)*

Free house ~ Licensee Sally Selvage ~ Real ale ~ Bar food (12-2, 6-9 (tapas 12-9); 12-9 Sun;) ~ Restaurant ~ (01449) 781234 ~ Children welcome ~ Dogs allowed in bar ~ Live music weekends ~ Open 12-11(10.30 Sun)

CRETINGHAM TM2260 Map 5
Bell
The Street

The licensee at this neatly kept village pub is a fisherman himself (with a boat at Southwold), so you can be sure that the fresh fish served here will be carefully selected. The changing menu is gently imaginative, and dishes are served in generous helpings: lunchtime baguettes (from £5 – crayfish is popular), ploughman's (from £5.50), and hot flaked sea trout salad (£6.50), lobster salad (around £4 per 100 grams), wilted rocket, black olive, red onion and parmesan tart (£4.50), leek, white onion and cheese risotto (£8.50), braised lamb shoulder with pease pudding (£10), crispy bass (11), and rib-eye steak with horseradish mash and veal jus (£13), with puddings such as date and pistachio bread and butter pudding (£3.75). The building is a lovely conversion of four cottages, with lots of exposed beams and standing timbers and a large old fireplace. The comfortably modernised lounge bar features a big hunting scene tapestry, and the quarry-tiled public bar has shove-ha'penny, dominoes and chess. Adnams Bitter and Greene King Abbot and a couple of guests such as Mauldons Black Adder and Woodfordes Wherry are well kept on handpump, they've good wines, and about 20 malt whiskies. The attractive garden has rustic tables on the sheltered grass in front and more on a lawn by rose bushes and a fine old oak tree; more reports please. *(Recommended by Comus and Sarah Elliott, Ian and Nita Cooper, John F Morton, Tracey and Stephen Groves, M G Hart)*

Free house ~ Licensee Lee Knight ~ Real ale ~ Bar food ~ Restaurant ~ (01728) 685419 ~ Children welcome ~ Dogs allowed in bar ~ Open 11-3, 6-11; 12-3, 7-10.30 Sun; closed Tues ~ Bedrooms: £45B/£65B

DENNINGTON TM2867 Map 5
Queens Head
A1120

Handy if you're passing, this Tudor pub is gorgeously picturesque, and prettily set in gardens alongside the church. It backs on to Dennington Park, which has swings and so forth for children, and there are seats on a side lawn, attractively planted with flowers, and sheltered by some noble lime trees, with a goldfish pond. The main neatly kept L-shaped room has carefully stripped wall timbers and beams, a handsomely carved bressumer beam, and comfortable padded wall seats on the partly carpeted and partly tiled floor. Adnams Bitter and a guest such as Woodfordes Wherry are well kept on handpump and served from the brick bar counter; piped music, cribbage, dominoes. Quite a choice of bar food might include sandwiches (from £2.60), soup (£3.25), whitebait or fried camembert (£3.95), ploughman's (from £4.75), vegetable balti, scampi or roast beef (£6.95), sausage pie (£7.75), coq au vin (£8.25), baked trout with honey and almonds (£8.50), duck in orange and basil (£12.25), and puddings such as orange and kiwi cheesecake, banana split or treacle tart (£3.50). With new tables and chairs, both dining areas are no smoking, and you can't smoke at the counter. *(Recommended by*

David and Jean Hall, David Boult , Edmund Coan, M and GR, John Saul, P and J Shapley, George Atkinson)

Free house ~ Licensees Hilary Cowie, Peter Mills ~ Real ale ~ Bar food (9-11, 12-2, 6.30-9) ~ Restaurant ~ (01728) 638241 ~ Children in family room ~ Open 11-3, 6-11; 12-3, 6-10.30 Sun; opens 6.30 in winter

DUNWICH TM4770 Map 5
Ship
St James Street

This deceptively large old brick pub is beautifully located in a charmingly peaceful little village – it's hard to imagine that centuries ago it was one of England's busiest ports. The cosy welcoming main bar is traditionally furnished with benches, pews, captain's chairs and wooden tables on its tiled floor, a woodburning stove (left open in cold weather) and lots of sea prints and nautical memorabilia. From the handsomely panelled bar counter, you can get well kept Adnams Bitter and Broadside and Mauldons served with antique handpumps; fruit machine, dominoes and cribbage. A simple conservatory looks on to an attractive sunny back terrace, and the large garden is very pleasant, with its well spaced picnic-sets, two large anchors, and enormous fig tree. Besides simple fresh fish from Lowestoft harbour, and home-made chips (cod £6.85 lunchtime, £8.65 in the evening), a quite short choice of reasonably priced tasty bar food at lunchtime includes home-made soup (£2.20), sausage and chips (£4.95), ploughman's (from £5.50 – available till 6pm, readers recommend the crab £6.55), and a hot dish of the day (£6.55), while in the evening there might be spinach flan or gammon and pineapple (£7.95), fishcakes (£9.45), and steak and ale casserole (£9.25), with home-made puddings (£4.25); children's meals (from £5.50). The restaurant is no smoking. There's plenty to do or look at around here – lots of surrounding walks, lovely coastal scenery, the RSPB reserve at Minsmere, and the nearby Dunwich Museum, though a consequence of this is that the pub can get busy during the holidays. *(Recommended by Carolyn Browse, Rob and Catherine Dunster, Peter Meister, MJVK, Fred and Lorraine Gill, Penny and Fraser Hutchinson, Alan Sadler, Stephen and Jean Curtis, Tracey and Stephen Groves, David Field, Pat and Clive Sherriff, Comus and Sarah Elliott, Ian and Jane Irving, Tina and David Woods-Taylor, Robert Lorimer, Eric Robinson, Jacqueline Pratt, Richard and Margaret McPhee, Clive and Vivienne Locks, H and P Cate, Louise English)*

Free house ~ Licensee Brett Stephenson ~ Real ale ~ Bar food (12-3, 6-9) ~ Restaurant (evening only) ~ (01728) 648219 ~ Children in restaurant ~ Dogs allowed in bar and bedrooms ~ Open 11-11; 12-10.30 Sun ~ Bedrooms: /£68B

EARL SOHAM TM2363 Map 5
Victoria 🍺 £
A1120 Yoxford—Stowmarket

The three Earl Soham beers at this unpretentious workaday little village pub are very well kept – not surprising as the brewery is right across the road; local farm cider too. There's an appealingly easy-going local atmosphere in the well worn bar (now completely no smoking) which is fairly basic and sparsely furnished, with stripped panelling, kitchen chairs and pews, plank-topped trestle sewing-machine tables and other simple scrubbed pine country tables with candles, tiled or board floors, an interesting range of pictures of Queen Victoria and her reign, a piano, and open fires; cribbage and dominoes. Very reasonably priced bar food could include sandwiches (from £2.50), soup (£3.50), ploughman's (from £4.25), popular corned beef hash (£4.95), vegetarian pasta dishes (£5.25), meat or vegetable lasagne (£6.30), pork and pineapple or lamb curry (£6.50), feta and onion tart, beef casserole or winter Sunday roast (£7.95) and home-made puddings (£3.25); service is very friendly (but can be slow at busy times). There are seats on the raised back lawn, with more out in front. The pub is quite close to a wild fritillary meadow at Framlingham, and a working windmill at Saxtead. *(Recommended by Comus and Sarah Elliott, Judith and Edward Pearson, Pam and David Bailey, Pete Baker, Mrs A Chapman,*

Mark, Amanda, Luke and Jake Sheard, TW, MW, Tom Gondris, Stephen P Edwards)

Free house ~ Licensee Paul Hooper ~ Real ale ~ Bar food (12-2, 7-10) ~ (01728) 685758
~ Children welcome ~ Dogs welcome ~ Open 11.30-3, 6-11; 12-3, 7-11 Sun

ERWARTON TM2134 Map 5
Queens Head ♀ ⬤
**Village signposted off B1456 Ipswich—Shotley Gate; pub beyond the attractive church
and the manor with its unusual gatehouse (like an upturned salt-cellar)**

The cosy coal fire and welcoming staff both help towards the happy homely
atmosphere at this relaxed 16th-c pub. The friendly bar has bowed black oak
beams in its shiny low yellowing ceiling, comfortable furnishings and several sea
paintings and photographs. A nice place to sit is at tables by the window, which
looks across fields to the Stour estuary, but get here early for one of these seats,
especially at the weekend when it can get busy. Adnams Bitter and Broadside and
Greene King IPA are well kept on handpump, they have a decent wine list, and
several malt whiskies. Along with a fairly extensive choice of specials such as red
lentil and spinach curry (£7.95), crab salad or lamb and apricot casserole (£8.95),
tasty bar food includes home-made soup (£3.25), ploughman's (£5.75), chicken
breast with peach and almond sauce, gammon and egg or home-made lasagne
(£7.95), and stuffed lemon sole with crabmeat (£8.95); puddings might be treacle
pudding, sticky toffee pavlova or lemon meringue pie (£3.95). The no smoking
conservatory dining area is pleasant; darts, bar billiards, shove-ha'penny, cribbage
and dominoes, and maybe piped music. The gents' has quite a collection of
navigational charts. There are picnic-sets under summer hanging baskets in front.
*(Recommended by Pamela Goodwyn, Mrs A Chapman, Colin and Dot Savill, Tony and
Shirley Albert, Mike and Mary Carter, Judi Bell)*

Free house ~ Licensees Julia Crisp and G M Buckle ~ Real ale ~ Bar food ~ Restaurant ~
(01473) 787550 ~ Children in restaurant ~ Open 11-3, 6.30-11; 11.30-3, 6.30-10.30 Sun

GREAT GLEMHAM TM3361 Map 5
Crown ⬤
Between A12 Wickham Market—Saxmundham and B1119 Saxmundham—Framlingham

This immaculately kept pub is light and airy and fairly smart, with quite an
emphasis on the enjoyable food (it's worth booking). Served in generous helpings,
and fairly priced, enjoyable dishes might include sandwiches (from £3.25), soup
(£3.95), baked potatoes (from £5.25), crispy whitebait (£5.25), ploughman's
(£6.25), sausage, egg and chips (£7.25), scampi and chips (£8.95), gammon and
pineapple (£9.25), with daily specials such as cottage pie (£8.95), leek and goats
cheese tart (£8.95), lamb casserole (£9.50), and fried rainbow trout with almonds
(£9.95). Nothing is too much trouble for the helpful staff or friendly licensees. Well
kept Adnams Bitter and Broadside are served from old brass handpumps, and
they've seven wines by the glass, a farm cider, freshly squeezed orange juice and
good coffee. Past the sofas on rush matting in the big entrance hall, an open-plan
beamed lounge has wooden pews and captain's chairs around stripped and waxed
kitchen tables, local photographs and interesting paintings on cream walls, fresh
flowers, and some brass ornaments; log fires in two big fireplaces. A tidy, flower-
fringed lawn, raised above the corner of the quiet village lane by a retaining wall,
has some seats and tables under cocktail parasols; disabled access. The pub is in a
particularly pretty village. *(Recommended by Comus and Sarah Elliott, J F M and M West,
Edmund Coan, Alison Style, David Field, Pamela Goodwyn, Leigh and Gillian Mellor,
Simon Cottrell, Clive and Vivienne Locks, Neil Powell)*

Free house ~ Licensees Barry and Susie Coote ~ Real ale ~ Bar food ~ (01728) 663693 ~
Children welcome ~ Dogs welcome ~ Open 11.30-3, 6.30-11; 12-3, 7-10.30 Sun; closed
Mon except bank hols

HORRINGER TL8261 Map 5

Beehive 🍴 ♀

A143

With good quality old country furniture on coir or flagstones, the rambling, welcoming little rooms at this civilised pub have a cottagey feel, largely because the owners have refrained from pulling walls down to create the usual open-plan layout. Despite some very low beams, stripped panelling and brickwork, good chalky heritage wall colours keep it fairly light and airy. Now completely no smoking throughout, it does get busy with diners, so if you want to eat here, you must arrive early, or book. The nicely balanced menu changes every day, but might typically include soundly imaginative and very well prepared dishes such as fish soup or country pâté (£4.95), courgette, roast pepper and blue cheese tart or tagliatelle with pesto and cream (£8.95), home-made pork, apple and sage sausages on creamy mash (£9.50), fillet of bream with dill and cream sauce (£12.95), and slow-roasted lamb with tomato herb sauce (£13.95), and puddings such as chocolate bread and butter pudding or lemon and lime cheesecake (£4.95). They've decent changing wines with half a dozen by the glass; Greene King IPA and a changing Greene King guest are well kept on handpump. An attractively planted back terrace has picnic-sets and more seats on a raised lawn. Their friendly, well behaved dog Muffin is a great hit with readers; other dogs are not really welcome. *(Recommended by John Saville, Ken Millar, Tony Brace, Simon Cottrell, Mr and Mrs Martin Joyce, Jo Lilley, Simon Calvert, Pam and David Bailey)*

Greene King ~ Tenants Gary and Dianne Kingshott ~ Real ale ~ Bar food (not Sun evening) ~ (01284) 735260 ~ Children welcome ~ Open 11.30-2.30, 7-11; 12-2.30, 7-10 Sun

LAVENHAM TL9149 Map 5 🏠

Angel ★ 🍴 ♀ 🍺 🛏

Market Place

The inviting appearance of this attractive Tudor inn will not disappoint once you're inside. Very smoothly run, with almost indulgently friendly service (but don't ask for chips), it's a longstanding readers' favourite for a drink, a meal or as a comfortable place to stay, and it's completely no smoking. The light and airy long bar area has plenty of polished dark tables, a big inglenook log fire under a heavy mantelbeam, and some attractive 16th-c ceiling plasterwork – even more elaborate pargeting in the residents' sitting room upstairs. Round towards the back on the right of the central servery is a further dining area with heavy stripped pine country furnishings. They have shelves of books, dominoes (and regulars who play), lots of board games and classical piped music. You can eat the excellent food in the bar or the restaurant. Lunchtime dishes could include ploughman's (£6.25), penne with chicken, bacon and chives (£6.25), local pork sausages with mash and onion gravy or tomato, mozzarella and basil tart (£6.95), with other dishes such as tomato lentil and vegetable soup (£3.95), smoked salmon and trout with lemon mayonnaise (£6.75), steak and ale pie or butternut, roast sweet potato and goats cheese strudel (£8.95), grilled halibut with fennel risotto and saffron sauce (£11.95), roast duck breast with braised red cabbage (£11.95), fillet steak with green peppercorn sauce (£16.95), and puddings such as lemon meringue roulade or steamed syrup sponge (£4.25). Four well kept beers, all from this part of the world, include Adnams Bitter and Broadside, Greene King IPA and Nethergate Augustinian on handpump, and they've nine decent wines by the glass or part bottle (you get charged for what you drink) from a good wine list, and over 20 malt whiskies. Picnic-sets out in front overlook the former market square, and there are tables under parasols in a sizeable sheltered back garden; it's worth asking if they've time to show you the interesting Tudor cellar. *(Recommended by Dr and Mrs R G J Telfer, Neil and Brenda Skidmore, Jeff and Wendy Williams, Tina and David Woods-Taylor, the Didler, Stephen and Jean Curtis, Des and Jen Clarke, Charles and Isabel Cooper, Mrs A Chapman, Alan Cole, Kirstie Bruce, Tracey and Stephen Groves, Pam and David Bailey, M Sharp, David J Bunter, Pamela Goodwyn,*

Michael and Ann Cole, J C Poley, Julian Templeman, Victoria Taylor, Margaret and Roy Randle,
Richard Pitcher, P and J Shapley, Pam and Alan Neale, Carolyn Dixon, John Saville,
Adele Summers, I A Herdman)

Free house ~ Licensees Roy Whitworth and John Barry ~ Real ale ~ Bar food (12-2.15,
6.45-9.15) ~ Restaurant ~ (01787) 247388 ~ Children in eating area of bar and restaurant
~ Dogs allowed in bedrooms ~ Classical piano Fri evenings ~ Open 11-11; 12-10.30 Sun ~
Bedrooms: £55B/£80B

LAXFIELD TM2972 Map 5

Kings Head ★ ◧ £

Behind church, off road toward Banyards Green

Full of character, the three charmingly old-fashioned rooms at this bewitchingly
unspoilt thatched 15th-c house have a warmly welcoming atmosphere. Lots of
people like the front room best, with a high-backed built-in settle on the tiled floor,
and an open fire. Two other equally unspoilt rooms – the card and tap rooms –
have pews, old seats, scrubbed deal tables and some interesting wall prints. There's
no bar; instead, the friendly licensees potter in and out of a cellar tap room to tap
pints of the well kept Adnams Best, Broadside, a seasonal ale and Fullers London
Pride straight from the cask; shove-ha'penny, cribbage, dominoes and piped music.
Outside, the garden has plenty of benches and tables, there's an arbour covered by
grape and hop vines, and a small pavilion for cooler evenings. Simple good value
bar food such as sandwiches (from £2.50, home-made soup or garlic mushrooms
(£3.50), baguettes (£4.50), ploughman's (£5), cottage pie or sausages and mash
(£5.50), good fresh crispy bacon salad (£6.95), grilled plaice (£8), a handful of daily
specials, and puddings such as apple and rhubarb crumble (£3.50). Please note that
they don't take credit cards. *(Recommended by the Didler, John and Enid Morris, Pam and
David Bailey, Dennis and Gill Keen, Mr and Mrs T B Staples, Pete Baker, Tracey and
Stephen Groves, Ian and Nita Cooper, Comus and Sarah Elliott, G P V Creagh, David Carr,
Alan Sadler)*

Adnams ~ Tenants George and Maureen Coleman ~ Real ale ~ Bar food (not Sun evening
Nov-April) ~ Restaurant ~ No credit cards ~ (01986) 798395 ~ Children in restaurant ~
Dogs allowed in bar ~ Open 12-3, 6-11(7-10.30 Sun)

LIDGATE TL7257 Map 5

Star ♀

B1063 SE of Newmarket

This little village pub is a relaxing place to stop for a meal or a drink. With lots of
pubby character, the cosy main room has handsomely moulded heavy beams, a
good big log fire, candles in iron candelabra on good polished oak or stripped pine
tables, bar billiards, dominoes, darts and ring the bull, and some antique catalan
plates over the bar; piped music. Besides a second similar room on the right, there's
a cosy little no smoking dining room on the left. The landlady is Spanish, and the
interesting (but not cheap) menu reflects this: fish soup, boquerones, grilled squid
or catalan salad (£5.90), paella, roast lamb in garlic and wine or lambs kidneys in
sherry (£14.50), cod in garlic mousseline, wild boar in strawberry sauce or
monkfish marinière (£15.50), and puddings such as strawberry cream tart and
chocolate roulade (£4.95), or an unusual cheeseboard (£4.95). They also do a two-
course lunch (£10.50). They've enjoyable house wines, and Greene King IPA,
Abbot and Old Speckled Hen are well kept on handpump. Tables are out on the
raised lawn in front, and in a pretty little rustic back garden *(Recommended by
Tony and Shirley Albert, Hywel Bevan, M and GR)*

Greene King ~ Lease Maria Teresa Axon ~ Real ale ~ Bar food (not Sun evening) ~
Restaurant ~ (01638) 500275 ~ Children welcome ~ Open 11-3, 6-11; 12-3, 7-11 Sun

---

We say if we know a pub has piped music.

NAYLAND TL9734 Map 5

Anchor ♀

Court Street; just off A134 – turn off S of signposted B1087 main village turn

This neatly refurbished dining pub has a vineyard and a smokehouse, and they serve their own wines, and smoked meats and fish. Yet another Suffolk pub to become completely no smoking this year, it's light and sunny inside, with interesting old photographs of pipe-smoking customers and village characters on its pale yellow walls, farmhouse chairs around a mix of tables, and coal and log fires at each end. Behind, a room with similar furniture and another fire leads into a small carpeted sun room. The changing menu might include soup (£3.50), baked goats cheese with caramelised apples (£4), smoked fish, meat and cheese platter (£5), ploughman's or gin and tonic cured salmon huffer (£6.50), sausage and garlic mash with thyme gravy (£7.50), battered fish or beef, onion and red wine pie (£8.50), baked salmon with creamy leeks and Pernod butter sauce (£9), wild mushroom, spinach and ricotta stuffed duck leg (£10), with puddings such as waffles with poached rhubarb and orange curd cream (£3.95). The separate restaurant, similarly light and airy, is up quite steep stairs. Served in elegant beer glasses, by friendly staff, Adnams and Greene King IPA are well kept on handpump, along with a couple of guests such as Greene King Old Speckled Hen and XX Mild, and ten wines by the glass. The bare-boards front bar has a more local feel; piped music, but not too intrusive. A gravel terrace behind has picnic-sets looking across to the peaceful River Stour and its quacking ducks. Next to the pub is an ongoing Heritage Farming Project. The farmland is being worked throughout the season by suffolk punch horses using traditional farming methods. The suffolk punch is one of the most endangered species in the world – even rarer than the giant panda. Visitors are welcome to watch or to try their hand at the reins. *(Recommended by MDN, Reg Fowle, Helen Rickwood, Derek Thomas, Charles and Pauline Stride, Clive and Vivienne Locks)*

Free house ~ Licensee Daniel Bunting ~ Real ale ~ Bar food (12-2(2.30 Fri, Sat); 6.30-9(9.30); 10-3, 5-9 Sun) ~ Restaurant ~ (01206) 262313 ~ Children welcome ~ Open 11-3, 5-11; 11-11 Sat; 10-9 Sun

ORFORD TM4250 Map 5

Jolly Sailor £

Quay Street

Firmly run and down-to-earth, this unspoilt 17th-c brick pub is built mainly from wrecked ships' timbers. The several snugly traditional rooms have lots of exposed brickwork, and are served from counters and hatches in an old-fashioned central cubicle. There's an unusual spiral staircase in the corner of the flagstoned main bar – which also has 13 brass door knockers and other brassware, local photographs, two cushioned pews and a long antique stripped deal table, and an open woodburning stove in the big brick fireplace (with nice horsebrasses above it); a small room is popular with the dominoes and cribbage players. Adnams Bitter and Broadside are well kept on handpump. A short choice of straightforward food in generous helpings could include tasty battered local cod, skate, rock eel or flounder with chips, home-made steak pie or home-cooked ham, egg and chips, chilli, and daily roasts (all £5.95), with a couple of evening specials such as cod mornay and chicken stir fry (£6.50); no sandwiches. The dining room and some tables in the bar are no smoking. There are lovely surrounding coastal walks and plenty of outside pursuits; several picnic-sets on grass at the back have views over the marshes. The landlord can seem a bit straightforward at times. *(Recommended by Stephen and Jean Curtis, Pat and Clive Sherriff, Klaus and Elizabeth Leist, David Carr, Simon Rodway, Ken Millar, Mr and Mrs John Taylor, Michael and Ann Cole, Mike and Shelley Woodroffe, David and Linda Holmes, Neil Powell)*

Adnams ~ Tenant Philip Attwood ~ Real ale ~ Bar food (not Mon evening, nor Mon-Thurs evenings Nov-Easter) ~ No credit cards ~ (01394) 450243 ~ Open 11.30-2.30, 7-11; 12-2.45, 7-10.30 Sun ~ Bedrooms: /£50

REDE TL8055 Map 5

Plough (🍴) ♀

Village signposted off A143 Bury St Edmunds—Haverhill

Featuring quite a lot of game and roundly robust flavours, the changing food at this thatched pink-washed pub is very well cooked: asparagus soup (£3.95), venison carpaccio (£5.95), grilled scallops (£6.95), smoked haddock risotto with saffron, fennel and peas or stuffed pigeon with green lentils, (£9.95), wild boar sausages and mash or oxtail braised in burgundy (£10.95), hock of venison braised with vegetables or plaice with prawns and wild mushrooms (£11.95) and some home-made puddings (£3.95). You may need to book to be sure of a table. Simple and traditional, the bar has copper measures and pewter tankards hanging from low black beams, decorative plates on a delft shelf and surrounding the solid-fuel stove in its brick fireplace, and red plush button-back built-in wall banquettes. Served from electric pumps by the friendly staff, Greene King Abbot and IPA and a guest such as St Austells Tribute are well kept under light blanket pressure and they've around 60 wines by the glass; piped pop music. There are picnic-sets in front, and a sheltered cottagey garden at the back; more reports please. *(Recommended by Philip and Susan Philcox, Adele Summers)*

Greene King ~ Tenant Brian Desborough ~ Real ale ~ Bar food (not Sun evening) ~ Restaurant ~ (01284) 789208 ~ Children in restaurant ~ Open 11-3, 6-11; 12-3, 7-10.30 Sun

SNAPE TM3959 Map 5 🏠

Crown (🍴) ♀ 🛏

B1069

Suffolk Dining Pub of the Year

Reader reports on this bustling inn are much improved this year – it now seems to be nicely on form and is doing well on all counts. Most people come here for the very good food, and indeed at busy times the tables may all be reserved for diners, and during the Festival they do a useful pre-concert short menu. Regularly changing dishes from the blackboard menu might include cream of celeriac, saffron and orange soup (£3.95), duck breast and pork pâté (£5.95), fried chorizo with rocket salad and poached egg (£6.50), smoked haddock fishcakes (£9.75), battered cod or tomato and brie tart (£9.95), steak and kidney pudding or chicken with mozzarella and parma ham filling (£10.95), and wild bass fillet on basil and lemon risotto (£12.75). The dining room is no smoking. With a warm welcome from the congenial landlady and her staff, the attractive bar is furnished with striking horseshoe-shaped high-backed settles around a big brick inglenook with a woodburning stove, spindleback and country kitchen chairs, and nice old tables on some old brick flooring; an exposed panel shows how the ancient walls were constructed, and there are lots of beams in the various small side rooms. The wine list is thoughtful, with 14 wines by the glass (including champagne), and they've Adnams Bitter, Broadside and a seasonal ale, which are well kept on handpump. A pretty roadside garden has tables under cocktail parasols. Up steep stairs and down twisting corridors the 14 bedrooms, with beamed ceilings, sloping floors, and doorways that you may have to stoop through, have been attractively refurbished in a contemporary style; they also serve good breakfasts. *(Recommended by Simon Cottrell, David and Jean Hall, Comus and Sarah Elliott, Phil and Heidi Cook, Simon Rodway, Pamela Goodwyn, David and Gilly Wilkins, Dr Peter D Smart, Peter and Pat Frogley, Mrs A Chapman, Ian and Jane Irving, Fred and Lorraine Gill, Mr and Mrs R W Glover, Adrian White, Mrs Jane Kingsbury, MDN, Roy and Lindsey Fentiman, Barry Collett, Clive and Vivienne Locks, Mrs S Lyons, Neil Powell)*

Adnams ~ Tenant Angelina Deacon ~ Real ale ~ Bar food ~ Restaurant ~ (01728) 688324 ~ Open 12-3, 6(7 Sun)-11 ~ Bedrooms: £70B/£80B

The knife-and-fork award distinguishes pubs where the food is of exceptional quality.

SOUTH ELMHAM TM3389 Map 5
St Peters Brewery
St Peter S Elmham; off B1062 SW of Bungay

The dramatically high-ceilinged hall (hung with an imposing chandelier) at the heart of this stunning medieval manor dates back to the late 13th c. It's now used as a dining hall (no smoking), with strikingly ancient features including elaborate woodwork, mullioned windows and a big flagstoned floor. From here a couple more rooms, also ancient and appealing, are reached up some steepish stairs – one is no smoking, while the other is a light, beamed room with comfortable armchairs and nice big rug. Extensions around the hall were completed in 1539 using materials from the recently dissolved Flixton Priory. Genuinely old tapestries and furnishings make having a drink in the small main bar feel more like a trip to a historic home than a typical pub outing, but the atmosphere is relaxed and welcoming, with candles and fresh flowers on the dark wooden tables, and comfortable seats – from cushioned pews and settles to a 16th-c French bishop's throne; piped music. The very good beers they brew here are made using water from a 100-metre (300-ft) bore hole, in brewery buildings laid out around a courtyard; they do tours Fri-Sun and bank holidays on the hour between 12 and 4pm, and there's a gift shop. On handpump they serve well kept St Peters Organic Best, Golden Ale and one dark beer from the range, while the rest of their ales are available by the bottle. It's best to book for the short choice of well presented and cooked food, which is fairly priced and served by friendly waitresses, and includes home-made soup (£3.95), baguettes (from £4.95), lasagne (£7.95), steak and ale pie or mixed vegetable and goats cheese strudel (£8.95), sirloin steak with pepper sauce (£9.95), puddings such as dark chocolate and bread and butter pudding and a delicious lemon cheesecake (£4.25) and farmhouse cheeses (£6.25). Outside, tables overlook the original moat. *(Recommended by David Barnes, J F M and M West, Peter Meister, Esther and John Sprinkle, M and GR, Dennis and Gill Keen, John Wooll, P and J Shapley, the Didler, Martin and Pauline Jennings, John Saville, Mr and Mrs W E Cross)*

Own brew ~ Licensees John Murphy and Janet Fogg ~ Real ale ~ Bar food ~ Restaurant ~ (01986) 782322 ~ Children in eating area of bar and restaurant ~ Open 11-11; 12-10.30 bank hols and Sun

SOUTHWOLD TM5076 Map 5
Crown
High Street

You do need to get here early as this rather smart (and now completely no smoking) old hotel is very popular, even attracting family groups. You are offered the menu fairly promptly on arrival, and most tables are occupied by diners who are here for the very good food. There's a separate restaurant. The delightfully seasonal menu changes every week, but might include gravadlax or greek salad (£5.50), mezze (£6.50), seafood platter (£10), salmon and haddock fishcakes (£10.50), crispy aromatic duck (£11.50), roast bell peppers with ratatouille, soft polenta and roquefort (£12.50), seafood cataplana for a minimum of two people (£13.50 each), and grilled rib-eye steak (£16.50) and puddings such as lemon and white chocolate cheesecake with lemon sauce (£5.50) and chocolate assiette (£6.50). With an appealingly relaxed atmosphere and a good mix of customers, the extended elegant beamed main bar has a stripped curved high-backed settle and other dark varnished settles, kitchen chairs and some bar stools, pretty flowers on the mix of kitchen pine tables, a carefully restored and rather fine carved wooden fireplace, and newspapers to read. The smaller back oak-panelled locals' bar has more of a traditional pubby atmosphere, with red leatherette wall benches and a red carpet; shove-ha'penny, dominoes and cribbage. Friendly and efficient staff serve three or four Adnams beers in top condition on handpump, and they've a splendid wine list, with a monthly changing choice of 20 interesting varieties by the glass or bottle, and quite a few malt whiskies. Tables out in a sunny sheltered corner are very pleasant. *(Recommended by John Wooll, David and Jean Hall,*

Simon Cottrell, Michael Dandy, Simon Rodway, MJVK, Steve Nye, John and Enid Morris, Pam and David Bailey, Rob Winstanley, M and GR, Comus and Sarah Elliott, Leigh and Gillian Mellor, Pat and Tony Hinkins, Brenda and Rob Fincham, David Carr, Tina and David Woods-Taylor, Anthony Rickards Collinson, David Boult, Charles and Isabel Cooper, John Saul, J Jennings, Richard Pitcher, Clive and Vivienne Locks, H and P Cate, the Didler, Mike and Sue Loseby)

Adnams ~ Manager Francis Guildea ~ Real ale ~ Bar food ~ Restaurant ~ (01502) 722275 ~ Children in front bar and restaurant ~ Dogs allowed in bar ~ Open 11-11; 12-10.30 Sun; 11-3, 6-11: 12-3, 6.30-10.30 Sun in winter ~ Bedrooms: £88B/£128B

Harbour Inn 🍺

Blackshore, by the boats; from A1095, turn right at the Kings Head, and keep on past the golf course and water tower

It's well worth arriving at this appealing old waterside pub early in good weather, so you can pick a seat at the front of the building and watch all the activity in the bustling Blyth Estuary quay. The genuine nautical character of the place only really shines through these days in winter, when the tourist bustle has subsided, but there are still plenty of clues – not to mention the friendly landlord who is a lifeboatman. The tiny, low-beamed, tiled and panelled front bar has antique settles, and the back bar has a wind speed indicator, model ships, a lot of local ship and boat photographs, smoked dried fish hanging from a line on a beam, a lifeboat line launcher and brass shellcases on the mantelpiece over a stove. This room has rustic stools and cushioned wooden benches built into its stripped panelling. Behind here, the dining extension is no smoking. Freshly prepared tasty bar food (which a couple of readers feel is pricey) includes soup (£4.25), filled baguettes (from £4.95), half a pint of prawns (£5.25, a pint £8.95), lasagne (£8.95), fish pie (£9.95), vegetable curry or grilled cajun chicken (£10.95), with fresh fish specials. Superbly kept Adnams Broadside and Southwold, and a seasonal guest on handpump; piped music. On former marshland, the back garden has lots of tables, and a little terrace with fine views across marshy fields towards the town and the lighthouse; look out for the 1953 flood level marked on the outside of the pub. *(Recommended by KC, David and Jean Hall, Peter Meister, Pat and Clive Sherriff, Neil and Lorna Mclaughlan, Pete Baker, Fred and Lorraine Gill, Simon Rodway, Richard Waller, Pauline Smith, Louise English, Peter and Pat Frogley, Barry Collett, Paul and Ursula Randall, Michael Dandy, the Didler, Mike and Sue Loseby)*

Adnams ~ Tenant Colin Fraser ~ Real ale ~ Bar food (12-2.30, 6-9) ~ (01502) 722381 ~ Children in bottom bar and restaurant ~ Dogs allowed in bar ~ Live music occasional Fri, most Sats, folk first and third Sun ~ Open 11-11; 12-10.30 Sun

Lord Nelson 🍺

East Street, off High Street (A1095)

Vibrant and convivial, this relaxed and easy-going seaside local can get very busy, but is so well run by its friendly and ever-present landlord that there's never any sense of strain, and the good-natured service is always quick and attentive. The partly panelled bar and its two small side rooms are kept spotless, with a small but extremely hot coal fire, light wood furniture on the tiled floor, lamps in nice nooks and corners, and some interesting Nelson memorabilia, including attractive nautical prints and a fine model of HMS *Victory*. They have good wines by the glass as well as perfectly kept Adnams Best and Broadside and another changing Adnams beer on handpump. Wholesome plain generous lunchtime food consists of well filled sandwiches (from £2.35 – the ham off the bone is very good), soup (£2.75), a huge proper ploughman's (£4.85), curry or chilli (£6.50), scampi (£6.85), lots of salads (from £6.50), rump steak (£10.45), one or two daily specials, and puddings such as cherry pie or sticky toffee (£3.10). They have daily papers out; no piped music or games machines. Disabled access is not perfect but is possible, and they help. There are nice seats out in front, with a sidelong view down to the sea, and in a sheltered back garden, with the brewery in sight (and often the appetising fragrance of brewing in progress). The seafront is just moments away. *(Recommended by Rob and Catherine Dunster, Pat and Tony Martin, Michael Dandy, the Didler, Comus and Sarah Elliott, Derek Field, David Carr, Pam and David Bailey, David Field, DM, Neil and Lorna Mclaughlan, Pete Baker, Dr and Mrs M E Wilson)*

Adnams ~ Tenant John Illston ~ Real ale ~ Bar food (not bank hol Mon evenings) ~ No credit cards ~ (01502) 722079 ~ Children in family room ~ Dogs welcome ~ Open 10.30(12 Sun)-11

STOKE-BY-NAYLAND TL9836 Map 5
Angel 🍴 ♀

B1068 Sudbury—East Bergholt; also signposted via Nayland off A134 Colchester—Sudbury

The comfortable main bar area at this elegant pub is calmly atmospheric, with handsome Elizabethan beams, some stripped brickwork and timbers, a mixture of furnishings including wing armchairs, mahogany dining chairs and pale library chairs, local watercolours, modern paintings and older prints, attractive table lamps and a huge log fire. Round the corner is a little tiled-floor stand-and-chat bar. Neatly uniformed smiling staff serve well kept Greene King IPA and a guest such as Fullers London Pride on handpump, and there's a decent wine list. Another room has a low sofa and wing armchairs around its woodburning stove, and mustard-coloured walls. Food is beautifully prepared and presented, and the changing menu includes more fresh fish dishes than usual: cream of tomato soup (£3.25), griddled sardines (£4.75), parma ham and melon (£6.95), sausage and spring onion mash with ale and onion sauce or leek, stilton and artichoke tart (£7.75), roast leg of lamb with rosemary and garlic jus (£9.25), grilled calamari with sweet chilli sauce or grilled mackerel (£10.50), fried bass on roast chicory with pepper sauce and rocket (£13.95), and home-made puddings such as baked rum and raisin cheesecake (£4.25); the restaurant is no smoking. There are seats and tables on a sheltered terrace. *(Recommended by Dr and Mrs R G J Telfer, Dr and Mrs T E Hothersall, Derek Thomas, MDN, J F M and M West, Ken Millar, David J Bunter, John and Enid Morris, David Twitchett, Alan and Jill Bull, Jeff and Wendy Williams, Charles Gysin, Eric Robinson, Jacqueline Pratt)*

Horizon Inns ~ Manager Neil Bishop ~ Real ale ~ Bar food (12-2, 6-9.30) ~ Restaurant ~ (01206) 263245 ~ Open 11-11(10.30 Sun) ~ Bedrooms: £70B/£85B

Crown ★ ♀
Park Street (B1068)

This radical refurbishment is a contemporary reinterpretation of what makes a good if rather upmarket pub. The careful interior design has a lot to do with this. Most of the pub is open to the three-sided bar servery, yet it's well divided, and with two or three more tucked-away areas too. The main area, with a big woodburning stove, has quite a lot of fairly closely spaced tables, in a variety of shapes, styles and sizes. Elsewhere, several smaller areas each have just three or four tables. Seating varies from deep armchairs and sofas to elegant dining chairs and comfortable high-backed woven rush seats – and there are plenty of bar stools. This all gives a good choice between conviviality and varying degrees of cosiness and privacy. With a subtle colour scheme of several gentle toning colours, cheerful wildlife and landscape paintings, quite a lot of attractive table lamps and carefully placed gentle spotlighting, low ceilings (some with a good deal of stripped old beams), and floors varying from old tiles through broad boards or dark new flagstones to beige carpet, the overall feel is of relaxation. There is a table of daily papers. They have Adnams Bitter and Greene King IPA and a couple of guests on handpump, good nicely served coffee (typically doing well over 100 cups a day), and take care with other drinks such as Pimms. An unusual feature is the glass-walled wine 'cellar' in one corner, and of about 200 wines on their list, around 30 are available by the glass. They sell wines by the half-case to take away, and suggest a different wine to go with each of their two dozen or so menu choices. The food is enterprising without being outlandishly unusual, choosing ingredients carefully (local free-range chicken, pork, lamb, game and vegetables, crab from East Mersea, wild scotch salmon), and might include soup (£3.95), soused herrings with dill sauce (£5.95), dressed crab (£7.95), spinach, walnut and goats cheese tart (£9.25), herb crusted pork fillet with potato and spinach gratin and red wine sauce (£10.95), calves liver with sage and bacon croquettes and black pudding (£11.25), beef fillet with smoked king prawns, garlic sauce and bubble and squeak (£16.95) and puddings such as golden syrup pudding or chocolate cookie cheesecake with chocolate sauce (£4.95). They are happy to do small helpings if you want. Service is good, prompt and thoughtful – and given a slightly continental touch by the wrap-around white aprons worn by all the friendly young staff; about half the pub is no smoking. A sheltered back terrace has cushioned teak chairs and tables under big canvas parasols with heaters, looking out over a neat lawn to a landscaped shrubbery that includes a small romantic ruined-abbey folly. There are many more picnic-sets out on the front terrace. Disabled access is good, and the car park is big. *(Recommended by Mr and Mrs Foulston, Keith Sale, MDN, John Prescott, David Twitchett, H Jones, J F M and M West, Alan Sadler, Pamela Goodwyn)*

Free house ~ Licensee Richard Sunderland ~ Real ale ~ Bar food (12-2.30, 6-9.30 (10 Fri, Sat); 12-9 Sun) ~ Restaurant ~ (01206) 262001 ~ Children in eating area of bar ~ Dogs allowed in bar ~ Open 11-11; 12-10.30 Sun

SWILLAND TM1852 Map 5

Moon & Mushroom ♀ ◀

Village signposted off B1078 Needham Market—Wickham Market, and off B1077

Happily, new licensees have changed very little at this cosy old place. The eight beers, tapped straight from casks functionally racked up behind the long counter, still come from independent East Anglian brewers such as Buffys, Crouch Vale, Mauldons and Woodfordes. They also serve 21 decent wines by the glass, and around 23 malt whiskies. With a good mix of locals and visitors, the homely interior is mainly quarry-tiled, with a small coal fire in a brick fireplace, old tables (with lots of board games in the drawers) arranged in little booths made by pine pews, and cushioned stools along the bar. The other nice touch here has always been the four hearty hotpots in the no smoking dark green and brown painted cottagey dining room, through a small doorway from the bar. These are served to you from Le Creuset dishes on a warming counter and might include beef cooked in beer with dumplings, pork cooked with three mustards, wine, cream and mushrooms or chicken breast in wine with herbs (all £8.95), and you then help yourself to a choice of half a dozen or so tasty vegetables. Another few dishes might include a good ploughman's (£4.95), salads (from £6.95), and salmon fillet with wine and herb sauce or spinach and mascarpone lasagne (£8.95), with puddings such as white chocolate and raspberry cheesecake or toffee and ginger pudding with butterscotch sauce (£3.75). They also do a Sunday roast. The entrance to the pub is through an archway of grapevines and creepers, and a little terrace in front has retractable awnings and outdoor heaters, flower containers, trellis and nice wooden furniture under parasols. *(Recommended by Pam and David Bailey, Mrs P Sarson, J F M and M West, Charles Gysin, Ian and Nita Cooper, Pamela Goodwyn, M and GR, M G Hart, Clive and Vivienne Locks, Carolyn Dixon, the Didler)*

Free house ~ Licensees Nikki Gavin and Martin Burgess ~ Real ale ~ Bar food (12-2(2.30 Sun), 6.30-8.45; not Sun evening) ~ Restaurant ~ (01473) 785320 ~ Children in restaurant ~ Dogs allowed in bar ~ Open 11.30-2.30, 6-11; 12-2.30, 7-10.30 Sun

WALBERSWICK TM4974 Map 5

Bell ♀ ⟺

Just off B1387

The best time to visit this likeable old pub is out of season, when it's less busy, particularly as they don't take bookings for bar food, and there are usually queues at peak times (when service can slow down). A novel but nice way to get here is on the little ferry from Southwold, ending with a short walk. The pub is in a great setting close to the beach (most of the well appointed bedrooms look over the sea or river), and tables on the sizeable lawn are sheltered from the worst of the winds by a well placed hedge. Inside is quite charming with brick floors, well worn uneven flagstones and wonky steps, and oak beams that were here 400 years ago when the sleepy little village was a flourishing port. The rambling traditional bar has curved high-backed settles, tankards hanging from oars above the counter, and a woodburning stove in the big fireplace; a second bar has a very large open fire. Served by friendly staff, the five well kept real ales here all come from Adnams, and they've ten wines by the glass, a dozen malt whiskies and pressed apple juice. As well as lunchtime sandwiches (from £4), enjoyable bar food, from a changing menu, might include home-made soup (£3.95), grilled herring with giant croûton and sweet chilli sauce or herby hummous with chilli oil, toasted pine nuts and pitta bread (£4.95), crayfish salad (£5.50), ploughman's (£6.50), sweet potato and cumin curry, battered haddock or chilli (£7.50), lamb tagine with couscous or fish pie (£8.50) and grilled tuna steak with tomato, chilli and caper salsa (£9.25), and home-made puddings such as tiramisu (£3.95); Sunday roast (£7.95). They call out your number when your food is ready. The bar, restaurant and dining room all have no smoking areas; piped music, darts, shove-ha'penny, cribbage and dominoes; boules outside. The landlord's daughter runs a ceramics business from a shed in the garden. (*Recommended by Louise English, David and Jean Hall, Comus and Sarah Elliott, TW, MW, Julie Scarsbrook, Roy and Lindsey Fentiman, the Didler, Peter Meister, Fred and Lorraine Gill, Phil and Helen Holt, Pat and Clive Sheriff, Blaise Vyner, Tina and David Woods-Taylor, MJVK, Rob Kelvey, Neil and Lorna Mclaughlan, Simon Rodway, Victoria Taylor, Alan Sadler, J Jennings, H and P Cate, Mike and Sue Loseby*)

Adnams ~ Tenant Sue Ireland Cutting ~ Real ale ~ Bar food (12-2(2.30 Sun and bank hols), 7(6 Fri, Sat, and every day July, Aug)-9) ~ Restaurant ~ (01502) 723109 ~ Children in eating area of bar ~ Dogs allowed in bar and bedrooms ~ Open 11-11; 11-11 Sat; 12-10.30 Sun; 12-3, 6-11 weekdays in winter ~ Bedrooms: /£80S(£100B)

WALDRINGFIELD TM2844 Map 5

Maybush

Off A12 S of Martlesham; The Quay, Cliff Road

There are dozens of well arranged tables on the verandah outside this busy family pub, all geared up for taking in views of the River Deben, which indeed all sorts of customers do. Inside, the spacious bar has quite a nautical theme, with lots of old lanterns, pistols and so forth, as well as aerial photographs, an original Twister board, and fresh flowers; though it's all been knocked through, it's divided into separate areas by fireplaces or steps; fruit machine. A glass case has an elaborate ship's model, and there are a few more in a lighter, high-ceilinged extension. A number of the dark wooden tables are set for eating, and though it can fill quickly at lunchtime (particularly in summer), service remains swift, and friendly. Adnams Best and Broadside, and Greene King IPA are well kept on handpump, and they've a good range of wines, with around nine or ten by the glass. Besides lunchtime sandwiches, straightforward bar food includes soup (£3.45), prawn cocktail (£4.95), cheese and vegetable pie or stilton beefburger, tiger prawns in filo pastry or steak and Guinness pie (£8.45), steaks (from £10.95) and grilled dover sole (£11.95), with daily specials and puddings listed on blackboards. The dining rooms are no smoking. River cruises are available nearby. (*Recommended by Mrs A Chapman, David Carr, Pamela Goodwyn, Louise English, Tracey and Stephen Groves*)

Punch ~ Lease Steve and Louise Lomas ~ Real ale ~ Bar food (12-2, 7-9; all day weekends and bank hols) ~ Restaurant ~ (01473) 736215 ~ Children in restaurant ~ Dogs allowed in bar ~ Open 11-11; 12-10.30 Sun

Post Office address codings confusingly give the impression that some pubs are in Suffolk when they're really in Norfolk or Cambridgeshire (which is where we list them).

LUCKY DIP

Besides the fully inspected pubs, you might like to try these Lucky Dips recommended to us and described by readers (if you do, please send us reports: www.goodguides.co.uk).

ALDEBURGH [TM4656]

☆ *Cross Keys* [Crabbe St]: 16th-c pub extended from low-beamed core with antique settles, Victorian prints, woodburners, well kept Adnams ales (the full range) and wines, brisk friendly service, ample enjoyable food, Sunday papers; can be crowded, loudspeaker food announcements, fruit machine; open all day July/Aug, children in eating areas, picnic-sets in sheltered back yard by promenade and beach; elegant bedrooms with own bathrooms *(MDN, Comus and Sarah Elliott, LYM)*

Mill [Market Cross Pl, opp Moot Hall]: Small 1920s seaside pub, friendly and relaxing, with good value fresh food from sandwiches and baguettes to very local fish and crabs, good service (humorous landlord), well kept Adnams ales, decent coffee, locals' bar, lots of pictures, cosy no smoking beamed dining room with *Gypsy Queen* model, sea view and strong RNLI theme, cream teas July/Aug; fruit machine; dogs welcome, open all day Fri/Sat and July/Aug, bedrooms *(Derek and Sylvia Stephenson, Colin and Janet Roe, David and Gilly Wilkins, Clive and Vivienne Locks, Michael Dandy, Keith and Janet Morris, the Didler)*

Wentworth [Wentworth Rd]: Hotel not pub, but has enjoyable reasonably priced bar lunches in a choice of welcoming areas, well kept Adnams and a good choice of wines by the glass; conservatory, seafront terrace tables, bedrooms *(Pam and David Bailey, Pamela Goodwyn)*

ALDRINGHAM [TM4461]

☆ *Parrot & Punchbowl* [B1122/B1353 S of Leiston]: Pleasant beamed pub with good fairly priced food inc local fish and speciality prime steaks, good wine choice, well kept Adnams and Greene King IPA, decent coffee, two-level restaurant, no piped music or machines; children welcome; nice sheltered garden, also family garden with adventure play area, good craft centre opp *(BB, Comus and Sarah Elliott, Simon Rodway)*

BARHAM [TM1251]

Sorrel Horse [Old Norwich Rd]: Cheerful and attractive pink-washed pantiled 17th-c country pub, nicely refurbished bar with magnificent log fire, lots of beams, lounge and two dining areas off, ample wholesome home cooking inc interesting specials, prompt friendly service, particularly well kept real ales, decent wines; children welcome, good garden with big play area, summer bouncy castle and barbecue, stables opp; comfortable bedrooms in converted barn, well placed for walks *(G Coates, Ian and Nita Cooper)*

BARTON MILLS [TL7273]

Bull [just S of Mildenhall; The Street]: Attractive rambling bars and dining area, wide choice of pubby food from sandwiches and baguettes up, big log fire, four changing real ales, games room; children welcome, 15 bedrooms with own bathrooms, open all day *(Alan M Pring, BB)*

BEYTON [TL9363]

White Horse [signed off A14 and A1088; Bury Rd]: Village-green pub very popular with older lunchers, good home-made food inc particularly good vegetarian choice, friendly waitresses, well kept Greene King IPA and Abbot, no music *(Mr and Mrs Staples)*

BILDESTON [TL9949]

☆ *Crown* [B1115 SW of Stowmarket]: Picturesque 15th-c timbered country local, neat beamed main bar with inglenook and comfortable banquettes, smaller more modern bar, good value food from soup and sandwiches up (good chips and puddings choice), no smoking dining room, well kept Adnams and Broadside and a guest beer tapped from the cask, kind relaxed service; may be piped music; children and dogs welcome, nice tables out in courtyard, more in large attractive garden with pet owl, quiet bedrooms *(Patrick Hancock, LYM, Colin and Janet Roe, Eric Robinson, Jacqueline Pratt)*

BLYTHBURGH [TM4575]

☆ *White Hart* [A12]: Friendly and roomy open-plan family dining pub with fine ancient beams, woodwork and staircase, full Adnams range kept well, good range of wines in two glass sizes, good coffee, charming informal service, robust sensibly priced blackboard food inc game and fish; children in eating area and restaurant, open all day, spacious lawns looking down on tidal marshes (barbecues), magnificent church over road, bedrooms *(B J Harding, Fred and Lorraine Gill, Comus and Sarah Elliott, LYM)*

BOXFORD [TL9640]

☆ *Fleece* [Broad St]: Quietly unpretentious partly 15th-c pub with particularly friendly landlord, well kept Adnams, good home-made food, cosy panelled bar on right, airy lounge bar with wonderful medieval fireplace, armchairs and some distinctive old seats among more conventional furnishings *(LYM, Paul and Angela Acton)*

BRENT ELEIGH [TL9447]

☆ *Cock* [A1141 SE of Lavenham]: Relaxed and unspoilt thatched local with piano in clean and cosy snug, benches, table and darts in second small room, antique flooring tiles, lovely coal fire, ochre walls with old photographs of local villages (the village church is well worth a look), well kept Adnams and Greene King IPA and Abbot, good organic farm cider, obliging landlord, no food beyond crisps and pickled eggs; picnic-sets up on side grass with summer hatch service, attractive inn-sign, bedrooms *(Tracey and Stephen Groves, the Didler, Giles and Annie Francis, BB, MLR)*

BUNGAY [TM3389]
Castles [Earsham St]: Small welcoming bar, enjoyable food in informal dining room *(anon)*

BURY ST EDMUNDS [TL8864]
Flying Fortress [Mount Rd, Gt Barton (out towards Thurston, parallel to A143)]: Much enlarged former HQ of USAF support group, on edge of housing estate now covering Rougham ex-airfield – the original for the classic war film *Twelve O'Clock High*, with World War II bomber models and evocative black and white pictures; comfortable modern lounge area, well kept Adnams and a house beer brewed by Mauldons from long bar, quick friendly service, good value food inc carvery (big echoic restaurant area); tables outside, old fire-engine for children to play on *(Pam and David Bailey)*
Linden Tree [Out Northgate/Station Hill]: Reliable family dining pub with wide choice of generous good value food from good baguettes up, friendly quick service, well kept ales, decent wines in two glass sizes, stripped pine bar, popular no smoking conservatory restaurant; good well kept garden *(Paul Humphreys)*
Rose & Crown [Whiting St]: Unassuming town local with simple excellent value lunchtime food, particularly well kept Greene King ales and a guest beer, pleasant lounge with lots of piggy pictures and bric-a-brac, good games-oriented public bar with darts, cards and dominoes, rare separate off-sales counter; no no smoking area, may be piped local radio *(Pete Baker, Keith and Janet Morris)*

CAMPSEY ASH [TM3356]
Dog & Duck [Station Rd]: Attractive family-friendly pub doing well under current welcoming and helpful management, good range of enjoyable food, well kept Adnams and Woodfordes Wherry tapped from the cask; tables out in front, nice garden with good play area, five bedrooms with own bathrooms *(Derek and Sylvia Stephenson, the Didler)*

CAVENDISH [TL8046]
☆ *Bull* [A1092 Long Melford—Clare]: Attractive 16th-c open-plan pub freshened up under warmly welcoming new management, good atmosphere and enjoyable food, well kept Adnams ales, good wines by the glass, heavy beams and timbers and fine fireplaces; children in eating areas, tables in garden, summer barbecues, car park (useful in this honeypot village) *(I J and S A Bufton, LYM, Adrian White, MDN, Mark Harrington, Marianne and Peter Stevens)*
☆ *George* [The Green]: Beautiful well restored ancient inn under new licensees, more restaurant-with-rooms than pub, good inventive modern food from interesting lunchtime sandwiches and light dishes to enterprising main dishes, good atmosphere and charming efficient service, beamed no smoking room, further large eating area with bar, good value wines, good coffees and teas; bedrooms *(Marianne and Peter Stevens, MDN, Tony and Margaret Cross, Sarah Flynn)*

CHELMONDISTON [TM2037]
Foresters Arms: New management doing sensibly limited choice of good food *(Peter Coode)*

CHELSWORTH [TL9848]
☆ *Peacock* [B1115 Sudbury—Needham Mkt]: Attractive and prettily set old dining pub enlivened by new licensees (who had the Brewers Arms at Rattlesden in its hey-day as one of the county's top dining pubs), good service and cooking and appealing choice, well kept real ales, lots of Tudor brickwork and exposed beams, big inglenook log fire, well spaced comfortable tables; nice small garden, comfortable bedrooms, pretty village *(LYM, MDN, R A P Cross)*

CHILLESFORD [TM3852]
Froize [B1084 E of Woodbridge]: Largely no smoking restaurant rather than pub (they open only when they serve food, ie not Mon, nor Sun-Weds evenings), good country cooking in pleasantly decorated bar and restaurant, good value two-course buffet-style lunch, wide choice of more elaborate evening meals, local pork, game and venison, generous Sun lunch, original puddings, well kept Adnams, decent wines by the glass, warmly welcoming service; may be cl Feb for hols *(Mrs Hilarie Taylor, David Boult, Pamela Goodwyn, LYM, Kerry and Tricia Thomas, Tony and Shirley Albert)*

CLARE [TL7645]
Globe [Callis St]: Well run, with low-priced enjoyable food all day, well kept beer, separate eating area; handy for the church *(Ron Deighton)*

COWLINGE [TL7154]
Three Tuns: Friendly and comfortable unspoilt village local with low beams and stone floors, good value generous home-made food from baguettes and baked potatoes to wide choice of freshly made pubby favourites, smaller children's helpings, efficient pleasant staff, well kept beer, separate dining area *(JDM, KM, Pam and David Bailey)*

CRATFIELD [TM3175]
Cratfield Poacher [Bell Green]: Welcoming local, enjoyable food inc special nights with music, well kept Adnams and Greene King IPA and Abbot *(TW, MW)*

CREETING ST MARY [TM1155]
Highwayman [A140, just N of junction with A14]: Much modernised two-bar pub with pleasant barn extension, relaxed atmosphere, welcoming staff, good value food inc interesting dishes and popular Sun lunch, Adnams, Fullers London Pride and Woodfordes Wherry, decent wines, gallery overflow; unobtrusive piped music; tables on back lawn with small pond, cl Mon and Tues/Weds lunchtime *(Pamela Goodwyn, Comus and Sarah Elliott, Ian and Nita Cooper)*

EAST BERGHOLT [TM0734]
☆ *Kings Head* [Burnt Oak, towards Flatford Mill]: Well kept attractive beamed lounge with comfortable sofas, interesting decorations, dining area off, good value

home-made blackboard food, well kept Greene King and guest ales, decent wines and coffee, quick pleasant service, friendly atmosphere; piped classical music; lots of room in pretty garden, flower-decked haywain, baskets and tubs of flowers in front *(Tony and Shirley Albert, Pamela Goodwyn, Mike and Mary Carter)*

FELIXSTOWE FERRY [TM3237]

☆ *Ferry Boat*: Relaxed and cottagey 17th-c pub tucked between golf links and dunes nr harbour, Martello tower and summer rowing-boat ferry, great for walks by sea; extended and much modernised as family pub, impressive blackboard choice of good value food from snacks to fresh fish, well kept Adnams Best and Greene King IPA and Old Speckled Hen, welcoming helpful service, good log fire; piped music; dogs welcome, tables out in front, on green opposite, and in securely fenced garden, busy summer wknds *(TW, MW, David Carr, Giles and Annie Francis, LYM, John Prescott, Charles and Pauline Stride, MLR)*

Victoria: Child-friendly riverside pub, substantial attractively priced straightforward food inc local fish, well kept Adnams and Greene King ales, good log fire in snug, friendly efficient service, sea views from no smoking upstairs dining area *(Pamela Goodwyn, Giles and Annie Francis, Mike and Mary Carter, J F M and M West, Ryta Lyndley)*

FRAMLINGHAM [TM2862]

☆ *Station Hotel* [Station Rd (B1116 S)]: High-ceilinged big-windowed bar with pine tables and chairs on stripped boards, interesting generous proper home cooking inc good fish dishes (an emphasis on smoked), four well kept Earl Soham ales and a guest beer, good choice of house wines, welcoming service, informal relaxed atmosphere, plenty of train pictures, small tiled-floor back snug; children welcome, picnic-sets in good-sized pleasant garden *(Pete Baker, BB)*

FRESSINGFIELD [TM2677]

☆ *Fox & Goose* [B1116 N of Framlingham; Church St]: Restaurant rather than pub, in beautifully timbered 16th-c building owned by the church; young chef/landlord does good kindly priced food, creative without being pretentious, inc light lunches and perhaps two-for-one bargains, comfortable armchairs and sofas in lounge for pre-dinner drinks (no bar counter), Adnams Best and Regatta tapped from the cask, fine wines, unstuffy personal service, two no smoking dining rooms, one with beams and modern art, the other cosy with a high-backed settle and log fire; children welcome, cl Mon *(TW, MW, KC, LYM, Peter and Jean Dowson)*

GRUNDISBURGH [TM2250]

Dog [The Green]: Well run carefully extended elegant period village pub with good proper cooking, not expensive, well kept ales inc Adnams, friendly landlord, tankards on oak beams, old pictures, restaurant; attractive village *(Anthony Rickards Collinson)*

HALESWORTH [TM3877]

☆ *Angel* [Thoroughfare (now pedestrianised)]: Civilised and comfortable 16th-c coaching inn with no smoking main saloon and livelier back bar (can be smoky) off interesting glazed inner courtyard with 18th-c clock and vines, very well kept reasonably priced Adnams ales, friendly efficient staff, enjoyable bar food from soup and sandwiches up, good range of coffees and cakes, italian restaurant, nice wines, great log fire; children welcome, seven well equipped bedrooms with good bathrooms, open all day *(John Wooll, TW, MW, Peter and Jean Dowson, Robert Lorimer, Steve Nye)*

☆ *White Hart* [Thoroughfare]: Roomy and well restored open-plan pub, warmly welcoming and locally popular especially for evening meals; well arranged and nicely furnished, with good home-made food inc fresh fish and excellent local veg, well kept Adnams and at least two guest beers *(Robert Lorimer)*

HARTEST [TL8352]

☆ *Crown* [B1066 S of Bury St Edmunds]: Child-friendly pink-washed pub by church behind pretty village green, smartly minimalist décor with quality tables and chairs on tiled floor, good log fire in impressive fireplace, wide choice of enjoyable food from baguettes up, well kept Greene King IPA, Abbot and Old Speckled Hen, decent house wines, quick friendly service, two no smoking dining rooms and conservatory; piped music; dogs welcome, tables on big back lawn and in sheltered side courtyard, good play area *(Adele Summers, Des and Jen Clarke, LYM, Marianne and Peter Stevens, Chris and Ali Charman)*

HAUGHLEY [TM0262]

Kings Arms [off A45/B1113 N of Stowmarket; Old St]: Varied pub food inc good salads and puddings in 16th-c timbered pub with airy 1950s back part refurbished to match, well kept Adnams Broadside and Greene King Abbot, decent wines, busy public bar with games, log fire; piped music; tables and play house in colourful back garden *(BB, J F M and M West)*

HESSETT [TL9361]

☆ *Five Bells* [The Street]: 18th-c pub opp spectacular Norman church, two congenial beamed bars with dining areas and log fires, well kept Greene King ales and a guest beer, attractively varied home cooking inc good family Sun lunch, good-humoured efficient staff, traditional games; dogs welcome, boules *(Derek Field, Joan Astley Cooper, J W Russell)*

HOXNE [TM1877]

☆ *Swan* [off B1118, signed off A140 S of Diss; Low St]: Outstanding well restored late 15th-c building, broad oak floorboards, handsomely carved timbering in the colourwashed walls, armchairs by deep-set inglenook log fire, no smoking snug, another huge log fire in dining room, well kept Adnams Bitter and Broadside and good guest beers tapped from the cask, bank hol beer festivals, enjoyable bar food from baguettes and light dishes up, friendly landlord, hard-working cheerful staff, lighted candles; children welcome, sizeable attractive garden behind, summer barbecues *(David Barnes, TW, MW, Comus and Sarah Elliott, Mrs A Chapman, LYM, Peter and Jean Dowson)*

HUNDON [TL7247]

☆ *Plough* [Brockley Green, SW towards Kedington]: Friendly neatly kept knocked-through bar, beams, timbers and stripped brick, scrubbed tables and open fire, tasty food from lunchtime sandwiches to some enterprising dishes (can take a while if they're busy), cheerful staff, Greene King IPA, Woodfordes Wherry and a guest beer, good choice of wines by the glass and malt whiskies, no smoking restaurant; children and dogs welcome, extensive attractive grounds with croquet, good tables and terrace, bedrooms *(Pam and David Bailey, Adele Summers, Alan Sadler, LYM, P and J Shapley, Eric Robinson, Jacqueline Pratt)*

HUNTINGFIELD [TM3473]

Huntingfield Arms [The Street]: Handsome building overlooking green, neat and unpretentious, light wood tables and chairs, beams and stripped brickwork, blazing woodburner in front room, decent home cooking inc good salads, fresh fish and great pudding choice, well kept Adnams and a guest beer, friendly attentive service, pleasant back games area with pool, restaurant; cl Sun evening *(Edmund Coan, Peter Bush, Robert Lorimer)*

IPSWICH [TM1844]

☆ *Fat Cat* [Spring Rd, opp junction with Nelson Rd]: Neatly kept pastiche of basic bare-boards pub with 15 or more well kept interesting ales mainly from small breweries, belgian imports, farm ciders, helpful friendly service and cheery regulars, snacks such as scotch eggs, filled rolls and pasties (or bring your own food), lots of enamel beer advertisements, no music or machines, cat called Dave; very little daytime parking nearby; back conservatory and terrace with summer thai barbecues, open all day *(Ian and Nita Cooper, BB, the Didler)*

Lord Nelson [Fore St]: Ancient local with bare boards and timbering, friendly prompt service, generous pub food inc good fresh specials, well kept Adnams ales tapped from the cask; handy for waterfront *(R T and J C Moggridge)*

Milestone [Woodbridge Rd]: Open-plan pub with up to a dozen or so real ales, farm ciders, several dozen whiskies, home-made food lunchtime and Mon-Weds evening; big-screen sports TV, live bands; large front terrace *(the Didler)*

IXWORTH [TL9370]

☆ *Pykkerel* [High St; just off A143 Bury—Diss]: Friendly and attractive Elizabethan pub with several rooms off central servery, good value food (not Sun evening) from sandwiches to interesting local fish choice, well kept Greene King ales, big fireplaces, antique tables and comfortable old settles, oriental rugs on polished boards, beams, stripped brickwork, panelling and paintings, restaurant; children and dogs welcome, comfortable bedrooms *(LYM, George Cowie, TW, MW, Pam and David Bailey)*

KEDINGTON [TL7046]

White Horse [Sturmer Rd (B1061)]: Reasonably priced home-made food, friendly service, no smoking dining room; open all day *(Adele Summers)*

KERSEY [TM0044]

☆ *Bell* [signed off A1141 N of Hadleigh; The Street]: Quaint flower-decked Tudor building in notably picturesque village, recently tastefully modernised low-beamed bar with log fire, two dining rooms, good welcoming service, wide choice of good sensibly priced food from sandwiches and bar lunches to more elaborate evening dishes, well kept Adnams and Greene King IPA, decent house wines; children allowed, open all day, sheltered back terrace with fairy-lit side canopy *(LYM, Pamela Goodwyn, Paul and Ursula Randall, Philip and Susan Philcox)*

LAVENHAM [TL9149]

Cock [Church St]: Comfortable and attractive thatched village pub with generous nicely prepared food from baguettes up, plush lounge, separate family dining room, basic bar (popular with young people wknds), Adnams and Greene King ales, good wine choice, quick friendly service, attentive and helpful; no dogs; seats out in front and back garden, nice view of church *(Des and Jen Clarke, Neil and Brenda Skidmore, the Didler, Adele Summers, MLR)*

Swan [High Street]: Smart, well equipped and by no means cheap hotel incorporating handsome medieval buildings, well worth a look for its appealing network of beamed and timbered alcoves and more open areas, inc peaceful little tiled-floor inner bar with leather chairs and memorabilia of its days as the local for US 48th Bomber Group, well kept Adnams and a guest such as Hook Norton, fairly short lunchtime bar menu, morning coffee, afternoon tea, good young staff often from overseas, lavishly timbered no smoking restaurant; children welcome, sheltered courtyard garden *(LYM, the Didler, MDN, David Barnes)*

LAYHAM [TM0340]

☆ *Marquis of Cornwallis* [Upper St (B1070 E of Hadleigh)]: Homely beamed 16th-c local under new management, quick attentive service, good value generous food inc good ploughman's and fresh veg, well kept Adnams and Greene King, good wines and coffee, buoyant evening atmosphere, plush lounge bar with warm coal fire, eating area, separate restaurant; good valley views, picnic-sets in extensive riverside garden, bedrooms handy for Harwich ferries, open all day Sat in summer *(Tom Gondris, David Barnes)*

Queens Head [The Street]: Well kept Adnams inc Mild in proper neatly kept local with nice landlord and decent food *(Giles and Annie Francis)*

LEVINGTON [TM2339]

☆ *Ship* [Gun Hill/Church Lane]: Nautical décor and pictures in charming old pub with cosy flagstoned dining room, very popular tasty food inc sensibly priced fresh fish and seafood, good choice of wines by the glass, Adnams and

Greene King kept under light blanket pressure, two no smoking areas; it's a compact place and they don't take bookings – you may have to share a table with strangers; no children inside, front picnic-sets with a bit of a sea view, attractive surroundings, good walks, cl Sun evening *(Pamela Goodwyn, Mr and Mrs M Hayes, Mike and Mary Carter, Edward Mirzoeff, LYM, Ian and Nita Cooper, Charles and Pauline Stride, Tony and Shirley Albert)*

LINDSEY TYE [TL9846]

Red Rose: Recently improved by enthusiastic new landlord, well cooked reasonably priced food, well kept changing real ales, friendly bar *(MDN)*

LONG MELFORD [TL8646]

Black Lion [Church Walk]: Comfortable hotel with deeply cushioned sofas, leather wing armchairs, swagged curtains in big windows with views over the green and large portraits in the bar, and leather dining chairs around handsome tables set for food (till 10 Fri, Sat) in no smoking dining area; changing menu, service by neatly uniformed staff, well kept (but not cheap) Adnams, and Nethergate IPA on handpump, good range of wines by the glass inc champagne, 20 malt whiskies, generous cafetière coffees; tortilla chips are set out in bowls; piped light classical music can be obtrusive; children in eating area of bar and restaurant, dogs in bar and bedrooms, appealing Victorian walled garden, breakfast served from 9am, open all day *(Michael and Ann Cole, Sarah Markham, Adele Summers, Tracey and Stephen Groves, MDN, Mr and Mrs M Hayes)*

MARKET WESTON [TL9777]

☆ *Mill* [Bury Rd (B1111)]: Opened-up pub with attractively priced lunches using local produce, OAP discounts, thoughtful evening menu, well kept Adnams, Greene King IPA, Woodfordes Wherry and an Old Chimneys beer from the village brewery, enthusiastic effective service, two log fires, dominoes; children welcome, small garden *(Derek Field)*

MELTON [TM2850]

Wilford Bridge [Wilford Bridge Rd]: Light, roomy and well organised, with emphasis on good value food from good sandwiches to local fish in two spacious bars and restaurant, steak nights Mon/Tues, takeaways, well kept Adnams and Greene King Old Speckled Hen, good wines by the glass, prompt friendly service even when busy; nearby river walks *(Pamela Goodwyn, Mrs A Chapman)*

MIDDLETON [TM4267]

Bell [off B1125 Leiston—Westleton; The Street]: Traditional pub, part thatched and beamed, full Adnams range kept well and tapped from the cask, enjoyable cheap food inc children's, woodburner in comfortable lounge, small back dining room, darts and open fire in small low-ceilinged public bar (dogs allowed); impromptu folk nights Weds; garden picnic-sets, pretty setting nr church, camping, handy for RSPB Minsmere and coast *(BB, Comus and Sarah Elliott)*

MONKS ELEIGH [TL9647]

☆ *Swan* [B1115 Sudbury—Stowmarket]: Proper pub with chef/landlord doing good freshly made rather restauranty food (and recipe books), real ales inc Adnams and Greene King, good value wines, welcoming efficient service, comfortably modernised lounge bar, open fire, two separate dining areas; bedrooms *(Derek Thomas, MDN, J F M and M West)*

NEWBOURNE [TM2643]

Fox [The Street]: Pleasant 17th-c village pub with new licensees working hard on the food side, good choice using fresh local produce, well kept Adnams, cosy unspoilt oak-beamed drinking area around log fire, separate family room, dining extension; pretty hanging baskets, lots of tables in attractive garden with pond *(Pamela Goodwyn, Wendy and Carl Dye, Comus and Sarah Elliott)*

ORFORD [TM4249]

Crown & Castle: Restaurant with rooms and bar used mainly for pre-dinner drinks (but some people do just drop in there and it has well kept guest beers and good wines by the glass); well worth knowing for wide choice of good food with a strong streak of individuality, and bright spacious garden bedrooms with modern bathrooms *(J F M and M West, TW, MW, A J Murray, Tracey and Stephen Groves)*

☆ *Kings Head* [Front St]: Bright and airy lounge bar overlooking churchyard, well kept Adnams ales, good coffee, good reasonably priced food from sandwiches through excellent local smokery products and proper children's specials to restaurant meals, decent wines, friendly efficient staff; live music Fri, attractive character bedrooms with own bathrooms, lots of flowers outside *(Neil and Lorna Mclaughlan, Gloria Bax, LYM, Jonathan and Gillian Shread, N R White)*

OTLEY [TM1852]

White Hart [Helmingham Rd (B1079)]: Reasonably priced food from baguettes up, pleasant attentive staff, Woodfordes ale, decent wines; sizeable pretty garden with tiling draughts board, handy for Helmingham Hall gardens *(Esther and John Sprinkle, J F M and M West)*

PAKENHAM [TL9267]

Fox [signed off A1088 and A143 S of Norwich]: Friendly beamed village local with popular licensees, well kept Greene King IPA and Abbot, reliable reasonably priced pub food with wkdy OAP discounts and some takeaways, log fire, small neat dining room, darts and quiz nights; quiet piped jazz; children welcome, tables in streamside garden with barbecue, boules and new summer bar *(Derek Field)*

POLSTEAD [TL9938]

☆ *Cock* [signed off B1068 and A1071 E of Sudbury, then pub signed; Polstead Green]: Black beams and timbers, dark pink walls, woodburner and open fire, random mix of unassuming furniture, good-natured local atmosphere, interesting reasonably priced food (not Sun evening) from big lunchtime rolls to good value Fri steak night, well kept ales such as Adnams Broadside, Greene King IPA and Woodfordes Wherry, good choice of wines and malt whiskies, good coffee, smarter light and airy barn restaurant; piped music; children welcome, picnic-sets out overlooking quiet green, side play area, cl Mon *(Pamela Goodwyn, BB, John Prescott, David Barnes)*

RAMSHOLT [TM3041]
☆ *Ramsholt Arms* [signed off B1083; Dock Rd]: Lovely isolated spot, with picture-window nautical bars overlooking River Deben, handy for bird walks and Sutton Hoo; quickly served wholesome food inc plenty of good value seafood and seasonal game, well kept Adnams Best and Broadside with a seasonal guest such as Nethergate, decent wines by the glass, winter mulled wine, easy-going contented bar (one of the dogs can let himself in) with good log fire, no smoking restaurant; longish steep walk down from car park, busy summer wknds; children very welcome, tables outside with summer afternoon terrace bar (not Sun), roomy bedrooms with stunning view, yacht moorings nearby – and the church is beautiful *(LYM, Mrs Hilarie Taylor, Comus and Sarah Elliott, Peter Meister, Pamela Goodwyn, J F M and M West, Stephen and Jean Curtis, P and J Shapley, Tracey and Stephen Groves)*

RATTLESDEN [TL9758]
Brewers Arms [off B1115 or A45 W of Stowmarket; Lower Rd]: Solidly built 16th-c village pub with nice pictures and bric-a-brac in book-lined beamed lounge, comfortable no smoking dining area (children allowed), well kept Greene King ales and plenty of malt whiskies, traditional pub games; piped music; french windows to garden; new tenants 2005 – reports please *(LYM, Ian and Nita Cooper)*

REDGRAVE [TM0477]
Cross Keys [The Street]: Friendly village local with comfortable lounge bar, substantial good value home cooking inc good sandwiches and bargain lunches, Adnams, Greene King and a guest beer, decent wines, daily papers; popular Sun quiz night *(J F M and M West)*

REYDON [TM4977]
Randolph [Wangford Rd]: Light and airy décor, scrubbed pine tables, friendly helpful staff, good choice of good food inc plenty of fish and interesting puddings, well kept Adnams beers and wines; children welcome in dining area, garden tables, bedrooms *(Comus and Sarah Elliott)*

ROUGHAM [TL9063]
Ravenwood Hall: Country house hotel with good welcoming service in charming lounge bar, good blackboard bar meal choice inc sandwiches, sausages and mash and fish and chips, two good log fires, lots of interesting touches, well kept Adnams Bitter and Broadside, good wines by the glass, mulled wine at Christmas, elaborate restaurant; children welcome, tables outside, wooded grounds, 14 bedrooms *(Comus and Sarah Elliott, J F M and M West)*

SAXON STREET [TL6759]
Reindeer [The Street]: Smart dining pub with enjoyable if not cheap food, friendly efficient staff, some real ales *(M and GR, Mike and Jennifer Marsh)*

SAXTEAD GREEN [TM2564]
☆ *Old Mill House* [B1119; The Green]: Roomy dining pub across green from windmill, beamed carpeted bar, neat country-look flagstoned restaurant extension, wooden tables and chairs, pretty curtains, friendly service, popular reasonably priced fresh food inc good puddings and nightly carvery, well kept ales inc Adnams, decent wines; discreet piped music; children very welcome, attractive and sizeable garden with terrace and good play area *(LYM, Philip and Susan Philcox)*

SHOTTISHAM [TM3144]
Sorrel Horse [Hollesley Rd]: Friendly new landlord in charming two-bar thatched Tudor local, well kept Greene King IPA tapped from the cask, limited tasty home-made food from granary baguettes up, helpful service, good log fire in flagstoned bar, attractive dining room; tables out on green of tucked-away village *(Comus and Sarah Elliott, the Didler, Geoff and Carol Thorp)*

SNAPE [TM3957]
☆ *Plough & Sail* [the Maltings]: Light and airy restyle now wearing in nicely, well kept Adnams ales, decent wines, enjoyable up-to-date food from snacks to full meals, attractive original core with sofas, settles and log fires; teak tables out in big enclosed flower-filled courtyard, open all day in summer, lovely surroundings with good walks *(Comus and Sarah Elliott, LYM, Klaus and Elizabeth Leist, Pamela Goodwyn, Clive and Vivienne Locks)*

SOMERLEYTON [TM4797]
Dukes Head [Slugs Lane (B1074)]: Old stone-built pub much extended for family dining, enjoyable food at sensible prices, Adnams and Oulton real ales; tables out on grass, country views, a stiff walk up from River Waveney *(Dr and Mrs M E Wilson)*

SOMERSHAM [TM0848]
☆ *Duke of Marlborough* [off A14 just N of Ipswich; Main Rd]: Pub/restaurant with sturdy pine tables on fresh stripped boards in big open room, appealing country prints and 16th-c inglenook, light and airy turkey-carpeted dining room, good service and atmosphere, good fresh food from lunchtime baguettes and baked potatoes to some interesting hot dishes and home-made shortbread, well kept Greene King IPA and Old Speckled Hen, decent wines, good coffee, pleasant and efficient young staff *(Pamela Goodwyn, BB, J F M and M West)*

SOUTHWOLD [TM5176]
Pier Pub [North Parade]: Part of new pier development, with lovely sea views, bijou end bar, two smallish rooms (one no smoking), well kept Adnams, decent wines, good tea, wide choice of good simple food at sensible prices, quick efficient service; children welcome, covered terrace *(John Wooll)*
☆ *Red Lion* [South Green]: Big windows

looking over green to sea, pale panelling, ship pictures, lots of brassware and copper, friendly prompt service, well kept Adnams Bitter and Broadside, popular reasonably priced food from sandwiches up inc good fish and chips, pub games, no smoking dining room; children and dogs welcome, lots of tables outside, right by the Adnams retail shop; bedrooms small but comfortable *(Robert Turnham, BB, Colin and Janet Roe, Pam and David Bailey, M and GR, Dr and Mrs M E Wilson, Michael Dandy)*

Sole Bay [East Green]: Bright and stylish café/bar décor and light wood furnishings, lively local atmosphere, well kept Adnams, cheerful and efficient smartly dressed staff, good simple food from impressive doorstep sandwiches up, conservatory; live music Fri; tables on side terrace, moments from sea and lighthouse *(Comus and Sarah Elliott, David Carr, MDN, LYM, Mrs A Chapman, Dr and Mrs M E Wilson, Paul and Ursula Randall)*

☆ *Swan* [Market Pl]: Smart hotel not pub, with relaxed and comfortable bar tucked away at the back, well kept Adnams and Broadside, full range of their bottled beers, fine wines and malt whiskies, good bar lunches (not cheap, but worth it) from enormous open sandwiches and ciabattas to ten or so main dishes, pricey coffee and teas in luxurious chintzy front lounge; good bedrooms inc garden rooms where (by arrangement) dogs can stay too *(LYM, Michael Dandy, Martin and Pauline Jennings, Dr and Mrs M E Wilson, George Atkinson)*

SPROUGHTON [TM1243]
Beagle [Old Hadleigh Rd]: Comfortable 1920s timber-framed pub redone as olde-worlde Vintage Inn with beamery and inglenooks, five open fires, usual value-conscious food all day inc interesting puddings, Adnams and Greene King IPA, good choice of reasonably priced wines by the glass, friendly efficient service, back conservatory *(Michael Dandy)*

STANTON [TL9673]
Rose & Crown [Bury Rd]: Comfortable dining pub with new people doing wide range of consistently good value generous food, pleasant service, neat conservatory restaurant; children welcome *(Mrs J A Jackson)*

STOWUPLAND [TM0759]
Crown [Church Rd (A1120 just E of Stowmarket)]: Traditional main bar with brasses and farm tools, well kept Greene King IPA, reliable solid pub food inc imaginative curries and meats from good local butcher, locals' lively back bar with darts, pool and big-screen sports TV *(Stephen P Edwards)*

STRADBROKE [TM2373]
White Hart [Church St]: Friendly local with lovely view of church, generous good value pub food, well kept Adnams and Greene King IPA, decent wines *(TW, MW)*

STUTTON [TM1434]
Gardeners Arms [Manningtree Rd, Upper Street (B1080)]: Enjoyable fresh home-made food inc good value Sun lunch, friendly

landlord, separate dining room; open all day *(Andrew Scarr)*

SUDBURY [TL8741]
☆ *Waggon & Horses* [Church Walk]: Comfortable compact bar with cheerful welcoming service, good choice of attractively priced fresh food inc good sandwiches even Sun afternoon, well kept beers, good house wines, interesting décor, log fire; pleasant walled garden with picnic-sets, handy for Gainsborough House *(MLR, Charles Gysin)*

THEBERTON [TM4365]
Lion [B1122]: Unpretentious village local with no smoking lounge, comfortable banquettes, lots of old local photographs, pictures, copper, brass, plates and bric-a-brac, fresh flowers, good value freshly made pub food inc children's, welcoming licensees, well kept Adnams, Woodfordes Wherry and a couple of stronger guest beers, games area with darts and pool; garden with picnic-sets, small terrace and camp site *(Comus and Sarah Elliott)*

THORNHAM MAGNA [TM1070]
Four Horseshoes [off A140 S of Diss; Wickham Rd]: Extensive thatched pub with dim-lit rambling well divided bar, very low heavy black beams, mix of chairs and plush banquettes, country pictures and farm tools, big log fireplaces, inside well, no smoking areas; Greene King ales, quick friendly service, wide food choice inc Sun lunch; piped music, games machine; bedrooms, picnic-sets on big sheltered lawn, open all day, handy for Thornham Walks and thatched church with ancient frescoes and fine retable *(Michael Dandy, Ian and Nita Cooper, LYM, David Barnes, N R White)*

THORPENESS [TM4759]
Dolphin: Attractive almost scandinavian décor, light and bright, with well kept Adnams, good wine range, relaxed helpful service, interesting photographs of this quaint purpose-built seaside holiday village with its boating lake, food from lunchtime sandwiches up; dogs welcome in public bar, sizeable and attractive garden with summer bar and barbecue, three comfortable bedrooms with own bathrooms *(Mrs Romey Heaton, Pamela Goodwyn, Comus and Sarah Elliott)*

TOSTOCK [TL9563]
Gardeners Arms [off A14 or A1088]: Yet another change of management in appealing low-beamed village pub, welcoming service, well kept Greene King ales and a guest such as Wadworths 6X, good-sized helpings of substantial pubby food inc fresh fish, reasonable prices, log fire, games in tiled public bar, no smoking dining area; picnic-sets in nicely planted sheltered garden *(LYM, Robert F Smith, Derek Field, J F M and M West, Tim and Suzy Bower, Ian and Nita Cooper)*

UFFORD [TM2952]
White Lion [Lower St]: Charming unspoilt 16th-c village pub tucked away not far from quiet stretch of River Deben, good value home cooking using local produce, sandwiches to steaks, Adnams tapped from the cask, good log

fire in central fireplace, flagstone floors, friendly service, no music; tables out on grass *(Pamela Goodwyn, Mrs Hilarie Taylor)*

WALBERSWICK [TM4974]

☆ *Anchor* [The Street]: Enthusiastic new landlord and landlady/chef doing enjoyable real food inc fresh local seafood, well kept Adnams Bitter, Broadside and Fisherman tapped from the cask, some good wines, comfortably modern hotel bar, roomy, airy and bright, with pine furnishings, no smoking area, cosy log fires, special events inc beer and food matching evenings; dogs welcome, neat garden behind, bedrooms *(Eddie Edwards, Julie Scarsbrook)*

WHERSTEAD [TM1641]

Oyster Reach [junction A137/B1456 N, just S of Ipswich]: Very old pub renamed (was Ostrich) and extensively reworked as good Beefeater, with light relaxing décor, welcoming service, good value food all day; bedrooms in attached Travel Inn *(Charles and Pauline Stride)*

WOODBRIDGE [TM2648]

Cherry Tree [opp Notcutts Nursery, off A12; Cumberland St]: Recently refurbished 17th-c inn, aircraft prints, beams and log fires, good variety of daily-changing food, friendly service, Adnams real ales, quiz night Thurs, live music Fri; garden with play area, three well equipped new bedrooms in adjoining barn conversion, open all day wknds *(Gill Kegel, MDN)*

Crown [Thoroughfare]: Cheerfully furnished two-level bar, well kept Greene King IPA and Abbot, attractive beamed restaurant; nice metal tables and chairs out on decking, comfortable well equipped bedrooms in former stable block *(Tracey and Stephen Groves)*

Olde Bell & Steelyard [New St, off Market Sq]: Unusual and unpretentious olde-worlde pub, steelyard still overhanging the street, good friendly mix of drinking and dining in bar, well kept Greene King, short but varied blackboard choice of home-made food from good filled baguettes to local fish, good service *(Ian and Nita Cooper, Barry Collett)*

Seckford Hall [signed off A12 bypass, N of town; Seckford Hall Rd, Great Bealings]: Civilised Tudor hotel not pub, but its dark and friendly comfortable bar has immaculately kept Adnams and good wines inc lots of half bottles; good value though not cheap fixed-price meals, garden with lake, leisure centre and swimming pool, good bedrooms *(Comus and Sarah Elliott)*

WORLINGWORTH [TM2267]

Swan [Swan Rd]: Cheerful character local with pine benches and tiled floors, enjoyable generous food, well kept Adnams tapped from the cask, good wines by the glass, welcoming service, separate games bar with pool; garden tables *(TW, MW)*

YOXFORD [TM3968]

☆ *Griffin* [High St]: 14th-c village pub with log fire and nice corner sofa in appealing main bar, good value generous food using local supplies, Adnams and changing guest beers, decent reasonably priced wines, friendly attentive staff, charming log-fire restaurant; comfortable beamed bedrooms, good breakfast *(Stephen and Jean Curtis, Comus and Sarah Elliott)*

Surrey

Surrey has a good many reliable pubs, often low-beamed buildings of considerable age. As there is a lot of money about in the county, many of its better pubs are rather upscale both in style and in price. But even in places which charge quite highly for their restauranty food, it's quite common to find good value two-course lunch deals. This is also a part of the world where there are several good examples of chain pubs, notably Vintage Inns and Chef & Brewers. Three pubs move up into the main entries here this year: the smart and spotless Fox & Hounds at Englefield Green, very handy for Windsor Park; the charmingly individual Parrot at Forest Green, doing very well under its new licensees, in good walking country with a lovely garden; and the Jolly Farmer near Worplesdon, another pub enjoying new management, and again well placed for walks. All three have good food. Other pubs particularly warmly commended in recent months are the 16th-c Dolphin in Betchworth (good food, wine and service in this homely pub), the smart upmarket Withies at Compton (food good if pricey, attentive service), the welcoming Marneys in Esher (nice to find such a relaxed and countrified pub on the outer fringes of London), the friendly and nicely placed King William IV at Mickleham (good food and beer), another Mickleham pub, the fine old Running Horses (enjoyable food here too), the old Skimmington Castle tucked away on Reigate Heath (good all round, a pub of great individuality), and the more contemporary Inn at West End (great wine choice, good food). Among all the pubs where food stands out as a particular draw, the King William IV at Mickleham gains the title of Surrey Dining Pub of the Year – good food in the cheerful surroundings of a proper pub. A few pubs to note particularly this year in the Lucky Dip section at the end of the chapter are the Mill at Elstead, Old School House at Ockley, Red Lion at Shamley Green, Brickmakers and Half Moon, both in Windlesham, and Wotton Hatch at Wotton. Drinks prices in the county are sky-high; the cost of a pint here is on average now over £2.50. Hogs Back is the main local beer to look out for.

BETCHWORTH TQ2149 Map 3

Dolphin ♀

Turn off A25 W of Reigate opposite B2032 at roundabout, and keep on into The Street; opposite the church

Real fires, good food and plenty of character combine to make this friendly 16th-c village pub somewhere to return to again and again. The neat and homely front room has kitchen chairs and plain tables on the 400-year-old scrubbed flagstones, and the carpeted back saloon bar is black-panelled, with robust old-fashioned elm or oak tables. There are three fires, a nice chiming longcase clock, silenced fruit machine, darts, cribbage and dominoes. As well as up to 18 wines by the glass, friendly staff serve well kept Youngs Bitter, Special, Waggle Dance and maybe a seasonal guest on handpump. It's best to arrive early, or book a table beforehand if you want to enjoy the generously served, good value bar food, which includes sandwiches (from £2.85), home-made soup (£3.15), ploughman's (from £5.65), very popular breaded plaice and chips (£7.95), beef or vegetable lasagne (£7.50) and steaks (from £9.95), with daily specials such as lemon sole goujons (£7.95), steak and mushroom pie (£8.15) and lamb shank (£8.75); puddings might be apple pie or chocolate fudge cake (from £3.65). There are some seats in the small laurel-shaded front courtyard, and behind are picnic-sets on a terrace and lawn by the car park, opposite the church. Parking can be very difficult in summer. No children under 14 inside. *(Recommended by John Ecklin, the Didler, DWAJ, Gordon Neighbour, Alan Sadler, Paul A Moore, Ian Phillips, Ron and Sheila Corbett)*

Youngs ~ Managers George and Rose Campbell ~ Real ale ~ Bar food (12-2.30, 7-10) ~ (01737) 842288 ~ Dogs welcome ~ Open 11-3, 5.30-11; 11-11 Sat; 12-10.30 Sun

BLACKBROOK TQ1846 Map 3

Plough ♀

On by-road E of A24, parallel to it, between Dorking and Newdigate, just N of the turn E to Leigh

Usefully placed for walks in the surrounding oak woods, this white-fronted pub is prettily adorned with hanging baskets and window boxes. The no smoking red saloon bar has fresh flowers on its tables and on the window sills of its large windows (which have new green and gold curtains). Down some steps, the public bar has brass-topped treadle tables, old saws on the ceiling, and bottles and flat irons; shove-ha'penny, cribbage and dominoes. Bar food includes lunchtime snacks such as local spicy sausage and chips (£4.75), ploughman's or grilled ham steak with chips (£5.75), nice bagels with fillings such as warm pastrami, mustard and coleslaw (£5.95), steak sandwich (£7.75), and blackboard specials such as tomato and basil soup (£3.95), baked avocado with crab (£6.25); moussaka (£7.95), chicken curry or brioche of wild mushroom in port wine sauce (£8.45), grilled monkfish wrapped with parma ham with rice (£13.95), steak (from £13.95); wide-ranging children's menu including filled baked potatoes (£3.75) and mini ploughman's or hot lunch (£4.25). Well kept Badger Best, K&B Sussex and Tanglefoot, and a guest such as Gribble Fursty Ferret on handpump, 18 wines by the glass, and several ports. There are tables and chairs outside on the terrace and a little swiss playhouse furnished with little tables and chairs in the secluded garden. One reader found on arrival that the pub was fully booked and they were not even allowed a drink, and we would be grateful to hear if this has happened to other readers. *(Recommended by Neil Hardwick, John Evans, Susan and John Douglas, Fr Robert Marsh, John Ecklin, C and R Bromage)*

Badger ~ Tenants Chris and Robin Squire ~ Real ale ~ Bar food (not Mon evening) ~ (01306) 886603 ~ Children welcome until 9pm ~ Dogs allowed in bar ~ Open 11-3, 6-11.30; 11-3, 7-10.30 Sun; closed 24-26 Dec

CHARLESHILL SU8944 Map 2

Donkey

B3001 Milford—Farnham near Tilford; coming from Elstead, turn left as soon as you see pub sign

Children are made to feel very welcome at this 18th-c cottage-like dining pub and they have their own play area and wendy house; the attractive garden also has a terrace and plenty of seats; you may meet two friendly donkeys called Pip and Dusty. Friendly staff serve lunchtime sandwiches (from £3; toasted sandwiches £3.50) and salads (from £7.50), and other menu items include starters such as soup (£3.75), liver and brandy pâté (£5.95) and scallops with crispy bacon in garlic and herb butter (£8.95), and main courses such as steak and Guinness pie (£10.95), steak (from £12.95), roast gressingham duck with blackcurrant and apricot brandy sauce (£14.95) and bass with king prawns (£15.95), as well as daily specials like home-made steak and kidney pie (£10.95) or lobster thermidor (£16.95). They also do two-course lunches from Monday to Thursday (£10.95) and a Sunday roast (£10.50). The bright saloon has lots of polished stirrups, lamps and watering cans on the walls, and prettily cushioned built-in wall benches, while the lounge has a fine high-backed settle, highly polished horsebrasses, and swords on the walls and beams; the dining conservatory is no smoking. All their wines are available by the glass, and you'll also find well kept Greene King IPA, Abbot and Old Speckled Hen on handpump; piped music. *(Recommended by James Price, John and Joyce Snell)*

Greene King ~ Lease Lee and Helen Francis ~ Real ale ~ Bar food (12-2.30, 6-9.30) ~ Restaurant ~ (01252) 702124 ~ Children welcome ~ Dogs allowed in bar ~ Open 12-3, 6-11(11.30 Sat); 12-10.30 Sun; 12-3, 6-10.30 Sun in winter

COBHAM TQ1060 Map 3
Cricketers

Downside Common; 3¾ miles from M25 junction 10; A3 towards Cobham, first right on to A245, right at Downside signpost into Downside Bridge Road, follow road into its right fork – away from Cobham Park – at second turn after bridge, then take next left turn into the pub's own lane

Crooked standing timbers create a comfortable open-plan layout in this characterful pub, which is warmed by a blazing log fire; watch your head on the low, heavy oak beams (some have crash-pads on them). In places you can see the wide oak ceiling boards and ancient plastering laths. Furnishings are quite simple, and there are horsebrasses and big brass platters on the walls; the stable bar and restaurant are no smoking. Fullers London Pride, Gales and Greene King Old Speckled Hen are kept under a light blanket pressure on handpump, and a good choice of wines including several by the glass; piped music. Elaborate bar food might include jerusalem artichoke soup (£4.75), whipped ash-rolled goats cheese and beetroot salad (£5.50), pressed ham hock and poached chicken terrine (£6.75), home-made gnocchi with wild mushrooms, walnuts and blue cheese sauce (£11.50), chargrilled cannon of exmoor lamb niçoise (£13.75) and bruschetta with celeriac remoulade and bass with slow-roasted tomatoes (£14.50); puddings could include mango crème brûlée or sticky toffee pudding with date ice-cream (£5.25); there's also a separate restaurant menu. White painted metal tables on a terrace with outdoor heaters, and in the delightful neatly kept garden (with standard roses, magnolias, dahlias, bedding plants, urns and hanging baskets) have views over the village green, where riders may have tethered their horses while they stop for a drink. Note that food times may change from those given below, and that it's worth arriving early (particularly on Sunday) to be sure of a table. *(Recommended by James Price, Mr and Mrs A H Young, Geoffrey Kemp, Gerry and Rosemary Dobson, LM, Vanessa Stilwell, John Saville, Mike and Lynn Robinson, Ian Phillips, Stephen Allford, Roger and Pauline Pearce, W W Burke, C J Roebuck)*

Enterprise ~ Tenant Mustafa Ozcan ~ Real ale ~ Bar food (12-9.30(8 Sun)) ~ Restaurant ~ (01932) 862105 ~ Children in family room ~ Dogs allowed in bar ~ Open 11-11; 12-10.30 Sun

COLDHARBOUR TQ1543 Map 3
Plough ◀

Village signposted in the network of small roads around Leith Hill

Some 800 feet above sea level in a peaceful hamlet in the Surrey hills, this own-brew inn is one of the highest pubs in south-east England, and after a good lunch or a drink you can stride up Leith Hill for far-ranging views. The two bars (each with a lovely open fire) have stripped light beams and timbering in the warm-coloured dark ochre walls, with quite unusual little chairs around the tables in the snug red-carpeted games room on the left (with darts), and little decorative plates on the walls; the one on the right leads through to the no smoking candlelit restaurant. From the pub's own Leith Hill Brewery, they serve Crooked Furrow and Tallywacker on handpump, along with three or four well kept real ales such as Charles Wells Bombardier, Ringwood Old Thumper and Shepherd Neame Early Bird and Spitfire; also Biddenden farm cider; darts, TV, cribbage and dominoes; at busy times it may be hard to find somewhere to sit if you're not dining. Enjoyable bar food includes soup (£3.95), deep-fried herring roe with horseradish or chicken liver and brandy pâté (£5.95), ploughman's (£6.95), sausage and mash or cheddar parsnip and parmesan roulade (£9.95), cajun spiced salmon fillet (£10.95) and confit of duck on mash with zesty orange jus (£12.95); puddings such as steamed fudge and walnut pudding or crumble of the day (£4.50). The front and the terraced gardens have picnic-sets, tubs of flowers and a fish pond full of water-lilies. *(Recommended by Jason Reynolds, Simon and Mandy King, Philip and Ann Board, Anthony Rogers, Paul Humphreys, Dick Pyper, C and R Bromage, Andy Trafford, Louise Bayly, A G Roby, R A Rosen, Peter Lewis, Mike and Mary Carter)*

Own brew ~ Licensees Richard and Anna Abrehart ~ Real ale ~ Bar food (12-2.30, 6-9.30(9 Sun)) ~ Restaurant ~ (01306) 711793 ~ Children in eating area of bar and also in barn on Sun ~ Dogs allowed in bar ~ Open 11.30-11; 12-10.30 Sun; closed 25-26 Dec, 1 Jan evening ~ Bedrooms: £59.50S/£69.50S

COMPTON SU9546 Map 2

Withies

Withies Lane; pub signposted from B3000

A mass of flowers borders the neat lawn in front of this very attractive and civilised 16th-c pub, and weeping willows overhang the immaculate garden, where there are dining tables under an arbour of creeper-hung trellises, more on a crazy-paved terrace and others under old apple trees. Inside is a low-beamed little bar, some fine 17th-c carved panels between the windows, and a splendidly art nouveau settle among the old sewing-machine tables; you'll find a good log fire in a massive inglenook fireplace; piped music. They do good straightforward pubby bar food such as soup (£3.75), sandwiches or filled baked potatoes (from £4.50), quiche or smoked salmon pâté (£4.75), ploughman's (£5.25), cumberland sausages with mash and onion gravy (£5.50) and seafood platter (£9.50). The no smoking restaurant is more formal, with an elaborate, and expensive menu, and is very popular with a well heeled local set. Even when it's busy, the pleasant uniformed staff remain helpful and efficient, though unfortunately they may try to keep your credit card while you eat. Badger K&B, Fullers London Pride, Greene King IPA and Hogs Back TEA are well kept on handpump. Polsted Manor and Loseley Park are a pleasant walk up the lane from here. *(Recommended by James Price, John Braine-Hartnell, Alan Cowell, Bob and Margaret Holder, John Evans, Ann and Stephen Saunders, Guy Consterdine, Gene and Kitty Rankin, Mrs G R Sharman, Ian Phillips, Nigel B Thompson, Wendy Arnold, R Lake)*

Free house ~ Licensees Brian and Hugh Thomas ~ Real ale ~ Bar food (12-2.30, 7-10) ~ Restaurant ~ (01483) 421158 ~ Children welcome ~ Open 11-3, 6-11; 12-4 Sun; closed Sun evening

EASHING SU9543 Map 2

Stag

Lower Eashing; Eashing signposted off A3 southbound, S of Hurtmore turn-off; or pub signposted off A283 just SE of exit roundabout at N end of A3 Milford bypass

Despite its Georgian brick façade, this pleasant pub (also known as the Stag on the River) tucked down a narrow lane dates back in part to the 15th c; inside you'll find an attractively opened-up interior with a charming old-fashioned locals' bar on the right with red and black flooring tiles by the counter. They serve well kept Courage Best, Fullers London Pride and Shepherd Neame Spitfire on handpump, and about 14 wines by the glass. A cosy gently lit room beyond has a low white plank ceiling, a big stag print and stag's head on the dark-wallpapered walls, some cookery books on shelves by the log fire, and sturdy cushioned housekeeper's chairs grouped around dark tables on the brick floor. An extensive blue-carpeted area rambles around on the left, with similar comfortable dark furniture, some smaller country prints and decorative plates on pink Anaglypta walls, and round towards the back a big woodburning stove in a capacious fireplace under a long mantelbeam. It's all rather smart yet cosily traditional; there is a table of conservative daily papers, and they are kind to visiting dogs. Lunchtime bar snacks include soup (£3.85), open ciabatta sandwiches (from £6.25), ploughman's (£6.45) and burgers or sausage and mash (£9.95), and blackboard specials such as nachos with tomato salsa (£6.25), home-made faggots with mash and apple and shallot sauce (£7.50) and sirloin steak (£15.25). Prices on the evening menu (available in the bar or restaurant) are more expensive and include dishes like fried tofu and chargrilled vegetable platter (£12.55) and chicken breast wrapped in parma ham (£14.55), as well as specials on the blackboard such as moules marinière (£6.50), lamb shank (£10.95) and seared duck breast (£13.25); no smoking restaurant. The riverside garden has a millstream, picnic-sets and other tables under cocktail parasols among mature trees, a terrace with some teak furniture, and more picnic-sets in a lantern-lit arbour. (*Recommended by Martin and Karen Wake, R B Gardiner, Gordon Stevenson, Susan and John Douglas, C J Roebuck*)

Punch ~ Lease Marilyn Lackey ~ Real ale ~ Bar food (12-2.30(3 Sun), 6-9.30; not Sun, Mon evenings) ~ Restaurant ~ (01483) 421568 ~ Children welcome ~ Dogs allowed in bar ~ Open 11-11; 12-10.30 Sun ~ Bedrooms: /£55S

ENGLEFIELD GREEN SU9772 Map 2
Fox & Hounds
Bishopsgate Road; off A328 N of Egham

We've had a number of enthusiastic reports from readers on this spotless 17th-c pub, on the edge of Windsor Park and a very short stroll from the main gate to the Savill Garden. It's a civilised place with good sturdy wooden tables and chairs, a good log fire in the big fireplace. Very good bar food includes an interesting choice of filled baguettes, soup (£4.50), spiced lamb koftas with cucumber raita and warm pitta (£6.25), thai fishcakes or chicken liver parfait (£6.95), cumberland sausages and mash (£8.25), wild mushroom and mascarpone risotto (£11.95), baked fillet of salmon with warm potato salad (£12.95), and roast shoulder of lamb or rib-eye steak (£13.95), and six to eight fish specials such as chargrilled butterfish (£14.50) or fillets of bass with creamed cabbage (£15.95). They also have a restaurant menu for the attractive candlelit back dining room. Well kept Brakspears, Greene King Abbot and Hogs Back Brewery TEA on handpump, and an extensive wine list as well as several malt whiskies. There are picnic-sets on the neat and pretty front lawn, and more on a back terrace. (*Recommended by Kevin Thomas, Nina Randall, Mike and Jennifer Marsh, Martin and Karen Wake, Ian Phillips, Robert Hay, Ellen Weld, David London, N R White*)

Old Monk ~ Real ale ~ Bar food (12-2.30 Mon-Thurs; 12-4 Fri-Sun; filled baguettes only Sun) ~ Restaurant ~ (01784) 433098 ~ Children welcome ~ Dogs allowed in bar ~ Live jazz Mon evening ~ Open 11-11; 12-10.30 Sun; 11-3, 5.30-11 Jan-Easter

ESHER TQ1566 Map 3
Marneys ♀
Alma Road (one way only), Weston Green; heading N on A309 from A307 roundabout, after Lamb & Star pub turn left into Lime Tree Avenue (signposted to All Saints Parish Church), then left at T junction into Chestnut Avenue

The Norwegian landlord has given an interesting slant to this cottagey pub beside a wooded common, and here and there you'll find his national flag and anthem on display. The food, too, tends towards the scandinavian style: the sensibly small choice features baguettes (from £5.75), scandinavian meatballs and red cabbage or good soused herring fillets (£8.25), frikadeller (danish meatcakes) (£8.50), and puddings such as almond and pear tart (£4); they usually have around nine specials on the board, such as grilled goats cheese crostini with roasted plum tomatoes and balsamic syrup or home-made prime steak burger with bacon and cheese (£8.95) and seared tuna with red pepper and pesto salsa (£9.95); they are happy to provide children's portions. There's not much room in the chatty low-beamed bar with its black and white plank panelling, shelves of hens and ducks and other ornaments, small blue-curtained windows, and perhaps horse racing on the unobtrusive corner TV; piped music. On the left, past a little cast-iron woodburning stove, a dining area (somewhat roomier but still small) has big pine tables, pews and pale country kitchen chairs, with attractive goose pictures; this leads on to a recently added decking area with seating and large tables. Well kept Bass, Courage Best and Flowers Original on handpump, just over a dozen wines by the glass (even pink champagne on our summer visit), enterprising soft drinks, norwegian schnapps and good coffee. Service by friendly uniformed staff is quick and efficient; and they have daily papers on sticks. The pleasantly planted sheltered garden has black picnic-sets and tables under green and blue canvas parasols, and the front terrace has dark blue cast-iron tables and chairs under matching parasols, with some more black tables too. *(Recommended by Alec and Barbara Jones, Ian Phillips, Martin and Karen Wake, Susan and John Douglas)*

Free house ~ Licensee Henrik Platou ~ Real ale ~ Bar food (12-2.15, 7-10; 12.30-3 Sun; not Sun or Mon evenings) ~ Restaurant ~ (020) 8398 4444 ~ Children in eating area of bar and restaurant ~ Dogs welcome ~ Open 11-11; 12-10.30 Sun

FOREST GREEN TQ1241 Map 3
Parrot
B2127 just W of junction with B2126, SW of Dorking

Overlooking the village cricket field, this quaint, extended old pub was recently taken over by the Gotto family, until this year a mainstay of our London chapter for the several pubs they made such a success of around the capital (see the Ship in our South London section). This latest venture is close to their farm, so most of the meat on the very good menu is their own. They hadn't been here for long when we visited, but signs of their sure-handed approach were already firmly evident, from the food and carefully chosen wines to the freshly squeezed orange juice behind the bar. It's a comfortably civilised place, and very attractive too, particularly in the bar, with its profusion of heavy beams, timbers and flagstones, and huge inglenook fireplace. There's plenty of space, with a couple of cosy areas hidden away behind the fireplace, and some more spread out tables opposite the long brick bar counter, which has a few unusual wooden chairs in front. Well kept Ringwood Best, a couple of Youngs beers, and perhaps a guest like Hogs Back TEA on handpump; newspapers are laid out for customers. A brass parrot sits beside a brick fireplace with a stove, then beyond here is a big, no smoking restaurant, less distinctive than the bar, but with the same enjoyably relaxed atmosphere. You can eat anywhere, from a frequently changing menu that might include lunchtime sandwiches, soup (£4), flaked smoked mackerel with beetroot and potato salad (£4.95), grilled sardines (£5.95), lots of their own lamb served as sausages, burgers or chops, and specials like lambs liver with crispy bacon creamy chive mash and red wine gravy (£9); they do a choice of good, popular Sunday roasts. Outside there's lots of room, with tables in front and among several attractive gardens, one with apple trees and rose beds; they plan to turn the rather run-down play area into a vegetable garden. The pub is handy for the good woodland walks in the hills around Abinger. *(Recommended by Jenny and Brian Seller, Evan Davies)*

Free house ~ Licensee Charles Gotto ~ Real ale ~ Bar food (12-3(4 weekends), 7-10; no food Sun evening) ~ Restaurant ~ (01306) 621339 ~ Well behaved children till 7pm ~ Dogs allowed in bar ~ Open 11-11; 12-10.30 Sun

LALEHAM TQ0568 Map 3
Three Horseshoes ♀
5 miles from M25 junction 13; A30 E, then at roundabout turn on to A308 (signposted Kingston, Sunbury), then at roundabout after another 1.3 miles turn right on to B377; in Laleham turn right on to B376 (Shepperton Road)

Not far from an idyllic, grassy stretch of the Thames, this much-smartened, ancient stone-flagged tavern (in a building dating from the 13th c) gets distinctly busy on summer days. The bar is airy with gentle lighting, cream walls, farmhouse tables, comfortable settees, newspapers to read, a fireplace with an open fire and some intimate little corners. A feng shui consultation determined the placing of the red, blue and green carpets. Bar food is served in generous helpings and includes soup

(£3.95), sandwiches (from £3.95), ham, egg and chips (£6.75), steak and ale pie (£7.50), grilled cajun chicken with caesar salad (£8.25), chicken breast stuffed with onion and cheese (£9.95) and puddings (£4.75); fish specials might include bass (£13.50) or dover sole (£19.95). Five areas, including the conservatory, snug room and restaurants are no smoking. Efficient bar staff serve well kept Courage Best, Fullers London Pride, Youngs Special and a couple of guests such as Brakspears and Shepherd Neame Spitfire on handpump and over a dozen wines by the glass; piped music (which can be obtrusive) and fruit machine. *(Recommended by Tom McLean, John Mitchell, Mayur Shah, Martin and Alison Stainsby, JMM)*

Unique (Enterprise) ~ Lease Sean Alderson ~ Real ale ~ Bar food (12-3.30, 6-9.30; 12-10 Sat; 12-9 Sun) ~ Restaurant ~ (01784) 455014 ~ Children welcome in restaurant if eating ~ Open 11-11; 12-10.30 Sun

LEIGH TQ2246 Map 3
Plough
3 miles S of A25 Dorking—Reigate, signposted from Betchworth (which itself is signposted off the main road); also signposted from South Park area of Reigate; on village green

A particularly inviting spot to head for in summer and with plenty of colourful hanging baskets, this weatherboarded pub stands by the village green, and its pretty side garden (fairy-lit in the evening) has picnic-sets under cocktail parasols. On the right as you come in, the cosy timbered no smoking dining lounge is decorated with lots of local prints on white walls. On the left, a simpler more local pubby bar has a good bow window seat, lots of different games including darts, shove-ha'penny, dominoes, table skittles, cribbage, Jenga, backgammon and shut the box; there's also piped music, an alcove fruit machine and occasional TV. Well kept real ales are Badger Best, Tanglefoot, Sussex, and a guest such as Gribble Fursty Ferret on handpump, and you can have a glass of anything on the decent wine list. The wide-ranging menu includes enjoyable snacks such as soup (£3.95), a big selection of sandwiches (from £3.95), baked potatoes (from £4.50), and ploughman's (from £5.95), liver and bacon (£7.95), steak pie (£8.50), roasted vegetable mexican-style tortilla wrap or bacon wrapped chicken (£9.95) and steaks (from £11.75), along with blackboard specials such as grilled oak turbot marinated in lime, chilli and ginger on stir-fried vegetables (£11.95), with puddings such as pavlova or apple pie (from £3.75); you may need to book at the weekend. Nearby parking is limited. *(Recommended by John Braine-Hartnell, David Crook, Alan Sadler, N R White)*

Badger ~ Tenant Sarah Bloomfield ~ Real ale ~ Bar food (12-9.30) ~ Restaurant ~ (01306) 611348 ~ Children in eating area of bar and restaurant ~ Dogs allowed in bar ~ Open 11-11; 12-10.30 Sun

LINGFIELD TQ3844 Map 3
Hare & Hounds 🍴 ◼
Turn off B2029 N at Crowhurst, Edenbridge signpost, into Lingfield Common Road

Interestingly individual and not over-smartened, this dining pub is a distinctive place for a meal. The smallish open-plan bar (mostly no smoking), light and airy by day, has soft lighting and nightlights burning on a good mix of different-sized tables at night – when it's full of the chatter of happy customers, some drinking, some eating, all mixing comfortably. Partly bare boards and partly flagstones, it has an eclectic variety of well worn scatter-cushioned dining chairs and other seats from pews to a button-back leather chesterfield, black and white pictures of jazz musicians on brown tongue-and-groove panelling, and occasional piped music. It opens into a quieter no smoking dining area with big abstract-expressionist paintings. They make their own soda bread, ice-cream and pasta, and the well presented, daily changing bar food (not cheap) might include starters such as soup (£3.95) and skate and parsley terrine or spiced sweet potato rolls with mushroom salad and chilli dip (£5.95) and main courses like cumberland sausages with cheddar mash (£7.95), deep-fried battered haddock or salt beef butternut squash

(£9.50), crispy twice-cooked duck with pork and shi-itake dumplings (£14.95) and fillet steak with lemon and cheddar stuffed baked potato, swiss chard and roast shallot jus (£15.95); vegetables are an extra £2.95. Flowers Original and Greene King Abbot and IPA are well kept on handpump, and there are decent wines. Tables are set out in a pleasant split-level garden, some on decking. This is good walking country near Haxted Mill; walkers can leave their boots in the porch, guarded by a life-size great dane statue. They hold irish theme nights around every two months. *(Recommended by John Saville, R and S Bentley, Derek Thomas, Tony and Wendy Hobden, Sharon and Alan Corper)*

Pubmaster ~ Lease Fergus Greer ~ Real ale ~ Bar food (12-2.30(3.30 Sun), 7-9.30) ~ Restaurant ~ (01342) 832351 ~ Children welcome if well behaved ~ Dogs allowed in bar ~ Open 11.30-11; 12-8.30 Sun

MICKLEHAM TQ1753 Map 3
King William IV 🍴 🍺

Byttom Hill; short but narrow steep track up hill just off A24 Leatherhead—Dorking by partly green-painted restaurant – public car park down here is best place to park; OS Sheet 187 map reference 173538

Surrey Dining Pub of the Year

Cut into the hillside above the A24 and well positioned for walks through the woods and up Box Hill and White Hill, this pub has panoramic views over the Surrey countryside. Needless to say, such an idyllic spot does draw the crowds on a sunny day and as they don't take bookings during the summer you will need to get here early to secure a table, and be aware that you will have to queue to place your order, but service should be quick enough after that. The snug plank-panelled front bar shares the same panoramic views as the garden. The more spacious back bar is quite brightly lit, with kitchen-type chairs around its cast-iron-framed tables, log fires, fresh flowers on all the tables, and a serviceable grandfather clock. There's a friendly atmosphere throughout. Very enjoyable bar food in huge helpings might include sandwiches (from £3.95), filled baked potatoes or ploughman's (from £6.75), aubergine and vegetable lasagne (£8.75), steak and kidney pie or seafood pie (£9.95), grilled catch of the day on stir-fried vegetables and pak choi with lemon rice (£12.95), fillet steak with wild mushroom and brandy cream sauce (£15.95), tapas platter (£17.50 for two) and puddings such as hot chocolate fudge cake or treacle, ginger and apple tart (£4.25). The choice is more limited on Sundays and bank holidays, and they don't do sandwiches at weekends. Very well kept Adnams Best, Badger Best, Hogs Back TEA and a monthly changing guest such as Hogs Back Hop Garden Gold on handpump; light piped music. The lovely terraced garden at the back is neatly filled with sweet peas, climbing roses and honeysuckle, and plenty of tables (some in an extended open-sided wooden shelter with gas heaters). Nearby parking can be difficult on the lane, so you may need to use the public car park at the bottom of the hill and take a character-forming walk up. *(Recommended by James Price, C and R Bromage, John Ecklin, Alan Sadler, Andrea Rampley, T R and B C Jenkins, Catherine and Richard Preston, Tracey and Stephen Groves, Ian Phillips, Clive and Janice Sillitoe, Rosemary and Tom Hall, N R White, Andy Trafford, Louise Bayly)*

Free house ~ Licensees Chris and Jenny Grist ~ Real ale ~ Bar food (12-2, 7-9.30; 12-5 Sun) ~ (01372) 372590 ~ Children over 12 ~ Open 11-3, 6-11; 12-10.30 Sun

Running Horses 🍷 🛏

Old London Road (B2209) 🏠

Continuing to receive good reports from readers for its food, this smart, substantial inn has two calmly relaxing bar rooms, neatly kept and spaciously open plan with fresh flowers (in summer) in an inglenook at one end, lots of race tickets hanging from a beam, some really good racing cartoons, hunting pictures and Hogarth prints, dark carpets, cushioned wall settles and other dining chairs around straightforward pubby tables and bar stools. Adnams, Fullers London Pride, Greene King Abbot and Youngs are well kept on handpump alongside good, if pricey, wines by the glass, from a serious list. As well as a tempting choice of bar food (not cheap) such as soup (£4.50), lunchtime chunky sandwiches (from £4.60), ciabatta toasties like bacon and brie or creamy oyster mushrooms and tarragon (£6.95), fritatta of mixed peppers, onion and potato (£7.50), tempura fish or vegetables and pineapple (£9.50), steak, Guinness and mushroom pudding (£12.50); there's also a more elaborate restaurant menu (which you can eat from in the bar), which might include cracked peppered fillet of beef carpaccio (£7.25), seared pheasant on chorizo and mushroom risotto (£16.95), roasted english veal with lemon thyme (£17.75) and sautéed cod fillet on a crab, coconut and coriander cake (£19.25) as well as puddings such as sticky date and sultana pudding with butterscotch sauce and toffee ice-cream or dark chocolate caramel and walnut torte (£5.25). The no smoking restaurant area leads straight out of the bar and although it is set out quite formally with crisp white cloths and candles on each table, it shares the thriving atmosphere of the bar; piped music and professional staff. There are picnic-sets on a terrace in front by lovely flowering tubs and hanging baskets, with a peaceful view of the old church with its strange stubby steeple. *(Recommended by Andrew York, Norma and Noel Thomas, Debbie and Neil Hayter, John Ecklin, S Topham, C J Roebuck, Susan and John Douglas, Gordon Stevenson)*

Punch ~ Lease Steve and Josie Slayford ~ Real ale ~ Bar food (12-2.30(3 Sat, Sun), 7-9.30(9 Sun)) ~ Restaurant ~ (01372) 372279 ~ Children over 14 only in bar ~ Dogs allowed in bar ~ Open 11.30-11; 12-10.30 Sun ~ Bedrooms: £94S/£105.75S

NEWDIGATE TQ2043 Map 3
Surrey Oaks ⬛
Off A24 S of Dorking, via Beare Green; Parkgate Road

Originally a wheelwright's cottage, this partly tile-hung 16th-c country pub has a nicely complicated garden with a terrace, and a rockery with pools and a waterfall – the play area and two goats help keep children amused. The welcoming landlord is keen on real ale and serves five well kept real ales on handpump, with Caledonian Deuchars IPA, Harveys Sussex Best and Timothy Taylors Landlord alongside guests such as Dark Star Landlord's Wit and Ossetts Silver King; they also do belgian bottled beers and farm cider. The pub is interestingly divided into four areas; in the older part locals gather by a coal-effect gas fire in a snug little beamed room, and a standing area with unusually large flagstones has a woodburning stove in an inglenook fireplace. Rustic tables are dotted around the light and airy main lounge to the left, and there's a pool table in the separate games room; fruit machine and piped classical music. The atmosphere is pubby, and families feel particularly welcome here. Reasonably priced tasty bar food includes filled baguettes (from £4), ploughman's (from £5.50), ham, eggs and chips or battered fish of the day (£7), sausage and mash (£7.50), with specials such as home-made asparagus quiche (£6.50), and gammon hock with parsley sauce or fried lamb chump chop with tomato, mushroom and tarragon sauce (£9); children's meals (£5); also occasional food theme evenings. *(Recommended by Fr Robert Marsh, C and R Bromage, Mike and Heather Watson, Tracey and Stephen Groves, Louise English)*

Punch ~ Lease Ken Proctor ~ Real ale ~ Bar food (12-1.45(2.15 Sat, Sun), 6.30-9; not Sun, Mon evenings) ~ Restaurant ~ (01306) 631200 ~ Children welcome ~ Dogs allowed in bar ~ Open 11.30-2.30, 5.30-11; 11.30-3, 6-11 Sat; 12-3, 7-10.30 Sun

OCKLEY TQ1439 Map 3
Kings Arms ♀ 🛏
Stane Street (A29)

This 17th-c country dining inn near the spacious village green and cricket pitch was sold as we were going to press, but we understand that the new owner is planning to keep things much as they were, and is keen for people to feel at ease just coming in for a drink. The heavily black-beamed and timbered bar, cosy and very softly lit, has three more or less distinct areas with turkey carpet throughout, button-back wall banquettes and cushioned captain's chairs, antique prints of racehorses, country scenes and so forth massed two or three deep on the wall, some nice examples of antique wood carving, and plenty of other highly polished bric-a-brac, for instance among the rather Victorian houseplants in the heavy-draped windows. They're hoping to broaden the range of food (still prepared by the same chef who was here under the former owner) which typically includes sandwiches (from £2.95), soup (£3.95), ploughman's or scampi and chips (£6.95), crab and prawn salad (£8.95), pies or roast mediterranean vegetable quiche (£9.95), steamed salmon with a dill and cucumber sauce (£10.95), 16oz gammon steak (£11.95), shoulder of lamb roasted with honey and mustard (£13.95) and scallops wrapped in bacon (£14.95). They have champagne by the glass among a good choice of other wines, and well kept Bass, Flowers IPA, Greene King Old Speckled Hen and Marstons Pedigree on handpump (no smoking at bar counter); polite service with a pleasantly individual touch by neatly uniformed staff; a good inglenook log fire; no piped music or fruit machines. The small no smoking restaurant (on the right as you come in from the car park) has crisp white table linen; its game soup is a hot tip. A back terrace has teak tables and chairs, with a few picnic-sets among neatly clipped shrubs on immaculate grass beyond. The garden has won local awards, and the owner is hoping to create a new garden room. More reports on the new regime please. *(Recommended by Richard Fedrick, Keith and Jenny Grant, John Ecklin, John Evans, Peter Lewis, C and R Bromage)*

Free house ~ Licensee Martin Clements ~ Real ale ~ Bar food (12-2(2.30 Sat, Sun), 7-9 (10 Fri)) ~ Restaurant ~ (01306) 711224 ~ Open 11-2.30(3 Sat), 6-11; 12-3, 7-10.30 Sun ~ Bedrooms: £50B/£70B

OTTERSHAW TQ0263 Map 3
Castle ▣

2.6 miles from M25 junction 11; heading S on A320, after A319 roundabout pass church on right, then after another 350 yards or so take sharp left turn into Brox Road

With its two friendly bars, this mid 19th-c local has a nicely unpretentious atmosphere. Under quite an armoury of venerable guns, the servery between the two separate bars has half a dozen well kept changing ales such as Adnams, Brakspears, Fullers London Pride, Greene King Abbot, Harveys Sussex Best and Youngs on handpump, and Addlestone's cider. Good winter log fires, horse tack on the walls, rustic paraphernalia on the black ceiling joists, small pictures and some stripped brickwork (including little stub walls making two or three snugly cushioned side booths) add to the relaxed country feel; the bar on the right opens into a dining area and small side conservatory. A wide range of popular home-made food runs from good value lunchtime sandwiches (from £2.15) and soup (£3.75) to other pubby dishes such as cheese and potato pie (£6.15), ploughman's (£6.75), salads, cottage pie or chicken curry (£7.25), and puddings such as apple strudel (£3.95); Sunday roast (£8.95). In the left-hand bar a low table made from a smith's bellows has a good collection of upmarket magazines; piped music. The sheltered garden has tables with rustic benches in pleasant creeper-hung booths, and picnic-sets on the front terrace are set well back from the fairly quiet road. Most of the pub, including one bar and the conservatory, is no smoking. *(Recommended by Gwyn Jones, R T and J C Moggridge, Fr Robert Marsh, Ian Phillips, JMM)*

Punch ~ Lease John Olorenshaw ~ Real ale ~ Bar food (12-2, 7-9.30; 12-4 Sun; not Sun evening) ~ (01932) 872373 ~ Children in conservatory ~ Dogs allowed in bar ~ Open 11-2.30, 5.30-11; 11-11 Sat; 12-10.30 Sun

REIGATE HEATH TQ2349 Map 3
Skimmington Castle

3 miles from M25 junction 8: through Reigate take A25 towards Dorking, then on edge of Reigate turn left past Black Horse into Flanchford Road; after ¼ mile turn left into Bonny's Road (unmade, very bumpy track); after crossing golf course fork right up hill

This remote country pub is on the Greensand Way and has lovely views from the crazy-paved front terrace and tables on the grass by lilac bushes; more tables at the back overlook the meadows and the hillocks (though you may find the views blocked by trees in summer). The bright main front bar leads off a small room with a central serving counter, with dark simple panelling and lots and lots of keys hanging from the beams. There's a miscellany of chairs and tables, shiny brown plank panelling, a brown plank ceiling, well kept Adnams, Harveys Sussex Best, Youngs Special and a couple of guest ales such as a Harveys seasonal brew and Theakstons on handpump, with 15 wines by the glass, Addlestone's farm cider, mulled wine in winter and even some organic spirits. The cosy back rooms are partly panelled too, with old-fashioned settles and windsor chairs; one has a big brick fireplace with its bread-oven still beside it – the chimney is said to have been used as a highwayman's look-out. Steps take you down to just three tables in a small but pleasant no smoking room at the back; shove-ha'penny, cribbage, dominoes, ring-the-bull, board games and piped music. The bar food is good and popular, so you need to get here early for a table as they don't take bookings. Swiftly served dishes could include soup (£3.25), sandwiches (from £3.40), ploughman's (from £4.95), home-made fish pie (£6.95), steak and kidney pie (£7.50), breaded haddock (£7.50), herb crusted salmon (£7.95), crayfish and cured salmon salad (£8.95), leg of lamb steak with spicy dressing (£9.95) and duck breast with sour cranberry sauce (£11.25), with irresistible puddings (£3.75). There's a hitching rail outside for horses. No children. *(Recommended by Gordon Stevenson, PL, James Price, Ian Phillips, Colin McKerrow, Conor McGaughey, C and R Bromage, Brian and Karen Thomas, DWAJ, Fr Robert Marsh, John and Elizabeth Cox)*

Punch ~ Tenants Anthony Pugh and John Davidson ~ Real ale ~ Bar food (12-2.15(2.30 Sun), 7-9.30(9 Sun)) ~ (01737) 243100 ~ Dogs welcome ~ Folk jam session second Sun in month ~ Open 11-3, 5.30(6 Sat)-11; 12-10.30 Sun; closed 1 Jan evening, 25 Dec, 26 Dec evening

WEST END SU9461 Map 2
Inn at West End 🍽 ♀
Just under 2½ miles from M3 junction 3; A322 S, on right

Wine is a strong feature of this friendly and efficiently run dining pub: the landlord is a wine merchant and holds periodic wine tastings; good house wines include a dozen by the glass, several sherries and 18 dessert wines, and they can supply by the case. They also hold gastronomic evenings. A strong emphasis is placed on the good (though not cheap), locally sourced food, which could include soup (£4.75), sandwiches (from £5), black pudding with caramelised apples on toasted brioche (£6.75), lightly curried smoked haddock kedgeree with poached egg (£7.75, or £11.75 as a main course), pasta carbonara (£8.75), cumberland sausage and mash (£12.50), plus specials such as game and hock terrine (£5.75), tomato and goats cheese tartlet (£12.50), pheasant casserole (£13.50) and roasted turbot with walnut and parsley crust (£17.95); desserts such as caramelised lemon tart with blackcurrant sorbet or chocolate mousse (£4.75); no smoking dining room and conservatory. Appealingly up-to-date, the pub is open-plan, with bare boards, attractive modern prints on canary yellow walls above a red dado, and a line of dining tables with crisp white linen over pale yellow tablecloths on the left. The bar counter, straight ahead as you come in, is quite a focus, with chatting regulars on the comfortable bar stools, well kept Courage Best and Fullers London Pride on handpump; seasonal drinks such as Pimms, bucks fizz and kir royale, and good coffee. The area on the right has a pleasant relaxed atmosphere, with blue-cushioned wall benches and dining chairs around solid pale wood tables, broadsheet daily papers, magazines and a row of reference books on the brick chimneybreast above a woodburning stove. This opens into a terracotta-tiled garden room, with a blue overhead awning, which in turn leads to a pergola-covered (with grapevine and clematis) terrace; on sunny bank holidays they have boules days here. *(Recommended by Mayur Shah, Alan Sadler, Edward Mirzoeff, Ian Phillips, Guy Consterdine, Shirley Mackenzie, KC, B and M Kendall, Ann Gray)*

Free house ~ Licensees Gerry and Ann Price, Lee Watts and Vicky Wolfe ~ Real ale ~ Bar food (12-2.30, 6-9.30; 12-3, 6-9 Sun) ~ Restaurant ~ (01276) 858652 ~ Well behaved children over 5 welcome in restaurant if dining ~ Dogs allowed in bar ~ Open 12-3, 5-11; 12-11 Sat; 12-10.30 Sun

WORPLESDON SU9854 Map 3

Jolly Farmer 🍺

Burdenshott Road, off A320 Guildford—Woking, not in village – heading N from Guildford on the A320, turn left at Jacobs Well roundabout towards Worplesdon Station; OS Sheet 186 map reference 987542

You can stroll straight into woodland from this smart, attractively placed dining pub, and in summer they have occasional barbecues in the large, sheltered back garden, which has grape vines and fruit trees, and picnic-sets under cocktail parasols. Despite the accent on food, there is still a proper bar, with comfortable modern furnishings and a fresh décor integrated well with the beams and woodwork. You can eat here, or in a dining extension with stripped brickwork and well spaced tables. The menu ranges from soup (£3.50), welsh rarebit (£4.25) and large open sandwiches (from £5, though they'll happily make more standard-size normal ones on request) to home-made beefburger (£7.95), roasted vegetable mille-feuille (£9.25), home-made fisherman's pie (£10.50), regular fresh fish specials (£11-£15) and 10oz rib-eye steak (£14.75), with puddings like fruit crumble (£4.95); on Sunday they have a shorter menu with roasts (£10.95-£12.95). Well kept Fullers Discovery and London Pride on handpump, plus one or two guests such as a Fullers seasonal brew and Hogs Back TEA, and a large wine list with 15 by the glass. The car park is shared with Whitmore Common. *(Recommended by James Price, C J Roebuck, Martin and Alison Stainsby, KC)*

Fullers ~ Managers Monica and John Howard ~ Real ale ~ Bar food (12-3, 6-9.30; 12-9.30 Fri, Sat;12-8 Sun) ~ Restaurant ~ (01483) 234658 ~ Children welcome in eating area of bar and restaurant until 9pm ~ Dogs allowed in bar ~ Open 12-11(10.30 Sun)

LUCKY DIP

Besides the fully inspected pubs, you might like to try these Lucky Dips recommended to us and described by readers (if you do, please send us reports: www.goodguides.co.uk).

ABINGER COMMON [TQ1146]
☆ *Abinger Hatch* [off A25 W of Dorking, towards Abinger Hammer]: Beautifully placed pub, very busy in summer, with heavy beams and flagstones, log fires, pews forming booths around oak tables in carpeted side area, popular changing food (not Sun evening) from generous sandwiches and baked potatoes up, Ringwood and other ales, young friendly staff; dogs welcome, piped music, children allowed only in plain extension; nr pretty church and pond in clearing of rolling woods, tables and friendly ducks in nice garden, summer barbecues, open all day *(M and GR, P and J Shapley, Philip and Ann Board, Mrs Sylvia Elcoate, LYM, Mike and Lynn Robinson, Barry Steele-Perkins, N R White)*
ADDLESTONE [TQ0464]
Waggon & Horses [Simplemarsh Rd]: Pretty and very welcoming suburban mock-Tudor local kept spotless, with genial bearded landlord and personable landlady, real ales such as Black Sheep, Ushers Best and Wychwood Hobgoblin, rows of cups and trophies; flowers and picnic-sets on small front terrace *(Ian Phillips)*
ALBURY [TQ0547]
☆ *Drummond Arms* [off A248 SE of Guildford;

The Street]: Unpretentiously civilised and traditional, with well kept ales such as Courage Best, Gales HSB, Greene King Old Speckled Hen and Charles Wells Bombardier, attentive helpful staff, attractive dining room, conservatory (children allowed here); piped music; pretty streamside back garden with duck island, tables by willows, fountain, covered terrace and barbecue, bedrooms, attractive village, pleasant walks nearby *(MDN, William Ruxton, LYM, Jason Reynolds, Ian Phillips, Paul A Moore)*
BETCHWORTH [TQ2150]
Red Lion [Old Rd, Buckland]: Light and airy dining pub under new Cypriot ownership, emphasis on wide choice of enjoyable food, steps down to stylish long flagstoned room and no smoking rather Tuscan-seeming candlelit dining room, modern furnishings, well kept Adnams Broadside and guest beers; may be piped music; children welcome, picnic-sets on lawn with play area and cricket ground beyond, dining terrace, bedroom block, open all day *(John Evans, D WAJ, Cathryn and Richard Hicks, Gordon Neighbour, LYM)*
BLETCHINGLEY [TQ3250]
☆ *Prince Albert* [Outwood Lane]: Attractive and friendly beamed local with cosy linked rooms,

panelling and simple furnishings, vintage car pictures, well kept ales such as Itchen Valley Fagins and Pure Gold, Shepherd Neame Bishops Finger and Wadworths 6X, decent house wines, popular food from baguettes to quite a range of fish, smallish restaurant, cribbage, dominoes; may be piped pop music; dogs and children welcome, open all day Sun (also Weds-Sat in summer), tables on terrace and in pretty garden *(Quentin and Carol Williamson, B and M Kendall, Dick and Madeleine Brown, Mrs B M Hill, John Ecklin, Ian Phillips, LYM, Geoffrey Kemp)*

William IV [3 miles from M25 junction 6; Little Common Lane, off A25 on Redhill side of village]: Peaceful old country pub down pretty lane, tile-hung and weatherboarded, three bar rooms and comfortably old-fashioned little back no smoking dining room, wide choice of food from sandwiches and baguettes to enjoyable Sun roasts, well kept ales such as Fullers London Pride, Greene King Old Speckled Hen, Harveys Best and Youngs Special, friendly unforced service, good wines, lots of bric-a-brac; two-level garden with summer barbecues *(LYM, Debbie and Neil Hayter, Michael and Ann Cole)*

BLINDLEY HEATH [TQ3645]

Blue Anchor [Eastbourne Rd]: Large well laid out main road pub with good value food inc home-made specials, friendly mainly young staff; tables in front garden *(Alan M Pring, N R White)*

BYFLEET [TQ0661]

Plough [High Rd]: Medley of furnishings in friendly local with well kept Courage Best, Fullers London Pride and guests such as Greene King IPA, Ringwood Best and Old Thumper, Shepherd Neame Bitter and Porter, Charles Wells Bombardier and Youngs, attractively priced straightforward food from sandwiches up, lots of farm tools, brass and copper, log fire, dominoes; picnic-sets in pleasant back garden *(Ian Phillips)*

CATERHAM [TQ3254]

Harrow [Stanstead Rd, Whitehill]: Doing well under new licensees, good atmosphere and reasonably priced enjoyable food; tables in garden, open country by North Downs Way *(Mike Walters, Alan Sadler)*

CHARLTON [TQ0868]

Harrow [Charlton Rd, Ashford Common; off B376 Laleham—Shepperton]: Thatched 17th-c pub with newish Indian licensees doing some good generous indian dishes (Sat food is all indian), massive helpings, quick pleasant service; garden tables *(Mayur Shah)*

CHERTSEY [TQ0466]

Crown [London St (B375)]: Relaxed traditional Youngs pub with button-back banquettes in spreading high-ceilinged bar, tall and very sonorous longcase clock, well kept ales, fine wines by the glass, nicely presented no-nonsense food from doorstep sandwiches and baked potatoes up, courteous attentive staff; neatly placed darts, discreet fruit machines; children and dogs welcome, garden bar with conservatory, tables in courtyard and

garden with pond; smart 30-bedroom annexe *(Shirley Mackenzie, Ian Phillips)*

Kingfisher [Chertsey Bridge Rd]: Vintage Inn pastiche of traditional pub using old materials, beautifully placed by busy bridge and Thames lock, well kept Bass and Fullers London Pride, good wine choice, reasonably priced food, good log fires, daily papers, warm medley of furnishings in spreading series of small intimate areas, subtle lighting, large-scale map for walkers; soft piped music; familes welcome if eating (otherwise no under-21s), riverside garden by road, open all day *(Ian Phillips)*

CHIDDINGFOLD [SU9635]

☆ *Swan* [A283 S]: Attractive country inn largely rebuilt internally (after 2003 fire) as comfortable dining pub, good choice of enjoyable food in light and airy dining bar and restaurant, several well kept ales, thoughtful wine choice, friendly attentive staff, no smoking area; comfortable attractive bedrooms *(LYM, Mr and Mrs M Pattinson, Michael B Griffith)*

Winterton Arms [Petworth Rd (A283), North Bridge]: Pleasant local atmosphere, enjoyable individually prepared food, friendly attentive staff, choice of well kept ales, no smoking restaurant area; dogs welcome, disabled access, good-sized garden with play area *(Jane and David Runham)*

CHILWORTH [TQ0347]

☆ *Percy Arms* [Dorking Rd]: Smart rather restauranty partly 18th-c pub with welcoming service by lots of helpful young staff, well kept Greene King IPA and Abbot and Wadworths 6X, good choice of wines by the glass, enjoyable fresh food from sandwiches, wraps and baguettes to steaks cut to your chosen weight, popular Sun carvery, roomy, comfortable and well lit main area, smaller public bar, restaurant; no dogs; children welcome, pretty views over vale of Chilworth to St Martha's Hill from big pleasant back conservatory and picnic-sets in extensive tidy garden, good walks *(Carolyn Graham, Philip and Ann Board, Julie Schofield, Ian Phillips)*

CHIPSTEAD [TQ2757]

Well House [Chipstead signed with Mugswell off A217, N of M25 junction 8]: Partly 14th-c, cottagey and comfortable, with lots of atmosphere, good value food (not Sun evening, and may take a time) from hefty sandwiches and baguettes to some interesting blackboard specials, efficient friendly staff, log fires in all three rooms (one bar is no smoking), well kept ales such as Adnams, Everards Tiger, Fullers London Pride, Hogs Back Hair of the Hog and Wadworths 6X; dogs allowed; attractive garden with well reputed to be mentioned in Domesday Book (loudspeaker food announcements though); delightful setting *(Ian Phillips, LYM, John Branston)*

CHOBHAM [SU9761]

Sun [4 miles from M3 junc 3]: Pleasant low-beamed timbered pub with Courage Directors, Fullers London Pride and Hogs Back TEA, indian-based food, friendly staff, lots of daily papers, two log fires, shining brasses *(LYM, Ian Phillips)*

COBHAM [TQ1059]

☆ *Plough* [Plough Lane, towards Downside]: Cheerful black-shuttered upmarket local with comfortable low-beamed lounge bar partly divided by L-shaped settles, huge log fire separating it from very popular restaurant area with pleasant French staff, quickly served enjoyable food from lunchtime sandwiches through good value two-course lunches to more expensive evening meals, real ales such as Hogs Back TEA and Charles Wells Bombardier, decent house wines, pine-panelled snug with darts, very smart new lavatories; tables outside *(John Ecklin, LYM, Sue and Mike Todd, Geoffrey Kemp)*
Running Mare [Tilt Rd]: Attractive old pub overlooking green, popular for its good food – very busy Sun lunchtime *(Sue Brown)*

CRANLEIGH [TQ0739]

Little Park Hatch [Bookhurst Rd, Parkmead estate – towards Shere]: Low beams, flagstones, huge inglenook with log fire, warm local atmosphere, wide food choice from snacks and sandwiches to main meals cooked largely by landlady, reasonable prices, friendly landlord, well kept real ales, small dining area; dogs welcome; big garden with adventure play area *(Shirley Mackenzie)*
Three Horseshoes [High St]: Friendly village local, well kept Greene King ales, lunchtime snacks; dogs welcome, good sheltered garden safe for children, open all day *(Mike and Lynn Robinson)*

DORKING [TQ1649]

☆ *Kings Arms* [West St]: Olde-worlde rambling 16th-c pub in antiques area, masses of timbers and low beams, nice lived-in old furniture in part-panelled lounge, warm relaxed atmosphere, well kept mainstream and interesting guest ales, friendly efficient service, good choice of economical home-made food from sandwiches up, attractive old-fashioned back dining area; piped music; open all day *(Conor McGaughey, Mike and Heather Watson, Andy Trafford, Louise Bayly)*

EAST CLANDON [TQ0651]

☆ *Queens Head* [just off A246 Guildford—Leatherhead; The Street]: Rambling dining pub popular with older people for home-made blackboard food from baguettes and baked potatoes to some good specials, relaxed atmosphere in small, comfortable and spotless connecting rooms, big inglenook log-effect fire, fine old elm bar counter, well kept ales such as Badger K&B, Hogs Back TEA and Youngs, quick attentive service; they may try to keep your credit card as you eat, no dogs, boots or overalls; children welcome, picnic-sets on pretty front terrace and in quiet side garden, handy for two NT properties, cl Mon *(John Evans, LYM, Ian Phillips, DWAJ, C and R Bromage, Sue and Mike Todd, Andy and Yvonne Cunningham, Philip and June Caunt, C J Roebuck, Jenny and Brian Seller)*

EFFINGHAM [TQ1153]

☆ *Plough* [Orestan Lane]: Friendly and well run Youngs pub with consistently well kept ales from traditional bar with handbag hooks, good value food inc enjoyable Sun lunch, good wine choice in two glass sizes, helpful staff, two coal-effect gas fires, beamery, panelling, old plates and brassware in long lounge, no smoking extension; attractive garden with play area, handy for Polesden Lacey (NT) *(Sue and Mike Todd, Gordon Stevenson, John Evans, Martin and Karen Wake, Stephen Funnell)*

ELLENS GREEN [TQ0936]

Wheatsheaf [B2128 N of Rudgwick]: New licensees doing enjoyable fairly priced fresh food, good service, no piped music *(Shirley Mackenzie, Mike and Heather Watson)*

ELSTEAD [SU9044]

☆ *Mill* [Farnham Rd (B3001)]: Majestic 17th/18th-c converted watermill with sprawling series of rambling linked rooms appealingly refurbished by Fullers in a range of their period house styles, from scrubbed pine farmhouse tables and chairs through high Victorian to modern, log fires, one in a huge inglenook, good lighting, waterwheel still in place (not used), well kept Fullers ales inc seasonal specials, wide choice of good value food, friendly service, no smoking dining room; large attractive well floodlit grounds by River Wey *(Tracey and Stephen Groves, D Marsh, Susan and John Douglas)*
Woolpack [B3001 Milford—Farnham]: Wide range of enjoyable if pricey food, well kept ales such as Fullers London Pride, Greene King Abbot and Youngs, high-backed settles in long airy main bar, open fires each end, second big room, country décor; children allowed, garden with picnic-sets, open all day wknds *(LYM, Ian Phillips, Gordon Stevenson, Ann Gray, Michael Sargent)*

ENGLEFIELD GREEN [SU9971]

Barley Mow [Northcroft Rd]: Pretty pub with good value food from good reasonably priced sandwiches up, well kept Courage Best and Directors, Fullers London Pride, Greene King Old Speckled Hen and Marstons Pedigree, friendly service and local regulars, usual refurbished interior, back dining area with no smoking section, darts; quiet piped music; pleasant back garden with play area, café tables out in front overlooking cricket green (summer steam fairs) *(KN-R, Martin Terry)*
Sun [Wick Lane, Bishopsgate]: Unassuming welcoming local, well kept Courage Best, Fullers London Pride, Greene King Abbot and Hogs Back TEA, good blackboard wine choice, long-serving landlord and efficient young staff, enjoyable food from good sandwiches and baguettes to Sun lunch, reasonable prices, daily papers, lovely log fire in back conservatory, biscuit and water for dogs, interesting beer bottle collection; quiet garden with aviary, handy for Savill Garden and Windsor Park *(Ian Phillips)*

EPSOM [TQ2158]

☆ *Derby Arms* [Downs Rd, Epsom Downs]: Comfortable dining pub very popular lunchtimes with older people for wide choice of reasonably priced food from good sandwich range up, decent wines, well kept Fullers London Pride and Shepherd Neame Spitfire, log fires, no smoking area; open all day Sun, nice tables outside, good views – opp racecourse grandstand (yet surprisingly little racing memorabilia) *(R T and J C Moggridge, Mrs G R Sharman, Gordon Neighbour, MRSM)*

ESHER [TQ1464]

Prince of Wales [West End Lane; off A244 towards Hersham, by Princess Alice Hospice]: Victorian pub tudorised as Chef & Brewer dining pub popular for wide choice of reasonably priced food, cosy candlelit corners, open fires, turkey carpets, old furniture, prints and photographs, well kept ales such as Courage Best, Fullers London Pride and Greene King Old Speckled Hen, good wine choice, daily papers; big shady garden, lovely village setting nr green and pond *(Derek and Heather Manning, Geoffrey Kemp)*

FARNHAM [SU8446]

Shepherd & Flock [Moor Park Lane, on A31/A324/A325 roundabout]: Flower-decked pub with good atmosphere, half a dozen or more well kept ales such as Gales Trafalgar, Hogs Back TEA, Itchen Valley Fagins and Wat Tyler, Ringwood Old Thumper, Sharps Doom Bar and Special and Weltons Rucked Off, enjoyable simple pub lunches, service good even when busy, modernised with rather austere décor; pleasant enclosed back garden with picnic-sets under cocktail parasols and barbecue, nicely tucked away from the traffic, open all day wknds *(Dr Martin Owton, Richard Houghton, Ian Phillips)*

FICKLESHOLE [TQ3960]

☆ *White Bear* [Featherbed Lane/Fairchildes Lane; off A2022 Purley Rd just S of A212 roundabout]: Rambling interestingly furnished partly 15th-c family country pub, popular with families even at midweek lunchtimes for good value food from fat fresh sandwiches up inc some interesting dishes, lots of small rooms, beams and flagstones, friendly landlady and young staff, well kept Everards Tiger, Fullers London Pride and Charles Wells Bombardier (they may offer samples), good coffee, restaurant; fruit machine, video game, piped music; children welcome, play area in pleasant sizeable garden, lots of picnic-sets under square white parasols on front terrace, open all day Sat *(LYM, Jenny and Brian Seller, LM)*

FRIDAY STREET [TQ1245]

Stephan Langton [signed off B2126, or from A25 Westcott—Guildford]: Simple walkers' pub with good fresh food (not Mon) inc home-baked bread and panini in bar and evening restaurant (not Sun/Mon), sensible prices but may be a long wait, good wines by the glass, well kept Adnams, comfortable bar, parlour-like lounge, traditional games; plenty of tables in front courtyard, more on back tree-surrounded stream-side terrace, peaceful spot surrounded by good walks, has been open all day summer *(James Price, LYM,*

Carolyn Graham, John Evans, Clive and Janice Sillitoe)

FRIMLEY GREEN [SU8856]

Old Wheatsheaf [Frimley Green Rd (B3411, was A321)]: Welcoming proper pub, wheelback chairs, banquettes and country prints in opened-up bar, Greene King ales, lots of sensibly priced sandwiches as well as baguettes, ploughman's and a few substantial bargain daily specials, quick service, evening restaurant; terrace tables *(KC, Mrs S M Prince)*

GRAYSWOOD [SU9134]

Wheatsheaf [Grayswood Rd (A286 NE of Haslemere)]: Civilised much modernised pub, light and airy, with enjoyable food in bar and restaurant (they bake their own bread), good range of well kept ales such as Ringwood and Timothy Taylors Landlord, friendly helpful service; conference/bedroom extension *(Ruth Nixon, Wendy Arnold)*

GREAT BOOKHAM [TQ1354]

Royal Oak [High St]: Comfortable heavy-beamed and flagstoned two-bar village local, reasonably priced food all day, changing ales such as Timothy Taylors Landlord and Wadworths 6X, service friendly and good-humoured even when busy, flame-effect fire in huge fireplace; public bar can get quite smoky evenings; some live music *(Andrew York)*

GUILDFORD [SU9949]

Kings Head [Quarry St]: Spotless pub with lots of beams and stripped brickwork, inglenook fire, cosy corners with armchairs, well kept Courage Best and Directors and Wychwood Hobgoblin, decent wines, reasonably priced standard food from baguettes and ploughman's up, polite service; no dogs, big-screen sports TV; picnic-sets in back courtyard with raised area giving castle views *(Ian Phillips, Wendy Arnold)*

☆ *Olde Ship* [Portsmouth Rd (A3100 S)]: Three cosy areas around central bar, ancient beams, flagstones, good log fire in big fireplace, candles and comfortable mix of furniture, no smoking zone (no mobile phones either), part with tables and chairs, good range of interesting but unpretentious and fairly priced bistro-style food inc good wood-fired pizzas, well kept ales inc Greene King, decent wines, quick, friendly and helpful; no music *(Tom and Ruth Rees, Michael Sargent, Mrs Rosemary Ingram)*

Weyside [Shalford Rd, Millbrook; across car park from Yvonne Arnaud Theatre, beyond boat yard]: Big popular two-level riverside pub, smart and contemporary with pale colours and tables (even the many riverside picnic-sets) painted a neat greyish off-white, lots of different areas from comfortable settees to conservatory dining area; enjoyable up-to-date food throughout, very good choice of wines by the glass, Fullers London Pride and Greene King Old Speckled Hen, polite service; big garden with moorings and terrace by River Wey, good walks, open all day *(Ian Phillips)*

HAMBLEDON [SU9639]

Merry Harriers [off A283; just N of village]: Good-natured old-fashioned country local popular with walkers, huge inglenook log fire, dark wood with cream and terracotta paintwork, pine tables, impressive collection of chamber-pots hanging from beams, well kept Greene King IPA and Abbot, Hogs Back TEA and Hop Back Crop Circle, farm cider, decent wines and coffee, daily papers and classic motorcycle magazines, reasonably priced fresh simple food from sandwiches up; pool room, folk night 1st Sun of month; big back garden in attractive walking countryside near Greensand Way, picnic-sets in front and over road – caravan parking *(Phil and Sally Gorton, N R White)*

HASCOMBE [TQ0039]

☆ *White Horse* [B2130 S of Godalming]: Picturesque old rose-draped pub, not cheap but good value, with attractively simple beamed public bar, traditional games and quiet small-windowed alcoves, more restaurant dining bar (children allowed), good bar food from sandwiches and baguettes up, well kept Adnams and Harveys, good wine list, log fires or woodburners; small front terrace, spacious sloping back lawn, pretty village on the Greensand Way and handy for Winkworth Arboretum, open all day wknds *(Jenny and Brian Seller, LYM, Gordon Stevenson, John Hale, C J Roebuck)*

HEADLEY [TQ2054]

Cock [Church Lane]: Much-modernised Tudor pub back to its proper name under new licensees after a decade as the Cock Horse, refurbished with several light and airy dining areas, attentive efficient staff, well kept ales, enjoyable food from good choice of baguettes and salads up; tables outside – attractive setting, good walks *(Mike and Heather Watson, C and R Bromage)*

HERSHAM [TQ1164]

Bricklayers Arms [Queens Rd]: Friendly and well kept, back servery doing wide choice of good value home-made food from sandwiches and snacks up, good choice of ales such as Flower IPA and Hogs Back TEA, decent wines, separate public bar with two pool tables; parking down by green in Faulkners Rd; small secluded garden, comfortable bedrooms *(C J Roebuck)*

HINDHEAD [SU8736]

Woodcock [Churt Rd (A287)]: Welcoming licensees, good value food inc good Sun carvery with fresh veg, Gales HSB; handy for Frensham Ponds *(Klaus and Elizabeth Leist)*

HOLMBURY ST MARY [TQ1144]

Royal Oak: Well run and relaxing low-beamed 17th-c coaching inn in pleasant spot by green and church, reliable generous food from sandwiches and baked potatoes up, good choice of well kept ales such as Greene King IPA, decent wines by the glass, quick friendly service, log fire; tables on front lawn, bedrooms, good walks *(R Lake, Martin Terry)*

HORSELL [SU9859]

Cricketers [Horsell Birch]: Friendly local with long neatly kept bar, quietly comfortable end sections, extended back eating area, carpet and shiny boards, good straightforward food (all

day Sun and bank hols), Adnams, Courage Best and Fullers London Pride, cheerful service, children well catered for; big well kept garden, and seats out in front overlooking village green *(Ian Phillips)*

Crown [Church Hill/High St]: Thriving atmosphere in pleasant pub with Badger Fursty Ferret, Fullers London Pride, Sharps Doom Bar and Charles Wells Bombardier *(Ian Phillips)*

Red Lion [High St]: Welcoming comfortably renovated pub with good food, well kept Courage Best, Fullers London Pride and Greene King IPA, decent wines, friendly staff, picture-filled converted barn where children allowed; ivy-clad passage to garden with picnic-sets under cocktail parasols and pleasant terrace, good walks nearby *(Ian Phillips)*

HORSELL COMMON [TQ0160]

Bleak House [Chertsey Rd, The Anthonys; A320 Woking—Ottershaw]: Newly reworked as upscale gastropub (no doubt suiting the new nearby McLarens motor-racing HQ), with grey split sandstone for floor and face of bar counter, tasteful mushroom and white décor with black tables, sofas and stools, attractively presented food from baguettes to aberdeen angus steak, Hogs Back TEA and Hop Garden Gold and Charles Wells Bombardier, lots of smart uniformed staff; pleasant back garden merging into woods with good shortish walks to sandpits which inspired H G Wells's *War of the Worlds (Ian Phillips)*

HURTMORE [SU9445]

Squirrels [just off A3 nr Godalming, via Priorsfield Rd]: Comfortable, fresh and airy bar with real ale, decent wines, some emphasis on the food side, friendly service, cosy corners, bar billiards, partly no smoking restaurant and conservatory; disabled facilities, sizeable pleasant garden with heated terrace and play area, comfortable well equipped bedrooms, good breakfast, open all day *(BB, Andrew and Diane Hall)*

LEATHERHEAD [TQ1656]

Running Horse [Bridge St]: Small pleasant local under new landlady, half a dozen real ales such as Fullers London Pride, Greene King IPA and Old Speckled Hen, Timothy Taylors Landlord and Youngs Special, good value straightforward food, no smoking eating area; close to River Mole *(Andy Trafford, Louise Bayly)*

LEIGH [TQ2147]

☆ *Seven Stars* [Dawes Green, S of A25 Dorking—Reigate]: Pretty country pub with airy and spacious flagstoned bar, good generous food inc enterprising dishes and Tues tapas night, good friendly service, Youngs ales, leather sofa and tub chairs by inglenook woodburner, pine tables and chairs; picnic-sets on front lawn and heated side terrace *(LYM, Glenn and Pauline Larder)*

LONG DITTON [TQ1666]

City Arms [Portsmouth Rd (A307)]: Under new management and completely refurbished, with comfortable furnishings, enjoyable standard food from baguettes and baked potatoes up, OAP discounts, a well kept real ale, helpful friendly family service *(Ted and Lyn Clarkson)*

MARTYRS GREEN [TQ0857]

Black Swan [handy for M25 junction 10; off A3 S-bound, but return N of junction]: Cheerful place, much enlarged, with a dozen or more well kept ales inc bargains, simple furnishings, well used back bar, usual food (queue to order) all day from breakfast on, friendly staff, log fires, restaurant; SkyTV, can get crowded with young people evenings, piped pop music may be loud then, biker night Weds, frequent discos and theme nights; plenty of tables in big woodside garden with barbecues and good play area – bouncy castle, playground-quality frames, roundabouts etc; dogs welcome, handy for RHS Wisley Garden, open all day *(Steve Felstead, Jason Reynolds)*

MILFORD [SU9542]

Red Lion [Portsmouth Rd (A3100 N)]: Welcoming newish licensees, wide choice of decent pub food, Courage Best and Directors *(June and Ken Brooks)*

MOGADOR [TQ2453]

Sportsman [from M25 up A217 past 2nd roundabout, then Mogador signed; edge of Banstead Heath]: Interesting, relaxed and welcoming low-ceilinged pub with new chef doing enterprising food from foreign cheeses to wild boar and exotic imaginatively prepared fish, well kept Shepherd Neame Spitfire and Youngs, friendly service, fresh flowers in dining room; dogs welcome if not wet or muddy, tables out on common, on back lawn, and some under cover (some M25 noise out here), on Walton Heath – a magnet for walkers and riders *(Conor McGaughey, C and R Bromage, N R White)*

NEWCHAPEL [TQ3642]

Blacksmiths Head [Newchapel Rd]: Well kept Fullers London Pride, Harveys Best and two guest beers, enjoyable food in bar and restaurant from interesting tapas up, welcoming licensees, friendly atmosphere, no music or machines; five good value bedrooms with own bathrooms *(anon)*

Wiremill [Wire Mill Lane; off A22 just S of B2028 by Mormon Temple]: Spacious big-windowed two-storey pub in lakeside mill thought to have been built with 16th-c ship's timbers, well kept Greene King ales, pleasant staff, up-to-date home-made food from baguettes and omelettes up; lots of tables out on terrace, lovely setting, bedrooms *(Michael and Ann Cole)*

NEWDIGATE [TQ1942]

Six Bells: Good atmosphere in popular refurbished local with good range of well kept ales, good value food, well kept Bass and Kings, friendly service and cheery landlord; children really welcome, plenty of tables in pleasant garden, lovely outlook over wooden-towered church *(Marc Hadley, Mark Killman)*

NUTFIELD [TQ3050]

☆ *Queens Head* [A25 E of Redhill]: Congenial atmosphere in tiled bar and carpeted restaurant, enjoyable nicely presented food, good helpful service, good wine list *(C S Turner, Mrs C Hewitt)*

OCKHAM [TQ0756]

☆ *Hautboy* [Ockham Lane – towards Cobham]: Remarkable red stone gothic folly, crypt bar with four well kept ales such as Adnams, Fullers London Pride and Greene King Old Speckled Hen, friendly helpful young staff, emphasis on upstairs brasserie bar like a 19th-c arts & crafts chapel, darkly panelled and high-vaulted, with oil paintings and minstrel's gallery, imaginative choice of enjoyable food from sandwiches, baguettes and baked potatoes up inc bargain two-course lunch, entertaining parrot; children welcome, tables on cricket-view terrace and in secluded orchard garden with play area, bedrooms; currently the best lunch place within easy reach of RHS Wisley *(LYM, MDN, O K Smyth, Stephen Funnell, Howard and Lorna Lambert, P and J Shapley)*

OCKLEY [TQ1439]

☆ *Old School House* [Stane St]: Very popular dining place, thriving atmosphere in pubby eating area around small bar counter with well kept Gales BB and Butser, good wines by the glass inc champagne, good generous food in nice variety from sandwiches up with some emphasis on fish (it's also signed as Bryce's Fish Restaurant), good value two-course lunch, prompt attentive young staff, wonderful log fire, smarter carpeted restaurant area; picnic-sets under cocktail parasols on sunny terrace with flowers around car park *(Bob and Maggie Atherton, C and R Bromage, Jeremy Woods, Gordon Stevenson, Tom and Ruth Rees, Terry Buckland, BB, Mrs J A Sales, Mike and Heather Watson)*

PIRBRIGHT [SU9454]

☆ *Royal Oak* [Aldershot Rd; A324S of village]: Relaxed and cottagey old Tudor pub now all no smoking, heavily beamed and timbered rambling side alcoves, several stripped brickwork, three real fires, well kept ales such as Black Sheep, Greene King IPA, Abbot and Old Speckled Hen, Hogs Back TEA and Hook Norton Old Hooky, good range of wines by the glass, no smoking dining area (food can take a while) and family room; disabled facilities, extensive colourful fairy-lit gardens, good walks, open all day *(James Price, KC, Ian Phillips, LYM, R T and J C Moggridge, Gill and Keith Croxton)*

PUTTENHAM [SU9347]

☆ *Good Intent* [signed off B3000 just S of A31 junction; The Street/Seale Lane]: Hands-on landlord and friendly efficient staff in beamed village local with good range of reasonably priced generous fresh food (not Sun/Mon evenings) from sandwiches and baked potatoes up, well kept ales such as Hogs Back TEA, Ringwood Best and Youngs Special, farm cider, decent wine choice, handsome log fire, pool, old photographs of the pub; dogs welcome, no children, picnic-sets in small sunny garden, good walks, open all day wknds *(Michael Sargent, BB, Sally, Andy and Oscar de la Fontaine, Dennis Jenkin, Phil and Sally Gorton, Ian Phillips)*

PYRFORD LOCK [TQ0559]

Anchor [3 miles from M25 junction 10 – S on A3, then take Wisley slip rd and go on past RHS garden]: Busy modern pub included for its position by bridge and locks on River Wey Navigation; low-priced food (popular lunchtime with families and older people), Courage Directors, Fullers London Pride and Greene King Abbot, canteenish conservatory, picture-window bar, upstairs room with narrow-boat memorabilia, big terrace; Tannoy food number announcements, juke box, sports TV, machines etc; open all day in summer *(DWAJ, LYM)*

RIPLEY [TQ0556]

☆ *Anchor* [High St]: 16th-c former almshouse, three interesting cool dark low-beamed connecting rooms and separate restaurant, wide choice of enjoyable promptly served mainly thai food, well kept ales such as Bass, Courage Best and Fullers London Pride, smart coffee, nautical memorabilia and photographs of Ripley's cycling heyday, coal-effect stove; public bar with games and two big loud music video screens; disabled facilities, tables in coachyard *(Ian Phillips, BB, C and R Bromage, KC)*

Jovial Sailor [Portsmouth Rd]: 19th-c pub much extended as large Chef & Brewer divided by standing timbers, popular almost across the board (the sort of place where you might find a group of young mothers, happily breast-feeding), well kept Hogs Back TEA and Hop Garden Gold and Youngs, good wine choice, their usual food all day, log fire; piped music; garden tables *(Ian Phillips, Julie Schofield)*

Seven Stars [Newark Lane (B367)]: Neatly kept 1930s pub popular lunchtimes for good value generous food from sandwiches and baked potatoes to plenty of seafood, lots of blackboards, good Sun lunches, well kept Fullers London Pride, Greene King Abbot and Old Speckled Hen, Marstons Pedigree, Shepherd Neame Spitfire and Wadworths 6X, decent wines, friendly efficient service, no smoking area; piped music; picnic-sets in large tidy garden behind *(Jason Reynolds, Sue and Mike Todd, Ian Phillips)*

Talbot [High St]: Substantial beamed coaching inn with good big log fireplaces in both roomy and traditional front bars, welcoming helpful staff, enjoyable if not cheap food from generous baguettes up, Greene King IPA, Hogs Back TEA and Shepherd Neame Spitfire, decent wine, daily papers, nice atmosphere, minimalist back brasserie; may be piped music; bedrooms, tables in back courtyard, antiques centre in outbuildings *(Ian Phillips)*

SEND [TQ0156]

New Inn [Cartbridge]: Nice spot by Wey Navigation canal, long bar with lots of appropriate old photographs, reasonably priced popular food in sizeable helpings from toasted sandwiches up, well kept Adnams Broadside, Fullers London Pride and guest beers such as Pilgrim Crusader and Shepherd Neame Spitfire, efficient cheerful service; piped music, smoking throughout; picnic-sets in front by road and in

garden by canal path (Tannoy food announcements out here) *(Ian Phillips, KC)*

SENDMARSH [TQ0455]

Saddlers Arms [Send Marsh Rd]: Friendly low-beamed local with creeper-covered porch, well kept Fullers London Pride, Shepherd Neame Spitfire and Youngs, enjoyable home-made unpretentious food, open fire, no smoking area, toby jugs, brassware etc; well behaved dogs welcome, picnic-sets out front and back *(Ian Phillips, Shirley Mackenzie)*

SHALFORD [SU9946]

Parrot [Broadford]: Big neatly kept canalside pub with nice décor, ample helpings of tasty good value bar food from good sandwiches up, separate pleasant conservatory grill restaurant, well kept Fullers London Pride, Greene King Abbot, Hogs Back TEA and Itchen Valley Fagins, quick friendly staff; attractive garden *(Fr Robert Marsh)*

SHAMLEY GREEN [TQ0343]

☆ *Red Lion* [The Green]: Smartly done-up dining pub with neat décor, dark polished furniture, rows of books, open fires, local cricketing photographs, welcoming service, reliable food all day from good well filled sandwiches with chips to steaks, children's helpings and unusual puddings, well kept Adnams Broadside and Youngs, farm cider, good choice of wines, cafetière coffee, smart restaurant; open all day, children welcome, sturdy tables in nice garden, bedrooms *(LYM, Shirley Mackenzie, Tony and Glenys Dyer, E H and J I Wild)*

SHEPPERTON [TQ0866]

Red Lion [Russell Rd]: Roomy and welcoming old wisteria-covered local across rd from Thames, well kept Brakspears, Courage Best, Fullers London Pride and Greene King Abbot, generous food from baked potatoes up inc very popular good value all-day Sun lunch, quick attentive service, interesting prints in cosy front bar, back bar for sports TV, restaurant; plenty of tables on terrace among fine displays of shrubs and flowers, more on lawn over road (traffic noise) with lovely river views and well run moorings *(Ian Phillips, Mayur Shah)*

SHERE [TQ0747]

☆ *White Horse* [signed off A25 3 miles E of Guildford; Middle St]: Lovely half-timbered pub extensively enlarged as Chef & Brewer, several rooms off small busy bar, uneven floors, massive beams, Tudor stonework, oak wall seats, two log fires, one in a huge inglenook, good choice of reasonably priced food all day from sandwiches and baguettes up (can sometimes take a while), nice staff, well kept beers such as Courage Best and Hogs Back TEA, lots of wines by the glass, good-sized children's area; tables outside, beautiful village, open all day *(LYM, John Ecklin, Norma and Noel Thomas, Andy Trafford, Louise Bayly, Mike and Heather Watson, A and B D Craig)*

SOUTH GODSTONE [TQ3549]

☆ *Fox & Hounds* [Tilburstow Hill Rd/Harts Lane, off A22]: Pleasant country pub with racing prints and woodburner in low-beamed bar, welcoming staff, tasty food from pubby staples to good seafood, nice puddings, well kept Greene King IPA, Abbot and Ruddles County from tiny bar counter, evening restaurant (not Sun/Mon evenings); may be piped music; children in eating area *(Mike and Heather Watson, LYM, Susan and John Douglas)*

STAINES [TQ0371]

Bells [Church St]: Quiet and friendly local, well kept Youngs ales, decent wines, prompt home-made lunchtime food from good sandwiches to popular good value Sun lunch, friendly staff, cosy furnishings, central fireplace, darts; tables in garden with terrace *(Ian Phillips)*

STOKE D'ABERNON [TQ1259]

Old Plough [Station Rd, off A245]: Comfortable local with well kept Courage Best and interesting guest beers such as Titanic, reasonably priced good sensible bar food, big window seats, coal fire, helpful staff, airy conservatory restaurant; sizeable garden, open all day *(BB, Stephen Funnell)*

SUTTON ABINGER [TQ1045]

Volunteer [Water Lane; just off B2126 via Raikes Lane, 1½ miles S of Abinger Hammer]: Picturesque pub in attractive setting above clear stream, three low-ceilinged olde-worlde linked rooms, well kept ales such as Badger Best and Harveys Best, decent wines, roaring fire, homely medley of furnishings, big rugs on bare boards or red tiles, no smoking area, restaurant; nice choice of enjoyable meals (not cheap); children and dogs welcome, good tables out on flowery terrace and suntrap lawns stepped up behind, has been open all day summer wknds, good walks *(LYM, Robin Cordell, Christopher and Elise Way, Brian Dawes)*

SUTTON GREEN [TQ0054]

Olive Tree [Sutton Green Road]: Welcoming modern dining pub with good honest food *(Mrs S M Prince)*

TANDRIDGE [TQ3750]

Barley Mow [Tandridge Lane, off A25 W of Oxted]: Generous well cooked reasonably priced food in several eating areas, friendly efficient staff, bar sensibly kept for drinkers – Badger IPA and other ales; big garden *(J and S French)*

THAMES DITTON [TQ1567]

Albany [Queens Rd, signed off Summer Rd]: Smartly refurbished dining pub in delightful spot by Thames, lots of tables on attractive terrace and lawn with lovely views across to Hampton Court grounds, main focus on waitress-service restaurant with decent fairly conventional food from sandwiches up, quick friendly staff, Adnams, Bass and Fullers London Pride, good choice of wines by the glass, log fire in one funny little corner, daily papers, river pictures, pleasant atmosphere, nice balconies, moorings, open all day *(Gordon Stevenson, Tom and Ruth Rees, Ian Phillips, A Rees, John and Glenys Wheeler, R Lake)*

Angel [Portsmouth Rd/Angel Rd (A307)]: Low-beamed 15th-c pub under new management, log fire, no smoking restaurant;

tables out in front overlooking cricket green, and in courtyard *(anon)*

THE SANDS [SU8846]

☆ *Barley Mow* [Littleworth Rd, Seale; E of Farnham]: Comfortable village pub with polished pine tables and simple chairs, a step or two down to small dining area, well kept Brakspears, Fullers London Pride and Greene King, good fresh food from lunchtime sandwiches up with good choice of unpretentious main dishes, evening food more restauranty with fish emphasis, great puddings; picnic-sets in secluded attractive garden, well placed for walks *(Paul and Brigid Wright)*

THURSLEY [SU9039]

☆ *Three Horseshoes* [Dye House Rd, just off A3 SW of Godalming]: Charming partly 16th-c country pub, closed since 1999 and now reopened after internal reworking, friendly service, well kept Fullers London Pride and Hogs Back TEA in front bar, enjoyable food here and in attractive restaurant area behind with beamery and paintings of local scenes, good range of reasonably priced wines; comfortable seats and tables in good-sized garden *(Martin and Karen Wake)*

WARLINGHAM [TQ3955]

☆ *Botley Hill Farmhouse* [Limpsfield Rd (B269)]: Busy more or less open-plan dining pub, low-ceilinged linked rooms up and down steps, soft lighting, spreading turkey carpet, quite close-set tables, big fireplace with copper and blacked pans above the log fire in one attractive flagstoned room, restaurant with overhead fishing net and seashells, small no smoking area; enjoyable food from lunchtime snacks up, well kept ales such as Greene King and Shepherd Neame Spitfire, good house wines, pleasant service; children welcome away from bar, cream teas, wknd entertainments (may be loud live bands outside), tables in courtyard, neat garden with play area and toddlers' park, ducks and aviary *(Alan M Pring, BB)*

WEST CLANDON [TQ0452]

☆ *Bulls Head* [A247 SE of Woking]: Friendly and comfortably modernised, based on 1540s timbered hall house, very popular esp with older people lunchtime for generous homely food from sandwiches, ploughman's and baked potatoes through hearty home-made proper pies to steak, small lantern-lit beamed front bar with open fire and some stripped brick, contemporary artwork for sale, older local prints and bric-a-brac, steps up to simple raised back inglenook dining area, efficient service, well kept Courage Best, Greene King Old Speckled Hen and Wadworths 6X, good coffee, no piped music, games room with darts and pool; no credit cards; children and dogs on leads welcome, tables and good play area in garden, convenient for Clandon Park, good walking country *(Ian Phillips, R Lake, Sue and Mike Todd, John Ecklin, Susan and John Douglas, Jenny and Brian Seller)*

Onslow Arms [A247 SE of Woking]: Rambling partly 17th-c country pub with dark nooks and corners, heavy beams and flagstones, warm seats by inglenook log fires, lots of brass and copper, good choice of food (not Sun evening) from sandwiches to main dishes, some with a french slant, two-course lunch deals in partly no smoking brasserie, well kept ales such as Courage Directors, Fullers London Pride and Charles Wells Bombardier, decent wines; children welcome (and dogs in bar), great well lit garden, open all day *(Mike and Heather Watson, LYM, John Ecklin, Ian Phillips, R A Rosen)*

WEST HORSLEY [TQ0853]

☆ *Barley Mow* [The Street]: Tree-shaded village pub with beams, flagstones, leather settees on bare boards, big log fire, well kept ales such as Fullers London Pride, Greene King IPA, Shepherd Neame Spitfire and Youngs, decent wines and spirits, inexpensive pubby food (not Sun evening), cheerful landlord and neat friendly staff, vintage and classic car pictures (may be an AC Cobra or Jaguar XK outside too), comfortable high-ceilinged softly lit dining room; dogs and children welcome, picnic-sets in garden, open all day *(Ian Phillips, Tony Hobden, C J Roebuck, Susan and John Douglas)*

King William IV [The Street]: Comfortable early 19th-c pub, refurbished and largely no smoking under its new licensees, with very low-beamed open-plan rambling bar, reasonably priced food from sandwiches up here and in updated conservatory restaurant, good choice of wines by the glass, three well kept ales, good coffee, log fires; children and dogs very welcome (board games and water bowls), good disabled access, small garden and terrace with gorgeous hanging baskets *(Kate Foulger Moorby)*

WESTHUMBLE [TQ1751]

Stepping Stones [just off A24 below Box Hill]: Refurbished and thriving after earlier fire damage, mainly no smoking, with comfortable seating areas and modern dining room, further back area used wknds if busy, good sensibly priced straightforward lunchtime food and more elaborate evening menu, good friendly service, circular bar with real ales such as Fullers London Pride, Greene King Abbot and Old Speckled Hen and Ringwood, open fire, no music; children and walkers welcome, terrace and garden with summer barbecue and play area *(Mike and Heather Watson, DWAJ, Sue and Mike Todd)*

WEYBRIDGE [TQ0764]

☆ *Old Crown* [Thames St]: Friendly and comfortably old-fashioned three-bar pub, very popular lunchtime for good value food from sandwiches and baked potatoes up esp fresh grimsby fish (served evening too), good specials; well kept Courage Best and Directors, John Smiths, Youngs Special and a guest beer, service good even when busy, no smoking family lounge and conservatory, no music or machines but may be sports TV in back bar; children welcome, suntrap streamside garden *(DWAJ)*

☆ *Prince of Wales* [Cross Rd/Anderson Rd off Oatlands Drive]: Congenial and attractively

restored, with relaxed country-local feel at lunchtime (may be busier evenings), reasonably priced generous blackboard food inc interesting dishes and Sun lunch with three roasts, well kept ales such as Adnams, Boddingtons, Fullers London Pride, Tetleys and Wadworths 6X, ten wines by the glass, friendly service, log fire in right-hand bar, daily papers, stripped pine dining room down a couple of steps (candlelit bistro feel there at night); big-screen TVs for major sports events *(David and Heather Stephenson, Ian Phillips, Minda and Stanley Alexander)*

WINDLESHAM [SU9464]

☆ *Brickmakers* [Chertsey Rd (B386, W of B383 roundabout)]: Bistro-feel dining pub, part of same good small local group as Fox & Hounds, Englefield Green, with enjoyable fresh seasonal food from good filled baguettes up, flagstones, pastel colours and different areas, one room with sofas and low tables, well kept Brakspears, Courage Best, Fullers London Pride and Marstons Pedigree, good choice of wines by the glass, nice coffee, welcoming service, log fire, conservatory; may be quiet piped classical music; well behaved children allowed, attractive courtyard with flower-filled pergola, heater, boules and barbecues *(Dr and Mrs M E Wilson, Martin and Karen Wake, Robert Hay, Ian Phillips)*

☆ *Half Moon* [Church Rd]: Popular family pub with attractive new barn-style restaurant out along covered flagstoned walkway, reliable food inc family Sun lunch and fresh veg, half a dozen interesting well kept changing ales alongside Brakspears and Fullers London Pride, Weston's farm cider, decent wines, good range of children's drinks, cheerful efficient staff, friendly labrador called Boddington, log fires, interesting World War II pictures, modern furnishings; piped music, silenced fruit machine; children welcome, picnic-sets in huge well kept garden with two new terraces and well used play area *(Guy Consterdine, Ian Phillips, Robert Hay, R Lake)*

Surrey Cricketers [Chertsey Rd (B386)]: Warm welcome, Fullers London Pride, Greene King IPA and Old Speckled Hen and Wadworths 6X, wide choice of good generous food from well filled baguettes to seafood and steaks, daily papers, lots of neat small tables on bare boards, pleasant back dining conservatory, separate skittle alley; garden *(Ian Phillips)*

Windmill [A30/B3020 junction]: Popular well run Vintage Inn dining pub, much extended and aged with beams and so forth in nicely decorated small rooms, good range of beers and wines by the glass, well thought out choice of reliable food, polite helpful staff, log fire, daily papers; handy for Ascot racecourse, some tables outside *(Peter Rozée)*

WITLEY [SU9439]

White Hart [Petworth Rd]: New licensees in attractive beamed Tudor local, well kept Shepherd Neame Best and Spitfire, fairly priced home-made food, daily papers, good oak furniture and log fire in cosy panelled inglenook snug where George Eliot drank, games in public bar, restaurant; piped music; tables on flower-filled cobbled terrace, lower meadow with picnic-sets and play area *(Gordon Stevenson, LYM, Mike and Heather Watson, Michael B Griffith)*

WOKING [SU9956]

Mayford Arms [Guildford Rd, Mayford (A320)]: Good value generous pubby food, Adnams and Courage Best, friendly staff, no smoking dining area; garden with play area *(Roger and Pauline Pearce, Ian Phillips)*

Wetherspoons [Chertsey Rd]: First visited by some readers in its former life as a Woolworths, now lots of intimate areas and cosy side snugs, good range of food all day, half a dozen or more reasonably priced changing ales, good value coffee, friendly helpful staff, interesting old local pictures, no music; a civilised retreat from an area which can at times leave something to be desired *(Tony Hobden, Ian Phillips)*

WONERSH [TQ0145]

☆ *Grantley Arms* [The Street]: Spacious recently spruced-up 16th-c timbered pub with good food in bar and restaurant, reasonable prices, friendly staff *(Shirley Mackenzie)*

WOOD STREET [SU9550]

Royal Oak [Oak Hill]: Brightly lit pub, comfortable and friendly, with well kept ales such as Arundel Gauntlet, Courage Best, Crouch Vale Blackwater Mild, Hogs Back and Three Rivers Aquarian, popular moderately priced food with lots of fresh veg and good home-made puddings *(Ian Phillips)*

WOODHAM [TQ0361]

Victoria [Woodham Lane]: Friendly local with pretty window boxes, popular food, good atmosphere, real ales such as Greene King IPA and Old Speckled Hen, Harveys and Timothy Taylors Landlord, lots of team events; big new back balcony/terrace, sheltered garden with good play area *(Ian Phillips)*

WORPLESDON [SU9654]

Fox [Fox Corner]: Smart and relaxing

modernised pub/restaurant, wicker chairs, pine tables, Courage Best and Greene King IPA, good variety of food, an area for the locals; big pretty garden with picnic-sets under dark green parasols, heated terrace *(Ian Phillips)*

WOTTON [TQ1247]

☆ *Wotton Hatch* [A25 Dorking—Guildford]: Attractive and well run Vintage Inn family dining pub, welcoming largely no smoking rambling rooms around 17th-c core, interesting furnishings and log fire, good generous reasonably priced food (all day Thurs-Sun and summer), hearty sandwiches till 5 (not Sun), well kept Bass and Fullers London Pride, good choice of decent wines, generous soft drinks inc freshly squeezed orange juice, hospitable landlord and staff, daily papers, conservatory; gentle piped music, no dogs; impressive views from neat garden, open all day *(Gordon Prince, Mrs J A Steff-Langston, LYM, John Ecklin, Gordon Stevenson, Mark Percy, Lesley Mayoh, Alan M Pring, R Lake)*

WRECCLESHAM [SU8344]

☆ *Bat & Ball* [approach from Sandrock Hill and rough unmade Upper Bourne Lane then narrow steep lane to pub]: Close-set numbered tables in neatly kept secluded recently refurbished valley-bottom pub, emphasis on wide range of above-average food (small helpings available) from ploughman's, baked potatoes and light dishes through typical favourites to more upmarket dishes, cabinet of salads and tasty puddings, up to half a dozen or more well kept ales such as Bass, Hop Back TEA, Ringwood Fortyniner, Timothy Taylors Landlord, Youngs Special and a beer brewed for them by Hampshire, good choice of wines by the glass, friendly staff, no smoking areas; they may try to keep your credit card while you eat, sports TV; disabled facilities, dogs and children allowed in one area with games machines, tables out on terrace and in garden with substantial play fort, open all day wknds *(BB, Sue Plant, KC, R Lake, D Marsh)*

Post Office address codings confusingly give the impression that some pubs are in Surrey when they're really in Hampshire or London (which is where we list them). And there's further confusion from the way the Post Office still talks about Middlesex – which disappeared in 1965 local government reorganisation.

Sussex

Over the years we've sifted through recommendations for nearly 900 pubs here in our own home county, and reckon that after thousands of reader reports and hundreds of editorial inspections we now have a pretty exact account of the county's top pubs. Sussex has quite a lot of nice cheerful proper pubs, rather than ultra-smart upscale or restaurical places. Often these are run by really good landlords and landladies – and it's this personal touch which wins them their place in the *Guide*. After several years in which there has been quite a flush of new main entries, we have just two here this year: the Greys in Brighton, serving good food and wines at appealing prices in a very relaxed and pubby environment; and the 14th-c Bull at Ditchling, with good food in attractive civilised surroundings. Other pubs on top form here now are the cheerful and chatty Stag at Balls Cross (a fine example of the difference a good landlord makes), the cottagey Cricketers Arms at Berwick (nice unpretentious food), the attractive Blackboys Inn (a nice friendly all-rounder, always busy), the Basketmakers Arms in Brighton (a splendid relaxed refuge from the nearby tourist haunts, with good cheap food), the Black Horse at Byworth (thriving under new licensees, gaining a Beer Award alongside its tasty food and lovely garden), the cheerfully old-fashioned Six Bells at Chiddingly (great value), the restaurant Jolly Sportsman at East Chiltington (super food), the Star & Garter at East Dean (another restaurant pub, earning its Food Award this year), the charming very well run Tiger tucked away at the other East Dean just outside Eastbourne, the Foresters Arms at East Hoathly (good food, and a nice little dining room), the friendly and bustling Star with its lovely garden by Old Heathfield church near Heathfield, the cheerful and interesting sausage-oriented Sussex Brewery at Hermitage over on the Hampshire border, the welcoming Queens Head at Icklesham (decent proper food, good beer range and nice garden), the friendly Keepers Arms at Trotton with its unusual décor reflecting the landlady's world travels (good interesting food), and the relaxed and enjoyable Giants Rest at Wilmington (great for a meal or a drink after a walk). For a special meal out, the Jolly Sportsman at East Chiltington is Sussex Dining Pub of the Year. Pubs we have high regard for in the Lucky Dip section at the end of the chapter are the Yew Tree at Arlington, Blue Ship in Billingshurst, Old House At Home at Chidham, Royal Oak at Chilgrove, Hatch at Colemans Hatch, Old Vine at Cousley Wood, restaurant Royal Oak at East Lavant, Huntsman at Eridge Station, Anglesey Arms at Halnaker, Woodmans Arms at Hammerpot (rebuilt and reopened after a fire), Duke of Cumberland Arms at Henley, Arun View in Littlehampton, Hollist Arms at Lodsworth, Blacksmiths Arms at Offham, Cock at Ringmer, White Horse at Rogate, Spur at Slindon and White Horse at Sutton. Drinks prices here are higher than the national average. The main local brewer is Harveys, and other local beers you are quite likely to come across here are (in a very rough order of frequency) Ballards, Arundel, Kings, Weltons and Dark Star. The widely available beer labelled K&B Sussex is actually a Badger beer, brewed down in Dorset (Badger closed the King & Barnes brewery in Horsham after they bought it and its tied pubs a few years ago).

ALCISTON TQ5005 Map 3
Rose Cottage
Village signposted off A27 Polegate—Lewes

For more than 40 years, this old-fashioned little cottage has been run by the same family. There's a good mix of locals and ramblers, cosy winter log fires, half a dozen tables with cushioned pews under quite a forest of harness, traps, a thatcher's blade and lots of other black ironware, and more bric-a-brac on the shelves above the stripped pine dado or in the etched-glass windows; in the mornings you may also find Jasper the parrot (it can get a little smoky for him in the evenings). There's a lunchtime overflow into the no smoking restaurant area. Using a local farmer's co-operative for their meat, a fishmonger on the beach at Eastbourne, as much organic produce as possible, and local eggs, honey, rabbits and seasonal game, the bar food at lunchtime might include home-made soup (£3.25), home-made pâté (£4.50), salads (from £5.95), ploughman's (£6.25), pork sausages with tomato chutney (£7.25), and honey-roast ham and poached egg (£6.50), with evening extras such as scotch steaks (from £10.25), and half a roast duckling with a changing sauce (£13.95), and fresh fish such as cheese-topped grilled garlic mussels (£4.95; main course £8.95), grilled salmon fillet with orange and ginger butter (£8.95), and whole grilled bass in coriander, parsley, lemon and garlic (£10.95). Well kept Harveys Best and a guest such as Wychwood Shires Bitter on handpump, a good little wine list with fair value house wines and a few nice bin ends, and local farm cider; the landlord is quite a plain-speaking character. There are gas heaters outside for cooler evenings, and the small paddock in the garden has ducks and chickens. Nearby fishing and shooting. The charming little village (and local church) are certainly worth a look. They only take bedroom bookings for two nights. (Recommended by D Marsh, Richard Haw, the Didler, Jenny and Peter Lowater, Dr D G Twyman, Michael and Ann Cole, John Beeken, C J Roebuck, Richard May, Mrs Phoebe A Kemp, Mary Rayner)

Free house ~ Licensee Ian Lewis ~ Real ale ~ Bar food ~ Restaurant ~ (01323) 870377 ~ Children allowed if over 10 ~ Dogs allowed in bar ~ Open 11.30-3, 6.30-11; 12-3, 6.30-10.30 Sun; closed 25 and 26 Dec ~ Bedrooms: /£50S

ALFRISTON TQ5203 Map 3
George
High Street

As two long-distance paths (the South Downs Way and Vanguard Way) cross in this lovely village, it makes good sense to drop in here for a rest. It's a 14th-c timbered inn and the long bar has massive low beams hung with hops, appropriately soft lighting, and a log fire (or summer flower arrangement) in a huge stone inglenook fireplace that dominates the room, with lots of copper and brass around it. Sturdy stripped tables have settles and chairs around them, and there's well kept Batemans XXXB. Greene King IPA, Abbot, and Old Speckled Hen on handpump; decent wines, champagne by the glass, dominoes and piped music. Bar food at lunchtime includes stir-fried tofu with spicy noodles (£5.50), tagliatelle carbonara (£5.95), ploughman's (£6.50), pork and leek sausages with onion gravy (£6.95), and steak, mushroom and Guinness suet pudding or ham and free-range eggs (£7.50), with evening choices such as chicken liver parfait with aubergine and olive relish (£4.95), tiger prawn satay with peanut sambal (£5.95), asparagus, pea and lemon risotto (£9.95), slow-braised knuckle of lamb with mint and chive mash and garlic and thyme sauce (£11.95), chicken breast with lime and coriander (£12.75), confit pork belly with red cabbage and bramley apple (£12.95), monkfish wrapped in parma ham on a mixed bean cassoulet (£15.95), and puddings like rosewater and orange cheesecake, chocolate pear and hazelnut tart or crème brûlée (£3.95). Besides the cosy candlelit no smoking restaurant, there's a garden dining room – or you can sit out in the charming flint-walled garden behind. (Recommended by Philip and Ann Board, Len Beattie, John Davis, Dr David Cockburn, Ann and Colin Hunt, Ian and Nita Cooper)

Greene King ~ Lease Roland and Cate Couch ~ Real ale ~ Bar food (12-2.30, 7-9(10 Fri/Sat)) ~ Restaurant ~ (01323) 870319 ~ Children in eating area of bar and restaurant ~ Dogs allowed in bar and bedrooms ~ Open 12-11; 12-10.30 Sun; closed 25 Dec ~ Bedrooms: £50S/£80B

AMBERLEY SO8401 Map 3
Black Horse
Off B2139

The restful garden of this pretty pub has fine views and is just the place to relax with a drink after a walk along the South Downs Way. The main bar has high-backed settles on flagstones, beams over the serving counter festooned with sheep bells and shepherds' tools (hung by the last shepherd on the Downs), and walls decorated with a mixture of prints and paintings. The lounge bar has many antiques and artefacts collected by the owners on their world travels; there are log fires in both bars and two in the no smoking restaurant. Well liked bar food includes home-made vegetable soup (£3.45), home-made chicken liver pâté (£3.95), deep-fried brie and camembert with cumberland sauce (£4.55), sandwiches with salad and chips or ploughman's (£5.95), lasagne or broccoli and pasta bake (£8.95), steak in ale pie (£8.95), and various curries or chicken with sauces such as bacon and stilton or prawn and lobster (£9.95); puddings (£4.25) and Sunday roast (£8.95). Well kept Greene King IPA and Wells Bombardier on handpump, and several malt whiskies; piped music. The garden is a restful place. More reports please. *(Recommended by Liz and Tony Colman, John Davis, Jude Wright)*

Pubmaster ~ Tenant Gary Tubb ~ Real ale ~ Bar food (12-3, 6-8.30(10 Sat); all day Sun) ~ Restaurant ~ (01798) 831552 ~ Children in eating areas but must be over 12 in evening restaurant ~ Dogs allowed in bar ~ Open 11-11; 12-10.30 Sun

ARLINGTON TQ5407 Map 3
Old Oak
Caneheath, off A22 or A27 NW of Polegate

Built in 1733 as an almshouse for the village, this first became a public house in the early 1900s. The open-plan, L-shaped bar has heavy beams, well spaced tables and comfortable seating, log fires, and Badger Best, Harveys Best and a guest such as Fullers London Pride tapped from the cask; several malt whiskies, piped music, darts, toad-in-the-hole and dominoes. Straightforward bar food includes home-made soup (£3.75), coarse pâté (£5.95), pasta or curry of the day (£7.25), home-made pie of the day or gammon and egg (£8.50), and daily specials. The dining area is no smoking, and the garden is attractive and peaceful. *(Recommended by Jenny and Peter Lowater, Fr Robert Marsh, Michael and Ann Cole, Alan Sadler, R and M Thomas, M and R Thomas, Ron Gentry, Paul A Moore)*

Free house ~ Licensees Mr J Boots and Mr B Slattery ~ Real ale ~ Bar food (12-2.30, 6.30-9.30; all day weekends) ~ Restaurant ~ (01323) 482072 ~ Children welcome ~ Dogs allowed in bar ~ Open 11-11; 11-10.30 Sun

BALLS CROSS SU9826 Map 2
Stag
Village signposted off A283 at N edge of Petworth, brown sign to pub there too

There's a good welcoming landlord in this charming little 16th-c pub. It's an unpretentious, convivial place and very popular locally – though visitors will find it easy to fall into conversation. The tiny flagstoned bar has a winter log fire in its huge inglenook fireplace, just a couple of tables, a window seat, and a few chairs and leather-seated bar stools; on the right a second room with a rug on its bare boards has space for just a single table. Beyond is an appealing old-fashioned no smoking dining room, carpeted, with a great many more or less horsey pictures. There are yellowing cream walls and low shiny ochre ceilings throughout, with soft lighting from little fringed wall lamps. On the left a separate carpeted room with a couple of big Victorian prints has tables skittles, darts, fruit machine, shove-ha'penny, cribbage and dominoes. Service is welcoming and committed, and they have well kept Badger Best, Fursty Ferret and Sussex on handpump, decent wines by the glass, summer cider and some nice malt whiskies. A wide choice of good value food using meat from a local butcher and game bagged by the landlord (they tell us prices have not changed since last year) includes filled rolls (from £4.25), ploughman's (from £5), filled baked potatoes (£5.25), mediterranean vegetable lasagne, macaroni cheese or ham and egg (£7), full breakfast (£7.50), seasonal pheasant casserole (£9), and venison casserole, calves liver and bacon or fish pie (£9). The good-sized garden behind, divided by a shrubbery, has teak or cast-iron tables and chairs, picnic-sets, and in summer a couple of canvas awnings; there are more picnic-sets out under green canvas parasols in front, and the hitching rail does get used. The veteran gents' is outside. *(Recommended by R B Gardiner, Phil and Sally Gorton, David Cosham, Mrs J A Sales, Peter Lewis)*

Badger ~ Tenant Hamish Barrie Hiddleston ~ Real ale ~ Bar food (not Sun evening) ~ Restaurant ~ (01403) 820241 ~ Children in restaurant and family room ~ Dogs allowed in bar and bedrooms ~ Open 11-3, 6-11; 12-3, 7-10.30 Sun ~ Bedrooms: £30/£60

BERWICK TQ5105 Map 3
Cricketers Arms
Lower Road, S of A27

Once two cottages, this little country pub is particularly special on a peaceful sunny afternoon when you can sit in the old-fashioned front garden amidst small brick paths and mature flowering shrubs and plants; there are more seats behind the building. Inside, the three small similarly furnished rooms (one is no smoking) have simple benches against the half-panelled walls, a pleasant mix of old country tables and chairs, burgundy velvet curtains on poles, a few bar stools and some country prints; quarry tiles on the floors (nice worn ones in the middle room), two log fires in little brick fireplaces, a huge black supporting beam in each of the low ochre ceilings, and (in the end room) some attractive cricketing pastels; some of the beams are hung with cricket bats. Good straightforward bar food includes garlic mushrooms (£5.95), duck and pistachio terrine with cranberry sauce, ploughman's, local sausages or home-baked ham and egg (all £6.50), warm salads (from £8.50), 12oz rib-eye steak (£12.95), and daily specials such as a vegetarian dish (£7.25), fresh dressed crab salad (£7.50), grilled tuna (£7.95), and steak, stilton and mushroom warm salad (£8.95); best to get here early to be sure of a seat as it does fill up quickly. Well kept Harveys Best and two seasonal ales tapped from the cask, and decent wine; cribbage, dominoes and an old Sussex coin game called toad in the hole. The wall paintings in the nearby church done by the Bloomsbury Group during WWII are worth a look. *(Recommended by Joel Dobris, Ann and Colin Hunt, Alan Cowell, Fr Robert Marsh, Sue Demont, Tim Barrow, Guy Vowles, M and R Thomas, the Didler, John Beeken, Kevin Thorpe, Paul Hopton, Percy and Cathy Paine, Mrs Phoebe A Kemp, Michael Sargent)*

Harveys ~ Tenant Peter Brown ~ Real ale ~ Bar food (12-2.15, 6.30-9) ~ (01323) 870469 ~ Children in family room ~ Dogs welcome ~ Open 11-3, 6-11 (all day July/August); 11-11 Sat; 12-10.30 Sun

BLACKBOYS TQ5220 Map 3
Blackboys Inn
B2192, S edge of village

After a walk along the Vanguard Way footpath, the South Downs Way or in the Woodland Trust land opposite, the garden of this pretty 14th-c weatherboarded house is a pleasant place to relax: plenty of rustic tables overlooking the pond, with more under the chestnut trees. Inside, the bustling locals' bar has a chatty and properly pubby atmosphere, and there's a string of old-fashioned and unpretentious little rooms with dark oak beams, bare boards or parquet, antique prints, copious curios (including a collection of keys above the bar), and usually, a good log fire in the inglenook fireplace. Enjoyable food includes snacks like filled baked potatoes and ploughman's, as well as flaked smoked haddock in cheese sauce (£3.50; big helping £6.95), moules marinière (£3.95; big helping £5.95), moussaka, home-made pie or scampi (£7.50), beef and root vegetable stew with dumplings (£8.95), crab mornay, garlic prawns, mussels, and queen scallops (£10.50), chicken stuffed with mediterranean vegetables (£11.50), pepper, parmesan and courgette tartlet (£11.95), 10oz entrecote steak (£11.95), and puddings like spotted dick and custard (£4.95). The restaurant and dining areas are no smoking; obliging, efficient service even when busy. Well kept Harveys Best, Pale Ale and a couple of guests like Armada or Knots of May on handpump, eight wines by the glass and Addlestone's cider; darts, fruit machine, juke box, cribbage and dominoes. *(Recommended by Len Beattie, Louise English, John Davis, John Hendy, Tony and Wendy Hobden, Michael and Ann Cole, R M Corlett, Angus Johnson, Carol Bolden, Susan and John Douglas)*

Harveys ~ Tenant Edward Molesworth ~ Real ale ~ Bar food (12-2.15, 6.30-9; not Sun evening) ~ Restaurant ~ (01825) 890283 ~ Children welcome ~ Dogs allowed in bar ~ Open 11-3, 5(6 Sat)-11; 11-11 Fri and Sat; 12-10.30 Sun

BODIAM TQ7825 Map 3
Curlew ⑪

B2244 S of Hawkhurst, outside village at crossroads with turn-off to Castle

There's no doubt that under the keen new licensee, emphasis here is firmly on the particularly good food. There's a relaxed, informal atmosphere and friendly staff, and the main bar has a heavily carved bar counter, well kept Badger Best, Fursty Ferret and Tanglefoot on handpump, two sizes of wine glass from a thoughtful list, and a woodburning stove. Off to the right is a smaller room with timbered red walls, mirrors that give an impression of more space, and a piano. The no smoking restaurant has black timbers and pictures that are mainly trompe-l'oeil ones of life-size wine bottles looking as if they are in wood-framed alcoves; some sunny watercolour landscapes, too, and interesting photographs in the gents'. Attractively presented, the food at lunchtime might include crunchy vegetable salad with mustard vinaigrette (£5.95), filled baguettes (from £6.95), smoked haddock risotto with poached egg and hollandaise sauce (£7.95), pasta with roasted red peppers, cherry tomatoes and parmesan (£8.50), good fish and chips with garlic mayonnaise (£9.95), sausage of the day with home-made tomato relish and red wine and onion jus (£10.95), and calves liver and bacon with caramelised onion gravy (£11.95); also, soup (£4.25), marinated tuna carpaccio with fennel and celeriac salad (£5.95), tiger prawn, crab and coriander salad with lemon ginger dressing (£7.50), moroccan vegetable tagine with tahini dressing (£12.95), roasted red snapper with lemon and lime potato cake and warm chickpea salad or roast chicken breast with wild mushrooms, asparagus and truffle foam (£14.95), and puddings like orange and dark chocolate marquise with passion fruit sorbet, summer fruit and champagne jelly with black pepper and lemon sorbet or rhubarb and cinnamon trifle with cognac crème anglaise (from £5.50). You can eat outside on the pretty terrace in fine weather, surrounded by flowering baskets and troughs. *(Recommended by Gene and Kitty Rankin, Peter Meister, Susan and John Douglas, Paul A Moore, JMC)*

Free house ~ Licensee Simon Lazenby ~ Bar food (not Sun evening or Mon) ~ Restaurant ~ (01580) 861394 ~ Children in eating area of bar and restaurant ~ Dogs allowed in bar ~ Open 11.30-11; 12-4 Mon and Sun; closed Sun and Mon evening

BRIGHTON TQ3105 Map 3
Basketmakers Arms ⑪ £

Gloucester Road – the E end, near Cheltenham Place; off Marlborough Place (A23) via Gloucester Street

Handy for The Lanes and close to the Theatre Royal, this bustling little backstreet corner pub is as popular as ever. There's a really cheerful, chatty atmosphere, and both the locals and staff behind the bar are friendly and welcoming; it's best to get here early, especially at weekends. The two small low-ceilinged rooms have brocaded wall benches and stools on the stripped wood floor, lots of interesting old tins all over the walls, cigarette cards on one beam with whisky labels on another, beermats, and some old advertisements, photographs and posters; quiet piped music. Good value enjoyable bar food includes lots of sandwiches (from £2.50; brie and avocado £3.25; steak in french bread £3.75), particularly good home-made meaty and vegetarian burgers (£2.95), baked potatoes with fillings such as beef, chilli and yoghurt (£3.60), ploughman's (£3.95), and specials such as bangers and mash in red onion and wine gravy (£4.50), thai green curry, steak in ale or fish pies (£4.95), and Friday beer-battered fish with home-made tartare sauce (£4.95); Sunday roasts (from £5.25). Well kept Gales Bitter, GB, HSB, and seasonal ales, and a guest such as Wells Bombardier on handpump, good wines (house wines come in three different glass sizes), over 80 malt whiskies, and good coffees; they do a splendid Pimms. There are three tables out on the pavement. *(Recommended by MLR, B and M Kendall, the Didler, LM, Ann and Colin Hunt, Andy Trafford, Louise Bayly, Tony Hobden, Tracey and Stephen Groves)*

Gales ~ Tenants P and K Dowd, A Mawer, J Archdeacon ~ Real ale ~ Bar food (12-3, 5.30-8.30; 12-7 Sat; 12-5 Sun; not Sat/Sun evenings) ~ (01273) 689006 ~ Children welcome until 8pm ~ Dogs welcome ~ Open 11-11; 12-10.30 Sun; closed 26 Dec

Greys

Southover Street, off A270 Lewes Road opposite The Level (public park)

Rather a curious hybrid this, with what amounts to a good little restaurant sharing one small L-shaped room with an unabashed and not at all smart pubby local. Furnishings are basic, with simple wall seats and stools around mixed pub tables on bare boards or reconstituted flagstones, ochre walls, and some brown-varnished plank panelling around a flame-effect stove below a big metal canopy, with piped music from the array of loudspeakers above it. The serving bar is on the right, with well kept Harveys Best and Timothy Taylors Landlord on handpump, Leffe and Hoegaarden on tap, a considerable range of belgian bottled beers, and a cheery local crowd on the bar stools and at the nearby tables. The five or six tables on the left, each with a little vase of flowers and lighted tea lamp, are the food bit – one corner table is snugged in by a high-backed settle, and another at the back is tucked into a quiet corner under the open stairs up to the lavatories (the stair wall is papered with posters and flyers from bands, singers and poets who have performed here). The food is good, with a shortish menu that changes every couple of months and might include coddled egg, toulouse sausages with creamy potato or an excellent seafood soup (£4.50), hearty peasant-style soups (£5.50), mushroom stroganoff (£9.50 – and strongly flavoured enough to appeal even to confirmed carnivores), delicious guinea fowl tenderly pot-roasted with peppers, oranges, lemons, tomatoes, raisins, onions and garlic (£10.75), grilled hake (£11) and seafood crumble (£11.75). Masses of vegetables and potatoes are served separately, and the short choice of enterprising puddings (£4.50) also comes in generous helpings (on our anonymous inspection visit, we found just one helping of poached peaches with raspberry purée and its little mound of crème patissière on sponge cake, served with three spoons, did handsomely for all three of us). The house wines, from burgundy, are excellent value. Service is informal, friendly and attentive. There is not much daytime parking on this steep lane or the nearby streets. No children inside. *(Recommended by Richard Houghton, Val and Alan Green)*

Free house ~ Licensees Chris Taylor and Gill Perkins ~ Real ale ~ Bar food (not Fri or Sun evenings, nor Mon) ~ (01273) 680734 ~ Regular live music Sun and/or Mon, usually £7 ~ Open 12-11(10.30 Sun); 5.30-11 Mon; closed Mon lunchtime

---

Ideas for a country day out? We list pubs in really attractive scenery at the back of the book – and there are separate lists for waterside pubs, ones with really good gardens, and ones with lovely views.

BURPHAM TQ0308 Map 3

George & Dragon 🍺

Warningcamp turn off A27 outside Arundel: follow road up and up

Now with new licensees, this bustling country pub is popular for its enjoyable food
and even on a damp, cold winter's day there is unlikely to be a spare table – best to
book ahead. The front part is a proper bar with old pale flagstones and a
woodburning stove in a big inglenook on the right, a carpeted area with an old
wireless set, nice scrubbed trestle tables, and bar stools along the counter serving
well kept Arundel Castle and Stronghold, and King Red River Ale on handpump.
A couple of tables share a small light flagstone middle area with the big
blackboard that lists changing dishes such as home-made soup (£5.25), smoked
chicken, pigeon breast and baby leek terrine with apple and cider brandy chutney
(£6.95), baked aubergine tian with warm lemon caper vinaigrette (£13.95), seared
fresh scallops with creamy spinach risotto, tiger prawns, sorrel and vermouth
beurre blanc or roasted rump of lamb with tarragon and mustard sauce (£16.95),
specials such as wild mushroom tortellini (£9.95) or sirloin steak in peppercorn
sauce (£15.95), and dark chocolate and Grand Marnier and white chocolate and
Cointreau terrine or mango and pawpaw crème brûlée (£5.25); the conservatory
extension overlooks the garden. The back part of the pub, entirely no smoking and
angling right round behind the bar servery, with a further extension beyond one set
of internal windows, has solid pale country-kitchen furniture on neat bare boards,
and a fresh and airy décor, with a little bleached pine panelling and long white
curtains. The garden has picnic-sets under cocktail parasols. Always popular with
local people in the know, the pub gets extremely busy on Goodwood race days.
*(Recommended by R T and J C Moggridge, John Davis, J P Humphery, Mike and Gill Gadsden,
John Hendy, A and B D Craig, Martin O' Keefe, Peter Lewis, Martin and Karen Wake,
Sue Demont, Tim Barrow)*

Free house ~ Licensees Alastair and Angela Thackeray ~ Real ale ~ Bar food (not Sun
evening) ~ Restaurant ~ (01903) 883131 ~ Children welcome ~ Open 11-11; 12-10.30
Sun

BYWORTH SU9820 Map 2

Black Horse 🍺

Off A283

Now a free house, this charming old country pub is doing very well at the moment,
and readers really enjoy the welcoming pubby atmosphere. The simply furnished
though smart bar has pews and scrubbed wooden tables on its bare floorboards,
pictures and old photographs on the walls, large open fires, and newspapers to
read. The back dining room has lots of nooks and crannies, and there's a mainly no
smoking upstairs restaurant with lovely views of the downs. At lunchtime, the well
liked straightforward food includes filled baguettes and baked potatoes (from
£3.95), and ham and egg, home-made burger, or ploughman's (£5.95); evening
dishes such as tasty soup or devilled whitebait (£3.95), home-made beef in beer pie
or chilli (£6.95), chicken tikka masala (£8.95), and steaks (from £8.95). Well kept
Cheriton Best Bitter, Diggers Gold and Pots Ale, and Fullers London Pride on
handpump; darts, cribbage and dominoes. The particularly attractive garden has
tables on a steep series of grassy terraces sheltered by banks of flowering shrubs
that look across a drowsy valley to swelling woodland. *(Recommended by
Gordon Neighbour, H H Hellin, John Davis, John Evans, R B Gardiner, David Coleman,
Phil and Sally Gorton, Colin McKerrow, David Cosham)*

Free house ~ Licensee Mark Robinson ~ Real ale ~ Bar food (12-2, 6-9) ~ Restaurant ~
(01798) 342424 ~ Children welcome ~ Dogs welcome ~ Open 11-11; 12-10.30 Sun

---

We say if we know a pub allows dogs.

CHARLTON SU8812 Map 2
Fox Goes Free
Village signposted off A286 Chichester—Midhurst in Singleton, also from Chichester—Petworth via East Dean

The bedrooms here have been upgraded (which now means dogs are no longer allowed in them), the furniture has been smartened up, and there's a new terraced area which enjoys the lovely downland views. It's a well run pub with cheerful, helpful staff and a good mix of customers. Throughout, there are now old irish settles, tables and chapel chairs, and the first of the dark and cosy series of separate rooms is a small bar with an open fireplace. Standing timbers divide a larger beamed bar which has a huge brick fireplace with a woodburning stove, and old local photographs on the walls. A dining area with hunting prints looks over the garden and the South Downs beyond. The family extension is a clever conversion from horse boxes and the stables where the 1926 Goodwood winner was housed; darts and fruit machine. Well kept Ballards Best, Fox Goes Free (brewed for the pub by Arundel) and a seasonal guest from Ballards like Golden Bine on handpump, and nine wines by the glass. Using as much fresh local produce as possible, the enjoyable food includes sandwiches, home-made steak and kidney pie, chilli and lasagne as well as baked goats cheese crottin with a red pepper coulis (£6.50), king prawn kebab with fresh lime and chilli dressing (£7.25), fried venison steak with boulangère potatoes and balsamic jus (£14.95), fried skate wing with a courgette and carrot salad (£15.95), and puddings such as warm chocolate brownie, chocolate fudge sauce or baked raspberry cheesecake with raspberry ripple ice-cream (£4.95). Best to book to be sure of a table. The attractive garden has plenty of picnic-sets among fruit trees. Goodwood Racecourse is not far away (on race days it does get very busy); it's also handy for the Weald and Downland Open Air Museum and there are some fine surrounding walks. *(Recommended by Wendy Arnold, R B Gardiner, Gene and Kitty Rankin, Richard Haw, Michael and Ann Cole, Michael B Griffith, Ann and Colin Hunt, Philip and Ann Board, Mrs Sheela Curtis, Gordon Neighbour, Susan and John Douglas, Dave Yates, Mrs J A Sales, Keith and Maureen Trainer, Jenny Garrett)*

Free house ~ Licensee David Coxon ~ Real ale ~ Bar food (12-2.30, 6.30-9.30; all day weekends) ~ (01243) 811461 ~ Children welcome ~ Dogs allowed in bar ~ Live music Weds evenings ~ Open 11-11; 12-10.30 Sun ~ Bedrooms: £50S/£70S

CHIDDINGLY TQ5414 Map 3
Six Bells ★ £
Village signed off A22 Uckfield—Hailsham

It's always the sign of a really well run pub when customers of widely different sorts are all chatting happily together. Cheerily old-fashioned with a good bustling atmosphere, you can be sure of a genuinely friendly welcome from the long-standing landlord. The bars have log fires as well as solid old wood furnishings such as pews and antique seats, lots of fusty artefacts and interesting bric-a-brac, and plenty of local pictures and posters. A sensitive extension provides some much needed family space; dominoes and cribbage. Particularly for this part of the country, the bar food is a bargain: straightforward but tasty, there might be french onion soup (£2.50), filled baguettes, steak and kidney pie (£3.50), baked potatoes (from £4.20), ploughman's (from £4.75), ravioli in spicy sauce, spare ribs in barbecue sauce, tuna pasta bake or chicken curry (from £5.50), and puddings like treacle tart or banoffi pie (£3). Well kept Courage Directors, Harveys Best and a guest such as John Smiths on handpump. Outside at the back, there are some tables beyond a big raised goldfish pond, and a boules pitch; the church opposite has an interesting Jefferay monument. Vintage and Kit car meetings outside the pub every month. This is a pleasant area for walks. *(Recommended by Guy Vowles, Michael and Ann Cole, B and M Kendall, Tony and Wendy Hobden, Humphry and Angela Crum Ewing, R M Corlett, Susan and John Douglas)*

Free house ~ Licensees Paul Newman and Emma Bannister ~ Real ale ~ Bar food (12-2.30; 6-9.30; 12-10 Sat, 12-9 Sun) ~ (01825) 872227 ~ Children in family room ~ Dogs allowed in bar ~ Live music Fri/Sat/Sun evenings and Sun lunchtime; jazz and folk every other Tues evening ~ Open 11-3, 6-11; 11-12 Sat; 12-10.30 Sun

CHILGROVE SU8214 Map 2
White Horse ♀ ⇌
B2141 Petersfield—Chichester

Totally no smoking now, this attractive former 18th-c coaching inn is civilised and quietly upmarket – but as there are plenty of tables for drinkers at the front, walkers and their dogs are still welcome; lots of fine walks nearby. The bar counter is made up from claret, burgundy and other mainly french wooden wine cases, and good wines by the glass, with an impressive range by the bottle, are a big plus here – in fact, every dish from the menu has a recommended wine to go with it; well kept Ballards on handpump. Dark brown deco leather armchairs and a sofa are grouped on dark boards here, and on either side are three or four well spaced good-sized sturdy tables with good pale spindleback side and elbow chairs on lighter newer boards; a feeling of freshness is accentuated by the big bow window, uncluttered cream walls and ceiling, and clear lighting; maybe piped music, well reproduced. Besides a good range of sandwiches, Spanish staff prepare enjoyable if not cheap light lunchtime dishes such as organic chicken liver parfait with roasted cherry compote, raspberry dressing and toasted brioche or oxtail ravioli with a rich sauce (£7.95), mediterranean fish soup (£8.95), fresh selsey crab and avocado (£9.95), and duo of hand-dived scallops and king prawns (£11.95); more substantial dishes include vegetable risotto in a smoked paprika cream and crispy parmesan disc or baked crab thermidor (£14.95), organic gloucester old spot pork cutlet with grilled pineapple and sherry gravy (£15.95), and best end of organic local lamb with shi-itake mushroom and cheddar timbale with stout jus (£17.95), with puddings like hot Valrhona chocolate fondant with crème anglaise, chocolate sauce and home-made orange ice-cream, star fruit and earl grey cheesecake or Baileys mousse served in a chocolate tower with coffee ice-cream and coffee sauce (from £6.95). The bar has a woodburner on one side, and a log fire on the other. Past here, it opens into a restaurant with comfortable modern seats and attractively laid tables – as in the bar, generously spaced out. Outside, one neat lawn has white cast-iron tables and chairs under an old yew tree, and another has wooden benches, tables and picnic-sets under a tall flag mast. Comfortable bedrooms and super continental breakfasts brought to your room in a wicker hamper. *(Recommended by John Davis, Phyl and Jack Street, Tracey and Stephen Groves, Stephen and Anne Atkinson)*

Free house ~ Licensee Charles Burton ~ Real ale ~ Bar food ~ Restaurant ~ (01243) 535219 ~ Children in eating area of bar ~ Dogs allowed in bar ~ Open 10-3, 6-11; 12-3 Sun; closed Sun evening, Mon ~ Bedrooms: £65B/£95B

COMPTON SU7714 Map 2
Coach & Horses ◖
B2146 S of Petersfield

Locals, walkers and their dogs, and those wanting a meal all mix happily in this 17th-c village local. There's an open fire in the roomy front public bar, and the Village Bar has pine shutters and panelling, and the original pitched pine block floor has been restored; an open fire in the roomy front public bar. It is here that the enjoyable food, cooked by the landlord, is served: home-made soup (£3.95), sandwiches or filled baguettes (from £4.10), black pudding, bacon and poached egg salad or lamb sweetbreads on spinach (£5.75), chicken and mushroom pie (£9.25), and baked aubergine with chargrilled peppers and brie or chicken breast with grain mustard and almond sauce (£9.75). The charming little plush beamed lounge bar serves as a relaxing ante-room to the attractive restaurant. Well kept Ballards Best, Cheriton Diggers Gold, Fullers ESB, Palmers 200 and Triple fff Altons Pride and Moondance on handpump; old-fashioned juke box, bar billiards and fruit machine.

There are tables out by the square in front; it's not far from Uppark (NT). *(Recommended by R T and J C Moggridge, Paul A Moore, Ann and Colin Hunt, Andy and Jill Kassube, Tracey and Stephen Groves, John Davis, Geoff and Linda Payne)*

Free house ~ Licensees David and Christiane Butler ~ Real ale ~ Bar food ~ Restaurant ~ (023) 9263 1228 ~ Children in eating area of bar and restaurant ~ Dogs allowed in bar ~ Open 11.30-3, 6-11; 12-3, 7-10.30 Sun; closed one week late Feb

COWBEECH TQ6114 Map 3
Merrie Harriers
Village signed from A271

The beamed and panelled bar in this ex-farmhouse has a log fire in the brick inglenook, quite a mix of tables and chairs, Harveys Sussex Best, King Spring Ale and Wadworths 6X on handpump, and nine wines by the glass. Good bar food might include cream of wild mushroom and marsala soup (£4.25), pot of hot smokie with gratin of leeks and cheddar (£4.95), whole roast quail stuffed with toulouse sausage (£6.50), mediterranean tart with chargrilled halloumi cheese or rare rib of local beef with sauté potatoes (£8.95), beer battered fillet of cod with home-made tartare sauce (£9.95), roast breast of corn-fed chicken on lemon and lime tagliatelle (£11.95), honey glazed confit of pork belly with caramelised apple (£12.95), seared wing of skate with garlic butter and shellfish or rack of lamb with lavender mash and cassis jus (£14.95), and puddings such as sticky toffee pudding with whisky butterscotch sauce, raspberry crème brûlée or apple crumble with cinnamon glaze (£4.50). The brick-walled and oak-ceilinged back restaurant is no smoking; piped music. There are rustic seats amongst colourful shrubs and pots in the terraced garden, and country views. More reports please. *(Recommended by Rob Winstanley, PL)*

Free house ~ Licensee Roger Cotton ~ Real ale ~ Bar food ~ Restaurant ~ (01323) 833108 ~ Children in eating area of bar and restaurant ~ Dogs allowed in bar ~ Monthly jazz ~ Open 11.30-3(4 Sat), 6-11; 12-4, 6-10.30 Sun

DITCHLING TQ3215 Map 3
Bull
High Street (B2112)

Unassuming from the outside, this 14th-c building is in a very pretty village. The invitingly cosy main bar on the right is quite large, rambling and pleasantly traditional with characterful and well worn old wooden furniture, beams and floorboards, and a blazing winter fire. To the left, the nicely refurbished rooms have a calm, restrained mellow décor and candles, and beyond that a snug area with chesterfields around a low table; piped music. Half the pub is no smoking. Well kept Adnams Broadside, Harveys Best, Hop Back Summer Lightning and Timothy Taylors Landlord on handpump, and a dozen wines by the glass. Using local produce, the well liked food might include lunchtime filled ciabattas and bar snacks, as well as soup (£4.50), marinated and roasted duck breast with toasted sesame salad, seared beef with cajun spiced ratatouille and pesto dressing or camembert roasted in its box with cranberry sauce (all £6.50), chicken caesar salad (£8.50), courgette, potato, mint and feta cake with red onion salad and sweet cumin dressing (£9), fish in ale batter or home-made beefburger (£9.50), seared tuna steak with niçoise salad (£11.50), and roast rack of local lamb with salsify and shallot ragoût (£13.50). Picnic-sets in the good-sized pretty downland garden which is gently lit at night look up towards Ditchling Beacon, and there are more tables on a suntrap back terrace; there is good wheelchair access. The charming old village is a popular base for the South Downs Way and other walks. *(Recommended by J P Humphery, Mr and Mrs John Taylor, N R White)*

Free house ~ Licensee Dominic Worrall ~ Real ale ~ Bar food (12-2.30, 7-9.30; 12-4 Sun) ~ (01273) 843147 ~ Children welcome ~ Dogs allowed in bar ~ Acoustic celtic music last Sun of month ~ Open 11-11; 12-10.30 Sun; closed evenings 25, 26 and 31 Dec ~ Bedrooms: /£80B

DONNINGTON SU8502 Map 2
Blacksmiths Arms
Turn off A27 on to A286 signposted Selsey, then almost immediately left on to B2201

The small low-ceilinged rooms in this little white roadside cottage are prettily decorated, and have Victorian prints on the walls, solid, comfortable furnishings, and a relaxed atmosphere; the back no smoking restaurant is very airy and pleasant. Well liked bar food includes soup (£4.25; soup and a sandwich £6.75), tartlet of caramelised onions, slow-roasted cherry tomatoes and St Augur cheese (£4.50), sandwiches (£4.50; filled baguettes £5.50), home-made chicken liver pâté with apple and grape chutney and damson jelly sauce (£4.95), filled baked potatoes (£5.75), home-cooked ham and egg (£7.50), ragoût of wild mushrooms glazed with goats cheese on vegetable spaghetti or sausage and mash with onion jus (£9.95), fresh selsey crab (£10.95), seared guinea fowl filled with green peppercorn and pistachio mousse with smoked bacon, shallot and fig jus (£11.95), and steaks (from £12.95); two-course Sunday lunch (£11.95). Well kept Fullers London Pride, Greene King Abbot, Oakleaf Bitter and Wells Bombardier on handpump. The big garden has a play area with swings, a climbing frame, two rabbits called Barnham and Blu, two dogs (Tess and Cleo), a cat (Amber), and four tortoises (only allowed in the garden on special occasions), and plenty of picnic-sets. *(Recommended by Bob and Margaret Holder, David Carr, Ann and Colin Hunt, Tony and Wendy Hobden, Martin and Karen Wake, Tracey and Stephen Groves, Ian Phillips, Susan and John Douglas, Tony and Shirley Albert, Bruce Bird)*

Punch ~ Tenants George and Lesley Ward ~ Real ale ~ Bar food (12-2.30, 6.30-9.30; not Sun evening) ~ Restaurant ~ (01243) 783999 ~ Children in eating area of bar and restaurant ~ Dogs allowed in bar ~ Open 11-3, 5.30-11; 12-4, 6-10.30 Sun

EAST ASHLING SU8207 Map 2
Horse & Groom ♀ ◀
B2178 NW of Chichester

The front part of this bustling country pub is a proper bar with old pale flagstones and a woodburning stove in a big inglenook on the right, a carpeted area with an old wireless set, nice scrubbed trestle tables, and bar stools along the counter serving well kept Brewsters Hophead, Harveys Best, Hop Back Summer Lightning and Youngs on handpump; several wines by the glass. A couple of tables share a small light flagstoned middle area with the big blackboard that lists daily changing dishes: sandwiches and filled baguettes (from £3), filled baked potatoes (from £4.25), ploughman's (from £5.95), home-cooked ham and eggs (£6.50), chicken breast in dijon mustard sauce or steak in ale pie (£10.25), lamb cutlets with rosemary jus (£10.95), whole baked plaice with lemon butter (£11.25), and king prawns in parsley butter (£12.95); the restaurant is no smoking. The back part of the pub, angling right round behind the bar servery, with a further extension beyond one set of internal windows, has solid pale country-kitchen furniture on neat bare boards, and a fresh and airy décor, with a little bleached pine panelling and long white curtains. French windows lead out to a garden with picnic-sets under cocktail parasols. Always popular with local people in the know, the pub gets extremely busy on Goodwood race days. *(Recommended by Ann and Colin Hunt, Mrs A P Lee, Roger Endersby, J Wakeling, Andy and Jill Kassube, Bruce Bird, Cynthia McKinley, Richard Waller, Pauline Smith, Tracey and Stephen Groves, Cathy Robinson, Ed Coombe, S G N Bennett, Barry Ashton, Walter and Susan Rinaldi-Butcher, Tony and Shirley Albert, Gordon Neighbour)*

Free house ~ Licensee Michael Martell ~ Real ale ~ Bar food (12-2, 6-9; not Sun evening) ~ Restaurant ~ (01243) 575339 ~ Children in eating area of bar and restaurant ~ Dogs allowed in bar and bedrooms ~ Open 12-3, 6-11; 12-6 Sun; closed Sun evening ~ Bedrooms: £40.50B/£60.75B

Pubs close to motorway junctions are listed at the back of the book.

EAST CHILTINGTON TQ3715 Map 3

Jolly Sportsman ⑪ ♀

2 miles N of B2116; Chapel Lane – follow sign to 13th-c church

Sussex Dining Pub of the Year

Although edging towards a restaurant, this tucked away and civilised place does still have some pubbiness. A couple of chairs by the fireplace are set aside for drinkers in the chatty little bar with stripped wood floors and a mix of furniture, and there are two well kept ales from breweries such as Brewsters, Dark Star or Mauldons tapped from the cask – as well as a remarkably good wine list with nine wines by the glass, farm cider and 68 malt whiskies. Most people do head, though, for the smart but informal no smoking restaurant with contemporary light wood furniture, and modern landscapes on green painted walls. As well as a set two-course (£12) and three-course (£15.75) lunch menu, there might be home-made soup (£5.25), duck liver parfait with onion marmalade and toasted brioche (£5.85), smoked haddock and chive gratinée (£6.75), crab ravioli with wild garlic dressing (£6.85), baked cornish mackerel with tzatziki (£10.85), roast chump of local lamb, aubergine and piquillo pepper stew (£14.75), gressingham duck breast with golden raisins and armagnac (£15.95), poached wild halibut fillet, samphire and capers (£16.85), and puddings such as chocolate tart, grappa panna cotta with raspberry prosecco jelly, and apricot, walnut and ginger toffee pudding (from £5.75). There are rustic tables and benches under gnarled trees in a pretty cottagey front garden with more on the terrace and the front bricked area, and the large back lawn with a children's play area looks out towards the South Downs; good walks nearby. *(Recommended by Cathy Robinson, Ed Coombe, Pamela Goodwyn, A C English, Margaret and Anthony D'Arcy, Michael and Ann Cole, Tracey and Stephen Groves, Roger Hancock, Tony Curtis, Alison Stewart)*

Free house ~ Licensee Bruce Wass ~ Real ale ~ Bar food (till 10 Fri and Sat; not Sun evening) ~ Restaurant ~ (01273) 890400 ~ Children welcome ~ Dogs welcome ~ Open 12-2.30, 6-11; 12-4 Sun; closed Sun evening, all day Mon (except bank hols)

EAST DEAN SU9012 Map 2

Star & Garter ⑪ ♀

Village signposted with Charlton off A286 in Singleton; also signposted off A285; note that there are two East Deans in Sussex (this one is N of Chichester) – OS Sheet 197 map reference 904129

Inside this quietly set brick and flint dining pub, it is more or less one roomy square area, with sturdy and individual mainly stripped and scrubbed tables in various sizes and an interesting variety of seating from country-kitchen chairs through chunky modern dining chairs to cushioned pews and some handsome 17th-c or 18th-c carved oak seats; broad stripped boards, a few stripped beams, and some stripped panelling and masonry. The high ceiling, big windows and uncluttered walls give a light and airy feel, and tables over on the right-hand side can be booked; helpful, welcoming owners and staff, an easy-going atmosphere, a rack of daily papers by the entrance, and piped music. The bar counter (with a few bar stools, often used for those reading menus) is over on the left, with a dozen or so well chosen wines by the glass, well kept Ballards Trotton, Best and Nyewood Gold tapped from casks in a back stillroom, a couple of farm ciders such as Weston's and Whitehead's, a dozen malt whiskies, and an espresso machine. As well as lunchtime filled baguettes (from £4.50) and ploughman's with home-made chutney (£6), the imaginative food might include home-made soup (£4.50), smoked chicken, chorizo and red onion or feta and roasted pepper salads (£5.50; main course £9.50), home-made steak and kidney pudding (£9.75), crab and sherry bake or chicken breast with a herb crust with bordelaise sauce (£11), roast pigeon breasts with raspberry and brandy sauce (£12), duck breast with stilton and port (£13), and rump of lamb with rosemary rösti in a sage, orange and redcurrant jus (£13.50); there's also a shellfish bar with dressed selsey crab (£8.50; large £10.50), hand-carved wild smoked salmon (£8.50; large £12), and platter (£32 for two). The sheltered terrace

behind has teak tables and chairs with big canvas parasols and heaters; steps go up
to a walled lawn with picnic-sets (there are also a few steps up to the front door).
The pub is well placed for walks, and on the South Downs Way. *(Recommended
by Jeremy and Angela Williams, Richard Haw, Ann and Colin Hunt, Mrs J A Sales,
Cathy Robinson, Ed Coombe, Mrs Brenda Calver, J P Humphery)*

Free house ~ Licensee Oliver Ligertwood ~ Real ale ~ Bar food (12-2.30, 6.30-10) ~
Restaurant ~ (01243) 811318 ~ Children in restaurant ~ Dogs welcome ~ Live music
Tues evening ~ Open 11.30-3, 6-11; 11-11 Sat; 12-10.30 Sun ~ Bedrooms:
£50S(£70B)/£80S(£100B)

EAST DEAN TV5597 Map 3

Tiger ♀

Pub (with village centre) signposted – not vividly – from A259 Eastbourne—Seaford;
note that there's another East Dean in Sussex, over near Chichester, see above entry

The delightful cottage-lined green here makes a perfect setting for this long low
white tiled pub with its lovely summer flowering climbers and window boxes.
Inside, there are just nine tables in the two smallish rooms (candlelit at night) so
space at peak times is very limited – particularly in winter when you can't stand
outside or sit on the grass; they don't, in the best pub tradition, take bookings so
you do have to arrive early for a table. There are low beams hung with pewter and
china, polished rustic tables and distinctive antique settles, and old prints and so
forth. Well kept Harveys Best with guests such as Brakspears Bitter or Flowers IPA
on handpump, and a good choice of wines with a dozen by the large glass; cribbage
and dominoes. They get their fish fresh from Hastings, their lamb from the farm on
the hill, all vegetables and eggs from another local farm, and meat from the local
butcher. From a sensibly short but ever changing menu, the imaginative food at
lunchtime might include a choice of around 14 or more different ploughmans
(£6.50), a bowl of feta, hummous, black olives and cherry tomato salad or haddock
and leek mornay (£7.95), casseroles of pork in cider or rich beef burgundy (£8.95),
home-made salmon fishcakes with lemon mayonnaise or fresh crab salad (£9.95),
and fresh large whole prawns (£10.95); in the evening, there might be locally
smoked breast of duck salad or hot smoked salmon with a pink peppercorn and
sweet chilli sauce (£8.95), chicken wrapped in bacon with a white wine sauce on
tagliatelle (£9.95), and fresh whole lobster (£14.95). At lunchtimes on hot days and
bank holidays they usually have only cold food. The South Downs Way is close by
so it's naturally popular with walkers, and the lane leads on down to a fine stretch
of coast culminating in Beachy Head. No children inside. *(Recommended by Philip and
Ann Board, Sue Demont, Tim Barrow, Mike Gorton, Andrea Rampley, John Beeken,
Miss Valerie Eckl, Sebastian and Paris Leach, Michael and Ann Cole, Jenny and Peter Lowater,
Michael B Griffith, Jennifer Fisher, Kevin Thorpe, Prof and Mrs S Barnett, Alan Sadler,
C J Roebuck, Geoff and Molly Betteridge)*

Free house ~ Licensee Nicholas Denyer ~ Real ale ~ Bar food ~ (01323) 423209 ~
Dogs welcome ~ Open 11-3, 6-11; 11-11 Sat; 12-10.30 Sun

EAST HOATHLY TQ5116 Map 3

Foresters Arms

Village signposted off A22 Hailsham—Uckfield (take south-easternmost of the two turn-
offs); South Street

Undergoing some exterior refurbishment as we went to press, this village pub has a
relaxed local atmosphere, and some emphasis on the well liked food. The bar has
two small linked rooms, with just a handful of tables on its parquet floor (one in a
bow window), simple pub seating including a sturdy winged settle, eau de nil
wallpaper and dark woodwork; the one on the right has a small art nouveau
fireplace under a big mirror, and its ceiling is papered with sheet music, from
J S Bach to 'Yes! We Have No Bananas!' and french songs of a similar vintage.
Back from here is a bigger room with mulberry walls and ceiling over a panelled
dado, a collection of musical instruments on one wall, a piano, and some sturdy

cushioned oak settles; darts, cribbage, dominoes and shove-ha'penny. Popular bar food might include sandwiches (from £3.50), deep-fried whitebait with home-made tartare sauce (£4.50), parma ham and goats cheese salad (£4.95), ploughman's or filo wrapped king prawns with sweet chilli dip (£5.95), mushroom korma (£6.75), ham and eggs (£6.95), sausage and mash (£7.95), mint marinated lamb chops (£9.95), and puddings like sticky toffee pudding or chocolate brownie (£3.95); take-away curry or fish and chips (£6). On the left, a charming library-style no smoking carpeted dining room, not cut off from the rest of the pub, has just five candlelit tables. Under high beams, hop bines and copper pans, the mahogany bar counter has well kept Harveys Best, Pale Ale and Old on handpump, ten wines by the glass, and good coffee. There may be unobtrusive piped music. Service is informal and friendly, and there is good wheelchair access. A few picnic-sets with cocktail parasols stand out in front. *(Recommended by BOB, John Beeken)*

Harveys ~ Tenants Gary Skipsey and Lindsay Coates ~ Real ale ~ Bar food (12-2.15, 7-9.15; not Sun evening or Mon or Tues lunchtime) ~ Restaurant ~ (01825) 840208 ~ Children in eating area of bar and restaurant ~ Dogs allowed in bar ~ Live music Thurs evening ~ Open 11-3, 5-11; 12-10.30 Sun; closed Mon and Tues lunchtime in winter

ELSTED SU8119 Map 2

Three Horseshoes 🍺

Village signposted from B2141 Chichester—Petersfield; also reached easily from A272 about 2 miles W of Midhurst, turning left heading W

This 16th-c pub used to be a drovers' rest and is set at the end of a hamlet below the sweep of the South Downs; the summer garden is lovely with free-roaming bantams, plenty of tables, pretty flowers and marvellous views. Inside, it is friendly and cheerful and the snug little rooms have ancient beams and flooring, antique furnishings, log fires, fresh flowers on the tables, attractive prints and photographs, candlelight, and a very congenial atmosphere. Well liked bar food includes home-made soup (£3.95), a generous ploughman's with a good choice of cheeses or mozzarella and bacon salad or avocado and stilton with mushroom sauce and topped with bacon (£6.95), seasonal game pie, chicken breast with wild mushrooms and madeira, cottage pie or roasted romano pepper with spinach, cheese and pine nuts (all £9.95), venison fillet with port and redcurrant (£15.95), and puddings like lemon and ginger crunch, raspberry and hazelnut meringue or summer strawberry and passion fruit cheesecake (£4.95). The dining room is no smoking. Well kept changing ales racked on a stillage behind the bar counter might include Ballards Best, Cheriton Pots Ale and Timothy Taylors Landlord with guests like Fullers London Pride or Hop Back Summer Lightning; summer cider; dominoes. *(Recommended by John Hale, Tony and Wendy Hobden, Ann and Colin Hunt, R B Gardiner, John Davis, Tony Radnor, William Ruxton, Martin Edwards, Roger Endersby, Michael B Griffith, Peter Lewis, Geoff and Linda Payne)*

Free house ~ Licensee Sue Beavis ~ Real ale ~ Bar food ~ (01730) 825746 ~ Well behaved children in eating areas ~ Dogs allowed in bar ~ Open 11-2.30, 6-11; 12-3, 7-10.30 Sun

FERNHURST SU8926 Map 2

Kings Arms ♀ 🍺

A286 towards Midhurst

Without losing its comfortable feel this 17th-c dining pub had a bit of a face-lift recently. The inside was completely repainted and updated, all the furniture was replaced – as was the crockery and glass – and more shelves and cabinets were added in the back bar area. A fireplace was opened up in the bar and a woodburner installed. The no smoking main area, on the left, is all set for eating, but keeps a traditional feel, especially at the far end with its big log fire under a long low mantelbeam. Past here is a smaller room, with a display of often intriguing bottle openers, as well as the main concentration of the wine-oriented pictures which form the pub's decorative theme. The choice of wines is good and interesting, with plenty by the glass. People dropping in just for a drink feel entirely at home, with friendly service, a table of local newspapers, and a pleasantly chatty seating area on the right. Well kept kept Hogs Back TEA and Crop Circle, Kings Horsham Best Bitter, Triple fff Moondance and Ringwood Fortyniner on handpump. Using seasonal local produce, well liked bar food includes lunchtime filled baguettes (from £7.50) and ploughman's (£7.95), as well as soup (£5), line-caught local trout seared with garlic (£6.25), coarse pork terrine with apple chutney (£6.50), corned beef hash with fried free-range egg (£10), beer battered cod fillet (£12), free-range chicken breast with pancetta and grain mustard sauce (£13.25), rack of local lamb with rosemary sautéed potatoes and redcurrant jus (£13.95), and puddings like rhubarb and custard fool, cardamom and cinnamon poached pears with crème anglaise or warm chocolate brownies (from £5). A fair-sized garden has green picnic-sets under cocktail parasols or shaded by a weeping willow; though it is completely screened from the road, there is some traffic noise. If you are heading south, take particular care leaving the car park. *(Recommended by Andy and Jill Kassube, Wendy Arnold, Mike Bowden, Martin and Karen Wake, John Evans, Edwina Messer)*

Free house ~ Licensees Michael and Annabel Hirst ~ Real ale ~ Bar food (12-2.30, 7-9.30 (best to check on bank hols)) ~ Restaurant ~ (01428) 652005 ~ Children in restaurant lunchtime only ~ Dogs allowed in bar ~ Open 11.30-3, 5.30(6.30 Sat)-11; 12-3 Sun; closed Sun evening

FITTLEWORTH TQ0118 Map 2

Swan 🛏

Lower Street

Perhaps the nicest place to sit in summer here is at one of the well spaced tables on the big back lawn, sheltered by flowering shrubs and a hedge sprawling with honeysuckle; there are also benches by the village lane in front of this pretty tile-hung inn. Inside, the beamed main bar is comfortable and relaxed with windsor armchairs and bar stools on the part stripped wood and part carpeted floor, there are wooden truncheons over the big inglenook fireplace (which has good winter log fires), and well kept Fullers London Pride and Gales HSB on handpump. The restaurant is no smoking. Bar food includes lunchtime open sandwich platters (£6.50), ploughman's (£6.75), home-made soup (£4.25), baked goats cheese tart with roasted red peppers (£5.95), tuna carpaccio (£6.35), vegetable stir fry (£8.95), fishy rarebit, pie of the day or liver and bacon (£9.95), cajun chicken (£11.95), and stir-fried oriental beef (£12.95). Good nearby walks in beech woods. *(Recommended by Jenny and Brian Seller, Brenda and Rob Fincham, Barry Collett, Cathy Robinson, Ed Coombe, Colin McKerrow, Alan Sadler, Tony and Wendy Hobden, Richard Waller, Pauline Smith, MRSM)*

Enterprise ~ Lease Mr and Mrs Warriner ~ Real ale ~ Bar food (not winter Sun evening) ~ Restaurant ~ (01798) 865429 ~ Children in eating area of bar and restaurant ~ Dogs allowed in bar ~ Open 11-3, 5-11; 12-4, 7-10.30 Sun ~ Bedrooms: £45B/£85B

FLETCHING TQ4223 Map 3

Griffin ★ ⊕ ♀ 🛏

Village signposted off A272 W of Uckfield

With plenty to do nearby, this civilised old inn is a good base for an overnight stay. The beamed and quaintly panelled bar rooms have quite a mix of customers, a bustling atmosphere, blazing log fires, old photographs and hunting prints, straightforward close-set furniture including some captain's chairs, and china on a delft shelf. There's a small bare-boarded serving area off to one side, and a snug separate bar with sofas and TV; the restaurant is no smoking. As well as weekday lunchtime filled ciabattas (from £5.95), the modern cooking might include home-made soup (£4.95), risotto of pancetta, spinach and pine nuts with parmesan (£6.50), chicken, pigeon and venison terrine with pear chutney or marinated fresh squid salad (£6.95), fresh crab bruschetta with spring onion, chilli and lemon aïoli (£7.50), chargrilled local sausages with onion gravy or sweet potato, oyster mushrooms and taleggio tart (£8.95), caesar salad with chicken breast, croûtons and anchovies or local venison cobbler (£9.50), honey-glazed confit of duck with puy lentils (£12.50), chargrilled rib-eye steak with home-made chips (£14.50), and puddings like chocolate brownie with chocolate sauce, vanilla and grappa panna cotta with spiced apricot and almond compote or treacle tart (£4.95). When busy, service can slow down. Well kept Badger Tanglefoot, Harveys Best, and Kings Horsham Best Bitter on handpump, and a fine wine list with 14 (including champagne) by the glass. The two acres of garden behind the pub look across fine rolling countryside towards Sheffield Park, and there are plenty of seats here and on the newly paved terrace with its new woodburning oven. *(Recommended by Joel Dobris, Liz and Tony Colman, Michael Porter, Leigh Lain Walker, Mrs Jane Kingsbury, A P Seymour, JMC, Peter Meister, Simon Rodway, Christopher Turner, Walter and Susan Rinaldi-Butcher, Philip Vernon, Kim Maidment, Uta and John Owlett, Mike Gorton, Susan May, N R White, Tom and Ruth Rees)*

Free house ~ Licensees J Pullan, T Erlam, M W Wright ~ Real ale ~ Bar food (12-2.30, 7-9.30(9 Sun)) ~ Restaurant ~ (01825) 722890 ~ Children in eating area of bar and restaurant ~ Dogs allowed in bar ~ Jazz Fri evening and Sun lunchtime ~ Open 12-3, 6-11; 12-11(10.30 Sun) Sat; closed 25 Dec ~ Bedrooms: /£95B

HEATHFIELD TQ5920 Map 3

Star 🍺

Old Heathfield – head East out of Heathfield itself on A265, then fork right on to B2096; turn right at signpost to Heathfield Church then keep bearing right; pub on left immediately after church

In warm weather, the prettily planted garden here with its rustic furniture under smart umbrellas and lovely views of rolling oak-lined sheep pastures is extremely popular. Turner thought it fine enough to paint. But inside on a cold day, this fine old pub is just as enjoyable, and you can expect a warm welcome from the friendly staff. With a bustling, relaxed atmosphere and a good mix of both locals and visitors, the L-shaped beamed bar has a good log fire in the inglenook fireplace, panelling, built-in wall settles and window seats, and just four or five tables; a doorway leads into a similarly furnished smaller room. The tables are candlelit at night. Chalked up on boards, the well liked food might include home-made soup (£4.75), home-made chicken liver or smoked mackerel pâté (£5.75), moules marinière (£6.50; main course £8.50), smoked ham and two free-range eggs (£7.95), cold meats and bubble and squeak (£8.50), home-made steak and mushroom pie or local fish and chips (£8.75), cumberland sausage with red wine and onion gravy (£9.50), pasta tossed with smoked salmon, sun-dried tomatoes, greek olives, basil, garlic and cream (£10.25), half shoulder of lamb in rosemary, garlic and redcurrant (£13.95), and half a free-range duckling with tangy honey and orange sauce (£14.95); efficient, courteous service. You must book to be sure of a table (and get there early to bag a parking space in the car park). Well kept Harveys Best, Shepherd Neame Best Bitter and a guest such as Welton Old Harry on handpump, half a dozen wines by the glass, Pimms by the jug, and a good bloody mary; piped music, shove-ha'penny, cribbage and bar billiards. *(Recommended by Marc Hadley, E G Parish, John Hendy , Matthew Lidbury, Susan and John Douglas, Ron Gentry)*

Free house ~ Licensees Mike Chappell and Fiona Airey ~ Real ale ~ Bar food (12-2.15, 7-9.30) ~ Restaurant ~ (01435) 863570 ~ Children in eating area of bar ~ Dogs welcome ~ Open 11.30-3, 5.30-11; 12-4, 7-10.30 Sun; closed evenings 25 and 26 Dec

---

Real ale to us means beer which has matured naturally in its cask – not pressurised or filtered. We name all real ales stocked. We usually name ales preserved under a light blanket of carbon dioxide too, though purists – pointing out that this stops the natural yeasts developing – would disagree (most people, including us, can't tell the difference!)

HERMITAGE SU7505 Map 2
Sussex Brewery
A259 just inside Sussex boundary, by Thorney Island turn just W of Emsworth

Handy for the ferries at Portsmouth, this is a cheerful pub with a bustling atmosphere and a good mix of customers. The bar is quite small, with sawdust (yes, real sawdust) on bare boards, an old wing armchair by the huge brick fireplace (with a good winter log fire – there's a second little blue-tiled Victorian fireplace opposite it, also used), simple seats, four tables (two painted as inn signs, one as thrown-down playing cards), and small brewery mirrors on yellowing walls. Well kept Youngs Bitter, Special and Waggle Dance and a guest beer such as Smiles Best on handpump from the dark brick counter, and up to a dozen wines by the glass; friendly helpful staff; no machines or piped music. At the end of the bar, a little flagstoned snug with small polished pews around just two tables is kept food-free at night; shove-ha'penny, cribbage and dominoes. Down a flagstoned passage, a snug pink-walled carpeted back no smoking dining room has comfortable plush chairs, and there's a second little no smoking dining room overlooking the garden. The main event on the menu are the speciality sausages, over 40 different and often unusual varieties such as chicken, roquefort and port, mushroom and tarragon, hot and spicy beef, pigeon, brandy, herbs and quince jelly, and local pork with real ale, cheese and grained mustard (from £6.10). Also, filled baked potatoes (from £4.35), ploughman's (from £5.95), salads (from £6.25), prawn curry or steak and mushroom in ale pudding (£7.25), poached smoked haddock (£10.90), and steaks (from £14.50). There are picnic-sets in a small enclosed back courtyard, with one or two more out by the side. (Recommended by Ann and Colin Hunt, Andy and Jill Kassube, J Metcalfe, Tony Hobden, Ian Phillips, Steve Whalley, Tracey and Stephen Groves, John Beeken, Mike and Mary Carter)

Youngs ~ Tenant David Roberts ~ Real ale ~ Bar food (12-2.30, 7-10) ~ Restaurant ~ (01243) 371533 ~ Children welcome ~ Dogs allowed in bar ~ Open 11-11; 12-10.30 Sun

HORSHAM TQ1730 Map 3
Black Jug ♀
31 North Street

Useful for the area, this is an airy open-plan turn-of-the-century-style room (now partly no smoking) with a large central bar, a nice collection of heavy sizeable dark wood tables, and comfortable chairs on a stripped wood floor; the cream walls are crammed with interesting old prints and photographs above a dark wood panelled dado, and there's a warm terracotta ceiling. A spacious no smoking conservatory has similar furniture and lots of hanging baskets; piped music. Well kept Greene King Old Speckled Hen, Everards Tiger, Jennings Golden Host, Marstons Pedigree, and Weltons Black Jug and maybe Horsham Old on handpump, 40 malt whiskies, and 24 wines by the glass. Bar food includes bread things (bloomers, bruschetta, sourdough bread and so forth with various toppings or fillings, from £4.25), wild mushroom and parmesan risotto (£4.95), home-made chicken liver pâté with home-made beetroot chutney (£5.50), herb omelette with cheese and red onion (£7.50), bangers and mash or smoked haddock and salmon fishcakes with dill and lemon mayonnaise (£7.95), chargrilled chicken caesar salad (£8.95), beef in ale with dumplings (£9.50), 10oz rib-eye steak with béarnaise sauce (£13.95), and home-made puddings like white chocolate mousse with Cointreau sauce or rhubarb and apple bread and butter pudding (£4.50). The pretty flower-filled back terrace has plenty of garden furniture by outside heaters. The small car park is for staff and deliveries only but you can park next door in the council car park. More reports please. (Recommended by Wombat, Guy Vowles, Martin and Karen Wake, Dave Lowe, Mark Killman)

Brunning & Price ~ Managers Myles Abell and Nick Stafford ~ Real ale ~ Bar food (all day) ~ (01403) 253526 ~ Children in restaurant until 6pm ~ Dogs allowed in bar ~ Open 12-11; 12-10.30 Sun

ICKLESHAM TQ8716 Map 3

Queens Head ♀ ◖

Just off A259 Rye—Hastings

Always welcoming and friendly, this handsome pub is consistently liked by our readers. The open-plan areas work round a very big serving counter which stands under a vaulted beamed roof, the high beamed walls and ceiling of the easy-going bar are lined with shelves of bottles and covered with farming implements and animal traps, and there are well used pub tables and old pews on the brown patterned carpet. Other areas (two are no smoking and popular with diners) have big inglenook fireplaces, and the back room is decorated with old bicycle and motorbike prints. Well kept Courage Directors and Greene King IPA and Abbot, with guests like Daleside Shrimpers, Grand Union Honey Porter and North Yorkshire Flying Herbert on handpump, Biddenden cider, and a dozen wines by the glass. Reasonably priced, decent home-made bar food includes sandwiches (from £2.45), soup (£3.50), filled baked potatoes (from £3.95), chicken liver pâté (£4.50), ploughman's (from £4.95), home-cooked ham and eggs (£5.95), thai vegetable curry (£7.25), home-made steak and kidney pudding (£9.95), steaks (from £9.95), seven fresh fish dishes (from £6.95), and puddings such as banoffi pie or fruit crumble (£3.25); prompt service from efficient staff. Shove-ha'penny, dominoes, cribbage, darts, fruit machine and piped music. Picnic-sets look out over the vast, gently sloping plain of the Brede Valley from the little garden, and there's an outside children's play area, and boules. Good local walks. *(Recommended by Colin McKerrow, Brian Root, Wombat, John Davis, Paul A Moore, Kevin Thorpe, John Hendy, E G Parish, Peter Meister, Michael and Ann Cole, Stephen C Harvey, Bruce Bird, Ian and Nita Cooper)*

Free house ~ Licensee Ian Mitchell ~ Real ale ~ Bar food (12-2.30, 6.15-9.30; all day Sat, Sun and bank hols; not 25 or 26 Dec) ~ (01424) 814552 ~ Well behaved children in eating area of bar until 8.30pm ~ Dogs welcome ~ Live jazz/blues/folk Thurs evening ~ Open 11-11; 12-10.30 Sun

LODSWORTH SU9223 Map 2

Halfway Bridge Inn ♀ ⇌

Just before village, on A272 Midhurst—Petworth

New licensees have taken over this civilised inn and have done some refurbishment both inside and out. The three or four bar rooms are comfortably furnished with good oak chairs and an individual mix of tables, and down some steps is the no smoking restaurant area; one of the log fires is contained in a well polished kitchen range. Well kept Arundel Gold, Ballards Best Bitter and Cheriton Pots Ale on handpump, and a thoughtful little wine list with a changing choice by the glass; piped music and TV. From a short menu, bar food now includes lunchtime sandwiches (from £5.25), soup (£4.75), fried whitebait with caper mayonnaise (£5), smoked caesar salad (£7.50), seared king scallops with sweet tomato salsa (£8.50), warm glazed ham, fried egg and bubble and squeak (£8.75), beer battered fish (£10.50), steak, kidney and mushroom suet pudding (£11), wild mushroom risotto (£12), calves liver and smoked bacon (£13.50), 10oz sirloin steak (£15), and puddings such as spiced apple and apricot crumble or crème brûlée with peanut butter cookies (£4.95). At the back there are new seats on a small terrace. More reports on the new regime, please. *(Recommended by Darren and Jane Staniforth, John Davis, JCW, Ann and Stephen Saunders, John Evans, Mrs Sheela Curtis, John Cooper, Bruce Bird, Basil Wynbergen, Martin and Karen Wake, Irene and Derek Flewin, Colin McKerrow)*

Free house ~ Licensee Nick Sutherland ~ Real ale ~ Bar food ~ Restaurant ~ (01798) 861281 ~ Children in eating area of bar and restaurant ~ Dogs allowed in bar ~ Open 11-11; 12-10.30 Sun ~ Bedrooms: £60B/£90B

It is illegal for bar staff to smoke while handling your drink.

OVING SU9005 Map 2

Gribble Inn ◗

Between A27 and A259 just E of Chichester, then should be signposted just off village road; OS Sheet 197 map reference 900050

As this 16th-c thatched pub is owned by Badger, you might find the own-brewed real ales from here at other pubs owned by the brewery as well: Gribble Ale, Pigs Ear, Plucking Pheasant, Reg's Tipple, Slurping Stoat and winter Wobbler, plus Badger Best and Fursty Ferret on handpump. Also decent wine and farm cider. There's a cottagey feel in the several linked rooms, and the chatty bar has lots of heavy beams and timbering, and old country-kitchen furnishings and pews. The dining room and family room are no smoking. The new licensees tell us bar food prices have not changed since last year: lunchtime sandwiches (from £4.95), ploughman's (£5.75), ham and eggs (£7.25), red pepper and spinach lasagne (£7.95), sausage and mash (£8.25), beer-battered fish or steak, ale and mushroom pie (£8.50), steaks (from £11.95), and puddings (£4.50). Cribbage, dominoes and a separate skittle alley. There's a covered seating area, and more chairs in the pretty garden with apple and pear trees. *(Recommended by J A Snell, Vanessa Stilwell, Ann and Colin Hunt, Andy and Jill Kassube, R B Gardiner, David H T Dimock, Mike and Lynn Robinson, Roy and Lindsey Fentiman, Val and Alan Green)*

Own brew ~ Managers Dave and Linda Stone ~ Real ale ~ Bar food (12-2.30, 6-9.30) ~ Restaurant ~ (01243) 786893 ~ Children in family room only ~ Dogs allowed in bar ~ Jazz first Tues of month, folk every Tues, mix of bands alternate Fri ~ Open 11-11; 12-10.30 Sun; 11-3, 5.30-11 winter weekdays

PETWORTH SU9921 Map 2

Welldiggers Arms

Low Heath; A283 towards Pulborough

Although there's likely to be a chatty group of locals around the bar, most visitors come to this country pub with its unassuming style and appearance to enjoy the food. The smallish L-shaped bar has low beams, a few pictures (Churchill and gun dogs are prominent) on shiny ochre walls above a panelled dado, a couple of very long rustic settles with tables to match, and some other stripped tables (many are laid for eating); a second rather lower side room has a somewhat lighter décor. No music or machines. Youngs on handpump, and decent wines. Popular home-made food includes sandwiches (from £3.50), french onion soup or ploughman's (£5.50), smooth duck pâté (£5.95), home-made cottage pie (£6.50), courgette, tomato and cheese bake (£7.25), home-cooked ham and egg (£7.50), grilled king prawns in garlic (£9.50), smoked haddock on spinach with chive butter sauce or steak, Guinness and stilton pie (£9.95), and steaks (from £14.50). Outside, screened from the road by a thick high hedge, are plenty of tables and chairs on pleasant lawns and a terrace, looking back over rolling fields and woodland. *(Recommended by John Davis, Mrs J A Sales, Peter Lewis)*

Free house ~ Licensee Ted Whitcomb ~ Real ale ~ Bar food (see opening hours) ~ (01798) 342287 ~ Children welcome ~ Dogs welcome ~ Open 11-3, 6-11; closed Mon; closed evenings Tues, Weds and Sun

RUSHLAKE GREEN TQ6218 Map 3

Horse & Groom

Village signposted off B2096 Heathfield—Battle

This is an attractive setting with the village green just across the little lane, and the cottagey garden has oak seats and tables made by the landlord, and pretty country views. Inside, the little L-shaped bar has low beams (watch your head) and is simply furnished with high bar stools and bar chairs, red plush cushioned wall seats and a few brocaded cushioned stools, and a brick fireplace with some brass items on the mantelpiece; horsebrasses, photographs of the pub and local scenes on the walls, and fresh flowers. A small room down a step has jockeys' colours and jockey photographs and watercolours of the pub. To the right of the entrance is the heavily beamed no smoking restaurant with guns and hunting trophies on the walls, plenty of wheelback chairs around pubby tables, and a log fire. Listed on boards by the entrance to the bar, the large choice of popular bar food might include home-made soup (£4.50), home-made chicken liver pâté (£5.50), asparagus sautéed with crispy pancetta and a smoked mozzarella croûton (£6.95), fresh scallops with spring onions, bacon and buttery oyster sauce in a puff pastry shell (£7.95), steak and kidney in Guinness pudding (£10.95), organic salmon fishcakes (£11.95), red thai tiger prawn curry (£12.95), halibut with parsley pesto on jerusalem artichokes and a red pepper coulis (£14.95), and marinated chump of lamb on dauphinoise potatoes with port wine sauce (£15.95). Well kept Harveys Best and Shepherd Neame Master Brew and Spitfire on handpump, and several wines by the glass. More reports please. *(Recommended by John Davis, Ron Gentry)*

Free house ~ Licensees Mike and Sue Chappel ~ Real ale ~ Bar food ~ Restaurant ~ (01435) 830320 ~ Children welcome ~ Dogs welcome ~ Open 11.30-3, 5.30-11; 12-3, 7-10.30 Sun

RYE TQ9220 Map 3
Mermaid ♀ ⇤

Mermaid Street

The beautiful black and white façade, with its distinctive sign hanging over the steeply cobbled street, has barely altered since this hotel was built in the 15th and 16th c. It's extremely civilised with prices to match, and the little bar is where those in search of a light lunch and a drink tend to head for: quite a mix of quite closely set furnishings such as Victorian gothic carved oak chairs, older but plainer oak seats and more modern ones in character, and a massive deeply polished bressumer beam across one wall for the huge inglenook fireplace. Three antique but not ancient wall paintings show old English scenes. Well kept Courage Best on handpump, a good wine list, and a short choice of bar food such as sandwiches (from £6), chargrilled chicken caesar salad (£8), open goats cheese and spinach omelette or moules marinière (£8.50), minute steak with blue cheese salad (£10.50), seafood platter for two (£29), and puddings (£5.50). The smart (expensive) restaurant is no smoking; piped music (bar only), dominoes and cribbage. Seats on a small back terrace overlook the car park – where there are morris dancers on bank holiday weekends. *(Recommended by Nick Lawless, Joel Dobris, Sue Demont, Tim Barrow, the Didler, John Davis, Jason Reynolds, Ann and Colin Hunt, Michael Dandy, Andrea Rampley, Sean and Sharon Pines)*

Free house ~ Licensees Robert Pinwill and Mrs J Blincow ~ Real ale ~ Bar food (12-2.30, 6.30-9) ~ Restaurant ~ (01797) 223065 ~ Children in eating area of bar and restaurant ~ Open 12-11(10.30 Sun) ~ Bedrooms: £85S(£90B)/£180B

Ypres Castle ♀ ◗

Gun Garden; steps up from A259, or down past Ypres Tower

From the large, sheltered garden here (and from the windows), you look over the River Rother with its working fishing fleet, and on further to Romney Marsh and the sea. Inside, the bars are traditionally furnished with antique furniture and rugs and there's a big eclectic art collection, and a winter log fire surrounded by comfortable chairs; above the bar on a piece of driftwood is a series of tiles depicting typical local marshy scenes. You can eat in the large no smoking room, the more informal bar area or the comfortable no smoking restaurant, and although bar food is served at lunchtime only, in the evening you can enjoy the restaurant food in the bar. From the lunchtime menu, there might be wild mushroom soup (£3.95), filled baguettes (from £4.25), filled baked potatoes (from £5.50), ploughman's (£5.95), home-cooked ham and egg (£6.75), game pâté (£6.95), prosciutto, fig and rocket salad (£8.95), and daily specials; in the evening there are main courses such as bell peppers filled with spicy vegetable risotto (£7.25), whole cracked local crab (£9.95), 10oz sirloin steak with brandy and peppercorn sauce (£12.95), roast duck breast with port and orange sauce or rack of local lamb with redcurrant and mint sauce (£12.50), and bass with local samphire (£14.95). Vegetables are extra which bumps up the price; friendly service. Well kept Adnams Broadside, Fullers London Pride, Harveys Best and Wells Bombardier on handpump, 12 wines by the glass, Biddenden cider and wine, and local fresh fruit juices; shove-ha'penny, cribbage, dominoes and piped music. During the September arts festival several events are held here. Locals tend to call the pub 'Wipers' in true WWI style. *(Recommended by Sue Austin, Gwyn Jones, Sue Demont, Tim Barrow, Stephen C Harvey, B and M Kendall, Peter Meister, Barry Ashton, Louise English)*

Free house ~ Licensees Tom Cosgrove and Michael Gage ~ Real ale ~ Bar food (12-2.30, 7-9; not Sun evening or winter Tues) ~ Restaurant ~ (01797) 223248 ~ Children allowed if eating but must be gone by 9pm ~ Dogs allowed in bar ~ Open 11.30-3, 6-11; all day during school hols; 11.30-11 Sat; 12-4 Sun; closed Sun evening, winter Tues ~ Live music Fri evening

SALEHURST TQ7424 Map 3
Salehurst Halt ♀
Village signposted from Robertsbridge bypass on A21 Tunbridge Wells—Battle Road

In summer, the charming and pretty back garden behind this little pub is a suntrap, and there are terraces and picnic-sets for outside meals; the front window boxes and tubs are most attractive. Quieter at lunchtime but more lively in the evening, the L-shaped bar has plain wooden tables and chairs on flagstones at one end, a cushioned window seat, beams, a little open brick fireplace, a time punch clock, and olde worlde pictures; lots of hops on a big beam divide this from the beamed carpeted area with its mix of tables, wheelback and farmhouse chairs, and a half wall leads to a no smoking dining area. Good interesting bar food includes lunchtime baguettes (around £5.95) as well as field mushroom stuffed with goats cheese (£5.95), home-cured salt beef (£6.95), wild smoked salmon with a ruby chard salad (£5.95; main course £8.95), warm chicken salad (£7.95), popular lunchtime home-made burgers (£8), beef in ale pie (£8.95), mediterranean vegetable couscous stack (£9.95), gressingham duck breast with teriyaki sauce and crispy noodles (£10.95), steaks (from £10.95; fillet steak on sweet potato dauphinoise topped with porcini mushroom pâté £16.95), and puddings such as home-made treacle sponge with custard or fruit crumbles (£4.25). Well kept Harveys Best and a guest beer on handpump, and good wines. Best to book in advance to be sure of a table at weekends; piped music. More reports please. *(Recommended by John Saville, Kevin Thorpe, M Sage, Ian and Nita Cooper)*

Free house ~ Licensees Claire and Hossein Refahi ~ Real ale ~ Bar food (not Sun evening or Mon) ~ Restaurant ~ (01580) 880620 ~ Children in restaurant ~ Dogs allowed in bar ~ Open 12-3, 6.30-11(10.30 Sun); closed Mon

SINGLETON SU8713 Map 2
Partridge
Just off A286 Midhurst—Chichester; heading S into the village, the main road bends sharp right – keep straight ahead instead; if you miss this turn, take the Charlton road, then first left

Once the Fox & Hounds, this has been renamed the Partridge. It's been extended to include a new long bar and additional roomy table area, but the polished wooden floors, flagstones and daily papers remain, as do the smaller rooms with red settles and good winter log fires. Much of the pub is no smoking. There's quite an emphasis on the well liked honest bar food which at lunchtime might consist of home-made soup (£4.50), pâté (£5.50), cheese platter with pickles (£6.95), pasta of the day (£8.75), steak in ale pie or lambs liver and bacon (£8.95), gammon with mustard and rosemary (£9.25), with more elaborate evening dishes such as pork loin coated with french mustard and sugar with creamy mustard and cider sauce (£9.95), and seared marlin with a warm potato and basil salad or game pie (£10.50); puddings (£4.50) and Sunday roast (£9.50). Well kept Fullers London

Pride and Ringwood Best on handpump, and decent wines by the glass; no music or machines. Beyond the new extension are a terrace and a big walled garden with colourful flowerbeds and fruit trees. The Weald & Downland Open Air Museum is just down the road, and Goodwood Racecourse is not far away. *(Recommended by PL, Ann and Colin Hunt, Derek and Maggie Washington, B J Harding, Ellen Weld, David London, Susan and John Douglas, Prof and Mrs S Barnett, Lionel and Sylvia Kopelowitz, Tom and Ruth Rees)*

Enterprise ~ Lease Tony Simpson ~ Real ale ~ Bar food (all day weekends) ~ (01243) 811251 ~ Children welcome ~ Dogs allowed in bar ~ Trad jazz third Tues of month ~ Open 11.30-3, 6-11; 11.30-11 Sat; 12-11 Sun

TROTTON SU8323 Map 2

Keepers Arms 🍴

A272 Midhurst—Petersfield; pub tucked up above road, on S side

This is a genuinely friendly place and certainly decorated in a highly individual style. The walls throughout are decorated with some unusual pictures and artefacts that reflect Jenny's previous long years of travelling the world, they have just bought two enormous african heads carved from single pieces of wood, and there is now an alligator head poking out of the woodburning stove during the summer. The beamed L-shaped bar has timbered walls and some standing timbers, sofas by the big log fire, and ethnic rugs scattered on the oak floor. Elsewhere, there are a couple of unusual adult high chairs at an oak refectory table, two huge Georgian leather high-backed chairs around another table, an interesting medley of old or antique seats, and dining tables decorated with pretty candelabra, and bowls of fruit and chillis. There's also a north african-style room with a cushioned bench around all four walls, with a large central table, rare ethnic fabrics and weavings, and a big moroccan lamp hanging in the centre. The popular restaurant is no smoking. Interesting piped music (which they change according to the customers) ranges from Buddha bar-type music to classical. Enjoyable bar food includes devilled kidneys (£5; main course £10), a lunchtime platter for two (£7 per person), cumberland sausage or hot ham and egg (£7.50), haggis, neeps and tatties (£10), thai-style salmon fishcakes with sweet chilli dipping sauce (£10.50), indonesian peanut chicken (£11), home-made pie of the day (£11.50), winter game pie (£13), hot selsey crab au gratin (£13.50), and fresh summer seafood platter (Fridays only and must be ordered by Wednesday lunchtime, £26); you must book for Sunday lunch. Well kept Ballards Best and Cheriton Diggers Gold and Pots Ale on handpump, and decent wines. Plenty of seats on the attractive, almost mediterranean-feeling south facing front terrace. Dogs lunchtime only. *(Recommended by R T and J C Moggridge, Michael and Ann Cole, Martin and Karen Wake, Nigel Clifton, Prof and Mrs S Barnett, Karen Eliot, Mrs Phoebe A Kemp, Liz and Brian Barnard)*

Free house ~ Licensee Jenny Oxley ~ Real ale ~ Bar food (not Sun evening, Mon) ~ Restaurant ~ (01730) 813724 ~ Children welcome ~ Dogs welcome ~ Live music monthly ~ Open 12-3, 6.30-11; 12-3 Sun; closed Sun evening, all Mon; Christmas

WARTLING TQ6509 Map 3

Lamb ♀

Village signposted with Herstmonceux Castle off A271 Herstmonceux—Battle

Quieter at lunchtime but more lively at night, this pleasant country pub is liked by both locals and visitors. There's a little entrance bar where locals popping in for a drink and a chat tend to gather: brocaded settles and stools and just a few tables on the green patterned carpet, a big blackboard with specials of the day, and a woodburning stove with logs stacked to one side. A narrow tiled floor area runs along the carved bar counter, and leads to the snug (mind your head on the low entrance beam) with a mix of cushioned chairs and more brocaded settles around straightforward pubby tables, and beams and timbering. The lounge has a mix of sofas and armchairs around low tables by the fireplace, and there's a restaurant, too; all the eating areas are no smoking. Piped music. Doors from here lead up steps to a back terrace with green picnic-sets, climbers on the gazebo, and flowering tubs and pots. Well kept Bass, Harveys Best and Kings Horsham Best Bitter on handpump, ten wines by the glass (including champagne), and friendly, helpful staff. Popular bar food might include soup with herb croûtons and home-made bread (£4.25), local goats cheese, toasted almond and fresh sage pâté (£5.50), local sausages and mash (£6.95), home-made pie of the day (£8.95), home-made vegetarian wellington of the day (£9.50), braised lamb shank with rosemary mash (£11.95), chicken on smoked cheddar mash with bacon and mushroom cream sauce (£12.50), local cod on grain mustard mash with fresh pea pesto (£13.95), and puddings such as iced dark chocolate and kirsch soaked cherry parfait or blackcurrant and vanilla crème brûlée (£4.95); best to book to be sure of a table. There are seats out in front. *(Recommended by Julian Petley, David Thompson, Mike Gorton, Tony and Wendy Hobden, Roy and Lindsey Fentiman, Colin and Janet Roe, Jenny and Peter Lowater, Ian and Nita Cooper)*

Free house ~ Licensees Robert and Alison Farncombe ~ Bar food (11.45-2.15, 6.45-9) ~ Restaurant ~ (01323) 832116 ~ Children in eating area of bar and restaurant ~ Dogs allowed in bar ~ Open 11-3, 6-11; 12-3, 6.30-10.30 Sun; closed Sun evening and Mon (but this may change)

WILMINGTON TQ5404 Map 3

Giants Rest

Just off A27

After a good walk, this friendly, well run and comfortable pub is a smashing place to enjoy a relaxing drink or a good meal. The long wood-floored bar and adjacent open areas, one with a log fire, are simply furnished with old pews and pine tables (each with its own bar game or wooden puzzle), and have well kept Harveys Best, Hop Back Summer Lightning and Timothy Taylors Landlord on handpump; decent wines. Well liked and generously served, the bar food might include soup (£3.50), bacon and garlic mushrooms or garlic prawns with lemon mayonnaise (£5), baked camembert in a box with crusty bread (for two, £6.50), filled baked potatoes or ploughman's (from £6.50), roasted vegetable moussaka (£8), hake, coriander, chilli, ginger and spring onion fishcakes, rabbit pie or home-cooked ham with bubble and squeak and home-made chutney (all £8.50), lamb off the bone in asparagus sauce or smoked duck and bacon salad (£10), and home-made puddings (£4). All the tables are no smoking. Sunday lunchtime is especially busy and there may not be much space for those just wanting a drink as most of the tables are booked by diners; piped music. Plenty of seats in the front garden, and the pub is watched over by the impressive chalk-carved Long Man of Wilmington at the foot of the South Downs. Elizabeth David the famous cookery writer is buried in the churchyard at nearby Folkington; her headstone is beautifully carved and features mediterranean vegetables and a casserole. Please note, they no longer do bedrooms. *(Recommended by John Hendy, Jenny and Peter Lowater, Philip and Ann Board, Anthony Longden, Mike Gorton, Fr Robert Marsh, Kevin Thorpe, Guy Vowles, Grahame Brooks, John Beeken, M and R Thomas, Paul Hopton)*

Free house ~ Licensees Adrian and Rebecca Hillman ~ Real ale ~ Bar food ~ Restaurant ~ (01323) 870207 ~ Children welcome ~ Dogs welcome ~ Open 11-3, 6-11; 11-11 Sat; 12-10.30 Sun

WINEHAM TQ2320 Map 3

Royal Oak £

Village signposted from A272 and B2116

There's quite a mix of customers in this old-fashioned and unchanging local – and dogs and children are allowed, too. It's been in the same family for over 50 years, and still has no fruit machines, piped music or even beer pumps. Logs burn in an enormous inglenook fireplace with a cast-iron Royal Oak fireback, and there's a collection of cigarette cards showing old English pubs, a stuffed stoat and crocodile, a collection of jugs, ancient corkscrews decorating the very low beams above the serving counter, and racing plates, tools and a coach horn on the walls; maybe a nice tabby cat, and views of quiet countryside from the back parlour. Well kept Harveys Best with a guest such as Wadworths 6X tapped from the cask in a stillroom; darts, shove-ha'penny, dominoes and cribbage. Bar snacks are limited to home-made winter soup (£2.75), simple sandwiches (from £2.50), and ploughman's (from £5). There are some picnic-sets outside – picturesque if you are facing the pub. *(Recommended by Brenda and Rob Fincham, John Davis, Lucy Wild, Richard May)*

Inn Business ~ Tenant Tim Peacock ~ Real ale ~ Bar food (served during opening hours) ~ No credit cards ~ (01444) 881252 ~ Children allowed away from main bar ~ Dogs allowed in bar ~ Open 11-2.30, 5.30(6 Sat)-11; 12-3, 7-10.30 Sun; closed evenings 25, 26 and 31 Dec

LUCKY DIP

Besides the fully inspected pubs, you might like to try these Lucky Dips recommended to us and described by readers (if you do, please send us reports: www.goodguides.co.uk).

ALFRISTON [TQ5203]
Olde Smugglers [Waterloo Sq]: Olde-worlde low-beamed white-panelled bar with big inglenook, plenty of bric-a-brac and smuggling mementoes, good value bar food from sandwiches to steaks, good choice of well kept real ales and of wines by the glass, friendly service; can get crowded as this lovely village draws many visitors; children allowed in eating area and conservatory, garden tables *(LYM, Ann and Colin Hunt, Michael and Ann Cole)*
☆ *Star* [High St]: Fascinating fine painted medieval carvings outside, heavy-beamed bar (busy lunchtime, quiet evenings) with chain-pub feel but some interesting features inc medieval sanctuary post, antique furnishings and big log fire in Tudor fireplace, some no smoking areas, bar food from sandwiches and baked potatoes up, well kept Bass, Fullers London Pride and Harveys Best, decent wines by the glass, good coffee, daily papers and magazines, easy chairs in comfortable lounge, restaurant; good modern bedrooms in up-to-date part behind, open all day summer *(the Didler, Tony and Wendy Hobden, LYM, Michael and Ann Cole, Mr and Mrs John Taylor)*
AMBERLEY [TQ0313]
☆ *Sportsmans* [Crossgates; Rackham Rd, off B2139]: Pleasant atmosphere in three bars and pretty little back conservatory (with terrific views, shared by tables on decking and by bedrooms), well kept changing real ales, lots of wines by the glass, neat well organised staff, generous reasonably priced food from sandwiches through sausage and mash, cottage pie and so forth to steaks; piped music may obtrude; children welcome *(LYM, Norma and Noel Thomas, Martin and Karen Wake, David H T Dimock, Francis Vernon, Cathy Robinson, Ed Coombe, Ron Gentry, Sue Demont, Tim Barrow)*
ANGMERING [TQ0604]
Lamb [The Square]: Friendly village pub with well spaced tables, lots of bric-a-brac and big fireplace, relaxed atmosphere, pleasant service,

enjoyable reasonably priced bar food (not Mon/Tues evenings) from sandwiches to huge mixed grill, well kept Harveys Best, Fullers London Pride and a guest beer, low-priced coffee; live music Sat, meat raffle Sun *(Tony and Wendy Hobden)*
☆ *Spotted Cow* [High St]: Appealing pub with smallish bar on left, long dining area with large no smoking conservatory on right, good generous food (very popular wkdy lunchtimes with older people) from imaginative sandwiches up, well kept ales such as Fullers London Pride, Greene King IPA and Old Speckled Hen, Marstons Pedigree and Ringwood Huffkin, good choice of wines by the glass, friendly and enthusiastic chef/landlord, smuggling history, sporting caricatures, cool and roomy in summer, two log fires winter, no piped music; children welcome, big garden with boules and play area; open all day Sun, afternoon jazz sometimes then, lovely walk to Highdown hill fort *(John Davis, Andy and Jill Kassube, John Beeken, W W Burke)*
ARDINGLY [TQ3429]
☆ *Gardeners Arms* [B2028 2 miles N]: Olde-worlde pub divided by standing timbers, with inglenooks, farm tools, horsebrasses, hunting horns and old local photographs, a mix of tables inc some nice old ones, hearty helpings of popular food from good baguettes up (need a table number before you queue to order), well kept Badger Best and Harveys, pleasant efficient service; may be piped pop music, no children inside; attractive wooden furniture on pretty terrace, with lots of picnic-sets in side garden; open all day at least wknds, opp S of England show ground and handy for Borde Hill and Wakehurst Place *(Susan and John Douglas, BB, Alec and Joan Laurence, David Coleman)*
Oak [Street Lane]: Beamed 14th-c dining pub handy for show ground, enjoyable reasonable priced family food (not Sun evening) inc good home-made pies, Harveys Best, Hop Back Summer Lightning and Kings Red River, good range of wines by the glass, helpful staff, olde-

worlde décor with lots of brass, bric-a-brac and lace curtains, magnificent old fireplace, bright comfortable restaurant extension; tables in pleasant garden, reservoir walks *(John Saville, Gary and Jane Turner)*

ARLINGTON [TQ5407]

☆ *Yew Tree* [off A22 nr Hailsham, or A27 W of Polegate]: Neatly modernised two-bar Victorian village local popular for wide choice of home-made food in hearty helpings (can ask for smaller) from hot filled rolls through familiar and more imaginative dishes to duck and wild boar, well kept Harveys Best, log fires, prompt cheery helpful service even when busy, darts, no smoking conservatory; children welcome, good big garden with play area by paddock with farm animals, good walks *(Graham and Carol Uren, BB, John Beeken, Andy Seares)*

ASHURST [TQ1716]

Fountain [B2135 S of Partridge Green]: Neatly kept 16th-c country pub with fine old flagstones, rustic tap room on right with some antique polished trestle tables and housekeepers' chairs by inglenook log fire, second inglenook in opened-up heavy-beamed snug, Fullers London Pride, Harveys and Kings Horsham; dogs welcome, no under-10s, prettily planted garden with duck pond *(Cathy Robinson, Ed Coombe, LYM, Brenda and Rob Fincham, M Sage)*

BARNHAM [SU9604]

☆ *Murrell Arms* [Yapton Rd]: Unspoilt and old-fashioned, masses of interesting bric-a-brac, nice old mixed furnishings and candles in bottles, cheerful public bar and simple tiny snug, very long-serving licensees, Gales and a guest beer from huge polished half-barrel bar counter, two open fires, darts, shove-ha'penny, reasonably priced straightforward bar food (not on Thurs folk night); no children or dogs; pretty flower-filled courtyard with big cider press and ancient wooden furniture under grape vine, picnic-sets in cottagey little enclosed garden up some steps, open all day wknds *(Gordon Neighbour, LYM)*

BATTLE [TQ7215]

Squirrel [North Trade Rd (A271 towards Herstmonceux)]: Generous home cooking inc their own hams and evenings with all-you-can eat curry/carvery etc, well kept beers, chatty licensees; children allowed in pool room, large family garden – but you can't eat out there on Sun till 1pm *(Klaus and Elizabeth Leist)*

BECKLEY [TQ8423]

Rose & Crown [Northiam Rd (B2088)]: Unspoilt character coaching inn, welcoming landlady, good value generous standard food from sandwiches, baguettes and baked potatoes up, well kept changing beers such as Fullers ESB, Harveys Best and Timothy Taylors Landlord, cosy eating area with log fire; children welcome, good views from garden with swing *(V Brogden)*

BEXHILL [TQ7208]

Denbigh [Little Common Rd (A259 towards Polegate)]: Straightforward pub with cheerful landlady and staff and good reasonably priced

food *(Klaus and Elizabeth Leist)*

Traffers [Egerton Rd]: Spotless pub with well kept Harveys and a guest beer, enjoyable lunchtime bar food, upstairs restaurant *(Percy and Cathy Paine)*

BILLINGSHURST [TQ0830]

☆ *Blue Ship* [The Haven; hamlet signposted off A29 just N of junction with A264, then follow signpost left towards Garlands and Okehurst]: Unpretentious pub in quiet country spot, beamed and brick-floored front bar with blazing inglenook log fire, scrubbed tables and wall benches, well kept Badger K&B and perhaps other Badger ales served from hatch, limited home-made food, two small carpeted back rooms (no smoking), darts, bar billiards, shove-ha'penny, cribbage, dominoes, reasonably priced traditional bar food (not Sun or Mon evenings), £1 fine for use of mobile phones, no credit cards; children in one back room, seats by trees or tangle of honeysuckle around front door *(Phil and Sally Gorton, the Didler, LYM, Mrs Romey Heaton, Roy and Lindsey Fentiman, S G N Bennett, Peter Lewis)*

BINSTED [SU9806]

☆ *Black Horse* [Binsted Lane; about 2 miles W of Arundel, turn S off A27 towards Binsted]: Pretty 17th-c local with ochre walls and open fire in big comfortably chatty bar, enjoyable food from generous sandwiches to interesting specials, wider range in back conservatory restaurant candlelit at night, well kept Adnams Regatta, Gales HSB, Harveys Best and Hop Back Summer Lightning, attentive service, darts and bar billiards one end, shelf of sweetie jars, greyhound racing trophies; piped music; tables on terrace, idyllic garden, views over valley; bedrooms *(BB, Jude Wright)*

BIRDHAM [SZ8199]

Bell [B2198 towards Somerley]: Much extended 1930s-ish pub recently done out with pine furniture in good-sized main bar area, oak in back part, wide choice of food strong on fish, real ales such as Adnams, Courage Best and Ringwood Best; piped music, games machine; children welcome, large garden with play area, summer bar and pigeon house *(Val and Alan Green, Mrs Brenda Calver, Fr Robert Marsh, Ann and Colin Hunt)*

BLACKHAM [TQ4839]

Sussex Oak [A264 towards E Grinstead]: Friendly and unpretentious, small bar with games room one side, small eating area the other, well kept Shepherd Neame ales, good choice of bar food from lunchtime baguettes up, no smoking restaurant; country views from peaceful garden *(LYM, Bruce Bird, Tony Hobden)*

BOARSHEAD [TQ5332]

Boars Head [Eridge Rd, off A26 bypass]: Good friendly service, well kept beer and good value fresh food in attractive old unspoilt pub with separate restaurant; quiet spot *(Richard May, C Whittington, Michael and Ann Cole, Ian Phillips)*

BODIAM [TQ7825]

Castle Inn: 18th-c country local, very handy for the Castle (and owned by National Trust), with Shepherd Neame ales, enjoyable blackboard food (simpler choice at quiet times), plain tables and chairs in bar, restaurant section – interesting painted ceiling; tables outside, summer barbecues *(Martin Terry, Dave Braisted)*

BOSHAM [SU8003]
Berkeley Arms [just outside old village]: Cheery local with straightforward food even on Sun night, well kept Gales, lounge with eating area, public bar *(Ann and Colin Hunt, C and R Bromage)*
White Swan [A259 roundabout]: Open-plan pub with well kept ales, good value coffee, welcoming service, log fire, usual pub food, skittle alley/function room; quiet piped music; children welcome, plenty of tables out on terrace *(Tony and Shirley Albert)*

BRIGHTON [TQ3104]
Bath Arms [Union St/Meeting House Lane, The Lanes]: Cheerful attentive service and good value bar food all day from sandwiches up, several high-ceilinged rooms with panelling and old fireplaces, lots of old photographs and cartoon prints, half a dozen real ales inc Harveys, decent coffee, new world wines; pavement tables *(Ann and Colin Hunt, John A Barker, Richard Waller, Pauline Smith)*
Battle of Trafalgar [Trafalgar Rd/Guildford Rd, Portslade (B2193)]: Friendly town local with well kept ales such as Adnams, Fullers London Pride, Harveys Best and Youngs Special (no coffee), lunchtime side servery doing hearty food from good doorstep sandwiches up, log fire; pub games, piped jazz and blues; lovely big garden, open all day Thurs-Sun *(Tony Hobden)*
☆ *Cricketers* [Black Lion St]: Cheerful down-to-earth town pub, friendly bustle at busy times, good relaxed atmosphere when quieter, ageing Victorian furnishings and loads of interesting bric-a-brac – even a stuffed bear; well kept Greene King Old Speckled Hen, Harveys, Charles Wells Bombardier and Youngs tapped from the cask, good coffee, usual well priced lunchtime bar food with fresh veg in upstairs bar, restaurant (where children allowed) and covered ex-stables courtyard bar; piped music; open all day *(Ann and Colin Hunt, LYM, Richard Waller, Pauline Smith)*
☆ *Evening Star* [Surrey St]: Chatty tap for good Dark Star microbrewery, with several well kept changing beers from other small breweries, bench seating on bare boards, enthusiastic landlord (may let you sample before you buy), changing farm ciders and perries, lots of country wines, good lunchtime baguettes (rolls Sun), good mix of customers; unobtrusive piped music, some live; tables outside, open all day *(MLR, Richard and Nicola Tranter, Bruce Bird, Tony Hobden)*
Reservoir [Howard Rd]: Friendly lounge-like pub in largely residential area, comfortable seats, well kept beer, bargain food offers; quiet piped music *(J Christey)*
Sussex Cricketer [Eaton Rd, Hove, by cricket ground]: Warm and comfortable Ember Inn with welcoming layout, well priced standard

food all day from sandwiches to nice puddings, well kept ales such as Harveys, decent wines by the glass, plush seating *(Andy and Jill Kassube, Tony and Wendy Hobden)*
West Quay [Brighton Marina]: Former Jacksons Wharf, attractively refurbished and reopened as a Wetherspoons Lloyds No 1, their usual food, friendly staff, big windows overlooking the water *(Klaus and Elizabeth Leist)*

BUCKS GREEN [TQ0733]
Fox [Guildford Rd (A281 W of Rudgwick)]: Ancient open-plan inglenook bar with good-sized restaurant specialising in good and generous if not cheap fish, well kept Badger beers, decent wines by the glass, welcoming efficient service by cheerful staff; play area *(J P Humphery)*

BURWASH [TQ6724]
☆ *Rose & Crown* [inn sign on A265]: Low-beamed timbered local tucked away down lane in pretty village, now under same management as Foresters in East Hoathly (see main entries); enjoyable food inc lots of seafood from fresh crab sandwiches up, well kept Harveys IPA and Best, decent wines, fine log fire in bar, pleasant restaurant area with new woodburner, good service; tables out in small quiet garden, bedrooms being refurbished, limited nearby parking *(BB, Tony and Wendy Hobden)*

BURWASH WEALD [TQ6523]
Wheel [A265 Burwash—Heathfield]: Tidy open-plan pub with comfortable sofas by good inglenook log fire, well kept Harveys and other ales, shortish choice of decent food, dining room leading out to garden; tables on sunny front terrace too, lovely walks in valley opp *(BB, Jason Caulkin)*

BURY [TQ0113]
☆ *Squire & Horse* [Bury Common; A29 Fontwell—Pulborough]: Sizeable roadside pub with wide range of popular generous home-made food inc some interesting blackboard dishes, well kept ales such as Brakspears, Harveys and Shepherd Neame, Sun bar nibbles, neatly kept partly divided U-shaped open-plan bar areas, heavy beams, pink plush wall seats, hunting prints and ornaments, flame-effect stove, flourishing two-level beamed restaurant with fresh flowers and another stove; green tables and chairs on pretty terrace; cl Sun evening, Mon *(BB, Bruce and Pat Anderson, John Evans, Melanie Ginger)*

CHAILEY [TQ3919]
☆ *Five Bells* [A275 9 miles N of Lewes]: Attractive rambling roadside pub, spacious and well appointed, with lots of different rooms and alcoves leading from low-beamed bar area with fine old brick floor, brick walls and inglenook, candles and fresh flowers, leather sofa by the log fire with another under window, dining extension, well kept Fullers London Pride, Greene King Old Speckled Hen and Harveys Best, decent wine choice, smallish but interesting range of well liked food inc OAP lunch discounts, good service; Fri jazz nights; picnic-sets in pretty garden with play

area *(Glenn and Gillian Miller, BB, J Stickland)*

CHELWOOD GATE [TQ4130]

Red Lion [A275, S of Forest Row junction with A22]: Cheerful dining pub, big tables, modern pictures and sculptures, pale colour-washed walls, enjoyable food from sandwiches and baked potatoes up, good welcoming service, fair-priced Shepherd Neame beers, decent wines, light and airy back room; polished wood floors make for lively acoustics; big sheltered side garden with well spaced tables, more out in front – handy for Ashdown Forest walks *(BB, Mrs Stella Knight)*

CHICHESTER [SU8605]

Bell [Broyle Rd]: Well kept changing ales such as Arundel Gold and Gales HSB, interesting wines, relaxing atmosphere, good food from separate counter inc super puddings, friendly attentive service, no smoking dining area (bar can get smoky); handy for theatre *(Tony Hobden, Ann and Colin Hunt, Richard Waller, Pauline Smith)*

Dolphin & Anchor [West St]: Well run Wetherspoons in former hotel opp cathedral, good value food inc good range of curries, six low-priced real ales; small family area till 7 (not wknds), very busy with young people Sat night, doorman and queues to get in; pleasant back terrace, open all day *(Craig Turnbull)*

George & Dragon [North St]: Bustling simply refurbished bare-boards bar with well kept real ales, decent house wines, wholesome plentiful food, pleasant service, conservatory; tables out on quiet back terrace, bedrooms *(Ann and Colin Hunt, Richard Waller, Pauline Smith)*

Old Cross [North St]: Nicely modernised open-plan dining pub in building dating from 16th c, wide blackboard food choice all day inc speciality pies, well kept Courage Best and Directors and Charles Wells Bombardier, good choice of wines by the glass, friendly efficient service, no smoking areas; dogs welcome, open all day *(Tony and Wendy Hobden, Mike and Lynn Robinson)*

CHIDHAM [SU7804]

☆ *Old House At Home* [off A259 at Barleycorn pub in Nutbourne; Cot Lane]: Cottagey old pub under new licensees, cheerful friendly service and warmly welcoming atmosphere, low beams and timbering, windsor chairs and long wall seats, log fire, well kept Adnams Broadside, Fullers London Pride, Ringwood Best and Youngs, plentiful food inc nice range of fresh fish, partly no smoking restaurant, no piped music or machines; children in eating areas, tables outside, remote unspoilt farm-hamlet location, nearby walks by Chichester Harbour, open all day wknds *(LYM, John Davis, Charles and Pauline Stride, Roger and Pauline Pearce, Paul A Moore, Tony and Shirley Albert, Ann and Colin Hunt)*

CHILGROVE [SU8116]

☆ *Royal Oak* [off B2141 Petersfield—Chichester, signed Hooksway down steep single track]: Charmingly tucked-away two-room country tavern dating from 15th c, no smoking beamed and brick-floored bar with steps down to attractive restaurant, smartly simple country-kitchen furnishings, huge log fires, three well kept changing ales plus a distinctive one brewed for the pub by Hampshire, chatty landlord, inexpensive hearty food inc lunchtime ploughman's, neat prompt service even when busy, games, provision for children; some live music Fri in summer; tables out in pretty garden, good walks, cl Mon and winter Sun evening *(R B Gardiner, J A Snell, Prof and Mrs S Barnett, Torrens Lyster, Michael B Griffith, John Davis, LYM, Ann and Colin Hunt, Bruce Bird, Martin Richardson)*

CLIMPING [TQ0001]

Black Horse: Good value dining pub with wide choice from sandwiches and baked potatoes up, Courage Best and Directors, friendly staff; walk to beach *(Fr Robert Marsh)*

COCKING CAUSEWAY [SU8819]

Greyhound [A286 Cocking—Midhurst]: Pretty tile-hung pub with cosy and welcoming olde-worlde beamed bar, old fireplaces, table lamps, fresh flowers, old prints, pewter pots and woodworking tools; inexpensive home cooking inc lots for children (who are well looked after), welcoming young staff, Ringwood Best; dovecote in side courtyard, picnic-sets on large lawn, play area and aviary, open all day *(Ron Gentry)*

COLEMANS HATCH [TQ4533]

☆ *Hatch* [signed off B2026, or off B2110 opp church]: Quaint and attractive weatherboarded Ashdown Forest pub dating from 1430, big log fire in quickly filling beamed bar, small back dining room with another log fire, good generous food from sandwiches, baked potatoes, giant ploughman's and filled ciabattas through imaginative salads to bass and steak, well kept Harveys Best, Larkins Best and one or two guest beers, friendly quick young staff, good mix of customers inc families and dogs; picnic-sets on front terrace and in beautifully kept big garden, open all day Sun and summer Sat *(Debbie and Neil Hayter, LYM, Simon and Sally Small, Peter Meister, John Davis)*

COOLHAM [TQ1423]

☆ *George & Dragon* [pub signed just off A272, about 1½ miles E of village; Dragons Lane]: Very low-beamed ancient pub, unpretentiously comfortable, with good fire in enormous inglenook fireplace, well kept Badger ales, generous home-made standard food from sandwiches, baguettes and baked potatoes up, small restaurant, back games bar with bar billiards; can get pretty busy; children allowed in games or eating areas, dogs allowed in bar, well spaced tables out in big attractive orchard garden, open all day wknds and handy for Hilaire Belloc's Shipley windmill (which is open then) *(John Beeken, LYM, Ron Gentry)*

Selsey Arms [A272/B2139]: Two linked areas, well kept Fullers London Pride and Harveys, chatty atmosphere, friendly considerate service even when busy, enjoyable blackboard food from filled rolls and baked potatoes up, cheerful fire, elderly labrador (likes snacks);

garden fenced off from road in front, another behind *(Terry Buckland, Peter Lewis)*

COPSALE [TQ1724]

Bridge House [signed off A24; Copsale Rd]: Friendly new licensees in modern local by Downs Link footpath, tasty reasonably priced pubby food, well kept Badger K&B and Tanglefoot, cheerful bar, no smoking dining room, games room; good-sized garden with play area *(Ron Gentry, C and R Bromage)*

COPTHORNE [TQ3239]

Cherry Tree [Copthorne Bank (pub just over Surrey border)]: Four or five linked areas in rambling extended 1920s pub with two bars and dining area, particularly friendly personable staff, Badger Best, K&B and Tanglefoot, enjoyable standard food from sandwiches and baked potatoes up, massive fireplace, daily papers; dogs welcome *(Ian Phillips)*

COUSLEY WOOD [TQ6533]

☆ *Old Vine* [B2100 Wadhurst—Lamberhurst]: Popular and attractive dining pub with lots of old timbers and beams, wide range of generous enjoyable food inc good fish, good house wines, four well kept ales, good if not always speedy service, rustic pretty restaurant on right, pubbier bare-boards or brick-floored area with woodburner by bar; they may try to keep your credit card while you eat, but otherwise friendly; a few tables out behind *(B J Harding, Oliver and Sue Rowell, BB, Robert Rice, Steve Harvey, Jamie May)*

COWFOLD [TQ2122]

Hare & Hounds [Henfield Rd (A281 S)]: Good friendly landlord in welcoming refurbished pub, part flagstoned, with good value food from well filled baguettes with chips up, five real ales mainly from Sussex brewers, decent wines, darts, no smoking family area *(Tony and Wendy Hobden, Jackie and Alan Moody, Paul Humphreys)*

CRAWLEY [TQ2836]

Snooty Fox [Haslett Ave, opp Three Bridges Stn]: Comfortable recently refurbished Steak & Ale pub, low-priced food, Bass and Wadworths 6X, no smoking area *(Tony Hobden)*

White Hart [High St]: Two-bar Harveys local with their full range, lunchtime food in bar and restaurant, pool and darts teams; live music Sun evening, open all day, busy market days (Thurs-Sat) *(Tony Hobden)*

CUCKFIELD [TQ3025]

White Harte [South Street; off A272 W of Haywards Heath]: Pretty partly medieval pub, comfortable beamed and timbered lounge with polished floorboards and ancient brick flooring, sturdy furnishings in public bar with blazing inglenook log fire and traditional games, well kept Badger Best, K&B and Tanglefoot; piped music, TV; dogs in bar, children welcome, tables in back yard, cl Mon lunchtime in winter *(Klaus and Elizabeth Leist, Ron Gentry, Terry Buckland, LYM, Francis Vernon)*

DALLINGTON [TQ6619]

Swan [Woods Corner, B2096 E]: Low-beamed country local with decent food, well kept Harveys Best and a guest beer, good wines by the glass and coffee, friendly staff, warm log fire in bare-boards bar with some sofas, small comfortable back dining room with far views to Beachy Head; steps down to smallish garden *(BB, Mike Gorton)*

DANEHILL [TQ4128]

☆ *Coach & Horses* [off A275, via School Lane towards Chelwood Common]: Well run pub in attractive countryside, emphasis on good if not cheap restauranty food (not Sun evening), well kept Harveys Best and Wychwood Shires, good wines by generous glass, little hatch-served public bar with simple furniture on highly polished boards and small woodburner, main bar on the left with big Victorian prints and mix of chairs around attractive old tables on fine brick floor, no smoking dining extension; well behaved children and dogs allowed, plenty of tables in big attractive garden with terrace under huge maple *(Karen Eliot, Tony and Wendy Hobden, Alan Sadler, Alan Cowell, B J Harding, Pete Walker, Ron Gentry, Dominic Morgan, Pierre Richterich, Roger Fox, N R White, Martin and Karen Wake, LYM)*

DELL QUAY [SU8302]

☆ *Crown & Anchor* [off A286 S of Chichester]: Modernised 15th-c pub in splendid spot on site of Roman quay overlooking Chichester Harbour – best at high tide and quiet times, can be packed at wknds; comfortable bow-windowed lounge bar, panelled public bar (dogs welcome), two open fires and lots of beams, well kept Courage Directors and Theakstons Best or John Smiths and Charles Wells Bombardier, very wide choice of wines by the glass, good popular food from all-day servery; terrace picnic-sets, nice walks *(Father David Cossar, Martin and Karen Wake, Ann and Colin Hunt, BB, Colin McKerrow, Mrs Sheela Curtis)*

DENTON [TQ4502]

Flying Fish [Denton Rd]: Attractive 17th-c flint village local by South Downs Way, hops and brassware in two small snug bars with well kept Shepherd Neame ales, French chef/landlord doing good well priced food from interesting baguettes up inc seasonal food esp game and fresh fish from nearby Newhaven, friendly prompt service, comfortable no smoking dining room; attractive garden behind, more tables out in front *(the Didler, Emily Mottram)*

DUNCTON [SU9617]

☆ *Cricketers* [set back from A285]: Yet another new licensee for this pretty little white country pub with its inglenook fireplace, cricketing pictures and bats on walls, and mix of country chairs around scrubbed wooden tables, steps down to no smoking room set for the decent bar food, well kept Youngs Bitter and couple of Ballards beers, several decent wines by the glass, shove-ha'penny, cribbage and dominoes; piped music; children and dogs welcome, picnic-sets in charming garden behind with creeper-covered bower and proper barbecue, open all day (*A and B D Craig, Roger Endersby, LYM, David Cosham, Cathy Robinson, Ed Coombe, Derek Thomas, Susan and John Douglas*)

EARTHAM [SU9409]

☆ *George* [signed off A285 Chichester—Petworth, from Fontwell off A27, from Slindon off A29]: Popular pub smartly refurbished in light wood, comfortable lounge, attractive pubbier public bar with games, old farm tools and photographs, welcoming helpful service and hands-on landlord, enjoyable home-made food at sensible prices, well kept Greene King ales, log fire, darts, backgammon, no smoking restaurant; piped music; easy disabled access, children welcome in eating areas, large pretty garden, attractive surroundings, open all day summer wknds (*Christine Crowther, LYM, Jude Wright*)

EASEBOURNE [SU8922]

☆ *White Horse* [off A272 just NE of Midhurst]: Cosy beamed village pub, large mainly bare-boards bar with several distinct areas inc fireside armchairs and small no smoking dining area, convivial landlord, efficient friendly service, traditional food from baked potatoes up (worth booking wknds), well kept Greene King IPA and Abbot, two open fires, no piped music; children and dogs welcome, tables on back grass and in courtyard (*T O'Brien, LYM, John Beeken, Dick Bensted-Smith*)

EAST HOATHLY [TQ5216]

Kings Head [High St]: Former coaching inn with log fire at one end of long comfortably worn in open-plan bar with some dark panelling and old local photographs, ancient woodburner and TV at the other end, now brewing its own 1648 ales, also a well kept guest beer such as Harveys or Hop Back, enjoyable bar food, good service, no piped music, restaurant; tables in garden up steps behind (*Kevin Thorpe, Bruce Bird*)

EAST LAVANT [SU8608]

☆ *Royal Oak* [signed off A286 N of Chichester; Pook Lane]: Restaurranty dining pub, not cheap but good relaxed atmosphere, prompt friendly service, candlelight and scrubbed tables, rugs on bare boards and flooring tiles, two open fires and a woodburner, racing prints, well kept Badger ales tapped from the cask, country wines, good house wines; attractively planted gardens inc secluded terrace with bookable tables (quiet exc for wknd light planes using Goodwood airfield), good walks; comfortable bedrooms, cl Sun pm, Mon (*Christopher and Elise Way, LYM, Lionel and Sylvia Kopelowitz, Dr D and Mrs B Woods, Richard Waller, Pauline Smith*)

EAST PRESTON [TQ0602]

Fletcher Arms [Station Rd]: Well kept ales such as Fullers London Pride, Greene King Old Speckled Hen and Ringwood Best, good cheap bar food (not Sun evening) inc OAP bargains, friendly helpful young staff, some unusual bric-a-brac, local photographs, lots of events; fruit machine; big well kept garden with pets corner, play area and barbecues (*Tony and Wendy Hobden*)

EASTBOURNE [TV6198]

Buccaneer [Compton St, by Winter Gardens]: Popular open-plan bar shaped like a galleon, raised no smoking side, Bass, Coors Burton, Tetleys and three guest beers, good value food (not Sun), theatre memorabilia; open all day (*the Didler*)

Toby Carvery [Willingdon Drove]: Chain dining pub with nostalgic show-business photographs, good service, good value carvery (*Ron and Sheila Corbett*)

ELSTED [SU8119]

Elsted Inn [Elsted Marsh]: Attractive two-bar country pub under new management, nice country furniture, wooden floors, old railway photographs, log fires, home-cooked food inc good sensibly priced Sun lunch (very popular), four well kept ales such as Ballards, Cheriton Pots and Timothy Taylors Landlord, traditional games; lovely enclosed downs-view garden with big terrace and summer barbecues, well appointed adjacent bedroom block (*John Davis, LYM, David Cosham, Ann and Colin Hunt*)

ERIDGE STATION [TQ5434]

☆ *Huntsman*: Good value generous home-made food (worth booking wknds) from sandwiches to some innovative dishes, quietly friendly landlord with considerable wine expertise, also well kept Badger Best, K&B and seasonal Fursty Ferret, farm cider, two recently redecorated bars; lacks a no smoking area; walkers and dogs welcome, new picnic-sets on front terrace and in big garden behind with decking, cl Mon (*Peter Meister, Tony and Wendy Hobden, Fr Robert Marsh, Paul A Moore, Bill and Pauline Harvey*)

EWHURST GREEN [TQ7924]

White Dog: Extensive and attractive partly 17th-c pub/restaurant in fine spot above Bodiam Castle, wide choice of good value food, welcoming helpful service, well kept ales inc Harveys and Youngs, log fire and polished flagstones, cheerful unpretentious atmosphere, evening restaurant; walkers and children welcome, bedrooms, tables in big garden making the most of the view (*PL, LYM, Vincent Board, Michael and Ann Cole, M Joyner*)

FELPHAM [SU9500]

Southdowns [Felpham Way (A259)]: Now an Ember Inn, neat and airy with separate areas inc no smoking, well kept real ales inc mini beer festivals, competitively priced standard food, smaller helpings of some dishes (*Tony Hobden*)

FERNHURST [SU9028]

☆ *Red Lion* [3m S of Haslemere; The Green, off A286 via Church Lane]: Pleasantly relaxed atmosphere in wisteria-covered 15th-c pub tucked quietly away by green nr church, heavy beams, attractive layout and furnishings, friendly attentive staff, good value food from interesting sandwiches and snacks to fresh fish, well kept Fullers ales, good wines, no smoking restaurant; children welcome, pretty gardens front and back (*Mrs Maricar Jagger, BB, H H Hellin, Roy and Lindsey Fentiman, Wendy Arnold, Simon Jones*)

FIRLE [TQ4607]
☆ *Ram* [village signed off A27 Lewes—Polegate]: Unpretentious and comfortably worn 17th-c village pub, very welcoming to families and booted walkers; big plain tables, log fires, no smoking snug, good-sized family room, well kept Harveys Best and seasonal Old and a guest such as Arundel, farm cider, popular food 12-5.30 (till 9 Fri-Sun) from baguettes and baked potatoes up, with three sizes of children's meals and cream teas (chocolates and books for sale too), traditional games inc toad in the hole; new children's room in adjoining stable, play equipment and nicely segregated table area in walled garden behind, open all day *(LYM, the Didier, John Davis, Kevin Thorpe, N R White)*

FISHBOURNE [SU8304]
Bulls Head [Fishbourne Rd (A259 Chichester—Emsworth)]: Relaxing and comfortable old village pub with pretty window boxes, fair-sized main bar, full Gales range kept well with Fullers London Pride, good varied quickly served food often using local produce (not Sun evening – Sun lunch very popular), children's helpings, friendly neatly dressed staff, log fire, children's area, restaurant with no smoking area; skittle alley, picnic-sets on terrace *(J A Snell, David H T Dimock, Ann and Colin Hunt, MRSM, C and R Bromage, Mrs Angela Bromley-Martin, Richard Waller, Pauline Smith)*
Woolpack [Fishbourne Rd W; just off A27 Chichester—Emsworth]: Big comfortably refurbished open-plan 1950s-ish roadside pub, nice variety of seats inc settees, smart no smoking dining area, enjoyable food, well kept Greene King Abbot, Youngs Special and two guest beers, friendly dog; dogs welcome, big garden with barbecues and spit-roasts, new hotel annexe *(Ann and Colin Hunt)*

FULKING [TQ2411]
☆ *Shepherd & Dog* [off A281 N of Brighton, via Poynings]: Charming partly panelled low-ceilinged country pub beautifully placed below downs, antique or stoutly rustic furnishings around log fire, attractive bow windows, well kept ales, wide food choice (all day wknds) from sandwiches and baked potatoes up inc lots of ploughman's and summer salads, no piped music; can be packed out, when staff can be inadequate; dogs and children welcome, pretty streamside garden with upper play lawn (loudspeaker food announcements out here), open all day *(LYM, John Hendy, Ron Gentry, Andrew Scarr)*

FUNTINGTON [SU7908]
Fox & Hounds: Friendly beamed family pub with wide food choice from sandwiches to popular Sun roasts, cottagey rooms, comfortable and attractive dining extension, welcoming service, well kept Badger Best, K&B and Tanglefoot, reasonably priced wines, good coffee, huge log fire, no music; garden behind, pair of nice inn signs – one a pack of hounds, the other a family of foxes *(R B Gardiner, Ian Phillips, Peter and Audrey Dowsett)*

GLYNDE [TQ4508]
Trevor Arms: Well kept Harveys ales and bargain food from ploughman's and baked potatoes to good Sun roasts, congenial landlord, small bar with corridor to no smoking room and big dining room, Glyndebourne posters and photographs; tables in large garden with downland backdrop, Glyndebourne musicians may play out here on summer Suns *(A J Bowen, John Davis, John Beeken)*

GODDARDS GREEN [TQ2820]
Sportsman: Family dining pub with wide choice of popular usual food from open sandwiches and baked potatoes up, friendly efficient waitress service, well kept Badger real ales, decent house wines, no smoking restaurant extension *(Ron Gentry, Terry Buckland, Tony and Wendy Hobden)*

GOLDEN CROSS [TQ5312]
Golden Cross Inn [A22 NW of Hailsham]: Small friendly Harveys pub with well kept beers, good traditional pub food (not Sun evening) inc lots of different fresh veg in partly no smoking saloon, separate public bar, welcoming courteous service *(Angus Johnson, Carol Bolden)*

GORING-BY-SEA [TQ1004]
Swallows Return [Titnore Lane, off A259/A2032 Northbrook College roundabout]: Vintage Inns barn conversion, their usual food all day inc sandwiches till 5, Bass and Harveys Best, good choice of wines by the glass, good coffee, log fire as well as central heating, no smoking end and upper gallery; open all day *(Tony and Wendy Hobden)*

GRAFFHAM [SU9217]
Foresters Arms: Big helpings of enjoyable home-made food in friendly smallish two-room 17th-c pub kept spotless, well kept ales such as Cheriton Pots, Harveys Best, Ringwood Best and Timothy Taylors Landlord, good wine choice, efficient service, big log fire in fine old fireplace, country sports pictures, daily papers and magazines, old pulpit as feature of small pretty no smoking restaurant (can be fully booked); tables in big pleasant garden, bedrooms, good walks *(Bruce Bird, Prof and Mrs S Barnett, Richard Waller, Pauline Smith)*
☆ *White Horse*: Spotless family pub with good food from familiar favourites to upscale dishes, well kept Badger Best and Tanglefoot, friendly licensees, log fires, walkers welcome, small dining room and conservatory restaurant with good South Downs views; terrace, big garden, open all day Sun in summer *(John Davis, William Ruxton)*

HALNAKER [SU9008]
☆ *Anglesey Arms* [A285 Chichester—Petworth]: Charmingly unpretentious bar with well kept Adnams Best and Youngs, friendly landlord and staff, reasonably priced good imaginative food and traditional games, simple but smart candlelit dining rooms with woodburners, stripped pine and some flagstones (children allowed), decent wines; garden tables *(Ann and Colin Hunt, Ian Wilson, R B Gardiner, John Davis, LYM, W W Burke)*

HAMMERPOT [TQ0605]

☆ **Woodmans Arms:** Pretty thatched pub impressively rebuilt after devastating 2004 fire, in its former 16th-c layout but with more headroom for the big beams, a more contemporary feel, and extension giving extra no smoking dining room; well kept Gales ales, attractively priced generous pubby food from sandwiches and baked potatoes up; piped music; open all day Fri/Sat and summer Sun *(LYM, Bruce Bird, Don and Thelma Anderson, Ann and Colin Hunt, Tony and Wendy Hobden)*

HANDCROSS [TQ2629]

Red Lion [High St]: Large Chef & Brewer nicely divided with plenty of tables and good no smoking area, emphasis on huge blackboard food choice from snacks to fish, real ales inc a guest such as Youngs, good wine list, lively atmosphere, quick friendly service; unobtrusive piped music *(Amanda Eames, Fred Chamberlain)*

Royal Oak [Horsham Rd (A279, off A23)]: Friendly low-beamed open-plan local, two smallish areas divided by big log-effect gas fire, chatty landlord, his sons doing good changing well crafted food from light dishes to seasonal game, prompt service even for big groups of ramblers, well kept Fullers London Pride, Harveys and Timothy Taylors Landlord, winter mulled wine, old photographs and curios, friendly dog called Harvey; tables in sunny forecourt, small garden behind, handy for Nymans *(Edward and Pat Wolfe, Terry Buckland, J P Humphery, C and R Bromage, N R White)*

Wheatsheaf [B2110 W]: Well kept Badger ales, good range of generous good value home-made food using local produce from sandwiches to steaks inc children's, welcoming service, two bars with lots of horse tack and farm tools, no smoking dining room; large garden with piped music and big play area *(Ron Gentry, Graham Breen)*

HARTFIELD [TQ4735]

Anchor [Church St]: Welcoming well worn-in 15th-c local with heavy beams and flagstones, little country pictures and houseplants, inglenook log fire and a woodburner, comfortable dining area, well kept Adnams, Bass, Flowers IPA, Fullers ESB and Harveys Best, pleasant helpful long-serving licensees, darts in lower room, usual bar food; piped music; children welcome, seats out on front verandah, garden with play area, open all day *(Joel Dobris, LYM, Alan Kilpatrick, Ron Gentry)*

Haywaggon [High St (A264)]: Friendly and busy, with two big log fires, pews and lots of large tables in spacious beamed bar, well kept ales inc Harveys, wide range of blackboard bar food, good choice of wines by the glass, nice dog, good value interesting food in former bakehouse restaurant; picnic-sets outside *(Bill and Pauline Harvey)*

HENFIELD [TQ2116]

White Hart [High St (A281)]: 16th-c village pub with interesting tiled roof, comfortable L-shaped lounge and big no smoking area, lots of panelling, tools hanging from low beams, horsebrasses, paintings, prints, photographs and fresh flowers, log fire, large civilised dining area with good choice of home-cooked food inc tempting puddings, friendly efficient service, well kept Badger, Harveys Best and Shepherd Neame, decent wines with choice of glass sizes; children welcome, garden with terrace and play area *(Ron Gentry)*

HENLEY [SU8925]

☆ **Duke of Cumberland Arms** [off A286 S of Fernhurst]: Pretty wisteria-covered 15th-c stone-built pub with big scrubbed pine or oak tables in two small rooms each with a log fire, low ceilings, white-painted wall boards and rustic decorations, well kept ales tapped from the cask such as Adnams Broadside, Brakspears, Hook Norton Best, Shepherd Neame Spitfire and Youngs Special, Rich's farm cider, good wine choice; pricey food (not Sun evening) from sandwiches up; beautiful hill views from gnarled seats in charming big sloping garden criss-crossed by stream and trout ponds, children and dogs welcome, open all day *(Roger Endersby, Torrens Lyster, Mrs Ann Gray, Martin and Karen Wake, Mrs Romey Heaton, J P Humphery, LYM, John Evans, Phil and Sally Gorton, Edwina Messer, Paul A Moore)*

HEYSHOTT [SU8918]

☆ **Unicorn** [well signed off A286 S of Midhurst]: Welcoming new licensees in small village-green local, well kept ales inc local Ballards, good if not cheap food from lunchtime sandwiches and baguettes up, cheerful service even when busy, comfortably cushioned bar, attractive dining area; children allowed, reasonable disabled access, pretty garden with barbecue, charming downland setting handy for South Downs Way *(Charles van der Lande, Cathy Robinson, Ed Coombe, Alan Cowell, John Davis, Geoff and Linda Payne)*

HOLTYE [TQ4538]

White Horse [Holtye Common; A264 East Grinstead—Tunbridge Wells]: Ancient gently refurbished village inn with welcoming atmosphere, good sensibly limited food, well kept Bass, Harveys and Charles Wells Bombardier, good service, log fire (which can smoke a bit sometimes), illuminated aquarium set into floor; good disabled facilities, marvellous view from back lawn, bedrooms *(R and S Bentley, Ian Phillips)*

HORSHAM [TQ1630]

Lynd Cross [Bishopric]: Wetherspoons in main shopping area, their reliable food and well kept beers; children in family area *(Tony Hobden)*

Malt Shovel [Springfield Rd]: Traditional flagstoned pub with up to nine well kept quickly changing real ales, Biddenden farm cider, enjoyable home cooking 12-6; sports TV – they're keen on rugby; open all day *(Robin Pine, Tony Hobden)*

HORSTED KEYNES [TQ3828]

Green Man [The Green]: Open-plan pub in attractive spot, well kept Greene King ales, decent wines by the glass, well served food from sandwiches to tuna steak, massive open fireplace, no smoking beamed dining area; piped classical music, no children inside; lots of tables out in front and on green, handy for Bluebell Line *(C and R Bromage, Neil Hardwick, G J C Moss, John Beeken)*

HUNSTON [SU8601]

Spotted Cow [B2145 S of Chichester]: Bright and welcoming flagstoned pub, smart contemporary mediterranean-style décor, small front bar, roomier side lounge with armchairs, sofas and low tables as anteroom for airy high-ceilinged restaurant, generous and enjoyable if not cheap fresh food from sandwiches to fish and good puddings, friendly landlord and cheerful efficient service, well kept Gales, big fires; good disabled access, children welcome to eat, big pretty garden, handy for towpath walkers *(Tony and Wendy Hobden, Ann and Colin Hunt)*

ISFIELD [TQ4516]

☆ *Halfway House* [Rose Hill (A26)]: Tastefully extended rambling pub with enjoyable good value home cooking inc Sun lunch and local game in season, chatty helpful staff, well kept Harveys ales inc a seasonal beer, low beams and timbers, dark pub furniture inc a couple of high-backed settles on turkey carpet, busy restaurant; children and dogs welcome, picnic-sets in small back garden *(BB, Jenny and Brian Seller, Michael and Ann Cole)*

Laughing Fish: Welcoming and hard-working licensees in simply modernised village local with good fresh inexpensive home-made food, four or five well kept Greene King and other ales, traditional games, no smoking bar; children and dogs welcome, tables in small pleasant walled garden with entertaining enclosed play area, right by Lavender Line *(BB, the Didler, Michael and Ann Cole)*

JEVINGTON [TQ5601]

☆ *Eight Bells*: Busy and neatly kept, fast friendly service, good value hearty home-made food (all day Sun) from good unusual lunchtime filled rolls and baked potatoes up, well kept Adnams Broadside, Flowers Original and Harveys Best and winter Old, simple furnishings, beams, parquet floor, flame-effect fire in inglenook; piped music, fruit machine; walkers welcome, South Downs Way, Weald Way and 1066 Trail all nearby, quiet village with interesting church; tables under cocktail parasols on front terrace, secluded downs-view garden with some sturdy tables under cover, open all day *(John Beeken, John Davis, Pam Adsley, BB, Ann and Colin Hunt, Kevin Thorpe)*

KINGSTON NEAR LEWES [TQ3908]

Juggs [village signed off A27 by roundabout W of Lewes]: Ancient rose-covered pub recently smartened up, with heavy 15th-c beams, lots of neatly stripped masonry, sturdy wooden furniture on bare boards and stone slabs, smaller eating areas inc no smoking family room off, good if not cheap choice of bar food from baguettes and baked potatoes up, well kept Shepherd Neame ales, good wine list, log fires, dominoes and shove-ha'penny; piped music may obtrude; nice seating areas outside,

compact well equipped play area *(PL, A J Bowen, Ian Phillips, LYM, John Beeken, Ann and Colin Hunt)*

KIRDFORD [TQ0126]

☆ *Half Moon* [opp church, off A272 Petworth—Billingshurst]: 17th-c tile-hung bar/restaurant, picturesque and charmingly set, doing well under current welcoming management, with enjoyable food, immaculate roomy and rambling largely no smoking low-beamed dining area, well kept Fullers London Pride from the curved counter in the attractive partly quarry-tiled bar, good wines by the glass, log fire; tables in pretty back garden and out in front *(Arnold Bennett, LYM, Derek Thomas, J P Humphery)*

LEWES [TQ4110]

Brewers Arms [High St]: Spotless friendly local dating from 16th c, back lounge bar, good choice of attractively priced food, well kept Harveys Best and two or three interesting guest ales, games room with pool and sports TV, 260-year list of landlords in public bar *(Dom Bradshaw, John Davis, the Didler, Quentin and Carol Williamson)*

John Harvey [Bear Yard, just off Cliffe High St]: Tap for nearby Harveys brewery (with separate good brewery shop), all their beers inc seasonal kept perfectly, some tapped from the cask, generous low-priced well prepared food from lunchtime sandwiches, baked potatoes and ciabattas up, efficient young staff, basic dark flagstoned bar with one great vat halved to make two towering 'snugs' for several people, lighter room on left; bar can get smoky, piped music and machines; a few tables outside, open all day, breakfast from 10am *(Bruce Bird, BB, Tracey and Stephen Groves, Dom Bradshaw)*

Kings Head [Southover High St]: Lively corner pub with Harveys Best and Fullers London Pride from central bar, generous reasonably priced pubby food from sandwiches and baked potatoes up, friendly attentive staff, raised no smoking area with flame-effect fire, sofa in side alcove, monarch portraits and collections of cup and cheese dishes, board games; back garden, bedrooms, handy for Southover Grange and Anne of Cleves House *(John Beeken)*

☆ *Lewes Arms* [Castle Ditch Lane/Mount Pl – tucked behind castle ruins]: Chatty unchanging and unpretentious corner local built into castle ramparts, old-fashioned layout and atmosphere with small front bar and hatchway, larger lounge with eating area off, well kept Greene King and Harveys ales, good orange juice, very reasonably priced simple lunchtime food from good baguettes and baked potatoes up, friendly staff, daily papers, local pictures, toad in the hole, no music; small terrace, open all day *(Sue Demont, Tim Barrow, Phil and Sally Gorton, Dom Bradshaw)*

☆ *Snowdrop* [South St]: Two spacious bar areas with the cliffs as a backdrop and an interesting maritime theme with figureheads, ship lamps etc, fairly straightforward bar food, well kept Adnams Broadside, Harveys Best and a guest beer, dominoes, spiral stairs up to more seats and pool; piped music, local bands Sat evening; children and dogs welcome, open all day *(BB, Dom Bradshaw, Fr Robert Marsh, A J Bowen, Ann and Colin Hunt, LM, Tony and Wendy Hobden, Guy Vowles, LYM)*

White Hart [High St]: Rambling central hotel with side coach entrance, well kept Harveys Best and Tom Paine, bargain straightforward bar food from sandwiches up, coffee lounge beside main bar, dining room with terrace tables and Ouse Valley views; swimming pool, health club, bedrooms *(John Beeken)*

LITLINGTON [TQ5201]

☆ *Plough & Harrow* [between A27 Lewes—Polegate and A259 E of Seaford]: Attractive neatly extended beamed flint pub under new management, good home-made food from light lunchtime snacks up, quick friendly service, well kept ales inc Badger and Harveys, decent wines by the glass, dining area done up as railway dining car (children allowed here); little suntrap front garden, attractive back lawn with children's bar and pretty views *(M and R Thomas, LYM)*

LITTLEHAMPTON [TQ0202]

☆ *Arun View* [Wharf Rd; W towards Chichester]: Roomy and comfortable 18th-c inn in lovely spot right on harbour with river directly below windows, worth booking for its interesting food with good fresh fish (very popular lunchtime with older people, a younger crowd evenings), sandwiches too, well kept ales such as Ringwood Best and Old Thumper and Youngs Special, good wine list, cheerful helpful service, flagstoned back bar with lots of drawings and caricatures, large no smoking conservatory and flower-filled terrace both overlooking busy waterway and pedestrian bridge; disabled facilities, summer barbecues evenings and wknds, winter live music, bright and modest good value bedrooms *(David Carr, Sue and Mike Todd, Mrs Sue Barlow, Craig Turnbull, Tony and Wendy Hobden)*

LITTLEWORTH [TQ1921]

Windmill [pub sign on B2135; village signed off A272 southbound, W of Cowfold]: Small spotless local with hospitable welcome, log fires in panelled flagstoned public bar and compact cosy beamed lounge/eating area (smoking allowed), enjoyable sensibly priced generous food, well kept Badger beers, bric-a-brac large and small inside and out, darts, dominoes, cards and bar billiards, two easy-going pub dogs, no music; children welcome, peaceful and attractive side garden *(Bruce Bird)*

☆ **LODSWORTH** [SU9223]

☆ *Hollist Arms* [off A272 Midhurst—Petworth]: Cheerful open-plan village pub overlooking small green, well kept Kings Horsham Best, Timothy Taylors Landlord and Youngs, good wines by the glass and coffee, good range of generous enjoyable bar food inc fresh fish and shellfish, popular Sun lunch, relaxed atmosphere, lively landlord and prompt charming service, interesting books and magazines, country prints, sofas by log fire for

no smoking dining room (must book for Sat night); may be piped classical music; children welcome, nice tree-lined back garden, good walks *(John Beeken, Bruce Bird, Martin and Karen Wake, Denis Dutton, Gerry and Rosemary Dobson, Mrs J A Sales, Peter Lewis)*

LURGASHALL [SU9327]

☆ *Noahs Ark* [off A283 N of Petworth]: Charmingly placed individually run 16th-c country local, two neat bars with log fires (one in a capacious inglenook), well kept Greene King IPA, Abbot and Old Speckled Hen, family room, darts, sandwiches, wraps, filled baked potatoes and enjoyable simple hot bar food (not Sun evening, can take a while when busy), restaurant; dogs and children welcome, picnic-sets on front grass facing cricket green, more in back garden, cl winter Sun evening *(Michael B Griffith, LYM, Klaus and Elizabeth Leist, Mike and Lynn Robinson, Alison and Graham Hooper)*

MAPLEHURST [TQ1924]

White Horse [Park Lane]: Peaceful beamed country local, four seating areas inc homely cosy corners and sun lounge (no smoking at lunchtime) with redundant church furniture and lots of plants, log fire, well kept Harveys Best, Weltons Pride & Joy and interesting guest beers, farm cider, bargain coffee, good value sandwiches, toasties, baked potatoes and one or two simple hot dishes, friendly licensees and good service, lots of traditional games, no music or machines; children welcome, pleasant garden with play area, beautiful wisteria in front, car enthusiasts' evenings *(Bruce Bird, Tony and Wendy Hobden, Mark Killman)*

MAYFIELD [TQ5826]

Middle House [High St]: Handsome 16th-c timbered inn of great potential, L-shaped beamed locals' bar with massive fireplace, well kept Adnams, Fullers London Pride, Greene King Abbot, Harveys Best and a guest beer, local cider, decent wines, quiet lounge with leather chesterfields around log fire in ornate carved fireplace, big menu, panelled no smoking restaurant; piped music; children welcome, terraced back garden with lovely views, slide and play house, open all day *(LYM, Conor McGaughey)*

Rose & Crown [Fletching St]: Pretty weather-boarded old pub, chef/landlord doing popular attractively priced food, well kept Greene King Abbot and Old Speckled Hen and Harveys Best, cheery if not always speedy service, cosy little low-beamed front rooms and pleasant restaurant, big inglenook fire, shove-ha'penny Mon and Fri; piped music, poor disabled access; children welcome, four attractive bedrooms, good breakfast, tables outside; open all day Sat *(LYM, Roger Noble, B and M Kendall)*

MIDHURST [SU8821]

Bricklayers Arms [Wool Lane/West St]: Two cosily welcoming olde-worlde bars, good local atmosphere, good value generous home-made food inc Sun roast, well kept Greene King IPA and Abbot, friendly efficient service, sturdy old oak furniture, 17th-c beams, old photographs and bric-a-brac *(Roger Endersby, June and Geoffrey Cox)*

MILLAND [SU8328]

☆ *Rising Sun* [Iping Rd junction with main rd through village]: Largely open-plan big-windowed pub, light and airy despite the close-set furnishings, with friendly service, French landlady cooking generous fresh interesting food inc some recipes from Normandy and good french country puddings, well kept Gales Butser, BB and HSB with a seasonal guest beer, sports TV, pool and fruit machine in separate games end; picnic-sets in good-sized neatly kept garden, good walking area *(Michael B Griffith, BB, Jean and Roy Benson)*

MILTON STREET [TQ5304]

Sussex Ox [off A27 just E of Alfriston – brown sign to pub]: Attractive country pub under friendly new licensees, magnificent downs views, smallish beamed and brick-floored bar with roaring woodburner, well kept real ales, separate restaurant; piped music; children allowed in good no smoking family room (book well ahead in summer), big lawn, lots of good walks *(LYM, Jenny and Peter Lowater)*

NORTHIAM [TQ8224]

Hayes Arms [Church Lane]: French family running this civilised Georgian-fronted hotel, enjoyable french food in comfortable and pleasant brasserie-style bar, heavy Tudor beams, log fire in big brick inglenook, small back restaurant; bedrooms *(V Brogden)*

NUTBOURNE [TQ0718]

Rising Sun [off A283 E of Pulborough; The Street]: Unspoilt creeper-covered village pub dating partly from 16th c, doing well under current friendly landlord; well kept Fullers London Pride and four changing ales such as Arundel Castle, Brakspears, Harveys Best and Skinners Betty Stogs, enjoyable fairly priced bar food, big log fire, daily papers, rough tables on bare boards, 1920s dance and fashion posters, chess and cosy games room, beamed restaurant; children and dogs allowed, two garden areas with small bare terrace under apple tree, handy for Nutbourne vineyard *(Peter D B Harding, Bruce Bird, John Beeken)*

NUTHURST [TQ1926]

☆ *Black Horse* [off A281 SE of Horsham]: Convivial 17th-c country pub with low black beams, flagstones, inglenook log fire and plenty of character in its several small rooms, well kept Harveys Best, Kings, Timothy Taylors Landlord and a guest such as Itchen Valley, good range of wines by the glass, friendly efficient service, no smoking snug and restaurant; may be piped music; children and dogs welcome, attractive woodland streamside back garden, more seats on front terrace, open for food all day wknds and bank hols *(Tony and Wendy Hobden, LYM, Ron Gentry, R Yates, John Davis, C and R Bromage)*

OFFHAM [TQ3912]

☆ *Blacksmiths Arms* [A275 N of Lewes]: Popular open-plan dining pub, open sandwiches, baked potatoes, ploughman's and usual pubby things

as well as good fresh fish and other specials, well kept Harveys Best, good professional service, huge end inglenook fireplace; french windows to terrace with picnic-sets, four new bedrooms with own bathrooms *(Fr Robert Marsh, Ann and Colin Hunt, LYM, Mr and Mrs Peter Chance, Ron Gentry, Geoff and Molly Betteridge, Mrs J A Jackson)*

Chalk Pit [A275 N of Lewes]: Bright and pleasant bar, well kept Harveys, good range of reasonably priced food all day, good Sun roasts, cheerful service, no smoking restaurant; bedrooms, open all day *(Ann and Colin Hunt)*

PAGHAM [SZ8998]

Lion [Nyetimber Lane]: Two-bar pub tastefully refurbished under new owners, good value food, well kept beers, low beams, small restaurant; big suntrap terrace *(Mrs Brenda Calver)*

PARTRIDGE GREEN [TQ1819]

Green Man [Jolesfield (B2135 N)]: Good well presented modern food with mediterranean touches such as unusual tapas-style starters in attractive bar and restaurant (more restaurant than pub), good-sized helpings, good wine choice, cheerful and helpful young staff, stripped pine tables on stripped floors, interesting mix of artworks on pastel walls; children welcome, garden *(Roger Price)*

PATCHING [TQ0705]

Fox [signed off A27 eastbound just W of Worthing]: Large no smoking dining area off roomy panelled bar, enjoyable reasonably priced generous food freshly made from imaginative sandwiches, baguettes and baked potatoes up, popular Sun roasts (book ahead for these), well kept Harveys Best, Shepherd Neame Spitfire and a seasonal guest beer, friendly attentive service, daily papers, hunting pictures; quiet piped music, nice big tree-shaded garden with play area, small caravan site, open all day wknds *(Bruce Bird, Tony and Wendy Hobden)*

PEASMARSH [TQ8823]

Cock Horse [Main St]: Warm welcome, tidy and cosy bar with log fire and plenty of character, well kept Harveys Best, well priced straightforward food from good sandwiches up; neat garden *(Ann and Colin Hunt, Paul A Moore)*

PETT [TQ8713]

Royal Oak [Pett Rd]: Well run friendly local (remembered rather surprisingly by some readers as a Temperance Inn), roomy bars, well kept real ales, good well presented food from generous sandwiches up, separate dining area *(Michael and Ann Cole)*

PETWORTH [SU9719]

☆ *Badgers* [Station Rd (A285 1½ miles S)]: Small drinking area by entrance, but most customers come to eat the up-to-date rather upmarket food, served at well spaced tables with mix from old mahogany to waxed stripped pine, charming wrought-iron lamps, log fires, well kept Badger Best and K&B, quite a range of wines; may be faint piped music; children in eating area of bar if over 5, stylish tables and seats out on terrace by water-lily pool,

bedrooms, cl winter Sun evenings
(Roger Endersby, John Evans, Arnold Bennett, Pamela and Merlyn Horswell, Walter and Susan Rinaldi-Butcher, LYM)

PEVENSEY [TQ6404]
Royal Oak & Castle [High St]: Right by formidable Roman/Norman castle ruins, interesting and sympathetic neo-colonial refurbishment, lots of wicker and basketwork, light and airy atmosphere, well kept Harveys, good value food inc good range of european dishes, friendly staff and customers, more formal back dining area; garden tables under canvas parasols, good play area *(Sue Demont, Tim Barrow)*

POUNDGATE [TQ4928]
Crow & Gate [A26 Crowborough—Uckfield]: Old pub extended as beamed Vintage Inn, good log fire, their usual food, well kept if not cheap Harveys Best, lots of wines by the glass, efficient service, no smoking area; good disabled access, children welcome, tables outside, play area *(R M Corlett)*

POYNINGS [TQ2611]
Royal Oak [The Street]: Large pleasantly refurbished beamed bar with wide choice of enjoyable food, good service, well kept Courage Directors, Greene King Old Speckled Hen and Harveys from three-sided servery, no smoking area, woodburner, no piped music; big attractive garden with barbecue, climbing frame and country/downs views *(John Beeken, Mr and Mrs John Taylor, J Varey)*

RINGMER [TQ4412]
☆ *Cock* [Uckfield Rd – blocked-off section of rd off A26 N of village turn-off]: Heavy 16th-c beams, flagstones and big inglenook log fire, great blackboard choice of good value food, helpful, friendly and efficient young staff, well kept Badger Tanglefoot, Fullers London Pride and Harveys Best and seasonal Old, good wines by the glass, modernised rooms off inc no smoking lounge and back restaurant; children allowed in overflow eating area; piped music; tables on small terrace and in big sloping fairy-lit garden with shrubs, fruit trees and lots of spring flowers, walks nearby *(LYM, A J Bowen, John Beeken, P W Taylor, M and R Thomas)*

RIPE [TQ5010]
☆ *Lamb* [signed off A22 Uckfield—Hailsham, or off A27 Lewes—Polegate via Chalvington; Church Lane]: Interestingly furnished partly panelled rooms around central servery, masses of attractive antique prints and pictures, nostalgic song-sheet covers, automotive memorabilia, Victorian pin-ups in gents', new chef doing good value fresh food inc imaginative dishes, well kept Harveys Best and a couple of interesting guest beers, good range of reasonably priced wines, several open fires, small dining room set out as farmyard stalls; bar billiards, TV; pleasant sheltered back garden with play area and barbecues *(BB, Tony and Wendy Hobden, John and Esme Walters)*

ROBERTSBRIDGE [TQ7323]
Ostrich [Station Rd]: Cheerful open-plan

former station hotel, enjoyable food from filled rolls up, Adnams, Harveys Best and a guest beer, coal fire, eye-catching artworks, games room; tables in attractive garden, bedrooms, open all day *(the Didler)*

RODMELL [TQ4105]
Abergavenny Arms [back rd Lewes—Newhaven]: Open-plan beamed and raftered village pub, largely no smoking, with some interesting bric-a-brac and furnishings, generous food from ploughman's to sensible hot dishes, well kept Harveys Best and guests such as Kings or Whites, quick friendly service, log fire, small no smoking section; they may try to keep your credit card while you eat; dogs on leads welcome, large two-level back terrace, good walks and handy for Virginia Woolf's Monks Cottage *(Bruce Bird, Tony and Wendy Hobden, Paul Hopton)*

ROGATE [SU8023]
☆ *White Horse* [East St; A272 Midhurst—Petersfield]: Rambling heavy-beamed local, country boots, waxed jackets and springer spaniels mixing easily with high heels and off-the-shoulder dresses to make for a charming relaxed atmosphere, flagstones, timbers and big log fire, step down to attractive candlelit dining area, well kept Harveys ales, good generous food (not Sun eve or Mon), hands-on licensees, traditional games, no music or machines; quiz and folk nights, open all day Sun, some tables out behind *(LYM, Pamela and Merlyn Horswell, Geoff and Linda Payne)*

ROTTINGDEAN [TQ3602]
Queen Victoria [High St]: Well kept Gales BB and Harveys BB, good value bar food from sandwiches and baguettes up, long bar with old local photographs, partitioned back dining room; piped classical music; back garden, interesting village handy for seaside walks *(John Beeken)*

ROWHOOK [TQ1234]
☆ *Chequers* [off A29 NW of Horsham]: Attractive 16th-c pub, relaxing beamed and flagstone front bar with portraits and inglenook fire, step up to low-beamed lounge, well kept Harveys, Youngs and two guest beers, decent wines by the glass, good coffee, friendly helpful staff, young chef/landlord doing up-to-date food from panini and light dishes up, good separate restaurant; piped music; children and dogs welcome, tables out on terraces and in pretty garden with good play area, attractive surroundings *(Roger Hancock, LYM, Martin and Karen Wake, Frances Mumford, Alan Sadler)*

RUNCTON [SU8900]
Royal Oak [Pagham Rd, S]: Very popular, with particularly good sizzling steak and mixed grill, friendly staff, well kept Gales HSB *(A and B D Craig)*

RUSPER [TQ2037]
Plough [signed from A24 and A264 N and NE of Horsham]: Friendly and nicely worn in country local dating from 16th c, padded very low beams, panelling and enormous inglenook with lovely log fire, well kept ales such as

Fullers London Pride, Greene King IPA, Abbot and Ruddles County and Kings Ale, good value food, quick pleasant service, dining area; children welcome, bar billiards and darts in raftered room upstairs; pretty front terrace, fountain in back garden, occasional live music *(Brian Root, LYM, Ian Phillips)*

RUSTINGTON [TQ0402]

Lamb [The Street]: Large Steak & Ale chain pub with settles and other mixed seating, no smoking dining area one side, games room with darts, pool and machines the other, food all day inc various deals, Greene King Old Speckled Hen, Harveys Best and Marstons Pedigree, efficient friendly service; piped music may obtrude *(Tony and Wendy Hobden)*

Windmill [Mill Lane (B2187)]: Efficient friendly service, Arundel and guest ales such as Dark Star, generous enjoyable food ordered from separate counter inc Thurs OAP lunches, no smoking restaurant; plenty of tables, some covered, in pleasant garden with neat lawn, miniature windmill, boules and play area *(Tony and Wendy Hobden, Bruce Bird)*

RYE HARBOUR [TQ9220]

☆ *Inkerman Arms* [Rye Harbour Rd]: Cosy and welcoming unpretentious local nr nature reserve, wide choice of good food inc lots of fresh local fish, fine home-made pies and old-fashioned puddings, well kept ales inc Harveys Best, pleasantly decorated main bar with secluded eating areas inc no smoking area; tables in small garden; cl Mon evening and winter Mon lunchtime *(John Davis, Hywel Bevan, R C Livesey, Pete Taylor, Mr and Mrs S Wilson)*

SCAYNES HILL [TQ3824]

Sloop [Freshfield Lock]: Named for the boats on the adjacent former Ouse Canal, pleasantly furnished linked areas inc no smoking section, promptly served blackboard food, well kept Greene King ales with one or two guest beers, decent wines, bar billiards and traditional games, lots of interesting photographs; may be piped music; children in eating areas, lots of tables in sheltered garden, open for food all day Sun *(LYM, Susan and John Douglas, Clive and Janice Sillitoe)*

SEAFORD [TV5199]

Golden Galleon [Exceat, A259 E]: Popular newly reworked Vintage Inns family dining pub in fine position, handy for the level walk down the valley to the sea, with plenty of tables outside, good choice of wines by the glass, well kept Adnams Broadside and perhaps Bass and Harveys Best, good service, reasonably priced usual food all day *(LYM, Philip and Ann Board, Dr David Cockburn, Michael and Ann Cole, Ron Gentry, Karen Eliot)*

Wellington [Steyne Rd]: Pleasant local with well kept real ales *(Chris Glasson)*

SELSEY [SZ8692]

Lifeboat [Albion Rd, nr seafront]: Convivial unpretentious bar (dogs allowed) with dining extension, wide choice of low-priced food from sandwiches to local fish and crab, well kept Fullers London Pride, friendly helpful staff;

tables out on big verandah – only main courses served at hatch here *(J A Snell, Phil and Sally Gorton, LM, Tony and Shirley Albert)*

SHOREHAM-BY-SEA [TQ2105]

Buckingham Arms [Brunswick Rd, by stn]: Big open-plan pub with lots of real ales inc interesting microbrews, good value lunchtime food from sandwiches up; no no smoking area; small garden behind *(Tony Hobden)*

Fly Inn [signed off A27, A259]: Not a pub, but this small bar in interesting 1930s art deco airport building has well kept changing ales such as Adnams Broadside and Weltone Wealden Best, enjoyable low-priced bar food from baked potatoes up inc popular all-day breakfast, congenial relaxed atmosphere, cheerful staff; piped music; terrace tables, uninterrupted views all round (downs views, plenty of light aircraft action); children welcome, small airport museum *(John Beeken, Louise English)*

☆ *Red Lion* [Upper Shoreham Rd, opp church]: Modest dim-lit low-beamed and timbered 16th-c pub with settles in snug alcoves, good value well presented individual food with sensibly limited lunchtime choice, well kept changing ales, post-Easter beer festival, decent wines, farm cider, friendly efficient staff, log fire in unusual fireplace, another open fire in no smoking dining room, further bar with covered terrace; piped music; pretty sheltered garden behind, good downs views and walks *(MLR, Bruce Bird, PL)*

SHORTBRIDGE [TQ4521]

Peacock [Piltdown; OS Sheet 198 map ref 450215]: Neatly rebuilt beamed and timbered bar, comfortable and welcoming, with big inglenook, enjoyable generous food served piping hot inc good fish, well kept Fullers London Pride and Harveys, restaurant; piped music; children welcome, good-sized garden *(John Davis, BB, Richard May, J P Humphery)*

SIDLESHAM [SZ8697]

☆ *Crab & Lobster* [Mill Lane; off B2145 S of Chichester]: Old country local with log fire in chatty traditional regulars' bar, side dining lounge, pretty back garden looking over to the bird-reserve of silted Pagham Harbour; reasonably priced food (not wkdy evenings in winter) inc good fresh local crab, reasonable prices, quick genial service, Ballards and other ales, decent wines, country wines, traditional games; dogs welcome, no children, music or machines *(LYM, Tracey and Stephen Groves, Tony and Wendy Hobden, John Coatsworth, Andy and Jill Kassube, Edwina Messer)*

SLINDON [SU9708]

☆ *Spur* [Slindon Common; A29 towards Bognor]: Civilised, roomy and attractive 17th-c pub, good choice of upmarket but good value food changing daily, well kept Courage Directors and Greene King Ruddles, cheerful efficient staff, welcoming atmosphere, two big log fires, pine tables, large elegant restaurant, games room with darts and pool (for over-18s), friendly dogs; children welcome, pretty garden (traffic noise) *(Mike Vincent, John Davis, John and Valerie Barnett, J C Bingham)*

SOUTH HARTING [SU7819]

Ship [North Lane (B2146)]: Welcoming 17th-c pub, unpretentious and informal, with good choice of good value food (not Sun evening, when there are bar nibbles) inc sandwiches on request in dimly lit main bar, fine log fire, old photographs, well kept ales inc Ballards, Cheriton Pots and Palmers, helpful landlord, friendly staff and dogs, plain wooden settles in locals' bar (dominoes, perhaps chestnuts to roast by its log fire); unobtrusive piped music; nice setting in pretty village *(Ann and Colin Hunt, Rona Murdoch)*

White Hart [B2146 SE of Petersfield]: Dating from 16th c, cool décor with well spaced tables on polished wood, lounge bar with lower level bar area, friendly efficient young staff, well kept Courage and Fullers London Pride, good wine range, interesting food choice from baguettes up, no smoking restaurant with huge fireplace; piped music; well behaved dogs allowed, walkers and children welcome, good walled garden with spectacular downs views, handy for Uppark *(Ann and Colin Hunt, Rona Murdoch)*

STAPLEFIELD [TQ2728]

☆ *Jolly Tanners* [Handcross Rd, just off A23]: Spotless and comfortable, good honest home-made food, well kept ales such as Dark Star Porter, Elgoods Black Dog, Fullers Chiswick and London Pride and Harveys Best, Australian staff efficient even under pressure, two good log fires, lots of china, brasses and old photographs, no smoking room; piped music, and they may try to keep your credit card while you eat; attractive garden with lots of space for children, terrace tables under cocktail parasols and picnic-sets on grass, by cricket green, quite handy for Nymans (NT) *(Terry Buckland, Roy and Lindsey Fentiman, Bruce Bird, Fred Chamberlain, Tony and Wendy Hobden)*

STEYNING [TQ1711]

White Horse [High St]: Pleasantly furnished and welcoming, with enjoyable food *(Roger Price)*

STOPHAM [TQ0318]

White Hart [off A283 E of village, W of Pulborough]: Interesting old heavily timbered, beamed and panelled pub with log fire and sofas in one of its three snug rooms, well kept ales, wide food choice from baguettes to venison, young enthusiastic staff, no smoking restaurant; piped music; children welcome, play area over road, tables out by River Arun *(Roger Endersby, LYM, Tony and Wendy Hobden, E H and J I Wild)*

STORRINGTON [TQ0814]

New Moon [High St]: Wide choice of reasonably priced food from sandwiches up (not Sun evening), Greene King IPA and Abbot, lower no smoking area; garden tables *(Tony and Wendy Hobden)*

STOUGHTON [SU8011]

☆ *Hare & Hounds* [signed off B2146 Petersfield—Emsworth]: Comfortable and airy pine-clad country dining pub with generous reasonably priced food inc good value Sun roast, four well kept real ales such as Timothy Taylors Landlord and Youngs Special (a little room for drinkers in main bar, small locals' bar), huge open fires, good helpful service; children in eating areas, tables on pretty front terrace and in back garden, lovely setting nr Saxon church, good walks nearby *(LYM, Ann and Colin Hunt, Cathy Robinson, Ed Coombe, John Davis, J A Snell)*

SUTTON [SU9715]

☆ *White Horse* [The Street]: Charming small and civilised country pub with island servery separating bare-boards and flagstoned bar (dogs welcome this side) from two-room barrel-vaulted dining area with stylishly simple furnishings and Rowlandson prints, warm welcome, good if not cheap food from interesting sandwiches and bar dishes to enterprising restaurant meals inc local game and fish, well kept Courage Best, Fullers London Pride, Shepherd Neame Spitfire and Youngs Special, short interesting wine choice, log fire; tables in garden up behind, good value bedrooms with excellent breakfast, quiet little hamlet nr Bignor Roman villa *(BB, John Davis, S Topham, Melanie Ginger, Prof and Mrs S Barnett)*

TELHAM [TQ7714]

Black Horse [A2100 Battle—Hastings]: Small low-beamed pub with good varied sensibly priced food inc evening grills, friendly landlord, Shepherd Neame beers, log fires, old-world décor with grandfather clock, upstairs skittle alley; unobtrusive piped music, monthly jazz nights, spring folk/jazz festival; garden with boules *(Ian and Nita Cooper)*

THAKEHAM [TQ1017]

☆ *White Lion* [off B2139 N of Storrington; The Street]: Heavily beamed two-bar 16th-c village pub, quiet and relaxing after being nicely cleaned up under new landlord (he's got rid of the piped music), several well kept ales such as Caledonian Deuchars IPA and Harveys, good choice of wines by the glass, robust home-made food from open kitchen, friendly informal service, big log fire, bare boards and traditional furnishings inc corner settles, bistro Thurs-Sat; dogs welcome, terrace tables, more on small lawn *(Tony and Wendy Hobden, Bruce Bird, John Beeken, Mrs M Rice, Terry Buckland)*

TURNERS HILL [TQ3435]

☆ *Crown* [East St]: Spacious pleasantly decorated dining pub, different levels inc attractive restaurant with pitched rafters, wide choice of reliable reasonably priced food, well kept ales such as Fullers and Harveys, good wine choice, log fire; soft piped music; children welcome, tables outside, pleasant valley views from back garden, two bedrooms *(BB, Debbie and Neil Hayter)*

Red Lion [Lion Lane, just off and parallel with B2028]: Convivial traditional local with welcoming licensees and splendidly broad range of customers giving properly pubby atmosphere, well kept Harveys PA, Best and seasonal beers, good choice of wines by the glass, good value food from filled rolls through simple hot dishes to good reasonably priced Sun roast, narrow high-beamed bar with small fire, three steps up to smallish low-ceilinged dining area with inglenook log fire, cushioned pews and built-in settles; can be a bit smoky, live music Fri; children and well behaved dogs welcome, picnic-sets in quiet side garden *(BB, Klaus and Elizabeth Leist, Mike Gorton, Terry Buckland, Richard May)*

UDIMORE [TQ8519]

Kings Head: Traditional chatty village pub with long-serving licensees, much character, open fires, low beams, plain tables and chairs on bare boards, well kept Fullers London Pride and Harveys from long bar, good-sized helpings of low-priced pubby food in dining area *(Peter Meister)*

☆ *Plough* [Cock Marling (B2089 W of Rye)]: Civilised pub with good home-made food, all fresh, running up to bass and duck, well kept Greene King ales and a guest such as Ringwood Fortyniner, reasonably priced wines, relaxed friendly service, woodburner, books for sale, open fire and country prints in small dining area; tables on good-sized suntrap back terrace *(Kevin Thorpe, Peter Meister, V Brogden)*

WADHURST [TQ6131]

☆ *Best Beech* [Mayfield Lane (B2100 a mile W)]: Pleasantly worn in dining pub with enjoyable food using some local produce in cosy eating area with lots of pictures, bar on left with wall seats, plenty of comfortable sofas, coal fire, well kept Adnams, Harveys and Youngs, good choice of wines by the glass, quick pleasant service; may be piped music; back restaurant, tables outside, good value bedrooms, good breakfast *(Richard Siebert, BB, Clive and Janice Sillitoe)*

WALDRON [TQ5419]

Star [Blackboys—Horam side road]: Lively village local with big inglenook log fire in panelled bar, well kept Harveys Bitter and seasonal Old, fair range of standard pub food from good ham baguettes to some interesting specials, friendly helpful if not always speedy service, no music, separate back dining room; pleasant garden, seats out in front overlooking pretty village *(Phil and Sally Gorton, BB)*

WARBLETON [TQ6018]

☆ *Warbil in Tun* [S of B2096 SE of Heathfield]: Pretty dining pub with good choice of good value food esp meat (helpful ex-butcher landlord), nice puddings, well kept reasonably priced Harveys Best, good coffee, welcoming and cosily civilised atmosphere, beams and red plush, huge log fireplace, no music; tables on roadside green, attractive tucked-away village *(Michael and Ann Cole)*

WARNHAM [TQ1533]

☆ *Sussex Oak* [just off A24 Horsham—Dorking; Church St]: Cheerful country pub with friendly staff, big inglenook log fireplace, mix of flagstones, tiles, wood and carpeting, heavy beams and timbers, sofas and bar billiards, well kept Adnams, Fullers London Pride, Timothy Taylors Landlord, Youngs and a guest beer from carved servery, plenty of wines

by the glass, **popular** food (not Sun/Mon evenings) from sandwiches and baked potatoes to steaks, high-raftered no smoking restaurant; piped music; children and dogs welcome, garden picnic-sets, open all day *(LYM, Ron Gentry, Peter Lewis, Malcolm Pearce)*

WARNINGLID [TQ2425]

Half Moon [The Street]: Welcoming new licensees giving big boost to this village pub, with delightful atmosphere, well kept beer, good wines, and now developing the food side *(J P Humphery, Sue Slade)*

WASHINGTON [TQ1213]

Frankland Arms [just off A24 Horsham—Worthing]: Wide choice of food all day from warm baguettes to good puddings, take-aways too, well kept Flowers Original, Fullers London Pride and a guest such as Arundel, good value wines by the glass, log fires, pleasant prompt service, well used bar (dogs welcome) and large comfortable no smoking dining area; disabled facilities, Post Office in outbuilding, tables in neat garden *(Tony and Wendy Hobden)*

WEST ASHLING [SU8107]

Richmond Arms [just off B2146; Mill Rd]: Village pub tucked away in pretty setting nr mill pond with ducks, gently refurbished by courteous new licensees, three Greene King and guest ales, bar food, good relaxed atmosphere, open fire, darts, pool and a skittle alley; children allowed, picnic-sets out by pergola, has been open all day Sun and summer Sat *(LYM, Ann and Colin Hunt)*

WEST DEAN [SU8512]

Selsey Arms [A286 Midhurst—Chichester]: Large welcoming late 18th-c two-bar pub with plentiful enjoyable food inc good home-made crisps, well kept Greene King IPA and Fullers London Pride, decent wines, roomy no smoking area, log fire *(John Davis, Sue and Mike Todd, Ann and Colin Hunt, R B Gardiner, Richard Waller, Pauline Smith)*

WEST HOATHLY [TQ3632]

Intrepid Fox [Hammingden Lane/North Lane, towards Sharpthorne]: Vinols Cross Inn renamed, warm and welcoming, with genial landlord, enjoyable generous food, good wine *(Selina Knight, Mrs F Reynolds)*

WESTERGATE [SU9305]

Labour in Vain: Three small linked areas with enjoyable reasonably priced straightforward food, well kept Badger K&B, Ballards Best, Harveys Best and Kings Old *(Tony and Wendy Hobden)*

WHATLINGTON [TQ7619]

Royal Oak [A21]: Steps between two long welcoming and relaxing beamed rooms with stripped pine tables and chairs, log fire, nooks and corners, feature well edged with flowers, generous enjoyable traditional food with good veg, decent wine, friendly service; tables in back garden *(J N Davidson, Pamela and Douglas Cooper, BB, Vincent Board, Veronica Ford)*

WINCHELSEA [TQ9017]

☆ *New Inn* [German St; just off A259]: Rambling open-plan beamed areas with emphasis on the enjoyable food esp fresh local fish, well kept Greene King ales, decent wines and malt whiskies, obliging helpful staff, log fire, Georgian décor with turkey carpet and some slate flagstones, separate public bar with darts; piped music may obtrude; children in eating area, pleasant walled garden, six pretty bedrooms (some sharing bathrooms), delightful setting opp pretty church – Spike Milligan buried in graveyard *(Joel Dobris, E G Parish, Peter Meister, LYM, Andrew Richard Smith, John Beeken)*

WISBOROUGH GREEN [TQ0526]

☆ *Three Crowns* [Billingshurst Rd (A272)]: Friendly new licensees in big immaculately kept pub with welcoming helpful service, nice mix of ages, good value straightforward food from sandwiches and baguettes up, small helpings available, open-plan bar stretching into no smoking dining room (worth booking), stripped bricks and beams, well kept ales inc Ballards Trotton, good coffee, games room; disabled facilities, sizeable back garden shaded by elm tree *(David Coleman, DWAJ, Peter Lewis, David A Hammond)*

WITHYHAM [TQ4935]

☆ *Dorset Arms* [B2110]: Cheerful new young landlord (Harveys' youngest tenant) in 16th-c pub handy for Forest Way walks, enjoyable traditional food from filled rolls up, reasonable prices, well kept Harveys Best, Armada, Porter and winter Old, decent wines inc local ones, attentive friendly service, sturdy tables and simple country seats on wide oak floorboards (sometimes a bit uneven – beware of wobbles), good log fire in Tudor fireplace, darts, dominoes, shove-ha'penny, cribbage, pretty no smoking restaurant; piped pop music, fruit machine; dogs welcome, white tables on brick terrace by small green *(LYM, Peter Meister, Debbie and Neil Hayter, Angus Johnson, Carol Bolden)*

WOODMANCOTE [SU7707]

Woodmancote Arms [the one nr Emsworth]: Cheerful village pub with friendly locals and their dogs, simple generous reasonably priced bar food, well kept Wadworths ales, decent wines, log fire in eating area, pretty and unpretentious restaurant; large games room for pool and darts *(Ann and Colin Hunt)*

WORTHING [TQ1404]

Cricketers [Broadwater St W, Broadwater Green (A24)]: Extended panelled local with well kept Bass, Fullers London Pride, Greene King IPA, Harveys and a guest beer, log fires, reasonably priced popular food, friendly staff, steps down to small lounge with no smoking dining room beyond; garden *(Tony and Wendy Hobden)*

George & Dragon [High St, Old Tarring]: Extended 17th-c pub with four areas inc airy lounge and no smoking restaurant, good value lunches inc OAP bargains, well kept Harveys Best, Charles Wells Bombardier, Youngs and a good guest beer, friendly efficient service, beams and panelling, bric-a-brac, brass platters and old photographs, no piped music; dogs allowed (not in attractive garden), open all day *(Bruce Bird)*

Hare & Hound [Portland Rd, N of Marks & Spencer]: Friendly bustling extended local with five well kept ales from several different breweries from central brass and oak bar, good value promptly served straightforward food (not Fri-Sun evenings) from sandwiches and baked potatoes up, helpful staff, jazz night Tues; canopied courtyard *(Craig Turnbull, R T and J C Moggridge, Tony and Wendy Hobden)*

Selden Arms [Lyndhurst Rd, between Safeway and hospital]: Friendly local with well kept Ringwood Fortyniner, Youngs and four changing ales from interesting small breweries, farm cider, lively landlady and locals, generous good value lunchtime food inc popular doorstep sandwiches, log fire, lots of old pub photographs; can get smoky; open all day *(Tony and Wendy Hobden, Bruce Bird)*

YAPTON [SU9704]

Maypole [signed off B2132 Arundel rd; Maypole Lane]: Chatty landlord and regulars, well kept Ringwood Best, Skinners Betty Stogs and several changing guests inc a local Mild, enjoyable generous lunchtime sandwiches and simple hot dishes, good value Sun roasts, log fire in cosy lounge, skittle alley, spring and autumn beer festivals, occasional live music, Sun meat raffle; can be smoky; seats outside, open all day *(Tony and Wendy Hobden, Bruce Bird)*

A very few pubs try to make you leave a credit card at the bar, as a sort of deposit if you order food. They are not entitled to do this. The credit card firms and banks which issue them warn you not to let them out of your sight. If someone behind the counter used your card fraudulently, the card company or bank could in theory hold you liable, because of your negligence in letting a stranger hang on to your card. Suggest instead that if they feel the need for security, they 'swipe' your card and give it back to you. And do name and shame the pub to us.

Warwickshire
(with Birmingham and West Midlands)

Just one new entry here this year: the Crabmill at Preston Bagot, a transformation of an interesting old pub into a stylishly up-to-date place, very popular for a rewarding meal out or a comfortable sit with a good drink or coffee. Other pubs notching up particularly warm reports these days are the gently upmarket ancient Kings Head at Aston Cantlow (imaginative food and charming service), the flamboyant Old Joint Stock in Birmingham (good drinks and reasonably priced food), the chatty old Turf in Bloxwich (a fine unspoilt real ale pub), the smartly upmarket Inn at Farnborough (delicious food at a price, and splendid choice of wines by the glass), the charmingly old-fashioned Case is Altered at Five Ways (a favourite unspoilt pub), the Malt Shovel at Gaydon (a splendid all-rounder, and very relaxing as a motorway break), the entirely no smoking Howard Arms at Ilmington (very good food and atmosphere), the cheery canalside Navigation at Lapworth (enjoyable no-nonsense food, good beer), and the civilised Bell at Welford-on-Avon (imaginative good food in a charming building – the service is charming, too). It is the Bell at Welford-on-Avon which takes the title of Warwickshire Dining Pub of the Year. In the Lucky Dip section at the end of the chapter, front-running pubs include the spectacular Bartons Arms in Birmingham, Boot at Lapworth (if you like the Crabmill and Kings Head at Aston Cantlow you'll certainly like this too), Old Swan in Netherton and Blue Boar at Temple Grafton. In the Warwickshire countryside drinks prices tend to be closely in line with the national average. You can find much cheaper beer in the friendly and unpretentious town locals of the West Midlands (and often bargain food too); Bathams and Holdens are particularly good value local brewers. The main regional brewer is Banks's of Wolverhampton.

ALDERMINSTER SP2348 Map 4
Bell 🍴 ♟

A3400 Oxford—Stratford

Cool green walls at this civilised dining pub are hung with huge modern prints, giving a spotlessly kept Georgian inn an interesting contemporary twist. Spacious and open plan, the communicating rooms of the bar have a counter fronted with rough timber from wine crates, stripped slatback chairs around wooden tables on flagstones and beautifully polished wooden floors, little vases of flowers, a solid fuel stove in a stripped brick inglenook, and white wicker chairs in the lounge. Emphasis is very much on the menu, which changes every few months, but might include soup (£3.95), filled lunchtime baguettes (from £4.50, not Sun), spinach and parmesan soufflé (£6.50), parsnip, sage and apricot roulade (£8.95), steak and kidney pudding (£10.95), casserole of minted lamb (£9.50). Also daily specials such as smoked haddock and mushroom au gratin (£5.50), lamb with almonds, ginger and garlic with spiced rice (£10.50), baked chicken supreme with mango and grain mustard (£10.95), and home-made puddings such as fruit crumble, steamed pudding of the day or chocolate, pistachio and brioche bread pudding (£4.95). Well kept Greene King IPA and Old Speckled Hen on handpump, alongside a good range of around 20 wines and champagne by the glass, freshly squeezed juice, cocktails, winter mulled wine and various teas. Other than the bar, the pub is no smoking. They have high chairs, and readers with children have felt particularly welcome. A conservatory and terrace overlook the garden and Stour Valley. *(Recommended by Roy Bromell, Annette and John Derbyshire, Susie Symes, Paul Humphreys, Jane Legate, Ian Phillips, Joan Crane, Eileen White, Les and Barbara Owen, Margaret Best, Michael and Jeanne Shillington, Dr P M O'Donnell, Iain R Hewitt, David Tett, Pat and Clive Sherriff)*

Free house ~ Licensees Keith and Vanessa Brewer ~ Real ale ~ Bar food ~ Restaurant ~ (01789) 450414 ~ Children welcome ~ Dogs allowed in bar and bedrooms ~ Open 11.30-3, 6.30-11(10.30 Sun); closed evenings 24-27 Dec, 1 Jan ~ Bedrooms: £27(£45S)(£52B)/£48(£55S)(£70B)

ARMSCOTE SP2444 Map 4
Fox & Goose 🍴 ♀ 🛏
Off A3400 Stratford—Shipston

Hovering comfortably somewhere between bistro and upmarket pub this stylishly simple blacksmith's forge has red painted walls in the small flagstoned bar, bright crushed velvet cushions plumped up on wooden pews, a big gilt mirror over a log fire, polished floorboards and black and white etchings. In a quirky tableau above the dining room's woodburning stove a stuffed fox stalks a big goose. Not cheap, but nevertheless very good, bar food is listed on a daily changing blackboard, and as well as sandwiches (£4.75), there might be grilled garlic sardines or home-cured gravadlax (£5.25), wild mushroom and spring onion risotto with a poached egg (£10.50), fried fillets of red mullet on a prawn and cognac sauce (£13.95), beef fillet with wild mushroom and red wine jus (£16.95) and home-made puddings such as strawberry eton mess (£4.95). Service from charming young staff is very helpful, but there isn't a designated no smoking area so one reader found the place a bit smoky. J W Lees (possibly changing to Hook Horton), and a Hook Norton seasonal beer are well kept on handpump, and they have mulled wine in winter, jugs of Pimms in summer, and well chosen wines including a choice of dessert wines. Bedrooms, which are named after characters in Cluedo, are mildly quirky, stylishly decorated and comfortable. Outside, the garden has an elegant vine-covered deck area overlooking a big lawn with tables, benches and fruit trees, and several of the neighbouring houses boast splendid roses in summer. *(Recommended by John Kane, Fred and Lorraine Gill, W W Burke, David Handforth, Mr and Mrs G S Ayrton, Paul Humphreys, Dr David Cockburn, Ian Phillips, Lee and Liz Potter, Roger and Maureen Kenning, KC, Rod Stoneman, Michael and Jeanne Shillington, Iain R Hewitt, Stephen Woad, Robin and Yvonne Calvert, D M Heath)*

Free house ~ Licensee Sarah Watson ~ Real ale ~ Bar food (12-2.30, 7-9.30) ~ Restaurant ~ (01608) 682293 ~ Children in restaurant ~ Dogs allowed in bar ~ Open 12-3, 6-11 ~ Bedrooms: £55B/£85B

ASTON CANTLOW SP1359 Map 4
Kings Head 🍴 ♀
Village signposted just off A3400 NW of Stratford

This lovely old black and white timbered Tudor pub really hits the mark with lots of readers. There's particular praise for the good often inventive food, but they also love the historic feel of the building, the relaxed and chatty and gently civilised atmosphere, and the high standard of enthusiastic service from attentive young staff. The creative menu changes very regularly and meals are freshly prepared. As well as lunchtime sandwiches (£4.95), dishes might include starters such as soup (£3.75), chicken caesar salad (£5.75) and artichoke, asparagus and walnut fettuccine (£5.75), main courses such as pea and broad bean risotto with parmesan and basil oil (£8.95), braised lamb chump (£12.50), baked lemon sole with chive butter sauce (£13.95) and puddings such as trio of chocolate mousses or summer fruit crumble (£4.95); the restaurant and bar have no smoking areas. The clean and comfortable village bar on the right is a nice mix of rustic surroundings with a subtly upmarket atmosphere, flagstones, low beams, and old-fashioned settles around its massive inglenook log fireplace. The chatty quarry-tiled main room has attractive window seats and oak tables. Three well kept real ales on handpump include Greene King Abbot, M&B Brew XI and a guest such as Hook Norton Old Hooky, also decent wines; piped jazz. The garden is lovely, with a big chestnut tree. This is a very pretty village; the pub is not far from Mary Arden's house in Wilmcote, and Shakespeare's parents are said to have married in the church next door. It's a real picture in summer, with wisteria and colourful hanging baskets. *(Recommended by John Kane, Mrs Ann Gray, Stan and Hazel Allen, Steve Cawthray, Richard Marjoram, Di and Mike Gillam, Stephen Woad, Karen Eliot, Simon and Sally Small, Susan and John Douglas, Therese Flanagan, Mike Gorton, Charles and Isabel Cooper, Les and Barbara Owen, Dr D Scott, John Saul, Paul and Gloria Howell)*

Furlong Leisure ~ Manager David Brian ~ Real ale ~ Bar food (12-2.30(3.30 Sun), 7-9.45(9.30 Sun)) ~ Restaurant ~ (01789) 488242 ~ Children welcome ~ Dogs allowed in bar ~ Open 11-3, 5.30-11; 11-11 Sat; 12-10.30 Sun

BIRMINGHAM SP0686 Map 4
Old Joint Stock ♛
Temple Row West

The sober exterior of this romanesque building gives little indication of the impressive flamboyance within – chandeliers hang from the soaring pink and gilt ceiling, gently illuminated busts line the top of the ornately plastered walls, and there's a splendid if well worn cupola above the centre of the room. Drinks are served from a handsome dark wood island bar counter, and big portraits and smart long curtains create an air of unexpected elegance. Around the walls are plenty of tables and chairs, some in surprisingly cosy corners, with more on a big balcony overlooking the bar, reached by a very grand wide staircase. It can get busy (it's a lunchtime favourite with local office workers), but effortlessly absorbs what seem like huge numbers of people. A separate room with panelling and a fireplace has a more intimate, clubby feel. This is the only pub we know of N of Bristol to be owned by the London-based brewer Fullers; it stocks their Chiswick, ESB, London Pride and one of their seasonal beers, which are well kept alongside a guest from the local Beowulf, and they have a decent range of about a dozen wines by the glass; helpful friendly service, teas, coffees. Usefully served all day, a nice variety of very fairly priced bar food includes soup (£3.25), sandwiches (from £3), bacon and brie panini (£5.75), sweet potato and goats cheese pie (£6.50), grilled tuna steak (£7.25), steak and stilton pie (£7.45) and fish and chips (£7.50). Daily papers, perhaps big-screen TV for major sporting events, and piped music (which can be quite loud). A small back terrace has some cast-iron tables and chairs. At busy times there might be a bouncer on the doors. *(Recommended by Rob and Catherine Dunster, Steve and Liz Tilley, Susan and John Douglas, John and Fiona McIlwain, Kevin Blake, Barry Collett, Richard Waller, Pauline Smith, Tony and Wendy Hobden, Colin Gooch)*

Fullers ~ Manager Alison Turner ~ Real ale ~ Bar food (12-9; not Sun) ~ (0121) 200 1892 ~ Dogs allowed in bar ~ Open 11-11; closed bank hols

BLOXWICH SJ9902 Map 4
Turf ♛
Wolverhampton Road, off A34 just S of A4124, N fringes of Walsall; aka Tinky's

This utterly uncontrived old-fashioned local is a fascinating reminder of how pubs used to be. It's been in the same family for over 130 years, and little changed during that time. What's particularly nice is that even though the unspoilt rooms are Grade II listed, it's far more than just a museum piece. It's alive and chatty with friendly locals happy to tell you the history of the place, and the particularly impressive changing range of beers, always very well kept, draws in a wider range of customers than you might expect. From the outside you could be forgiven for thinking it's no longer in business, as it appears to be a rather run-down terraced house. Once through the front door it still doesn't immediately look like a pub, but more like the hall of a 1930s home; the public bar is through a door on the right. Reminiscent of a waiting room, it has wooden slatted benches running around the walls, with a big heating pipe clearly visible underneath; there's a tiled floor, three small tables, and William Morris curtains and wallpaper around the simple fireplace. The bar counter has four changing real ales from brewers such as Bathams, Beowulf, Holdens, RCH and Titanic. There's hatch service (friendly and chatty) out to the hall, on the other side of which is the smoking room, slightly more comfortable, with unusual padded wall settles with armrests. There's also a tiny back parlour with chairs around a tiled fireplace. It almost goes without saying that there's no music or machines. The pub's basic charms won't appeal to those who like their creature comforts; the no-frills lavatories are outside, at the end of a simple but pleasant garden, and they don't do food. *(Recommended by Kerry Law, Simon Smith, the Didler, Pete Baker, RWC, Mike Begley, Paul and Gloria Howell)*

Free house ~ Licensees Doris and Zena Hiscott-Wilkes ~ Real ale ~ No credit cards ~ (01922) 407745 ~ Open 12-3, 7-11(10.30 Sun)

BRIERLEY HILL SO9187 Map 4
Vine ◀ £

Delph Road; B4172 between A461 and (nearer) A4100

This genuine chatty beer drinker's local, truly west midlands in character, is warmly welcoming with a friendly down-to-earth landlord and staff. It's known locally as the Bull & Bladder, in reference to the good stained-glass bull's heads and very approximate bunches of grapes in the front bow windows. It can get crowded in the plainer front bar, which has wall benches and simple leatherette-topped oak stools. The extended and comfortably refurbished snug on the left (partly no smoking for the first time this year) has solidly built red plush seats, and the back bar has brass chandeliers – as well as darts, dominoes and a big-screen TV. A couple of tables and fruit machines stand in a corridor. Some of the memorabilia here, including one huge pair of horns over a mantelpiece, relates to the Royal Ancient Order of Buffalos, who meet in a room here. As it's the tap for the next-door Bathams brewery, the Bitter and Mild, and perhaps Delph Strong in winter, are in top condition, and very cheap. So too is the simple but tasty fresh lunchtime snacks, which are limited to samosas (65p), sandwiches (from £1), and curry, faggots and peas, or steak and kidney pie (£2.50). There are tables in a back yard, and the car park is opposite. *(Recommended by Gill and Tony Morriss, the Didler, Martin Grosberg, Paul and Gloria Howell)*

Bathams ~ Manager Melvyn Wood ~ Real ale ~ Bar food (12-2 Mon-Fri) ~ No credit cards ~ (01384) 78293 ~ Children in family room ~ Dogs allowed in bar ~ Open 12-11(10.30 Sun)

EASENHALL SP4679 Map 4 🏠
Golden Lion 🛏

Village signposted from B4112 Newbold—Pailton, and from B4455 at Brinklow; Main Street

Enthusiastic licensees put great effort and goodwill into running this comfortable no smoking hotel pub. Forming part of an expanding establishment, the spotlessly kept refurbished tiled and flagstoned bar still has many of its original features, including low beams, timbers and a fine carved settle. Yellow walls have occasional stencilled lion motifs or latin phrases, while a slightly raised area has a comfortable little alcove with padding overhead; the lower level has a brick fireplace. Greene King Abbot, Old Speckled Hen and Ruddles and possibly a guest are well kept on handpump, and service is efficient and welcoming, even at busy times. Bar food includes lunchtime sandwiches (from £4.20), vegetable spring rolls (£4.60), ploughman's (£6.60), local sausages in red wine and onion gravy with mustard grain mash (£8.95), penne with tomato, chilli and garlic topped with melted cheese (£9.35), lamb cutlets with rosemary and redcurrant gravy (£13.75), additional evening dishes such as roast salmon fillet with chilli and coriander sauce on egg noodles (£11.95), and daily specials; two-course Sunday lunch (£13.50). There are tables at the side, and a good few picnic-sets on a spacious lawn. *(Recommended by Rob and Catherine Dunster, Clive and Fran Dutson, Simon Cottrell, Ian Phillips)*

Free house ~ Licensee James Austin ~ Real ale ~ Bar food (12-2, 6-10) ~ Restaurant ~ (01788) 832265 ~ Children in eating area of bar ~ Open 11(12 Sun)-11 ~ Bedrooms: £52B/£72.50B

EDGE HILL SP3747 Map 4
Castle
Off A422

At its best by far on a sunny day when you can sit outside, this crenellated octagon tower (also known as the Round Tower or Radway Tower) is a folly that was built in 1749 by a Gothic Revival enthusiast to mark the spot where Charles I raised his standard at the start of the Battle of Edge Hill. The big attractive garden has lovely glimpses down through the trees of the battlefield, and it's said that after closing time you can hear ghostly sounds of battle – a phantom cavalry officer has even been seen galloping by in search of his severed hand. Inside, there are arched doorways, and the walls of the lounge bar, which has the same eight sides as the rest of the main tower, is decorated with maps, pictures and a collection of Civil War memorabilia. The current licensee was leaving just as we went to press, but as it's always been the building and its setting that have captured readers' fancy that didn't seem grounds for a demotion. Upton House is nearby on the A422, and Compton Wynyates, one of the most beautiful houses in this part of England, is not far beyond. *(Recommended by Gill and Tony Morriss, Jill Bickerton, Susan and John Douglas, W M Paton, Martin and Pauline Jennings, Iain R Hewitt, B Brewer, Rob and Catherine Dunster)*

Opening times and other details not available at time of going to press: (01295) 670255

FARNBOROUGH SP4349 Map 4
Inn at Farnborough 🍴 ♈
Off A423 N of Banbury

The emphasis at this elegant old golden stone house is on fine dining in a civilised environment. From a beautifully put together changing blackboard menu (though it's not cheap), very well prepared dishes, using local produce where possible, might include cream of white onion and port soup (£4.95), ham hock and foie gras terrine with toasted brioche and warm cider apple chutney (£7.95), salmon fishcakes with spinach and mushrooms and chive hollandaise (£12.95), roast pork fillet wrapped in parma ham with oxford blue mash and cider apple sauce (£13.95), roast duck breast with celeriac and potato gratin and black cherry jus (£14.95), fried bass fillet with saffron fricassee of king scallops, mussels and tiger prawns (£15.95) and daily specials such as somerset brie and caramelised onion focaccia or ploughman's (£5.95), and organic burger (£10.95). The set menu (two-course £10.95, three-course £12.95) is good value. Service is professional and courteous. The stylishly refurbished interior is a pleasant mix of the traditional and contemporary, with plenty of exposed stonework, and thoughtful lighting. The beamed and flagstoned bar has neat blinds on its mullioned windows, a chrome hood over a warm log fire in the old stone fireplace, plenty of fresh flowers on the modern counter, candles on wicker tables, and smartly upholstered chairs, window seats and stools. A stable door leads out to chic metal furnishings on a decked terrace. The no smoking dining room has a comfortably roomy seat in a fireplace, nice wooden floors, a good mix of mismatched tables and chairs, and well chosen plants. Well kept Greene King Abbot and a couple of guest beers such as Greene King Ruddles County and Hook Norton Best on handpump, and a good extensive wine list with about 17 by the glass. A machine dispenses Havana cigars; piped music. The landscaped garden is really delightful with a lovely sloping lawn, plenty of picnic-sets (one under a big old tree) and wandering hens. *(Recommended by John Kane, Karen Eliot, Mrs E Widdowson, Gerry and Rosemary Dobson, Michael Jones, Arnold Bennett, George Atkinson, Michael and Anne Brown, Humphry and Angela Crum Ewing, Rob and Catherine Dunster, Iain R Hewitt, KN-R, Simon Jones, Heather Couper)*

Free house ~ Licensees Anthony and Jo Robinson ~ Real ale ~ Bar food (12-3, 6-10; 12-10 Sat, Sun) ~ Restaurant ~ (01295) 690615 ~ Children in eating area of bar and restaurant ~ Dogs allowed in bar ~ Open 12-3.30, 6-11.30; 12-11.30 Sat; 12-10.30 Sun

FIVE WAYS SP2270 Map 4
Case is Altered ◗▩

Follow Rowington signposts at junction roundabout off A4177/A4141 N of Warwick, then right into Case Lane

Even on a Monday lunchtime the buzz of happy grown-up chatter, undisturbed by children, games machines, piped music or even food service, fills the old-fashioned rooms of this delightful white cottage. A door at the back of the building leads into a modest little room with a rug on its tiled floor and an antique bar billiards table protected by an ancient leather cover (it takes pre-decimal sixpences). From here, the simple little main bar has a fine old poster showing the old Lucas Blackwell & Arkwright brewery (now flats) and a clock with its hours spelling out Thornleys Ale – another defunct brewery; there are just a few sturdy old-fashioned tables, with a couple of stout leather-covered settles facing each other over the spotless tiles. The homely lounge (usually open only weekend evenings and Sunday lunchtime) is reached through the front courtyard or back car park. Behind a wrought-iron gate is a little brick-paved courtyard with a stone table. Greene King IPA, Hook Norton Old Hooky and Hooky Dark, a local brew and a national guest, are all served by a rare type of handpump mounted on the casks that are stilled behind the counter. A reader has told us there is disabled access. *(Recommended by the Didler, Ted George, R J Herd, Pete Baker, Mike Begley)*

Free house ~ Licensee Jackie Willacy ~ Real ale ~ No credit cards ~ (01926) 484206 ~ Open 12(11.30 Sat)-2.30, 6-11; 12-2, 7-10.30 Sun

GAYDON SP3654 Map 4
Malt Shovel

Under a mile from M40 junction 12; B4451 into village, then left and right across B4100; Church Road

Well worth knowing about, this busy pub is very handy if you're looking for a break from the M40, but also deserving of praise in its own right. It has a good relaxed atmosphere and a decent choice of well kept beers, and the tasty food is fairly priced and served in generous helpings. Get there early though as they will stop taking orders if it gets too busy. Its slightly unusual layout sees a sort of pathway in mahogany-varnished boards running through bright carpeting to link the entrance, the bar counter on the right and the log fire on the left. The central area has a high pitched ceiling, with milk churns and earthenware containers in a loft above the bar, where five beers from brewers such as Adnams, Castle Eden, Fullers, Greene King Abbot and Shepherd Neame are well kept on handpump alongside nine decent wines by the glass, and filter coffee. Three steps take you up to a snug little space with some comfortable sofas overlooked by a big stained-glass window and reproductions of classic posters. At the other end is a busy lower-ceilinged no smoking dining area with flowers on the mix of kitchen, pub and dining tables. Enjoyable food, cooked by the chef-landlord, includes lunchtime sandwiches (£3.15) and ploughman's or breakfast (£5.50), as well as soup (£3.15), stilton and port mushrooms (£3.95), battered haddock (£5.95), roast pepper, mozzarella and olive salad (£7.15), three-cheese vegetable lasagne (£7.95), wild boar and apple sausages braised in calvados and cider with mustard mash (£8.45), daily specials such as butternut squash and sweet potato pasta bake (£6.95), home-made pies with good pastry (£7.45) and grilled bass with beetroot salsa (£10.95), and puddings such as Amaretti iced nougat or warm chocolate brioche (from

£3.50). Service is friendly and efficient; maybe piped music; darts, fruit machine. The springer spaniel is Rosie, and the jack russell is Mollie. *(Recommended by Karen Eliot, Jill Bickerton, Ian Phillips, Peter and Audrey Dowsett, Roger, Debbie and Rebecca Stamp, Rob and Catherine Dunster, Fergus Dowding, Tina and David Woods-Taylor, J Stickland, Craig Turnbull, Mark and Ruth Brock, Bruce and Sharon Eden)*

Enterprise ~ Lease Richard and Debi Morisot ~ Real ale ~ Bar food (12-2, 6.30-9) ~ Restaurant ~ (01926) 641221 ~ Children in restaurant ~ Dogs allowed in bar ~ Open 11-3, 5-11; 11-11 Sat; 12-10.30 Sun

GREAT WOLFORD SP2434 Map 4

Fox & Hounds

Village signposted on right on A3400 3 miles S of Shipston-on-Stour

The cosy low-beamed bar at this welcoming 16th-c stone inn has a nice collection of chairs and old candlelit tables on spotless flagstones, antique hunting prints, and a roaring log fire in the inglenook fireplace with its fine old bread oven. An old-fashioned little tap room serves well kept Hook Norton and a couple of guests such as Brains Reverend James and Timothy Taylors Landlord on handpump, and over 150 malt whiskies; piped music. You will probably need to book, particularly at the weekend, as they do reserve all tables throughout the pub. Good bar food includes lunchtime sandwiches (from £4.25), ploughman's (£7.45) and ham, egg and chips (£7.95), as well as daily specials that might be soup (£3.75), brie and bacon parcels with cumberland sauce (£5.50), battered haddock (£9.50), scallops on wild mushroom risotto (£12.75), roast partridge on puy lentils with onion, bacon and redcurrant jus (£13.75), rib-eye steak (£17), and puddings such as brioche bread and butter pudding or almond meringue with Cointreau chantilly cream and caramelised orange (£4.50). The dining area is no smoking. A terrace has solid wood furniture and a well. *(Recommended by K H Frostick, P and J Shapley, Sir Nigel Foulkes, Val and Brian Garrod, Pat and Roger Fereday, WAH, Margaret and Roy Randle, Chris Glasson, Iain R Hewitt, Les and Barbara Owen, R Huggins, D Irving, E McCall, T McLean)*

Free house ~ Licensees Paul and Veronica Tomlinson ~ Real ale ~ Bar food (not Sun evening) ~ (01608) 674220 ~ Children in eating area of bar ~ Dogs welcome ~ Open 12-2.30(3 Sat), 6-11; 12-3, 6(7.30 winter)-10.30 Sun; closed Mon and first two weeks in Jan ~ Bedrooms: £45B/£70B

HIMLEY SO8990 Map 4

Crooked House ★

Pub signposted from B4176 Gornalwood—Himley, OS Sheet 139 map reference 896908; readers have got so used to thinking of the pub as being near Kingswinford in the Midlands (though Himley is actually in Staffs) that we still include it in this chapter – the pub itself is virtually smack on the county boundary

When subsidence caused by mine workings underneath this old pub threw the building 15 degrees out of true they propped it up, rehung the doors and straightened the floors. The result leaves your perceptions spinning in a way that can really feel like being at sea. On one table a bottle on its side actually rolls 'upwards' against the apparent direction of the slope, and for a 10p donation you can get a big ball-bearing from the bar to roll 'uphill' along a wainscot. Being quite high on novelty value it does draw in summer tourists (and even coach groups), but it's quieter out of season. There's a conservatory, a large, level and more modern extension with local antiques, and a spacious outside terrace. Most of the pub is no smoking, and there's a friendly atmosphere throughout. Very reasonably priced Banks's Bitter and Mild and a couple of guests from brewers such as Hopback and Smiles are well kept on handpump alongside a farm cider; piped music. Good value bar food includes soup (£2.75), filled baguettes (£3.25), battered cod (£6.99), tomato and mozzarella pudding (£7.25), steak and kidney pudding (£7.50), braised lamb knuckle (£8.95), daily specials such as cod with mushrooms, peppers and vermouth (£8.95) and puddings such as gooseberry and apple treacle crunch

(£3.50). *(Recommended by Pam and John Smith, Phil and Jane Hodson, Patrick Hancock, Ian Phillips, the Didler, Dr and Mrs A K Clarke, Paul and Gloria Howell)*

Banks's (W & D) ~ Tenant Brett Harrison ~ Real ale ~ Bar food (12-9(9.30 Fri, Sat; 8 Sun), not 2.15-5.30 in winter) ~ (01384) 238583 ~ Children in eating area of bar and restaurant ~ Dogs allowed in bar ~ Open 11.30-11; 12-10.30 Sun; 11.30-3, 5-11 weekdays winter

ILMINGTON SP2143 Map 4
Howard Arms 🍴 ♀ 🛏
Village signposted with Wimpstone off A3400 S of Stratford

This beautifully kept golden-stone inn is another this year to join the growing ranks of completely no smoking pubs, and it's perhaps what one would expect from an elegant dining pub of this calibre. The stylishly simple interior is light and airy, with a few good prints on attractively painted warm golden walls, rugs on broad polished flagstones, and a nice mix of furniture from hardwood pews to old church seats. A nice choice of beers includes well kept Everards Tiger, North Cotswold Genesis and a guest such as Wizard One for the Toad, as well as organic juices, organic wines and ten wines by the glass. The imaginative menu changes two or three times a week, and is carefully written on boards above a huge stone inglenook (with a log fire that burns most of the year). Given the tremendous quality of the freshly prepared food prices are fair: soup (£3.75), fried squid with garlic, parsley and bacon stuffing (£6), wild mushroom stroganoff or beef, ale and mustard pie (£9.50), roast pork fillet with apricot and bacon stuffing and thyme jus or sauté of veal kidneys and lamb sweetbreads, shallots, sage and beurre noisette (£11.50), fried bass with wilted spinach and creamed fennel sauce (£14) and puddings such as white chocolate torte with poached blackberries and apple, pear and blackberry flapjack crumble (from £4.50); you will need to book and beware, they are inflexible even to the minute, about food service times. The garden is lovely in summer with fruit trees sheltering the lawn, a colourful herbaceous border, and a handful of tables on a neat York stone terrace; the chocolate-spotted dalmatian is called Loulou, and her new wire haired german pointer companion is Nola. The pub is nicely set beside the village green, and there are lovely walks on the nearby hills (as well as strolls around the village outskirts). *(Recommended by Mr and Mrs G S Ayrton, Bernard Stradling, John Kane, Ian and Jane Irving, Michael and Jenny Back, Dr David Cockburn, Di and Mike Gillam, David Handforth, Clive and Fran Dutson, Paul Humphreys, Norman and Sarah Keeping, Elaine and Tony Barker, Nicholas and Dorothy Stephens, Hugh Spottiswoode, Peter Saville, Therese Flanagan, Nigel and Sue Foster, Les and Barbara Owen, David and Ruth Shillitoe, Anthony Moody, Roger Braithwaite, Ian and Joan Blackwell, Karen and Graham Oddey, Theo, Anne and Jane Gaskinskin)*

Free house ~ Licensees Rob Greenstock and Martin Devereux ~ Real ale ~ Bar food (12-2, 7-9(9.30 Fri, Sat); 6.30-8.30 Sun) ~ Restaurant ~ (01608) 682226 ~ Children welcome till 7.30pm ~ Open 11-3(3.30 Sat), 6-11; 12-3.30, 6-10.30 Sun ~ Bedrooms: £75B/£97B

LAPWORTH SP1970 Map 4
Navigation 🍺
Old Warwick Road S of village (B4439 Warwick—Hockley Heath); by Grand Union Canal, OS Sheet 139 map reference 191709

This bustling canalside pub is filled with the happy chatter of cheery locals, canal-users and friendly staff. Beer is very well kept, and though by no means exotic, the bar food is tasty and served in generous helpings: sandwiches (from £4.95), goats cheese salad (£6.95), vegetarian quiche (£8.50), tasty battered cod, smoked gammon, egg and chips or beef and ale casserole (£8.95), fillet steak (£12), and puddings such as chocolate bread and butter pudding (£3.50). Bass, M&B Brew XI and a guest such as Everards Beacon on handpump are on offer alongside a changing farm cider, and around 30 malt whiskies. The beamed bar is genuinely rustic, with an undulating flagstoned floor, high-backed winged settles, seats built in around its window bay, a warming coal fire in a high-manteled inglenook, one or two bits of brightly painted canal ware, and cases of stuffed fish. The fish theme is developed in the lounge, which has more cases of stuffed fish, oak and carpet floors, and pews; fruit machine and TV (rarely on). The quieter no smoking dining room at the back (they call it the Conga Lounge) has a fresher contemporary feel with modern art on light mushroom walls, high-backed leather chairs on oak floors, and wooden venetian blinds. This room has a pleasant outlook over the sheltered flower-edged lawn, and on down to the busy canal behind. This is a great place in summer when hatch service to aluminium and wicker chairs on the terrace lets you make the most of its pretty canalside setting; they do ice-creams then too, and the pub and gardens are prettily lit at night. *(Recommended by Dr and Mrs A K Clarke, Arnold Bennett, John Saville, Mrs B M Hill, David Edwards, Dr D J and Mrs S C Walker, M Joyner, L Elliott, Joyce and Geoff Robson, Steve Kirby, Paul and Gloria Howell, Richard Endacott)*

Unique (Enterprise) ~ Lease Andrew Kimber ~ Real ale ~ Bar food (12-2(3 Sun), 6-9) ~ (01564) 783337 ~ Children welcome ~ Dogs allowed in bar ~ Open 11-3, 5.30-11; 11-11 Sat; 12-10.30 Sun

LITTLE COMPTON SP2630 Map 4
Red Lion
Off A44 Moreton-in-Marsh—Chipping Norton

This traditional 16th-c cotswold stone local is handy for a decent meal in a pleasantly welcoming atmosphere – and a very fairly priced pint. The simple but comfortably old-fashioned low-beamed plush lounge has snug alcoves and a couple of little tables by the log fire. The plainer public bar has another log fire, Donnington BB and SBA on handpump and an extensive wine list; juke box, darts, pool, cribbage, dominoes and fruit machine. It does get busy here so you may need to book, especially at weekends. Bar food includes soup (£3.50), very good filled baguettes (from £4.25), ploughman's (£5.25), tagliatelle niçoise (£7.95), 16oz rump (£16.75), and daily specials such as antipasti platter (£5.75), smoked salmon creole with spicy prawn filling and tortilla chips (£5.95), salmon and asparagus lasagne (£8.95), grilled pork loin with pink peppercorn, brandy and cream (£9.95) and grilled barracuda with pineapple salsa (£11.95); the restaurant is no smoking. The well maintained garden is well enclosed and rather pretty, with lots of white plastic furniture, and this is a handy base for exploring the Cotswolds. *(Recommended by Brian Root, Ann and Colin Hunt, John and Johanne Eadie, Dr and Mrs R G J Telfer, Margaret and Roy Randle, R Huggins, D Irving, E McCall, T McLean, Michael Dandy)*

Donnington ~ Tenant David Smith ~ Real ale ~ Bar food ~ Restaurant ~ (01608) 674397 ~ Children in restaurant and eating area of bar, over 8 if staying ~ Open 11-2.30, 6-11; 12-3, 7-10.30 Sun ~ Bedrooms: £45B/£55B

LONG ITCHINGTON SP4165 Map 4
Duck on the Pond
Just off A423 Coventry—Southam; The Green

It's worth striking a little way off your route for a meal at this warmly welcoming pub. Using thoughtfully sourced ingredients, enjoyable food includes soup (£3.95), salmon and prawn fishcakes with chilli and plum jam (£4.95), grilled goats cheese rolled in hazelnuts on rocket and orange salad (£5.25), battered haddock (£9.95), penne with mediterranean roast vegetables (£11.95), fried duck breast with honey and cloves on sautéed leeks and bacon with orange caramelised butter fondant potato (£13.95) and daily specials such as salmon cured with beetroot and ginger (£5.95) and grilled tuna with niçoise salad and a poached egg (£12.95) and seared rib of beef with truffle mash (£13.95). The surprisingly eclectic interior of this spacious place (now completely no smoking) is vaguely reminiscent of a 1970s french bistro. The central bar has dark pine ceiling planks, royal blue banquettes, some barrel tables, bacchanalian carvings around its coal fire and a few big wading bird decoys. Wicker panels provide an unusual frontage to the bar counter, which has Charles Wells Bombardier and a guest such as Greene King Old Speckled Hen on handpump, and about eight wines by the glass. On each side of the bar, sizeable dining areas have pine furniture (some tables painted in light red chequers), a wall of wine bottles, big Edwardian prints on sienna red walls, a crystal chandelier and a grandfather clock. The piped pop or jazzy soul music may be loud but is well reproduced. Tables and chairs in front look down on a pond, which does indeed have ducks; the main road is quite busy. *(Recommended by Darren and Jane Staniforth, Dennis and Gill Keen)*

Charles Wells ~ Lease Andrew and Wendy Parry ~ Real ale ~ Bar food (12-2, 6.30-9.30; 12-9.30 Sat, Sun) ~ Restaurant ~ (01926) 815876 ~ No children Fri, Sat evenings ~ Open 12-2.30, 5-11; 12-11(10.30 Sun) Sat; closed Mon except bank hols

PRESTON BAGOT SP1765 Map 4
Crabmill
B4095 Henley-in-Arden—Warwick

Anyone who knew this rambling pub a few years ago (as we did) will be amazed at it now. What had become most kindly described as place of great potential – it was originally a cider mill – has been transformed into a really stylish place, with a thriving civilised atmosphere. It's kept its snug corners and (after careful sandblasting) its low beams, and even the flagstones in the bar area, which has some stripped pine country tables, but the bar itself is now a gleaming steel construct under well placed downlighters, and that rather sets the up-to-date tone. The stylish two-level lounge area has a good relaxed feel, thanks to its gentle colours, soft leather settees and easy chairs, low tables, big table lamps and one or two rugs on bare boards; there's an elegant and roomy low-beamed dining area, with candles and fresh flowers. They have well kept Greene King Abbot, Tetleys and Wadworths 6X on handpump, excellent coffee, and eight wines by the glass; service by cheerful young staff is courteous and professional. The modern food, most enjoyable, might include soup (£3.95), salmon kofta with couscous and mint yoghurt or antipasto (£6.50), roast butternut squash, feta and rosemary risotto (£10.95), honey-braised pork belly with mustard mash and apple and calvados sauce (£11.95), bass fillets with smoked salmon and dill rösti, spinach and crab bisque or sirloin steak with crevettes and garlic butter (£14.95), and a handful of daily specials such as crab and crayfish salad with guacamole crostini (£6.95) and red snapper fillet with samphire, bok choi and harissa, ginger and lime butter (£14.50); it gets very busy at weekends. Piped music is well chosen and well reproduced. There are lots of tables, some of them under cover, out in a large attractively reworked garden with a play area, open all day. *(Recommended by Denise Greenhalgh, Peter Evans, Mrs P Burvill, Susan and John Douglas, George Atkinson, Gavin and Helen Griggs)*

Enterprise ~ Lease Sarah Robinson ~ Real ale ~ Bar food (12-2.30(3.30 Sun), 6.30-9.30) ~ Restaurant ~ (01926) 843342 ~ Children welcome ~ Dogs allowed in bar ~ Open 11-11; 12-6 Sun; closed Sun evening

PRIORS MARSTON SP4857 Map 4
Holly Bush
Village signposted from A361 S of Daventry (or take the old Welsh Road) from Southam); from village centre follow Shuckburgh signpost, then take first right turn by phone box

Stylish refurbishments at this golden stone 13th-c inn (once the village bakehouse) have kept, and even enhanced the considerable character of the interesting old building. The main part is divided into small beamed rambling rooms by partly glazed timber dividers, keeping a good-sized bar as well as the main dining area, and there are flagstones, some bare boards, a good deal of stripped stone, and good sturdy tables in varying sizes. A log fire blazes in the big stone hearth at one end, and the central lounge area has a woodburning stove. Beside a second smaller and smarter no smoking dining area is a back snug with temptingly squashy leather sofas and a woodburning stove. Good food (from the bar and restaurant menu) might include soup (£3.95), baguettes (£5.95), chicken, bacon and avocado salad (£8.25), steak and ale pie (£8.75), grilled asparagus on black olive and tomato couscous (£9.50), rump steak with green peppercorn sauce (£11.95), baked bass with herb butter (£13.50), and puddings such as crème brûleé with fruit coulis or sticky toffee with butterscotch sauce (£4.50); friendly informal service from amiable staff. They have Fullers London Pride, Hook Norton Old Hooky and a guest such as Timothy Taylors Landlord well kept on handpump from the copper-topped bar counter, alongside a farm cider, and decent wines by the glass; there may be piped music; pool. The sheltered garden behind has tables and chairs on the lawn, and this is an attractive village. We have not yet heard from readers who have stayed here, and look forward to reports on this aspect. *(Recommended by Jane Legate, Arnold Bennett, Di and Mike Gillam)*

Free house ~ Licensee Richard Saunders ~ Real ale ~ Bar food ~ Restaurant ~ (01327) 260934 ~ Children in eating area of bar and restaurant ~ Dogs allowed in bar and bedrooms ~ Open 12-2, 5.30-11; 12-3, 6-11(7-10.30 Sun) Sat ~ Bedrooms: £40S/£45B

SEDGLEY SO9193 Map 4

Beacon ★ ◨

Bilston Street (no pub sign on our visit, but by Beacon Lane); A463, off A4123 Wolverhampton—Dudley

To get the full effect, once you've parked, it's worth ignoring the side entrance and walking round to the front of this plain-looking old Victorian brick house. Up a couple of steps, the front door opens into a plain quarry-tiled drinking corridor where you may find a couple of cheery locals leaning up against the walls going up the stairs, chatting to the friendly waistcoated barman propped in the doorway of his little central serving booth. Go through the door into the little snug on your left and you can easily imagine a 19th-c traveller tucked up on one of the wall settles, next to the imposing green-tiled marble fireplace with its big misty mirror, the door closed for privacy and warmth and a drink handed through the glazed hatch. The dark woodwork, turkey carpet, velvet and net curtains, heavy mahogany tables, old piano and little landscape prints all seem unchanged since those times. Another simple snug on the right has a black kettle and embroidered mantel over a blackened range, and a stripped wooden wall bench. The corridor then runs round the serving booth, past the stairs and into a big well proportioned dark-panelled smoking room with sturdy red leather wall settles down the length of each side, gilt-based cast-iron tables, a big blue carpet on the lino, and dramatic sea prints. Round a corner (where you would have come in from the car park) the conservatory is densely filled with plants, and has no seats. Alongside a couple of guests from brewers such as Archers or York, the beautifully aromatic Sarah Hughes (a former landlady) beers served here – Dark Ruby, Pale Amber and Surprise Bitter – are brewed in the traditional Victorian brewery at the back, which you can arrange to look round. The only food served is cheese and onion cobs (£1). A children's play area in the garden has a slide, climbing frame and roundabout. *(Recommended by Ian Phillips, the Didler, Pete Baker, Paul and Gloria Howell)*

Own brew ~ Licensee John Hughes ~ Real ale ~ No credit cards ~ (01902) 883380 ~ Dogs welcome ~ Open 12-2.30, 5.30-11; 12-3, 6-11 Sat; 12-3, 7-10.30 Sun

SHIPSTON-ON-STOUR SP2540 Map 4

White Bear

High Street

One reader felt this lively town local had quite a continental feel – perhaps it's the relaxed atmosphere, or the tables on the pavement outside, or all the pictures, clearly chosen by a francophile, that are dotted around. Tucked behind a fine Georgian brick frontage, the long narrow front bar on the left has massive stripped settles and attractive lamps, and interesting pictures from charming pen and wash drawings of Paris café society, through sporting and other cartoons of Alken and Lawson Wood, and bright modern ones by Tibb on the rag-rolled walls. The back lounge is more plainly furnished and decorated, with comfortable modern furniture, and big Toulouse-Lautrec and other prints of french music-hall life. A separate bar on the right has a woodburning stove in a big painted stone fireplace. Well kept Adnams, Bass, Hook Norton Old Hooky and a guest such as Titanic Iceberg on handpump, with eclectically chosen wines, including bin ends and a good selection of ports and wines by the glass; polite, knowledgeable service; daily papers. Bar food might include soup (£3.50), crab fritters (£5.80), home-made burger and chunky chips (£8.95) and steak, onion and Guinness pie (£9.10); part of the restaurant is no smoking; fruit machine, juke box and TV. (Recommended by Des and Jen Clarke, W W Burke, Ian Phillips, Michael and Jeanne Shillington, Mr and Mrs D S Price)

Punch ~ Lease George Kruszynskyi ~ Real ale ~ Bar food (12-2(2.30 Fri, Sat), 6.30-9.30 (10 Fri, Sat); not Sun evening) ~ Restaurant ~ (01608) 661558 ~ Children welcome ~ Dogs welcome ~ Live music Sun evening ~ Open 11-11; 12-10.30 Sun ~ Bedrooms: £40S/£65B

SHUSTOKE SP2290 Map 4
Griffin 🍺 £

5 miles from M6, junction 4; A446 towards Tamworth, then right on to B4114 and go straight through Coleshill; pub is at Church End, a mile E of village

The finest feature at this unpretentious country local must be the interesting range of up to ten changing and very well kept real ales. Dispensed from a servery under a very low heavy beam, they come from an enterprising range of brewers such as Banks's, Bathams, Everards, Exmoor, Fullers Marstons Pedigree, RCH; also 22 english wines, farm cider, mulled wine and hot punch in winter. Almost always bustling with a cheery crowd, the low-beamed L-shaped bar has log fires in two stone fireplaces (one's a big inglenook) with warming log fires. Besides one nice old-fashioned settle the décor is fairly simple, from cushioned café seats (some quite closely packed) to sturdily elm-topped sewing trestles, lots of old jugs on the beams, beer mats on the ceiling and a fruit machine. As well as a choice of 20 warwickshire cheeses (you can buy them to take away), good value straightforward but tasty lunchtime bar food, served by friendly efficient staff, includes pie and chips, broccoli bake, lasagne and cod, chips and mushy peas (£5.50-£5.75); you may need to arrive early to get a table. There are old-fashioned seats and tables outside on the back grass, a play area and a large terrace with plants in raised beds. (Recommended by John Dwane, Brian and Jacky Wilson, Derek and Sylvia Stephenson, David Green, Richard Waller, Pauline Smith)

Free house ~ Licensee Michael Pugh ~ Real ale ~ Bar food (12-2; not Sun or evenings) ~ No credit cards ~ (01675) 481205 ~ Children in family room ~ Dogs welcome ~ Open 12-2.30, 7-11; 12-3, 7-10.30 Sun

WELFORD-ON-AVON SP1452 Map 4
Bell 🍴

Off B439 W of Stratford; High Street

Warwickshire Dining Pub of the Year

This charming old 17th-c brick pub deserves accolade for the high all round praise it wins from readers. It's obviously superbly run, and though emphasis is on the very good imaginative menu, this lovely old building still makes a delightful place for a civilised drink. The very attractive interior is divided into five comfortable areas, each with its own character, from the cosy terracotta-painted bar to the light and airy terrace room with its peach and terracotta wash. Flagstone floors, stripped, well polished antique or period-style furniture, and three real fires (one in an inglenook) give it quite a pubby feel. Flowers Original, Hobsons, Hook Norton Old Hooky and a guest such as Deuchars IPA are well kept on handpump, and they've a wide choice of wines including local ones; piped music. Using local produce where possible, food is served by charmingly efficient staff and might include chicken liver pâté with onion marmalade (£5.50), smoked trout, asparagus and brie tart (£5.75), lemon and green pea risotto with rocket and parmesan or pork and leek sausages on bubble and squeak (£9.50), steak and Guinness pie (£9.95), garlic roasted cod or roast duck breast with spinach and kumquat sauce (£12.95) and puddings such as panna cotta with balsamic strawberries and orange tart (£4.75); several no smoking areas. In summer the creeper-covered exterior is hung with lots of colourful baskets, and there are seats on a vine-covered terrace. The riverside village has an appealing church and pretty thatched black and white cottages. *(Recommended by Susan and John Douglas, Oliver Richardson, Peter Coxon, Glenwys and Alan Lawrence, Martin and Pauline Jennings, Margaret Dickinson, John and Johanne Eadie, Martin O' Keefe, John Kane, Les and Barbara Owen, Michael and Jeanne Shillington, K H Frostick, Gerry and Rosemary Dobson)*

Laurel (Enterprise) ~ Lease Colin and Teresa Ombler ~ Real ale ~ Bar food (11.30-2.30, 6.30-9.30(6-10 Fri, Sat); 12-9.30 summer Sun) ~ Restaurant ~ (01789) 750353 ~ Children welcome ~ Open 11.30-3, 6.30(6 Fri, Sat)-11; 12-10.30(12-5, 6.30-10.30 winter) Sun

WHARF SP4352 Map 4

Wharf Inn

A423 Banbury—Southam, near Fenny Compton

Feeling almost on top of the South Oxford Canal, this open-plan pub is right by Bridge 136, with its own moorings (and space for caravans). Inside, a smart dining area on the left has tall windows (the end ones give the effect of hanging right over the water), plain solid tables, high-backed chairs and a big oriental rug on mainly wood strip or tiled floors, and modern artwork on fresh cream walls. A small central flagstoned bar has Adnams and Brakspears and one or two guests such as Bass or Fullers London Pride on handpump, about ten vodkas, a decent wine list and good freshly ground coffee, all served by very friendly helpful staff. On the right is a pair of soft brown leather settees by a feature coffee table, a few more tables with deco armed chairs, a modern woodburning stove, and some appealing mainly water-related pictures; a little room beyond has a pile of children's books. Lighting throughout is good. Tasty bar food includes full english breakfast (£6.50); the menus change four times a year but might include soup (£3.95), sandwiches (from £5.95), vegetarian penne pasta or thai chicken curry (£6.95), sausage and mash, steak and kidney pudding, paella (£7.95), steaks (from £8.95), roast lamb shank with rosemary (£10.95), and puddings such as chocolate and orange torte with pistachio ice-cream (£4.95); decent children's meals. The slightly sloping waterside garden has picnic-sets and a playhouse on high stilts; disabled access and facilities; faint piped pop music, fruit machine, and no smoking areas are dotted throughout. *(Recommended by Rob and Catherine Dunster, Ted George, Meg and Colin Hamilton, Iain R Hewitt, Karen Eliot, Joyce and Geoff Robson)*

Punch ~ Lease Penelope Waller ~ Real ale ~ Bar food (12-3.30, 5-9.30) ~ Restaurant ~ (01295) 770332 ~ Children welcome away from bar ~ Dogs allowed in bar ~ Open 10-11(12 Sat, 11 Sun)

LUCKY DIP

Besides the fully inspected pubs, you might like to try these Lucky Dips recommended to us and described by readers (if you do, please send us reports: www.goodguides.co.uk).

ALCESTER [SP0957]
☆ *Holly Bush* [Henley St]: Warren of unpretentious 17th-c panelled rooms off central bar, enjoyable food (not Mon) from good value baguettes to generous and often interesting blackboard food at fair prices, good relaxed atmosphere, hard-working landlady and pleasant staff, well kept Uley and several changing ales such as Brakspears, Cannon Royall, Hadrian & Border and Okells, farm cider, dozens of whiskies, steps down to no smoking area, Jun and Oct beer festivals, no piped music; disabled access, pleasant

sheltered back garden, open all day *(Gill and Tony Morriss, Pete Baker, B M Eldridge, G Coates)*
Lord Nelson [Priory Rd]: Small pleasant rooms, lovely log fire, good range of well kept ales, enjoyable reasonably priced bar food, friendly staff, warm atmosphere; bedrooms, cl Mon lunchtime *(B M Eldridge)*
ANSLEY [SP2991]
Boot [Birmingham Rd]: Neatly kept and quiet at lunchtime, with food from bargain sandwiches to full meals, welcoming landlady *(Ian Blackwell)*

BARFORD [SP2660]
Joseph Arch [A429, handy for M40]: Two well
kept changing ales, good malt whiskies,
friendly staff and enjoyable reasonably priced
food in pub named for founder of agricultural
workers' union (born and died nearby)
(Colin Mason)

BARSTON [SP2078]
☆ *Bulls Head* [from M42 junction 5, A4141
towards Warwick, first left, then signed down
Barston Lane]: Unassuming partly Tudor
village local, comfortable lounge with pictures
and plates, oak-beamed bar with a little Buddy
Holly memorabilia, well kept Adnams, Bass
and a couple of guest beers, friendly efficient
service, enjoyable traditional food from
sandwiches to good fresh fish (not Sun; limited
for vegetarians), log fires, separate dining
room; good-sized secluded garden alongside,
hay barn behind, open all day wknds
*(Geoffrey and Penny Hughes, Pete Baker,
Bob Ellis, Clive and Fran Dutson)*
Malt Shovel [Barston Lane]: Attractive dining
pub with shuttered upper floor, light and airy
inside with stylish country-modern décor,
generous brasserie-style food inc interesting
starters, three well kept real ales, good choice
of wines, helpful young staff, converted barn
restaurant; pleasant garden *(E G Parish)*

BILSTON [SO9496]
Sir Henry Newbolt [High St]: Wetherspoons
shop conversion, some seating in big bays, well
kept real ales inc interesting guests, their usual
keenly priced food; no smoking area, good
disabled access *(G Coates)*
Trumpet [High St]: Holdens and a guest beer,
good free nightly jazz bands; trumpets and
other instruments hang from ceiling, lots of
musical memorabilia and photographs, back
conservatory *(the Didler)*
White Rose [Temple St]: Friendly and lively
traditional town pub with up to a dozen or so
well kept interesting ales from small breweries,
also belgian beers and unusual lagers,
reasonably priced substantial food all day inc
Sun carvery, long narrow bar, no smoking
eating area; children welcome, tables outside,
open all day, Sun afternoon break *(Ian and
Liz Rispin, Paul and Gloria Howell)*

BIRMINGHAM [SP0786]
Anchor [Bradford St, Digbeth]: Well kept
changing ales mainly from small breweries, lots
of bottled beers and frequent themed beer
festivals in well preserved Edwardian pub, two-
part front public bar (one no smoking) with
carefully restored art nouveau windows, bench
seating, tall counter and much polished
brasswork and mirrors, back lounge set for
eating (well priced simple food till 6 inc huge
chip butties), friendly staff, games area with
pool and sports TV; tables out behind, handy
for coach stn, open all day *(Martin Grosberg,
Richard Waller, Pauline Smith)*
☆ *Bartons Arms* [High St, Aston (A34)]:
Magnificent Edwardian pub, a trouble-free
oasis in rather a daunting area, imposing series
of well restored richly decorated rooms from
the palatial to the snug, original tilework

murals, stained glass and mahogany,
decorative fireplaces, sweeping flight to
handsome rooms upstairs, well kept Oakham
and guest beers from ornate island bar with
snob screens in one section, interesting
imported bottled beers and frequent mini beer
festivals, good choice of keenly priced thai
food (not Mon), good landlord and young
staff; comedy nights, open all day *(BB,
Kerry Law, Simon Smith, Theocsbrian,
John Dwane, the Didler, Steve Jennings,
Richard Waller, Pauline Smith)*
Bennetts [Bennetts Hill]: Attractively converted
opulent bank with egyptian/french theme, big
mural, high carved domed ceiling, snugger side
'board room' and 'library' with lots of old
pictures, ironwork and wood (not books you'd
want to read), relaxed atmosphere,
comfortable seats inc armchair and leather
settee, well kept ales inc Banks's and Marstons
Pedigree, decent house wines, good coffee,
friendly staff, dining area; piped music may
be rather loud; good wheelchair access, but
parking restrictions *(Pamela and
Merlyn Horswell, Kevin Blake, John and
Yvonne Davies)*
Black Eagle [Factory Rd, Hockley]:
Welcoming late 19th-c pub with particularly
well kept Ansells Mild, Marstons Pedigree and
two or three guest beers, generous popular
home-made food inc bargain specials, good
traditional landlord and efficient service, small
bare-boards bar, three-part lounge inc one
section with banquettes, bay window and old
pictures, some original Minton tilework,
compact back dining room, summer beer
festival with live music; shaded tables in small
garden, open all day Fri, cl Sun evening
*(John Dwane, G Coates, Simon Pyle,
Richard Waller, Pauline Smith)*
Brasshouse [Broad St]: Handsome and
comfortable bank conversion with lots of dark
oak and brass, enjoyable reasonably priced
food from chip butties to steaks, prompt
friendly service, well kept ales such as Greene
King Old Speckled Hen, unusual collection of
builders' hard hats, attractive dining area; very
handy for National Sea Life Centre and
convention centre *(John and Yvonne Davies,
Colin Gooch)*
Church Inn [Gt Hampton St, Hockley]:
Comfortable and friendly, with meaty helpings
of good value food, well kept Bathams and
guests such as Adnams, Batemans, Black
Sheep, Jennings and Greene King, dozens of
whiskies, long-serving landlord and good staff;
good juke box; open all day wkdys, cl Sun
(Steve Jennings)
Lord Clifden [Gt Hampton St]: Popular food
from sandwiches to steaks and Sun lunch, well
kept beers such as Timothy Taylors Landlord,
friendly service, contemporary artwork and
sporting memorabilia; Thurs quiz night, live
music Sat; plenty of tables out behind with
ping-pong marquee *(anon)*
☆ *Metro* [Cornwall St]: Long softly lit chatty bar
with bays of banquettes and stylish mirrored
panels, good interesting main-course

sandwiches here and upmarket meals in light and airy candlelit modern restaurant with abstract art, helpful service; cl Sun *(Susan and John Douglas)*

☆ *Tap & Spile* [Gas St]: Nicely placed with picnic-sets by Gas Street canal basin, attractive back-to-basics yet quite cottagey décor, stripped brickwork, bare boards and reclaimed timber, old pine pews and settles, lots of prints, three levels, real ales such as Fullers London Pride, Greene King Old Speckled Hen, Charles Wells Bombardier and Youngs, low-priced bar food till 5.30 from baguettes to scampi; piped music, darts, dominoes, fruit machine, no children; open all day *(LYM, Dave Braisted)*

Toby Carvery [Harborne Rd/Richmond Hill Rd, Edgbaston]: Useful for University, typical chain pub with reasonable bar and restaurant food (nicely al dente veg), well kept Bass, linked bars with eclectic furnishings *(KC)*

Walk About [Langley Buildings, Regency Wharf, Broad St]: Popular australian bare-boards theme bar, australian flags and staff, big-screen sporty videos, hot quick tasty basic food; a friendly cavern of a place with lots of bare brickwork and pipework, rather loud piped music (sometimes live), evening dress code *(Colin Gooch)*

Woodman [Albert St]: Victorian etched windows and fittings in friendly and lively L-shaped main bar, hatch service to relaxing back smoke room with original tiling and coal fire, good baguettes, well kept Bass, Ansells Mild, Courage Directors, Greene King and a guest beer, friendly unhurried service, interesting juke box *(the Didler, Pete Baker)*

BISHOP'S TACHBROOK [SP3161]
Leopard [nr M40 junction 13, via A452; Oakley Wood Rd]: Relaxing upmarket country pub/restaurant with well kept Black Sheep, Greene King IPA and Abbot and Hook Norton Best in small bar, steps down to modern lounge/dining area and larger restaurant (children welcome here) with country views, enjoyable generous food from bar snacks to more sophisticated dishes, attentive young staff; lots of lunchtime business customers *(George Atkinson)*

BRANDON [SP4076]
Royal Oak [Station Rd]: Rambling areas on different levels, leather armchairs in comfortable lounge, several real ales, friendly staff, usual pub lunches from filled baguettes to steaks, interesting menu in restaurant with no smoking area, joists and deep glass-covered well; pretty front garden overlooking main railway line *(Suzanne Miles)*

BRINKLOW [SP4379]
Bulls Head [A427, fairly handy for M6 junction 2]: Much enjoyed by families, with play areas indoors and outdoors, enjoyable generous food from fresh sandwiches up inc plenty of vegetarian and children's dishes, particularly friendly bar staff, well kept ales such as Badger Best, Flowers Original, Hook Norton Best and Marstons Pedigree, collection of old pub signs, no smoking area, shove-

ha'penny and table skittles; heated terrace *(Duncan Cloud, Bernie Adams, Alan Johnson, R Lindsay, Mrs S Gaade)*

BROOM [SP0853]
Broom Tavern [High St; off B439 in Bidford]: Attractive and comfortable 16th-c timber-framed pub in pretty village by River Arrow, relaxed and welcoming, with enjoyable food inc some imaginative starters, OAP lunches in ample helpings, attentive young staff, big log fire, heavy beams, hunting and country life cartoons; children welcome *(Phyllis McCombie)*

BUBBENHALL [SP3672]
Three Horseshoes [Spring Hill]: Sympathetic conversion of village pub into pleasant pub/restaurant, new pine furniture, some leatherette banquettes, good range of mid-priced home-made food from good baguettes up, M&B Brew Xl, Hook Norton Old Hooky and Charles Wells Bombardier, large restaurant; piped pop music may be loud; bedrooms *(Geoffrey and Penny Hughes, Rob and Catherine Dunster, Nigel and Sue Foster, Mrs S Gaade)*

COVENTRY [SP3279]
Malt Shovel [Spon End; B4101 just W of centre]: Olde-worlde local in terrace of preserved ancient buildings, basic seating in small busy bar with log fire, second room on right with another, back games area, further drinking area, two well kept ales, friendly staff, food confined to Sun lunch; occasional music evenings in marquee-covered back courtyard; disabled access at a pinch, open all day, cl Mon/Tues lunchtime *(G Coates)*

☆ *Old Windmill* [Spon Street]: Well worn timber-framed 15th-c pub which unlike other buildings in this reconstituted medieval street has always been here; lots of tiny old rooms, exposed beams in uneven ceilings, carved oak seats on flagstones, woodburner in a fine inglenook, Courage Directors, Greene King IPA and Old Speckled Hen, Theakstons Old Peculier, Wychwood Hobgoblin and a changing guest beer, basic lunchtime bar food (not Mon) served from the kitchen door, partly no smoking restaurant; popular with students and busy at wknds, fruit machine and juke box, no credit cards; open all day *(LYM, the Gray family, the Didler)*

Town Wall [Bond St, among car parks behind Belgrade Theatre]: Busy Victorian town local with Adnams Bitter and Broadside, Bass and M&B Brew XI, farm cider, nice hot drinks choice, good generous lunchtime doorstep sandwiches, filled rolls and cheap hot dishes, can order bargain evening party buffets, unspoilt basic (and sometimes smoky) front bar and famously tiny and clubby snug, engraved windows and open fires, bigger fresher back lounge with actor and playwright photographs – it's behind Belgrade Theatre; big-screen sports TV; open all day *(Alan Johnson, BB, Suzanne Miles, Ted and Lyn Clarkson)*

☆ *Whitefriars* [Gosford St]: Pair of well preserved medieval town houses, restored 2000 – three genuinely old-fashioned and dark historic rooms on both floors, the nicest downstairs at the front, with lots of ancient beams, timbers and furniture, flagstones, cobbles and real fires; up to nine well kept changing ales (more during beer festivals) – Church End prominent; basic sensibly priced food from sandwiches, ploughman's and baked potatoes up, daily papers; frequent live music Sun, folk on Weds, quiz nights, special offers for students (university nearby); no children (but shelter on good-sized terrace behind), open all day *(Alan Johnson, BB)*

DUDLEY [SO9390]

Lamp [King St/Blowers Green Rd (A461/A454)]: Extended pub with well kept Bathams, good range of malt whiskies, surprisingly good view from the upstairs Panorama room, good value wkdy lunchtime food in homely restaurant area, handsome tiled corridor to lavatories; annexe bedrooms, open all day *(Martin Grosberg)*

Park [George St/Chapel St]: Welcoming and pleasantly refurbished in up-to-date style, tap for adjacent Holdens brewery, their beers kept well and priced attractively, as is the good no-nonsense lunchtime food inc hot beef, pork and chicken sandwiches, conservatory, small games room; sports TV; attractive octagonal conservatory *(Colin Fisher, the Didler)*

DUNCHURCH [SP4871]

☆ *Dun Cow* [A mile from M45 junction 1: on junction of A45 and A426)]: Handsomely beamed largely no smoking Vintage Inn with good log fires and other traditional features, good range of wines by the glass, well kept ales such as Bass, Hancocks and Marstons Pedigree, reasonably priced food all day from sandwiches up in bar and restaurant; piped music; children welcome, tables out in attractive former coachyard and on sheltered side lawn, comfortable bedrooms, open all day *(George Atkinson, Alain and Rose Foote, Dr and Mrs R G J Telfer, P Tailyour, LYM, Roger and Jenny Huggins, Dr D Jeary, Les and Barbara Owen, David Green)*

EARLSWOOD [SP1174]

Red Lion [Lady Lane (past the Lakes)]: Imposing twin-gabled black and white Georgian pub, traditional food all day (busy wknds), several small but high-ceilinged rooms each with its own character, sturdy tables and chairs, some wall settles, no smoking back room with open fire, chandeliers and bigger tables; disabled access, skittle alley, Stratford Canal moorings *(Mrs P Burvill)*

ETTINGTON [SP2550]

Houndshill House [A422 towards Stratford; aka Mucky Mongrel]: Civilised dining pub, very popular with families and OAPs, with friendly landlord, tasty traditional food, stripped stone and beams, efficient service even when busy, good choice of wines, well kept ales; children welcome, tables in big attractive garden with play area well away from buildings, good views from front, good well equipped bedrooms, camp site *(Joyce and Maurice Cottrell)*

FILLONGLEY [SP2787]

Cottage [Black Hall Lane]: Consistently enjoyable reasonably priced food, Church End real ale, pleasant rather restauranty atmosphere *(Tim Phillips)*

HALESOWEN [SO9683]

Hawne Tavern [Attwood St]: Well worn in sidestreet local, well kept Banks's, Bathams and lots of guest beers, good value cheap food inc big baguettes, good staff, quiet lounge; bar with pool, TV and juke box *(the Didler)*

Somers Club [The Grange, Grange Hill (B4551 S)]: Early Georgian mansion, now an easy-going sports and social club – visitors can sign in; comfortable bar with half a dozen or more well kept real ales from long counter inc Banks's, Bathams and Old Swan, simple snacks, friendly regulars; bowling green in grounds behind *(the Didler)*

Waggon & Horses [Stourbridge Rd]: Unpretentious gently refurbished bare-boards local with long narrow bar leading to more spacious lounge, well kept Bathams, a house beer and up to a dozen or so interesting changing ales from small independent brewers, country wines, chatty regulars, good snacks, brewery memorabilia; TV, Tues music night; open all day *(the Didler, Martin Grosberg)*

HARBOROUGH MAGNA [SP4779]

Old Lion [3 miles from M6 junction 1; B4122]: Friendly service in busy village local with Greene King ales, good helpings of food from sandwiches, baguettes and baked potatoes up inc OAP lunches, bar with pool etc, no smoking dining area off, more formal restaurant; children welcome, family events, open all day wknds *(Alan Johnson, Roger and Jenny Huggins)*

HATTON [SP2467]

Waterman [A4177, by Grand Union Canal]: Good-sized pub above Hatton flight of 21 locks, views as far as Warwick from sunny balcony and huge garden; Bass and Tetleys, friendly efficient service even when very busy (as it can be), generous food inc children's, smart new lavatories; good circular walks nearby, moorings *(Edward Leetham)*

HOCKLEY HEATH [SP1572]

Wharf [Stratford Rd (A3400)]: Friendly modernised local, open-plan but cosily divided, with lounge extension overlooking canal, quick generous food from hot meat rolls to carvery, attractive prices, Marstons and guest beers, good canal photographs; children welcome, attractive garden with adventure playground by Stratford Canal, interesting towpath walks *(Edward Leetham)*

KENILWORTH [SP2872]

Clarendon Arms [Castle Hill]: Busy traditional pub opp castle, huge helpings of good value food in several rooms, some no smoking, off long partly flagstoned bar (which can be smoky and noisy), largish peaceful upstairs dining room, plenty of atmosphere, efficient and friendly obliging staff, good range of well served beers, wines and other drinks; best to book wknds *(Bob and Margaret Holder, Alan Johnson, John and Yvonne Davies,*

Roger Huggins, Tom and Alex McLean,
David Glynne-Jones, Joan and Tony Walker)

Virgin & Castle [High St]: Maze of intimate
rooms off inner servery, small snugs by
entrance corridor, flagstones, heavy beams, lots
of woodwork inc booth seating, coal fire,
decent food from generous sandwiches and
baked potatoes to japanese and filipino
specialities, friendly staff, well kept ales inc
guests, good coffee, no smoking room, upstairs
games bar, restaurant; frequent live music,
open all day, children in eating area, tables in
sheltered garden (Anne Wickens, LYM)

KNOWLE [SP1876]

☆ **Herons Nest** [Warwick Rd S]: Vintage Inn
dining pub in former hotel, dining tables in
several individual rooms inc no smoking areas,
some flagstones and high-backed settles, hops
on beams, interesting décor, open fires, wide
choice of sensibly priced food inc children's
helpings (may be a wait at busy times), plenty
of good value wines by the glass, good fruit
juices, well kept Bass and Tetleys, friendly
staff; tables in garden by Grand Union
Canal, moorings, bedrooms, open all day
(Edward Leetham, David Green, L Elliott)

LAPWORTH [SP1670]

☆ **Boot** [B4439, by Warwickshire Canal]: Good
food suiting deepish pockets (may be a security
guard to protect all that expensive metalwork
in the car park) from baguettes and tasty
starters/light dishes to steaks and fish inc some
unusual dishes, well kept Greene King Old
Speckled Hen and Tetleys, upscale wines (big
glasses), good service by smart young staff,
daily papers, lots of board games, cartoons;
piped nostalgic pop music; good lavatories,
beautifully done waterside garden, pleasant
walks (Edward Leetham, R A K Crabtree,
B M Eldridge, M Joyner, Susan and
John Douglas, George Atkinson)

LEAMINGTON SPA [SP3165]

Cask & Bottle [Kennedy Sq/Lansdowne St]:
Former Greyhound, renamed after reworking
with lots of blond wood and metal (makes the
friendly L-shaped bar rather loud when busy),
well kept Boddingtons, Greene King Abbot,
Wadworths 6X and a quickly changing guest
beer, cheap cheerful food inc bargain wkdy
sandwiches and popular Sun lunch, some side
alcoves, huge table for groups one end; big-
screen sports TV (Steve and Liz Tilley)

Somerville Arms [Campion Terr]: Neat and
cosy character local with tiny unspoilt
Victorian back lounge, half a dozen or more
well kept ales such as Adnams, Fullers London
Pride and Greene King IPA, friendly staff,
darts; quiz and music nights; tables out on
wide pavement, cl lunchtime (Steve and
Liz Tilley)

LONG COMPTON [SP2832]

Red Lion [A3400 S of Shipston-on-Stour]:
Stripped stone, bare beams, panelling,
flagstones, old-fashioned built-in settles among
other pleasantly assorted old seats and tables,
old prints and team photographs, good value
food from good generous sandwiches up in bar
and restaurant, children's helpings, well kept

ales such as Greene King, Hook Norton and
Websters, welcoming service, log fires and
woodburners, simple public bar with pool; pub
dog and cat, unobtrusive piped music; dogs
and children welcome, big back garden with
picnic-sets and climber, bedrooms
(Theocsbrian, LYM, Phil and Jane Hodson,
KC)

LONG ITCHINGTON [SP4165]

Blue Lias [Stockton Rd, off A423]: Well placed
on Grand Union Canal, with pleasant staff,
reasonably priced pubby food, well kept ales
such as Everards Tiger, snug eating booths;
plenty of tables in waterside grounds, also a
separate outbuilding bar with tables under a
dome (Bernie Adams, Ted George, Charles and
Pauline Stride)

LOWER BRAILES [SP3039]

George [B4035 Shipston—Banbury]:
Handsome old stone-built inn with cheery and
roomy flagstoned front bar, dark oak tables,
nice curtains and inglenook log fire (not always
lit), panelled oak-beamed back bar with soft
lighting and green décor, well kept Hook
Norton ales, darts, country-style flagstoned
wknd restaurant; live music most Sat and Mon
evenings and Sun afternoon; provision for
children, aunt sally in sizeable neatly kept
sheltered garden with terrace and covered area,
six comfortable bedrooms, lovely village
(Steve Jennings, LYM, JHBS, Pete Baker,
Theocsbrian)

LOWER GORNAL [SO9191]

Fountain [Temple St]: Lively two-room local
with keen and helpful landlord and staff, well
kept Enville, Everards, Holdens and up to six
changing ales (beer festivals Easter and Oct),
two farm ciders, country wines, enjoyable
inexpensive food, back dining area, pigs-and-
pen skittles; piped music can be loud
(the Didler, Paul and Gloria Howell)

Old Bulls Head [Redhall Rd]: Victorian local
now brewing its own Black Country ales in
back microbrewery, busy front bar with no
smoking area, pub games behind; some live
music; open all day wknds (from 4 wkdys)
(the Didler)

LOWSONFORD [SP1868]

Fleur de Lys [off B4439 Hockley Heath—
Warwick; Lapworth St]: Prettily placed by
Warwickshire Canal, largely no smoking, with
log fires, lots of beams, good seating inc sofas,
several well kept real ales, decent wines inc
many by the glass, enjoyable food esp pies in
bar and dining room, reasonable prices, quick
friendly service; waterside garden, open all day
(Roger Braithwaite, LYM, Mick and
Moira Brummell)

LOXLEY [SP2552]

☆ **Fox** [signed off A422 Stratford—Banbury]:
Cheerful pub under new management,
inventive good value food from innovative
sandwiches and starters/light dishes to fish
specialities, well kept Bass, Flowers IPA and
Hook Norton Best, quick welcoming service,
partly divided lounge with panelling, a few
pictures and plates, settles and brocaded
banquettes, pleasant dining area; piped music;

tables in good-sized garden behind, sleepy village handy for Stratford *(Joan and Tony Walker, Geoffrey and Penny Hughes)*

MONKS KIRBY [SP4682]

☆ *Bell* [just off B4027 W of Pailton]: Open-plan dimly lit dark-beamed and timbered bar divided into separate areas, flagstoned and cobbled floor, well kept Bass and Flowers Original, relaxed informal service led by welcoming long-serving Spanish landlord, very wide choice of largely spanish food inc starters doubling as tapas, fine range of spanish wines and of brandies and malt whiskies, no smoking dining area, enjoyably appropriate piped music; children and dogs welcome, streamside back terrace with country view, may be cl Mon *(Mr and Mrs J E C Tasker, Barbara and Peter Kelly, LYM, Susan and John Douglas, Brian and Pat Wardrobe, R T and J C Moggridge, Ian and Nita Cooper, Tim West, Julie Hill, Jane Davies)*

☆ *Denbigh Arms* [Main St]: Small friendly 17th-c beamed pub opp church, old photographs and interesting 18th-c pew seating, big helpings of enjoyable straightforward food inc OAP bargain, well kept Greene King Abbot, Timothy Taylors Landlord and Theakstons XB, good wine choice, no smoking family room; upstairs folk club 2nd Sun of month; play area *(Bernie Adams, Alan Johnson, Rob and Catherine Dunster, Mrs S Fairbrother, Ian and Nita Cooper)*

NETHERTON [SO9387]

☆ *Old Swan* [Halesowen Rd (A459 just S of centre)]: Friendly and traditional, brewing its own good cheap Original, Dark, Entire and occasional other beers, lots of whiskies, wide choice of good cheap food inc some imaginative twists and Sun lunches in no smoking room on left (worth booking well ahead), airy front room with fine mirrors and open fire, steps down to comfortable and cheery back snug with nice old solid fuel stove, red and cream décor, decorative swan ceiling, cards and dominoes; no children, regular sing-alongs, open all day *(the Didler, Martin Grosberg, LYM, Nigel Epsley, Richard Houghton, Pete Baker, Paul and Gloria Howell)*

OLD HILL [SO9685]

Waterfall [Waterfall Lane]: Down-to-earth good value local, friendly staff, well kept Holdens, good value plain home-made food from hot filled baguettes with chips to Sun lunch, tankards and jugs hanging from boarded ceiling, lounge with no smoking eating area; piped music; children welcome, back garden with play area, open all day wknds *(Gill and Tony Morriss, the Didler)*

OLDBURY [SO9989]

Waggon & Horses [Church St, nr Savacentre]: Copper ceiling, original etched windows, open fire and Black Country memorabilia in busy town pub with well kept Enville White, Old Swan Entire and two or three guest beers, wide choice of generous lunchtime food (not Sun) from sandwiches and baguettes up inc lots of puddings, decent wines, friendly efficient

service even when busy, ornate Victorian tiles in corridor to lively comfortable no smoking back lounge with tie collection, side room with high-backed settles and big old tables, bookable upstairs bistro; opens noon *(Pete Baker)*

OXHILL [SP3149]

Peacock: Welcoming helpful licensees, good blackboard choice of changing fresh food, reasonable prices *(David and Juliette Wylie)*

PRINCETHORPE [SP3870]

Woodhouse [B4453 towards Cubbington]: Pleasantly placed hotel with consistently good bar food, well kept Bass, Boddingtons and Worthington, proper coffee, good service, restaurant popular with local retirees, exquisite puddings; lawns with play area, bedrooms *(Elaine and Tony Barker, W W Burke)*

PRIORS HARDWICK [SP4756]

☆ *Butchers Arms* [off A423 via Wormleighton or A361 via Boddington, N of Banbury; Church End]: Upmarket old-fashioned restaurant in pleasantly reworked 14th-c building, oak beams, flagstones, panelling, antiques and soft lighting, huge choice of good if pricey food inc fixed price lunches, very friendly Portuguese landlord, punctilious formal service, distinguished wine list (the beer is keg), small bar with inglenook log fire used mainly by people waiting for a table, also simple public bar; country garden *(Arnold Bennett, Hugh Spottiswoode, BB, Michael and Jeanne Shillington, Howard and Margaret Buchanan)*

RATLEY [SP3847]

☆ *Rose & Crown* [off A422 NW of Banbury]: Cosy and charming ancient golden stone beamed pub, well kept Charles Wells Eagle and Bombardier, enjoyable food from good sandwiches up, new kitchen and back restaurant, friendly helpful service, woodburner in flagstoned area on left, big log fireplace in carpeted area on right; dogs and children welcome, tables in small gravel garden, nr lovely church in small sleepy village *(BB, T Walker, R J Herd)*

RED HILL [SP1356]

Stag [Alcester Rd (A46 Alcester—Stratford)]: Lots of linked small timbered rooms around central bar, some with pine tables, others with comfortable sofas, well kept Greene King ales, good value if not cheap straightforward food inc extensive help-yourself salad bar, Sun carvery 12-7, open fires; piped music; children welcome, large terrace with tables and chairs under cocktail parasols (traffic noise out here) *(Rob Weeks)*

RUGBY [SP4873]

William Webb Ellis [Warwick St]: Name and décor refer to the start and development of rugby football; sensibly priced food from sandwiches on home-made bread through light dishes to pubby favourites using fresh local produce, wide wine choice and quirky cocktails, live jazz Sun lunchtime *(anon)*

SHIPSTON-ON-STOUR [SP2540]

☆ *Black Horse* [Station Rd (off A3400)]: 16th-c thatched pub, homely and relaxed, with reasonably priced carefully cooked food (not Sun evening) inc wkdy OAP bargain lunches, well kept Greene King IPA, Abbot and Ruddles County and a guest beer, friendly staff and locals, interesting ornaments and good inglenook log fire in spotless low-beamed bar, second room with darts, small dining room; back garden with terrace and barbecue *(JHBS)*

Coach & Horses [New St (A3400, S end of village)]: Busy local with full Hook Norton range and good value food; nice summer flower displays, aunt sally *(Geoff Calcott)*

☆ *Horseshoe* [Church St]: Pretty timbered inn with open-plan largely modern bar, lots of maroon plush, coal-effect fire in big fireplace with copper pans above, good generous blackboard food (not Sun evening) inc hefty mixed grill, OAP discounts and popular Sun carvery, eat in bar or appealing no smoking chintzy restaurant, friendly staff, three well kept ales such as Archers and Hook Norton, decent coffee, darts, no piped music (live Weds); children very welcome, small flower-decked back terrace; bedrooms pretty, bright and clean *(BB, John and Bridget Levick, JHBS, Sharon Redshaw)*

STONNALL [SK0703]

Royal Oak [just off A452 N of Brownhills; Main St]: Popular welcoming pub with well kept Hook Norton, Charles Wells Bombardier and good range of changing guest beers, farm cider, jovial attentive landlord and helpful staff, enjoyable evening food in beamed bar and small restaurant, also Sun lunch, no music *(Clifford Blakemore)*

STOURBRIDGE [SO8984]

Royal Exchange [Enville St]: Bar and lounge linked by long passageway, friendly regulars, Bathams Bitter and Mild; large back terrace, open all day from 1pm *(Martin Grosberg)*

Shrubbery Cottage [Heath Lane, Old Swinford (B4186 S)]: Recently refurbished local with full Holdens range kept well, popular good value lunchtime food inc black country specialities, welcoming staff and regulars, L-shaped bar with darts one end, people playing cards and dominoes the other; central wide-screen sports TV *(Pete Baker)*

STRATFORD-UPON-AVON [SP2055]

Dirty Duck [Waterside]: Bustling 16th-c pub nr Memorial Theatre, lots of signed RSC photographs, well kept Flowers IPA, Greene King Old Speckled Hen and Wadworths 6X, open fire, interesting choice of enjoyable food, helpful friendly young staff, modern conservatory restaurant suiting larger parties; children allowed in dining area, attractive small terrace looking over riverside public gardens – which tend to act as summer overflow *(LYM, David Glynne-Jones, Carolyn Browse, Kevin Blake, Ann Gray)*

☆ *Garrick* [High St]: Ancient pub, no smoking throughout, and much enjoyed both for that and for its character, with heavy beams and timbers, odd-shaped rooms and simple furnishings on bare boards; Flowers Original, Greene King Abbot, Hook Norton Old Hooky and Wadworths 6X at sensible prices, good-

natured staff, bar food from sandwiches and light dishes up all day, small air-conditioned back restaurant; piped music, TV, fruit machine; children welcome, open all day *(Patrick Hancock, Bob and Margaret Holder, Duncan Cloud, Sue Dibben, Ted George, A J Knight, LYM, Val and Alan Green, Paul and Gloria Howell, Frank and Chris Sharp, David Glynne-Jones, Edward Mirzoeff)*

Golden Bee [Sheep St]: Airy and spacious Wetherspoons with light wood furniture, separate no smoking areas, usual range of cheap real ales, good value large meals, family eating area, good service (can slow at busy times) *(Ted George)*

Pen & Parchment [Bridgefoot, by canal basin]: Shakespeare theme in L-shaped split-level lounge and snug, rustic-style beams, balusters, bare boards and tiles or flagstones, small alcoves and no smoking area, big open fire in old fireplace, pleasant pubby atmosphere, wide wine choice, four well kept real ales, prompt helpful service, usual food; tables out among shrubs and ivy, pretty hanging baskets, good canal basin views; busy road *(Alain and Rose Foote, Roger and Anne Newbury, Dave Braisted)*

Shakespeare Hotel [Chapel St]: Smart hotel based on handsome lavishly modernised Tudor merchants' houses, comfortable lounge with plush settees and armchairs, character bar, beams and huge log fire, grandfather clock in hallway, good attentive staff, pricey drinks but they come with nibbles, good restaurant; tables in sheltered courtyard, bedrooms comfortable and well equipped *(LYM, Kevin Blake)*

☆ *West End* [Bull St]: Attractively modernised old pub in quiet part of old town, friendly new management and staff, thriving atmosphere, good value nicely presented seasonal food, good wine choice, changing guest beers, interesting soft drinks range inc plenty of coffees, nice film star photographs; well chosen piped music; appealing terrace *(Sue Dibben, Maurice Ribbans, Margaret and Roy Randle, M C and S Jeanes)*

☆ *Windmill* [Church St]: Cosy and relaxing old pub with town's oldest licence, beyond the attractive Guild Chapel; unpretentious but civilised, with very low black beams, cosy and attractive carpeted front room, varnished boards in main one, big log fire, wide choice of good value food from sandwiches to substantial Sun lunch and some unusual main dishes, well kept sensibly priced Flowers Original and Greene King IPA, friendly efficient staff, carpeted dining area; piped music, sports TV; tables outside, open all day from noon *(Derek and Sylvia Stephenson, Ted George, Paul and Gloria Howell)*

STRETTON-ON-FOSSE [SP2238]

☆ *Plough* [just off A429]: Olde-worlde 17th-c village pub with welcoming licensees and happy staff, bustling mix of villagers and visitors, wide choice of generous home-made food from baguettes through OAP lunches to wknd spit roasts on the inglenook log fire (chain drive from windscreen wiper motor), Ansells Bitter and Mild, Shepherd Neame Spitfire and a guest beer, small bar and larger lounge, stripped stone and some flagstones, jugs and mugs on oak beams, small attractive candlelit dining room on right, darts; dogs welcome, a few tables outside, cl Mon lunchtime *(Geoffrey and Penny Hughes, K H Frostick, JHBS, BB, J C Burgis)*

SUTTON COLDFIELD [SP1195]

Bottle of Sack [Birmingham Rd (A5127)]: Popular two-floor Wetherspoons local, usual reasonably priced food, well kept Shepherd Neame Spitfire, big side conservatory; wheelchair access, but limited nearby parking *(Michael Tack)*

TEMPLE GRAFTON [SP1255]

☆ *Blue Boar* [a mile E, towards Binton; off A422 W of Stratford]: Good atmosphere in extended country dining pub with above-average generous food from sandwiches and baked potatoes up, good value Sun lunch, pleasant attentive service, well kept ales such as Brakspears, Greene King Old Speckled Hen, Hook Norton and Theakstons XB, good coffee and wine choice, beams, stripped stonework and log fires, comfortable dining room (past glass-top wall with golden carp) and good no smoking section and attractive farmhouse-kitchen mural, traditional games in flagstoned side room; children welcome, picnic-sets outside, pretty flower plantings, comfortable well equipped bedrooms, open all day summer wknds *(Susan and John Douglas, R J Herd, LYM, Dennis Jenkin, Michael and Jeanne Shillington, Grahame Brooks)*

TIPTON [SO9792]

Rising Sun [Horseley Rd (B4517, off A461)]: Welcoming Victorian local with well kept Banks's, Oakham and guest beers in lined glasses, farm cider, back lounge with coal fires, alcoves and original bare boards and tiles, lunchtime food; tables outside *(G Coates, the Didler)*

UPPER BRAILES [SP3039]

☆ *Gate*: Attractive and tidily old-fashioned low-beamed village pub, sizeable part-panelled bar, smaller lounge with stripped stone, old bread oven and lots of brass, welcoming landlord, wife cooks good generous well priced country food (not Sun evening, Mon or lunchtime Tues) inc good fresh fish Tues/Weds, well kept Hook Norton and guest beers, big log fire; piped music in stripped stone restaurant; dogs and well behaved children welcome, tables in extensive back garden with wendy house, pretty hillside spot, plenty of footpaths, cl Mon *(JHBS)*

UPPER GORNAL [SO92921]

☆ *Britannia* [Kent St (A459)]: Chatty and welcoming 19th-c Bathams local, their cheap Best and Mild kept superbly, tiled floors, coal fires in front bar and no smoking back room down corridor, sports TV; nice flower-filled back yard, open all day Sat *(the Didler, Paul and Gloria Howell)*

Jolly Crispin [Clarence St (A459)]: Friendly well run 18th-c local with up to a dozen interesting quickly changing ales, two farm ciders, compact front bar, wall seats and mixed tables and chairs on tiled floor, lots of aircraft pictures in larger back room, lunchtime bar food, beer festivals; open all day, cl lunchtime Mon/Tues *(the Didler, Paul and Gloria Howell)*

WARWICK [SP2967]

Saxon Mill [Guy's Cliffe, A429 just N]: Converted mill with long history, pleasantly refurbished under new management, wheel turning slowly behind glass, mill race under glass floor-panel, contemporary chairs and tables on polished boards and flagstones below the beams, cosy corners with leather armchairs and big rugs, willing staff, good reasonably priced food in upstairs restaurant; teak tables out on terraces in lovely setting by broad willow-flanked river, delightful views, open all day *(LYM, Dr W I C Clark)*

WELFORD-ON-AVON [SP1452]

Four Alls [Binton Rd]: Attractive modern décor in recently refurbished riverside Wayside Inn, light and comfortable, with good cheerful antipodean service, wide choice of enjoyable generous standard food inc OAP specials and decent grills, no smoking eating area, three real ales, good wines by the glass; attractive terrace with heaters *(Andrew Richardson, Martin and Pauline Jennings)*

WELLESBOURNE [SP2755]

Kings Head: Vintage Inn dining pub with contemporary furnishings in high-ceilinged lounge bar, log fire and smaller areas leading off, lively public bar with games room, wide choice of keenly priced wines, well kept Bass, good value food from wraps and sandwiches up, friendly staff; piped music, no dogs; proper tables and chairs on small front terrace, more in prettily placed back garden facing church, bedrooms (handy for Stratford but cheaper), open all day *(J F M and M West, LYM, Martin and Karen Wake)*

☆ *Stags Head* [old centre, Bridge St/ Walton Way]: Picturesque 17th-c thatched and timbered pub with good atmosphere in small simply furnished beamed lounge bar, flagstoned passage to larger stone-floored public bar, friendly licensees, good service even when busy, good value enjoyable usual food from baked potatoes up, well kept ales such as Badger Best, Bass, Fullers London Pride, Greene King Abbot, Marstons Pedigree and Timothy Taylors Landlord, lots of local history and photographs; picnic-sets in garden and out in front, bedrooms, lovely setting in group of Elizabethan cottages *(BB, Sarah Akhtar)*

WHATCOTE [SP2944]

☆ *Royal Oak*: Dating from 12th c, quaint low-beamed small room with Civil War connections and lots of knick-knacks and curios, wide choice of good value fresh food from nice sandwiches to venison and good steaks, cheery landlord, three well kept Hook Norton ales, decent wines, good log fire in huge inglenook, restaurant; children welcome, picnic-sets in informal garden *(George Atkinson, LYM, Kevin Blake)*

WHICHFORD [SP3134]
Norman Knight: Welcoming flagstoned pub
with well kept Hook Norton Best and
changing beers from its back Wizard brewery,
enterprising landlord, nicely priced food
(lunchtime and Fri/Sat evening) inc good Sun
roasts; regular live music, can be rather smoky;
dogs welcome, tables out by attractive village
green, cl Mon lunchtime (*JHBS, Tina and
David Woods-Taylor, Stuart Turner*)

WILLENHALL [SO9698]
Malthouse [New Rd]: Wetherspoons, lighter
and brighter than most, reminiscent of 1920s
cruise ship upper deck outside, with art deco
interior, well kept ales inc guests, usual well
thought out menu all day till 10, exemplary
lavatories; busy with young people Sat night;
good disabled access and facilities, open all day
(*G Coates*)

WILLOUGHBY [SP5267]
Rose [just off A45 E of Dunchurch; Main St]:
Partly thatched beamed pub pleasantly opened
up and refurbished without losing character,
Greene King Abbot, Hook Norton Best and
Timothy Taylors Landlord, enthusiastic
landlord, welcoming cheerful staff, good range
of baguettes and limited lunchtime hot dishes,
evening restaurant; lots of outside seating at
front and in garden with play area, flowers
everywhere (*George Atkinson*)

WITHYBROOK [SP4384]
Pheasant [B4112 NE of Coventry, not far from
M6, junction 2]: Friendly well used dining pub
with very wide choice of generous food, real
ales, good coffee, big log fires, lots of dark
tables with plush-cushioned chairs; piped
music; children welcome, tables under lanterns
on brookside terrace, open all day Sun
(*LYM, Alan Johnson, Bernie Adams, Mr and
Mrs J E C Tasker*)

WOLLASTON [SO8884]
Unicorn [Bridgnorth Rd (A458)]: Cosy
traditional Bathams pub, their Bitter and Mild

well kept and cheap, unpretentious L-shaped
bar and unspoilt back parlour, lots of brasses
and knick-knacks, sandwiches; tables outside,
open all day, Sun afternoon break (*Gill and
Tony Morriss, the Didler*)

WOLVERHAMPTON [SO9198]
☆ *Great Western* [Corn Hill/Sun St, behind BR
station]: Well run and down to earth, tucked
interestingly away by cobbled lane down from
main line station to GWR low-level one, with
particularly well kept Bathams, Holdens Bitter,
Golden Glow, Special and perhaps Sham Rock
Stout, winter mulled wine (no tea or coffee),
friendly no-nonsense service, cheap hearty
home-made lunchtime food (not Sun) from
filled cobs up served incredibly promptly,
interesting railway and more recent motorcycle
photographs, traditional front bar, other
rooms inc separate no smoking bar and neat
dining conservatory; SkyTV; picnic-sets in yard
with good barbecues, open all day (*the Didler,
BB, Pete Baker, Paul and Gloria Howell*)
Mermaid [Bridgnorth Rd (A454 W)]: Large
friendly efficient roadside pub, above-
average food lunchtime and early evening
inc very generous ploughman's; handy for
NT Wightwick Manor (*Tony Brace,
Gloria Bax*)

WOOTTON WAWEN [SP1563]
Bulls Head [just off A3400 Birmingham—
Stratford]: Attractive black and white dining
pub with low Elizabethan beams and timbers,
some emphasis on roomy restaurant with rich
colours, brocaded seats and tapestries,
enjoyable if not cheap food inc good light
lunch dishes, welcoming traditional bare-
boards bar, four real ales, good house wines,
friendly young staff; children welcome (small
helpings available for them), garden tables,
handy for one of England's finest churches and
Stratford Canal walks (*Anthony R Locke,
LYM, Elizabeth and Bart Sheehan,
Lucien Perring*)

'Children welcome' means the pub says it lets children inside without any special
restriction. If it allows them in, but to restricted areas such as an eating area or family
room, we specify this. Places with separate restaurants often let children use them,
hotels usually let them into public areas such as lounges. Some pubs impose an evening
time limit — let us know if you find this.

Wiltshire

We are very enthusiastic about this year's new entries here: the quirkily unspoilt Dumb Post at Bremhill, with masses of character; the chatty and nicely reworked George at Codford, its imaginative cooking bringing it a Food Award; the thriving Three Tuns at Great Bedwyn, its popular food relying on local produce; the very neat and well run Bridge Inn by the canal at Horton; the bustling and welcoming Old Royal Ship at Luckington (a nice all-rounder); and the entirely no smoking Bridge Inn at West Lavington, a good lunch stop if you're near. Other places coming in for particular praise from readers recently are the Dandy Lion in Bradford-on-Avon (unusual character for a town pub, and enjoyable food), the ancient thatched Compasses tucked away near Chicksgrove (good all round), the quirky and welcoming Two Pigs in Corsham (good beers and live music), the Forester at Donhead St Andrew (the commendable food and service make us have high hopes of their two new bedrooms), the charming Horseshoe at Ebbesbourne Wake (a favourite country pub), the Linnet at Great Hinton (good food, especially those home-baked breads), the Neeld Arms at Grittleton (good atmosphere, food and beers in this proper country pub, nice bedrooms too), the smart and civilised Lamb at Hindon (its new ownership linking it with a good London restaurant seems to be working out very well), the Malet Arms at Newton Tony (hearty home-made food, good beers, and plenty of character), the Vine Tree at Norton (good locally sourced food, lots of wines, attentive service and buoyant atmosphere), the nicely set Silver Plough at Pitton (reliable food), the intriguing old Haunch of Venison in Salisbury (no major changes, thank goodness, but we have a feeling its food is becoming more interesting), the Spread Eagle at Stourton (the new landlord's impressive restaurant background is beginning to pay dividends here), and the Pear Tree at Whitley (very good food in this welcoming and civilised place, nice to stay in). Several of these stand out as rewarding places for a special meal out – most notably, the Forester, the George, the Linnet, the Vine Tree, and the Pear Tree. By a short lead, the Vine Tree at Norton takes the crown as Wiltshire Dining Pub of the Year. This is a very rewarding county for pubs, with the Lucky Dip section at the end of the chapter consequently being a rich hunting-ground. We'd particularly note the Beehive near Bradford-on-Avon, Horse & Groom at Charlton, Kings Head at Chitterne, Flemish Weaver in Corsham, Cross Keys at Corsley, Bath Arms at Crockerton, Beckford Arms at Fonthill Gifford, Crown at Giddeahall, Ivy at Heddington, Toll Gate at Holt, Who'd A Thought It at Lockeridge, Wheatsheaf at Lower Woodford, Kings Arms at Monkton Farleigh, Old Mill in Salisbury, Benett Arms at Semley, Bridge Inn at Upper Woodford, Poplars at Wingfield, White Horse at Winterbourne Bassett and Five Bells in Wootton Bassett. Drinks prices here are close to the national average, with Wadworths of Devizes dominating the local beer scene; other smaller local brewers to look out for are Hop Back, Archers, Moles and Stonehenge.

AXFORD SU2370 Map 2

Red Lion ♀

Off A4 E of Marlborough; on back road Mildenhall—Ramsbury

Attractively placed in a Kennett Valley hamlet close to Savernake Forest, this pretty flint-and-brick pub has a wide range of home-made food, from bar snacks (not Saturday evening or Sunday lunch) like lunchtime filled rolls (from £4.95), soup (£4.25), pies like turkey and ham, salmon and asparagus and creamy garden vegetable (£8.50), and poached salmon with white wine and cream sauce or gammon steak (£8.50), to more elaborate à la carte meals such as cardomom chicken with crème fraîche, ginger and coriander (£12.75), or oxtail braised in Guinness with horseradish and black pepper mash (£13.75), and lots of interesting fish dishes such as whole skate wing grilled with turmeric and black mustard seed (£13.50), whole bass with wasabi butter (£13.75), and grilled fillet of sea trout with a white wine and saffron sauce (£14.50); the children's menu is better than the norm. Food is cooked freshly to order, so there may be a wait. The restaurant and bar eating areas are no smoking. The beamed and pine-panelled bar has a big inglenook fireplace, and a pleasant mix of comfortable sofas, cask seats and other solid chairs on the parquet floor; the pictures by local artists are for sale. There are lovely views over a valley from good hardwood tables and chairs on the terrace outside the restaurant, and you get the same views from picture windows in the restaurant and lounge. Along with 16 sensibly priced wines by the glass, and around two dozen malt whiskies, you'll find well kept Hook Norton, Fullers London Pride and a guest like Ramsbury Gold on handpump; good choice of non-alcoholic drinks too. The sheltered garden has picnic-sets under parasols and swings. *(Recommended by Bernard Stradling, J Stickland, David Heath, Derek and Sylvia Stephenson, Alec and Barbara Jones, Sir Nigel Foulkes, Karen Comber, Mr and Mrs B Thorne, Mary Rayner, Alan and Paula McCully, Mr and Mrs Peter Llewellyn)*

Free house ~ Licensee Seamus Lecky ~ Real ale ~ Bar food ~ Restaurant ~ (01672) 520271 ~ Children in eating area of bar and restaurant ~ Open 12-2.30, 6.30-11; 12-3, 7-10.30 Sun; closed 25 Dec

BECKHAMPTON SU0868 Map 2

Waggon & Horses

A4 Marlborough—Calne

Useful for a good value, honest lunch, this handsome old pub has long been a welcome sight for travellers on what used to be notorious as the coldest stretch of the old Bath road. Straightforward but generously served, the bar food includes soup (£2.25), sandwiches (from £3.25), spicy thai crab cake (£3.75), chilli or breaded cod (£5.95), tasty fillet steak (£12.95), and specials like mushroom stroganoff (£6.50), or lamb and spinach curry (£6.95); it's especially popular with older visitors, and there's a good value OAP weekday lunch special (£3.95). The dining area is no smoking. Attentive staff serve well kept Wadworths IPA, JCB, 6X and a couple of guests such as McMullen Country Best and St Austell Tribute on handpump or tapped straight from the cask, and there are a dozen wines by the glass; piped music, darts, pool, dominoes, fruit machine and TV. The relaxing open-plan bar has beams in the shiny ceiling where walls have been knocked through, shiny wood floors, mustard walls, an old-fashioned high-backed settle on one side of the room with a smaller one opposite, leatherette stools, and comfortably cushioned wall benches. One reader found the food service stopped abruptly. Silbury Hill (a vast prehistoric mound) is just towards Marlborough from here, and Avebury stone circle and the West Kennet long barrow are very close too. *(Recommended by Frank Willy, Dr and Mrs A K Clarke, Susan and Nigel Wilson, R C Livesey, David Crook, Paul A Moore, Sheila and Robert Robinson)*

Wadworths ~ Manager Doug Shepherd ~ Real ale ~ Bar food (not Sun evening) ~ (01672) 539418 ~ Children in restaurant ~ Open 11-2.30, 5.30-11; 11-3, 6-11 Sat; 12-3, 6-10.30 Sun

BERWICK ST JAMES SU0639 Map 2
Boot ⊕

B3083, between A36 and A303 NW of Salisbury

This friendly flint and stone pub is the sort of comfortably traditional place you might want as your local. The partly carpeted flagstoned bar has a contented cosy atmosphere, a huge winter log fire in the inglenook fireplace at one end, sporting prints over a smaller brick fireplace at the other, and houseplants on its wide window sills. A charming small back no smoking dining room has a nice mix of dining chairs around four tables, and deep pink walls with an attractively mounted collection of celebrity boots. The blackboard menu lists a good choice of reasonably priced food, made using lots of local produce (vegetables may even come from the garden), such as tasty lunchtime baguettes (from £4.95), and ploughman's (£5.95), soup (£4.95), breaded brie with raspberry coulis (£5.75), chilli con carne (£8.95), red thai chicken curry or salmon supreme with a lemon and thyme risotto (£9.95), calves liver and bacon with mustard mash and onion gravy, slow-roast shoulder of lamb, or bass with ginger, spring onion and soy sauce (all £10.95), steaks (from £13.95), puddings (£4.75), and children's meals; as food is cooked to order, service can slow down at busy times. Wadworths IPA and 6X along with a changing guest such as Ruddles Best are well kept on handpump, and they also have half a dozen malts and farm cider; piped jazz. Very neatly kept, the sheltered side lawn has pretty flowerbeds, and some well spaced picnic-sets. Though dogs are welcome, they must be on a lead. *(Recommended by M G Hart, David and Wendy Puttock, DC, Sarah and Anthony Bussy, Fiona Eddleston, Sebastian and Paris Leach, John A Barker, W W Burke, Sheila Manchester, Alistair Forsyth, Tonya Govender, Joyce and Geoff Robson)*

Wadworths ~ Tenant Kathie Duval ~ Real ale ~ Bar food (12-2.30, 6.30-9.30; not Mon, or Sun evening) ~ Restaurant ~ (01722) 790243 ~ Children welcome ~ Dogs welcome ~ Open 12-2.30(3 Sat), 6-11; 12-3, 7-10.30 Sun; closed Mon lunchtime exc bank hols

BERWICK ST JOHN ST9422 Map 2
Talbot

Village signposted from A30 E of Shaftesbury

In a peaceful and pretty village, surrounded by thatched old houses, this attractive pub has a single long bar with nicely shaped heavy black beams and crossbeams with bevelled corners. It's simply furnished with cushioned solid wall and window seats, spindleback chairs, a high-backed built-in settle at one end, and a huge inglenook fireplace with a good iron fireback and bread ovens. Reasonably priced bar food includes lunchtime sandwiches (from £2.75), ploughman's (from £4.50), baguettes (from £4.50), cheese and mushroom omelette (£5), sausage and mash (£5.75), changing specials like steak and kidney pie (£7.50), beef stroganoff or lamb shank in rosemary and red wine (£8.95), and evening extras like grilled cajun chicken (£7.95); Sunday roasts (£7). Bass, Ringwood Best, Wadworths 6X and a guest such as Archers SSB are well kept on handpump, and they've farm cider; darts, cribbage. There are seats outside. More reports please. *(Recommended by D P and M A Miles, Colin and Janet Roe, David and Elizabeth Briggs)*

Free house ~ Licensees Pete and Marilyn Hawkins ~ Real ale ~ Bar food (not Sun evening, or Mon) ~ (01747) 828222 ~ Children in eating area of bar and restaurant ~ Dogs allowed in bar ~ Open 12-2.30, 6.30-11; 12-5 Sun; closed Sun evening, Mon exc bank hol lunchtime

BOX ST8369 Map 2

Quarrymans Arms

Box Hill; coming from Bath on A4 turn right into Bargates 50 yds before railway bridge, then at T junction turn left up Quarry Hill, turning left again near the top at grassy triangle; from Corsham, turn left after Rudloe Park Hotel into Beech Road, then third left on to Barnetts Hill, and finally right at the top of the hill; OS Sheet 173 map reference 834694

Reached by a sinuous drive down a warren of lanes, this unpretentious low stone pub is a warmly welcoming place, with its good food and wide range of drinks both big draws. Once the local of the Bath stone miners, it has quite a lot of mining-related photographs and memorabilia dotted around the interior, and the licensees run interesting guided trips down the mine itself. One modernised room with an open fire is entirely set aside for drinking, with very well kept Butcombe, Moles Best, Wadworths 6X and maybe a guest on handpump, as well as good wines, over 60 malt whiskies, ten or so old cognacs, and various coffees. It's not the smartest of pubs, but beautifully sweeping views from big windows in the no smoking dining room are usually enough to distract visitors from the mild untidiness. The fairly priced menu includes sandwiches (£2.50), soup (£2.95), macaroni cheese (£5.25), scampi, ham, egg and chips or all day breakfast (£5.95), moules marinière (£5.25; £8.25 main), spaghetti carbonara (£7.95), various stir fries (£8.25), and lots of daily specials such as home-made faggots and mushy peas (£7.50), steak and ale pie (£7.95), fish risotto (£9.25), and chicken breast wrapped in pancetta with a creamy pesto sauce (£9.50); pleasant informal service. The pub is ideally placed for cavers, potholers and walkers, and the atmosphere is easy-going; cribbage, dominoes, shove-ha'penny, fruit machine and piped music. An attractive outside terrace has picnic-sets, and they play boules here (with football and cricket teams, too). *(Recommended by Gene and Kitty Rankin, Dr and Mrs C W Thomas, Dr and Mrs A K Clarke, Tom Bottinga, M Sage, Dr and Mrs M E Wilson)*

Free house ~ Licensees John and Ginny Arundel ~ Real ale ~ Bar food (11.30-3, 6-9) ~ Restaurant ~ (01225) 743569 ~ Children welcome ~ Dogs allowed in bar ~ Open 11-11; 12-10.30 Sun ~ Bedrooms: £25(£35B)/£50(£65B)

BRADFORD-ON-AVON ST8261 Map 2

Dandy Lion

35 Market Street

Busy, traditional and friendly, this thriving town pub has delighted readers in recent months, particularly those who found free cake and biscuits on the bar when they popped in for morning coffee. A good place to spend an afternoon with a drink and the papers, it has an enjoyably continental feel, and a good mix of customers. Big windows, either side of the door, look out on to the street, and have a table and cushioned wooden armchair each. Working in, the pleasantly relaxed long main bar has nice high-backed farmhouse chairs, old-fashioned dining chairs, a long brocade-cushioned settle on the stripped wooden floor (there's a couple of rugs, too), sentimental and gently erotic pictures on the panelled walls, an overmantel with brussels horses, and fairy-lit hops over the bar counter. Up a few steps at the back, a snug little bare-boarded room has a lovely high-backed settle and other small ones around sturdy tables, a big mirror on a mulberry wall, and a piano; piped jazz. The upstairs restaurant is candlelit at night, and has an area with antique toys and baskets of flowers; it's no smoking in here (as is the back bar at lunchtimes). Butcombe, Wadworths IPA, 6X and a seasonal ale are well kept on handpump, they've a dozen wines by the glass, and they do good coffees; welcoming service. Served only at lunchtime, good straightforward bar food includes soup (£4.50), filled rolls or panini (from £4.75). baked potatoes (from £5.25), spaghetti carbonara or fish and chips (£7.25), and specials such as wild mushroom risotto (£6.95) or venison casserole (£8.25); on Sunday they have a choice of roasts (£7.95). In the evening, the pub is popular with a young crowd (especially weekends, when parts can get smoky). They have evening poetry readings, and

occasional jazz. *(Recommended by Paul and Shirley White, Dr and Mrs A K Clarke,*
Sue Demont, Tim Barrow, Dr and Mrs M E Wilson, David and Pam Wilcox, Michael Butler,
Mrs Margo Finlay, Jörg Kasprowski, Douglas and Ann Hare, David Crook, Ian Phillips,
Mike Gorton)

Wadworths ~ Tenant Jennifer Taylor ~ Real ale ~ Bar food (12-2.15 (3 Sun); not 25 or 26
Dec) ~ Restaurant ~ (01225) 863433 ~ Children welcome ~ Open 10.30-3,
6-11; 10.30-11 Sat; 11.30-3.30, 7-11 Sun

BREMHILL ST9772 Map 2
Dumb Post
Off A4/A3102 just NW of Calne; Hazeland, just SW of village itself, OS Sheet 173 map
reference 976727

You could easily drive past this unspoilt and quirky old place without realising
what it is, and we half suspect that's the way they like it; run by and for people who
like their pubs unpretentious and brimming with genuine character, it may not suit
those with fussier tastes. The main lounge is a glorious mix of mismatched, faded
furnishings, vivid patterned wallpaper, and stuffed animal heads, its two big
windows boasting an unexpectedly fine view down over the surrounding
countryside; not huge (it has a half dozen or so tables), it has something of the air
of a once-grand hunting lodge. There's a big woodburner in a brick fireplace and a
log fire on the opposite side of the room, comfortably-worn armchairs and plush
banquettes, a standard lamp, mugs, bread and a sombrero hanging from the beams,
and a scaled-down model house between the windows; in a cage is an occasionally
vocal parrot, Oscar. The narrow bar leading to the lounge is more dimly lit, but has
a few more tables, exposed stonework, and quite a collection of toby jugs around
the counter; there's a plainer third room with a pool table. Three well kept beers
such as Archers SSB, Butcombe Gold and Wadworths 6X on handpump; friendly
service. The lunchtime bar food is simple, hearty and well liked by locals: toasted
sandwich (£2.40), soup (£3.10), sausage, egg and chips (£4.90), and steak and
kidney or home-made cottage pie (£5.55). There are a couple of picnic table sets
outside, and some wooden play equipment. A peaceful spot, in good walking
country. Note the limited lunchtime opening times. *(Recommended by Dick and*
Madeleine Brown)

Free house ~ Licensee Mr Pitt ~ Real ale ~ Bar food (12-2) ~ No credit cards ~
(01249) 813192 ~ Children in eating area of bar ~ Dogs allowed in bar ~ Open 12-2
(not Mon-Weds), 7-11; 12-3, 7-11 Sat; 12-4, 7-10.30 Sun; closed Mon-Weds lunchtimes

BRINKWORTH SU0184 Map 2
Three Crowns ♀
The Street; B4042 Wootton Bassett—Malmesbury

The elaborate menu at this popular place covers an entire wall, but though the very
good food is clearly at the heart of things it still feels like a proper pub, with a nice
atmosphere and friendly staff. That said, meal prices are now firmly at the top of
the pub range, though helpings can be substantial, and all main courses are served
with half a dozen fresh vegetables. The choice changes every day, and besides
lunchtime snacks such as filled rolls (from £6.25), filled baked potatoes (from
£6.95), and ploughman's (from £6.95) might include include vegetable strudel
(£14.50), steak and kidney or chicken korma pie (£14.95), fresh asparagus baked in
filo pastry with Boursin cheese and a champagne sauce (£15.95), half a locally
smoked chicken with a sherry and cream sauce, and a hint of dijon mustard
(£17.45), half a roasted duck with a cassis, redcurrant jelly and cream sauce, and
fresh strawberries (£18.95), and strips of crocodile marinated in herbs and spices,
then sautéed with garlic, mushrooms and sun-dried tomato, and flamed with
whisky (£19.95). It can get very crowded, so it's worth arriving early if you want a
table, or be prepared to wait. Most people choose to eat in the conservatory or the
light and airy garden room; both are no smoking. The bar part is more traditional,
with big landscape prints and other pictures, some horsebrasses on dark beams, a

dresser with a collection of old bottles, tables of stripped deal, and a couple made from gigantic forge bellows, big tapestry-upholstered pews and blond chairs, and log fires; sensibly placed darts, shove-ha'penny, dominoes, cribbage and chess, fruit machine and piped music. Drinkers have a good range of real ales to choose from, with Archers Village, Castle Eden Bitter, Fullers London Pride, Greene King IPA and Wadworths 6X on handpump, and they have a long wine list, with around 20 (including champagne) by the glass, and mulled wine in winter. There's a terrace with outdoor heating to the side of the conservatory. The garden stretches around the side and back, with well spaced tables and a climbing frame, and looks over a side lane to the church, and out over rolling prosperous farmland. *(Recommended by Andrew Shore, Maria Williams, Brenda and Rob Fincham, James Morrell, Gordon Neighbour, KC, Tom and Ruth Rees, Mrs Pat Crabb, Veronica Turner, Ian Phillips, Malcolm Ward, Martin and Karen Wake)*

Enterprise ~ Lease Anthony Windle ~ Real ale ~ Bar food (12-2(3 Sun), 6-9.30; not 25-26 Dec) ~ Restaurant ~ (01666) 510366 ~ Children allowed in dining areas and garden ~ Dogs allowed in bar ~ Open 11-3(4 Sat), 6-11; 12-5, 6-10.30 Sun; closed 25-26 Dec

CHICKSGROVE ST9729 Map 2

Compasses ★ 🍴 🍷 🛏

From A30 5½ miles W of B3089 junction, take lane on N side signposted Sutton Mandeville, Sutton Row, then first left fork (small signs point the way to the pub, in Lower Chicksgrove; look out for the car park)

Reassuringly unchanging and peaceful, this ancient thatched house continues to be a real favourite with some readers, in part because of its history and atmosphere, but also thanks to its friendly welcome and good, generously served food. The bar has old bottles and jugs hanging from beams above the roughly timbered counter, farm tools and traps on the partly stripped stone walls, and high-backed wooden settles forming snug booths around tables on the mainly flagstoned floor. Well kept Bass, Chicksgrove Churl (brewed for the pub by Wadworths), Wadworths 6X and a guest like Hidden Pint from the nearby Dinton Brewery on handpump, several wines by the glass, and ten malt whiskies; cribbage, dominoes, bagatelle and shove-ha'penny. Besides snacks such as filled onion bread (from £3.95), ham, egg and chips or 6oz rib-eye steak (£6.45), the daily changing menu might include baked red pepper with garlic and anchovies (£5.25), smoked duck and red onion tartlet (£5.45), steak and kidney pie with suet (£8.95), wild mushrooms with blue vinney cheese, apple and cider sauce with caper risotto (£9.95), duck breast wrapped in bacon with chinese jus or monkfish steak marinated in thai spices (£12.95), and lamb fillet with mint and redcurrant jus (£14.95), with puddings such as raspberry, lemon, ginger and coriander tart (£4.25); main courses come with a good selection of vegetables, and they do good children's meals. Service can be slow when it's busy. The dining room is no smoking. The quiet garden and flagstoned farm courtyard are very pleasant places to sit; they've an enclosed garden behind, and two terraces. There's a nice walk to Sutton Mandeville church and back along the Nadder Valley. *(Recommended by David and Ruth Hollands, Dr D E Granger, Colin and Janet Roe, Ken and Sylvia Jones, Phyl and Jack Street, Edmund Coan, Sebastian and Paris Leach, Edward Mirzoeff, Helen and Brian Edgeley, Roger and Pauline Pearce, Mrs Belinda Mead, Ian Wilson, M Sage, Mike and Brenda Roberts, Mary Kirman and Tim Jefferson, Paul Humphreys, Richard and Nicola Tranter, Robert Blevin, Bill and Jessica Ritson, Mrs J H S Lang)*

Free house ~ Licensee Alan Stoneham ~ Real ale ~ Bar food (not Sun evenings, or Mon exc bank hols) ~ Restaurant ~ (01722) 714318 ~ Children welcome ~ Dogs welcome ~ Open 12-3, 6-11; 12-3, 7-8.30 Sun; closed Mon exc bank hols (when closed the next day instead) ~ Bedrooms: £45B/£75B

The letters and figures after the name of each town are its Ordnance Survey map reference. *Using the Guide* at the beginning of the book explains how it helps you find a pub, in road atlases or large-scale maps as well as in our own maps.

CODFORD ST9639 Map 2

George 🍽 ♈

Just off A36 W of A303 intersection; High Street

They take food very seriously at this nicely refurbished old inn, but in a refreshingly flexible way; the landlord likes to mix together whatever fresh ingredients he might have lying around that day, and if you're staying, you'll find that instead of presenting you with a breakfast menu, he'll pop out and ask what you'd like him to make. Vegetarians get the same treatment at other times, while others will find a changing menu that might include lunchtime sandwiches, soup (£3.95), rosette of ripe avocado and oak smoked salmon with lemon and poppy seed dressing (£6.50), cumberland sausage with seed mustard mash and red onion gravy (£7.95), rib-eye steak with home-made chips (£10.95), caramelised breast of gressingham duck with wild mushroom risotto and madeira and earl grey jus (£12.95), and roasted fillet of turbot with fresh asparagus, chilli and coriander mash, and spring onion and ginger cream sauce (£14.95). Fish comes fresh from Brixham five times a week, they make their own (delicious) bread, and the puddings are excellent – we especially enjoyed an iced banana parfait with amaretto ice-cream and home-made honeycomb. The knocked through L-shaped bar has been refurbished in an unfussy but warmly comfortable way, with exposed brickwork, candles on the well spaced tables, fresh flowers and big house plants, modern art and an ornate mirror on the red-painted walls, contemporary lighting, and some artfully arranged twigs and leaves; there's a long pine counter, and a log fire. Particularly appealing is the very nice lounge with sofas and big piles of magazines; it's no smoking, as is the top end of the bar. Well kept Timothy Taylors Landlord and a changing guest like Butcombe or Ringwood Best, and a good wine list; piped music. Service is friendly and attentive. Tables on the narrow front terrace overlook the road; on fine evenings these have candles too. The bedrooms have unusually comfortable beds. *(Recommended by Richard J Mullarkey)*

Enterprise ~ Lease Boyd McIntosh and Joanne Fryer ~ Real ale ~ Bar food (not Tues, or Sun evening) ~ (01985) 850270 ~ Well behaved children welcome ~ Open 12-3, 6.30-11; 12-3, 7-10.30 Sun; closed Tues, and Sun evening ~ Bedrooms: £45B/£65B

CORSHAM ST8670 Map 2

Two Pigs 🍺

A4, Pickwick

You can depend on a fine beer and a friendly welcome at this delightfully eccentric little beer lover's pub. Always chatty and friendly, the atmosphere is at its headiest on Monday nights, when live blues draws a big crowd into the narrow and dimly lit flagstoned bar. Amassed by the individualistic landlord, you'll find a zany collection of bric-a-brac including enamel advertising signs on the wood-clad walls, pig-theme ornaments, and old radios. A good mix of customers gathers around the long dark wood tables and benches, and friendly staff serve well kept Hop Back Summer Lightning and Stonehenge Pigswill, along with a couple of changing guests from small independent brewers like Teignworthy; piped blues. A covered yard outside is called the Sty. Beware of their opening times – the pub is closed every lunchtime, except on Sunday; no food (except crisps) or under-21s. *(Recommended by Dr and Mrs A K Clarke, R Huggins, D Irving, E McCall, T McLean, Mr and Mrs P R Thomas, Catherine Pitt, P R and D Thomas)*

Free house ~ Licensees Dickie and Ann Doyle ~ Real ale ~ No credit cards ~ (01249) 712515 ~ Blues Mon evening ~ Open 7-11; 12-2.30, 7-10.30 Sun

---

Anyone claiming to arrange or prevent inclusion of a pub in the *Guide* is a fraud. Pubs are included only if recommended by genuine readers and if our own anonymous inspection confirms that they are suitable.

DEVIZES SU0061 Map 2

Bear ♀ ◀

Market Place

Completely refurbished over the last couple of years, this old coaching inn has provided shelter to distinguished guests as diverse as King George III and Dr Johnson. The big main carpeted bar has log fires, black winged wall settles and muted cloth-upholstered bucket armchairs around oak tripod tables; the classic bar counter has shiny black woodwork and small panes of glass. Separated from the main bar by some steps, a room named after the portrait painter Thomas Lawrence (his father ran the establishment in the 1770s) has dark oak-panelled walls, a parquet floor, a big open fireplace, shining copper pans, and plates around the walls; it's partly no smoking. Well kept Wadworths IPA, 6X and a seasonal guest on handpump, as well as a good choice of wines (including 16 by the glass), quite a few malt whiskies, and freshly squeezed juices. Lunchtime bar food (which not all readers consider the pub's main strength) might include home-made soup (£2.95), sandwiches (from £2.75), ploughman's (from £4.95), and thai fishcakes, stuffed peppers or fish and chips (all £5.95); prices for the same dishes go up in the evenings. There are buffet meals in the Lawrence Room, and you can eat these in the bar too. A courtyard has some outside tables. It's only a stone's throw from here to Wadworths brewery, where you can buy beer in splendid old-fashioned half-gallon earthenware jars. *(Recommended by the Didler, Dr and Mrs A K Clarke, Alan Sadler, Blaise Vyner, Tina and David Woods-Taylor, Ian Phillips, Mary Rayner, D H Lloyd, Bill and Jessica Ritson)*

Wadworths ~ Tenant Andrew Maclachlan ~ Real ale ~ Bar food (11.30-2.30, 7-9.30) ~ Restaurant ~ (01380) 722444 ~ Children welcome ~ Dogs allowed in bar ~ Weekly jazz ~ Open 11-11; 12-10.30 Sun; closed 25-26 Dec ~ Bedrooms: £60B/£85B

DONHEAD ST ANDREW ST9124 Map 2

Forester ◀ ♀

Village signposted off A30 E of Shaftesbury, just E of Ludwell; Lower Street

Doing well under its current licensees (who this year have opened a couple of very nice bedrooms), this 14th-c thatched pub, in a charming village, impresses with its very good, carefully sourced food: no wonder several readers have admitted that they can scarcely stay away. Using wherever possible organic or free-range produce, the changing menu might include chicken liver and foie gras parfait with toasted brioche and apricot and ginger chutney (£5.95), seared scallops with garlic potato purée, chorizo sausage, and a caper and sultana dressing (£7.95), game pie (£9.25), baked goats cheese gnocchi with sweet chestnuts, portobello mushrooms and a herb crust (£9.95), confit of duck with roasted apple and bubble and squeak (£11.95), pan-seared tuna steak with couscous and chilli jam or pot-roasted pheasant with cabbage, bacon and game jus (£12.95), braised ham hock crépinettes with garlic mash, haricot blanc and watercress sauce (£13.50), and calves liver with sage and leek mash, bacon and wholegrain mustard sauce (£13.95); they do children's helpings of most dishes, and have a good children's menu too (from £3.95). Warmly welcoming and well organised, the appealing bar has stripped tables, wooden floors, a log fire in its big inglenook fireplace, and usually a few local regulars around the servery; well kept Ringwood Best, Wadworths 6X and a guest like Sharps on handpump, and a very good choice of wines by the glass. The comfortable main dining room has country-kitchen tables in varying sizes, nicely laid out with linen napkins, and attractive wrought-iron candlesticks – they sell these, if you like the design. A second smaller and cosier dining room is, like the first, no smoking. Service is pleasant and helpful, and there are no machines or piped music. Tables out on the good-sized terrace have fine country views, and there are good walks nearby, for example to the old and 'new' Wardour castles. The neighbouring cottage used to be the pub's coach house. *(Recommended by Michael Doswell, Bill and Sally Imeson, Penny Simpson, Edmund Coan, Peter Salmon, Colin and Janet Roe, Ian Cox, OPUS, Mary Kirman and Tim Jefferson, Roger Wain-Heapy, Richard and Nicola Tranter)*

Free house ~ Licensee Martin Hobbs ~ Real ale ~ Bar food ~ Restaurant ~
(01747) 828038 ~ Dogs allowed in bar ~ Open 11-3, 6-11 (11-11 July/Aug); 11-11 Sat;
11-3, 6-10.30, all day Jun-Sept Sun ~ Bedrooms: £50S/£65S

EBBESBOURNE WAKE ST9824 Map 2

Horseshoe ★ 🍺 🛏️

On A354 S of Salisbury, right at signpost at Coombe Bissett; village is around 8 miles
further on

Readers continue to be delighted by this charmingly unspoilt old country pub,
recent reports highlighting the food ('the best ploughman's ever', said one reader),
the atmosphere ('we were treated like old friends', says another), and the welcome,
with readers commenting on how friendly they found the licensees, the locals, and
the two jack russells. Tucked away in fine downland, it also has pleasant views over
the steep sleepy valley of the River Ebble from seats in its pretty little garden; look
out for the three goats in a paddock at the bottom of the garden. Inside, there are
fresh home-grown flowers on the tables in the beautifully kept bar, with lanterns, a
large collection of farm tools and other bric-a-brac crowded along its beams, and
an open fire; a conservatory extension seats ten people. Well kept Archers,
Ringwood Best, Wadworths 6X and a guest like Adnams Broadside or Fullers
London Pride are tapped from the row of casks behind the bar, and they also stock
farm cider, country wines and several malt whiskies. Served with a huge variety of
well cooked seasonal vegetables (and good chips), enjoyable bar food includes
lunchtime ham and eggs (£6.75), curry (£9.25), faggots (£9.50), steak and kidney
pie (£9.75), lambs liver and bacon (£9.75), and evening dishes such as lamb cutlets
in port sauce (£12.95), fillet steak or half a honey-roasted duckling in gooseberry
sauce (£15), popular Sunday roasts, and good puddings like treacle tart (£3.95).
Booking is advisable for the small no smoking restaurant, especially at weekends
when it can fill quite quickly. There are good walks nearby. *(Recommended by the
Didler, Andrea Rampley, Dr D G Twyman, David Kirkcaldy, Terry and Linda Moseley, Pat and
Robert Watt, OPUS, Colin and Janet Roe, Keith and Jean Symons, Anthony Longden,
Rosemary and Tom Hall, H W Roberts, Dr Michael Smith, Mike and Linda Hudson, Pam and
David Bailey)*

Free house ~ Licensees Tony and Pat Bath ~ Real ale ~ Bar food (not Sun evenings or
Mon) ~ Restaurant ~ (01722) 780474 ~ Children in restaurant ~ Open 12-3, 6.30-11;
12-4, 7-10.30 Sun; closed Sun evenings winter; closed Mon lunchtime exc bank hols,
26 Dec ~ Bedrooms: £45B/£60(£65B)

GREAT BEDWYN SU2764 Map 2

Three Tuns

Village signposted off A338 S of Hungerford, or off A4 W of Hungerford via Little
Bedwyn; High Street

Once the village bakery (and still with its original bread oven), this busy place really
is thriving under its current licensees, and though there's plenty of space, it does fill
up fast at weekends – particularly on Sunday lunchtimes when locals gather for the
weekly meat raffle. Most people are here for the food, but there's a wonderfully
chatty, genuinely pubby atmosphere too: you don't feel out of place if you just want
a drink. The traditional décor is lifted out of the ordinary by some quirky touches,
such as life-size models of the Blues Brothers at separate tables in the beamed, bare-
boards front bar, and a similarly incongruous female mannequin in the back
restaurant. Almost every inch of the walls and ceiling is covered by either the usual
brasses, jugs, hops and agricultural implements, or more unusual collections such as
ribbons from ships' hats, showbiz photos, and yellowing cuttings about the royal
family, all of which reflect stages of the landlord's career. There's a profusion of
chalked-up quotes and pithy comments (mostly from the licensees), as well as an
inglenook fireplace, and lighted candles in the evenings. Relying heavily on local
produce, the changing menus might include soup (£3.95), goats cheese and sun-
dried tomato filo parcels with honey and walnut dressing (£5.50), home-made

curries (from £6.95), spaghetti with cheese sauce, red onions, leek and courgettes (£8.95), seafood chowder or seared calves liver with bacon (£11.95), venison casserole (£12.95), fresh monkfish stuffed with basil leaves, peppers, spinach, onion and leeks, on a red pepper coulis (£13.95), and daily specials; good Sunday roasts. They also do a take-away menu. Well kept Flowers IPA, Fullers London Pride and Wadworths 6X on handpump, good wine list, with several by the glass, espresso machine, and over 40 malt whiskies; helpful friendly service, piped music. The restaurant is no smoking. The whitewashed building has quite a few plants in front, and a pleasant raised garden behind. *(Recommended by Penny Simpson, Ian Phillips)*

Punch ~ Lease Alan and Janet Carr ~ Real ale ~ Bar food (not Sun evenings) ~ Restaurant ~ (01672) 870280 ~ Children in eating area of bar and restaurant ~ Open 11.30-3, 6-11; 12-3, 7-10.30 Sun

GREAT HINTON ST9059 Map 2
Linnet 🍴

3½ miles E of Trowbridge, village signposted off A361 opposite Lamb at Semington

Very much somewhere to come to for an imaginative meal, rather than just a drink, this attractive brick pub enjoys such a reputation for its food that if you want to be sure of a table at weekends, it's best to book a few weeks in advance. Everything on the menu is home-made, from the bread (readers have enjoyed onion, rosemary and hazelnut), to the sausages and ice-cream. Served by attentive staff in the little bar or restaurant, the changing menu might include at lunchtimes filled focaccia or salads (from £7.50), smoked salmon and cod fishcakes (£7.25), and grilled rib-eye steak with blue cheese and bacon fritters in port sauce (£9.95), with evening dishes such as steamed salmon with roasted pepper, baby sweetcorn and lemon risotto with prawn sauce (£11.50), pork tenderloin filled with apple, red onion and truffles with honey and mustard sauce (£12.95), and fried rib-eye steak with braised calves kidneys stuffed with fried onions and herbs in thyme sauce (£15), with puddings such as lemon meringue cheesecake (£4.60). The set lunch (£11.50 for two courses; £13.95 for three courses) is excellent value. The bar to the right of the door has a cream carpet and lots of photographs of the pub and the brewery, and there are bookshelves in a snug end part. The cosy restaurant is candlelit at night. As well as more than two dozen malt whiskies, and quite a few wines (with eight by the glass), they serve well kept Wadworths 6X, and maybe a seasonal guest on handpump; piped music. In summer, the flowering tubs and window boxes with seats dotted among them are quite a sight. *(Recommended by Ken and Sylvia Jones, Danielle Nay, Dr and Mrs A K Clarke, Andrew Shore, Maria Williams, Mike Gorton, Mr and Mrs A H Young, Mr and Mrs Peter Llewellyn, Glenwys and Alan Lawrence, Michael Doswell, Bernard Stradling)*

Wadworths ~ Tenant Jonathan Furby ~ Real ale ~ Bar food (not Mon) ~ Restaurant ~ (01380) 870354 ~ Children welcome ~ Dogs allowed in bar ~ Open 11-2.30, 6-11; 12-3, 7-10.30 Sun; closed Mon

GRITTLETON ST8680 Map 2 🏠
Neeld Arms ♀ 🍺 🛏

Off A350 NW of Chippenham; The Street

Well liked for its particularly convivial atmosphere, this 17th-c black-beamed pub is the sort of place that stays well organised even when busy – just as well, as during the Badminton Horse Trials they serve an average of 150 lunches a day. It's largely open-plan, with some stripped stone, a log fire in the big inglenook on the right and a smaller coal-effect fire on the left, flowers on tables, and a pleasant mix of seating from windsor chairs through scatter-cushioned window seats to some nice arts and crafts chairs and a traditional settle. The parquet-floored back dining area has yet another inglenook, with a big woodburning stove; even back here, you still feel thoroughly part of the action. Well kept beers such as Bass, Bath Spa and Wadworths IPA and 6X on handpump at the substantial central bar counter, and a good choice of reasonably priced wines by the glass. Enjoyable food from changing blackboards might include soup (£2.95), lunchtime ciabattas (£4.25, not Sunday), ploughman's (£4.95), fish, chips and mushy peas (£6.95), salmon and dill fishcakes (£7.25), and sausages or pie of the week (£7.50), with evening dishes such as lemon tarragon chicken (£8.50), local venison with redcurrant jus (£10.50), lamb shank with redcurrant and rosemary (£11.95), and good home-made puddings (£4.25); they do Sunday roast with local beef (£7.25), and plenty of game in season. There's an outdoor terrace, with pergola. Look out for Soaky, the golden retriever who likes slops. *(Recommended by Richard Stancomb, Anthony Barnes, Peter Neate, Simon and Mandy King, Kevin Thorpe, R Huggins, D Irving, E McCall, T McLean, Stephen Woad, Michael Doswell, Mike Pugh, Dr Alan and Mrs Sue Holder, Andrew Scarr, Pete Devonish, Ian McIntyre)*

Free house ~ Licensees Charlie and Boo West ~ Real ale ~ Bar food ~ (01249) 782470 ~ Children welcome ~ Dogs welcome ~ Open 12-3, 5.30-11; 11.30-3.30, 5.30-12 Sat; 12-3.30, 7-11 Sun ~ Bedrooms: £40S(£40B)/£60S(£70B)

HEYTESBURY ST9242 Map 2 🏠
Angel 🗪

High Street; just off A36 E of Warminster

Nicely refurbished under its current landlord, this enjoyable and quietly upmarket dining pub is in a quiet village just below the Salisbury Plain. With a good open fire and plenty of comfortable armchairs and sofas, the spacious homely lounge on the right opens into the stylish restaurant with high-back leather chairs and wooden tables. This in turn opens on to an attractive secluded courtyard garden. On the left, a long beamed bar has a convivial evening atmosphere, open fire, some attractive prints and old photographs, and straightforward tables and chairs; piped music. Good food might include lunchtime rolls and ploughman's, cornish crab gratin with free-range egg (£7.95), scottish beefburger or pork sausages, mash and onion gravy (£8.95), fish pie (£9.95), portobello and porcini mushroom tart with roasted shallot purée and parmesan crisps (£10.95), local pork fillet with sauerkraut and black pudding croquette and calvados sauce (£13.95); the restaurant specialises in steaks (from £14.95). They do a good value two-course lunch for £8, Mon-Thurs. Nine wines are available by the glass, and beers include Greene King IPA, Morland Original and Wadworths 6X on handpump. *(Recommended by Edward Mirzoeff, Hugh Roberts, Keith and Jean Symons, M G Hart, Dr and Mrs A K Clarke, MRSM, Ian Phillips)*

Greene King ~ Lease Tim Etchells ~ Real ale ~ Bar food ~ Restaurant ~ (01985) 840330 ~ Children in eating area of bar and restaurant ~ Dogs allowed in bar and bedrooms ~ Open 12-11; 12-10.30 Sun ~ Bedrooms: £60B/£75B

HINDON ST9132 Map 2 🏠
Lamb

B3089 Wilton—Mere

A minor refurbishment has left this deeply civilised solidly built hotel more atmospheric than ever, its darkly elegant, well furnished rooms full of warmth and character. The two flagstoned lower sections of the roomy long bar have a very long polished table with wall benches and chairs, blacksmith's tools set behind a big inglenook fireplace, high-backed pews and settles, and at one end a window seat (overlooking the village church) with a big waxed circular table. Deep red walls add to the comfortable, relaxed feel. Up some steps a third, bigger area has lots more tables and chairs – though it can fill up fast and at busy times you may not be able to find a seat. Big blackboards list the enjoyable bar food, which might include baguettes (from £4.50), soup (£3.95), ploughman's (£5.50), cod in beer batter with minted peas (£8.25), sautéed gnocchi with peppers, parmesan, rocket and basil pesto (£8.50), steak and mushroom pie (£8.90), 10oz chopped steak burger (£8.95), moroccan marinated free-range chicken with spiced couscous and spinach (£10.75), pan-fried bass with pak choi and a sesame and ginger dressing (£12.50), 28-day matured scottish rump steak (£14.95), a game dish of the day (with which there's an optional donation to the Countryside Alliance), and puddings such as bread and butter pudding (£3.95); they do a Sunday roast (£8.25), and you can usually get cream teas throughout the afternoon. From the polished dark wooden counter, pleasant staff serve Youngs Bitter, Special and seasonal brews on handpump, and a good choice of wines by the glass; the extensive range of whiskies includes all the malts from the Isle of Islay, and they have a wide choice of Havana cigars. There are picnic-sets across the road (which is a good alternative to the main routes west); parking is limited. The pub is now linked to the Boisdale restaurant in Belgravia. *(Recommended by B J Harding, Phil and Sally Gorton, John Evans, Ian Phillips, Colin and Janet Roe, Mrs J H S Lang)*

Free house ~ Licensee Nick James ~ Real ale ~ Bar food (12-2.30, 6.30-9.30) ~ (01747) 820573 ~ Children in eating area of bar ~ Dogs welcome ~ Open 11-11; 12-11 Sun ~ Bedrooms: £65B/£90B

HORTON SU0363 Map 2
Bridge Inn ◗
Signposted off A361 Beckhampton road just inside the Devizes limit; Horton Road

Nicely placed by a humpy bridge over the Kennet & Avon Canal, this started life around 1800 as a flour mill and bakery, relying on the canal for transport. It has old black and whites of brightly dressed bargee families and their steam barges among other old photographs and country pictures on the red walls above a high panelled dado. In the carpeted area on the left all the sturdy pale pine tables are set for the landlord/chef's good range of enjoyable food, using all local supplies, such as filled rolls (from £3.50), soup (£3.75), cod and pancetta fishcakes or fried camembert (£4.95), ploughman's (from £5.50), spinach and mascarpone lasagne (£7.95), steak and ale pie (£8.95), trout stuffed with prawns with dill butter (£9.25), 8oz sirloin steak (£11.95), and similar specials such as game pie (£8.95). Puddings such as chocolate fudge cake come with a jug of cream. This dining part has a log fire in the front area, and an end no smoking room. On the right of the bar is a pubbier bit with similar country-kitchen furniture on reconstituted flagstones, and some stripped brickwork, with superbly kept Wadworths IPA, 6X and a seasonal ale tapped straight from the cask, and eight decent wines by the glass. Service by the helpful staff is well organised; disabled lavatories. There may be quiet piped music. The safely fenced garden has picnic-sets, and an aviary with two or three dozen white fantail doves. *(Recommended by Dr and Mrs A K Clarke, Mark and Joanna, Keith and Sally Jackson, Howard and Margaret Buchanan)*

Wadworths ~ Tenants Sue Jacobs and Kevin Maul ~ Real ale ~ Bar food (12-2.15, 7-9.15) ~ Restaurant ~ (01380) 860273 ~ Children welcome ~ Dogs allowed in bar ~ Open 11.30(12 Sun)-3(2.30 in winter), 6.30-11

KILMINGTON ST7736 Map 2
Red Lion £ ⇔
B3092 Mere—Frome, 2½ miles S of Maiden Bradley; 3 miles from A303 Mere turn-off

Popular with walkers (you can buy locally made walking sticks), this down-to-earth ivy-covered country inn has a good local pubby atmosphere, particularly in the evenings. The snug low-ceilinged bar is pleasantly furnished with a curved high-backed settle and red leatherette wall and window seats on the flagstones, photographs of locals pinned up on the black beams, and a couple of big fireplaces (one with a fine old iron fireback) with log fires in winter. A newer big-windowed no smoking eating area is decorated with brasses, a large leather horse collar, and hanging plates. Dogs are allowed in the bar – but not at lunchtime; sensibly placed darts, dominoes, shove-ha'penny and cribbage. Butcombe, Butts Jester and a regularly changing guest such as Ale Fresco are well kept on handpump, and they've farm cider, pressés, and monthly changing wines (all of which you can have by the glass). Served only at lunchtime, the straightforward bar menu includes soup (£1.50), sandwiches (from £3, toasted from £3.50), ploughman's (from £4.50), pasties (£4.50), salads (£4.95), steak and kidney or lamb and apricot pie (£5.25), meat or vegetable lasagne (£7.40), and perhaps a couple of daily specials. There are picnic-sets in the big attractive garden (look out for Kim the labrador). A gate gives on to the lane which leads to White Sheet Hill, where there is riding, hang gliding and radio-controlled gliders. Dating back to the 15th c, the pub is owned by the National Trust. Stourhead Gardens are only a mile away. *(Recommended by Mike Gorton, Colin and Janet Roe, Andrea Rampley, D M Tyley, Steve Jackson)*

Free house ~ Licensee Chris Gibbs ~ Real ale ~ Bar food (12-1.50; not 25-26 Dec or1 Jan) ~ No credit cards ~ (01985) 844263 ~ Children welcome in eating area of bar till 8.30pm ~ Dogs allowed in bar ~ Open 11.30-2.30, 6.30-11; 12-3, 7-10.30 Sun; closed evening 25 Dec ~ Bedrooms: /£40

LACOCK ST9168 Map 2

George

West Street; village signposted off A350 S of Chippenham

Licensed continuously since the 17th c, this unspoilt and homely pub is one of the oldest buildings in this much-loved National Trust village. Comfortable and warmly welcoming, the low-beamed bar has upright timbers in the place of knocked-through walls making cosy rambling corners, candles on tables (even at lunchtime), armchairs and windsor chairs, seats in the stone-mullioned windows, and flagstones just by the counter; piped music (which can be quite loud). The treadwheel set into the outer breast of the original great central fireplace is a talking point – worked by a dog, it was used to turn a spit for roasting. Outside, there are picnic-sets with umbrellas in the attractive back garden (which has plenty of space to run round), and they've recently updated the play area; a bench in front overlooks the main street. There's a decent choice of good value wines, and reasonably priced Wadworths IPA, JCB and 6X on handpump; friendly service from the long-standing landlord and his family. Bar food might include vegetarian dishes such as wild mushroom lasagne or lemon and thyme risotto (£7.95), home-made steak and ale pie (£7.95), breaded scampi (£8.95), chicken breast stuffed with wild mushrooms wrapped in bacon with red wine sauce (10.95), and salmon with asparagus sauce (£11.50), with lunchtime baguettes and ploughman's (from £4.95). It can get busy with tourists, so booking may be a good idea. The barn restaurant is no smoking. *(Recommended by Andy and Jill Kassube, Andrew Shore, Maria Williams, Brian Root, Sue and Mike Todd, Meg and Colin Hamilton, Kevin Thorpe, Louise English, Dr and Mrs A K Clarke, Nicholas and Dorothy Stephens, Roger and Jenny Huggins, Fiona Eddleston, Dr and Mrs M E Wilson, Alan Sadler, Anne Morris)*

Wadworths ~ Tenant John Glass ~ Real ale ~ Bar food ~ Restaurant ~ (01249) 730263 ~ Children in eating area of bar and restaurant ~ Open 10-3, 5-11; 10-11 Fri, Sat; 10-10.30 Sun; 10-3, 5-11 Fri in winter

Red Lion

High Street

Open all day under its new managers, this imposing Georgian inn is owned by the National Trust and handy for a visit to Lacock Abbey or the Fox Talbot Museum. With a good pubby atmosphere, the long and airy pink-painted bar has distressed heavy dark wood tables and tapestried chairs, turkey rugs on the partly flagstoned floor, a fine old log fire at one end, aged-looking paintings, and branding irons hanging from the ceiling. The cosy snug has comfortable leather armchairs. Wadworths IPA, JCB, 6X and seasonal beers are well kept on handpump, and they've around 18 malt whiskies; fruit machine and piped music. Lunchtime bar food includes sandwiches and baked potatoes (from £3.95), ploughman's (£5.50), soup (£3.95), and daily specials such as beef and Guinness casserole, fish pie or moroccan lamb (£7.50), with evening extras like roasted pepper, red onion and goats cheese tart (£7.25), pork tenderloin with apples in a calvados cream sauce (£9.25) and steaks (from £9.95); turkey-dinosaur-style children's meals. The restaurant is no smoking. In fine weather, seats outside are a pleasant place for a drink. *(Recommended by Dr and Mrs A K Clarke, Betsy and Peter Little, R Huggins, D Irving, E McCall, T McLean, Frank Willy, Roger and Jenny Huggins)*

Wadworths ~ Managers Joe and Jessica Caudle ~ Real ale ~ Bar food (12-2, 6-9) ~
(01249) 730456 ~ Children in eating area of bar and restaurant ~ Dogs allowed in bar ~
Open 11.30-11; 11.30-11 Sat; 12-10.30 Sun ~ Bedrooms: £55B/£75B

Rising Sun 🍺

Bewley Common, Bowden Hill – out towards Sandy Lane, up hill past Abbey; OS Sheet
173 map reference 935679

Just outside the village, this cheerily unpretentious stone pub has a delightful
garden, its big two-level terrace offering views extending up to 25 miles over the
Avon valley; it's a marvellous place to enjoy the sunset with a well kept beer.
Popular with chatting locals, the three welcoming little rooms have been knocked
together to form one simply furnished area, with a mix of old chairs and basic
kitchen tables on stone floors, stuffed animals and birds, country pictures, and open
fires. Welcoming staff serve the full range of Moles beers on handpump (and if you
can't decide which one to have you'll probably be offered a taster), with Moles Tap
Bitter, Best, Molecatcher, Molennium and seasonal ales like Holy Moley and Moel
Moel, and they keep the brewery's Black Rat cider too. There's darts, cribbage,
dominoes, board games, and unobtrusive piped music. Good helpings of enjoyable
bar food include lunchtime snacks such as baguettes (from £3.75) and baked
potatoes (from £4.50), breaded chicken or fish platter (£6.95), sizzling chicken
tortillas (£7.95), and lamb chops in minted gravy (£8.45), with specials such as
venison casserole (£9.95) or wild boar steaks (£10.95). They do children's meals,
and there's a children's play area. *(Recommended by Peter Meister, Dr and Mrs
A K Clarke, Roger and Jenny Huggins, Kevin Thorpe, Jane and Mark Hooper, A P Seymour)*

Moles ~ Managers Roger Catte, Peter and Michelle Eaton ~ Real ale ~ Bar food (12-2, 6-9;
not Sun evening, or Mon lunch) ~ (01249) 730363 ~ Children allowed until 8.15pm in bar,
and in restaurant at lunchtimes ~ Dogs allowed in bar ~ Live entertainment every Weds
evening ~ Open 12-3, 6-11; 12-11 Sat, Sun; 12-3, 6-11 Sat in winter; closed Mon lunchtime

LOWER CHUTE SU3153 Map 2
Hatchet

The Chutes well signposted via Appleshaw off A342, 2½ miles W of Andover

Reassuringly unchanging, this 16th-c thatched cottage particularly stands out for its
appearance; it's one of the most charming looking pubs we know. With a peaceful
local feel, the very low-beamed bar has a mix of captain's chairs and cushioned
wheelbacks around oak tables, and a splendid 17th-c fireback in the huge fireplace
(which has a roaring log fire in winter); cribbage, dominoes and piped music. They
serve well kept Adnams, Otter and Timothy Taylors Landlord on handpump, and a
range of country wines. Thursday night is curry night, when you can eat as much as
you like (£7.25). Other bar food includes lunchtime baguettes (from £4.95),
ploughman's (£6.50), liver and bacon, chicken tortillas, smoked haddock florentine
and mushroom tortellini with sun-dried tomatoes and pesto (all £7.95), and daily
specials like mushroom and red pepper stroganoff (£7.95) and lamb shank (£8.25);
they do a good value Sunday roast. The restaurant is no smoking (other parts can
be smoky at times). There are seats out on a terrace by the front car park, or on the
side grass, and there's a children's sandpit. They have only twin bedrooms.
*(Recommended by J Stickland, Lynn Sharpless, Bill and Jessica Ritson, Mrs J H S Lang,
Mr and Mrs R Davies)*

Free house ~ Licensee Jeremy McKay ~ Real ale ~ Bar food (12-2.15, 6.30-9.45) ~
Restaurant ~ (01264) 730229 ~ Children in restaurant and family room ~ Dogs allowed in
bar ~ Open 11.30-3, 6-11; 12-3.30, 7-10.30 Sun ~ Bedrooms: £50S/£50S

The 🍺 symbol shows pubs which keep their beer unusually well,
have a particularly good range or brew their own.

LUCKINGTON ST8384 Map 2
Old Royal Ship
Off B4040 SW of Malmesbury

Dating from the 17th c, this has been pleasantly opened up, making in effect one long bar divided into three areas. The central servery has well kept Archers Village, Bass, Wadworths 6X and Youngs Waggledance on handpump, with farm cider, ten decent wines in two glass sizes, and good coffee; skittle alley and piped music. On the right are neat tables, spindleback chairs and small cushioned settles on dark bare boards, with a small open fireplace and some stripped masonry. On the left, past an area with corks packed into its ceiling, there is more of a mix of tables and chairs, and a small step up to a carpeted section partly divided by rubber plants and dracaenas. In here, an extraordinary trompe l'oeil stone staircase disappears up into a fictitious turret. The dining areas are no smoking. Flowers on the tables, some rather lively yellow paintwork and bright curtains add quite a touch of colour. All this space quickly fills in the evenings (it's a favourite with the young farmers and with people out celebrating), and at lunchtime – especially during the Badminton horse trials. Decent bar food includes sandwiches, deep-fried whitebait or deep-fried chicken goujons with chilli dip (£5.50), breaded plaice (£7.95), gammon and egg (£9.25), chicken caesar salad (£9.95), and steaks (from £12.50). Service is welcoming and helpful. The garden beyond the car park has boules, and a play area with a big wooden fort. *(Recommended by Dr and Mrs A K Clarke, Richard Stancomb, KN-R, J L Wedel)*

Free house ~ Licensee Helen Johnson-Greening ~ Real ale ~ Bar food (12-2.30, 6-9.30) ~ Restaurant ~ (01666) 840222 ~ Children in restaurant only ~ Open 11.30-3, 6-11; 11.30-11 Sat; 12-4, 7-10.30 Sun

MALMESBURY ST9287 Map 2
Smoking Dog ◀
High Street

This double-fronted mid-terrace 17th-c pub gets particularly lively on the spring bank holiday weekend, when their annual sausage and beer festival offers a chance to sample dozens of different bangers and around 30 often unusual brews from around the country. The rest of the year they have half a dozen real ales tapped straight from the cask or on handpump: alongside well kept Archers Best, Brains Revd James and Buckley's Best, changing guests might include Charles Wells Bombardier, Shepherd Neame Bishops Finger and Wadworths 6X. They also do nine wines by the glass. The two smallish front bars have a sociable local atmosphere, with flagstones, dark woodwork, cushioned bench seating, big pine tables and a blazing log fire. A flagstoned corridor with local notices on the walls leads to a bare-boards no smoking restaurant. Tasty bar food includes good baguettes and ciabattas (from £4.95), ploughman's (£5.75), a local sausage of the week (£5.75), potato, broccoli and leek galette with cream, garlic and cheese (£7.25), and home-made chicken jalfrezi (£8.75); in the evening you can choose from the restaurant menu which has things like grilled smoked haddock with ale and cheese (£10.50), calves liver with bacon, onions and basil gravy (£10.95), and sirloin steak (£12.25), with puddings such as italian baked chocolate torte (£4.95). On Sunday they do a range of roasts (£7.50; three courses £13.95) and other choices may be more limited then. Recently landscaped, the garden has pleasant views out over the town. *(Recommended by Deborah Boyle, Lesley and Peter Barrett, Dr and Mrs A K Clarke, R Huggins, D Irving, E McCall, T McLean, Jenny and Brian Seller, R M Corlett, DAV, Mike Pugh)*

Brains ~ Manager Martin Bridge ~ Real ale ~ Bar food (not Sun evening) ~ Restaurant ~ (01666) 825823 ~ Children in eating area of bar and restaurant ~ Dogs allowed in bar ~ Live vocalist one Thurs evening every two months ~ Open 12-11(10.30 Sun); closed 25 Dec evening

NEWTON TONY SU2140 Map 2

Malet Arms
Village signposted off A338 Swindon—Salisbury

Very much at the heart of the peaceful village, this tiled flintstone pub is well liked by readers for its hearty, home-made food – though it's the kind of place you'd come for a meal rather than a snack. Chalked up on a blackboard, the choice changes regularly but might typically include home-made soup (£4.25), beautifully presented smoked trout pâté with whisky and horseradish (£5.75), thai spiced salmon and shrimp fishcakes (£8.25), sweet potato curry with coconut and mango (£8.95), spicy north african lamb tagine or wild mushroom risotto (£9.25), popular rump steak sandwich (£9.50), and moules marinière (£10.50). The landlady's puddings receive plenty of praise; favourites include the Mars Bar cheesecake and hot ginger pudding with fresh figs, mascarpone and honey (£4.60), and she's currently turning her hand to regional english puddings like canterbury or manchester tart. In winter they do Sunday roasts (£8.25) and plenty of local game (especially venison), and in summer you'll find tasty locally smoked food. The two low-beamed interconnecting rooms have nice furnishings including a mix of different-sized tables with high winged wall settles, carved pews, chapel and carver chairs, and there are lots of pictures, mainly from imperial days. The main front windows are said to have come from the stern of a ship. There's a log and coal fire in a huge fireplace – no longer so smoky after recent work on the chimney. There's an attractive and homely back dining room on the right; it's no smoking in here. Wadworths 6X is tapped from oak casks, and they also have well kept Palmers IPA, Stonehenge Heelstone and a guest (usually from a local brewery) like Ramsbury Gold on handpump; decent wines, farm cider, 16 malt whiskies, vintage calvados, and an espresso machine. The two pub jack russells, Badger and Piper, have been joined by a black labrador named Shovel, and there's an african grey parrot called Steerpike. The small front terrace has old-fashioned garden seats, with some picnic-sets on the grass there; a back garden has more, along with a wendy house. There's also a little aviary, and a horse paddock behind. You can play cricket on the playing field opposite – the landlord (an aficionado) tells us there are new nets up this year. The pub looks over a chalk stream that you ford to drive to it – it's best to use an alternative route in winter, when it can be quite deep.
(Recommended by M G Hart, Mark Barker, John Coatsworth, Dr D G Twyman, Glen and Nola Armstrong, David and Elizabeth Tyzack, Kevin Thorpe, J Stickland, Bob and Margaret Holder, Colin Moore, Grahame Brooks, Gillian Rodgers, Evelyn and Derek Walter, Ian Phillips, Patrick Hall, Michael Doswell)

Free house ~ Licensee Noel Cardew ~ Real ale ~ Bar food (12-2.30, 6.30-10 (7-9.30 Sun)) ~ (01980) 629279 ~ Children in restaurant and family room ~ Dogs allowed in bar ~ Open 11-3, 6-11; 12-3, 7-10.30 Sun; closed 25-26 Dec, 1 Jan

NORTON ST8884 Map 2

Vine Tree
4 miles from M4 junction 17; A429 towards Malmesbury, then left at Hullavington, Sherston signpost, then follow Norton signposts; in village turn right at Foxley signpost, which takes you into Honey Lane

Wiltshire Dining Pub of the Year
They put real care into sourcing fresh, local ingredients at this civilised dining pub (in an attractively converted 18th-c mill house), though they don't have to try too hard to find their Sunday roasts; the beef comes from their own farm next door. Besides baguettes made with home-baked bread (from £5.75, not Friday or Saturday evenings), a wide choice of imaginative seasonally changing dishes might include soups like mussel and saffron or white bean and thyme (from £3.95), jugged hare terrine with rosemary and prunes (£5.95), tea-smoked quail with foie gras on a sweet cured bacon salad (£6.50), seared scallops wrapped in prosciutto with a roasted red pepper coulis (£6.95 starter, £13.95 main), pumpkin ravioli with walnut sauce (£9.95), locally shot wood pigeon (£12.75), roast partridge with

juniper sauce and bubble and squeak or chicken breast stuffed with seafood with a mild red thai curry cream (£13.95), braised shoulder of lamb with irish stew and herb dumplings (£14.95), wild bass fillet with scallop, leek and herb risotto and a vanilla bean jus (£15.75), and puddings like espresso crème brûlée or an excellent sticky toffee pudding (£5.25); they have some unusual farmhouse cheeses, and proper home-made children's meals. It's best to book if you want to eat here, especially at weekends. Three beautifully kept little rooms open together, with limited edition and sporting prints, a mock-up mounted pig's mask (used for a game that involves knocking coins off its nose and ears), lots of stripped pine, big church candles on the tables (the lighting's very gentle), and some old settles; look out for Clementine, the friendly and docile black labrador. One dining area is no smoking. There are picnic-sets in a two-acre garden which includes a pretty walled terrace with a lion fountain and urns of flowers; two boules pitches. Although the emphasis is on eating, drinkers do pop in, and there's a buoyant atmosphere, with quite a mix of customers. Helpful attentive staff serve well kept beers like Bath Spa and Butcombe Bitter, and around 24 wines are available by the glass, from an impressive list (they do monthly tutored tastings); also quite a choice of malt whiskies and armagnacs. They have a busy calendar of events, with outdoor music in summer, vintage car rallies and lots going on during the Badminton horse trials. That said, it's not the easiest place to find, so it can feel more remote than its proximity to the motorway would suggest. *(Recommended by Richard Stancomb, Dr and Mrs A K Clarke, Simon and Mandy King, M G Hart, Alice Harper, Betsy and Peter Little, John and Joan Nash, Miss A G Drake, J Stickland, Simon Collett-Jones, Mrs Pat Crabb, Mr and Mrs Peter Llewellyn, Matthew Shackle, Andrea and Guy Bradley, Adelle Wheeler, Guy Vowles, John and Gloria Isaacs)*

Free house ~ Licensees Charles Walker and Tiggi Wood ~ Real ale ~ Bar food (12-2(2.30 Sat, 3 Sun), 7-9.30(10 Fri, Sat)) ~ Restaurant ~ (01666) 837654 ~ Children welcome ~ Dogs welcome ~ Occasional jazz and blues ~ Open 12-3(3.30 Sat), 6-11; 12-10.30 Sun; closed 25 Dec

PITTON SU2131 Map 2
Silver Plough ♀
Village signposted from A30 E of Salisbury (follow brown tourist signs)

About to be refurbished as we went to press (with new carpets, curtains and seat covers), this pleasant and nicely set country dining pub has plenty to keep your eyes busy: the black beams in the comfortable front bar are strung with hundreds of antique boot-warmers and stretchers, pewter and china tankards, copper kettles, toby jugs, earthenware and glass rolling pins, painted clogs, glass net-floats, and coach horns and so forth. Seats include half a dozen cushioned antique oak settles (one elaborately carved, beside a very fine reproduction of an Elizabethan oak table), and the timbered white walls are hung with Thorburn and other game bird prints, original Craven Hill sporting cartoons, and a big naval battle glass-painting. The back bar is simpler, but still has a big winged high-backed settle, cased antique guns, substantial pictures, and – like the front room – flowers on its tables. There's a skittle alley next to the snug bar; cribbage, shove-ha'penny, and piped music. Popular, generously served bar food includes baguettes (from £5.50), ploughman's (£6.50), various salads (from £5.95; they do two sizes), and steak and kidney pie or beef or vegetable lasagne (£8.25), with à la carte dishes like spinach and brie filo parcels (£10.95), and salmon on herb mash with dill and caper berry sauce or half a honey roast duck with plum sauce (£14.95); children's meals (£4.75). On Sunday the menu is more limited, and they do a choice of roasts. The restaurant and half the main bar are now no smoking, as is the snug at lunchtimes. Badger Best, Sussex Bitter, Tanglefoot and a seasonal brew like Fursty Ferret are well kept on handpump under light blanket pressure; they've a fine wine list including eight by the glass, and some well priced and carefully chosen bottles, a good range of country wines, and a worthy choice of spirits. A quiet lawn has picnic-sets and other tables under cocktail parasols. The pub is well placed for good downland and woodland walks. *(Recommended by James Price, Phyl and Jack Street, Dr D G Twyman, Brenda and Rob Fincham, J P Humphery, Fr Robert Marsh, Liz and Tony Colman,*

Keith and Margaret Kettell, Michael Butler, Anthony Longden, Kevin Blake, Bernard Stradling, Peter Neate)

Badger ~ Tenants Hughen and Joyce Riley ~ Real ale ~ Bar food (12-2, 6-9) ~ Restaurant ~ (01722) 712266 ~ Children in family room ~ Open 11-3, 6-11; 12-3, 6.30-10.30 Sun ~ Bedrooms: /£50S

POULSHOT ST9559 Map 2
Raven 🍺
Village signposted off A361 Devizes—Seend

The generously served bar food, well cooked by the landlord, is what readers most like about this classic country pub, prettily placed across from the village green. Two intimate black-beamed rooms are well furnished with sturdy tables and chairs and comfortable banquettes; the lounge and dining room are no smoking. Very well kept Wadworths IPA, 6X and maybe a seasonal ale are tapped straight from the cask; efficient, obliging service. Bar food includes filled ciabattas (from £4.95), soup (£3.35), deep fried tiger prawns in filo pastry (£5.15), steak and kidney pie (£8.95), smoked haddock pie (£9.65), pork stroganoff (£11.80), and specials like spicy five bean casserole (£7.80), salmon fishcakes with lemon butter sauce or lamb and apricots (£8.80), and stilton chicken (£9.20); good puddings include crème brûlée or bread and butter pudding (£3.55). The gents' is outside. More reports please. *(Recommended by Paul A Moore, Mr and Mrs J Brown)*

Wadworths ~ Tenants Philip and Susan Henshaw ~ Real ale ~ Bar food (not Mon (except bank hol lunch)) ~ Restaurant ~ (01380) 828271 ~ Children in restaurant ~ Dogs allowed in bar ~ Open 11-2.30, 6.30-11; 12-3, 7-10.30 Sun; closed Mon except bank hol lunchtime

RAMSBURY SU2771 Map 2
Bell
Signed off B4192 NW of Hungerford, or A4 W

Nicely positioned in a smartly attractive village, this spotlessly kept dining pub has a pleasantly relaxed, chatty atmosphere. Comfortably modernised, the airy bar has exposed beams, cream-washed walls, and two woodburning stoves; fresh flowers on polished tables add a welcome touch of colour. Victorian stained-glass panels in one of the two sunny bay windows look out onto the quiet village street. Bar food might include sausages and mash, fish and chips, burger, and beef stir fry (£8), or you can eat from the more elaborate à la carte menu in the bar, with dishes such as smoked duck salad or black pudding with scallops and shallot jus (£7), bass with cherry tarte tatin and vermouth cream or lamb chump with potato purée, ratatouille and rosemary coulis (£14), with puddings such as treacle tart (£6); they do two courses for £19.50. The friendly landlord and staff serve well kept Wadworths IPA, 6X and an occasional guest beer. There are picnic-sets on the raised lawn; roads lead from this quiet village into the downland on all sides. The planned bedrooms haven't materialised yet but are still in the pipeline. More reports please. *(Recommended by Peter B Brown, Michael Gray, Mark and Ruth Brock)*

Free house ~ Licensee Jeremy Wilkins ~ Real ale ~ Bar food (not Sun evening) ~ Restaurant ~ (01672) 520230 ~ Children welcome ~ Dogs allowed in bar ~ Open 12-3, 5.30-11; 12-3, 7-10.30 Sun

ROWDE ST9762 Map 2
George & Dragon 🍴 ♀
A342 Devizes—Chippenham

This attractive old dining pub, completely no smoking now, has changed hands since our last edition, but is being run along the same lines with many of the old team, so fingers crossed standards will remain as high. It's best known for the wide choice of seafood, not cheap, but delivered fresh from Cornwall, with the choice typically including grilled sardines (£6.50), grilled lemon sole (£14.50), thai curry with hake, salmon and squid (£15), roast monkfish with parsnip mash and red wine jus (£16.50), and lobster linguini with chilli tomato sauce (£17.50). Non-fishy choices include tomato and tarragon soup (£3.50), beef carpaccio with rocket and parmesan (£7), pork and peanut satay balls with apricot sauce (£7, £9.50 main course), cheese soufflé (£7.50, £9.50 main course), duck breast in a potato rösti with walnut and grape salad (£14), and sirloin steak with blue cheese crust (£14.50); they do a selection of cheeses (£7). The bar is tastefully furnished, with plenty of dark wood, and a log fire; the bare-floored dining room has quite plain tables and chairs, and is close enough to the bar to keep a pleasant chatty atmosphere. Butcombe and a guest like Ringwood Fortyniner on handpump, and they've organic cider, a good wine list, continental beers and lagers, and a wide range of teas and coffees; shove-ha'penny, cribbage and dominoes. A pretty garden at the back has tables and chairs; the Kennet & Avon Canal is nearby. *(Recommended by Tina and David Woods-Taylor, Mike Gorton, Mary Rayner, Mr and Mrs F J Parmenter)*

Free house ~ Licensees Philip and Michelle Hale, Christopher Day ~ Real ale ~ Bar food (not Mon, or Sun evening) ~ Restaurant ~ (01380) 723053 ~ Children welcome ~ Dogs allowed in bar ~ Open 12-3(4 Sat), 7-11; 12-4 Sun; closed Mon lunchtime, all first week of Jan

SALISBURY SU1429 Map 2
Haunch of Venison
Minster Street, opposite Market Cross

The licensees of this cosy and genuinely interesting old pub are about to celebrate their 25th year here. Dating back to 1320 when it was used by craftsmen working on the Cathedral spire, its two tiny downstairs rooms are quite spit-and-sawdust in spirit, with massive beams in the white ceiling, stout oak benches built into the timbered walls, black and white floor tiles and an open fire. A tiny snug (popular with locals, but historically said to be where the ladies drank) opens off the entrance lobby. Courage Best, Wadworths 6X and a guest such as Hop Back Summer Lightning are served on handpump from a unique pewter bar counter, with a rare set of antique taps for gravity-fed spirits and liqueurs. They've also 55 malt whiskies, decent wines and a range of brandies; chess, dominoes and piped music. Halfway up the stairs is a panelled no smoking room they call the House of Lords, which has a small-paned window looking down on to the main bar, and a splendid fireplace that dates back to the building's early years; behind glass in a small wall slit is the smoke-preserved mummified hand of an 18th-c card sharp still clutching his cards. Bar food in here includes a few dishes from the upstairs restaurant, as well as things like venison sausage toad in the hole or faggots with bubble and squeak (£4.90), salmon and crab fishcakes (£5.50), and smoked haddock chowder with poached egg (£6.90). *(Recommended by David Carr, Dr D G Twyman, Andrea Rampley, the Didler, Peter and Anne Hollindale, Dr and Mrs A K Clarke, Ann and Colin Hunt, Howard and Margaret Buchanan, Kevin Blake, Ken and Joyce Hollis, Bill and Jessica Ritson)*

Scottish Courage ~ Lease Anthony Leroy, Rupert Willcocks ~ Real ale ~ Bar food ~ Restaurant ~ (01722) 322024 ~ Children in restaurant ~ Dogs allowed in bar ~ Open 11-11; 12-10 Sun; closed 25 Dec

SEEND ST9461 Map 2
Barge
Seend Cleeve; signposted off A361 Devizes—Trowbridge, between Seend village and signpost to Seend Head

Its lovely setting means this attractive canalside pub is always buzzing, but readers like the way service remains efficient and friendly even at the busiest times. The bar has an unusual barge-theme décor, and intricately painted Victorian flowers cover the ceilings and run in a waist-high band above the deep green lower walls. A distinctive medley of eye-catching seats includes milk churns, unusual high-backed chairs (made from old boat-parts), a seat made from an upturned canoe, and the occasional small oak settle among the rugs on the parquet floor, while the walls have big sentimental engravings. The watery theme continues with a well stocked aquarium, and there's also a pretty Victorian fireplace, big bunches of dried flowers, and red velvet curtains for the big windows; fruit machine and piped music. Outside, the neatly kept waterside garden is an excellent place to watch the bustle of boats on the Kennet & Avon Canal – old streetlamps let you linger there after dark, and moorings by the humpy bridge are very useful for thirsty bargees. Butcombe, Wadworths IPA and 6X, and a guest like Marstons Pedigree are well kept on handpump, and they've lots of malt whiskies, a good choice of wines by the glass, and mulled wine in winter; good coffee too. Uniformed staff serve generous well liked lunchtime bar food from a changing menu that might include good sandwiches (from £3.95; soup and a sandwich £5.95), and filled baked potatoes (from £5.25), home-cooked ham and eggs (£8.50), several vegetarian dishes like baked field mushrooms topped with herb breaded goats cheese with spicy plum sauce (£9), tasty steak, mushroom and ale pie (£9.50), rump steak (£9.95), chicken breast wrapped in bacon with stilton and leek sauce (£10.50), and good fish specials such as marlin loin with a catalan mussel and rocket salad (£12); home-made puddings (£4.25). The restaurant extension is no smoking. They recommend booking for meals, especially at weekends. *(Recommended by Kevin Thorpe, Norman and Sheila Davies, Peter and Audrey Dowsett, Keith and Margaret Kettell, Dr and Mrs A K Clarke, Paul and Shirley White, Michael Doswell, Pat and Robert Watt, Keith and Sally Jackson, Mark Flynn, Alan Sadler, Ian Moody, Dr and Mrs M E Wilson, Joyce and Geoff Robson, Mark and Mary Fairman)*

Wadworths ~ Tenant Christopher Moorley Long ~ Real ale ~ Bar food (12-2(2.30 weekends and bank hols), 7-(10 Fri, Sat)9.30) ~ Restaurant ~ (01380) 828230 ~ Children welcome ~ Dogs allowed in bar ~ Open 11-2.30, 6-11 (all day in school summer hols); 12-11(10.30 Sun) Sat

STOURTON ST7734 Map 2 🏠

Spread Eagle

Church Lawn; follow Stourhead brown signs off B3092, N of junction with A303 just W of Mere

Owned by the National Trust, and delightfully set among other elegant National Trust stone buildings at the head of Stourhead Lake, this civilised old pub has a new landlord this year, who plans to refurbish the bar and bedrooms and introduce an emphasis on fresh food from the estate. The interior has antique panel-back settles, a mix of new and old solid tables and chairs, handsome fireplaces with good winter log fires, smoky old sporting prints, prints of Stourhead, and standard lamps or brass swan's-neck wall lamps. One room by the entrance has armchairs, a longcase clock and a corner china cupboard. There's a welcoming atmosphere, and service from the mostly young staff is friendly (though it can slow down at busy times). The new menu includes lunchtime filled rolls (from £3.10), baked potatoes (£4.95), and ploughman's (£5.95), soup (£3.50); sweet onion tart with roasted vegetables and basil (£5.95), lincolnshire sausages with bubble and squeak and mustard sauce (£7.25), braised lamb shank with red wine and oranges (£10.50), and evening extras like venison and juniper casserole (£10.25). The middle bar and restaurant are no smoking. Butcombe, Wadworths 6X and a guest like Wessex Crockerton Classic are well kept on handpump. There are benches in the courtyard behind. A bonus when staying here is that you can wander freely around the gardens outside their normal opening times – a nice way of enjoying them away from the crowds. *(Recommended by Meg and Colin Hamilton, R Michael Richards, Dr and Mrs M E Wilson, John Doe, Ian Phillips, S Topham, Gill and Keith Croxton, P R and D Thomas, Mike Turner, John and Joan Nash, David Hoult, Paul Humphreys)*

Free house ~ Licensees Stephen Ross, Karen Lock ~ Real ale ~ Bar food (12-9) ~ Restaurant (evening) ~ (01747) 840587 ~ Children in restaurant ~ Open 9-11; 12-10.30 Sun ~ Bedrooms: £60B/£90B

If we know a pub does summer barbecues, we say so.

WEST LAVINGTON SU0052 Map 2

Bridge Inn

A360 S of Devizes; Church Street

Now completely no smoking, this quietly civilised village pub is doing well under its current licensees, whose thoughtful range of good food and carefully chosen drinks attracts a wonderfully varied mix of locals and visitors, on our last visit including an elderly gentleman with a crossword and a bowl of soup, a biker couple enjoying well filled baguettes, and several smart families perusing the bin-ends. The light, spacious bar comfortably mixes contemporary features such as spotlights in the ceiling with firmly traditional fixtures like the enormous brick inglenook, on our visit filled with big logs and candles; at the opposite end is a smaller modern fireplace, in an area set mostly for eating. Pictures on the cream-painted or exposed brick walls are for sale, as are local jams, and there are plenty of fresh flowers on the tables and bar; timbers and the occasional step divide the various areas. The monthly changing menu might include soup (£3), red onion marmalade and smoked bacon tartlets with tarragon dressing (£4.95), sun-dried tomato and black olive soufflé with ratatouille (£8.95), baked lemon sole with shallot and dill cream sauce (£10.50), and pan-fried pheasant breast with onion and sage stuffing and a morello cherry sauce (£12.95); they do a two- or three-course set Sunday lunch. One of the licensees is French, and his native specialities may pop up on the specials board. Three well kept changing beers like Brakspears, Butcombe Gold and Sharps Doombar on handpump, good wines; piped music in the evenings. At the back is a nice raised lawn area with several tables under a big tree; there's a new boules pitch outside too. *(Recommended by Richard Stancomb, J H Bescoby, B and F A Hannam, Bill and Jessica Ritson)*

Enterprise ~ Lease Cyrille and Paula Portier, Dave Hamilton ~ Real ale ~ Bar food ~ Restaurant ~ (01380) 813213 ~ Children in eating area of bar and restaurant ~ Dogs allowed in bar ~ Live jazz Sun evenings ~ Open 12-3, 6-11; 12-3, 6-10.30 Sun; closed Mon

WHITLEY ST8866 Map 2

Pear Tree 🍴 ♀ 🛏️

Off B3353 S of Corsham, at Atworth 1½, Purlpit 1 signpost; or from A350 Chippenham—Melksham in Beanacre turn off on Westlands Lane at Whitley 1 signpost, then left and right at B3353

This honey-coloured stone farmhouse has this year once again delighted readers with its imaginative food; one says that on a busy evening laughter and conversation echo deafeningly round the barn-like main dining room as if it were the Albert Hall. With an emphasis on local produce (except for the fish, delivered fresh daily from Looe), the seasonally changing menu might include bar bites like pâté on toast with pear chutney (£2.25) and mini fishcakes with caper mayonnaise (£2.50), toasted sandwiches (£5.50), goats cheese salad with roast beetroot (£5.75), smoked chicken, pancetta, deep-fried avocado and grilled courgette salad (£5.95 starter, £9.75 main course), spring vegetable risotto with mint, basil and parmesan (£11.25), home-made pork sausages with braised lentils, roasted peppers, basil and rocket (£11.50), boneless skate wing with potato gnocchi, broad beans, asparagus, fennel, chilli, basil and lemon (£13.75), slow-cooked shoulder of lamb with black olive mash, sautéed artichokes, ratatouille and lamb sauce (£14.25), and grilled rare breed pork loin with potato and black pudding cake, asparagus and apple sauce (£15.95), with puddings such as roast italian white peach with honey, home-made vanilla ice-cream and amaretto (£4.95) and some unusual cheese (£5.50); they do a set lunch menu (£14 two courses, £16 three courses). Twenty-five or so decent wines are available by the glass (including champagne), and Wadworths 6X, and a couple of changing guests such as Bath Ales Gem are well kept on handpump; lots of speciality teas too. The front bar has quite a pubby feel, with cushioned window seats, some stripped shutters, a mix of dining chairs around good solid tables, a variety of country pictures and a Wiltshire Regiment sampler on the walls, a little fireplace on the left, and a lovely old stripped stone one on the right. Candlelit at night, the popular but unhurried big back no smoking restaurant (you may need to book) has green dining chairs, quite a mix of tables, and a pitched ceiling at one end with a quirky farmyard theme – wrought-iron cockerels and white scythe sculpture. A bright spacious garden room opens on to a terrace with good teak furniture and views over the carefully maintained gardens, which are prettily lit at night to show features like the ruined pigsty; they've recently added a new terrace; boules. Service is helpful and courteous; you'll be made welcome if you want just a drink, but you could feel left out if you don't have something to eat. Half of the eight well equipped bedrooms are in a courtyard block behind, and the rest are above the pub; excellent breakfasts. *(Recommended by Lyn Huxtable, Richard Seers, Di and Mike Gillam, Paul Humphreys, Mike Pugh, Alan Sadler, Joyce and Maurice Cottrell, Dr and Mrs A K Clarke, Danielle Nay, David Boult, Gwen Griffiths, Andrew Shore, Maria Williams, Keith Rutter, Inga Davis, Therese Flanagan, Sebastian Snow, Paul and Ursula Randall, M and GR, Mr and Mrs Peter Llewellyn, Mr and Mrs A H Young, John and Jane Hayter, A P Seymour, Bill and Jessica Ritson)*

Free house ~ Licensees Martin and Debbie Still ~ Real ale ~ Bar food (12-2.30(3 Sun), 6.30-9.30(10 Fri, Sat)) ~ Restaurant ~ (01225) 709131 ~ Children in eating area of bar and restaurant ~ Open 11-3, 6-11; 12-10.30 Sun; closed 25-26 Dec, 1 Jan ~ Bedrooms: £70B/£95B

LUCKY DIP

Besides the fully inspected pubs, you might like to try these Lucky Dips recommended to us and described by readers (if you do, please send us reports: www.goodguides.co.uk).

ALDBOURNE [SU2675]
Blue Boar [The Green (off B4192)]: Homely and relaxed, with inexpensive generous food from sandwiches up, three well kept Wadworths ales, good choice of wines and soft drinks, farm tools, boar's head and flame-effect woodburner in Tudor bar with darts, extensive more modern back lounge/dining area; may be quiet piped music; children welcome, seats out facing pretty village green nr church and neatly kept small back country garden, open all day *(Mary Rayner)*
ALVEDISTON [ST9723]
☆ *Crown* [off A30 W of Salisbury]: 15th-c thatched inn doing well under friendly newish licensees, three cosy very low-beamed partly panelled rooms, deep pink paintwork, two inglenook fireplaces, no smoking dining area, good service, well kept Ringwood Best and guest beers, good value imaginative food, darts, cribbage, dominoes; piped music; children welcome, dogs allowed in bar, neatly kept attractive garden, good bedrooms, pretty spot *(Dr Sally Hanson, Dave Braisted, LYM, Dr Michael Smith, Colin and Janet Roe, Douglas and Ann Hare)*
AVEBURY [SU1069]
Red Lion [A361]: Much-modernised and substantially extended from pretty thatched front part, in the heart of the stone circles; quick friendly service even when packed, well kept ales such as Stonehenge and Wadworths 6X, good wine by the glass, open fires, well run food bar, reasonable prices, no smoking area and restaurant extension – huge choice inc Sun carvery; may be piped music; children welcome *(LYM, T R and B C Jenkins, Mary Kirman and Tim Jefferson, Mr and Mrs G Ives)*

BADBURY [SU1980]
Plough [A346 just S of M4 junction 15]: Large friendly rambling bar area, light and airy no smoking dining room (children allowed) looking over road to Vale of the White Horse, pianola and papers to read, well kept Arkells 2B, 3B and Kingsdown, decent wines, wide blackboard choice of usual food inc afternoon snacks, friendly efficient service; darts, piped music; children welcome, play area in sunny garden above, handy for Great Western Hospital, open all day *(Mrs Pat Crabb, Dr and Mrs A K Clarke, Mark and Ruth Brock)*
BARFORD ST MARTIN [SU0531]
☆ *Barford Inn* [B3098 W of Salisbury (Grovely Rd), just off A30]: Panelled front bar with big log fire, other chatty interlinking rooms and bars, no smoking restaurant, pleasant atmosphere, enjoyable food, well kept Badger Best and K&B; disabled access and lavatories, children welcome, dogs allowed in bar, terrace tables, more in back garden, charming comfortable bedrooms, open all day (has been cl Sun afternoon) *(LYM, M G Hart)*
BIDDESTONE [ST8673]
Biddestone Arms [off A420 W of Chippenham; The Green]: Well kept roomy village pub, mostly set out for eating – hearty food inc two-course midweek bargain lunch; good welcoming service, Wadworths 6X, games in cosy public bar, swings in fairylit garden with roses, attractive village with lovely pond *(BB, Michael Doswell)*
☆ *White Horse* [The Green]: Busy 16th-c village local, wide choice of sensibly priced hearty pub food and filled rolls in unusual stencilled lounge and partly no smoking dining area, well kept Butcombe and Wadworths 6X, quick friendly service, small hatch-served bar with

shove-ha'penny, darts and table skittles, games machine; children welcome; overlooks duck pond in picturesque village, tables in good garden with play area, aviary and rabbits; bedrooms *(Michael Doswell)*

BISHOPSTONE [SU2483]

True Heart [signed off A419/B4192 at Wanborough; High St]: Spacious old country pub nr Ridgeway with emphasis on wide range of reasonably priced food (cooked to order so may be a wait), real ales, good soft drinks choice, light and airy bar with darts and steps up to no smoking eating area, corridor to small dining room; quiet piped music; children and dogs welcome, picnic-sets in garden with terrace, bedrooms *(CMW, JJW)*

BOX [ST8268]

Bear [High St (A4)]: 18th-c, with quiet lounge set for enjoyable reasonably priced food, welcoming staff, well kept Wadworths 6X and Wickwar Cotswold Way, log fires, lively locals' bar with cards and dominoes; bedrooms, backs on to cricket ground *(Colin Hobbs, Roger and Jenny Huggins)*

Queens Head [High St]: Open-plan local with old-world dark wood décor, prompt friendly service, three real ales, bargain food from snacks and light dishes such as baked potatoes up, valley views *(Guy Vowles)*

BRADFORD-ON-AVON [ST8260]

Barge [Frome Rd]: Pub part (not on canal) with well kept real ale, café (no real ale) with steps up to waterside tables and more on own barge, softly coloured lamps out here; friendly licensees, efficient service, a welcome for children, well priced food from lunchtime sandwiches and baguettes to some interesting dishes and choice of Sun roasts; sensibly priced bedrooms *(Keith and Sally Jackson, John and Joan Nash)*

☆ *Beehive* [A363 out towards Trowbridge]: Cheerful old-fashioned L-shaped pub nr canal on outskirts, new landlady keeping up its high local reputation for friendly service and half a dozen interesting well kept ales, generous good value food, not ambitious but thoroughly enjoyable, good range of wines, cosy log fires, candlelit tables, 19th-c playbills, cricketing prints and cigarette cards, darts; children and dogs welcome; attractive good-sized back garden now nicely taken in hand, play area, barbecues *(Dr and Mrs M E Wilson, BB, Dr and Mrs A K Clarke, Pete Baker, Mike Gorton, Sue Demont, Tim Barrow, Richard Greenway, Mark Flynn)*

Cross Guns [Avoncliff, outside town]: Listed for its position, with floodlit gardens steeply terraced above the bridges, aqueducts and river; stripped-stone low-beamed bar with 16th-c inglenook, upstairs river-view restaurant, well kept house beer, Bass, Worthington and a guest beer, lots of malt whiskies and country wines; loudspeaker food announcements, piped music, and the pub can get very busy indeed, when housekeeping can come under pressure; children welcome, open all day *(Dr and Mrs A K Clarke, Michael Bayne, LYM, Ian Phillips, Roger Wain-Heapy)*

Three Horseshoes [Frome Rd, by station car park entrance]: Comfortable and chatty old pub with quickly served good substantial food (and new tapas bar), well kept Butcombe and Wadworths 6X, friendly service, plenty of nooks and corners, small restaurant; tables on terrace with big barbecue *(Ted George, Dr and Mrs A K Clarke)*

BROMHAM [ST9665]

Greyhound [off A342; High St]: Simple furnishings in friendly locals' bar, beams hung with enjoyable bric-a-brac, log fires, even a well, interesting choice of good value generous home-made food using local ingredients, good unassuming restaurant service, well kept Wadworths, good wine choice; big garden *(Martin and Alison Stainsby)*

BROUGHTON GIFFORD [ST8764]

Bell on the Common [The Common]: Imposing rose-draped stone-built pub on huge informal village green, traditional furnishings, friendly service, well kept Wadworths from handpumps on back wall, big coal fire, homely food, dining lounge full of copper and old country prints, rustic bar with local photographs old and new, small pool room with darts and juke box, quiz night; children welcome, charming garden (occasional pig roasts and live music), bowls club next door *(Dr and Mrs A K Clarke, Michael Doswell, Dr and Mrs M E Wilson)*

BURTON [ST8179]

Old House At Home [B4039 Chippenham—Chipping Sodbury]: Spacious stone-built dining pub behind attractive ivy-covered exterior, good-sized helpings of enjoyable rather upmarket food inc splendid puddings, attentive staff, well kept Wadworths 6X, good choice of wines by the glass, log fire; piped music, has been cl Tues lunchtime *(John and Gloria Isaacs, Tom Evans)*

BUSHTON [SU0677]

Trotting Horse: Home-made food (not Sun evening or Mon), three real ales and good soft drinks choice, good-sized bar with lots of pleasant nooks and crannies, no smoking dining extension, games area with darts, bar billiards, juke box, games machine and TV; bedrooms *(CMW, JJW)*

CASTLE COMBE [ST8477]

☆ *Castle Inn*: Welcoming and helpful new landlady in smart and attractive old-world country hotel with good atmosphere in comfortable and pleasantly furnished beamed bar, individual touches such as faux cats on seats, enjoyable standard bar food from ciabattas and ploughman's up, Moles real ale, afternoon teas, restaurant and conservatory with tented ceiling; tables and chairs out on pretty terrace, 13 well equipped bedrooms, beautiful village *(Peter and Audrey Dowsett)*

White Hart [signed off B4039 Chippenham—Chipping Sodbury]: Attractive ancient stone-built pub, beams, panelling, flagstones, seats in stone-mullioned window, lots of old local photographs; Wadworths ales, nice staff, log fires, wide food choice, smaller lounge, family room, games room; walkers welcome (handy for Macmillan Way), tables in sheltered courtyard; in centre of this honeypot village, so can be very busy *(LYM, Richard Stancomb, Peter and Audrey Dowsett)*

CASTLE EATON [SU1495]

Red Lion [The Street]: Thames-side dining pub with cosy linked rooms inc sizeable pleasant conservatory, good choice of beers, log fire, welcoming landlady; children welcome, shrubby riverside garden, popular with walkers on Thames Path *(LYM, Peter and Audrey Dowsett, R Huggins, D Irving, E McCall, T McLean)*

CHAPMANSLADE [ST8247]

Three Horseshoes [A3098 Westbury—Frome; High St]: 16th-c beamed country inn with good attractively priced food, well kept Bass, Butcombe and Sharps, sensibly priced good wines, helpful service, big fires each end of neatly furnished carpeted bar, lots of brass and pewter, extra dining room up steps; pleasant garden with superb views *(Dr and Mrs M E Wilson)*

CHARLTON [ST9688]

☆ *Horse & Groom* [B4040 towards Cricklade]: Appealing stone-built inn under friendly and obliging new young landlord, smart but relaxing bar with fine old furnishings, stripped stone and log fire, simpler right-hand bar with hops on beams, wide choice of good freshly made food in bar and restaurant, well kept ales, decent wines; dogs welcome, tables out under trees, comfortable bedrooms *(Dr and Mrs A K Clarke, LYM, Mark and Joanna, R Huggins, D Irving, E McCall, T McLean)*

CHILMARK [ST9732]

☆ *Black Dog* [B3089 Salisbury—Hindon]: Warmly welcoming and helpful new South African landlord and staff in comfortably modernised and attractive 15th-c beamed pub with enjoyable food from sandwiches and baguettes up, well kept local ales such as Hop Back, good value house wines, several smallish relaxing rooms with a log fire in each (armchairs by one and fossil ammonite in another's fireplace), good local atmosphere (regulars turn up on horseback); dogs welcome, tables out in good-sized roadside garden with terrace *(Julie and Bill Ryan, Douglas and Ann Hare, LYM, Dr Michael Smith, Edward Mirzoeff)*

CHIPPENHAM [ST9073]

Kingfisher [Hungerdown Lane]: Welcoming local with well kept Wadworths 6X, interesting malt whiskies and brandies, good lunchtime sandwiches and salads, fine old prints; soft piped music, board games, frequent music and good quiz nights; tables outside *(Richard Pierce, Dr and Mrs A K Clarke)*

Old Road Tavern [Old Rd, by N side of station]: Traditional games-oriented public bar, two-part lounge, well kept Courage Best, Fullers London Pride, Greene King Old Speckled Hen and a guest beer, cheap lunchtime food from sandwiches up; frequent wknd live music; pleasant secluded little back garden *(Pete Baker)*

CHITTERNE [ST9843]

☆ *Kings Head* [B390 Heytesbury—Shrewton]: Relaxed and understated Salisbury Plain oasis, despite out-of-the-way setting well liked for enjoyable food from bar snacks to inventive meals inc good fish; well kept Butcombe and Wadworths 6X, friendly service, good log fire, simple traditional décor with wooden floors, panelled dado and chunky old pine tables with lighted candles, no music or machines, lovely hanging baskets; tables on back terrace, pretty village, good walks *(Meg and Colin Hamilton, Kit Stallard, BB, J Stickland)*

CLYFFE PYPARD [SU0776]

Goddard Arms: Cheery 16th-c local with log fire and raised dining area in split-level main bar, small sitting room with another fire and two old armchairs, down-to-earth chatty and welcoming licensees, well kept Wadworths 6X and guest beers like local Ramsbury, good value straightforward fresh food, daily papers, artwork for sale, pool room with darts, cribbage etc; sports TV, no credit cards; picnic-sets in back courtyard, bedrooms, also new bunkhouse accommodation in former back skittle alley, tiny pretty thatched village in lovely countryside, open all day wknds *(Pete Baker, Mrs Pat Crabb, BB)*

COLLINGBOURNE DUCIS [SU2453]

☆ *Shears* [Cadley Rd]: Popular racing-country pub with good fresh imaginative food in bar and restaurant, generous helpings and reasonable prices, well kept beers; good value bedrooms *(J Stickland)*

COLLINGBOURNE KINGSTON [SU2355]

Barleycorn [A338]: Smartly kept village pub with several well kept ales such as Hook Norton Old Hooky, Charles Wells Bombardier and Wadworths, wide blackboard choice of affordable food from fresh sandwiches to massive steaks, decent wines, friendly service, a warm welcome for coach parties, pool room, attractive restaurant, exemplary lavatories; piped music; tables in small garden *(Peter and Audrey Dowsett, J Stickland)*

CORSHAM [ST8770]

☆ *Flemish Weaver* [High St]: Attractive and civilised mellow stone building, sensitively modernised keeping slate floor and ceiling planking, sensibly short choice of enjoyable food listing local suppliers (some organic), from good lunchtime baguettes and platters up, friendly attentive service, well kept Banks's Original, Bath Barnstormer and Moles, decent wines, good coffee, fresh flowers, no smoking room; piped music (may be classical, and turned down on request); tables in back courtyard, handy for Corsham Court *(P R and D Thomas, Gloria Bax, Michael Doswell, BB)*

CORSLEY [ST8246]

☆ *Cross Keys* [Lyes Green (off A362 SE of Frome)]: Smart dining pub with old scrubbed tables and good log fires in comfortable quarry-tiled L-shaped bar and partly no smoking dining area on right with gleaming glasses and lighted candles, more formal separate dining room too, good interesting changing food from freshly baked lunchtime baguettes and other bar dishes up, wider evening choice with some emphasis on fish, well kept Wadworths ales, good wine choice; piped pop music; attractive garden, handy for Longleat *(Michael Doswell, Ken and Sylvia Jones, Mr and Mrs A H Young, BB)*

CORSLEY HEATH [ST8145]

Royal Oak [A362 Frome—Warminster]: Large comfortable 19th-c pub very popular lunchtime for generous reasonably priced home-made food from sandwiches and baked potatoes through chilli and spaghetti to duck and steaks, friendly landlady and attentive staff, Wadworths real ales, roomy beamed and panelled bar (no dogs), good fire, big pleasant back family room with pool table, no smoking restaurant; big garden, handy for Longleat *(Neil and Anita Christopher)*

CORTON [ST9340]

☆ *Dove* [off A36 at Upton Lovell, SE of Warminster]: Cottagey country pub in lovely valley, attractively furnished partly flagstoned main bar with huge central log fire and good pictures, wide range of enjoyable food at all price levels from baguettes to fresh fish and steaks, well kept Hop Back and Timothy Taylors, good wines by the glass, friendly landlord and attentive staff, daily papers, no smoking conservatory; piped music; children welcome, tables on neat back lawn, comfortable wheelchair-friendly bedrooms, good fishing available *(LYM, John Hale, Dr and Mrs M E Wilson, Andrea Rampley, Rex Martyn, Richard and Nicola Tranter)*

CRICKLADE [SU1093]

Red Lion [High St]: Fine old 16th-c former coaching inn, interesting signs and bric-a-brac in large yet cosy bar, half a dozen or more well kept changing ales (they may offer tasters), farm ciders, good choice of malt whiskies, friendly landlord and pleasant staff, no music or mobile phones; neat garden, open all day *(Mr and Mrs G S Ayrton, R Huggins, D Irving, E McCall, T McLean, Richard Houghton, CMW, JJW)*

Vale [High St]: Beams, stripped bricks and timbers, plenty of famous-guest pictures, dining rooms off pleasant bar with woodburner in each room, wide food choice from lunchtime sandwiches, panini, baguettes and wraps to hearty evening dishes and popular Sun roasts, helpful friendly staff, well kept ales such as Batemans, Greene King IPA, Abbot and Ruddles County, Smiles and Wadworths 6X, local art for sale; piped music; bedrooms *(Mr and Mrs G S Ayrton, R Huggins, D Irving, E McCall, T McLean)*

White Hart [High St]: Large open-plan bar on several levels, Arkells real ale, wide food choice, friendly service, side pool table *(Peter and Audrey Dowsett)*

CROCKERTON [ST8642]

☆ *Bath Arms* [just off A350 Warminster—Blandford]: Attractive old dining pub with talented chef/landlord doing good food packed with flavour, attractively presented and reasonably priced; beers include two brewed locally by Hobdens for the pub, good wines by

the glass, pleasant informal atmosphere with plenty of well spaced tables in long two-roomed beamed bar and dining area, traditional décor, log fire; piped music may obtrude; picnic-sets in good-sized garden, not far from Longleat *(Michael Doswell, BB, Edward Mirzoeff)*

CRUDWELL [ST9492]

Wheatsheaf: Pleasant L-shaped bar, more bistro than pub in style, with good choice of food (blackboard dominates one wall), three real ales, good house wines *(R Huggins, D Irving, E McCall, T McLean)*

DERRY HILL [ST9570]

Lansdowne Arms [Church Rd]: Striking and stately stone-built pub opposite one of Bowood's grand gatehouses, several civilised areas with relaxed period flavour, hearty log fire and candles in bottles, well kept Wadworths IPA, JCB, 6X and Red Shoot Forest Gold, good value wines by the glass, prompt attentive cheerful service, wide food choice from good range of huge sandwiches with chips up in bar and restaurant; faint piped music; fine views, picnic-sets in neat side garden, good play area *(Dr and Mrs A K Clarke, BB, Meg and Colin Hamilton)*

DOWNTON [SU1721]

Wooden Spoon [High St (A338 S of Salisbury)]: Convivial family-run local with good sensibly priced food from sandwiches and baguettes to wide choice of hot dishes using local produce, inc good steaks, casseroles and popular Sun lunch (when they may want your table for a second sitting), real ales such as Fullers, Ringwood and Youngs, good value wines; children welcome *(Tony Shepherd, Mark Barker)*

EAST KNOYLE [ST8731]

Fox & Hounds [off A350 S of A303]: Lovely out-of-the-way setting, superb views from green opp, good blackboard choice of fairly priced fresh food in bar and small conservatory restaurant, Smiles and Youngs ales, farm cider, good choice of chilled wines, comfortable seats, pleasant layout, quaint décor *(Mrs H E Cunliffe)*

☆ *Seymour Arms* [The Street; just off A350 S of Warminster]: Roomy creeper-covered stone-built black-beamed pub, good freshly made generous food inc interesting specials, attentive service, well kept Wadworths IPA, 6X and JCB, warmly friendly, spotless and comfortable rambling bar areas, cosy part with high-backed settle by log fire; tables in garden with play area, good value bedrooms *(Dr and Mrs A K Clarke, BB, Pam Parkinson)*

EASTON ROYAL [SU1961]

Bruce Arms [Easton Rd]: Nicely basic 19th-c local with two long scrubbed antique pine tables on bar's brick floor, piano in homely parlour, well kept Wadworths and guest ales, Pewsey organic cider, good filled rolls; open all day Sun *(the Didler, Phil and Sally Gorton)*

EDINGTON [ST9353]

☆ *Lamb* [Westbury Rd (B3098)]: Cheerful open-plan beamed village pub with assorted pine furniture on bare boards, good log fire, food from soup, hot panini and ploughman's through some modern dishes to local steaks and game (young landlady's husband does the cooking, jovial father runs the bar), popular Sun lunch, well kept ales such as Otter, Ringwood Fortyniner and Charles Wells Bombardier, good changing wine choice at attractive prices, daily papers, dining room; piped music, lacks a no smoking area; children and dogs welcome, pleasant garden tables (access to pretty village's play area beyond), great views, good walks, cl Sun evening and Mon lunchtime *(Alec and Susan Hamilton, Dr and Mrs M E Wilson, Fr Robert Marsh, Mike Gorton, Dr and Mrs A K Clarke, Pete and Lynda Russell)*

FARLEIGH WICK [ST8063]
Fox & Hounds [A363 Bath—Bradford, 2½ miles NW of Bradford]: Well extended low-beamed rambling pub with good welcoming service, real ales such as Butcombe, Courage and Marstons Pedigree, decent food, large comfortable dining area; attractive garden *(Dr and Mrs A K Clarke, MRSM, Dr and Mrs M E Wilson, Mrs S A Brooks)*

FONTHILL GIFFORD [ST9231]
☆ *Beckford Arms* [off B3089 W of Wilton at Fonthill Bishop]: Light and airy country inn, welcoming and informally civilised, with good if not cheap bar food, well kept Greene King Abbot, Milk Street Gulp, Timothy Taylors Landlord and a guest beer, cat dozing by big inglenook log fire, picture-window back garden room looking on to terrace, restaurant, locals' bar with darts, pool, games machine and TV; piped music; well behaved children and dogs welcome, wooded garden, open all day, comfortable bedrooms *(Peter Salmon, LYM, A Rees, Paul and Ursula Randall, Dr D G Twyman, Owen Upton, M Sage, Mary Kirman and Tim Jefferson, Penny Simpson, M C Stephenson, A P Seymour)*

FORD [ST8474]
White Hart [off A420 Chippenham—Bristol]: Comfortable heavily black-beamed stone-built country inn in attractive stream-side grounds, perhaps best seen as a restaurant with rooms, though it does have a good range of well kept real ales and good log fire in its ancient fireplace, good choice of wines by the glass, wide choice of restaurant food (all day Sun); bar food, piped music, bar may be smoky; children in restaurant, tables outside, pleasant bedrooms, open all day wknds *(Tom and Ruth Rees, Dr and Mrs A K Clarke, Dr Brian and Mrs Anne Hamilton, John Coatsworth, Oliver and Sue Rowell, Simon Cottrell, John Close, Brian and Karen Thomas, Veronica Turner, LYM, Matthew Shackle, Andrew Shore, Maria Williams, A P Seymour, Nigel and Sue Foster)*

FOVANT [SU0028]
Pembroke Arms [A30 W of Salisbury]: Cheerful creeper-covered two-bar local nr the giant regimental badges cut into the downs, with lots of touching and interesting local World War I mementoes, good reasonably priced food from baguettes up, well kept

Ringwood ales, good friendly service, daily papers, log fire, no smoking lounge bar and restaurant; picnic-sets in neat and tidy tiered side garden, comfortable bedrooms, good breakfast, open all day wknds, cl Mon lunchtime *(BB, Paul Humphreys)*

FOXHAM [ST9977]
Foxham Inn [NE of Chippenham]: Small country pub recently carefully refurbished in traditional style with woodburner, wide food choice from ciabattas and baguettes to sensibly priced main dishes and puddings (with pudding wines), enterprising wine list, compact no smoking restaurant; provision for dogs and children, terrace tables, extensive views from front, peaceful village, cl Mon *(anon)*

FROXFIELD [SU2968]
☆ *Pelican* [A4]: 18th-c former coaching inn with good food choice at moderate prices from baguettes and baked potatoes to game and fresh fish from Poole; Boddingtons, Fullers London Pride, Morrells Oxford Blue and Wadworths 6X, welcoming service, relaxed atmosphere, pleasant clean décor in bars and dining area; attractive streamside garden with dovecote and duck pond, bedrooms with own bathrooms *(Ian Phillips)*

GIDDEAHALL [ST8574]
☆ *Crown* [A420 Chippenham—Ford; keep eyes skinned as no village sign]: Interesting Tudor pub with attractive rambling beamed and flagstoned bar, several small rooms off, wide choice of enjoyable if not cheap food, friendly staff, well kept changing ales such as Courage, Fullers London Pride and Greene King Ruddles; some live music; comfortable bedrooms *(Dave Irving, LYM, Pete and Rosie Flower, Ewan McCall, Roger Huggins, Tom and Alex McLean, Peter and Audrey Dowsett)*

GREAT BEDWYN [SU2764]
Cross Keys [High St]: Cheerful relaxed village pub with comfortable chairs and settles, good range of generous attractively priced bar food inc good vegetarian choice, Wadworths ales, decent wines, willing friendly service; tables in garden with terrace, bedrooms – nr Kennet & Avon Canal and Savernake Forest *(Betsy and Peter Little, Mrs Pat Crabb, Keith and Sally Jackson)*

GREAT DURNFORD [SU1337]
☆ *Black Horse* [off A345 Amesbury—Devizes]: Cheerful pub with good value food from baguettes up, some nice alcoves and two no smoking rooms, one with ship pictures, models and huge ensigns, the other with a big inglenook woodburner, well kept Ringwood and other ales, darts, shove-ha'penny, table skittles, pinball, cribbage, dominoes and ring the bull; piped blues and jazz; children and dogs welcome, picnic-sets in big riverside garden with good play area and barbecues, decent bedrooms, cl Sun evening and Mon in winter *(Dr D G Twyman, Mark Flynn, Graham Chamberlain, LYM)*

GREAT WISHFORD [SU0735]
☆ *Royal Oak* [off A36 NW of Salisbury]: Wide choice of enjoyable food and friendly helpful

service in appealing two-bar pub with big family dining area and restaurant, pleasant décor with beams, panelling, rugs on bare boards and log fires, well kept real ales, decent wines; pretty village (LYM, S E Milton-White)

HEDDINGTON [ST9966]

☆ *Ivy*: Picturesque thatched 15th-c village pub with good inglenook log fire in simple old-fashioned L-shaped bar, heavy low beams, timbered walls, assorted furnishings on parquet floor, brass and copper, prompt friendly service, well kept Wadworths IPA, 6X and a seasonal beer tapped from the cask, good plain fresh home-made food (not Sun-Weds evenings) from great lunchtime club sandwiches up, back family eating room, sensibly placed darts, piano, dog and cat; may be piped music; disabled access, open all day wknds, picnic-sets in front garden, attractively set hamlet (Michael Doswell, the Didler, LYM, Pete Baker, Guy Vowles, Dr and Mrs M E Wilson)

HINDON [ST9032]

Angel [B3089 Wilton—Mere]: New management yet again for 18th-c flagstoned coaching inn, well kept ales such as Archers from chrome bar counter, decent wines, big fireplace, no smoking lounge, dining area and long cream restaurant with huge window showing kitchen; piped music; children in eating area, dogs allowed in bar and bedrooms, tables outside, open all day in summer, has been cl Sun evening (LYM, Peter Dixon, Colin and Janet Roe)

HODSON [SU1780]

☆ *Calley Arms* [not far from M4 junction 15, via Chiseldon; off B4005 S of Swindon]: Relaxed and welcoming big bar with raised no smoking dining area, good well priced food (not Sun/Mon evenings) inc some unusual dishes and cut-price small helpings, cheerful prompt considerate service, well kept Wadworths ales with a guest, dozens of malt whiskies, farm ciders, country wines, darts and open fire one end; piped music; children welcome, picnic-sets in garden with dovecote, plenty of good walks (Ned Kelly)

HOLT [ST8561]

☆ *Toll Gate* [Ham Green; B3107 W of Melksham]: Appealing individual décor and furnishings, good fresh food inc imaginative dishes in bar and high-raftered ex-chapel restaurant up steps, five well kept interesting changing ales, good choice of wines by the glass, farm cider and good coffee, friendly attentive service, log fire; piped music; dogs welcome, no under-10s, picnic-sets out on back terrace, comfortable bedrooms, cl Sun evening, Mon (Sharon and Nick Mather, Dr and Mrs A K Clarke, M G Hart, Andrew Shore, Maria Williams, Sue Demont, Tim Barrow, John and Penny Spinks, LYM, Norman and Sarah Keeping, W F C Phillips, Ian Phillips, Mr and Mrs P R Thomas, David and Jean Hall)

HONEYSTREET [SU1061]

Barge [off A345 W of Pewsey]: Early 19th-c open-plan pub by Kennet & Avon Canal, not

overmodernised, with original carpentry and fittings still in downstairs lavatories; log fires, well kept ales such as Butcombe, Flowers and Wychwood, farm ciders, interesting crop circle photographs in back room, friendly cats and dogs, pool; may be quiet piped music, live Sat; waterside picnic-sets, bedrooms, camping field – nice setting, good downland walks (Dr and Mrs M E Wilson, J Stickland, Guy Vowles, Howard and Margaret Buchanan)

HOOK [SU0785]

Bolingbroke Arms [B4041, off A420 just W of M4 junction 16]: Well spaced tables in informal airy bare-boards bar with lots of light pine, darker tables in pleasantly decorated restaurant very popular with older lunchers, friendly attentive staff, well kept beer, good-sized helpings of food from sandwiches and baked potatoes up; piped music (Mr and Mrs G S Ayrton)

HORNINGSHAM [ST8041]

☆ *Bath Arms* [by entrance to Longleat House]: Civilised old stone-built inn on sloping green, cosy and well appointed, with lots of old woodwork, interesting local photographs, wide choice of good value home-made food from sandwiches up inc children's menu, well kept Youngs ales, good wine choice, daily papers, friendly service, side restaurant and conservatory; attractive garden with new terrace, bedrooms well equipped, clean and comfortable, pretty village (BB, John Coatsworth)

HURDCOTT [SU1633]

Black Horse [signed off A338 N of Salisbury]: Pretty black and white pub with reliable generous food inc good Sun roasts (best to book at wknds), Wadworths 6X, quick welcoming service, attractive décor, no smoking conservatory restaurant, no machines; dogs on leads and children allowed away from bar, tables in pretty garden (David and Elizabeth Briggs)

KINGTON LANGLEY [ST9277]

Hit or Miss [handy for M4 junction 17, off A350 S; Days Lane]: Cottagey pub with emphasis on left-hand restaurant with good log fire, also small rather plush low-beamed cricket-theme bar with no smoking area, appetising food from generous baguettes through familiar pub dishes to exotics such as ostrich, kudu and crocodile, popular Sun lunch, well kept Fullers London Pride and Timothy Taylor Landlord, friendly service from chatty interested landlady and smartly dressed landlord, darts and pool in room off; tables out in front (Mark and Joanna, Michael Doswell, BB)

LACOCK [ST9168]

Carpenters Arms [Church St]: Country prints, log fire and panelled dado in cottagey-style rambling bar, wide choice of quickly served home-made food, well kept Wadworths 6X and a guest such as Exmoor, back restaurant with fish tank; children in eating area, bedrooms (LYM, Kevin Thorpe)

LANDFORD [SU2419]

☆ *Cuckoo* [village signed down B3079 off A36,

then right towards Redlynch]: Unpretentious and individualistic thatched cottage with friendly chatty local atmosphere in four simple rooms, well kept Hop Back Summer Lightning and Ringwood Best tapped from the cask, traditional games; tables in pleasant garden area, on edge of New Forest (LYM, Alan Clark)

LIMPLEY STOKE [ST7861]

Hop Pole [off A36 and B3108 S of Bath]: Largely panelled 16th-c stone-built two-bar pub with recent successive management changes, looking promising under convivial new couple; log fire, well kept Bass, Butcombe, Courage Best and a guest beer, wide choice of bar food, traditional games; TV, piped music; children in eating areas, nice enclosed garden behind (LYM, Dr and Mrs M E Wilson)

LOCKERIDGE [SU1467]

☆ *Who'd A Thought It* [signed just off A4 Marlborough—Calne just W of Fyfield]: Friendly and lively local with interesting well illustrated and annotated collection of cooperage tools in two main linked rooms set for good sensibly priced well presented food from good value baguettes and very popular OAP lunch to some interesting dishes, small side drinking area, well kept Hook Norton Old Hooky and Wadworths IPA and 6X, good choice of decent wines by the glass, caring landlord, coal or log fire, family room - good for children; piped music; pleasant back garden with play area, delightful quiet scenery, lovely walks (Tim and Rosemary Wells, J Stickland, BB, Jenny and Brian Seller, Mark and Ruth Brock)

LONGBRIDGE DEVERILL [ST8640]

George [A350/B3095]: Extended village pub, spacious and relaxed even when busy, with pleasant efficient service, good reasonably priced food inc popular Sun carvery, well kept Gales, restaurant (Sue Plant, Colin and Janet Roe)

LOWER WOODFORD [SU1235]

☆ *Wheatsheaf* [signed off A360 just N of Salisbury]: Prettily set 18th-c dining pub, large and efficiently run, with big helpings of enjoyable reasonably priced food, well kept Badger Best, IPA and Tanglefoot, good wines, log fire, comfortable furnishings on oak floor with miniature footbridge over indoor goldfish pool; piped music; children welcome, good disabled access, baby-changing, good big tree-lined garden with play area (Peter B Brown, LYM, J Stickland, Pat and Robert Watt, Mark Flynn, Tony and Caroline Elwood)

LUDWELL [ST9022]

Grove Arms [A30 E of Shaftesbury]: Hotel's bright and roomy bar with linked dining area, well kept changing beers inc interesting ones from small breweries, good varied food from small selection of lunchtime snacks such as generously garnished sandwiches to attractively priced main meals, welcoming well trained staff, spotless housekeeping, restaurant; children welcome, bedrooms (Gloria Bax, Alan M Pring, Colin and Janet Roe, D G T Horsford, Pat and Robert Watt)

MAIDEN BRADLEY [ST8038]

Somerset Arms [Church St]: Relaxed, welcoming and child-friendly village pub, nicely restored and decorated without being spoilt, helpful caring licensees, good honest attractively priced food, well kept Wadworths and a guest such as Butcombe, tempting whiskies, daily papers and magazines; bedrooms (Edward Mirzoeff, Rachel Manolsen, Steve Jackson, Gauri Divan)

MALMESBURY [ST9387]

Whole Hog [Market Cross]: Friendly town-centre bar with basic furnishings on bare boards, market cross view from bar stools at window counter, piggy theme, well kept ales such as Archers, Ramsbury and Wadworths 6X, generous cheapish food, daily papers, restaurant (not Sun evening); games machines, popular with young people evenings (R Huggins, D Irving, E McCall, T McLean)

MARDEN [SU0857]

Millstream [off A342]: Pleasantly refurbished and extended bar/restaurant with enjoyable changing fresh food inc their own bread and ice-creams, well kept Wadworths ales and good wines inc champagne by the glass, beams, flagstones, open fires and woodburners, attentive service, maps and guides as well as daily papers; children and well behaved dogs welcome, pleasant garden, cl Mon (Bill and Jessica Ritson)

MARLBOROUGH [SU1869]

Castle & Ball [High St]: Georgian coaching inn with seats out under projecting colonnade, plenty of atmosphere in comfortably worn in public areas, decent generous food inc good speciality pie in pleasant eating area, well kept Greene King ales, good range of well listed wines by the glass, young enthusiastic staff; good value bedrooms (Derek and Sylvia Stephenson, Tim and Rosemary Wells, Dr and Mrs A K Clarke, Paul Humphreys, A P Seymour, Michael Sargent)

Green Dragon [High St]: Bustling town pub with friendly service, full Wadworths range kept well, reasonably priced lunchtime bar food (plenty of eating areas), big coal-effect gas fire, stripped brickwork, lots of blue and white plates, leatherette wall banquettes, pine furniture, steps down to back games room, skittle alley; back terrace, bedrooms, pretty little breakfast room (Ann and Colin Hunt)

☆ *Wellington Arms* [High St]: Thriving atmosphere in cosy well run pub, neatly refurbished, with good value sensible home-made pub food in eating area down steps, bargains Weds and Fri evenings, well kept Timothy Taylors Landlord and Wadworths 6X, friendly staff and locals, newspapers on canes, back no smoking area, Sun quiz night; tables in attractive back courtyard, bedrooms (BB, Paul Humphreys)

MERE [ST8132]

☆ *George* [The Square]: Comfortably modernised 16th-c inn, good enterprising cooking, welcoming licensees, quick helpful service, well kept Badger IPA and Best, reasonable prices, open fire, well spaced tables in attractive restaurant; good bedrooms *(BB, Julian Snell, B and F A Hannam)*

MILDENHALL [SU2169]

☆ *Horseshoe*: Relaxed and neatly kept traditional 17th-c thatched pub with sensibly priced bar and restaurant food, well kept ales such as Archers and Wadworths, good value wines, friendly helpful service even when busy, three attractive partly partitioned beamed rooms, small no smoking dining room; bedrooms, picnic-sets out on grass, pleasant village setting, good Kennet Valley and Savernake Forest walks *(Phyl and Jack Street, Mary Rayner)*

MINETY [SU0390]

White Horse [Station Rd]: Unusual upstairs layout – stripped brick and stone bar with well kept real ales such as Adnams Regatta and Wadworths 6X from central servery, good baguettes and limited though innovative choice of lunchtime hot dishes, pleasant no smoking evening restaurant with sofas and armchairs on landing, impressive décor; children very welcome, balcony tables overlooking pond below *(Chris and Ann Coy)*

MONKTON FARLEIGH [ST8065]

☆ *Kings Arms* [signed off A363 Bradford—Bath]: Imposing 17th-c building in lovely village, good choice of home-made food (all day wknds) from sandwiches and baked potatoes up in L-shaped beamed lounge and no smoking tapestry restaurant end with huge inglenook, pewter and panelling, well kept Butcombe, Courage Best, Shepherd Neame Spitfire and Wychwood Hobgoblin, farm cider, unusual wines, quick service, well separated lively games end with darts and bar billiards, good live music Fri; rustic tables in front partly flagstoned courtyard, aviaries and guinea-pigs in well tended two-level back garden, open all day wknds *(Dr and Mrs M E Wilson, Michael Doswell, Dr and Mrs A K Clarke, Mrs S A Brooks, Ian Phillips)*

NETHERHAMPTON [SU1129]

☆ *Victoria & Albert* [just off A3094 W of Salisbury]: Cosy black-beamed bar in simple thatched cottage with nicely cushioned old-fashioned wall settles on ancient floor tiles, efficient pleasant service, real ales such as Butcombe and Moles, Black Rat farm cider, reasonably priced food, no smoking restaurant; children welcome, hatch service for sizeable garden behind, handy for Wilton House and Nadder Valley walks *(Colin and Janet Roe, Richard Fendick, Dr and Mrs A K Clarke, LYM)*

NOMANSLAND [SU2517]

Lamb [signed off B3078 and B3079]: Lovely New Forest village-green setting with friendly donkeys and ponies for unpretentious pub with long bar and small no smoking dining room, friendly attentive service, wide range of good value straightforward food inc lots of pasta and fish, children's menu, Fullers London Pride, Gales HSB and Ringwood Best and Fortyniner, short sensible wine list, end pool table; tables out on terrace, green and garden behind, good walks, open all day *(Catherine Kelly, BB)*

NORTH NEWNTON [SU1357]

Woodbridge [A345 Upavon—Pewsey]: Enjoyable straightforward food inc interesting local cheeses in two bars and small dining area, well kept Wadworths ales, friendly landlord, blazing log fire; plenty of tables and play area in sizeable garden backing on to River Avon, space for tents or caravans, fly fishing passes available, pleasant bedrooms (three with own bathroom) *(Peter Meister, LYM)*

NORTH WROUGHTON [SU1482]

Check Inn [Woodland View (A4361 just S of Swindon)]: Busy extended local with prompt friendly service, up to ten well kept interesting changing ales in oversized lined glasses, lots of bottled imports, farm cider, good soft drinks choice, good value generous food, log fire, glossy pine furniture, various comfortable areas inc children's and large no smoking area; traditional games and machine; disabled access, heated front terrace, garden bar, bedrooms, open all day Fri-Sun *(Richard Houghton)*

NUNTON [SU1526]

☆ *Radnor Arms* [off A338 S of Salisbury]: Pretty ivy-clad village pub very popular for enjoyable food inc fish and local game, friendly staff (very helpful with wheelchairs), well kept Badger inc Tanglefoot; three pleasantly decorated and furnished linked rooms inc cheerfully busy yet relaxing bar and staider restaurant, log fires, amiable labrador; can get rather crowded, booking essential at wknds; attractive garden popular with children *(Dr Michael Smith, Dr D G Twyman, Don and Thelma Anderson)*

OGBOURNE ST ANDREW [SU1871]

☆ *Silks on the Downs* [A345 N of Marlborough]: Former Wheatsheaf renamed, more restaurant than pub, civilised and rather upmarket, though there is a bar, and they do have baguettes (at a price) and Adnams and Wadworths 6X as well as decent wines; stylish décor with some good prints and photographs as well as racing silks, generous enjoyable food from open kitchen; well behaved children allowed, a few black-painted tables outside, bedrooms, cl Sun evening *(LYM, V Brogden, Mary Rayner, A P Seymour)*

PEWSEY [SU1561]

☆ *French Horn* [A345 towards Marlborough; Pewsey Wharf]: Pleasantly refurbished old pub popular for food from interesting filled baps up, entirely home-made (from bread to ice-cream), well kept Wadworths IPA and 6X, good choice of wines by the glass, chatty landlord and cheery informal service, two-part back bar divided by log fire open to both sides, steps down to pleasant and rather smart flagstoned front dining area (children allowed here); piped music; picnic-sets on back terrace, many more in well fenced wood-chip area with robust timber play area above barges moored on Kennet & Avon Canal *(Michael Doswell, BB, K H Frostick, Keith and Sally Jackson, Mary Rayner)*

REDLYNCH [SU2021]

☆ *Kings Head* [off A338 via B3080; The Row]: Charming low-ceilinged cottagey 16th-c pub under new management, two carpeted bays, one a pleasant small conservatory, off beamed main bar, nice mix of furnishings and ornaments, interesting blackboard choice of good generous food, quick friendly service, Courage Best and Directors and Wadworths 6X, good house wine and cafetière coffee, log fire and woodburner; dogs welcome, picnic-sets in side garden, nice Pepper Box Hill walks nearby, bedrooms *(BB, Phyl and Jack Street, MRSM)*

SALISBURY [SU1430]

☆ *Avon Brewery* [Castle St]: Long and narrow city bar, busy and friendly, with dark mahogany, frosted and engraved bow windows, friezes and attractive pictures, two open fires, sensibly priced food (not Sun evening) from sandwiches up, well kept Boddingtons, Fullers London Pride and Ind Coope Burton, decent wines; may be classical piped music; long sheltered courtyard garden overlooking river, open all day *(David Carr, LYM)*

Corn Market Inn [Market Pl]: Comfortable and handy for shops, with good value bar food inc generous sandwiches, well kept Wadworths 6X, good friendly service, pictures *(Ann and Colin Hunt)*

Kings Head [Bridge St]: Wetherspoons Lloyds No 1 on site of former hotel, variety of seating in large bar with separate TV area (and piped music), no smoking gallery upstairs, their usual menu (inc breakfast); bedrooms *(Craig Turnbull)*

☆ *Old Mill* [Town Path, W Harnham]: Charming 17th-c pub/hotel in glorious tranquil out-of-centre setting, pleasant beamed bars with prized window tables, enjoyable bar food from sandwiches up, friendly staff, well kept real ales, good wines and malt whiskies, good value restaurant lunch; children welcome, picnic-sets in small floodlit garden by duck-filled millpond, a stroll across water meadows from cathedral (classic view of it from bridge beyond garden), bedrooms *(P R and D Thomas, David Carr, Dr D G Twyman, LYM)*

Red Lion [Milford St]: Attractive Best Western hotel with mix of old-fashioned seats and modern banquettes in popular two-roomed panelled bar opening into other spacious and interesting areas, well kept Bass and Ringwood, smart efficient service, food from sandwiches up; children in eating areas, loggia courtyard seats, comfortable bedrooms *(Colin and Janet Roe, LYM, Ann and Colin Hunt, W W Burke)*

Three Crowns [Town Path]: New licensees doing good well presented straightforward food inc bargain lunches Mon-Thurs in welcoming little pub well restored after a fire; tables in flower-decked courtyard *(David and Elizabeth Briggs)*

☆ *Wig & Quill* [New St]: Low-beamed and subtly lit 16th-c former shop with ornate rugs, open fires, worn leather armchairs, stuffed birds and low arches to connecting rooms; friendly landlord, Wadworths IPA, JCB and

6X and guest beers tapped from the cask, decent wines and interesting long summer drinks, good value standard food from sandwiches up, tiled back bar with pool and darts; open all day, dogs allowed, nice small courtyard behind with cathedral views *(John and Gloria Isaacs, David Carr)*

Wyndham Arms [Estcourt Rd]: Friendly modern corner local with well kept Hop Back beers (originally brewed here, now from Downton), country wines, simple bar food, small no smoking front room, longer main bar; children welcome in front room, open all day wknds, cl lunchtime other days *(the Didler)*

SANDY LANE [ST9668]

George [A342 Devizes—Chippenham]: Stone-built beamed pub, well worn in, with wide choice of enjoyable food from doorstep sandwiches to full meals, well kept ales inc Wadworths, decent wines, pleasant efficient staff, interesting décor, back bar-restaurant, no smoking area; car park on dodgy bend; tables on front terrace, more in back garden with play area *(LYM, Mr and Mrs P R Thomas)*

SEEND [ST9562]

Three Magpies [Sells Green – A365 towards Melksham]: Partly 18th-c pub popular for its good value straightforward home-made food from sandwiches and baked potatoes up, efficient service, well kept Wadworths IPA and 6X, decent choice of wines by the glass; big garden with play area, good adjacent camp site *(Joyce and Maurice Cottrell)*

SEMINGTON [ST9259]

☆ *Lamb* [The Strand; A361 Devizes—Trowbridge]: Busy dining pub with good blackboard choice of consistently good food inc fresh fish in attractive linked rooms, reasonable prices, carefully chosen wines, well kept Butcombe, Ringwood Best and a guest such as Titanic, good coffee, buoyant atmosphere, helpful friendly service, woodburner and log fire; children in eating area, helpful to wheelchairs, attractive walled garden; cl Sun evening *(Miss M W Hayter, Dr and Mrs A K Clarke, Dr and Mrs M E Wilson, LYM, Ken and Sylvia Jones)*

Somerset Arms [A350 2 miles S of Melksham]: Cosy 16th-c coaching inn, heavy-beamed long bar, real and flame-effect fires, high-backed settles, plenty of tables, lots of prints and brassware, wide range of decent food in bar and restaurant from sandwiches and chips to some imaginative dishes, good atmosphere, cheerful service, Badger beers, good coffee; piped music; pleasant garden behind, short walk on busy road from Kennet & Avon Canal *(Dr and Mrs A K Clarke, Colin McKerrow)*

SEMLEY [ST8926]

☆ *Benett Arms* [off A350 N of Shaftesbury]: Bustling character village inn across green from church, welcoming landlord and good relaxed atmosphere, well kept ales such as Brakspears, Ringwood Best and Youngs, decent wines and good range of other drinks, enjoyable food, log fire, traditional games, no music, restaurant; children and well behaved dogs allowed, pleasant tables outside *(OPUS, LYM,*

Colin and Janet Roe, Dr and Mrs A H Young,
Dr and Mrs M E Wilson, Dr Alan and
Mrs Sue Holder)

SHAW [ST8765]

Golden Fleece [A365 towards Atworth]:
Former coaching inn with good atmosphere in
low-ceilinged L-shaped bar and long
sympathetic front dining extension, good range
of food inc generous bargain lunches – very
popular with older people, good welcoming
service, well kept ales such as Butcombe,
Fullers London Pride, Greene King and Smiles;
garden tables *(Brian Pearson, Dr and Mrs
A K Clarke, K R Harris)*

SHERSTON [ST8586]

Carpenters Arms [Easton (B4040)]: Cosy
small-roomed low-beamed local, settles and
shiny tables, log fire, well kept beers, decent
wines, good choice of reasonably priced food,
willing if not always speedy informal service,
attractive modern conservatory and dining
rooms, no piped music; TV in locals' bar;
tables in pleasant garden with play area
*(Dr and Mrs A K Clarke, Andrew Scarr,
Peter and Audrey Dowsett, John and
Gloria Isaacs)*

Rattlebone [Church St (B4040 Malmesbury—
Chipping Sodbury)]: Rambling beamed and
stone-walled 17th-c village pub, cosy corners
with pews, settles and country-kitchen chairs,
log fire, decent wines, Youngs beers, public bar
with pool, table football and other games,
partly no smoking dining area (no food Sun
evening); TV; children in restaurant, skittle
alley, picnic-sets in back garden, open all
day *(Dr and Mrs A K Clarke, LYM,
Richard Stancomb, R Huggins, D Irving,
E McCall, T McLean, Betsy and Peter Little,
James Woods, Andrew Scarr, Peter and
Audrey Dowsett)*

SOUTH MARSTON [SU1988]

Carriers Arms [Highworth Rd]: Vast choice
of well presented usual food (not Sun evening)
in enjoyably compact bar, larger lounge or
restaurant, friendly service, Ushers ales,
decent wine, pleasant décor
(Mrs M Sainsbury)

SOUTH WRAXALL [ST8364]

Long Arms [Upper S Wraxall, off B3109 N of
Bradford-on-Avon]: Cheerful cosily refurbished
country local with friendly landlord, good
value popular food inc good Sun lunch and
OAP lunches Tues-Fri, well kept Wadworths,
good range of wines by the glass, log fire;
pretty garden *(Dr and Mrs A K Clarke,
Mark Flynn)*

STAVERTON [ST8560]

Old Bear [B3105 Trowbridge—Bradford-on-
Avon]: Wide choice of good food inc fish and
upmarket dishes from huge ciabattas up in
neatly kept long bar divided into four sections,
Bass, Flowers, Milk Street Funky Monkey and
Wadworths 6X, smart staff, nice mix of seats
inc some high-backed settles, stone fireplaces
(biggest in end dining area), back restaurant
(booking recommended Sun lunchtime); village
dominated by huge Nestlé factory *(BB, Dr and
Mrs M E Wilson)*

STIBB GREEN [SU2262]

☆ *Three Horseshoes* [just N of Burbage]: Friendly
and spotless old-world local, warmly
welcoming, with good simple home-made food
(not Sun evening or Mon) cooked by landlady
– pies are her speciality; sensible prices and
quick service, well kept Wadworths IPA and
6X, farm cider, inglenook log fire in
comfortable beamed front bar, second no
smoking bar, dining room with railway
memorabilia and pictures (landlord is an
enthusiast); attractive garden, cl Mon
(Mrs Anthea Post, Pete Baker)

SUTTON BENGER [ST9478]

Wellesley Arms [handy for M4 junction 17, via
B4122 and B4069; High St]: Beamed Cotswold
stone pub with several Duke of Wellington
pictures and exposed stonework in lounge,
Wadworths ales, separate dining room, big-
screen TV and pool in bar, occasional live
music; handy for M4 (some traffic noise for
picnic-sets out behind) *(Richard Stancomb,
Richard Pierce, BB)*

SWINDON [SU1584]

Beehive [Prospect Hill]: Character multi-level
Victorian local tucked behind the college, plain
and unaffected, lively mix from students to
older people with a faintly bohemian streak,
well kept Greene King ales, convivial helpful
staff, lunchtime snacks, peanuts on the bar;
open all day *(Dave Irving)*

Glue Pot [Emlyn Sq]: Tap for Archers Brewery,
with their ales and perhaps a guest beer kept
well, good soft drinks choice, high-backed
settles around pine tables, pub games; tables on
terrace – in Brunel's Railway Village; open all
day (cl Sun afternoon), and perhaps best in
daytime, with lunchtime snacks *(Dave Irving)*

Kings Arms [Wood St]: Comfortable early
Victorian hotel with big modern bar and
various eating areas off, well kept Arkells 2B,
3B, Kingsdown and Moonlight, friendly staff,
good reasonably priced food; disabled access,
bedrooms *(Ian Phillips)*

Savoy [Regent Circus]: Busy Wetherspoons in
excellently converted cinema, seven ales,
decent food, affordable prices, split-level
seating areas, books and lots of film
memorabilia, comfortable atmosphere, decent
wine, quick friendly service even when busy,
no smoking areas, no piped music; open all
day *(Dave Irving, Tim and Rosemary Wells)*

Steam Railway [Newport St]: Large pub, nine
real ales from long bar, food till early evening,
lots of panelling; two TVs, pool, youngsters'
bar on left; open all day *(CMW, JJW)*

Victoria [Victoria Rd]: Small split-level pub
with well kept Shepherd Neame Spitfire and
Wadworths 6X, good value organic food
freshly made (so may take a while), carpeted
area away from bar, abstract artworks for sale,
gig posters (frequent live music in basement),
corner TV *(Jeremy King)*

TISBURY [ST9429]

Crown [Church St]: Attractive extended pub
doing well under new licensees, new chef
boosting the food side, good wines, Shepherd
Neame Spitfire *(Douglas and Ann Hare)*

TROWBRIDGE [ST8557]
Sir Isaac Pitman [Castle Pl]: Useful
Wetherspoons well done out in elm-coloured
wood, comfortable alcoves and different levels
below cupola, the shorthand Sir Isaac invented
along the beams, no smoking area, good value
beer and food, pleasant staff *(Mike Gorton,
Dr and Mrs M E Wilson, Dr and Mrs A K
Clarke)*
UPPER WOODFORD [SU1236]
☆ *Bridge Inn*: Good sensibly priced food from
ploughman's with unsalted butter and lots of
bread (handy for ducks in attractive riverside
garden across road) to wide menu and
blackboard specials, quick friendly service, well
kept Hop Back ales, good house wines,
upmarket newspapers, big flower prints on eau
de nil walls, log fire, neat country-kitchen
tables on expanse of newish wooden flooring,
rather smart games room with pool and
leather chesterfields; best to book wknds
*(BB, Howard and Margaret Buchanan,
Richard Fendick)*
UPTON LOVELL [ST9441]
☆ *Prince Leopold*: Prettily tucked away in quiet
thatched village, with cheerful staff,
imaginative food from interestingly filled
ciabattas up, well kept Ringwood Best and
Boondoggle and John Smiths, decent good
value wines, dark Victorian bar décor, airy
newish dining extension with river views from
end tables; tables in small attractive garden
beside the clear Wylye trout stream,
comfortable quiet bedrooms *(Dr and Mrs M E
Wilson, Richard Fendick)*
UPTON SCUDAMORE [ST8647]
Angel [off A350 N of Warminster]: Big dining
pub with bustling modern feel, contemporary
pictures for sale in long two-part dining room,
good choice of food from open kitchen, well
kept Butcombe, Wadworths 6X and a guest
beer, good changing wine choice, friendly
effective service, traditional games; piped
music, TV; sheltered flagstoned back terrace
with big barbecue, bedrooms in house across
car park *(LYM, Dr and Mrs A K Clarke,
Mr and Mrs Peter Llewellyn, Mike and
Mary Carter)*
WANBOROUGH [SU2083]
Cross Keys [Burycroft, Lower Wanborough]:
Welcoming much extended village pub with
solid wood floor, alcoves and individual décor
inc lots of bric-a-brac, well kept Wadworths,
good choice of food (even Sun evening) inc
succulent local ham, good service, back
restaurant *(Dr and Mrs A K Clarke,
Francis Johnston)*
Harrow [3 miles from M4 junction 15; Lower
Wanborough signed off A346]: Pretty thatched
pub with long low-beamed stepped bar, big
inglenook log fire, pine panelling, candles in
bottles, settles and bay window alcoves, well
kept ales such as Greene King Old Speckled
Hen, Hook Norton Old Hooky and Youngs
Special, friendly staff, decent food (not Sun
evening), daily papers, no piped music, simple
beamed and flagstoned stripped stone dining
room with another open fire; live music Sun

night, cast-iron tables and picnic-sets outside
(Dr and Mrs A K Clarke, BB, A P Seymour)
☆ *Plough* [High St, Lower Wanborough]:
Thriving down-to-earth atmosphere in long
low thatched stone-built pub with three old-
world rooms, huge centrepiece inglenook log
fire in one, good honest well priced home-
made food (not Sun), quick friendly service,
well kept ales such as Archers Village, Bass and
Wadworths 6X; open all day Sat *(R Huggins,
D Irving, E McCall, T McLean, A P Seymour)*
WEST LAVINGTON [SU0053]
Stage Post [High St (A360)]: Comfortably
refurbished L-shaped bar, big glazed front
dining area, enjoyable food from baguettes
and baked potatoes to steaks, welcoming
service, well kept real ale, good wine choice
inc bin ends; pool room with TV; reasonably
priced bedrooms with own bathrooms
(Mrs E A Stephens)
WESTBURY [ST8751]
Horse & Groom [Alfred St]: Now brewing its
own good real ales, guest beers too, home-
made food with OAP discounts, cheerful
service *(Mike Pugh)*
WESTWOOD [ST8159]
☆ *New Inn* [off B3109 S of Bradford-on-Avon]:
Comfortably traditional country pub with
several linked rooms, beams and hops, stripped
stone, traditional scrubbed tables on new slate
floor, good fires, fresh flowers and candles,
generous helpings of good varied food in bar
and no smoking restaurant, real ales inc
Wadworths 6X, efficient friendly service from
smartly dressed young staff; piped radio; a few
tables out behind, walks nearby, pretty village,
cl Sun evening and Mon *(D P and M A Miles,
BB, John and Angela Main, W F C Phillips)*
WILTON [SU0931]
☆ *Pembroke Arms* [Minster St (A30)]: Elegant
Georgian hotel handy for Wilton House with
genial new licensees and chef who also made
nearby Barford Inn a popular main entry,
spacious comfortable hotelish bar with big sash
windows, fireplace, fresh flowers and candles,
one Badger beer, good coffee and lots of wines,
no smoking restaurant with excellent
lunchtime salad bar, wide range of influences
and ingredients, filled ciabattas too, friendly
service; some outside tables, attractive
bedrooms with marble bathrooms *(BB,
Edward Mirzoeff)*
WINGFIELD [ST8256]
☆ *Poplars* [B3109 S of Bradford-on-Avon (Shop
Lane)]: Attractive and friendly country local
very popular for good sensibly priced
interesting food, especially with older people at
lunchtime, but drinkers and chatters very
welcome too, with well kept Wadworths ales,
friendly fast service even when busy, enjoyable
atmosphere, no juke box or machines, light
and airy no smoking family dining extension;
tables out by own cricket pitch *(Dr and
Mrs A K Clarke, Dr and Mrs M E Wilson,
LYM, Susan and Nigel Wilson)*
WINSLEY [ST7960]
Seven Stars [off B3108 bypass W of Bradford-
on-Avon (pub just over Wilts border)]: Big

stripped-stone open-plan pub, welcoming and relaxed, with low beams, soft lighting, snug alcoves, log-effect gas fires, well kept Bass, Butcombe, Wadworths 6X and a guest beer, good wine choice, enjoyable food (not cheap but worth it) inc good vegetarian choice, friendly attentive service, no smoking dining area; discreet piped music; picnic-sets out on pleasant terrace, attractive village *(Jenny Brand, Dr and Mrs M E Wilson, MRSM, Meg and Colin Hamilton)*

WINTERBOURNE BASSETT [SU1075]
☆ *White Horse* [off A4361 S of Swindon]: Wide choice of reliable fresh generous food inc several fish dishes, popular bargain lunches Mon-Sat and good Sun roast, in neat and well cared for big-windowed recently extended bar (the new part blends in well), comfortable dining room and warm conservatory, welcoming efficient service, well kept Wadworths, good wines by the glass and coffee, goldfish tank; quiet piped music; tables on good-sized side lawn, pleasant setting *(Sheila and Robert Robinson, BB, Mrs Pat Crabb, Evelyn and Derek Walter, Tony Baldwin)*

WOODBOROUGH [SU1159]
Seven Stars [off A345 S of Marlborough; Bottlesford]: Pretty thatched pub with a good welcome and perhaps a blessing from the new landlord, enjoyable more routine food now (used to be french), Fullers London Pride, Wadworths 6X and a changing guest beer, a good choice of wines and friendly staff, with hunting prints, attractively moulded panelling, hot coal fire in the old range at one end, big log fire the other, nice mix of antique settles and country furniture, cosy nooks, no smoking dining extension; piped music; children and dogs welcome, extensive riverside gardens, open all day Sun *(H Frank Smith, Ron Shelton, Lawrence Pearse, Guy Vowles, LYM, A P Seymour, Bill and Jessica Ritson)*

WOODFALLS [SU1920]
Old Inn [The Ridge]: Nicely cleaned up by helpful and welcoming new licensees, enjoyable home-made food with a modern twist to some traditional dishes, decent wines, no smoking area; children welcome, lovely village in pretty countryside *(Dizzy Riches)*

WOOTTON BASSETT [SU0682]
☆ *Five Bells* [Wood St]: Friendly and rather enterprising town local with great atmosphere, well kept ales such as Cains Raisin, Fullers London Pride, Shepherd Neame Spitfire and Youngs, food a decided cut above the usual pub style, with good value substantial sandwiches, and some interesting notions like their Weds sausage night (may also be special menus during major sports matches); tables in good recently done shaded courtyard, open all day Fri-Sun *(Tim and Rosemary Wells, Dr and Mrs A K Clarke, BB, Ian Phillips, Mike Thomas)*

WOOTTON RIVERS [SU1963]
☆ *Royal Oak* [off A346, A345 or B3087]: 16th-c beamed and thatched pub, wide range of reliable food from lunchtime sandwiches, ciabattas and baguettes to plenty of specials and full meals (for which they add a 10% service charge), friendly L-shaped dining lounge with woodburner, timbered bar with small games area, well kept Fullers London Pride, Wadworths 6X and perhaps a guest beer, good wine list; children welcome, tables out in yard, pleasant village, bedrooms in adjoining house *(Ann and Colin Hunt, Simon Watkins, James Woods, LYM, Geoff Pidoux, Andrew Shore, Maria Williams, Nigel Howard, Ned Kelly, A P Seymour, Mrs J H S Lang)*

YATTON KEYNELL [ST8676]
Bell [B4039 NW of Chippenham]: Cosy village pub with good value home-made food, well kept Bass and Smiles, nicely decorated bar and country-feel dining area; well spaced picnic-sets in good-sized fenced garden *(Michael Doswell)*

Several well known guide books make establishments pay for entry, either directly or as a fee for inspection. These fees can run to many hundreds of pounds. We do not. Unlike other guides, we never take payment for entries. We never accept a free meal, free drink, or any other freebie from a pub. We do not accept any sponsorship – let alone from commercial schemes linked to the pub trade. All our entries depend solely on merit.

Worcestershire

It's a real pleasure to welcome back to the main entries that old favourite the Fleece at Bretforton, which kept our hopes up with a stalwart if limited service of food and drinks from its barn while the pub itself was being restored after a fire; this lovely old place, largely no smoking now, is fully back in action. Other pubs here on great current form are the Jockey at Baughton, all no smoking now (its newish landlord settling in well, with good food and wines), the very foody and well run Admiral Rodney at Berrow Green, the friendly Bear & Ragged Staff at Bransford (universal praise for its locally sourced food, from bar snacks to more elaborate meals), the smart and trendy Childswickham Inn (stylish restaurant food, good wines and a nice little bar), the well run restauranty Fountain at Clent (now entirely no smoking), the Old Chequers at Crowle (a splendid food break from the motorway), the friendly and charmingly furnished Bell & Cross at Holy Cross (gaining a Wine Award to join its Food Award this year), the Walter de Cantelupe at Kempsey (exemplary ploughman's and interesting drinks – nice bedrooms, too), the cheery King & Castle in Kidderminster (what a bargain, the food and beer at this interesting steam railway bar), the Nags Head in Malvern (a distinctive favourite, great for beer), the good value and warmly welcoming Bell at Pensax (a nice all-rounder), and the riverside Anchor at Wyre Piddle. Of the foodier pubs in this distinguished company, it's the Bear & Ragged Staff at Bransford which stands out as Worcestershire Dining Pub of the Year. Pubs to note particularly in the Lucky Dip section at the end of the chapter are the Lygon Arms at Feckenham, Peacock at Forhill, Three Kings at Hanley Castle, Swan at Hanley Swan, Bulls Head at Inkberrow, Ship in Tenbury Wells and French House at Upton Snodsbury. Drinks tend to be a little cheaper in Worcestershire than in the country generally; locally brewed beers worth looking out for include Wyre Piddle, Cannon Royall, St Georges and (from the Talbot at Knightwick) Teme Valley – though you are at least as likely to find 'interlopers' such as Hook Norton, Enville and Hobsons. It's also very much worth looking out for the good local apple juices which are increasingly widely available here, alongside the county's great traditional speciality, cider.

BAUGHTON SO8741 Map 4

Jockey ♀

4 miles from M50 junction 1; A38 northwards, then right on to A4104 Upton—Pershore

Readers very much enjoy the food at this no smoking dining pub. The interior is open-plan but partly divided by stripped brick and timbering, with a mix of good-sized tables, a few horse-racing pictures on the butter-coloured walls, and a cream Rayburn in one brick inglenook; piped music. The food includes specials such as sweet and sour spare ribs (£10.95), and up to half a dozen fish dishes such as shark steak with cajun mixed spices (£13.50) and poached lemon sole (£16.50). Other enjoyable dishes might include soup (£3.95), exotic seafood basket (£5.50), steak and ale pie (£10.50), slow-braised lamb shank (£12.95), duck breast with orange and Grand Marnier sauce (£13.95), and peppered sirloin steak (£14.95), with puddings such as home-made treacle and orange pudding (£3.95); they also do lunchtime sandwiches (from £4.95), and ploughman's (£5.95). Attentive staff serve three changing real ales such as Highgate Saddlers, Theakstons Black Bull and Wychwood Shires XXX, and they've a rewarding choice of wines, with a dozen by the glass. There are picnic-sets out in front, with an array of blue flowers (out here, but not inside, you can hear the motorway in the distance). No children. *(Recommended by Mrs S Lyons, Denys Gueroult, Geoffrey and Penny Hughes, Nigel Long, Ron and Val Broom, Derek and Sylvia Stephenson, Glen and Nola Armstrong, Rod Stoneman, Stuart Paulley)*

Free house ~ Licensee Mark Welsh ~ Real ale ~ Bar food (12-2, 6-9) ~ Restaurant ~ (01684) 592153 ~ Dogs allowed in bar ~ Open 12-3, 6-11; closed Sun evening and Mon

BERROW GREEN SO7458 Map 4
Admiral Rodney ✦ ⇌
B4197, off A44 W of Worcester

The licensees are putting increasing emphasis on the food at this attractively arranged and efficiently run country inn, a good place for a special meal or weekend away. Pleasantly light and roomy throughout, the bare-boards entrance bar is still a place you can just enjoy a drink; with high beams and a sunny bow window, it has big stripped kitchen tables and cushioned chairs, a traditional winged settle, and a woodburning stove in a fireplace that opens through to the comfortable no smoking lounge area. This has some carpet on its slate flagstones, dark red settees, a table of magazines and rack of broadsheet newspapers, quite a few board games, and prints of the Battle of the Saints, where Lord Rodney obliterated the French fleet in the Caribbean. A separate skittle alley has pool; also darts, Jenga, cribbage and dominoes. It's popular with older crowds at lunchtime, and in the evening you'll find locals dropping in for a chatty drink. Besides a couple of tasty fresh cornish fish specials such as bass steamed with wild mushroom and cream sauce or herb-crusted tuna steak (£12.50), enjoyable dishes include soup (£3.95), lunchtime sandwiches (from £3.95; may not be available at busy times), broccoli and stilton tart (£7.25), stir-fried pork with noodles (£7.75) home-made pie, chicken curry or lasagne (£7.95), and mixed grill (£12.95), with puddings such as warm chocolate cake or pear and almond tart (£4.25); on Sundays they do roasts (£7.75) with a vegetarian and fish option too. A rebuilt barn stepping down through three levels forms a charming red restaurant (mostly no smoking). Alongside well kept Wye Valley Bitter, they've three changing guests such as Archers Golden, Beartown Black Bear and Woods Quaff, and you'll find a tempting choice of wines and malt whiskies, Glebe Farm apple juice and Weston's perry; cheerful service from the hands-on licensees. Out on a terrace and neat green, solid tables and chairs look over the Lower Teme valley (two of the three bedrooms share the views), and this is good walking territory. *(Recommended by Martin and Pauline Jennings, Lynda and Trevor Smith, Nick and Lynne Carter, Denys Gueroult, Annette Tress, Gary Smith, John and Patricia White)*

Free house ~ Licensees Gillian and Kenneth Green ~ Real ale ~ Bar food (12-2, 6.30-9(9.30 Sat); 12-2.30, 6.30-9 Sun) ~ Restaurant ~ (01886) 821375 ~ Children welcome ~ Dogs allowed in bar and bedrooms ~ Folk night first Weds of month, and live music on bank hols ~ Open 11-3, 5-11; 11-11 Sat; 12-10.30 Sun; closed Mon lunchtime exc bank hols ~ Bedrooms: /£55B

BEWDLEY SO7875 Map 4
Little Pack Horse ✦
High Street; no nearby parking – best to park in main car park, cross A4117 Cleobury road, and keep walking on down narrowing High Street

Enjoyable and reasonably priced food makes this interesting old timber-framed pub worth seeking out, and there's a splendid miscellany of old advertisements, photos and other memorabilia on display – even old boots and a mortar bomb. Cosily pubby and bustling, with a pleasant mix of old furnishings, it's nicely warmed by a woodburning stove in winter; the atmosphere is welcoming, and service is cheerful and efficient. You'll find a wide choice of bar food, and lots of dishes come in two sizes. The reasonably priced menu includes sandwiches (from £3.20), chicken and spinach terrine with cumberland sauce (£4.25), moroccan vegetable and chick pea couscous (£4.30, £5.60 large), tasty pies (from £5.20), scampi and chips (£5.85, £7.25 large), cajun chicken breast (£6.90), minted lamb steak with redcurrant glaze (£8.90), and steaks (from £11.25), with three or four specials like trout (£8.50) or duck (£9.50) and puddings such as home-made apple and rhubarb crumble (£3); the dining area is no smoking. Alongside Greene King IPA, they have a guest ale such as Everards Tiger or Fullers London Pride; there may be piped music, and two of the dining areas are no smoking. It's best to leave your car in the public car park near the river in this rewarding old town, and walk up. *(Recommended by T R and B C Jenkins, Stuart Paulley, Paul and Gloria Howell)*

Punch ~ Lease Michael Stewart Gaunt ~ Real ale ~ Bar food (12-2.15, 6-9.30; 12-9.30 weekends) ~ Restaurant ~ (01299) 403762 ~ Children allowed in restaurant till 9pm ~ Dogs allowed in bar ~ Open 12-3, 6-11; 12-11(10.30 Sun) Sat

BIRTSMORTON SO7935 Map 4
Farmers Arms 🏠 £
Birts Street, off B4208 W

This friendly, old-fashioned half-timbered village local remains reassuringly unchanged in its atmosphere, and has nothing in the way of piped music or fruit machines. The neatly kept big room on the right, which has a no smoking area, rambles away under very low dark beams, with some standing timbers, and flowery-panelled cushioned settles as well as spindleback chairs; on the left an even lower-beamed room seems even cosier, and in both the white walls have black timbering; the local cribbage and darts teams play here, and you can also play shove-ha'penny or dominoes. Sociable locals gather at the bar for Hook Norton Hooky and Old Hooky well kept on handpump, and there's also a changing guest from a brewer such as St Georges. Good value simple dishes (with prices much as they were last year) typically include sandwiches (from £1.70), soup (£2), ploughman's (from £3), well cooked macaroni cheese (£3.50), fish and chips (£4.75), chicken and vegetable curry (£4.70), lasagne (£5.15), steak and kidney pie (£5.70), gammon (£6.95) and steak (£8.25), with good puddings such as apple pie or spotted dick (from £2.20). You'll find seats out on the large lawn, and the pub is surrounded by plenty of walks. Please treat the opening hours we give below as approximate – they may vary according to how busy or quiet things are. *(Recommended by the Didler, Pam and David Bailey, Derek and Sylvia Stephenson, Martin and Pauline Jennings)*

Free house ~ Licensees Jill and Julie Moore ~ Real ale ~ Bar food (12-2, 6.30(7 Sun)-9.30) ~ No credit cards ~ (01684) 833308 ~ Children welcome ~ Dogs welcome ~ Open 11-4, 6-11; 12-4, 7-10.30 Sun

BRANSFORD SO7852 Map 4
Bear & Ragged Staff 🍽️ ♀
Off A4103 SW of Worcester; Station Road
Worcestershire Dining Pub of the Year

They make much use of local produce in the food here, and readers are highly appreciative of both what comes out of the kitchen and the welcome from friendly staff. The cheerful interconnecting rooms give fine views over rolling country, and in winter you'll find an open fire; cribbage and piped music (which can be obtrusive). In fine weather, the garden and terrace are enjoyable places to sit (pleasant views from here too). The tempting changing bar specials might typically include home-made faggots, haddock and chips or curry of the day (£9.95), chargrilled rib-eye steak (£13.50), with around four fresh fish specials such as chargrilled marlin steak (£13.25) and steamed monkfish tail with spinach, wild mushroom and orange-scented cream (£13.95), and puddings such as delicious raspberry and lemon grass crème brûlée or white and dark chocolate cheesecake (£4.50); they also do lunchtime sandwiches with dressed salad and crisps (from £4.95; not Sunday). There are proper tablecloths, linen napkins and fresh flowers on the tables in the restaurant, which has a more expensive menu; all dining areas are no smoking. They've a good range of wines to choose from too, lots of malt whiskies, quite a few brandies and liqueurs, and Robinsons Unicorn and a guest such as St Georges Best are well kept on handpump. Good disabled access and facilities. *(Recommended by Mr and Mrs P H Griffiths, Mr and Mrs B Jeffery, A J Wright, Brenda and Rob Fincham, Rodney and Norma Stubington, Ray and Winifred Halliday, Mr and Mrs Donald Bostock, Jeff and Wendy Williams, Mr and Mrs J Tout, Sallie Hammond)*

Free house ~ Licensees Lynda Williams and Andy Kane ~ Real ale ~ Bar food (not Sat evening) ~ Restaurant ~ (01886) 833399 ~ Children in eating area of bar and restaurant till 9pm ~ Open 12-2, 6(6.30 Sat)-11; 12-2, 7-10.30 Sun

BREDON SO9236 Map 4
Fox & Hounds

4½ miles from M5 junction 9; A438 to Northway, left at B4079, then in Bredon follow signpost to church and river on right

This 15th-c stone and timber thatched pub stands by the village church, and is especially pretty in summer, when it's decked with brightly coloured hanging baskets; some of the picnic-sets are under Perspex. The open-plan carpeted bar has low hop-hung beams, stone pillars and stripped timbers, a central woodburning stove, upholstered settles, a variety of wheelback, tub and kitchen chairs around handsome mahogany and cast-iron-framed tables, dried grasses and flowers, a toy fox dressed in hunting scarlet, and elegant wall lamps. There's a smaller side bar, and the restaurant and part of the main bar are no smoking. Friendly efficient staff serve Banks's Bitter and Greene King Old Speckled Hen along with a guest such as Timothy Taylors Landlord on handpump, and Minchew's farm cider and perry in bottles (possibly from the cask too); piped music. Besides baguettes (from £4.95), straightforward bar food might include home-made soup (£3.95), ploughman's (from £6.50), and breaded plaice (£7.95), with other dishes such as steak (from £11.50) and fish specials; on Sunday they do a choice of roasts (from £8). *(Recommended by Ian and Denise Foster, JHW, David J Austin, Chris Flynn, Wendy Jones, Ken Millar, Dr and Mrs A K Clarke, Felicity Stephens, David Fox, Di and Mike Gillam)*

Enterprise ~ Lease Cilla and Christopher Lamb ~ Real ale ~ Bar food (12-2, 6.30-9(9.30 Sat-Sun)) ~ Restaurant ~ (01684) 772377 ~ Children welcome ~ Dogs allowed in bar ~ Open 12-3, 6.30(6 summer)-11

BRETFORTON SP0943 Map 4
Fleece ★ £

B4035 E of Evesham: turn S off this road into village; pub is in centre square by church; there's a sizeable car park at one side of the church

Happily now restored and reopened after a disastrous fire in 2004, this enchanting medieval thatched pub is very much back to what it was. Locals helped rescue the ancient contents from the flames, and scorch marks have been left as a memento on one of the benches; photographs of the fire damage leave you wondering how they've managed to get it back into shape so quickly. Before becoming a pub in 1848 the Fleece was a farm owned by the same family for nearly 500 years, and was left to the National Trust in 1977. Many of the furnishings, such as the great oak dresser that holds a priceless 48-piece set of Stuart pewter, are heirlooms passed down through that family for many generations, and now back in place. The rooms have massive beams and exposed timbers, and despite the fire you can still see marks scored on the worn and crazed flagstones to keep out demons. There are two fine grandfather clocks, ancient kitchen chairs, curved high-backed settles, a rocking chair, and a rack of heavy pointed iron shafts, probably for spit roasting (though there have been all sorts of esoteric guesses), in one of the huge inglenook fireplaces – the three log fires have been allowed to come back into action. Plenty of oddities include a great cheese-press and set of cheese moulds, and a rare dough-proving table; a leaflet details the more bizarre items. The whole pub apart from the small room called the brewhouse is no smoking. They serve well kept Hook Norton Old Hooky, Uley Pigs Ear and around four guests from breweries such as Bathams, Salopian, Tetleys and Wye Valley from handpump, along with farm cider. They have darts, cribbage, dominoes, shove-ha'penny and various board games, but no piped music or fruit machines. Straightforward reasonably priced bar food includes sandwiches (from £3.50), faggots and mash (£5.50), baked stuffed aubergine with ratatouille filling (£6.25), home-made steak and kidney pie or warm chicken and stilton on mixed leaves with avocado (£7.25), poached salmon (£7.95), and puddings such as chocolate brandy cake (£3.25). They hold the annual asparagus auctions (end of May) and village fête (August bank holiday Monday), there's sometimes morris dancing, and the village silver band plays here regularly too; in summer musical and theatrical events are performed on a stage in the garden. The lawn around the beautifully restored thatched and timbered barn is a lovely place to sit, among the fruit trees, and at the front by the stone pump-trough; there are more picnic-sets in the front courtyard. The pub gets very busy in summer. *(Recommended by Rob Weeks, Paul Humphreys, Martin and Pauline Jennings)*

Free house ~ Licensee Nigel Smith ~ Real ale ~ Bar food (12-2.30, 6.30-9; 12-4 Sun; not Sun evening) ~ (01386) 831173 ~ Children welcome ~ Folk Thurs from 8.30; monthly live act (folk or blues) ~ Open 11-11; 11-3, 6-11 in winter; 11-11 Sat; 12-10.30 Sun

BROADWAY SP0937 Map 4
Crown & Trumpet ◧
Church Street

In a handsome, much-visited Cotswold village, this cheerful, down-to-earth 17th-c pub has seasonal beers (one for each season) brewed for the pub by the local Stanway Brewery; also well kept on handpump are Greene King Old Speckled Hen, Hook Norton Old Hooky and Timothy Taylors Landlord, plus hot toddies and mulled wine. The relaxed beamed and timbered bar has antique dark high-backed settles, good big tables and a blazing log fire; outside hardwood tables and chairs among flowers on a slightly raised front terrace are popular with walkers – even in adverse weather. The pub hosts regular live music and has a range of pub games, including darts, shove-ha'penny, cribbage, dominoes, ring-the-bull and Evesham quoits; they've also a fruit machine, TV and piped music. Straightforward bar food such as baguettes and wraps (from £3.95), various pies (from £6.95), seafood mornay (£8.95), and puddings (£3.45); they do Sunday roasts. *(Recommended by M Joyner, David J Austin, James Woods, Di and Mike Gillam, Tracey and Stephen Groves, Dr G and Mrs J Kelvin, Ted George, Hugh Pollard, Paul and Gloria Howell)*

Laurel (Enterprise) ~ Lease Andrew Scott ~ Real ale ~ Bar food (12-2.15(3 Sat-Sun in winter), 6-9.15; 12-9.15 Sat-Sun in summer) ~ (01386) 853202 ~ Children welcome ~ Dogs welcome ~ Live music Sat evening, blues every second Thurs, jazz every third Thurs ~ Open 11-11; 12-10.30 Sun ~ Bedrooms: £43S(£48B)/£58S(£65B)

CHILDSWICKHAM SP0738 Map 4
Childswickham Inn ♀
Village signposted off A44 just NW of Broadway

Upmarket and sophisticated, this imaginatively run and innovative gastropub has an eclectic cuisine that embraces both modern and traditional, but is also a place where you are welcome just to come in for a drink. It's been carefully expanded, and the main area, largely no smoking, is for eating in, with a mix of chairs around kitchen tables, big rugs on boards or broad terracotta tiles, more or less abstract contemporary prints on walls painted cream and pale violet or mauve, candlesticks in great variety, a woodburning stove and a piano; piped music. At lunchtime, it's popular with older folk, but in the evenings and at weekends you'll find a broader mix. Skilfully cooked imaginative restaurant food changes daily but might include basil, mozzarella and vine tomato salad (£5.90), steamed mussels with chorizo, tomato and fresh herb broth (£6.95), roasted vine tomato, chargrilled vegetable and walnut tagliatelle (£10.95), fried breast of chicken (£15.90), baked hake steak with fennel, orange and star anise salad (£17.90), and fillet steak topped with baked mushroom and port and madeira sauce (£18.95), with over 20 puddings such as french lemon tart, damson ice-cream or chocolate, prune and armagnac terrine (all £4.95). Off to the right is a modern-style lounge-like bar (snacks only, such as baguettes, in here), light and airy, with Greene King Old Speckled Hen and Hook Norton Hooky on handpump (from a counter that seems made from old doors), a good choice of over 50 french, italian and other wines (with ten sold by the glass), and good coffee in elegant cups; service is friendly and attentive. This small carefully lit room has a similarly modern colour-scheme with paintings by local artists, leather armchairs and sofas, and bamboo furniture. The entrance lobby has the biggest doormat we have ever seen – wall to wall – with good disabled access and facilities. A large sunny deck outside has tables, and the garden is nicely cottagey, with a lawn and borders. *(Recommended by David and Sue Sykes, Roger Braithwaite, A S and M E Marriott, Bernard Stradling, Paul and Gloria Howell)*

Punch ~ Lease Guy Justin Brookes ~ Real ale ~ Restaurant (not Sun evening or Mon lunch) ~ (01386) 852461 ~ Children in restaurant ~ Dogs allowed in bar ~ Open 12-3, 6-11; 12-10.30 Sun; closed Mon lunch except bank hols

CLENT SO9279 Map 4
Fountain

Off A491 at Holy Cross/Clent exit roundabout, via Violet Lane, then turn right at T junction; Adams Hill/Odnall Lane

Now no smoking throughout, this restauranty pub near the breezy Clent Hills gets heavily booked up (with an older set at lunchtime) and it's worth booking a table for the delicious food. As well as interesting lunchtime sandwiches (from £4.25, not Sunday), the menu might include lunchtime specials such as liver and bacon (£7.95), and herb-roasted salmon or pork with peppercorn and cream sauce (£8.95), with other dishes such as generous portions of home-made soup (£3.95), duck and orange terrine (£4.25), goats cheese and mushroom filo (£10.95), and steaks with around half a dozen sauces (from £12.50), while puddings might be chocolate and caramel parfait or chocolate and kumquat truffle (from £3.75); there are also various Sunday roasts (from £8.95); children's helpings available until 7.30pm from £5.95; service is very friendly and efficient. With a buoyant atmosphere, the long carpeted dining bar – four knocked-together areas – is filled mainly by sturdy pine tables and country-kitchen chairs or mate's chairs, with some comfortably cushioned brocaded wall seats. There are nicely framed local photographs on the ragged pinkish walls above a dark panelled dado, pretty wall lights, and candles on the tables. Banks's Mild and Bitter, and a couple of guests such as Hydes Jekylls Gold Premium Ale and Marstons Pedigree are very well kept on handpump, and they've decent wines served in cut glass, and ten malts; also a choice of speciality teas and good coffees, and freshly squeezed orange juice; alley skittles. There are a few picnic-sets out in front. They have plans to add bedrooms. Note that they may close in the evening on winter Sundays. *(Recommended by Margaret Drazin, Lynda and Trevor Smith, J and P Blake, J C Churchill-Wood, Mrs Pat Crabb, Theo, Anne and Jane Gaskin)*

Union Pub Company ~ Lease Richard and Jacque Macey ~ Real ale ~ Bar food (12-2.15, 6-8.30(9 Fri); 12-2, 6-9 Sat; 12-4.30 Sun; not Sun or bank hol Mon evenings) ~ Restaurant ~ (01562) 883286 ~ Children welcome ~ Open 11-11; 12-10.30 Sun

CROWLE SO9256 Map 4
Old Chequers 🍴 ♀

2½ miles from M5 junction 6; A4538 towards Evesham, then left after ½ mile; then follow Crowle signpost right to Crowle Green

You can eat really well at this especially well run pub that is within easy access of the motorway. Generously served, well prepared food typically features soup (£2.95), ploughmans' (£6.50), thai chicken curry (£10.95), loin of lamb with sauce of the day (£13.50), scottish rib-eye steak with port and stilton sauce (£15.50), together with specials such as vegetable biryani (£8.50), lamb moussaka (£8.95), and fillet of plaice or rabbit casserole (£10.95). Much modernised, the pub rambles extensively around an island bar, with plush-seated mates' chairs around a mix of pub tables on the patterned carpet, some brass and copper on the swirly-plastered walls, lots of pictures for sale at the back, and a coal-effect gas fire at one end (there's central heating too). A big square extension on the right, with shinily varnished rustic timbering and beamery, has more tables. Banks's Bitter and Timothy Taylors Landlord are well kept on handpump with a guest such as Enville Bitter, and they've good value house wines. Disabled access; piped music; one bar area is no smoking. Outside, there are picnic-sets on the grass behind, among shrubs and small fruit trees – a pleasant spot, with pasture beyond. *(Recommended by Mike and Mary Carter, Pat and Tony Martin, Joan and Tony Walker, Karen Eliot, Dave Braisted, Ian and Jo Argyle, John and Wendy Allin, Christopher Turner, M G Hart, Mr and Mrs F E Boxell, Mr and Mrs A H Young, M Joyner, Stuart Paulley, Kay and Alistair Butler, David Green)*

Free house ~ Licensees Steven and Ian Thomas ~ Real ale ~ Bar food (12-1.45, 7-9.45; not Sun evening) ~ (01905) 381275 ~ Children over 14 and in evening only ~ Open 12-2.30, 7-11; 12-3 Sun; closed Sun evening, 26 Dec-1 Jan

DEFFORD SO9143 Map 4
Monkey House

A4104 towards Upton – immediately after passing Oak public house on right, there's a small group of cottages, of which this is the last

A miraculous survival and in the same family for some 150 years, this enchantingly simple black and white thatched cider-house hardly resembles a pub at all at first sight, and there's no inn sign. Very cheap Bulmer's Medium or Special Dry cider is tapped from barrels, poured by jug into pottery mugs (some locals have their own) and served from a hatch beside the door. As a concession to modern tastes, beer is sold too, in cans. Apart from crisps and nuts they don't do food, but you can bring your own. In the summer you could find yourself sharing the garden with the hens and cockerels that wander in from an adjacent collection of caravans and sheds; there's also a pony called Mandy, Tapper the jack russell, and Marie the rottweiler. Alternatively you can retreat to a small and spartan side outbuilding with a couple of plain tables, a settle and an open fire. The pub's name comes from the story of a drunken customer who, some years ago, fell into bramble bushes and swore that he was attacked by monkeys. Please note the limited opening times. *(Recommended by Derek and Sylvia Stephenson, Pete Baker, Dr G and Mrs J Kelvin, RWC, the Didler, Dr and Mrs A K Clarke, David J Austin, Annabel Viney)*

Free house ~ Licensee Graham Collins ~ No credit cards ~ (01386) 750234 ~ Children welcome ~ Open 11-2 Fri, Sat, Mon; 6-10 Weds-Sat; 12-2, 7-10 Sun; closed Mon evening, Weds-Thurs lunchtime, all Tues

---

Post Office address codings confusingly give the impression that some pubs are in Worcestershire, when they're really in Gloucestershire, Herefordshire, Shropshire, or Warwickshire (which is where we list them).

HOLY CROSS SO9278 Map 4
Bell & Cross 🍽 ♗

4 miles from M5 junction 4: A491 towards Stourbridge, then follow Clent signpost off on left

With welcoming staff and terrific food, this distinctive and well run pub continues to bring praise from readers, and it's still the sort of place you can just come in to enjoy a drink. Delicious dishes, from a changing menu, include lunchtime snacks (not Sunday) such as leek and potato soup with chives and port (£3.95), sandwiches (from £4.25, baguettes and panini from £4.95), fishcakes with prawns, peking duck rolls or chicory smoked chicken and avocado salad with roasted tomato (£5.95), and oak smoked salmon (£6.95), with other dishes such as roasted corn-fed chicken with potato, white beans and chorizo (£11), slow-cooked belly of pork with honey glazed apple and fondant potato (£11.75), grilled fillet of sea bream with prawn basil and tomato linguini (£11.75), and rib-eye steak (£13.50), with a few daily specials such as grilled fillets of cornish mackerel with sautéed fennel, prawn and dill white wine sauce (£12.50) or chargrilled cutlet of free-range pork, confit potato with smoked bacon and tomato ragoût (£12.95); puddings might include white chocolate and rhubarb crème brûlée (£4.95). The Sunday menu includes traditional roasts (£10.95); they do children's meals (£5.25). With a classic unspoilt early 19th-c layout, the five small rooms and kitchen open off a central corridor with a black and white tiled floor: they give a choice of carpet, bare boards, lino or nice old quarry tiles, a variety of moods from snug and chatty to bright and airy, and an individual décor in each – theatrical engravings on red walls here, nice sporting prints on pale green walls there, racing and gundog pictures above the black panelled dado in another room. Two of the rooms have small serving bars, with well kept Banks's Bitter and Mild, Marstons Pedigree and maybe a guest such as Timothy Taylors Landlord on handpump. You'll find over 50 wines (with 14 sold by the glass), a variety of coffees, daily papers, coal fires in most rooms, perhaps regulars playing cards in one of the two front ones, and piped music; all dining areas are no smoking. You get pleasant views from the garden terrace. The pub cat is called Pumba. *(Recommended by Drs E J C Parker, Margaret Drazin, Pete Baker, Stuart Paulley, Nigel Long, Brenda and Rob Fincham, KC, J and P Blake, J C Churchill-Wood, Mike and Linda Hudson)*

Enterprise ~ Tenants Roger and Jo Narbett ~ Real ale ~ Bar food (12-2, 6.30-9.15(9.30 Fri-Sat); 12-2, 7-9 Sun) ~ Restaurant ~ (01562) 730319 ~ Children in restaurant ~ Dogs allowed in bar ~ Open 12-3, 6-11; 12-4, 7-10.30 Sun; closed 25 Dec

KEMPSEY SO8548 Map 4 🏠
Walter de Cantelupe ♗ 🛏

A38, handy for M5 junction 7 via A44 and A4440

Alongside well kept real ales on handpump such as Cannon Royall Kings Shilling, Hobsons Best, and Timothy Taylors Landlord, this efficiently run free house has a guest ale such as Olde Swan in winter, a farm cider in summer, and locally grown and pressed apple and pear juices; they also stock a good choice of wines by the glass (they have regularly changing bin ends, and english wines from a local vineyard). Boldly decorated in red and gold, the bar area has an informal and well worn in mix of furniture, an old wind-up HMV gramophone and a good big fireplace. The dining area has various plush or yellow leather dining chairs, an old settle, a sonorous clock, and candles and flowers on the tables. Cooked by the friendly landlord, using lots of local produce, enjoyable well presented dishes might be lunchtime sandwiches (from £3), home-made soup (£3.60), very good ploughman's (£5.60), sausages and mash (£7.25; with vegetarian sausages £6.50), chicken balti (£7.50), and gammon, egg and chips (£7.60), with specials such as home-made baked beans in a real tomato and Guinness sauce served on toast (£3.95), chicken liver pâté (£4), beef and ale pie (£8.50), and poached salmon salad (£8.75), with puddings such as sticky ginger pudding with ginger wine and toffee sauce (£3.95); you can buy jars of home-made chutney and marmalade. The dining area is no smoking; cribbage, dominoes and table skittles. There's a pretty suntrap walled garden at the back; the sociable labrador is called Monti. *(Recommended by Paul Kemp, David and Christine Vaughton, Jack Clark, Dr and Mrs A K Clarke, P R Morgan, Theocsbrian, Pat and Tony Martin)*

Free house ~ Licensee Martin Lloyd Morris ~ Real ale ~ Bar food (12-2(2.30 Sat), 6.30-9.30(10 Fri-Sat); not Sun evening; not Mon except bank hols) ~ Restaurant ~ (01905) 820572 ~ Children in restaurant until 8.15pm ~ Dogs allowed in bar and bedrooms ~ Live folk evening second Sun ~ Open 12-2, 6-11; 11-2.30(3 summer), 6-11 Sat; 12-3, 7-10.30 Sun; closed Mon except bank hols ~ Bedrooms: £40.50S(£49.50B)/£55S(£77B)

KIDDERMINSTER SO8376 Map 4
King & Castle 🍺 £
Railway Station, Comberton Hill

Steam trains hissing by the platform immediately outside this painstakingly re-created station refreshment room memorably evoke the great age of the railways at the terminus of the Severn Valley Railway, and with beer perhaps only £1.10 a pint you may indeed think you've gone on a journey back in time. Inside the building you get the feeling of a better-class Edwardian establishment that has let its hair down to embrace more informal modern ways. You'll find a good mix of customers, and the atmosphere is lively and sometimes noisily good-humoured; it can get rather smoky. Furnishings are solid and in character, and there's the railway memorabilia that you'd expect. Bathams and Wyre Piddle Royal Piddle are superbly kept alongside a couple of changing guests from brewers such as Enville Nailmaker and Mild Exmoor Gold on handpump, and they've ten malt whiskies; piped music. The reasonably priced straightforward menu includes sandwiches (from £1.50), toasties (from £2.50), basket meals such as sausage and chips (£2.75), all-day breakfast (£4.75), broccoli and cream cheese bake, scampi or chicken kiev (£5.25), and traditional puddings such as chocolate pudding (£2.50); they also do Sunday roasts (£4.75), and children's meals (£2.75). The cheerful landlady and friendly staff cope well with the bank holiday and railway gala day crowds (you'd be lucky to find a seat then); dogs are very welcome. You can use a Rover ticket to shuttle between here and the Railwaymans Arms in Bridgnorth (see Shropshire chapter). *(Recommended by Gill and Tony Morriss, John Tavernor, Theocsbrian, B M Eldridge, Theo, Anne and Jane Gaskin, Paul and Gloria Howell)*

Free house ~ Licensee Rosemary Hyde ~ Real ale ~ Bar food (12-2(2.30 Sat-Sun), 6-8 Fri-Sat, 7-9 Sun; not Mon-Thurs evenings) ~ No credit cards ~ (01562) 747505 ~ Children welcome if seated in eating area of bar till 9pm ~ Dogs welcome ~ Open 11-3, 5-11; 11-11 Sat; 12-10.30 Sun

KNIGHTWICK SO7355 Map 4
Talbot 🍷 🍺 🛏
Knightsford Bridge; B4197 just off A44 Worcester—Bromyard

Nicely placed by a bridge over the River Teme and looking out to rolling, wooded hills, this 15th-c coaching inn brews its own very reasonably priced beers, This, That, T'Other and Wot ales using locally grown hops and well kept on handpump; they also have a guest such as Hobsons Bitter and sometimes a farm cider, as well as ten different wines by the glass and 15 malt whiskies. With a good log fire in winter, the heavily beamed and extended lounge bar opens on to a terrace and an arbour with roses and clematis. There are a variety of interesting seats from small carved or leatherette armchairs to the winged settles by the tall bow windows, and a vast stove squats in the big central stone hearth. The well furnished back public bar has pool on a raised side area, darts, fruit machine, video game and juke box; dominoes and cribbage. The restaurant is no smoking. Freshly prepared with local ingredients (some of the vegetables are grown in the pub's organic garden), good bar food includes a couple of lunchtime snacks such as rolls (£2), ploughman's (£6), vegetarian quiche (£7.50), with other well presented (though not cheap) dishes such as soup (£4), salmon gravadlax or beetroot terrine (£5.50), rabbit casserole, fisherman's pie, chicken and leek pie or lentil and sweet potato curry (£12), with puddings such as chocolate truffle cake or apple and apricot pie (£5); cheerfully attentive service. There are some old-fashioned seats in front of the pub, with more on a good-sized lawn under the lane by the river (they serve out here too). Some of the bedrooms are above the bar. They hold a farmers' market here on the second Sunday in the month. (Recommended by Dave Braisted, Gill and Tony Morriss, Guy Vowles, JHW, O K Smyth, George Atkinson, Dick and Madeleine Brown, Pat and Tony Martin)

Own brew ~ Licensees Wiz and Annie Clift ~ Real ale ~ Bar food (12-2, 6-30-9.30(7-9 Sun)) ~ Restaurant ~ (01886) 821235 ~ Children in eating area of bar and restaurant ~ Dogs allowed in bar ~ Open 11-11; 12-10.30 Sun ~ Bedrooms: £45S/£80B

MALVERN SO7845 Map 4
Nags Head ◖

Bottom end of Bank Street, steep turn down off A449

Open all day, this is a pleasantly traditional place to come down to if you've built up a thirst walking on the north end of the Malvern Ridge: the pub attracts a good mix of customers (with plenty of locals), and the mood is chatty and easy-going, with friendly young staff. It has a terrific choice of 11 real ales well kept on handpump: along with Banks's, Bathams, Greene King IPA, Marstons Pedigree and Woods Shropshire Lad, you'll find changing guest beers from brewers such as Brains, Enville, Greene King and Wye Valley. They also keep a fine range of malt whiskies, belgian beers and decent wines by the glass. There's a good variety of places to sit: a series of snug individually decorated rooms with one or two steps between some, all sorts of chairs including some leather armchairs, pews sometimes arranged as booths, a mix of tables with some sturdy ones stained different colours, bare boards here, flagstones there, carpet elsewhere, and plenty of interesting pictures and homely touches such as house plants and shelves of well thumbed books; there's a coal fire opposite the central servery; broadsheet newspapers and a good juke box; piped music, shove-ha'penny, cribbage and dominoes. Lunchtime bar food might include sandwiches (from £3, goats cheese ciabatta £4.50), soup (£4), ploughman's (£6.50), sausages and mash (£6.80), moroccan vegetable tagine (£7), fish pie (£8), and vegetable stir fry (£8.60), with puddings (£4). In the evenings they do meals only in the extension barn dining room; they don't take bookings, and it fills up quickly so get here early. Outside are picnic-sets and rustic tables and benches on the front terrace and in a garden, there are heaters, and umbrellas for wet weather. (Recommended by Mike Pugh, Chris Flynn, Wendy Jones, Ray and Winifred Halliday, Guy Vowles, Dr and Mrs Jackson, Andy Trafford, Louise Bayly, Barry Collett, Theocsbrian, Mike and Mary Clark)

Free house ~ Licensee Duncan Ironmonger ~ Real ale ~ Bar food (12-2) ~ Restaurant ~ (01684) 574373 ~ Children in restaurant ~ Dogs allowed in bar ~ Open 11-11; 12-10.30 Sun

PENSAX SO7269 Map 4
Bell ◖ £

B4202 Abberley—Clows Top, SE of the Snead Common part of the village

The licensees really make an effort to create an enjoyable and extremely welcoming atmosphere at this mock-Tudor local, which attracts a nice mix of customers. Along with Hobsons, you'll find at least four well kept changing real ales from brewers such as Cannon Royall, Hook Norton, Holdens, Woods and Wye Valley on handpump, and they've Weston's Old Rosie cider and Herefordshire County perry on handpump too; over the last weekend of June they hold a beer festival. The L-shaped main bar has a restrained traditional décor, with long cushioned pews on its bare boards, good solid pub tables, and a woodburning stove; dominoes, darts and shove-ha'penny. Beyond a small area on the left with a couple more tables is a more airy dining room, with french windows opening on to a wooden deck that on hot days can give a slightly californian feel; the pub has a log fire for our more usual weather. Besides good value lunchtime weekday specials such as steak and ale pie, vegetable stir fry, cornish pasty or sausage and mash (all £4.95), hearty enjoyable dishes, using locally sourced meat and vegetables, could include generous sandwiches (£3.50), faggots, chips and mushy peas (£6.95), pork chop with dijon sauce (£8.95), and steaks (from £11.95); Sunday roast (£6.95); children's menu (£3.95); they were hoping to add more fish and pasta choices at the time of going to press. Picnic-sets in the back garden look out over rolling fields and copses to the Wyre Forest. *(Recommended by Gill and Tony Morriss, Lynda and Trevor Smith, Colin Fisher, David Eberlin, Guy Vowles)*

Free house ~ Licensees John and Trudy Greaves ~ Real ale ~ Bar food (12-2, 6-9; 12-3 Sun; not Sun evening; not Mon lunchtime exc bank hols) ~ Restaurant ~ (01299) 896677 ~ Children in restaurant and family room ~ Dogs allowed in bar ~ Open 12-2.30, 5-11; 12-10.30 Sun; closed Mon lunch except bank hols

WYRE PIDDLE SO9647 Map 4

Anchor

Village signposted off A4538 WNW of Evesham

This black and white riverside pub is a lovely place to sit outside on the large back lawn (which is floodlit at night), with the Malverns and Bredon Hill as the backdrop, and with 100 feet of private moorings on the River Avon you can even arrive by boat and pop in for a pint or a meal; on fine summer Wednesdays they may have live jazz outside. You get good river views too (though only if you arrive early) from the big airy back bar, where they serve Banks's Bitter, Marstons Pedigree, Timothy Taylors Landlord, local Wyre Piddle and a monthly guest such as Charles Wells Bombardier under light blanket pressure, 12 wines by the glass (including champagne) and summer Pimms; fruit machine and piped music. The friendly and neatly kept little lounge has a good flame-effect gas fire in its attractively restored inglenook fireplace, comfortably upholstered chairs and settles, and two beams in the shiny ceiling. The no smoking dining area has rugs on stripped wood floors and wooden tables and chairs. Big helpings of swiftly served bar food might include home-made soup (£3.25), lunchtime sandwiches (from £3.60), steak and ale pie of roasted vegetable plait (£7.50), roast shank of lamb (£9.25), fresh fish from Birmingham market such as fillet of haddock (£9.50), and half a roast duck (£10.50), with puddings (£3.25); they also do a children's menu (from £3.25). *(Recommended by KN-R, Mr and Mrs Colin Roberts, Mr and Mrs A J Edwards, Dr L Kaufman, John Saville, Theo, Anne and Jane Gaskin, Paul and Gloria Howell)*

Enterprise ~ Lease Nigel and Hilary Green ~ Real ale ~ Bar food (not 1 Jan, 25-26 Dec) ~ Restaurant ~ (01386) 552799 ~ Children welcome ~ Dogs allowed in bar ~ Live music Fri evening; live jazz Weds evening in summer ~ Open 12-3, 6-11; 12-11(10.30 Sun) Sat; 12-3, 6-11 Sat in winter

---

LUCKY DIP

Besides the fully inspected pubs, you might like to try these Lucky Dips recommended to us and described by readers (if you do, please send us reports: www.goodguides.co.uk).

ASHTON UNDER HILL [SO9938]
Star [Elmley Rd]: Agreeable pub in quiet village below Bredon Hill, lots of tables in spacious carpeted bar, well kept Greene King IPA and Hook Norton Old Hooky, decent bar food and small modest restaurant; good garden, cl Mon/Tues lunchtimes *(Dr A Y Drummond)*
BADSEY [SP0743]
✩ *Round of Gras* [B4035 2 miles E of Evesham]: Warm, comfortable and largely no smoking, with substantial well priced fresh food inc seasonal local asparagus feasts, welcoming landlord, good range of well kept ales inc Uley

Old Spot as a regular, Weston's farm cider, country wines, log fire, lots of polished wood, panelling and farm tools, raised restaurant section; children welcome, pleasant fair-sized tree-shaded garden, open all day wknds *(BB, Mr and Mrs A P Reeves)*
BELBROUGHTON [SO9177]
✩ *Queens* [Queens Hill (B4188 E of Kidderminster)]: Newish landlord in bustling 18th-c traditional village pub by Belne Brook, enjoyable food, well kept Banks's, Marstons Pedigree and guest beers, friendly efficient service, comfortable alcove seating, bigger tables in no smoking family

area, fresh flowers; picnic-sets on small roadside terrace, pleasant village (*John and Laney Woods, Roy and Lindsey Fentiman, John Westley*)

BEWDLEY [SO7875]

Black Boy [Wyre Hill, off A456]: Welcoming traditional timbered inn dating from 17th c or earlier, well kept Enville, Fullers London Pride, Greene King Abbot and a local guest ale such as Woods or Wye Valley, interesting good value food from low-priced sandwiches up, long bar/lounge with cosy drinking area and log fire, caring service, large sleepy pub cat, local papers, restaurant; tables outside, handy for River Severn (*Gill and Tony Morriss, Paul and Gloria Howell*)

BRADLEY GREEN [SP9861]

Red Lion [Droitwich Rd]: Efficiently organised pub with pleasant staff, bargain carvery (other food too), no smoking in eating area, well kept Greene King Abbot; popular with W Midlands coach parties; handy for NT Hanbury Hall (*Martin and Pauline Jennings*)

BRANSFORD [SO8053]

Fox [A4103 Worcester—Hereford]: Good atmosphere in spacious Chef & Brewer well divided to give cosy areas, wide range of well priced food, pleasant staff, Hobsons Best and Town Crier (*Nigel and Sue Foster*)

CALLOW END [SO8349]

Blue Bell [Upton Rd]: Up-to-date Banks's pub with two bars and dining area, their real ales, generous fresh food inc interesting dishes and two-for-one bargains, pleasant staff (*M Joyner*)

Old Bush [Upton Rd]: Friendly pub with pleasant staff, well kept Banks's and Marstons Bitter and Pedigree, good choice of bar food (*Colin Fisher*)

CHADDESLEY CORBETT [SO8973]

Fox [A448 Bromsgrove—Kidderminster]: Spacious and comfortable, with several eating and drianking areas, good value interesting bar and restaurant food, four well kept real ales inc Enville and Hobsons Town Crier (*Gill and Tony Morriss*)

Swan [off A448 Bromsgrove—Kidderminster]: Friendly spacious lounge with high beams and roaring woodburner, smaller proper locals' bar, good solid furniture, well kept Bathams Bitter and Mild, good plain food from hot pork sandwiches to attractively priced restaurant specials; some live music; good-sized garden (*Theocsbrian*)

CLENT [SO9279]

Hill Tavern [Adams Hill]: At foot of Clent Hills (right by the car park), good value bar food, Courage Directors, skittle alley; pleasant terrace (*Dave Braisted*)

DODFORD [SO9372]

Dodford Inn [Whinfield Rd]: Friendly unpretentious walkers' pub in extensive grounds, quiet spot overlooking wooded valley, lots of footpaths; relaxed peaceful atmosphere, traditional décor and simple furnishings, attractively priced home cooking in hearty helpings, two well kept changing ales such as Robinsons Samuel Oldknow and Wychwood Goliath, central fire, darts; live

music Weds; children and dogs welcome, disabled access (though tables close together) and facilities, garden with terrace and play area (*G Coates*)

DRAKES BROUGHTON [SO9248]

☆ *Plough & Harrow* [A44 NW of Pershore]: Popular dining pub with partly no smoking extended and refurbished restaurant area, comfortable and attractive rambling lounge, good friendly helpful service, well kept mainstream beers and a weekly guest ale, sensible prices and cut-price small helpings for the elderly, log fire; may be two sittings on busy days; good disabled access, pleasant terrace, big orchard-side garden with play area, open all day (*Mr and Mrs F E Boxell, Mr and Mrs J C Lodge, Chris Flynn, Wendy Jones*)

DUNHAMPSTEAD [SO9160]

☆ *Firs* [just SE of Droitwich, towards Sale Green – OS Sheet 150 map ref 919600]: Welcoming and pretty country dining pub with good bar food from enterprisingly filled baguettes and baked potatoes up, well kept Banks's and Marstons, flowers on tables, comfortable no smoking dining conservatory; booking advised wknds; dogs allowed in side bar, tables on flower-filled terrace and in small grassy garden, nice spot not far from canal – good walks (*Lynda and Trevor Smith, LYM*)

EARLS CROOME [SO8642]

Yorkshire Grey [A38, N of M50 junction 1]: Bustling entirely no smoking pub newly refurbished under new landlord, friendly atmosphere, fair-priced enjoyable food inc some enterprising dishes, well kept Greene King Old Speckled Hen, sensibly priced wines, log fire, candlelit restaurant; disabled access, garden tables (*Paul Kemp, C Howard, Mrs S Lyons, Reg Fowle, Helen Rickwood*)

ELDERSFIELD [SO8131]

☆ *Greyhound* [signed from B4211; Lime St (don't go into Eldersfield itself), OS Sheet 150 map ref 815314]: Unspoilt country local with welcoming young licensees, good inexpensive country cooking (not Mon) by landlord, well kept ales such as Butcombe and Woods Parish tapped from the cask, big woodburner and friendly tabby cat in appealing black-beamed ochre-walled public bar, horse-racing pictures in candlelit carpeted no smoking room, lively skittle alley, strikingly modern lavatories with interesting mosaic in gents'; picnic-sets in small front garden, swings and dovecote out behind (*the Didler, BB, D A J and Mrs Tompsett*)

FAR FOREST [SO7175]

Horse & Jockey: Truly child-friendly pub with imaginative range of good food at attractive prices, good service, Black Sheep, Greene King IPA and Tetleys, good wine choice, pleasant restaurant with well spaced tables (*Drs E J C Parker*)

FECKENHAM [SP0061]

☆ *Lygon Arms* [B4090 Droitwich—Alcester]: Welcoming licensees, good food using fresh ingredients inc fish delivered daily, small helpings of main courses available, well kept Boddingtons, Flowers IPA, Greene King Old Speckled Hen and Hobsons, reasonably priced wines, traditional bar, attractive and popular two-room dining conservatory *(Martin and Pauline Jennings, Dave Braisted)*

FLADBURY [SO9946]

Chequers [Chequers Lane]: Attractive upmarket dining pub dating from 14th c, huge old-fashioned range with log fire at end of long bar, lots of local prints, good generous food from sandwiches to steaks, well kept Fullers London Pride, Hook Norton Best and Wyre Piddle Piddle in the Hole at reasonable prices, quick friendly service, charming beamed back restaurant with carvery; children welcome, large pleasant garden with play area, peaceful pretty village, comfortable well equipped bedroom extension *(M S Catling, Mr and Mrs G S Ayrton, Mr and Mrs F E Boxell, Martin and Pauline Jennings)*

FLYFORD FLAVELL [SO9754]

☆ *Boot* [off A422 Worcester—Alcester; Radford Rd]: Convivial Georgian-fronted country pub, log fire in ancient heavily beamed and timbered partly no smoking back core now mainly for dining, comfortable modern conservatory, little old-world beamed front bar with small inglenook log fire, cards and pool, up to half a dozen real ales, reasonably priced food from lunchtime sandwiches up; piped music, fruit machine; children and dogs allowed, pretty garden with heaters and lighting, comfortable bedrooms, open all day Sun *(M Joyner, Dr Paull Khan, Mr and Mrs W D Borthwick, George Atkinson, Richard Evans, Moira and John Cole, John and Johanne Eadie, LYM, Rod Stoneman, Barry Collett, Annabel Viney, Theo, Anne and Jane Gaskin)*

FORHILL [SP0575]

☆ *Peacock* [handy for M42, junctions 2 and 3; pub at junction Lea End Lane and Icknield St]: Appealing, quietly placed and well run no smoking Chef & Brewer with wide range of generous enjoyable food, plenty of tables in comfortably fitted knocked-through beamed rooms, woodburner in big inglenook, well kept Enville, Hobsons Best, Theakstons Old Peculier and two second beams; reliable acceptably priced food from baguettes and baked potatoes up, friendly prompt helpful service; piped classical music; children welcome, picnic-sets on back terrace and front grass, open all day *(Stan and Hazel Allen, LYM, Dennis and Gill Keen, P J Holt, David Edwards, M G Hart, Nigel and Sue Foster)*

HALLOW [SO8258]

Royal Oak [Main Rd (A443 N of Worcester)]: Good home-made mainstream food with some individual touches, cheerful helpful service, nice house wines, interesting photographs, splendid vintage toy pedal car; good-sized garden *(Peter and Anne Hollindale)*

HANLEY CASTLE [SO8341]

☆ *Three Kings* [Church End, off B4211 N of Upton upon Severn]: Quaint and well worn-in country local, a friendly and homely favourite, with huge inglenook and hatch service in little tiled-floor tap room, consistently well kept Butcombe, Hobsons Best and two or three changing beers from small breweries usually

inc a Mild, Nov beer festival, farm cider, dozens of malt whiskies, two other larger rooms, one with fire in open range, low-priced food (not Sun evening – singer then); be prepared for a possibly longish wait other times), seats of sort outside; family room, bedroom *(Gill and Tony Morriss, the Didler, Pete Baker, LYM, MLR)*

HANLEY SWAN [SO8142]

☆ *Swan* [B4209 Malvern—Upton]: Reopened at the end of 2004 after lengthy refurbishment and extension, attractive contemporary rustic décor and furnishings with log fire, settees and armchairs in former dining area, pleasant new dining area (both areas used for the popular Sun lunch), efficient welcoming service, good interesting menu from good choice of sandwiches up, good value small help-yourself wkdy hot buffet, Adnams, Shepherd Neame Spitfire, Tetleys and a guest beer; disabled access, tables on good-sized side lawn with play area, nice spot facing green and big duck pond, five good new bedrooms *(BB, Colin Fisher, GSB, Ron and Val Broom, Martin and Pauline Jennings)*

HOLT HEATH [SO8063]

Red Lion [Witley Rd (A443/A4133)]: Sparkling clean olde-worlde pub with sociable staff, good local beer range, very wide choice of enjoyable food from black country specialities to awesome exotica, cigarette cards and team photographs in long bar, restaurant *(Mr and Mrs F E Boxell)*

INKBERROW [SP0157]

☆ *Bulls Head* [A422 Worcester—Alcester]: Handsome Georgian inn doing well under current management, steps between levels, good village atmosphere in much older heavily beamed, timbered and partly flagstoned bar with woodburner in big fireplace, comfortable banquettes and other seats, two comfortable dining areas, decent food inc good roasts, well kept ales such as Banks's and Marstons Pedigree, good house wines, neat attentive staff, lots of pictures and disaster posters, darts; garden behind with terrace and play area *(Mrs Lynda Mills, BB, Mike and Mary Carter)*

KIDDERMINSTER [SO8679]

Old Waggon & Horses [Ismere (A451 towards Stourbridge)]: Interesting and enjoyable freshly cooked food inc good vegetarian choice in solid former carriers' pub with friendly service, good range of well kept local beers, etched windows and hatch-style bar front in quarry-tiled public bar, cosy L-shaped lounge and dining room with knick-knacks *(Mr and Mrs F E Boxell)*

KINNERSLEY [SO8743]

New Royal Oak [off A38 S of Worcester]: Welcoming pub with horse-racing memorabilia in cosy bar, Courage Directors and Charles Wells Bombardier, friendly landlord, separate conservatory restaurant *(Dave Braisted)*

LEIGH SINTON [SO7850]

☆ *Royal Oak* [Malvern Rd]: Well run dining pub with cheerful cartoons in low-beamed bar, careful service by relaxed and responsive staff, reliably enjoyable and competitively priced food very popular with older lunchers, notable Sun lunch and bargain Mon buffet, reasonably priced wines, plenty of locals, attractive restaurant; charming flower-filled garden behind with covered seating *(JCW, JHW, Mrs G P Hall, Denys Gueroult)*

LULSLEY [SO7455]

Fox & Hounds [signed a mile off A44 Worcester—Bromyard]: Tucked-away country pub with decent food from enjoyable sandwiches and baguettes to good Sun lunch, well kept real ale, nice wines, smallish parquet-floored bar stepping down into neat dining lounge, open fire, pretty little restaurant on left, attractive conservatory; dogs welcome, quiet and colourful enclosed side rose garden *(Lynda and Trevor Smith, BB)*

MALVERN WELLS [SO7742]

Railway Inn [Wells Rd (A449 towards Ledbury)]: Tidy pub nicely placed in Malvern Hills, with wide choice of enjoyable food inc Sun evening, friendly staff, Banks's, Marstons Pedigree and a guest beer, restaurant, separate skittle alley and pool table; terrace tables, fine views *(Chris Flynn, Wendy Jones, Philip and Cheryl Hill)*

MARTLEY [SO7560]

Crown: Reopened after extension and upmarket refurbishment, comfortable contemporary furniture on bare wood floors, modern artwork, friendly staff, good interesting lunchtime light dishes at appealing prices, more substantial evening menu, good wines by the glass and nice coffee; lovely walks nearby *(Caroline and Michael Abbey)*

OMBERSLEY [SO8463]

Cross Keys [A449, Kidderminster end]: Friendly efficient service, neat and comfortable beamed front bar, enjoyable attractively presented food from light bar meals to the conservatory restaurant's fish specialities, well kept and chosen real ales *(Mrs B J Edwards, Mr and Mrs F E Boxell, Paul and Gloria Howell)*

Crown & Sandys [A4133]: Big popular open-plan bistro pub with imaginative if not cheap food from lunchtime sandwiches up, fine choice of wines by the glass inc champagnes, uniformed staff, airy modern décor but keeping beams, settles and nice log fire in old fireplace, limestone-floor conservatory leading to terrace with fountain and sizeable garden beyond; loud acoustics, with flagstones or wooden flooring and piped music; children welcome, smartly refurbished bedrooms, open all day wknds *(Chris Flynn, Wendy Jones, B A and D Marsh, JHW, LYM, Alec Whitfield, Paul and Gloria Howell)*

PERSHORE [SO9445]

☆ *Brandy Cask* [Bridge St]: Plain high-ceilinged bow-windowed bar, back courtyard brewery producing their own attractively priced real ales, well kept guest beers too, Aug beer festival, coal fire, enjoyable fresh food from sandwiches to steaks, quaintly decorated no smoking dining room, quick friendly helpful service; well behaved children allowed; long attractive garden down to river (keep a careful eye on the children), with terrace, vine arbour and koi pond *(the Didler, BB, Derek and Sylvia Stephenson)*

Millers Arms [Bridge St]: Spacious but cosy beamed pub with well kept Wadworths IPA, 6X and Farmers Glory, good friendly service, separate no smoking dining area with bargain food *(Mr and Mrs A P Reeves)*

Star [Bridge St]: Well kept traditional town pub with coal fire in snug timbered bar, friendly Scottish licensees, bargain food from bacon and other rolls up *(Caroline and Michael Abbey)*

ROMSLEY [SO9679]

Swallows Nest [B4551, handy for M5 junctions 3 and 4]: Large Vintage Inn, linked areas inc no smoking and family rooms, unhurried welcome and pleasant efficient service, good atmosphere, Bass and Tetleys, wide choice of wines by the glass, decent varied food *(KC)*

SEDGEBERROW [SP0238]

Queens Head [Main St (B4078, just off A46 S of Evesham)]: Friendly village pub under welcoming newish licensees, enjoyable traditional pub food, well kept Wickwar Cotswold Way and one or two guest beers, farm cider, no smoking dining end allowing children, central area where the locals congregate, far end with piano, darts and comfortable settees among more usual pub furnishings, collection of old 3-D relief advertisements; open all day wknds *(Pete Baker)*

SEVERN STOKE [SO8544]

Rose & Crown [A38 S of Worcester]: Attractive 16th-c black and white pub, low beams, knick-knacks and good fire in character front bar, well kept Banks's and Marstons, good value generous food, friendly staff, back room where children allowed; big garden with picnic-sets and play area *(Dave Braisted)*

SHATTERFORD [SO7981]

☆ *Bellmans Cross* [Bridgnorth Rd (A442)]: Dining pub popular with business people at lunchtime, interesting and attractively presented bar food from baguettes up, smart tasteful restaurant, French chefs and bar staff, pleasant deft service, neat timber-effect bar with well kept Bass, Greene King Old Speckled Hen and a guest beer, good choice of wines by the glass inc champagne; picnic-sets outside, handy for Severn Woods walks *(BB, Lynda and Trevor Smith, Theo, Anne and Jane Gaskin, Dave Braisted)*

SHENSTONE [SO8673]

Plough: Secluded and unspoilt two-bar country local in pleasant surroundings, particularly well kept Bathams ales at attractive prices, friendly regulars, no food *(Colin Fisher)*

SNEACHILL [SO9053]

Nightingale [A44]: Roomy Vintage Inn with some character and interesting old photographs, friendly attentive young service, well kept real ales and good wines by the glass, sensible choice of good ample food all day *(Martin and Pauline Jennings)*

STOKE PRIOR [SO9666]
Gate Hangs Well [Woodgate Rd, off B4091
Hanbury Rd via Moorgate Rd]: Much
extended dining pub, open-plan but well
divided, keeping balance between its popular
carvery (and other good value generous food)
and its bar side, with good local atmosphere,
well kept Banks's and Marstons Pedigree,
friendly service, conservatory and country
views *(Dave Braisted)*

STOKE WHARF [SO9468]
Navigation [Hanbury Rd (B4091), by
Worcester & Birmingham Canal]: Friendly
good value pub popular for good food inc
Thurs paella night and (by prior arrangement)
fantastic seafood platter, changing real ales
(Geoffrey and Penny Hughes, Dave Braisted)

STOKE WORKS [SO9365]
Boat & Railway [Shaw Lane, by Bridge 42 of
Worcester & Birmingham Canal]: Popular
and unpretentious, with happy old-fashioned
atmosphere, efficient service with a smile,
well kept Banks's, Hansons and Marstons
Special, bargain generous lunchtime food;
pretty hanging baskets, pleasant waterside
terrace *(Bob and Bridget Attridge,
Dave Braisted)*

STOURPORT ON SEVERN [SO8070]
Old Beams [Dunley Rd (A451 towards Gt
Witley, just over Walshes Meadow bridge)]:
Comfortable and attractive, divided into areas
by stub walls with arched timbered openings,
enjoyable food in eating area at one end,
well kept real ale, nice staff; piped music; has
been open all day in summer *(Ted and
Shirley Wills)*

TENBURY WELLS [SO5968]
Pembroke House [Cross St]: 16th-c, with good
atmosphere, good reasonably priced food
(booking recommended evenings), generous
helpings with lots of veg, well kept Hobsons
and a guest beer *(David and Lesley Elliott)*
☆ *Ship* [Teme St]: Bright rather café-style no
smoking dining room with consistently good
freshly made food from generous sandwiches
to fish and Sun lunch, reasonable prices,
thoughtful and genuine smiling service, easy
mix of customers, fresh flowers, well kept
Fullers London Pride and Hobsons Best, decent
wines, good coffee, small L-shaped bar with
lots of dark wood inc fine Elizabethan beams,
little hunting prints and other pictures; piped
music; picnic-sets in coach yard and on neat
sheltered back lawn, comfortable bedrooms
*(E S Hales, BB, David and Lesley Elliott,
Francis Johnston)*

UPHAMPTON [SO8464]
Fruiterers Arms [off A449 N of Ombersley]:
Homely country local (looks like a private
house with a porch) brewing its own good
Cannon Royall Arrowhead, Mild, Muzzle
Loader and seasonal ales, also farm cider,
inexpensive fresh lunchtime sandwiches, simple
rustic Jacobean panelled bar serving lounge
with comfortable armchairs, beamery, log fire,
lots of photographs and local memorabilia; no
music, plain pool room; garden, some seats out
in front *(MLR, Pete Baker)*

UPPER ARLEY [SO7679]
Harbour [off B4194 NW of Bewdley; or off
A442 then footbridge]: Picturesque old-
fashioned pub in delightful country setting,
good value bar food, good range of well kept
ales, pleasant staff, warm welcoming
atmosphere, restaurant; tables and play area in
big field nr Severn, handy for Severn Valley
Railway station *(B M Eldridge)*

UPTON SNODSBURY [SO9454]
☆ *French House* [Worcester Rd (A422
Worcester—Stratford)]: Extensive series of
linked convivial carpeted rooms with
welcoming accommodating landlord and
cheerful staff, enjoyable food, well kept Tetleys
and a couple of guest beers, cheapish wines,
high-spirited frenchified décor with masses of
pictures and bric-a-brac, a lot of it quirkily
interesting, ceilings wicker or entirely wine
bottles, two grandfather clocks, balustraded no
smoking area up three steps, mix of seating
from dining tables to leather chesterfields;
piped music; tables out on terrace and grass,
comfortable bedrooms, open all day Sun
*(Barry Collett, LYM, Jill and
Graham Matthews, Kevin Blake)*

UPTON UPON SEVERN [SO8540]
Swan [Waterside]: Popular low-beamed main
bar in charming riverside setting, well kept
Banks's, Marstons Pedigree and guest beers,
two open fires and boating memorabilia,
quieter separate hotel lounge bar with sizeable
newly refurbished dining room off, good value
well presented generous standard food,
attentive staff; waterside garden with
summer barbecues, bedrooms *(BB, Nick and
Lynne Carter)*

WELLAND [SO8039]
☆ *Anchor* [Drake St (A4104 towards Upton)]:
Pretty flower-covered Tudor cottage with wide
choice of food from baguettes and baked
potatoes up, chatty and welcoming L-shaped
bar with some armchairs, comfortable and
nicely set spreading no smoking dining area
with fine views, five or six real ales, all wines
available by the glass (large measures for wine
and spirits), shove-ha'penny, dominoes, chess,
Jenga; may be unobtrusive piped music, and
despite general warm approval some recent
niggles; children in restaurant, charming
garden, field for tents or caravans, good
appealingly furnished bedrooms, cl Sun
evening *(Mike and Mary Carter, Dr J Puszet,
Chris Flynn, Wendy Jones, Martin and
Pauline Jennings, Joyce and Maurice Cottrell,
Keith and Maureen Trainer, G S R Cox,
David Green, Mike Green, LYM,
Barry Collett, Bernard Stradling, Sue Holland,
Dave Webster, Dave Braisted)*

WOLVERLEY [SO8379]
Lock [Wolverley Rd (B4189 N of
Kidderminster, by Staffs & Worcs Canal)]:
Cottagey-looking pub with bay window
overlooking a lock on the quaint canal as it
negotiates the red sandstone bluff into which
the pub is set; pleasant and comfortable, with
generous well prepared straightforward food,
Banks's and related ales, good prices; lovely

spot, some waterside tables *(Ted and Shirley Wills)*

WORCESTER [SO8455]

Old Rectifying House [North Parade]: Interesting flagstoned building overlooking River Severn, recently reworked with brasserie dining area downstairs and bar up, enjoyable up-to-date food from light dishes to good fish choice, reasonable prices, well kept Greene King Old Speckled Hen, decent wines; piped music, jazz Sun afternoon and alternate Weds; open all day *(Craig Turnbull, Ryta Lyndley)*

If a pub tries to make you leave a credit card behind the bar, be on your guard. The credit card firms and banks which issue them condemn this practice. After all, the publican who asks you to do this is in effect saying: 'I don't trust you'. Have you any more reason to trust his staff? If your card is used fraudulently while you have let it be kept out of your sight, the card company could say you've been negligent yourself – and refuse to make good your losses. So say that they can 'swipe' your card instead, but must hand it back to you. Please let us know if a pub does try to keep your card.

Yorkshire

This huge area has a remarkably rich range of good pubs, from idiosyncratic town taverns, or very simple moorland pubs surrounded by glorious walks, to smart and civilised dining pubs and inns or restaurants-with-rooms. Over the years we've built up dossiers of readers' reports on nearly 2,000 Yorkshire pubs, and the editors have anonymously inspected several hundred of these themselves. So this edition's entries are a very careful distillation of the best that Yorkshire has to offer. They include several new main entries: the Blue Bell at Alne, a welcoming dining pub that's now no smoking throughout; the Wheatsheaf at Burn, with a fine beer range and very cheap straightforward food; the Bridge Inn beautifully placed at Grinton, a most enjoyable all-rounder; the Black Sheep Brewery in Masham, not exactly a pub, but an excellent substitute; the Black Swan in Middleham, another fine all-rounder; the pretty Star at North Dalton, with very good imaginative food and good wines by the glass; the Old Bridge in Ripponden, a nicely placed pub back in the *Guide* after a break of several years, doing enjoyable food these days, and good on the drinks side too; the Rose & Crown at Sutton-on-the-Forest, an appealing pub with good food that's interesting without being pretentious, and good wines by the glass; the Falling Stone at Thwing, with its own good beers brewed on a nearby farm, and award-quality food; and the Blacksmiths at Westow, an upmarket dining pub with excellent food, that's kept a nicely traditional bar – pleasant simple bedrooms, too. Favourite pubs that have been in the *Guide* for longer include the unique Birch Hall at Beck Hole (a happy cross between sweetie shop and village tavern), the gaslit White Horse in Beverley (a Victorian local, quite without frills), the White Lion in lovely scenery at Cray (decent pubby food and four local real ales), the smart and civilised Blue Lion at East Witton (very good restauranty food in rather an upmarket atmosphere), the Tempest Arms at Elslack (genuinely friendly, with good food, beer and wine – all hugely enjoyed by many readers), the Carpenters Arms at Felixkirk (another notably friendly place, with good food and drinks), the General Tarleton at Ferrensby (a super place for a meal out, nice to stay at, too), the Star at Harome (a charming all-rounder, with good lunchtime sandwiches and ploughman's as well as their excellent restauranty – and restaurant-priced – food), the Stone Trough at Kirkham (well run, with enjoyable food in both pub and restaurant), the friendly Charles Bathurst in lovely scenery at Langthwaite (a nice place to stay in, or just to drop into for a good meal or a drink), the Chequers at Ledsham (great to find such a good place so close to the A1), the memorable little Sandpiper in Leyburn (doing very well all round these days), the Wellington at Lund (another very rewarding all-rounder), the friendly and well run Kings Head in Masham, the Boars Head in Ripley (this smart well run hotel's bar is properly pubby – and very friendly), the Fat Cat in Sheffield (their own good Kelham Island beers, and enjoyable food at ridiculously low prices), the smart Three Acres at Shelley (good interesting food, and super on the drinks side), the Fox & Hounds in the pretty village of Sinnington (very good interesting food, yet keeping a nicely pubby feel), the St Vincent Arms at Sutton upon Derwent (fine range of beers, and good home cooking), the Sportsmans Arms at Wath in Nidderdale (so nicely run, best thought of as a restaurant-with-rooms in glorious countryside), and the Maltings in York (great choice of beers and other drinks, good value simple food). Repeatedly, good food comes up as a strong point in these top Yorkshire pubs, many of them old favourites. But it's a newcomer, the Blacksmiths at Westow, which wins the title of Yorkshire Dining Pub of the Year. In the Lucky Dip section at the end of the chapter, pubs to note particularly are, in North Yorkshire, the Falcon at Arncliffe, Three Hares at Bilbrough, Falcon at Cloughton, Bryherstones at Cloughton Newlands, Olde Sun at Colton, Royal Oak at Dacre Banks, Queens Head at Finghall, Devonshire in Grassington, restauranty Roasted Pepper at Husthwaite, Kings Head and Racehorses in Kettlewell, Black Bull at Moulton, Farmers Arms at Muker, Castle Arms at Snape, Railway Inn at Spofforth, Tan Hill Inn, and in York the Ackhorne, Black Swan, Blue Bell and Three Legged Mare. In West Yorkshire we'd pick out the restauranty Kaye Arms on Grange Moor and the Bay Horse at Kirk Deighton, in East Yorkshire the Three Cups at Stamford Bridge (it's almost smack on the border), and in South Yorkshire the Devonshire Cat in Sheffield. Drinks prices in Yorkshire are generally well below the national average. John Smiths, produced in Yorkshire for the Scottish & Newcastle brewing combine, is a national beer brand, and generally available. A clutch of independently owned local breweries also produces beers that often show as the cheapest on offer in pubs here, most notably Black Sheep, Theakstons (recently bought back from Scottish & Newcastle by Theakston family members – another family member started Black Sheep) and Timothy Taylors. We also found Sam Smiths, Clarks, York, Daleside, Brown Cow and Wold Top at good prices – particularly the first two. And several of our main entries now brew their own beers, also at attractive prices.

ALDBOROUGH SE4166 Map 7
Ship

Village signposted from B6265 just S of Boroughbridge, close to A1

Handy for the A1, this is a creeper-clad village pub with a heavily beamed bar, some old-fashioned seats around heavy cast-iron tables, lots of copper and brass on the walls, and a coal fire in the stone inglenook fireplace. The licensees who moved in last year have brought Mog the cat and fish in two tanks. Decent, straightforward food includes snacks such as sandwiches or filled baked potatoes (from £4.95), and ploughman's (£5.95), as well as home-made soup (£3.95), garlic mushrooms (£4.75), home-made chicken liver pâté (£4.95), tortilla wraps (from £6.95), sausages with red onion gravy (£7.50), spinach and ricotta cannelloni or home-made steak and kidney pie (£7.95), steaks (from £11.95), and seared tuna steak with basil pesto or cherry barbary duck (£12.95); Sunday roast (£7.50). The restaurant is no smoking. Well kept John Smiths, Theakstons Best and Timothy Taylors Landlord on handpump, a decent wine list, and quite a few malt whiskies; piped music and dominoes. There are seats on the front terrace. The Roman town with its museum and Roman pavements is nearby. (Recommended by Peter and Jean Hoare, Clare and Peter Pearse, Andy and Jill Kassube, Roger and Kathleen Lucas, Janet and Peter Race, Jim Auld, Simon Turner, Paul Humphreys, Michael Doswell, Peter and Anne Hollindale, Jonathan Tong, David Collison)

S&N ~ Lease Joanne Thirkell ~ Real ale ~ Bar food (12-2, 5.30-9.30) ~ Restaurant ~ (01423) 322749 ~ Children welcome ~ Singer and guitar last Sat of month ~ Open 11.30-3, 5.30-11.30; 11.30-12 Sat; 11.30-11.30 Sun ~ Bedrooms: £40S/£80S

ALNE SE4965 Map 7

Blue Bell

Off A19 NW of York; Main Street

The first pub in the area to ban smoking throughout, this rather restauranty dining pub is particularly welcoming. There are neatly set tables in the two linked carpeted front areas, with a coal fire on the left and a coal-fired stove on the right, old engravings on cream walls, and stripped joists in the dark red ceiling. The furnishings are an appealing mix of styles and periods; on the left there's a splendid big bow-window seat around one good-sized round table. Behind is a small sun lounge with a sofa, and beyond that, forming an L, what looks an older part of the building, with dark tables on quarry tiles; a little Dickensian bow window opens on to a sort of external corridor around the angle of this L. They have well kept Black Sheep, John Smiths and Timothy Taylors Landlord on handpump, and service is friendly and helpful; piped music. The food includes black pudding tower with caramelised apple and fruit chutney or home-made pâté (£4.75), mushrooms pots with cheese, onions, bacon and cream (£5.25), deep-fried haddock with home-made tartare sauce (£7.25), steak in ale pie (£8.95), vegetable, goats cheese and brie strudel with a tomato and basil sauce (£9.95), oriental steam-infused bass fillets with fresh herbs and lemon zest, roasted rare breed suckling pig with apple and cider sauce or lamb noisettes on a white onion bread croûton topped with pâté and served with a rich madeira sauce (£11.95), half a roast duckling with orange and plum sauce (£12.95), and puddings like sticky toffee pudding or lemon and lime délice (from £4.50); two-course Sunday lunch (£9.95). They have a winning way with game and the like (good local partridge breast, and top marks for their boned and stuffed quail with polenta and wine gravy). A neat garden behind has metal tables and chairs on a small terrace, and some pretty arbour seats. We have not yet heard from any readers who have stayed here, but would expect this to be a nice place to stay in. *(Recommended by Marlene and Jim Godfrey, John Knighton)*

Free house ~ Licensee Michael Anson ~ Real ale ~ Bar food (6-9(10 Sat); 12-3 Sun) ~ Restaurant ~ (01347) 838331 ~ Children welcome ~ Open 6-11; 12-3 Sun; closed weekday lunchtimes and Sun evening

APPLETON-LE-MOORS SE7388 Map 10

Moors

Village N of A170 just under 1½ miles E of Kirkby Moorside

Surprisingly bare of the usual bric-a-brac, this unassuming, mainly no smoking little stone-built pub is strikingly neat and fresh. Sparse decorations include just a few copper pans and earthenware mugs in a little alcove, a couple of plates, one or two pieces of country ironwork, and a delft shelf with miniature whiskies; the whiteness of walls and ceiling is underlined by the black beams and joists, and the bristly grey carpet. Perfect for a cold winter evening, there's a nice built-in high-backed stripped settle next to an old kitchen fireplace, and other seating includes an unusual rustic seat for two cleverly made out of stripped cartwheels; plenty of standing space. To the left of the bar, where you'll probably find a few regulars chatting on the backed padded stools, there's a games room with a pool table (the one place you can smoke) and darts; dominoes. Well kept Black Sheep on handpump, and quite a few malt whiskies. Evening food could include home-made soup (£2.95), home-made chicken liver pâté (£3.95), mushroom quiche (£8.50), local trout (£8.75), chicken breast stuffed with cheese, wrapped in bacon and served with a leek sauce (£9.50), lamb shoulder with apricot stuffing (£9.75), sirloin steak (£11.95), daily specials such as lamb casserole (£8.50), seasonal game pie, and italian chicken or guinea fowl in port (£9.50), and home-made puddings like bilberry flan or sticky toffee pudding (£3.50). There are tables in the walled garden with quiet moors views, and moors walks straight from here to Rosedale Abbey or Hartoft End. The bedrooms are in what used to be a barn behind. More reports please. *(Recommended by Michael and Ann Cole)*

Free house ~ Licensee Janet Frank ~ Real ale ~ Bar food ~ Restaurant ~ No credit cards ~
(01751) 417435 ~ Children in eating area of bar and restaurant ~ Dogs allowed in bar ~
Open 7-11; 12-3, 7-10.30 Sun; closed Mon ~ Bedrooms: £30S/£50B

ASENBY SE3975 Map 7

Crab & Lobster ♀ ⇌

Village signposted off A168 – handy for A1

The rambling, L-shaped bar here still has an interesting jumble of seats from
antique high-backed and other settles through settees and wing armchairs heaped
with cushions, to tall and rather theatrical corner seats; the tables are almost as
much of a mix, and the walls and available surfaces are quite a jungle of bric-a-
brac, with standard and table lamps and candles keeping even the lighting
pleasantly informal. There's also a no smoking dining pavilion with big tropical
plants, nautical bits and pieces, and Edwardian sofas. Bar food includes smoked
haddock and cod fishcakes with a poached egg and fennel butter sauce or egg pasta
with chargrilled peppers, plum tomatoes, pesto and parmesan (£6; main course
£12), chicken, basil and brie wrapped in bacon with garlic creamed mushrooms
(£14), braised lamb shank with dried fruit couscous (£14.50), posh fish and chips
with crushed peas and lobster tartare sauce (£16), and puddings such as sticky
toffee pudding with butterscotch sauce or plum and apple crumble with clotted
cream (£6). Well kept Marstons Pedigree and John Smiths on handpump, and 15
wines by the glass from an interesting list; piped music. The gardens have bamboo
and palm trees lining the paths, there's a gazebo at the end of the walkways, and
seats on a mediterranean-style terrace. The opulent bedrooms (based on famous
hotels around the world) are in the surrounding house which has seven acres of
mature gardens, and 180-metre golf hole with full practice facilities. More reports
please. *(Recommended by Janet and Peter Race, Dr and Mrs R G J Telfer, Patrick and
Phillipa Vickery, Edward and Deanna Pearce, Alan Jones, Jack Morley)*

Vimac Leisure ~ Licensee Mark Spenceley ~ Real ale ~ Bar food (12-2.30, 7-9.30) ~
Restaurant ~ (01845) 577286 ~ Children in eating area of bar and restaurant ~ Dogs
allowed in bedrooms ~ Lunchtime jazz Sun; some evenings, too ~ Open 11.30-12; 12-12
Sun ~ Bedrooms: /£150B

BECK HOLE NZ8202 Map 10

Birch Hall

Signed off A169 SW of Whitby, from top of Sleights Moor

Unique, and in a beautiful steep valley, this is a charming pub-cum-village shop.
There are two rooms (one is no smoking) with the shop selling postcards, sweeties
and ice-creams in between, and hatch service to both sides. Furnishings are simple –
built-in cushioned wall seats and wooden tables (spot the one with 136 pennies, all
heads up, embedded in the top) and chairs on the floor (flagstones in one room,
composition in the other), some strange items such as french breakfast cereal boxes
and a tube of Macleans toothpaste priced 1/3d, and well kept Black Sheep Bitter
and Durham Bonny Lass and Malton Double Chance on handpump; several malt
whiskies. Bar snacks like locally-made pies (£1.50), butties (£2.10), and home-made
scones and cakes including their lovely beer cake (from 90p); friendly, welcoming
staff; dominoes and quoits. Outside, an ancient oil painting of the view up the
steeply wooded river valley hangs on the pub wall, there are benches out in front,
and steep steps up to a little steeply terraced side garden with a moorland view.
This is a lovely spot with marvellous surrounding walks – you can walk along the
disused railway line from Goathland; part of the path from Beck Hole to Grosmont
is surfaced with mussel shells. *(Recommended by Paul Newberry, Michael and Ann Cole,
Christopher Turner, David and Ruth Hollands, John Fiander, Patrick Hancock, the Didler,
Colin and Dot Savill, Pete Baker, David Carr, C E Reid, Pat and Tony Martin)*

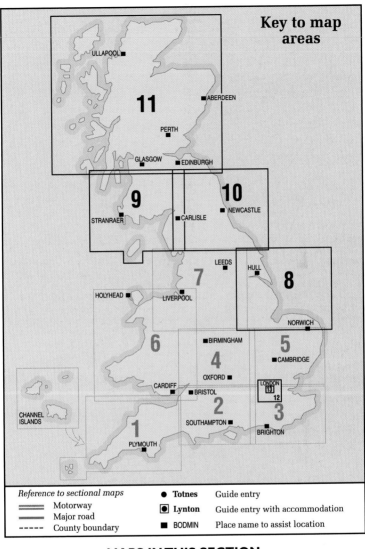

Key to map areas

Reference to sectional maps
≡≡≡ Motorway
≡≡≡ Major road
----- County boundary

● **Totnes**   Guide entry
◉ **Lynton**   Guide entry with accommodation
■ **BODMIN**   Place name to assist location

MAPS IN THIS SECTION

For Maps 1 – 7 see earlier colour section

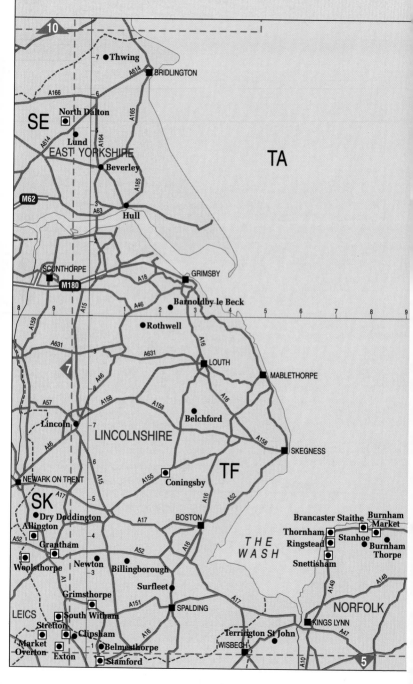

10

● Thwing
A614
■ BRIDLINGTON
A166
SE
North Dalton ◉
A165
A614
Lund ●
A164
EAST YORKSHIRE
● Beverley
A165
M62
A63 3
Hull
A15 2
A18
A46
SCUNTHORPE
M180
A159
A15
1
● GRIMSBY
A46 2 Barnoldby le Beck
8 9
A631
● Rothwell
9
A631
A16
7
A46
■ LOUTH
8
A57
A158
A158
A16
■ MABLETHORPE
● Belchford
Lincoln ◉ 7
LINCOLNSHIRE
A158
A46
A158
■ SKEGNESS
6
A15
TF
NEWARK ON TRENT
A155 ◉
A17
5
Coningsby
A16
A52
SK
● Dry Doddington
A17
A16
Allington ●
BOSTON ■
Brancaster Staithe ◉ ■ Burnham
A52
4
A52
Thornham ◉ Market
Grantham ◉
THE
Ringstead ◉ Stanhoe ◉
Newton ◉
WASH
● Burnham
Woolsthorpe ◉
Billingborough ●
A16
Thorpe
3
Snettisham ◉
Grimsthorpe ◉
Surfleet ●
A149
A148
LEICS
A151
SPALDING ■
A17
NORFOLK
South Witham ◉
Stretton ◉
Terrington St John ●
■ KINGS LYNN
Clipsham ◉
A16
A47
Market
Belmesthorpe ●
WISBECH ■
Overton ◉
Exton ◉ ◉ Stamford
A10
5

TA

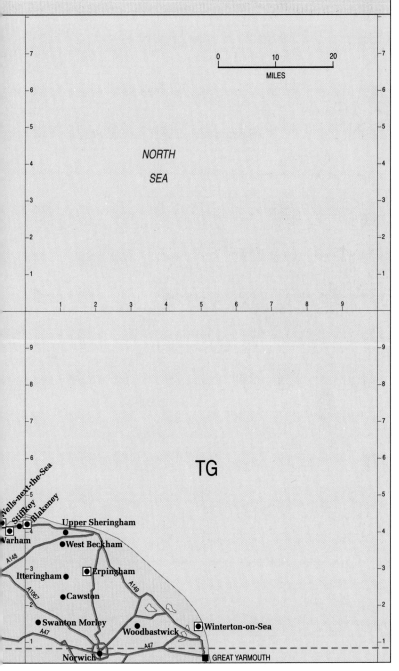

0   10   20
MILES

NORTH

SEA

TG

Wells-next-the-Sea
Stiffkey
Blakeney
Upper Sheringham
Warham
West Beckham
A148
Erpingham
Itteringham
A149
Cawston
A1067
Swanton Morley
Woodbastwick
Winterton-on-Sea
A47
Norwich
A47
GREAT YARMOUTH

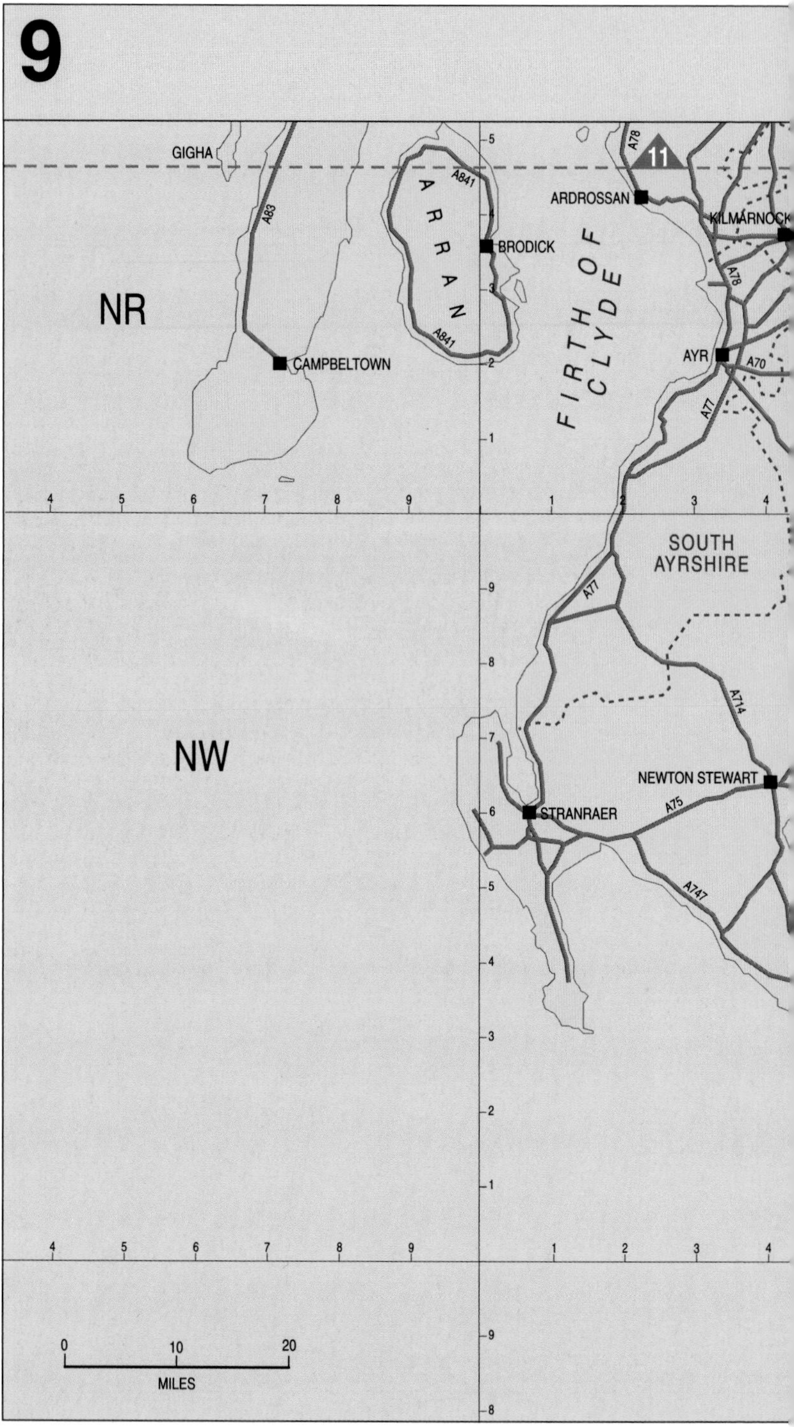

GIGHA

A841

A R R A N

A841

ARDROSSAN

KILMARNOCK

A78

BRODICK

A78

NR

FIRTH OF CLYDE

AYR

A70

CAMPBELTOWN

A841

A77

SOUTH AYRSHIRE

A77

A714

NW

A75

NEWTON STEWART

STRANRAER

A77

A747

A83

0   10   20

MILES

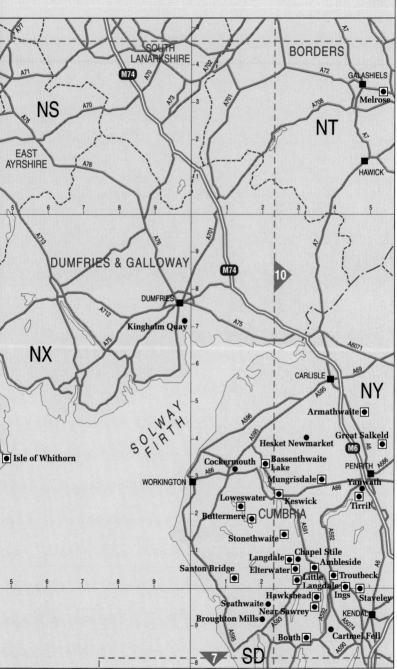

SOUTH
LANARKSHIRE

BORDERS

M74

GALASHIELS

Melrose

NS

NT

EAST
AYRSHIRE

HAWICK

DUMFRIES & GALLOWAY

M74

10

DUMFRIES

Kingholm Quay

NX

SOLWAY
FIRTH

CARLISLE

NY

Armathwaite

Isle of Whithorn

Great Salkeld

M6

Hesket Newmarket

PENRITH

Cockermouth

Bassenthwaite
Lake

WORKINGTON

Mungrisdale

Yanwath

Loweswater

Keswick

Tirril

Buttermere

CUMBRIA

Stonethwaite

Chapel Stile

Langdale

Ambleside

Santon Bridge

Elterwater

Troutbeck

Little
Langdale

Ings

Staveley

Hawkshead

Seathwaite

Near Sawrey

KENDAL

Broughton Mills

Bouth

Cartmel Fell

SD

7

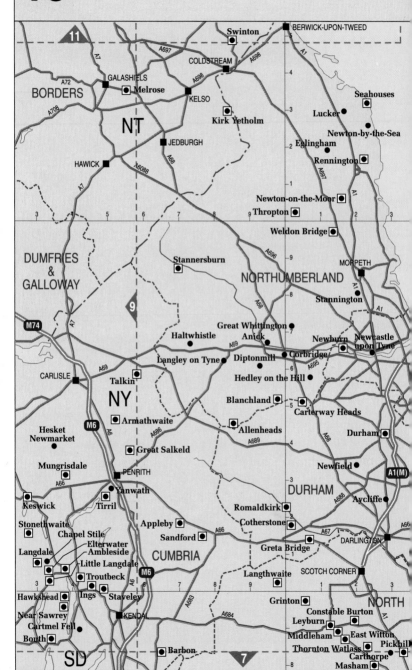

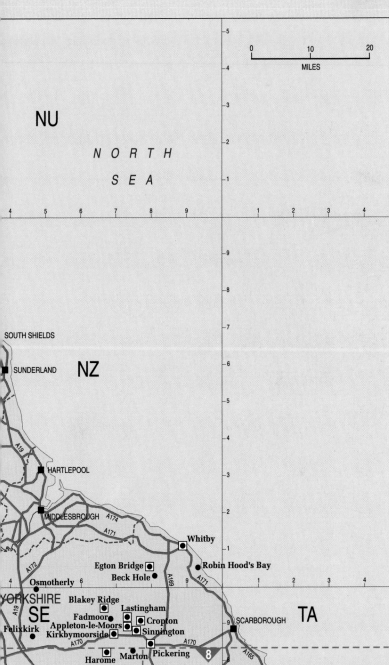

NU

N O R T H

S E A

0   10   20
MILES

SOUTH SHIELDS

■ SUNDERLAND   NZ

■ HARTLEPOOL

■ MIDDLESBROUGH   A174

A171

● Whitby

Egton Bridge ◉
      Beck Hole ●

● Robin Hood's Bay

● Osmotherly

YORKSHIRE   Blakey Ridge
                    ◉
SE   Fadmoor ●   ◉ ◉ Lastingham
       ● Appleton-le-Moors ◉ ◉ Cropton
Felixkirk ● Kirkbymoorside ◉ ● Sinnington
A170

● Harome ◉ Marton ● Pickering 8

■ SCARBOROUGH   TA

A170   A165

A172

A19

A19

A172

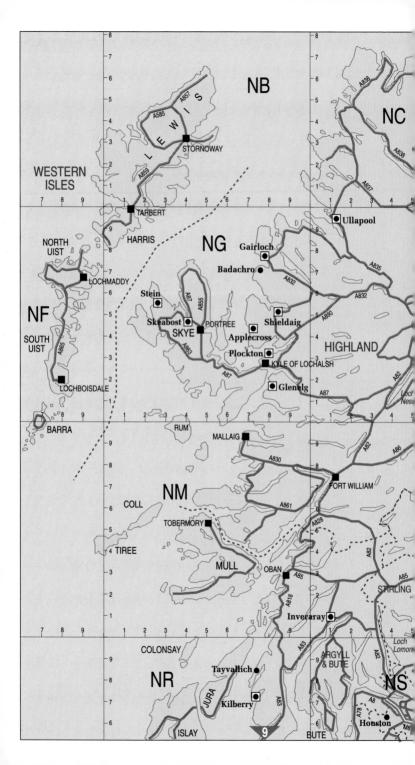

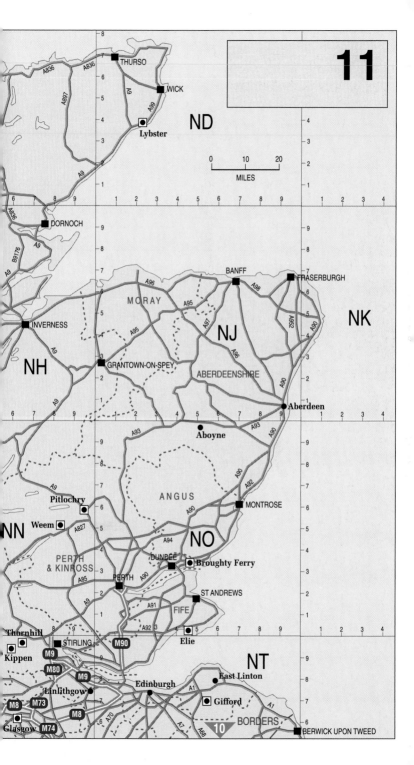

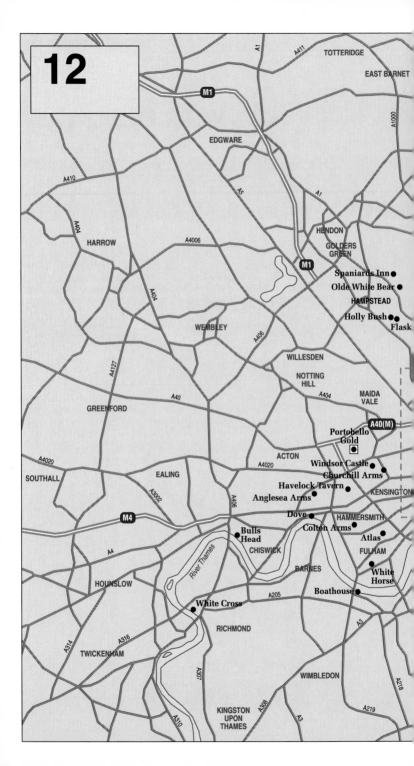

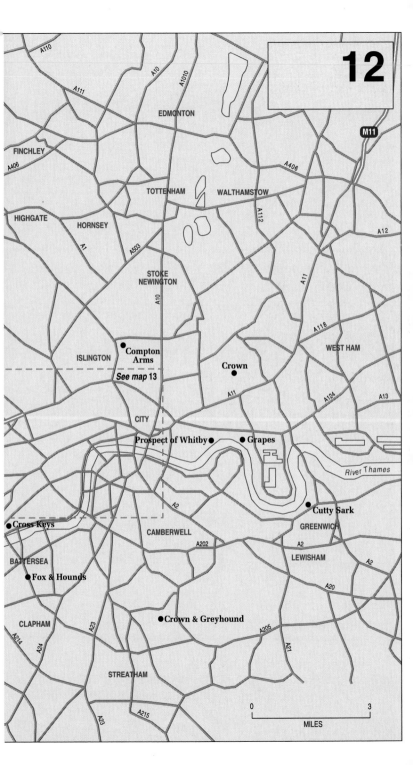

A110
A10
A1010
A111
EDMONTON
M11
FINCHLEY
A406
A406
A12
TOTTENHAM
WALTHAMSTOW
HIGHGATE
HORNSEY
A112
A1
A503
A12
STOKE
NEWINGTON
A11
A10
A118
WEST HAM
ISLINGTON
●Compton
Arms
●Crown
See map 13
A11
A124
A13
CITY
A11
●Grapes
Prospect of Whitby●
River Thames
A2
●Cutty Sark
●Cross Keys
GREENWICH
CAMBERWELL
A202
A2
LEWISHAM
A2
BATTERSEA
●Fox & Hounds
A20
CLAPHAM
A23
A214
A24
●Crown & Greyhound
A205
A21
STREATHAM
A215
A23

0   3
MILES

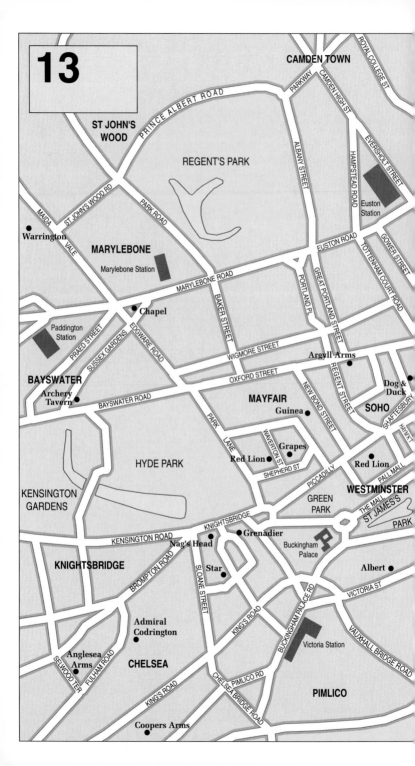

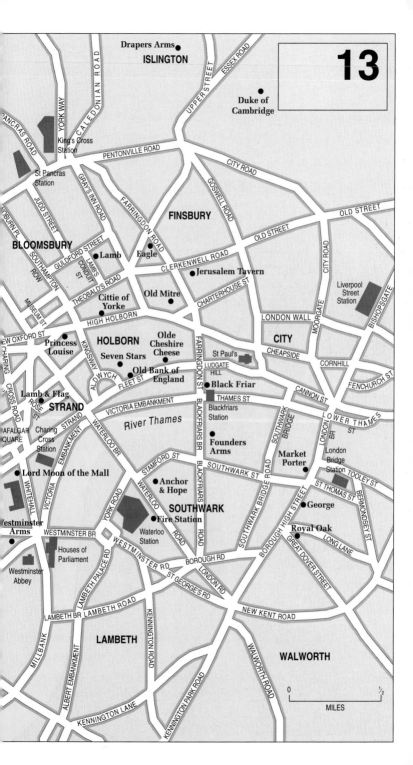

13

Drapers Arms •
ISLINGTON

UPPER STREET

ESSEX ROAD

•
Duke of
Cambridge

CALEDONIAN ROAD

YORK WAY

PANCRAS ROAD

King's Cross
Station

PENTONVILLE ROAD

CITY ROAD

St Pancras
Station

GRAY'S INN ROAD

FARRINGDON ROAD

GOSWELL ROAD

OLD STREET

JUDD STREET

FINSBURY

OLD STREET

CITY ROAD

OBURN PL

BLOOMSBURY

GUILDFORD STREET

LAMB'S

• Lamb

Eagle •

CLERKENWELL ROAD

• Jerusalem Tavern

OLD STREET

Liverpool
Street
Station

BISHOPSGATE

SOUTHAMPTON
ROW

CONDUIT
ST

THEOBALD'S ROAD

Cittie of
Yorke

Old Mitre •

CHARTERHOUSE ST

LONDON WALL

MORGATE

M USEUM ST

HIGH HOLBORN

CITY

EW OXFORD ST

Olde
Cheshire
Cheese

HOLBORN

St Paul's

CHEAPSIDE

CORNHILL

CHARING

Princess
Louise •

Seven Stars

KINGSWAY

Olde Bank of
England

FARRINGDON ST

LUDGATE
HILL

• Black Friar

CANNON ST

FENCHURCH ST

ALDWYCH

FLEET ST

Lamb & Flag •

ROSE

STRAND

STRAND

VICTORIA EMBANKMENT

BLACKFRIARS BR

THAMES ST

Blackfriars
Station

LOWER THAMES
ST

LONDON BR

CROSS ROAD

EMBANKMENT

WATERLOO BR

River Thames

SOUTHWARK
BRIDGE

AFALGAR
QUARE

Charing
Cross
Station

STAMFORD ST

•
Founders
Arms

SOUTHWARK ST

• Market
Porter

London
Bridge
Station

TOOLEY ST

• Lord Moon of the Mall

VICTORIA

YORK ROAD

WATERLOO

BLACKFRIARS BR

SOUTHWARK ST

SOUTHWARK BRIDGE ROAD

BOROUGH HIGH STREET

ST THOMAS ST

BERMONDSEY ST

WHITEHALL

• Anchor
& Hope

SOUTHWARK

• George

estminster
Arms

WESTMINSTER BR

Fire Station •

Waterloo
Station

WATERLOO
ROAD

Royal Oak •

LONG LANE

Houses of
Parliament

WESTMINSTER RD

BOROUGH RD

GREAT DOVER STREET

Westminster
Abbey

LAMBETH PALACE RD

ST GEORGE'S RD

LONDON RD

MILLBANK

LAMBETH BR

LAMBETH ROAD

KENNINGTON ROAD

NEW KENT ROAD

ALBERT EMBANKMENT

LAMBETH

WALWORTH

WALWORTH ROAD

KENNINGTON LANE

KENNINGTON PARK ROAD

0   ½

MILES

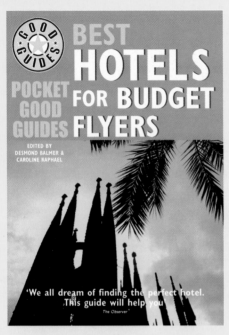

From affordable B&Bs to hip designer hotels, exclusive boutique hotels to characterful guesthouses, this handy guide covers over 50 destinations and 200 places to stay.

✱ Essential reading for the dedicated European traveller

✱ A wide range of choices – from affordable B&Bs to luxury hotels

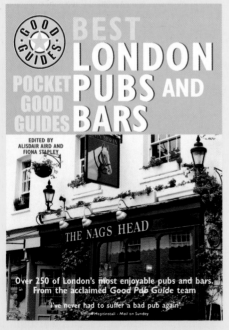

From the national institution that is *The Good Pub Guide* comes this fantastic pocket guide to the capital's finest pubs and bars. Sit back, relax with a drink and enjoy London living at its best.

✱ Over 250 of London's best watering-holes

✱ Includes the finest food pubs and bars

Free house ~ Licensees Neil and Glenys Crampton ~ Real ale ~ Bar food (available during all opening hours) ~ No credit cards ~ (01947) 896245 ~ Children in small family room ~ Dogs welcome ~ Open 11-11; 12-10.30 Sun; 11-3, 7.30-11 in winter

BEVERLEY TA0340 Map 8

White Horse £

Hengate, close to the imposing Church of St Mary's; runs off North Bar

Known locally as 'Nellies', this fine unspoilt pub has a carefully preserved Victorian feel and is quite without frills. The basic but very atmospheric little rooms are huddled together around the central bar, with brown leatherette seats (high-backed settles in one little snug) and basic wooden chairs and benches on bare floorboards, antique cartoons and sentimental engravings on the nicotine-stained walls, a gaslit pulley-controlled chandelier, a deeply reverberating chiming clock, and open fires – one with an attractively tiled old fireplace. Well kept and very cheap Sam Smiths OB on handpump, and simple food (they tell us prices have not changed this year) such as sandwiches, bangers and mash or pasta provençale (£3.95), steak in ale pie (£4.50), lasagne (£4.95), gammon with parsley sauce (£5.50), lamb shank (£6.95), and puddings like spotted dick and custard (£2). A separate games room has darts, fruit machine, trivia and two pool tables – these and the no smoking room behind the bar are the only modern touches. John Wesley preached in the back yard in the mid-18th c. *(Recommended by Marlene and Jim Godfrey, the Didler, Paul and Ursula Randall, Pete Baker, David Carr, Mark Walker, Len Beattie)*

Sam Smiths ~ Manager Anna ~ Real ale ~ Bar food (11-3 Mon-Sat; 12-2.30 Sun) ~ No credit cards ~ (01482) 861973 ~ Children welcome away from bar until 8pm ~ Dogs allowed in bar ~ Open 11-11; 12-10.30 Sun

BLAKEY RIDGE SE6799 Map 10

Lion 🍺 🛏

From A171 Guisborough—Whitby follow Castleton, Hutton le Hole signposts; from A170 Kirkby Moorside—Pickering follow Keldholm, Hutton le Hole, Castleton signposts; OS Sheet 100 map reference 679996

With stunning views and lots of surrounding hikes (the Coast to Coast Footpath is close by), it's not surprising that this bustling pub is very busy in summer, and the very good value bedrooms do get booked up weeks in advance. The beamed and rambling bars have warm open fires, a few big high-backed rustic settles around cast-iron-framed tables, lots of small dining chairs, a nice leather settee, and stone walls hung with some old engravings and photographs of the pub under snow (it can easily get cut off in winter). Generous helpings of good basic bar food include lunchtime sandwiches (from £2.95) and filled baked potatoes (from £3.25), as well as giant yorkshire pudding and gravy or soup (£2.25), home-cooked ham and egg, lasagne, chicken curry, battered cod, and leek and mushroom crumble (all £7.50), daily specials such as steak in Guinness pie or a roast (£7.50), 10oz fillet steak (£12.95), and puddings like sticky toffee sponge or profiteroles with chocolate sauce (£2.95). Three restaurants are no smoking. Well kept Greene King Old Speckled Hen and Theakstons Best, Old Peculier, Black Bull and XB on handpump; piped music, dominoes and fruit machine. *(Recommended by Mrs P Hall, Dr J Barrie Jones, Dr David Cockburn, Peter Coxon, Mark and Ruth Brock, Sylvia and Tony Birbeck)*

Free house ~ Licensee Barry Crossland ~ Real ale ~ Bar food (12-10) ~ Restaurant ~ (01751) 417320 ~ Children welcome ~ Dogs allowed in bar and bedrooms ~ Live music every third Thurs ~ Open 11(10.30 Sat)-11; 12-11 Sun ~ Bedrooms: £18(£37.50B)/£50(£60B)

By law pubs must show a price list of their drinks. Let us know if you
are inconvenienced by any breach of this law.

BOROUGHBRIDGE SE3966 Map 7 🏠

Black Bull ♀

St James Square; B6265, just off A1(M)

A bad fire destroyed the bedrooms in the more modern wing of this attractive old town centre inn, but by the time this edition is published, they should be open again. The main bar area has a relaxed, friendly atmosphere, a big stone fireplace and brown leather seats, and is served through an old-fashioned hatch; there's also a cosy and attractive snug with traditional wall settles. The restaurant and part of the bar area are no smoking. Enjoyable bar food includes soup (£2.95), sandwiches (from £2.85; hot roast loin of pork topped with bramley apple compote £4.25), chinese-style duck salad (£5.50), pork and chive sausages with onion gravy (£5.95), roasted peppers, red onions and wild mushroom pizza (£6.50), gammon and egg or home-made pie of the day (£6.95), thai beef with noodles and vegetables (£7.50), smoked chicken with tagliatelle in a creamy garlic sauce (£7.85), chargrilled tuna steak (£9.50), steaks (from £10.25), and puddings (£3). Well kept Black Sheep Bitter, John Smiths, and a guest such as Roosters Yankee on handpump, enjoyable wines (with ten by the glass), and quite a few malt whiskies; dominoes. Service is friendly and attentive, the two borzoi dogs are called Charlie and Sadie, and the two cats Mimi and Cyny; the local mummers perform here three or four times a year. The hanging baskets are lovely. *(Recommended by Anthony Barnes, Dr Peter D Smart, the Didler, Charles and Pauline Stride, Ian and Nita Cooper)*

Free house ~ Licensees Anthony and Jillian Burgess ~ Real ale ~ Bar food (12-2, 6-9) ~ Restaurant ~ (01423) 322413 ~ Children welcome ~ Dogs welcome ~ Open 11-11; 12-10.30 Sun ~ Bedrooms: £40S/£60S

BRADFIELD SK2392 Map 7

Strines Inn

From A57 heading E of junction with A6013 (Ladybower Reservoir) take first left turn (signposted with Bradfield) then bear left; with a map can also be reached more circuitously from Strines signpost on A616 at head of Underbank Reservoir, W of Stocksbridge

This 13th-c inn is surrounded by superb scenery on the edge of the High Peak National Park and there are fine views from the picnic-sets; a safely fenced in children's playground, and some rescued animals. The main bar has a welcoming atmosphere, black beams liberally decked with copper kettles and so forth, quite a menagerie of stuffed animals, homely red-plush-cushioned traditional wooden wall benches and small chairs, and a coal fire in the rather grand stone fireplace; there's a good mixture of customers. A room off on the right has another coal fire, hunting photographs and prints, and lots of brass and china, and on the left is another similarly furnished room; two rooms are no smoking. Well liked bar food includes home-made soup (£2.70), sandwiches (from £2.10; hot panini bread with roast pork £3.70), filled baked potatoes (from £3.35), garlic mushrooms (£3.95), filled giant yorkshire puddings (from £5.95), liver and onions (£6.50), mediterranean vegetable hotpot (£6.95), pie of the day (£7.25), steaks (from £8.95), daily specials such as home-made vegetable chilli (£5.95), and home-made shepherd's pie or cajun chicken (£6.95), and puddings like home-made apple and blackberry crumble (£3.30). Well kept Badger Tanglefoot, Banks's Mansfield Dark Bitter, and Marstons Pedigree on handpump, and several malt whiskies; piped music. The bedrooms have four-poster beds (one has an open log fire). *(Recommended by the Didler, Matt Waite, R T and J C Moggridge, Greta and Christopher Wells, Peter F Marshall, Bob)*

Free house ~ Licensee Bruce Howarth ~ Real ale ~ Bar food (12-3, 6-9 winter weekdays; all day weekends and summer weekdays) ~ (0114) 285 1247 ~ Children welcome ~ Dogs welcome ~ Open 10.30-11; 10.30-10.30 Sun; 10.30-3, 6-11 weekdays in winter ~ Bedrooms: /£67.50B

There are report forms at the back of the book.

BREARTON SE3261 Map 7

Malt Shovel ⑪ ◀

Village signposted off A61 N of Harrogate

Although this 16th-c village pub is slightly off the beaten track, it is handy for
Harrogate and Knaresborough. Several heavily-beamed rooms radiate from the
attractive linenfold oak bar counter with plush-cushioned seats and a mix of tables,
an ancient oak partition wall, tankards and horsebrasses, an open fire, and
paintings by local artists (for sale) and lively hunting prints on the walls. The dining
area is no smoking. Under the new licensees, bar food now includes sandwiches
(from £3.50), ploughman's (£5.75), meaty or vegetarian lasagne (£5.95), sausage
and mash (£6.75), lamb curry or steak in ale pie (£6.95), haddock and chips
(£7.95), seafood gratin (£8.20), daily specials, and puddings (£3.75). Well kept
Black Sheep Bitter, Daleside Bitter, and Theakstons Best, and a guest such as
Salamander Golden Salamander on handpump, and several malt whiskies. You can
eat outside on the small terrace where they have outdoor heaters. More reports
please. *(Recommended by G Dobson, Jo Lilley, Simon Calvert, Ken Black, Paul Boot, Tim and
Ann Newell, Mr and Mrs Staples, Pierre Richterich, Mike Tucker, Peter and Jean Dowson,
Ian and Nita Cooper)*

Free house ~ Licensees Jamie and Hayley Stewart ~ Real ale ~ Bar food (not Sun evening
or Mon) ~ No credit cards ~ (01423) 862929 ~ Children welcome ~ Dogs welcome ~
Open 11.45-3, 6.45-11; 11/45-3, 7-10.30 Sun; closed Mon

BURN SE5928 Map 7

Wheatsheaf ◀ £

A19 Selby—Doncaster; Main Road

This roadside mock-Tudor pub is very nicely done up inside, for example with
gleaming copper kettles, black dagging shears, polished buffalo horns and the like
around its good log and coal fire, and a drying rack with bunches of herbs above it.
There are masses more to look at on the walls, from the decorative mugs above one
bow-window seat to cases of model vans and lorries on the pink-painted walls. The
highly polished pub tables in the partly divided open-plan bar have comfortable
seats around them, and the atmosphere is welcoming and chatty, with a friendly
landlord and neat efficient young staff. Good value food might include sandwiches
or burgers (£1.95), ploughman's (£2.95), steak pie, lamb rogan josh, vegetarian
dishes, lasagne, and chilli con carne (all £4.95), and sirloin steak (£6.50); notable
fish and chips (OAPs £1.95; medium £4.50; jumbo £5.50), and Sunday lunch (from
£4.50). They have well kept changing ales such as Black Sheep Best, Elgoods
Cambridge, Ossett Pale Gold, John Smiths, Timothy Taylors Landlord and
Wharfedale Folly on handpump at attractive prices, over 50 malt whiskies, and
australian wines at exceptionally low mark-ups. A pool table is out of the way on
the left, cribbage, dominoes, fruit machine, TV, and there may be unobtrusive piped
music. A small garden behind has picnic-sets on a heated terrace. *(Recommended by
J A Ellis, Matt Waite)*

Free house ~ Licensee Andrew Howdall ~ Bar food (12-2 daily and 6.30-8.30 Thurs-Sat) ~
Restaurant ~ (01757) 270614 ~ Children welcome ~ Dogs welcome ~ Local live bands
and theatre companies monthly Weds or Sat ~ Open 12-11(10.30 Sun)

BURTON LEONARD SE3364 Map 7

Hare & Hounds

Village signposted off A61 Ripon—Harrogate (and easily reached from A1(M) exit 48)

There's a bustling, friendly atmosphere and a good mix of customers in this well
run country pub. The large turkey-carpeted main area is divided by a two-way
stone fireplace with a log fire, and the traditional furnishings include flowery-
cushioned captain's chairs, wall pews, grey plush stools and so forth; the restaurant
and lounge are no smoking. The ceiling has a couple of beech branches strung with
white fairy lights, there are some olde-worlde prints and decorative plates, and an

eye-catching long bar counter, under gleaming copper and brass pans and measures; well kept Black Sheep, Tetleys, and Timothy Taylors Landlord on handpump, up to 15 wines by the glass, and 30 malt whiskies; dominoes. Enjoyable bar food includes lunchtime sandwiches and filled baguettes (from £3.95), as well as home-made soup (£4.50), creamy garlic mushrooms (£5.85), cajun vegetable curry (£8.95), home-made steak and kidney pie, chicken with a leek, bacon, cream and white wine sauce, smoked haddock and broccoli mornay, and gammon and egg (all £9.95), breast of duck with a port, orange and summer berry sauce (£12.95), rack of lamb with mint and redcurrant sauce (£13.95), steaks (from £13.95), and puddings (£3.95). On the left as you go in, a bright little room has a pink sofa and easy chairs, and local village prints and old postcards. The flowering tubs and window boxes outside are very pretty all year round; seats in the back garden. More reports please. *(Recommended by R E Dixon, Janet and Peter Race, R J Herd, DC)*

Free house ~ Licensees Sarah and Tony Porter ~ Real ale ~ Bar food (12-2, 6-9; not Tues) ~ Restaurant ~ (01765) 677355 ~ Children in eating area of bar and restaurant ~ Open 12-3, 5.30-11; closed Tues

BYLAND ABBEY SE5579 Map 7

Abbey Inn 🍴 🛏️

The Abbey has a brown tourist-attraction signpost off the A170 Thirsk—Helmsley

Under the instructions of Henry VIII, what was at one time the largest ecclesiastical building in Europe was closed and eventually fell into ruins. This inn was built, also by monks, 300 years later. The two no smoking characterful front rooms have big fireplaces, oak and stripped deal tables, settees, carved oak seats, and Jacobean-style dining chairs on the polished boards and flagstones; there are various stuffed birds, little etchings and china cabinets, and some discreet stripping back of plaster to show the ex-abbey masonry. The Library has lots of bookshelves and a large single oak table (ideal for a party of up to ten people), and the big back room has lots of rustic bygones; piped music. Imaginative food at lunchtime might include soup with ciabatta croûtons (£4.75), chicken liver and wild mushroom pâté with plum and apple chutney or antipasti (£6.50), main course £8.50), lemon peppered chicken salad (£6.75), main course £8.75), roasted red pepper filled with wild mushroom risotto with tomato and garlic sauce (£8.75), roasted barnsley chop lancashire hotpot-style (£9.75), crispy cod loin on minted pea purée (£10.25), and calves liver with crispy bacon and onion gravy (£12); evening choices such as home-made soup (£4.75), crispy courgette ribbons with herb salad and mango avocado salsa (£6.50), thinly sliced halibut with a timbale of fresh crab and celeriac remoulade (£7.95), corn-fed chicken on sunblush tomato and black olive salad with basil couscous (£11), braised lamb shank with port and rosemary reduction or griddled rack of venison with port and thyme sauce (£14), and puddings like iced pistachio and mascarpone parfait with port figs or glazed espresso crème brûlée with home-made white chocolate and raspberry ice-cream (£4.95). Well kept Black Sheep Bitter and Tetleys on handpump, and an interesting wine list with 20 (plus champagne) by the glass. Plenty of room outside on the terrace and in the garden. *(Recommended by Dr Pete Crawshaw, A and B Myers, Michael Ward, Mike and Lynn Robinson, A S and M E Marriott, Edward and Deanna Pearce, Marlene and Jim Godfrey, Peter Burton, Walter and Susan Rinaldi-Butcher, Ian and Rose Lock)*

Free house ~ Licensees Jane and Martin Nordli ~ Real ale ~ Bar food (not Sun evening or Mon lunchtime) ~ Restaurant ~ (01347) 868204 ~ Children welcome ~ Open 12-3, 6.30-11; 12-5 Sun; closed Sun evening and Mon lunchtime ~ Bedrooms: /£95B

'Children welcome' means the pub says it lets children inside without any special restriction. If it allows them in, but to restricted areas such as an eating area or family room, we specify this. Some pubs may impose an evening time limit. We do not mention limits after 9pm as we assume children are home by then.

CARTHORPE SE3184 Map 10

Fox & Hounds 🕮 ♀

Village signposted from A1 N of Ripon, via B6285

Handy for a break on the A1 northbound, this neatly kept and well run extended dining pub is popular for its interesting food; best to book a table in advance – especially at weekends. The cosy L-shaped bar has quite a few mistily evocative Victorian photographs of Whitby, a couple of nice seats by the larger of its two log fires, plush button-back built-in wall banquettes and chairs, plates on stripped beams, and some limed panelling; piped light classical music. There is some theatrical memorabilia in the corridors, and an attractive high-raftered no smoking restaurant with lots of neatly black-painted farm and smithy tools. Served by attentive staff, the food might include sandwiches, home-made soups (£3.45), grilled black pudding with caramelised apple and onion marmalade (£4.95), smoked salmon pâté (£5.25), fresh crab tartlet (£5.95), chicken filled with coverdale cheese in a creamy sauce (£10.95), pheasant breast with a pear and thyme stuffing wrapped in bacon with a red wine sauce (£11.95), fried bass on potato rösti with red pepper sauce (£12.95), rack of lamb on a blackcurrant croûton with redcurrant gravy (£13.50), half a roasted gressingham duckling with orange sauce and parsley and thyme stuffing (£14.95), grilled fillet steak with mango and horseradish relish (£14.95), and daily specials, with delicious puddings such as sticky orange marmalade sponge, white chocolate and irish cream cheesecake or raspberry and almond tart (from £4.85). On Tuesdays to Thursdays they also offer a two-course (£12.95) and three-course (£14.95) set meal. Well kept Black Sheep on handpump, and from their extensive list they will open any wine for you just to have a glass. More reports please. *(Recommended by Janet and Peter Race, Michael Doswell, JWAC, Wendy and Carl Dye, Mr and Mrs I Templeton, Adam and Joan Bunting, R N and M I Bailey, Peter Hacker)*

Free house ~ Licensees Howard and Bernie Fitzgerald ~ Real ale ~ Bar food (not Mon) ~ Restaurant ~ (01845) 567433 ~ Children in restaurant until 8.30pm ~ Open 12-2.30, 7-11(10.30 Sun); closed Mon

CHAPEL LE DALE SD7477 Map 7

Hill Inn ◀

B5655 Ingleton—Hawes, 3 miles N of Ingleton

Extremely welcoming and helpful licensees run this friendly inn. There are fine views to Ingleborough and Whernside and wonderful remote walks, but it is essential to phone beforehand to check their opening times. There are old pine tables and benches on the stripped wooden floors, nice pictures on the walls, stripped-stone recesses, a warm log fire, and up to half a dozen well kept real ales on handpump: Black Sheep Best, Special and Riggwelter, Dent Aviator and Best, and Theakstons Best. The dining room is no smoking, and there's a well worn-in sun lounge. They tell us the good, enjoyable food cooked by the licensees is the same as last year: lunchtime sandwiches (from £4.60) and sausage and mash with red wine and onion gravy (£8.25), as well as more elaborate evening meals such as blue cheese and polenta tart with sautéed vegetables and a home-made tomato sauce (£9.25), grilled salmon on chive mash with a light thai curry sauce (£9.85), beef in ale casserole or chicken provençale (£9.95), lamb shank with home-made mint sauce or confit of duck with herb mash and apple sauce (£10.95), and super puddings such as warm chocolate pudding with white chocolate sauce and home-made vanilla ice-cream, sticky toffee pudding or crème brûlée with orange salad and home-made orange and yoghurt ice-cream (£4.65); the home-baked bread is very good, and there may be sugar sculptures to look at. More reports please. *(Recommended by Mike Turner, Karen Eliot, Tony and Maggie Harwood, Helen Pollard, Richard and Anne Ansell, Richard Mason, J Conti-Ramsden, Rona Murdoch)*

Free house ~ Licensee Sabena Martin ~ Real ale ~ Bar food (not Mon) ~ Restaurant ~ (015242) 41256 ~ Children in eating area of bar and restaurant ~ Dogs allowed in bar ~ Folk club penultimate Sat of month; folk night last Fri of month (if anyone turns up) ~

Open 6.30-11; may open all day Sun and Sat; closed all Mon, also Tues-Fri lunchtimes ~
Bedrooms: /£65S

CONSTABLE BURTON SE1791 Map 10
Wyvill Arms 🍽 ♉ ◼
A684 E of Leyburn

There are plans to add both a bistro and a dining room extension here, and the
whole place is now no smoking. The small bar area has a mix of seating, a finely
worked plaster ceiling with the Wyvill family's coat of arms, and an elaborate stone
fireplace. The second bar, where food is served, has semicircled, upholstered
alcoves, a seventies juke box with music for all ages, hunting prints and old oak
tables; the reception area of this room includes a huge chesterfield which can seat
up to eight people, another carved stone fireplace, and an old leaded church
stained-glass window partition. Both rooms are hung with pictures of local scenes.
Popular, enjoyable food includes light lunches such as soup (£3.50), filled baguettes
(from £3.95), and scrambled egg and smoked salmon (£5.45), as well as duck liver
mousse (£4.70), moules marinière (£4.95), rarebit and smoked haddock with roast
cherry tomatoes (£5.20), sardines with tomato and capers on toast (£5.70), spicy
suckling pig stir fry (£5.75), banana stuffed chicken with thai curry sauce and sticky
coconut rice (£11.95), roasted fillet of lamb with a herb crust and parsnip purée
(£12.95), monkfish wrapped in parma ham with exotic mushrooms and a red wine
and butter sauce or aberdeen angus rib-eye steak with bordelaise sauce (£14.95),
and shin of veal braised in madeira with a three-mustard sauce (£15.45); they make
all their own bread, butter, ice-creams and sorbets. Well kept Black Sheep, John
Smiths Bitter and Theakstons Best with a guest like Hydes Cloud Nine on
handpump, and a dozen wines by the glass; cribbage, dominoes, darts and piped
music. There's a herb and vegetable garden behind the pub, and several large
wooden benches with large white parasols for outdoor dining. Constable Burton
Gardens are opposite and worth a visit. Although dogs are allowed in the bar, they
are not welcome in the dining room. *(Recommended by E D Fraser, John Close, Ian and
Nita Cooper, Anna Cooper, Mrs J Doherty, Ben and Helen Ingram, Andrew Shore,
Maria Williams, Richard and Anne Ansell, Jack Morley, Mike and Jayne Bastin)*

Free house ~ Licensee Nigel Stevens ~ Real ale ~ Bar food (not Mon except bank hols) ~
Restaurant ~ (01677) 450581 ~ Children welcome ~ Dogs allowed in bar and bedrooms
~ Open 12-3, 6(7 Sun)-11; closed Mon except bank hols ~ Bedrooms: £40B/£60B

CRAY SD9379 Map 7
White Lion ◼ 🛏
B6160, Upper Wharfedale N of Kettlewell

The countryside surrounding this warmly friendly former drovers' hostelry is
superb, and walkers are made most welcome. The simply furnished bar has an open
fire, a traditional atmosphere, seats around tables on the flagstone floor, shelves of
china, iron tools and so forth, and a high dark beam-and-plank ceiling; there's also
a no smoking family room. As well as lunchtime filled yorkshire puddings (from
£2.95), filled baguettes (from £3.50), and ploughman's (£4.75), the enjoyable bar
food might include home-made soup (£2.95), home-made smoked trout pâté or
mushrooms stuffed with sun-dried tomato, dates and pecan nuts with cheese on top
(£3.95), king prawns in garlic butter (£4.50), home-made steak and mushroom pie,
home-made pork casserole or chicken fried with smoked bacon (all £7.95), home-
made vegetable lasagne (£8.50), duck breast with a raspberry and redcurrant sauce
(£9.95), and steaks (from £10.95). If you eat between 5.45 and 6.15pm you get a
20% discount on some items. Well kept Moorhouses Bitter, Timothy Taylors
Landlord, and maybe Copper Dragon Golden Pippin and Scotts 1816 on
handpump, nine wines by the glass, and around 20 malt whiskies; dominoes,
cribbage, shove-ha'penny, ring the bull and giant Jenga. In fine weather, you can sit
at picnic benches above the very quiet steep lane or on the great flat limestone slabs
in the shallow stream which tumbles down opposite. *(Recommended by Mr and*

Mrs Maurice Thompson, Ben Whitney and Pippa Redmond, Kevin Thorpe, MDN, the Didler,
Tony and Betty Parker, B and M Kendall, Kerry Law, Simon Smith, Di and Mike Gillam,
Eddie Edwards, Peter F Marshall, Tony and Ann Bennett-Hughes, Lynda and Trevor Smith)

Free house ~ Licensees Kevin and Debbie Roe ~ Real ale ~ Bar food (12-2, 5.45-8.30) ~
(01756) 760262 ~ Children in family room ~ Dogs allowed in bar and bedrooms ~
Open 11-11; 12-10.30 Sun ~ Bedrooms: £40S/£60S

CRAYKE SE5670 Map 7
Durham Ox
Off B1363 at Brandsby, towards Easingwold; West Way

The old-fashioned lounge bar here has venerable tables and antique seats and settles
on the flagstones, pictures and photographs on the dark red walls, interesting
satirical carvings in its panelling (Victorian copies of medievel pew ends), polished
copper and brass, and an enormous inglenook fireplace. In the bottom bar is a
framed illustrated acount of the local history (some of it gruesome) dating back to
the 12th c, and a large framed print of the original famous Durham Ox which
weighed 171 stones. Bar food includes sandwiches, home-made soup (£3.95), crispy
belly of pork with sweet soy dressing and asian-style salad (£5.95), pasta with sun-
dried tomatoes, chargrilled artichokes, courgettes and pesto sauce (£11.95), roasted
red snapper fillets with a saffron vegetable sauce or veal escalopes with a lemon and
parsley emulsion (£14.95), chicken breast with green peppercorn sauce(£15.90),
steaks (from £15.95), daily specials and puddings like white chocolate mousse with
raspberry coulis and berries or sticky toffee pudding with caramel sauce (from
£4.95). The restaurant is no smoking; piped music. Well kept Adnams Bitter,
Greene King Old Speckled Hen, John Smiths and Timothy Taylors Landlord on
handpump, and 12 wines by the glass. There are seats outside on a terrace and in
the courtyard, and the comfortable bedrooms are in converted farm buildings. The
tale is that this is the hill which the Grand Old Duke of York marched his men up;
the view from the hill opposite is marvellous. More reports please. *(Recommended by*
Edward and Deanna Pearce, Peter Burton)

Free house ~ Licensee Michael Ibbotson ~ Real ale ~ Bar food (12-2.30, 6-9.30(8.30 Sun))
~ Restaurant ~ (01347) 821506 ~ Children in eating area of bar ~ Dogs allowed in
bedrooms ~ Jazz Thurs evening ~ Open 12-3, 6-11.30; 12-11 Sat; 12-10.30 Sun ~
Bedrooms: £60B/£80B

CROPTON SE7588 Map 10
New Inn 🍺 🛏
Village signposted off A170 W of Pickering

It's the good own-brewed beers that draw customers to this comfortably
modernised village inn: Endeavour Ale, King Billy, Two Pints, and Yorkshire
Moors Bitter, which they keep well on handpump, and a guest such as Theakstons
Best. The traditional village bar has Victorian church panels, terracotta and dark
blue plush seats, lots of brass, and a small fire. A local artist has designed historical
posters all around the no smoking downstairs conservatory. Bar food includes
lunchtime sandwiches (from £3.75), as well as soup (£3.50), haddock cakes with a
sour cream and chive dip (£4.50), ploughman's (£7.50), steak in stout pie (£7.95),
sausages with yorkshire pudding and real ale gravy or broccoli and stilton quiche
(£8.50), pork in a creamy mango and curry sauce (£9.50), and steaks (from
£11.95). The elegant no smoking restaurant is furnished with genuine Victorian
and early Edwardian pieces. Darts, pool, juke box, fruit machine and piped music.
There's a neat terrace, a garden with a pond, and a brewery shop. *(Recommended by*
Michael and Ann Cole, Marlene and Jim Godfrey, Tracey and Stephen Groves, Christine and
Neil Townend, Colin and Dot Savill, Dr David Cockburn, Esther and John Sprinkle, O K Smyth,
Christine and Phil Young, John and Sylvia Harrop, Sylvia and Tony Birbeck)

Own brew ~ Licensee Philip Lee ~ Real ale ~ Bar food (12-2, 6-9) ~ Restaurant ~
(01751) 417330 ~ Children in family room ~ Dogs allowed in bar ~ Open 11-11; 12-10.30
Sun ~ Bedrooms: £41B/£70B

EAST WITTON SE1586 Map 10

Blue Lion (m) ♀ ⇐

A6108 Leyburn—Ripon

Smart and rather civilised, this well run dining pub is at its best when genial Mr Klein himself is around. The big squarish bar has a friendly atmosphere, high-backed antique settles and old windsor chairs on the turkey rugs and flagstones, ham-hooks in the high ceiling decorated with dried wheat, teazles and so forth, a delft shelf filled with appropriate bric-a-brac, several prints, sporting caricatures and other pictures on the walls, a log fire, and daily papers; the friendly labrador is called Archie. Excellent, restaurant-quality food includes home-made tagliatelle carbonara (£4.80; main course £9.80), terrine of duck and orange (£5.75), warm onion and blue wensleydale cheese tart with tomato chutney (£5.85), baked goats cheese on hazelnut brioche with chargrilled red peppers (£6.25), whitby crab and beetroot salad with curried lemon dressing (£6.95), beef and onion suet pudding with dark onion sauce (£12.95), poached fillet of smoked haddock topped with a poached egg, leek and mushroom sauce and toasted with gruyère (£14.25), cassoulet of goose leg confit with toulouse sausage, haricot beans, tomato and ham (£14.55), slow-braised leg of lamb with garlic mash (£14.95), chargrilled fillet of beef with shiraz sauce, sautéed shallots, lardons and mushrooms (£18.95), and puddings such as dark chocolate terrine with pistachios and raspberry sauce, pineapple syrup sponge with custard or apple tatin with cinnamon ice-cream (from £5.25). Well kept Black Sheep Bitter and Riggwelter, and Theakstons Best on handpump, and an impressive wine list with quite a few by the glass. Picnic-sets on the gravel outside look beyond the stone houses on the far side of the village green to Witton Fell, and there's a big, pretty back garden. *(Recommended by S and N McLean, Neil Whitehead, Ian and Nita Cooper, Ian Arthur, Mrs Yvette Bateman, John Close, Jane Taylor, David Dutton, the Didler, Lynda and Trevor Smith, Gerry and Rosemary Dobson, Pat and Sam Roberts, Peter Hacker, Rod Stoneman, Christopher JDarwent, Dr and Mrs T E Hothersall, Peter Abbott, Dr Pete Crawshaw, I A Herdman)*

Free house ~ Licensee Paul Klein ~ Real ale ~ Bar food ~ (01969) 624273 ~ Children in eating area of bar and restaurant ~ Dogs allowed in bar and bedrooms ~ Open 11-11; 12-10.30 Sun ~ Bedrooms: £59.50S/£79S(£89B)

EGTON BRIDGE NZ8005 Map 10

Horse Shoe

Village signposted from A171 W of Whitby; via Grosmont from A169 S of Whitby

Charmingly placed in a hamlet by the Esk, this peaceful inn offers a friendly welcome to both locals and visitors. The bar has old oak tables, high-backed built-in winged settles, wall seats and spindleback chairs, a big stuffed trout (caught near here in 1913), pictures on the walls, and a warm log fire; the restaurant is no smoking. A new raised garden supplies the kitchen with home-grown produce: sandwiches, field mushroom filled with spinach and cheddar (£4.60), aubergine with parmesan cheese or venison sausages with red onion chutney (£4.80), garlic and chilli prawns (£6), wild mushroom risotto (£7.90), chicken breast stuffed with brie, wrapped in bacon (£8.90), fish chowder (£9.50), lamb fillet on bubble and squeak (£9.60), honey-roast duck breast with berry and cassis sauce (£11), and monkfish in light batter with mediterranean sauce (£12). Well kept Black Sheep and John Smiths with guests from Adnams, Copper Dragon and Durham on handpump, and quite a few malt whiskies; the area around the bar is no smoking. Darts, dominoes, cribbage and piped music. The attractive gardens have pretty roses and mature redwoods, and there are comfortable seats on a quiet terrace and lawn beside a little stream (where there are ducks). Fishing is available on a daily ticket from Egton Estates. A different way to reach this beautifully placed pub is to park by the Roman Catholic church, walk through the village and cross the River Esk by stepping stones. Not to be confused with a similarly named pub up at Egton. *(Recommended by Matt and Vicky Wharton, Joyce and Maurice Cottrell, Greta and Christopher Wells, Tracey and Stephen Groves, Clare and Peter Pearse, Patrick Hancock,*

*Pete Baker, John Dwane, David Carr, Richard and Karen Holt, Mark and Angela Stephens,
Derek and Sylvia Stephenson, John and Yvonne Davies, Dr and Mrs R G J Telfer)*

Free house ~ Licensees Tim and Suzanne Boulton ~ Real ale ~ Bar food ~ Restaurant ~
(01947) 895245 ~ Children in restaurant and small back family room only ~ Dogs allowed
in bar ~ Open 11.30-3(3.30 Sat), 6.30-11; 12-3.30, 6-10.30 Sun; closed 25 Dec ~
Bedrooms: /£45(£55S)

ELSLACK SD9249 Map 7

Tempest Arms 🍴 ♀ 🍺

Village signposted just off A56 Earby—Skipton

With this pub's genuinely friendly welcome and good bustling atmosphere, it would
be hard not to enjoy your visit here. The series of quietly decorated areas has three
log fires (one in a dividing fireplace), comfortable plum or chocolate plush
cushioned armchairs, cushioned built-in wall seats, stools and lots of tables; there's
also quite a bit of stripped stonework, nice prints on the cream walls, and perhaps
Molly the friendly black labrador. Several parts of the bar and the dining room are
no smoking; piped music in one area only, and winter darts and dominoes. Well
kept Black Sheep, a beer from Copper Dragon, Theakstons Best, Timothy Taylors
Best and Wharfedale Folly Ale on handpump, ten wines by big or small glass from
a good list, and several malt whiskies. Very good food from a menu that can be
used for both the bar and restaurant might include sandwiches, home-made
yorkshire pudding with onion gravy (£2.95), home-made soup (£3.50), home-made
onion bhajis with raita and fruity mango chutney (£3.95), sautéed queenie scallops
with palma ham, cream and brandy gratinated with swiss cheese (£6.50),
cumberland sausage on mustard mash with caramelised red onion and red wine
glaze, bacon chop with fresh pear and stilton or roast vegetable roly-poly (£8.95),
red beef curry (£9.95), smoked haddock with swiss cheese, prawn sauce and a
poached egg (£9.95), duck and vegetable wraps with sweetened hoisin and honey
glaze (£10.50), specials such as chicken stroganoff (£9.99), steak frites (£10.50),
and lamb on the bone with minted gravy (£10.95), and puddings like sticky toffee
pudding or giant chocolate muffin with runny chocolate sauce (£4.25). Tables
outside are largely screened from the road by a raised bank. *(Recommended by
Patrick Hancock, Jo Lilley, Simon Calvert, Jim and Maggie Cowell, Karen Eliot, Steve Whalley,
B and M Kendall, Fred and Lorraine Gill, Graham and Doreen Holden, Stephen Buckley)*

Free house ~ Licensees Martin and Veronica Clarkson ~ Real ale ~ Bar food (12-2.30, 6-9;
12-7.45 Sun) ~ Restaurant ~ (01282) 842450 ~ Children in eating area of bar and
restaurant ~ Open 11-11; 12-10.30 Sun ~ Bedrooms: £59.95B/£74.95B

FADMOOR SE6789 Map 10

Plough 🍴 ♀

Village signposted off A170 in or just W of Kirkbymoorside

Overlooking the village green, this neatly kept dining pub is run by friendly people.
The elegantly simple little rooms have rugs on seagrass, richly upholstered
furnishings, and yellow walls, well kept Black Sheep Best, Tetleys, and maybe
Timothy Taylors Landlord on handpump, and an extensive wine list. The popular,
often interesting bar food includes home-made soups like cream of ham and pea or
broccoli and stilton (£4.95), smooth chicken liver and brandy pâté with home-made
fruit chutney (£5.50), local black pudding with blue stilton salad topped with warm
croûtons or english breakfast tartlet topped with a warm poached egg and creamy
mushroom sauce (£5.95), seared king scallops with wild mushrooms, sweet chilli
and spring onions (£7.95), home-made steak in ale pie (£8.50), battered whitby
haddock with home-made tartare sauce (£9.75), chicken breast with a creamy
cheddar cheese and mustard sauce (£10.50), sliced confit of belly pork on steamed
apple and shallot risotto with a cider and cream sauce (£10.95), slow-roasted shank
of lamb on leek mash with red wine and rosemary sauce (£11.50), roast boneless
half gressingham duckling with an orange, mandarin and brandy sauce (£12.95),
steaks (from £12.95), and puddings such as white chocolate and Baileys crème

brûlée, caramelised lemon tart with redcurrant compote or hot chocolate fudge brownie with hot chocolate sauce and chocolate ice-cream (£4.95); two-course set meal (£12.95; not Saturday evening or Sunday lunchtime). The dining areas are no smoking; piped music and dominoes. There are seats on the terrace. *(Recommended by Peter Burton, I D Barnett, Peter and Eleanor Kenyon, Christopher Turner)*

Holf Leisure Ltd ~ Licensee Neil Nicholson ~ Real ale ~ Bar food (12-1.45, 6.30-8.45; 12-2, 7-8.30 Sun) ~ Restaurant ~ (01751) 431515 ~ Children welcome ~ Open 12-2.30, 6.30-11; 12-3, 7-10.30 Sun; closed 25 and 26 Dec, 1 Jan

FELIXKIRK SE4785 Map 10

Carpenters Arms 🍽 ♀
Village signposted off A170 E of Thirsk

Readers very much enjoy their visits to this warmly inviting pub in a picturesque small moors-edge village. You can be sure of a genuinely friendly welcome, and there are three or four cosy areas that ramble around the bar counter (made partly from three huge casks) dark beams and joists hung with carpentry tools and other bric-a-brac, comfortable seats around tables with check tablecloths and little lighted oil burners, and a couple of huge japanese fans by the stone fireplace. The bar and restaurant are no smoking; piped music and dominoes. Good, popular food includes home-made soup (£3.25), coarse pork and pistachio terrine with home-made chutney (£5.25), twice-baked three cheese and fine herb soufflé (£5.95), grilled black pudding, fried foie gras, spiced apple and sultana chutney and scrumpy dressing (£8.95), asparagus, vine tomato and mint pesto tagliatelle with parmesan (£9.50), fillets of bass on saffron mash with sauce vierge (£12.50), calves liver with bubble and squeak and crispy pancetta (£12.95), steaks (from £13.50), honey and soy glazed duck breast with stir-fried vegetables and plum sauce (£13.95), roast rump of lamb with chargrilled mediterranean vegetables with rocket pesto (£14.50), and puddings such as banana spring rolls with chocolate sauce and chocolate ripple ice-cream, pink peppercorn meringue with fresh strawberries, thyme cream and strawberry coulis or sticky toffee pudding with butterscotch sauce (£4.50); interesting cheeses, and two-course lunch menu (£11.95). Well kept Black Sheep Best, John Smiths and a couple of weekly guests like Greene King Old Speckled Hen or Timothy Taylors Landlord on handpump, and a good wine list with ten by the glass. There are two dalmatians, Lloyd and Lola. The church is prettily floodlit at night. *(Recommended by Walter and Susan Rinaldi-Butcher, Edward and Deanna Pearce, Michael Ward, Peter Burton, Anna Cooper, P S Hoyle, Christine and Phil Young, Peter and Jean Dowson, Judith and Edward Pearson, J Crosby)*

Free house ~ Licensee Karen Bumby ~ Real ale ~ Bar food (not Sun evening or Mon) ~ Restaurant ~ (01845) 537369 ~ Children welcome ~ Open 11.30-3, 6.30-11; 12-3 Sun; closed Sun evening, 25 Dec and evenings 26 Dec and 1 Jan

FERRENSBY SE3761 Map 7

General Tarleton 🍽 ♀ 🛏
A655 N of Knaresborough

As well as being a super place to stay, this rather smart and comfortable old coaching inn remains extremely popular for its excellent food (though plenty of locals pop in for a drink and a chat), and service is unfailingly courteous and helpful. The beamed and carpeted bar has brick pillars dividing up the several different areas to create the occasional cosy alcove, some exposed stonework, and neatly framed pictures on the red walls; there's a mix of country kitchen furniture and comfortable banquettes, a big open fire, and a door leading out to a pleasant tree-lined garden with smart green tables. As well as quite pricey changing specials such as cream of mushroom and tarragon soup (£4.95), roast fillet of whitby cod with spinach, prawn and chive beurre blanc (£10.95), grilled morecambe bay brill with garlic and herb butter (£13.95), roasted goosnargh duck breast with fresh ginger, bell pepper and maple glaze (£14.50), and chargrilled T-bone steak with béarnaise sauce (£19.95); the better value menu offers roast butternut squash and coconut soup (£4.95), grilled goats cheese with beetroot and horseradish salad (£5.95), queenie scallops (£5.95; main course £8.85), ham hock and foie gras terrine (£6.95), sausages with mash and red onion gravy (£7.50), lunchtime open sandwiches on home-made muffins or toasted walnut bread (from £7.95), fish in beer batter (£9.95), steak in ale pudding (£10.95), braised belly of rare breed pork (£12.50), fish pie (£12.95), and puddings like vanilla panna cotta with fresh raspberries, warm apple cobbler pudding or warm banana bread pudding with a melting chocolate centre and malt ice-cream (from £4.95); good breakfasts. Well kept Black Sheep Best and Timothy Taylors Landlord on handpump, over 20 good wines by the glass, and quite a few coffees. The covered courtyard eating area, and the restaurant, are no smoking. *(Recommended by R E Dixon, Brian Kneale, Janet and Peter Race, M Sharp, Patrick Hancock, DC, Edward and Deanna Pearce, A Allcock, Judith and Edward Pearson, David and Pam Lewis)*

Free house ~ Licensee John Topham ~ Real ale ~ Bar food (12-2.15, 6-9.15(8.30 Sun)) ~ Restaurant ~ (01423) 340284 ~ Children welcome ~ Dogs allowed in bedrooms ~ Open 12-3, 6-11(10.30 Sun) ~ Bedrooms: £85B/£97B

GOOSE EYE SE0240 Map 7
Turkey 🍺
Just S of Laycock on road to Oakworth and Haworth, W of Keighley; OS Sheet 104 map reference 028406

Tucked away in a village at the bottom of a steep valley, this busy place has a friendly landlord and locals, their own-brewed beer, roaring winter log fires, and plenty of character. There are various cosy and snug alcoves, brocaded upholstery, and walls covered with pictures of surrounding areas; the restaurant is no smoking. You can visit the microbrewery – they ask for a donation for Upper Wharfedale Fell Rescue: Turkey Bitter, John Peel and winter Dark Mild, and changing guest beers on handpump. Over 40 whiskies. Generous helpings of decent, straightforward bar food include home-made soup (£2.10), sandwiches (from £3.50), vegetable lasagne (£5.80), home-made pie (£6.40), steaks (from £7.20), home-made daily specials (from £6), and puddings (from £2.40); Sunday lunch (£6.40). Piped music, and a separate games area with pool, fruit machine and TV. More reports please. *(Recommended by Greta and Christopher Wells, Mrs J Doherty, DC, Geoffrey and Brenda Wilson)*

Own brew ~ Licensee Harry Brisland ~ Real ale ~ Bar food (not Mon or Tues lunchtimes; all day Sun) ~ Restaurant ~ (01535) 681339 ~ Children welcome ~ Dogs allowed in bar ~ Live entertainment first and third Sun of month ~ Open 12-3, 5.30-11; 12-11 Fri and Sat; 12-10.30 Sun; closed Mon and Tues lunchtimes

GRINTON SE0598 Map 10
Bridge Inn 🍺 🛏
B6270 W of Richmond

A proper pub this, with a reassuring sign welcoming dogs and muddy boots. The cheerful gently lit red-carpeted bar has well kept Jennings Cumberland, Dark Mild, Cocker Hoop and a guest on handpump, a good collection of malt whiskies, nice wines by the glass, and a good log fire; darts, pool and piped music. Under the friendly young landlord service is warm-hearted and helpful. There are bow window seats and a pair of stripped traditional settles among more usual pub seats, all well cushioned. On the right a few steps take you down into a dark red walled room with darts and a well lit pool table; there may be piped nostalgic pop music. Besides sandwiches and hot baguettes (which they serve all day; £4.95), the food shows that a chef of real talent is working here now. Our anonymous winter inspection meal included delicious freshwater prawns with garlicky sauce and lime and tomato couscous (£12.95) and a lamb and barley casserole (very tender lamb from the opposite hillside, £7.95); the fresh vegetables were just right. Other dishes, served generously, might include soup (£3.10), filled baked potatoes (from £3.95), chicken liver pâté with spicy red onion marmalade or thai fishcakes with sweet

chilli sauce (£4.95), steak in ale pie (£6.95), aubergine and wild mushroom tower
or spicy chicken with onion bhaji dumplings (£7.95), duck breast with carrot and
cauliflower mousse and an orange and brandy sauce (£12.95), 10oz sirloin steak
(£13.95), daily specials such as local blue cheese and red onion tart with tomato
chutney (£7.95), marinated venison steak with a red wine and shallot reduction
(£13.95), and fried fillet of red snapper in tarragon butter on a tomato risotto with
parmesan crisps (£14.95), and puddings like three chocolate brownie with
chocolate sauce, fresh fruit crumbles, and a rich ginger sponge with sticky toffee
sauce (£4.25); good coffee. On the left is an extensive two-part dining room, past
leather armchairs and a sofa by a second log fire (and a glass chess set); the décor is
in mint green and shades of brown, with a modicum of fishing memorabilia. This is
a pretty Swaledale village, surrounded by good walks; there are picnic-sets outside,
and the inn is right opposite a lovely church known as the Cathedral of the Dales.
The bedrooms are neat and simple, with a good breakfast. *(Recommended by
Andrew York, Matthew Shackle, David Reid, David Field, Blaise Vyner, Tony and Betty Parker,
Dave Braisted, Clive Gibson, Karina Spero, Edward and Deanna Pearce)*

Jennings (W & D) ~ Lease Andrew Atkin ~ Real ale ~ Bar food (all day) ~ Restaurant ~
(01748) 884224 ~ Children welcome ~ Dogs allowed in bar ~ Local live music Thurs
evenings ~ Open 12-11 ~ Bedrooms: £42S/£64S

HALIFAX SE1026 Map 7 🏠

Shibden Mill 🍽 ♀

Off A58 into Kell Lane at Stump Cross Inn, near A6036 junction; keep on, pub
signposted from Kell Lane on left

Tucked into a leafy enclave, with a stream rushing noisily past the car park, this
hidden-away country inn comes as a nice surprise. It's run by helpful and friendly
people and the rambling bar has cosy side areas with enticing banquettes heaped
softly with cushions and rugs; tables and chairs are well spaced, but candles in
elegant iron holders give a feeling of real intimacy. There are old hunting prints,
country landscapes and so forth, and a couple of big log fireplaces. They offer a
dozen wines (and two champagnes) by the glass, and have John Smiths, a softly
flavoured golden beer brewed for them by Moorhouses, Theakstons XB and a guest
like Copper Dragon Golden Pippin kept well on handpump. Good, enjoyable bar
food includes home-made soup (£3.75), sandwiches on home-made bread (£5.25),
roasted red pepper and gruyère tart (£6.75), cold ham hock with egg, chips and
green tomato chutney (£6.95), ploughman's and scotch egg with their own
preserves (£8), cottage pie (£8.25), home-made pork and chive sausages with onion
sauce or lambs liver (£8.50), black pudding cake with smoked bacon, poached egg
and mustard sauce (£8.75), more exotic dishes such as aubergine and confit potato
timbale (£10.95), braised shank of lamb with a cassoulet of chorizo and haricot
beans (£14.95), and fillet of beef with haggis risotto cake and Drambuie sauce
(£17.95), and puddings like chocolate torte with warm pear and plum chutney,
caramelised peppered pineapple with crème de cacao sauce or toffee and banana
crumble with banana ice-cream (£4.50); side orders are £1.95 extra; piped music.
The restaurant is upstairs. There are plenty of good teak tables and chairs out on an
attractive terrace, with lots of heaters; the building is prettily floodlit at night. More
reports please. *(Recommended by Paul Leason, R and P A Mitchell, Mrs J Doherty,
Geoffrey and Brenda Wilson, Kate Charman, Greta and Christopher Wells, Ian and
Nita Cooper, Jo Lilley, Simon Calvert)*

Free house ~ Licensee Glen Pearson ~ Real ale ~ Bar food (12-2, 6-9.30; all day Sun) ~
Restaurant ~ (01422) 365840 ~ Children welcome ~ Dogs allowed in bar ~ Open
12-2.30, 5.30-11; 12-11 Sat; 12-10.30 Sun ~ Bedrooms: £68B/£85B

We accept no free drinks, meals or payment for inclusion. We take no
advertising, and are not sponsored by the brewing industry – or by anyone else.
So all reports are independent.

HAROME SE6582 Map 10

Star ★ ⑪ ♀ ◑ 🛏

Village signposted S of A170, E of Helmsley

As well as running this first class inn, the friendly young licensees have opened a café in the Walled Garden at Scampston Hall, and now own a traditional butcher in the Market Place in Helmsley which specialises in home-made terrines, british cheeses, cooked meats and so forth. Their bakery/delicatessen, The Corner Shop, selling take-away meals and snacks as well as all manner of delicious goodies, is doing very well indeed, too. The 14th-c pub itself is pretty and thatched and although the emphasis is, not surprisingly, on the super food, there is a proper pubby atmosphere in the bar. This has a dark bowed beam-and-plank ceiling, well polished tiled kitchen range, plenty of bric-a-brac, interesting furniture (this was the first pub that 'Mousey Thompson' ever populated with his famous dark wood furniture), a fine log fire, and daily papers and magazines; as they don't take bar reservations, it's best to arrive early to get a seat. There's also a private dining room and a popular coffee loft in the eaves, and a separate no smoking restaurant. The inventive food uses fish that is delivered daily from Hartlepool, local hen, duck and guinea fowl eggs, three types of honey from the village, and their own herbs and vegetables; lots of british cheeses, too. Changing daily, there might be lunchtime sandwiches or buns (from £7.50) and posh ploughman's (£9.50), as well as pressed local pigeon terrine with pickled mushrooms, toasted rye bread and stewed fig chutney (£7.25; main course £12.50), home-grown purple sage and onion risotto with deep-fried onion fritters and cotherstone cheese salad (£7.50; main course £13.50), brandade of oak-smoked salmon and salted cod with wild garlic, poached egg and chervil butter (£9.25; main course £16.50), braised faggots of wild rabbit with lemon thyme, bubble and squeak rösti, smoked bacon and onion juices (£14.50), honey-roast rare breed ham knuckle with flat parsley mash and english mustard cream (£14.75), free range chicken with french-style fresh peas and york ham lardons, sherried lovage juices and parmentier potatoes (£16.50), loin of lamb with a little kidney and mutton stew, rosemary potato, caper and pearl barley juices (£18.95), and puddings such as steamed ale cake with rich toffee sauce and Theakstons ice-cream, apple mousse with cider raisins and walnut brittle or a taste of all the puddings in miniature (from £6.50). Well kept Black Sheep Special, Cropton Two Pints, Theakstons Old Peculier and a guest such as Fullers London Pride or John Smiths on handpump, home-made juices and liqueurs, farm cider, and ten wines by the glass from a fairly extensive wine list; good coffees with home-made chocolates, and piped music. There are some seats and tables on a sheltered front terrace with more in the garden with fruit trees. Eight superbly equipped, stylish bedrooms in converted farm buildings plus three suites in a thatched cottage, and there's a private dining room, too. They have a village cricket team.
(Recommended by Michael and Ann Cole, David Thornton, Edward and Deanna Pearce, W W Burke, Mrs Yvette Bateman, Dr and Mrs S Donald, A C English, Tracey and Stephen Groves, G Dobson, Geoff and Angela Jaques, David and Ruth Hollands, Walter and Susan Rinaldi-Butcher, Paul and Ursula Randall, Ian and Rose Lock, C E Reid, Dr D Scott)

Free house ~ Licensees Andrew and Jacquie Pern ~ Real ale ~ Bar food (11.30-2, 6.30-9.30; 12-6 Sun; not Mon) ~ Restaurant ~ (01439) 770397 ~ Children welcome ~ Open 11.30-3, 6.30(6.15 Sat)-11; 12-11 Sun; closed Mon lunchtime and two weeks Jan ~ Bedrooms: /£140B

HEATH SE3519 Map 7

Kings Arms

Village signposted from A655 Wakefield—Normanton – or, more directly, turn off to the left opposite Horse & Groom

A bit of a surprise being so close to industrial Wakefield, this is an old-fashioned pub that makes the most of the village green setting opposite surrounded by 19th-c stone merchants' houses. In fine weather you can sit at seats along the front of the building, and there are picnic-sets on a side lawn, and a nice walled flower-filled garden. Inside, the gas lighting adds a lot to the atmosphere, and the original bar has a fire burning in the old black range (with a long row of smoothing irons on the mantelpiece), plain elm stools and oak settles built into the walls, and dark panelling. A more comfortable extension has carefully preserved the original style, down to good wood-pegged oak panelling (two embossed with royal arms), and a high shelf of plates; there are also two other small flagstoned rooms, and the conservatory opens on to the garden. Good value bar food includes sandwiches (from £2.25; hot sausage and onion £2.95), home-made soup (£2.75), mushroom stroganoff (£5.25), liver and onions in rich gravy or beef in ale pie (£6.45), rump steak (£8.50), and puddings like treacle sponge and custard (£2.95). Well kept Clarks Classic Blonde, Timothy Taylors Landlord, and a guest like Clarks Rams Revenge on handpump; quiz night Tuesdays. The landlord tell us that with four exits to the pub, customers do leave without paying, so they ask for ID – though most people prefer to leave their credit card in the till. *(Recommended by Richard and Karen Holt, Steve Kirby, Greta and Christopher Wells, the Didler, Patrick Hancock, Ian Phillips)*

Clarks ~ Manager Alan Tate ~ Real ale ~ Bar food (12-2(2.30 weekends), 6-9.30) ~ (01924) 377527 ~ Children in eating area of bar and restaurant ~ Open 11.30-11; 12-10.30 Sun; 11.30-3, 5.30-11 weekdays in winter

HETTON SD9558 Map 7

Angel 🍴 ♀

Just off B6265 Skipton—Grassington

This has long been a favourite with many of our readers, so we are keeping our fingers crossed that the new licensees will continue in the same vein. The four timbered and panelled rambling rooms still have lots of cosy alcoves, comfortable country-kitchen chairs or button-back green plush seats, Ronald Searle wine snob cartoons and older engravings and photographs, log fires, and in the main bar a Victorian farmhouse range in the big stone fireplace; two rooms are no smoking, as is the restaurant. Good bar food includes butternut squash and sage risotto (£4.75; main course £8.95), asian-style crispy belly pork on a warm noodle salad (£5.95), seared tuna loin with tomato tartare and garlic crisps (£6.25), pork sausages with red onion gravy (£8.25), chicken, mushroom and tarragon fettuccine in a creamy white wine sauce (£9.50), cornfed chicken breast with honey roasted parsnips and a red wine cranberry sauce (£12.95), roasted venison with artichoke dauphinoise and a thyme red wine sauce (£13.95), and specials such as cream of mushroom and broccoli soup (£3.95), roasted pigeon breast with a fricassee of sautéed spinach and wild mushrooms (£9.95), and poached smoked haddock with wholegrain mustard beurre blanc topped with poached egg (£11.25). Two-course lunch (£8.75). Well kept Black Sheep Bitter and Timothy Taylors Landlord on handpump, 25 wines by the glass, including champagne, and quite a few malt whiskies. Wooden seats and tables under colourful sunshades on the terrace. More reports on the new regime, please. *(Recommended by Pat and Clive Sherriff, Brenda and Rob Fincham, P J Holt, M and GR, J S Burn, Jo Lilley, Simon Calvert, Fred and Lorraine Gill, A Darroch Harkness, Mrs M E Mills, Jack Morley, Keith and Margaret Kettell, Marlene and Jim Godfrey, Linda Somers, Revd D Glover, John Mitchell, Stephen Buckley, Dr Ian S Morley, Air Commodore and Mrs A Curry, Tim Nicoll, W K Wood)*

Free house ~ Licensees Bruce Elsworth and Luc Daguzan ~ Real ale ~ Bar food (12-2.15, 6-9.30(10 Sat)) ~ Restaurant ~ (01756) 730263 ~ Children welcome ~ Dogs allowed in bedrooms ~ Open 12-3, 6-11; 12-2.30, 6-10.30 in winter; closed 25 Dec, 1 Jan, 1 week Jan ~ Bedrooms: /£120B

Real ale may be served from handpumps, electric pumps (not just the on-off switches used for keg beer) or — common in Scotland — tall taps called founts (pronounced 'fonts') where a separate pump pushes the beer up under air pressure. The landlord can adjust the force of the flow – a tight spigot gives the good creamy head that Yorkshire lads like.

HULL TA0927 Map 8
Minerva ¶

Park at top of pedestrianised area at top of Queen's Street and walk over Nelson Street or turn off Queen's Street into Wellington Street, right into Pier Street and pub is at top; no parking restrictions weekends, 2-hour stay Mon-Fri

Overlooking the Humber Estuary and handy for the nearby The Deep (Europe's deepest aquarium), this busy pub has seats out in front from which you can watch the passing boats; you can also watch them from the piers on each side, too. Inside, several rooms ramble all the way round a central servery, and are filled with comfortable seats, quite a few interesting photographs and pictures of old Hull (with two attractive wash drawings by Roger Davis) and a big chart of the Humber. A tiny snug has room for just three people, and a back room (which looks out to the marina basin) houses a profusion of varnished woodwork; two coal fires in winter. They hold three beer festivals a year – at Easter, mid-July, and whenever the Sea Shanty Festival is on – August/September. Otherwise, they keep Tetleys with guests like Acorn Summer Pale, Gales HSB, and York Yorkshire Terrier on handpump. Under the new licensee, bar food includes soup (£2.25), sandwiches or filled baked potatoes (from £2.75), burger, cheese platter, vegetarian pasta or battered fish (£4.95), ham and eggs (£5.75), chicken with barbecue sauce and bacon (£5.95), beef in ale pie (£6.45), steaks (from £6.95), minted lamb shoulder (£8.95), and puddings (£3.25). The bar and restaurant are no smoking. Fruit machine, TV, darts and piped music. *(Recommended by Paul and Ursula Randall, the Didler, Kay and Alistair Butler, Patrick Hancock, David Carr)*

Spirit Group ~ Manager Adam Brailsford ~ Real ale ~ Bar food (all day) ~ Restaurant ~ (01482) 326909 ~ Children in restaurant if eating ~ Open 11-11; 12-10.30 Sun; closed 25 Dec

Olde White Harte ★

Off 25 Silver Street, a continuation of Whitefriargate; pub is up narrow passage, and should not be confused with the much more modern White Hart nearby

You can almost feel the history in this beautifully preserved ancient tavern. It's tucked away in a cosy courtyard amongst narrow alleyways, and the three bars have some fine features. The downstairs one has attractive stained-glass windows that look out above the bow window seat, carved heavy beams support black ceiling boards, and there are two big brick inglenooks with a frieze of delft tiles. The curved copper-topped counter serves well kept Caledonian Deuchars IPA, Marstons Pedigree, McEwans 80/-, and Theakstons Old Peculier on handpump, and straightforward bar food; the restaurant is no smoking. It was in the heavily panelled room up the oak staircase that in 1642 the town's governor Sir John Hotham made the fateful decision to lock the nearby gate against Charles I, depriving him of Hull's arsenal; it didn't do him much good, as in the Civil War that followed, Hotham, like the king, was executed by the parliamentarians. There are seats in the courtyard, and outside heaters. *(Recommended by Matt Waite, Patrick Hancock, the Didler, David Carr)*

Scottish Courage ~ Lease Bernard Copley ~ Real ale ~ Bar food (12-2(3 Sun); they may do evening food by the time this edition is published) ~ Restaurant ~ (01482) 326363 ~ Children in restaurant ~ Open 11-11; 12-10.30 Sun

KETTLESING SE2256 Map 7
Queens Head ¶

Village signposted off A59 W of Harrogate

At lunchtime, this friendly stone-built pub – under new licensees this year – fills up quickly with customers keen to enjoy the good food. The L-shaped, carpeted main bar is decorated with Victorian song sheet covers, lithographs of Queen Victoria, little heraldic shields, and a delft shelf of blue and white china. There's also a quietly chatty atmosphere, and lots of quite close-set elm and other tables around its walls, with cushioned country seats. Nicely presented, the bar food includes soup (£3.95), deep-fried brie with a ginger and apricot compote (£4.50), devilled whitebait (£4.50), sandwiches (from £4.75), a plate of cheese and meats with bread (£7.95), gammon with peaches or local free-range eggs (£8.95), speciality sausages (£9.50), home-made lasagne, scrumpy beef casserole or minty lamb curry (£9.75), and 10oz sirloin steak (£14.95). Coal or log fires at each end and maybe unobtrusive piped radio. A smaller bar on the left, with built-in red banquettes, has cricketing prints and cigarette cards, coins and banknotes, and in the lobby there's a life-size portrait of Queen Elizabeth I. Two rooms are no smoking. Well kept Black Sheep Bitter, Theakstons Old Peculier and a quickly changing guest on handpump. Seats in the neatly kept suntrap back garden, and benches in front by the lane. More reports please. *(Recommended by John and Sylvia Harrop, DC, Graham Holden, Julie Lee, Brian and Janet Ainscough, Roger and Anne Newbury)*

Free house ~ Licensees Louise and Glen Garbutt ~ Real ale ~ Bar food ~ (01423) 770263 ~ Children in eating area of bar, restaurant and family room ~ Open 11-3, 6.30-11; 12-10.30 Sun ~ Bedrooms: £73.50S(£55B)/£88S(£65B)

KIRKBYMOORSIDE SE6987 Map 10

George & Dragon 🛏

Market Place

This pretty little town has its market day on Wednesday, so lunchtime then is a good time to visit this 17th-c coaching inn. The pubby front bar has leather chesterfields as well as the brass-studded solid dark red leatherette armchairs set around polished wooden tables, burgundy and cream walls and panelling stripped back to its original pitch pine, horsebrasses hung along the beams, newspapers to read, and a blazing log fire; piped music. There's also an attractive beamed bistro, and a no smoking restaurant. Well liked bar food includes home-made soup (£3.25), chicken liver terrine with home-made plum chutney (£4.50), pasta with smoked bacon, mushrooms and creamy mature cheddar sauce (£6.95), whitby haddock in beer batter (£7.25), gammon and eggs or steak in ale pie (£7.50), daily specials such as moules marinière (£5.50), smoked salmon pâté (£5.95), vegetable lasagne (£8.95), spicy mexican lamb (£9.95), and daube of beef (£12.95), and puddings like ginger sponge pudding or walnut and caramel tart (£3.95); two-course lunch (£9.95), and three-course Sunday lunch (£11.50). The evening menu is more elaborate (and more expensive). Well kept Black Sheep Bitter, Tetleys and Timothy Taylors Landlord on handpump, ten wines by the glass and 25 malt whiskies. There are seats under umbrellas in the back courtyard and a surprisingly peaceful walled garden for residents to use. More reports please. *(Recommended by Dr David Cockburn, I D Barnett, Pat and Tony Martin, Derek and Sylvia Stephenson, Mark and Ruth Brock)*

Free house ~ Licensee Elaine Walker ~ Real ale ~ Bar food (12-2.15, 6.30-9.15) ~ Restaurant ~ (01751) 433334 ~ Children welcome ~ Dogs allowed in bar and bedrooms ~ Open 11-11; 12-10.30 Sun ~ Bedrooms: £54B/£89B

KIRKHAM SE7466 Map 7

Stone Trough 🍴 ♀ 🍺

Kirkham Abbey

Bustling and friendly, this country inn is popular as both somewhere to drop in for a pint and a chat or for an enjoyable meal. The several beamed and cosy rooms have warm log fires, well kept Black Sheep Best Bitter, Tetleys, Timothy Taylors Landlord and a couple of guests such as Malton Golden Chance and Theakstons Old Peculier on handpump, and ten wines by the glass; two lounge areas and the restaurant are no smoking. Good, often imaginative food includes soup (£3.95), coarse pork terrine with spiced apple chutney (£4.95), sandwiches (lunchtime only, from £4.95), wild mushroom, spinach and asparagus tartlet with beetroot and walnut salad (£5.25), pork and herb sausages in sage mash with real ale gravy and caramelised red onion marmalade (£7.25), seafood pasta with green thai cream sauce or chicken and wild mushroom risotto (£9.25), confit belly pork on thyme mash with sherry jus and sweet pepper relish (£10.50), slow-cooked lamb shank with garlic mash and redcurrant and rosemary jus (£10.95), chargrilled rib-eye steak with peppercorn butter (£13.50), daily specials, and puddings such as spiced apple and pear crumble or dark and white chocolate pavé with black cherry compote (£4.25). Pool, fruit machine, dominoes, shove-ha'penny and piped music; TV in the pool room. From the seats outside, there are lovely views down the valley, and the inn is handy for Kirkham Abbey and Castle Howard. *(Recommended by Christopher Turner, Marlene and Jim Godfrey, Edward Leetham, Michael Doswell, Pat and Graham Williamson, J Crosby)*

Free house ~ Licensees Sarah and Adam Richardson ~ Real ale ~ Bar food (12-2, 6.30-8.30; not Mon except bank hols) ~ Restaurant ~ (01653) 618713 ~ Well behaved children welcome ~ Open 12-2.30, 6-11; 11.45-10.30 Sun; closed Mon except bank hols; 25 Dec

LANGTHWAITE NY9902 Map 10
Charles Bathurst 🍽 🍺 🛏
Arkengarthdale, a mile N towards Tan Hill; generally known as the CB Inn

This is a nice place to stay and the bedrooms are pretty and comfortable – but it's also appropriately pubby too, with a friendly welcome from the helpful landlord, and a good mix of locals and visitors. There's a long bar with light pine scrubbed tables, country chairs and benches on stripped floors, plenty of snug alcoves, and a roaring fire; the wooden floored dining room (with views of Scar House – a shooting lodge owned by the Duke of Norfolk) is no smoking, as are the other dining areas. The island bar counter has well kept Black Sheep Best Bitter and Riggwelter, John Smiths and Theakstons Best on handpump, and a good choice of wines. Piped music, darts, pool, TV and dominoes. Cooked by the licensee, the popular food might include lunchtime filled baguettes, celery and cheddar soup with sun-dried tomato bread (£3.85), black pudding, olives, pancetta, croûtons and avocado salad (£4.95), smoked and cured fish platter with horseradish chantilly (£5.50), tomato tartlet with goats cheese, red onion confit and pesto (£8.95), fillet of bass with garlic and herb butter (£10.50), boned guinea fowl stuffed with ham and lime duxelle and madeira (£11.25), leg of lamb steak with pea purée (£11.95), and puddings such as sticky toffee pudding with caramel sauce, chocolate tart with raspberry coulis or poached pears in spiced red wine (£3.75). Best to book to be sure of a table. There are fine views over Langthwaite village and Arkengarthdale. *(Recommended by Lynda and Trevor Smith, David Field, Anthony Barnes, David Reid, Pam Stacey, Janet and Peter Race, Ben and Helen Ingram, Ellen and Jeremy Clark-King, Rod Stoneman, Jo Lilley, Simon Calvert, Peter and Anne-Marie O'Malley, Dr and Mrs T E Hothersall, Mark and Ruth Brock, J Crosby, David and Jean Hall)*

Free house ~ Licensees Charles and Stacy Cody ~ Real ale ~ Bar food ~ (01748) 884567 ~ Children welcome ~ Dogs welcome ~ Open 11-11; 12-10.30 Sun; closed 25 Dec ~ Bedrooms: /£85B

LASTINGHAM SE7391 Map 10
Blacksmiths Arms 🍺
Off A170 W of Pickering at Wrelton, forking off Rosedale road N of Cropton; or via Appleton or Hutton-le-Hole

This year, the no smoking main dining room, the bar area and three bedrooms in this neatly kept stone inn have been refurbished. The cosily old-fashioned beamed bar has a log fire in an open range, traditional furnishings, well kept Copper Dragon Best Bitter, Phoenix White Monk, and Theakstons on handpump, and several wines by the glass. Decent bar food includes lunchtime snacks like home-made soup, filled baked potatoes, open sandwiches and ploughman's (from £3.65), starters that include deep-fried brie wedges with cranberry dip or spicy chicken wings (from £2.50), main courses such as home-made steak in ale of minty lamb pie, hotpot in a yorkshire pudding or a roast of the day (from £7.95), and puddings (£3.65); best to book at weekends. There are seats in the back garden and the village is very pretty. It's worth a visit to the church as it has a unique Saxon crypt built as a shrine to St Cedd. As the inn is at the foot of the moors, it's popular with walkers. *(Recommended by Colin and Dot Savill, Dr David Cockburn, Dr and Mrs Jackson, C E Reid)*

Free house ~ Licensee Peter Trafford ~ Real ale ~ Bar food (not winter Tues lunchtime) ~ Restaurant ~ (01751) 417247 ~ Children in eating area of bar ~ Open 12-11(10.30 Sun); 12-2.30, 6-11 Mon-Thurs in winter; closed winter Tues lunchtime and two weeks Nov ~ Bedrooms: /£60B

LEDSHAM SE4529 Map 7
Chequers ◗
Claypit Lane; a mile SW of A1(M) junction 42, and some 4 miles N of junction M62

As well as plenty of locals this bustling and friendly stone-built village pub has plenty of return visitors, too – it is so handy for the A1. The old-fashioned little central panelled-in servery has several small, individually decorated rooms leading off with low beams, lots of cosy alcoves, a number of toby jugs, log fires, and well kept Brown Cow Bitter, John Smiths, Theakstons Best, Timothy Taylors Landlord and a guest beer on handpump. Popular bar food includes snacks such as filled baguettes (from £4.95), smoked salmon with scrambled eggs (£6.85), and sausage and mash or steak and mushroom pie (£9.85), as well as more fancifully described dishes such as tian of whitby crab, smoked trout and mackerel (£7.85), black pudding tower nestled on herb dusted sautéed potatoes masked by a dijon and tarragon cream (£7.95), cornfed chicken enveloping red pepper and mushroom duxelle presented across caramelised orange with a glaze of tarragon cream (£13.95), salmon loin baked whilst sheeted with smoked mozzarella atop thyme and lemon steeped courgettes and splashed with a sweet chilli dressing (£14.95), specials such as chorizo, chicken strips and bacon lardons in garlic scented oil and thrown over a nest of fancy leaves (£7.65), crayfish tails amidst egg noodles with diced peppers and sesame oil (£7.95), a wedge of brie enveloped in puff pastry, baled and served upon a stilton cream broken with dollops of red onion marmalade (£13.95), and tarragon dusted pork loin medallions stacked alternatively with black pudding and caramelised apples (£16.65), and puddings like raspberry cheesecake, chocolate velvet torte or sticky toffee pudding with caramel sauce (from £4.45). A sheltered two-level terrace behind the house has tables among roses, and the hanging baskets and flowers are very pretty. More food reports please. *(Recommended by David Thornton, Ray and Winifred Halliday, the Didler, Philip and June Caunt, Paul Boot, Matt Waite, Peter and Eleanor Kenyon, Darly Graton, Graeme Gulibert, Joyce and Geoff Robson, Christine and Neil Townend, Lawrence Pearse, Bill and Marian de Bass, Richard Cole, Di and Mike Gillam, K M Crook, Alison and Pete, JWAC)*

Free house ~ Licensee Chris Wraith ~ Real ale ~ Bar food (12-2.15, 6-9.15; 12-9.15 Sat; not Sun) ~ Restaurant ~ (01977) 683135 ~ Children welcome ~ Dogs welcome ~ Open 11-3, 5-11; 11-11 Sat; closed Sun

LEEDS SE3033 Map 7
Whitelocks ★ ◗ £
Turks Head Yard; alley off Briggate, opposite Debenhams and Littlewoods; park in shoppers' car park and walk

There are few city centre pubs that remain as beautifully preserved as this atmospheric pub – it has hardly changed since Victorian times. There's always a good mix of customers (it does get packed at peak times) and a lively atmosphere, and the long and narrow old-fashioned bar has polychrome tiles on the bar counter, stained-glass windows and grand advertising mirrors, and red button back plush banquettes and heavy copper-topped cast-iron tables squeezed down one side. Under the new licensee, food includes giant yorkshire puddings (from £1.95), sandwiches and filled baguettes (from £3.75), a home-made pie of the day (£5.75), and tasty sausage and mash (£5.95). Well kept John Smiths, Theakstons Best and Old Peculier, and five quickly changing guest beers on handpump. *(Recommended by David Carr, the Didler, Jo Lilley, Simon Calvert, Dr and Mrs A K Clarke, Chris Parsons, David and Nina Pugsley, B and M Kendall)*

Spirit ~ Manager Darren Hancock ~ Real ale ~ Bar food (12-7 Mon-Sat, 12-4 Sun) ~ Restaurant ~ (0113) 245 3950 ~ Children in restaurant if eating ~ Open 11-11; 12-10.30 Sun

LEYBURN SE1191 Map 10
Sandpiper ⊕ ♀
Just off Market Place

Set away from the main bustle of the town, this 17th-c stone cottage is extremely popular for its super food, and readers have enjoyed staying overnight, too. But despite the food emphasis, the cosy small bar and upper room beyond are liked by locals for a drink and a chat. This bar has a couple of black beams in the low ceiling, antlers, brass jugs and a few tables and chairs, and the back room up three steps has attractive Dales photographs. Down by the nice linenfold panelled bar counter there are stuffed sandpipers, more photographs and a woodburning stove in the stone fireplace; to the left is the no smoking restaurant. At lunchtime, the good food might include sandwiches (from £4; club sandwich £6.50), caesar salad (£5.50; main course £8.50), pressed ham hock, chicken and mushroom terrine (£6), fish in ale batter (£8.75), mushrooms, spinach and leek with pasta (£8.95), gammon with onions and mustard (£9.25), and crispy duck leg with plum and orange sauce or braised beef olive on garlic mash (£11); evening dishes such as warm goats cheese and asparagus salad (£5.75), fishcakes with a fine herb sauce (£6.25; main course £11.50), caramelised belly pork with braised lentils and foie gras (£6.50), moroccan spiced chicken with couscous (£11.50), seared swordfish with honey and soy (£13.75), local lamb with garlic sauce (£14), fillet of pork wrapped in parma ham with roasted peppers, sunblush tomatoes and creamed pasta (£14.50), and puddings like terrine of three chocolates with pistachio sauce, summer pudding or sticky toffee pudding with butterscotch sauce (£4.75). Well kept Black Sheep Best Bitter and Special, and a guest from Copper Dragon on handpump, around 100 malt whiskies, a decent wine list with eight by the glass, and friendly, cheerful staff; piped music and dominoes. There are green cast-iron tables on the front terrace amidst the lovely hanging baskets and flowering climbers. *(Recommended by M S Catling, John Coatsworth, B and M Kendall, Richard and Anne Ansell, Janet and Peter Race, Margaret and Roy Randle, Anna Cooper, Ben and Helen Ingram, Michael Doswell, Michael Butler, David Hoult, Keith and Avril Stringer, J Crosby)*

Free house ~ Licensees Jonathan and Michael Harrison ~ Real ale ~ Bar food (12-2.30 (2 Sun), 6.30-9(9.30 Fri and Sat); not Mon) ~ Restaurant ~ (01969) 622206 ~ Children in eating area of bar but must leave restaurant by 8pm at weekends ~ Dogs allowed in bar ~ Open 11.30-3, 6.30-11; 12-3, 7-10.30 Sun; closed Mon ~ Bedrooms: £60S(£65B)/£70S(£75B)

LINTHWAITE SE1014 Map 7
Sair ◖
Hoyle Ing, off A62; 3½ miles after Huddersfield look out for two water storage tanks (painted with a shepherd scene) on your right – the street is on your left, burrowing very steeply up between works buildings; OS Sheet 110 map reference 101143

It's the large choice of own-brewed beers on handpump that remain the draw to this unspoilt and old-fashioned pub: Linfit Bitter, Dark Mild, Special, Swift, Gold Medal, Autumn Gold, Old Eli, English Guineas Stout, Leadboiler, Enochs Hammer, and occasional brews like Smoke House Ale, Springbok Bier, Xmas Ale and Ginger beer. Weston's farm cider and a few malt whiskies; weekend sandwiches. The four rooms are furnished with pews or smaller chairs on the rough flagstones or wooden floors, and there are open fires in every room; one room is no smoking. The room on the left has dominoes, a juke box, shove-ha'penny and cribbage; piano players welcome. In summer, there are plenty of seats and tables in front of the pub that have a striking view across the Colne Valley. The Huddersfield Narrow Canal is now restored through to Ashton; in the 3½ miles from Linthwaite to the highest, deepest and longest tunnel in Britain are 25 working locks and some lovely countryside. More reports please. *(Recommended by the Didler)*

Own brew ~ Licensee Ron Crabtree ~ Real ale ~ No credit cards ~ (01484) 842370 ~ Children welcome in three rooms away from bar ~ Dogs welcome ~ Open 7(5 Fri)-11; 12-11 Sat; 12-10.30 Sun

LINTON SE3946 Map 7

Windmill

Leaving Wetherby W on A661, fork left just before hospital and bear left; also signposted from A659, leaving Collingham towards Harewood

Bustling and friendly, this popular dining pub is run by helpful and efficient people. The small beamed rooms have walls stripped back to bare stone, polished antique oak settles around copper-topped cast-iron tables, pots hanging from the oak beams, a high shelf of plates, and log fires; the restaurant is no smoking. Well liked and attractively presented, the bar food at lunchtime includes sandwiches on granary bread, baguette or folded flat naan and served with salad and potato crisps (from £3.95), chicken liver parfait with plum and apple chutney (£5.95), and filled baked potatoes (from £5.95), with evening dishes such as fresh white crabmeat with asparagus (£5.95), goats cheese with lemon marmalade (£4.15), chicken with butternut squash mash and grain mustard sauce (£9.95), cajun monkfish (£11.95), and puddings such as bread and butter pudding, glazed lemon tart or sticky toffee pudding (£3.95). Well kept John Smiths, Theakstons Best and a couple of guests like Daleside Bitter and Greene King Ruddles County on handpump, and several wines by the glass; piped music, fruit machine and TV. The pear tree outside was raised from seed brought back from the Napoleonic Wars, and there are seats in the sheltered garden and on the sunny terrace at the back. *(Recommended by R A K Crabtree, B and M Kendall, Dr Peter D Smart, Michael Butler, Joyce and Geoff Robson, Richard Cole, Kevin Blake, Alex and Claire Pearse, A S and M E Marriott)*

Scottish Courage ~ Lease Janet Rowley and John Littler ~ Real ale ~ Bar food (12-2, 5.30-9; not Sun evening) ~ Restaurant ~ (01937) 582209 ~ Children in restaurant ~ Dogs allowed in bar ~ Open 11-3, 5-11; 11-11 Sat; 12-10.30 Sun

LINTON IN CRAVEN SD9962 Map 7

Fountaine

Just off B6265 Skipton—Grassington

This busy pub looks down over the village green to the narrow stream that runs through this delightful hamlet; it's a fine place to end up after walking in the Dales. The original small rooms are furnished with stools, benches and other seats, and they keep Black Sheep Best Bitter, John Smiths, Tetleys Bitter and Timothy Taylors Landlord on handpump; six wines by the glass and a dozen malt whiskies. Bar food includes home-made soup (£3.50), lunchtime sandwiches (from £3.50), pork pie with mushy peas (£4.25), and ploughman's or coarse pork terrine with black pudding and bacon and home-made chutney (£5.25), gammon and egg (£7.50), pork, apple and thyme sausages with parmesan mash and red onion gravy or home-made steak and mushroom in ale pie (£7.75), daily specials such as lambs kidneys or smoked chicken and mango salad (£4.95), veal escalope (£12), fillet steak (£14.95), and puddings like sticky toffee pudding glazed lemon tart with dark chocolate sauce or raspberry bakewell tart (£3.95). The restaurant and one other room are no smoking. Darts, dominoes and piped music. The pub is named after the local lad who made his pile in the Great Plague – contracting in London to bury the bodies. *(Recommended by Mr and Mrs D J Nash, Pat and Clive Sherriff, Michael Butler, Graham and Doreen Holden, Lynda and Trevor Smith, R L Gorick, Alyson and Andrew Jackson, Len Beattie)*

Free house ~ Licensee George Knight ~ Real ale ~ Bar food (all day) ~ Restaurant ~
(01756) 752210 ~ Children welcome ~ Dogs allowed in bar ~ Open 11-11;
12-10.30 Sun

LITTON SD9074 Map 7

Queens Arms ◀

From B6160 N of Grassington, after Kilnsey take second left fork; can also be reached off B6479 at Stainforth N of Settle, via Halton Gill

In fine weather you can make the most of the seats outside; the views over the fells are stunning, and there's a safe area for children in the two-level garden. It's a super little inn with a good mix of customers and a cheerful welcome, and the main bar on the right has a good coal fire, stripped rough stone walls, a brown beam-and-plank ceiling, stools around cast-iron-framed tables on the stone and concrete floor, a seat built into the stone-mullioned window, and signed cricket bats. The left-hand room is an eating area with old photographs of the Dales around the walls. Well kept Litton Ale and Potts Beck Ale on handpump from their own microbrewery; the family room is no smoking. Good, popular bar food includes home-made soup (£2.95), sandwiches (from £4.50), filled baked potatoes (from £4.95), home-made rabbit pie (£8.60), gammon and egg (£8.95), daily specials such as local blue cheese, onion, mushroom and black olive tart (£8.50), roast lamb or beef (£8.95), stilton chicken (£9.95), and a massive mixed grill (£17.50), and puddings like rhubarb crumble, bread and butter pudding or syrup tart (£4). Darts, dominoes, cribbage and piped music. Plenty of surrounding walks – a track behind the inn leads over Ackerley Moor to Buckden, and the quiet lane through the valley leads on to Pen-y-ghent. Walkers enjoy staying here very much – and there is a walkers' room (price on request). *(Recommended by Mr and Mrs Maurice Thompson, A and B Myers, Kerry Law, Simon Smith, Richard Houghton, Lawrence Pearse, Fred and Lorraine Gill, Dr D and Mrs B Woods, Greta and Christopher Wells, MDN, B and M Kendall)*

Free house ~ Licensees Tanya and Neil Thompson ~ Real ale ~ Bar food (not Mon or Jan)
~ (01756) 770208 ~ Children in family room ~ Dogs welcome ~ Open 12-3, 7-11; closed
Mon and all Jan ~ Bedrooms: /£66S

LOW CATTON SE7053 Map 7

Gold Cup

Village signposted with High Catton off A166 in Stamford Bridge or A1079 at Kexby Bridge

Neatly kept and friendly, this white-rendered house has comfortable, communicating rooms with a fire at one end, plush wall seats and stools around good solid tables, some decorative plates and brasswork on the walls, and a relaxed atmosphere; the back bar has a woodburning stove in a brick fireplace. Good, popular food includes home-made soup or home-made yorkshire pudding with onion gravy (£3), apricot and stilton pâté (£3.75), free-range omelettes (lunchtime only £5.25), roast turkey with cranberry sauce or chicken chasseur (£6.85), grilled gammon with cheese and pineapple or leek and wensleydale potato cakes with tomato and basil sauce (£7.50), chicken fillet with bacon and mushroom sauce (£7.75), and puddings such as chocolate and brandy torte with cappuccino ice-cream, poached pear in madeira, and mocha crème brûlée (£3.25). The restaurant is no smoking (as is the area at the bar) and has solid wooden pews and tables, said to be made from a single oak tree, and pleasant views of the surrounding fields. Well kept Jennings Cumberland and John Smiths on handpump; piped music, pool, fruit machine, TV and dominoes. The garden has a grassed area for children, and the back paddock houses Billie the goat and Polly the shetland who are kept in check by Candy the horse; they also own Boris and Marilyn (retired greyhounds), and have fishing rights on the adjoining River Derwent. *(Recommended by M Mennell, Debbie Reynolds, Sheila Brudenell, Roger A Bellingham, H Bramwell, Mr and Mrs P M Jennings, Pat and Tony Martin)*

Free house ~ Licensees Pat and Ray Hales ~ Real ale ~ Bar food (12-2.30, 6-9.30; all day weekends; not Mon lunchtime) ~ No credit cards ~ (01759) 371354 ~ Children in eating area of bar and restaurant ~ Dogs allowed in bar ~ Open 12-3, 6-11; 12-11(10.30 Sun) Sat; closed Mon lunchtime

LUND SE9748 Map 8

Wellington 🍴 ♀
Off B1248 SW of Driffield

Our readers are very fond of this well run, bustling and neatly kept pub, and on a cold day, the cheerful fires and friendly service are most welcome. Many customers do come to eat, and as well as the restaurant, there is a back dining area where you cannot reserve a table; they've sensibly kept the main bar a haven for drinkers only in the evening. The most atmospheric part is the cosy Farmers Bar, a small heavily beamed room with an interesting fireplace and some old agricultural equipment; the neatly kept main bar is much brighter, with a brick fireplace and bar counter, well polished wooden banquettes and square tables, dried flowers, and local prints on the textured cream-painted walls; two areas are no smoking. Off to one side is a plainer flagstoned room, while at the other a york-stoned walkway leads to a room with a display case showing off the village's Britain in Bloom awards. Good enjoyable bar food at lunchtime includes soup of the day (£3.75), smoked haddock fishcakes or chicken liver parfait with redcurrant and orange sauce (£5.50), beer battered local haddock (£9.50), fresh tuna on caesar salad (£9.95), and fresh local crab with herb mayonnaise or calves liver with sage and onion mash and real ale gravy (£11.95), with evening choices such as grilled sardines with garlic butter (£5.50), smoked chicken with chorizo, bacon and pine nuts (£6.75), chicken breast stuffed with mild irish blue cheese on chargrilled vegetable ratatouille (£13.50), loin of english lamb with minted hollandaise (£16.95), and medallions of beef fillet with cracked pepper and garlic (£18.95); puddings like sticky orange and apricot pudding with Grand Marnier custard or warm chocolate and pear frangipane tart with vanilla bean ice-cream (from £4.75). Well kept Black Sheep Best Bitter, John Smiths, and Timothy Taylors Landlord with a changing local guest like Copper Dragon Scotts 1816 on handpump, a good wine list with a helpfully labelled choice by the glass, and 30 malt whiskies. Piped music, darts, pool, TV and fruit machine. A small courtyard beside the car park has a couple of benches. *(Recommended by Michael Butler, C A Hall, Roger A Bellingham, Mark and Cath Caley, Paul Boot, Paul and Ursula Randall, Peter and Caroline Barker, Derek and Sylvia Stephenson, Keith and Margaret Kettell, J Crosby)*

Free house ~ Licensees Russell Jeffery and Sarah Jeffery ~ Real ale ~ Bar food (not Mon) ~ Restaurant (Tues-Sat evenings) ~ (01377) 217294 ~ Children in eating area of bar lunchtime only ~ Open 12-3, 6.30-11; 12-3, 7-10.30 Sun; closed Mon lunchtime

MARTON SE7383 Map 10

Appletree 🍴 ♀ 🍺
Village signposted off A170 W of Pickering

There's no doubt that the emphasis in this spotlessly kept dining pub is firmly placed on the well prepared food, though they do have two or three real ales, too. The relaxed beamed lounge bar has comfortable settees in red or blue around polished low tables, an open fire in the stone fireplace, and a modicum of carefully placed decorations on the eau de nil walls. Most customers head for the terracotta-walled dining room, which has well spaced farmhouse tables, fresh flowers, and masses of candles at night. Both dining rooms and half the bar area are no smoking. Good interesting food might include chicken and duck liver pâté with mulled wine marmalade or seafood fishcakes with sweet pepper and chilli coulis and lime cream (£5.50), grilled sardines (£5.90), tartlet of wild mushrooms with leek ragoût and truffle oil (£9), venison suet pudding (£11), beef daube with horseradish cream (£13), roast rump of lamb with rosemary and lamb jus (£14), deep-fried halibut fillets with banana and horseradish tartare sauce (£15), and puddings like white chocolate pyramid, golden and black treacle tart, and raspberry mousse (from £3.90); Sunday evening posh pie and pea supper (£6.50); they grow some of their own herbs and vegetables, and produce their own flavoured breads, chutneys, preserves, flavoured oils and butters and so forth. Well kept John Smiths, and guests such as Batemans Miss Saucy or Youngs St Georges on handpump, and 15 wines by two sizes of glass from a thoughtful list. There are cast-iron tables and chairs out on a sheltered flagstoned terrace behind, with plant pots and a small water feature, and looking out through young silver birches to an orchard garden with fruit trees. More reports please. *(Recommended by Peter Burton, Alan Cowell, I D Barnett, Michael Doswell, A and B Myers)*

Free house ~ Licensees Melanie and T J Drew ~ Bar food (12-2, 6.30-9; not Mon or Tues) ~ Restaurant ~ (01751) 431457 ~ Children welcome ~ Open 11.45-2.30, 6.30-11; 12-3, 7-10.30 Sun; closed Mon, Tues, 25 Dec, first two weeks Jan

MASHAM SE2381 Map 10
Black Sheep Brewery 🍺
Crosshills

Though far from being a pub, this does do the food and drink side of a pub's work perfectly well. A huge upper warehouse room has a bar serving well kept Black Sheep Best, Special and Riggwelter from handpump, good wines by the glass, and a good choice of soft drinks. They do a wide range of enjoyable food, which at lunchtime includes home-made soup (£3.75), sandwiches (from £3.75; minute steak baguette £5.50), filled baked potatoes (from £4.25), home-made fishcakes (£4.95), omelettes (from £5), and hot crispy duck, black pudding and bacon salad (£5.25); also, cumberland sausage with mustard mash and onion sauce (£6.95), smoked haddock fillet with spinach and parmesan mash and a fish sauce (£7.50), ploughman's, gammon and eggs or steak in ale casserole (£7.95), chicken supreme filled with wensleydale cheese wrapped in bacon with a tomato and sage sauce (£8.95), and puddings such as treacle tart, jam roly-poly or apple pie (£3.60); cream teas (£3.75), plus cakes and tray bakes, milk shakes, lots of coffees and hot chocolates, and an ice-cream menu. Most of the good-sized tables have cheery american-cloth patterned tablecloths and brightly cushioned green café chairs; there are some modern pubbier tables near the bar. There's a good deal of bare woodwork, with some rough stonework painted dark red or dark green, and green-painted steel girders and pillars. This big area is partly divided up by free-standing partitions and some big plants; there's a thriving easy-going mix of ages, from what look like school groups (they usually seem to take the open metal steps up to an upper gallery) through family outings to the elderly. Service is prompt and friendly; piped music. There are interesting brewery tours, and a shop selling both beers and more or less beer-related items from pub games and T-shirts to pottery and fudge. A glass wall lets you see into the brewing exhibition centre. There are picnic-sets out on the grass. *(Recommended by Mr and Mrs Maurice Thompson, Neil and Angela Huxter, Paul and Ursula Randall, M and GR, Gerry and Rosemary Dobson, Ian and Nita Cooper)*

Free house ~ Licensee Paul Theakston ~ Bar food (12-2.30, 7-9.30; 12-3 weekends) ~ Restaurant ~ (01765) 680100 ~ Children welcome ~ Open 11-5; 11-midnight Thurs, Fri and Sat; 12-5 Sun; best to phone for opening hours in winter

Kings Head 🍷 🛏️
Market Square

Readers very much enjoy their visits to this well run and handsome stone inn. It's in a super spot opposite the broad partly tree-shaded market square, and in summer the hanging baskets and window boxes in front of the building are very pretty; seats on the back terrace with a few in front, too. There's a thriving atmosphere in the two opened-up rooms of the bar, as well as traditional pine tables and chairs on the wood-stripped floor, a roaring fire in the imposing fireplace, a big clock (from Masham Station), and well kept Theakstons Best, Black Bull, XB and Old Peculier on handpump, and an extensive wine list with over 20 by the glass. Good, very popular bar food includes sandwiches, home-made soup (£3.75), chicken skewers with apple chutney (£4.45), black pudding and bacon stack with a creamy dijonnais and leek sauce or home-made salmon fishcake with tarragon crème fraîche (£4.95), sausage and mash with red onion gravy (£6.45), chicken caesar salad or brie and broccoli parcel with red pepper sauce (£7.95), steaks (from £10.75), cod on lemon and chardonnay risotto (£12.95), venison in red wine sauce (£13.50), and puddings like chocolate brownie skewer with marshmallows and strawberries or treacle sponge (from £4.95); helpful, friendly service. The restaurant is no smoking; piped music, darts, fruit machine, TV and dominoes. There are bedrooms in the back courtyard area with rooms for disabled customers and for families; they hold a civil wedding licence. *(Recommended by David and Ruth Shillitoe, Peter F Marshall, Janet and Peter Race, Richard and Anne Ansell, John Coatsworth, Edward and Deanna Pearce, Dr and Mrs Jackson, Jack Morley, K M Crook, Mike and Jayne Bastin)*

S&N ~ Manager Philip Capon ~ Real ale ~ Bar food (12-2.45, 6-9.45; all day Sat and Sun) ~ Restaurant ~ (01765) 689295 ~ Children in eating area of bar and restaurant ~ Dogs allowed in bedrooms ~ Open 11-11; 12-10.30 Sun ~ Bedrooms: £50B/£65B

MIDDLEHAM SE1288 Map 10

Black Swan 🍷

Market Place

In a rather steep and pretty village, this 17th-c stone inn is in the heart of racing country and is popular with trainers and stable staff. The immaculately kept heavy-beamed bar has high-backed settles built in by the big stone fireplace, racing memorabilia on the stripped stone walls, horsebrasses and pewter mugs, and John Smiths Bitter, Theakstons Best, Black Bull and Old Peculier, and Wensleydale Tony's Tipple on handpump; a decent little wine list with several by the glass, and piped music, darts, TV, shove-ha'penny and cribbage. Well liked bar food includes lunchtime snacks such as soup (£3.50), sandwiches or filled baguettes (from £3.25), filled baked potatoes (from £3.75), platters (from £5.25), and beefburgers (from £5.65), as well as sausages with a free-range egg or lasagne (£6.95), home-made steak pie or stilton pasta bake (£7.50), battered haddock or home-made chicken curry (£7.95), and seasonal game dishes; evening extras like 16oz gammon and egg (£9.95), and steaks (from £13.45). You may smoke only in the bar area. The dining room has been refurbished. There are tables on the cobbles outside and in the sheltered back garden which has been opened up and re-planted. Good walking country. *(Recommended by R E Dixon, Michael Tack, Blaise Vyner, Greta and Christopher Wells, Ian and Nita Cooper, Mike and Margaret Newton, K M Crook)*

Free house ~ Licensees John and James Verbeken ~ Real ale ~ Bar food ~ Restaurant ~ (01969) 622221 ~ Children in eating area of bar and family room ~ Dogs allowed in bar ~ Open 11-3.30, 6-11; 11-11 Sat; 12-10.30 Sun ~ Bedrooms: £35S/£65S(£70B)

White Swan 🍷 🛏

Market Place

If you are lucky, you can bag one of the seats in the window of the bar in this pleasant coaching inn that look across the cobbled market square to the ruined turrets of Middleham Castle beyond. The beamed and flagstoned entrance bar has a relaxed pubby atmosphere, a long dark pew built into a big window, a mix of chairs around a handful of biggish tables, well kept Black Sheep Best Bitter, Special and Riggwelter and John Smiths on handpump from the curved counter, 15 wines by the glass, and 20 malt whiskies; friendly attentive service and a good inglenook log fire. A second beamed room on the right has a variety of tables and dining chairs, a red oriental rug on its black boards, and like the first room, is candlelit. There's a third broadly similar room behind, a no smoking restaurant and, by the time this edition is published, a new dining room; piped music and dominoes. Enjoyable bar food includes home-made soup (£3.25), sandwiches (from £3.50), tagliatelle with blue cheese and spinach or tomatoes and herbs (£7.95), fried chicken with leeks on a honey and mustard cream sauce (£8.50), pies such as chicken or steak in ale (£8.95; a pie for two £15.95), pork fillet in cider sauce with lyonnaise potatoes (£9.75), salmon fillet with garlic and parsley mash and a creamy wine sauce (£12.95), daily specials like home-made prawn cakes with lemon mayonnaise (£4.50), queen scallops in chilli and coconut (£5.25), and calves liver with mushroom and smoked bacon gravy (£9.25), and puddings such as sticky toffee pudding with caramel sauce (£4); they also serve morning coffee and afternoon tea. Seven new bedrooms have been added this year. *(Recommended by B and M Kendall, Janet and Peter Race, Dr and Mrs M W A Haward, Michael Doswell, Ian and Nita Cooper, Ben and Helen Ingram)*

Free house ~ Licensees Andrew Holmes and Paul Klein ~ Real ale ~ Bar food (12-2.15, 6.30-9.15) ~ Restaurant ~ (01969) 622093 ~ Children welcome ~ Dogs welcome ~ Open 10-11; 12-10.30 Sun; closed 25 Dec ~ Bedrooms: £47.50S(£59B)/£69B

MILL BANK SE0321 Map 7
Millbank 🍴 🍷
Mill Bank Road, off A58 SW of Sowerby Bridge

There is superb walking country close to this well run dining place, with the Calderdale Way easily accessible from the pub. Cottagey and traditionally Pennine from the outside, it has a calm, clean-cut minimalist modern décor and local photographs for sale. The interior is divided into the tap room, bar and no smoking restaurant, with well kept Tetleys and Timothy Taylors Landlord on handpump, and 20 wines by the glass including champagne, port and pudding wines; also, a specialised gin list. Discreet background music of a jazzy flavour. Outside, the terrace has a glass roof and fold-away windows that make the most of the glorious setting overlooking an old textile mill. Below this is a garden adorned with metal sculptures made from old farm equipment. From an interesting menu, there might be pea and mint soup (£4.95), parmesan gnocchi with roast pepper and aubergine salad (£4.95; main course £9.95), sandwiches (from £4.95), chicken liver and foie gras parfait with grape chutney (£5.95), lemon and rosemary sausages with polenta chips (£8.95), olive and feta samosa with roast red onion, cucumber pickle and tomato butter (£9.95), beef in Guinness with horseradish mash or suckling pig with roast root vegetables and black pudding hash brown (£13.95), poached halibut with mussel, spring onion and saffron tagliatelle (£14.95), and puddings such as chocolate fondant cake with pistachio ice-cream or banana and caramel cheesecake (from £5.50); there's also a good value set price two-course menu (£11.95). More reports please. *(Recommended by Dr and Mrs Guy Cocker, Mike and Melanie Powell)*

Timothy Taylors ~ Licensee Joe McNally ~ Real ale ~ Bar food (12-2.30, 6-9.30; 12.30-4.30, 6-8 Sun; not Mon lunchtime) ~ (01422) 825588 ~ Children welcome ~ Dogs allowed in bar ~ Open 12-3, 5.30-11; 12-10.30 Sun; closed Mon lunchtime; first two weeks Oct, first two weeks Jan

NORTH DALTON SE9352 Map 8
Star 🍴 🍷
B1246 Pocklington—Driffield

This 18th-c brick-built pub makes one of the most attractive pub pictures we've seen, its walls rising almost straight out of a sizeable village pond. It's nice inside, too, a civilised place, recently refurbished in a relaxed gently upmarket country style, with a mix of candlelit tables in the main right-hand eating area, and some deeply comfortable seats with a good coal fire in the smart but properly pubby bar; there's a growing collection of breweriana. They have well kept ales such as John Smiths and Theakstons XB on handpump, decent house wines with a dozen by the glass, 20 malt whiskies, and a good choice of other drinks, and service is attentive; piped music. The food stands out for its quality in this part of Yorkshire, and at lunchtime, it might include two home-made soups (£3.50), sandwiches with home-made chips (from £5.25; avocado, tomato and mozzarella £5.50), coarse pork and black pudding terrine with red onion and apple chutney (£9.50), trio of crab cakes

(£9.95), and prawn, mango and king prawn salad with thai-style chilli dressing or roast chicken, chorizo and asparagus risotto (£10.50); also, grilled sardines in garlic and parsley butter with toasted anchovy and olive bread (£5.50), filo basket of chicken livers and chorizo in marsala and cream sauce (£5.95), smoked duck breast and apple salad topped with crispy leek (£6.50), layered chargrilled aubergine, smoked mozzarella and red pepper on a tomato and herb sauce (£12.50), pork fillet wrapped in smoked bacon with prune confit and port reduction (£13.95), fresh halibut on a lime, basil and caper butter (£15.95), medallions of beef fillet with a baby steak and Guinness suet pudding (£17.95), and puddings such as steamed chocolate sponge marbled with white chocolate and covered in chocolate sauce, lemon and ginger mousse, and boozy cherry and frangipane tart (from £4.50). The no smoking restaurant was originally a victorian pig sty. The pub dog is called Deefer. As we went to press, the bedrooms were under refurbishment *(Recommended by Dr Ian S Morley, C A Hall, Michael Swallow)*

Free house ~ Licensee Anne-Marie Thomson ~ Real ale ~ Bar food (not Sun evening, not Mon) ~ Restaurant ~ (01377) 217688 ~ Children in restaurant ~ Open 12-2.30, 6-11; 12-4, 6-10.30 Sun; closed Mon

NOSTERFIELD SE2780 Map 7

Freemasons Arms 🍺

B6267

Popular locally, but with a welcome for strangers too, this is a chatty pub with lots to look at. The low black beams are hung with gas masks, steel helmets, miners' lamps, pewter tankards and so forth, there are big prints of Queen Victoria, many old enamel advertising signs, and Union flags propped in corners; the cosy feel is boosted by the warm lighting, the candles on the tables and the hot coal fires. Using only local produce, the well liked bar food includes sandwiches (from £3.95), caesar salad (£4.25), baked goats cheese with rocket salad and red onion jam (£4.95), salmon fillet wrapped in parma ham with roasted mediterranean vegetables (£12.50), 12oz free-range pork chop with thyme mash and cider jus or rump of lamb with creamed savoy cabbage and smoked bacon (£12.95), and puddings such as eton mess (£3.95). The main bar area has just two or three tables with close wooden booth seating on its flagstones; there are more tables with pews and settles in the carpeted room on the left. Well kept Black Sheep, Tetleys and Timothy Taylors Landlord on handpump, and ten wines by the glass; piped music and dominoes. There are a few picnic-sets out in front, with pretty flower tubs and baskets. They now have a self-catering flat to let. No children inside. *(Recommended by Mr and Mrs Maurice Thompson, Janet and Peter Race, Michael Doswell, Pete Baker)*

Free house ~ Licensee Kris Stephenson ~ Real ale ~ Bar food (not Mon) ~ (01677) 470548 ~ Dogs allowed in bar ~ Open 12-3, 6-11; 12-10.30 Sun; closed Mon

NUNNINGTON SE6779 Map 7

Royal Oak 🍴

Church Street; at back of village, which is signposted from A170 and B1257

Very popular and consistently reliable, this is an attractive and neatly kept little pub with a genuinely friendly welcome from the attentive staff. The bar has high black beams strung with earthenware flagons, copper jugs and lots of antique keys, one of the walls is stripped back to the bare stone to display a fine collection of antique farm tools, and there are open fires; carefully chosen furniture such as kitchen and country dining chairs or a long pew around the sturdy tables on the turkey carpet, and a lectern in one corner. The dining room is no smoking. Good bar food includes home-made soup (£4.35), sandwiches (from £4.75), chicken liver pâté with home-made chutney (£5.75), mushrooms stuffed with garlic butter and stilton (£5.95), seafood hors d'oeuvres (£6.50), ploughman's (£7.50), lasagne, sweet and sour vegetables, steak and kidney casserole with herb dumpling, pork fillet in barbecue sauce or chicken breast in cheese and mustard sauce (all £9.95), fisherman's pot (£10.25), crispy roast duckling with orange sauce (£11.95), 12oz sirloin steak (£14.95), and puddings (£4.75). Well kept Tetleys, Theakstons Black Bull and Old Peculier and Wold Top Bitter on handpump. Handy for a visit to Nunnington Hall (National Trust). *(Recommended by Edward and Deanna Pearce, Simon J Barber, Peter Burton, Roger A Bellingham, Michael J Caley, Pat and Graham Williamson, Mr and Mrs P M Jennings)*

Free house ~ Licensee Anthony Simpson ~ Real ale ~ Bar food (not Mon) ~ Restaurant ~ (01439) 748271 ~ Children in restaurant ~ Open 12-2.30, 6.30-11; 12-2.30, 7-10.30 Sun; closed Mon

OSMOTHERLEY SE4499 Map 10

Golden Lion 🍴 🍺

The Green, West End; off A19 N of Thirsk

On the green of a small pretty village, this old stone-built dining pub remains extremely popular for its good, interesting food; you must book to be sure of a table, especially at weekends. The roomy beamed bar on the left, simply furnished with old pews and just a few decorations on its white walls, has a pleasantly lively atmosphere, candles on tables, well kept Hambleton Bitter, Timothy Taylors Landlord and maybe John Smiths on handpump, a decent wine list and 45 malt whiskies; one side of the pub is no smoking. On the right, a similarly unpretentious eating area, brightened up with fresh flowers, has good value generous food which might include sandwiches, french onion soup with gruyère cheese croûton (£3.95), rough pâté with onion and apricot relish, goats cheese and red pepper terrine or spicy pork ribs (£5.50), home-made lamb burger with mint jelly (£6.50), spaghetti with mussels or fresh baby clams or fresh white crab with brown crab mayonnaise (£6.95), home-made lasagne or lentil burgers (£7.50), steak and kidney pie (£8.95), salmon with creamy basil sauce or home-made chicken kiev (£9.95), pork and parma ham with sage and marsala wine sauce (£10.95), and calves liver and onions (£11.95); several teas and coffees. There's also an airy dining room, mainly open at weekends; piped music. Benches out in front look across the village green to the market cross. As the inn is the start of the 44-mile Lyke Wakes Walk on the Cleveland Way, and quite handy for the Coast to Coast Walk, it is naturally popular with walkers. *(Recommended by David and Ruth Shillitoe, Michael Doswell, Blaise Vyner, Tracey and Stephen Groves, Dr Peter D Smart, Pat and Tony Martin, Dr and Mrs R G J Telfer)*

Free house ~ Licensee Christie Connelly ~ Real ale ~ Bar food (12-3, 6-9) ~ Restaurant ~ (01609) 883526 ~ Children in eating area of bar ~ Open 12-3.30, 6-11; 12-11(10.30 Sun) Sat; closed 25 Dec

PICKERING SE7983 Map 10 🏠

White Swan 🍴 🍷 🛏

Market Place, just off A170

There's no doubt that this is a smart old coaching inn with quite an emphasis on the very good, interesting restaurant-style food and comfortable bedrooms, but there is still a relaxed small bar with a charming country atmosphere, panelling, a log fire and just three or four tables; bar billiards and dominoes. Opposite, a no smoking bare-boards room with a few more tables has another fire in a handsome art nouveau iron fireplace, a big bow window, and pear prints on its plum-coloured walls. The no smoking restaurant has flagstones, a fine open fire, rich tweed soft furnishings, comfortable settles and gothic screens. Attractively presented food might include lunchtime sandwiches (from £4.95; crab and watercress £5.25), as well as soup with home-made bread (£3.95), local cheeses with grape chutney and celery (£5.25), spinach and ricotta gnocchi with tomato and basil vinaigrette or smoked chicken caesar salad (£5.95), potted nidderdale smoked trout with horseradish cream and lovage salad (£6.25), hand-dived scallops with chilli, rocket and crème fraîche (£8.95), posh fish and chips or whole dressed whitby crab (£10.95), lemon roast chicken with herb, broad bean and parmesan salad or goats cheese and spring onion tart with red pepper chutney (£12.95), sage roasted pork fillet, chorizo sausage and fine bean and new potato salad (£13.95), and marinated leg of lamb with rösti and mint sauce (£14.95), with puddings such as rich chocolate cake with boozy cherries, glazed lemon tart with raspberry sauce or summer fruit pudding (£4.95). Well kept Black Sheep Bitter and Special and guests such as Cropton Yorkshire Moors Bitter or Timothy Taylors Landlord on handpump, good house wines (by two sizes of glass; pudding wines and superb list of old St Emilions), and quite a few malt whiskies. The old coach entry to the car park is very narrow. *(Recommended by David Carr, Mrs Yvette Bateman, Peter Burton, Mrs Hannah Colton, Joyce and Maurice Cottrell, Sylvia and Tony Birbeck, Christopher Turner, Judith and Edward Pearson, J Crosby)*

Free house ~ Licensees Marion and Victor Buchanan ~ Real ale ~ Bar food ~ Restaurant ~ (01751) 472288 ~ Children in restaurant and family room ~ Dogs allowed in bar and bedrooms ~ Open 10-11; 12-10.30 Sun ~ Bedrooms: £89B/£139B

PICKHILL SE3584 Map 10

Nags Head 🍴 ♀ 🛏

Take the Masham turn-off from A1 both N and S, and village signposted off B6267 in Ainderby Quernhow

Certainly handy as a break from the busy A1, this is a particularly well run and very popular place where you can be sure of a friendly welcome from the polite, obliging staff. The busy tap room on the left has beams hung with jugs, coach horns, ale-yards and so forth, and masses of ties hanging as a frieze from a rail around the red ceiling. The smarter lounge bar has deep green plush banquettes on the matching carpet, pictures for sale on its neat cream walls, and an open fire. The enjoyable food might include well liked sandwiches, home-made asparagus or leek and potato soup (£2.50; cullen skink £4.50), warm goats cheese and red onion confit tartlet (£5.25), foie gras mousse with madeira jelly and toasted brioche (£6.25), hors d'oeuvres (£7.95), spring vegetable risotto (£9.25), lambs liver with red onion gravy and crisp pancetta (£10.95), pork belly slow-roasted in spices with honey-glazed apple and five spice juices or cold roast sirloin of beef salad (£11.95), wild venison pie (£12.95), halibut fillet with saffron mash and champagne velouté (£13.95), and puddings like hot chocolate fondant with griottine cherries, crème caramel with sultanas or sticky toffee pudding with butterscotch sauce (£4.50); good breakfasts. The library-themed restaurant is no smoking. Well kept Black Sheep Bitter and Special, Hambleton Bitter and Timothy Taylors Landlord on handpump, a good choice of malt whiskies, vintage armagnacs, and a carefully chosen wine list with several by the glass. One table is inset with a chessboard, and they also have cribbage, dominoes and shove-ha'penny. There's a front verandah, a boules and quoits pitch, and nine-hole putting green. *(Recommended by David Miles-dinham, Charles and Pauline Stride, R N and M I Bailey, R F Ballinger, Oliver Richardson, Phil and Helen Holt, Adam and Joan Bunting, Alan Jefferson, Walter and Susan Rinaldi-Butcher, J F M and M West, Michael and Anne Brown, Mr and Mrs John Taylor, Alison and Pete)*

Free house ~ Licensees Edward and Raymond Boynton ~ Real ale ~ Bar food (12-2, 6-9) ~ Restaurant ~ (01845) 567391 ~ Children in restaurant ~ Dogs allowed in bedrooms ~ Open 11-11; 12-10.30 Sun; closed 25 Dec ~ Bedrooms: £50S(£55B)/£75B

RIPLEY SE2861 Map 7

Boars Head 🍴 ♀ 🍺 🛏

Off A61 Harrogate—Ripon

Even though the bar here is attached to a smart and comfortable hotel, it remains a genuinely friendly place with a relaxed and proper pubby feel and is still very much used by locals – they also keep a fine range of real ales. It's a long flagstoned room with green checked tablecloths and olive oil on all the tables, most of which are arranged to form individual booths. The warm yellow walls have jolly little drawings of cricketers or huntsmen running along the bottom, as well as a boar's head (part of the family coat of arms), an interesting religious carving, a couple of cricket bats, and well kept Black Sheep Best Bitter, Hambleton (Village Brewer) White Boar, Theakstons Best and Old Peculier and a beer called Crackshot (brewed for them by Daleside but following the Ingilby family's own 17th-c recipe) on handpump; an excellent wine list (with ten or so by the glass), and around 20 malt whiskies. From a menu that changes every two weeks, the interesting bar food might include soup (£3.75), nice sandwiches (from £4; soup and a sandwich £6.50), terrine of smoked salmon and horseradish with citrus sauce or goats cheese and crispy chorizo (£5.95; main course £11), risotto of roast garlic and goats cheese (£9.95), cumberland sausage with cranberry and thyme potatoes or seared lambs liver with sweet and sour onions and smoked bacon (£10.95), roast chicken supreme with spring greens and crispy leeks (£11.50), duck breast with honey-roast figs and chorizo oil (£13.50), and puddings such as dark chocolate fondant with poached pear or mixed berry crumble (£4.50); efficient staff even when very busy. The no smoking areas are clearly marked; piped music. Some of the furnishings in the hotel came from the attic of next door Ripley Castle, where the Ingilbys have lived for over 650 years. A pleasant little garden has plenty of tables. *(Recommended by John and Wendy Allin, Andrew and Samantha Grainger, Tim and Ann Newell, Marlene and Jim Godfrey, A S and M E Marriott, Stephen R Holman, David and Ruth Hollands, Michael Doswell, M J Winterton, Dr D Scott)*

Free house ~ Licensee Sir Thomas Ingilby ~ Real ale ~ Bar food ~ Restaurant ~ (01423) 771888 ~ Children welcome ~ Dogs allowed in bedrooms ~ Pianist Sat evening in restaurant ~ Open 11-11; 12-10.30 Sun ~ Bedrooms: £105B/£125B

RIPPONDEN SE0419 Map 7
Old Bridge ♀ ◖

From A58, best approach is Elland Road (opposite Golden Lion), park opposite the church in pub's car park and walk back over ancient hump-backed bridge

If you are not finding it easy to locate this 14th-c pub (and there's no traditional pub sign outside) – head for the church. It is by the medieval pack-horse bridge over the little River Ryburn, and there's a little garden overlooking the water. Inside, the three communicating rooms (one of which is no smoking) are each on a slightly different level. There's a relaxed atmosphere, oak settles built into the window recesses of the thick stone walls, antique oak tables, rush-seated chairs, a few well chosen pictures and prints, and a big woodburning stove. As well as the popular weekday lunchtime cold meats and salad buffet and sandwiches, the well liked bar food includes soup (£3.50), devilled whitby crab or dolcelatte cheesecake with pickled pears (£4.50), mushroom, spinach and asparagus pasta bake (£7), spanish chicken casserole, meat and potato pie or smoked haddock and spinach pancakes (£7.50), slow-roasted shoulder of local lamb in honey and rosemary (£9.95), and puddings such as bilberry crème brûlée or sticky toffee pudding (£3.50). Well kept Black Sheep Special, Copper Dragon Black Gold, Ossett Silver King and Timothy Taylors Best Golden Best, and Landlord on handpump, a dozen wines by the glass, 30 malt whiskies, and a good choice of foreign bottled beers. *(Recommended by Matt Waite, James Storey, Mrs Yvette Bateman, Roger and Anne Newbury, GSB)*

Free house ~ Licensees Tim and Lindsay Eaton Walker ~ Real ale ~ Bar food (12-2, 6.30-9.30; not Sat or Sun evening) ~ (01422) 822595 ~ Children in eating area of bar until 8pm but must be well behaved ~ Open 12-3, 5.30(5 Fri)-11; 12-11 Sat; 12-10.30 Sun

ROBIN HOOD'S BAY NZ9505 Map 10
Laurel ◖

Village signposted off A171 S of Whitby

At the bottom of a row of fishermen's cottages, at the heart of one of the prettiest and most unspoilt fishing villages on the North East coast, sits this charming little pub. The beamed and welcoming main bar is neatly kept, and is decorated with old local photographs, Victorian prints and brasses, and lager bottles from all over the world; the snug is no smoking, there's a roaring open fire, and sandwiches are served on winter Saturday lunchtimes only. Well kept Jennings Cumberland,

Tetleys and a guest such as Greene King Old Speckled Hen on handpump; darts, shove-ha'penny, dominoes, cribbage and piped music. In summer, the hanging baskets and window boxes are lovely. They have a self-contained apartment for two people. More reports please. *(Recommended by John Dwane, David Carr)*

Free house ~ Licensee Brian Catling ~ Real ale ~ Bar food ~ No credit cards ~ (01947) 880400 ~ Children in snug bar only ~ Dogs welcome ~ Open 12-11; 12-10.30 Sun; weekday opening time 2pm in winter

SAWLEY SE2568 Map 7
Sawley Arms ♀
Village signposted off B6265 W of Ripon

Run by Mrs Hawes for 36 years now, this is a spotlessly kept, no smoking dining pub that is ultra-civilised in an old-fashioned, decorous sort of way. The small turkey-carpeted rooms have log fires and comfortable furniture ranging from small softly cushioned armed dining chairs and settees, to the wing armchairs down a couple of steps in a side snug; maybe daily papers and magazines to read, piped music. The conservatory is liked by customers. Bar food includes soup with croûtons (£3.90), lunchtime sandwiches (from £5.50), salmon mousse (£5.95), home-made steak pie (£8.50), corn-fed chicken breast in a creamy mushroom sauce (£8.50), plaice mornay (£9.75), and daily specials; good house wines. In fine weather there are tables and chairs in the pretty garden, and the flowering tubs and baskets are lovely; two stone cottages in the grounds for rent. Fountains Abbey (the most extensive of the great monastic remains – floodlit on late summer Friday and Saturday evenings, with a live choir on the Saturday) – is not far away.
(Recommended by Walter and Susan Rinaldi-Butcher, JHBS, Margaret Dickinson, Janet and Peter Race)

Free house ~ Licensee Mrs June Hawes ~ Bar food (not Mon evening) ~ Restaurant ~ (01765) 620642 ~ No children under 9 ~ Open 11.30-3, 6.30-10.30; 12-3, 6-8 Sun; closed winter Sun evening, Mon evenings, 25 Dec

SHEFFIELD SK3687 Map 7
Fat Cat ◖ £
23 Alma Street

With its own-brewed, very popular Kelham Island beers and six guests all well kept on handpump, this back street pub has a fine bustling atmosphere and plenty of thirsty customers. There's a Brewery Visitor's Centre (you can book brewery trips (0114) 249 4804) with framed beer mats, pump clips and prints on the walls: Kelham Island Bitter, Pale Rider and two of their own guests, plus Boggart Hole Clough Sun Dial, Camerons Long Leg, Copper Dragon Best Bitter, McMullen AK, Oakwell Old Tom Mild and Timothy Taylors Landlord. Also, foreign bottled beers, two belgian draught beers, fruit gin, country wines and farm cider. Incredibly cheap, enjoyable bar food includes sandwiches (from 70p), soup (£2), ploughman's (£3), steak pie, mixed bean cobbler, spanish chicken, mushroom tortilla, and cheese and vegetable pasta (all £3.50), and puddings like jam roly-poly or apple crumble (£1.50). The two small downstairs rooms have brewery-related prints on the walls, coal fires, simple wooden tables and cushioned seats around the walls, and jugs, bottles, and some advertising mirrors; the one on the left is no smoking; cribbage and dominoes, and maybe the pub cat wandering around. Steep steps take you up to another similarly simple room (which may be booked for functions) with some attractive prints of old Sheffield; there are picnic-sets in a fairylit back courtyard.
(Recommended by Jo Lilley, Simon Calvert, Patrick Hancock, David Carr, B and M Kendall, the Didler, C J Fletcher, Keith and Chris O'Neill, Bob, James A Waller)

Own brew ~ Licensee Stephen Fearn ~ Real ale ~ Bar food (12-2.30, 6-7.30; not Sat or Sun evening) ~ No credit cards ~ (0114) 249 4801 ~ Children in no smoking room ~ Dogs welcome ~ Open 12-3, 5.30-11; 12-11 Fri and Sat; 12-3, 7-10.30 Sun; closed 25 and 26 Dec

---

Pubs brewing their own beers are listed at the back of the book.

New Barrack ● £

601 Penistone Road, Hillsborough

Friendly, enthusiastic new licensees have taken over this freshly decorated sizeable pub. It's got a lively atmosphere helped by regular live music, a curry night (Tuesdays), a weekly quiz evening (Thursdays), and up to nine real ales. Well kept on handpump there are four regulars such as Abbeydale Moonshine, Barnsley Bitter, and Castle Rock Harvest Pale and Wildlife, and five constantly changing guests; also, real cider, seven continental draught lagers, lots of continental bottled beers and a wide range of malt whiskies. The comfortable front lounge has red leather banquettes, old pine floors, a woodburning stove, and collections of decorative plates and of bottles, and there are two smaller rooms behind – one with high ceilings and benches, stools and tables around the edges, and the third room (no smoking) is more set up for eating; TV, darts, cribbage, dominoes and piped music. Tasty bar food now includes sandwiches (from £1.80; fresh baked baguettes from £3.95; steak sandwich £4.95), burgers (from £2.20), pie and peas (£3.30), all-day breakfast (£3.40), pizzas (from £4.50; 40p per extra topping), chilli (£4.95), spicy vegetable gumbo or chicken piri-piri (£5.25), and mixed grill (£9.90). Daily papers and magazines to read; maybe quiet piped radio. There's a small walled back garden. Local parking is not easy. More reports please. *(Recommended by David Carr, the Didler, Patrick Hancock, G Coates, Anne and Paul Horscraft)*

Tynemill ~ Manager Kevin Woods ~ Real ale ~ Bar food (10-2.30, 5(7 Sun)-9) ~ (0114) 234 9148 ~ Children welcome ~ Dogs welcome ~ Live music monthly Fri evening, alternate Sun evening and folk monthly Mon ~ Open 11-11; 12-10.30 Sun

SHELLEY SE2112 Map 7

Three Acres ⊕ ♉ ● 🛏

Roydhouse (not signposted); from B6116 heading for Skelmanthorpe, turn left in Shelley (signposted Flockton, Elmley, Elmley Moor) and go up lane for 2 miles towards radio mast

For a special meal out, this civilised and very well run former coaching inn remains popular with our readers. The roomy lounge bar has a relaxed, friendly atmosphere, tankards hanging from the main beam, button-back leather sofas, old prints and so forth, and well kept Black Sheep, Tetleys and Timothy Taylors Landlord on handpump, over 40 whiskies and an exceptional (if not cheap) choice of wines, with 13 by the glass. To be sure of a place, it's best to book (quite a way ahead) – try to get a table with a view. The restaurant and bar dining rooms are no smoking; piped music. Good, interesting food includes a fine choice of sandwiches (from £5.25; vegetarian club with mozzarella, plum tomato, basil, rocket, avocado and pine nuts dressed with sun-dried tomato pesto £5.95; open steak on toasted olive and tomato bread with caramelised sweet pepper marmalade topped with mustard and horseradish butter £8.95), as well as soups (from £4.95), potted shrimps or chicken liver parfait with toasted onion bread (£6.95), omelette arnold bennett or six rock oysters (£7.95), fresh dressed cornish crab on asparagus and samphire (£8.95; main course £15.95), thai green vegetable curry (£11.95), steak, kidney and mushroom pie with home-made brown sauce or lunchtime roast of the day (£13.95), fresh haddock in a light crispy sunblushed tomato and basil batter with home-made tartare sauce (£14.95), calves liver and dry cured bacon with bubble and squeak and caramelised onion gravy or chargrilled gloucester old spot chop with savoury herb coating topped with shallot and grain mustard butter with apple and black pudding compote and lyonnaise potatoes (£15.95), assiette of english lamb (£16.95), and home-made puddings such as hot cherries with chocolate brownie and vanilla bean ice-cream, orange and lemon tart with lime sorbet and confit zest, and coffee cream profiteroles with white chocolate sauce (£5.50). There's a delicatessen next door with take-home meals; helpful, welcoming service, even when really pushed. There are fine views across to Emley Moor. *(Recommended by Mrs Yvette Bateman, Mrs R A Cartwright, Jo Lilley, Simon Calvert, J R Ringrose, Brenda and Rob Fincham, Anthony Moody, M and GR, W K Wood, Peter Fitton, Mr and Mrs J Hutton, Richard Cole, Dr Michael Smith, Martin and Sue Day, Michael Butler)*

Free house ~ Licensees Neil Truelove and Brian Orme ~ Real ale ~ Bar food ~ Restaurant ~ (01484) 602606 ~ Children welcome ~ Open 12-3, 6-11; closed 25 Dec-2 Jan ~ Bedrooms: £60B/£80B

SINNINGTON SE7485 Map 10

Fox & Hounds 🍴 ♟ 🛏

Just off A170 W of Pickering

After a stroll through the pretty village, this neat and pleasant 18th-c coaching inn is just the place to enjoy a drink or a good meal. The beamed bar has various pictures and old artefacts, a woodburning stove and comfortable wall seats and carver chairs around the tables on its carpet. The curved corner bar counter has well kept Black Sheep Special and John Smiths on handpump, seven wines by the glass and some rare malt whiskies. At lunchtime, the well liked bar food might include home-made soup (£3.45), caesar salad (£4.45; main course £7.25), sandwiches (from £4.50; flatbreads with toppings like chargrilled vegetables and taleggio cheese £6.95), cherry vine tomato and melted cheese tartlet (£5.45), confit of duck on lavender mash with a honey and orange syrup (£6), fresh battered haddock (£7.45), spanish sausages with sweet pepper and tomato rice (£7.95), steak and Guinness pie (£7.95), and roast belly pork with fricassee of broad beans, butterbeans and asparagus (£8.75); evening choices such as field mushroom rarebit with pork stuffing, cheese and a sage and tomato concasse (£5.45), local smoked salmon with sour cream, blinis and roe (£6.50), parmesan tartlet of crab and saffron leeks topped with goats cheese, red pepper and crème fraîche (£7.25), leek risotto with roasted red onions, pepper, chestnut mushrooms and chilli oil and parmesan taco (£9.25), cornfed poussin with garlic and thyme and a red plum chutney and tarragon oil (£11.95), roasted veal escalope filled with parma ham, dolcelatte and sage with green pasta and tomato coulis (£13.45), and 10oz rib-eye steak with red pepper marmalade, roquefort cheese and rosemary (£14.25). Daily specials like whitby oak roast salmon rillette (£6.25), roasted mackerel fillets with a mushroom and tarragon fish cream (£10), and grilled whole lemon sole with a nut brown pomegranate and saffron butter (£13.25), and home-made puddings like orange and maple bavarois on white chocolate marquise with a rich orange compote, bread and butter pudding or miniature sherry trifle (£4.65). The lounge bar and restaurant are no smoking; piped music, dominoes and darts. Picnic-sets out in front and in the garden. *(Recommended by David and Ruth Hollands, C A Hall, Mark Walker, Alison and Pete, Michael Butler)*

Free house ~ Licensees Andrew and Catherine Stephens ~ Real ale ~ Bar food ~ Restaurant (evening) ~ (01751) 431577 ~ Children in eating area of bar and family room ~ Dogs allowed in bar and bedrooms ~ Open 12-2.30, 6(6.30 in winter and on Sun)-11 ~ Bedrooms: £59S(£69B)/£90S(£100B)

SUTTON-ON-THE-FOREST SE5864 Map 7

Rose & Crown 🍴 ♟

B1363 N of York

On a broad village street with good grass verges each side, this spotless and smartly refurbished beamed pub draws enthusiastic customers for its dining room food, and does not neglect the bar side. On the right a small parquet-floored bar has old engravings on sage green walls, well kept Black Sheep and Timothy Taylors Golden Best and Landlord on handpump from an intricately carved counter, ten wines by the glass from an interesting list, old-fashioned pub seating, a couple of dimpled copper tables, and some bric-a-brac on the mantelpiece. The L-shaped no smoking dining room on the left is bigger, with an attractive collection of dining chairs around the well spaced mixed mahogany tables on its polished boards, more etchings on its cream walls, and a red-painted former inglenook; it opens on to a terrace with good teak or metal tables and chairs, and a neatly kept garden beyond. Service is friendly and attentive, and the food quality gains from the choice being kept shortish: home-made soup (£3.95), braised ham rillette with apricot and ginger chutney (£4.95), salad of baby gems, grilled pancetta, soft boiled egg, garlic croûtons and honey and mustard dressing (£5.25), chicken caesar salad (£9.50), risotto of button mushrooms (£10.95), braised belly pork with cider and onion jus (£11.95), sweet chilli confit duck legs with stir-fried noodles and soy dressing or seared escalope of salmon with tiger prawn bisque (£12.50), chunky roast whitby cod with creamed leeks and potted shrimps (£13.95), grilled sirloin steak with pepper sauce (£14.95), daily specials, and puddings such as warm banana tarte tatin with coconut ice-cream and rum and sultana caramel, iced lemon parfait with Pimms and summer fruit consommé or dark chocolate and orange torte with passion fruit sorbet (£4.50); coffee is good. *(Recommended by Michael Doswell, Pat and Graham Williamson)*

Free house ~ Licensee Mr Middleton ~ Real ale ~ Bar food (12-2, 6-9; not Sun evening or Mon) ~ Restaurant ~ (01347) 811333 ~ Children welcome ~ Dogs allowed in bar ~ Open 12-2.30, 6-11; 12-3.30 Sun; closed Sun evening, Mon

SUTTON UPON DERWENT SE7047 Map 7
St Vincent Arms ⑪ ♀ ◖
B1228 SE of York

Readers consistently enjoy their visits to this well run and unchanging local and there's always a welcome for both regulars and visitors, too. The parlour-like panelled front bar has traditional high-backed settles, a cushioned bow-window seat, windsor chairs and a gas-effect coal fire; another lounge and separate dining room open off. To be sure of a seat, it's best to get here early. As well as sandwiches, the good, popular food includes home-made soup (£3.50), baked mushroom topped with goats cheese and a pesto dressing (£5), smoked haddock risotto, cornish crab mayonnaise or confit of duck with hoisin sauce and cucumber salad (£5.50), vegetable stir fry (£7), griddled chicken caesar salad (£8), steak and mushroom in ale pie (£8.20), beef stroganoff or thai chicken breast (£10.50), steaks (from £12.50), rack of lamb with a herb crust and a port and rosemary sauce (£13.50), daily specials like mushroom and pancetta risotto (£5), gratin or queenie scallops (£6), calves liver with pancetta and a red wine sauce or veal cutlet milanese (£11), and fillet of turbot on crushed potatoes with beurre blanc (£14), and home-made puddings such as treacle tart, crème brûlée or apple pie (from £3.80). All the eating areas are no smoking. Up to ten real ales on handpump or tapped from the cask: Fullers Chiswick, London Pride, ESB and seasonal ales, Marstons Pedigree, Old Mill Bitter, Timothy Taylors Landlord, Charles Wells Bombardier and York Yorkshire Terrier; nine wines by the glass, and several malt whiskies. There are seats in the garden. The pub is named after the admiral who was granted the village and lands by the nation as thanks for his successful commands – and for coping with Nelson's infatuation with Lady Hamilton. Handy for the Yorkshire Air Museum. *(Recommended by Derek and Sylvia Stephenson, Paul and Ursula Randall, Tim and Liz Sherbourne, Roger A Bellingham, Andy and Jill Kassube, Pat and Tony Martin, Peter and Anne-Marie O'Malley, Brian P White)*

Free house ~ Licensees Phil, Simon and Adrian Hopwood ~ Real ale ~ Bar food ~ Restaurant ~ (01904) 608349 ~ Children welcome ~ Dogs allowed in bar ~ Open 11.30-3, 6-11; 12-4, 7-10.30 Sun

THORNTON IN LONSDALE SD6976 Map 7
Marton Arms ◖ 🛏
Off A65 just NW of Ingleton (or can be reached direct from Ingleton)

With up to 15 real ales and 350 malt whiskies, this well liked pub remains popular with many of our readers. On handpump and well kept, the breweries might include Beartown, Black Sheep, Caledonian, Cropton, Dent, Sarah Hughes, McGuinness, Moorhouses, Salamander, Storm, Theakstons, Timothy Taylors and Titanic; four-pint take-aways, too. Also, Stowford Press and Weston's farm cider, all sorts of unusual spirits, a decent choice of wines and an enterprising range of soft drinks, as well as proper tea and coffee. Service is friendly and attentive. The beamed partly no smoking bar is inviting, with stools on blackboards by the long counter, and lots of stripped pine tables, pews and built-in wall seats in the carpeted main part – light and airy, with biggish black and white local photographs; some train memorabilia. A curtained-off flagstoned public bar has bar billiards, and both seating areas have open log fires. Generously served bar food such as home-made soup (£3.75), creamy garlic mushrooms (£4.35), sandwiches (from £4.65), 8oz burgers (from £5.10), home-made pizzas (from £6.50), cumberland sausage (£7.25), all-day breakfast (£7.95), vegetarian pasta (£8.25), steak and kidney pudding (£9.45), home-made game pie (£9.85), steaks (from £10.25), minted shoulder of lamb (£10.25), puddings (£3.95), and Sunday roast (£9.50). The dining room is no smoking. There are picnic-sets out on the front terrace, with more behind. Two of the bedrooms are equipped for disabled people; good breakfasts, which suit this great walking country. The 13th-c church opposite is where Sir Arthur Conan Doyle was married. *(Recommended by Andy and Jill Kassube, Patrick Hancock, Jo Lilley, Simon Calvert, Tony and Maggie Harwood, Michael Doswell, Steve Whalley, Len Beattie, John and Sylvia Harrop, Rob Razzell, Alex and Claire Pearse)*

Enterprise ~ Lease Graham Wright ~ Real ale ~ Bar food (12-2.30, 5.30-9; all day weekends and bank hols) ~ Restaurant ~ (0152 42) 41281 ~ Children welcome ~ Open 12-2.30, 5.30-11; 12-11 Fri and Sat; 12-10.30 Sun ~ Bedrooms: £46S/£72S

THORNTON WATLASS SE2486 Map 10

Buck ⬤ ⬅

Village signposted off B6268 Bedale—Masham

The place to head for in this genuine, friendly local is the pleasantly traditional right-hand bar with upholstered old-fashioned wall settles on the carpet, a fine mahogany bar counter, a high shelf packed with ancient bottles, several mounted fox masks and brushes, a brick fireplace, and a relaxed atmosphere; piped music. The dining room is no smoking. The Long Room (which overlooks the cricket green) has large prints of old Thornton Watlass cricket teams, signed bats and cricket balls and so forth. As well as specials that change every two weeks such as potted shrimps (£4.95), mussels with cream and pesto sauce (£5.50; main course £7.75), tagliatelle with spinach and nutmeg in a creamy tomato sauce (£7.95), thai green chicken curry (£9.50), and seared salmon fillet with a hot lemon-thyme dressing (£10.50), there might be soup (£3.25), home-made chicken liver pâté or smoked haddock fishcakes (£4.75), ploughman's (£5.95), omelettes (from £5.95), lasagne (£7.50), steak and kidney pie (£7.95), gammon and egg (£9.95), and steaks (from £10.95). Well kept Black Sheep Bitter and John Smiths, and a couple of guests like Durham White Crystal or Titanic Lifeboat on handpump, 40 malt whiskies, and half a dozen wines by the glass; darts, cribbage and dominoes. The sheltered garden has an equipped children's play area and summer barbecues, and they have their own cricket team; quoits. More reports please. *(Recommended by Oliver Richardson, Walter and Susan Rinaldi-Butcher, Matthew Hall, Anthony Barnes, Mrs P Wynne)*

Free house ~ Licensees Michael and Margaret Fox ~ Real ale ~ Bar food (12-2, 6.15-9.30; 12-9.30 Sun) ~ Restaurant ~ (01677) 422461 ~ Children welcome ~ Dogs allowed in bedrooms ~ Jazz alternate Sun lunchtimes ~ Open 11-11; 12-10.30 Sun; closed evening 25 Dec ~ Bedrooms: £50S/£65(£70B)

THWING TA0570 Map 8

Falling Stone ⑪

Off B1253 W of Bridlington; Main Street

The name is for a meteorite which fell on a field of the farm four or five miles away, where the pub's good Wold Top beers are brewed: Wold Top, Wold Gold, and Falling Stone are kept well on handpump, with a guest such as York. Their wines are reasonably priced. The carpeted bar on the right has attractively upholstered stools, bar stools and wall seats, with some button-back banquettes, a modicum of china on its cream walls, and steps up to a comfortable back pool room. Service is friendly, and the atmosphere relaxed and chatty; there may be well reproduced piped music, and the chess set gets a good deal of use. On the left is an extensive no smoking dining area, part conservatory, with white table linen neatly contrasting with the grey carpet; the cheerful street-scene pictures are by the landlady. A blackboard above the bar's warm coal and log fire lists the good food, which at lunchtime (not Sunday) might include big ciabatta sandwiches such as black pudding and poached egg (from £5), home-made pork and black pudding sausage on bubble and squeak (£5.50), home-made gnocchi with smoked haddock and a poached egg with basil, cream and parmesan (£7.50), and fresh salmon with asparagus hollandaise (£7.95); also, home-made salmon fishcakes with their own tartare sauce or warm salad of pigeon breast with croûtons, lardons and walnut dressing (£4.75), home-made chicken liver pâté with caramelised red onion marmalade (£4.95), calves liver with black pudding and pancetta with roasted shallots and balsamic jus (£10.50), duck breast with a salad of watercress, orange and dolcelatte with honey dressing or fresh wild bass with sauce vierge (£11.95), rack of lamb with rosemary, thyme and redcurrant jus (£12.95), sirloin steak with cream, pepper and brandy sauce and home-made chips (£13.50), and seafood platter (£16.95). *(Recommended by Marlene and Jim Godfrey, Fred and Lorraine Gill, Dr Ian S Morley, C A Hall)*

Wold Top ~ Lease Richard Ferebee ~ Bar food ~ Restaurant ~ (01262) 470403 ~ Children in eating area of bar ~ Open 12-3, 6(5 Sat)-11; 12-3, 7-10.30 Sun; closed Mon and Tues lunchtime

WASS SE5679 Map 7
Wombwell Arms 🛏

Back road W of Ampleforth; or follow brown tourist-attraction sign for Byland Abbey off A170 Thirsk—Helmsley

In a pretty village below the Hambleton Hills, this inn now has new licensees. The two character bars, both with log fires, are cosy and neatly kept and the two no smoking restaurants are incorporated into a former 17th-c granary. They use only fresh produce from local suppliers for their food: ciabatta sandwiches, home-made soup (£3.95), salmon fishcake with pink hollandaise (£4.75), a changing pâté (£4.95), black pudding on croûtons topped with a lightly fried egg and bacon (£5.65), spicy vegetarian ravioli (£9), steak, mushroom and Guinness pie (£9.25), chicken brochette with bacon, crème fraîche and mint sauce (£10.95), game casserole (£11.85), king prawns and scallops (£13.45), rump of lamb with a rosemary, cranberry and port sauce (£13.75), crispy duckling with orange sauce (£14.95), and home-made puddings (£4.25). Well kept Black Sheep Bitter and Timothy Taylors Landlord on handpump, several malt whiskies, and seven wines by the glass. More reports please. *(Recommended by Sue Holland, Dave Webster, Steve Whalley, Nigel Epsley, Jeff and Cindy Copland, Dr and Mrs R G J Telfer, Janet and Peter Race, Michael Doswell, Edward and Deanna Pearce, Jeff and Wendy Williams, Russell Burr, Mike and Lynn Robinson, Richard and Karen Holt, Paul and Ursula Randall, Pat and Stewart Gordon, J Crosby)*

Free house ~ Licensees Steve and Mary Wykes ~ Real ale ~ Bar food ~ Restaurant ~ (01347) 868280 ~ Children welcome ~ Dogs allowed in bar ~ Open 11.30-2.30(4.30 Sat), 6.15-11; 12-3.30, 6.15-10.30 Sun; closed Sun evening in winter~ Bedrooms: £42S/£70S

WATH IN NIDDERDALE SE1467 Map 7
Sportsmans Arms 🍴 ♀ 🛏

Nidderdale road off B6265 in Pateley Bridge; village and pub signposted over hump-back bridge on right after a couple of miles

Strictly speaking, this 17th-c mellow sandstone building is more of a civilised restaurant-with-bedrooms than a pub, but it does have a welcoming bar where locals do drop in for just a drink. It's been run by the charming Mr Carter for 28 years now and you can be sure of a genuinely warm welcome from both him and his courteous and friendly staff. The food remains excellent and they use the best local produce – game from the moors, fish delivered daily from Whitby, and nidderdale lamb, pork and beef. In the bar and changing daily, there might be freshly made soup with assorted breads (£3.75), terrine of local game with rhubarb chutney or warm salad of chicken livers and black pudding (£5.50), a choice of three cheeses (£6), local sausages with red onion and chickpea gravy or king scallops with garlic and gruyère (£8.50), slow-cooked venison with butter onions and mushrooms (£10.50), rib-eye steak with rocket aïoli and fries (£11.50), breast of chicken stuffed with banana, pilaff rice, and curry sauce (£12.50), monkfish wrapped in pancetta on fennel with a chive beurre blanc (£13.50), and puddings such as double chocolate roulade with chocolate ice-cream, their favourite summer or winter pudding, or roasted plums with cinnamon and mascarpone (£5); they also offer a two-course lunch (£10). The restaurant is no smoking. Well kept Black Sheep and a guest such as Butcombe Blonde on handpump, a very sensible and extensive wine list with a dozen by the glass, over 30 malt whiskies and several russian vodkas; open fires and quiet piped music. Benches and tables outside. Seats outside in the pretty garden. As well as their own fishing on the River Nidd, this is an ideal spot for walkers, hikers and ornithologists, and there are plenty of country houses, gardens and cities to explore. Children are tolerated but there are no facilities for them. *(Recommended by Anne Walford, John Close, Keith Moss, Marlene and Jim Godfrey, Barry and Patricia Wooding, Michael Jones, R A K Crabtree, Lynda and Trevor Smith, H Bramwell, John Saul, David and Ruth Hollands, T Walker, Stephen Woad)*

Free house ~ Licensee Ray Carter ~ Real ale ~ Bar food ~ Restaurant ~ (01423) 711306 ~ Dogs allowed in bar ~ Open 12-2.30, 6.45-11; closed 25 Dec ~ Bedrooms: £65S/£100B

WESTOW SE7565 Map 7

Blacksmiths 🍴 🍷 🛏️

Off A64 York—Malton; Main Street

Yorkshire Dining Pub of the Year

Taken over in 2003 by an Eddlethorpe farming family, what was the Blacksmiths Arms, an unassuming village local, has been carefully reworked into an upmarket dining pub. But the locals haven't been left out: there's usually a group of them on the left of the small black-beamed bar area, perhaps watching football on TV. There are traditional high-backed settles around sturdy stripped tables, each with a fat candle, a big open woodburning stove in the capacious brick inglenook, and a few small engravings (farm animals, scenes from *Mr Sponge's Sporting Tour* and the like) on the cream walls. A brightly lit focal serving bar has well kept John Smiths, Timothy Taylors Landlord and Tetleys on handpump, and they have good new world wines by the glass, their own sloe liqueur, and a nice range of soft drinks; wooden games and TV. The main, no smoking dining area on the right, open to the bar, is basically two linked smallish rooms, with a medley of comfortable dining chairs including some distinctive antiques around candlelit stripped dining tables; mixed old cutlery on linen napkins and nice glassware and china set the tone. Food is good, up to date in both presentation and content, using some produce from the family farm (which unusually does a nice line in sloe gin and chocolates). Besides tasty home-baked bread, it might include soup (£3.95), flaked smoked mackerel and smoked salmon salad with beetroot and sour cream (£4.95), toasted goats cheese with pesto dressing (£5.75), king prawn pasta with oven-dried cherry tomatoes and shellfish cream or peppered asparagus with parma ham, rocket and grain mustard dressing (£6.25), grilled trout with capers and watercress and lemon parsley butter (£9.75), roast rump of lamb with port and redcurrant jus (£13.75), breast of gressingham duck with sloe gin (£13.95), seared fillet of halibut with shrimp and cockle chowder (£14.75), and puddings such as iced banana parfait with crushed walnuts and caramel sauce or mango panna cotta with Harbrow liqueur (£4.50). Service is cheerful and efficient. There are picnic-sets in a side rockery. The bedrooms are in a newly done cottagey building behind; breakfasts are good. They have a pétanque pitch. *(Recommended by Sue Ashton, Giles and Annie Francis, Christopher Turner, Tim and Suzy Bower)*

Free house ~ Licensee Julia Brown ~ Bar food (not Mon or Tues; not lunchtimes except Sun (12-3.30)) ~ Restaurant ~ (01653) 618365 ~ Children welcome ~ Dogs allowed in

bar and bedrooms ~ Open 6-11; 12-10.30 Sun; closed Mon; closed lunchtimes except Sun
~ Bedrooms: £30S/£60S

WHITBY NZ9011 Map 10
Duke of York ◀
Church Street, Harbour East Side

It's the position that makes this busy pub worth a visit. The famous 199 Steps that
lead up to the abbey (one reader tells us that tradition says if you miscount you
have to start all over again) are close by, and there's a splendid view over the
harbour entrance and the western cliff from the windows. The comfortable beamed
lounge bar has plenty of atmosphere and decorations that include quite a bit of
fishing memorabilia – best to arrive early to be sure of a table. Bar food includes
fresh crab or prawn sandwiches (£3.75) or large fillet of fresh cod or fresh crab
salad (£6.95), as well as other sandwiches (from £2.95), vegetable lasagne or chilli
(£6), steak in ale pie (£6.50), and puddings (£3). Well kept Courage Directors, John
Smiths, and a changing guest on handpump, decent wines by two sizes of glass, and
quite a few malt whiskies; piped music (which some customers feel is unnecessary),
darts and fruit machine. Try to get a bedroom overlooking the water – it's also
quieter. There is no nearby parking. More reports please. *(Recommended by
Michael and Ann Cole, Tracey and Stephen Groves, David Carr, David and Ruth Hollands,
Edward and Deanna Pearce, John Fiander, Derek and Sylvia Stephenson, Mrs Yvette Bateman,
Dr J Barrie Jones, the Didler, Janet and Peter Race, Stuart Orton, LS, Kevin Thorpe)*

Enterprise ~ Lease Lawrence Bradley ~ Real ale ~ Bar food (all day) ~ (01947) 600324 ~
Children welcome ~ Live music Mon ~ Open 11-11; 12-10.30 Sun ~ Bedrooms: /£50B

WIDDOP SD9531 Map 7
Pack Horse ◀
The Ridge; from A646 on W side of Hebden Bridge, turn off at Heptonstall signpost (as it's a sharp turn, coming out of Hebden Bridge road signs direct you around a turning circle), then follow Slack and Widdop signposts; can also be reached from Nelson and Colne, on high, pretty road; OS Sheet 103 map reference 952317

For anyone crossing Heptonstall Moor, this isolated, traditional and friendly pub is
quite a haven; leave your boots and backpacks in the porch. The bar has warm
winter fires, window seats cut into the partly panelled stripped stone walls that take
in the moorland view, sturdy furnishings, and well kept Black Sheep Bitter, Greene
King Old Speckled Hen, Thwaites Bitter and a changing guest on handpump,
around 130 single malt whiskies, some irish ones as well and eight wines by the
glass; efficient service. Bar food includes home-made pâté (£3.50), sandwiches or
baps (from £3.50), home-made steak and kidney pie, ploughman's or mushroom
stroganoff (£5.95), steaks (from £9.95), roast rack of lamb (£10.95), and specials
such as queenie scallops with garlic butter and gruyère (£4.95; main course £9.95),
and venison in sloe gin, pheasant breast with stuffing and a red wine sauce, and
bass grilled with prawns (all £9.95). The restaurant is open only on Saturday
evenings. The friendly golden retrievers are called Paddy and Murphy. Seats outside
and pretty summer hanging baskets. *(Recommended by Greta and Christopher Wells,
Len Beattie, Nigel Epsley, MJVK, Ian and Nita Cooper, Martin and Sue Day)*

Free house ~ Licensee Andrew Hollinrake ~ Real ale ~ Bar food (not Mon or weekday
winter lunchtimes) ~ Restaurant ~ (01422) 842803 ~ Children in eating area of bar until
8pm ~ Dogs welcome ~ Open 12-3, 7-11; 12-11 Sun; closed weekday lunchtimes in
winter; closed Mon ~ Bedrooms: /£48B

If you have to cancel a reservation for a bedroom or restaurant, please telephone or
write to warn them. You may lose your deposit if you've paid one.

YORK SE5951 Map 7

Maltings 🍺 £

Tanners Moat/Wellington Row, below Lendal Bridge

Deservedly popular and well run, this lively small pub has a good mix of customers and a friendly, chatty atmosphere – and, of course, a fine range of real ales. The tricksy décor is entirely contrived and strong on salvaged somewhat quirky junk: old doors for the bar front and much of the ceiling, enamel advertising signs for the rest of it, what looks like a suburban front door for the entrance to the ladies', partly stripped orange brick walls, even a lavatory pan in one corner. There are six or seven particularly well kept changing beers on handpump with Black Sheep and Roosters, and five changing guests, with frequent special events when the jovial landlord adds many more. He also has two or three continental beers on tap, up to four farm ciders, a dozen or so country wines, and more irish whiskeys than you normally see. In generous helpings, the well liked and very good value food might include sandwiches (from £2.85), extremely good, truly home-made chips (£2.50) with chilli or curry (£3.50), filled baked potatoes (from £3.75), haddock (£4.95), and beef in ale pie or stilton and leek bake (£5.25); get there early to be sure of a seat. The day's papers are framed in the gents'; fruit machine. Nearby parking is difficult; the pub is very handy for the Rail Museum. *(Recommended by Dr and Mrs A K Clarke, David Carr, Patrick Hancock, Fred and Lorraine Gill, the Didler, Nick Holding, Martin Grosberg, Andy and Jill Kassube, Tracey and Stephen Groves, Esther and John Sprinkle, Mark Walker, Andy Lickfold, Eric Larkham)*

Free house ~ Licensee Shaun Collinge ~ Real ale ~ Bar food (12-2 weekdays, 12-4 weekends; not evenings) ~ No credit cards ~ (01904) 655387 ~ Children allowed after food service and must be well behaved ~ Jazz Mon, blues Tues ~ Open 11-11; 12-10.30 Sun; closed 25 Dec

---

LUCKY DIP

Besides the fully inspected pubs, you might like to try these Lucky Dips recommended to us and described by readers (if you do, please send us reports: www.goodguides.co.uk).

ADDINGHAM [SE0749]
☆ *Fleece* [Main St]: 18th-c pub locally popular for food from good hearty sandwiches and generous well priced blackboard meals using fresh local meat, whitby fish and smoked fish, popular Sun roasts (all day then), some unusual veg, pleasant mainly young staff, well kept Black Sheep, Timothy Taylors Landlord and Tetleys, good choice of wines by the glass, low ceilings, flagstones, candles and log fire, no smoking dining area, tap room with darts and dominoes; very busy wknds; children welcome, tables outside *(Tina and David Woods-Taylor, Marlene and Jim Godfrey, C A Hall)*

AINDERBY STEEPLE [SE3392]
☆ *Wellington Heifer* [A684, 3 miles from A1]: Wide choice of enjoyable fresh food inc good Sun lunch served quickly, cheerfully and generously in long friendly low-ceilinged bar, two-level lounge and dining room, log fires, good beer range *(Ian and Linda Barnes)*

ALLERTHORPE [SE7847]
☆ *Plough* [Main St]: Clean and airy two-room lounge bar with wide daily-changing choice of good sensibly priced food inc local game and nice puddings, friendly welcome, well kept Greene King Old Speckled Hen, Marstons Pedigree, Theakstons Best and Tetleys, decent house wines, well served coffee, snug alcoves,

hunting prints, World War II RAF and RCAF photographs, open fires, restaurant, games extension with pool; piped music; tables out in pleasant garden, handy for Burnby Hall *(LYM, R T J and J J Hubbard, Mr and Mrs P M Jennings)*

AMPLEFORTH [SE5878]
White Horse [West End]: Imaginative choice of good generous freshly made food in well appointed no smoking dining room, good genial service, relaxed atmosphere, well kept Black Sheep, open fires, good choice of wine, usual games (no fruit machines or piped music); sunny terrace, three bedrooms with own bathrooms *(Michael Butler)*
☆ *White Swan* [off A170 W of Helmsley; East End]: Three separate interestingly furnished and decorated rooms, good food from sandwiches up in bar and no smoking candlelit restaurant, friendly efficient staff, good atmosphere, John Smiths and Tetleys, blazing log fires, comfortable squashy seating, sporting prints, public bar with darts and dominoes; children welcome, attractive back terrace *(LYM, Dr and Mrs R G J Telfer)*

APPLETON ROEBUCK [SE5542]
Shoulder of Mutton [Chapel Green]: Cheerful and attractive unpretentious pub in nice spot overlooking village green, wide choice of

enjoyable bargain food in bar and restaurant, well kept cheap Sam Smiths on all four handpumps, prompt friendly service even on a busy Sun lunchtime (can be crowded with caravanners summer); bedrooms *(Peter Coxon, Alison and Pete)*

APPLETREEWICK [SE0560]

☆ *Craven Arms* [off B6160 Burnsall—Bolton Abbey]: Attractively placed creeper-covered 17th-c beamed pub with down-to-earth settles, flagstones and brown-painted ply panelling, well kept Black Sheep Bitter and Special and summer guest beers inc one brewed for them in Burnley, enjoyable reasonably priced home-made food from good baguettes up, small no smoking dining room, no piped music; walking boots welcome (plenty of surrounding walks), nice views from front picnic-sets, more seats in back garden *(LYM, Mr and Mrs Staples, Michael Butler, Lawrence Pearse)*

New Inn: Stone-built country local, unpretentious bar with good value simple wknd food inc good sandwiches, real ales such as Daleside, John Smiths and Theakstons, helpfully described bottled imports, eccentric décor and interesting photographs (HQ of local soi-disant dangerous sports club), nice pub cat, pool table in main sitting area, family room; machines and piped music, may be cl Mon lunchtime; in fine spot, lovely views, garden, good walking; bedrooms *(LYM, Stefanie and Christian Mohr, Pat and Graham Williamson, Alison and Pete)*

ARNCLIFFE [SD9473]

☆ *Falcon* [off B6160 N of Grassington]: Ideal setting on moorland village green for a favourite basic country tavern, same family for generations, no frills, coal fire in small bar with elderly furnishings, interesting photographs and humorous sporting prints, well kept Timothy Taylors Landlord tapped from cask to stoneware jugs in central hatch-style servery, generous plain lunchtime and early evening sandwiches and snacks from old family kitchen with range, airy back sunroom (children allowed here lunchtime) looking on to pleasant garden; cl winter Thurs evenings; plain bedrooms (not all year), good breakfast and evening meal *(B and M Kendall, Neil and Angela Huxter, the Didler, Kerry Law, Simon Smith, Richard and Anne Ansell, Ben Whitney and Pippa Redmond, MDN, LYM, Fred and Lorraine Gill)*

ASKHAM BRYAN [SE5548]

Nags Head [Main St]: Well kept Black Sheep and John Smiths, bargain food inc daily roast, good atmosphere *(Andy and Jill Kassube)*

ASKRIGG [SD9591]

Crown [Main St]: Neatly kept open-plan local in popular and attractive James Herriot village, helpful friendly staff, several separate areas off main bar with blazing fires inc old-fashioned range, relaxed atmosphere, cheap home-cooked food inc cut-price small helpings, fine ploughman's, good value Sun lunch and good puddings choice, well kept Black Sheep and Theakstons XB; children and walkers welcome, tables outside *(David Field,*

John Fiander, John and Enid Morris, Julia and Richard Tredgett, Alan and Carolin Tidbury, Peter Abbott)

☆ *Kings Arms* [signed from A684 Leyburn—Sedbergh in Bainbridge]: Early 19th-c coaching inn, thriving pubby atmosphere in flagstoned main bar with roaring log fire, attractive traditional furnishings and décor, well kept ales such as Black Sheep, John Smiths, Theakstons Best and Old Peculier, decent wines by the glass, good choice of malt whiskies, good interesting food choice, quick polite service, another open fire in no smoking dining room, pool in barrel-vaulted former beer cellar; bedrooms run separately as part of Holiday Property Bond complex behind *(Roger and Anne Newbury, Michael Tack, John and Enid Morris, LYM, John Fiander, Revd John E Cooper, Mike and Jayne Bastin)*

ASKWITH [SD1648]

☆ *Black Horse* [back rd Otley—Ilkley]: Biggish open-plan family pub in lovely spot with superb Wharfedale views from dining conservatory and good terrace; wide choice of usual food cooked well at sensible prices (best to book Sun lunch), well kept Timothy Taylors Landlord, courteous helpful staff, open fire *(Dr Pete Crawshaw)*

AUSTWICK [SD7668]

Game Cock [just off A65 Settle—Kirkby Lonsdale]: Prettily placed below the Three Peaks, good fire in homely old-fashioned beamed bare-boards back bar, good choice of fairly priced food from sandwiches up, well kept Thwaites, nice coffee, friendly obliging staff, two dining rooms (and modern front conservatory-type extension); dogs welcome, tables out in front with good play area, neat bedrooms, good walks all round *(BB, Tony and Maggie Harwood, Karina Spero)*

AYSGARTH [SE0188]

Palmer Flatt: Moorland hotel in great scenery nr broad waterfalls, medley of largely modernised bars but some interesting ancient masonry at the back recalling its days as a pilgrims' inn, well kept beers, bar food and restaurant; tables outside, fishing rights, space for caravans, bedrooms *(LYM, Mr and Mrs Maurice Thompson)*

BAINBRIDGE [SD9390]

☆ *Rose & Crown*: Upgraded inn overlooking moorland village green, nice mix of hotel with friendly and pubbily old-fashioned front bar, beams, oak panelling, old settles and big log fire, well kept Black Sheep and Websters, good coffee, reasonably priced wines by the glass, enjoyable food from good baguettes up in bar and spacious no smoking restaurant; children welcome, busy back extension popular with families, open all day, bedrooms *(LYM, Peter Abbott, Mr and Mrs Maurice Thompson)*

BARKISLAND [SE0520]

New Rock: Modest hilltop pub popular for incredibly cheap good food esp bargain steaks – well worth booking; well trained staff, beautiful labradors, keg beers; children welcome (not late evening), cl wkdy lunchtimes *(Herbert and Susan Verity)*

BECKWITHSHAW [SE2853]

Pine Marten [Otley Rd, Beckwith Knowle; B6162 towards Harrogate]: Conversion of rambling Victorian house, large rooms, mullioned windows, panelling, open fires, good food all day inc unusual dishes, welcoming service, Bass, Greene King Old Speckled Hen and Tetleys, decent wines, no smoking areas; handy for Harlow Carr gardens *(Mike Turner)*

BEVERLEY [TA0339]

☆ *Corner House* [Norwood]: Open-plan largely bare-boards reworking with some leather settees and easy chairs each end as well as pews and stripped solid tables, modern prints and some blue and pink décor, soft lighting, good value fresh up-to-date food from baguettes up, big wknd breakfast from 10, long counter with well kept ales such as Black Sheep, Fullers London Pride, Greene King Abbot, Roosters Yankee, Timothy Taylors Landlord and Tetleys, good wines, farm cider, wide range of fresh fruit juices, hot beverages, daily papers; piped pop music, and popular with young people; disabled access and facilities, tables outside, open all day Fri-Sun *(Fred and Lorraine Gill, David Carr, Len Beattie, BB)*

Dog & Duck [Ladygate]: Cheerfully busy two-bar local handy for playhouse and Sat market, cheap home-made usual lunchtime food using local produce from sandwiches to bargain Sun lunch, well kept Greene King Abbot, John Smiths and an interesting guest beer, good value wines and good range of malt whiskies, helpful friendly staff, coal fires; piped music, games machine; good value bedrooms up outside iron staircase in courtyard – secure parking *(Mark Walker)*

Molescroft Inn [Molescroft Rd (A164/B1248 NW)]: Comfortable pub with changing ales such as Badger Tanglefoot and Marstons Pedigree from central bar, good value pubby food from sandwiches and baked potatoes up *(Pat and Tony Martin)*

Woolpack [Westwood Rd, W of centre]: Small welcoming pub in former 19th-c cottage pair, very popular under current jovial landlady, limited choice of good value fresh generous food Weds-Sat evenings and Sun lunchtime (best to book), well kept Burtonwood and guest beers, decent wines by the glass, cheerful efficient service, cosy snug, real fires, simple spotless furnishings, no pretentions, brasses, teapots, prints and maps; subdued piped music, no nearby parking; open all day Sun, has been cl Mon-Thurs lunchtimes *(Paul and Ursula Randall, Len Beattie, J Crosby)*

BILBROUGH [SE5346]

☆ *Three Hares* [off A64 York—Tadcaster]: Back to a relaxed local village-pub atmosphere under new landlord, with good value food from good sandwiches to full meals (and take-away regional delicacies), friendly staff, well kept Black Sheep and Timothy Taylors Landlord, good wine choice, sofas and log fire; has been cl Mon *(Andy and Jill Kassube, Dr Ian S Morley)*

BINGLEY [SE1039]

☆ *Brown Cow* [Ireland Bridge; B6429 just W of junction with A650]: Genuine and unpretentious, open-plan but snugly divided, with good coal fires, easy chairs, toby jugs, lots of pictures, panelling; well kept Timothy Taylors ales with an unusual guest beer, good reasonably priced food from sandwiches to steaks, no smoking restaurant, friendly staff; may be piped music; children welcome, tables on sheltered terrace, pleasant spot by river *(Jane Taylor, David Dutton, LYM, Mrs Dilys Unsworth)*

Dick Hudsons [Otley Rd, High Eldwick]: Comfortable and appealingly old-world Vintage Inn, with popular food, Bass and Tetleys, good choice of wines by the glass, quick service; tables out by cricket field, tremendous views and good walks, open all day *(Anne and David Robinson, Stuart Paulley)*

Fisherman [Wagon Lane, by Leeds & Liverpool Canal]: Straightforward waterside pub in nice spot by bridge, wide choice of food from sandwiches to full meals inc a daily-changing school pudding in bar and partly no smoking dining room, Black Sheep and Tetleys, cheerful helpful staff; children welcome (crayons and colouring pictures) *(Anne and David Robinson, Pat and Graham Williamson, Tony Hobden)*

BIRSTALL [SE2126]

☆ *Black Bull* [Kirkgate, off A652; head down hill towards church]: Medieval stone-built pub opp part-Saxon church, dark panelling and low beams in long row of five small linked rooms, traditional décor complete with stag's head and lace curtains, lively local atmosphere, good cheap home-made food inc bargain early meals and good value Sun lunch, good service, well kept mainstream ales such as Boddingtons and InBev Trophy, upstairs former courtroom (now a function room, but they may give you a guided tour); no no smoking area; children welcome, quiz night Mon *(BB, Michael Butler)*

BIRSTWITH [SE2459]

☆ *Station Hotel* [off B6165 W of Ripley]: Welcoming interesting stone-built Dales local under hard-working young couple, smartly modernised spotless lounge, short choice of good value lunchtime food freshly made from local supplies, wider evening range, well kept Black Sheep and another real ale, good coffee, nice china; tables outside, picturesque valley *(R E Dixon, Brian and Janet Ainscough)*

BLAXTON [SE6700]

Blue Bell [Thorne Rd]: Pleasant local in former mining area, varied good value food inc popular Sun lunch, three well kept ales inc Theakstons Old Peculier, good service, daily papers, darts, conservatory; piped music, TV, machines at one end; picnic-sets outside, open all day wknds *(CMW, JJW)*

BOROUGHBRIDGE [SE3966]

Three Horseshoes [Bridge St]: Spotless unspoilt 1930s pub/hotel run by same family from the start, character landlord, friendly locals, huge fire in lounge, darts, dominoes and cards in public bar (not always open), original features inc slide-down snob screens, good plain home cooking from sandwiches to steaks in bars and restaurant, well kept Camerons Strongarm and Tetleys, splendidly tiled ladies'; bedrooms, open all day Sun *(Pete Baker, the Didler)*

BRADFIELD [SK2692]
Old Horns [High Bradfield]: Friendly old stone-built pub with comfortable divided L-shaped bar, lots of pictures, no smoking area, good value home-made food, efficient service, real ales and continental beers on tap; children welcome, picnic-sets and play area outside, hill village with stunning views, interesting church, good walks *(Matthew Lidbury)*

BRADFORD [SE2230]
Greyhound [Tong Lane, off B6135 – not far from M62 junction 27, via A650]: Well divided open-plan local, low ceilings and some flagstones, well kept Greene King Abbot and Tetleys, buoyant atmosphere, lots of cricket photographs (cricket field alongside), small restaurant *(Michael Butler)*
Symposium [Albion Rd, Idle]: Part of Market Town Taverns, with good choice of ales, foreign bottled beers, food inc popular Sun lunch and wkdy bargains, and wines, no smoking bar area and back dining snug; wheelchair access not great; open all day Fri-Sun *(Andy and Jill Kassube)*

BRIDGE HEWICK [SE3370]
Black-a-moor [Boroughbridge Rd (B6265 E of Ripon)]: Dining pub currently doing well, with enjoyable food and strong local support *(Janet and Peter Race)*

BRIDLINGTON [TA1767]
Black Lion [High St]: Former 18th-c coaching inn, oak-panelled bar and restaurant, friendly service, wide choice of enjoyable food, well kept ales such as John Smiths; tables outside *(Colin Gooch)*
Marine Bar [Expanse Hotel, N Marine Dr]: Plush seating, modern artwork, real ales inc guest beers, plentiful low-priced fresh food such as filled baked potatoes and local haddock; overlooks North Sea, bedrooms in hotel part *(Colin Gooch)*
Pavilion Bar [Jeromes, Esplanade]: Wicker chairs, modern art, huge lamps, lots of glass and iron pillars in former Floral Hall Theatre, attentive friendly staff, well kept Marstons Pedigree and John Smiths, usual food lunchtime and early evening; piped music; good disabled access and facilities, children welcome (indoor play area – small fee), small stage for entertainment, tables outside *(Colin Gooch)*

BRIGHOUSE [SE1323]
Red Rooster [Brookfoot; A6025 towards Elland]: Flagstoned alehouse with well kept changing ales such as Caledonian Deuchars IPA, Ossett, Roosters Yankee and Thwaites Lancaster Bomber, brewery memorabilia, open fire, separate areas inc one with pin table, no food or machines; small terrace *(the Didler, Andy and Jill Kassube)*

BROUGHTON [SD9450]
Bull: Neatly modernised old-fashioned pub popular for good wholesome food in bar and restaurant, pleasant busy atmosphere, polished brass and china, happy staff, well kept Black Sheep and Tetleys *(LYM, Hunter and Christine Wright)*

BURGHWALLIS [SE5311]
☆ *Burghwallis* [signed off A1 southbound, S of Pontefract; Scorcher Hills Lane]: Bargain hot food counter inc carvery (all day Sun) and a few fresh hot dishes for former village social club's huge dining area, well kept nicely priced Old Mill and Tetleys, good choice of wines by the glass, quick cheerful service, full-sized billiards table in separate games area with green leather wall seating; very popular with older lunchers *(Andrew Crawford, BB)*

BURNISTON [TA0193]
Three Jolly Sailors [A171 N of Scarborough; High St]: Very popular for good value generous lunches inc local fish, roomy fresh bright lounge with eating area, public bar and conservatory, interesting décor, real ales *(Janet and Peter Race, Geoff and Angela Jaques)*

BURNSALL [SE0360]
Fell Hotel: Elegant restauranty pub/hotel with light woodwork, blue, mauve and green chairs around low tables, three real ales from long bar, quiet atmosphere, good service, enjoyable if not cheap food, dramatic views esp from conservatory; good disabled access, comfortable bedrooms *(Hunter and Christine Wright)*
Red Lion [B6160 S of Grassington]: Popular 16th-c inn in lovely spot by River Wharfe, looking across village green to Burnsall Fell, tables out on front cobbles and on big back terrace; attractively panelled sturdily furnished front area with log fire linking into large back area with second sitting area and servery, several well kept ales inc Timothy Taylors Landlord, interesting wine choice by glass or bottle (they import direct), imaginative but pricey bar food, no smoking in dining room, bar parlour and conservatory; they may try to keep your credit card while you eat; children welcome, comfortable bedrooms (dogs allowed in bar), open all day, fishing permits *(Jim Abbott, Dudley and Moira Cockroft, LYM, Mrs P J Carroll, Alyson and Andrew Jackson)*

BURNT YATES [SE2561]
New Inn [Pateley Bridge Rd]: Appealing well run pub with friendly licensees and staff, decent pubby food and wines, well kept ales inc Theakstons, good atmosphere, interesting décor inc lots of antiques, nicely panelled back room; chalet bedrooms *(Tim and Ann Newell)*

CADEBY [SE5100]
Cadeby Inn [Main St]: 18th-c dining pub with up-to-date minimalist décor, stripped stone, pale carpet and polished beams, modern furniture in several linked areas, separate public bar with well kept Batemans XB, John Smiths, Tetleys and Wentworth Bluebell, good wines by the glass, pleasant staff, daily papers, open fires; tables out in sunny garden *(WAH,*

LYM, Derek and Sylvia Stephenson, Kay and Alistair Butler)

CALDER GROVE [SE3017]

Navigation [just off M1 junction 39; A636 signposted Denby Dale, then 1st right – Broad Cut Rd]: Good motorway break – cheery waterside stone-built local with interesting old canal photographs, two well kept ales, good simple food, low prices, panelled bar and ceiling, family room; tables outside with play area, walks by Calder & Hebble Canal *(LYM, JHBS)*

Red Kite [Denby Dale Rd (A636, by M1 junction 39)]: Vintage Inn done like a Georgian house adjoining a cottage row, pleasant inside, with their usual food and wide range of wines by the glass, Bass and Tetleys, log fire, daily papers; bedrooms in adjacent Holiday Inn *(Ian Phillips, Richard and Karen Holt)*

CARLTON [SE0684]

☆ *Foresters Arms* [off A684 W of Leyburn]: Welcoming low-beamed pub with good choice of enjoyable food inc unusual dishes, helpful service, decent wines by the glass, log fires, no smoking restaurant, darts and dominoes; landlord brewing his own Wensleydale ales; children welcome, bench seats out among tubs of flowers, pretty village at the heart of the Yorkshire Dales National Park, comfortable bedrooms, lovely views *(Michael Swallow, LYM, Steve and Barbara Bamford, Jack Morley)*

CARLTON HUSTHWAITE [SE4976]

Carlton Inn: Cosy pleasantly modernised dining pub with enjoyable medium-range food inc bargain lunches and three-course candlelit dinners, well kept real ale, cheerful service, speedy even when full *(Janet and Peter Race)*

CASTLEFORD [SE4225]

Shoulder of Mutton [Methley Rd]: Wide choice of real ales, friendly landlord and locals, nice atmosphere (but a lot of them smoke) *(Tony Hobden)*

CHAPELTOWN [SK3596]

Commercial [Station Rd]: Friendly three-room pub noted for half a dozen well kept interesting ales inc Wentworth, lots of pump clips in small no smoking snug, good choice of good value food all day (not Sun evening) inc good roasts and hot meat sandwiches on Sun, pictures and fans in lounge/dining room, games room with pool off L-shaped bar; no music or dogs, picnic-sets in small garden, open all day Fri-Sun *(Jo Lilley, Simon Calvert)*

CHURCH FENTON [SE5136]

White Horse [Main St]: Enjoyable home-made food at attractive prices, well kept ales such as Copper Dragon and John Smiths, welcoming service, games room with dominoes and pool, dining room/conservatory; garden tables *(C A Hall)*

CLAPHAM [SD7469]

New Inn [off A65 N of Settle]: Welcoming riverside pub in famously pretty village, log fires, landlady's tapestries and caving and other cartoons in small comfortable lounge, public bar with games room, well kept Daleside, Dent and Tetleys, good honest food in bars and restaurant, friendly service; handy for round walk to Ingleborough Cavern and more adventurous hikes, bedrooms *(Len Beattie)*

CLIFTON [SE1622]

☆ *Black Horse* [Westgate/Coalpit Lane; signed off Brighouse rd from M62 junction 25]: 17th-c pub with pleasant décor majoring on racing, golf and football, front part focused on wide choice of popular generous food from interesting ciabattas and other snacks to restaurant meals inc good value set dinners, smaller back area by bar counter mainly just standing room, beam and plank ceiling, open fire, well kept ales such as Boddingtons, InBev Trophy and Timothy Taylors Landlord, decent wines; 21 comfortable bedrooms, pleasant village *(Howard Martin, BB, Michael Butler)*

CLOUGHTON [TA0094]

Blacksmiths Arms [High St]: Cosy friendly local with good simple food on special nights (Weds salmon and steak, Thurs fish and chips), open fire, separate restaurant; bedrooms *(anon)*

☆ *Falcon* [pub signed just off A171 out towards Whitby]: Big dependable open-plan bar, neatly kept and well divided, light and airy, with comfortable banquettes and other seats on turkey carpet, good value honest food in quantity (no booking, but worth the wait for a table), well kept John Smiths and Theakstons Best and XB, good friendly family service, log fire in big stone fireplace, distant sea view from end windows; piped music; picnic-sets on walled lawn, good bedrooms with own bathrooms *(Patrick Renouf, BB, DJH)*

CLOUGHTON NEWLANDS [TA0195]

☆ *Bryherstones* [Newlands Rd, off A171 in Cloughton]: Several interconnecting rooms inc pink-décor dining room up on right and cosy flagstoned stable-theme room on left, lighter bare-boards back room with pool and interesting see-through woodburner, good reasonably priced generous food inc two- and three-course bargains and some unusual dishes, four well kept ales inc Timothy Taylors Landlord and Tetleys, over 50 whiskies, friendly efficient service, rustic bygones; children welcome (dogs too, it seems), picnic-sets and play area in sheltered back garden; has been cl Mon-Weds off season *(Edward Leetham, BB, Joan York)*

Hayburn Wyke Hotel [just N of village, which is off A171]: Down very long steep zigzag drive, great spot nr NT Hayburn Wyke, spectacular Cleveland Way coastal path and Scarborough—Whitby path/bicycle trail; bar pleasantly brightened up with lighter colours and higher ceiling, efficient cheerful service, good value straightforward food inc popular Sun carvery, well kept Black Sheep Special, Tetleys and Theakstons, coal fire, big café-style dining area, pool, table football and video game in bare-boards games area, monthly karaoke; well behaved children welcome, picnic-sets out on terrace and grass, play areas, comfortably refurbished bedrooms, good breakfast *(Edward Leetham, BB, Geoff and Angela Jaques)*

COLTON [SE5444]

☆ *Olde Sun* [off A64 York—Tadcaster]:
Immaculate 17th-c beamed pub under
enthusiastic new young management, several
linked low-ceilinged rooms with nice collection
of old chairs inc an antique settle around good
solid tables, coal fires, some emphasis on the
food side with wide choice changing monthly,
well kept John Smiths, Timothy Taylors
Landlord, Tetleys and a guest such as Bass,
decent wines, new delicatessen specialising in
local produce; picnic-sets on quiet front
terrace, has been cl Mon *(Mrs Jean Mitchell,
Les and Sandra Brown, BB)*

COWLING [SD9743]

Harlequin [A6068 Keighley Rd, NE of Colne]:
Stylish dining pub with good freshly made
food in bar and restaurant, well kept Timothy
Taylors Landlord; cl Mon/Tues *(Peter Abbott)*

COXWOLD [SE5377]

Fauconberg Arms [off A170 Thirsk—
Helmsley]: Picturesque old pub in delightful
unchanging village, well kept Black Sheep,
John Smiths and Theakstons Best, log fire in
attractively furnished lounge bar, back locals'
bar with pub games and TV, no smoking
restaurant with own comfortable pre-meal
drinks area; dogs and children welcome, open
all day in summer *(LYM, Mike and
Lynn Robinson, Dr and Mrs Jackson)*

DACRE BANKS [SE1961]

☆ *Royal Oak* [B6451 S of Pateley Bridge]: Solid
and comfortable stone-built pub with
Nidderdale views, interesting old photographs,
well kept Rudgate ales and Tetleys, good wine
choice, friendly staff, generous enjoyable food
from sandwiches up (they help with individual
dietary requirements), good log fire in no
smoking dining area; pool, dominoes, cribbage,
TV and piped music; children in eating areas,
terrace tables and informal back garden, three
good value character bedrooms, good
breakfast *(Peter J and Avril Hanson, LYM,
Andrew Shore, Maria Williams, Ben Whitney
and Pippa Redmond, Mrs Diane M Hall,
Paul and Ursula Randall, Geoff and
Teresa Salt, Steve Kirby, Dr Pete Crawshaw,
Alison and Pete)*

DALEHOUSE [NZ7717]

Fox & Hounds [Dalehouse Bank, off A174 at
Staithes]: Small spotless country pub with fox
and hounds theme throughout, busy local front
bar, very friendly attentive staff, well kept
Theakstons, good usual home-made food from
generous sandwiches through kippers and fresh
fish to steaks, no smoking side room
(Edward and Deanna Pearce)

DALTON [NZ1108]

Travellers Rest [off A66 NW of Scotch
Corner]: Surprisingly inventive good food in
small tucked-away old stone-built dining pub
with pleasant warm atmosphere, friendly
service, real ales, good wines, good coffee with
petits fours; quiet hamlet *(Michael Doswell)*

DEWSBURY [SE2622]

Huntsman [Walker Cottages, Chidswell Lane,
Shaw Cross – pub signed]: Cosy converted
cottages alongside urban-fringe farm, low

beams, lots of brasses and agricultural bric-a-
brac, friendly locals, well kept Black Sheep,
John Smiths and Timothy Taylors Landlord,
warm fire, small no smoking front extension;
no food evening or Sun/Mon lunchtime, busy
evenings *(Michael Butler)*

Leggers [Robinsons Boat Yard, Savile Town
Wharf, Mill St E (SE of B6409)]: Friendly if
basic wharfside hayloft conversion, low-
beamed upstairs bar with two egyptian beers
brewed downstairs, several guest beers inc
Roosters, pies and sandwiches or filled rolls
all day, real fire, helpful staff, daily papers,
lots of old brewery and pub memorabilia,
pool; open all day, and they do Calder boat
trips *(the Didler, Michael Butler,
Tony Hobden)*

☆ *West Riding Licensed Refreshment Rooms*
[Station, Wellington Rd]: Busy three-room
early Victorian station bar on southbound
platform, particularly well kept Anglo Dutch
(from the related local brewery), Black Sheep,
Timothy Taylors and other changing ales inc
great value cheap Mild, farm ciders, bargain
wkdy lunchtime food on scrubbed tables, pie
night Tues, curry night Weds, daily papers,
friendly staff, coal fire, lots of steam
memorabilia inc paintings by local artists; no
smoking area just til 6, jazz nights, lavatories
can come under pressure; disabled access, open
all day *(Andy and Jill Kassube, the Didler,
Jim and Maggie Cowell, Richard and
Karen Holt, Tony Hobden)*

DONCASTER [SE5703]

Corner Pin [St Sepulchre Gate W, Cleveland
St]: Well kept John Smiths and two interesting
changing guest beers, plushly refurbished
beamed lounge with old local pub prints, welsh
dresser and china, good value traditional food
from fine hot sandwiches to cheap Sun roast,
friendly landlady and locals, cheery bar with
darts, games machine and TV; open all day
(the Didler, Patrick Hancock)

Hare & Tortoise [Parrots Corner, Bawtry Rd,
Bessacarr (A638)]: Former surgeon's house
redone as relaxed and civilised Vintage Inn
pub/restaurant suiting all ages, varying-sized
antique tables in eight small rooms off bar,
sensibly priced food all day, friendly efficient
young staff, real ales and well chosen wines,
log fire *(Stephen Woad)*

Leopard [West St]: Lively and friendly, with
superb tiled façade, well kept John Smiths, one
or two local Glentworth and guest beers, cheap
basic lunchtime food, lounge with lots of bric-
a-brac, children's games and nostalgic juke
box, basic bar area with pool and darts; TV
and games machine, good live music upstairs,
can get very busy; open all day, disabled access
(Patrick Hancock, the Didler)

Plough [W Laith Gate, by Frenchgate shopping
centre]: Old-fashioned small local with well
kept low-priced real ales, old town maps,
friendly staff, bustling front room with darts
and dominoes (and sports TV), quieter back
lounge; tiny central courtyard, open all day
Tues, Fri, Sat *(the Didler, Pete Baker,
Patrick Hancock)*

DORE [SK3081]
Dore Moor Inn [A625 Sheffield—Castleton]:
Busy extended Vintage Inn on edge of Peak
District looking down on Sheffield, popular for
early evening family meals; good value ample
food, fine choice of wines by the glass, good
coffee with refills, Bass and Tetleys, hard-
working friendly staff, superb central log fires,
lots of stripped pine, nice flower arrangements
(Michael Butler, Bob)

DOWNHOLME [SE1197]
☆ *Bolton Arms* [off A6108 Leyburn—
Richmond]: Consistently good interesting
blackboard food cooked to order by landlord
in small Dales dining pub, two neat carpeted
pubby areas divided by smallish entrance bar,
lots of little pictures, log fire, steps up to red-
walled conservatory dining room with great
Swaledale views, well kept Black Sheep and
Timothy Taylors Landlord, good short wine
choice; best to book evenings, esp wknds; neat
garden, two good value bedrooms sharing
bathroom (Anna Cooper, Michael Doswell,
BB)

DRIFFIELD [TA0257]
Bell [Market Pl]: Elegant and well run 18th-c
coaching inn with good bistro-style bar food
inc good value imaginative lunchtime buffet,
cheerful welcoming staff and well kept beer
from small breweries such as Daleside and
Hambleton in long spaciously comfortable red
plush bar, former Corn Exchange used as
stripped-brick eating area with lots of leafy-
looking hanging baskets, delightful old-
fashioned restaurant; comfortable bedrooms
(Derek and Sylvia Stephenson, Paul and
Ursula Randall)

EASINGWOLD [SE5270]
George [Market Pl]: Trim and cheerful market
town hotel popular with older people,
comfortable quiet corners even when busy,
well kept Black Sheep and Timothy Taylors
Landlord, good food in bar and no smoking
dining room, friendly helpful staff;
comfortable bedrooms, good breakfast
(Janet and Peter Race, Philip and June Caunt,
J Crosby)

EAST MARTON [SD9050]
☆ *Cross Keys* [A59 Gisburn—Skipton]: Roomy
and civilised, attractively set back behind small
green nr Leeds & Liverpool Canal (and
Pennine Way), abstract prints on canary walls
contrasting with heavy beams, antique oak
furniture and big log or coal fire, good range of
generous food from sandwiches served with
roasted veg up, well kept ales such as Black
Sheep, Copper Dragon Bitter and Orange
Pippin, Timothy Taylors Landlord and
Theakstons Cool Cask, decent wines, quick
friendly helpful service, more restauranty
dining room; quiet piped music; tables outside
(LYM, Steve Whalley, Malcolm M Stewart,
Tony Hobden)

EGTON BRIDGE [NZ8005]
☆ *Postgate* [signed off A171 W of Whitby]:
Welcoming moorland village local, proper
home cooking from sandwiches to good fish
choice, helpful landlady, well kept Theakstons,

beams, ochre walls and dark panelling, quarry
tiles, rustic bric-a-brac, coal fire in old kitchen
range, traditional games in public bar, small
restaurant; tables on sunny flagstoned terrace,
has been open all day, nice bedrooms (LYM,
Tim Walker, LS)

ELLAND [SE1121]
☆ *Barge & Barrel* [quite handy for M62 junction
24; Park Rd (A6025, via A629 and B6114)]:
Large welcoming pub, tap for local E&S
Elland ales, guest beers too, farm cider,
pleasant staff, huge helpings of low-priced
tasty lunchtime food (not Weds), real fire,
family room (with air hockey); piped radio,
live music some Suns; seats by Calder &
Hebble Canal, limited parking, open all day
(JHBS, the Didler)
Oddfellows [Elland Lane]: Neatly kept
comfortable tap for E&S beers, also three guest
beers, sandwiches, baked potatoes and a few
simple hot dishes (Pat and Tony Martin,
the Didler)

ELLERBY [NZ7914]
Ellerby Hotel [just off A174 Whitby rd;
Ryeland Lane]: Small hotel in same welcoming
family for 20 years, completely no smoking,
with good pub atmosphere, bar meals from
pies to imaginative meat and fish dishes, well
kept Courage Directors and John Smiths
Magnet, log fire, good restaurant; bedrooms
comfortable and well priced, with enormous
breakfast (Richard and Karen Holt)

ELVINGTON [SE6947]
Grey Horse [Main St (B1228 SE of York)]:
Bustling village local with warmly friendly
staff, wide choice of enjoyable food, well kept
changing ales such as Black Sheep, John Smiths
and Timothy Taylors Landlord, woodburners
and comfortable restaurant extension; tables
outside, bedrooms, open all day wknds
(Jane Greenwood)

FINGHALL [SE1889]
☆ *Queens Head* [off A684 E of Leyburn]: Warm
and comfortable, with good log fires each end,
some panelling, low black beams and lit
candles, settles making stalls around big tables,
friendly helpful young management, well
rounded choice of enjoyable reasonably priced
food, well kept Black Sheep, Johns Smiths and
Theakstons, interesting range of well priced
wines, good soft drinks, elegant and roomy no
smoking back Wensleydale-view restaurant; no
dogs; wheelchair access, disabled facilities,
garden tables sharing view, open all day
(Fiona Salvesen, Anna Cooper, Leslie J Lyon,
Mrs Hilary Nicholson, BB)

FLAMBOROUGH [TA2270]
☆ *Seabirds* [Tower St (B1255/B1229)]: Friendly
village pub under newish licensees (more
reports please), shipping-theme bar,
woodburner and local pictures in comfortable
lounge, enjoyable bar food from sandwiches to
steaks, extended no smoking restaurant, well
kept John Smiths and a guest beer, decent wine
list, dominoes; piped music, games machine,
TV; children and dogs welcome, tables in
sizeable garden (Dr and Mrs T E Hothersall,
LYM, Dr Alan and Mrs Sue Holder)

FLOCKTON [SE2314]
Sun [off A642 Wakefield—Huddersfield at Blacksmiths Arms]: Comfortably worn in beamed pub with lots of brasses, open fires in bar and dining area, reasonably priced food (not Sun evening) from sandwiches to cheap Sun roast, three real ales, good service; piped music; children welcome, garden tables with lovely views, open all day *(Geoffrey and Brenda Wilson)*

GALPHAY [SE2572]
☆ *Galphay Inn* [off B6265 W of Ripon]: Attractive small stone-built country dining pub stylishly refurbished under new licensees, good food inc succulent seasonal game and carefully chosen local ingredients with some imaginative cooking, good friendly service, well kept Timothy Taylors Landlord, enterprising wine choice, good coffee, interesting etchings in partly panelled newly carpeted bar with woodburner, modern wildlife prints in elegant terracotta dining room; teak tables and chairs on new heated decking out behind *(R E Dixon, Hunter and Christine Wright, Michael Doswell, Stephen Woad, BB)*

GANTON [SE9877]
Greyhound [Main Rd (A64 Malton—Scarboro)]: Under new licensees, with fresh and airy uncluttered décor, friendly helpful staff, well presented standard pub food from sandwiches up; well placed for the championship golf course *(DB)*

GARGRAVE [SD9253]
Masons Arms [Church St/Marton Rd (off A65 NW of Skipton)]: Busy well run pub, attractive and homely, well kept Boddingtons, Timothy Taylors Landlord and Tetleys, good friendly service, generous quickly served food from good sandwiches up, copper-canopied log-effect gas fire dividing two open-plan areas, one no smoking; well behaved children welcome, tables in garden, bowling green behind – charming village on Pennine Way, between river and church and not far from Leeds & Liverpool Canal *(Geoffrey and Brenda Wilson)*

GARSDALE HEAD [SD7992]
Moorcock [junction A684/B6259; marked on many maps, nr Garsdale stn on Settle—Carlisle line]: Isolated stone-built inn doing well under friendly new landlord, well kept Timothy Taylors Landlord and guest beers, good choice of generous bar food inc decent vegetarian selection, pleasant no smoking lounge bar with cosy corners; occasional live music, tables outside with views of viaduct and Settle—Carlisle railway, bedrooms *(Len Beattie, John Keeler)*

GILLAMOOR [SE6890]
☆ *Royal Oak* [off A170 in Kirkbymoorside]: Well run traditional stone-built village inn with some emphasis on the good value food side, good service under friendly hands-on landlady, well kept Black Sheep Bitter and Riggwelter, John Smiths and Tetleys, good coffee and reasonably priced wines, roomy turkey-carpeted bar, heavy dark beams, log fires in two tall stone fireplaces (one with a great old-fashioned iron kitchen range), flowers and candles throughout, no music; comfortable bedrooms, good breakfast, attractive village handy for Barnsdale Moor walks *(Michael Doswell, BB, R Pickles)*

GILLING EAST [SE6176]
Fairfax Arms [Main St (B1363)]: Country pub doing well under hospitable new licensees, looking up to castle in attractive village with miniature steam railway, enjoyable food in bar and restaurant, well kept Jennings, friendly attentive staff; picnic-sets under cocktail parasols out by stream *(Walter and Susan Rinaldi-Butcher, Colin and Dot Savill)*

GOLDSBOROUGH [NZ8314]
Fox & Hounds [off A174 NW of Whitby]: Snug and homely, short choice of good food changing daily, welcoming chef/landlord, well kept beers *(Mark and Angela Stephens)*

GRANGE MOOR [SE2215]
☆ *Kaye Arms* [A642 Huddersfield—Wakefield]: Very good family-run eating place, too restauranty for the main entries but well up to that standard: civilised, friendly and busy, enterprising proper food, sandwiches too (they bake and sell their own bread), courteous efficient staff, exceptional value house wines from imaginative list, hundreds of malt whiskies, no smoking room; handy for Yorkshire Mining Museum, cl Mon lunchtime *(David and Catherine Whiting, Michael Butler, Pierre Richterich, LYM, Dr and Mrs S Donald)*

GRANTLEY [SE2369]
Grantley Arms [off B6265 W of Ripon]: Attractive stone-built pub in quiet Dales village, comfortable and tasteful, with beams, brasses and big coal fire, interesting if not cheap food (all day Sun, not Tues lunchtime or Mon), well kept Black Sheep and Timothy Taylors Landlord, decent wines, attentive service, candles and fresh flowers, paintings by landlady, no smoking area; children welcome if eating *(Mr and Mrs R K Blackman, Angus Johnson, Carol Bolden, Christopher J Darwent)*

GRASSINGTON [SE0064]
☆ *Devonshire* [The Square]: Handsome small hotel with good window seats and tables outside overlooking sloping village square, good range of well presented generous food from sandwiches to bargain two-course lunches in big popular restaurant, interesting pictures and ornaments, beams and open fires, pleasant family room, good service from cheerful chatty uniformed staff even though it's busy, buoyant mix of locals and visitors, well kept ales inc Black Sheep Best and Timothy Taylors Landlord, decent wines; comfortable bedrooms, open all day Sun *(LYM, Fred and Lorraine Gill, Mr and Mrs A J Edwards, Rod Stoneman, B and M Kendall)*
Foresters Arms [Main St]: Locally popular opened-up old coaching inn with friendly efficient staff, well kept Black Sheep, Tetleys Mild, Timothy Taylors Landlord and changing guest beers, good value straightforward food, pool, dining room; sports TV; children

welcome, reasonably priced bedrooms, open all day *(B and M Kendall, Fred and Lorraine Gill, the Didler)*

Grassington House [The Square]: Hotel doing enjoyable varied bar food, good atmosphere and service, well kept beers, decent wines; bedrooms *(Margaret and Roy Randle)*

GREAT AYTON [NZ5610]
Royal Oak [off A173 – follow village signs; High Green]: Wide range of generous good traditional food, well kept Courage Directors and Theakstons, unpretentious convivial bar with good log fire, beam-and-plank ceiling, bulgy old partly panelled stone walls, traditional furnishings inc antique settles, pleasant views of elegant village green from bay windows, long dining lounge (children welcome), separate appealingly old-fashioned restaurant; comfortable bedrooms *(LYM, Blaise Vyner)*

GREAT OUSEBURN [SE4562]
☆ *Crown* [off B6265 SE of Boroughbridge]: Cheerful country pub very popular for wide choice of good generous elegantly presented food (all afternoon Sat/Sun) from baguettes to some interesting dishes and big steaks, restaurant quality at sensible prices, early evening bargains, tip-top cheeses, well kept Black Sheep, Hampleton, John Smiths and Theakstons, good choice of wines, good friendly service, lots of Edwardian pictures and assorted bric-a-brac, no smoking new back dining extension; may be piped music; well behaved children welcome, tables in garden with enclosed terrace and play area, cl wkdy lunchtimes, open all day wknds and bank hols *(LYM, Michael Swallow, Michael Doswell)*

GRENOSIDE [SK3394]
Cow & Calf [3 miles from M1 junction 35; Skew Hill Lane]: Three connected rooms, one no smoking, high-backed settles, stripped stone and beams, low-priced lunchtime food inc three roasts, well kept low-priced Sam Smiths OB; tea and coffee, friendly staff, cosy fire; disabled access, children welcome, family room in block across flower-decked walled former farmyard with picnic-sets, splendid views over Sheffield, open all day wknds *(LYM, CMW, JJW, Lucien Perring)*

GREWELTHORPE [SE2376]
☆ *Crown* [back rd NW of Ripon]: Open fire in bustling two-room Dales bar, well furnished and welcoming, with good value generous food (not Mon lunchtime but all day Fri-Sun), well kept Jennings ales, separate back dining room; picnic-sets out in front, pleasant small village, good walks nearby *(M J Winterton)*

GUNNERSIDE [SD9598]
Kings Head [B6270 Swaledale rd]: Small open-plan flagstoned local in pretty riverside Dales village, friendly staff, well kept Black Sheep and Hambleton, good value simple home-made food, old village photographs; unobtrusive piped music, smoking allowed throughout; children welcome, some tables out by bridge, good walks nearby, open all day *(Tim and Rosemary Wells)*

HACKNESS [SE9788]
Everley: Comfortable lounge bar in stone-built hotel in pretty valley setting, well kept beers such as John Smiths and Greene King Ruddles County, landlady (who taught at catering college) cooks good food specialising in puddings, beautiful views from restaurant; bedrooms *(Colin and Dot Savill)*

HALIFAX [SE0924]
☆ *Shears* [Paris Gates, Boys Lane; OS Sheet 104 map ref 097241]: Down steep cobbled lanes among tall working textile mill buildings, roomy locals' bar with bays of plush banquettes and plenty of standing space, well kept Timothy Taylors Best, Golden Best, Landlord and Ram Tam and a guest beer, proficient service, good cheap lunchtime food from hot-filled sandwiches up, local sports photographs; big-screen sports TV; seats out above the Hebble Brook *(the Didler, BB)*

HARMBY [SE1289]
Pheasant [A684 about 1½ m E of Leyburn]: Small comfortable cheery local, well kept Black Sheep and Theakstons, bar with racing photographs, lounge *(Ian and Nita Cooper)*

HARPHAM [TA0961]
St Quintin Arms [Main St]: Comfortable and well run old white-painted village pub, friendly licensees and staff, wide choice of enjoyable good value food (not Tues lunchtime or Mon), well kept mainstream ales, moderately priced wines, attractive décor, spotless housekeeping, small dining room; attractive garden with lawn and trellis, four good value bedrooms *(Donald and Margaret Wood, Paul and Ursula Randall)*

HARROGATE [SE3155]
Coach & Horses [West Park]: Welcoming pub with well kept local ales such as Black Sheep, Daleside, Timothy Taylors and Tetleys, reasonably priced bar food, no piped music; open all day *(anon)*

Gardeners Arms [Bilton Lane (off A59 either in Bilton itself or on outskirts towards Harrogate – via Bilton Hall Dr)]: Small 16th-c stone-built house converted into friendly old-fashioned local, totally unspoilt with tiny bar and three small rooms, tiled floors, panelling, old prints and little else; very cheap well kept Sam Smiths OB, decent bar lunches, coal fire in big stone fireplace; tables in good-sized surrounding streamside garden, lovely peaceful setting *(the Didler, D W Stokes)*

Kestrel [A658/A661 E]: Vintage Inn built to look like a converted farmhouse, half a dozen or more snug and welcoming linked areas, flagstones and three log fires, enjoyable food all day, well kept Bass and Tetleys; open all day *(JHBS)*

☆ *Old Bell* [Royal Parade]: Busy bar with up to eight well kept ales such as Black Sheep, Copper Dragon, Daleside and Timothy Taylors Landlord from handsome bar counter, lots of continental bottled beers, friendly caring service, enjoyable food inc popular Fri fish night, no smoking second bar and quiet upstairs no smoking evening restaurant, no

music or machines; no children; open all day *(Patrick Hancock, Dr and Mrs A K Clarke, D W Stokes, Ben Whitney and Pippa Redmond, Jo Lilley, Simon Calvert, Andy and Jill Kassube, T and P, J Stickland, Drs M J and P M Cox)*
Winter Gardens [Royal Baths, Crescent Rd]: Wetherspoons transformation of former ballroom in landmark building, comfortable sofas in lofty hall, upper no smoking gallery, cheap well kept Theakstons and other ales; very busy late evening; attractive terrace, open all day *(Dr and Mrs A K Clarke, David Crook)*

HARTHILL [SK4980]

Beehive [Union St]: Smart two-bar village pub with chef/landlord doing wide choice of enjoyable well priced food (not Mon lunchtime) inc proper pies and Sun lunch, well kept Fullers London Pride, Timothy Taylors Landlord and Tetleys, good choice of wines and soft drinks, lounge no smoking at meal times; games room with pool, fruit machine, piped music; children welcome, picnic-sets in attractive garden, walks nearby *(Tony Hobden)*

HARTSHEAD [SE1822]

Gray Ox [not far from M62 junction 25, via A644 SE, left on A62, left on B6119, then 2nd left on Hartshead Lane]: Popular stone-built moorland dining pub under new ownership, great views, beams, flagstones and latticed windows, comfortable carpeted areas off inc no smoking room, wide choice of generous food from sandwiches to upmarket main dishes and popular Sun lunch (all afternoon), well kept Jennings ales; open all day Sun, picnic-sets outside *(Geoffrey and Brenda Wilson, Derek Earnshaw, BB, Michael Butler)*

HAWES [SD8789]

Fountain [Market Pl]: Bright and friendly open bar and lounge, quick helpful staff, well kept ales such as Black Sheep and Boddingtons, good value simple food from reasonably priced sandwiches up, lots of posters from local operatic society's past productions; may be piped radio; bedrooms *(Mr and Mrs John Taylor, Peter Abbott)*
☆ *White Hart* [Main St]: Old-fashioned local bustling wknds and Tues market day, quieter on left, wide choice of good value generous food from sandwiches to some interesting hot dishes in beamed bar and dining room, hot fire, well kept Black Sheep or Theakstons and Charles Wells Bombardier, decent carafe wines, cheerful helpful staff, brisk service, daily papers, darts and dominoes, juke box; occasional craft fairs upstairs, good value bedrooms, good breakfast *(BB, Don and Shirley Parrish, John Fiander, Mr and Mrs Maurice Thompson, George Atkinson)*

HAWORTH [SE0336]

Haworth Old Hall [Sun St]: Friendly open-plan 17th-c building and panelled building with valley views, three eating areas off long bar, log fire, stripped stonework, appropriately plain furnishings, up to five well kept Jennings ales, quick service by well trained cheerful staff, generous food from good sandwiches

up; piped music; plenty of tables out in front, open all day, bedrooms, good breakfast *(Peter F Beever, Peter F Marshall)*

HEBDEN BRIDGE [SD9927]

☆ *White Lion* [Bridge Gate]: Solid stone-built inn with busy comfortable bar and country-furnished no smoking bare-boards back area with coal fire, good choice of sound reasonably priced home cooking all day (just lunchtime Sun), fish specialities, well kept Boddingtons, Timothy Taylors Landlord and a guest beer, pleasant service; disabled access and facilities, attractive secluded riverside garden, comfortable bedrooms *(MJVK, John Fiander, G Coates)*

HECKMONDWIKE [SE2223]

☆ *Old Hall* [New North Rd (B6117)]: Interesting largely 15th-c building, once home of Joseph Priestley, with lots of beams and timbers, mullioned windows, stripped masonry, snug low-ceilinged alcoves and upper gallery room, no smoking area, straightforward bar food (not Sun evening, nothing hot Mon-Weds, cheap well kept Sam Smiths OB, darts, dominoes; fruit machine, piped music, TV; children welcome, open all day *(LYM, Michael Butler)*

HELMSLEY [SE6183]

Feathers [Market Pl]: Substantial stone inn refurbished under newish management, several rooms inc no smoking restaurant, comfortable seats, oak and walnut tables, nice prints, heavy medieval beams, panelling and huge inglenook log fire, sensibly priced generous all-day bar food from sandwiches up, well kept Black Sheep; service good even when busy; children in eating area, tables in attractive back garden, bedrooms, open all day *(Fred and Lorraine Gill, LYM, Janet and Peter Race)*

HELWITH BRIDGE [SD8169]

Helwith Bridge Inn [off B6479 N of Stainforth]: Warm and cosy village inn, up to six real ales in flagstoned bar; by Settle—Carlisle railway *(Mr and Mrs Maurice Thompson)*

HEPWORTH [SE1606]

Butchers Arms [off A616 SE of Holmfirth; Towngate]: Friendly L-shaped bar, dark beams, partly panelled stone walls, pine tables on light wood floor, large log fire in dining room, good choice of interesting food inc good value special lunches and Sun roasts, well kept Marstons Pedigree, Theakstons XB and Timothy Taylors Landlord, cheerful landlord and good courteous service, pool and darts one end, pictures for sale; piped music; dogs welcome, open all day Fri/Sat, good animal sculpture nearby *(Dr Michael Smith)*

HIGH HOYLAND [SE2710]

Cherry Tree [Bank End Lane; 3 miles W of M1 junction 38]: Friendly and attractive split-level stone-built village pub, low beams, brasses, cigarette card collections, open fire, friendly staff, well kept local Eastwood & Sanders, John Smiths and Tetleys, good soft drinks choice, good range of enjoyable simple food cooked to order (so may be a wait if busy) inc popular Sun lunch, dining areas (one no smoking) each end of bar and separate small restaurant; piped music; children welcome, front picnic-sets under cocktail parasols with lovely views over Cannon Hall Country Park *(CMW, JJW, Michael Butler, DC)*

HIGHBURTON [SE1913]

Smiths Arms [Towngate (off A629 SE of Huddersfield)]: Lively village local with well kept Black Sheep and Tetleys, flagstones and low ceilings, lots of bric-a-brac, brasses and cigarette card collections; tables outside *(Michael Butler)*

HOLME [SE1005]

☆ *Fleece* [A6024 SW of Holmfirth]: Cosy pleasant L-shaped bar, well kept Theakstons and a guest beer, good coffee, popular fresh pub food inc OAP bargains and some special nights, warmly welcoming jovial landlord, great staff, real fire, conservatory with nice flowers, pool/darts room; quiet piped music; attractive village setting just off Pennine Way below Holme Moss TV mast, great walks (they have plenty of leaflets, even walking socks and gloves for sale) *(Stuart Paulley, Christine and Neil Townend)*

HOLMFIRTH [SD1108]

Ford [A635 towards Manchester]: Enjoyable food in bar and bistro restaurant *(Christine and Neil Townend)*

Rose & Crown [aka The Nook; Victoria Sq]: Family-run stone-built local, friendly and unpretentious, with several rooms, low beams, tiled floor, half a dozen well kept ales such as Black Sheep, Jennings, Moorhouses Black Cat Mild and Timothy Taylors Landlord, real fire, pool room; occasional folk nights, tables outside, open all day *(the Didler)*

HORBURY [SE3018]

Boons [Queen St]: Lively, chatty and comfortably unpretentious, with well kept local Clarks, John Smiths, Timothy Taylors Landlord and three or four quickly changing guest beers, some flagstones, bare walls, rugby league memorabilia, back tap room with pool and TV; very popular, can get crowded, no children; courtyard tables *(Michael Butler)*

Bulls Head [Southfield Lane]: Large relaxed pub well divided into more intimate areas, panelling and wood floors, library room, no smoking snug, popular food in bar and restaurant (busy wknds), Black Sheep and John Smiths, lots of wines by the glass; big car park *(Michael Butler)*

HORNSEA [TA2047]

Victoria [Market Pl]: Stripped pine in bar, pleasant dining room, good value varied pub food (also breakfast and tea), well kept ales *(Fred and Lorraine Gill)*

HORSFORTH [SE2438]

Town Street Tavern [Town St]: New Market Town Taverns pub, now no smoking, with well kept Black Sheep, Caledonian IPA, Timothy Taylors Landlord and four or five well kept changing guest beers, Erdinger wheat beer and an imported guest beer on tap, lots of continental bottled beers, friendly knowledgeable staff; upstairs bistro *(Andy Hemingway, Tony Hobden)*

HORTON IN RIBBLESDALE [SD8172]

☆ *Crown* [B6479 N of Settle]: Pretty pub by river, well placed for walkers (Pennine Way goes through car park, short walk from Settle—Carlisle line station), dark woodwork and lots of brass in low-ceilinged locals' bar and larger lounge, good fire in both, cheap and cheerful home cooking, well kept Black Sheep and Theakstons, nice wines by the glass, friendly helpful staff, restaurant; big garden behind, good value comfortable bedrooms *(Peter Heaton, Joyce and Maurice Cottrell, A H C Rainier, Sue Demont, Tim Barrow)*

HOVINGHAM [SE6675]

Malt Shovel [Main St]: Attractive and comfortably unpretentious, with friendly staff, enjoyable sensibly priced food, well kept Sam Smiths, good coffee with cream jug; children welcome *(Mr and Mrs John Taylor, Shirley and Clive Pickerill)*

HUBBERHOLME [SD9278]

George: New owners in beautifully placed ancient Dales inn with River Wharfe fishing rights, heavy beams, flagstones and stripped stone, simple bar food from sandwiches to steak and local lamb, well kept Black Sheep Bitter and Special and a guest beer, dominoes; children welcome, tables outside, bedrooms, cl Mon in winter *(LYM, Malcolm and Lynne Jessop, David and Jean Hall)*

HUDDERSFIELD [SE1416]

Head of Steam [Station, St Georges Sq]: Railway memorabilia, model trains, cars, buses and planes for sale, pies, ciabattas, baked potatoes and good value Sun roasts, four rooms inc comfortable no smoking eating area by platform, hot coal fire, front room with breweriana, long bar with up to eight well kept changing ales such as Black Sheep, Coach House, Holts and Phoenix, lots of bottled beers, farm ciders, Gales fruit wines; jazz nights, can be very busy; open all day *(Christine and Neil Townend, Andy and Jill Kassube, John Fiander, Martin Grosberg)*

High Park [Bradley Rd, Bradley]: Attractively done out and very neatly kept, with well kept Hardys & Hansons beers, good attractively priced food, quick friendly service, no smoking family area *(John Fiander)*

Sands House [Greenhead Ave]: Popular dining pub with decent food, mainstream real ales, downstairs dining room, lots of woodwork, contemporary clocks and watches; piped music; children in eating area, garden with play area *(BB, Dr Michael Smith)*

Star [Albert St, Lockwood]: Well kept E&S, Timothy Taylors and several changing beers inc a Mild in a friendly atmosphere, continental beers, farm cider, several well organised beer festivals, bric-a-brac and customers' paintings, no juke box, pool or machines – or food (may be pie and peas Tues); cl Mon, and lunchtime Tues-Thurs *(Andy and Jill Kassube)*

HULL [TA0927]

Bay Horse [Wincolmlee]: Popular unassuming corner local tied to Batemans, their beers kept well, good value basic food inc good home-made pies, pleasant licensees, open fire, raftered extension lounge/dining room, interesting brewery memorabilia; open all day *(the Didler)*

Olde Black Boy [High St, Old Town]: Appealing little black-panelled low-ceilinged front smoke room with carved fireplace, lofty 18th-c back vaults bar with leather seating, interesting Wilberforce-related posters etc, good value food lunchtime (not Sun) and late afternoon (not wknds), also Sun breakfast, friendly service, well kept real ales, country wines, old jugs and bottles, upstairs pool room and overflow wknd bar; darts, piano Thurs, games machine; children allowed, open all day *(the Didler, BB, David Carr)*

Olde Blue Bell [alley off Lowgate; look out for huge blue bell over pavement]: Friendly traditional 17th-c local with well kept cheap Sam Smiths OB, good value simple lunchtime food, three rooms off corridor, remarkable collection of bells, coal fire; open all day exc Sun afternoon *(BB, the Didler, David Carr)*

HUSTHWAITE [SE5275]

☆ *Roasted Pepper* [Low St]: Upmarket restaurany pub with good enterprising food from tapas and elaborate ciabattas up, small helpings of main dishes available, good choice of wines by the glass (keg beers), friendly efficient staff, lively atmosphere, imaginative hispanic-flavour décor with warm cream and brown tones, stylish dark mexican furnishings on quarry tiles or sunken bare bricks; terrace tables, cl Mon *(Dr and Mrs R G J Telfer, Janet and Peter Race, Mike and Lynn Robinson, JHBS, John and Verna Aspinall)*

HUTTON-LE-HOLE [SE7089]

Crown [The Green]: Bustling friendly pub overlooking pretty village green with wandering sheep in classic coach-trip country, good sandwiches and huge helpings of plain hot food, cheery service, well kept Black Sheep, lots of whisky-water jugs; children welcome, near Folk Museum – so may be morris dancers – and handy for Farndale walks *(Edward and Deanna Pearce, Michael Butler)*

ILKLEY [SE1346]

Cow & Calf [Hangingstone Rd (moors rd towards Hawksworth)]: Vintage Inn in stunning spot with lovely views over Ilkley and Wharfedale, their usual reliable food with inventive heart-warming touches, well kept Bass and Tetleys and fine choice of wines by the glass, courteous young staff, old-world décor, log fire in food-free snug; children welcome, good bedrooms *(R A K Crabtree, Karen Eliot, Stephen Buckley, Geoffrey and Brenda Wilson)*

INGLETON [SD6973]

☆ *Wheatsheaf* [High Street]: New licensees for pleasant 17th-c coaching inn in attractive village with long open-plan bar, pool table, big log fire, and family area; bar food has been reasonably priced and decent (and children and dogs have been allowed), with no smoking restaurant, well kept Black Sheep Bitter and Special, Tetleys and Timothy Taylors Golden

Best, and quite a few whiskies; piped music; seats in back garden, bedrooms with own bathrooms, open all day summer wknds *(Karen Eliot, LYM)*

JEATER HOUSES [SE4394]

Haynes Arms [A19 N of Thirsk]: Useful for its long opening hours, with varied food lunchtime and from 5.30, well kept ales, good log fire; children welcome, lovely area *(Tim and Ann Newell)*

KEIGHLEY [SE0941]

Airedale Heifer [Bradford Rd, Sandbeds (B6265 towards Bingley)]: Spreading series of rustic rooms, smart and civilised atmosphere, enjoyable food inc carvery; subdued piped classical music; lovely garden, with tables in front and behind *(Mrs Dilys Unsworth)*

Boltmakers Arms [East Parade]: Split-level open-plan local with particularly well kept Timothy Taylors Landlord, Best, Golden Best and guest beers, good value basic food all day, affable landlord, coal fire, nice brewing pictures; open all day, short walk from Worth Valley Railway *(the Didler)*

Globe [Parkwood St]: Comfortable local by Worth Valley steam railway track, wkdy lunches, Timothy Taylors ales; open all day *(the Didler)*

KETTLEWELL [SD9672]

Bluebell [Middle Lane]: Roomy knocked-through 17th-c pub with snug simple furnishings, low beams and flagstones, cosy welcoming atmosphere, friendly landlord and regulars, well kept Black Sheep, Tetleys and Theakstons Old Peculier, sensibly priced food from sandwiches up in bar and attractive restaurant, children's room; pool room, piped music; seats out on cobbles facing Wharfe bridge, more on good-sized back terrace, decent bedrooms mainly in annexe *(Mr and Mrs Maurice Thompson, LYM, Michael Butler, Margaret and Roy Randle)*

☆ *Kings Head*: Cheerful and welcoming old local away from centre of Calendar Girls village, lively flagstoned main bar with log fire in big inglenook, comfortable tartan-carpeted snug around corner, discreet dining room, well kept Black Sheep, local Littondale ales and Tetleys, reliable good value straightforward food with good veg, friendly helpful staff; four comfortable bedrooms with own bathrooms *(Edmund Coan, Michael Butler, Lawrence Pearse, Dr D and Mrs B Woods, O K Smyth, B and M Kendall)*

☆ *Racehorses* [B6160 N of Skipton]: Comfortable, civilised and friendly, with generous good value food inc lunchtime rolls and baguettes and local game, well kept Black Sheep Best and Special and Timothy Taylors Landlord, good wine choice, efficient helpful staff, log fires; dogs welcome in front bar, picnic-sets (tops rather low, relative to seats) on attractive terrace, well placed for Wharfedale walks, good bedrooms with own bathrooms, open all day *(Mr and Mrs Maurice Thompson, Michael Butler, BB, MDN, Margaret and Roy Randle, Len Beattie, Dr D and Mrs B Woods)*

KILHAM [TA0664]

Star [Church St]: Neatly kept and cosy old pub, two front rooms now opened together for more space, warm fires, friendly licensees and easy-going local atmosphere, well kept Archers Golden, Marstons Pedigree and Jennings Wards Best, good coffee, enjoyable freshly made fairly priced food (not Sun evening) in bar and popular rustic flagstoned barn restaurant, darts, dominoes; plans for two bedrooms, pretty village *(Di and Mike Gillam, Dr Ian S Morley, Tim Nicoll, Paul and Ursula Randall)*

KILNSEA [TA4015]

☆ *Crown & Anchor* [Kilnsea Rd]: Welcoming family-friendly pub in great remote location overlooking eroding Spurn Point nature reserve and Humber Estuary, single bar opening into two beamed lounges and linen-set restaurant, prints and bric-a-brac, friendly staff, well kept Tetleys and perhaps a guest beer such as Timothy Taylors Landlord, low-priced wines, above-average reasonably priced generous pub food inc good fresh fish; piped music; picnic-sets in back garden and out in front facing estuary, four bedrooms with own bathrooms, open all day *(DC, Paul and Ursula Randall, J Crosby)*

KIRK DEIGHTON [SE3950]

☆ *Bay Horse* [B6164 N of Wetherby]: Cosy beamed dining lounge with comfortable banquettes and dark pink décor, rugs on dark flagstones, nice mix of seating and tables, good food from good lunchtime sandwiches (home-baked bread) and enterprising light dishes to imaginative fresh restaurant meals and tempting puddings, friendly efficient service, well kept Black Sheep, Jennings Cumberland and Tetleys, good coffee, simpler newly flagstoned public bar by entrance *(Les and Sandra Brown, Michael Doswell, BB)*

KIRKBY MALHAM [SD8960]

Victoria: Pleasantly understated Victorian décor, good friendly service, enjoyable pub food, well kept Black Sheep, Timothy Taylors Golden Best, Theakstons Best and (a new one to us) Granny Mouse, good wine choice, separate restaurant (not always in use); attractive good value bedrooms, lovely village with interesting church – quieter than nearby Malham though busy with walkers at lunchtime *(Tim and Rosemary Wells)*

KIRKBYMOORSIDE [SE6986]

Kings Head [High Market Pl]: 16th-c inn now tied to Jennings, their beers kept well, hard-working friendly tenants, well priced food all home-made inc local fish, game and meat, interesting vegetarian menu, friendly service (newish licensees much in evidence), well kept beer, cosy lounge and pleasant new conservatory opening into sheltered courtyard and attractive garden, good log fire; children welcome, comfortable good value bedrooms *(I D Barnett, Judith and Edward Pearson)*

KIVETON PARK [SK5082]

Station Hotel [B6059 opp stn]: Good value pub food inc enterprising children's dishes, friendly service, stripped brick dining area

through arch off lounge, separate bar; children welcome *(Anne and Paul Horscraft)*

KNARESBOROUGH [SE3557]

☆ *Blind Jacks* [Market Pl]: Charming and friendly multi-floor traditional tavern in 18th-c building, simple but attractive furnishings, brewery posters etc, well kept changing ales such as Black Sheep, Timothy Taylors (inc their great Dark Mild), Village and White Boar, farm cider and foreign bottled beers, bubbly atmosphere downstairs, quieter up; well behaved children allowed away from bar, open all day wknds, cl Mon till 5.30; Beer Ritz two doors away sells all sorts of rare bottled beers *(Andrew Hewitt, Jo Lilley, Simon Calvert, David Carr, LYM, the Didler, Patrick Hancock)*

LANGDALE END [SE9391]

Moorcock [off A170 E of Scarborough, or A171 via Hackness]: Delightfully old-fashioned stone-built terrace pub in charming moorland valley village, old enamel advertisements outside, welcoming owners and staff, two rooms served by hatch from back room, children allowed in one, another with music and pool, changing well kept interesting real ales, bar food, warm fire, quarry tiles and simple furnishings *(LYM, Christine and Phil Young)*

LANGSETT [SE2100]

Wagon & Horses [A616 Stocksbridge—Huddersfield]: Welcoming and comfortable main-road moors pub, blazing log fire, stripped stone and woodwork, well kept Theakstons, enjoyable food inc good value Sun lunch, magazines to read *(James A Waller)*

LANGTHWAITE [NZ0002]

☆ *Red Lion* [just off Reeth—Brough Arkengarthdale rd]: Homely unspoilt 17th-c pub, individual and relaxing, in charming Dales village with ancient bridge; basic cheap nourishing lunchtime food, well kept Black Sheep Bitter and Riggwelter and John Smiths, country wines, tea and coffee, character firm-viewed landlady; well behaved children allowed lunchtime in very low-ceilinged side snug; the ladies' is a genuine bathroom; seats outside, good walks all around, inc organised circular ones from the pub – maps and guides for sale *(LYM, Tony and Ann Bennett-Hughes)*

LAUGHTON EN LE MORTHEN [SK5189]

Travellers Rest [Brookhouse, towards Thurcroft]: Pleasant 1970s-style stone-built pub with enjoyable food, popular bargain Sun roasts (till 6), three real ales, no smoking lounge/dining room, public bar with darts and pool; quiet piped music; children welcome, streamside picnic-sets outside, play area, pleasant village, open all day *(CMW, JJW)*

LEALHOLM [NZ7607]

Board [off A171 W of Whitby]: In wonderful moorland village spot by wide pool of River Esk, two tidy refurbished bars, stripped stone, Jennings Cumberland, Theakstons Black Bull and a guest such as Ring o' Bells Porkers Pride, big log fire, darts, new restaurant; TV; secluded riverside garden, open all day Sat, cl wkdy winter lunchtimes *(Kevin Thorpe)*

LEAVENING [SE7863]

Jolly Farmers [Main St]: Pleasantly unpretentious village local, good choice of well kept changing ales such as Timothy Taylors Landlord, good wholesome food with lots of fresh veg in separate dining room, reasonable prices, friendly licensees; good bedrooms *(Christopher Turner)*

LEEDS [SE3033]

Adelphi [Hunslet Rd]: Well restored handsome Edwardian mahogany screens, panelling, tiling and cut and etched glass, several rooms, impressive stairway; particularly well kept Tetleys Bitter, Mild and Imperial (virtually the brewery tap), prompt friendly service, good spread of lunchtime cheap food from hot baguettes etc, crowded but convivial then; live jazz Sat *(the Didler, C J Fletcher)*

Duck & Drake [Kirkgate, between indoor market and Parish Church]: A dozen or more well kept reasonably priced ales such as Black Sheep, John Smiths, Old Mill and Timothy Taylors from well worn in two-bar pub's central servery, farm cider too, good coal fires, basic furniture, bare boards and beer posters and mirrors; low-priced wkdy lunchtime bar snacks, games room with Yorkshire doubles dartboard as well as pool etc; juke box, loud big-screen TV, games machines, quiz nights, jazz nights Mon and Thurs; open all day *(the Didler, Pete Baker, C J Fletcher, Martin Grosberg)*

Garden Gate [Whitfield Pl, Hunslet]: Newish licensees in down-to-earth local ripe for restoration and interesting for its untouched flagstoned Victorian layout and intricate glass, ceramics and woodwork, with various rooms off central drinking corridor, well kept Tetleys Bitter and Mild, farm cider, no food; open all day *(BB, the Didler)*

Grove [Back Row, Holbeck]: Unspoilt 1930s-feel local, three or four rooms off drinking corridor, up to eight changing ales inc a Mild; folk nights; open all day *(the Didler)*

Horse & Trumpet [The Headrow]: Late Victorian, with fine façade, lovely stained-glass ceiling and separate rooms inc handsome snug and comfortable back parlour, lunchtime food, Tetleys and several interesting changing guest beers, busy friendly staff, lots of music hall playbills; open all day *(David Carr)*

Railway Hotel [Calverley Bridge, Rodley; off A6120 Horsforth ring road]: Friendly waterside pub quietly set on Leeds & Liverpool Canal, good wine choice, decent sandwiches; lovely walks *(Greta and Christopher Wells)*

Roundhay Fox [by Roundhay Park, Princes Avenue]: Pleasant atmosphere in popular Vintage Inn, plenty of space, friendly staff, good range of sensibly priced food, guest beers, open fire; courtyard tables *(DAV, A S and M E Marriott, M Joyner)*

Viaduct [Lower Briggate]: Pleasantly furnished long narrow bar, lots of wood, well kept Tetleys and guest ales, popular lunchtime food, friendly helpful staff, no smoking area; actively caters for disabled customers, attractive back garden, open all day exc Sun afternoon *(the Didler)*

☆ *Victoria* [Gt George St, just behind Town Hall]: Opulent bustling early Victorian pub with grand cut and etched mirrors, impressive globe lamps extending from the majestic bar, imposing carved beams, booths with working snob-screens in lounge, smaller rooms off; well kept Black Sheep, Tetleys Best and Mild and changing guest beers, friendly efficient service by smart bar staff, reasonably priced food all day till early evening from sandwiches and light dishes up in luncheon room with end serving hatch, no smoking room; open all day *(the Didler, C J Fletcher, David Carr, M and GR)*

LELLEY [TA2032]

Stags Head [Main St; NE of Preston]: Recent major refurbishment, comfortable restaurant and more tables in bar, enjoyable enterprising fresh food, helpful cheerful efficient service, John Smiths and Marstons Pedigree, decent wines by the glass; TV *(Paul and Ursula Randall)*

LEVEN [TA1045]

New Inn [just off A165/A1035; South St]: Good-sized dining area, bargain Sun lunches, bar with pool, occasional live entertainment; good value recently refurbished bedrooms, good breakfast, pleasant village *(Michael Butler)*

LEVISHAM [SE8391]

Horseshoe [off A169 N of Pickering]: Neat pub in delightful unspoilt village a steep walk up from station, new owners running it as more of a pub/restaurant, limited choice of enjoyable if not cheap food, simple décor, log fire in stone fireplace, no smoking dining area, well kept real ales, good wine choice; quiet piped classical music; picnic-sets on attractive green, plenty of good walks *(Michael and Ann Cole, LYM)*

LEYBURN [SE1190]

Bolton Arms [Market Pl]: Substantial stone-built inn at top of market place, good friendly service, well kept Black Sheep and John Smiths, good value home-made pub food; bedrooms *(Gerry Miller)*

Golden Lion [Market Pl]: Relaxing panelled and bay-windowed two-room bar, light and airy, with log-effect gas fire in eating area, varied good value generous food, well kept Black Sheep, decent coffee, friendly efficient service, paintings for sale, evening restaurant; very busy on Fri market day; dogs allowed, tables out in front, good value bedrooms, open all day *(BB, Michael Tack)*

LIVERSEDGE [SE2023]

Black Bull [Halifax Rd]: Popular local now tied to Ossett, with their real ales inc a Mild and guest beers; limited sandwiches, may be thai curry Tues evening *(Andy and Jill Kassube)*

LOCKTON [SE8488]

Fox & Rabbit [just off A169 N of Pickering]: Taken over by two enthusiastic young brothers, one cooks enjoyable honest food for bar or no smoking dining room, sandwiches too, comfortable plush banquettes, brasses, real fires, well kept real ale, friendly helpful service; tables outside and in sun lounge, nice spot on moors edge, good views *(LYM, Ian Ward, Colin and Dot Savill)*

LOFTHOUSE [SE1073]

Crown [the one in Nidderdale]: Prettily placed Dales pub, friendly and relaxed, with hearty simple bar food and well kept Black Sheep Bitter and Special, small public bar, eating extension where children allowed; bedrooms, outside gents' *(Michael Butler)*

LONG MARSTON [SE5051]

Sun [B1224 Wetherby—York]: Friendly local with very cheap well kept Sam Smiths, good value usual food inc challenging mixed grills, friendly helpful staff, log fire and several pleasant areas; garden with big play area *(Judith and Edward Pearson)*

LOW BENTHAM [SD6469]

Punch Bowl: Warm welcome from rather special landlady, enjoyable home-made food inc Fri bargain and popular Sun lunch, log fire, no smoking dining room *(Karen Eliot)*

LOW BRADFIELD [SK2691]

Plough [New Rd]: Good value freshly made food, good changing range of real ales inc Caledonian Deuchars IPA, comfortable banquettes, lots of brass and copper, old lamps and bric-a-brac, two fires, restaurant; children welcome, picnic-sets in attractive garden, nice setting *(Matthew Lidbury)*

MALHAM [SD9062]

Listers Arms [off A65 NW of Skipton]: Creeper-covered stone-built inn in nice spot by river, good walking country; easy-going open-plan lounge, busy wknds, good value wholesome food inc hot-filled ciabattas, small helpings available, well kept changing ales inc Boddingtons, Caledonian Deuchars IPA and Timothy Taylors Landlord, lots of continental beers and malt whiskies, good service, roaring fire, big-windowed bare-boards lower room good for families; children and dogs welcome, seats out overlooking small green, more in back garden, comfortable modern bedrooms with own bathrooms *(Anna Graham, R T J and J J Hubbard, Alun Howells)*

MALTON [SE7871]

Crown [Wheelgate – aka Suddabys and signed as that not Crown]: In same family for generations, chatty basic town bar with strong horse-racing links (and racing TV on bar), good Malton Crown Double Chance (low price), Golden Chance and a seasonal beer from their back brewhouse, well kept guest beers, popular pub (not Sun, sandwiches only Tues, bookings only evenings), daily papers; lots of local notices, beer festivals Jun and Dec; children welcome in back courtyard nicely redone as conservatory (occasional live music here), good value bedrooms *(BB, Kevin Thorpe, John Tavernor, Roger A Bellingham)*

Wentworth Arms [Town St, Old Malton]: Enjoyable generous food from well filled baguettes up in bar and big dining room, well kept ales inc local guest beers, decent wines,

friendly local atmosphere, quick service; children welcome *(Marlene and Jim Godfrey, C A Hall, Brian and Ruth Archer, Pat and Tony Martin)*

MANFIELD [NZ2213]

Crown [Vicars Lane]: Old-fashioned village local with warmly welcoming regulars, Village White Boar and Bull and half a dozen interesting changing guest beers, enjoyable pub food from good sandwiches up; pool, unobtrusive juke box, Tues quiz night *(Andrew York, Tim Wellock, Granville Chambers)*

MANKINHOLES [SD9523]

Top Brink Inn [Lumbutts]: Small busy moorland village pub very popular for its good value well cooked straightforward food inc good steaks, efficient friendly young staff, well kept ales such as Boddingtons and Timothy Taylors Landlord; children welcome, fine views from conservatory and terrace tables, quite close to Pennine Way and nice walks to nearby monument on Stoodley Pike *(Nigel Siesage, Len Beattie, Andy and Jill Kassube)*

MARSDEN [SE0412]

Railway Hotel [Station Rd]: Welcoming unpretentious tavern with well kept Burtonwood and other ales, enjoyable reasonably priced food from baguettes and filled baked potatoes to steak, good carvery Sun lunch, bargain wkdy early suppers, smaller no smoking area off large main part; wheelchair access *(Pam and John Smith, Stuart Paulley, John Fiander)*

☆ *Riverhead* [Peel St, next to Co-op; just off A62 Huddersfield—Oldham]: Busy basic pub in converted grocer's, spiral stairs down to microbrewery (tours available) producing good range of interesting beers named after local reservoirs, the higher the reservoir, the higher the strength, inc Mild, Stout and Porter, farm cider, enjoyable food upstairs, no food or machines; unobtrusive piped music; wheelchair access, streamside tables, cl wkdy lunchtimes, open from 4pm, all day wknds, handy for Huddersfield Broad Canal and moorland walks *(the Didler, John Fiander)*

Tunnel End [Reddisher Rd (off A62 via Peel St)]: Friendly licensees, well kept ales such as Black Sheep and Timothy Taylors Landlord, generous unpretentious food inc Sun roasts, four good-sized but homely rooms (one no smoking), hot log fire in back room; overlooks mouth of recently restored Standedge Canal Tunnel – at three miles under the Pennines, the UK's longest *(Clifford Payton, Dr Michael Smith)*

MARSKE BY THE SEA [NZ6222]

Mermaid [Redcar Rd]: Unpretentious dining pub with quick service in bargain carvery (choice of three roasts), also reasonably priced restaurant menu running up to steak; keg beers *(BB, C A Hall)*

MASHAM [SE2281]

☆ *White Bear* [Wellgarth, Crosshills; signed off A6108 opp turn into town]: Bright and cheerful beamed and stone-built pub, small lino-floor public bar with darts, comfortable larger bare-boards lounge with coal fire, well kept Theakstons Best, Mild, Black Bull and Old Peculier, decent wines by the glass, good fairly priced food choice (not Sun evening) from sandwiches up, neat efficient staff; piped radio; metal tables and chairs out on terrace, open all day *(Janet and Peter Race, the Didler, BB)*

MEXBOROUGH [SK4799]

Concertina Band Club [Dolcliffe Rd]: Friendly pubby club welcoming visitors, brewing its own good changing ales, also well kept guest beers; large bar with stage and small games area with pool, other games and SkyTV; cl Sun lunchtime *(the Didler)*

MIDDLESBROUGH [NZ4717]

Cambridge [Cambridge Rd]: Neatly kept hotel with freshly made good value food in lounge bar, friendly helpful staff, Sam Smiths under blanket pressure, separate tap room; bedrooms *(C A Hall)*

MILL BANK [SE0221]

Alma [1½ miles off A58 at Triangle pub; Four Lane Ends]: Two cosy front bar rooms with pine furniture and country/fishing décor, home-made bar food and Timothy Taylors real ales, restaurant dishes in bright and airy bare-boards extension with fine Pennine views; bedrooms *(Herbert and Susan Verity)*

MIRFIELD [SE2017]

Hare & Hounds [Liley Lane (B6118 2m S)]: Good views towards Huddersfield from Vintage Inn very popular early evenings for respectable wholesome food, Bass, Boddingtons and John Smiths, lots of decent wines by the glass, no smoking eating area; Thurs quiz night; tables outside *(Andy and Jill Kassube, Michael Butler)*

MOULTON [NZ2303]

☆ *Black Bull* [just off A1 nr Scotch Corner]: Interesting black-beamed bar with individual comfortably worn in furnishings and big log fire, some good substantial and unusual lunchtime bar dishes, side dark-panelled seafood bar with close-set tables and high seats at marble-topped counter, evening restaurant meals (Brighton Belle dining car as well as polished conservatory), good wines, sherries and spirits (keg beers), jolly waitresses (management can sometimes seem a bit stiff); no under-7s; courtyard seats under trees, cl Sun *(David Field, Greta and Christopher Wells, LYM, Alan Cole, Kirstie Bruce, Marlene and Jim Godfrey, Mr and Mrs J E C Tasker, Michael and Anne Brown)*

MUKER [SD9097]

☆ *Farmers Arms* [B6270 W of Reeth]: Basic family-friendly walkers' pub in beautiful valley village, well placed both for rewarding walks and interesting drives, warm open fire, friendly staff and locals, well kept Black Sheep and Theakstons, wines, teas and coffees, enjoyable food from sandwiches to generous pies, casseroles and so forth, flagstones and carpeting, darts and dominoes; tables outside, self-catering studio flat *(Richard and Anne Ansell, LYM, Ben Whitney and Pippa Redmond, Rona Murdoch,*

Matthew Shackle, Tony and Ann Bennett-Hughes, Michael Gallagher, David and Jean Hall)

NEWTON-ON-OUSE [SE5160]

Dawnay Arms [off A19 N of York]: Attractive comfortably worn in 18th-c inn nr Beningbrough Hall, lots of beamery, brass and copper, good log fire, decent bar food from sandwiches up inc early-evening bargains, well kept Copper Dragon Golden Pippin and Greene King IPA, Old Speckled Hen, dozens of malt whiskies, good coffee, no smoking river-view restaurant; piped music, no dogs; children in eating area, neat lawn running down to moorings on River Ouse, tables on terrace, play area *(Dr and Mrs R G J Telfer, LYM, Roger A Bellingham)*

NEWTON-ON-RAWCLIFFE [SE8190]

Mucky Duck: Old-fashioned chatty country pub overlooking sleepy village green and pond, genial landlord, wife cooks generous inexpensive traditional food, well kept beer with a monthly guest, attentive service, cosy bar with railway memorabilia, TV and music in another room; tables outside, back field for caravans *(Frank Willy, Michael and Ann Cole)*

NORLAND [SE0622]

Blue Ball: Enjoyable food from sandwiches, baguettes and baked potatoes to several roasts on Sun, good puddings, Black Sheep and Timothy Taylors Landlord; plenty of tables outside, good views *(Pat and Tony Martin)*

NORTH STAINLEY [SE2876]

Staveley Arms [A6108 Ripon—Masham]: Neatly kept old country pub with high beams and flagstones, separate dining area, wide blackboard choice of decent generous bar food, popular carvery Thurs-Sat evening and Sun lunch, Black Sheep and good value wines, friendly helpful staff, some rustic bric-a-brac; handy for Lightwater Valley, bedrooms comfortable and well priced *(Janet and Peter Race)*

NORTHALLERTON [SE3693]

Golden Lion [High St]: Large Georgian ex-coaching inn, generous food in two big bars and attractive dining room, well kept beers inc Hambleton and John Smiths, good coffee; 25 bedrooms *(Roger A Bellingham)*

NORWOOD GREEN [SE1326]

☆ *Olde White Beare* [signed off A641 in Wyke, or off A58 Halifax—Leeds just W of Wyke; Village St]: Large 17th-c building well renovated and extended, with character tap room, larger split-level lounge, beams and panelling, brasses, good personal service, well kept Boddingtons, Timothy Taylors and Tetleys, friendly staff, limited but interesting choice of enjoyable food in handsome barn restaurant, also bar food, bargain early suppers and popular Sun lunch; tables outside front and back, barbecues, Calderdale Way and Brontë Way pass the door *(Len Beattie)*

NUN MONKTON [SE5057]

Alice Hawthorn [off A59 York—Harrogate; The Green]: Modernised beamed dining pub on broad village green with pond and lovely avenue to church and Rivers Nidd and Ouse;

lots of brass etc in bar with big brick inglenook fireplace, another open fire in restaurant, several changing real ales, big helpings of reasonably priced home-made food *(BB, Alex and Claire Pearse)*

OSMOTHERLEY [SE4597]
Queen Catherine [West End]: Good family pub, welcoming atmosphere, roomy modern décor with old local prints, popular reasonably priced hearty food inc good Sun lunch with proper yorkshire puddings, Tetleys and a well kept guest beer such as Hambleton, friendly service, jazz night every other Sun; simple but comfortable bedrooms with own bathrooms, good breakfast *(C A Hall, Mr and Mrs J E C Tasker)*

☆ OSSETT [SE2719]
Brewers Pride [Low Mill Rd/Healey Lane (long cul-de-sac by railway sidings, off B6128)]: Warmly friendly basic local brewing its own good beers, four well kept guest beers, cosy front room and bar both with open fires, brewery memorabilia and flagstones, small games room, enjoyable lunchtime food (not Sun) and pie or curry night Weds; quiz night Mon, popular folk club Thurs; big back garden with local entertainment summer wknds, nr Calder & Hebble Canal, open all day Fri-Sun *(the Didler)*

OUTLANE [SE0818]
Swan [just off A640 Huddersfield—Rochdale by M62 junction 23, handy for junction 24 too]: Comfortable open-plan pub with good range of sensibly priced home cooking inc hot and cold sandwiches, bargain specials and (all afternoon) good value Sun lunch, Black Sheep and Timothy Taylors, friendly landlord and good service, no smoking area; unobtrusive piped music, pool table in side area *(J R Ringrose, Stuart Paulley)*

OVERTON [SE2516]
Black Swan [off A642 Wakefield—Huddersfield; Green Lane]: Traditional local, two knocked-together low-beamed rooms with lots of brasses and bric-a-brac, well kept John Smiths; Thurs quiz night (may be free food) *(Michael Butler)*

☆ OXENHOPE [SE0434]
Dog & Gun [Long Causeway; off B6141 towards Denholme]: Beautifully placed roomy moorland pub with warm welcome, good varied generous home cooking from sandwiches to lots of fish and Sun roasts, smart helpful waitress service, full Timothy Taylors beer range kept well, beamery, copper, brasses and delft shelves of plates and jugs, big log fire each end, padded settles and stools, a couple of smaller rooms, attractive small bistro-style restaurant, nice views *(Geoffrey and Brenda Wilson, John and Joan Calvert)*

PENISTONE [SE2402]
Cubley Hall [Mortimer Rd, out towards Stocksbridge]: Spacious and lively centre for events as well as family meals and drinks, in handsome rambling building with panelling, elaborate plasterwork, mosaic tiling and plush furnishings, roomy conservatory, wide choice of bar food all day, well kept Greene King Abbot and Old Speckled Hen, Marstons Pedigree and Charles Wells Bombardier, decent wines, no smoking room; piped music, fruit machine, TV; children welcome (and can be over-evident), big garden with plenty of tables, good playground and distant views, bedrooms with own bathrooms, open all day *(RJH, LYM, Trevor and Judy Pearson, Graham Holden, Julie Lee, Matthew Lidbury)*

PINCHINTHORPE [NZ5714]
Pinchinthorpe Hall [A173 W of Guisborough]: Partly medieval hotel/restaurant, not pub, but brews its own good North Yorkshire organic ales, and has reliably good fresh food (may be a wait) at sensible prices in bistro; bedrooms *(Blaise Vyner)*

POOL [SE2445]
☆ White Hart [just off A658 S of Harrogate, A659 E of Otley]: Reliable and relaxing Vintage Inn family dining pub, four mainly no smoking and flagstoned olde-worlde rooms with assorted farmhouse furnishings, two big log fires and country décor, friendly service even when busy, well kept Tetleys and Worthington, good choice of wines by the glass, their usual food from lunchtime sandwiches to steaks and Sun roasts; piped music; children welcome, pleasant tables outside, good walking country, open all day *(June and Ken Brooks, Michael Butler, Ray and Winifred Halliday, Roy and Lindsey Fentiman, LYM, Dave Braisted, Pat and Graham Williamson)*

REETH [SE0399]
Black Bull [B6270]: Friendly village pub in fine spot at foot of broad sloping green, traditional dark beamed and flagstoned L-shaped front bar cosy at night, Black Sheep real ale, enjoyable reasonably priced nourishing food, open fires, helpful staff; piped music in pool room; children welcome, tables outside, comfortable bedrooms with lovely Dales views, good breakfast *(LYM, Tony and Ann Bennett-Hughes)*

Kings Arms [Market Pl (B6270)]: Popular beamed dining pub by green, pine pews around walls, log fire in 18th-c stone inglenook, quieter room behind; reasonably priced food, well kept Black Sheep, full Theakstons range and a guest beer; may be piped music; children very welcome, tables outside, bedrooms *(Dr and Mrs M W A Haward, David Reid)*

RIBBLEHEAD [SD7678]
Station Hotel [B6255 Ingleton—Hawes]: Terrific spot alone on the moors by Ribblehead Viaduct (Settle—Carlisle trains), kind licensees, good log fire in woodburner, well kept Black Sheep, Copper Dragon Golden Pippin and an interesting guest beer, low-priced wine, huge helpings of food from sandwiches to steaks, basic pub furnishings, central pool table, darts, dining room with viaduct mural (the bar has relevant photographs, some you can buy); video game, piped music; open all day in season, some picnic-sets outside, good value simple bedrooms and next-door bunkhouse, good wholesome breakfast *(BB, JHBS)*

RICHMOND [NZ1700]
Holly Hill Inn [Holly Hill, Slee Gill]: Friendly pub overlooking castle and River Swale, comfortable lounge, Black Sheep and Timothy Taylors Landlord, enterprising food in bar and pleasant restaurant, games on upper level; piped music *(anon)*

RILLINGTON [SE8574]
Coach & Horses [Scarborough Rd]: Unpretentious neatly kept village local with vast china cat collection in spotless lounge, generous straightforward home-made food at bargain prices inc proper pies and Sun roast, friendly landlord, well kept Tetleys *(Colin and Dot Savill)*

☆ *One-Eyed Rat* [Allhallowgate]: No-frills friendly bare-boards pub with interesting well kept ales such as Black Sheep, Durham White Velvet, Mallard IPA, Salamander Vesuvius and Timothy Taylors Landlord, farm cider, lots of country wines, log fire, cigarette cards, framed beer mats, bank notes and old pictures, bar billiards (no food, juke box or music); tables in pleasant outside area *(Mr and Mrs P G Mitchell, Jack Clark)*
Royal Oak [Kirkgate]: Leather-seat oak settles and cast-iron framed tables on flagstones, two or three well kept ales, smiling service *(Dr D E Granger)*

ROBIN HOOD'S BAY [NZ9504]
Bay Hotel [The Dock, Bay Town]: Unpretentious old village inn with fine sea views from cosy picture-window upstairs bar (downstairs only at busy times), friendly staff, three well kept ales, log fires, good value generous food in bar and separate dining area; open all day, tables outside, cosy bedrooms *(Edward Leetham)*
Olde Dolphin [King St, Bay Town]: Snug 18th-c inn stepped up above sea front in attractive little town; unpretentious basic bar with friendly service, convivial atmosphere, well kept ales inc Caledonian Deuchars IPA, good open fire, good value generous plain food inc local seafood, popular back games room allowing children; well behaved dogs welcome in bar, piped music, can get crowded wknds, long walk back up to village car park; Fri folk club, cheap simple bedrooms *(John Dwane, Dr and Mrs Jackson)*

☆ *Victoria* [Station Rd]: Clifftop Victorian hotel with great bay and sea views from bustling straightforwardly modernised bar, well kept Camerons ales and a guest beer such as Durham from curved counter, quick friendly service, wide choice of reasonably priced enjoyable fresh generous food, large no smoking green-walled family room; children and dogs welcome, useful car park, play area in big garden overlooking village, nine tidy comfortable bedrooms with own bathrooms, good breakfast *(John Dwane, Derek and Sylvia Stephenson)*

ROECLIFFE [SE3765]
Crown [W of Boroughbridge]: Thriving pub with good choice of well presented enjoyable food from good sandwiches and snack lunches

to interesting full meals, well kept Black Sheep, Daleside, John Smiths and Timothy Taylors, competent friendly staff, flagstoned bar, lounge with caricatures of famous Yorkshire folk, spacious dining room; front benches overlook quaint village green, lovely village, bedrooms, unobtrusive touring caravan site *(Judith and Edward Pearson)*

SALTBURN-BY-THE-SEA [NZ6621]
☆ *Ship* [A174 towards Whitby]: Beautiful setting among beached fishing boats, sea views from tasteful nautical-style black-beamed bars and big plainer summer dining lounge with handsome ship model; wide choice of inexpensive usual food, well kept Tetleys, quick friendly service, evening restaurant (not Sun), children's room and menu; busy at holiday times; tables outside, smuggling exhibition next door *(Mike and Lynn Robinson, LYM, David and Ruth Shillitoe)*

SAWDON [TA9484]
☆ *Anvil* [Main St]: Comfortable easy chairs among other seats in attractive high-raftered former smithy with woodburner and featuring the former smith's hearth, lower-ceilinged second bar leading through to neat dining room, turkey carpet throughout; has had well kept changing ales such as B&T Golden Fox, Badger Best, Caledonian Deuchars IPA and Six Nations and Copper Dragon Golden Pippin, and good hearty home-made food, but the friendly landlord who with his family made its atmosphere so good left in July 2005 – too late for us to gauge its subsequent appeal (so reports please!); comfortable warm bedrooms *(Patrick Renouf, Richard Haw, BB)*

SCARBOROUGH [TA0487]
Highlander [Esplanade]: Clean, bright and comfortable, with magnificent collection of whiskies (tartan curtains and carpet too), well kept Tetleys and changing ales such as Fullers London Pride, good value pub food from generous sandwiches and toasties up, friendly obliging service, civilised atmosphere, sea views from front bar; front courtyard tables, bedrooms, handy for South Bay beach *(Fred and Lorraine Gill, David Carr, Martin and Jane Taylor)*
Hole in the Wall [Vernon Rd]: Three-room Victorian pub, easy-going and down to earth, with well kept Greene King IPA, John Smiths and Charles Wells Bombardier, darts, dominoes, pool; juke box or piped music, games machine, TV; children and dogs welcome, open all day Fri/Sat and in summer Mon-Thurs *(David Carr, Andrew York, the Didler, Kevin Blake, LYM)*
Indigo Alley [N Marine Rd]: Bustling high-ceilinged pub stripped to bare boards and painted bright yellow, central bar with up to five changing real ales such as Roosters, Leffe on tap, bottled imports, no food or machines, lots of standing room, piped music from big speakers – live Tues-Thurs and Sun; open till midnight Fri/Sat in summer, cl lunchtime *(BB, Eric Larkham)*
Lord Rosebery [Westborough]: Large handsome Wetherspoons in former Co-op (and

once the local Liberal HQ), very busy and lively evenings, in traffic-free central shopping area; galleried upper bar, well kept beers such as Black Sheep, enjoyable quickly served food inc Sun roast, obliging staff, no smoking area, local prints; disabled facilities, open all day *(David Carr, Colin Gooch, Kevin Blake)*

Scarborough Arms [North Terr]: Comfortable mock-Tudor pub, walls decorated with weaponry, good value filling meals (not Sun evening), well kept Marstons, John Smiths Bitter and Magnet and a guest beer, helpful landlady, friendly staff, warm open range, darts, pool; children welcome, good outside seating, open all day *(LS)*

Tap & Spile [Falsgrave Rd]: Three rooms, bare boards or flagstones, four changing well kept ales, farm cider, efficient good-humoured staff, good value home-made food lunchtime and early evening, no smoking room; frequent live music; terrace with barbecues *(the Didler)*

SCAWTON [SE5483]

☆ *Hare* [off A170 Thirsk—Helmsley]: Attractive dining pub with well spaced stripped pine tables, heavy beams and some flagstones, old-fashioned range and woodburner, appealing prints, well kept Black Sheep, Jennings Cumberland and John Smiths, good enterprising rather upmarket food, no smoking restaurant (allowing children) and part of bar; piped music; open all day summer, cl Mon *(Michael and Ann Cole, Christine and Phil Young, Walter and Susan Rinaldi-Butcher, Peter and Anne Hollindale, LYM)*

SEAMER [TA0183]

Copper Horse [just S of Scarboro; Main St]: Good choice of generous tasty food in friendly no smoking dining areas off main bar, bright and clean with beams, brasses, bare stone, part wood-floored and part carpeted, pleasant helpful service; pretty village *(Joan York)*

SETTLE [SD8163]

Golden Lion [B6480 (main rd through town), off A65 bypass]: Lively mix in old-fashioned market town inn with surprisingly grand staircase sweeping down into spacious baronial-style high-beamed hall bar, enormous log fireplace, comfortable settles, plush seats, brass, prints and chinese plates on dark panelling; well kept local and guest ales, decent wines by the glass, well priced straightforward food (all day wknds); music video may obtrude, public bar with darts, pool, fruit machine and TV; children in eating area, 12 recently well refurbished bedrooms, open all day *(Richard and Anne Ansell, LYM, Michael Butler, Karen Eliot, Sue Demont, Tim Barrow)*

Royal Oak [Market Pl (B6480, off A65 bypass)]: Large market-town inn with lots of highly waxed ornate oak panelling in spotless roomy and congenial partly divided open-plan bar, well kept local ales and others such as Charles Wells Bombardier, comfortable seats around brass-topped tables, restaurant, no smoking area; may be live music Sat; children welcome, bedrooms with own

bathrooms, open all day *(Paul Davies, LYM, Michael Butler)*

SEWERBY [TA2068]

Ship [Cliff Rd]: Welcoming pub overlooking North Sea, lots of sea pictures, nautical bric-a-brac and jugs hanging from beams, good value pubby food, well kept Mansfield ales, good service, small traditional dining room with comfortable wall settles and sea and cricket memorabilia, games/children's room with arcade games; large garden above cliff with big play area, snack bar; very handy for Sewerby Hall, with its land train connection to Bridlington *(Colin Gooch)*

SHEFFIELD [SK3687]

Bankers Draft [Market Pl]: Good value Wetherspoons bank conversion, clean, tidy and very popular, bars on two roomy floors, standard food all day, good range of real ales, decent wines, friendly staff, lots of old prints, no smoking areas; good disabled facilities, open all day from 10.30 *(P G Topp, Patrick Hancock, C J Fletcher)*

Bath [Victoria St, off Glossop Rd]: Cosy local, two small well restored rooms with nice woodwork, tiles and glass, well kept changing local real ales *(the Didler)*

☆ *Cask & Cutler* [Henry St; Shalesmoor tram stop right outside]: Convivial and cheery alehouse, half a dozen or more good often rare changing ales, occasional Port Mahon beers from its own back microbrewery, interesting dutch and belgian bottled beers, farm ciders and perry, coal fire in no smoking lounge on left, friendly licensees, cat and lovable dog, appropriate posters, occasional hot snacks or cobs, daily papers, pub games, good Nov beer festival; wheelchair access, tables in nice back garden, open all day Fri/Sat, cl Mon lunchtime *(David Carr, Patrick Hancock, Andrew York, the Didler)*

Cocked Hat [just off Attercliffe Common (A6178)]: Largely open-plan, tasteful dark colours, brewery memorabilia, well kept Marstons Pedigree, good value lunchtime food, welcoming landlord; quiet evenings *(Patrick Hancock, James A Waller)*

☆ *Devonshire Cat* [Wellington St (some local parking)]: Bright and airy stylishly modern café/bar with plenty of room inc no smoking area, polished light wood, some parquet, big modern prints, friendly staff knowledgeable about the dozen well kept mainly Yorkshire real ales inc Abbeydale and Kelham Island, more tapped from the cask, eight foreign beers on tap, masses of bottled beers in glass-walled cool room, two farm ciders, tea and coffee, good value food more interesting than usual from end servery, plenty of board games, good smoke extraction; well reproduced piped music, wide-screen TV, silenced games machine, ATM, live music Weds, quiz night Mon; good disabled access and facilities, open all day *(Patrick Hancock, Richard Houghton, the Didler, Mrs Jane Kingsbury, David Carr, C J Fletcher, Bob, BB)*

Gardeners Rest [Neepsend Lane]: Well kept Timothy Taylors and several guest beers (often the full range from one microbrewery), farm cider, continental beers on tap and in bottle, friendly beer-enthusiast landlord, no smoking lounge with old brewery memorabilia, lunchtime food, daily papers, games inc bar billiards (free Mon), changing artwork; frequent live music, poetry/story-telling nights, quiz Sun, Oct beer festival; disabled access and facilities, conservatory and tables out behind overlooking River Don, open all day *(David Carr, the Didler, Patrick Hancock)*

☆ *Hillsborough* [Langsett Rd/Wood St; by Primrose View tram stop]: Pub-in-hotel with its own well kept Crown, Edale and Wellington ales at attractive prices, also lots of guest beers, friendly staff, bare-boards bar, lounge, no smoking room with fire, views to ski slope from attractive back conservatory and terrace tables, daily papers, good filled rolls, limited hot food Weds evening; TV, Tues quiz night; good value bedrooms with own bathrooms, covered parking, real ale bar open evenings only, from 6 (4.30 Thurs-Sat) *(the Didler, Patrick Hancock, CMW, JJW)*

☆ *Kelham Island Tavern* [Kelham Island]: Friendly, comfortable and relaxed backstreet local with well kept Acorn Barnsley, Pictish Brewers Gold and several interesting beers from other small brewers, continental imports, farm cider, nice artwork, filled cobs and other food (not Sun), good-sized no smoking room, Sun folk night; disabled facilities *(the Didler, Patrick Hancock, Richard Houghton, C J Fletcher)*

Red Deer [Pitt St]: Lively backstreet local among Univ buildings, plenty of well kept popular real ales from central bar, wide choice of good value simple lunchtime food, extended lounge with pleasant raised back area; open all day wkdys *(Michael Ward, Patrick Hancock, the Didler, David Carr, Bob)*

Red Lion [Charles St, nr stn]: Traditional local, comfortable rooms off welcoming central bar, ornate fireplaces and coal fires, attractive panelling and etched glass, good simple lunchtime food, small back dining room, pleasant conservatory, usually have well kept Stones and Theakstons *(the Didler, Patrick Hancock, Bob, Pete Baker)*

Rose & Crown [Stour Lane, Wadsley]: Inexpensive tasty home-made food, cosy and welcoming; tables outside *(Matthew Lidbury)*

Springvale [Commonside]: Spacious studenty pub with good choice of beers such as Caledonian Deuchars IPA and Greene King, friendly service; big-screen sports TV *(Matthew Lidbury)*

Union [Union Rd, Netheredge]: Well run and spotless, with well kept ales such as Greene King Abbot and Old Speckled Hen, good value hearty food, lots of bric-a-brac *(Patrick Hancock, Peter F Marshall)*

Walkley Cottage [Bole Hill Rd]: Chatty 1930s pub popular for good value generous freshly made food (not Sun evening) inc bargain OAP lunch Mon-Thurs and good Sun roast, no smoking dining area, half a dozen or so well kept ales, farm cider, good coffee and soft drinks choice, daily papers, games room; quiet piped music, Mon music quiz; children and dogs welcome (pub dog called Max), views from picnic-sets in small back garden with swings, lovely hanging baskets, open all day *(CMW, JJW, Patrick Hancock)*

Wisewood [Loxley Rd]: Smallish and friendly, with good beer choice, pool; attractive garden *(Matthew Lidbury)*

SHEPLEY [SE1810]

Clothiers Arms [Station Rd, Stocksmoor (off A629 N, via Thunderbridge)]: Good atmosphere in softly lit rooms, polite helpful staff, enjoyable straightforward food, conservatory extension; balcony tables, quiet countryside *(Roger A Bellingham)*

SHERIFF HUTTON [SE6566]

Castle Inn [village green]: Well kept cheap Sam Smiths OB, wholesome reasonably priced straightforward food from sandwiches and baked potatoes up *(Pat and Tony Martin)*

SICKLINGHALL [SE3648]

☆ *Scotts Arms* [Main St]: Hospitable olde-worlde pub with long blackboard menus of good generous food, friendly service, nice rambling layout, low beams, old timbers, log fire in double-sided fireplace, well kept Timothy Taylors Landlord and Theakstons Old Peculier, good coffee and wine range, daily papers; big garden with play area *(Dr Pete Crawshaw, LYM)*

SKEEBY [NZ1902]

Travellers Rest [Richmond Rd (A6108)]: Neatly kept and friendly, copper and pewter on beams, coal fire, pub food from baguettes up, well kept Black Sheep, Greene King Old Speckled Hen and John Smiths; walking parties welcome, tables outside *(Michael Doswell, Roger Braithwaite)*

SKELTON [SE3668]

Black Lion [off B6265]: Enjoyable lunches in pleasant dining room, more elaborate evening menu; tables outside, caravan site behind *(Janet and Peter Race)*

SKIPTON [SD9851]

☆ *Narrow Boat* [Victoria St; pub signed down alley off Coach St]: No smoking town pub nr canal in small Market Town Taverns group, up to half a dozen well kept ales from mainly Yorkshire small breweries inc local Copper Dragon and a Mild (they may give you tasters), belgian beers too, good variety of fairly priced food (not Fri/Sat evening) from ciabattas and potato wedges up, good wine choice, friendly service, dark woodwork and upper gallery, no piped music; no children, some jazz and folk music, quiz Weds; tables outside, open all day *(D J Etheridge, MLR, Andy and Jill Kassube, Rona Murdoch, Tony Hobden)*

☆ *Royal Shepherd* [Canal St; from Water St (A65) turn into Coach St, then left after bridge over Leeds & Liverpool Canal]: Busy old-fashioned sociable local with big bar, snug and dining room, open fires, well kept Black Sheep and two local Copper Dragon ales, decent wine, unusual sensibly priced whiskies, cheery landlord and brisk service, low-priced standard food from sandwiches and baked potatoes up, photographs of Yorks CCC in its golden days; games and piped music; children welcome in side room, tables out in pretty spot by canal *(Meg and Colin Hamilton, George Atkinson)*

☆ **Woolly Sheep** [Sheep St]: Full Timothy Taylors range kept well in big bustling town pub with usual cheap generous food (plenty for children), prompt friendly enthusiastic service, two beamed bars off flagstoned passage, exposed brickwork, stone fireplace, lots of sheep prints and bric-a-brac, roomy comfortable lunchtime dining area; can be smoky, unobtrusive piped music; spacious pretty garden, six good value bedrooms, good breakfast *(MLR, Clive Flynn, Tim and Rosemary Wells)*

SKIPWITH [SE6638]

Drovers Arms [follow Escrick sign off A163 NE of Selby]: Comfortable two-room country pub in smart village by Skipwith Common nature reserve, good log fires, cheerful young licensees, obliging service, well kept beers such as Black Sheep and Shepherd Neame Spitfire, fine range of house wines, enterprising changing home-made food from proper sandwiches to good Sun roasts, separate dining room; wheelchair access *(Daniel Reid)*

SLAITHWAITE [SE0513]

Rose & Crown [Cop Hill, up Nabbs Lane then Holme Lane]: Great Colne Valley and moor views, three refurbished rooms off friendly bar, log fire in lounge, end restaurant, well kept Black Sheep beers, wide choice of malt whiskies, changing blackboard food on novel square plates, pleasant service; piped music turned off on request; good walks *(Dr Michael Smith)*

White House [Chain Rd (B6107 Meltham—Marsden)]: Attractive moorland inn under new family, enjoyable home-made food, well kept ales such as Timothy Taylors Landlord, good service, good choice of wines by the glass, small bar with log fire, comfortable lounge on right, attractive restaurant area on left; children welcome, tables out on front flagstones *(Anna Prior)*

SNAINTON [TA9182]

Coachman [Pickering Rd W (A170)]: Recently reopened as good pub/restaurant with varied and interesting choice, real ales such as Black Sheep *(Peter Burton)*

SNAPE [SE2684]

☆ **Castle Arms** [off B6268 Masham—Bedale]: Spotless comfortably updated low-ceilinged pub with good fresh enterprising food from interesting sandwiches up in flagstoned bar with big inglenook coal fire, second flagstoned room and attractive rather smart small carpeted dining room, relaxed happy atmosphere and considerate helpful service, well kept Black Sheep Best, Gales BB, Hambleton Best and John Smiths, decent wines, good coffee, sporting prints; unobtrusive piped music; children and dogs welcome, tables in charming courtyard, pretty village very handy for Thorp Perrow, comfortable bedrooms *(Michael Doswell, Edward and Deanna Pearce, Alistair Stead,*

Dr and Mrs P Truelove, BB)

SOUTH ANSTON [SK4681]

Loyal Trooper [3 miles from M1 junction 31]: Cheerful three-room village local with well kept Adnams and Timothy Taylors Landlord, good value straightforward food (not Sun, not Fri/Sat evening), TV in lounge, lively public bar; no no smoking area *(LYM, Tony Hobden)*

SOUTH CAVE [SE9231]

☆ **Fox & Coney** [Market Pl (A1034)]: Pleasant pub with well kept Caledonian Deuchars IPA, Timothy Taylors Landlord and Wychwood Hobgoblin from central servery, generous enjoyable standard food from baguettes to steaks, bright and comfortable warmly Victorian open-plan main bar and dining areas, friendly efficient staff, coal fire; bedrooms in adjoining hotel *(Paul and Ursula Randall, Dr D J and Mrs S C Walker, Steve Whalley)*

SOUTH DALTON [SE9645]

☆ **Pipe & Glass** [West End, just off B1248 NW of Beverley]: Friendly dining pub in charming secluded setting, stripped-stone beamed bar with some high-backed settles, old prints, log fires and bow windows, well kept beers inc one brewed for them by Cropton, enjoyable bar food all day, more formal large attractively laid conservatory restaurant overlooking Dalton Park (must book wknds); may be quiet piped music; children welcome, tables in garden with splendid yew tree, three comfortable bedrooms with good breakfast, open all day *(LYM, Kevin Blake)*

SOUTH KILVINGTON [SE4284]

Old Oak Tree: Spacious rambling low-ceilinged pub, three linked rooms and long pretty back conservatory, old photographs and so forth, good vegetarian specialities as well as meaty things, plenty of puddings, well kept Tetleys, relaxed friendly and informal atmosphere; rustic tables on sloping lawn *(Edward and Deanna Pearce)*

SOWERBY BRIDGE [SE0623]

Rams Head [Wakefield Rd]: Brews its own good well priced Ryburn ales, with open fire in well divided stripped stone lounge bar, good value home-made food in no smoking L-shaped dining area; service can slow *(Pete Baker, G Coates, Tony and Wendy Hobden)*

White Horse [Spring Gardens (A646 N)]: Friendly community local with public bar and lounge off main serving area, well kept Tetleys Bitter and Mild and a beer from E&S Elland *(Pete Baker)*

SPOFFORTH [SE3650]

☆ **Railway Inn** [A661 Harrogate—Wetherby; Park Terr]: Simple little pub made special by welcoming hard-working landlord who goes out of his way to make sure everything is right; wide choice of good low-priced home-made food from sandwiches to steaks, well kept Sam Smiths, straightforward furnishings in basic locals' bar and unfussy no smoking lounge, real fires, no juke box; no credit cards, Weds quiz nights; tables and swing in garden behind *(BB, Stuart Paulley, B and M Kendall)*

SPROATLEY [TA1934]
Blue Bell [Main Rd (B1238)]: Welcoming
village local, cosy lounge bar and other rooms
inc separate dining room, straightforward
food, decent wines, real ale, friendly service
(A J Bowen)

SPROTBROUGH [SE5302]
☆ *Boat* [3½ miles from M18 junction 2, less from
A1(M) junction 36 via A630 and Mill Lane;
Nursery Lane]: Roomy stone-built ex-
farmhouse thoroughly refurbished as Vintage
Inn dining pub early in 2004, keeping
something of the feel of several snug flagstoned
areas, log fires in big stone fireplaces, latticed
windows, dark beams, sensibly priced food
from sandwiches and crusty buns to steak all
day till 10pm, well kept Black Sheep, John
Smiths and Tetleys, 15 wines by the glass,
prompt uniformed service; piped music, games
machine, no dogs; tables in big sheltered
prettily lit courtyard, River Don walks, open
all day *(GSB, LYM, JHBS)*

STAMFORD BRIDGE [SE7055]
☆ *Three Cups* [A166 W of town]: Spacious
Vintage Inn family dining pub in timbered
country style, glass-topped 20-metre well in
bar, reliable food all day, good range of wines
by the glass, well kept Bass and Tetleys, good
welcoming staff and relaxed atmosphere; good
disabled access, children welcome, good play
area behind, bedrooms, open all day *(LYM,
Walter and Sue Anderson, Roger A Bellingham,
Pat and Graham Williamson)*

STANNINGTON [SK3189]
Robin Hood [Greaves Lane, Little Matlock]:
Friendly and comfortable stone-built country
pub with good views and walks, wide
blackboard choice of good value largely freshly
made food inc children's, two unusual real
ales, good soft drinks choice, two big rooms
(dogs allowed in tap room), beams, brass,
copper and pictures; play area, cl Mon/Tues
lunchtime in winter *(CMW, JJW)*

STUTTON [SE4841]
☆ *Hare & Hounds* [Manor Rd]: Pleasantly
refurbished stone-built pub with cosy low-
ceilinged rooms, wide choice of enjoyable food
(not Sun evening) with some new dishes
alongside old favourites, quick pleasant service
even when busy (helpful with wheelchairs),
well kept cheap Sam Smiths OB, decent wine,
well behaved children in restaurant; has been
cl Mon, tables, some under marquee, in long
prettily planted sloping garden with playthings
(LYM, Geoffrey and Brenda Wilson)

SUTTON BANK [SE5283]
Hambleton Hotel [Hambleton; A170 Thirsk—
Scarboro]: Roadside pub with enjoyable
reasonably priced pub food in three areas, well
kept Hambleton beer, friendly licensees;
caravan site behind, on Cleveland Way,
popular with walkers *(Hunter and
Christine Wright)*

SWAINBY [NZ4702]
Black Horse [High St]: Pleasant spot by stream
in nice village, appealing beamed bar with
plenty to look at, wide range of generous
appetising home-made food from substantial

doorstep sandwiches to good value Sun roasts,
well kept Camerons Strongarm and John
Smiths, service friendly and efficient even
when busy; well spaced picnic-sets in good-
sized attractive garden with play area
(Michael Doswell, Geoff and Angela Jaques)

TAN HILL [NY8906]
☆ *Tan Hill Inn* [Arkengarthdale rd Reeth—
Brough, at junction Keld/W Stonesdale rd]:
Old stone pub in wonderful setting on Pennine
Way – Britain's highest, and second most
remote, nearly five miles from the nearest
neighbour, basic, bustling and can get
overcrowded, full of bric-a-brac and pictures
inc interesting old photographs, simple sturdy
furniture, flagstones, ever-burning big log fire
(with prized stone side seats); well kept
Theakstons Best, XB and Old Peculier (in
winter the cellar does chill down – whisky with
hot water's good then), help-yourself coffee,
generous food from good sandwiches to usual
hot dishes and hearty yorkshire puddings, pool
in family room; may be piped radio, often
snowbound; swaledale sheep show here last
Thurs in May; children and dogs welcome,
bedrooms, inc some in extension with own
bathrooms, open all day *(LYM, Michael Tack,
Rona Murdoch, David Reid)*

THIXENDALE [SE8461]
Cross Keys [off A166 3 miles N of
Fridaythorpe]: Unspoilt welcoming country
pub in deep valley below the rolling Wolds,
cosy L-shaped bar with fitted wall seats,
relaxed atmosphere, well kept Jennings, Tetleys
and a guest beer, sensible home-made
blackboard food; large pleasant garden behind,
popular with walkers, handy for Wharram
Percy earthworks *(the Didler)*

THORGANBY [SE6942]
☆ *Jefferson Arms* [off A163 NE of Selby, via
Skipwith]: New licensees for this dining pub
(they now close only on Mon), with armchairs,
sofas and log fires as well as the marble-topped
tables and bentwood chairs, two
conservatories, quite an emphasis on what has
been good food, well kept Marstons Pedigree,
Timothy Taylors Landlord and perhaps a guest
beer; piped music; children welcome,
bedrooms; more reports on new regime please
*(Barbara and Derek Thompson, David and
Catherine Whiting, LYM)*

THORNTON [SE0933]
☆ *Ring o' Bells* [Hill Top Rd, off B6145 W of
Bradford]: Spotless 19th-c moortop dining pub
very popular for wide choice of well presented
good home cooking inc fresh fish, speciality
pies, superb steaks, good puddings, bargain
early suppers, separate-sittings Sun lunch (best
to book), well kept Black Sheep, Courage
Directors and Websters Green Label, crisp
efficient service, pleasant bar, popular air-
conditioned no smoking restaurant and
pleasant conservatory lounge; wide views
towards Shipley and Bingley *(Nigel and
Sue Foster, Andy and Jill Kassube)*

THORNTON DALE [SE8383]
New Inn [The Square]: Early 18th-c beamed
coaching inn under new licensees, old-world

style, well kept Black Sheep and Timothy
Taylors Landlord, good home-made food using
local ingredients; courtyard tables, attractive
roomy bedrooms with own bathrooms, good
breakfast, pretty village in walking area
(Michael Butler)

TICKHILL [SK5993]
Scarbrough Arms [Sunderland St (A631)]:
Cheerful village pub, small low-ceilinged
central bar with coal fire, barrel tables and lots
of brass, more conventional dining area,
traditional public bar, good reasonably priced
genuine home cooking (lunchtime, not Sun) inc
imaginative vegetarian dishes, well kept John
Smiths and a guest beer such as Cottage,
friendly efficient staff; no credit cards; tables
out on lawn with swings, interesting village
(Derek and Sylvia Stephenson)

TOTLEY [SK3080]
Crown [Hillfoot Rd]: Old-fashioned country
inn with friendly landlord and good staff, five
well kept ales such as Fullers London Pride and
Tetleys, short choice of good plain home-
cooked food; no children
(DC, James A Waller)

UGTHORPE [NZ7911]
Black Bull: Small-roomed 17th-c local, wide
choice of enjoyable food using local produce
from good sandwiches and baked potatoes to
steaks, fish and good value Sun lunch, friendly
licensees, cosy bar with darts, dominoes and
quoits, pleasantly decorated no smoking
restaurant overlooking back garden
(Eric Addison)

WAINSTALLS [SE0428]
Cat i' th' Well: Picturesque country pub in fine
spot towards the windy top of Luddenden
Dean, three snug linked areas, fresh and
untwee, with 19th-c panelling from nearby
demolished hall, nice balance between drinking
and dining, above-average food from good
sandwich choice and huge ploughman's up,
well kept Timothy Taylors Best and Landlord
and a guest beer, quick friendly service, no
smoking area; piped music; tables outside,
walkers welcome, handy for Calderdale Way
(Carol Jones, Rona Murdoch)

WAKEFIELD [SE3320]
Fernandes Brewery Tap [Avison Yard,
Kirkgate]: Tap for Fernandes microbrewery on
upper floor of 19th-c malt store, their beers
and interesting guests kept well, farm cider,
interesting breweriana, friendly atmosphere,
bare boards and rafters; cl Mon-Thurs
lunchtime, open all day Fri-Sun with
lunchtime soup and sandwiches then,
brewery shop *(the Didler, Patrick Hancock,
Tony Hobden)*
Henry Boons [Westgate]: Well kept Clarks
(from next-door brewery), Black Sheep,
Timothy Taylors and Tetleys, in two-room
bare-boards local, friendly staff, barrel tables
and breweriana, side pool area; juke box,
machines, live bands; open all day (till 1am
Fri/Sat) *(the Didler, Patrick Hancock)*
Redoubt [Horbury Rd, Westgate]: Busy and
friendly traditional pub, four compact rooms
off long corridor, well kept Tetleys Bitter and

Mild and Timothy Taylors Landlord, rugby
league photographs and memorabilia, pub
games; family room till 8, open all day
(Michael Butler, the Didler)
Talbot & Falcon [Northgate]: Smart and
popular town pub with friendly long bar,
panelling and lots of prints, back lounge, Black
Sheep and Tetleys, foreign bottled beers,
popular reasonably priced lunchtime food,
quick service; TV, games machines; bedrooms,
open all day *(Tony Hobden)*
Wagon [Westgate End]: Busy friendly local
specialising in well kept ales mainly from
interesting small breweries, lunchtime food,
reasonable prices, log fire, side pool room;
benches outside, open all day *(the Didler)*
Wakefield Labour Club [Vicarage St]: Red
wooden shed rather like a works canteen
inside, small and chatty – it is a club, but you
can just sign in; changing keenly priced real
ales usually inc Ossett, belgian beers, farm
cider; picnic-sets outside, cl lunchtime Mon-
Thurs and Sun evening *(the Didler)*

WALES [SK4782]
Duke of Leeds [Church St]: Comfortable
18th-c stone-faced village pub under friendly
new licensees, well kept ales such as John
Smiths and Theakstons, good wine and soft
drinks choice, good range of fresh lunchtime
and evening food, quick service, long no
smoking dining lounge and smaller room
where smoking allowed, lots of brass and
copper, flame-effect gas fire; quiet piped music,
Sun quiz night; children welcome, nearby
walks *(CMW, JJW)*

WALKINGTON [SE9937]
Dog & Duck [B1230, West End]: Popular well
run pub with welcoming licensees, good choice
of food from good value sandwiches to bargain
Sun roasts in long beamed lounge bar or small
restaurant, well kept Camerons, Mansfield and
Marstons Pedigree, back games bar with pool;
charming village *(Michael Butler)*

WALTON [SE4447]
Fox & Hounds [Hall Park Rd, off back rd
Wetherby—Tadcaster]: Recently reworked into
dining pub by ex-restaurateur licensees of
nearby Bay Horse at Kirk Deighton, enjoyable
food inc popular Sun lunch (should book),
thriving atmosphere, well kept John Smiths
and a guest such as Black Sheep or Caledonian
Deuchars IPA *(Les and Sandra Brown)*

WELBURN [SE7168]
Crown & Cushion [off A64]: Comfortable
village pub with good home cooking from well
made sandwiches and ploughman's up, good
service, well kept Camerons and Tetleys,
decent wine, games in public bar, restaurant,
children in eating areas, amusing pictures in
gents'; piped music, and some talk of the
cheerful warmly welcoming landlord's retiring,
as we went to press; attractive small back
garden with terrace, handy for Castle Howard
*(LYM, Christopher Turner, Peter and
Anne Hollindale, Walter and Susan Rinaldi-
Butcher)*

WENTWORTH [SK3898]
☆ *George & Dragon* [3 miles from M1 junction

36; Main St]: Friendly rambling split-level bar, half a dozen well kept ales such as Kelham Island, Timothy Taylors Best and Landlord and local Wentworth ones, flagstones and assorted old-fashioned furnishings, ornate stove in lounge, generous good value food inc traditional puddings in bar and restaurant, good service; high chairs provided; may be piped music, small back games room with darts and machine; benches in front courtyard, tables out on big back lawn, crafts and antiques shop – pleasant village (LYM, R T and J C Moggridge, Pat and Tony Martin, Patrick Hancock, Derek and Sylvia Stephenson, Jo Lilley, Simon Calvert)

☆ Rockingham Arms [3 miles from M1 junction 36; B6090, signed off A6135; Main St]: Welcoming Steak & Ale pub with comfortable traditional furnishings, open fires, stripped stone, rooms off inc a no smoking dining/family room, good food choice all day (freshly made so can take a while), sensible prices, Theakstons ales and two local Wentworth ones, good choice of wines by the glass, no smoking room; quiet piped music, TV; dogs allowed in part (meals available for them), tables in attractive garden with own bowling green, bedrooms, open all day (Derek and Sylvia Stephenson, CMW, JJW, BB)

WEST BURTON [SE0186]

Fox & Hounds [on green, off B6160 Bishopdale—Wharfedale]: Friendly local on long green of idyllic Dales village, good friendly service, well kept Black Sheep and Tetleys, wide choice of generous usual food inc good sandwiches, residents' dining room; nearby caravan park; children and dogs welcome, good modern bedrooms, lovely walks and waterfalls nearby (Abi Benson, Gerry Miller, Keith and Avril Stringer, B and M Kendall)

WEST TANFIELD [SE2678]

☆ Bruce Arms [A6108 N of Ripon]: Thriving dining pub with good rather upmarket food inc interesting dishes in intimate log-fire bar or smallish dining room (often fully booked at night), friendly service (LYM, Janet and Peter Race)

☆ Bull [Church St (A6108 N of Ripon)]: Open-plan but the feel of two smallish rooms, snug and cosy, with warm Victorian décor and comfortable pub furniture; popular food all day inc good generous baguettes with chips and salad (served outside too) and some enterprising hot dishes, well kept Black Sheep ales, decent wines, quick pleasant service, small restaurant; children allowed away from bar, tables on terraces in attractive garden behind sloping steeply to River Ure (Edward and Deanna Pearce, BB, Janet and Peter Race)

WETHERBY [SE4048]

Swan & Talbot [handy for A1; North St]: Traditional well decorated town pub, linked rooms each side of main bar, good choice of reasonably priced tasty food, three changing well kept ales, pleasant chatty staff (Edward Leetham)

WHISTON [SK4490]

Chequers [under 2 miles from M1 junction 33, via A630, A631, A618: Pleasley Rd/Chaff Lane]: Much modernised 1930s pub, up to five real ales, food lunchtime and evening inc well priced Sun roast, lounge/dining area, coal-effect fire, tap room with games; piped pop music (CMW, JJW)

Golden Ball [nr M1 junction 33, via A618; Turner Lane, off High St]: Spotless extended Ember Inn, wide food choice inc good value mixed grill, real ales such as Badger Tanglefoot, Bass, Caledonian Deuchars IPA, Stones, Timothy Taylors Landlord and Tetleys, several wines by the glass, good soft drinks choice, daily papers, log fire, no smoking room; quiet piped music, machines, quiz nights, no children inside; picnic-sets outside, open all day (CMW, JJW, Peter F Marshall)

WHITBY [NZ9010]

Middle Earth Tavern [Church St]: Quiet spot facing river and harbour, Black Sheep and Tetleys, bar food; tables outside (David Carr)

WHIXLEY [SE4457]

Anchor [New Rd]: Family-friendly pub just outside village, traditional generous food inc bargain lunchtime sliced roasts particularly popular with OAPs, cheery efficient service, well kept John Smiths and Tetleys, straightforward main eating extension off original core with some character – coal fire in small lounge, lots of eccentric teapots (Janet and Peter Race, Donald and Margaret Wood)

WIGGLESWORTH [SD8056]

☆ Plough [B6478, off A65 S of Settle]: Friendly dining pub with wide range of good reasonably priced bar food inc good Sun lunch, well kept Black Sheep and Tetleys, attractive bar with log fire, little rooms off, some simple yet cosy, others more plush, inc no smoking panelled dining room, snug and attractive newly refurbished conservatory restaurant with panoramic Dales views; pleasant garden, homely and comfortable bedrooms also with views (Peter F Marshall, Norma and Noel Thomas)

WRAGBY [SE4117]

Spread Eagle [A638]: Popular traditional local with bric-a-brac in four appealing low-beamed rooms, good value bar snacks and bargain lunches, well kept low-priced Sam Smiths, friendly helpful staff, photographs of regulars as youngsters in tap room, evening restaurant; quiz night, popular wknds; tables in back garden with play area, handy for sumptuous Nostell Priory (NT) (Geoffrey and Brenda Wilson)

WYKE [SE1426]

Wyke Lion [A641 Bradford—Brighouse, just off A58]: Popular Vintage Inn, with their usual good value food, well kept beers and friendly staff (Geoffrey and Brenda Wilson)

WYKEHAM [SE9783]

Downe Arms [Main Rd (A170 Scarboro—Pickering)]: Comfortable and spacious bars and barn-style dining room, stripped pine and cottagey furnishings, John Smiths and Theakstons, family room, pool; piped music; play area, bedrooms *(Janet and Peter Race)*

YORK [SE5951]

☆ *Ackhorne* [St Martins Lane, Micklegate]: Good changing real ales from Roosters, Caledonian and other small brewers, up to four farm ciders, perry, country wines, foreign bottled beers and good coffee; beams and bare boards, leather wall seats, Civil War prints, bottles and jugs, carpeted snug one end, good value home-made food (not Sun) from good choice of sandwiches up, friendly landlord and family, helpful service, open fire, daily papers, traditional games, silenced games machine; Sun quiz night; new suntrap back terrace (steps a bit steep), open all day *(the Didler, Roger A Bellingham, Patrick Hancock, Dr David Cockburn, David Carr, Esther and John Sprinkle, Peter Coxon, Alison and Pete, Pat and Tony Martin, Eric Larkham)*

☆ *Black Swan* [Peaseholme Green (inner ring road)]: Marvellous timbered and jettied Tudor building, compact panelled front bar, crooked-floored hall with fine period staircase, black-beamed back bar with vast inglenook, cheerful service, low-priced usual food from baked potatoes and baguettes up, well kept ales such as Fullers London Pride, Greene King Abbot, John Smiths and York Yorkshire Terrier, decent wines; piped music, jazz and folk nights; useful car park *(Patrick Hancock, Peter Coxon, the Didler, David Carr, LYM, Paul and Ursula Randall, Kevin Blake, Alison and Pete)*

☆ *Blue Bell* [Fossgate]: Classic little Edwardian pub with well kept ales such as Camerons Strongarm, Caledonian Deuchars IPA, Greene King Abbot, John Smiths, Timothy Taylors Landlord and Charles Wells Bombardier, nice wines, tiny tiled-floor front bar with roaring fire, panelled ceiling, stained glass, bar pots and decanters, corridor to back smoke room not much bigger, hatch service to middle bar, good friendly service, lamps and flickering candles, chatty local atmosphere (given its size, can get crowded), good value sandwiches and tapas all day, pub games; open all day *(Nick Holding, Patrick Hancock, Paul and Ursula Randall, Pete Baker, Peter Coxon, the Didler, Tracey and Stephen Groves, Alison and Pete, Eric Larkham)*

Dormouse [Shipton Rd, Clifton Park]: Purpose-built Vintage Inn, well designed and given plenty of character and atmosphere, with friendly efficient staff, their usual reasonably priced food, wide choice of good value wines, Bass and Tetleys; good disabled access *(Walter and Sue Anderson, John Knighton)*

Golden Ball [Cromwell Rd/Bishophill]: Unspoilt and buoyant 1950s local feel in friendly and well preserved four-room Edwardian pub, enjoyable straightforward wkdy lunchtime food, well kept Marstons Pedigree, John Smiths and a guest beer, bar billiards, cards and dominoes; TV, can be lively evenings, live music Thurs and Sun; pleasant small walled garden *(the Didler, Pete Baker,*

Peter Coxon, Alison and Pete)

Golden Fleece [Pavement]: Timothy Taylors Landlord and guest beers often from York Brewery, usual bar food all day (till 5 Sun), long corridor from bar to back lounge (beware the sloping floors – it dates from 1503), lots of ghost stories and pictures; children welcome, bedrooms *(Peter Coxon, Nick Holding, Esther and John Sprinkle)*

Golden Slipper [Goodramgate]: Dating from 15th c, renovated carefully to keep distinctively old-fashioned almost rustic local feel in its neat unpretentious bar and three small rooms, one lined with books, good cheap plain food from sandwiches, baguettes and baked potatoes to tender roast beef, well kept Caledonian Deuchars IPA, Greene King Old Speckled Hen and John Smiths, cheerful staff; tables in back courtyard *(Karen Eliot, Peter Coxon, David Carr, Paul and Ursula Randall)*

Hole in the Wall [High Petergate]: Rambling much modernised open-plan pub handy for Minster, beams, stripped masonry, lots of prints, turkey carpeting, lots of low plush stools, well kept Banks's, Mansfield and Marstons Pedigree, good coffee, very busy lunchtime for well priced food noon onwards inc generous Sun lunch, friendly service; juke box, games machines, piped music not too loud, live some nights; children welcome, open all day *(Martin and Sarah, Mr and Mrs John Taylor, LYM, Tracey and Stephen Groves, Esther and John Sprinkle)*

☆ *Last Drop* [Colliergate]: Former law office dating from 17th c, restored by York Brewery in basic traditional style, several of their own beers and one or two expertly kept guests, decent wines and country wines, enthusiastic landlord and friendly helpful young staff, bare boards, barrel tables and comfortable seats, big windows overlooking pavement, no music, machines or children, nice simple fresh food 12-4 from sandwiches and panini up (local cheeses recommended); piped music can obtrude, no children, can get very busy lunchtime, attic lavatories; tables out behind, open all day *(Peter Coxon, Fred and Lorraine Gill, Martin Grosberg, Patrick Hancock, Dr David Cockburn, Nick Holding, David R Brown, Mark Walker, Esther and John Sprinkle)*

☆ *Lendal Cellars* [Lendal]: Cheerful bustling split-level ale house down steps in broad-vaulted 17th-c cellars carefully spotlit to show up the stripped brickwork, stone floor, interconnecting rooms and alcoves, well kept changing ales such as Boddingtons, Caledonian Deuchars IPA, Marstons Pedigree and Theakstons at fair prices, farm cider, decent coffee, good choice of wines by the glass, foreign bottled beers, daily papers, cheerful staff, children allowed for good plain food 11.30-7(5 Fri/Sat), two-for-one bargains; good piped music, popular with students; open all day *(Peter Coxon and Maurice Cottrell, Patrick Hancock, the Didler, LYM)*

Masons Arms [Fishergate]: 1930s local, two

fires in panelled front bar with blow lamps and pig ornaments, no smoking second room, attractive fireplaces, good range of beers inc guests, generous interesting home-made food, friendly service; comfortable bedroom block with own bathrooms (no breakfast), tables out in front and on back riverside terrace *(Martin and Sarah, Eric Larkham)*

Minster Inn [Marygate]: Well preserved modest Edwardian local, three chatty rooms (one no smoking) off central corridor, bric-a-brac and dark old tables and settles, fires and woodburners, friendly landlord, well kept changing ales such as Burtonwood Top Hat, Darwin Ghost and Hanby Drawwell, sandwiches, traditional table games; piped music; tables out behind *(Tracey and Stephen Groves, Eric Larkham)*

Olde Starre [Stonegate]: City's oldest licensed pub, and a magnet for tourists, with 'gallows' sign across York's prettiest street, original panelling and prints, green plush wall seats, several other little rooms off porch-like lobby, well kept changing ales such as Caledonian Deuchars IPA, John Smiths, Theakstons Best and York Yorkshire Terrier from long counter, cheerful young staff, low-priced food; piped music may be loud, fruit and games machines; open all day, children welcome away from bar, flower-filled back garden and front courtyard with Minster glimpsed across the rooftops *(Patrick Hancock, Peter Coxon, Nick Holding, LYM, Dr and Mrs Jackson)*

Postern Gate [Piccadilly]: Wetherspoons in new building, with four regular and six guest beers, food all day inc breakfasts (not Sun) from 10am; family room *(David Carr)*

☆ *Red Lion* [Merchantgate, between Fossgate and Piccadilly]: Low-beamed rambling rooms with plenty of atmosphere, some stripped Tudor brickwork, relaxed old-fashioned furnishings, well kept Black Sheep and John Smiths, reasonably priced bar lunches, good attentive staff; piped music; children welcome to eat at lunchtime, picnic-sets outside *(Peter Coxon, Nick Holding, LYM, Mark Walker, Dave Braisted)*

Rook & Gaskill [Lawrence St]: Tied to York Brewery, with all their beers kept well and lots of guests, traditional décor, dark wood tables, banquettes, chairs and high stools, cheerful knowledgeable service, limited bar food; jazz and folk nights *(Paul and Ursula Randall, Peter Coxon)*

☆ *Royal Oak* [Goodramgate]: Comfortably worn in three-room black-beamed 16th-c pub remodelled in Tudor style 1934, warm welcoming atmosphere, cosy corners with blazing fires, good value generous homely food (limited Sun evening) inc fresh veg and home-baked bread served 11.30-8, no sandwiches till 3, speedy service from cheerful bustling young staff, reliably well kept Greene King Abbot, Timothy Taylors Landlord, Tetleys and a guest beer, decent wines, good coffee; prints, swords, busts and old guns, no smoking family room; piped music, can get crowded, outside gents'; handy for Minster, open all day *(Peter Coxon, Patrick Hancock, Nick Holding, BB, Paul and Ursula Randall, Kevin Blake)*

Snickleway [Goodramgate]: Snug and interesting little open-plan pub, cosy nooks and crannies, lots of antiques, copper and brass, good coal fires, cheerful landlord, well kept Black Sheep, Greene King Old Speckled Hen and John Smiths, good value fresh well filled doorstep sandwiches and light snacks lunchtimes, prompt service, splendid cartoons in gents', exemplary ladies'; unobtrusive piped music *(Tim and Sue Halstead, Paul and Ursula Randall, David Carr, Esther and John Sprinkle, Kevin Blake)*

Swan [Bishopgate St, Clementhorpe]: Unspoilt 1950s feel, friendly and chatty, hatch service to lobby for two small rooms off main bar, great staff, particularly well kept Timothy Taylors Landlord and other changing ales; can be smoky, piped music may obtrude, popular with young people wknds; small pleasant walled garden, nr city walls *(Fred and Lorraine Gill, Pete Baker, the Didler, Peter Coxon, R Brackenbury)*

☆ *Tap & Spile* [Monkgate]: Friendly open-plan late Victorian pub with changing well kept ales such as Downton Chimera Gold, Exmoor Hound Dog, Hook Norton Double Stout, Roosters Yankee and Springfield Roaring Meg, farm cider and country wines, decent wines by the glass, bookshelves, games in raised back area, cheap straightforward lunchtime bar food (not Mon); children in eating area, tables on heated terrace and in garden, open all day *(the Didler, LYM, Patrick Hancock, David Carr, Paul and Ursula Randall, Peter Coxon)*

☆ *Three Legged Mare* [High Petergate]: Bustling open-plan light and airy modern café-bar with York Brewery's full beer range kept well, good range of belgian Trappist beers, quick cheerful service (staff know about beers), generous interesting sandwiches and one or two other reasonably priced lunchtime snacks, some comfortable sofas, back conservatory; no children, can be smoky; disabled facilities (other lavatories down noisy spiral stairs), tables in back garden with replica of the original three-legged mare – a local gallows used for multiple executions *(Andrew York, Dr David Cockburn, Peter Coxon, Pat and Tony Martin, Paul and Ursula Randall, David Carr, Fred and Lorraine Gill, Esther and John Sprinkle, Eric Larkham)*

☆ *York Arms* [High Petergate]: Snug and cheerful little basic panelled bar (beware the sliding door), big modern back lounge, cosier partly panelled no smoking parlour full of old bric-a-brac, prints, brown-cushioned wall settles, dimpled copper tables and an open fire; quick helpful service, well kept Sam Smiths OB, tasty sensibly priced simple food lunchtime to early evening (not Sun-Tues), no piped music; by Minster, open all day *(Patrick Hancock, BB, Esther and John Sprinkle)*

York Brewery Tap [Toft Green, Micklegate]: Upstairs lounge at York Brewery, their own full cask range in top condition, also bottled beers, nice clubby atmosphere with friendly staff happy to talk about the beers, lots of breweriana and view of brewing plant, comfortable settees and armchairs, magazines and daily papers; no food, brewery tours by arrangement, shop; children allowed, open 11.30-7, cl Sun, annual membership fee £3 unless you live in York or go on the tour

(the Didler, Esther and John Sprinkle, Paul and Ursula Randall, Eric Larkham)
Yorkshire Terrier [Stonegate]: Recently opened by York Brewery, their full range from smallish bar, dining room tucked behind a front brewery shop, another no smoking room upstairs, soup, sandwiches and limited range of moderately priced food noon till 4 inc Sun *(Paul and Ursula Randall)*

Bedroom prices normally include full English breakfast, VAT and any inclusive service charge that we know of. Prices before the '/' are for single rooms, after for two people in double or twin (B includes a private bath, S a private shower). If there is no '/', the prices are only for twin or double rooms (as far as we know there are no singles). If there is no B or S, as far as we know no rooms have private facilities.

LONDON
SCOTLAND
WALES
CHANNEL ISLANDS

London

It's scary days for drinks prices in London pubs. In our price survey this year we found several which priced their very cheapest beer at £3 a pint, and the average price of a pint here is now only a very few pence short of £2.50. So particular praise for Sam Smiths the Yorkshire brewer, which holds the price of a pint down to a very pocket-friendly £1.70 or so in its good London pubs; and for Wetherspoons the pub chain, which also keeps beer prices down to well below £2 a pint. Beers from Fullers and Youngs, the two London brewers, also tend to compare well on price with most out-of-London brews. Five new entries here span a tremendous range of styles. In Central London, the Princess Louise, back in the *Guide* after a break of several years, has a rich High Victorian décor (even the gents' is Listed; good value food and drink, and nice atmosphere). Three are in South London: the Anchor & Hope, a lively and informal gastropub with particularly good though expensive food; the Royal Oak, a careful re-creation of a Victorian alehouse, with nice country-style cooking; and the Old Jail out at Biggin Hill, utterly countrified and one of the very few fringe-of-London pubs worth making a special trip to. The final newcomer, the Warrington, in West London, is a remarkably ornate art nouveau building, from its grand Mackintosh-style windows to its opulent interior (almost with a hint of the 19th-c bordello); good beers and wines, too, and nice thai food. Central London pubs on top form are the Black Friar (another art nouveau spectacular), the Cittie of Yorke (great booth-lined bar, great value beer), the Cross Keys (attractively individual décor, good food), the Jerusalem Tavern (lovely atmosphere, good food and beer), the Lamb & Flag (a splendidly old-fashioned retreat from Covent Garden, with bargain food and a fine beer range), the Lord Moon of the Mall (one of the best Wetherspoons, in a fine location), the fascinating Olde Cheshire Cheese (oozing with history, and bargain beer), the nicely tucked-away Olde Mitre (newish landlord settling in well, good value snacks, and gains a Beer Award this year), the cheerful little Seven Stars (nice food these days, and an expansion into the next-door shop will give much-needed extra space). In East London, the Grapes and Prospect of Whitby are both very much enjoyed for their buoyant atmosphere. In North London, the Drapers Arms has top-notch food in nicely relaxed surroundings; the Duke of Cambridge scores on its very good organic food and drinks; and the Flask and Holly Bush are well liked for their villagey style – the Holly Bush is another pub that's at least starting down the organic path. In South London, two favourites are the Founders Arms (making the most of its spectacular riverside site) and the Market Porter (a dozen quickly changing good beers, great atmosphere, and now virtually doubled in size). Currently tops in West London are the Atlas (one of the best London pubs for food), and the civilised White Horse, with its excellent range of drinks, good service and nice food. Of those pubs scoring particularly highly for their good imaginative food, it is the Drapers Arms in North London which takes the title of London Dining Pub of the Year. In the Lucky Dip section at the end of the chapter, Central London pubs which have been earning high praise recently are the Audley, Bleeding Heart, Buckingham Arms, Chandos, Cross Keys, Duke, O'Conor Don, Old

Coffee House and Salisbury; in North London, the Head of Steam and Rising Sun; and in South London, the Mayflower and Trafalgar. We have listed the pubs in these areas by postal district, and we have separated off the outer London suburbs. These come last, after the Central, East, North, South and West numbered postal districts.

CENTRAL LONDON Map 13

Admiral Codrington ♀

Mossop Street, SW3; ⊖ South Kensington

Positively buzzing on our last evening visit, this popular pub is the kind of place where half the customers arrive by taxi, but nevertheless its clientele can be rather more varied than the heart-of-Chelsea location might suggest. The chief draw remains the sunny back dining room, mainly because of the very good food, but also because of its design – particularly impressive in fine weather when the retractable glass roof slides open. The menu in this part might include diver-caught scallops with chilled red pepper gazpacho and baby summer vegetables (£8.25), salmon and smoked haddock fishcakes (£10.75), cod baked with tomatoes and mushrooms in a soft herb crust (£11.75), slow-roasted shoulder of lamb with spiced aubergine caviar and mint dressing (£12.95), line-caught bass with fresh baby fennel (£14.75), and good puddings or farmhouse cheeses (£5.25). It's worth booking, particularly at weekends. The more pubby bar was elegantly reworked by designer Nina Campbell; it's an effective mix of traditional and chic, with comfortable sofas and cushioned wall seats, neatly polished floorboards and panelling, spotlights in the ceiling and lamps on elegant wooden tables, a handsome central counter, sporting prints on the yellow walls, and houseplants around the big bow windows. There's a model ship in a case just above the entrance to the dining room. A separate lunchtime bar menu might include eggs benedict or florentine (£5.25 starter, £7.75 main course), ravioli of ricotta and lemon with fresh pesto (£6.95 starter, £9.95 main course), crostini of devon crab and wild rocket salad (£7.75), chicken caesar salad (£7.95), and rib-eye burgers (£9.95); Sunday roasts. At weekends they serve brunch from 11. Well kept Black Sheep and Charles Wells Bombardier on handpump (not cheap, even for round here), and an excellent wine list, with nearly all available by the glass; various coffees, and a range of Havana cigars; friendly service from smartly uniformed young staff. There may be piped pop or jazz – though in the evenings especially it will be drowned out by the sound of animated conversation; the dining room is quieter. At the side is a nice little terrace with tables, benches and heaters. More reports please. *(Recommended by Ian Phillips, Andrew York, Joel Dobris)*

Punch ~ Lease Langlands Pearse ~ Real ale ~ Bar food (12-2.30 (3.30 Sat, 4 Sun), 7-11) ~ Restaurant ~ (020) 7581 0005 ~ Children in eating area of bar and restaurant ~ Dogs allowed in bar ~ Open 11-11; 12-10.30 Sun; closed 25-26 Dec

Albert

Victoria Street, SW1; ⊖ St James's Park

A useful spot for all-day food, this bustling 19th-c pub still has some of its original Victorian fixtures and fittings – notably the heavily cut and etched windows which run along three sides of the open-plan bar, giving the place a surprisingly airy feel. Always busy – especially on weekday lunchtimes and after work – it also has some gleaming mahogany, an ornate ceiling, and good solid comfortable furnishings. A wonderfully diverse mix of customers takes in tourists, civil servants and even the occasional MP: the division bell is rung to remind them when it's time to get back to Westminster. Service from the big island counter is efficient and friendly – particularly obliging to people from overseas. They have Courage Best (at a surprisingly friendly price for this prime location) and Directors, Fullers London Pride, Charles Wells Bombardier and a guest like Marstons Pedigree on handpump, and a good choice of wines by the glass. Promptly served, good value bar food includes sandwiches (from £4.65), salads from a cold counter, soup (£3.25), burgers (from £4.75, including vegetarian), sausage and mash or fish and chips (£6.25), and changing hot specials like turkey casserole or sweet and sour chicken (£5.75) from a servery. The no smoking upstairs restaurant has a better than average carvery (all day inc Sunday, £16.50 for three courses and coffee, £12.65 for two); it may be worth booking ahead. The handsome staircase that leads up to it is lined with portraits of prime ministers. The back bar is no smoking, other areas can feel smoky at times; piped music, fruit machine. Handily placed between Victoria and Westminster, the pub was one of the few buildings in this part of Victoria to escape the Blitz, and is one of the area's most striking sights (though it's now rather dwarfed by the surrounding faceless cliffs of dark modern glass). *(Recommended by Ian Phillips, Val and Alan Green, Tracey and Stephen Groves, R T and J C Moggridge, Michael Butler, Michael Dandy)*

Spirit Group ~ Manager Liz Cairns ~ Real ale ~ Bar food (11(12 Sun)-10) ~ Restaurant ~ (020) 7222 5577 ~ Children in restaurant and family room ~ Open 11-11; 12-10.30 Sun; closed 25 Dec

Archery Tavern 🍺

Bathurst Street, W2, opposite the Royal Lancaster hotel; ⊖ Lancaster Gate

A handy stop if you're visiting this side of Hyde Park, and a welcoming retreat from the Bayswater bustle, this nicely kept Victorian pub is next to a little mews housing some riding stables, so you can sometimes hear the sound of hooves clopping past the door. Taking its name from an archery range that occupied the site for a while in the early 19th c, it has several comfortably relaxing, pubby areas around the central servery. On the green patterned walls are a number of archery prints, as well as a history of the pub and the area, other old prints, dried hops, and quite a few plates running along shelves. Well kept Badger Best, King &Barnes Sussex and Tanglefoot on handpump, and several malt whiskies. A back room has bare boards, and a fireplace; darts, TV, a big stack of board games, cribbage, dominoes, fruit machine, piped music (loudish at times). Bar food typically includes sandwiches (from £3.95), stuffed peppers (£5.45), salmon, lemon and lime fishcakes or lamb stew and dumplings (£5.95), fish and chips (£6.25), steak and ale pie (£6.95), 8oz rump steak (£7.95), daily specials, and Sunday roasts (£6.95). There's lots more seating in front of the pub, under hanging baskets and elaborate floral displays, and some nicely old-fashioned lamps. Dogs should be kept on a lead. *(Recommended by Dr and Mrs A K Clarke, Ian Phillips, Joe Green, Thomas Agosti, Brian and Rosalie Laverick, the Didler, C J Fletcher)*

Badger ~ Manager Mac Mac Glade ~ Real ale ~ Bar food (12-3, 6-9.30 weekdays, 12-9(9.30 Sat) weekends) ~ (020) 7402 4916 ~ Children welcome ~ Dogs welcome ~ Open 11-11; 12-10.30 Sun

Argyll Arms 🍺

Argyll Street, W1; ⊖ Oxford Circus, opposite tube side exit

With its wonderful old glass and secluded little snugs, this bustling Victorian pub is much more distinctive than its Oxford Circus location might lead you to expect. Particularly unusual are the three atmospheric little cubicle rooms at the front, essentially unchanged since they were built in the 1860s. All oddly angular, they're made by wooden partitions with remarkable frosted and engraved glass, with hops trailing above. A long mirrored corridor leads to the spacious back room. Well kept Charles Wells Bombardier, Fullers London Pride, Youngs, and maybe a changing guest on handpump; they hope to have five or six beers on in the winter, and also have several malt whiskies. Served all day, changing bar food might typically include doorstep sandwiches (from £3.90), an all-day breakfast (£5.25), fish and chips (£6.95, or £9.95 for an especially big helping), and beef and ale pie (£7.50). Service is generally prompt and friendly; newspapers to read, two fruit machines. Open till midnight Thurs-Sat (and serving food through to the end of the evening), the quieter upstairs bar overlooks the pedestrianised street – and the Palladium theatre if you can see through the impressive foliage outside the window; divided into several snugs with comfortable plush easy chairs, it has swan's-neck lamps, and lots of small theatrical prints along the top of the walls. Under the current manager the piped music is quieter than it has been in the past. The pub can get very crowded (and can seem less individual on busier evenings), but there's space for drinking outside. *(Recommended by DC, the Didler, Ian Phillips, R T and J C Moggridge, Patrick Hancock, Dr and Mrs M E Wilson, Andrew York, Tracey and Stephen Groves)*

Mitchells & Butlers ~ Manager Graham Pearson ~ Real ale ~ Bar food (12-10 (11.30 Thurs-Sat)) ~ (020) 7734 6117 ~ Children in upstairs bar till 9pm ~ Open 11-11 (midnight Thurs-Sat); 12-10.30 Sun; closed 25 Dec

Black Friar

Queen Victoria Street, EC4; ⊖ ⇌ Blackfriars

Very much enjoyed by readers again this year, this distinctive old favourite stands out for its unique décor, which includes some of the best Edwardian bronze and marble art nouveau work to be found anywhere. The inner back room has big bas-relief friezes of jolly monks set into richly coloured florentine marble walls, an opulent marble-pillared inglenook fireplace, a low vaulted mosaic ceiling, gleaming mirrors, seats built into rich golden marble recesses, and tongue-in-cheek verbal embellishments such as Silence is Golden and Finery is Foolish. See if you can spot the opium-smoking hints modelled into the fireplace of the front room. Well kept Adnams, Fullers London Pride and Timothy Taylors Landlord on handpump, and a decent range of wines by the glass; fruit machine. Served all day, bar food includes sandwiches (from £3.95), soup (£3.95), a good steak sandwich (£5.50), pork and herb sausages with mash and onion gravy (£5.75), a vegetarian dish of the day (£5.95), and battered cod and chips or smoked haddock fishcakes (£6.95); prompt, friendly service. An area around the bar is no smoking. The pub does get busy (and can be smoky then), and in the evenings lots of people spill out on to the wide forecourt, near the approach to Blackfriars Bridge; there's some smart new furniture out here. If you're coming by Tube, choose your exit carefully – it's all too easy to emerge from the network of passageways and find yourself on the wrong side of the street, or marooned on a traffic island. *(Recommended by Sue Demont, Tim Barrow, the Didler, John and Gloria Isaacs, Ian Phillips, Andrew York, Dr and Mrs A K Clarke, Andy Trafford, Louise Bayly, Eithne Dandy, Kevin Blake, N R White, Susan and John Douglas, Alison and Pete, R Huggins, D Irving, E McCall, TMcLean)*

Mitchells & Butlers ~ Manager David Tate ~ Real ale ~ Bar food (12-9) ~ (020) 7236 5474 ~ Open 11-11; 12-11 (10.30 Sun) Sat; 11.30-11 winter

Cittie of Yorke 🏮

High Holborn, WC1 – find it by looking out for its big black and gold clock; ⊖ Chancery Lane

Very popular again with readers this year, this unique old place scores highly for its refreshingly cheap real ale, but most of all for its remarkable and quite unexpected back bar. Like a vast baronial hall, it has thousand-gallon wine vats resting above the gantry, big bulbous lights hanging from the soaring high-raftered roof, and an extraordinarily extended bar counter stretching off into the distance. A favourite with lawyers and City types, it does get busy in the evenings, but there's plenty of space to absorb the crowds – and indeed it's at the busiest times that the pub is at its most magnificent. Most people tend to congregate in the middle, so you may still be able to bag one of the intimate, old-fashioned and ornately carved booths that run along both sides. The triangular Waterloo fireplace, with grates on all three sides and a figure of Peace among laurels, used to stand in the Hall of Grays Inn Common Room until less obtrusive heating was introduced (thanks to the readers who sent us more thorough notes on its history). Well kept Sam Smiths OB on handpump (appealingly priced at around a pound less than the typical cost of a London pint); helpful, polite service from smartly dressed staff; fruit machine. A smaller, comfortable panelled room has lots of little prints of York and attractive brass lights, while the ceiling of the entrance hall has medieval-style painted panels and plaster York roses. Served from buffet counters in the main hall and cellar bar, bar food includes sandwiches (from £3.25), and half a dozen daily-changing hot dishes such as steak and kidney pie or lasagne (£4.95). A pub has stood on this site since 1430, though the current building owes more to the 1695 coffee house erected here behind a garden; it was reconstructed in Victorian times, using 17th-c materials and parts. *(Recommended by John Evans, Joe Green, Patrick Hancock, Dr and Mrs A K Clarke, the Didler, Paul Boot, Darren Le Poidevin, Ian Phillips, John and Gloria Isaacs, Catherine and Richard Preston, Barry Collett, Peter Coxon, Kevin Blake)*

Sam Smiths ~ Manager Stuart Browning ~ Real ale ~ Bar food (12-3, 5-9) ~ (020) 7242 7670 ~ Children in eating area of bar ~ Open 11.30(12 Sat)-11; closed Sun, bank hols, 25-26 Dec

Coopers Arms

Flood Street, SW3; ⊖ Sloane Square, but quite a walk

Notably relaxed and friendly, this spacious open-plan pub combines well liked food, beer and wine with a particularly good, properly pubby atmosphere; readers have described it as a cross between a bar and a front room. The bar food mixes familiar favourites with modern tastes to excellent effect, and might typically include leek and potato soup (£3.95), grilled goats cheese and red pepper crostini with rocket and pine nuts (£5.75), bangers and mash (£8.50), harissa lamb steak with moroccan vegetable couscous and herb yoghurt (£9.25), crumbed veal escalope with grilled mediterranean vegetable stack (£9.95), and pan-roasted bass fillet with salad niçoise and salsa verde (£10.95), with puddings like home-made white chocolate ice-cream (£3.95); pleasant helpful staff. Interesting furnishings include kitchen chairs and some dark brown plush chairs on the floorboards, a mix of nice old good-sized tables, and a pre-war sideboard and dresser; also, LNER posters and maps of Chelsea and the Thames on the walls, an enormous railway clock, a fireplace with dried flowers and a tusky boar's head, and tea-shop chandeliers. Well kept Youngs Bitter, Special and seasonal St Georges or Waggledance on handpump, with 14 wines by the glass. *(Recommended by Jarrod and Wendy Hopkinson, Ian Phillips, Tracey and Stephen Groves, Sue Demont, Tim Barrow)*

Youngs ~ Tenants Caroline and Simon Lee ~ Real ale ~ Bar food (12.30-2.30(3 Sat, Sun)3, 6.30-9.30 (not Sun evening)) ~ (020) 7376 3120 ~ Children in eating area of bar ~ Dogs allowed in bar ~ Open 11-11; 12-10.30 Sun; closed Good Fri, 25-26 Dec, 1 Jan

Cross Keys

Lawrence Street, SW3; ⊖ Sloane Square, but some distance away

Readers have enjoyed the food at this bustling Victorian pub over the last few months, but it's the eclectic décor that's really got them excited; there's an unusual array of brassware hanging from the rafters, including trumpets and a diver's helmet, as well as animal-skin prints on the furnishings, and quite a mix of sculptures, paintings and objects. The roomy high-ceilinged flagstoned bar also has an island servery, a roaring fire, lots of atmosphere, and a good range of customers; there's a light and airy conservatory-style back restaurant, with an ironic twist to its appealing gardening décor. Enjoyably upscale bar food includes crab gazpacho (£4.50), half a dozen rock oysters with shallot vinegar and rustic bread (£7.50), baked scallop and salmon en croûte (£8.50), toulouse sausages with mash and lentil jus (£8.90), and specials like braised ox tongue, gherkins and mustard sauce (£12.50), and roasted pork belly with apple, mash and calvados jus (£13.50). Courage Directors and Wadworths 6X on handpump (not cheap, even for this area), and a good choice of wines by the glass. Attentive young staff; piped music. Attractive outside with its foliage and flowers, this like most pubs in the area can be busy and lively on Saturday evenings. *(Recommended by Tracey and Stephen Groves, Derek Thomas, Andrea Rampley, Esther and John Sprinkle, David and Nina Pugsley)*

Free house ~ Licensee Oliver Delestrade ~ Bar food (12-3, 6-8 Mon-Fri (no food

weekends)) ~ Restaurant ~ (020) 7349 9111 ~ Children in restaurant ~ Dogs allowed in
bar ~ Open 12-11; 12-10.30 Sun; closed bank hols

Dog & Duck ◖

Bateman Street, on corner with Frith Street, W1; ✪ Tottenham Court Road/Leicester
Square

Afternoons are probably the best time to fully appreciate the décor of this pint-sized
corner house – in the evenings it can be very busy indeed, packing a lot of
atmosphere into a small space. Essentially unchanged for 40 years, it's a real Soho
landmark, friendly and welcoming, with some interesting detail and individual
touches. On the floor near the door is an engaging mosaic showing a dog with its
tongue out in hot pursuit of a duck; the same theme is embossed on some of the
shiny tiles that frame the heavy old advertising mirrors. There are some high stools
by the ledge along the back wall, and further seats in a slightly roomier area at one
end; the piped music is usually drowned out by the good-natured chatter. The
unusual little bar counter serves very well kept Fullers London Pride, Timothy
Taylors Landlord, Youngs and maybe a guest like Adnams; also Addlestone's cider,
and decent wines by the glass. There's a fire in winter. Served all day, good value
bar snacks include sausage sandwiches (£4.50), summer salads, and fish and chips
(£6.95). In good weather especially, most people tend to spill on to the bustling
street, though even when the pub is at its busiest you may find plenty of space in
the rather cosy upstairs bar. One reader has found they may not always open
promptly. The pub is said to be where George Orwell celebrated when the
American Book of the Month Club chose *Animal Farm* as its monthly selection.
Ronnie Scott's jazz club is near by. *(Recommended by Joe Green, Patrick Hancock, LM,
Dr and Mrs M E Wilson, Darren Le Poidevin, Tim Maddison, Dr and Mrs A K Clarke,
Ian Phillips, Mike Gorton, R Huggins, D Irving, E McCall, T McLean, C J Fletcher, Tracey and
Stephen Groves)*

Mitchells & Butlers ~ Real ale ~ Bar food (12-9) ~ (020) 7494 0697 ~ Open 12-11;
12-10.30 Sun; closed 25 Dec

Eagle ⊗ ⟙

Farringdon Road, EC1; opposite Bowling Green Lane car park;
✪ ⇌ Farringdon/Old Street

We're surprised not to have had more reports on this excellent food pub this year,
but are happy to confirm it's business as usual. There's a real emphasis on the
distinctive mediterranean-style meals, but despite that the atmosphere always feels
chatty and pubby, with a buzzing informality that belies the quality of the cooking.
Served from an open kitchen that dominates the busy single room, typical dishes
might include a genovese minestrone soup (£5), bucatini piccoli with roast fennel,
chilli, garlic and lemon (£7), marinated rump steak sandwich (£8.50), grilled napoli
sausages with green lentils and mustard leaves (£9.50), poached smoked haddock
with mash and soft boiled egg (£10.50), grilled bass with turnip tops, chilli and
aïoli or lamb chops with arrocina beans and tapenade (£12), and grilled sirloin
steak with sautéed potatoes and peppers (£13); they also do unusual spanish,
sardinian or goats milk cheeses (£6.50), and portuguese custard tarts (£1.20). On
weekday lunchtimes especially, dishes from the blackboard menu can run out or
change fairly quickly, so it really is worth getting here as early as you possibly can if
you're hoping to eat. Furnishings are basic but stylish – school chairs, a random
assortment of tables, a couple of sofas on bare boards, and modern paintings on the
walls (there's an art gallery upstairs, with direct access from the bar). During the
week it's generally very busy indeed around meal times (and can occasionally be
slightly smoky then), so isn't the sort of place you'd go for a quiet dinner, or a
smart night out; it's generally quieter at weekends. Well kept Charles Wells Eagle
and Bombardier on handpump, good wines including a dozen by the glass, good
coffee, and properly made cocktails; piped music (sometimes loud). The Eagle was
London's first gastropub, and its continued success does mean you may have to

wait for a table, or at least not be shy about sharing. *(Recommended by Ian Phillips, Dr and Mrs M E Wilson, Jo Lilley, Simon Calvert, Darren Le Poidevin, Richard Siebert, Tim Maddison, Patrick Hancock)*

Free house ~ Licensee Michael Belben ~ Real ale ~ Bar food (12.30-3(3.30 weekends), 6.30-10.30 (not Sun)) ~ (020) 7837 1353 ~ Children welcome ~ Dogs welcome ~ Open 12-11(5 Sun); closed Sun evening, bank hols and a week at Christmas

Grapes

Shepherd Market, W1; ⊖ Green Park

Engagingly old-fashioned and genuinely atmospheric, this characterful pub is enjoyable at lunchtime when you can more easily take in its traditional charms, but is perhaps at its best when it's so very busy in the evenings, and the cheery bustle rather adds to the allure. The dimly lit bar has plenty of plush red furnishings, stuffed birds and fish in glass display cases, wooden floors and panelling, a welcoming coal fire, and a snug little alcove at the back. A good range of six or seven well kept beers on handpump (as in most Mayfair pubs fairly pricey) usually takes in Bass, Flowers IPA, Fullers London Pride, Marstons Pedigree and Timothy Taylors Landlord; fruit machine. No food, but, very appealingly, they say that customers are welcome to bring in their own if they're buying drinks. Service can sometimes slow down at the busiest times, and it can get smoky then; you'll generally see smart-suited drinkers spilling onto the square outside. The pub is in the heart of Shepherd Market, one of central London's best-kept secrets. *(Recommended by Patrick Hancock, the Didler, Barry and Anne, J F M and M West, Thomas Agosti, Dr and Mrs M E Wilson, Eric Robinson, Jacqueline Pratt, Ian Phillips)*

Free house ~ Licensees Gill and Eric Lewis ~ Real ale ~ Open 11(12 Sat)-11; 12-10.30 Sun

Grenadier

Wilton Row, SW1; the turning off Wilton Crescent looks prohibitive, but the barrier and watchman are there to keep out cars; walk straight past – the pub is just around the corner; ⊖ Hyde Park Corner/Knightsbridge

Patriotically painted in red, white and blue, this very snug and individual pub was once the mess for the officers of the Duke of Wellington. His portrait hangs above the fireplace, alongside neat prints of Guardsmen through the ages. It doesn't take many people to fill up the tiny bar, but despite its charms it rarely gets too crowded, so you should generally be able to plonk yourself on one of the stools or wooden benches. Well kept Charles Wells Bombardier, Courage Best, Fullers London Pride, and Youngs from handpumps at the rare pewter-topped bar counter, though on Sundays especially you'll find several of the customers here to sample their famous bloody marys, made to a unique recipe. The bar food has rather upped its game under the new manager; everything is home-made, down to the batter on the fish fingers. Snacks like a pork and leek sausage (£1 each), or bowls of chips (£2) and nachos (£3.50) are popular with after-work drinkers, and they also do more substantial things like sandwiches (from £4.50), english breakfast (£6.50), sausage and mash (£7.50), aberdeen angus burger with goats cheese and red onion relish (£8.25), and fresh fish and chips (£8.75); choice of Sunday roasts. At the back is an intimate restaurant. There's a single table outside in the peaceful mews. Thanks to the active poltergeist this is said to be London's most haunted pub. *(Recommended by Jason Reynolds, Ian Phillips, Jo Lilley, Simon Calvert, N R White)*

Spirit Group ~ Manager Chris Buckley ~ Real ale ~ Bar food (12-2.30, 6-9.30) ~ Restaurant ~ (020) 7235 3074 ~ Dogs allowed in bar ~ Open 12-11(10.30 Sun)

Our pocket London guide published last year, besides including many of the pubs in this chapter (a few of them described in more detail), adds another 150 or so places which are not listed here: *Best London Pubs and Bars*, Ebury Press, £5.99.

Guinea

Bruton Place, W1; ⊖ Bond Street/Green Park/Oxford Circus/Piccadilly Circus

Even on winter weekday evenings the smart mews outside this handily-positioned little pub acts as something of an overflow – it can be standing room only inside. The lunchtime bar food is the main draw, and in particular their award-winning steak and kidney pie (£6.95), which easily lives up to the hype; they also do a steak and mushroom pie, but beyond that the menu is limited to a vegetarian sandwich (£4.95) and rather elaborate grilled ciabattas (£6.95; these have won prizes too). Well kept Youngs Bitter, Special, and seasonal brews from the striking bar counter, which has some nice wrought-iron work above it. The look of the place is appealingly simple, with bare boards, yellow walls, old-fashioned prints, and a red-planked ceiling with raj fans, but the atmosphere is chatty and civilised, with plenty of suited workers from Mayfair offices (it's quieter at the weekend). Three cushioned wooden seats and tables are tucked to the left of the entrance to the bar, with a couple more in a snug area at the back, underneath a big old clock; most people tend to prop themselves against a little shelf running along the side of the small room. Take care to pick the right entrance – it's all too easy to walk into the quite separate upscale Guinea Grill which takes up much of the same building; uniformed doormen will politely redirect you if you've picked the door to that by mistake. *(Recommended by Ian Phillips, R Huggins, D Irving, E McCall, T McLean, the Didler, Mayur Shah, Andy and Jill Kassube)*

Youngs ~ Manager Carl Smith ~ Real ale ~ Bar food (12.30-2.30 Mon-Fri only) ~ Restaurant ~ (020) 7409 1728 ~ Children in restaurant ~ Open 11-11; 6.30-11 Sat; closed Sat lunchtime, all day Sun, bank hols

Jerusalem Tavern ★ ◀

Britton Street, EC1; ⊖ ⇌ Farringdon

A reader visiting this carefully restored old coffee house for the first time admits to becoming rather over-excited and taking far too many photos, so overwhelmed were they by the atmosphere, the food, and of course the beer. Now one of our most popular London main entries, it's the only place to stock the whole range of brews from the Suffolk-based St Peters other than the brewery itself, with half a dozen tapped from casks behind the little bar counter, and the rest available in their elegant, distinctively shaped bottles. Depending on the season you'll find St Peters Best, Fruit Beer, Golden Ale, Grapefruit, Strong, Porter, Wheat Beer, Winter and Spiced Ales, and you can buy them to take away too. Particularly inviting when it's candlelit on a cold winter's evening, the pub is a vivid re-creation of a dark 18th-c tavern, seeming so genuinely old that you'd hardly guess the work was done only a few years ago. The current building was developed around 1720, originally as a merchant's house, then becoming a clock and watchmaker's. It still has the shop front added in 1810, immediately behind which is a light little room with a couple of wooden tables and benches, a stack of *Country Life* magazines, and some remarkable old tiles on the walls at either side. This leads to the tiny dimly lit bar, which has a couple of unpretentious tables on the bare boards, and another up some stairs on a discreetly precarious-feeling though perfectly secure balcony – a prized vantage point. A plainer back room has a few more tables, a fireplace, and a stuffed fox in a case. There's a relaxed, chatty feel in the evenings, although these days it's getting harder to bag a seat here then, and it can feel crowded at times. Blackboards list the simple but well liked lunchtime food: good big doorstep sandwiches (from £5), and a couple of changing hot dishes such as chicken, bacon and asparagus pie, tuna niçoise salad, or stuffed aubergines (all between £6 and £8). The menu depends on what the helpful staff have picked up that day from the local markets, including Smithfield. There may be a couple of tables outside. Note the pub is once again closed at weekends. The brewery's headquarters in South Elmham is a main entry in our Suffolk chapter. *(Recommended by Paul Hopton, Ian Phillips, Sue Demont, Tim Barrow, Patrick Hancock, Dr and Mrs A K Clarke, the Didler, Brian and Rosalie Laverick, Anthony Longden, R Huggins, D Irving, E McCall, T McLean, Mike Gorton, Nigel and Sue Foster, Esther and John Sprinkle, Andy and Jill Kassube, Jo Lilley, Simon Calvert, Joe Green)*

St Peters ~ Manager Steve Medniuk ~ Real ale ~ Bar food (11.30-3) ~ (020) 7490 4281 ~
Children welcome ~ Dogs allowed in bar ~ Open 11-11; closed weekends and
bank hols

Lamb ★ ◀

Lamb's Conduit Street, WC1; ⊖ Holborn

'A treasure to be preserved' wrote one reader after a recent visit to this old
favourite. It's one of London's most famous pubs, standing out for its unique
Victorian fittings and atmosphere, with the highlight the bank of cut-glass
swivelling 'snob-screens' all the way around the U-shaped bar counter. Sepia
photographs of 1890s actresses on the ochre panelled walls, and traditional cast-
iron-framed tables with neat brass rails around the rim add to the overall effect.
Consistently well kept Youngs Bitter, Special and seasonal brews like St Georges
and Waggledance on handpump, and around 40 different malt whiskies. Lunchtime
bar food includes a popular hot ham baguette, with the meat carved on the counter
(weekdays only, £4.95), as well as ploughman's (£4.95), vegetable curry (£5.95),
sausage and mash (£6.35), fish and chips (£6.75), good pies such as beef and ale or
pork and cider (£7.45), and cajun chicken (£8.95); Sunday roasts (£6.95). Shove-
ha'penny, cribbage, dominoes; no machines or music. A scouple of areas are no
smoking, including the snug room at the back. There are slatted wooden seats in
front, and more in a little courtyard beyond. It can get very busy, especially in the
evenings, but can be rather peaceful after lunch. Like the street, the pub is named
for the Kentish clothmaker William Lamb who brought fresh water to Holborn in
1577. Note they don't allow children. *(Recommended by Ian Phillips, Paul Boot,
Darren Le Poidevin, Derek Thomas, the Didler, C J Fletcher, Joe Green, Patrick Hancock,
Mike Gorton, James A Waller, Anthony Longden, Kevin Blake, Sue Demont, Tim Barrow,
Dr and Mrs M E Wilson)*

Youngs ~ Manager Michael Hehir ~ Real ale ~ Bar food (12-2.30, 6-9(not Sun evening)) ~
(020) 7405 0713 ~ Open 11-11; 12-4, 7-10.30 Sun

Lamb & Flag ◀ £

Rose Street, WC2, off Garrick Street; ⊖ Covent Garden/Leicester Square

As ever this historic Covent Garden pub has been much enjoyed by readers this
year, who particularly like its lively atmosphere and old-fashioned style. Unspoilt
and in places rather basic, it's enormously popular with after-work drinkers and
visitors; it can be empty at 5pm and heaving by 6, and even in winter you'll find an
overflow of people drinking and chatting in the little alleyways outside. The
upstairs Dryden Room is often less crowded than downstairs, and has jazz every
Sunday evening. Access throughout has been improved in recent years; the more
spartan front bar now leads easily into the back, without altering too much the
snug feel of the place. The low-ceilinged back bar has high-backed black settles and
an open fire, and in Regency times was known as the Bucket of Blood from the
bare-knuckle prize-fights held here. Half a dozen well kept real ales typically
include Charles Wells Bombardier, Courage Best and Directors, Marstons Pedigree,
Ridleys IPA, and Youngs Special; as in most pubs round here, the beer isn't cheap,
but on weekdays between 11 and 5 you should find at least one offered at a
substantial saving. Also, a good few malt whiskies. The bar food – lunchtimes only
– is simple but very good value, including soup (£2.50), toasted sandwiches (£2.50),
filled baked potatoes (£3.50), ploughman's or good doorstep sandwiches (£3.95), a
few daily changing specials like toad in the hole, steak and kidney pie or fish and
chips (£4.25), and a choice of roasts (£6.50); pleasant service. There's a TV in the
front bar. The pub has a lively and well documented history: Dryden was nearly
beaten to death by hired thugs outside, and Dickens made fun of the Middle
Temple lawyers who frequented it when he was working in nearby Catherine
Street. *(Recommended by David Carr, Andrea Rampley, Mike Gorton, Dr and Mrs A K Clarke,
Jo Lilley, Simon Calvert, Jarrod and Wendy Hopkinson, Ian Phillips, the Didler, R T and
J C Moggridge, Roger and Jenny Huggins, Barry and Anne, LM, Derek Thomas,*

*Mrs Hazel Rainer, Fr Robert Marsh, Anthony Longden, B and M Kendall, N R White,
Neil Powell)*

Free house ~ Licensees Terry Archer and Adrian and Sandra Zimmerman ~ Real ale ~ Bar
food (11-3 weekdays, 11-5 Sat, 12-5 Sun) ~ (020) 7497 9504 ~ Children in eating area of
bar 11-5 only ~ Jazz Sun evenings ~ Open 11-11(10.45 Fri, Sat); 12-10.30 Sun; closed
24-26 Dec, 1 Jan

Lord Moon of the Mall 🍴 £
Whitehall, SW1; ↔ ⇌ Charing Cross

More individual than many Wetherspoons pubs, this well run and nicely converted
former bank is a useful pit-stop for families and visitors touring the nearby sights,
not least because the food is far cheaper than you'll find anywhere else in the area.
The impressive main room has a splendid high ceiling and quite an elegant feel, with
old prints, big arched windows looking out over Whitehall, and a huge painting that
seems to show a well-to-do 18th-c gentleman; in fact it's Tim Martin, founder of the
Wetherspoons chain. Once through an arch the style is more recognisably
Wetherspoons, with a couple of neatly tiled areas and bookshelves opposite the long
bar; silenced fruit machines, trivia, and now a cash machine. They usually have
seven or eight real ales, with the regulars Fullers London Pride, Greene King Abbot,
Marstons Pedigree and Shepherd Neame Spitfire; the guests can be quite unusual,
and the prices for all of them are much less than the London norm. They have
occasional beer festivals, and also keep Weston's cider. Bar food – served all day – is
from the standard Wetherspoons menu: sandwiches (from £2.39), five bean chilli
(£5.75), bangers and mash (£5.79), aberdeen angus steak pie (£5.99), a big mexican
platter for sharing (£7.99), and children's meals; after 2pm (all day weekends) they
usually have a two-for-one meal offer for £6.99. The terms of the licence rule out
fried food. Service can slow down at lunchtimes, when it does get busy. The back
doors (now only an emergency exit) were apparently built as a secret entrance for
the bank's account holders living in Buckingham Palace (Edward VII had an account
here from the age of three); the area by here is no smoking. As you come out,
Nelson's Column is immediately to the left, and Big Ben a walk of ten minutes or so
to the right. *(Recommended by Ian Phillips, Sue Demont, Tim Barrow, Dr and Mrs A K Clarke,
Roger and Jenny Huggins, Piotr Chodzko-Zajko, Dr and Mrs M E Wilson, Barry Collett,
Meg and Colin Hamilton, Mrs Hazel Rainer, B Shelley, Joe Green)*

Wetherspoons ~ Manager Mathew Gold ~ Real ale ~ Bar food (10-10; 12-9.30 Sun) ~
(020) 7839 7701 ~ Children welcome till 7pm if eating ~ Open 10-11; 10-10.30 Sun

Nags Head 🍴
Kinnerton Street, SW1; ↔ Knightsbridge

One of London's most unspoilt pubs (and indeed one of our own favourites), this
quaint little gem has the feel of an old-fashioned local in a sleepy country village. So
calming is the atmosphere, and so utterly removed from modern life does it feel that
you can scarcely believe you're only minutes from Harrods and the hordes of
Knightsbridge; its timeless appeal is summed up rather well by a reader who found
it 'like an Ealing comedy film set'. Hidden away in an attractive and peaceful mews,
it rarely gets too busy or crowded, and there's a snugly relaxed and cosy feel in the
small, panelled and low-ceilinged front room, where friendly regulars sit chatting
around the unusual sunken bar counter. There's a log-effect gas fire in an old
cooking range (seats by here are generally snapped up pretty quickly), then a
narrow passage leads down steps to an even smaller back bar with stools and a mix
of comfortable seats. The well kept Adnams Best, Broadside and seasonal brews are
pulled on attractive 19th-c china, pewter and brass handpumps, while other
interesting old features include a 1930s what-the-butler-saw machine and a one-
armed bandit that takes old pennies. The piped music is rather individual: often
jazz, folk or 1920s-40s show tunes. There are a few seats and sometimes a couple
of tables outside. Bar food (less distinctive than the rest of the pub) includes
sandwiches (from £4), ploughman's or salads (from £6.50), sausage, mash and

beans, chilli con carne, steak and mushroom pie, daily specials, and a choice of roasts (£6.95); there's a £1.50 surcharge added to all dishes in the evenings, and at weekends. Service is friendly and efficient. Many readers will be delighted to learn they have a fairly hard-line policy on mobile phone use. *(Recommended by Andrea Rampley, the Didler, Derek Thomas, Pete Baker, Ian Phillips, Sue Demont, Tim Barrow, Giles and Annie Francis, Michael Butler, Phil and Sally Gorton, LM, John and Gloria Isaacs)*

Free house ~ Licensee Kevin Moran ~ Real ale ~ Bar food (11-9.30) ~ No credit cards ~ (020) 7235 1135 ~ Children in eating area of bar ~ Dogs allowed in bar ~ Open 11-11; 12-10.30 Sun

Old Bank of England ♀
Fleet Street, EC4; ⊖ Temple

A recent refurbishment has left this spectacularly converted former branch of the Bank of England looking more impressive than ever, the new red colour scheme somehow better suiting the gilt and creating a wonderful air of opulence. The soaring, spacious bar takes your breath away when you enter: three gleaming chandeliers hang from the exquisitely plastered ceiling, high above an unusually tall island bar counter, crowned with a clock. The end wall has big paintings and murals that look like 18th-c depictions of Justice, but in fact feature members of the Fuller, Smith and Turner families, who run the brewery the pub belongs to. There are well polished dark wooden furnishings, plenty of framed prints and, despite the grandeur, some surprisingly cosy corners, with screens between some of the tables creating an unexpectedly intimate feel. Tables in a quieter galleried section upstairs offer a birds-eye view of the action, and some smaller rooms (used mainly for functions) open off; several areas are no smoking. Well kept Fullers Chiswick, ESB, London Pride and seasonal brews on handpump, a choice of malt whiskies, and around a dozen wines by the glass. Available all day, the good bar food has an emphasis on home-made pies such as sweet potato and goats cheese (£6.95), chicken, ham and leek (£7.25), and steak and ale (£7.80), but also includes sandwiches (from £3.75), soup (£3.25), welsh rarebit (£4.50), bangers and mash (£6.50), beer battered cod (£7.95), chicken cordon bleu (£8.25), and 10oz rump steak (£10.95); they now do full afternoon teas (£14.95). At lunchtimes the piped music is generally classical or easy listening; it's louder and livelier after work, when the pub can get busy. In winter the pub is easy to spot by the Olympic-style torches blazing outside the rather austere Italianate building. Note they don't allow children, and are closed at weekends. Pies have a long if rather dubious pedigree in this area; it was in the vaults and tunnels below the Old Bank and the surrounding buildings that Sweeney Todd butchered the clients destined to provide the fillings in his mistress Mrs Lovett's nearby pie shop. *(Recommended by Paul Boot, Ian Phillips, Dr and Mrs A K Clarke, the Didler, Kevin Blake, Barry Collett)*

Fullers ~ Manager James Carman ~ Real ale ~ Bar food (12-9(8 Fri)) ~ Restaurant ~ (020) 7430 2255 ~ Open 11-11; closed weekends, bank hols

Olde Cheshire Cheese
Wine Office Court, off 145 Fleet Street, EC4; ⊖ ≹ Blackfriars

This atmospheric 17th-c former chop house is the London pub we've had most reports on this year. Readers very much enjoy exploring its warren of dark, historic little rooms, and though it can get busy with tourists, there are plenty of hidden corners to absorb the crowds. Over the years Congreve, Pope, Voltaire, Thackeray, Dickens, Conan Doyle, Yeats and perhaps Dr Johnson have called in, and many parts appear hardly to have changed since. The unpretentious rooms have bare wooden benches built in to the walls, bare boards and, on the ground floor, high beams, crackly old black varnish, Victorian paintings on the dark brown walls, and big open fires in winter. A particularly snug room is the tiny one on the right as you enter, but the most rewarding bit is the Cellar Bar, down steep narrow stone steps that look as if they're only going to lead to the loo, but in fact take you to an unexpected series of cosy areas with stone walls and ceilings, and some secluded alcoves. Well kept Sam Smiths OB on handpump, as usual for this brewery, extraordinarily well priced (almost £1 less than beers in some other London pubs). Usually served all day, well liked bar food includes good sandwiches or hot panini (from £3.25), good value straightforward dishes like shepherd's pie or pasta (£5), and some more expensive specials; they also do a lunchtime pie and mash buffet (12-2) in the cellar bar (part of which is no smoking then). Helpful service from smartly dressed staff. It's much quieter at weekends than during the week. In the early 20th c the pub was well known for its famous parrot that for over 40 years entertained princes, ambassadors and other distinguished guests; she's still around today, stuffed and silent, in the restaurant on the ground floor. *(Recommended by Richard Marjoram, Jason Reynolds, Dr and Mrs A K Clarke, Ian Phillips, Steve Kirby, Patrick Hancock, the Didler, Dr J Barrie Jones, Simon and Sally Small, Barry and Anne, Mike Gorton, Andy Trafford, Louise Bayly, Bruce Bird, Barry Collett, Jo Lilley, Simon Calvert, N R White, Anthony Longden, Tich Critchlow, Alison and Pete)*

Sam Smiths ~ Manager Gordon Garrity ~ Real ale ~ Bar food (12-9 Mon-Fri; 12-5 Sat; not Sun (though restaurant open then)) ~ Restaurant ~ (020) 7353 6170/4388 ~ Children in eating area of bar and restaurant ~ Open 11-11; 12-3 Sun; closed Sun evening

Olde Mitre 🍺 £

Ely Place, EC1; the easiest way to find it is from the narrow passageway beside 8 Hatton Garden; ⊖ Chancery Lane

A reader recently revisited this atmospheric old tavern because it had once been his father's local, and was delighted to find everything appeared to be as it had been 40 years ago, right down to the lampshades. A real hidden treasure, the pub can be notoriously difficult to find; it's best approached from Hatton Garden, where an easily missed sign on a lamppost points the way down a narrow alley. The cosy small rooms have lots of dark panelling, as well as antique settles and – particularly in the back room, where there are more seats – old local pictures and so forth. It gets good-naturedly packed between 12.30 and 2.15, filling up again in the early evening, but in the early afternoons and by around nine becomes a good deal more tranquil. An upstairs room, mainly used for functions, may double as an overflow at peak periods. Well kept Adnams Bitter and Broadside, Tetleys and a carefully chosen guest like Orkney Dark Isle; obliging staff. No music, TV or machines – the only games here are darts, cribbage and dominoes. Served all day, bar snacks are limited to scotch eggs or pork pies (£1), and really good value toasted sandwiches with cheese, ham, pickle or tomato (£1.50). There are some pot plants and jasmine in the narrow yard between the pub and St Ethelreda's church. Note the pub doesn't open at weekends. The iron gates that guard one entrance to Ely Place are a reminder of the days when the law in this district was administered by the Bishops of Ely. *(Recommended by Ian Phillips, Dr J Barrie Jones, Patrick Hancock, the Didler, Steve Kirby, R Huggins, D Irving, E McCall, T McLean, Dr and Mrs A K Clarke, Peter Coxon, Tracey and Stephen Groves, Neil Powell, Joe Green)*

Spirit Group ~ Manager Eamon Scott ~ Real ale ~ Bar food (11.30-9.30) ~ (020) 7405 4751 ~ Open 11-11; closed weekends, bank hols

Princess Louise

High Holborn, WC1; ⊖ Holborn

The finest craftsmen of the day created this splendid Victorian gin-palace, which survives essentially intact. The gloriously opulent décor includes magnificent etched and gilt mirrors, brightly coloured and fruity-shaped tiles, and slender portland stone columns soaring towards the lofty and deeply moulded crimson and gold plaster ceiling. Quieter corners have comfortable green plush seats and banquettes. Its architecural appeal is unique (even the gents' has its own preservation order) but the pub also scores for its friendly, bustling atmosphere, and good value food and drink. Very nicely priced Sam Smiths OB on handpump from the long main bar, which might also have several wines by the glass; good service. Hot food is served upstairs (open only on weekdays), with things like home-made lasagne and pies

(£5.50), but downstairs sandwiches, baguettes and ploughman's (£5.25) are available pretty much all day. Though it can get crowded during the week (especially in winter), it's usually quieter later on in the evening, or on a Saturday lunchtime. *(Recommended by Dr and Mrs A K Clarke, Patrick Hancock, the Didler, Ian Phillips, C J Fletcher, Tracey and Stephen Groves)*

Sam Smiths ~ Licensee Campbell Mackay ~ Real ale ~ Bar food (12-2.30, 6-8.30) ~ (020) 7405 8816 ~ Dogs allowed in bar ~ Open 11-11; 12-11 Sat; 12-10.30 Sun; closed 25-26 Dec, 1 Jan

Red Lion ◀

Waverton Street, W1; ⊖ Green Park

Standing out for its very relaxed and distinctly un-London atmosphere, this comfortably civilised pub is in one of Mayfair's quietest and prettiest corners, where the sudden appearance of what appears to be a smart village local is a real but welcome surprise. On some evenings after work it can be very busy indeed, but it always keeps its warmly cosy feel. The main L-shaped bar has small winged settles on the partly carpeted scrubbed floorboards, and London prints below the high shelf of china on its dark-panelled walls. Well kept beers such as Charles Wells Bombardier, Fullers London Pride, Greene King IPA and Youngs Ordinary on handpump, and they do rather good bloody marys (with a daunting Very Spicy option); also a dozen malt whiskies, and around 14 wines by the glass. Good, honest bar food (served from a corner at the front) includes sandwiches (from £3.45; toasted from £4), soup (£2.95), ploughman's (£5.50), cumberland susage and mash (£5.95), battered haddock (£6.45), goats cheese penne pasta (£6.95), steak and stilton pie (£7.95), and daily specials. The restaurant is no smoking. The gents' usually has a copy of *The Times* at eye level. On Saturday evenings they generally have a pianist. *(Recommended by Thomas Agosti, Dr and Mrs A K Clarke, Dr and Mrs M E Wilson, Ian Phillips, Tracey and Stephen Groves, Barry Collett)*

Spirit Group ~ Manager Greg Peck ~ Real ale ~ Bar food (12-3 (not Sat), 6-9.30) ~ Restaurant ~ (020) 7499 1307 ~ Children welcome ~ Dogs allowed in bar ~ Piano Sat evening ~ Open 11.30-11; 6-11 Sat; 12-3, 6-10.30 Sun; closed Sat am, all day 25-26 Dec, 1 Jan

Red Lion ◀

Duke of York Street, SW1; ⊖ Piccadilly Circus

Filling up fast thanks to its busy location in the heart of the West End, this is perhaps central London's most perfectly preserved Victorian pub. 'Mirrors, mirrors, mirrors' observed one reader, and the gleaming glasswork isn't the only feature of note: the series of small rooms also has a good deal of polished mahogany, as well as crystal chandeliers and cut and etched windows, and a striking ornamental plaster ceiling. There's a good, bustling atmosphere, so it's worth getting here at opening time to appreciate its period charms more peacefully. Five well kept real ales such as Adnams, Fullers London Pride, Greene King IPA, Hook Norton Old Hooky, and Wadworths 6X; friendly efficient service. Simple lunchtime snacks include sandwiches (£3), filled baguettes (£4), and sausage and chips (£6); diners have priority on a few of the front tables, and there's a minuscule upstairs eating area. It can be very crowded at lunchtime (try inching through to the back room where there's sometimes more space); many customers spill out on to the pavement, in front of a mass of foliage and flowers cascading down the wall. The piped music can be loud at times. No children inside. *(Recommended by the Didler, Mayur Shah, Ian Phillips, Sue Demont, Tim Barrow, Roger and Jenny Huggins, Dr and Mrs M E Wilson, Mike Gorton)*

Mitchells & Butlers ~ Manager Michael Brown ~ Real ale ~ Bar food (12-3) ~ Restaurant ~ (020) 7321 0782 ~ Open 11.30(12 Sat)-11; closed Sun; bank hols

Seven Stars ◗

Carey Street, WC2; ❷ Holborn (just as handy from Temple or Chancery Lane, but the walk through Lincoln's Inn Fields can be rather pleasant)

Lack of space has been the only issue readers have had with this cosy little pub since the current licencees arrived, so it's good news that they're expanding into the neighbouring building, until recently an antique shop specialising in secondhand legal wigs. What's especially nice is that as this next-door property's shopfront was quite a draw for tourists, it will continue to display its original name and wigs in the window, although hidden behind will be more space for eating and drinking. Facing the back of the Law Courts, the pub has long been a favourite with lawyers and reporters covering notable trials nearby, so its other two unspoilt little rooms have plenty of caricatures of barristers and judges on the red-painted walls, along with posters of legal-themed British films, big ceiling fans, and a relaxed, intimate atmosphere; checked tablecloths add a quirky, almost continental touch. The landlady is quite an authority on food (she recently presented a BBC series on the topic), so several of the tables are set for eating the good bar food, served all day from a changing blackboard menu that might include things like half a dozen oysters (£6), extra mature cheddar with relish, salad and oatcakes (£6.50), Country Scramble (a chunk of sourdough with smoked pork, sliced potato, onion, parsley and thyme in eggs, £7.50), caesar salad with poached egg or charcuterie with artisan bread and onion relish (£8), free-range norfolk chicken stew with barley (£8.50), minced chuck steak hamburger (£8.75), and plenty of seasonal game; at times you may also find vintage port with fruit cake. Well kept Adnams Best and Broadside on handpump, with a couple of changing guests like Fullers London Pride and Harveys Sussex; service is prompt and very friendly. The pub can fill up very quickly, and on busy evenings customers sometimes spill on to the quiet road in front; it generally quietens down after 8pm. The Elizabethan stairs up to the lavatories are rather steep, but there's a good strong handrail. The pub cat may take umbrage if you move the newspaper he likes to sleep on (indeed one reader describes the pussy as pushy). *(Recommended by Patrick Hancock, Ian Phillips, LM, Sue Demont, Tim Barrow, R Huggins, D Irving, E McCall, T McLean, the Didler, Jarrod and Wendy Hopkinson, Mike Gorton, Barry Collett, Ian and Nita Cooper)*

Free house ~ Licensee Roxy Beaujolais ~ Real ale ~ Bar food (12-9) ~ (020) 7242 8521 ~ Dogs allowed in bar ~ Open 11-11; 12-11.30 Sat; closed Sun, and some bank hols (usually inc Christmas)

Star ◗

Belgrave Mews West, SW1, behind the German Embassy, off Belgrave Square; ❷ Knightsbridge

Said to be where the Great Train Robbery was planned, this timeless pub has a restful local feel outside peak times (when it can be busy), and always impresses in summer with its astonishing array of hanging baskets and flowering tubs. The small entry room, which also has the food servery, has stools by the counter and tall windows; an arch leads to a side room with swagged curtains, well polished wooden tables and chairs, heavy upholstered settles, globe lighting and raj fans. The back room has button-back built-in wall seats, and there's a similarly furnished room upstairs (particularly enjoyed by readers, though it's not always open). Very well kept Fullers Chiswick, ESB, London Pride and seasonal brews on handpump. Under the new managers the seasonally changing bar menu might include ham, egg and chips or sausage of the week and mash (£6.45), mediterranean vegetable bake, beer-battered cod or pies like steak and ale or lamb and apricot (£7.25), and rib-eye steak (£11.45). *(Recommended by Sue Demont, Tim Barrow, Ian Phillips, the Didler, Mike Tucker, N R White)*

Fullers ~ Managers Jason and Karen Tinklin ~ Real ale ~ Bar food (12-2.30, 6-9.30(9 Sat, 8.30 Sun)) ~ (020) 7235 3019 ~ Children welcome ~ Dogs allowed in bar ~ Open 11-11; 12-10.30 Sun

Westminster Arms ◀

Storey's Gate, SW1; ⊖ Westminster

If you hear something a bit like a telephone bell in this friendly and unpretentious Westminster local, it's the Division Bell, reminding MPs to go back across the road to vote. It's the handiest pub for the Abbey as well as the Houses of Parliament, and can be packed after work with government staff and researchers, but the turnover of customers is usually quite quick, and there's an appealing mix of people. A good range of seven well kept real ales takes in Adnams Best and Broadside, Ansells, Fullers London Pride, Greene King Abbot, Youngs and a guest like Thwaites Lancaster Bomber; they also do decent wines, and several malt whiskies. The plain main bar has simple old-fashioned furnishings, with proper tables on the wooden floors, a good deal of panelling, and a fruit machine; there's not a lot of room, so go early for a seat. Bar food is served in the downstairs wine bar (a good retreat from the ground-floor bustle), with some of the tables in cosy booths; typical dishes include filled baguettes (£4), various salads or ploughman's (£6.50), cottage pie (£6.50), steak and kidney pie (£6.95), fish and chips (£7.95), and daily specials; you can get most of the same dishes in the more formal upstairs restaurant, but they may be slightly more expensive. Both these areas are no smoking at lunchtime, and there's piped music (but not generally in the main bar). There are a couple of tables by the street outside. *(Recommended by Sue Demont, Tim Barrow, Ian Phillips, Tracey and Stephen Groves, the Didler, Mayur Shah, Dr and Mrs A K Clarke, Jarrod and Wendy Hopkinson, Mike Begley)*

Free house ~ Licensees Gerry and Marie Dolan ~ Real ale ~ Bar food (12-7 weekdays, 12-4 Sat, Sun) ~ Restaurant (weekday lunchtimes (not Weds)) ~ (020) 7222 8520 ~ Children in eating area of bar and restaurant ~ Open 11-11; 11-6 Sat; 12-5 Sun; closed 25 Dec

EAST LONDON Map 12

Crown ♀

Grove Road/Old Ford Road, E3; ⊖ Mile End

Like its sister pub the Duke of Cambridge (see North London main entries), this idiosyncratic pub stands out for its painstakingly sourced organic food and drinks, offering flavours you won't come across anywhere else. Despite the big windows, it's dim inside, thanks to the very dark ceiling, some dark brown walls, and soft lighting (evidently powered by solar or wind generation) from lamps that include some big retirees from a hospital operating theatre. There is an easy-going jumble of mainly stripped tables in all sorts of sizes on the dark floorboards, with a similar mix of chairs; a couple of corners have well worn easy chairs, and big abstracts decorate the walls. Good freshly cooked food makes its entrance down broad stairs below a crystal chandelier; changing twice a day, the big blackboard might include roast tomato soup with tapenade (£4.50), bruschetta with chicken livers, dandelion leaves and crème fraîche (£6), bacon wrapped scallops with tartare potato cake and basil crème (£10.50), pan-fried red mullet with linguini, lemon and chilli sauce or chargrilled chicken thighs with sun-dried tomato, sweet potato and parsley salad (£12), roast pollock in salsa verde, new potato and mussel stew (£12.50), and home smoked lamb fillet with potato aubergine and feta gratin (£13), with puddings like white chocolate and berry cheesecake (£5); children's helpings. They may have special weekday lunch offers, and on Monday evenings if you're dining the wines may be half price. A fine choice of organic wines and other drinks (the only non-organic tipples are the single malt whiskies and tequila) includes on handpump the local Pitfield beers East Kent Goldings and SB (named after the pub's hands-on owner) and St Peters Organic Best. Part of the bar and all of the restaurant are no smoking. The relaxed mix of customers may include the odd friendly dog, and there are some pleasant courtyard tables. The pub is on quite a busy roundabout facing Victoria Park with its popular boating lake. More reports please. *(Recommended by Catherine Cronin)*

Free house ~ Licensee Geetie Singh ~ Real ale ~ Bar food (12-4 (not Mon), 6.30-10.30 (10 Sun)) ~ Restaurant ~ (020) 8981 9998 ~ Children welcome ~ Dogs allowed in bar ~ Open 12.30-11; 12-10.30 Sun; closed till 5pm Mon, all 25 Dec

Grapes

Narrow Street, E14; ⊖ Shadwell (some distance away) or Westferry on the Docklands Light Railway; the Limehouse link has made it hard to find by car – turn off Commercial Road at signs for Rotherhithe tunnel, then from the Tunnel Approach slip road, fork left leading into Branch Road, turn left and then left again into Narrow Street

The ultra-modern surroundings of this warmly welcoming 16th-c tavern make the fact it's survived so unscathed all the more remarkable. In a peaceful spot well off the tourist route, it's one of London's most engaging riverside pubs, little changed since Dickens used it as the basis of his Six Jolly Fellowship Porters in *Our Mutual Friend*, and described it as 'A tavern of dropsical appearance'. Back then frequent visitors weren't always so well rewarded: watermen would row out drunks from here, drown them, and sell the salvaged bodies to the anatomists. The back part is the oldest (and in winter when the fire is lit perhaps the cosiest), with the small back balcony a fine place for a sheltered waterside drink; steps lead down to the foreshore. The chatty, partly panelled bar has lots of prints, mainly of actors, and old local maps, as well as some elaborately etched windows, plates along a shelf, and newspapers to read. Well kept Adnams, Bass and Marston Pedigree on handpump, a choice of malt whiskies, and a good wine list; efficient, friendly service. Good bar food includes soup (£3.25), sandwiches (from £3.25), ploughman's (£4.75), a pint of shell-on prawns (£5.25), bangers and mash (£6.25), home-made fishcakes with caper sauce (£6.50), dressed crab (£7.75), and a highly regarded, generous Sunday roast (no other meals then, when it can be busy, particularly in season). Booking is recommended for the very good upstairs fish restaurant, which has fine views of the river (the pub was a favourite with Rex Whistler, who used it as the viewpoint for his rather special river paintings). Shove-ha'penny, table skittles, cribbage, dominoes, chess, backgammon; there may be piped classical or jazz. *(Recommended by LM, Joan E Hilditch, Tracey and Stephen Groves, John and Gloria Isaacs, N R White)*

Spirit Group ~ Manager Barbara Haigh ~ Real ale ~ Bar food (not Sun evening) ~ Restaurant ~ (020) 7987 4396 ~ Dogs allowed in bar ~ Open 12-3, 5.30-11; 12-11 Sat; 12-10.30 Sun; closed 25-26 Dec, 1 Jan

Prospect of Whitby

Wapping Wall, E1; ⊖ Wapping

The river views from here can hardly be bettered, but it's the building and the entertaining way they play on its history that readers enjoy the most. Claiming to be the oldest pub on the Thames (it dates back to 1543), for a long while it was better known as the Devil's Tavern, thanks to its popularity with smugglers and other ne'er-do-wells. Some of the capital's best-known figures were frequent callers: Pepys and Dickens both regularly popped in, Turner came for weeks at a time to study the scene, and in the 17th c the notorious Hanging Judge Jeffreys was able to combine two of his interests by enjoying a drink at the back while looking down over the grisly goings-on in Execution Dock. With such a lively history it's no wonder they do rather play on it; the tourists who flock here lap up the colourful tales of Merrie Olde London, and only the most unromantic of visitors could fail to be carried along by the fun. The pub is an established favourite on the evening coach tours, but is usually quieter at lunchtimes. Plenty of bare beams, bare boards, panelling and flagstones in the L-shaped bar (where the long pewter counter is over 400 years old), and a river view towards Docklands from tables in the waterfront courtyard. Well kept Charles Wells Bombardier, Fullers London Pride and Greene King Old Speckled Hen on handpump, and quite a few malt whiskies. Under the new manager the bar menu has changed, but you can still get sandwiches and changing hot dishes all day. One room (with good river views) is no smoking; fruit machine, golf game. *(Recommended by Piotr Chodzko-Zajko, the Didler, Bill Sykes, Dr and Mrs M E Wilson, Tracey and Stephen Groves, Eric Robinson, Jacqueline Pratt, D J and P M Taylor)*

Spirit Group ~ Real ale ~ Bar food (12-9.30) ~ Restaurant ~ (020) 7481 1095 ~ Children welcome ~ Dogs welcome ~ Open 12-11; 12-10.30 Sun

NORTH LONDON Maps 12 & 13

Chapel ⑪ ♀

Chapel Street, NW1; ⊖ Edgware Road

This child-friendly gastropub can get very busy very quickly, and on days when the much-modernised interior feels a little frenetic, it's rather nice to bag a spot on the spacious and rather calming outside terrace. The atmosphere is always cosmopolitan – perhaps more relaxed and civilised at lunchtime, when it's a favourite with chic local office workers, then altogether busier and louder in the evenings. The choice of imaginative and well served and presented meals changes every day, but might include soups such as courgette and watercress (£4), baked goats cheese with honey and rosemary or moules marinière (£5.50), grilled aubergine with ratatouille and pecorino (£8.50), penne with meatballs, tomato sauce and parmesan (£9), free-range chicken fricassee with mustard, crème fraîche, roast parsnips and mash (£12), pan-fried veal escalope with sautéed potatoes, red cabbage and haricots blancs (£13), and grilled lamb loin chops with gratin potato, baby carrots, rosemary and balsamic jus (£13.50). Prompt, charming service from helpful staff, who may bring delicious warm walnut bread to your table while you're waiting. Light and spacious, the cream-painted rooms are dominated by the open kitchen; furnishings are smart but simple, with plenty of plain wooden tables around the bar, a couple of comfortable sofas at the lounge end, and a big fireplace. You may have to wait for a table during busier periods. Well kept Adnams and Greene King IPA on handpump, a good range of interesting wines (up to half by the glass), cappuccino and espresso, fresh orange juice, and a choice of tisanes such as peppermint or strawberry and vanilla. In the evening, trade is more evenly split between diners and drinkers, and the music can be more noticeable then, especially at weekends. A couple of readers have found it a little smoky this year. *(Recommended by Sebastian and Paris Leach, Mayur Shah, Ian Phillips, Sue Demont, Tim Barrow, Steve Harvey, Dr and Mrs M E Wilson)*

Punch ~ Lease Lakis Hondrogiannis ~ Real ale ~ Bar food (12-2.30, 7-10) ~ (020) 7402 9220 ~ Children welcome ~ Dogs welcome ~ Open 12-11(10.30 Sun); closed 25-26 Dec

Compton Arms £

Compton Avenue, off Canonbury Road, N1; ⊖ Highbury & Islington

An unexpected bonus at this tiny, well run pub is its very pleasant back terrace, with tables among flowers under a big sycamore tree; there may be heaters in winter, and barbecues in summer. Like an appealing village local, the unpretentious low-ceilinged rooms are simply furnished with wooden settles and assorted stools and chairs, with local pictures on the walls; there's a TV for sport, but the only games are things like chess, Jenga and battleships. Well kept Greene King Abbot, IPA and Old Speckled Hen and a changing guest like Wadworths 6X on handpump; friendly service. Decent bar food such as baguettes (£3.95), filled baked potatoes (£3.95), various burgers (£4.95), fish and chips or steak and ale pie (£5.95), and eight different types of sausage served with mashed potato and home-made red onion gravy (£5.95); their Sunday roasts come in two sizes, normal (£4.95), and large (£5.95). The pub is hidden away in a peaceful mews, though as it's deep in Arsenal country can get busy on match days. *(Recommended by Darren Le Poidevin, Tim Maddison, Sue Demont, Tim Barrow, Joe Green)*

Greene King ~ Managers Scott Plomer and Eileen Shelock ~ Real ale ~ Bar food (12-2.30, 6-8.30; 12-4 Sat/Sun; no food Mon) ~ (020) 7359 6883 ~ Children in eating area of bar and family room ~ Open 12-11(10.30 Sun)

Drapers Arms ⊗ ♀

Barnsbury Street; ⊖ Highbury & Islington

London Dining Pub of the Year

A meal at this top-notch gastropub isn't exactly cheap, but the fresh, carefully judged flavours and tempting presentation make it a particularly rewarding and memorable experience. The choice might include lunchtime sandwiches (from £5.95), chilled squash and fresh ginger soup (£5), bubble and squeak, poached egg and hollandaise with bacon (£5.50 starter, £7.50 main course), seared squid and chorizo salad or roast red pepper, goats cheese and pesto tart (£6.50), chermoula marinated poussin with fattoush (£12.50), roasted bream on bruschetta with piperade and bayonne ham or wild boar sausage toad in the hole (£13.50), linguini with chilli and tiger prawns (£14), and rabbit with baby leeks and polenta croûtons (£14.50), with puddings like lemon posset with cinnamon and pistachio biscuits or a first-rate sticky toffee (£5.50). Service is helpful and unobtrusive. Big colourful bunches of flowers, inset shelves of paperbacks and board games, and a couple of groups of sofas and armchairs offset what might otherwise seem rather a severe open-plan layout and décor, with high-backed dining chairs or booths on dark bare boards, high ceilings, a few big drapery prints on dusky pink walls, and a pair of large fireplaces and mirrors precisely facing each other across the front area; the overall effect is not unlike a bright, elegant wine bar. The choice of wines by the glass (including champagne) is excellent, and they have Courage Best and Greene King Old Speckled Hen on handpump, with a guest like Hook Norton Old Hooky, and a dozen malt whiskies; there may be piped jazz and swing. The dining room is no smoking. The pub is a striking Georgian townhouse, in a quiet residential street away from Islington's main drag; perhaps its slightly hidden location explains why we don't receive more reports on what in our view is now London's best pub for a special meal out. (Recommended by Aidan Wallis)

Free house ~ Licensees Mark Emberton and Paul McElhinney ~ Real ale ~ Bar food (12-3, 7-10.30 (6.30-9.30 Sun)) ~ Restaurant ~ (020) 7619 0348 ~ Children welcome till 8pm ~ Dogs allowed in bar ~ Open 12-11;·12-10.30 Sun; closed 25-27 Dec, 1-2 Jan

Duke of Cambridge ⊗ ♀ ◧

St Peter's Street, N1; ⊖ Angel, though some distance away

The organic food and drink at this trailblazing cornerhouse are still the main draw, but it also boasts a warmly inviting atmosphere; it's the kind of place that somehow encourages conversation, so instead of noise from piped music, games or machines, there's a steady stream of civilised chat from the varied customers. The big, busy main room is simply decorated and furnished, with lots of chunky wooden tables, pews and benches on bare boards, a couple of big metal vases with colourful flowers, daily papers, and carefully positioned soft lighting around the otherwise bare walls. A corridor leads off past a few tables and an open kitchen to a couple of smaller candlelit rooms, more formally set for eating, and there's a new conservatory. The excellent range of impeccably sourced drinks and food may cost slightly more than you'd pay for a non-organic meal, but it's usually worth the extra to enjoy choices and flavours you won't find anywhere else. Changing twice a day, the blackboard menu might include things like celeriac, chickpea and cabbage soup (£4.50), chicken liver pâté with pickled cucumber, red onion chutney and toast (£6.50), a dozen oysters with shallot vinegar (£9), tagliatelle with lemon cream, parsley and parmesan (£9.50), grilled herring fillets with braised puy lentils and grain mustard sauce (£12), boiled ham hock with mustard, mashed potato and savoy cabbage (£12.50), roast herb crusted organic salmon fillet on butter bean and chorizo stew (£13), grilled venison steak with spinach, chips and redcurrant jus (£14.50), and puddings like apple pie with cinnamon custard (£4.50); children's helpings. They make all their own bread, pickles, ice-cream and so on. On handpump are four organic real ales: from London's small Pitfield Brewery Eco Warrior and SB (named for the pub's owner), St Peters Best, and a guest such as East Kent Goldings or Shoreditch Organic Stout. They also have organic draught lagers and cider, organic spirits, and a very wide range of organic wines, many of which are available by the glass. The full range of drinks is chalked on a blackboard, and also includes good coffees and teas, and a spicy ginger ale. Most of the pub is no smoking. It's worth arriving early to eat, as they can get vey busy. This was London's first organic pub, and the licensee runs the Crown in Victoria Park (see East London main entries) along similar lines. *(Recommended by Darren Le Poidevin, Alistair Forsyth, Susan May)*

Free house ~ Licensee Geetie Singh ~ Real ale ~ Bar food (12.30-3(3.30 Sat, Sun), 6.30-10.30(10 Sun)) ~ Restaurant ~ (020) 7359 3066 ~ Children welcome ~ Dogs allowed in bar ~ Open 12-11(10.30 Sun); closed 25-26 Dec

Flask ♀

Flask Walk, NW3; ⊖ Hampstead

A peaceful, properly old-fashioned local with a rather villagey feel, this is a popular haunt of Hampstead artists, actors and characters. The snuggest and most individual part is the cosy lounge at the front, with plush green seats and banquettes curving round the panelled walls, a unique Victorian screen dividing it from the public bar, and an attractive fireplace. A comfortable orange-lit room with period prints and a few further tables leads into a rather smart dining conservatory, which with its plants, prominent wine bottles and neat table linen feels a bit like a wine bar. A couple of white iron tables are squeezed into the tiny back yard. Well kept Youngs Bitter, Special and seasonal brews on handpump, around 18 wines by the glass, and decent coffees – they have a machine that grinds the beans to order. Bar food might include sandwiches, soup, daily changing specials like chicken casserole, lamb curry or spiced minced beef pie with a cheese and leek mash topping (from £5.50), and fish and chips (£6.50). A plainer public bar (which you can get into only from the street) has leatherette seating, cribbage, backgammon, lots of space for darts, fruit machines, trivia and big-screen SkyTV. There are quite a few tables out in the alley. Small dogs are allowed in the front bars only. The pub's name is a reminder of the days when it distributed mineral water from Hampstead's springs. *(Recommended by the Didler, MDN, Jo Lilley, Simon Calvert, Patrick Hancock, Steve Harvey, Derek Thomas, N R White, Tim Maddison)*

Youngs ~ Manager John Cannon ~ Real ale ~ Bar food (12-3(4 Sun), 6-8.30; not Sun or Mon evening) ~ Restaurant ~ (020) 7435 4580 ~ Dogs allowed in bar ~ Open 11-11; 12-10.30 Sun

Holly Bush ◀

Holly Mount, NW3; ⊖ Hampstead

Originally the stable block of a nearby house, this timeless old favourite is well liked for its food and range of drinks, but it's the atmosphere that most stands out, particularly in the evenings, when a good mix of chatty locals and visitors fills the old-fashioned and individual front bar. Under the dark sagging ceiling are brown and cream panelled walls (decorated with old advertisements and a few hanging plates), open fires, bare boards, and cosy bays formed by partly glazed partitions. Slightly more intimate, the back room, named after the painter George Romney, has an embossed red ceiling, panelled and etched glass alcoves, and ochre-painted brick walls covered with small prints; piped music. With carefully sourced ingredients (most of their meat is organic), bar food might include welsh rarebit (£5), various sausages with cheddar mash and gravy (£8.50), pies like chicken, mushroom and London Pride (£9) or beef and Harveys (£9.50), roasted free-range chicken in beer and paprika sauce (£10.50), rabbit in mustard and pilsner sauce (£11.50), and some good, unusual cheeses (£7). Well kept Adnams Bitter and Broadside, Fullers London Pride, Harveys Sussex and an unusual guest like Kelham Island Pale Island on handpump, plenty of whiskies, and a seasonally changing wine list; friendly service. The upstairs dining room (with table service Weds-Sun) is no smoking. There are tables on the pavement outside. The pub is reached by a delightful stroll along some of Hampstead's most villagey streets. *(Recommended by*

Paul Boot, Derek Thomas, the Didler, Tim Maddison, Jo Lilley, Simon Calvert, Steve Harvey)

Punch ~ Lease Nicolai Outzen ~ Real ale ~ Bar food (12.30-4, 6.30-10 weekdays; 12-10 Sat, 12-9 Sun) ~ Restaurant ~ (020) 7435 2892 ~ Children in eating area of bar and restaurant ~ Dogs allowed in bar ~ Open 11-11(10.30 Sun); closed 1 Jan

Olde White Bear

Well Road, NW3; ⊖ Hampstead

This neo-Victorian pub has a wonderfully clubby feel that attracts a splendidly diverse mix of customers, and is reckoned by many to be Hampstead's friendliest pub. The dimly lit knocked-through bar is smart but relaxed, with elegant panelling, wooden venetian blinds, and three separate-seeming areas: the biggest has lots of Victorian prints and cartoons on the walls, as well as wooden stools, cushioned captain's chairs, a couple of big tasselled armchairs, a flowery sofa, a handsome fireplace and an ornate Edwardian sideboard. A brighter section at the end has elaborate brocaded pews, while a central area has dried flower arrangements and signed photographs of actors and playwrights. Bar food is served all day, from a range including soups like chickpea and leek (£4), good elaborate sandwiches (from £4.50), skewered tempura prawns (£5.50), goats cheese and red pepper quiche (£7), warm chorizo sausage salad with green beans, peppers and new potatoes (£7.50), spicy meatballs in tomato sauce, ginger and honey-glazed chicken on a bed of polenta or salmon fishcakes with a dill and caper sauce (all £8), and seared tuna loin on pak choi (£9.50); they do a choice of popular Sunday roasts. Adnams, Fullers London Pride, Greene King Abbot and Youngs on handpump; over a dozen wines by the glass, and a decent range of whiskies. There are a few tables in front, and more in a courtyard behind. Soft piped music, cards, chess, TV, and excellent Thursday quiz nights. Parking may be a problem at times – it's mostly residents' permits only nearby (there are no restrictions on Sundays). The pub is handy for the Heath. *(Recommended by Jo Lilley, Simon Calvert, Sue Demont, Tim Barrow, the Didler, Patrick Hancock, N R White, Tim Maddison)*

Punch ~ Lease Christopher Ely ~ Real ale ~ Bar food (12-9) ~ (020) 7435 3758 ~ Children welcome ~ Dogs allowed in bar ~ Thurs quiz night (starts 9) ~ Open 11-11; 11-11 Sat; 12-10.30 Sun

Spaniards Inn 🍷

Spaniards Lane, NW3; ⊖ Hampstead, but some distance away, or from Golders Green station take 220 bus

A new manager has arrived at this busy former toll house, famed for its tales of hauntings and highwaymen, and an outside bar has opened in the charming garden, nicely arranged in a series of areas separated by judicious planting of shrubs. A crazy-paved terrace with slatted wooden tables and chairs opens onto a flagstoned walk around a small lawn, with roses, and a side arbour of wisteria and clematis. They have regular barbecues out here in summer, though you'll need to move fast to bag a table. Dating back to 1585, the low-ceilinged oak-panelled rooms of the attractive main bar are full of character, with open fires, genuinely antique winged settles, candle-shaped lamps in shades, and snug little alcoves. There's an impressive range of drinks, with between five and eight real ales at a time, typically including Caledonian Deuchars IPA, Fullers London Pride, Marstons Old Empire, Roosters Yankee and Youngs Special, some unusual continental draught lagers, and 18 wines by the glass – though in summer you might find the most popular drink is their big jug of Pimms. Served all day, bar food might include ciabattas (from £4.95), cottage pie (£6), pasta with roasted vegetables and green basil pesto or an enormous greek salad (£6.50), cumberland sausages (£7.50), piri-piri lamb with mediterranean couscous (£8.50), and cod and chips (£10); they do a paella on Saturdays (£7.50), and a choice of roasts on Sundays. The food bar is no smoking at lunchtimes; upstairs, the Georgian Turpin Room is no smoking all day. The pub is believed to have been named after the Spanish ambassador to the court of James I, who had a private residence here. More recently it drew headlines for introducing the world's first automatic dog-wash, perfect for cleaning canines who've enjoyed themselves a little too enthusiastically on the Heath. It's fairly handy for Kenwood. Parking can be difficult. *(Recommended by Jo Lilley, Simon Calvert, Ian Phillips, R T and J C Moggridge, John Saville, Tracey and Stephen Groves)*

Mitchells & Butlers ~ Manager David Nichol ~ Real ale ~ Bar food (11-10) ~ (020) 8731 6571 ~ Children in eating area of bar ~ Dogs welcome ~ Open 11-11(10.30 Sun)

SOUTH LONDON Maps 12 & 13
Anchor & Hope ⊗
The Cut, SE1 (B300, turning E off A301 Waterloo Road, S of Waterloo Station); ⇌ Waterloo East, ⊖ ⇌ Waterloo

It's no great shakes from the outside, but don't be fooled: this relaxed and informal gastropub has quickly won an excellent reputation for its unusual food – not cheap, but thoughtfully prepared using excellent ingredients. Changing twice a day, the blackboard menu might include gazpacho (£4.40), baked summer vegetables with butterbeans and goats curd (£10), tripe and chips (£11), preserved rabbit with anchovies, olives and noodles (£11.80), braised lamb shank with butterbeans, aïoli and tomato (£12.80), roasted plaice, chips and tartare sauce (£14), roast beef rump with russian salad or excellent scallops and ratatouille (£16), and raspberry and almond tart (£5). It's very much of the Eagle school (bare boards and no booking), and appeals to the same sort of people, but here there's a separate dining room, and on arrival you can add your name to the list to be seated there. Alternatively you can join the throng in the bar, which shares the same menu, but the dining room tables are better for an unhurried meal; those in the bar are rather low and small. That doesn't put off most people: our last visit was on a typically busy weekday evening, when the diners we came across were so enjoying their food they scarcely noticed they were perched precariously over the tiniest of tables. There's a piano in one corner, but otherwise the bar is fairly plain, with dark red-painted walls and big windows that open up in summer. On the other side of a big curtain, the dining room is similar, but with contemporary paintings on the walls; it's no smoking in here. Well kept Charles Wells Bombardier and Eagle on handpump, along with a guest like Butcombe (again, not cheap); there's a good wine list, but a popular choice before dinner is one of their sherries. The atmosphere is relaxed but vibrantly chatty – it's the kind of place where strangers cheerfully ask what you're eating; at busy times there can be a slight air of chaos, and service, though prompt and friendly, can be confused then. There are a few metal tables in front on the street. *(Recommended by Dr and Mrs M E Wilson, Ian Phillips, Derek Thomas, Sue Demont, Tim Barrow)*

Charles Wells ~ Licensee Robert Shaw ~ Real ale ~ Bar food (12-2.30 (not Mon), 6-10.30) ~ Restaurant ~ (020) 7928 9898 ~ Children welcome ~ Open 11-11(closed till 5pm Mon); closed Sun

Boathouse
Brewhouse Lane, Putney Wharf, SW15; ⇌ Putney or ⊖ Putney Bridge, then cross the Thames – from the bridge you can see the pub on your left

A strikingly converted former vinegar factory in a bustling new waterside development, this has quickly become one of the area's busiest pubs, and on fine days you'll find plenty of people packed onto the sunny front terrace, enjoying fine views of Putney Bridge and the river. The view is just as good from the comfortable bar in the building's glazed front extension, and even better from the balcony of the upstairs dining room. As well as its huge walls of glass – creating a very light, spacious feel – the bar has several sofas and low, modern tables on rugs on the polished wooden floors; also fresh flowers and newspapers, a large, slightly incongruous candelabrum, and a big plasma TV screen for sports. Well kept Youngs Original, Special and seasonal brews on handpump from the long counter, and amost a dozen wines by the glass; piped music. Up some steps is a cosier galleried room, more traditional, with panelling, a mix of leatherette and upholstered armchairs, a couple of discreet rowing oars, and another sofa tucked under the stairs. Around the walls is a variety of water- or boating-themed artwork – most interesting are the period Underground posters advertising the Boat Race (the race starts near here), many of which line the warren of corridors leading to the gents'. Good bar food (served all day at weekends) might include sandwiches (from £4.25), soup (£3.75), various salads and sharing platters like chicken, guacamole and spicy bean wraps with sour cream and sweet chilli (£6.25), cumberland sausage and mash (£6.75), and chilli (£6.95); there's a separate and rather more interesting menu for the balcony bar and upstairs dining room, which might typically include rocket and saffron risotto (£7.25), fish and chips (£8.95), thai spiced crab cakes with roast fennel salad (£10.50), and specials like roast pheasant with red wine sauce and braised savoy cabbage (£11.50) or pan-fried calves liver with mustard mash and sage jus (£12.50). The dining room is no smoking, and has its own bar; there are monthly opera or jazz nights in here too. The pub can be busy with under-30s in the evening (though the dining room usually has a wider mix of customers then) when service can slow down, but it's quieter and rather relaxing during the day. *(Recommended by Susan and John Douglas)*

Youngs ~ Managers Elizabeth and Andrew Ford ~ Real ale ~ Bar food (12-3, 6-10 (12-10 weekends)) ~ Restaurant ~ (020) 8789 0476 ~ Children in eating area of bar and restaurant ~ Dogs allowed in bar ~ Monthly opera or jazz nights ~ Open 11-11; 12-10.30 Sun

Crown & Greyhound

Dulwich Village, SE21; ⇌ North Dulwich

One reader has been enjoying this relaxed Victorian pub for nearly 40 years. Refurbished but retaining many of its original features, the roomy main bar area at the front is pleasantly furnished, with some quite ornate plasterwork and lamps over on the right, and a variety of nicely distinct seating areas, some with traditional upholstered and panelled settles, others with stripped kitchen tables on stripped boards; there's a coal-effect gas fire and some old prints. A big back dining room and no smoking conservatory opens into the garden, one of the pub's main draws. It's been recently spruced up with new furniture and parasols, some of its tables are shaded by a chestnut tree, and they've added french boules; there are regular barbecues out here in summer. As well as Fullers London Pride they have four changing real ales (very much at central London prices), often including some unusual brews; beer festivals on bank holidays. The lunchtime menu might include big ciabattas (from £4.60), sausages with chive mash and red onion gravy or well liked burgers (from £6.90), and specials such as chicken in mustard sauce, lamb in red wine or cod mornay (all £6.95). Best to arrive early for their popular Sunday carvery (£8.90), as they don't take bookings; the pub can be popular with families then. Known locally as the Dog, it was built at the turn of the century to replace two inns that had stood here previously, hence the unusual name. Busy in the evenings, but quieter during the day, it's handy for walks through the park, and for the Dulwich picture gallery. *(Recommended by Mrs Maricar Jagger, Pete Walker, Piotr Chodzko-Zajko, Dave W Holliday, Dr and Mrs M E Wilson)*

Mitchells & Butlers ~ Manager Duncan Moore ~ Real ale ~ Bar food (12-10(9 Sun)) ~ (020) 8299 4976 ~ Children in restaurant ~ Dogs welcome ~ Open 11-11; 12-10.30 Sun

Cutty Sark

Ballast Quay, off Lassell Street, SE10; ⇌ Maze Hill, from London Bridge; or from the river front walk past the Yacht in Crane Street and Trinity Hospital

A new licensee has arrived at this attractive late 16th-c white-painted house since our last edition, but apart from introducing a wider range of food has no plans for major changes. That's not a huge surprise: the pub's unspoilt appearance and old-fashioned feel are very much the main draw, and you can almost imagine smugglers and blackguards with patches over their eyes in the dark, flagstoned bar, which has rough brick walls, wooden settles, barrel tables, open fires, low lighting and narrow openings to tiny side snugs. There's an elaborate central staircase. Well kept Adnams Broadside, Batemans XXXB, Fullers London Pride, Greene King Old Speckled Hen and Youngs Special on handpump, with a good choice of malt whiskies and a range of organic wines; fruit machine, juke box. In a roomy eating area, good, promptly served bar food includes sandwiches (from £3.95), and changing hot dishes like bangers and mash (£7.95), sweet chilli salmon on a bed of noodles (£9.95), and garlic peppered rib-eye steak (£11.95). There are splendid views of the Thames and the Millennium Dome from the busy terrace across the narrow cobbled lane (where the concrete tables strike a slightly incongruous note); or, better still, from the upstairs room with the big bow window – itself notable for the way it jetties over the pavement. The pub is alive with young people on Friday and Saturday evenings, but can be surprisingly quiet some weekday lunchtimes. They have jazz festivals two or three times a year, and morris dancers occasionally drop by. Parking is limited nearby. *(Recommended by Tony Brace, the Didler, Michael Butler, Andy Trafford, Louise Bayly, John Saville, N R White)*

Free house ~ Licensee Katie Jackson ~ Real ale ~ Bar food (12-9(10 Sat)) ~ Restaurant ~ (020) 8858 3146 ~ Children upstairs till 9pm ~ Dogs allowed in bar ~ Open 11-11; 12-10.30 Sun

Fire Station 🍽 ♀

Waterloo Road, SE1; ⊖ ⇌ Waterloo

Not the place to come for a quiet meal, this conversion of the former LCC central fire station is vibrantly busy after work, when loud chat and music combine in a cheery cacophony that most readers thoroughly enjoy, but some find a little overpowering. Though some original features remain, it now looks like a cross between a warehouse and a schoolroom, with plenty of wooden pews, chairs and long tables (a few spilling on to the street), some mirrors and rather incongruous pieces of dressers, and brightly red-painted doors, shelves and modern hanging lightshades; the determinedly contemporary art round the walls is for sale, and there's a table with newspapers to read. Well kept Adnams, Fullers London Pride, Shepherd Neame Spitfire, Youngs and a guest on handpump, as well as a number of european bottled beers, variously flavoured teas, several malt whiskies and a good choice of wines. They serve a range of bar meals between 11 and 5.30, which might include interestingly filled panini (£5.95) and ciabattas (£6.50), but it really is worth paying the extra to eat from the main menu, served from an open kitchen in the spacious back dining room. Changing daily, this has things like soup (£4.25), confit of rabbit on a pineapple and beansprout salad (£6.95), baked pear and blue cheese tart (£9.95), sage and pumpkin tortellini (£10.95), fish of the day (£11.95), stuffed corn fed chicken breast wrapped in parma ham with vegetable risotto (£12.50), and tandoori seared yellow fin tuna loin (£12.95); some dishes can run out, so get there early for the best choice. They also do a set menu at lunchtimes and between 5.30 and 7, with two courses for £11.95, or three for £14.50. You can book tables. There may be a cover charge for the bread, and they'll add a 5% service charge for groups of five or more. Piped modern jazz and other music fits into the good-natured hubbub; it's calmer at lunchtimes, and at weekends. There's a TV for rugby matches. It's very handy for the Old Vic and Waterloo Station. *(Recommended by Keith and Chris O'Neill, Dr and Mrs M E Wilson, Ian Phillips, Michael Butler, Paul A Moore, R T and J C Moggridge, E G Parish, Mrs Hazel Rainer, Mayur Shah, Nina Randall, Giles and Annie Francis)*

Wizard ~ Manager Philippe Ha Yeung ~ Real ale ~ Bar food (12-2.45, 5.30-10.45; 11-10.45 Sat, 12-9.30 Sun) ~ Restaurant ~ (020) 7620 2226 ~ Children in eating area of bar and restaurant ~ Open 11-11; 12-10.30 Sun; closed 25-26 Dec

---

People named as recommenders after the main entries have told us that the pub should be included. But they have not written the report – we have, after anonymous on-the-spot inspection.

Founders Arms

Hopton Street (Bankside), SE1; ⊖ ⇌ Blackfriars, and cross Blackfriars Bridge

Most customers at this big, modern place sit outside and it's no wonder: the panorama from the waterside terrace is among the best from any pub along the Thames, particularly in the City, with fine views of the river, St Paul's, and the Millennium Bridge; there are plenty of picnic table sets to take it all in. Rather like a huge conservatory, this is the handiest pub for visiting Tate Modern, and Shakespeare's Globe is a short stroll away. If you're inside, the lighting is nice and unobtrusive so that you can still see out across the river at night. It can get busy, particularly on weekday evenings, when it's popular with young City types for an after-work drink. Well kept Youngs Bitter, Special and seasonal brews from the modern bar counter angling along one side; also, coffee, tea and hot chocolate. Served pretty much all day (starting at 9 for breakfast), the promptly served bar food includes sandwiches (from £3.95), panini (from £4.95), soup (£3.95), sausages and mash (£7.50), fresh fish in beer batter (£7.70), pasta with roasted pepper, sun-dried tomato, artichoke, garlic and pesto (£7.85), loin of pork with paprika, calvados and pineapple sauce (£8.35), steak and ale pie (£8.75), and daily specials; Sunday roasts. Efficient, neat and cheerful service. One raised area is no smoking; piped music, fruit machine. Like many City pubs, it may close a little early on quieter nights. *(Recommended by John Wooll, Meg and Colin Hamilton, Keith and Chris O'Neill, John Coatsworth, Patrick Hancock, D J and P M Taylor, Michael Butler, the Didler, Mrs Pat Crabb, Ian Phillips, Dr and Mrs M E Wilson, N R White)*

Youngs ~ Managers Mr and Mrs P Wakefield ~ Real ale ~ Bar food (12-8.30(7 Sun, 8 in summer)) ~ (020) 7928 1899 ~ Children in eating area of bar until 8.30pm ~ Open 11-11; 12-10.30 Sun

Fox & Hounds ⬛ ⵆ

Latchmere Road, SW11; ⇌ Clapham Junction

The food is the draw at this big Victorian local; it's the second of the small group run by the two brothers who transformed the Atlas (see West London, below), so there's a similar emphasis on the excellent mediterranean cooking. Changing every day, the menu might include spring pea soup with parma ham (£4), pan-fried king prawns with asparagus, green bean and cherry tomato salad or roast butternut squash risotto (£7.50), grilled tuscan sausages with black pepper and fennel (£9), portuguese mussel stew (£10.50), turkish lamb meatballs with cumin and coriander, tomato and cayenne pepper sauce and couscous salad (£11.50), and pan-fried whole lemon sole with puy lentils, tomato, thyme and chilli (£12.50), blueberry cheesecake (£4), and creamy italian cheeses with pear and grilled bread (£5). The pub can fill quickly, so you may have to move fast to grab a table. The spacious, straightforward bar has bare boards, mismatched tables and chairs, two narrow pillars supporting the dark red ceiling, photographs on the walls, and big windows overlooking the street (the view partially obscured by colourful window boxes). There are fresh flowers and daily papers on the bar, and a view of the kitchen behind. Two rooms lead off, one more cosy with its two red leatherette sofas. Well kept Caledonian Deuchars IPA, Fullers London Pride and Harveys Sussex on handpump; the carefully chosen wine list (which includes a dozen by the glass) is written out on a blackboard. It's still very much the kind of place where locals happily come to drink – and they're a more varied bunch than you might find filling the Atlas; the varied piped music fits in rather well. The garden has been extensively refurbished, with plenty of new planting and big parasols and heaters for winter. The same team have another two similarly organised pubs: the Cumberland Arms near Olympia, and the Swan in Chiswick. *(Recommended by Pete Walker, Sue Demont, Tim Barrow, Russell Lewin, Keith and Chris O'Neill)*

Free house ~ Licensees Richard and George Manners ~ Real ale ~ Bar food (12.30-3 Fri, Sat, Sun, 7-10.30(10 Sun); no lunch Mon-Thurs) ~ (020) 7924 5483 ~ Children welcome in eating area till 7pm ~ Dogs welcome ~ Open 12-3 (not Mon), 5-11 Mon-Thurs; 12-11 Fri, Sat; 12-10.30 Sun; closed Mon lunchtime; 24 Dec-1 Jan; Easter Sat and Sun

George ★ 🍺

Off 77 Borough High Street, SE1; ⊖ ⇌ Borough or London Bridge

As they say on their new menu, the last major changes to this splendid-looking building were in 1676. It's perhaps the country's best example of a historic coaching inn, and is preserved by the National Trust. The tiers of open galleries look down over a bustling cobbled courtyard with plenty of picnic-sets, and maybe morris men and even Shakespeare in summer. Inside, the row of no-frills ground-floor rooms and bars all have square-latticed windows, black beams, bare floorboards, some panelling, plain oak or elm tables and old-fashioned built-in settles, along with a 1797 'Act of Parliament' clock, dimpled glass lantern-lamps and so forth. The snuggest refuge is the room nearest the street, where there's an ancient beer engine that looks like a cash register. Two rooms are no smoking at lunchtimes. In summer they open a bar with direct service into the courtyard. It's now tied to Greene King, so has that brewery's Abbot and IPA, and a beer made by them for the pub, as well as Fullers London Pride, and a changing guest like Shepherd Neame Spitfire on handpump; mulled wine in winter, tea and coffee. Good value lunchtime bar food includes baguettes (from £4.50) and wraps (from £4.75), soup (£2.95), filled baked potatoes (from £3.50), ham, egg and chips or scampi (£5.45), spinach and mixed mushroom cannelloni (£5.95), sausage and mash (£5.95), fish and chips (£6.45), and steak and ale pie (£6.75). A splendid central staircase goes up to a series of dining rooms and to a gas-lit balcony; darts, trivia. What survives today is only a third of what it once was; the building was 'mercilessly reduced' as E V Lucas put it, during the period when it was owned by the Great Northern Railway Company. Unless you know where you're going (or you're not in one of the many tourist groups that flock here in summer) you may well miss it, as apart from the great gates and sign there's little to indicate that such a gem still exists behind the less auspicious-looking buildings on the busy high street. (Recommended by Andy and Jill Kassube, Mike Gorton, Ian Phillips, CMW, JJW, the Didler, Andrea Rampley, Simon Collett-Jones, Joe Green, B and M Kendall, Jo Lilley, Simon Calvert, N R White, Peter Coxon, R Huggins, D Irving, E McCall, T McLean)

Greene King ~ Manager Scott Masterson ~ Real ale ~ Bar food (12-5) ~ Restaurant (5-10) ~ (020) 7407 2056 ~ Children in eating area of bar ~ Open 11-11; 12-10.30 Sun

Market Porter 🍺

Stoney Street, SE1; ⊖ ⇌ London Bridge

A recent refurbishment has doubled the size of this busily pubby place, which has probably the largest and most interesting selection of real ales we've ever come across. They've added some more pumps, and now serve around a dozen, with the Harveys Best joined by a constantly changing range of beers you're probably never heard of, let alone tasted; when we last called the choice included Cropton Brewery Yorkshire Moors, Goachers Mild, Marlows Rebellion, Ringwood Best, Suddabys Coffee Porter and W J King Ace of Ales, all perfectly kept and served. The pub opens between 6 and 8.30 on weekday mornings to serve the workers and porters from Borough Market (they do breakfasts then), and the only criticism we've heard in recent years is that it's sometimes so busy you can't see which beers are available; it feels very bustling indeed at lunchtimes (when it can be noisy with the chatter), but is usually quieter in the afternoons. The main part of the bar has rough wooden ceiling beams with beer barrels balanced on them, a heavy wooden bar counter with a beamed gantry, cushioned bar stools, an open fire, and 20s-style wall lamps; it gets more old-fashioned the further you venture in. Sensibly priced lunchtime bar food includes sandwiches (from £3.45), and panini (from £3.95), caesar salad (£4.95), sausages and mash (£5.75), a changing home-made pie (£6.25), and sirloin steak (£8.25); good Sunday roasts. Obliging, friendly service; darts, fruit machine, TV and piped music. A cosy partly panelled room has leaded glass windows and a couple of tables. The company that owns the pub has various others around London; ones with similarly unusual beers (if not quite so many) can be found in Stamford Street and Seymour Place. (Recommended by Derek Thomas, Brian and Rosalie Laverick, the Didler, Mike Gorton, Patrick Hancock, Ian Phillips, Ted George,

Joe Green, R T and J C Moggridge, R Huggins, D Irving, E McCall, T McLean, Nigel and Sue Foster, Dr and Mrs M E Wilson, Valerie Baker, Sue Demont, Tim Barrow, Susan and John Douglas, Mike and Sue Loseby, Rob Razzell)

Free house ~ Licensee Nick Turner ~ Real ale ~ Bar food (12-2.30 (not Sat)) ~ Restaurant ~ (020) 7407 2495 ~ Children in restaurant ~ Open 6-8.30am weekdays, then 11-11; 12-11 Sat; 12-10.30 Sun

Old Jail

Map 3; Jail Lane, Biggin Hill (first turn E off A233 S of airport and industrial estate, towards Berry's Hill and Cudham); no station near

Very close to the border with Kent, this interesting old pub feels so much in the heart of the countryside it's easy to forget you're only ten minutes or so away from the bustle of Croydon and Bromley. A highlight is the lovely big garden, with well spaced picnic-sets on the grass, several substantial trees, and a nicely maintained play area; it's a popular spot for families on fine weekends. Inside, several traditional beamed and low-ceilinged rooms ramble around a central servery, with the nicest parts the two cosy little areas to the right of the front entrance; divided by dark timbers, one has a very big inglenook fireplace with lots of logs and brasses, and the other has a cabinet of Battle of Britain plates (it can be smoky in here at busy times). The pub was a mainstay of RAF pilots based at Biggin Hill, so there are wartime prints and plates in other parts too, especially around the edge of the dining room, up a step beyond a second, smaller fireplace. There's also a plainer, flagstoned room; discreet fruit machine, low piped music. Well kept Greene King IPA, Harveys and Shepherd Neame Spitfire on handpump, with an occasional guest. A standard menu takes in sandwiches (from £2.25), soup (£2.95), filled baked potatoes (from £3.30), and ploughman's (£5.95), but the food to go for is the wide choice of good, blackboard specials, which might include warm bacon and brie baguette (£3.25), local sausages and mash (£7.95), salmon and leek fishcakes or medallions of pork with a mustard cream sauce (£8.45), and roast rump of lamb with a rosemary potato cake and mediterranean vegetables in tomato sauce (£11.85); they do a choice of roasts on Sundays (£8.50). With nice hanging baskets in front on the narrow leafy lane, the attractive building wasn't itself part of any jail, but was a beef shop until becoming a pub in 1869. *(Recommended by LM, Ian Phillips, Alan M Pring, GHC)*

Punch ~ Tenant Richard Hards ~ Real ale ~ Bar food (12-2, 7-9.30 (not Sun evening)) ~ (01959) 572979 ~ Children welcome ~ Dogs allowed in bar ~ Open 11-3, 6-11 (all day Fri in summer); 11-11 Sat; 12-10.30 Sun

Royal Oak ◧

Tabard Street, SE1; ⊖ Borough

Despite being slightly off the beaten track, this wonderfully characterful Victorian corner house can get very busy with a real mix of customers who've actively sought it out, partly for the relaxed, chatty atmosphere, but also for the full range of impeccably kept beers from Sussex brewer Harveys, which you won't find anywhere else in town. Best-loved among these is perhaps their Sussex Best, but you'll also find their stronger Armada, as well as Mild, Pale Ale and changing seasonal brews. The brewery transformed the pub when they took over, and painstakingly re-created the look and feel of a traditional London alehouse – so successfully that you'd never imagine it wasn't like this all along. Two small L-shaped rooms meander around the central wooden servery, which has a fine old clock in the middle. They're done out in a cosy, old-fashioned style: patterned rugs on the wooden floors, plates running along a delft shelf, black and white scenes or period sheet music on the red-painted walls, and a good mix of wooden tables and chairs. It almost goes without saying, but there's no music or machines. Well liked by readers, good honest bar food includes impressive doorstep sandwiches, and generously served daily specials such as pork chop (£5.75), rabbit casserole or various roasts (£6.95), scallops and bacon or braised lamb shank (£7.95), and halibut steak (£8.75). *(Recommended by the Didler, Sue Demont, Tim Barrow, Nigel Brown, Tracey and Stephen Groves, C J Fletcher, C M Harnor)*

Harveys ~ Tenants John Porteous, Frank Taylor ~ Real ale ~ Bar food (12-2.45, 6-9.15 weekdays; 6-9.15 Sat, 12-5 Sun) ~ (020) 7357 7173 ~ Dogs allowed in bar ~ Open 11-11; 6-11 Sat; 12-6 Sun; closed bank hols

White Cross ♀

Water Lane; ⊖ ⇌ Richmond

This perfectly-set Thames-side pub has a certain wistful charm in winter, but is at its best in summer when the busy paved garden in front can be packed with people enjoying the river views. It can feel rather like a cosmopolitan seaside resort, and there's an outside bar then (they may use plastic glasses for outside drinking). Inside, the two chatty main rooms have something of the air of the hotel this once was, with local prints and photographs, an old-fashioned wooden island servery, and a good mix of variously aged customers. Two of the three log fires have mirrors above them – unusually, the third is below a window. A bright and airy upstairs room has lots more tables, and a pretty cast-iron balcony opening off, with a splendid view down to the water, and a couple more tables and chairs. Well kept Youngs Bitter, Special and seasonal beers on handpump, and a dozen or so carefully chosen wines by the glass; service is friendly and civilised, even when the pub is at its busiest. From a servery at the foot of the stairs, lunchtime bar food includes good sandwiches (from £3), salads (from £5.95), a variety of sausages (£6.75), and plenty of daily-changing specials, including a roast. Fruit machine, dominoes. It pays to check the tide times if you're leaving your car by the river; the water can rise rapidly, and you might return to find it marooned in a rapidly swelling pool of water. It's not unknown for the water to reach right up the steps into the bar. Boats leave from immediately outside for Kingston and Hampton Court. *(Recommended by the Didler, David and Nina Pugsley, Barry Collett)*

Youngs ~ Managers Ian and Phyl Heggie ~ Real ale ~ Bar food (12-3) ~ (020) 8940 6844 ~ Children in garden area only ~ Dogs welcome ~ Open 11-11; 12-10.30 Sun; closed 25 Dec (exc 12-2)

WEST LONDON Maps 12 & 13

Anglesea Arms ◀

Selwood Terrace, SW7; ⊖ South Kensington

Feeling both cosy and smart at the same time (much of the smartness due to the well heeled young locals), this is a characterful and genuinely old-fashioned pub, with a sensible choice of well prepared food, and a particularly friendly and chatty atmosphere. The traditional bar has the air of a late Victorian local, with a mix of cast-iron tables on the bare wood-strip floor, panelling, and big windows with attractive swagged curtains; at one end several booths with partly glazed screens have cushioned pews and spindleback chairs. The traditional mood is heightened by some heavy portraits, prints of London, and large brass chandeliers. On busy days you'll need to move fast to grab a seat, but most people seem happy leaning on the central elbow tables. A good choice of real ales takes in Adnams Bitter and Broadside, Brakspears Special, Fullers London Pride, Youngs and a weekly changing guest like Archers Golden; also a few bottled belgian beers, around 20 whiskies, and a varied wine list, with everything available by the glass. A few steps down is a separate eating area, with a Victorian fireplace. The shortish menu changes every day but typically includes good sandwiches, served with their home-made chips (from £4.95), leek, potato and stilton soup (£3.75), dorset crab on toasted sourdough bread (£5.45), pork, apple and sage burger or battered haddock (£8.95), roast vine tomato, mozzarella and fresh basil fettuccine with olives (£10.95), pan-fried bass with garlic, theyme, sautéed green beans and fresh shallots, and sirloin steak with horseradish sauce and watercress (£12.95); it's worth booking in advance for their good all-day Sunday roasts (from £8.95). The dining room is no smoking. Service is friendly and helpful. In summer the place to be is the leafy front patio (with outside heaters for chillier evenings). *(Recommended by T Fry, Ian Phillips, the Didler, Tracey and Stephen Groves, Mrs B M Hill, Dr and Mrs M E Wilson, Paul A Moore)*

Free house ~ Licensee Jenny Podmore ~ Real ale ~ Bar food (12-3, 6.30-10 weekdays; 12-5, 6-10(9.30 Sun) weekends) ~ Restaurant ~ (020) 7373 7960 ~ Children in eating area of bar and restaurant ~ Dogs allowed in bar ~ Open 11-11; 12-10.30 Sun

Anglesea Arms 🍽 ♀
Wingate Road, W6; ⊖ Ravenscourt Park

This rather off-the-beaten-path pub may at first glance appear rather ordinary, but it's lifted well beyond that by the superior food served in the bustling eating area at the back. Changing every lunchtime and evening, the imaginative blackboard menu might include starters such as ham hock and pea terrine with sauce gribiche and toast or warm spinach and mushroom tart with seasonal leaves (£4.95), and sautéed scallops with cauliflower, capers and vegetable crisps (£6.20), main courses like roast fillet of cod with peas, broad beans, lardons, mash and chive velouté (£11.50), or chargrilled wild venison with dauphinoise potatoes, rosemary and red wine (£13.95), puddings like orange posset with raspberry coulis and biscotti (£4.25), and some unusual farmhouse cheeses (£4.95); they usually do a set menu at lunchtimes. Though the dining room leads off the bar it feels quite separate, with skylights, closely packed tables, and a big modern painting along one wall; directly opposite is the kitchen, with several chefs frantically working on the meals. It's no smoking in here, and you can't book, so best to arrive early for a table, or be prepared to wait – it gets very busy after around 7.30. It feels a lot more restauranty than, say, the Eagle, though you can also eat in the bar: rather plainly decorated, but cosy in winter when the roaring fire casts long flickering shadows on the dark panelling. Neatly stacked piles of wood guard either side of the fireplace (which has a stopped clock above it), and there are some well worn green leatherette chairs and stools. Fullers London Pride, Greene King IPA and Old Speckled Hen on handpump with a wide range of carefully chosen wines listed above the bar. Several tables outside overlook the quiet street (not the easiest place to find a parking space). *(Recommended by David Edwards, Simon Rodway, John Chute, Richard Siebert, the Didler)*

Enterprise ~ Lease Fiona Evans and Jamie Wood ~ Real ale ~ Bar food (12.30-2.30 (Sat 3.30 Sun), 7-10.30) ~ Restaurant ~ (020) 8749 1291 ~ Children in eating area of bar and restaurant ~ Dogs allowed in bar ~ Open 11-11; 12-10.30 Sun; closed 24-31 Dec

Atlas 🍽 ♀
Seagrave Road, SW6; ⊖ West Brompton

Influenced by recipes from North Africa, Turkey and Italy, the innovative food at this souped-up local really is excellent, with a creative combination of flavours that results in a very satisfying, enjoyable meal. The menu changes twice a day but might include things like sweet potato and carrot soup with coriander (£4), very good antipasti (£7), grilled quail with pomegranate sauce, chickpea and parsley salad and marinated goats cheese (7.50), grilled tuscan sausages with fennel and black pepper, baked parmesan polenta, and roasted red onions with red wine and orange (£9), tunisian beef tagine with tomato, dates, apricot, turmeric and lemon rice with toasted pine nuts (£10.50), grilled whole mackerel with wild herb couscous, mint yoghurt, red onion and lemon zest (£12.50), and grilled lamb chops with sage, spiced black beans and tomato and chilli jam (£13); their delicious chocolate and almond cake (£4) is usually the only pudding, though they also have soft italian cheese with pear and grilled bread (£5). A downside is simply the place's popularity – tables are highly prized, so if you're planning a meal, arrive early, or swoop quickly. Perhaps more of a black mark is that you may be asked to leave your credit card behind the bar when you order. With a pleasantly bustling feel in the evenings (it's maybe not the place for a quiet dinner), the long, simple knocked-together bar has been well renovated without removing the original features; there's plenty of panelling and dark wooden wall benches, a couple of brick fireplaces, a mix of school chairs, and well spaced tables. Smart young people figure prominently in the mix, but there are plenty of locals too, as well as visitors to the Exhibition Centre at Earls Court (one of the biggest car parks is next door). Well kept Adnams Broadside, Caledonian Deuchars IPA and Fullers London Pride on handpump, and a very good, carefully chosen wine list, with plenty by the glass; big mugs of coffee; friendly service. The piped music is unusual – on various visits we've come across everything from salsa and jazz to vintage TV themes; it can be loud at times. Down at the end is a TV (though big sports events are shown in a room upstairs), by a hatch to the kitchen. Outside is an attractively planted narrow side terrace, with an overhead awning; heaters make it comfortable even in winter. This was the first of a small chain of pubs set up by two brothers; another of the group, the Fox & Hounds, is a main entry in the South London section. *(Recommended by Joel Dobris, Evelyn and Derek Walter, Brenda and Rob Fincham, Dr and Mrs M E Wilson, Tim Maddison)*

Free house ~ Licensees Richard and George Manners, James Gill, Toby Gellis ~ Real ale ~ Bar food (12.30-3, 7-10.30(10 Sun)) ~ (020) 7385 9129 ~ Children welcome till 7pm ~ Dogs welcome ~ Open 12-11(10.30 Sun); closed 24 Dec-1 Jan, and Easter Sat and Sun

Bulls Head

Strand-on-the-Green, W4; ⇌ Kew Bridge

If you get here early enough you should be able to bag one of the tables by the little windows of this atmospheric Thames-side pub, with nice views past attractively planted hanging flower baskets to the river. Comfortably refurbished by Chef & Brewer, a series of cosy rooms rambles up and down steps, with old-fashioned benches built into the simple panelling; black-panelled alcoves make useful cubby-holes, much enjoyed by readers on chilly autumn days. Lots of empty wine bottles are dotted around, and there's plenty of polished dark wood and beams. Served all day, the big menu takes in everything from good sandwiches and filled baguettes (£4.99), through fish and chips (£6.25) and beef and ale pie (£6.95) to green thai curry (£11.25); fresh fish is delivered daily, and there's a separate blackboard with fish specials. Popular Sunday roasts. The downstairs area is no smoking. Three well kept real ales include Fullers London Pride and a changing combination of guests like Adnams Broadside, Charles Wells Bombardier, Timothy Taylors Landlord and Youngs; good service from friendly uniformed staff. The pub can fill up fast. They do pitchers of Pimms in summer, and newspapers are laid out for customers. The original building served as Cromwell's HQ several times during the Civil War. *(Recommended by John Saville, R T and J C Moggridge, Ian Phillips, Russell Lewin, Roger Thornington)*

Spirit Group ~ Manager Andy Cockran ~ Real ale ~ Bar food (12-10) ~ (020) 8994 1204 ~ Children welcome ~ Open 11-11; 12-10.30 Sun

Churchill Arms ◀

Kensington Church Street, W8; ⊖ Notting Hill Gate/High Street Kensington

The wonderfully cheery atmosphere at this bustling old favourite owes a lot to the genial Irish landlord, who's just celebrated his 20th year here. He's very much in evidence, delightedly mixing with customers as he threads his way through the evening crowds, and the atmosphere is very much that of a friendly local; even at its busiest, you can quickly feel at home. In recent years he's put a lot of effort into the extraordinary summer floral displays outside, with every inch of the walls covered with hanging baskets and window boxes; another of his hobbies is collecting butterflies, so you'll see a variety of prints and books on the subject dotted around the bar. There are also countless lamps, miners' lights, horse tack, bedpans and brasses hanging from the ceiling, a couple of interesting carved figures and statuettes behind the central bar counter, prints of American presidents, and lots of Churchill memorabilia. Well kept Fullers Chiswick, ESB, London Pride, and seasonal beers on handpump, with a good choice of wines. The spacious and rather smart plant-filled dining conservatory may be used for hatching butterflies, but is better known for its big choice of excellent authentic thai food, such as a very good, proper thai curry, or various rice, noodle or stir-fried dishes (all £5.85); it's no smoking in here. They do food all day, with other choices including lunchtime baguettes, and a good value Sunday roast (£5.75). Fruit machine, TV; they have their own cricket and football teams. There can be quite an overspill onto the street, where there are some chrome tables and chairs. Even early in the week this isn't really a place for a quiet pint; it can get a bit smoky too. Look out for special events and decorations around Christmas, Hallowe'en, St Patrick's Day and Churchill's birthday (30 November) – along with more people than you'd ever imagine could feasibly fit inside. *(Recommended by Ian Phillips, Tracey and Stephen Groves, Darren Le Poidevin, Pete Walker, LM, Andy and Jill Kassube)*

Fullers ~ Manager Jerry O'Brien ~ Real ale ~ Bar food (12-9.30 (9 Sun)) ~ Restaurant ~ (020) 7727 4242 ~ Children in restaurant ~ Dogs allowed in bar ~ Open 11-11; 12-10.30 Sun; closed evening 25 Dec

Colton Arms

Greyhound Road, W14; ⊖ Barons Court

Like an old-fashioned country pub in town, this genuinely unspoilt little gem (described by readers as 'enchanting' this year) has been kept exactly the same by its dedicated landlord for the last 40 years. The main U-shaped front bar has a log fire blazing in winter, highly polished brasses, a fox's mask, hunting crops and plates decorated with hunting scenes on the walls, and a remarkable collection of handsomely carved 17th-c oak furniture. That room is small enough, and the two back rooms are tiny; each has its own little serving counter, with a bell to ring for service. Well kept Caledonian Deuchars IPA, Fullers London Pride and Wychwood Hobgoblin on handpump (when you pay, note the old-fashioned brass-bound till); the food is limited to sandwiches (weekday lunchtimes only, from £2.60). Pull the curtain aside for the door out to a charming back terrace with a neat rose arbour. The pub is next to the Queens Club tennis courts and gardens *(Recommended by Ian Phillips, Susan and John Douglas, Tracey and Stephen Groves)*

Enterprise ~ Tenants N J and J A Nunn ~ Real ale ~ Bar food (12-2 (not Sun)) ~ No credit cards ~ (020) 7385 6956 ~ Dogs welcome ~ Open 12-3, 5.30-11 Mon-Fri; 12-3.30, 7-11 Sat; 12-4, 7-10.30 Sun; closed 25 Dec, evening 26 Dec, all day Easter Sat, and Easter Sun lunch

Dove

Upper Mall, W6; ⊖ Ravenscourt Park

One of London's most famous riverside pubs, reached by a nice stroll along the Thames footpath, this old-fashioned tavern is said to be where 'Rule Britannia' was composed. The best bit is the delightful back terrace, where the main flagstoned area, down some steps, has a few highly prized teak tables and white metal and teak chairs looking over the low river wall to the Thames reach just above Hammersmith Bridge; there's a tiny exclusive area up a spiral staircase. You'll often see rowing crews out on the water. By the entrance from the quiet alley, the front bar is cosy and traditional, with black panelling, and red leatherette cushioned built-in wall settles and stools around dimpled copper tables; it leads to a bigger, similarly furnished room, with old framed advertisements and photographs of the pub. They stock the full range of Fullers beers, with well kept ESB, London Pride and seasonal beers on handpump; no games machines or piped music. Bar food includes sandwiches, steak and mushroom pie or sausages and mash (£8.25), and daily specials; as we went to press they were also doing a range of all-day snacks. The pub isn't quite so crowded at lunchtimes as it is in the evenings. A plaque marks the level of the highest-ever tide in 1928. *(Recommended by R T and J C Moggridge, Patrick Hancock, the Didler, David Edwards, Simon Rodway)*

Fullers ~ Real ale ~ Bar food (12-2.30, 5-9 Mon-Sat; 12-4 Sun) ~ (020) 8748 9474 ~ Dogs welcome ~ Open 11-11; 12-10.30 Sun

Havelock Tavern 🍴 ♀

Masbro Road, W14; ⊖ ⇌ Kensington (Olympia)

Though it looks rather ordinary, this blue-tiled cornerhouse is a well regarded gastropub, very popular locally for its classy food. Changing twice every day (and generally posted up on their website, www.thehavelocktavern.co.uk), the menu might include things like pea and mint soup (£4), chorizo and chickpea terrine, with gherkins, toast and apple chutney (£6), steamed mussels with melted onions, cider and thyme (£6.50 starter, £8.50 main course), chargrilled fillets of mackerel with baby spinach, new potatoes, smoked bacon, pea and mint (£8.50), penne with buffalo mozzarella, cherry tomatoes, basil, pine nuts and pecorino (£9), chargrilled lamb chop with spiced red lentils, spinach and raita (£10), seared scallops with spiced red lentils, spinach, coriander and lemon (£12), and some unusual cheeses served with apple chutney (£6); you can't book tables. Until 1932 the building was two separate shops (one was a wine merchant, but no one can remember much about the other), and it still has huge shop-front windows along both street-facing walls. The L-shaped bar is plain and unfussy: bare boards, long wooden tables, a mix of chairs and stools, a few soft spotlights, and a fireplace. A second little room with pews leads to a small paved terrace, with benches, a tree, and wall climbers. Well kept (though not cheap) Brakspears, Fullers London Pride and Marstons Pedigree on handpump from the elegant modern bar counter, and a good range of well chosen wines, with around a dozen by the glass; mulled wine in winter, and in May and June perhaps home-made elderflower soda. No music or machines, but backgammon, chess, Scrabble and other board games. Plenty of chat from the mostly smart customers – at busy times it can seem really quite noisy (and can be a little smoky). You may have to wait for a table in the evenings (when some dishes can run out quite quickly), but it can be quieter at lunchtimes, and in the afternoons can have something of the feel of a civilised private club. On weekdays, nearby parking can be limited, though restrictions stop at 5. *(Recommended by Simon Rodway, Mandy and Simon King, Derek Thomas, Ian Phillips, Jack Clark, Mayur Shah, Karen and Graham Oddey)*

Free house ~ Licensees Peter Richnell, Jonny Haughton ~ Real ale ~ Bar food (12.30-2.30(3 Sun), 7-10(9.30 Sun)) ~ No credit cards ~ (020) 7603 5374 ~ Children welcome ~ Dogs welcome ~ Open 11-11; 12-10.30 Sun; closed 22-26 Dec

Portobello Gold ♀ 🍴

Portobello Road, W11; ⊖ Notting Hill Gate

An engaging combination of pub, hotel, restaurant and even Internet café, this Notting Hill stalwart has bounced back from a disastrous fire last autumn. Our favourite part, the rather exotic-seeming back dining room, was particularly affected, but it's been restored in a similar style, with big tropical plants, an impressive wall-to-wall mirror, comfortable wicker chairs, stained wooden tables, and a cage of vocal canaries adding to the outdoor effect. In the old days – when we remember this being a Hells Angels hangout – this was the pub garden, and in summer they still open up the sliding roof. The walls here and in the smaller, brightly painted front bar are covered with changing displays of art and photography; the bar also has a nice old fireplace, cushioned pews, daily papers, and, more unusually, several Internet terminals (some of which disappear in the evening). The atmosphere is cheerfully relaxed, and at times almost bohemian. The Gold was the first place in the UK to serve oyster shooters (a shot glass with an oyster, parmesan, horseradish, crushed chillies, Tabasco and lime), and the good bar food still has something of an emphasis on oysters and seafood. The menu typically includes soup (£4.50), toasted sandwiches (from £5.50), cajun jumbo shrimp (from £5.75), ploughman's (£6), half a dozen irish rock oysters or mussels cooked in a variety of ways (£7), wild boar and apple sausages (£7.50), spicy lamb burger with hummous (£8.50), chicken fajitas (£8.75), fish and chips (£9.95), and puddings like chocolate and amaretti torte served in two sizes (£2.55 small, £4.50 large). They have a good children's menu, and a separate menu for those watching their weight. In the evenings they do a two-course set menu for £20, and they also serve afternoon teas. You can eat from the same menu in the bar or dining room (part of which is no smoking). Opening at 10 for coffee and fresh pastries, the bar has well kept Brakspears and Shepherd Neame Spitfire, as well as a couple of draught belgian beers, Thatcher's farm cider, a good selection of bottled beers from around the world, and a wide range of interesting tequilas and other well sourced spirits; the wine list is particularly good (the landlady has written books on matching wine with food). They also have a cigar menu and various coffees. Polite, helpful young staff; piped music, TV (used only for cricket), chess, backgammon. There are one or two tables and chairs on the pretty street outside, which, like the pub, is named in recognition of the 1769 battle of Portobello, fought over control of the lucrative gold route to Panama. A lively stall is set up outside during the Notting Hill Carnival. Parking nearby is metered; it's not always easy to bag a space. The bedrooms all have free Internet access, and there's a spacious apartment with rooftop terrace (and putting green). *(Recommended by Ian Phillips, Stephen R Holman, Sue Demont, Tim Barrow)*

Unique (Enterprise) ~ Lease Michael Bell and Linda Johnson-Bell ~ Real ale ~ Bar food (12-11(9 Sun)) ~ Restaurant ~ (020) 7460 4910 ~ Children in eating area of bar and restaurant till sundown ~ Dogs allowed in bar ~ Open 10am-midnight; 10-10.30 Sun ~ Bedrooms: /£75S

Warrington ♀ ▣ £
Warrington Crescent, W9; ⊖ Maida Vale

A striking building on the corner of a smart residential street, this late Victorian gin-palace is well worth a look for its opulent art nouveau décor. The main bar has two exquisitely tiled pillars, but the highlight is the splendid marble and mahogany bar counter, topped by an extraordinary structure that's rather like a cross between a carousel and a ship's hull, with cherubs thrown in for good measure. The drawings of nubile young women here and above a row of mirrors on the opposite wall are later additions, very much in keeping with the overall style, and hinting at the days when the building's trade was rather less respectable than it is today. Throughout are elaborately patterned tiles, ceilings and stained glass, and a remarkable number of big lamps and original light fittings; there's a small coal fire, and high ceiling fans for summer. At the end is a particularly comfortable area with tables around a long curved cushioned wall seat, and alcoves containing elegant light fittings in the shape of dancers. It's very much a bustling local, with a real buzz of conversation from the broad mix of customers; some areas can get smoky at times. There's a similar but simpler public bar, with darts and a big-screen TV for sports. Well kept Fullers ESB and London Pride, Shepherd Neame Spitfire, Youngs Special and a changing guest like Caledonian Deuchars IPA on handpump; all their 20 wines are available by the glass, and the bottles are displayed around the top of the bar counter. Service is friendly and efficient. Though it looks thoroughly english, the upstairs evening restaurant is a very good value thai, with main courses at around £6, and specials rarely more than £7.85; it's no smoking in here. The same food is available in the bar at lunchtimes. No music, but quite a few games machines. There are plenty of picnic sets to the side of the pub, overlooking the street, with heaters for winter. *(Recommended by Tracey and Stephen Groves, Alan and Carolin Tidbury, Rob Razzell)*

Free house ~ Licensee John Brandon ~ Real ale ~ Bar food (12-2.30) ~ Restaurant (6-10.30) ~ (020) 7286 2929 ~ Dogs welcome ~ Open 11-11; 12-10.30 Sun

---

Bedroom prices normally include full English breakfast, VAT and any inclusive service charge that we know of. Prices before the '/' are for single rooms, after for two people in double or twin (B includes a private bath, S a private shower). If there is no '/', the prices are only for twin or double rooms (as far as we know there are no singles).

White Horse ♀ ◥

Parsons Green, SW6; ⊖ Parsons Green

The expertly selected range of drinks is one of the highlights of this very well run pub, but the attentive service impresses too: one reader visiting on a rare quiet day was pleasantly surprised that the barman was happy to fetch a particular bottle of wine from the cellar and open it just for one glass. They're keen to encourage people to match the right drink to their food (and particularly to select beers as they might wines), so every item on the menu, whether it be scrambled egg or raspberry and coconut tart, has a suggested accompaniment listed beside it, perhaps a wine, perhaps a bottled beer. Six perfectly kept real ales might include Adnams Broadside, Brakspears, Fullers ESB, Harveys Sussex, Oakham JHB and Roosters Yankee; they also have five well chosen draught beers from overseas such as Sierra Nevada Pale Ale or Alaskan Smoked Porter, as well as 15 Trappist beers, around 50 other foreign bottled beers, a dozen malt whiskies, and a constantly expanding range of good, interesting and reasonably priced wines. The good bar food might include sandwiches (£4.50), ploughman's (with some unusual cheeses, £5.50), roast pumpkin salad with pine nuts, goats cheese, red onion and rosemary (£7.75), cep risotto with shaved parmesan and rocket (£8.25), pork sausages and mash with cabbage and beer onion gravy or salt and lemon pepper squid with tomato and coriander (£8.75), irish stew (£9.75), pan-fried mullet on paella rice with chorizo and saffron (£10.75) and chargrilled rib-eye steak with handcut chips and green peppercorn butter (£13.75). There's usually something to eat available all day; at weekends they do a good brunch menu, and in winter they do a popular Sunday lunch. Looking very smart these days, the stylishly modernised U-shaped bar has plenty of sofas, wooden tables, huge windows with slatted wooden blinds, and winter coal and log fires, one in an elegant marble fireplace. The pub is usually busy (and can feel crowded at times), but there are enough smiling, helpful staff behind the solid panelled central servery to ensure you'll rarely have to wait too long to be served. All the art displayed is for sale. The back restaurant is no smoking. On summer evenings the front terrace overlooking the green has something of a continental feel, with crowds of people drinking al fresco; in spring and summer you'll usually find an excellent barbecue out here Fri-Sun, when the pub's appeal to smart young people is more apparent than ever. They have quarterly beer festivals, often spotlighting regional breweries. (Recommended by LM, the Didler, Jack and Jill Gilbert, Martin and Karen Wake, Ian Phillips, Sue Demont, Tim Barrow, Tracey and Stephen Groves)

Mitchells & Butlers ~ Manager Mark Dorber ~ Real ale ~ Bar food (12-3.30, 6-10; snacks 3.30-6) ~ Restaurant ~ (020) 7736 2115 ~ Children in eating area of bar and restaurant ~ Dogs allowed in bar ~ Open 11-11; 11-10.30 Sun; closed 25-26 Dec

Windsor Castle

Campden Hill Road, W8; ⊖ Holland Park/Notting Hill Gate

This atmospheric Victorian pub now has barbecues most summer days in its big, tree-shaded garden, easily one of the best pub gardens in London. It's always busy out here when the sun's shining, but there's quite a secluded feel thanks to the high ivy-covered sheltering walls. The garden has its own bar in summer, as well as heaters for cooler days, and lots of tables and chairs on the flagstones. The pub's appeal is just as strong in winter, when the series of tiny unspoilt rooms, with their time-smoked ceilings and dark wooden furnishings, seems especially cosy and inviting. Each has to be entered through a separate door, so it can be quite a challenge finding the people you've arranged to meet – more often than not they'll be hidden behind the high backs of the sturdy built-in elm benches. A cosy pre-war-style dining room opens off, and soft lighting and a coal-effect fire add to the wonderfully old-fashioned feel. Served pretty much all day, bar food includes ciabattas (from £5.25), chicken caesar salad or lamb and mint burger (£7.50), aberdeen angus beefburger (£8.50), steamed mussels (£7.95), various sausages with mash and onion gravy (£9), fish and chips (£9.25), and specials like roast bass with spicy couscous (£13.50); they do a choice of roasts on Sunday (£9.95), when the range of other dishes may be more limited. Three real ales such as Adnams Broadside, Caledonian Deuchars IPA and Timothy Taylors Landlord on handpump, along with decent house wines, various malt whiskies, jugs of Pimms in summer, and perhaps mulled wine in winter. No fruit machines or piped music. Usually fairly quiet at lunchtime – when several areas are no smoking – but the pub can be packed some evenings. The bones of Thomas Paine are said to be buried in the cellar, after his son sold them to the landlord to settle a beer debt. (Recommended by Tracey and Stephen Groves, Jo Lilley, Simon Calvert, Giles and Annie Francis, Susie Symes, Ian Phillips)

Mitchells & Butlers ~ Manager Richard Bell ~ Real ale ~ Bar food (12-4, 5-10; 12-9 Sun) ~ (020) 7243 9551 ~ Dogs welcome ~ Open 12-11(10.30 Sun)

LUCKY DIP

Besides the fully inspected pubs, you might like to try these Lucky Dips recommended to us and described by readers (if you do, please send us reports: www.goodguides.co.uk).

CENTRAL LONDON

EC1

☆ **Bishops Finger** [W Smithfield, opp Bart's]: Comfortable and smartly civilised, with yellow walls, big windows and close-set elegant tables on polished boards, full Shepherd Neame beer range kept particularly well, plenty of wines by the glass, several ports and champagnes, decent coffee, daily papers, lunchtime food from open kitchen inc ciabattas, speciality sausages, a few dishes such as lamb chops and Thurs/Fri fish and chips, friendly service, more room upstairs; children welcome, a couple of tables outside, open all day, cl wknds (Ian Phillips, Jarrod and Wendy Hopkinson, Dr and Mrs A K Clarke, LYM, Michael Dandy)

☆ **Bleeding Heart** [Bleeding Heart Yard, off Greville St]: Airy contemporary bar with café tables on scrubbed boards, neat staff, well kept Adnams Bitter, Broadside and a seasonal beer from ornate mahogany-and-mirrors counter, good choice of wines by the glass; emphasis on good if not cheap french food in downstairs open-kitchen candlelit restaurant – an extraordinary maze of cellars (beware the 12½ % service charge); breakfast from 7, cl wknds (Sue Demont, Tim Barrow, BB, John Evans, Tracey and Stephen Groves)

Butchers Hook & Cleaver [W Smithfield]: Attractive bank conversion, now a Fullers Ale & Pie House, their full ale range kept well, good value food from nibbles and baguettes up, wkdy breakfast from 7.30am, friendly staff, relaxed atmosphere, nice mix of chairs inc some button-back leather armchairs, wrought-iron spiral stairs to pleasant mezzanine with waitress service; big-screen sports TV; open all day (BB, Ian Phillips, Michael Dandy)

☆ **Hand & Shears** [Middle St]: Traditional Smithfield pub dating from 16th c, three rooms around central servery, hubbub of lively conversation, Courage ales, quick friendly service, interesting bric-a-brac, reasonably priced food – evening too; open all day but cl weekends (LYM, Tracey and Stephen Groves)

Living Room [West Smithfield]: Cosy, elegant and unusual piano bar/restaurant; open all day till late (cl Sat lunchtime and Sun evening), other branches in London and other big cities (Ron Deighton)

Melton Mowbray [Holborn]: Large popular pastiche of Edwardian pub with lots of woodwork, etched glass, front button-back banquettes (opening in summer on to pavement café tables), back booths, small back mezzanine gallery; well kept Fullers ales, good food service – Melton Mowbray pies among other dishes (Dr and Mrs M E Wilson)

Mill [St John St]: Modernised corner pub with brasserie feel especially downstairs, foreign beers on tap, good coffees, enjoyable up-to-date food; fold-away walls opening to pavement picnic-sets (Ian Phillips)

Printworks [Farringdon Rd/Ray St]: Civilised Wetherspoons in former basement printworks of the old Guardian newspaper office, their usual food and good beer choice inc lots of bottled beers from around the world (Keith and Chris O'Neill)

Sekforde Arms [Sekforde St]: Small and comfortably simple corner local with friendly licensees, full Youngs beer range kept well, wide choice of well priced standard food (busy at lunchtime), nice pictures inc Spy caricatures, upstairs restaurant, darts, cards and board games; pavement tables (the Didler, C J Fletcher, Andy and Jill Kassube)

Sutton Arms [Carthusian St]: Uncluttered L-shaped bar with small tables on bare boards and little décor beyond big brewery mirrors and four large busts on prints, friendly staff, Adnams and Fullers London Pride, unusual lagers, upstairs dining room (Ian Phillips, Tracey and Stephen Groves)

EC2

☆ **Dirty Dicks** [Bishopsgate]: Popular re-creation of traditional City tavern with barrel tables in bare-boards bar, interesting old prints inc one of Nathaniel Bentley the strange original Dirty Dick, Youngs full beer range kept well, enjoyable food inc open sandwiches, baguettes and reasonably priced hot dishes, pleasant service, cellar wine bar with wine racks overhead in brick barrel-vaulted ceiling; loads of character – fun for foreign visitors *(LYM, the Didler, Stephen and Jean Curtis)*

☆ *Fox* [Paul St]: Basic well worn furnishings in lively bare-boards bar, intimate smarter upstairs dining room with friendly helpful service and appealing canopied terrace, good enterprising fixed-price lunches (same small group as Eagle in Farringdon Rd – see main entries), well kept Charles Wells Bombardier, decent wines, good coffee; may be piped jazz; dogs welcome, open all day, cl wknds *(LYM, Richard Siebert, Jo Lilley, Simon Calvert)*

☆ *Hamilton Hall* [Bishopsgate; also entrance from Liverpool St station]: Big busy Wetherspoons showpiece, flamboyant Victorian baroque décor, plaster nudes and fruit mouldings, chandeliers, mirrors, upper mezzanine, good-sized no smoking mezzanine, comfortable groups of seats, reliable food all day from well filled sandwiches and baked potatoes to steaks and good curry nights, lots of well kept real ales inc interesting guest beers, decent wines, good prices; silenced machines, can get crowded; tables outside, open all day *(Ian Phillips, Kevin Blake, LYM)*

Old Dr Butlers Head [Masons Ave]: 17th-c beamed City pub with more seating than usual, bare boards, dark wood, cream paint, small-paned windows, small tables around big irregularly shaped main room, raised back area with more tables, full Shepherd Neame ale range kept well (tasters offered), prompt friendly service, substantial bar food from filled cobs up, panelled upstairs lunchtime chop house *(Derek Thomas, Susan and John Douglas, Rona Murdoch)*

EC3

Hoop & Grapes [Aldgate High St]: Originally late 17th-c, dismantled and rebuilt 1983, with Jacobean staircase, carved oak doorposts and age-blackened oak serving counter; long narrow beamed and timbered bar with popular lunchtime food, Adnams and Fullers London Pride, back games area with pool; SkyTV; open all day *(Anthony Double)*

Jamaica Wine House [St Michael's Alley, Cornhill]: In a warren of small alleys, Courage and Charles Wells Bombardier as well as their wide choice of wines, downstairs bar and dining area *(Ian Phillips)*

Lamb [Grand Ave, Leadenhall Mkt]: Old-fashioned stand-up bar with bustling atmosphere (can get very busy), well kept Youngs ale, engraved glass, plenty of ledges and shelves, spiral stairs up to small light and airy no smoking carpeted gallery overlooking market's central crossing, corner servery doing good hot carvery rolls; also basement bar with shiny wall tiling and own entrance *(Valerie Baker, Dr and Mrs M E Wilson, Ian Phillips, N R White)*

New Moon [Gracechurch St]: Long busy bare-boards bar, fancy plasterwork in high red ceiling, Adnams and Fullers London Pride *(Dr and Mrs M E Wilson)*

Ship [Talbot Ct, off Eastcheap]: Quaint and interesting bare-boards courtyard pub full of City types, well kept Bass, Fullers London Pride and Greene King IPA and Old Speckled Hen, simple low-priced lunchtime food *(Ian Phillips)*

Swan [Ship Tavern Passage, off Gracechurch St]: Bustling narrow flagstoned bar, larger carpeted upstairs room, neatly kept Victorian panelled décor, friendly staff, generous lunchtime sandwiches, particularly well kept Fullers and a guest such as Caledonian Deuchars IPA; can get packed early wkdy evenings *(Tracey and Stephen Groves, N R White)*

EC4

Centre Page [Knightrider St]: Row of window booths in narrow entrance room, more space beyond, Dickensian style, pleasant efficient staff, simple appetising menu, well kept Fullers London Pride and Marstons Pedigree, good tea; piped chamber music *(Tim and Ann Newell, N R White)*

Cockpit [St Andrews Hill/Ireland Pl, off Queen Victoria St]: Lots of atmosphere in friendly little corner pub nr St Pauls, Courage Best and Directors and Marstons Pedigree, food from sandwiches and baked potatoes through cornish pasties and omelettes to steak and kidney pie and fish and chips *(Ian Phillips)*

Old Bell [Fleet St, nr Ludgate Circus]: Fine old traditional tavern backing on to St Brides the wedding-cake church, brass-topped tables, stained-glass bow window, good choice of well kept changing ales from island servery, friendly service, good value standard food, coal fire, lively atmosphere, some tables tucked away to give a sense of privacy; can get smoky when crowded *(BB, Ian Phillips, Jarrod and Wendy Hopkinson, the Didler, N R White)*

SW1

☆ *Buckingham Arms* [Petty France]: Chatty and welcoming 18th-c Youngs local with elegant mirrors and woodwork, unusual long side corridor fitted out with elbow ledge for drinkers (and SkyTV for motor sports), well kept ales, good value food lunchtime and evening, reasonable prices, service friendly and efficient even when busy, no music; dogs welcome, handy for Buckingham Palace, Westminster Abbey and St James's Park, open all day *(LYM, Dr and Mrs A K Clarke, Tracey and Stephen Groves, A Boss, the Didler, Mike Tucker)*

Cask & Glass [Palace St]: Inviting panelled room overflowing into street in summer – colourful flowers then; good range of well kept Shepherd Neame beers, friendly local atmosphere, good value lunchtime sandwiches, old prints and model aircraft; handy for Queen's Gallery *(R T and J C Moggridge)*

☆ *Fox & Hounds* [Passmore St/Graham Terr]: Small cosy bar with well kept ales such as Adnams, Bass, Greene King IPA and Harveys, bar food, friendly staff, wall benches, big hunting prints, old sepia photographs of pubs and customers, some toby jugs, hanging plants under attractive skylight in back room, coal-effect gas fire and organ; can be very busy Fri night, quieter wkdy lunchtimes *(Dr and Mrs A K Clarke, the Didler)*

Gallery [Lupus St, opp Pimlico tube station]: Modern light and airy décor, attractive prints and bric-a-brac, no smoking area, Bass, Courage Best, Greene King Abbot and Shepherd Neame Spitfire, reliable varied food; disabled access and lavatories (conventional ones down stairs) *(Mark Doughty)*

Golden Lion [King St]: Rather distinguished bow-fronted building opp Christies auction rooms, well kept ales inc Fullers London Pride, decent wines by the glass, good value food, friendly atmosphere; if downstairs bar busy, seats and tables usually available both in passageway alongside or upstairs in theatre bar *(Dr and Mrs M E Wilson, J F M and M West, Craig Turnbull)*

Jugged Hare [Vauxhall Bridge Rd/Rochester Row]: Popular Fullers Ale & Pie pub in impressive former colonnaded bank with balustraded balcony, chandelier, prints and busts; their ales kept well, friendly efficient service, reasonably priced traditional food from sandwiches up, no smoking back area; fruit machine, unobtrusive piped music; open all day *(BB, the Didler, Sue Demont, Tim Barrow, Mark Doughty, Andy and Jill Kassube)*

Marquis of Granby [Romney St/Dean Bradley St]: Big open-plan pub, well kept Fullers London Pride and a guest beer such as Timothy Taylors Landlord, cosy old settles and chandeliers behind long straight bar, lunchtime food, very busy then and early evenings; open all day, cl wknds *(Tracey and Stephen Groves)*

☆ *Morpeth Arms* [Millbank]: Roomy and comfortable nicely preserved Victorian pub facing MI6 HQ across River Thames, some etched and cut glass, old books and prints, photographs, earthenware jars and bottles, full Youngs beer range kept well, good choice of reasonably priced food from sandwiches up, good choice of wines, helpful well organised service even when it's packed at lunchtime (useful overflow upstairs), quieter evenings; seats outside (a lot of traffic), handy for Tate Britain *(BB, Dr and Mrs A K Clarke, Tracey and Stephen Groves, the Didler, R T and J C Moggridge, John Saville, Mike Gorton, Mark Doughty)*

Orange Brewery [Pimlico Rd]: Friendly panelled bar, all-day cheap food inc various pies and good sausages, well kept Fullers London Pride and Greene King Abbot, no smoking eating area; some seats outside *(LYM, Roger Thornington)*

Paxtons Head [Knightsbridge]: Peaceful Victorian pub, Adnams, Fullers London Pride and Charles Wells Bombardier from large attractive central bar with gas lamps and etched glass and mirrors from Paxton's Crystal Palace, standard pub food and full asian menu in upstairs restaurant, nice little cellar overflow bar *(Ian Phillips)*

Red Lion [Parliament St]: Convivial pub nr Houses of Parliament, with Division Bell – used by MPs and Foreign Office staff; parliamentary cartoons and prints, well kept real ale, decent wines by the glass, good range of food from good panini up, efficient staff, small narrow no smoking upstairs dining room; also cellar bar and *(Dr and Mrs A K Clarke, John and Gloria Isaacs)*

Three Crowns [Babmaes St]: Smart pub just off Jermyn St, comfortable armchairs, button-back settees and bentwood chairs, dark oak panelling and ceiling, Adnams, Courage and Charles Wells Bombardier, friendly service *(Dr and Mrs M E Wilson)*

Two Chairmen [Warwick House St]: Pleasant tucked-away pub with Courage Best and Fullers London Pride, daily papers, pubby food upstairs *(Ian Phillips)*

Walkers of Whitehall [Whitehall]: Pleasant three-bar pub with comfortable sofas in basement, Fullers London Pride and Greene King Old Speckled Hen on handpump *(Robert Lester)*

Wetherspoons [Victoria station]: Cheap ever-changing real ales inc interesting guest beers, wide choice of reasonably priced food all day, decent wines, prompt friendly service, good housekeeping; great for people-watchers, with glass-walled upper level and tables outside overlooking the main concourse and platform indicators *(Sue Demont, Tim Barrow)*

SW3

Builders Arms [Britten St]: Smart bistro-style pub, light and colourful, with bookshelves and artwork, good food (drinkers welcomed too), good choice of wines by the glass, new no smoking dining area; attractive street *(Derek Thomas)*

Crown [Dovehouse St]: Small modern pub recently revitalised by welcoming young licensees, homely but stylish, with clear windows and soft pastel colours, lovingly prepared unpretentious food, well kept Adnams and Fullers, quick unobtrusive service *(Victoria Fuller)*

W1

Angel in the Fields [Thayer St/Marylebone High St]: Proper workmanlike pub with well kept Sam Smiths, more room upstairs *(LYM, Tracey and Stephen Groves)*

☆ *Audley* [Mount St]: Classic Mayfair pub, civilised and relaxed, with opulent red plush, rich mahogany and engraved glass, clock hanging in lovely carved wood bracket from ornately corniced ceiling, well kept Courage Directors and Youngs from long polished bar, good food (reasonably priced for the area) and service, good coffee, upstairs panelled dining room, large no smoking area; open all day *(Dr and Mrs A K Clarke, LYM, Kevin Blake, Catherine and Richard Preston)*

Barley Mow [Dorset St]: Workmanlike 18th-c pub, its small basic front bar made unusual by the three swiftly-bagged 19th-c cubicles opening on to serving counter (where poor farmers pawned their watches to the landlord in privacy); Adnams Broadside, Greene King IPA, Marstons Pedigree and Charles Wells Bombardier, all-day panini, good value lunchtime two-for-one offers, wooden floors and panelled walls, old pictures, tiny back parlour; piped music, TV; pavement café tables *(Ian Phillips, Dr and Mrs M E Wilson, Nick Holding, the Didler, Sue Demont, Tim Barrow, BB)*

☆ *Clachan* [Kingly St]: Lovely wooden bar, ornate plaster ceiling supported by two large fluted and decorated pillars, comfortable screened leather banquettes, smaller drinking alcove up three or four steps, Adnams, Fullers London Pride and Greene King IPA, good service from hard-working smart staff, above-average food inc scotch eggs and pork pies; can get busy, but very relaxed in afternoons *(BB, Sue Demont, Tim Barrow)*

Cock [Great Portland St]: Big corner local with enormous lamps over picnic-sets outside, florid Victorian/Edwardian décor with handsome wood and plasterwork, some cut and etched glass, high tiled ceiling and mosaic floor, velvet curtains, coal-effect gas fire, well kept cheap Sam Smiths OB from all four handpumps, popular food (not Fri-Sun evenings) in upstairs lounge with two more coal-effect gas fires, ploughman's downstairs to 12-6, friendly efficient service; can get smoky *(the Didler, Dr and Mrs M E Wilson, Nick Holding, Ian Phillips)*

De Hems [Macclesfield St]: Typical London pub recycled as pastiche of a dutch bar (but roomier and less intimate than those tend to be), old dutch engravings, big continental founts and good range of interesting bottled beers, friendly service *(Jasmeet Fyfe, Tracey and Stephen Groves)*

Dover Castle [Weymouth Mews]: Simple yet quite elegant and comfortably old-fashioned, with panelling and old prints, charming back snug, cheap Sam Smiths OB, good range of bar food inc substantial all-day breakfast *(Dr and Mrs A K Clarke, Nick Holding, John and Gloria Isaacs)*

Duke of Wellington [Crawford St]: Friendly little pub with lots of pictures, toby jugs and Wellington memorabilia, warm and comfortable; salt beef speciality, well kept Adnams and Charles Wells Bombardier, simple pub food lunchtime and evening, genial relaxed antipodean staff; pavement tables *(Ian Phillips, Tracey and Stephen Groves)*

Fitzroy [Charlotte St]: Traditional pub with grand mahogany servery, maroon leather and handsome frosted glass and mirrors, photographs of customers Augustus John, Dylan Thomas and the young Richard Attenborough, George Orwell's NUJ card and so forth, quieter carpeted downstairs bar with white-painted brickwork, wooden settles, a couple of snugs and perhaps poetry readings, low-priced Sam Smiths OB, good value food inc filled baguettes, expert friendly staff; may be piped music; plenty of tables out under cocktail parasols, popular in summer *(Ian Phillips, Rob Razzell)*

French House [Dean St]: Theatre memorabilia, good wines by the glass (keg beers) and lively chatty atmosphere – mainly standing room *(Tracey and Stephen Groves)*

Golden Eagle [Marylebone Lane]: Tastefully renovated Victorian pub with traditional features but modern feel, well kept St Austell and other beers, fresh flowers, friendly service; piano singalong Thurs and Fri *(Tim Maddison)*

Hope [Tottenham St/Whitfield St]: Cosy two-floor proper traditional local with well kept Adnams, Everards Tiger, Fullers London Pride, Timothy Taylors Landlord and Charles Wells Bombardier, lunchtime sausages; pavement tables *(Tim Maddison, Sue Demont, Tim Barrow)*

John Snow [Broadwick St]: Character pub with low-priced Sam Smiths OB, food in upstairs lounge, ornately framed and elaborately engraved glass, engravings of old London and Thames, documentation of Dr Snow who discovered that cholera was water-borne in 1854 – a pump outside was implicated *(Ian Phillips)*

Kings Arms [Shepherd Market]: Minimalist décor, good value standard bar food from sandwiches up, changing real ales; upper gallery, summer pavement overflow *(LYM, Ian Phillips)*

Newman Arms [Rathbone St/Newman Passage]: Well kept Fullers and Youngs in small panelled bar with nautical memorabilia, home-made pies in small room upstairs, good friendly staff and character landlord of the old school *(Tim Maddison)*

☆ *O'Conor Don* [Marylebone Lane]: Civilised family-run bare-boards pub, genuinely and unobtrusively irish, with pubby tables and chairs on dark bare boards, elbow shelf right around frosted glass windows, high plastered ceiling, good value unusual menu inc good baguettes, waitress drinks service (to make sure the Guinness has settled properly), warm bustling atmosphere, daily papers, good upstairs restaurant with daily fresh Galway oysters; may be piped 1970s pop music, basement bar open till late Thurs; handy for the Wallace Collection *(BB, John and Gloria Isaacs, Ian Phillips, Tim Maddison)*

☆ *Old Coffee House* [Beak St]: Civilised and welcoming pub with wide choice of bargain lunchtime food (not Sun) in upstairs food room full of prints and pictures, well kept Courage Directors, Marstons Pedigree and Youngs Special, some interesting bric-a-brac; fruit machine, piped music, children allowed upstairs 12-3, open all day exc Sun afternoon; very popular with wknd shoppers and tourists *(Patrick Hancock, LYM, Ian Phillips, Peter Coxon)*

Red Lion [Kingly St]: Narrow rather dark front bar with deep leather banquettes, back bar with darts, well kept low-priced Sam Smiths, bargain simple lunchtime food from baguettes up in comfortable upstairs lounge *(Ian Phillips, DC, BB)*

Three Tuns [Portman Mews S]: Large bare-boards front bar and sizeable lounge/dining area with beams and nooks and crannies, Courage Directors, Charles Wells Bombardier and Youngs Special, pubby food from panini up *(Ian Phillips)*

☆ *Toucan* [Carlisle St]: Small Guinness pub that grows on you, five taps for it in relaxed dark and cosy basement bar with toucan paintings and vintage Guinness advertisements, lots of whiskeys and good irish piped music, enjoyable food 11-5 such as Guinness pie, irish stew, Galway oysters, good service though they say Peter the long-serving expert barman is now in Italy; plainer upstairs overflow bar, quiet TV in both bars; open all day, cl till 5.30 Sun *(BB, Rona Murdoch, Tim Maddison)*

Waxy O'Connors [Rupert St]: Small ordinary street entry to entertaining 3D maze of communicating areas on several levels, largely gothic décor, friendly young staff, good if not cheap food 12-7, keg beers; can be packed at night with young up-front people (good piped rock music), quiet daytime – open all day *(BB, Sue Demont, Tim Barrow, Peter Coxon)*

W2

☆ *Mad Bishop & Bear* [Paddington station]: Up escalators from concourse, city-pub décor in cream and pastels, ornate plasterwork, etched mirrors and fancy lamps inc big brass chandeliers, parquet, tiles and carpet, booths with leather banquettes, lots of wood and prints, a guest beer and full Fullers beer range kept well from long counter, good wine choice, friendly smartly dressed staff, wide choice of good value food from breakfast (7.30 on) and sandwiches to Sun roasts, big no smoking area, train departures screen; soft piped music, fruit machine; open all day, tables out overlooking concourse *(Susan and Nigel Wilson, Dr and Mrs A K Clarke, BB, Dr and Mrs M E Wilson, Roger Huggins, Tom and Alex McLean)*

WC1

Bull & Mouth [Bloomsbury Way/New Oxford St]: Light and roomy, with good service, great beer choice, wide choice of enjoyable food *(Stephen R Holman)*

Calthorpe Arms [Grays Inn Rd]: Relaxed and civilised corner pub with plush wall seats, Youngs beers, big helpings of popular food upstairs lunchtime and evening, good staff under friendly long-serving landlord; nice pavement tables, open all day *(Patrick Hancock, the Didler, C J Fletcher)*

Dolphin [Red Lion St]: Small and cottagey, high stools and wide shelves around the walls, old photographs, horsebrasses, hanging copper pots and pans and so forth inside, simple wkdy lunchtime food, and real ales such as Bass, Boddingtons, Brakspears and Fullers London Pride; seats and flower-filled window boxes outside, open all day wkdys, plus Sat lunchtime *(Ian Phillips, the Didler)*

☆ *Duke* [Roger St]: Quietly placed and unpretentious, with emphasis on surprisingly good distinctive modern food at reasonable prices; real ales such as Adnams and Greene King, friendly helpful staff, cool and welcoming young atmosphere (big Lichtenstein-style pictures), Formica-top tables and café chairs on worn lino in main bar, fresh colours, daily papers and relaxed village-local atmosphere in longer back room with log-effect gas fire, upstairs dining room; piped music *(Tracey and Stephen Groves, Ian Phillips, BB, Dr and Mrs M E Wilson)*

Harrison [Harrison St]: Good atmosphere and décor in recently refurbished backstreet pub, emphasis on enjoyable lunchtime food, not excessively priced *(Jonathon Judge)*

Museum Tavern [Museum St/Gt Russell St]: Traditional high-ceilinged Victorian pub facing British Museum, busy lunchtime and early evening, but can be quite peaceful other times, well kept Courage Directors, Fullers London Pride, Theakstons Old Peculier and Youngs Bitter and Special, several wines by the glass, good hot drinks, straightforward food from end servery; one or two tables out under gas lamps, open all day *(LYM, Ian Phillips, Craig Turnbull, Barry Collett)*

Pakenham Arms [Pakenham St]: Relaxed unspoilt split-level local, quiet at lunchtime and wknds, well kept real ales, friendly staff, generous food, big open doors making it light and airy in summer; picnic-sets outside, lots of flowers *(C J Fletcher, Patrick Hancock, Stephen and Jean Curtis)*

Plough [Museum St/Little Russell St]: Neatly kept two-bar Bloomsbury local with well kept Adnams, Fullers London Pride, Charles Wells Bombardier and Youngs, upstairs no smoking room with ploughman's and simple reasonably priced hot food *(Ian Phillips)*

Queens Larder [Queen Sq]: Small pleasant pub on corner of traffic-free square and cobbled Cosmo Place, also known as Queen Charlotte (where she stored goodies for her mad husband George III whose hospital was nearby); small tables around attractive and subtly lit U-shaped bar, well kept Adnams, Bass, Fullers London Pride and guest beers, decent low-priced food in attractive upstairs room; plenty of tables outside *(Sue Demont, Tim Barrow, LYM, Tracey and Stephen Groves)*

Rugby [Great James St]: Sizeable corner pub with well kept Shepherd Neame ales inc their seasonal beer from central servery, decent usual food, good service; tables on pleasant terrace *(the Didler)*

Swintons [Swinton St]: Modern wkdy dining pub, friendly service, extensive wine list as well as draught and bottled beer; no TVs or machines *(Martin Ballans)*

Union [Lloyd Baker St]: Victorian pub converted to bar/restaurant while keeping much period décor and furnishings, well kept Courage Directors and Fullers London Pride, sensibly short choice of enjoyable food, pleasant service *(Nigel and Sue Foster)*

WC2

☆ *Chandos* [St Martins Lane]: Busy downstairs bare-boards bar with snug cubicles, lots of theatre memorabilia on stairs up to more comfortable lounge with opera photographs, low wooden tables, panelling, leather sofas, orange, red and yellow leaded windows; well kept cheap Sam Smiths OB, prompt cheerful mainly antipodean service, generous reasonably priced food from sandwiches to Sun roasts, air conditioning, darts and pinball; can get packed early evening, piped music and games machines; note the automaton on the roof (working 10-2 and 4-9); children upstairs till 6, open all day from 9 (for breakfast) *(Susan and Nigel Wilson, Ian Phillips, Patrick Hancock, LYM, Craig Turnbull, Bruce Bird)*

Coach & Horses [Wellington St]: Small friendly and spotless irish pub with imported Dublin Guinness (at a price) from old-fashioned copper-topped bar, well kept mainstream real ales, lots of whiskeys, barman with computer-like drinks order memory, good lunchtime hot roast beef baps; can get crowded, handy for Royal Opera House *(Giles and Annie Francis)*

Cove [Piazza, Covent Garden]: Cornish-style nautical-theme bar above cornish pasty shop, small (may be crowded) with wood and flagstones, seats out on balcony overlooking cobbled piazza with its entertainers; Skinners Cornish Knocker and Betty Stogs and St Austell HSD and Tribute, pasties from downstairs *(Catherine Pitt)*

☆ *Cross Keys* [Endell St/Betterton St]: Friendly and cosy, refreshingly un-Londonish, with masses of photographs and posters inc Beatles memorabilia, brassware and tasteful bric-a-brac on the dark dim-lit walls, relaxed chatty feel, bargain food inc impressive range of lunchtime sandwiches and a few hot dishes, well kept Courage Best and guests such as Charles Wells Bombardier and Youngs, decent wines by the glass, quick service even at busy times; small upstairs bar, often used for functions; fruit machine, gents' down stairs; picnic-sets out on cobbles tucked behind a little group of trees, pretty flower tubs and hanging baskets, open all day *(the Didler, Ian Phillips, John and Gloria Isaacs, LYM, David Crook, Sue Demont, Tim Barrow)*

Globe [Bow St]: Nicholsons pub opposite Royal Opera House, their usual menu, Adnams, Fullers London Pride and Greene King IPA *(anon)*

Marquis of Granby [Chandos Pl]: Long narrow squeezed-in pub with high window stools overlooking street, well kept Adnams, Fullers London Pride and Greene King IPA, reasonably priced pub food, daily papers; open all day *(the Didler, Ian Phillips)*

Montagu Pyke [Charing Cross Rd]: Wetherspoons Lloyds No 1 with emphasis on lagers and cocktails, four well kept real ales too, and worth knowing particularly at quieter times of day for its bargain prices for food and drinks inc coffee, and what is at those times a very spacious and leisurely spread of different comfortable areas with minimalist up-to-date décor; plasma TV screens, quiet piped music then; open all day *(LYM, Ian Phillips)*

Moon Under Water [Leicester Sq]: Well placed Wetherspoons with reasonably priced beers and generous good value food all day *(B Shelley)*

Prince of Wales [Drury Lane]: Big neatly kept corner pub with smart friendly staff, Fullers London Pride, Greene King Abbot, Charles Wells Bombardier and Youngs, simple pubby food *(Ian Phillips)*

☆ *Salisbury* [St Martins Lane]: Stunning Victorian décor fresh from recent renovation, gilded figurines and gleaming mahogany, theatrical sweeps of red velvet, huge sparkling mirrors and cut and etched glass, well upholstered banquettes, well kept Courage Directors, McMullens Country and Frolic, Charles Wells Bombardier and Youngs Bitter and Special, decent house wines, friendly helpful staff, pubby food from sandwiches and ploughman's up, no smoking back room *(Derek Thomas, BB, Mike Gorton, the Didler, Paul Boot, Dr and Mrs A K Clarke, Susan and John Douglas, Ian Phillips, Peter Coxon, John and Gloria Isaacs)*

Sherlock Holmes [Northumberland St; aka Northumberland Arms]: Fine collection of Holmes memorabilia, inc complete model of his apartment, also silent videos of black and white Holmes films; well kept Fullers London Pride and a beer brewed for the pub, usual furnishings, quick service from lunchtime food counter, young staff, upstairs restaurant; busy lunchtime *(Dr and Mrs A K Clarke, BB, John Saville)*

Ship & Shovell [Craven Passage, off Craven St]: Two bars facing each other across passage under Charing X station, four Badger real ales kept well, decent reasonably priced food from wide range of baguettes, bloomers and ciabattas up, good friendly service, bright lighting, pleasant décor inc interesting prints, mainly naval (to support a fanciful connection between this former coal-heavers' pub properly called Ship & Shovel with Sir Cloudesley Shovell the early 18th-c admiral), compact back section; TV, can be smoky *(Ian Phillips, Patrick Hancock, the Didler, John and Gloria Isaacs, Ian and Nita Cooper)*

Welsh Harp [Chandos Pl]: Unpretentious and friendly, with some interesting if not always well executed star portraits on its red walls, lovely front stained glass, congenial seating layout with nice high benches around back tables and along wall counter, seats too at unusual counter facing pavement across fully opening windows, unusual well kept ales such as Elgoods, Harveys and York, good collection of whiskeys and whiskies *(Tim Maddison, BB, Dr and Mrs M E Wilson)*

EAST LONDON

E1

Captain Kidd [Wapping High St]: Great Thames views from large open-plan nautical-theme pub's jutting bay windows in renovated Docklands warehouse stripped back to beams and basics, good choice of hot and cold food all day inc several puddings, cheap Sam Smiths keg beers, obliging bow-tied staff, lively bustle; sports TV; chunky tables on roomy back waterside terrace *(Catherine Cronin, Eric Robinson, Jacqueline Pratt)*

☆ *Dickens Inn* [Marble Quay, St Katharines Way]: Outstanding position looking over smart docklands marina to Tower Bridge, oddly swiss-chalet look from outside with its balconies and window boxes, interesting stripped-down bare boards, baulks and timbers interior, wide choice of enjoyable food, well kept ales inc Greene King Old Speckled Hen, limited choice of decent wines by the glass, friendly prompt service, three floors inc pizza/pasta upstairs and smarter restaurant above that; popular with overseas visitors, tables outside *(John Saville, the Didler, LYM, Dr and Mrs M E Wilson, Andy Trafford, Louise Bayly)*

Pride of Spitalfields [Heneage St]: Compact East End local with well kept Fullers London Pride and an interesting changing guest beer, friendly staff and regulars, interesting prints and nice lighting *(Tracey and Stephen Groves)*

White Swan [Alie St]: Unobtrusively smart, light and well decorated, with armchairs and sofas as well as wooden furniture on bare boards, well kept Shepherd Neame beers, small choice of reasonably priced pub lunches, young welcoming staff *(Nigel and Sue Foster)*

Williams [Artillery Lane]: Busy pub with well kept Greene King IPA and Abbot, lunchtime food, wooden floor and period fittings *(Nigel and Sue Foster)*

E2

☆ *Approach Tavern* [Approach Rd]: Imposing high-ceilinged Victorian pub with comfortable seating and easy-going unpretentious atmosphere, some emphasis on fairly priced enjoyable food inc good Sun roasts and delicious puddings, well kept Fullers and Ridleys ales, considerate service, upstairs art gallery; children welcome, railed and heated front terrace *(BB, Catherine Cronin, Catherine Worsley, Tim Maddison)*

E8

Dove Arms [Broadway Market]: Dining tables, some in alcoves, in Victorian main bar, other rooms behind, lots of continental bottled beers (some used in their cooking); pavement tables *(John Wooll)*

Prince George [Parkholme Rd]: Stately mid-Victorian pub in enclave of attractive streets, heavy drapes for tall windows, well kept Fullers London Pride from large central servery, homely areas behind, small pool room off; occasional football on inconspicuous TV; tables out on small railed front terrace *(Tim Maddison)*

E10

King William IV [High Rd Leyton]: Has come up in the world, with very decorative façade, enjoyable food and good drinks *(Ron Deighton)*

Lion & Key [High Rd Leyton]: Well kept beer, warm welcome, good atmosphere *(Ron Deighton)*

E11

Duke of Edinburgh [Nightingale Lane]: Comfortably unspoilt two-bar mock-Tudor local, warm and friendly, with bargain generous home cooking from hot sandwiches up lunchtime (not Sun) and all afternoon, well kept Adnams and Youngs, decent wine, cheerful helpful staff, plenty of prints and plates, even an aquarium, darts, cards and shove-ha'penny; sports TV; garden tables, open all day *(Robert Lester, Pete Baker)*

E14

Bootys [Narrow St]: 19th-c bar with reasonably priced home-made food, friendly staff, spectacular Thames (and London Marathon) view *(Andy Trafford, Louise Bayly)*

George [Glengall Grove]: Cheery East End pub with Courage Best and Greene King Ruddles County, good conservatory seafood restaurant, locals' back bar and snug for Isle of Dogs old guard, younger-feeling front bar *(Ian Phillips)*

Narrow Street Pub & Dining Room [Narrow St]: Stylish up-to-date pastel décor, pale floors, stainless bar and open kitchen doing good value bar snacks and more expensive restaurant meals, dutch wheat beer on tap, great Thames views; piped music may obtrude evenings; children welcome, big heaters for picnic-sets on spacious if breezy terrace, open all day *(K Hutchinson, Tracey and Stephen Groves)*

Spinnaker [Harbour Exchange Sq, over Millwall Dock]: Picture-window views across Millwall Dock, Greene King IPA and another real ale, low-priced pubby food from sandwiches up, pool *(Ian Phillips)*

E17

College Arms [Forest Rd]: Cheap beer, enjoyable food, good crowd, cosy atmosphere; open all day *(Ron Deighton)*

Flower Pot [Wood St]: Friendly single bar with good atmosphere and particularly well kept Bass and Charles Wells Bombardier *(Ron Deighton)*

Goose & Granite [Hoe St/Selborne Rd, by Walthamstow Central station]: Chain pub with low-priced beers, other drinks, and food; good atmosphere, open all day *(Ron Deighton)*

Lord Raglan [Shernhall St]: Enjoyable food, well kept Greene King Old Speckled Hen, good atmosphere, pool, conservatory; small heated back terrace *(Ron Deighton)*

Rose & Crown [Hoe St]: Pleasant two-bar pub, bargain food, well kept beer, three tables upstairs; sports TV *(Ron Deighton)*

NORTH LONDON

N1

Alma [Newington Green Rd]: Relaxed local bar with sofas, big tables and open fire, candlelit restaurant area with deep red and mulberry décor, up-to-date food inc wkdy lunch deals and summer picnic take-aways, delicatessen counter, cheerful staff; children and dogs welcome, small sheltered fairy-lit garden, open all day, cl Mon lunchtime *(anon)*

☆ *Island Queen* [Noel Rd]: High-ceilinged Victorian pub handy for Camden Passage antiques area, well kept Fullers London Pride, a guest beer, lots of imported beer and good value wines from island bar, sensibly short choice of fresh often unusual food, pleasant staff, dark wood and decorative big mirrors, upstairs room; children welcome *(LYM, John Wooll)*

Wenlock Arms [Wenlock Rd]: Popular open-plan carpeted local in a bleak bit of London, warmly welcoming service, central bar serving ten or so well kept changing small-brewery ales from central servery, always inc a Mild, also farm cider and perry, foreign bottled beers, doorstep sandwiches inc good salt beef, alcove seating, piano in pride of place, coal fires, darts, back pool table; piped music; open all day, modern jazz Tues, trad Fri, piano Sun lunch *(Catherine Pitt, Tim Maddison)*

N4

Salisbury [Grand Parade, Green Lanes]: Grandiose late Victorian former hotel with spacious richly ornamented bars and dining room, dark velvet, leather and mahogany, intricate tiling and mirrors, well kept Fullers ales, czech lagers on tap; open all day, till 1am Thurs-Sat (no food Sun evening) *(R T and J C Moggridge, Tim Maddison)*

N6

Gatehouse [North Rd]: Wetherspoons pub with consistently good food, good range of well kept beers at low prices, effective service, no smoking area; upstairs theatre, tables in back yard *(Robert Gomme)*

N16

Daniel Defoe [Stoke Newington Church St]: Relaxing and informal proper pub with good mix of seating and table sizes in spacious bar, well kept Charles Wells Bombardier, a beer brewed by them for the pub and a guest beer such as St Austell Tribute, interesting lagers *(Tracey and Stephen Groves)*

Prince [Kynaston Rd]: Textbook cooking of good ingredients in neighbourhood gastropub with well kept Adnams Broadside and good choice of other drinks, scrubbed tables, candles, metal spiral staircase; trendy piped music *(Tracey and Stephen Groves)*

Shakespeare [Allen Rd]: Friendly and relaxed bare-boards local with classical figures dancing on walls, real ales and good choice of other drinks from central Victorian bar; tables out on narrow side terrace *(Tim Maddison)*

N20

☆ *Orange Tree* [Totteridge]: Attractive light and airy décor in rambling largely no smoking Vintage Inn, good value standard food from sandwiches up served efficiently even on busy

wknds, well kept Bass and Fullers London Pride, good choice of wines by the glass, freshly squeezed orange juice and coffee, friendly efficient staff, inglenook log fires; welcoming to children (and walkers, who leave boots in porch), tables out in pleasant surroundings by duck pond (still a village feel), open all day *(John Wooll, Jasmeet Fyfe, LYM, Ian Phillips)*

NW1

☆ *Head of Steam* [Eversholt St]: Large friendly and unpretentious Victorian-look bar up stairs from bus terminus and overlooking it, no smoking area, lots of railway nameplates, other memorabilia and enthusiast magazines for sale, also Corgi collection, unusual model trains and buses; fine array of interesting well kept ales (also take-away) changing from session to session, most from little-known small breweries, monthly themed beer festivals, Weston's farm cider and perry, lots of bottled beers and vodkas, kind service, simple cheap bar lunches, downstairs restaurant; TV, bar billiards, games machine, security-coded basement lavatories; open all day *(Sue Demont, Tim Barrow, BB, the Didler, Dr and Mrs A K Clarke, C J Fletcher, Dr J Barrie Jones, Dr D J and Mrs S C Walker, Darren Le Poidevin, Brian and Rosalie Laverick, Nigel Brown)*

Ice Wharf [Suffolk Wharf, Jamestown Rd]: New very modern Wetherspoons with usual good value food and drinks inc a few real ales such as Fullers London Pride, Greene King Abbot and Shepherd Neame Spitfire and plenty of lagers, daily papers; shiny french-look metal tables and chairs out on big canalside terrace by pretty little footbridge, right on the lock, extensive canal views *(Ian Phillips)*

Metropolitan [Baker St station, Marylebone Rd]: Busy Wetherspoons in ornate Victorian hall, lots of tables on one side, very long bar the other; their usual good beer choice and prices, no smoking areas, lack of piped music and so forth; can be packed Fri night *(Tracey and Stephen Groves)*

Queens [Regents Park Rd]: Long narrow bare-boards bar with mahogany, stained glass and african art, secluded corners inc quiet enclosed area up a few steps, smart end mirrors, well kept Youngs, lots of wines by the glass, pleasant service, upstairs restaurant with outdoor terrace and open kitchen doing innovative food inc asian dishes; dogs welcome *(John and Hiro Charles)*

NW3

Duke of Hamilton [New End]: Attractive family-run Fullers local, good value, with good range of seating (tall central servery gives an intimate feel to the two bars with their small tables and bric-a-brac), well kept London Pride, ESB and a seasonal beer, farm cider and malt whiskies; open all day, suntrap terrace, next to New End Theatre *(Patrick Hancock, the Didler, Tracey and Stephen Groves)*

Wells [Well Walk]: Relaxed lounge bar with

some leather armchairs and chess sets, Brains SB, decent if not cheap wines by the glass, obliging service (barman likes making cocktails), small choice of traditional british food, more formal upstairs dining area *(Tracey and Stephen Groves)*

NW4

Load of Hay [Brent St]: Large pub, quiet during the day, Fullers and three guest beers, daily papers, big room with TV and fish tank, separate dining area; picnic-sets outside *(Catherine Pitt)*

NW5

Assembly House [Kentish Town Rd/Leighton Rd]: Grandiose tall building, spacious and comfortable, with lovely stained-glass coachlight dominating back bar area, Greene King Old Speckled Hen, bar food; quiet piped music *(Ian Phillips)*

Junction Tavern [Fortess Rd]: Former corner Victorian local reworked as gastropub, good fresh food with some enterprising dishes, good atmosphere, well reproduced piped music; back conservatory, seats outside *(Ian Birrell)*

NW7

☆ *Rising Sun* [Marsh Lane/Highwood Hill, Mill Hill]: Energetic and considerate new Irish landlady in beautiful wisteria-covered local dating from 17th c, nicely worn-in cottagey bar and tiny low-ceilinged snug on right, lots of dark panelling, timber and coal fires, antique tables, prints and old local photographs, big plainer lounge on left, well kept Adnams, Greene King Abbot and Youngs Special, good wines by the glass and malt whiskies, enjoyable quickly served food from sandwiches up, polite and helpful well turned out staff; children welcome, picnic-sets on suntrap back terrace, good walks nearby, open all day *(John Wooll, Ian Phillips, Tracey and Stephen Groves, Tim Maddison)*

NW8

Lords Tavern [St Johns Wood Rd]: Next to Lords Cricket Ground, light and airy with lots of glass and modern bare-boards décor, Fullers London Pride and Youngs, good wine choice, decent food, friendly service; tables out on decking *(BB, Michael Dandy)*

New Inn [Allitsen Rd/Townsend Rd]: Cheerful 19th-c local with good atmosphere, enjoyable food from sandwiches to spicy thai dishes, well kept Greene King IPA and Abbot; TV, juke box and fruit machine; dogs welcome, tables outside, good value bedrooms *(John and Hiro Charles, Esther and John Sprinkle)*

SOUTH LONDON

SE1

Anchor [Bankside]: Much refurbished riverside pub, now mainly a biggish two-level open bar (its former creaky little black-panelled beamed rooms and passageways now generally closed off), Courage Best and Directors, a dozen wines by the glass, jugs of Pimms, winter mulled wine, various teas and coffees, ready-made baguettes, all-day simple low-priced hot dishes upstairs, some parts no smoking; great Thames views from outside tables, summer barbecues, children in top restaurant and family room, bedrooms in Premier Lodge behind, open all day *(R E Dixon, the Didler, Esther and John Sprinkle, LYM, Craig Turnbull, Roger Cox, Michael Butler, Mrs Pat Crabb, N R White)*

Barrow Boy & Banker [Borough High St, by London Bridge station]: Large smart banking hall conversion with upper gallery, full Fullers beer range kept well, decent wines, good manageress and efficient young staff, popular food *(Valerie Baker)*

Bridge House [Tower Bridge Rd]: Relaxed upmarket Adnams pub, their real ales and good wine choice, enjoyable food, friendly efficient service, modern décor with sofas *(N R White)*

Duke of York [Borough Rd]: Airy burgundy and cream décor, sofas and light wood furniture, polished boards, panelling and chandeliers, well kept Shepherd Neame real ales and shelves of belgian beers, good service; piped music; picnic-sets and floral displays outside *(Susan and John Douglas, Tracey and Stephen Groves)*

Hartley [Tower Bridge Rd]: Former Pagoda renamed, busy modernised bar with interesting food inc good Sun lunches (booking advised), good choice of wines by the glass *(Valerie Baker)*

☆ *Hole in the Wall* [Mepham St]: Well kept changing ales such as Adnams Bitter and Broadside, Fullers London Pride, Ridleys IPA, Charles Wells Bombardier and Youngs Bitter and Special, plenty of lagers, and good malts and irish whiskeys, in welcoming no-frills drinkers' dive, in railway arch virtually underneath Waterloo – rumbles and shakes with the trains; small front bar, nice medley of tables set well back from long bar in back room; loudish juke box, pinball and games machines, bargain basic food all day (cl wknd afternoons) *(Ian Phillips, LYM, Tracey and Stephen Groves)*

☆ *Horniman* [Hays Galleria, off Battlebridge Lane]: Good stop on Thames walks, spacious, bright and airy drinking hall with lots of polished wood, comfortable seating inc a few sofas, no smoking area, Adnams, Fullers London Pride and Greene King IPA, choice of teas and coffees at good prices, lunchtime bar food from soup and big sandwiches up, snacks other times, efficient service coping with large numbers after work; unobtrusive piped music; fine Thames views from picnic-sets outside, open all day *(Ian Phillips, Patrick Hancock, LYM, N R White)*

Kings Arms [Roupell St]: Bustling and friendly well preserved pub, two distinctive curved rooms with attractive prints, well kept Adnams, Fullers London Pride and guest beers, cheap and cheerful thai food at long trestle tables in back bar, good service; can be smoky

(Tracey and Stephen Groves, Sue Demont, Tim Barrow)

☆ **Lord Clyde** [Clennam St]: Unpretentious panelled L-shaped local, well kept Adnams Best, Fullers London Pride, Greene King IPA, Shepherd Neame Spitfire and Youngs Special, good value straightforward home-made food wkdy lunchtimes and early evenings, welcoming staff, darts in small hatch-service back public bar; striking tiled façade, open all day (Sat early evening break, cl 7 Sun) *(Pete Baker, C J Fletcher, Mike and Sue Losebey)*

Mulberry Bush [Upper Ground]: Attractively modernised sympathetically lit Youngs pub, very handy for South Bank complex; open-plan with lots of wood, slightly raised turkey-carpeted balustraded area and small tiled-floor no smoking back conservatory, decent wines, welcoming service, updated bar food, spiral stairs to bistro *(Stephen R Holman)*

☆ **Old Thameside** [Pickfords Wharf, Clink St]: Good 1980s pastiche of ancient tavern, two floors, hefty beams and timbers, pews, flagstones, candles; splendid river view upstairs and from charming waterside terrace; well kept Tetleys and Marstons Pedigree with guests such as Adnams and Fullers, friendly staff, fresh baguettes from salad bar, lunchtime hot buffet; pool down spiral stairs, piped music, service can slow when busy after work; open all day but cl 3 at wknds *(LYM, Esther and John Sprinkle, N R White)*

Pineapple [Hercules Rd]: Friendly and relaxed flower-decked refuge, comfortable and peaceful, with low-priced honest food from toasties and baked potatoes up, Bass, Fullers London Pride and Youngs, interesting maps of the area in the late 18th c, games room on right; picnic-sets out in front *(Ian Phillips, Michael Butler)*

Pommelers Rest [Tower Bridge Rd]: Wetherspoons with prompt friendly service, their usual food all day, well kept real ales, large no smoking family room *(C J Fletcher)*

Ring [Blackfriars Rd/The Cut, opp Southwark tube station]: Neat and bright, with stripped pale boards, lots of boxing photographs and memorabilia, thai food, Bass and Fullers London Pride *(Ian Phillips)*

Studio Six [Gabriel's Wharf, Upper Ground]: Bustling South Bank bar/bistro in two linked timber-framed buildings, glazed all round, picnic-sets on two terraces (one heated), good well priced modern food all day inc mezze and lots of fish, good choice of belgian beers on tap, decent wines, Boddingtons, efficient service; soft piped music; children welcome, great location, open all day *(Michael Butler, BB, Sue Demont, Tim Barrow)*

White Hart [Cornwall Ave/Whittlesey St]: Recently refurbished in upcoming area, comfortable sofas, stripped boards and so forth, Fullers London Pride, sensibly priced up-to-date food *(Ian Phillips)*

SE3

Hare & Billet [Eliot Cottages, Hare & Billet Rd]: Pleasant and chatty open-plan pub dating from 16th c, panelling, bare boards, good solid furniture and open fire, raised middle section, good value food, real ales such as Adnams, Bass, Fullers London Pride and Wadworths 6X, good choice of wines, view over Blackheath; open all day *(BB, N R White)*

Railway [Lee Rd/Blackheath Village]: Comfortable modern refurbishment, Adnams Broadside, Shepherd Neame Spitfire and Youngs, good choice of lagers and bottled beers inc belgian fruit beers, lots of wines by the glass inc champagne, enjoyable up-to-date food (all day wknds); garden behind *(Valerie Baker)*

SE5

Phoenix [Windsor Walk, Denmark Hill]: Striking and unusual Victorian railway hall converted to civilised contemporary pub, spiral stairs to upper gallery, well kept real ales, interesting up-to-date food all day from ciabattas and focaccia through light dishes to enjoyable main courses and traditional puddings *(LYM, Steve Harvey)*

SE10

Greenwich Union [Royal Hill]: Tied to small nearby Meantime brewery in nearby Charlton, with their own interesting keg and bottled beers and one real ale, friendly service and relaxing atmosphere, enjoyable fresh food (not Sun evening) inc tapas and two-sitting Sun lunch, up-to-date yellow décor, flagstones, some button-back leather chairs and settees, daily papers and pub games, may be free nibbles, small back conservatory; can get smoky if crowded, well reproduced piped music (live Tues and fortnightly Weds); children welcome, picnic-sets on small back terrace, open all day *(Richard Houghton, the Didler, N R White, Ben Bacon)*

☆ **Plume of Feathers** [Park Vista]: Well run low-ceilinged Georgian local with cheerful efficient service, good value food from sandwiches, baguettes and well filled baked potatoes up inc good curries and kebabs, well kept Adnams, Fullers London Pride and a couple of guest beers, flame-effect fire in large attractive fireplace, sea pictures and plates on ochre walls, back dining area; SkyTV sports; children welcome, play room across walled back terrace (Greenwich Park playground too), handy for Maritime Museum *(Esther and John Sprinkle, Pete Baker, N R White)*

☆ **Richard I** [Royal Hill]: Quietly old-fashioned pubby atmosphere in friendly no-nonsense traditional two-bar local with well kept Youngs, food inc notable sausages, good staff, no piped music, bare boards, panelling; tables out in front, pleasant back terrace with wknd barbecues, busy summer wknds and evenings *(the Didler, Humphry and Angela Crum Ewing, N R White)*

☆ **Trafalgar** [Park Row]: Substantial 18th-c building with river views from big windows in four elegant rooms inc pleasant end dining room and central bar, careful colour schemes, oak panelling and good maritime prints, well kept Flowers Original, Fullers London Pride, Nelsons Blood and Trafalgar and a couple of interesting guest beers, good house wines, helpful young staff, good atmosphere, popular food inc speciality whitebait and some imaginative dishes; can get noisy and smoky when packed Fri/Sat evenings, may be piped music; handy for Maritime Museum *(Gloria Bax, Roger and Jenny Huggins, N R White, Mr and Mrs A H Young, E G Parish, Ian Phillips)*

Yacht [Crane St]: Neatly modernised with stripped basic décor, good value food inc particularly good fish and chips, well kept Adnams, Fullers London Pride, Greene King and Shepherd Neame Spitfire, good river view from spacious room up a few steps from bar, cosy banquettes, light wood panelling, portholes, yacht pictures *(Roger and Jenny Huggins, John Walker, N R White, B J Harding)*

SE11

Prince of Wales [Cleaver Sq]: Comfortably traditional Edwardian pub in smart quiet Georgian square, burgundy décor, pictures of notorious Londoners, well kept Shepherd Neame ales, bar food from good sandwiches and wraps up, arch to small saloon *(BB, Giles and Annie Francis, Tracey and Stephen Groves)*

SE16

Blacksmiths Arms [Rotherhithe St (Nelson Dock)]: Smart Fullers local in up-and-coming area, friendly staff, well cooked straightforward blackboard pub food, London Pride, ESB and a guest such as Adnams *(Nigel and Sue Foster)*

☆ *Mayflower* [Rotherhithe St]: Cosy old riverside pub with thriving local atmosphere, surprisingly wide choice of enjoyable generous food (not Sun night) from ciabattas up, black beams, high-backed settles and coal fires, good Thames views from calm upstairs restaurant (cl Sat lunchtime), well kept Greene King IPA, Abbot and Old Speckled Hen, good coffee and good value wines, friendly efficient staff; unobtrusive nostalgic piped music; children welcome, tables out on nice jetty/terrace over water, open all day, in unusual street with lovely Wren church *(David Edwards, M A and C R Starling, LYM, Roy and Lindsey Fentiman, the Didler, Susan and John Douglas, Nigel and Sue Foster, N R White)*

SE26

☆ *Dulwich Wood House* [Sydenham Hill]: Well run extended Youngs pub in Victorian lodge gatehouse complete with turret, well kept ales, decent wines, attractively priced straightforward food cooked to order popular at lunchtime with local retired people, friendly service; steps up to entrance (and stiff walk up from station), can get smoky when crowded, no children in bar; lots of tables in big pleasant back garden (no dogs) with old-fashioned street lamps and barbecues, handy for Dulwich

Wood walks *(Vanessa Stilwell, N R White, Ian and Nita Cooper)*

SW9

Clapham North [Clapham Rd, opp the tube stn]: Modernised corner pub with high-perch alcove seating and shiny overhead metal ducting, wide choice of wines, up-to-date food from sandwiches to rib-eye steak, daily papers, pleasantly relaxed mix of customers; piped music fairly loud; live music Thurs, wknd DJs, open all day till late *(Ian Phillips)*

SW11

Eagle [Chatham Rd]: Attractive old backstreet local, well kept ales such as Flowers IPA, Fullers London Pride and Timothy Taylors Landlord, friendly helpful service, leather sofas in fireside corner of L-shaped bar; big-screen sports TV; back terrace with marquee, small front terrace too *(Sue Demont, Tim Barrow)*

Falcon [St Johns Hill]: Edwardian pub with remarkably long light oak bar snaking through several rooms, period partitions, cut glass and mirrors, friendly service, well kept Fullers London Pride, pub food from sandwiches and baked potatoes up, daily papers; big-screen TV *(R T and J C Moggridge, Ian Phillips)*

SW12

Grove [Oldridge Rd]: Bright and comfortable Youngs pub with their beer kept well, friendly staff, part with sofas and armchairs, upper bar for dining (imaginative menu), no smoking area; unobtrusive piped music *(Sue Demont, Tim Barrow)*

☆ *Nightingale* [Nightingale Lane]: Cosy and civilised early Victorian local, small woody front bar opening into larger back area and attractive family conservatory, good bar food, well kept Youngs, sensible prices, friendly staff; small secluded back garden *(Sue Demont, Tim Barrow, BB)*

SW13

Coach & Horses [Barnes High St]: Cosy Youngs local with their full beer range, enjoyable reasonably priced bar food, friendly staff; good back garden, open all day *(Anthony Double)*

Red Lion [Castelnau]: Big smartly refurbished Fullers pub with impressive Victorian woodwork, enjoyable food inc children's helpings and particularly popular Sun lunch, good choice of wines by the glass, polite service, three separate areas; big garden with good play area and barbecue *(BB, Peter Rozée)*

Sun [Church Rd]: Attractive spot with tables over road overlooking green and duck pond, several areas around central servery, softly lit cosy corners with sofas as well as lots of tables and chairs, tuscan wall colours and tracked spotlights, well kept Greene King ales and good range of belgian beers, speedy cheerful service even though busy, enjoyable modern food from ciabattas and panini up; piped music *(Jenny and Brian Seller, Gloria Bax, Peter Rozée, Andrew and Diane Hall)*

White Hart [The Terrace]: Pleasant open-plan pub with Youngs Bitter and seasonal Winter Warmer, good river views *(Robert Lester)*

SW15

☆ *Dukes Head* [Lower Richmond Rd]: Classic Victorian pub, spacious and grand yet friendly, light and airy civilised lounge with big ceiling fans, tables by window with great Thames view, well kept Youngs, 20 wines by the glass, good value fresh lunchtime food, pleasant service, coal fires, smaller more basic locals' bar; plastic glasses for outside *(R T and J C Moggridge, Susan and John Douglas, BB)*

SW18

Brewery Tap [Wandsworth High St]: Former Lamb, with all Youngs draught ales, bargain pub food from sandwiches and baked potatoes up, cheerful Australian staff, adjoining Youngs shop and brewery with their lovely dray horses *(Ian Phillips)*

☆ *Cats Back* [Point Pleasant]: Tiny and thoroughly individual back street boozer, for years a local secret, now better known thanks to redevelopment of up-and-coming area near nice riverside park; packed with eccentric mix of the sorts of things that might have ended up unsold at a collectables auction, motley furnishings from pews and scrubbed pine tables to a worn gilt three-piece suite and parts of a tree trunk, dimmed chandeliers and lots of lit candelabra, well kept and interesting changing ales such as Adnams, O'Hanlons Wheat Beer, Ringwood and/or Youngs Original and Waggle Dance, lunchtime food from sandwiches up, Sun roasts, good service, blazing fire in small fireplace, lively yet relaxing atmosphere; well chosen piped music, can get smoky; open all day *(Guy Vowles, Susan and John Douglas, BB)*

Ship [Jews Row]: As we went to press in July, the Gottos who in their 25 years here made this Thames-side Youngs pub so individual and so enjoyable for its relaxed atmosphere, real food and good drink were losing their tenancy, so we don't yet know how things will turn out; the décor has been mainly light and airy conservatory-style, with a pleasant mix of furnishings, a basic public bar, and an attractive good-sized terrace; dogs and children have been welcome, and it's been open all day; news please *(LYM)*

SW19

Alexandra [Wimbledon Hill Rd]: Busy refurbished Youngs pub with central no smoking bar and two other rooms, efficient service, adjoining upmarket wine bar; attractive roof terrace, tables also out in mews *(N R White)*

Crooked Billet [Wimbledon Common]: Olde-worlde pub popular for its position by common, lovely spot in summer; full Youngs range kept well, friendly efficient service, daily papers, lots of old prints, nice furnishings inc high-backed settles on broad polished oak boards, restaurant in 16th-c barn behind; can

be smoky, plastic glasses for outdoor drinking; open all day *(R T and J C Moggridge, Edward Mirzoeff, N R White)*

Fox & Grapes [Camp Rd]: By common, with contemporary food inc tapas, well kept ales, attractive mural behind no smoking bar's food servery, big-screen sports TV in larger high-beamed bar; piped music; open all day, children welcome till 7, pleasant on summer evenings when you can sit out on the grass *(BB, N R White)*

Hand in Hand [Crooked Billet]: Relaxed and cheerfully welcoming U-shaped bar serving several small areas, some tiled, others carpeted, very well kept Youngs (full range), good wine choice, straightforward food inc home-made pizzas and huge burgers, friendly efficient service, log fire; rather spartan no smoking family annexe with bar billiards, darts etc; tables out in front courtyard with vine and hanging baskets, benches out by common (plastic glasses there); can be very crowded with young people esp summer evenings *(BB, N R White)*

Rose & Crown [Wimbledon High St]: Refurbished 17th-c pub with alcove seating in roomy bar, well kept Youngs beers, enjoyable food, good friendly staff, back dining conservatory; tables in neat former coachyard, new bedrooms *(LYM, MRSM, John Coatsworth, N R White)*

WEST LONDON

SW6

Duke of Cumberland [New Kings Rd, Parsons Green]: Huge Edwardian pub, attractive decorative tiles and interesting panel fleshing out his life, sofas, coffee tables and candles; well kept Youngs Bitter and Special, cheerful at wknd lunchtimes, relaxed for wkdy lunchtime food such as sandwiches, baked potatoes and pies (no food Fri-Sun evenings); big-screen sports TV in sanded-floor main bar (smaller quieter carpeted back areas with log fire), piped pop music, some live; open all day, a few tables out in side street *(BB, the Didler, Ian Phillips)*

Southern Cross [New Kings Rd]: Comfortable leather tub chairs, Greene King IPA and Old Speckled Hen, enjoyable sensibly priced bar food from sandwiches to pasta, melts, fish and chips and so forth; discreet TV screens for rugby, upstairs pool room, stairs down to lavatories *(Ian Phillips)*

Wheatsheaf [Fulham Rd, opp fire station and Parsons Green Lane]: Big newly refurbished pub with some leather settees, high tables and stools, and more orthodox tables and chairs, mainly pale boards, some carpet, just a few pictures on the cream walls above pale sage-green panelling, wide choice of wines by the glass, Greene King IPA and Abbot, silenced big-screen TV *(Ian Phillips)*

SW10

Hollywood Arms [Hollywood Rd]: Comfortable Victorian-look front bar with charming staff, good simple food in skylit carpeted back restaurant with banquettes and prints on warm earth-tone walls, upstairs cocktail lounge *(Joel Dobris)*

W4

Swan [Evershed Walk, Acton Lane]: Former local appealingly freshened up as food pub, run by same team as Atlas (see West London main entries) and Fox & Hounds (South London), similar informal style and enjoyable up-to-date food, good range of wines by the glass, three real ales *(anon)*

W6

Latymers [Hammersmith Rd]: Big lively café/bar with minimal décor, lots of steel and glass inc ornate mirrored ceiling, well kept Fullers ales and friendly bar staff; three TV screens, may be unobtrusive piped music; good generous authentic thai food in comfortable and spacious back restaurant with cheerful attentive staff in thai dress, take-aways too *(Susan and John Douglas)*

W8

☆ *Scarsdale Arms* [Edwardes Sq]: Busy Georgian pub in lovely leafy square, keeping a good deal of character, with stripped wooden floors, two or three fireplaces with good coal-effect gas fires, lots of knick-knacks, ornate bar counter; well kept Fullers London Pride and Charles Wells Bombardier, good wine choice, enjoyable blackboard food inc unusual dishes, pleasant service; tree-shaded front courtyard with impressive show of flower tubs and baskets, open all day *(LYM, Joel Dobris)*

W14

Old Parrs Head [Blythe Rd]: Attractively restored Victorian façade, smartish inside with stripped pub and entertaining modern prints, friendly atmosphere, enjoyable interesting bar food, Fullers London Pride and Marstons Pedigree, decent wines, back candlelit thai restaurant; tables outside *(Ian Phillips)*
Warwick Arms [Warwick Rd]: Early 19th-c, with lots of woodwork, comfortable atmosphere, friendly regulars (some playing darts or bridge), good service, well kept Fullers beers from elegant Wedgwood handpumps, limited tasty food (not Sun evening), sensible prices, no piped music; open all day, tables outside, handy for Earls Court and Olympia *(Giles and Annie Francis, the Didler)*

OUTER LONDON

BARNET [TQ2396]
Lord Nelson [West End Lane]: Open-plan pub with plenty of tables, decent lunchtime food, quick friendly service, well kept real ales; no children or dogs inside, small front terrace with masses of flower baskets and tubs *(John Wooll)*
☆ *Olde Mitre* [High St]: Small early 17th-c local (remains of a famous coaching inn), bay windows in low-beamed panelled front bar with fruit machines, three-quarter panelled

back area on two slightly different levels, bare boards, lots of dark wood, open fire, pleasant atmosphere, friendly service, well kept Adnams and Timothy Taylors Landlord; open all day *(John Wooll, LYM)*

BECKENHAM [TQ3769]
George [High St]: Busy weatherboarded pub with friendly efficient service, real ale and bar food; can get crowded and smoky evenings; side garden with terrace *(N R White)*
Jolly Woodman [Chancery Lane]: Small recently refurbished traditional local with friendly atmosphere, good range of well kept ales, good value changing lunchtime food; can get crowded evenings; seats out in cosy garden and tiny street *(N R White)*

BRENTFORD [TQ1777]
Griffin [Brook Rd S]: Welcoming home of Griffin Brewery – a cornerstone of what we think is the only UK football ground with a pub on each of its four corners *(Keith and Chris O'Neill)*

BROMLEY [TQ4069]
Red Lion [North Rd]: Traditional backstreet local, soft lighting and shelves of books, chatty atmosphere with good range of real ales; picnic-sets on front terrace *(N R White)*
Two Doves [Oakley Rd (A233)]: Popular local notable for its picturesque garden with terrace tables; plenty of character inside, with friendly service, real ales and no smoking back conservatory *(N R White)*

CHISLEHURST [TQ4469]
Crown [School Rd]: Smartly refurbished, with new wooden furniture on flagstones, well prepared food in several dining areas, good helpful staff, well kept Shepherd Neame beers; tables out overlooking green *(B and M Kendall)*
Ramblers Rest [Mill Place; just off Bickley Park Rd and Old Hill, by Summer Hill (A222)]: White weatherboarded local in picturesque hillside setting on edge of Chislehurst Common, real ales, pleasant atmosphere; garden behind, grassy slope out in front (plastic glasses for there), handy for Chislehurst Caves *(N R White)*
Sydney Arms [Old Perry St]: Friendly atmosphere, brisk service even when busy, good range of good value food even on Sun, well kept real ales, big conservatory; pleasant garden good for children, almost opp entrance to Scadbury Park, country walks *(B J Harding, Martin and Pauline Jennings)*
Tigers Head [Watts Lane/Manor Park Rd (B264 S of common, opp St Nicholas Church)]: Pleasantly airy Chef & Brewer overlooking church and common, dating from 18th c and pleasantly divided into cosy low-beamed areas, efficient service even when quite busy, wide food choice inc variety of fish and Sun lunch, good wine list, well kept beers; smart casual dress code, no under-21s; side terrace tables, good walks nearby *(R T and J C Moggridge, N R White)*

DOWNE [TQ4361]
Queens Head [High St]: Civilised and comfortable, with Darwin texts and splendid

log fire in lounge, good value food from sandwiches to popular Sun roasts, well kept Adnams Bitter and Broadside, good smiling service, plush dining room; big-screen TV in public bar (can be noisy), well equipped children's room; picnic-sets on pavement, more in small pleasant back courtyard with aviary, handy for Darwin's Down House, open all day *(N R White)*

ENFIELD [TQ3599]

Pied Bull [Bullsmoor Lane (A1055); handy for M25 junction 25, by A10]: Rustic red-tiled 17th-c pub, spotless and now entirely no smoking, with local prints on boarded walls, low beam-and-plank ceilings, lots of comfortable and friendly little rooms and extensions, turkey rugs on bare boards, friendly staff, well kept Adnams, Fullers London Pride and Greene King Old Speckled Hen, wide choice of sensibly priced food; conservatory, pleasant garden *(Ian Phillips, E Michael Holdsworth)*

HAMPTON [TQ1469]

Jolly Coopers [High St]: Victorian local with four well kept ales such as Courage Best and Hop Back Summer Lightning, flame-effect gas fire, back dining extension with good shortish choice of interesting freshly cooked food, very friendly landlady *(Gerry and Rosemary Dobson)*

HAMPTON COURT [TQ1668]

Kings Arms [Hampton Court Rd, by Lion Gate]: On the edge of Hampton Court grounds, pleasantly spruced up, with oak panels, beams, stripped brickwork and good open fires, relaxed atmosphere, well kept Badger beers, good choice of wines by the glass, attractively priced usual food from sandwiches up, pleasant efficient service; piped music; children and dogs welcome, picnic-sets on hedged front terrace with shrub tubs, open all day *(Susan and John Douglas, LYM)*

ILFORD [TQ4589]

Dick Turpin [Aldborough Rd N, off A12 Newbury Park]: Recently refurbished former Beefeater, with enjoyable food in bar and restaurant, Flowers IPA *(Robert Lester)*

Red House [Redbridge Lane E]: Large multi-level Beefeater with good value food; bedrooms in adjoining Travelodge *(Robert Lester)*

ISLEWORTH [TQ1576]

Red Lion [Linkfield Rd]: Friendly unspoilt backstreet local with at least eight real ales and lots of belgian beers; live music wknds, theatre company, three annual beer festivals with bands; dogs and children welcome, terrace tables and garden, barbecues *(J Bean)*

KESTON [TQ4164]

Fox [Heathfield Rd]: Roomy and up-to-date open-plan pub with well kept Adnams and Fullers London Pride, popular traditional food from sandwiches and baguettes up, friendly and helpful young staff, red décor; can be a bit smoky; garden behind with decking, terrace and piped music *(LM)*

KEW [TQ1977]

Coach & Horses [Kew Green]: Spotless Youngs pub, their full beer range kept well,

range of coffees, enjoyable food from good value doorstep sandwiches and enterprising panini to good steaks and fish, no smoking restaurant area; tables on front terrace, nice setting *(P R Morgan, LM)*

KINGSTON [TQ1769]

Park [New Rd]: Friendly local with well kept Fullers London Pride and Youngs, filled rolls, large beer mat collection; lovely front terrace with lots of hanging baskets, handy for Richmond Park *(Kevin Blake)*

LEAVES GREEN [TQ4161]

Kings Arms [Leaves Green Rd (A233)]: Friendly low-beamed weatherboarded pub with real ale, back restaurant; piped music; tables out on small front terrace and in big back garden *(N R White)*

LONGFORD [TQ0576]

White Horse [Bath Rd, off A3044 (and A4)]: Brasses on low 16th-c black beams, fireplace between the two areas, comfortable seats, cosy and friendly with pot plants in windows and rustic decorations such as antique rifles and equestrian bronzes, big helpings of good value lunchtime bar food, good service, well kept Fullers London Pride; fruit machine, piped music; flower tubs and picnic-sets outside, one in a little barn, surprisingly villagey surroundings despite the parking meters, open all day *(R T and J C Moggridge)*

MALDEN RUSHETT [TQ1763]

☆ *Star* [Kingston Rd (A243 just N of M25 junction 9)]: Reliable family dining pub right on Surrey border, consistently good reasonably priced food from baguettes and baked potatoes to a good range of hot dishes, good friendly service and atmosphere, nice log fire; quiet piped music *(DWAJ)*

RICHMOND [TQ1874]

Racing Page [Duke St]: Well done open-plan racing décor, wooden furniture on bare boards, wide choice of reasonably priced generous thai food, attentive friendly service, decent wines, well kept Courage-related ales; big-screen SkyTV sports; nice spot nr theatre and green *(Mayur Shah)*

Sun [Parkshot, just off shopping centre]: Reliable three-room Fullers local covered with rugby memorabilia, generous bargain food, well kept ales; uncrowded wkdy lunchtimes *(Mayur Shah)*

White Swan [Old Palace Lane]: Civilised old pub with dark-beamed open-plan plush bar, relaxed and chatty, well kept real ales, good freshly cooked wholesome bar lunches, coal-effect gas fires, upstairs restaurant; piped music may obtrude; children allowed in conservatory, pretty little paved garden below railway, barbecues *(LYM, N R White)*

New Inn [Petersham Rd (A307, Ham Common)]: Attractive and comfortable Georgian pub in good spot on Ham Common, comfortable banquettes and stools, brown décor, good home-made food from herby panini and other snacks up, pleasant dining area, well kept Adnams Broadside, Courage Best and Greene King IPA, quick friendly service, big log fire one side, coal the other;

disabled facilities, picnic-sets out among flowers front and back *(LM, Mary Ellen Cummings)*

STANMORE [TQ1692]

Man in the Moon [Buckingham Parade, The Broadway]: L-shaped Wetherspoons with exceptional beer range, central tables, nice row of booths with tasteful stained-glass effect (also on ceiling) *(Tracey and Stephen Groves)*

TEDDINGTON [TQ1671]

Tide End Cottage [Broom Rd/Ferry Rd, nr bridge at Teddington Lock]: Friendly low-ceilinged local in Victorian cottage terrace, lots of river, fishing and rowing memorabilia and photographs in two little rooms united by big log-effect gas fire, well kept Greene King ales, good reasonably priced straightforward bar food from sandwiches and café-type meals to huge Sun roasts served 12-5 (can get busy then); sports TV in part-tented back bar, minimal parking; no river view, but some tables on back terrace *(Sue Demont, Tim Barrow)*

TWICKENHAM [TQ1673]

☆ *White Swan* [Riverside]: Unpretentious take-us-as-you-find-us 17th-c Thames-side house up steep anti-flood steps, little waterside lawn across quiet lane, traditional bare-boards bar with big rustic tables and blazing fires, back room full of rugby memorabilia, well kept Courage Directors, Greene King IPA and Shepherd Neame Spitfire, good choice of wines by the glass, winter mulled wine, sandwiches and one or two blackboard hot dishes, summer wkdy lunchtime buffet; backgammon, cribbage, piped blues or jazz, winter Weds folk

night; children welcome, open all day summer *(Ian Phillips, LYM, Roger Huggins, Tom and Alex McLean)*

Sussex Arms [Staines Rd]: Fairly small open-plan pub doing well under friendly and helpful new licensees, well kept Fullers London Pride and Youngs, good value generous home-made food; big-screen sports TVs; new children's garden *(Len Clark)*

UXBRIDGE [TQ0582]

Load of Hay [Villier St, off Cleveland Rd opp Brunel University]: Cheap food inc popular Sun roast in rambling low-key local with mixed bag of furniture, four well kept rotating beers, impressive fireplace in no smoking back part; dogs welcome, flower-filled back garden, pergola with vine *(Dr B and Mrs P B Baker)*

WOODFORD [TQ4291]

Crown & Crooked Billet [Cross Rd, just S of Manor Rd (B173)]: Cosy and welcoming, with reasonably priced food and well kept beer *(Ron Deighton)*

WOODFORD GREEN [TQ4091]

Castle [High Rd (A104)]: Massive well refurbished Harvester almost opp the green, reasonably priced food inc early bargains, Bass *(Robert Lester)*

Cocked Hat [Southend Rd (A1400), just off M11 terminal roundabout]: Main-road Harvester with good value food, Bass *(Robert Lester)*

Cricketers [High Rd]: Winston Churchill memorabilia, enjoyable reasonably priced food (get there early to be sure of the specials), good friendly management; no food Sun evening *(Ron Deighton)*

Scotland

With Scotland leading the way where we hope England will soon follow, smoking becomes illegal in pubs and hotels here from April 2006 – so our comments in the text about smoking in individual pubs and inns can be disregarded after that. Another important difference to note from England is that up here, away from the big cities, hotels often play the role that in England is played by pubs, so you will find quite a few such hotels among the main entries. Places on notably good form these days include the cheery and interesting Fishermans Tavern in Broughty Ferry, the Café Royal and Guildford Arms in Edinburgh (appreciated particularly for their décor, with proper pubby virtues too), Kays Bar there (lots of good beers and whiskies, nice atmosphere), the Starbank out towards the fringes of Edinburgh (great welcome and service, good food and drink), the friendly Ship by the sea at Elie (gains a Place to Stay Award this year), the Counting House in Glasgow (great décor, good beers and prices, and now already entirely no smoking), the Fox & Hounds in Houston (a good all-rounder, brewing its own fine beers), the interesting George in Inveraray (plenty of character, and a nice place to stay), the nicely placed Steam Packet at Isle of Whithorn (good food, service, wines and bedrooms), the unpretentiously cosy and comfortable Cross Keys at Kippen, the Border at Kirk Yetholm (a welcoming new entry, gently updated by friendly new licensees, enjoyable food and drink), the Burts Hotel in Melrose (warm welcome, good food, nice bedrooms), the Moulin in Pitlochry (another place brewing its own good beers, nice to stay in too, with enjoyable food), the beautifully set Plockton Hotel (a particular favourite, good food, great service, excellent place to stay in), the Stein Inn in a glorious spot on Skye (great character and welcome, good all round), and the civilised Wheatsheaf at Swinton (good food, welcoming staff, lovely bedrooms). For the second year running, the Plockton Hotel at Plockton carries off the title of Scotland Dining Pub of the Year. We have divided the Lucky Dip section at the end of the chapter into the counties used as postal addresses (putting Glasgow under Lanarkshire, and Edinburgh under Midlothian). In this section, pubs and inns currently showing particularly well are the Bridge of Orchy Hotel, Oyster at Connel and Clachaig at Glencoe (Argyll), Clachan at Dalry and Masonic Arms in Gatehouse of Fleet (Kirkcudbrightshire), Pot Still in Glasgow (Lanarkshire), Standing Order in Edinburgh (Midlothian), Byre at Brig o' Turk and Loch Tummel Inn (Perthshire), and on the islands the Rodel Hotel (Harris) and on Skye the Ardvasar Hotel, Eilean Iarmain at Isle Ornsay and Sligachan Hotel. Drinks prices here tend to be rather higher than south of the Border. It's well worth trying some of the beers from Scotland's growing band of small independent brewers – now numbered in dozens. Caledonian is very widely available. Others that you are quite likely to come across are (in a very rough order of frequency) Houston, Isle of Skye, Belhaven, Harviestoun, Orkney, Atlas, Broughton, Cairngorm, Fyne, Inveralmond, Isle of Arran, Black Isle, Moulin, An Teallach and Kelburn.

ABERDEEN NJ9305 Map 11

Prince of Wales ❦ £

St Nicholas Lane

A nice old tavern right in the heart of the city, this bustling place has a bar counter in its cosy central flagstoned area that some say is the longest in Scotland. Screened booths are furnished with pews and other wooden furniture, while a smarter main lounge has some panelling and a fruit machine. A good range of eight real ales includes Caledonian 80/-, Theakstons Old Peculier, and a beer named for the pub from Inveralmond, along with guests from brewers such as Atlas, Isle of Skye and Orkney. Friendly staff serve generous helpings of good value bar food such as sandwiches (from £1.30), filled baguettes or baked potatoes (£3.50), macaroni cheese (£4), steak pie (£4.50), and breaded haddock or beef stroganoff (£4.80), with puddings such as chocolate fudge cake (£1.50). At lunchtime a busy mix of locals and visitors often makes for standing room only. *(Recommended by Joe Green, the Didler, Pete Walker, Mark Walker)*

Free house ~ Licensee Kenny Gordon ~ Real ale ~ Bar food (11.30(12 Sun)-2.30 (4 Sat, Sun)) ~ (01224) 640597 ~ Children allowed in eating area of bar at lunchtime ~ Traditional folk music Sun evening, pop quiz Mon ~ Open 10-12

ABOYNE NO5298 Map 11

Boat ❦

Charlestown Road (B968, just off A93)

Right by the River Dee, this welcoming country inn is relaxed and pubby. Pleasantly served by prompt, friendly staff, lunchtime bar food includes soup (£2.50), sandwiches (from £3), mince, tatties and skirlie (£6.50), lasagne, very good fresh battered haddock (£7.95), and daily specials (including more good fish), while in the evening they add things like baked aubergine layered with peppers and goats cheese with tomato salsa and toasted pine nuts (£8.75) and beef daube (£10.95), with puddings such as rhubarb brûlée (£4.50); children's meals. They use plenty of fresh local produce, and are happy to accommodate special requests. Well kept Bass along with a couple of real ales from brewers such as Caledonian, Houston, Inveralmond and Isle of Skye; also, 40 malt whiskies. As you step inside, the first thing you'll notice is the model train, often chugging around just below the ceiling, making appropriate noises. There are also scottish pictures and brasses and an openable woodburning stove in the two areas downstairs, a bar counter that runs down the narrower linking section, and games along in the public-bar end. Spiral stairs take you up to a roomy additional dining area, which is no smoking. The pub used to serve the ferry that it's named for; there are tables outside, and they have a self-catering flat. *(Recommended by David and Betty Gittins, Mike and Shelley Woodroffe, Callum and Letitia Smith-Burnett, Michael Lamm, Lucien Perring)*

Free house ~ Licensee Wilson Forbes ~ Real ale ~ Bar food (12-2(2.30 Sat, Sun), 5.30-9 (9.30 Fri, Sat)) ~ Restaurant ~ (01339) 886137 ~ Children in eating area of bar and restaurant ~ Dogs allowed in bar and bedrooms ~ Open 11-2.30, 5-11(12 Fri); 11-midnight Sat; 11-11 Sun; closed 25-26 Dec and 1-2 Jan

APPLECROSS NG7144 Map 11

Applecross Inn ★ 🍽 🛏

Off A896 S of Shieldaig

Getting to this remote inn is quite an experience, with the exhilarating drive over the pass of the cattle (Beallach na Ba) one of the highest in Britain. The alternative route, along the single-track lane winding round the coast from just south of Shieldaig, has equally glorious sea loch and then sea views nearly all the way. You arrive to a marvellous waterside setting, looking across to Skye's Cuillin Hills, and tables in the nice shoreside garden are perfect for soaking it all in. The fresh seafood is a big draw, and most of the ingredients they use are local. Up on chalkboards, the menu might include crab and brandy bisque (£4.25), whole prawns from the bay tossed in hot lemon and garlic butter (£6.95), battered haddock (£7.95), and seared king scallops in garlic butter with crispy bacon (£12.95), with non-fishy dishes such as garlic mushrooms in cream sauce (£4.95), haggis in drambuie with oatcakes (£5.95), and venison casserole with apple and mustard mash (£10.95), with home-made puddings such as raspberry cranachan or fruit crumble (£3.50); they also do very good sandwiches. You must book for the small no smoking restaurant. With a friendly mix of locals and visitors, the no-nonsense bar has a woodburning stove, exposed stone walls, and upholstered pine furnishings on the stone floor; well kept Isle of Skye Blaven and Red Cuillin, and over 50 malt whiskies. There's also a no smoking dining area, with lavatories for the disabled and baby changing facilities; pool (winter only), dominoes, and juke box (musicians may take over instead). *(Recommended by G D Brooks, W Holborow, JDM, KM, Dr D J and Mrs S C Walker, Jeff and Wendy Williams, John and Claire Pettifer, Dr D E Granger, A J Bowen, Kay and Alistair Butler, Michael Lamm, Tim Maddison, GSB, Mr and Mrs M Stratton)*

Free house ~ Licensee Judith Fish ~ Real ale ~ Bar food (12-9) ~ Restaurant ~ (01520) 744262 ~ Children welcome till 8.30pm ~ Dogs allowed in bar and bedrooms ~ Live entertainment Thurs evenings ~ Open 11-11.30(12 Fri); 12.30-11 Sun; closed 25 Dec, 1 Jan ~ Bedrooms: £30/£60(£70B)

BADACHRO NG7773 Map 11
Badachro Inn ⑪

2½ miles S of Gairloch village turn off A832 on to B8056, then after another 3¼ miles turn right in Badachro to the quay and inn

Another remote and beautifully set waterside pub, this convivial black and white painted house has a terrace which virtually overhangs the water (there are more seats on an attractively planted lochside lawn); inside too you can make the most of the view, as the no-smoking dining conservatory overlooks the bay. There's an appealing local atmosphere in the bar, and gentle eavesdropping suggests that some of the yachtsmen have been calling in here annually for decades – the talk is still very much of fishing and boats. There are some interesting photographs and collages on the walls, and they put out the Sunday newspapers. The quieter dining area on the left has big tables by a huge log fire. Friendly staff serve a couple of well kept beers from the Isle of Skye, Black Isle or An Teallach breweries on handpump, and they've over 50 malt whiskies, and a good changing wine list, with almost a dozen by the glass; piped music, cribbage, shove-ha'penny and dominoes. Look out for the sociable pub spaniel Casper. Enjoyable food – with the good fresh fish earning the place its food award – includes snacks such as sandwiches (from £3.65), baked potatoes (from £3.45), beef and spring onion burger (£3.95), and ploughman's (£6.75), and changing specials such as sweet potato and turnip soup (£2.35), grilled goats cheese and salad (£6.95), fish pie or locally smoked haddock topped with welsh rarebit (£9.95), roast leg of lamb with yorkshire pudding (£9.95), baked chicken breast with potato, celeriac and garlic mash (£10.50), and locally caught monkfish kebab with rosemary, peppers and tomatoes (£13.95), and puddings such as treacle sponge (£4.25). The pub is in a tiny village, and the quiet road comes to a dead end a few miles further on at the lovely Redpoint beach. The bay is very sheltered, virtually landlocked by Eilean Horrisdale just opposite. There are three pub moorings (free for visitors), and showers are available at a small charge. Usefully, there's Internet access. *(Recommended by P R Morley, Brian and Anita Randall, Tim Maddison, Michael Lamm, A J Bowen)*

Free house ~ Licensee Martyn Pearson ~ Real ale ~ Bar food (12-3, 6-9; not 25 Dec) ~ Restaurant ~ (01445) 741255 ~ Children welcome ~ Dogs allowed in bar ~ Open 12-12; 12.30-11 Sun; Jan-Mar open weekdays only 4.30-11, Sat 12-12, and Sun 12.30-6; closed 25 Dec

---

If we know a pub has an outdoor play area for children, we mention it.

BROUGHTY FERRY NO4630 Map 11

Fishermans Tavern ♀ 🍺 🛏

Fort Street; turning off shore road

In a row of 17th-c fishermen's cottages, this welcoming town pub particularly impresses with its range of beers, as they have half a dozen brews changing almost every day; their website (www.fishermans-tavern-hotel.co.uk) has updates about which are currently on, though you might typically find Belhaven 80/-, Inveralmond Lia Fail, Timothy Taylors Landlord and guests from brewers such as Adnams, Bass, Caledonian, Fullers, and Orkney, on handpump or tall fount air pressure. They also have a dozen wines by the glass, some local country wines, draught wheat beer, and a good range of malt whiskies. There's an enjoyable atmosphere, and the staff and locals are friendly. A little carpeted snug on the right has nautical tables, light pink soft fabric seating, basket-weave wall panels and beige lamps, and is the more lively bar; on the left is a secluded lounge area with an open coal fire. The carpeted back bar (popular with diners) has a Victorian fireplace; dominoes, TV and fruit machine, and a coal fire. One room is no smoking. Though toasties are always available, the rest of the enjoyable bar food is served lunchtimes only, from a menu that might include soup (£2.25), sandwiches (from £3.40), vegetable biryani (£7), smokie pie or venison casseroled in red wine (£7.50), seafood crêpes with parmesan (£7.90), and plenty of fresh fish specials (not Mon); children's meals (£4.75). They do a two-course lunch for £8.45, and have disabled lavatories, and baby changing facilities. On summer evenings there are tables on the front pavement, and they might have barbecues in the secluded walled garden (where they hold an annual beer festival on the last weekend in May). Recently updated, the bedrooms extend into the neighbouring cottages; the residents' lounge has a seaview (the bay is just around the corner). One reader found they prefer guests not to take breakfast until the last minute. The landlord has another pub nearby, and also runs the well preserved Speedwell Bar in Dundee. *(Recommended by Jo Lilley, Simon Calvert, Callum and Letitia Smith-Burnett, Charles and Pauline Stride, Kay and Alistair Butler, Peter Abbott, Steve Whalley)*

Free house ~ Licensee Jonathan Stewart ~ Real ale ~ Bar food (12-2.30(Sat, Sun 12.30-3); not evenings) ~ (01382) 775941 ~ Children in eating area of bar ~ Dogs allowed in bar ~ Folk band Thurs night from 10 ~ Open 11-12(1 Thurs, Sat); 12.30-12 Sun ~ Bedrooms: £39B/£62B

EAST LINTON NT5977 Map 11

Drovers 🍺

Bridge Street (B1407), just off A1 Haddington—Dunbar

If you're coming to this pleasant old inn with six or more people they'll lay on a courtesy bus that runs as far as Edinburgh. The main bar feels a bit like a cosy living room, with wooden floors, a basket of logs in front of the woodburning stove, and comfortable armchairs. There's a goat's head on a pillar in the middle of the room, fresh flowers and newspapers, lighted candles, and a mix of prints and pictures on the half panelled, half magenta-painted walls; piped music. A similar room leads off, and a door opens out on to a walled lawn with tables. Adnams Broadside, Belhaven Best and Caledonian Deuchars IPA are well kept on handpump, and they've a couple of weekly changing guests such as Batemans XXX, Greene King Abbot, or Hook Norton Old Hooky. Bar food takes in baguettes (£3.25), salmon fillet with stir-fried vegetables and noodles (£6.25), steak and ale pie (£6.95), and steaks (from £7.95), with a daily changing set menu that includes main courses such as roast duck breast on salad with honey and orange jus (two courses £16.95, three courses £22). The upstairs restaurant is no smoking. The pub is on a pretty village street; readers have enjoyed its window boxes in spring. *(Recommended by Pat and Sam Roberts, Christine and Malcolm Ingram, Dr and Mrs Guy Cocker, Steve Whalley, Michael Butler)*

London and Edinburgh Inns ~ Manager Sue Campbell ~ Real ale ~ Restaurant ~ (01620) 860298 ~ Children welcome ~ Dogs allowed in bar ~ Open 11-11(12 Thurs); 11-1 Fri, Sat; 12.30-12 Sun

EDINBURGH NT2574 Map 11

Abbotsford ◀

Rose Street; E end, beside South St David Street

The refreshingly uncluttered interior of this single-bar pub is pleasantly traditional, with dark wooden half-panelled walls, an impressive highly polished Victorian island bar counter, long wooden tables and leatherette benches, and a welcoming log-effect gas fire. There are prints on the walls, a rather handsome plaster-moulded high ceiling, and a nicely old-fashioned atmosphere; fruit machine, and TV. Well kept Broughton Exciseman, Greenmantle IPA and a beer brewed for them by Atlas are served in the true Scottish fashion from a set of air pressure tall founts, along with a couple of changing guests from brewers such as Crouch Vale. They have around 72 whiskies. Reliable and good value, lunchtime bar food includes sandwiches (from £1.75), steak and kidney pie, a daily roast or haggis, neeps and tatties (£6.75), scampi (£6.95), and good home-made puddings. Efficient service from dark-uniformed or white-shirted staff; be warned that they close quite promptly after last orders. *(Recommended by Paul Hopton, R M Corlett, the Didler, Patrick Hancock, Joe Green, Esther and John Sprinkle, Janet and Peter Race)*

Free house ~ Licensee Colin Grant ~ Real ale ~ Bar food (12-3) ~ Restaurant ~ (0131) 225 5276 ~ Children welcome ~ Open 11-11; closed Sun, and 25 Dec, 1 Jan

Bow Bar ★ ◀

West Bow

The splendid range of real ales – and the way they serve them – is one of the main draws to this cheerfully traditional alehouse: eight superbly kept beers are served from impressive antique founts made by Aitkens, Mackie & Carnegie, with a typical selection including Belhaven 80/-, Caledonian Deuchars IPA, Timothy Taylors Landlord, and various changing guests like Atlas Nimbus, Fyne Ales Maverick, Hopback GFB, Kelburn Red Smiddy and Stewarts No 3. But that's not the only highlight – the grand carved mahogany gantry has a massive array of over 140 malts, including cask strength whiskies, and there's a good choice of rums and gins too. Busy and friendly with a good chatty atmosphere, the simple, neatly kept rectangular bar has a fine collection of appropriate enamel advertising signs and handsome antique trade mirrors, sturdy leatherette wall seats and heavy narrow tables on its wooden floor, and café-style bar seats. The only food they serve is tasty pies (from £1.40), and toasties (from £1.60). It's tucked away just below the castle. *(Recommended by David Crook, R M Corlett, Patrick Hancock, the Didler, Paul Hopton, Simon and Amanda Southwell, Joe Green, Mark Walker)*

Free house ~ Licensee Helen McLoughlin ~ Real ale ~ Bar food (12-2.30, not Sun) ~ (0131) 226 7667 ~ Dogs welcome ~ Open 12-11.30; 12.30-11 Sun; closed 25-26 Dec, 1-2 Jan

Café Royal

West Register Street

When this vibrant Victorian pub was built it was a showcase for the latest in gas and plumbing fittings, and its beautifully ornate interior continues to dazzle today. The floor and stairway are laid with marble, chandeliers hang from the magnificent ceilings, and the big island bar is graced by a carefully re-created gantry. The high-ceilinged café rooms have a particularly imprssive series of highly detailed Doulton tilework portraits of historical innovators Watt, Faraday, Stephenson, Caxton, Benjamin Franklin and Robert Peel (forget police – his importance here is as the introducer of calico printing). There are some fine original fittings in the downstairs gents', and the stained-glass well in the seafood and game restaurant is well worth a look. Alongside a decent choice of wines, with a dozen by the glass, they've 25 malt whiskies, and well kept Caledonian Deuchars IPA and 80/- on handpump, with perhaps a couple of scottish guests like Arran Blonde and Orkney Dark Island; there's a TV, fruit machine and piped music. The restaurant specialises in seafood and game, so the bar menu has plenty of these too; as well as sandwiches (from £3.95), you might find mussels (half a kilo £6.75, or a kilo – that's a lot of mussels – for £9.95), oysters (from £6.95), good sausage and mash (£6.95), braised lamb shank (£7.65), several fish specials such as seared swordfish steak (£9.95), and puddings such as sticky toffee pudding (£2.95). It can get very busy, and the décor is perhaps best appreciated on quiet afternoons. *(Recommended by Pat and Stewart Gordon, Michael Butler, Joe Green, the Didler, Patrick Hancock, R M Corlett, David Crook, Theocsbrian, Esther and John Sprinkle, Mark Walker, John and Fiona McIlwain)*

Spirit Group ~ Manager Dave Allan ~ Real ale ~ Bar food (11(12.30 Sun)-10) ~ Restaurant ~ (0131) 556 1884 ~ Children in restaurant ~ Open 11(12.30 Sun)-11(12 Thurs, 1 Fri-Sat); closed 25 Dec

Guildford Arms 🍺
West Register Street

The choice of ten well kept real ales is a big part of this bustling pub's appeal, but its chief glory is the splendid Victorian décor. The main bar has lots of mahogany, glorious colourfully painted plasterwork and ceilings, big original advertising mirrors, and heavy swagged velvet curtains at the arched windows. The snug little no smoking upstairs gallery restaurant gives a dress-circle view of the main bar (notice the lovely old mirror decorated with two tigers on the way up), but watch out: prices can be higher up here. The beers on handpump might include Caledonian Deuchars IPA and 80/-, Harviestoun Bitter & Twisted, Orkney Dark Island, Timothy Taylor Landlord, and guests like Kelham Island Pale Rider and Stewarts Pentland IPA; the helpful, friendly staff may offer a taste before you buy. Also, 16 wines by the glass (including champagne), and a good choice of malt whiskies. The lunchtime menu includes sandwiches, soup (£2.95), pan-fried black pudding with mushroom sauce and crispy pancetta (£3.55), shetland mussels with tomato and chilli or garlic and cream sauce (small £4.25, large £7.95), breaded haddock (£6.85), and steak and ale pie (£6.95), while in the evenings (when food is served only in the gallery restaurant) they might have lambs liver with crispy bacon and rosemary onion gravy on mustard mash (£8.95), and salmon with avocado salsa (£11.75). There's a TV, fruit machine, and piped music. This is the flagship of a small regional group of pubs and bars. *(Recommended by Pat and Stewart Gordon, R M Corlett, Joe Green, David Crook, the Didler, Michael Butler, Simon and Amanda Southwell, Patrick Hancock, Paul Hopton, Nigel Espley, Liane Purnell, Peter Abbott, Esther and John Sprinkle, Mark Walker, John and Fiona McIlwain, Janet and Peter Race)*

Free house ~ Licensee Scott Wilkinson ~ Real ale ~ Bar food (12(12.30 Sun)-2.30; 6-9.30(10 Fri, Sat)) ~ Restaurant (12(12.30 Sun)-2.30, 6-9.30(10 Fri, Sat)) ~ (0131) 556 4312 ~ Children over 14 in restaurant ~ Dogs allowed in bar ~ Jazz, folk or blues nightly in August, plus ten-day midsummer blues festival ~ Open 11(12.30 Sun)-11(midnight Fri, Sat)

Kays Bar 🍺 £
Jamaica Street W; off India Street

Always buzzing with an eclectic mix of customers, this busy backstreet pub is bigger than you might think from the outside. The cosy interior is decked out with various casks and vats, old wine and spirits merchant notices, gas-type lamps, well worn red plush wall banquettes and stools around cast-iron tables, and red pillars supporting a red ceiling. A quiet panelled back room leads off, with a narrow plank-panelled pitched ceiling and a collection of books ranging from dictionaries to ancient steam-train books for boys; lovely warming coal fire in winter. In days past, the pub was owned by John Kay, a whisky and wine merchant; wine barrels were hoisted up to the first floor and dispensed through pipes attached to nipples which can still be seen around the light rose. Nowadays, there's an interesting range of up to eight superbly kept real ales on handpump, including Belhaven 80/-, Caledonian Deuchars IPA, McEwans 80/-, Theakstons Best, and guests from brewers such as Fraioch, Greene King, Hook Norton and Isle of Arran. The choice of whiskies is impressive too, with around 60 malts between eight and 50 years old, and ten blended whiskies. Service is friendly and obliging; TV, dominoes and cribbage, Scrabble and backgammon. Straightforward but good value lunchtime bar food includes soup (£1.25), haggis and neeps or mince and tatties, steak pie and filled baked potatoes (£3.25), and lasagne, beefburger and chips or chicken balti (£3.70). *(Recommended by the Didler, R T and J C Moggridge, R M Corlett, Patrick Hancock, Peter F Marshall, John and Fiona McIlwain, Tich Critchlow)*

Free house ~ Licensee David Mackenzie ~ Real ale ~ Bar food (12-2.30; not on rugby international days) ~ (0131) 225 1858 ~ Dogs welcome ~ Open 11-12(1 Fri, Sat); 12.30-11 Sun

Starbank ♀ ● £

Laverockbank Road, off Starbank Road, just off A901 Granton—Leith

Readers have this year especially enjoyed the service at this stylish but friendly and relaxed pub, which also boasts a great range of drinks and marvellous views over the Firth of Forth from the long light and airy bare-boarded bar. Around eight well kept real ales include Belhaven 80/- and St Andrews, Caledonian Deuchars IPA, Timothy Taylors Landlord and guests from breweries all over Britain such as Harviestoun, Jennings, Springhead and Wychwood. Nearly all of their wines are served by the glass, and there's a tempting selection of malt whiskies. Tasty bar food (with most prices once again unchanged since last year) includes soup (£1.50), herring rollmop salad (£2.50), a daily vegetarian dish (£4.50), ploughman's or seafood salad (£5.50), haddock mornay or sliced breast of chicken with chasseur sauce (£6), and poached salmon with lemon butter or minute steak with pepper sauce (£6.50), and puddings (£2.50). The conservatory restaurant is no smoking, and there's a sheltered back terrace. Parking on the adjacent hilly street. *(Recommended by Pat and Stewart Gordon, Ken Richards, R T and J C Moggridge, Paul and Ursula Randall, R M Corlett, Callum and Letitia Smith-Burnett, Peter Abbott, Mark O'Sullivan, Paul Hopton, R N Lovelock, Maurice and Gill McMahon)*

Free house ~ Licensee Valerie West ~ Real ale ~ Bar food (12-2.30, 6-9; 12(12.30 Sun)-9 weekends) ~ Restaurant ~ (0131) 552 4141 ~ Children welcome till 9pm ~ Dogs allowed in bar ~ Live music first Sat evening of month, and jazz second Sun afternoon of month ~ Open 11-11(12 Thurs-Sat); 12.30-11 Sun

ELIE NO4900 Map 11

Ship ⇌

The Toft, off A917 (High Street) towards harbour

Tables on the terrace outside this popular harbourside pub look down onto Elie's broad sands and across the bay, and on summer Sundays you can watch the progress of their cricket team (they have regular barbecues then too). The upstairs restaurant enjoys the same beach views. The unspoilt, villagey beamed bar has a buoyant nautical feel, with friendly locals and staff, warming winter coal fires, and partly panelled walls studded with old prints and maps. There's also a simple carpeted back room; cribbage, dominoes and shut the box. Very well liked bar food includes good soup (£2.50), haggis, neeps and tatties with a whisky sauce (£4), haddock and chips (£7.50), burgers (£7.95), steak and ale or seafood pie (£8), and daily specials, including fresh fish; they do a good Sunday lunch. In summer they have a seafood lunch menu served in the garden, with things like mussels (£6), smoked haddock and gruyère quiche (£8) and dressed crab salad (£9.95). Well kept Caledonian Deuchars IPA, several wines by the glass, and half a dozen malt whiskies. Recently well refurbished (and earning a stay award this year), the comfortable bedrooms are in a guesthouse next door. An unmanned tourist booth in the garden has leaflets on the local area. *(Recommended by Paul and Ursula Randall, David and Katharine Cooke, Peter and Anne Hollindale, Michael Butler)*

Free house ~ Licensees Richard and Jill Philip ~ Real ale ~ Bar food (12-2.30, 6-9(9.30 Fri, Sat); Sun 12.30-3, 6-9) ~ Restaurant ~ (01333) 330246 ~ Children in eating area of bar and restaurant ~ Dogs allowed in bar ~ Open 11-12(1 Fri, Sat); 12.30-12 Sun; closed 25 Dec ~ Bedrooms: £45B/£70B

GAIRLOCH NG8077 Map 11

Old Inn 🍴 ♈ 🍺 🛏

Just off A832/B8021

The setting of this particularly friendly 18th-c inn is delightful – it nestles at the bottom of Flowerdale Glen, tucked comfortably away from the modern waterside road. Picnic-sets are prettily placed outside by the trees that line the stream as it flows past under the old stone bridge, and on the opposite side are more trees with high crags above (look out for eagles). There are pleasant wooded walks up the glen, the ancestral home of Clan MacKenzie, to the Flowerdale waterfall. The well kept changing beers are a big draw, with usually around five on offer: a typical selection might be Adnams, Cairngorms Tradewinds, Greene King Abbot, and Isle of Skye Red Cuillin and Blind Piper (a blend of Isle of Ske ales made for the pub and named after a famed 17th-c local piper). They have a lot of fairly priced wines by the glass, a decent collection of malt whiskies, and you can get speciality coffees. The food is popular, and fresh locally landed fish is a speciality, with bouillabaisse, seared scallops, and langoustines commonly on the board, and mussels, crabs, lobster, skate, haddock and hake often cropping up too. The regular bar menu includes soup (£3.25), pizzas (from £5.50), venison burger (£6.50), venison and wild boar sausages (£7.50), fish pie (£8.45), fresh pasta with smoked salmon, vodka and pink peppercorns (£7.50), seafood grill (£10.50), with specials like saddle of mountain hare stuffed with haggis (£13.50), and puddings such as clootie dumpling and custard (£3.75); they also do lunchtime open sandwiches (from £4.50), and a three-course scottish set menu for £12.25. The landlady makes her own chutneys and preserves – and grows many of the herbs they use (they also track down organic vegetables). Credit (but not debit) cards incur a surcharge of £1.75. It's nicely decorated with paintings and murals on exposed stone walls, and the cheerfully relaxed public bar has chatty locals; darts, TV, fruit machine and juke box. The eating areas and lounge are no smoking. The pub is only yards away from the little fishing harbour, and handy for pleasant beaches. More reports please. *(Recommended by Nelly Flowers, Roger and Anne Newbury, Brian and Anita Randall, Paul and Ursula Randall, Mr and Mrs M Stratton)*

Free house ~ Licensees Alastair and Ute Pearson ~ Real ale ~ Bar food (12-2, 7-9; 12-10 in summer) ~ Restaurant ~ (01445) 712006 ~ Children welcome ~ Dogs allowed in bar and bedrooms ~ Scottish music Fri evenings ~ Open 11-1(12 Sat); 12.30-11.30 Sun ~ Bedrooms: £35B/£69B

GIFFORD NT5368 Map 11

Tweeddale Arms 🛏

S of Haddington; High Street (B6355)

Under new management since the spring, this comfortable white-painted hotel is probably the oldest building in this appealing Borders village, but sits among a row of similarly attractive houses looking across the village green to a 300-year-old avenue of lime trees. Its various rooms each has its own character, with the bar particularly well liked by locals, who come both for food and for cheerfully rumbunctious games of cribbage and dominoes; the modernised lounge, though still chatty, is perhaps more reserved. Two changing real ales might include Caledonian Deuchars IPA and Greene King Old Speckled Hen, and they've quite a few malt whiskies, including the local Glenkinchie. If you're staying, the tranquil hotel lounge is particularly relaxing, with antique tables and paintings, chinoiserie chairs and chintzy easy chairs, an oriental rug on one wall, a splendid corner sofa and magazines on a table. Bar food includes soup (£2.50), fresh battered haddock (£8.25), beef and ale pie, lasagne or cold meat platter (£8.75), and changing specials like poached haddock mornay (£8.25). Fruit machine, TV and piped music. *(Recommended by Dr and Mrs R G J Telfer, Archie and Margaret Mackenzie, Steve Whalley)*

London and Edinburgh Inns ~ Manager Martin Ferguson ~ Real ale ~ Bar food ~ Restaurant ~ (01620) 810240 ~ Children in eating area of bar and restaurant ~ Dogs allowed in bar and bedrooms ~ Open 11-11 ~ Bedrooms: £60B/£75B

GLASGOW NS5965 Map 11
Babbity Bowster 🍴 ♀
Blackfriars Street

Particularly lively on Saturday evenings when there's live music, this cheery 18th-c
town house is quite a Glasgow institution, and has something of the feel of a
continental café-bar. The simply decorated light interior has fine tall windows, well
lit photographs and big pen-and-wash drawings of the city, its people and
musicians, dark grey stools and wall seats around dark grey tables on the stripped
wooden boards, and a peat fire. The bar opens on to a pleasant terrace with tables
under cocktail parasols, trellised vines and shrubs, and adjacent boules; they may
have barbecues out here in summer. You'll find well kept Caledonian Deuchars IPA
and a couple of guests like Hampshire Mayhem and Houston Peter's Well on air
pressure tall fount, and a remarkably sound collection of wines, malt whiskies, and
farm cider; good tea and coffee too. A short choice of interesting well cooked bar
food might include hearty home-made soup (£2.95), croques monsieur or haggis,
neeps and tatties (£4.95; they also do a vegetarian version), panini (from £5.65),
stovies (£5.75), mussels (£6.50), and toulouse sausage (£6.95), with daily specials,
and puddings such as clootie dumpling (£2.95). The airy upstairs restaurant has
more elaborate meals. A big ceramic of a kilted dancer and piper in the bar
illustrates the mildly cheeky 18th-c Lowland wedding pipe tune (Bab at the
Bowster) from which the pub takes its name – the friendly landlord or his staff will
be happy to explain further. *(Recommended by Mark and Ruth Brock, Tracey and
Stephen Groves, Tony and Wendy Hobden, Stephen and Jean Curtis)*

Free house ~ Licensee Fraser Laurie ~ Real ale ~ Bar food (12-10) ~ Restaurant ~
(0141) 552 5055 ~ Children in eating area of bar and restaurant ~ Live music on Sat ~
Open 11(12.30 Sun)-12; closed 25 Dec ~ Bedrooms: £40S/£55S

Bon Accord 🍺 £
North Street

Glasgow's finest pub for real ales, this friendly alehouse changes its ten well kept
beers so often that they get through an average of 500 different brews each year.
With an emphasis on smaller brewers from all around Britain, the range might
typically include beers from Brakspears, Broughton, Caledonian, Durham, Hop
Back, Fullers, Harviestoun, Houston, Kelham Island and Marstons. Whisky
drinkers have lots to keep them happy too, with over 140 malts to choose from,
and all 13 of their wines are available by the glass. There's a friendly atmosphere,
and you'll find a good mix of customers (women find it welcoming here). The
interior is neatly kept, partly polished bare-boards and partly carpeted, with a mix
of tables and chairs, terracotta walls, and pot plants throughout; TV, fruit machine,
cribbage, chess and background music. Reasonably priced bar food includes baked
potatoes or baguettes (£2.95), lasagne (£4.65), scampi (£4.80), and steak (£8.95);
they do a two-course special (£3.95). It's open mike night on Tuesday, there's a
quiz on Wednesday and a band on Saturday. *(Recommended by Nelly Flowers,
Ian Baillie, Patrick Hancock, Nick Holding)*

Scottish Courage ~ Lease Paul McDonagh ~ Real ale ~ Bar food (12(12.30 Sun)-7
(8 Weds)) ~ (0141) 248 4427 ~ Children until 8pm but only if eating ~ Live entertainment
Tues-Sat ~ Open 11-12; 12.30-11 Sun

Counting House 🍺 £
St Vincent Place/George Square

Now completely no smoking, this big, busy Wetherspoons conversion (once a
branch of the Royal Bank of Scotland) stays atmospheric and briskly efficient even
when crowded. The imposing interior is stunning, rising into a lofty, richly
decorated coffered ceiling which culminates in a great central dome, with well lit
nubile caryatids doing a fine supporting job in the corners. You'll also find the sort
of decorative glasswork that nowadays seems more appropriate to a landmark pub

than to a bank, as well as wall-safes, plenty of prints and local history, and big windows overlooking George Square. Away from the bar, several areas have solidly comfortable seating, while a series of smaller rooms – once the managers' offices – lead around the perimeter of the building. Some of these are surprisingly cosy, one is like a well stocked library, and a few are themed with pictures and prints of historical characters such as Walter Scott or Mary, Queen of Scots. The central island servery has fairly priced Caledonian 80/- and Deuchars IPA, Courage Directors and Cairngorm Wildcat, along with well kept guests such as Marstons Pedigree and Orkney Dark Island on handpump. They also do a good choice of bottled beers and malt whiskies, and a dozen wines by the glass; fruit machines. Friendly efficient staff serve the usual good value Wetherspoons food, with breakfasts (from £2.79, available till midday), sandwiches (from £2.29), panini (from £2.99), haggis, neeps and tatties (£3.49), wraps (from £3.59), chilli con carne or sausages and mash (£5.29), breaded scampi (£5.35), chicken jalfrezi (£5.79), steaks (from £7.15), specials like venison casserole (£7.49), Sunday roasts, and puddings such as treacle sponge (£2.69); they do two meals for £6.50. Tuesday is steak night, and Thursday curry night. The pub is a handy place to wait if catching a train from Queen Street station. *(Recommended by David Crook, Patrick Hancock, Dave Braisted, Nick Holding, Doug Christian, Tony and Wendy Hobden)*

Wetherspoons ~ Manager Stuart Coxshall ~ Real ale ~ Bar food (10am-11pm) ~ (0141) 225 0160 ~ Children in eating area of bar till 7pm ~ Open 10-12

GLENELG NG8119 Map 11

Glenelg Inn 🍽

Unmarked road from Shiel Bridge (A87) towards Skye

On a sunny day tables in the beautifully kept garden of this charming inn have lovely views across the water to Skye; Glenelg is the closest place on the mainland to the island, and there's a little car ferry across in summer. Feeling a bit like a mountain cabin (and still decidedly pubby given the smartness of the rest of the place), the unpretentious green-carpeted bar gives an overwhelming impression of dark wood, with lots of logs dotted about, a big fireplace, and only a very few tables and well worn cushioned wall benches – when necessary crates and fish boxes may be pressed into service as extra seating. Black and white photographs line the walls at the far end around the pool table, and there are various jokey articles and local information elsewhere; fruit machine, darts, winter pool and piped music (usually scottish). They don't have real ales (although hope to in the future), but there's a good collection of malt and cask strength whiskies; the locals are welcoming. At lunchtime they do only snacks such as soup (£3), filled granary rolls (£5), or big salads, while in the evening you can choose from tasty dishes such as roast guinea fowl and barley stew, curried venison burger or roast pepper and onion tart (£9), with puddings such as maple and pecan cheesecake (£3). They also do an outstanding four-course evening meal in the no smoking dining room (£35). The friendly staff or rather forthright landlord can organise local activities, and there are plenty of enjoyable walks nearby. Some of the bedrooms have great views; more are planned, and they do bargain rates in winter. Getting here is an experience, with the single-track road climbing dramatically past heather-blanketed slopes and mountains with spectacular views to the lochs below. *(Recommended by John Ballard, JDM, KM, Kay and Alistair Butler, W Holborow, G D Brooks)*

Free house ~ Licensee Christopher Main ~ Bar food (12-2, 6-9; not Sun evening) ~ Restaurant ~ (01599) 522273 ~ Children welcome ~ Dogs allowed in bar ~ Ceilidh Sat evening ~ Open 12-2.30, 5-11; 12-2.30 Sun; closed Sun in winter (except for residents); closed Christmas ~ Bedrooms: /£100B

You can send us reports through our web site: www.goodguides.co.uk
or directly to us at: The Good Pub Guide, FREEPOST TN1569,
Wadhurst, E Sussex TN5 7BR.

HOUSTON NS4166 Map 11

Fox & Hounds ◖

South Street at junction with Main Street (B789, off B790 at Langbank signpost E of Bridge of Weir)

This enjoyable village pub has a good welcome and popular food, but it's most notable as the home of the Houston Brewery, which produces its award winning beers in what was once a disused cellar. Their tasty Barochan, Killellan and St Peters Well are kept in top condition alongside a couple of seasonal brews like Big Lusty May or Warlock Stout, and a changing guest such as Deuchars IPA on handpump; a window in the bar looks into the brewery, which now sends its cask and bottled beers throughout the UK. You'll also find eight wines by the glass, around 100 malt whiskies, various teas and freshly squeezed orange juice. The clean plush hunting-theme lounge has comfortable seats by a fire and polished brass and copper; piped music. Popular with a younger crowd, the lively downstairs bar has a large-screen TV, pool and fruit machines. Served upstairs (downstairs they only do sandwiches), a good choice of enjoyable bar food might include soup (£2.95), chargrilled venison sausages with mash and onion gravy (£6.95), steak, mushroom and ale pie or large baked mushrooms stuffed with herb ratatouille (£7.50), apple, celery and mushroom stroganoff (£7.95), their own beer-battered scampi (£9.50), and steaks (from £12.95); they do children's meals (from £1.95), and the restaurant has a more elaborate menu. There are no smoking areas in the lounge and restaurant. They have several summer beer festivals, and a music fest in winter. The same family has been in charge for 27 years. *(Recommended by Jean and Douglas Troup, Mike and Shelley Woodroffe, Stephen and Jean Curtis, Martin and Sue Day)*

Own brew ~ Licensee Jonathan Wengel ~ Real ale ~ Bar food (12-2.30, 5.30-10; 12-10 Sat, Sun) ~ Restaurant ~ (01505) 612448 ~ Children in restaurant and no smoking part of bar ~ Dogs allowed in bar ~ Occasional live music and winter music fest ~ Open 11-12 (1am Fri and Sat); 12-12 Sun

INVERARAY NN0908 Map 11

George 🛌

Main Street E

Run by the same family since 1860, this comfortably modernised inn is the nicest place to stay in the area, and has a bustling dark bar that oozes character from its bare stone walls. Showing plenty of age in its exposed joists, old tiles and big flagstones, it has antique settles, cushioned stone slabs along the walls, carved wooden benches, nicely grained wooden-topped cast-iron tables, lots of curling club and ships' badges, and a cosy log fire in winter. Swiftly served by friendly staff (you order at the table), generously served enjoyable bar food includes soup (£2.30), ploughman's (£4.95), haggis, neeps and tatties (£5.25), steak pie (£5.75), good scampi and chips (£6.75), and evening dishes like salmon fillet grilled with tomatoes, olives, capers and mozzarella (£8.50), roast fillet of pork with sun-dried tomato, spinach and pine nut stuffing, arran mustard mash and apple and calvados jus (£9.25), and steaks (from £13.50); proper children's meals (£2.95). There's a new no smoking conservatory restaurant, and tables in a very pleasant, well laid-out garden. Two well kept changing beers include one from Fyne or Houston along with a guest such as Caledonian Deuchars IPA on handpump, and they've over 100 malt whiskies; darts, dominoes and TV, but no bar games in summer. Nicely placed in the centre of this little Georgian town, stretching along Loch Fyne in front of Inveraray Castle, the pub is well placed for the great Argyll woodland gardens, best for their rhododendrons in May and early June; there are good nearby walks – you may spot seals or even a basking shark or whale. The individually decorated bedrooms (reached by a grand wooden staircase) have jacuzzis or four-poster beds. *(Recommended by Paul Leason, Derek and Sylvia Stephenson, Mrs B M Hill, Philip and June Caunt, Patrick Hancock, A H C Rainier, Jenny and Brian Seller, OPUS)*

Free house ~ Licensee Donald Clark ~ Real ale ~ Bar food (12-9) ~ Restaurant ~
(01499) 302111 ~ Children welcome ~ Dogs welcome ~ Open 11-12 ~ Bedrooms:
£35B/£60S(£60B)

ISLE OF WHITHORN NX4736 Map 9

Steam Packet 🍽 ♀ 🛏

Harbour Row

Much enjoyed by readers this year (some of whom particularly enjoyed a stay out
of season), this friendly inn has big picture windows ideal for catching the action
in the picturesque working harbour, with its bustle of yachts and inshore fishing
boats. Swiftly served by helpful but unfussy staff, the food is good, with changing
evening specials such as pheasant with black pudding and a calvados jus (£8.75),
or barbary duck breast on beetroot with a honey and mustard suce (£8.75); other
well prepared dishes might include filled rolls (from £2.50), glamorgan sausages
or prawn cocktail (£6.95), gammon steak (£6.95), steamed mussels with tomato
and pesto sauce (£10.50), and steaks (from £12.95), with puddings such as
chocolate terrine with mixed fruits or rhubarb tartlet with stem ginger cream
(£3.50); they do children's meals (£2.50). The comfortable low-ceilinged bar is
split into two: on the right, plush button-back banquettes and boat pictures, and
on the left, green leatherette stools around cast-iron-framed tables on big stone
tiles, and a woodburning stove in the bare stone wall. Bar food can be served in
the lower-beamed dining room, which has excellent colour wildlife photographs,
rugs on its wooden floor, and a solid fuel stove, and there's also a small eating
area off the lounge bar. The conservatory is no smoking. Theakstons XB is well
kept on handpump, along with a guest such as Houston Blonde Bombshell, and
they've two dozen malt whiskies and a good wine list with half a dozen by the
glass; pool and dominoes. There are white tables and chairs in the garden.
Several of the recently refurbished bedrooms have good views. Boat trips leave
from the harbour; you can walk up to the remains of St Ninian's Kirk, on a
headland behind the village. *(Recommended by Dr and Mrs T E Hothersall, Mike and
Lynn Robinson, Stan and Hazel Allen, Richard J Holloway, JWAC, John and Angie Millar,
Julian and Linda Cooke)*

Free house ~ Licensee John Scoular ~ Real ale ~ Bar food (12-2, 6.30-9; not 25 Dec) ~
Restaurant ~ (01988) 500334 ~ Children welcome away from bar ~ Dogs allowed in bar
and bedrooms ~ Open 11-11(12 Sat); closed Mon-Thurs 2.30-6 in Nov, Jan and Feb
winter; closed 25 Dec ~ Bedrooms: £30B/£60B

KILBERRY NR7164 Map 11

Kilberry Inn 🛏

B8024

New licensees have arrived at this homely whitewashed inn and introduced a
greater emphasis on food – no mean feat considering the location is so remote that
local ingredients sometimes arrive by school bus. Getting here is quite an adventure,
the very leisurely drive along the single-track road letting you make the most of the
breathtaking views over rich coastal pastures to the sea and the island of Gigha
beyond; you'll know you've arrived when you spot the old-fashioned red telephone
box outside the low corrugated-roofed building. The menu might include green pea
soup (£4.25), warm red onion tartlet with polenta crust glazed with St Molio
cheese (£5.75), queen scallops toasted with garlic butter (£6.95 starter, £9.95
main), cottage pie with braised red cabbage (£8.95), and venison sausages with
buttery mash and tomato, red pepper and hot smoked paprika sauce (£9.25), with
evening extras like cod roasted with chorizo, basil, baby plum tomatoes and Tio
Pepe (£11.95) and puddings like chocolate espresso cake (£4.75). The small beamed
dining bar, tastefully and simply furnished, is relaxed and warmly sociable, with a
good log fire; piped music. The pub is completely no smoking; there's no real ale,
but they do bottled beers from Loch Fyne, and have a selection of malt whiskies
(with quite a few local ones). The bedrooms are stylishly attractive. *(Recommended*

by Ian Ness, Les and Sandra Brown, John and Ann Carter, Patrick Hancock, Christine and Neil Townend, Mrs Ruth McCaul, Catherine Kent, Colin Baigent)

Free house ~ Licensees Clare Johnson and David Wilson ~ Bar food (not Mon) ~ Restaurant ~ (01880) 770223 ~ Children in restaurant and family room ~ Dogs welcome ~ Open 12.30-3, 6.30-11; 12.30-3 Sun; closed Mon, and winter also closed Tues-Thurs and all Jan and Feb ~ Bedrooms: £39.50S/£79S

KINGHOLM QUAY NX9773 Map 9
Swan

B726 just S of Dumfries; or signposted off B725

In a quiet spot overlooking the old fishing jetty on the River Nith, this is a comfortable, well run pub useful for families. A short selection of pubby food is promptly served in the well ordered lounge with its little coal fire, or at busy times in the restaurant, from a menu that typically includes soup (£2.60), haggis with melted cheese (£3.60), liver and bacon (£6.25), steak pie or chicken with leeks and white wine (£6.50), spinach and ricotta cannelloni or chilli (£6.70), and battered haddock (£6.95), with evening specials such as rack of ribs or seafood risotto (£8.50), and steaks (from £8.50); puddings might include sticky toffee pudding (£3.20). Many dishes can be served in half helpings, and the food service area is no smoking. The neat and nicely furnished public bar has well kept Theakstons Best on handpump, and good house wines; TV and quiet piped music. The small garden has tables and a play area. They can get busy on Sundays. Handy for the Caerlaverock nature reserve with its multitude of geese, the pub is a pleasant two-mile walk from Dumfries along the river using the tarmacked cycle path. *(Recommended by Richard J Holloway, Nick and Meriel Cox, Nick Holding, Michael and Marion Buchanan, Christine and Malcolm Ingram, David A Hammond, Maurice and Gill McMahon)*

Free house ~ Licensees Billy Houliston, Tracy Rogan and Alan Austin ~ Real ale ~ Bar food (12-2, 5-8.45 (9 Fri, Sat); Sun 11.45-12.15, 4.45-8.30) ~ Restaurant ~ (01387) 253756 ~ Children welcome ~ Open 11.30-2.30, 5-10(11Thurs-Sat); 11.30-11 Sun

KIPPEN NS6594 Map 11
Cross Keys 🛏

Main Street; village signposted off A811 W of Stirling

Very cosy with its dark panelling and subdued lighting, this unpretentious and comfortable 18th-c inn has a strong local following, but extends a warm welcome to visitors. The straightforward lounge has a good log fire, and there's a coal fire in the attractive no smoking family dining room. Generously served by friendly staff, and making good use of fresh, local produce, the enjoyable bar food might include soups like pea and mint (£2.45), smoked salmon and prawn marie rose parcel (£4.75), home-made lasagne or gammon and pineapple (£7.25), and steak and mushroom pie or lamb casserole (£7.75), with puddings such as home-made sticky toffee pudding (£4.45); they also do sandwiches (from £2.95), and you can get smaller helpings. Well kept Harviestoun Bitter & Twisted on handpump, and they've more than 30 malt whiskies; cards, dominoes, TV, and maybe a radio in the separate public bar. Tables in the garden have good views towards the Trossachs. The brightly lit exterior is a cheering sight on a cold winter night. *(Recommended by Kay and Alistair Butler, Nick Holding, Dr A McCormick, Tracey and Stephen Groves)*

Free house ~ Licensees Mr and Mrs Scott ~ Real ale ~ Bar food (12-2, 6-9; 12.30-9 Sun; not 25 Dec, 1 Jan) ~ Restaurant ~ (01786) 870293 ~ Children welcome ~ Dogs allowed in bar and bedrooms ~ Open 12-2.30, 5.30-11(12 Fri); 12-12 Sat; 12.30-11 Sun ~ Bedrooms: /£70S(£70B)

Pubs with particularly interesting histories, or in unusually interesting buildings, are listed at the back of the book.

KIRK YETHOLM NT8328 Map 10

Border 🛏

Village signposted off B6352/B6401 crossroads, SE of Kelso; The Green

This substantially built small hotel, with its front picnic-sets among tubs of flowers, comes as a particularly welcome sight for anyone who has completed the 256-mile march up the Pennine Way long-distance walk. If you have done the full walk, and have with you a copy of the guide to the walk written and drawn by Alfred Wainwright, they will give you a free pint of beer. Originally Wainwright left some money at the inn, to pay for walkers claiming just a half-pint, but that's long gone, and the hotel now foots the bill itself. It's by no means just walkers who will enjoy the pub. Under its friendly new chef/landlord and his wife, the food has taken a quantum leap forward. The cooking is careful and inventive without being at all pretentious, which makes sure that the quality of the carefully sourced fresh local ingredients shines through. It might include sandwiches and toasties (from £2.50), home-made soup (£2.95), mushrooms stuffed with haggis and glazed with whisky sauce (£4.25), smoked salmon with red onions and capers or crayfish and prawn cocktail (£5.95), roast of the day (£6.95 – popular with walkers), home-made venison burger with mozzarella and barbecue sauce (£7.25), steak pie with proper suet pastry or thai vegetable patties with chilli sauce (£7.95), steaks (from £9.95), and home-made puddings like cranachan or bread and butter pudding (£3.95); plenty of autumn game and summer fish. The public bar has been gently freshened up, but is still cheerfully unpretentious, with snug side rooms. It has beams, flagstones and a log fire, and a signed photograph of Wainwright and various Pennine Way souvenirs, as well as appropriate Borders scenery etchings and murals. They have well kept Broughton Greenmantle and a changing scottish guest beer on handpump, decent wines by the glass, a good range of malt whiskies, and a water bowl for dogs; service is warm and efficient. There's a roomy pink-walled dining room, a comfortably refurbished lounge with a second log fire, and a neat conservatory. A sheltered back terrace has more picnic-sets. *(Recommended by Adam Peters, Mathew Horsman)*

Free house ~ Licensees Philip and Margaret Blackburn ~ Real ale ~ Bar food ~ Restaurant ~ (01573) 420237 ~ Children welcome ~ Dogs allowed in bar and bedrooms ~ Open 11-midnight ~ Bedrooms: £45B/£80B

LINLITHGOW NS9976 Map 11

Four Marys 🍺 £

High Street; 2 miles from M9 junction 3 (and little further from junction 4) – town signposted

Steeped in history and very handy for the Palace, this bustling pub has eight very well kept real ales on handpump, with swiftly changing guests such as Arran Blonde and Houston Texas joining the regular Atlas Latitude, Belhaven 80/- and St Andrews, and Caledonian Deuchars IPA on handpump. Dating from the 16th c, it takes its name from the four ladies-in-waiting of Mary, Queen of Scots, and there are masses of mementoes of the ill-fated queen, such as pictures and written records, a piece of bed curtain said to be hers, part of a 16th-c cloth and swansdown vest of the type she's likely to have worn, and a facsimile of her death-mask. The L-shaped bar also has mahogany dining chairs around stripped period and antique tables, a couple of attractive antique corner cupboards, and an elaborate Victorian dresser serving as a bar gantry. The walls are mainly stripped stone, including some remarkable masonry in the inner area; piped music. Readers recommend the haggis, neeps and tatties (£5.95), while other generously served good value bar food includes warm baguettes and baked potatoes (from £3.95), soup (£2.10; good cullen skink £2.50), burgers (from £5.25), macaroni cheese (£5.50), home-made curry, steak pie or lambs liver and bacon (£6.25), steaks (£10.95), and specials like pork fillet in a creamy peppercorn sauce (£6.95) or salmon wih tarragon and white wine (£7.95); children's menu. Service is charming, and the restaurant is no smoking. During their May and October beer festivals they have 20 real ale pumps and live entertainment.

Parking can be difficult. The atmosphere is a lot livelier now than during its days as an apothecary's shop, where David Waldie experimented with chloroform – its first use as an anaesthetic. *(Recommended by Pete Walker, Nick Holding, Peter F Marshall, Callum and Letitia Smith-Burnett)*

Belhaven ~ Managers Eve and Ian Forrest ~ Real ale ~ Bar food (12-3, 5-9 weekdays, 12(12.30 Sun)-9 weekends; all day May-Oct) ~ Restaurant ~ (01506) 842171 ~ Children in restaurant ~ Open 12(12.30 Sun)-11(12 Sat)

LYBSTER ND2436 Map 11
Portland Arms 🛏

A9 S of Wick

A good base for exploring the spectacular cliffs and stacks of the nearby coastline, this big welcoming hotel is our most northerly main entry. One area has been attractively laid out as a cosy country kitchen room with an Aga, pine furnishings and farmhouse crockery; the smart bar-bistro has warm colours and fabrics, solid dark wood furnishings, softly upholstered chairs and a cosy fire. Bar food includes sandwiches (£3, £3.50 toasted), rollmop herring (£3.50), vegetable lasagne (£7.50), home-made steak pie or scampi and chips (£8), salads (£8.50), and steaks (from £12.50), with interesting (but not cheap) specials such as mini beef and haggis bridie with neeps and tatties and whisky gravy (£4.50), steamed cabbage parcels filled with couscous, sun-dried tomatoes and stilton with a pepper and lemon sauce (£9), medallions of beef with haggis, black pudding and a port jus (£16), roasted saddle of lamb with pea and mint mash and madeira sauce (£16.75), and seared fresh tuna with mascarpone and pepper sauce (£17); home-made puddings such as oaty fruit crumble (£4.50). All main courses come with home-made oatcakes. One reader had trouble being served food while a function was on. They serve a good selection of malt whiskies (the beers are keg); dominoes, trivia, piped music. Two eating areas are no smoking. The hotel was built as a staging post on the early 19th-c Parliamentary Road. The friendly staff can arrange fishing and so forth. *(Recommended by Robert F Smith, Dr D G Twyman, Dr A McCormick, Alan Wilcock, Christine Davidson)*

Free house ~ Licensee Robert Reynolds ~ Bar food (12-2.30, 5-8.45; 12-10 in summer) ~ Restaurant ~ (01593) 721721 ~ Children in eating area of bar and restaurant ~ Open 12-11(12 Sat); 12-3, 5-11 weekdays in winter ~ Bedrooms: £55B/£80B

MELROSE NT5434 Map 9
Burts Hotel 🍽 🛏

B6374, Market Square

Always busy and cheerful, this comfortably sophisticated hotel is an ideal base for exploring the Border towns – of which Melrose is perhaps the most villagey. The inviting L-shaped lounge bar has lots of cushioned wall seats and windsor armchairs, and scottish prints on the walls. There are 80 malt whiskies to choose from, and Caledonian Deuchars IPA and 80/- and a guest such as Timothy Taylors Landlord are well kept on handpump; there's a good wine list too, with half a dozen by the glass. Excellent, swiftly served food might include soup (£2.95), grilled sardines with garlic butter (£4.50), breaded haddock (£7.95), vegetable and gruyère strudel on a bed of creamed leeks (£8), chicken curry (£8.50), braised rump of local lamb casserole with garlic and rosemary mash (£9.25), and aberdeen angus fillet steak (£15.95), with puddings such as passion fruit crème brûlée (£4.95); efficient friendly service. The restaurant and half the bar are no smoking. In summer you can sit out in the well tended garden. *(Recommended by Dr Pete Crawshaw, Pat and Stewart Gordon, Mike and Lynn Robinson, Edward Perrott, Peter Abbott, Mark Walker, Julian and Linda Cooke, John and Sylvia Harrop, Mrs J H S Lang, Lucien Perring)*

Free house ~ Licensees Graham and Anne Henderson ~ Real ale ~ Bar food (12-2, 6-9.30, not 25-26 Dec) ~ Restaurant ~ (01896) 822285 ~ Children welcome in eating area of bar and family room; must be over 10 in restaurant ~ Dogs allowed in bar and bedrooms ~ Open 11-2.30, 5-11; 12-2.30, 6-11 Sun; closed 26 Dec ~ Bedrooms: £54B/£100B

PITLOCHRY NN9459 Map 11

Moulin 🍺 🛏

Kirkmichael Road, Moulin; A924 NE of Pitlochry centre

A well liked place to stay, with good food, this imposing 17th-c white-painted inn particularly impresses with its real ales, described by one reader as the best beers he's tasted this year. Brewed in the little stables across the street, Ale of Atholl, Braveheart, Moulin Light and the stronger Old Remedial are superbly kept on handpump, and they also have around 40 malt whiskies, and a good choice of wines by the glass. Although it has been much extended over the years, the bar, in the oldest part of the building, still seems an entity in itself, nicely pubby, with plenty of atmosphere. Above the fireplace in the smaller room is an interesting painting of the village before the road was built (Moulin used to be a bustling market town, far busier than upstart Pitlochry), while the bigger carpeted area has a good few tables and cushioned banquettes in little booths divided by stained-glass country scenes, another big fireplace, some exposed stonework, fresh flowers, and golf clubs and local and sporting prints around the walls; bar billiards, shove ha'penny, cribbage, dominoes and an old-fashioned fruit machine. The extensive bar menu includes soup (£2.75), mussels with garlic and cream (£5.75, £8.95 main), deep fried haggis with a piquant sauce (£4.65), steak and ale pie (£6.95), stuffed peppers or fish, chips and mushy peas (£7.45), game casserole or lamb shank (£7.95), seafood pancake (£8.25), and daily specials, with puddings such as sticky whisky fudge cake or honey sponge and custard (£2.90); from 12 till 6pm they also serve baked potatoes and sandwiches (from £4.45), and they do children's meals. In the evening, readers enjoy eating in the no smoking restaurant. Service is friendly; the landlord is a real motor racing fan. Surrounded by tubs of flowers, picnic-sets outside look across to the village kirk; there are rewarding walks nearby. The rooms are comfortable and breakfasts are good; they offer good value three-night breaks out of season. *(Recommended by Pat and Stewart Gordon, Andy and Jill Kassube, G Dobson, Charles and Pauline Stride, Paul and Ursula Randall, R N Lovelock, Kay and Alistair Butler, Alex and Claire Pearse, Mr and Mrs Maurice Thompson)*

Own brew ~ Licensee Heather Reeves ~ Real ale ~ Bar food (12-9) ~ Restaurant ~ (01796) 472196 ~ Children in eating area of bar and restaurant ~ Dogs allowed in bar ~ Open 12-11(11.45 Sat) ~ Bedrooms: £45S(£45B)/£55S(£55B)

PLOCKTON NG8033 Map 11

Plockton Hotel ★ 🍽 🛏

Village signposted from A87 near Kyle of Lochalsh

Scotland Dining Pub of the Year

'Absolutely excellent in every respect' is one reader's verdict on this bewitching family-run hotel, and that's pretty much the general consensus, especially from people who stay here. Half the comfortable bedrooms have extraordinary views over the loch, service from the friendly staff is charming, and the food is very good too. Forming part of a long, low terrace of stone-built houses, the inn is set in a lovely National Trust for Scotland village. Tables in the front garden look out past the village's trademark palm trees and colourfully flowering shrub-lined shore, and across the sheltered anchorage to the rugged mountainous surrounds of Loch Carron; a stream runs down the hill into a pond in the landscaped back garden. With a buoyant bustling atmosphere, the welcoming comfortably furnished lounge bar has window seats looking out to the boats on the water, as well as antiqued dark red leather seating around neat Regency-style tables on a tartan carpet, three model ships set into the woodwork, and partly panelled stone walls. The separate public bar has darts, pool, shove-ha'penny, dominoes, TV and piped music. Well cooked, using lots of fresh local ingredients, the food might include lunchtime sandwiches, soup (£2.75, with home-made bread), hot smoked mackerel and mozzarella smokies (£4.25), herring in oatmeal or fish and chips (£7.75), venison casserole (£8.75), fresh local langoustines (£9.25 starter, £18.50 main), baked lamb shank with red wine and rosemary sauce (£12.25), good steaks (from £13.25), monkfish and bacon brochettes (£13.50), and fish specials such as hand-dived scallops and steamed local mussels; they also do children's meals. It's a good idea to book at busy times (when service can slow down). The snug and Courtyard restaurant are no smoking. Well kept Caledonian Deuchars IPA and Isle of Skye Hebridean Gold on handpump, and bottled beers from the Isle of Skye brewery, along with a good collection of malt whiskies, and a short wine list. Most bedrooms are in the adjacent building – one has a balcony and woodburning stove, and a four-poster will be in place soon. Expect good breakfasts. A hotel nearby changed its name a few years ago to the Plockton Inn, so don't get the two confused. *(Recommended by Les and Sandra Brown, Bruce and Penny Wilkie, GSB, JDM, KM, John and Claire Pettifer, Patrick Hancock, Dr and Mrs M W A Haward, Jeff and Wendy Williams, Joan and Tony Walker, Carol and Phil Byng, Ian and Jane Irving, Tracey and Stephen Groves, W Holborow)*

Free house ~ Licensee Tom Pearson ~ Real ale ~ Bar food (12(12.30 Sun)-2, 6-9 (9.15 Sun)) ~ Restaurant ~ (01599) 544274 ~ Children in eating area of bar and restaurant ~ Dogs allowed in bar ~ Traditional music summer Weds evenings ~ Open 11-12; 12.30-11 Sun; closed 25 Dec, 1 Jan ~ Bedrooms: £55S(£55B)/£90B

SHIELDAIG NG8154 Map 11
Tigh an Eilean Hotel 🛏
Village signposted just off A896 Lochcarron—Gairloch

A welcome sight in this beautiful but sparsely populated part of the Highlands, this civilised hotel's eagerly anticipated new bar extension is now expected to be completed by early 2006 (until then the quite basic Shieldaig Bar remains fairly separate to the rest of the hotel). It's in a beautiful position looking over the forested Shieldaig Island to Loch Torridon and then out to the sea beyond, with tables in a sheltered little courtyard well placed to enjoy the view. Fresh fish and seafood, all hand-dived or creel-caught by local fishermen, feature heavily on the bar menu, and particularly among the daily specials, which might take in whole local langoustines with a lemon grass, chilli and coriander dipping sauce (£2 each), razor clam fritters with romesco sauce (£4.50), venison liver with red wine gravy (£7.25), grilled bream with lemon and garlic butter (£9.50), and their popular seafood stew (12.95); other dishes include burgers (from £3.25), haggis, neeps and tatties (£6.50), and scampi (£7.75), and they do soup (£2.50) and sandwiches (£2.50) all day; children's meals. Isle of Skye Red Cuillin on handpump, along with maybe a summer guest from the Black Isle brewery, as well as several wines by the glass, and a dozen malt whiskies; winter darts, dominoes and background music. The National Trust Torridon estate and the Beinn Eighe nature reserve aren't too far away. *(Recommended by Charles and Pauline Stride, Tim Maddison, Dr D J and Mrs S C Walker)*

Free house ~ Licensees Cathryn and Christopher Field ~ Real ale ~ Bar food (12-2.30, 7-8.30) ~ Restaurant ~ (01520) 755251 ~ Children welcome in restaurant and eating areas of bar till 9pm ~ Dogs allowed in bedrooms ~ Trad music sessions some Fri or Sat nights ~ Open 11-11; 12-10 Sun ~ Bedrooms: £62.50B/£130B

SKEABOST NG4148 Map 11
Skeabost House Hotel ★ 🛏
A850 NW of Portree, 1½ miles past junction with A856

With glorious views over Loch Snizort, this splendidly grand-looking hotel has come a long way since it origins as a Victorian hunting lodge; carefully redesigned and beautifully decorated throughout, it's now an ultra-stylish and civilised place for an upmarket stay. It's quite a size too, with 12 acres of secluded woodland and gardens, and its own golf course. The old high-ceilinged bar is now mostly for residents, but there's a wholly separate public bar with darts, pool, TV, juke box and even its own car park. They no longer do real ale, but have over 100 malt whiskies, including their own and some rare single-year bottlings. Enjoyable food (which you can eat in the bar) might include soup (£3.50), mussels (£6), burger

(£7.25), lamb hotpot (£8.25), wild mushroom and asparagus risotto (£8.50), oysters (£9), steaks (from £12), and langoustines (£14.50), with puddings such as banana cheesecake (£4.25); they also do bar snacks on Saturday, and three-course meals on Sunday. All the eating areas are no smoking. A fine panelled billiards room leads off the stately hall. The hotel is said to have some of the best salmon fishing on the island. They have occasional concerts on the lawn, and on Saturday nights there's live music in the bar. The price we show for bedrooms is for the cheapest room; prices can be much higher. More reports please. *(Recommended by Joan and Tony Walker)*

Free house ~ Licensee Helen Myers ~ Bar food (10-11) ~ Restaurant ~ (01470) 532202 ~ Children in eating area of bar and family room ~ Dogs allowed in bar ~ Live music Sat nights ~ Open 11-2, 5-11; 11-12.30 Sat; 12-11 Sun ~ Bedrooms: £124.80B/£138B

STEIN NG2656 Map 11

Stein Inn 🛏

End of B886 N of Dunvegan in Waternish, off A850 Dunvegan—Portree; OS Sheet 23 map reference 263564

Skye's oldest inn boasts a prime waterfront spot in this untouched little hamlet, with views over the sea to the Hebrides. The tables outside are an ideal place to sit with a whisky (they've over 100 to choose from), and watch the sunset. Inside, the original public bar has great character, with its sturdy country furnishings, flagstone floor, beam and plank ceiling, partly panelled stripped-stone walls and peat fire. The atmosphere can be surprisingly buzzing, and there's a good welcome from the owners and the evening crowd of local regulars (where do they all appear from?). Good service from the smartly uniformed staff. The dining room and both the large and small lounges are no smoking, and there's a games area with pool table, darts, dominoes and cribbage, and maybe piped radio. Caledonian Deuchars IPA and Isle of Skye Red Cuillin are well kept on handpump, along with a guest like Cairngorm Black Gold. Making good use of local fish and highland meat, the short choice of bar food might include good value sandwiches, various salads (from £5.95), breaded haddock (£6.50), and 8oz sirloin steak (£11.25), with specials such as home-made soup (£2.30), feta cheese and spinach pastry parcels (£6.55), venison pie (£6.85), and fresh fillet of sea trout with parsley butter (£9.50), with puddings such as rich chocolate sponge (£4.10), and local cheeses (£4.75). There's a lively children's inside play area, and showers for yachtsmen. Some of the bedrooms have sea views, and breakfasts are good – readers tell us it's well worth pre-ordering the tasty smoked kippers if you stay here. Useful campsites nearby. *(Recommended by Walter and Susan Rinaldi-Butcher, Joan and Tony Walker, Patrick Hancock, Emma and Will, Jeff and Wendy Williams, Ian and Jane Irving, Tracey and Stephen Groves, Gill Cathles, Mrs Jane Kingsbury, Mr and Mrs M Stratton)*

Free house ~ Licensees Angus and Teresa Mcghie ~ Real ale ~ Bar food (12-4, 6-9.30; 12-4, 6.30-8 Nov-Mar) ~ Restaurant ~ (01470) 592362 ~ Children in eating area of bar, family room and restaurant till 8.30pm ~ Dogs welcome ~ Open 11-12(12.30 Sat); 11.30-11 Sun; 12(12.30 Sun)-11 winter; closed 25 Dec, 1 Jan ~ Bedrooms: £25S/£50S(£66B)

SWINTON NT8448 Map 10 🏠

Wheatsheaf 🍴 🍷 🛏

A6112 N of Coldstream

In a pretty village just a few miles from the River Tweed, this consistently enjoyable, civilised inn is well liked for its very good food, excellent accommodation, and friendly staff who seem genuinely keen to please. There's plenty of choice on the imaginative changing menu: skilfully cooked with fresh local ingredients, lunchtime dishes might include soup (£3.50), smoked haddock scotch egg with curried mango mayonnaise (£5.25), pork fillet and chicken liver terrine with warm red onion marmalade (£5.65), organic pork and leek meatballs in cider gravy (£7.45), fresh crab, red chilli and lemon oil linguini (£7.85), and spinach and pine kernel crêpe with mature cheese sauce (£8.20), with specials such as braised shank of border lamb with spring onion and potato mash (£8.25) or seared fillets of bass on spinach with lemon butter sauce (£11.65), and evening meals like breast of duck on parsnip mash with fresh plum and port sauce (£15.85) and peppered fillet of wild venison on creamed celeriac with a juniper and redcurrant sauce (£16.95); the puddings and Sunday roasts are highly praised, and they also do lunchtime ciabattas. It's a good idea to book, particularly from Thursday to Saturday evening. Carefully thought-out, the main bar area has an attractive long oak settle and comfortable armchairs, and sporting prints and plates on the bottle-green wall covering; a small lower-ceilinged part by the counter has pubbier furnishings, and small agricultural prints on the walls, especially sheep. A further lounge area has a fishing-theme décor (with a detailed fishing map of the River Tweed). The front conservatory has a vaulted pine ceiling and walls of local stone; all the dining areas are no smoking. Caledonian Deuchars IPA and a guest such as Broughton Reiver are well kept on handpump, and they have around 40 malt whiskies, and a fine choice of wines (with ten by the glass); organic fruit juices too. Readers especially enjoy staying here, and the breakfasts are good, with freshly squeezed orange juice. The friendly licensees have brightened up the exterior with new window boxes and hanging baskets. *(Recommended by Dr and Mrs S Donald, Carol and Phil Byng, R Macfarlane)*

Free house ~ Licensees Chris and Jan Winson ~ Real ale ~ Bar food (12-2, 6-9(8.30 Sun); not Sun evening Dec and Jan) ~ Restaurant ~ (01890) 860257 ~ Children welcome ~ Open 11-2.30, 6-11; 12-2.30, 6-10.30 Sun; closed Sun evening in Dec and Jan; 25-27 Dec, 2-4 Jan ~ Bedrooms: £65B/£98B

TAYVALLICH NR7386 Map 11

Tayvallich Inn 🍴

B8025, off A816 1 mile S of Kilmartin; or take B841 turn-off from A816 2 miles N of Lochgilphead

The speciality here is the fresh seafood caught by the fishing boats out on Loch Sween just across the lane, and the daily specials depend very much on what they've landed. The simply furnished bar and restaurant has this year been swapped around, so the bar is now the conservatory, with sliding glass doors opening onto a terrace with lovely views over the yacht anchorage and water; there's new decking and awning out here, and a garden too. Service is friendly, and people with children are made to feel welcome. Inside are exposed ceiling joists, pale pine chairs, benches and tables on the quarry-tiled floors, and local nautical charts on the cream walls; piped music. The good food might include deep-fried whitebait (£5.25), pan-fried queen scallops with black pudding and pancetta or steamed mussels with shallots, garlic, fresh thyme and cream (£5.95), langoustines grilled with tarragon butter (£6.95 starter, £14.95 main course), filo parcel stuffed with couscous, goats cheese, roast peppers and vine tomatoes (£7.95), haddock in beer batter (£8.50), roasted cod with a pesto crust on a bed of baby vine tomatoes (£9.95), chicken ballotine stuffed with wild mushroom mousseline wrapped in parma ham (£10.95), and lobster roasted with herbs (£17.95); they serve fresh milk shakes. There are 18 malt whiskies including a full range of Islay malts, and Loch Fyne Maverick and Pipers Gold on handpump. Until it was turned into a restaurant in the early 1970s, this was the village bus station. More reports please. *(Recommended by Mrs B M Hill, Ken Richards)*

Free house ~ Licensee Roddy Anderson ~ Bar food (12-10 Easter-Oct; 12-2, 6-10 winter weekdays (not Mon, or Tues lunch)) ~ Restaurant ~ (01546) 870282 ~ children welcome till 8pm ~ Dogs allowed in bar ~ Live music two Sats a month ~ Open 11-11(1 Sat); 12-12 Sun; 12-3, 5.30-11 in winter, when also closed Tues lunchtimes and all day Mon

---

Anyone claiming to arrange or prevent inclusion of a pub in the *Guide* is a fraud. Pubs are included only if recommended by genuine readers and if our own anonymous inspection confirms that they are suitable.

THORNHILL NS6699 Map 11

Lion & Unicorn

A873

Readers enjoy the friendly atmosphere and the warming fires at this attractive partly 17th-c pub. With new carpets this year, the open-plan front room has beams and stone walls, and comfortable seating; the restaurant (half no smoking) still has its original massive fireplace, almost big enough to drive a car into. Friendly obliging staff serve a well kept weekly changing real ale such as Harviestoun Bitter and Twisted – it's cheaper in the public bar than it is in the lounge. Served all day, well liked bar food includes soup (£2.95), baked potatoes (from £4.75), steak pie or battered haddock (£7.25), scampi (£7.50), a couple of vegetarian dishes such as goats cheese and tomato puff pastry tart (£7.95) or home-made vegetable lasagne (£8.25), and puddings such as apple pie and sticky toffee pudding (from £3.95). Juke box, pool, fruit machine, TV, darts, cribbage, dominoes and piped music. There's a play area in the garden. *(Recommended by Nick Holding, Ian Baillie, Michael Butler)*

Free house ~ Licensees Fiona and Bobby Stevenson ~ Real ale ~ Bar food (12-9) ~ Restaurant ~ (01786) 850204 ~ Children welcome away from bar ~ Open 11-12(1 Sat); 12.30-12 Sun ~ Bedrooms: £45B/£70B

ULLAPOOL NH1294 Map 11

Ferry Boat 🍺

Shore Street; coming from the S, keep straight ahead when main A835 turns right into Mill Street

Popular with locals as well as tourists, this friendly inn has a new licensee this year, though bar a lick of paint and some rewiring not much has changed. The unassuming pubby bar has big windows with good views over Loch Broom, yellow walls, brocade-cushioned seats around plain wooden tables, quarry tiles by the corner serving counter and patterned carpet elsewhere, a stained-glass door hanging from the ceiling, and a fruit machine; cribbage, dominoes and piped music. A smaller more peaceful room has a coal fire, and a delft shelf of copper measures and willow-pattern plates. Now served all day, good, hearty bar food includes soup (£2.25), sandwiches (from £3), cheese platter (£4.25), haggis, neeps and tatties or venison sausages (£5.95), and gammon and egg or local haddock (£9.25), with puddings such as chocolate and ginger cheesecake (£3.10); you can usually get scones and cakes too. In the evening (when dogs are allowed in the bar) food is served in the restaurant if busy. Three well kept changing real ales like Cairngorm Highland IPA, Flowers IPA, and Wadworths 6X on handpump. In summer you can sit on the wall across the road and take in the fine views to the tall hills beyond the attractive fishing port, with its bustle of yachts, ferry boats, fishing boats and tour boats for the Summer Isles. *(Recommended by Kay and Alistair Butler, Mr and Mrs M Stratton, Mike and Sue Loseby)*

Punch ~ Licensee Terry Flower ~ Real ale ~ Bar food (12-8) ~ Restaurant ~ (01854) 612366 ~ Children in eating area of bar and restaurant ~ Dogs allowed in bedrooms ~ Thurs evening folk music ~ Open 11(12.30 Sun)-11; closed 25 Dec ~ Bedrooms: £38S/£76S

WEEM NN8449 Map 11

Ailean Chraggan 🍽 ♀ 🛏

B846

Readers who enjoy this welcoming little family-run hotel will be pleased to hear they now have real ales, with a couple of beers from the Inveralmond Brewery, usually Lia Fail, Ossian or Thrappledouser; they also have a good range of scottish bottled beers. A lovely place to stay or come for a meal, it has fine views to the mountains beyond the Tay from its two outside terraces, sweeping up to Ben Lawers (the highest in this part of Scotland). You can eat in either the comfortably carpeted modern lounge or the dining room, and good changing dishes might include soup (£2.95), sandwiches (from £2.60), wood pigeon with black pudding and bacon (£4.95), mussels marinière with garlic toast (£5.35 starter, £9.95 main course), ratatouille stuffed peppers topped with cheese (£9.45), slow-braised lamb shank with vegetables on creamy mash (£10.95), pan-seared venison steak with sautéed wild mushrooms and cranberry jus (£12.85), fresh west coast scallops on a bed of swede and leek risotto (£15.65), and puddings like key lime pie with lime marmalade ice-cream (£4.25); they do children's meals too (£3.95). It's a good idea to book at busy times. They've a very good wine list, and there are around 100 malt whiskies; winter darts and dominoes. All areas apart from the bar are no smoking; the atmosphere is friendly, and you're likely to find chatty locals in the bar. They can arrange fishing nearby. *(Recommended by Walter and Susan Rinaldi-Butcher, Mark Flynn, John Ballard, Paul and Ursula Randall, Mr and Mrs M Stratton, Charles and Pauline Stride, Dr and Mrs M W A Haward)*

Free house ~ Licensee Alastair Gillespie ~ Real ale ~ Bar food ~ Restaurant ~ (01887) 820346 ~ Children welcome ~ Dogs allowed in bar and bedrooms ~ Open 11-11(12.45 Sat, 11.45 Sun) ~ Bedrooms: £55B/£90B

LUCKY DIP

Besides the fully inspected pubs, you might like to try these Lucky Dips recommended to us and described by readers (if you do, please send us reports: www.goodguides.co.uk).

ABERDEENSHIRE

ABERDEEN [NJ9305]
Grill [Union St]: Old-fashioned traditional local with well kept Boddingtons, Caledonian 80/-, Courage, Isle of Skye Red Cuillin and McEwans 80/-, enormous range of malt whiskies, polished dark panelling, match-strike metal strip under bar counter, basic snacks; can be smoky, open all day *(the Didler, Joe Green)*
CRATHIE [NO2293]
Inver [A93 Balmoral—Braemar]: Sensitively refurbished 18th-c inn by River Dee, pleasant bar, quiet lounge with open fire, good range of reasonably priced home-cooked food from excellent toasties up, good-humoured informal service, well kept beer, decent wine by the glass, lots of whiskies; bedrooms *(J F M and M West)*
GLENKINDIE [NJ4413]
Glenkindie Arms [A97]: Rotating real ale such as Belhaven or Camerons, wide food choice with accent on fresh fish *(David and Betty Gittins)*
MUIR OF FOWLIS [NJ5612]
Muggarthaugh [Tough, just off A980]: Good friendly service in two bars and no smoking dining room, Cairngorm Stag and Caledonian Deuchars IPA, generous helpings of good value fresh food inc some imaginative dishes and perfectly cooked veg, nice wine choice; bedrooms, open for most of day at least in summer, handy for Craigievar (which has no catering), cl Mon *(David and Betty Gittins)*

ANGUS

BROUGHTY FERRY [NO4630]
Ship [Fisher St]: Handsomely refurbished front bar with impressive mahogany bar (keg beers), stately model sailing ship, other mainly local nautical items and ornate plaster ceiling with chandeliers, simpler back lounge with burgundy banquettes, plenty of dark nautical-feel plank panelling with brass fittings throughout, good generous food inc massive seafood platter in separate upstairs bistro, good friendly staff; open all day *(Steve Whalley)*
KIRRIEMUIR [NO3853]
Hooks [Bank St]: Unpretentious small town pub with stable bar, good cheap mince cobbler, Irish Magnet cider *(Dave Braisted)*

ARGYLL

ARDUAINE [NM7907]
Lord of the Isles [Craobh Haven, signed off A816 S]: Pub/hotel on beautiful coast, with well kept scottish real ales and plenty of malt whiskies, enjoyable food in bar and restaurant inc local seafood; bedrooms *(Hugh Roberts)*
BALLACHULISH [NN0858]
Isles of Glencoe: Lochside hotel and leisure complex, short but good bar menu; bedrooms, wonderful location *(Pamela and Merlyn Horswell)*
BELLOCHANTUY [NR6631]
Hunting Lodge Hotel [A83 N of Campbeltown]: Welcoming licensees, good range of food and of whiskies *(Sarah and Peter Gooderham)*
BRIDGE OF ORCHY [NN2939]
☆ *Bridge of Orchy Hotel* [A82 Tyndrum—Glencoe]: Comfortable bar with nice views, wide choice of good fairly priced food in bar and restaurant, welcoming atmosphere and friendly Canadian service, particularly well

kept Caledonian 80/- and Fyne Maverick, dozens of malt whiskies, good choice of house wines, interesting mountain photographs; lovely bedrooms, good value bunkhouse, spectacular spot on West Highland Way (and if it's on time the sleeper from London gets you here for breakfast) *(Derek and Sylvia Stephenson, Dr A McCormick)*

CAIRNBAAN [NR8390]

Cairnbaan Hotel [B841, off A816 N of Lochgilphead]: Charming spot overlooking busy canal lock and swing bridge, with walk to four central locks; attractive and immaculately kept small bar with bare boards, bookshelves and restful décor, enjoyable bar food in carpeted conservatory, Fyne real ale, good stylish restaurant; tables on flagstoned terrace, good bedrooms, open all day *(Richard J Holloway)*

CONNEL [NM9034]

☆ *Oyster*: Recently refurbished and renamed 18th-c inn opp former ferry slipway, attractive bar and restaurant, good thriving atmosphere, enjoyable well prepared standard food, keg beers but good range of wines by the glass and of malt whiskies, good helpful service even when busy; comfortable bedrooms *(Charles and Pauline Stride, Maurice and Gill McMahon)*

CRINAN [NR7894]

☆ *Crinan Hotel* [B841, off A816]: Elegant hotel by Crinan Canal's entrance basin, picture-window views of fishing boats and yachts wandering out towards the Hebrides, smart nautical cocktail bar, simple public bar opening on to side terrace, coffee shop with sandwiches etc, good if pricey restaurant food, good wines, whiskies and soft drinks (keg beer); children and dogs welcome, open all day, comfortable bedrooms, outstanding breakfast *(LYM, Jenny and Brian Seller, OPUS)*

GLENCOE [NN1058]

☆ *Clachaig* [old Glencoe rd, behind NTS Visitor Centre]: Extended inn doubling as mountain rescue post and cheerfully crowded with outdoors people in season, with mountain photographs in flagstoned walkers' bar (two woodburners and pool), quieter pine-panelled snug and big modern-feeling dining lounge; cheerful service even when packed, hearty bar food all day, wider evening choice, a hundred or so malt whiskies, enterprising well kept quickly changing ales such as Atlas Three Sisters, Cairngorm Highland and Stag, Heather Fraoch, Isle of Skye Cuillin Dark Mild and St Peters Elderberry, unusual bottled beers, annual beer festival, children in no smoking restaurant; live music Sat; simple bedrooms, nourishing breakfast, spectacular setting surrounded by soaring mountains *(LYM, Richard and Anne Ansell, Dr Pete Crawshaw)*

KILCHRENAN [NN0323]

Kilchrenan Inn [B845]: Simple pub fitted out in local pine, window seat and rustic furniture, interesting old photographs, sandwiches and short blackboard choice of good food inc freshly caught trout here or in separate dining room, quiet relaxed atmosphere, friendly staff and regulars, good malt whiskies, perhaps a real ale; dogs welcome, garden tables, lovely drive along Loch Awe to the pub and beyond to Ardanaiseig gardens *(Dave Braisted, Simon Jones)*

KINLOCHLEVEN [NN1862]

Tailrace [Riverside Rd]: Friendly nicely decorated pub with well kept Atlas Blizzard from nearby brewery, bar food too *(R M Corlett)*

OBAN [NM8630]

☆ *Oban Inn* [Stafford St, near North Pier]: Cheerful 18th-c harbour-town local, pubby beamed and slate-floored downstairs bar, partly panelled upstairs bar with button-back banquettes around cast-iron-framed tables, coffered woodwork ceiling and little stained-glass false windows, no smoking children's area, well kept McEwans 80/-, 45 malt whiskies, good value bar food served all day; fruit machine, juke box, piped music; dogs allowed in bar, open all day *(LYM, Mrs B M Hill, Simon Jones)*

TARBERT [NR8768]

Columba [Pier Rd]: Civilised and well preserved 1900s pub named for the then daily ferry from Glasgow, attractive and congenial bar, enjoyable food using local fish and fresh produce here and in charming restaurant; seven comfortable Edwardian-décor bedrooms with own bathrooms *(Richard J Holloway)*

AYRSHIRE

AYR [NS3321]

Geordies Byre [Main St]: Friendly welcome, well stocked bar inc Caledonian Deuchars IPA, alcoves and interesting memorabilia; no food *(Tony and Maggie Harwood)*

BARR [NX2794]

☆ *Kings Arms* [Stinchar Rd]: Former coaching inn, good generous food all home-made (even the bread), good local produce and choice of whiskies, friendly landlord, cosy bar; six comfortable and attractive bedrooms *(Mrs Catherine Draper)*

FAIRLIE [NS2055]

Village Inn [Bay St]: Enjoyable food inc fresh simply cooked tasty seafood, friendly staff, a couple of mainstream ales, nicely furnished neatly kept lounge bar, conservatory restaurant *(R M Corlett)*

SYMINGTON [NS3831]

☆ *Wheatsheaf* [just off A77 Ayr—Kilmarnock; Main St]: Busy rambling 17th-c pub in quiet pretty village, charming and cosy, two dining rooms with wide blackboard choice of consistently good original food served all day esp fish and local produce, friendly quick service, racehorse décor; keg beers, must book wknd, can be seething with customers lunchtime; attractively set tables

outside, open all day *(Nick Holding,
Christine and Malcolm Ingram, Mrs Edna
M Jones, Gordon Scarlett)*

BERWICKSHIRE

AUCHENCROW [NT8560]

☆ *Craw* [B6438 NE of Duns; pub signed off
A1]: Attractive cottagey beamed country
local, quiet and friendly, with two well kept
changing ales such as Mordue, wide choice
of enjoyable fresh food inc good fish,
woodburner, no smoking back eating areas;
children welcome, tables on back terrace and
out on green, bedrooms, open all day wknds
(BB, Comus and Sarah Elliott)

LAUDER [NT5347]

Black Bull [Market Pl]: Comfortably
refurbished 17th-c inn with good choice of
interesting food; children welcome, open all
day, bedrooms *(Dr and Mrs S Donald,
LYM, Mr and Mrs H Hine)*

WESTRUTHER [NT6350]

☆ *Old Thistle*: Current licensees cooking
rather more food lunchtime and evening,
and still do superb local aberdeen angus
steaks; gently updated 18th-c traditional bar
with thriving local atmosphere, comfortable
dining lounge and racing-theme restaurant
with photographs and framed silks; children
welcome, cl Mon *(BB, Michael Lamm)*

CAITHNESS

KEISS [ND3461]

Sinclair Bay Hotel [Main St]: Friendly and
unpretentious family-run hotel with games in
locals' bar, good range of enjoyable reasonably
priced home-made food in lounge bar; good
value bedrooms *(Charles and Pauline Stride)*

MEY [ND2872]

Castle Arms: 19th-c former coaching inn,
quiet décor in understated stripped pine and
so forth, good usual bar food from toasties
up, wider choice for high teas and dinners in
dining room, very pleasant helpful service,
decent wines by the glass, photographs of
the late Queen Mother during her Caithness
holidays; eight bedrooms in back extension,
well placed for N coast of Caithness and for
Castle of Mey (which has no refreshments)
(J F M and M West)

CLACKMANNANSHIRE

POOL OF MUCKHART [NO0001]

Inn at Muckhart [A91 NE of Dollar]: Low
building with welcoming landlady and quick
efficient service, good value wholesome
substantial food, local Devon Bitter
(David and Katharine Cooke)

DUMFRIESSHIRE

AULDGIRTH [NX9186]

Auldgirth Inn [just E of A76, about 8 miles
N of Dumfries]: Ancient whitewashed stone-
built inn, comfortable bar in side annexe

with brasses, plates, pictures and a good log
fire, well kept Houston ales, above-average
food from simple bar meals to more
elaborate dishes, good cheerful service,
separate dining room (bookable tables, but
the bar – where you can't book – seems
more warmly inviting); tables outside, three
bedrooms *(Nick Holding)*

CARSETHORN [NX9959]

Steamboat [off A710 at Kirkbean]: Decent
generous home-made food, good service,
estuary views from front dining room,
seafaring items in adjoining little bar;
cl wkdy lunchtimes at least out of high
season *(Stan and Hazel Allen)*

CROCKETFORD [NX8372]

Galloway Arms [A75 Carlisle—Stranraer]:
Useful for serving decent standard bar food
all day (also more restauranty dining room
evening meals), attentive friendly staff;
comfortable bedrooms, own bathrooms
(Stan and Hazel Allen, Nick Holding)

DUMFRIES [NX9776]

Cavens Arms [Buccleuch St]: Attractively
spruced up under new licensees, lots of
wood in air-conditioned outer no smoking
area where you may find retired ladies
lunching (still a sign of high civilisation for a
scottish town pub), enjoyable food (all day
Fri-Sun, not Mon), friendly service, well kept
Caledonian Deuchars IPA, Greene King
Abbot and up to half a dozen changing guest
beers; no children, open all day *(Joe Green,
Nick Holding)*

MOFFAT [NT0805]

☆ *Black Bull* [Churchgate]: Attractive and well
kept small hotel, plush softly lit bar with
Burns memorabilia, enjoyable unpretentious
generous food from sandwiches to local
ingredients cooked imaginatively, pleasant
staff cope well even with the coach parties
from the nearby Woollen Mill gift shop, well
kept Caledonian Deuchars IPA, McEwans
80/- and Theakstons XB, several dozen malt
whiskies, friendly public bar across
courtyard with railway memorabilia and
good open fire, simply furnished tiled-floor
dining room; decent piped music, side games
bar with juke box, big-screen TV for golf;
children welcome, tables in courtyard,
12 comfortable good value bedrooms, open
all day *(Lee and Liz Potter, Gwyn and
Anne Wake, LYM, Nick Holding,
George Atkinson, David and
Heather Stephenson)*

Buccleuch Arms [High St]: Friendly
accommodating owners and attentive helpful
staff in rather old-fashioned Georgian
coaching inn with roomy carpeted bar and
lounge areas, good range of food from
sandwiches with chips up, informal upstairs
restaurant, keg beer but interesting wines;
soft piped music; modern bedrooms
(George Atkinson)

Moffat House [High St]: Large comfortably
plush bar of Best Western hotel in Adam
house, relaxed and quiet, with coal fire,
welcoming helpful service, consistently good

value bar food from sandwiches up, conservatory coffee lounge, restaurant; children welcome, stunning gardens, comfortable bedrooms, good breakfast *(Christine and Neil Townend, John and Yvonne Davies, George Atkinson)*

MONIAIVE [NX7790]

George [High St]: 17th-c inn with interesting if well worn old-fashioned flagstoned bar of considerable character, well kept Belhaven, decent wine, log fire, good service, reasonably priced lunchtime food; dogs welcome, may be cl lunchtime *(Stan and Hazel Allen, LYM)*

NEW ABBEY [NX9666]

Abbey Arms [The Square]: Friendly staff, a well kept changing real ale such as Black Sheep, pubby food from generous baguettes up, no smoking dark pink dining room; bar can be smoky; dogs welcome *(Stan and Hazel Allen, Andy and Ali, R T and C Moggridge)*

THORNHILL [NX8795]

Buccleuch & Queensberry [Drumlanrig St (A76)]: Substantial red sandstone Georgian former coaching inn with comfortable banquettes in traditional main beamed bar, good coal fire in the smoking area, friendly service, food from interesting sandwiches and baked potatoes to some good value main dishes, well kept Caledonian 80/- and a changing guest beer; access to three miles of fishing on the River Nith – the inn is popular with sporting folk; children welcome, comfortable bedrooms with good breakfast, attractive small town *(LYM, Nick Holding, WAC)*

DUNBARTONSHIRE

ARROCHAR [NN2903]

Village Inn [A814, just off A83 W of Loch Lomond]: Fine sea and hill views from simple all-day dining area with heavy beams, bare boards and big open fire, steps down to unpretentious bar, well kept changing real ales such as Orkney Dark Island, several dozen malt whiskies, good coffee; piped music, juke box, can be loudly busy Sat in summer; children welcome in eating areas ill 8, tables out on deck and lawn, comfortable bedrooms with own bathrooms, good breakfast, open all day *(A H C Rainier, Ian Baillie, LYM, Peter and Pat Frogley, Tracey and Stephen Groves)*

LUSS [NS3498]

Inverbeg Inn [A82 about 3 miles N]: Useful lunch stop across road from Loch Lomond with tables overlooking it, lounge often crowded for straightforward waitress-served food inc several haggis dishes (also restaurant), well kept real ales, friendly attentive staff, games in simple public bar, private jetty with boat trips; bedrooms inc quiet water's-edge lodges with bathrooms suiting disabled – great views *(LYM, Sarah and Peter Gooderham)*

EAST LOTHIAN

GIFFORD [NT5368]

Goblin Ha' [Main St]: Long public bar with pews, well worn leatherette banquettes and lively local atmosphere, well kept Caledonian Deuchars IPA, Hop Back Summer Lightning, Marstons Pedigree and Timothy Taylors Landlord, friendly service, varied food from simple bar lunches to more exotic or elaborate things, roomy and peaceful front dining lounge and airy back conservatory (which feel more part of the hotel); children in lounge, tables and chairs in good big garden with small play area, bedrooms, open all day Fri-Sun *(Dr Peter D Smart, Steve Whalley)*

GULLANE [NT4882]

☆ *Old Clubhouse* [East Links Rd]: Two spotless bars with Victorian pictures and cartoons, prewar sheet music and other memorabilia, stuffed birds, open fires, well kept McEwans 80/- and guests such as Shepherd Neame Spitfire and Timothy Taylors Landlord, wide range of enjoyable generous bar food, fast friendly service, views over golf links to Lammermuirs; children welcome, open all day *(David and Heather Stephenson, John Hillman)*

HADDINGTON [NT5173]

☆ *Waterside* [Waterside; just off A6093, over pedestrian bridge at E end of Town]: Attractively set riverside dining pub with plush bar, long cushioned benches and bigger tables in second room, more formal stripped-stone dining conservatory, modestly priced popular food from sandwiches to good fish and meat, well kept ales such as Bass and Caledonian Deuchars IPA, good range of wines; children welcome, no dogs, tables out overlooking the water, open all day wknds *(LYM, Nick Holding, Mark O'Sullivan)*

FIFE

ABERDOUR [NT1885]

Aberdour Hotel [High St (A921)]: Friendly nicely decorated hotel bar with coal fire, red plush banquettes, friendly service, good choice of malt whiskies, real ales such as Caledonian, Courage or Theakstons, good choice of traditional scottish food at pub prices in restaurant; open all day Thurs-Sun; 16 modernised bedrooms *(G Coates)*

ANSTRUTHER [NO5603]

Dreel [High St W]: Cosy low 16th-c building in attractive spot with garden overlooking Dreel Burn, plenty of low beams and timbers, small two-room bar popular with locals, back pool room, open fire and stripped stone in dining room, pleasant conservatory eating area, good value generous varied bar food inc fresh fish, well kept ales such as Fullers ESB and Tetleys, welcoming efficient staff; dogs welcome, open all day *(Michael Butler)*

CERES [NO3911]

Meldrums [Main St]: Small hotel with well kept Caledonian Deuchars IPA in well run cottagey parlour bar, pleasant atmosphere, roomy clean and attractive beamed dining lounge with good choice of enjoyable reasonably priced bar lunches, helpful friendly service even when busy; seven well appointed bedrooms, charming village nr Wemyss Pottery (*Clifford Payton, Michael Butler*)

INVERNESS-SHIRE

AVIEMORE [NH8612]

Cairngorm [Grampian Rd (A9)]: Lively friendly bar, wide choice of good value food inc useful teen menu, generous highland buffet Thurs, pleasant helpful waiting service in eating area and restaurant, a real ale and good choice of other drinks; sports TV; children welcome (*Christine and Phil Young, Graham Findlay*)

☆ *Old Bridge* [Dalfaber Rd, southern outskirts off B970]: Busy well kept inn with stripped stone and wood, local books and memorabilia, roaring open fire, good value food from sandwiches to carvery in bar (short but enterprising lunchtime choice) or large restaurant extension, cheerful landlady, well kept changing ales such as Adnams and Caledonian, decent wines; quiet piped music, Tues ceilidh; children welcome, pleasant surroundings (*Andy and Jill Kassube, R T and J C Moggridge, Christine and Phil Young, Christine and Neil Townend*)

FORT WILLIAM [NN1073]

Ben Nevis Bar [High St]: Roomy beamed bar with good value simple food such as haggis, prompt cheery service, McEwans 80/-, harbour views from upstairs restaurant; TV, games, may be live music (*George Atkinson, Dave Braisted, Sarah and Peter Gooderham*)

Grog & Gruel [High St]: Busy alehouse-style pub in pedestrian part, barrel tables, dark woodwork and bygones, friendly helpful staff, half a dozen well kept changing ales such as Atlas Latitude and Orkney Skullsplitter, wide range of good value food all day from baguettes, pasta and pizzas to upstairs tex-mex restaurant; piped music, machines; dogs and children welcome, live music nights, open all day (*Dave Braisted, Mike and Lynn Robinson*)

GLENUIG [NM6576]

Glenuig Inn [A861 SW of Lochailort, off A830 Fort William—Mallaig]: Small basic and friendly bar on picturesque bay, limited choice of good home-cooked food, fresh seafood as available from Mallaig, McEwans 80/- and Theakstons Best, some fine malt whiskies, chatty fishermen and other locals; big simple bedrooms, also bunkhouse accommodation popular with walkers and divers; open all day summer, more restricted winter (*Tim Roe*)

INVERGARRY [NH1001]

Tomdoun Hotel: Enjoyable bar food in well placed fishing hotel; bedrooms (*Celeste Labistour*)

INVERNESS [NH6446]

☆ *Clachnaharry Inn* [High St, Clachnaharry (A862 NW of city)]: Congenial and cosily dim beamed bar, simple top lounge, more comfortable bottom lounge with picture windows looking over Beauly Firth, warm chatty atmosphere, plenty of friendly efficient staff, bargain freshly cooked food all day from big baked potatoes up, half a dozen well kept ales such as Adnams, Caledonian, Cairngorm, Greene King and Isle of Skye, great log fire as well as gas stove; children welcome, tables out overlooking railway, lovely walks by big flight of Caledonian Canal locks, open all day (*Richard Houghton, Joe Green*)

Phoenix [Academy St]: Several well kept changing ales in bare-boards 1890s bar with much dark brown varnish and granite trough at foot of island servery, neat adjoining dining room with some booth seating; sports TVs (*Paul and Ursula Randall, Joe Green*)

☆ *Snow Goose* [Stoneyfield, about ¼ mile E of A9/A96 roundabout]: Reliable well run Vintage Inn dining pub, the most northerly of this chain, with well presented bar food at attractive prices in comfortable and relaxing informal country-feel room areas, beams and flagstones, several log fires, soft lighting, interesting décor, pleasant young helpful staff, decent wine by the glass; comfortable bedrooms in adjacent Travelodge (*Dr D G Twyman, Walter and Susan Rinaldi-Butcher, John and Claire Pettifer, Pamela and Merlyn Horswell, J F M and M West*)

KINGUSSIE [NH7500]

Scot House [Newtonmore Rd]: Clean and bright, with enjoyable fairly priced bar food from sandwiches and baked potatoes up, well kept beer, decent wine by the glass, rather pink décor; bedrooms (*Michael Lamm*)

ONICH [NN0263]

Nether Lochaber Hotel [A82]: Sensibly priced bar food in small 18th-c hotel's typically unassuming side bar (from outside looks like a shed), friendly landlady, bright cheerful dining room with log fire; simple bedrooms with own bathrooms, good breakfast, new bunkhouse (*Mr and Mrs M Stratton*)

TOMICH [NH2925]

Tomich Hotel: Welcoming newish licensees in former hunting lodge, good value food in homely bar and hotel dining room, local Black Isle bottled beers, comfortable residents' lounge; bedrooms, pretty village (*Richard Jones*)

TORLUNDY [NN1477]

Factors Inn [A82 NE of Fort William]: Smart and upmarket, with small but imaginative choice of good food, good choice of wine, local real ale, friendly staff; children welcome, pleasant surroundings *(Christine and Phil Young, Sarah and Peter Gooderham)*

STONEHAVEN [NO8785]
☆ *Marine Hotel* [harbour]: Friendly harbourside pub with several real ales such as Timothy Taylors Landlord, large lively stripped stone bar with log fire, coffee and tea, polite service, small lounge bar, good attractively priced food esp fresh local fish and superb view in upstairs no smoking restaurant; games room with juke box or piped music, TV; dogs and children welcome, open all day, bedrooms *(Esther and John Sprinkle, Mark Walker)*
Queens [Allardice St]: Good friendly service in small local front bar, big open back lounge popular with young people wknds, pool; keg beers, no food; bedrooms, open all day *(Mark Walker)*
☆ *Ship* [Shore Head]: Doing well under welcoming newish landlord, thriving local atmosphere, two well kept real ales, good choice of whiskies, good generous food from good value light dishes up in simply furnished bar (which can be smoky), small lounge off, and smarter no smoking back restaurant area, quick friendly service, games area; children welcome in lounge and restaurant, tables out overlooking pretty harbour with plenty going on, bedrooms, open all day *(Charles and Pauline Stride, Esther and John Sprinkle, Mark Walker)*

KINNESSWOOD [NO1702]
Lomond [A911 Glenrothes—Milnathort, not far from M90 junctions 7/8]: Enjoyable fresh food from sandwiches up in bar and restaurant of well appointed and friendly small inn with lovely sunset views over Loch Leven, well kept real ales, decent wines, cheerful helpful staff, log fire; 12 comfortable bedrooms *(Christine and Neil Townend)*

CASTLE DOUGLAS [NX7662]
Douglas Arms [King St]: Pleasant hotel bar, half given over to enjoyable food using local produce, well kept real ales, decent prices, friendly personable staff; good bedrooms *(Stan and Hazel Allen)*
COLVEND [NX8555]
Clonyard House: Small hotel nr Solway coast said to have enchanted tree in its pleasant wooded grounds; three bar rooms well used by locals, decent food here and in conservatory or separate no smoking restaurant, half price for children for most dishes, reasonably priced wine by the glass, polite service; dogs welcome, tables outside

with play area, bedrooms and cosy log-cabin chalets *(Stan and Hazel Allen)*
DALRY [NX6281]
☆ *Clachan* [A713 Castle Douglas—Ayr]: Cheerful bar, attractively refurbished yet pleasantly traditional with plenty of dark wood and log fires, good inexpensive wine list, fine selection of malts, enjoyable food using local meat, game and fish, from good sandwiches and toasties up, friendly willing service, another log fire in beamed and timbered restaurant, interesting fishing and shooting frieze; bedrooms with own bathrooms *(Dave Braisted, Mrs Maureen Robertson, Edward and June Sulley)*
GATEHOUSE OF FLEET [NX6056]
☆ *Masonic Arms* [Ann St]: Welcoming and comfortable two-room bar, friendly staff, cheerful atmosphere, a well kept ale brewed for them by Sulwath and a guest beer, good choice of wines and whiskies, good range of enjoyable generous fresh food in dining room and no smoking conservatory from lunchtime sandwiches and traditional pubby dishes to more imaginative cooking, quick service even when busy; children and dogs welcome, garden, cl Mon and Tues in winter *(Stan and Hazel Allen, JWAC, Nick Holding, Mrs Veronica Mellor, Jonathan Tong)*
HAUGH OF URR [NX8066]
Laurie Arms [B794 N of Dalbeattie]: Warmly welcoming village pub with log fires in both bars, three or four well kept changing ales such as Black Sheep, Greene King, Houston or Harviestoun, enjoyable reasonably priced bar food from sandwiches to good steaks, more adventurous choice in adjacent restaurant with own bar, decent wine, good robust landlord, attractive décor with various knick-knacks, Bamforth comic postcards in the lavatories; tables outside *(Nick Holding, Mark O'Sullivan, Joe Green)*
KIPPFORD [NX8355]
Anchor [off A710 S of Dalbeattie]: Busy down-to-earth waterfront inn in lovely spot overlooking big natural harbour and peaceful hills, friendly staff, food from sandwiches up which can be most enjoyable, local Sulwath beers, lots of malt whiskies, coal fire in traditional back bar, no smoking lounge bar, upstairs summer dining room; piped music, games room with table football and board games, also juke box, TV and machines; children welcome, tables outside, good walks and birdwatching, open all day in summer; more reports please *(Stan and Hazel Allen, Derek and Sylvia Stephenson, David and Heather Stephenson, LYM, Michael Doswell)*
KIRKCUDBRIGHT [NX6851]
Royal [St Cuthbert St]: Well used local with enjoyable cheap food in friendly bar and restaurant, decent wines; dogs welcome *(Stan and Hazel Allen)*
☆ *Selkirk Arms* [High St]: Nice atmosphere and quiet modern décor in 18th-c Best Western hotel's comfortable partly panelled

lounge bar with well kept local Sulwath Criffel and another of their ales, good food inc scottish dishes and plenty of fresh local fish in bar and restaurant, friendly efficient service; children welcome in lounge and restaurant, tables in garden with 15th-c font, good value bedrooms *(Nick Holding, BB, Derek and Sylvia Stephenson)*

ST JOHNS TOWN OF DALRY [NX6281]
Lochinvar [Main St (A702)]: Old-fashioned pub with enjoyable standard food, good wine by the glass, obliging Yorkshire landlord; 15 bedrooms *(Stan and Hazel Allen)*

LANARKSHIRE

BIGGAR [NT0437]
Crown [High St (A702)]: Two real ales and above-average food all day, coal fire in front bar, old-fashioned no smoking panelled back room with old local pictures; open all day *(Nick Holding)*

GLASGOW [NS5965]
Auctioneers [North Court, St Vincent Pl]: This former auction house, a previous main entry, was closed for refurbishment as we went to press in summer 2005, and we're told to expect a more modern look, which may mean the end of the mass of auction-style bric-a-brac that till now has appealed to us, but may suit its growing popularity with a young crowd who have enjoyed the four big screens for sports TV, as well as their well kept Caledonian Deuchars IPA, Orkney Dark Island and perhaps a guest beer, bargain wines, and low-priced bar food; children welcome 12-5 if eating, open all day *(LYM)*

☆ *Blackfriars* [Bell St]: Lively fusion of bare-boards tavern and cosmopolitan café, good range of continental draught and bottled beers as well as well kept ales such as Black Sheep, Carlsberg Burton and Charles Wells Bombardier, farm cider, plenty of wines by the glass and malt whiskies, cheerful service, good range of bar snacks and lunches, lots of events posters, daily papers, candles on tables; TV, piped music, loudish some evenings; Sun night basement comedy club, Sat band nights *(LYM, Doug Christian)*

Clockwork Beer Co [1153 Cathcart Rd]: Comfortable brightly decorated two-level café-bar in unappealing area, microbrewery on view brewing interestingly flavoured beers, also six or more weekly-changing guest beers on tall fount air pressure, good range of continental beers, farm cider, dozens of malt whiskies, speciality fruit schnapps, scottish and other country wines, good conventional wines, unusual fruit juices; good reasonably priced food all day, half helpings for children, good vegetarian choice, friendly service, daily papers, spiral stairs to gallery with TV, piano, games tables, books, toys and no smoking area; unobtrusive piped music, jazz Tues; disabled facilities and baby-changing, children

welcome till 8pm, open all day *(Nick Holding, Richard Houghton, G Coates)*

☆ *Horseshoe* [Drury St, nr Central station]: Classic high-ceilinged standing-room pub with enormous island bar, gleaming mahogany and mirrors, snob screens, other high Victorian features and interesting music-hall era memorabilia; friendly jovial staff and atmosphere, well kept Caledonian Deuchars IPA and 80/- and Orkney Red MacGregor, lots of malt whiskies, amazingly cheap food in plainer upstairs bar, no smoking restaurant (where children allowed); games machine, piped music; open all day *(Patrick Hancock, LYM, Ian Baillie, Pete Walker, Nick Holding)*

☆ *Pot Still* [Hope St]: Comfortable and welcoming, with over 500 interesting malt whiskies, bare boards and panelling, big carpets, raised back leather seating area, reasonably priced food all day (menu limited evenings), well kept McEwans 70/-, 80/- and Export and changing guest beers such as Atlas, Caledonian, Houston, Isle of Arran or Orkney Dark Island, interesting bottled beers, decent wines, knowledgeable and friendly staff helpful in choosing your drink; open all day *(BB, Owen Duffy, Doug Christian)*

State [Holland St]: Lots of carved wood inc handsome oak island servery in high-ceilinged bar with marble pillars, half a dozen or so well kept changing ales inc rarities, very cheap enjoyable basic lunchtime food from sandwiches up, friendly staff, armchair among other comfortable seats, coal-effect gas fire in big wooden fireplace, old prints and theatrical posters; piped music, games machine, wknd live music *(Patrick Hancock, Nick Holding)*

LOTHIAN

EDINBURGH [NT2673]
Worlds End [High St (Royal Mile)]: Small pub in 17th-c building, interesting nooks to sit in, well kept Caledonian 80/- *(Esther and John Sprinkle)*

MIDLOTHIAN

BALERNO [NT1666]
Johnsburn House [Johnsburn Rd]: Lovely old-fashioned beamed pub in 18th-c former mansion with masterpiece 1911 ceiling by Robert Lorimer; well kept Caledonian Deuchars IPA and interesting changing ales, coal fire, panelled dining lounge with good food inc shellfish and game, more formal evening dining rooms; children welcome, open all day wknds, cl Mon *(the Didler)*

CARLOPS [NT1656]
Allan Ramsay [A702]: Welcoming late 18th-c pub, several interconnecting beamed rooms, eating areas each end (wide choice of good generous food all day), helpful service, well kept Caledonian Deuchars IPA, good coffee, two fires, lots of bric-a-brac, fresh

flowers, witches' sabbath mural recalling
local legend which the eponymous poet
versified; piped music, games machine
and TV; children welcome *(R T and
J C Moggridge)*

CRAMOND [NT1876]

☆ *Cramond Inn* [Cramond Glebe Rd (off A90
W of Edinburgh)]: Softly lit smallish rooms
nicely refurbished by Sam Smiths in old-
fashioned style, their beers at low prices,
wide range of popular pubby food inc some
local dishes such as haggis and bashed neeps,
good friendly service and atmosphere, two
good coal and log fires; picturesque Firth of
Forth village at mouth of River Almond,
delightful views from tables out on grass by
car park *(Dr and Mrs T E Hothersall, LYM,
Michael Butler, Peter Abbott, Maurice and
Gill McMahon)*

EDINBURGH [NT2573]

☆ *Bannermans* [Cowgate]: Friendly
subterranean warren of simple flagstoned
rooms with barrel-vaulted ceilings, bare
stone walls, wood panelling and pillars at
front, medley of interesting old furnishings,
well kept Caledonian Deuchars IPA,
McEwans 80/- and guest beers in one room
(helpful staff may offer tasters), good bottled
beer choice, around 30 malts, nice chilli fries
with cheese and other snacks 12-5; piped
music (not too loud at lunchtime), games
machine, perhaps big-screen sports TV;
younger crowd in evenings, with DJs,
discos, live music and karaoke; children
allowed till 6, open all day till 1am
*(LYM, Patrick Hancock, Nigel Espley,
Liane Purnell)*

☆ *Bennets* [Leven St]: Ornate Victorian bar
with original glass, mirrors, arcades,
panelling and tiles, friendly service, well kept
ales inc Caledonian Deuchars IPA from tall
founts, over a hundred malt whiskies, bar
snacks and bargain homely lunchtime hot
dishes (children allowed in eating area then),
second bar with counter salvaged from old
ship; open all day, cl Sun *(LYM, the Didler)*
Berts Bar [William St]: Well done up in
traditional style, with well kept Caledonian
Deuchars IPA and other ales inc two from
Arran, cheap tasty simple food, long narrow
bar, room off with lovely tiled fireplace and
rugby shirt collection *(Patrick Hancock,
R M Corlett, Joe Green)*

☆ *Caledonian Ale House* [Haymarket Terr, by
station]: Long convivial Victorian-style bar
with well kept Caledonian and scottish guest
beers such as Arran Gold, imported beers on
tap and in bottle, simple furnishings on bare
boards, good range of enjoyable food in
upstairs bistro (booking recommended wknd
evenings), good service; sports TVs
*(Michael Butler, Andrew York, John and
Julie Moon)*
Canons Gait [Canongate]: Smart Royal
Mile bar with plush booth seating, pleasant
atmosphere, attractively priced lunchtime
food inc local produce, real ales such as
Belhaven St Andrews and Caledonian

Deuchars IPA and 80/-, bare-boards
basement bar; piped music; open all day
(R E Dixon, Esther and John Sprinkle)
Cask & Barrel [Broughton St]: Bare-boards
traditional drinkers' pub, half a dozen well
kept mainly scottish beers inc Caledonian
80/- from U-shaped bar, helpful service,
good value bar food esp stovies Mon-Fri;
sports TVs *(R M Corlett, BB)*
Cloisters [Brougham St]: Friendly and
interesting ex-parsonage alehouse mixing
church pews and gantry recycled from
redundant church with bare boards and lots
of brewery mirrors; Caledonian Deuchars
and 80/-, half a dozen or so interesting guest
beers, friendly atmosphere, food till 3 (4 Sat)
inc breakfasts and lunchtime toasties;
lavatories down spiral stairs, folk music Fri
and Sat; open all day *(Patrick Hancock,
the Didler)*
Doric [Market St]: Bar with plenty of
atmosphere, well kept Caledonian Deuchars
IPA and McEwans 80/-, decent wines, good
value enjoyable bar food, good mix of
customers and friendly young staff, wider
range of food in relaxing upstairs bistro
(often booked solid) *(Janet and Peter Race,
Nigel Espley, Liane Purnell)*
Jolly Judge [James Court, by 495
Lawnmarket]: Interesting and comfortable
basement of 16th-c tenement with
traditional fruit-and-flower-painted wooden
ceiling, relaxed atmosphere, friendly service,
Caledonian 80/- and a guest beer, changing
malt whiskies, hot drinks, lovely fire, quickly
served lunchtime bar meals (children
allowed then) and afternoon snacks; piped
music, games machine; open all day, cl Sun
lunchtime *(LYM, Mark Walker)*

☆ *Kenilworth* [Rose St]: Welcoming
Edwardian pub with ornate high ceiling,
carved woodwork and tiles, huge etched
brewery mirrors and windows, red leather
seating around tiled wall; central bar with
well kept Caledonian Deuchars IPA and
guest beers, hot drinks inc espresso, good
generous bar food lunchtime and evening,
quick friendly attentive service, back family
room; piped music, discreetly placed games
machines, TV, may be live music Sat; tables
outside, open all day *(Michael Butler,
Janet and Peter Race, BB, R T and
J C Moggridge, the Didler)*
Malt & Hops [The Shore, Leith]: Good
changing choice of well kept ales such as
Caledonian Deuchars IPA, Marstons
Pedigree, Inveralmond Independence and
Kelburn Red Smiddy, interesting panelled
décor with bric-a-brac, photographs, lots of
pump clips and brewery mirrors; seats
outside, open all day *(Esther and
John Sprinkle)*
Malt Shovel [Cockburn St]: Three levels, lots
of panelling, stained glass and mirrors, soft
leather sofas in top room, changing real ales
such as Arran from long serving bar, friendly
young staff, home-made bar food; piped
music, TV; open all day *(R M Corlett,*

Nigel Espley, Liane Purnell)

☆ **Milnes** [Rose St/Hanover St]: Well reworked traditional city pub rambling down to several areas below street level and even in yard; busy old-fashioned bare-boards feel, dark wood furnishings and panelling, cask tables, lots of old photographs and mementos of poets who used the 'Little Kremlin' room here, wide choice of well kept real ales, open fire, reasonably priced bar food *(the Didler, Janet and Peter Race, Edward Mirzoeff, BB, J M Tansey, R M Corlett)*

Mitre [High St, nr Festival Theatre]: Busy interesting pub with enjoyable pubby food inc haggis and bashed neeps, Caledonian and Tetleys *(Esther and John Sprinkle)*

Oxford [Young St]: Friendly unspoilt pub with two built-in wall settles in tiny bustling front bar, quieter back room, lino floor, well kept Belhaven Best and 80/- and scottish guest beers (may offer tasters), cheap filled cobs; lavatories up a few steps *(Joe Green, Nigel Espley, Liane Purnell, J M Tansey)*

Peacock [Lindsay Rd, Newhaven]: Good honest food all day esp fresh fish in hefty helpings in neat plushly comfortable pub with several linked areas inc conservatory-style back room leading to garden, McEwans 80/- and a guest such as Orkney Dark Island, efficient service; very popular, best to book evenings and Sun lunchtime; children welcome, open all day *(Charles and Pauline Stride, LYM)*

Queens Arms [Frederick St]: Nice basement pub with interesting Mary, Queen of Scots memorabilia, big log fire, good staff, enjoyable pubby food from nicely served sandwiches and baguettes up, Caledonian Deuchars IPA and McEwans 70/- *(Esther and John Sprinkle)*

Royal McGregor [High St]: Family-run long modern traditional-style bar with enjoyable real food in raised back area from sandwiches up (with good bread or oatcakes), well kept ales such as Caledonian Deuchars IPA, Inveralmond Red Smiddy and Kelburn Independence, good staff, old local prints; open all day *(Esther and John Sprinkle)*

☆ **Standing Order** [George St]: Grand Wetherspoons conversion of former bank in three elegant Georgian houses, imposing columns, enormous main room with elaborate colourful high ceiling, lots of tables, smaller side booths, other rooms inc two no smoking rooms with floor-to-ceiling bookshelves, comfortable green sofa and chairs, Adam fireplace and portraits; civilised atmosphere, friendly helpful staff, good value food (inc Sun evening), coffee and pastries, real ales inc interesting guest beers from very long counter; wknd live music, extremely popular Sat night; disabled facilities, open all day *(Joe Green, Patrick Hancock, BB, R M Corlett)*

Thomsons [Morrison St]: Gently refurbished, with fine woodwork behind

bar, interesting glass and bar fittings, eight well kept beers inc rarities, lunchtime food; open all day, cl Sun *(R M Corlett, Joe Green)*

Waterline [Shore, Leith]: Relaxed and inviting, largely no smoking, Caledonian Deuchars IPA and Inveralmond Independence, good range of wines by the glass and malt whiskies, new décor with big comfortable sofas and nautical touches such as charts on ceiling, decent food in bar and in back restaurant with second bar; overlooking the water *(Esther and John Sprinkle)*

White Hart [Grassmarket]: One of Edinburgh's oldest pubs, basic and easy-going, now entirely no smoking, with relaxing atmosphere, well kept Caledonian Deuchars IPA and 80/-, food all day, efficient young staff; piped music; pavement tables, open all day *(Mark Walker)*

MUSSELBURGH [NT3472]

Volunteer Arms [N High St; aka Staggs]: Same family since 1858, unspoilt busy bar, dark panelling, old brewery mirrors, great gantry with ancient casks, Caledonian Deuchars IPA and 80/- and a guest beer; dogs welcome, open all day *(Joe Green, the Didler)*

MORAYSHIRE

LOSSIEMOUTH [NJ2270]

Skerry Brae [Stotfield Rd]: Modern conversion of old stone building with generous helpings of good usual food inc fresh local seafood, changing well kept ales such as Isle of Skye Red Cuillin, conservatory bar with great views over golf links to Moray Firth and Sutherland hills, and perhaps RAF Tornadoes landing; terrace tables, bedrooms *(Mark O'Sullivan)*

NAIRNSHIRE

CAWDOR [NH8450]

☆ **Cawdor Tavern** [just off B9090]: Elegant panelled lounge, nice features in public bar, good lunchtime bar food from sandwiches to seasonally changing hot food with local influences, more restaurany in evening with some stylish upmarket cooking and partly no smoking restaurant, great choice of malt whiskies, well kept Cairngorm Stag, pleasant attentive staff; pub games, also piped music and TV; children in eating areas, dogs allowed in bar, tables on attractive front terrace, open all day wknds and summer *(Dr D G Twyman, LYM, R T and J C Moggridge, Ken Millar, Christine and Neil Townend)*

PEEBLESSHIRE

INNERLEITHEN [NT3336]

Traquair Arms [B709, just off A72 Peebles—Galashiels]: Unpretentious bar with warm fire, wide choice of bar food all day, another open fire in spacious dining room (all dining areas are no smoking), Broughton Clipper and an ale from nearby Traquair House; piped music; children and dogs welcome; bedrooms, open all day; changed hands summer 2005 – reports please *(Derek and Sylvia Stephenson, Christine and Malcolm Ingram, LYM, JWAC, Anthony Barnes, Graham Findlay)*

PERTHSHIRE

BLACKFORD [NN8908]
Blackford Hotel [Moray St, just off A9]: Attractive recently modernised hotel, enjoyable simple food all day, changing real ale such as Shepherd Neame Spitfire, spacious restful lounge; piped music; bedrooms *(Mark O'Sullivan)*
BLAIR ATHOLL [NN8765]
Atholl Arms: Sizeable hotel with stable-theme pubby bar, full range of Moulin real ales (same ownership), well priced good food all day from sandwiches to interesting dishes and local wild salmon and meat, helpful friendly staff; 31 good value bedrooms, open all day *(Andy and Jill Kassube, Brian and Anita Randall, Mr and Mrs Maurice Thompson)*
BRIG O' TURK [NN5306]
Byre [A821 Callander—Trossachs, just outside village]: Beautifully placed byre conversion under friendly new management, cast-iron framed tables in flagstoned bar, good unusual home-made bar food all day at fair prices, Tetleys, roomier high-raftered restaurant area; tables out on extensive new decking, three bedrooms, good walks, open all day, has been cl Thurs in winter *(Nick Holding, LYM, Maurice and Gill McMahon, Michael Butler)*
KENMORE [NN7745]
Kenmore Hotel [A827 W of Aberfeldy]: Civilised small hotel in pretty 18th-c village by Loch Tay, comfortable traditional front lounge with warm log fire and long poem pencilled by Burns himself on the chimney-breast, dozens of malt whiskies helpfully arranged alphabetically, polite uniformed staff, restaurant; bar food from sandwiches and baguettes up in light and airy back bar and terrace overlooking River Tay – this part seems a magnet for young people, with pool and winter darts, also juke box, TV, fruit machine, and entertainment Weds and Sun; children and dogs welcome, good bedrooms, open all day *(LYM, GSB, Graham Findlay, Michael Butler)*
KILLIN [NN5732]
Falls of Dochart [Gray St]: Former coaching inn near the falls, popular with visitors for both food and drink, large open fire, scottish beers; bedrooms with own bathrooms *(Mr and Mrs Maurice Thompson)*
KILMAHOG [NN6008]
Lade [A84 just NW of Callander, by A821 junction]: Proper pub now brewing its own organic Waylade, Ladeback and Lade Out,

well kept guest beers too, several small separate areas, beams, panelling, stripped stone, Highland prints and cigarette card collection, good range of wines by the glass, wide range of substantial good value food from lunchtime sandwiches to more ambitious restaurant dishes, no smoking conservatory opening on to terrace and pleasant garden with three fish ponds; children in eating area and family room, open all day wknds *(LYM, Maurice and Gill McMahon, Michael Butler)*
KIRKTON OF GLENISLA [NO2160]
Glenisla Hotel [B951 N of Kirriemuir and Alyth]: New management in 17th-c former coaching inn, lively local atmosphere and good log fire in beamed bar, comfortable sunny lounge and attractive high-ceilinged dining room, with games area in converted stable block; has had well kept ales such as Houston and Inveralmond, and enjoyable food in bar and restaurant; piped music, occasional live; children and dogs welcome, bedrooms being upgraded, good walks, has been open all day in season – more reports please *(Kay and Alistair Butler, LYM)*
LOCH TUMMEL [NN8160]
☆ *Loch Tummel Inn* [B8019 4 miles E of Tummel Bridge]: Lochside former coaching inn with great views over water to Schiehallion, lots of walks and local wildlife, big woodburner in cosy partly stripped stone bar, good food inc game and home-smoked salmon here and in converted hayloft restaurant, well kept local Moulin ales, good choice of wines and whiskies, helpful young Australian staff, no music or machines; attractive loch-view bedrooms with log fires, even an open fire in one bathroom, good breakfast, fishing free for residents; has been cl winter *(Andy and Jill Kassube, Paul and Ursula Randall, LYM, J F M and M West)*
MEIKLEOUR [NO1539]
☆ *Meikleour Hotel* [A984 W of Coupar Angus]: Two quietly well furnished lounges, one with stripped stone and flagstones, another more chintzy, both with open fires, welcoming landlord, polite helpful staff, three well kept ales such as Fyne and Inveralmond, local bottled water, good reasonably priced bar food inc fine sandwiches, back public bar; understated pretty building, picnic-sets in pleasant garden with tall pines and distant Highland view, comfortable bedrooms, good breakfast *(Stamford J Cartwright, Lee and Liz Potter, GSB, Christine and Neil Townend)*
PERTH [NO1223]
☆ *Greyfriars* [South St]: Small, comfortable and very friendly, with pretty décor, good value lunchtime food from baguettes and baked potatoes up, four well kept changing ales inc good Friars Tipple brewed for them by local Inveralmond, friendly staff and core of local regulars; small restaurant upstairs *(Peter Bell, Nick Holding, R T and J C Moggridge, Christine and Neil Townend, Richard Houghton)*

PITLOCHRY [NN9163]

☆ *Killiecrankie Hotel* [Killiecrankie, off A9 N]: Comfortable and splendidly placed largely no smoking country hotel with extensive peaceful grounds and dramatic views, attractive panelled bar (may have piped music), airy conservatory extension, food here and in rather formal restaurant, friendly efficient service, extensive wine list; children in bar eating area, bedrooms, open all day in summer *(Joan and Tony Walker, LYM, Dr and Mrs R G J Telfer)*

RANNOCH STATION [NN4275]

Moor of Rannoch Hotel [at end of B846]: Among moors and mountains (but trains from Oban etc, or by direct sleeper link from London Euston), friendly owners, bar, comfortable lounge with big soft armchairs and lots to read, enjoyable reasonably priced food in small dining room, good bottled beers; bedrooms *(Gill Cathles)*

RATTRAY [NO1945]

Old Cross [The Cross, Alyth Rd]: Unpretentious pub and restaurant under new young management, enjoyable low-priced home cooking inc bargain set menu *(A Rellie)*

STRATHYRE [NN5617]

Munro Inn [A84 N of Callander]: Well placed Victorian inn with lounge and public bars (dogs welcome), log fire, lots of malt whiskies, food all day, conservatory dining room, library, children's games room, internet café; nine well equipped bedrooms with own bathrooms, on Rob Roy Way, open all day *(anon)*

ROSS-SHIRE

CROMARTY [NH7867]

Cromarty Arms [Church St]: Friendly and roomy open-plan bar with reasonably priced food, pleasant staff, something of a 1950s feel, pool in annexe; sports TV; bedrooms *(Pamela and Merlyn Horswell)*

FORTROSE [NH7256]

Anderson [Union St, off A832]: Good small 19th-c hotel which takes its pub side seriously, with approaching 200 malt whiskies, a well kept changing real ale, dozens of bottled belgian beers, settees by the log fire, friendly knowledgeable landlord, and enjoyable bar food esp steaks in bar and restaurant; children welcome, comfortable bedrooms, open all day *(Ruth Green)*

KYLE OF LOCHALSH [NG7627]

Lochalsh Hotel [Ferry Rd]: Large friendly hotel lounge bar with civilised armchairs and sofas around low tables, plainer eating area, enjoyable simple bar food from generous double sandwiches to dishes of the day, pleasant Skye views, quick friendly service, good coffee; bedrooms *(Joan and Tony Walker)*

LOCHCARRON [NG9039]

Rockvilla: Good choice of food inc sandwiches and some local specialities in small hotel's light and comfortable bar,

quick friendly service, loch view; bedrooms *(G D Brooks)*

ROSEMARKIE [NH7357]

Crofters [Marine Terr]: Café with proper bar behind, good value home-made food, pleasant service; big garden overlooking Moray Firth *(Pamela and Merlyn Horswell)*

SHIEL BRIDGE [NG9319]

Kintail Lodge: Good food inc local game, wild salmon and own smokings, also children's helpings, in simple front bar or attractive conservatory restaurant with magnificent view across Loch Duich to Skye and its mountains, plenty of malt whiskies, decent wines; good value big bedrooms, bunkhouse *(Dave Braisted)*

ULLAPOOL [NH1294]

Seaforth [Quay St]: Roomy harbour-view bar with Hebridean and Isle of Skye ales, good range of malt whiskies, enjoyable local seafood in bar or upstairs restaurant, efficient service; live music most nights, open till late *(anon)*

ROXBURGHSHIRE

MELROSE [NT5434]

☆ *Kings Arms* [High St]: Late 18th-c inn, friendly and busy, with pews in bare-boards beamed bar, comfortable character lounge, well kept Tetleys and Charles Wells Bombardier, wide choice of good value generous food inc fine aberdeen angus steaks, cosy log fire, good choice of malt whiskies, attentive service; big-screen sports TV; children welcome, bedrooms, open all day *(Peter Abbott)*

SELKIRKSHIRE

TUSHIELAW [NT3018]

Tushielaw Inn [Ettrick Valley, B709/B7009 Lockerbie—Selkirk]: Former coaching inn in lovely spot by River Ettrick, unpretentiously comfortable little bar attracting an interesting mix of customers, open fire, local prints and photographs, home-made bar food inc good aberdeen angus steaks, decent house wines, a good few malt whiskies, darts, cribbage, dominoes, shove-ha'penny and liar dice, partly no smoking dining room; children welcome, terrace tables, bedrooms, open all day Sat in summer, cl Sun night and in winter all day Mon *(LYM, Nick Holding)*

STIRLINGSHIRE

BALMAHA [NS4290]

Oak Tree: On Loch Lomond's quiet side, recently built with recycled beams, timbers and panelling, pubby bar with lots of old photographs, farm tools and the like, log fire and pleasant tartan décor, enterprising choice of enjoyable food, perhaps a real ale such as Caledonian Deuchars IPA, restaurant; children welcome, plenty of tables out around ancient oak tree, eight bedrooms, bunkhouse *(Ian Baillie, Charles and Pauline Stride)*

DRYMEN [NS4788]

Winnock [The Square]: Well kept Caledonian 80/- in big Best Western hotel's modern stripped-stone and beamed lounge bar, comfortable and tidy, with blazing coal or wood fire, neat and helpful young staff, good choice of malt whiskies, steps down to popular restaurant area; piped music; big garden with picnic-sets, 48 bedrooms *(Ian Baillie, Tracey and Stephen Groves)*

STIRLING [NS7993]

☆ *Portcullis* [Castle Wynd]: Attractive former 18th-c school below castle, overlooking town and surroundings, entry through high-walled courtyard, spacious and elegant high-ceilinged stripped-stone bar with inglenooks and brocades, friendly service, pleasant atmosphere, nice choice of sandwiches and enjoyable hot dishes (not Mon evening, best to book other evenings), well kept Isle of Skye Red Cuillin and Orkney Dark Island from handsome bar counter, good choice of whiskies, log fire; lush sheltered terrace garden, good bedrooms *(Nick Holding, Tracey and Stephen Groves, Tom McLean)*

SUTHERLAND

LAIRG [NC5224]

Crask Inn [A836 13 miles N towards Altnaharra]: Good home-made food from soup and toasted sandwiches to low-priced 7.30ish evening meal such as venison or wild salmon in pleasant separate dining room, comfortably basic bar with woodburner and perhaps sheepdogs milling around (the friendly licensees keep sheep), Black Island organic bottled beers, no piped music; dogs welcome, bedrooms, and simple nearby bunkhouse *(Gill Cathles, Mike and Lynn Robinson)*

TONGUE [NC5957]

Ben Loyal Hotel [A836]: Great views up to Ben Loyal and out over Kyle of Tongue, good bar food, imaginative restaurant meals using local (even home-grown) produce, friendly owners, prompt service; keg beers, traditional live music in lounge bar in summer; tables in garden behind, dogs welcome outwith meal times, comfortable good value bedrooms in annexe (hotel itself more pricey) *(Mike and Lynn Robinson)*

Tongue Hotel [A836]: Friendly tartan-upholstered locals' side bar, wide choice of enjoyable food here or (slightly higher price) in hotel's restaurant upstairs, one real ale, good choice of malt whiskies; dogs welcome, bedrooms *(Mike and Lynn Robinson)*

WIGTOWNSHIRE

PORTPATRICK [NW9954]

Crown [North Crescent]: Waterside hotel in delightful harbourside village, good atmosphere in rambling old-fashioned bar with cosy nooks and crannies, several dozen malt whiskies, decent wine by the glass, pleasant staff, attractively decorated early 20th-c dining room (half no smoking) opening through quiet no smoking conservatory into sheltered back garden; TV, games machine, piped music; children and dogs welcome, tables out in front, open all day *(Stan and Hazel Allen, David A Hammond, LYM, Michael Lamm)*

SANDHEAD [NX0949]

Tigh na Mara [Main St]: Decent bar food in pleasant surroundings, friendly staff; bedrooms *(Dr and Mrs R G J Telfer)*

WIGTOWN [NX4355]

Ploughman [Bank St]: Reliable pub food, real ales such as Houston, decent wines, good attentive staff, simple café-style surroundings; bedrooms in Wigtown House Hotel, handy for Scotland's book town *(Stan and Hazel Allen)*

SCOTTISH ISLANDS

ARRAN

WHITING BAY [NS0425]

Eden Lodge: Enjoyable fresh blackboard food inc good puddings and fine collection of whiskies in partly stone-floored bar with cheerful atmosphere, airy décor and big contemporary pictures; great sea and coast views from beachside terrace picnic-sets and attractive modern bedrooms, open all year *(anon)*

GIGHA

GIGHA [NR6549]

Gigha Hotel: Well kept, nicely furnished and clean, with pine-décor public bar, sofas in drawing-room bar, decent food inc afternoon teas; garden tables, bedrooms, lovely spot overlooking the Sound and Kintyre *(Sarah and Peter Gooderham)*

HARRIS

RODEL [NG0483]

☆ *Rodel Hotel* [A859 at southern tip of South Harris]: Attractive and very comfortably refurbished hotel with well done new woodwork and local art in two bars and dining room, enjoyable bar lunches, keg beer; four bedrooms and self-catering, beautiful setting in small harbour *(Walter and Susan Rinaldi-Butcher)*

ISLAY

PORTNAHAVEN [NN1652]

An Tighe Seinnse [Queen St]: Small cosy end-of-terrace harbourside pub in remote fishing village, doing well under newish licensees; small bar and room off, good choice of malt whiskies, well kept local Islay real ale, open fire, good food from things that children like such as pizzas to speciality fresh fish and shellfish *(David Hoult)*

JURA

CRAIGHOUSE [NR5266]

Jura Hotel: Superb position next to the famous distillery, looking east over the Small Isles to the mainland, enjoyable inexpensive home-made bar food, agreeable owner, good restaurant; tables and seats in garden down to water's edge, bedrooms – the island is great for walkers, birdwatchers and photographers *(Richard J Holloway)*

NORTH UIST

LANGASS [NF8365]

Langass Lodge [off A867 Lochmaddy—Clachan]: Sporting hotel's relaxing panelled bar open to non-residents, good home-made bar food from sandwiches and other lunchtime snacks to more elaborate evening dishes, all local produce and catches, Isle of Skye Red Cuillin real ale and dozens of malt whiskies; bedrooms, tables in beautiful garden with wonderful views across hillside to lochan, short walk up to standing stones, RSPB walks to see otters, seals etc *(Gill Cathles)*

ORKNEY

STROMNESS [HY2509]

Ferry Inn [John St]: Very busy from breakfast time till 1am, enjoyable food from pubby things to restaurant dishes (best to book at wknds), lively young crowd evenings; 12 bedrooms *(Charles and Pauline Stride)*

TANKERNESS [HY5000]

Quoyburray Inn: Large bar with pleasant helpful staff and good mix of customers (HQ of local rugby team), enjoyable generous reasonably priced pubby food, also spoots (local razor clams) and more expensive seafood, Orkney bottled beers *(Kay and Alistair Butler)*

WESTRAY [HY4348]

Pierowall Hotel: Friendly and comfortable pub/hotel nr ferry, main bar largely given over to eating, from sandwiches and light snacks up inc good freshly landed fish, bottled Orkney beer, pool room and separate dining area; spacious bedrooms with bay or hill views *(Peter Meister)*

RAASAY

RAASAY [NG5436]

Outdoor Centre Café Bar: Bright décor, local art and books, interesting home-made food all day, Isle of Skye bottled beers, views across the sound towards Sconser, perhaps archers on the lawn or even a sea eagle; open all day till 11 *(Tracey and Stephen Groves)*

SKYE

ARDVASAR [NG6303]

☆ *Ardvasar Hotel* [A851 at S of island, nr Armadale pier]: Lovely sea and mountain views from comfortable white stone inn in peaceful very pretty spot, with friendly owner and staff, good home-made food inc local fish (children welcome in eating areas), prompt service, lots of malt whiskies, two or three well kept real ales, two bars and games room; TV, piped music; tables outside, bedrooms, good walks, open all day *(Walter and Susan Rinaldi-Butcher, LYM, Tracey and Stephen Groves, Mrs Jane Kingsbury)*

CARBOST [NG3731]

☆ *Old Inn* [B8009]: Unpretentious simply furnished bare-boards bar in idyllic peaceful spot close to Talisker distillery, friendly staff, limited bar food inc good fresh langoustines, perhaps a real ale such as Isle of Skye Red Cuillin, peat fire, darts, pool, cribbage and dominoes; TV, piped traditional music; children welcome, terrace with fine Loch Harport and Cuillin views (bar's at the back though), sea-view bedrooms in annexe (breakfast for non-residents too if you book the night before), bunkhouse and showers for yachtsmen, open all day, cl afternoons in midwinter *(Tom McLean, LYM, Tracey and Stephen Groves, David and Betty Gittins)*

ISLE ORNSAY [NG7012]

☆ *Eilean Iarmain* [off A851 Broadford—Armadale]: Bar adjunct to smart hotel in beautiful location, with tolerant willing staff inc students at the island's gaelic college, enjoyable often interesting bar food from same kitchen as charming sea-view restaurant, good choice of vatted (blended) malt whiskies inc its own Te Bheag, limited bar food, open fire; piped gaelic music; children welcome, very comfortable bedrooms *(Walter and Susan Rinaldi-Butcher, LYM, John and Elspeth Howell, Mrs Jane Kingsbury, W Holborow)*

PORTREE [NG4843]

☆ *Isles* [Somerled Sq]: Friendly 18th-c inn with decent food (nice slate table mats), well kept Caledonian Deuchars IPA, engaging Jacobean feel in interesting bar – perhaps granny in rocking chair by peat fire; bedrooms *(James Morrell, Dave Braisted)*

SLIGACHAN [NG4930]

☆ *Sligachan Hotel* [A87 Broadford—Portree, junction with A863]: Remote inn with almost a monopoly on the Cuillins, capacious, comfortable and well run, with well laid-out huge modern pine-clad bar (children's play area, games room) separating the original basic climbers' and walkers' bar from the plusher more sedate hotel side; up to half a dozen scottish real ales, dozens of malt whiskies on optic, quickly served popular food all day from home-made cakes with tea or coffee through decent straightforward bar food to fresh local seafood, fine log or coal fire, welcoming staff, good meals in hotel restaurant; piped highlands and islands music, very lively some nights, with summer live music and big campsite opp; children welcome, tables outside, bedrooms good value, open all day *(Roger and Anne Newbury, BB, Tom Espley, Tracey and Stephen Groves)*

UIG [NG3964]
Pier Inn [ferry terminal, A87]: Brightly lit bar right on pier, decent reasonably priced food

in modern café-style conservatory eating extension overlooking water, well kept Isle of Skye Red Cuillin from neighbouring brewery, efficient service, friendly cream labrador; prominent games machines; tables on terrace with good view of all the pierhead goings-on *(George Atkinson, Tracey and Stephen Groves)*

A very few pubs try to make you leave a credit card at the bar, as a sort of deposit if you order food. They are not entitled to do this. The credit card firms and banks which issue them warn you not to let them out of your sight. If someone behind the counter used your card fraudulently, the card company or bank could in theory hold you liable, because of your negligence in letting a stranger hang on to your card. Suggest instead that if they feel the need for security, they 'swipe' your card and give it back to you. And do name and shame the pub to us.

Wales

Across the Principality, pubs on top form these days are the stylish Harbourmaster overlooking Aberaeron's pretty harbour (good food, wines and bedrooms), the traditional riverside Nags Head at Abercych (brewing its own good beer, with enjoyable food), the Penhelig Arms looking across the water in Aberdovey (good food especially fish, nice bedrooms), the cheerful Black Lion at Abergorlech (pubby food and a lovely position), the Pen-y-Bryn up the hill in Colwyn Bay (great choice of drinks, enjoyable food all day), the Bear in Crickhowell (a favourite all-rounder, of great character), the restauranty Nantyffin Cider Mill just outside, the ancient Blue Anchor at East Aberthaw (back in the *Guide* after restoration of last year's fire damage, looking splendid under its new thatch), the Griffin at Felinfach (super cooking of good local ingredients and even their own fresh veg, gaining it a Food Award this year), the friendly and elegant Pant-yr-Ochain in its splendid grounds at Gresford (good food, drink and service, largely no smoking), the Old Black Lion in Hay-on-Wye (good food and beer, a place of character that's nice to stay in), the Queens Head near Llandudno Junction (consistently good food), the Druid at Llanferres (back in the *Guide* after a break of a few years, with a number of worthwhile improvements), the White Swan at Llanfrynach (another that has been in the *Guide* in the past, doing very well again these days with its cheerful service, attractive layout and fine garden), the splendidly designed Corn Mill by the river in Llangollen (food, beer and wine all good), the Hawk & Buckle tucked away high in the hills at Llannefydd (regaining its place in the *Guide* after a break of several years, with food that's a cut above these days), the bistro-style Glasfryn in Mold (good drinks and interesting food), the Cross Foxes above the river at Overton Bridge (great choice of drinks, good food and an appealing layout), the lovely Sloop by the sea at Porthgain, the Royal Oak in Saundersfoot (good beer, fresh fish, a new tapas bar next door, and hoping to be entirely no smoking by 2006), the Bell at Skenfrith (a newcomer to the *Guide*, a smart and extensive dining pub with good food), the individual Cherry Tree at Tintern (good changing beers, a successful recent refurbishment giving rather more room), the Groes at Ty'n-y-groes (an enjoyable food pub, nice to stay in too, with plenty of character), and the friendly Nags Head in Usk (good food in a fine old building). For a particularly enjoyable meal in charming surroundings, the Pant-yr-Ochain at Gresford takes the title of Wales Dining Pub of the Year. We have listed the Lucky Dip entries at the end of the chapter under the various regions which are still more recognisable to most visitors than the new administrative areas which have replaced them. Pubs to note particularly here are, in Clwyd, the White Lion at Llanelian-yn-Rhos; in Dyfed, the Old Point House at Angle, St Govans Country Inn at Bosherston, Druidstone Hotel at Broad Haven, Dyffryn Arms at Cwm Gwaun, Georges in Haverfordwest, Butchers Arms at Llanddarog, Farmers Arms at Mathry and Royal Oak in Newport; in Gwent, the Raglan Arms at Llandenny, Walnut Tree at Llandewi Skirrid, Greyhound at Llantrisant Fawr and Moon & Sixpence at Tintern; in Gwynedd, the Castle Hotel in Conwy, Ty Coch at Porth Dinllaen and Cwellyn Arms at Rhyd Ddu; in Mid Glamorgan, the Prince of Wales at Kenfig; in Powys, the Tai'r Bull at Libanus, Coach &

Horses at Llangynidr, Radnor Arms at Llowes and Star at Talybont-on-Usk; in South Glamorgan, the Caio Arms in Cardiff and Bear in Cowbridge; and in West Glamorgan, the Joiners Arms at Bishopston. Drinks prices are a little lower than the average over in England. Brains is the main local brewer (and also brews Hancocks for the Coors brewing combine). Small independent brewers haven't blossomed here in recent years quite as much as they have in Scotland – perhaps because here in Wales it's easier to get hold of good beers from England. Local brewers we have found supplying at least some of our main entries this year are (in a very rough order of frequency) Felinfoel, Evan Evans, Plassey, Breconshire, Tomos Watkins, Bragdy Ynys Môn and Bullmastiff, and we found nearly another dozen or so selling to the Lucky Dip pubs.

ABERAERON SN4562 Map 6

Harbourmaster 🍴 🍷 🛏️

Harbour Lane

On the yacht-filled harbour among a charming array of colourwashed buildings, this tastefully smartened-up hotel is a lovely spot to enjoy a meal and makes a splendidly civilised alternative to the area's true pubs. Buzzing with locals and visitors, and modern rustic in style, the wine bar (which may be a bit smoky) has dark wood panelling, sofas, and chunky blocks of wood as low tables or stools on dark wood floors; piped music. Tapas dishes served in here might include grilled mackerel or grilled aubergines with pesto (£5.50), grilled crevettes in chilli butter (£7.50) and mixed tapas (£9.50); well kept Brains SA and Buckleys Best on handpump, and a good wine list, with a constantly changing selection sold by the glass. The owners are chatty and welcoming, and service is good. In the no smoking restaurant, new light wood furniture looks stylishly modern on light wood floors against light and dark blue walls. Here, the imaginative menu might include soup (£4), fishcakes (£6.50), oysters (£7.50 for six), duck pâté (£5.50), antipasti platter for two (£12), lemon sole with sweet potato chips and red pepper coulis (£14.50), chargrilled welsh black beef fillet (£17.50), and blueberry and brazil nut brûlée with hazelnut ice-cream (£4.95) – a place for a special occasion. More reports please. *(Recommended by Glenys and John Roberts, Pamela and Merlyn Horswell, Ron and Sheila Corbett, Blaise Vyner, John Hale, V Brogden)*

Free house ~ Licensees Glyn and Menna Heulyn ~ Real ale ~ Bar food (12-2, 6.30-9) ~ Restaurant ~ (01545) 570755 ~ Children in restaurant ~ Open 11(6 Mon)-11; 12-10.30 (12-4 winter) Sun; closed Mon lunchtime ~ Bedrooms: £55S/£95B

ABERCYCH SN2441 Map 6

Nags Head 🍺

Off B4332 Cenarth—Boncath

Many of the customers at this beautifully placed riverside pub come from miles around. The dimly lit beamed and flagstoned bar has a comfortable old sofa in front of the big fireplace, clocks showing the time around the world, stripped wood tables, a piano, photographs and postcards of locals, and hundreds of bottles of beer displayed around the brick and stone walls – look out for the big stuffed rat. A plainer no smoking small room leads down to a couple of big dining areas (one of which is also no smoking), and there's another little room behind the bar. Besides the much-liked beer brewed on the premises (named Old Emrys after one of the regulars), they serve Greene King Abbot and a guest such as Breconshire Golden Valley; piped music and TV. Popular bar food served in huge helpings includes soup (£3.25), breaded brie wedges with home-made pear and ginger chutney (£4.25), vegetable chilli (£6.95), battered cod or lasagne (£7.25), steak and kidney pudding (£7.50), and daily specials such as local faggots (£7.50), crab salad or thai green vegetable curry (£8.95), and lamb steak with rosemary and redcurrant (£9.95); they do smaller helpings of some dishes (from £4.95) and children's meals. Service is pleasant and efficient. Lit by fairy lights in the evening, the pub is tucked away in a little village and beautifully set next to a river. Tables under cocktail parasols across the quiet road look over the water, and there are nicely arranged benches, and a children's play area; they sometimes have barbecues out here in summer. *(Recommended by Gene and Kitty Rankin, R Michael Richards, Colin Moore, David and Nina Pugsley)*

Own brew ~ Licensee Steven Jamieson ~ Real ale ~ Bar food (12-2, 6-9) ~ Restaurant ~ (01239) 841200 ~ Children welcome ~ Dogs allowed in bar ~ Open 11.30-3.30, 6-11.20; 12-10.30 Sun; closed Mon

ABERDOVEY SN6296 Map 6
Penhelig Arms ⊕ ♀ ⇌
Opposite Penhelig railway station

Fresh locally caught fish is a speciality at this splendidly located, efficiently run and welcoming 18th-c hotel by the harbour wall on the Dyfi estuary, and the impressive wine list includes some 300 bottles, with around 30 sold by the glass. Good log fires in the small original beamed bar make it especially cosy in winter, and there's nothing in the way of fruit machines or piped music. In addition to lunchtime sandwiches (from £2.95), the daily lunch and dinner menus (which they serve in the dining area of the bar and restaurant, both of which are no smoking; you do need to book) could include cream of mushroom soup (£3.50), dressed local crab (£6.95), steak and Guinness sausages with mash (£7.95), grilled fillet of plaice (£10.95), fried pork loin with mustard and tarragon sauce (£10.75), roast whole bream with rocket and pistachio salsa (£12.75), and whole bass (£13.50), with puddings such as summer pudding or caramelised lemon and lime tart (£4.50). They have three well kept beers such as Hancocks HB, Greene King Old Speckled Hen and Wye Valley Butty Bach on handpump, two dozen malt whiskies, fruit and peppermint teas, and various coffees; dominoes. Bedrooms are very comfortable, some with balconies overlooking the estuary, and the breakfasts varied and good. *(Recommended by V Brogden, Peter Meister, Gerry and Rosemary Dobson, E M Probyn, Prof Keith and Mrs Jane Barber, David Glynne-Jones, Revd D Glover, Earl and Chris Pick, Mike and Mary Carter, Di and Mike Gillam, Colin Moore, Comus and Sarah Elliott)*

Free house ~ Licensees Robert and Sally Hughes ~ Real ale ~ Bar food ~ Restaurant ~ (01654) 767215 ~ Children in eating area of bar and restaurant ~ Dogs allowed in bar ~ Open 11-4, 5-11; 11-11 Sat; 12-10.30 Sun; 11-3, 6-11 weekends in winter ~ Bedrooms: £49S/£78S

ABERGORLECH SN5833 Map 6
Black Lion
B4310 (a pretty road roughly NE of Carmarthen)

You feel a long way from anywhere in this tranquil spot in the wooded Cothi Valley, and the little 17th-c coaching inn is a good place to make for if you are visiting the nearby Dolaucothi Gold Mines at Pumsaint or strolling through the plantations of Brechfa Forest. Picnic-tables, wooden seats and benches have lovely views, and the garden slopes down towards the River Cothi where there's a Roman triple-arched bridge. The plain but comfortably cosy stripped-stone bar is traditionally furnished with plain oak tables and chairs, high-backed black settles facing each other across the flagstones by the gas-effect log fire, and has horsebrasses and copper pans on the black beams, old jugs on shelves and fresh flowers and paintings by a local artist. The dining extension (candlelit at night) has french windows opening on to a newly landscaped enclosed garden. Reasonably priced bar food includes soup (£2.50), sandwiches (from £2.75), sausage and mash (£4.95), excellent ploughman's (£5.50), curry or vegetable and stilton crumble (£6.50), home-made chicken and leek pie or steak and kidney pudding (£6.95), and 8oz sirloin steak (£9.95), with puddings such as home-made sherry trifle or apple crumble (£3.50); on Sunday you can also get roasts (£5.95, plus £2 for each extra course), and in summer they do afternoon teas. Evan Evans Best (brewed nearby in Llandeilo) and a guest such as Buckleys Best or Youngs are kept under a light blanket pressure on handpump; mulled wine in winter and lots of fruit juices; daily papers, sensibly placed darts, chess, cribbage, dominoes, draughts, monthly quiz nights and piped music. *(Recommended by Mrs Edna M Jones, Norman and June Williams, Richard Siebert, JWAC, Martin Frith, Annabel Viney)*

Free house ~ Licensees Michelle and Guy Richardson ~ Real ale ~ Bar food ~ Restaurant ~ (01558) 685271 ~ Children welcome in eating area of bar and restaurant until 9pm ~ Dogs allowed in bar ~ Open 12-3, 7-11; 12-11(10 Sun) Sat; closed Mon exc bank hols

BEAUMARIS SH6076 Map 6
Olde Bulls Head ♀ 🛏
Castle Street

Not much has changed in the beamed bar of this roomy 15th-c inn since Charles Dickens popped in for a drink in 1859 (another visitor was Samuel Johnson); a rare 17th-c brass water clock, a bloodthirsty crew of cutlasses and even an oak ducking stool are tucked among the snug alcoves, and are interesting reminders of the town's past. The bar also has lots of copper and china jugs, comfortable low-seated settles, leather-cushioned window seats, and a good log fire. They don't serve food in this room, so it's perfect for conversation and a drink, and it's open all day; Bass and Hancocks are well kept alongside a guest from a brewery such as Bragdy Ynys Môn. Quite a contrast, the popular no smoking brasserie behind is lively and contemporary with piped music and a menu that includes enjoyable dishes such as home-made soup (£3.35), sandwiches (from £4.50), deep-fried crab cakes (£4.25), salads (from £6.75), wild mushroom risotto or chicken, leek and mushroom pie (£7.50), grilled pork cutlet with celeriac mash (£8.25), roast tranche of halibut with herb crust and welsh rarebit sauce (£9.75), and baked bass with buttered fennel and salsa verde (£10.75), with puddings such as baked rice pudding with poached rhubarb or dark chocolate and raspberry bakewell tart (from £4.75); vegetable side dishes (from £1.50); children's menu. They don't take bookings in here, but do for the smart no smoking restaurant upstairs. The brasserie wine list incudes ten available by the glass; the restaurant wine list runs to 120 different bottles. The entrance to the pretty courtyard is closed by what is listed in *The Guinness Book of Records* as the biggest simple-hinged door in Britain (11 feet wide and 13 feet high). Named after characters in Dickens's novels, the bedrooms are very well equipped and are in both contemporary and traditional styles. *(Recommended by Gordon Prince, Revd D Glover, J Roy Smylie, Andy Sinden, Louise Harrington, Dr and Mrs M E Wilson, A J Law, Gerry and Rosemary Dobson)*

Free house ~ Licensee David Robertson ~ Real ale ~ Bar food (12-2, 6-9) ~ Restaurant ~ (01248) 810329 ~ Children in bar until 8pm and in brasserie ~ Open 11-11; 12-10.30 Sun ~ Bedrooms: £70B/£95B

CAPEL CURIG SH7258 Map 6
Bryn Tyrch
A5 W of village

You could hardly be closer to the high mountains of Snowdonia here, in this isolated inn, with some choice and challenging walking right on the doorstep. Wholesome food, with an emphasis on vegetarian and vegan dishes, is generously served to meet the healthy appetite of anyone participating in the local outdoor attractions – very much what this place is about. Big picture windows run the length of one wall, with views across the road to picnic-sets on a floodlit patch of grass by a stream running down to a couple of lakes, and the peaks of the Carneddau, Tryfan and Glyders in close range. Comfortably relaxed, the bar has several easy chairs round low tables, some by a coal fire with magazines and outdoor equipment catalogues piled to one side, and a pool table in the plainer hikers' bar; the dining area and part of the main bar are no smoking. Bar food includes soup (from £3.80), grilled goats cheese salad or chorizo with strips of mixed peppers and grated welsh cheese (£4.85), broccoli, cauliflower and stilton crumble, local lamb-and-leek sausages and mash or chicken breast with courgettes and mushroom sauce (all £8.95), smoked haddock, prawn and mushroom pie or beef and Guinness pie (£9.50), specials and home-made puddings such as apple crumble or chocolate pudding (from £4.25); they have a short list of specials such as chicken kebabs (£8.95) and braised local lamb shank (£10.50). You can also pop in here for a cup of one of the many coffee blends or Twinings teas that are listed on a blackboard, and served with a piece of vegan cake. Well kept Flowers, Brains SA, and Camerons Castle Eden on handpump, and quite a few malt whiskies; pool, shove-ha'penny and dominoes. There are tables on a steep little garden at the side. More reports please; we would also like to hear from readers who stay here (some rooms have views; £10 cleaning charge for dogs). *(Recommended by Richard and Anne Ansell, John and Joan Nash, KC, Rona Murdoch)*

Free house ~ Licensee Rita Davis ~ Real ale ~ Bar food (12-2.30, 5.9.30; all day in summer) ~ Restaurant ~ (01690) 720223 ~ Children welcome ~ Dogs allowed in bedrooms ~ Open 12-11(10.30 Sun); closed Mon, Tues Nov-Feb (but open school and bank hols) ~ Bedrooms: £40(£45B)/£56(£64B)

COLWYN BAY SH8478 Map 6

Pen-y-Bryn ♀

B5113 Llanwrst Road, on S outskirts; when you see the pub turn off into Wentworth Avenue for its car park

Readers enthuse about the delicious food (served all day), terrific views and attractive, light and airy interior of this modern, open-plan pub beside the sea. Working around the three long sides of the bar counter, the mix of seating and well spaced tables, oriental rugs on pale stripped boards, shelves of books, welcoming coal fires, profusion of pictures, big pot plants, careful lighting and dark green school radiators are all typical of the pubs in this small chain; the back part of the pub is no smoking. Besides Flowers Original, Fullers London Pride, Thwaites and up to three guests such as Archers and Weetwood Old Dog kept under light blanket pressure on handpump, they have well chosen good value wines including just over a dozen by the glass, 60 malts and several irish whiskeys, proper coffee and freshly squeezed orange juice; cribbage, dominoes, chess, faint piped music. Friendly efficient staff serve bar food which might include sandwiches (from £3.45), roasted carrot and rosemary soup (£3.95), pear, leek and roquefort tart or spicy beef and stir-fried vegetable wrap (£4.95), ploughman's (£6.95), pork-and-leek sausages with cheddar cheese mash (£7.95), porcini mushroom ravioli (£8.95), smoked haddock and leek risotto (£9.50), chinese-style shoulder of pork with stir-fried vegetables and noodles (£10.50), 10oz rump steak (£13.95), and puddings such as hazelnut tart or rhubarb and custard trifle (from £4.45). Outside there are sturdy tables and chairs on a side terrace and a lower one, by a lawn with picnic-sets. *(Recommended by E G Parish, Gwyn and Anne Wake, Paul Boot, Joan E Hilditch, R T J and J J Hubbard, Alan and Paula McCully, KC)*

Brunning & Price ~ Managers Graham Arathoon and Graham Price ~ Real ale ~ Bar food (12-9.30(9 Sun)) ~ (01492) 533360 ~ Children under 12 welcome till 7.30pm ~ Open 11.30-11; 12-10.30 Sun; closed 25-26 Dec

CRESSWELL QUAY SN0406 Map 6

Cresselly Arms

Village signposted from A4075

If you time the tides right, you can arrive by boat at this marvellously unchanged alehouse (one reader said it was like stepping back half a century), placed by a tidal creek of the Cresswell River and often full of locals; seats outside make the most of the view. The pub has a relaxed and jaunty air in the two simple comfortably old-fashioned communicating rooms, which have red and black floor tiles, built-in wall benches, kitchen chairs and plain tables, an open fire in one room, a working Aga in the other, and a high beam-and-plank ceiling hung with lots of pictorial china. A third red-carpeted no smoking room is more conventionally furnished, with red-cushioned mate's chairs around neat tables. Well kept Worthington BB and a winter guest beer are tapped straight from the cask into glass jugs by the landlord, whose presence is a key ingredient of the atmosphere; fruit machine. No children. *(Recommended by Phil and Sally Gorton, Pete Baker, the Didler, R M Corlett)*

Free house ~ Licensees Maurice and Janet Cole ~ Real ale ~ No credit cards ~ (01646) 651210 ~ Open 12-3, 5-11; 11-11 Sat; 12-3, 5(7 winter)-10.30 Sun

CRICKHOWELL SO2118 Map 6
Bear ★ ⑪ ♀ ◀ ⌂
Brecon Road; A40

Right in the centre of this delightful little town, this civilised old coaching inn manages to blend traditional charms with efficient service, and is a welcoming place to stay. Its comfortably decorated, heavily beamed lounge has fresh flowers on tables, lots of little plush-seated bentwood armchairs and handsome cushioned antique settles, and a window seat looking down on the market square. Up by the great roaring log fire, a big sofa and leather easy chairs are spread among rugs on the oak parquet floor. Other good antiques include a fine oak dresser filled with pewter and brass, a longcase clock, and interesting prints. Well kept Bass, Brains Rev James, and Greene King Ruddles Best and Ruddles County on handpump, as well as 24 malt whiskies, vintage and late-bottled ports, unusual wines (with over a dozen by the glass) and liqueurs (with some hops tucked in among the bottles) and local apple juice; the family lounge is no smoking. Friendly helpful staff serve bar food which includes sandwiches (from £2.50; baguettes from £3.50), soup (£3.50), chicken liver parfait with cumberland sauce and toasted brioche (£5.25), goats cheese and fried onion pie, sausages and mash or diced lamb with cumin and apricots and savoury rice (£7.95), salmon fishcakes (£8.25), chicken supreme in thai marinade with shredded vegetables and coconut rice (£9.50), and steak (from £12.50), with puddings such as dark chocolate and orange mousse or bread and butter pudding (£4.25); bar specials could include home-made cottage pie (£5.75) or maple syrup glazed bacon with baked barbecue beans (£9.50); the more elaborate restaurant menu is pricier, and their Sunday lunch is very popular. You can eat in the garden in summer; disabled lavatories. *(Recommended by Bob and Valerie Mawson, Tom and Ruth Rees, Jarrod and Wendy Hopkinson, Ann and Colin Hunt, Dr and Mrs C W Thomas, Alan Strong, Andrew Shore, Maria Williams, J C Poley, John Urquhart, Susie Symes, Norman and Sarah Keeping, Patrick Hancock, A S and M E Marriott, Terry and Linda Moseley, Mark and Ruth Brock, Joyce and Maurice Cottrell, David and Nina Pugsley, Charles and Isabel Cooper, Julia and Richard Tredgett, Brian and Jacky Wilson, Nigel Howard, Steve Cawthray, Alan and Paula McCully, Basil and Jard Jarvis, B P Abrahams, Colin Moore, Anthony Barnes, Mike Pugh, Jo Lilley, Simon Calvert, Colin Morgan, Di and Mike Gillam, Mike and Mary Carter)*

Free house ~ Licensee Judy Hindmarsh ~ Real ale ~ Bar food (12-2, 6-10; 12-2, 7-9.30 Sun) ~ Restaurant ~ (01873) 810408 ~ Children in family lounge and over 8 in restaurant ~ Dogs welcome ~ Open 11-3, 6-11; 12-3, 7-11 Sun ~ Bedrooms: £58S/£77S(£87B)

Nantyffin Cider Mill ♀
1½ miles NW, by junction A40/A479

You can see the old cider press that gives this L-shaped pink-washed brasserie style pub its name in the raftered barn that has been converted into a striking no smoking restaurant, and they serve farm cider too. With warm grey stonework, the interior has fresh and dried flowers, good solid comfortable tables and chairs and a woodburner in a fine broad fireplace. The counter at one end of the main open-plan area has Wadworths Henrys IPA and a guest such as Shepherd Neame on handpump, as well as thoughtfully chosen new world wines (a few by the glass or half bottle), Weston's Old Rosie cider on handpump, Pimms and home-made lemonade in summer, and hot punch and mulled wine in winter. From a changing

menu, not-cheap restauranty food could include soup (£3.50), hand-rolled fresh pasta ravioli filled with smoked chicken and mushrooms (£6.25), sweetcorn, brie and leek fritters (£10.50), confit of lamb with herb mash and rosemary garlic sauce (£11.95), roast supreme of home-reared chicken (£12.95), grilled rib-eye of beef with chips and mushrooms (£14.95), vegetable side dishes (£2.50), and puddings such as chocolate affogato pot or rhubarb and ginger crumble (£4.95); on weekdays they also do a two-course meal for £10. The River Usk is on the other side of a fairly busy road, and there are charming views from the tables out on the lawn above the pub's neat car park; a ramp makes disabled access easy.
(Recommended by Bob and Valerie Mawson, Terry and Linda Moseley, Mike Pugh, R T and J C Moggridge, David and Nina Pugsley)

Free house ~ Licensees Glyn Bridgeman and Sean Gerrard ~ Real ale ~ Bar food (12-2.30, 6.30-9.30) ~ Restaurant ~ (01873) 810775 ~ Children welcome ~ Dogs allowed in bar ~ Open 12-3, 6.30-10(11 Sat); closed Sun evening, Mon except bank hols

EAST ABERTHAW ST0367 Map 6
Blue Anchor 🍺
B4265

This charming medieval thatched pub is open again, if anything better than ever after restoration of 2004 fire damage (the thatch alone took several months to redo – and looks wonderful now). Full of character, its warren of snug low-beamed rooms dates back as far as 1380. There are massive stone walls and tiny doorways, and open fires everywhere, including one in an inglenook with antique oak seats built into its stripped stonework. Other seats and tables are worked into a series of chatty little alcoves, and the more open front bar still has an ancient lime-ash floor. Friendly, helpful staff serve five well kept real ales – besides a changing guest from a brewer such as Tomos Watkin, you'll find Brains Buckleys Best, Theakstons Old Peculier, Wadworths 6X and Wye Valley Hereford Pale Ale on handpump; fruit machine, darts, trivia machine and dominoes. It's nice to know that much of the fruit and vegetables served here is cultivated by the landlord's enthusiastic gardening father on his two-acre vegetable patch. As well as lunchtime sandwiches (from £3.90), and filled baked potatoes (from £4.75), enjoyable bar food might include soup (£3.25), home-made chicken liver terrine (£3.75), lamb and leek casserole or filo parcel of leeks, apricots and caerphilly cheese with rocket and pineapple salad (£6.95), marinated beef with oriental-style noodles and crispy seaweed (£7.50), seared calves liver and bacon on celeriac and potato mash with red wine jus or grilled pork chops with stilton (£7.95), 8oz rump steak (£8.95) and pudddings such as steamed ginger and apricot sponge or meringue nests with summer fruits (£3.50); piped music in the no smoking restaurant. Rustic seats shelter peacefully among tubs and troughs of flowers outside, with more stone tables on a newer terrace. From here a path leads to the shingly flats of the estuary. The pub can get very full in the evenings and on summer weekends. *(Recommended by R Michael Richards, Ian Phillips)*

Free house ~ Licensee Jeremy Coleman ~ Real ale ~ Bar food (12-2, 6-8; not Sat evening, not Sun lunchtime) ~ Restaurant ~ (01446) 750329 ~ Children welcome ~ Dogs allowed in bar ~ Open 11-11; 12-10.30 Sun

FELINFACH SO0933 Map 6
Griffin 🍴 ♀
A470 NE of Brecon

The licensees take great pride in sourcing local ingredients at this dining pub, and grow most of the vegetables themselves. Table settings are classy, and the good food might include lunchtime dishes such as potato and leek soup (£4.80), open sandwiches (£5.95), sausage and mash (£7.95), plaice fillet, chicken breast or morel mushroom and asparagus risotto (£9.95). A pricier evening menu includes dishes such as french onion soup (£4.80), wild mushroom tagliatelle (£6.50), breast of corn-fed chicken, creamed wild mushrooms and mash (£15.50), local rib-eye steak

(£15.95), and rack of lamb with spring vegetables, dauphinoise potatoes and red pepper jus (£16.50). They have a good choice of wines including several by the glass, welsh spirits, and Evan Evans and Tomos Watkins OSB well kept on handpump. Inside, the back bar is quite pubby in an up-to-date way, with three leather sofas around a low table on pitted quarry tiles, by a high slate hearth with a log fire, and behind them mixed stripped seats around scrubbed kitchen tables on bare boards, and a bright blue-and-ochre colour scheme. It has a few modern prints, and some nice photoprints of a livestock market by Victoria Upton. An upright piano stands against one wall – the acoustics are pretty lively, with so much bare flooring and uncurtained windows. The two smallish no smoking front dining rooms, linking through to the back bar, are attractive: on the left, mixed dining chairs around mainly stripped tables on flagstones, and white-painted rough stone walls, with a cream-coloured Aga in a big stripped-stone embrasure; on the right, similar furniture on bare boards, with big modern prints on terracotta walls, and good dark curtains. There may be piped Radio Wales in the bar. We have not yet heard from any readers who have stayed here, but would expect good news about their white bedrooms; there's a £10 supplement for dogs. Wheelchair access is good, and there are tables outside. *(Recommended by Bob and Valerie Mawson, Rodney and Norma Stubington, Pamela and Merlyn Horswell, John Holroyd, Andy Sinden, Louise Harrington)*

Free house ~ Licensee Charles Inkin ~ Real ale ~ Bar food (12.30-2.30, 6.30-9.30(9 Sun)) ~ Restaurant ~ (01874) 620111 ~ Children in eating area of bar and restaurant ~ Dogs allowed in bar and bedrooms ~ Open 12-3, 6-11; 12-11 Sat-Sun; closed Mon lunchtime except bank hols ~ Bedrooms: £67.50B/£92.50B

GRESFORD SJ3555 Map 6

Pant-yr-Ochain 🍴 ♀

Off A483 on N edge of Wrexham: at roundabout take A5156 (A534) towards Nantwich, then first left towards the Flash

Wales Dining Pub of the Year

Run with considerable flair and attention to detail, this elegant 16th-c country house continues its winning ways, with delicious food and a good choice of real ales and wines. In attractive grounds and with its own lake, it has been thoughtfully refurbished inside – interesting for the reader who used to come to tea here as a little boy over 50 years ago, when his father was vicar of Gresford. The light and airy rooms are stylishly decorated, with a wide range of interesting prints and bric-a-brac on walls and on shelves, and a good mix of individually chosen country furnishings, including comfortable seats for relaxing as well as more upright ones for eating. There is a good open fire, and one area is set out as a library, with floor to ceiling bookshelves. Excellent food, from a well balanced daily changing menu, might typically include mushroom and tarragon soup (£3.95), sandwiches (from £4.25), lamb terrine with roasted plums (£5.25), crab cakes with pickled cucumber salad (£5.25), ploughman's (£6.95), butternut squash ravioli with rocket and herb oil (£8.75), steak and bacon burger topped with cheddar cheese served with hand-cut chips (£9.25), crispy duck confit leg with pear salad (£9.95), tiger prawn and clotted cream quiche with hot potato salad (£10.95), and 10oz welsh rump steak with bourguignon sauce and hand-cut chips (£14.25), with puddings such as warm blackberry bakewell tart with clotted cream or lemon posset with grilled figs (£4.45); arrive early if you want a seat in the conservatory (which was about to be rebuilt, with a slate roof, as we went to press). Well kept on handpump are Caledonian Deuchars IPA, Flowers Original, Timothy Taylors Landlord, locally brewed Plassey Bitter and Weetwood Old Dog, as well as a guest such as Storm Bosley Cloud, and they have a good range of decent wines (strong on up-front new world ones), and more than 50 malt whiskies. Service is friendly and professional; apart from one bar the pub is entirely no smoking, and disabled access is good; piped music, board games and dominoes. *(Recommended by Mrs P J Carroll, Paul Boot, Revd D Glover, John Hendy, Brenda and Rob Fincham, Maurice and Della Andrew, Oliver and Sue Rowell, MLR, Esther and John Sprinkle, John and Helen Rushton, Susan Brookes, David Glynne-Jones, Bruce and Sharon Eden)*

Brunning & Price ~ Licensee Lynsey Prole ~ Real ale ~ Bar food (12-9.30(9 Sun)) ~
(01978) 853525 ~ Children welcome away from bar till 6pm ~ Open 12-11(10.30 Sun)

HAY-ON-WYE SO2342 Map 6

Kilverts 🛏

Bullring

Open all day, this is a pleasantly unrushed and welcoming town-centre inn that
makes a comfortable place for a meal or a drink, and you can watch the world go
by from tables in a small front flagstoned courtyard (with outdoor heaters) or while
away the hours by the fountain in a pretty terraced back garden. Calm and
understated, the airy high-beamed bar has some stripped stone walls, *Vanity Fair*
caricatures, a couple of standing timbers, candles on well spaced mixed old and
new tables, and a pleasant variety of seating. Enjoyable bar food from a sensibly
balanced menu is served in generous helpings, and includes lunchtime filled
baguettes or sandwiches (from £3.75), home-made soup (£3.95), about a dozen
pizzas (£5.50-£7.50), thai-style fishcakes (£5.50), spaghetti carbonara (£7.75),
curry and rice or beer battered haddock and chips (£9.25), beef and ale pie (£9.95),
grilled bass with fennel, lime and tarragon glaze (£10.25), spinach and mushroom
roulade filled with mint and cream cheese on mediterranean vegetables (£11.95),
baked chicken breast stuffed with stilton and peaches (£12.95), and 12oz sirloin
steak (£13.95); no smoking restaurant. They've an extensive wine list with about a
dozen by the glass, as well as three real ales such as Brains Rev James, Hancocks
HB and Wye Valley Butty Bach on handpump, a decent choice of wines by the glass
and good coffees; piped music. There's a £5.50 cleaning charge for dogs in the
comfortable bedrooms. *(Recommended by Sue Demont, Tim Barrow, Ann and Colin Hunt,
Peter and Jean Hoare, Mike Pugh, George Atkinson, Andy and Jill Kassube, Brian Brooks,
Martin Grosberg, MLR, Mrs Hazel Rainer)*

Free house ~ Licensee Colin Thomson ~ Real ale ~ Bar food (12-2, 7-9.30) ~ Restaurant
~ (01497) 821042 ~ Children welcome in eating area of bar until 9pm ~ Dogs welcome ~
Open 9-11 ~ Bedrooms: £50S/£70S(£80B)

Old Black Lion 🍴 🍺 🛏

Lion Street

Right in the heart of town, this welcoming and neatly kept old hotel dates back in
part to the 13th c and is near the site of the former town wall – the gate in this part
used to be called the Lion Gate. Peaceful and spotlessly kept, and with a snugly
enveloping atmosphere, the comfortable low-beamed bar has crimson and yellow
walls, nice old pine tables, and an original fireplace. The food here is good (if not
cheap), and the restaurant menu can be eaten in the bar too. The bar and restaurant
menus could include celeriac, fennel and rosemary soup (£4.95), lunchtime
sandwiches (£5.25), warm fillets of smoked eel in cream, spinach and garlic, on
tomato toast (£5.85), steak and kidney pie with cabbage mash (£9.95), moroccan
lamb with date and apricot compote and couscous (£10.50), grilled plaice with
herb butter or wild mushroom and leek crêpes with cheese sauce (£12.50), duck
breast with honey and five spice glaze on braised red cabbage with apples and
sultanas (£16.50), beef wellington or fried venison on parsnip purée with
blackberry and gin sauce (£17.50), puddings such as citrus tart or ginger crème
brûlée (£4.25); Sunday lunch (£8); no smoking restaurant. As well as Old Black
Lion (a good beer brewed for them by Wye Valley) on handpump, they serve a
changing Wye Valley real ale, and good value wines; service is very friendly and
enthusiastic. There are tables out behind on a sheltered terrace. Comfortably creaky
bedrooms make this an atmospheric place to stay, and they can arrange pony
trekking and golf, and trout and salmon fishing on the Wye. *(Recommended by
Andy and Jill Kassube, Kerry Law, Simon Smith, Sue Demont, Tim Barrow, Pam and
David Bailey, Ann and Colin Hunt, Mike and Mary Carter, Michael and Ann Cole, Keith and
Jean Symons, David Field, Tony Hall, Melanie Jackson, David and Jean Hall, Mrs Hazel Rainer,
Colin Morgan, Kay and Alistair Butler, MLR)*

Free house ~ Licensee Vanessa King ~ Real ale ~ Bar food (12-2.30, 6.30-9.30) ~
Restaurant ~ (01497) 820841 ~ Children over 5 welcome in evening if away from main bar
~ Open 11-11; 12-10.30 Sun; closed two weeks in Jan ~ Bedrooms: £50S(£42.50B)/£80B

LLANBERIS SH6655 Map 6
Pen-y-Gwryd £ 🛏
**Nant Gwynant; at junction of A498 and A4086, ie across mountains from Llanberis – OS
Sheet 115 map reference 660558**

A long-established haunt of mountaineers and in a spectacularly remote position
among the peaks of Snowdonia this fascinating old inn doubles up as a mountain
rescue post and even has its own chapel (built for the millennium and dedicated by
the Archbishop of Wales) and sauna. It has been in the same family for years, and the
team that first climbed Everest in 1953 used it as a training base, leaving their
fading signatures scrawled on the ceiling. One snug little room in the homely slate-
floored log cabin bar has built-in wall benches and sturdy country chairs to let you
gaze at the surrounding mountain landscapes – like precipitous Moel Siabod
beyond the lake opposite. A smaller room has a worthy collection of illustrious
boots from famous climbs, and a cosy panelled smoke room has more fascinating
climbing mementoes and equipment; darts, pool, shove-ha'penny, bar billiards and
dominoes. There's a sociable atmosphere, and the landlady is chattily helpful.
Alongside well kept Bass, they've home-made lemonade in summer, mulled wine in
winter, and sherry from their own solera in Puerto Santa Maria. Simple good-value
home-made lunchtime bar food (you order it from a hatch) from a short menu
could include soup (£2.95), spanish tortilla or pork burger in home-made bap (£5),
and fillet of salmon, chicken, leek and mushroom pie or pork and smoked bacon
terrine (all £6); they also have an evening menu for the no smoking restaurant.
Comfortable but basic bedrooms, excellent traditional breakfasts, dogs £2 a night.
(Recommended by Peter Meister, Tony and Maggie Harwood, Rona Murdoch)

Free house ~ Licensee Jane Pullee ~ Real ale ~ Bar food (lunchtime only) ~ Restaurant
(evening) ~ No credit cards ~ (01286) 870211 ~ Children in eating area of bar, restaurant
and family room ~ Dogs allowed in bar and bedrooms ~ Open 11-11(10.30 Sun); closed
Nov-Dec, Mon-Thurs Jan-Feb ~ Bedrooms: £30(£36B)/£60(£72B)

LLANDDAROG SN5016 Map 6
White Hart 🍺
Just off A48 E of Carmarthen, via B4310; aka Yr Hydd Gwyn

Brewed on site, five tasty Coles beers, four on handpump and one on air pressure,
are served at this pretty thatched pub (the full name is the White Hart Thatched Inn
and Brewery) using water from their own bore-hole: they produce ales, lagers and
stouts. The rooms are packed with bric-a-brac, lots of 17th-c welsh oak carving, a
tall grandfather clock, stained glass, a collection of hats and riding boots, china,
brass and copper on walls and dark beams, antique prints and even a suit of
armour. The heavily carved fireside settles by the huge crackling log fire are the best
place to sit. There are steps down to the high-raftered dining room, also
interestingly furnished; table skittles, shove-ha'penny and piped music. Generous
helpings of bar food from the servery include sandwiches (from £3.25), toasties and
baked potatoes (from £3.50), pizza (from £4.95), faggots, peas and gravy (£5.75),
ploughman's (from £6.50) and plaice and chips or pie of the day (£6.75). The
restaurant menu (which you can also eat from in the bar) includes japanese prawns
(£5.75), cheese and broccoli bake (£10.95), salmon fillet or pork loin (£11.95),
chicken chasseur (£12.95), steaks (from £13), and puddings (£3.95); the specials
board features roasts (£8.45), fish such as whole lemon sole (£11.95) and perhaps
16oz rib-eye steak or half a duck (£16.50); 5% surcharge on credit cards. A black
mark is that they charge 50p for a pint of tap water, though they do tell us that
they don't charge if you are eating. There are picnic-sets out on a terrace and a
children's play area; they can put a ramp in place for disabled access. Look out
for Homer the great dane. *(Recommended by Dr and Mrs A K Clarke, Don and*

Thelma Anderson, David and Nina Pugsley, Michael and Alison Sandy, P Price, Dave Irving, Mike Pugh)

Own brew ~ Licensees Marcus and Cain Coles ~ Real ale ~ Bar food (11.30-2, 6.30-10; 12-2, 7-9.30 Sun) ~ Restaurant ~ (01267) 275395 ~ Children in eating area of bar and restaurant ~ Open 11.30-3, 6.30-11; 12-3, 7-10.30 Sun

LLANDEILO SN6222 Map 6
Castle ◀

Rhosmaen Street (A483)

New licensees at this town pub are supporters of the 'slow food movement', and are putting emphasis on local ingredients, such as fish smoked in a local smokery. Bar food changes daily and might include sandwiches (from £3), warm salad of chorizo black pudding with roasted peppers (£4.50; £5.50 main), cheese and red onion pasty (£5), smoked trout salad (£6.25), citrus and coriander roast chicken leg with basmati rice and chilli sauce (£6.50), and welsh black sirloin steak (£13), with puddings such as Baileys bread and butter pudding (£3.95); the evening restaurant menu, also available in the bar, has more expensive dishes using similar ingredients, and includes a two-course set menu for £20, and they also do Sunday lunch in the no smoking restaurant. Six real ales are well kept on handpump, including Hancocks HB and usually Hop Back Summer Lightning, as well as four guests from brewers such as Adnams, Brakspears, Smiles and Wychwood; also farm cider tapped from the cask, and a decent choice of wines. The little tiled and partly green-painted back bar is perhaps the most interesting room, with a big fireplace and friendly locals sat in settles around the edge chatting; caricatures of locals hang on the walls alongside railway memorabilia; a TV in here is occasionally on for major sporting events or concerts. Freshly painted red, the front bar now has stripped bare-board floors, and a blue and green painted no smoking side area has lots of pictures; piped music in one room, cribbage, dominoes, Scrabble, chess and other board games. They plan to add a food servery facing into the courtyard area, and five ensuite bedrooms. More reports on the new regime, please. *(Recommended by the Didler, Dr and Mrs A K Clarke, Mike Pugh)*

Enterprise ~ Lease Gary Chambers ~ Real ale ~ Bar food (12-2.30, 5.30-7.30) ~ Restaurant ~ (01558) 823446 ~ Children in eating area of bar and restaurant ~ Dogs allowed in bar ~ Open 12-11(10.30 Sun)

LLANDUDNO JUNCTION SH8180 Map 6
Queens Head ⓨ ♀

Glanwydden; heading towards Llandudno on B5115 from Colwyn Bay, turn left into Llanrhos Road at roundabout as you enter the Penrhyn Bay speed limit; Glanwydden is signposted as the first left turn off this

The pleasant welcome and consistently high standards of food at this unassuming looking village pub bring readers back again and again. The menu changes every week and features lots of fresh local produce; well presented dishes could include soup (£3.95, tasty fish soup £4.35), open sandwiches (from £6.25), a generous seafood platter (£7.50; £16.50 main), home-made lasagne (£8.75), sausage and mash (£8.95), steak and mushroom pie or green thai chicken curry (£9.25), steak (from £12.50), rack of lamb (£13.25), and monkfish and prawn kebab (£13.50); efficient service; no smoking eating area. Despite the emphasis on dining, locals do pop in for a drink, and you'll find well kept Ind Coope Burton, Tetleys and a weekly guest beer on handpump, as well as decent wines (including some unusual ones and ten by the glass), 20 malt whiskies and good coffee. The spaciously comfortable modern lounge bar – partly divided by a white wall of broad arches – has brown plush wall banquettes and windsor chairs around neat black tables, and there's a little public bar; unobtrusive piped music. There are some tables out by the car park and you can rent the stone cottage across the road. *(Recommended by Revd D Glover, Yvonne and Mike Meadley, KC, Mr and Mrs Colin Roberts, Peter Fitton, Mr and Mrs A B Moore)*

Free house ~ Licensees Robert and Sally Cureton ~ Real ale ~ Bar food (12-2, 6-9; 12-9
Sun) ~ Restaurant ~ (01492) 546570 ~ Children over 7 in restaurant and eating area of
bar ~ Open 11.30-3, 6-11; 11.30-11 Sun

LLANFERRES SJ1860 Map 6 🏠

Druid 🛏

A494 Mold—Ruthin

Dating back to the 17th c and originally a farmhouse, this extended whitewashed
inn in the Alyn valley has glorious views across to the Clwydian Range; you can
enjoy the setting from tables outside at the front and from the broad bay window in
the civilised, smallish plush lounge. You can also see the hills from the bigger
beamed and characterful back bar, also carpeted (with quarry tiles by the log fire),
with its two handsome antique oak settles as well as a pleasant mix of more
modern furnishings; the attractive dining area is no smoking. You might meet the
resident three-legged cat, Chu. Welcoming staff serve a wide range of generous
changing bar food such as soup (£3.25), granary baps (£3.95), mussels (£4.95),
home-made lamb and leek pie (£8.50), mixed vegetables in a creamy chilli sauce or
asparagus wrapped in ham with cheese sauce (£8.95), steak and oyster pie or
chicken fillet with creamy chilli sauce (£9.95), thai-style fish curry or whole bass
with coriander butter (£10.95), and braised shoulder of welsh lamb with mint and
tarragon gravy (£13.95); they do lots of daily fresh fish specials. Burtonwood Bitter
and a couple of guests such as Highgate Davenports Bitter, Marstons Pedigree or
Youngs Waggle Dance are well kept on handpump; around two dozen malt
whiskies; a games room has darts and pool, along with dominoes, cribbage, shove-
ha'penny, bagatelle, board games, also TV and perhaps piped music. The bedrooms
have recently been refurbished. *(Recommended by KC, John and Helen Rushton,
G T Harding)*

Burtonwood (W & D) ~ Tenant James Dolan ~ Real ale ~ Bar food (12-2.30, 6-9.15;
12-9.30 Sat-Sun and bank hols) ~ Restaurant ~ (01352) 810225 ~ Children welcome ~
Dogs allowed in bar and bedrooms ~ Welsh sing-along first Sat of month ~ Open 12-3,
5.30-11; 12-11 Sat and bank hols; 12-10.30 Sun ~ Bedrooms: £40S/£55S

LLANFRYNACH SO0725 Map 6

White Swan ♀

Village signposted from B4558, off A40 E of Brecon – take second turn to village, which is also signed to pub

Popular with walkers, this pretty black and white dining pub is supremely well
placed for hefty climbs up the main Brecon Beacons summits as well as
undemanding saunters along the towpath of the Monmouthshire and Brecon Canal.
The charming secluded back terrace has stone and wood tables with a good choice
of sun or shade, and is attractively divided into sections by low plantings and
climbing shrubs, with views out over peaceful paddocks. There's a cheerfully
buoyant atmosphere in the bar side, which is on the right as you come in from the
back, the original part stripped stone and flagstones, with sturdy oak tables and
nice carver chairs in a polished country-kitchen style, a woodburning stove, and
leather sofas and armchairs in two groups around low tables. This part opens into
an apricot-walled high-ceilinged extension, light and airy, with bare boards and
different sets of chairs around each table. Well kept Hancocks HB and a guest from
a brewery such as Breconshire on handpump, good wines and coffees; piped music.
There's also a sizeable nicely furnished separate no smoking restaurant with heavy
beams, modern prints on its stripped stone walls, a big woodburning stove in a
huge fireplace. Readers like the food; served only at lunchtime, the bar menu could
include cockle and laver bread tart topped with baked egg and carmarthshire
ham (£5.45), duck liver terrine (£5.95), roasted red pepper stuffed with goats
cheese or filled baguettes and ciabattas (£6.95), ploughman's (£7.95), and gammon
steak and mash (£9.95), with puddings (£4.25) as well as specials such as supreme
of salmon (£11.95) and peppered loin of wild boar with herb mash (£13.95); there

is a more elaborate evening restaurant menu. Service is cheerful and attentive. *(Recommended by Bob and Valerie Mawson, Mrs C Sleight, Mrs M E Mills, David and Nina Pugsley, Elven Money)*

Free house ~ Licensee Richard Griffiths ~ Real ale ~ Bar food (lunchtime) ~ Restaurant ~ (01874) 665276 ~ Children welcome ~ Open 12-3, 7(6.30 Sat)-11; 12-3.30, 7-10.30 Sun; closed Mon (exc bank hols) and Tues, 1 Jan, 25-26 Dec

LLANGEDWYN SJ1924 Map 6
Green Inn
B4396 ¾ mile E of Llangedwyn

During the summer the attractive garden across the road from this 300-year-old pub comes into its own, with picnic-sets down towards the river, and they often have a marquee hosting such events as live country and western music. Inside the building it is nicely laid out with various snug alcoves, nooks and crannies, a good mix of furnishings including oak settles and attractively patterned fabrics, and a blazing log fire in winter. Besides well kept Tetleys, they've usually three changing guests such as Greene King Abbot, Oast House Old and St Georges Bitter on handpump and a decent wine list; darts, dominoes, TV, fruit machine and piped music. Straightforward bar food includes soup (£2.75), lunchtime sandwiches (£3.95), steak and kidney pie (£6.95), roast green peppers stuffed with broccoli and brie (£8.25), grilled whole plaice or 10oz rump steak (£9.95), and puddings (£3.95); they also do Sunday roasts (£7.95 or £9.95 for four courses) and Wednesday curry nights. A no smoking restaurant upstairs opens in the evening. As it's on a well used scenic run from the Midlands to the coast, the pub can get busy in summer. The pub has some fishing available to customers – day permit £4. More reports please. *(Recommended by Dave Braisted, Ian Phillips, GSB, Esther and John Sprinkle)*

Free house ~ Licensees Emma Richards and Scott Currie ~ Real ale ~ Bar food (12-2, 6-9; 12-9 Sat-Sun in summer) ~ Restaurant ~ (01691) 828234 ~ Children in eating area of bar and restaurant ~ Dogs allowed in bar ~ Open 12-3, 5-11; 12-11 Sat-Sun

LLANGOLLEN SJ2142 Map 6
Corn Mill ♀
Dee Lane, off Castle Street (A539) just S of bridge

From this imaginatively converted watermill there's a fascinating view from the external decking (set out with teak tables and chairs), cantilevered over the River Dee, rushing over rocks below; across the river you can see steam trains puffing away at the nearby station and maybe a horse-drawn barge on the Llangollen Canal, and attached to the mill itself a great waterwheel. Inside, it has been interestingly refitted with pale pine flooring on stout beams, a striking open stairway with gleaming timber and tensioned steel rails, mainly stripped stone walls, and quite a bit of the old mill machinery, pulleys and so forth. A lively bustling chatty feel greets you, with quick service from plenty of neat young staff, good-sized dining tables, big rugs, nicely chosen pictures (many to do with water) and lots of pot plants; the loft, wheelhouse and conservatory are no smoking. Good changing food could include cream of chicken soup with crusty bread (£3.75), sandwiches (from £4.25), pressed ham terrine or black pudding topped with welsh rarebit and with spiced apple sauce (£4.75), pressed ham terrine with piccalilli and crusty bread (£4.75), salmon and smoked haddock fishcakes (£7.95), ploughman's or welsh pork and herb sausage with spring onion mash (£8.25), pasta with artichoke hearts, sweet roast shallots and tomatoes (£9.25), stuffed pork loin with cider and leek sauce (£9.95), fried free-range chicken breast (£10.95), and 10oz rib-eye steak (£14.50), with puddings such as strawberry cheesecake (£4.25) or double chocolate muffin (£4.50). One of the two serving bars, away from the water, has a much more local feel, with pews on dark slate flagstones, daily papers, and regulars on the bar stools; piped music. Well kept Plassey and four or five guests such as Archers, Boddingtons, Caledonian Deuchars and Phoenix on handpump, more than 30 malt whiskies and a good wine choice that includes pudding wines.

(Recommended by John Wooll, Peter and Audrey Dowsett, Mike and Mary Carter, Pamela and Merlyn Horswell, MLR, John Whitehead, David Atkinson, Esther and John Sprinkle, Mrs Hazel Rainer, W Andrew, Lawrence Pearse, Mrs S E Griffiths, Brian Brooks, Bruce and Sharon Eden)

Brunning & Price ~ Licensee Andrew Barker ~ Real ale ~ Bar food (12-9.30(9 Sun)) ~ (01978) 869555 ~ Children in eating area of bar and restaurant ~ Open 12-11(10.30 Sun)

LLANNEFYDD SH9871 Map 6
Hawk & Buckle

Village well signposted from surrounding main roads; one of the least taxing routes is from Henllan at junction of B5382 and B5429 NW of Denbigh

This pleasant little 17th-c coaching inn has a splendid, peaceful position high up in the hills above Rhyl and Prestatyn, and from the well equipped, comfortable modern bedrooms you can see as far as the Lancashire coast – you may even be able to spot Blackpool Tower, some 40 miles away, and even Cumbria beyond. There's an eye-catching mosaic mural on the way through into the back bedroom extension. The long knocked-through black-beamed lounge bar has comfy upholstered settles around its walls and facing each other across the open fire, and a neat red carpet in the centre of its tiled floor. The buzzy locals' side bar has pool and unobtrusive piped music. Tasty bar food might include dishes such as soup (£3.25), steak pie (£7.95), fried chicken breast with leeks, mushroom and smoked bacon (£8.95), shoulder of roast lamb (£10.50), and half a roast duck (£13.95), with home-made puddings (£3.50); the dining room is no smoking. Brains SA is well kept on handpump and there is an extensive list of wines. More reports please. *(Recommended by Ian Saunders)*

Free house ~ Licensees David Topping and David Corlus ~ Bar food (not Sun or Mon evenings) ~ Restaurant ~ (01745) 540249 ~ Children in restaurant ~ Open 6-11; 12-3, 7-10.30 Sun ~ Bedrooms: £55S/£65S

MOLD SJ2465 Map 6
Glasfryn 🍽 🍷

N of the centre on Raikes Lane (parallel to the A5119), just past the well signposted Theatr Clwyd

The enthusiastic young licensees have struck a winning formula here at this upbeat bistro-style pub – just across the road from Theatr Clwyd – with interesting well prepared food served all day and a great choice of drinks. Open-plan rooms have both spaciousness and nice quiet corners, with an informal and attractive mix of country furnishings, and interesting decorations; about half the pub is no smoking. Besides a good variety of around a dozen wines by the glass and around 100 whiskies, they've well kept Flowers, Plassey Bitter, Thwaites, Timothy Taylors Landlord and three guests such as Caledonian Deuchars, Coniston Bluebird and Weetwood Old Dog on handpump. An inviting range of interesting reasonably priced bar food might include tomato and basil soup (£3.95), sandwiches (from £4.50), roasted red pepper filled with mozzarella and tomato (£4.75), peppered mackerel fillet with salad (£5.95), ploughman's (£7.50), asparagus and wild mushroom pastry, cold ham with free-range eggs and chips, or smoked haddock and salmon fishcakes (£8.25), braised shoulder of welsh lamb with mash, green beans and honey rosemary sauce (£12.95), grilled 10oz rump steak with pepper sauce and chips (£13.95), whole grilled lemon sole with potato and red onion salad (£15.50), and puddings such as cherry and almond tart with vanilla sauce, profiteroles with chocolate sauce or summer pudding (£4.50). Outside, sturdy timber tables on a big terrace give superb views to the Clwydian Hills – idyllic on a warm summer's evening. *(Recommended by John Wooll, June and Ken Brooks, Oliver and Sue Rowell, Brenda and Rob Fincham, Maurice and Della Andrew, Chris Flynn, Wendy Jones, Esther and John Sprinkle, KC, Brian Brooks)*

Brunning & Price ~ Manager James Meakin ~ Real ale ~ Bar food (12-9.30(9 Sun)) ~ (01352) 750500 ~ Children welcome away from bar until 6pm ~ Dogs allowed in bar ~ Open 11.30-11; 12-10.30 Sun

MONKNASH SS9270 Map 6

Plough & Harrow 🍺 £

Signposted Marcross, Broughton off B4265 St Brides Major—Llantwit Major – turn left at end of Water Street; OS Sheet 170 map reference 920706

It's worth coming here just to see the building, built with massively thick stone walls and dating back nearly nine centuries; it was originally part of a monastic grange. The dimly lit unspoilt but welcoming main bar (which used to be the scriptures room and mortuary) seems hardly changed over the last 70 years. There's a log fire in a huge fireplace with a side bread oven large enough to feed a village, as well as a woodburning stove with polished copper hot water pipes. The heavily black-beamed ceiling has ancient ham hooks, an intriguing arched doorway to the back, and a comfortably informal mix of furnishings that includes three fine stripped pine settles on the broad flagstones. The room on the left has lots of Wick rugby club memorabilia (it's their club room); daily papers, darts, dominoes, cribbage and piped music. Up to 11 well kept real ales on handpump or tapped from the cask include Archers Golden, Wye Valley Hereford Pale Ale, Worthington BB and thoughtfully sourced guest ales from brewers such as Cotswold Spring, Kelham Island and Tomos Watkins. Bar food could include soup (£2.95), filled baguettes (from £4.95), three cheese ploughman's or spaghetti bolognese (£5.95), beef cooked in Guinness or liver, bacon and mash (£6.95), cod and chips (£7.95) and puddings such as rhubarb crumble (£3.95); the specials menu might feature faggots and peas, lasagne or glamorgan sausages (all £5.95), and gammon and chips (£6.95). It can get crowded at weekends, when it's popular with families. It's in a peaceful spot not far from the coast near Nash Point, with an enjoyable walk from here down to the sea, where you can pick up a fine stretch of the coastal path along the top of remarkable candy-striped cliffs full of blow holes and fissures. There are picnic-sets in the front garden, which has a boules pitch, and they hold barbecues out here in summer. *(Recommended by Anthony Lee, David and Nina Pugsley, Ian Phillips, John and Joan Nash)*

Free house ~ Licensee Paula Jones ~ Real ale ~ Bar food (12-2(2.30 Sat-Sun), 6-9) ~ Restaurant ~ (01656) 890209 ~ Children in eating area of bar and restaurant ~ Dogs allowed in bar ~ Live music Sun evening ~ Open 12-11(10.30 Sun)

OLD RADNOR SO2559 Map 6

Harp 🛏

Village signposted off A44 Kington—New Radnor in Walton

On a hill looking across to the heights of Radnor Forest, this wonderfully evocative stone-built pub stands in the tiniest of villages – perhaps explaining why they don't open weekday lunchtimes. In the evening and at weekends chatty locals gather in the old-fashioned brownstone public bar, which has high-backed settles, an antique reader's chair and other elderly chairs around a log fire; cribbage, dominoes. The snug slate-floored lounge has a handsome curved antique settle and another log fire in a fine inglenook, and there are lots of local books and guides for residents. You'll find two well kept real ales on handpump from brewers such as Ansells and Bishops Castle; friendly, helpful service. Fairly simple bar food might include soup (£3.50), filled baguettes (from £4.95), ploughman's, home-made faggots or pork-and-herb sausages and mash (£5.95), lasagne or pasta and stilton bake (£6.95), cod and chips (£7.95), chicken wrapped in bacon with stilton sauce (£9.25) and rump steak (£10.95), with puddings such as home-made sticky toffee pudding (£3.50); on busy evenings, they sometimes don't serve food at all, so best to book. Note they don't allow large dogs in the bedrooms. Outside, there's plenty of seating – either under the big sycamore tree, or on the grass. The impressive church is worth a look for its interesting early organ case (Britain's oldest), fine rood screen and ancient font. *(Recommended by Peter Cole, Mr and Mrs M B Dalling, MLR, the Didler, Anne Morris)*

Free house ~ Licensees Erfyl Protheroe and Heather Price ~ Real ale ~ Bar food (12-2, 7-9) ~ Restaurant ~ (01544) 350655 ~ Children in eating area of bar and restaurant ~ Dogs allowed in bar and bedrooms ~ Open 6-11; 12-3, 6-11(10.30 Sun) Sat; 7pm evening opening winter; closed lunchtimes and Mon ~ Bedrooms: £30(£35B)/£55(£64B)

OVERTON BRIDGE SJ3542 Map 6

Cross Foxes 🍴 ♀

A539 W of Overton, near Erbistock

Much liked for its imaginative food, this very well run 18th-c coaching inn has daily changing food posted on a big blackboard by the entrance. As well as sandwiches (from £4.50) and ploughman's (£7.50), the choice might include soup (£3.75), salmon and haddock fishcake or baked stuffed aubergine with herb crust (£4.75; £8.50 as a main course), filo parcel filled with goats cheese and herbs with plum compote (£5), duck, cranberry and lemon terrine with pickled red cabbage (£5.25), pork sausages with leek mash and onion gravy (£8), steakburger with melted cheese and bacon with hand-cut chips and chunky coleslaw (£8.75), sweet potato, chickpea and spinach curry with mushroom pilau rice (£9.75), salmon supreme with crushed new potatoes, leeks and saffron cream sauce (£10.75), gressingham duck breast with celeriac mash, buttered carrots and port and cranberry sauce (£14), and puddings such as rich chocolate tart (£4.75). The River Dee sweeps past below, and the end room on the left (with big windows all round its walls) and picnic-sets out on a crazy-paved terrace give a great view of it. A grassy bank spreads down from the terrace, with a swing and slide – all safely fenced off from the water. The building is leased from Marstons (Wolverhampton & Dudley) by Brunning & Price, and has several linked but distinct areas, each with its own character, and all having framed pictures in abundance. Throughout is a good mix of individual tables in varying sizes, with big candles at night, grey carpet here, bare boards there, oriental rugs on quarry tiles elsewhere, mixed dining chairs in some places and built-in padded banquettes in others. They have good log fires, and the lighting is carefully thought out. They have well kept Banks's, Mansfield Riding, Marstons and a guest such as Caledonian Deuchars IPA on handpump, 25 malts, several armagnacs and a good changing choice of around 25 wines by the glass, and good coffee. Service is kind and efficient, and the lounge and conservatory are no smoking. *(Recommended by Mrs P J Carroll, Paul and Margaret Baker, Esther and John Sprinkle, Roger and Anne Newbury, Mike and Mary Carter)*

Brunning & Price ~ Manager Paul Fletcher ~ Real ale ~ Bar food (12-9.30(9 Sun)) ~ (01978) 780380 ~ Children under 5 until 7pm and under 11 until 8pm, in dining areas ~ Dogs allowed in bar ~ Open 12-11(10.30 Sun)

PEMBROKE FERRY SM9603 Map 6

Ferry Inn

Nestled below A477 toll bridge, N of Pembroke

Attractively set by the water's edge below the Cleddau Bridge, this was where the old ferry used to stop years ago, and aptly enough it has quite a nautical feel, with lots of seafaring pictures and memorabilia, a lovely open fire and good views over the water. Some comfortable seating areas are painted a cosy red. Bass, Felinfoel Double Dragon and a guest such as Sharps Eden Ale are well kept on handpump; fruit machine, board games and unobtrusive piped music. Following a refitting of the kitchen, they now do a wider selection of home-made specials (mostly fish), such as mussels (£7.50), plaice (£9.50), bean and celery chilli or local lamb with caerphilly cheese (£9.95) and brill (£15.30); other generously served bar food could include home-made hummous with pitta bread (£3.95), chicken liver pâté (£4.25), fillet of fried plaice (£6.75), curry (£7.25), steak and kidney pudding (£8.95) and minted lamb kebabs (£9.95), with puddings such as belgian chocolate tart or gooseberry and apple treacle crunch (£3.50). The pub is in an appealing spot overlooking the Cleddau estuary, and in warm weather it's nice to sit out on the terrace by the water. Note that the all day opening hours are limited to the summer holiday. More reports please. *(Recommended by Don and Thelma Anderson, Norman Lewis)*

Free house ~ Licensee Jayne Surtees ~ Real ale ~ Bar food (12-2, 7-9.30) ~ (01646) 682947 ~ Children in restaurant ~ Open 11.30-11; 12-10.30 Sun; 11.30-3, 6.30(7 Mon)-11; 12-2.30, 7-10.30 Sun winter

PORTHGAIN SM8132 Map 6

Sloop

Off A487 St Davids—Fishguard

On the Pembrokeshire Coast Path and in a tiny harbour village tucked into a cove, this lovely old white-painted pub is crammed with seafaring memorabilia. Inside, the walls of the plank-ceilinged bar are hung with lobster pots and fishing nets, ships' clocks and lanterns, and even relics from wrecks along this stretch of the coast. Down a step, another room leads round to a decent-sized eating area, with simple wooden chairs and tables, cushioned wall seats, and a freezer with ice-creams for children; well kept Brains Rev James, Felinfoel and Worthingtons on handpump, and wine by the glass in three different sized glasses. Rather than having a number for food service, many of the tables are named after a wrecked ship. Straightforward bar food (with children's portions for some items) includes soup (£3.80), lunchtime baguettes (from £4.40), moules marinière (£5.90), vegetable lasagne (£6.90), ploughman's (£7.45), crab salad (£11.90, if available), steak (from £13.75), and daily specials (perhaps unavailable during the summer holiday) such as steak and kidney pie (£7.95) and lamb shank on creamy mash (£13.95); the dining area is no smoking. There's a well segregated games room (used mainly by children) which has a fruit machine, juke box, pool, dominoes and Scrabble. It can get very busy here in summer, when they may extend food serving times. Tables on the terrace overlook the harbour, with outdoor heaters for cooler weather. *(Recommended by Mrs Julie Thomas, R Michael Richards, John and Enid Morris, R E Greenhalgh, B and F A Hannam, Mike Pugh, Tony and Betty Parker, Glenwys and Alan Lawrence, Pat and Stewart Gordon, Mark and Mary Fairman, Comus and Sarah Elliott)*

Free house ~ Licensee Matthew Blakiston ~ Real ale ~ Bar food (12-2.30, 6-9.30) ~ (01348) 831449 ~ Children welcome ~ Open 9.30-11; 9.30-10.30 Sun

PRESTEIGNE SO3265 Map 6

Radnorshire Arms

High Street; B4355 N of centre

In a quiet street of an enchanting little border town stands this striking half-timbered hotel, built in Elizabethan times for Christopher Hatton, one of Elizabeth I's favourite courtiers. Past renovations have revealed secret passages and priest's holes, with one priest's diary showing he was walled up here for two years. Although it's now part of a small chain of hotels, it's full of individuality and historical charm – a great place for morning coffee or afternoon tea. Discreet well worn-in modern furnishings blend in pleasantly with venerable dark oak panelling, latticed windows and elegantly moulded black oak beams (some decorated with horsebrasses); piped music. You'll find three well kept beers on handpump such as Cains, a welsh brew such as Felinfoel Double Dragon and Shepherd Neame Lancaster Bomber, and they've wine from Herefordshire as well as several malt whiskies. Friendly staff serve dishes from a bar menu which includes soup (£3.85), triple sandwiches (£4.15), welsh rarebit or baguettes (£4.95), carvery (£7.95), and puddings such as home-made apple. orange and cinnamon crumble (£3.45). There are lots of tables on an elegant sheltered flower-bordered lawn, which used to be a bowling green. More reports please. *(Recommended by Pam and David Bailey)*

Free house ~ Licensee Philip Smart ~ Real ale ~ Bar food ~ Restaurant ~ (01544) 267406 ~ Children in eating area of bar and restaurant ~ Dogs allowed in bar and bedrooms ~ Open 11-3, 5-11; 11-11 Sat; 12-10.30 Sun ~ Bedrooms: £68B/£86B

Please keep sending us reports. We rely on readers for news of new discoveries, and particularly for news of changes – however slight – at the fully described pubs. No stamp needed: The Good Pub Guide, FREEPOST TN1569, Wadhurst, E Sussex TN5 7BR or send your report through our web site: www.goodguides.co.uk

RAGLAN SO3608 Map 6

Clytha Arms 🍷 🍴 🛏

Clytha, off Abergavenny road – former A40, now declassified

They offer an excellent choice of drinks at this beautifully positioned old country inn, in extensive and well cared-for grounds on the edge of Clytha Park, and the food is generally much enjoyed by readers too. The building has long verandahs and diamond paned windows and inside it's comfortable, light and airy with scrubbed wood floors, pine settles, big faux fur cushions on the window seats by big windows, a good mix of old country furniture and a warming coal fire. Don't miss the murals in the lavatories. Run by charming licensees, it's the sort of relaxed place where everyone feels welcome, from locals who've walked here for a pint in the spotlessly kept bar (solidly comfortable furnishings and a couple of good fires), to diners in the contemporary linen-set restaurant. The reasonably priced bar menu includes sandwiches (from £3.95), soup (£5.25), cider baked ham with potato salad (£6.95), mussels (£7.50), wild boar sausages with potato pancakes (£7.95), wild mushroom omelette or chicken breast with parmesan crust (£8.50), and smoked haddock with local cheese (£9.25). The restaurant menu is pricier and more elaborate. An impressive choice of drinks includes Bass, Felinfoel Double Dragon and Hook Norton Old Hooky, three interesting changing guest beers (around 300 different ones a year) from brewers such as Caledonian, Carters and Fullers, an extensive wine list with about a dozen or so by the glass, a good choice of spirits, farm cider and even home-made perry. The restaurant and lounge are no smoking; darts, shove-ha'penny, boules, table skittles, bar billiards, cribbage, dominoes, draughts and chess. The two friendly labradors are Beamish and Stowford and there's an english setter. The bedrooms are very comfortable. *(Recommended by Guy Vowles, James Morrell, William Orchard, the Didler, Nigel and Karen Smith, Richard Haw, Ann and Colin Hunt, M and J Lindsay, Steve Whalley, Mike and Mary Carter, Lynda Payton, Sam Samuells, Mike Pugh, Ian Phillips, Alan and Paula McCully, Terry and Linda Moseley, MLR, John and Joan Nash, Geoff and Marianne Millin, David and Nina Pugsley, Andy Trafford, Louise Bayly, Simon Cleasby)*

Free house ~ Licensees Andrew and Beverley Canning ~ Real ale ~ Bar food (12.30-2.15, 7-9.30; not Sun evening or Mon) ~ Restaurant ~ (01873) 840206 ~ Children in eating area of bar and restaurant ~ Dogs allowed in bar ~ Open 12-3, 6-11; 12-11 Sat; 12-10.30 Sun; closed Mon lunchtime ~ Bedrooms: £50B/£70B

RED WHARF BAY SH5281 Map 6

Ship 🍷 🍴

Village signposted off B5025 N of Pentraeth

Sit on one of the benches placed against the white wall of this slate-roofed inn and you get a superb sweeping view of vast tidal sands enclosed by dunes and rounded headlands around a big bay on the north coast of Anglesey. Inside is old-fashioned and interesting, with lots of nautical bric-a-brac in big welcoming rooms on each side of the busy stone-built bar counter, both with long cushioned varnished pews built around the walls, glossily varnished cast-iron-framed tables and roaring fires. The restaurant and two bars are no smoking; piped Classic FM (in lounge only). They have more than 50 malt whiskies, as well as well kept Adnams, Brains and Tetleys, as well as a guest from a brewer like Greene King on handpump, and there's a wider choice of wines than is usual for the area (with about ten by the glass). The interesting menu (which includes quite a few seafood dishes) includes lunchtime sandwiches (from £3.45), soup (£3.50), welsh perl wen cheese with fruit chutney, celery, apple salad and tomato bread (£6.95), poached salmon and smoked trout salad (£7.95), baked shoulder of welsh spring lamb (£13.95), and seafood platter for two (£19.95), with specials such as fried fillet of local bass with creamed fennel (£13.50) and grilled rib-eye of welsh beef (£13.95); puddings such as rhubarb and strawberry crème (£4.55). You'll need to arrive early for a table at the weekend when it can get quite crowded, and they will ask to keep your credit card behind the bar in a locked numbered box (to which you are given the key) if you want to run a tab. *(Recommended by Yvonne and Mike Meadley, Revd D Glover, R T J and J J Hubbard, J Roy Smylie, Dr and Mrs M E Wilson, Tony and Maggie Harwood, Gerry and Rosemary Dobson)*

Free house ~ Licensee Neil Kenneally ~ Real ale ~ Bar food (12-2.30, 6-9; 12-9 Sat-Sun) ~ Restaurant ~ (01248) 852568 ~ Children in eating area of bar and restaurant ~ Open 11-11; 12-10.30 Sun

RHYD-Y-MEIRCH SO2907 Map 6
Goose & Cuckoo 🍺

Upper Llanover signposted up narrow track off A4042 S of Abergavenny; after ½ mile take first left, then keep on up (watch for hand-written Goose signs at the forks)

Near the end of a tiny lane a long way above the Usk valley, this welcoming, simple place is well positioned for walks along the nearby Monmouthshire and Brecon Canal towpath or over the hilltops towards Blorenge and Blaenavon. It's basically one small rustically furnished room with a woodburner in an arched stone fireplace, but what makes it special, apart from the setting, is the warmth of welcome you get from the friendly licensees. They have well kept Evans and Jones Premium Welsh and Wadworths Henrys and one or two guests (often local ones) such as Bullmastiffs or Felinfoel Double Dragon on handpump, and more than 75 whiskies, and good coffees; daily papers, cribbage, darts, dominoes, draughts, shove-ha'penny, quoits and boules. A fairly short choice of enjoyably simple home-made food includes home-baked rolls (from £1.80), bean soup (£2.40), baked potatoes or lasagne (£5.50), a variety of ploughman's (£6), turkey and ham pie, liver and bacon casserole, spaghetti bolognese or chilli con carne (all £6.50), with specials such as steak and kidney pie or corn beef pie (£6.50) and home-made puddings (£2.50); you may have to wait. A small picture-window extension makes the most of the view down the valley (unfortunately spoilt to some extent by a new building). There are a variety of rather ad hoc picnic-sets out on the gravel below, and the licensees keep sheep, geese and chickens. The bedroom has two single beds. *(Recommended by Terry and Linda Moseley, Bruce Bird, Charles and Pauline Stride, Guy Vowles, Louise Barrett, John Fiander, John and Gloria Isaacs, Mike Pugh)*

Free house ~ Licensees Michael and Carol Langley ~ Real ale ~ Bar food (12-2.30, 7-9) ~ No credit cards ~ (01873) 880277 ~ Children welcome ~ Dogs allowed in bar ~ Open 11.30-3, 7-11; 11.30-11 Sat; 12-10.30 Sun; closed Mon exc bank hols ~ Bedroom: £25S/£50S

ROSEBUSH SN0729 Map 6
Tafarn Sinc

B4329 Haverfordwest—Cardigan

You're likely to hear Welsh speakers at this thoroughly quirky maroon-painted corrugated iron shed, built in 1876 as a rudimentary hotel serving the adjacent railway halt for a long-abandoned railway serving a now-defunct quarry beneath the Preseli hills. The halt itself has been more or less re-created, even down to life-size dummy passengers waiting out on the platform, and the sizeable garden is periodically enlivened by the sounds of steam trains chuffing through – actually broadcast from a replica signal box. Though not exactly elegant, inside is really interesting, almost a museum of local history, with sawdust on the floor. With an appealingly buoyant atmosphere, the bar has plank panelling, an informal mix of chairs and pews, woodburners, and well kept Cwrw Tafarn Sinc (brewed specially for the pub), and a weekly changing guest such as Ridleys Prospect on handpump; piped music, darts and TV; some readers have reported that the staff could be more welcoming at times. Basic food includes home-made faggots with onion gravy, vegetable lasagne, or lamb burgers (all £7.90), steaks (from £9.90), and puddings (£3.90). There's a no smoking dining room. *(Recommended by Phil and Sally Gorton, the Didler, John and Enid Morris, Alan and Paula McCully)*

Free house ~ Licensee Brian Llewelyn ~ Real ale ~ Bar food (12-2, 6-9) ~ Restaurant ~ (01437) 532214 ~ Children in eating area of bar and restaurant ~ Open 12-11(10.30 Sun); closed Mon

SAUNDERSFOOT SN1304 Map 6
Royal Oak ♀ ◀
Wogan Terrace (B4316)

This well run and friendly village local is a good place to come for fish dishes (the owners have also recently opened up a tapas bar next door); booking is advised during the holiday season, particularly for the outside tables (under heaters) that overlook the harbour. The food choice features about ten fresh fish dishes a day, served with a good range of sauces, and with prices varying depending on the season: pint of prawns (£6.25), beer-battered haddock (£9.25), tuna steak topped with garlic prawns (£13.95), hake (£14.95) and grilled whole bass (£17.95). Other food includes lunchtime sandwiches (from £3.95), home-made lasagne (£8.45), local pork and garlic sausages or curry (£8.95), cauliflower and broccoli bake (£9.95), sizzling platter of chicken and ribs (£10.95), lamb cannon or 8oz fillet steak (£16.95), with puddings such as cheesecake of the day or lemon mousse (from £3.95); two-course Sunday lunch (£8.50, three courses £10.50). Service is pleasant and attentive. There's a cheerful atmosphere in the dining area and carpeted lounge bar, which has captain's chairs and wall banquettes. Frequented by chatty locals, the small public bar has a TV; piped music. Around five well kept real ales on handpump include Greene King Abbot and IPA, Ind Coope Burton, Worthington BB, and a couple of guests such as Greene King Old Speckled Hen and Plassey Dragons Breath. They've also over 30 malt whiskies and an interesting choice of wines (lots of new world ones), with about a dozen by the glass. The dining room is no smoking; they hope to make the entire pub no smoking by 2006. *(Recommended by the Didler, P Price, Brian and Ruth Archer, Alastair Stevenson)*

Free house ~ Licensees T S and T L Suter ~ Real ale ~ Bar food (12-2.30, 6-9.30) ~ Restaurant ~ (01834) 812546 ~ Children in restaurant ~ Dogs allowed in bar ~ Open 11-11; 12-10.30 Sun

SHIRENEWTON ST4894 Map 6
Carpenters Arms
Mynydd-bach; B4235 Chepstow—Usk, about ½ mile N

Originally a smithy, this quaint stone-built pub has blacksmith's bellows hanging from the planked ceiling of one of the interconnecting rooms, and here and there you'll also find chamber-pots, an attractive Victorian tiled fireplace, and a collection of chromolithographs of antique royal occasions. Furnishings run the gamut too, from one very high-backed ancient settle to pews, kitchen chairs, a nice elm table, several sewing-machine trestle tables and so forth; it's popular with locals (especially for Sunday lunch); shove-ha'penny, cribbage, dominoes, backgammon, and piped pop music. Bass, Fullers London Pride, Marstons Pedigree and Shepherd Neame Spitfire are kept under a light blanket pressure on handpump with an occasional seasonal guest. Straightforward bar food typically includes soup (£2.50), spicy king prawns (£4), steak and mushroom pie or spinach and mushroom in filo pastry (£6.95), trout (£9.95) and puddings (£2.95). Tables are set outside at the front, where there are hanging baskets in summer; no smoking family room. New licensees took over in 2005; more reports on the new regime please. *(Recommended by BOB, Mr and Mrs J Brown, Stephen and Jean Curtis, Ian Phillips)*

Punch ~ Lease Gary and Sandra Hayes ~ Real ale ~ Bar food (12-9.30; 12-3, 6-9.30 in winter) ~ (01291) 641231 ~ Children in family room ~ Dogs welcome ~ Open 12-11; 11-10.30 Sun; 12-3, 6-11(10.30 Sun) in winter

---

Real ale to us means beer which has matured naturally in its cask – not pressurised or filtered. We name all real ales stocked. We usually name ales preserved under a light blanket of carbon dioxide too, though purists – pointing out that this stops the natural yeasts developing – would disagree (most people, including us, can't tell the difference!)

SKENFRITH SO4520 Map 6

Bell ♀ ⇐

Just off B5421, NE of Abergavenny and N of Monmouth

The meals are the thing here: certainly not cheap, but consistently good, using named local suppliers of carefully chosen fresh ingredients such as welsh black beef. It might include roast tomato soup with basil oil (£4.50), pavé of watermelon, feta and pine nut salad with rocket oil (£5.95), goats cheese and walnut panna cotta with redcurrant jam (£6.50), fillet of line caught john dory, taboulet and fricassee of fresh peas, broad beans and chargrilled artichokes or all-spice marinated duck breast, pavé of quince, red onion jam and orange and madeira reduction (£17.50), roast rump of lamb with basil mash and a sauce of button onion and tomato (£17.95), half a cornish lobster (£19.50), and puddings such as chocolate and Baileys tart with mint pesto and white chocolate ice-cream, summer berry tian with lemon crème fraîche or lime and mango cheesecake with orange reduction (£5.50). The owners are welcoming and enthusiastic, and service is cheerful and attentive. The big back bare-boards dining area is very neat, light and airy, with dark country-kitchen chairs and rush-seat dining chairs, church candles and flowers on the dark tables, canary walls and a cream ceiling, and brocaded curtains on sturdy big-ring rails. The flagstoned bar on the left has a rather similar décor, with old local and school photographs, and a couple of pews as well as tables and café chairs, and well kept Breconshire Golden Valley, Freeminer, Hook Norton Best, and Timothy Taylors Landlord on handpump from an attractive bleached oak bar counter. They have good wines by the glass and half-bottle, and make good coffee. There may be piped nostalgic pop music in here, and besides a well lit pool table a corner games room has darts and perhaps a children's trike. The lounge bar on the right, opening into the no smoking dining area, has a nice Jacobean-style carved settle and a housekeeper's chair by a log fire in the big fireplace. The atmosphere is relaxed and gently upmarket (the lavatories are labelled Loos). There are good solid round picnic-sets as well as the usual rectangular ones out on the terrace, with steps up to a sloping lawn; it's a quiet spot. Across the access road is a pretty bridge over the River Monnow. *(Recommended by Alec and Barbara Jones, Pamela and Merlyn Horswell, Bernard Stradling, Ron and Sheila Corbett, Mark and Mary Fairman, Duncan Cloud)*

Free house ~ Licensee Janet Hutchings ~ Real ale ~ Bar food (12-2.30, 7-9.30(9 Sun)) ~ Restaurant ~ (01600) 750235 ~ Children welcome but must leave restaurant by 8pm ~ Dogs allowed in bar and bedrooms ~ Open 11-11; 12-10.30 Sun; may close Mon in winter ~ Bedrooms: /£95B

ST HILARY ST0173 Map 6

Bush £

Village signposted from A48 E of Cowbridge

Tucked behind the village church, this cosily old-fashioned 16th-c stone and thatch pub had a new licensee in 2005 and we hope it continues its strong previous form. Comfortable and welcoming, it has a lovely log fire, stripped old stone walls, and windsor chairs around copper-topped tables in the low-beamed carpeted lounge bar, while the other bar is pubbier with old settles and pews on aged flagstones, and a pleasant mix of locals and visitors. Bass, Greene King Old Speckled Hen, Hancocks HB and two or three guests such as Greene King Abbot and Felinfoel Double Dragon are well kept on handpump or tapped from the cask; TV, cribbage, dominoes and subdued piped music. Good value enjoyable bar food includes sandwiches (from £2.25), soup (£2.95), laver bread and bacon (£3.95), trout fillet grilled with bacon (£5.50), tagliatelle provençale or baked ham and parsley sauce (£6.95), chicken curry or steak and ale pie (£7) and sirloin steak (£10). They also have a restaurant menu which is available in the bar, with items such as seared tiger prawns with thai-style noodles (£5.95), roast red mullet (£8.95), roast rump of welsh lamb with spiced couscous (£9), and roast duck breast, beluga lentils and chorizo with caramelised pear (£11.50). The restaurant and lounge bar are no smoking during food service. There are tables and chairs in front, and more in the back garden; reasonable disabled access. Reports on the new regime please. *(Recommended by David and Ruth Shillitoe, David and Nina Pugsley, Ian Phillips, Glenwys and Alan Lawrence)*

Punch ~ Tenant Phil Thomas ~ Real ale ~ Bar food (12-2.30, 6.30-9.30) ~ Restaurant ~ (01446) 772745 ~ Children welcome ~ Open 12-11(10.30 Sun)

TINTERN SO5200 Map 6
Cherry Tree ◖

Pub signed up narrow Raglan road off A466, beside Royal George; parking very limited

With excellent beer and a warm welcome from the staff, this 16th-c cottage-like pub continues to be popular with readers, most of whom have found the recent extension to blend sympathetically with the original. The original beamed and stone-built bar has a walnut serving counter in one area and a good open fire in another; cribbage, darts, cards, dominoes and piped music; it leads into the new bar area; a slate floor extends throughout. Generous good value food, made using lots of fresh local ingredients, might include sandwiches (from £2), soup (£3.50), ham and eggs, mushroom and ricotta tortellini, vegetarian lasagne or spicy meat balls with couscous (£5.95), beef and ale pie (£7.95); they now also do a range of curries, such as chicken madras (£7.95), prawn and spinach saag, swordfish and king prawn kashmiri or tuna and prawn yellow thai curry (£8.95); changing daily specials could include wild boar in star anise or roasted butternut squash (£8.95), and lamb shanks in rosemary and raspberry (£9.95). Tapped straight from the cask, Hancocks HB is well kept alongside up to five changing guests from brewers such as Bath, Cottage, Sharps and Wye Valley. They also serve farm cider, and home-made country wines, and have two beer and cider festivals a year. It's in a quiet and attractive spot, yet only half a mile or so from the honey-pot centre of Tintern, and there are tables out in a charming garden, and on a green patio; disabled access is difficult. Look out for Guinness the dog. *(Recommended by the Didler, Pete Baker, Kerry Law, Simon Smith, John and Gloria Isaacs, R T and J C Moggridge, Tim and Ann Newell, Piotr Chodzko-Zajko, LM, A S and M E Marriott, Bruce Bird)*

Free house ~ Licensees Jill and Steve Pocock ~ Real ale ~ Bar food (12-7 Mon-Thurs; 12-5 Fri-Sun) ~ Restaurant ~ (01291) 689292 ~ Children under 12 in eating area of bar until 8pm ~ Dogs allowed in bar ~ Live music twice a month ~ Open 12-11; 12-3, 5-11 winter ~ Bedrooms: /£60B

TRELLECK SO5005 Map 6
Lion ◖

B4293 6 miles S of Monmouth

Often busy, this stone-built pub has a wide choice of food, and as the landlord's parents are Hungarian the menu features some interesting authentic hungarian specialities such as sweet peppers stuffed with minced pork and rice with sweet tomato sauce (£9.75) and erdö pulyka – fried diced turkey in creamy dill sauce (£11.25). Bar food includes two sausages and chips (£4.75), ploughman's (£5.50), vegetarian hotpot (£7.30), plaice and chips (£7.50), chicken tikka masala (£7.75), and home-made cottage pie (£8.25), while specials (£9-£13.95) could include tuna steak, mixed grill or potato and red cabbage layer cake. A step leads up to the no smoking dining area. The unpretentious open-plan bar has one or two black beams in its low ochre ceiling, a mix of furnishings including some comfortable brocaded wall seats and tub chairs, old red plush dining chairs, a hop-hung window seat, varying-sized tables, and log fires in two fireplaces opposite each other. A small fish tank occupies a wall recess, and there's another bigger one in the lobby by the lavatories; piped music, cribbage, dominoes and shove-ha'penny. A colourful galaxy of pump clips in the porch and on a wall show the range of rapidly changing guest beers from brewers such as Archers and Cottage, which are well kept alongside Bath SPA and Wye Valley Butty Bach, and they've around 30 malt whiskies. One or two readers have found the choice of beers restricted and availability of food erratic. There are some picnic-sets and an aviary out on the grass. The pub is opposite the church, and close by is a group of prehistoric standing stones; bedrooms in a nearby cottage. *(Recommended by Mike Pugh, Charles and Pauline Stride, Piotr Chodzko-Zajko, LM, Derek and Sylvia Stephenson, Bruce Bird, Guy Vowles)*

Free house ~ Licensees Tom and Debbie Zsigo ~ Real ale ~ Bar food (12-2, 6(7 Mon)-9.30; not Sun evening) ~ Restaurant ~ (01600) 860322 ~ Children welcome ~ Dogs allowed in bar ~ Live music on bank hols ~ Open 12-3, 6(7 Mon)-11; 12-3, 6.30-11 Sat; 12-3 Sun; closed Sun evening ~ Bedrooms: £40S/£65S

TY'N-Y-GROES SH7672 Map 6

Groes 🍴 ♀ ⇌

B5106 N of village

They specialise in Welsh and British food (not cheap) at this elegantly romantic hotel: ingredients are locally sourced, such as lamb and salmon from the Conwy valley, and game birds come from local shoots; they bake their own bread and grow their own herbs. Run by the same family for the last 20 years, and said to have been the first Welsh pub to be properly licensed – in 1573 – it enjoys magnificent views over the Vale of Conwy and the distant mountains. Past the hot stove in the entrance area, the spotlessly kept, homely, rambling, low-beamed and thick-walled rooms are nicely decorated with antique settles and an old sofa, old clocks, portraits, hats and tins hanging from the walls, and fresh flowers. A fine antique fireback is built into one wall, perhaps originally from the formidable fireplace in the back bar, which houses a collection of stone cats as well as cheerful winter log fires; the restaurant, family room and conservatory are no smoking. There's also an airy verdant no smoking conservatory. Well presented dishes might include soup (£3.95), sandwiches (from £4.75), freshly made linguini pasta, smoked chicken and carbonara sauce (£6.50), sausages, bacon and mash or welsh hill lamb shepherd's pie (£7.95), haddock, prawn and mushroom mornay (£8.75), poached salmon with hollandaise sauce (£10.65), and steaks (from £13.95), with daily specials such as game casserole (£10.50), local lamb steak (£11.75) and bass (£12.50). As well as puddings such as white chocolate and vanilla bean panna cotta or sticky toffee pudding (from £4.75), they do delicious home-made ice-creams, with a few unusual flavours such as lemon curd and poppy seed, or rose petal. Ind Coope Burton and Tetleys are well kept on handpump, and they've a good few malt whiskies, kir, and a fruity Pimms in summer; light classical piped music at lunchtimes, nostalgic light music at other times and a live harpist every now and then. The neatly kept, well equipped bedroom suites (some have terraces or balconies) have gorgeous views, and in summer it's a pleasure to sit outside in the pretty back garden with its flower-filled hayricks, and there are also some seats on the flower-decked roadside. They now also rent out a well appointed wooden cabin (the High Cabin), idyllically placed nearby. *(Recommended by Spider Newth, Tony and Betty Parker, Brenda and Rob Fincham, Mike and Jayne Bastin, A J Bowen, Jacquie and Jim Jones, Terry and Linda Moseley, Dennis Jenkin, Sarah and Peter Gooderham, Brian and Janet Ainscough, J C Poley, Dr Pete Crawshaw, Andy Sinden, Louise Harrington, Jo Lilley, Simon Calvert, Mike and Mary Carter, Margaret and Jeff Graham)*

Free house ~ Licensee Dawn Humphreys ~ Real ale ~ Bar food (12-2.15, 6.30-9) ~ Restaurant ~ (01492) 650545 ~ Children in eating area of bar and family room; must be over 10 in restaurant ~ Dogs welcome ~ Open 12-3, 6-11; 12-11 Sat-Sun ~ Bedrooms: £79B/£95B

USK SO3801 Map 6

Nags Head 🍴 ♀

The Square

'The Key family make your visit very special; why can't all pubs be as kind and welcoming to customers?' remarked one reader of this old coaching inn, run by the same family for over 37 years. With a friendly chatty atmosphere, the beautifully kept traditional main bar has lots of well polished tables and chairs packed under

its beams (some with farming tools), lanterns or horsebrasses and harness attached, as well as leatherette wall benches, and various sets of sporting prints and local pictures – look out for the original deeds to the pub. Tucked away at the front is an intimate little corner with some african masks, while on the other side of the room a passageway leads to the pub's own busy coffee bar (open between Easter and autumn). Built in the old entrance to the courtyard, it sells snacks, teas, cakes and ice-cream, and tables spill out from here on to the front pavement. A simpler room behind the bar has prints for sale, and perhaps a knot of sociable locals. Generously served dishes (concentrating on local produce) could include home-made soup (£3.90), frogs legs in hot provençal sauce or whitebait (£6), sausages (£6.50), home-made steak pie (£7), vegetable bake or glamorgan sausage (£7.75), delicious rabbit pie (£8), and interesting specials including seasonal game dishes (lovely on a cold winter evening), such as wild boar steak in apricot and brandy sauce (£13), pheasant in port (£14) and stuffed partridge (£15.50). You can book tables, some of which may be candlelit at night; nice proper linen napkins. They do 15 wines by the glass (nice glasses), along with well kept Brains SA, Buckleys Best and Rev James on handpump, 12 malt whiskies and Thatcher's Gold farm cider; quiet classical piped music; two rooms are no smoking. The centre of Usk is full of pretty hanging baskets and flowers in summer, and the church is well worth a look.
(Recommended by Dr Oscar Puls, Dr and Mrs C W Thomas, Brian Brooks, Eryl and Keith Dykes, Ann and Colin Hunt, Terry and Linda Moseley, Joyce and Maurice Cottrell, Roy and Lindsey Fentiman, Ian Phillips, Mike Pugh, Prof Keith and Mrs Jane Barber, Mr and Mrs A Williams, A S and M E Marriott, Pam and Alan Neale, Bruce Bird, Eileen McCall)

Free house ~ Licensee the Key family ~ Real ale ~ Bar food (12-2, 5.30-9.30) ~ Restaurant ~ (01291) 672820 ~ Children welcome ~ Dogs welcome ~ Open 11-2.30, 5.30-11; 12-3, 6-10.30 Sun

---

LUCKY DIP

Besides the fully inspected pubs, you might like to try these Lucky Dips recommended to us and described by readers (if you do, please send us reports: www.goodguides.co.uk).

ANGLESEY

BEAUMARIS [SH6076]

George & Dragon [Church St]: Cheery bar with nice local atmosphere, good value food, well kept Robinsons, friendly staff, Tudor beams and timbers, good lighting and gleaming brass, original fireplace and section of wattle and daub wall, welcoming landlord happy to show rare bits of wall paintings and painted beams upstairs; may be live entertainment *(Dr and Mrs M E Wilson)*
Liverpool Arms [Castle St]: Friendly pub/hotel with good helpful service, banquettes in alcoves, naval memorabilia, sweet little snug, wide range of good value generous fresh food all day, Brains ale; piped music; bedrooms (each named for an admiral) with own bathrooms, nice spot nr seafront *(Mr and Mrs Bentley-Davies)*
Sailors Return [Church St]: Bright cheery partly divided open-plan bar with comfortable banquettes and open fire, some emphasis on generous good value food from sandwiches and baguettes up inc a dish of the day, smiling helpful service, well kept Bass and perhaps one or two other real ales, decent wines, bookable tables in no smoking dining area; unobtrusive piped music;

children welcome in eating area, dogs in bar, comfortable bedrooms *(Terry and Linda Moseley, Paul Humphreys, Michael and Alison Sandy, Keith and Chris O'Neill, LYM, John and Helen Davey, Gerry and Rosemary Dobson, J C Brittain-Long)*

MENAI BRIDGE [SH5572]

Bridge Inn [bridge roundabout, Telford Rd (A5/A545); aka Tafarn y Bont]: Lots of rooms inc back dining room and conservatory, attractive décor with wood floors and pine much in evidence, bay windows, interesting choice of enjoyable food, good service, Banks's, Marstons Pedigree and a guest beer; smart chrome and wood furniture out on back terrace, more seating out in front *(Tony and Maggie Harwood)*
Liverpool Arms [St Georges Pier]: Cheerful low-beamed four-roomed local, well kept Courage Directos, Flowers IPA and Original and a guest such as Charles Wells Bombardier, decent wines, quick friendly service, wide choice of home-made food inc some rather different dishes, generous sandwiches, interesting mostly maritime photographs and prints, no smoking

panelled dining room, popular conservatory catching evening sun; one or two terrace tables *(John Tavernor, Pete and Kate Holford)*

RHOSCOLYN [SH2675]

White Eagle [off B4545 S of Holyhead]: Welcoming newish licensees, splendid remote setting with panoramic views towards Snowdonia from no smoking dining area, enjoyable food (all day in summer) inc good fresh seafood specials, four well kept interesting changing ales such as Marstons Bitter, Smiles Slap & Tickle and Weetwood Eastgate, friendly prompt service; children welcome, good large garden, lane down to beach, open all day in summer *(Brian and Anna Marsden)*

CLWYD

BODFARI [SJ0970]

☆ *Dinorben Arms* [off A541, near church]: Attractive black and white hillside pub nr Offa's Dyke, three well worn beamed and flagstoned rooms, old-fashioned settles, three open fires, a glassed-over old well, lots of hanging whisky-water jugs, over 260 malt whiskies, popular food from sandwiches and bar snacks to restaurant dishes and hot and cold buffet with carve-yourself joints, welcoming landlord, quick friendly service, well kept Banks's, Marstons Pedigree and a guest such as Batemans XB, good wines, darts and pool, light and airy garden room; fruit machine, TV, piped classical music; children welcome, grassy play area, charming views from pretty brick terraces, open all day wknds *(LYM, Esther and John Sprinkle, KC)*

CARROG [SJ1143]

Grouse [B5436, signed off A5 Llangollen—Corwen]: Small unpretentious pub with stunning views over River Dee and beyond from bay window, well kept Lees ales, good choice of well prepared food all day from good sandwiches, friendly staff and regulars, local pictures, pool in games room; piped music, narrow turn into car park; wheelchair access, tables in pretty walled garden with sunny terrace, handy for Llangollen steam railway, bedrooms *(John Oates, Denise Walton, Gill and Tony Morriss, Michael and Jenny Back)*

CHIRK [SJ2937]

Bridge Inn [Chirk Bank, B5070 S (just over Shrops border)]: Friendly old local short walk below Llangollen Canal nr aqueduct, enjoyable quickly served bar food, well kept Banks's and related ales, water-jugs on beams, back eating area; children welcome, picnic-sets on raised terrace *(Peter and Audrey Dowsett)*

Golf Club-House [Chirk Marina, on Shrops Union Canal W of village past station and castle]: Not a pub but open to all, popular with canal users, real ale, good value bar meals, friendly staff, spacious dining areas *(Peter and Audrey Dowsett)*

COLWYN BAY [SH8278]

Mountain View [Mochdre, S off A55—A470 link rd]: Roomy big-windowed recently refurbished modern pub with pine tables and chairs in divided bar, generous reliable food, full Burtonwood beer range kept well, children in no smoking eating area, darts, dominoes, table football, pool; piped music, games machine, juke box; tables on front terrace, bright window boxes *(KC, LYM)*

CROSS LANES [SJ3746]

Cross Lanes Hotel [Bangor Rd (A525 Wrexham—Bangor-is-y-coed)]: Good atmosphere and well kept Plassey real ales in hotel bar with good adjoining brasserie; bedrooms *(Esther and John Sprinkle)*

DYSERTH [SJ0579]

New Inn [Waterfall Rd (B5119)]: Welcoming helpful service, well kept Banks's Original, Mansfield Cask and Marstons Pedigree and Burton, enjoyable home-made food with proper pastry for the pies, several rooms served from central bar *(Pete and Kate Holford)*

GRAIANRHYD [SJ2156]

Rose & Crown [B5430 E of Ruthin]: Welcoming new landlord in two-room local in remote part of Clwydian Hills, enjoyable good value food, well kept real ales, two rooms both with coal fires, interesting 1950s bric-a-brac, darts, dominoes, pool; may be well reproduced piped music; children welcome, picnic-sets outside with pretty hill views, has been cl lunchtimes Mon-Thurs *(LYM, KC)*

GRAIG FECHAN [SJ1454]

Three Pigeons [signed off B5429 S of Ruthin]: Extended family-run two-bar largely 18th-c inn with enjoyable inexpensive food from baguettes, baked potatoes and basket meals up, well kept Bass, Greene King IPA, Hancocks HB and a guest beer, decent wines by the glass, games room, no smoking restaurant with great country views; children allowed if eating, big garden with barbecue, terraces and same views, good walks *(Ted and Lyn Clarkson)*

GWYDDELWERN [SJ0746]

☆ *Ty Mawr*: Medieval half-timbered stone-built inn with massive stone fireplace, throne-like chairs and wooden settles, lots of bottled traditional and belgian beers, wide choice of tasty and interesting reasonably priced food, prompt friendly service, erratic sloping floor upstairs with charming restaurant; children welcome *(Emma and Will, Amanda Greenwood, Rona Murdoch)*

HALKYN [SJ2070]

Blue Bell [Rhosesmor Rd (B5123)]: 18th-c, in fine spot on Halkyn Mountain, remarkable views in clear weather, warm welcome, real fires, particularly well kept changing ales inc one brewed in Wales for the pub, food from light dishes to substantial meals using local supplies *(anon)*

HIGHER KINNERTON [SJ3261]
Royal Oak [Kinnerton Lane, off A55/A5104 SW of Chester; also signed off A483]: Ancient picturesque coaching inn with good choice of interesting food inc fresh fish all day in dining area, decent wines, friendly staff and atmosphere, lots of small rooms, log fires, settles and cosy armchairs, low oak beams hung with jugs, teapots, copper kettles and chamber-pots, interesting collection of soda syphons; tables in small garden, barbecues and play area *(Peter Kingsford)*

HOLYWELL [SJ1876]
Calcot Arms [A5026]: Wide choice of reasonably priced well presented food inc good value small-appetite dishes, pleasant staff, Thwaites real ale; views across River Dee *(KC)*

LLANELIAN-YN-RHOS [SH8676]
☆ *White Lion* [signed off A5830 (shown as B5383 on some maps) and B5381, S of Colwyn Bay]: 16th-c inn with friendly and helpful family service, huge choice of good reasonably priced bar food from sandwiches and baguettes to good value full meals, well kept Marstons Bitter, Pedigree and a guest such as Caledonian Deuchars IPA, good range of wines, lots of malt whiskies, traditional flagstoned snug bar with antique settles and big fire, dining area on left with jugs hanging from beams, teapots above window, further comfortable more spacious no smoking dining area up broad steps, grotto filled with lion models, dominoes, cribbage; piped music; children in eating areas, rustic tables outside, good walking nearby, comfortable bedrooms *(Michael and Jenny Back, LYM)*

LLANGOLLEN [SJ2342]
Sun Trevor [Sun Bank (A539 towards Trevor)]: Spectacular views down over River Dee and canal, enjoyable reasonably priced home-made food from sandwiches up in attractive inglenook bar and small restaurant, inglenook fireplace, friendly efficient landlord and staff, well kept real ales and good wine choice, no piped music; handy for walkers *(Peter and Audrey Dowsett, Helen Clarke)*

LLOC [SJ1476]
Rock [St Asaph Rd (A5151)]: Bright décor, interesting choice of enjoyable food in busy bar with good log fire or (if you have a main dish) dining room – freshly made so can take a while *(KC)*

PONTBLYDDYN [SJ2761]
New Inn [A5104, just S of A541 3 miles SE of Mold]: Interesting choice of good food in unassuming building's attractive upstairs dining room, good service with attention to detail; piped music *(KC)*

RUTHIN [SJ1258]
Castle Hotel [St Peters Sq]: Small town hotel with several bars, interesting foreign beers and cocktails in back one, notable cooking at attractive prices, pleasant small restaurant *(John Wooll)*

TAL-Y-CAFN [SH7871]
☆ *Tal-y-Cafn Hotel* [A470 Conway—Llanwrst]: Cheerful bustle in comfortable lounge bar with jugs hanging from ceiling and log fire in big inglenook, wide choice of good value satisfying home cooking in huge helpings, Bass, Boddingtons and Tetleys; children welcome, seats in spacious garden, pleasant surroundings, handy for Bodnant Gardens *(LYM, KC)*

WREXHAM [SJ3350]
Horse & Jockey [Hope St]: Small thatched pub (a surprising sight in centre), several small linked low-beamed areas around central servery with changing ales such as Greene King Old Speckled Hen, Plassey and Tetleys, good choice of bottled beers, local lager, friendly helpful staff and locals, reasonably priced pubby lunchtime food from sandwiches and baked potatoes up, family area and back dining area; sports TV, may be piped music; open all day *(Martin Grosberg)*

DYFED

ABERAERON [SN4462]
Royal Oak [North Rd (A487)]: Good atmosphere in big invitingly cosy and popular front lounge, good food with some interesting specials, friendly prompt service, well kept beers, good choice of wines by the glass *(Jackie and Alan Moody, Andy Sinden, Louise Harrington)*

ALLTWALIS [SN4431]
Masons Arms [A485 about 7 miles N of Carmarthen]: Attractively furnished, with welcoming helpful staff, enjoyable food, well kept real ale such as Batemans, good coffee, nicely arranged tables; piped music; open all day *(Martin Griffin)*

ANGLE [SM8703]
☆ *Old Point House* [signed off B4320 in village, along long rough waterside track; East Angle Bay]: Idyllic spot overlooking Milford Haven, dating from 14th c, unspoilt but comfortable, with good food (almost all fresh local fish), well kept Felinfoel Double Dragon, flagstoned bar with open fire, small lounge bar, lots of charm and character, run by local lifeboat coxswain – many photographs; plenty of tables and ancient slate seats out by the shore *(Stephen and Jean Curtis, Maurice and Della Andrew, Glenwys and Alan Lawrence, Douglas and Ann Hare)*

BANCYFELIN [SN3218]
Fox & Hounds [off A40 W of Carmarthen; High St]: Some emphasis on good popular food in dining lounge/restaurant, also locals' bar; well priced beers *(Stuart Lane)*

BONCATH [SN2038]
Boncath Inn [B4332 Cenarth—Eglwyswrw]: Large village pub, attractive traditional décor with farm tools and photographs of former railway, good changing choice of four or five well kept if not cheap real ales, enjoyable food; prominent pool table;

open all day *(Colin Moore, Helene and Richard Lay)*

BOSHERSTON [SR9694]

☆ *St Govans Country Inn* [off B4319 S of Pembroke]: Cheerful, friendly and comfortably modernised, with good climbing photographs and murals of local beauty spots in big open-plan bar, log fire in large stone fireplace, helpful service, well kept changing ales such as Adnams, Brains Rev James, Fullers London Pride and Tetleys, cheap unpretentious food, no smoking dining area, dominoes, board games, pool (winter only); piped music, TV, fruit machine; children and dogs welcome, picnic-sets on front terrace, good value spotless bedrooms, good breakfast, handy for water-lily lakes, beach and cliffy coast *(Matthew Lidbury, LYM, Peter Davey, Mike Pugh, Richard Haw, John R Muller, Comus and Sarah Elliott)*

BROAD HAVEN [SM8616]

☆ *Druidstone Hotel* [N of village on coast rd, bear left for about 1½ miles then follow sign left to Druidstone Haven – inn a sharp left turn after another ½ mile; OS Sheet 157 map ref 862168, marked as Druidston Villa]: Happily informal converted country house in a grand spot above the sea, an individualistic favourite of the editors for well over 20 years, ruled out of the main entries only by its club licence (you can't go for just a drink and have to book to eat or stay there); terrific views, inventive home cooking with fresh ingredients and a leaning towards the organic, folksy cellar bar with well kept Worthington BB tapped from the cask, good wines, country wines and other drinks, ceilidhs and folk jamborees, chummy dogs (dogs welcomed), all sorts of sporting activities from boules to sand-yachting; attractive high-walled garden, spacious homely bedrooms, even an eco-friendly chalet, cl Nov and Jan, restaurant cl Sun evening *(John and Enid Morris, Mike Pugh, Robert Wivell, LYM, Colin Moore)*

CAIO [SN6739]

☆ *Brunant Arms* [off A482 Llanwrda—Lampeter]: New licensees in unpretentious and interestingly furnished village pub, five well kept changing real ales, decent house wines, good log fire, rather more elaborate food choice (can take a while), stripped stone public bar with games inc pool; juke box, TV; children and dogs welcome, small Perspex-roofed verandah and lower terrace, bedrooms with own bathrooms, has been open all day wknds; more reports on new regime please *(LYM, Geoff and Carol Thorp, Richard Siebert)*

CAPEL BANGOR [SN6580]

☆ *Tynllidiart Arms* [A44]: Quaint roadside cottage with woodburner in big stripped-stone bare-boards bar, has its own tiny brewery (in what used to be the gents') with four well kept ales inc a Stout, good friendly landlord, nice atmosphere, limited good well presented food, also large upstairs dining

room; well behaved children and dogs allowed *(Sion Edwards)*

CAREW [SN0403]

☆ *Carew Inn* [A4075, just off A477]: Cheerful old beamed pub with back garden overlooking spectacular castle ruins, outdoor heaters, good play area, more tables out in front, unpretentious old-fashioned furnishings inside, with interesting prints, well kept ales such as Brains and Worthington, reasonably priced food, friendly service, cosy no smoking upstairs dining room, traditional games; piped music, live Thurs and summer Sun; children and dogs welcome, open all day wknds and summer *(V Brogden, P Price, Mr and Mrs A H Young, the Didler, LYM, Colin Moore, Brian and Jacky Wilson)*

CARMARTHEN [SN4120]

Coracle [Cambrian Pl, by market]: Roomy and attractive, with slate-tiled floor, enjoyable food, well kept and well priced real ale, pleasant upper mezzanine dining area *(Stuart Lane)*

Drovers Arms [Lammas St]: Small family-run hotel with homely and civilised front bar, easy chairs in lounge, good value standard food, perhaps a well kept ale such as Felinfoel Double Dragon, welcoming service, back restaurant; comfortable bedrooms, good breakfast inc cockles and laver bread *(Stuart Lane)*

Queens [Queen St]: Two lively rooms either side of bar, good value low-priced food all day from tempting sandwiches up, well kept Bass, Worthington and guest beers, efficient friendly service (long-serving tenant also has adjoining Hamiltons wine bar/restaurant); very busy wknd evenings; children welcome, tables on small back terrace, open all day *(Stuart Lane)*

Rose & Crown [Lammas St]: Well refurbished, with enjoyable food, Bass, Fullers London Pride and Greene King Old Speckled Hen, good service, pleasant décor; back terrace tables *(Stuart Lane, Martin Griffin)*

Spread Eagle [Queen St]: Big upstairs open bar/restaurant very popular since full-scale refurbishment, enjoyable good value food; keg beer *(Stuart Lane)*

Stag & Pheasant [Spilman St]: Large open-plan pub with enjoyable food and particularly well kept Worthington and guest ales; open all day *(Stuart Lane)*

Yr Hen Dderwyn [King St]: Wetherspoons with enjoyable food and low-priced beer in good surroundings; children welcome, roadside tables *(Stuart Lane)*

CENARTH [SN2641]

Three Horseshoes [A484 Cardigan—Newcastle Emlyn]: Cosy and attractive beamed pub, generous reasonably priced popular food inc fresh seafood, well kept Bass and Buckleys, thatched former medieval brewhouse at the back; open all day (not winter Sun afternoons), seats in garden and on front terrace, nice village, lovely salmon falls nearby *(Jackie and Alan Moody)*

CILGERRAN [SN1943]
Pendre Inn [off A478 S of Cardigan; High St]: Friendly local under new licensees again, good atmosphere, straightforward food, well kept real ale, pleasant service, massive medieval stone walls and broad flagstones *(LYM, John and Enid Morris, Neil F Mason, Colin Moore, David and Nina Pugsley)*

CILYCWM [SN7540]
Neuadd Fawr Arms: Welcoming traditional village local in interesting building with simple old-world furnishings, good range of real ales, good choice of reasonably priced fresh homely food in bar and dining room, friendly staff and lots of cheerful Welsh-speaking regulars; good spot by churchyard above River Gwenlas, among lanes to Llyn Brianne *(BB, Geoff Palmer, Pat and Stewart Gordon)*

CROESGOCH [SM8430]
Artramont Arms [A487 Fishguard—St David's, by Porthgain turn]: Friendly roadside pub, light and bright, with efficient service, good choice of sensibly priced fresh food, well kept Brains SA and Felinfoel Double Dragon, daily papers, large bar with pool, small snug, separate dining area with charming conservatory; dogs welcome, good enclosed garden for children *(Mike Pugh, Alan and Paula McCully)*

CROSS [SN6564]
Rhos yr Hafod [B4577/B4337]: Helpful welcoming new landlord, decent food with some emphasis on evening dining, well kept Brains Buckleys, comfortable seating, old Cardiganshire pictures, book swap; attractive outside seating area *(B and M Kendall)*

CWM GWAUN [SN0035]
Dyffryn Arms [Cwn Gwaun and Pontfaen signed off B4313 E of Fishguard]: Classic unspoilt country tavern in lush green valley, very relaxed, basic and idiosyncratic, with veteran landlady (her farming family have run it since 1840, and she's been in charge for one-third of that time); 1920s front parlour with plain deal furniture inc rocking chair and draughts boards inlaid into tables, coal fire, well kept Bass served by jug through a hatch, pickled eggs, time-warp prices, Great War prints and posters, darts; pretty countryside, open more or less all day (may close if no customers) *(Phil and Sally Gorton, Colin Moore, RWC, the Didler, LYM, Giles and Annie Francis)*

DALE [SM8105]
Griffin: Friendly no-frills waterside pub by Milford Sound, popular with yachtsmen, sailboarders and field studies groups; two smallish bars, plenty of wood and sailing pictures, usual food inc seafood, real ales such as Brains Rev James, welcoming service, good view of estuary, boats and ships; children allowed when eating, can sit out on sea wall *(Norma and Noel Thomas)*

DINAS [SN0139]
Ship Aground [A487]: 18th-c smugglers' pub done up with nautical trappings, helpful landlady, good value food from proper old-fashioned ploughman's up, wide evening choice inc local fish and seafood, well kept Brains, some interesting ropework; open all day in summer *(BB, Pat and Robert Watt)*

FELINDRE FARCHOG [SN0939]
Olde Salutation [A487 Newport—Cardigan]: Smart, friendly and spacious antiqued pub with well kept local James Williams and guest beers, good value food from toasties and baguettes to bass, local beef and seasonal local sea trout, wide choice in evening restaurant, good landlord, comfortable matching seats and tables; bedrooms, fishing and good walks by nearby River Nevern *(Blaise Vyner, Colin Moore)*

FISHGUARD [SM9537]
☆ *Fishguard Arms* [Main St (A487)]: Tiny front bar with a couple of well kept changing real ales served by jug at unusually high counter, warmly friendly staff, open fire, rugby photographs, traditional games in back room, may be tasty bar nibbles Sun; has been open all day Sun, cl Mon *(LYM, the Didler, Brian and Ruth Archer, Patrick Renouf)*

Royal Oak [Market Sq, Upper Town]: Darkly beamed and stripped stone front bar leading through panelled room to big no smoking picture-window dining extension, pictures commemorating defeat here of bizarre french raid in 1797, three well kept ales from bar counter carved with welsh dragon, decent well priced generous food, woodburner; bar billiards, games machine; pleasant terrace *(the Didler, Mike Pugh, BB, Anne Morris)*

☆ *Ship* [Newport Rd, Lower Town]: Cheerful atmosphere and seafaring locals in dim-lit red-painted local nr old harbour, friendly staff, well kept Bass tapped from the cask, homely food from sandwiches and cawl up, coal fire, lots of boat pictures, model ships; children welcome, toys provided *(LYM, Brian and Ruth Archer)*

FRESHWATER EAST [SS0298]
Freshwater Inn: Old village pub brightened up under friendly new licensees, popular food, two or three real ales, lovely bay views from lounge; dining room, pool in public bar; well behaved children welcome, tables in nice garden, open all day summer (busy evenings then) *(Angie Coles, Douglas and Ann Hare)*

HAVERFORDWEST [SM9515]
☆ *Georges* [Market St]: Behind front eclectibles shop and small coffee bar/teashop area is long narrow celtic-theme bar with small stable-like booths – not a pub, but has well kept Brains SA and Rev James and a guest beer, interesting reasonably priced wines esp new world, pleasantly relaxed but efficient service even when busy, informal and relaxed rather whimsical atmosphere; larger upstairs restaurant, generous interesting

home-made food using good meat, fresh veg and good fish and vegetarian ranges; no dogs; back crafts shop/showroom, lovely walled garden, open 10.30-5.30 Mon-Thurs, 10.30-10.30 Fri/Sat *(V Brogden, David and Nina Pugsley, Mike Pugh)*

HERBRANDSTON [SM8607]

Taberna: Well kept beer, friendly people, impressive straightforward food in bar and restaurant *(Stephen and Jean Curtis, John and Enid Morris)*

LAMPETER [SN5748]

Castle Hotel [High St]: Well kept Brains IPA and SA at sensible prices, enjoyable food from good value snacks to full meals *(Martin Griffin)*

Kings Head [Bridge St]: Good helpings of enjoyable low-priced food, well kept Brains and guest ales such as Shepherd Neame Bishops Finger; garden tables, reasonably priced bedrooms *(Martin Griffin)*

LAMPHEY [SN0100]

Dial: Victorian pub with big light and airy bar and adjacent family dining room with show of decorative plates, good varied home-made food inc some enterprising specials, friendly helpful staff, real ales, good value house wine, games room with pool; piped music; small front terrace, bedrooms *(Ian Moody)*

LAWRENNY [SN0106]

Lawrenny Arms: Hard-working new licensees, enjoyable food inc some interesting dishes, well kept Brains Rev James; terrace tables, attractive spot *(R M Corlett)*

LETTERSTON [SM9429]

Harp [Haverfordwest Rd (A40)]: Roadside dining pub with dark wood and careful décor in smart lounge bars and restaurant, good generous food inc lots of fresh fish, well kept Tetleys, friendly obliging service; open all day *(Patrick Renouf)*

LITTLE HAVEN [SM8512]

☆ *St Brides Hotel* [in village itself, not St Brides hamlet further W]: Compact and unassuming stripped-stone bar and linking dining area, new owners doing good range of enjoyable popular food (busy evenings even into Oct), well kept Brains Rev James and Worthington, good wine choice, friendly staff, open fire, no piped music, interesting well in back corner grotto may be partly Roman; Pay & Display parking; big good value bedrooms, some in annexe over rd by sheltered sunny terraced garden, short stroll from the sea *(Tim and Liz Sherbourne, John and Enid Morris, LYM, Mr and Mrs A H Young, Roger and Cynthia Calrow)*

Swan [Point Rd]: This attractive seaside pub, a popular main entry, was boarded up, evidently for sale, as we went to press in summer 2005 *(LYM)*

LLANDDAROG [SN5016]

☆ *Butchers Arms*: Cheery bustle in heavily black-beamed local with three smallish eating areas rambling off central bar, good generous home cooking from sandwiches

through hearty country dishes to some interesting specials and good profiteroles (menu willingly adapted for children), friendly helpful staff, well kept Felinfoel Best and Double Dragon tapped from the cask, good wines by the glass, conventional pub furniture, fairylights and candles in bottles, woodburner in biggish fireplace; piped pop music; tables outside, delightful window boxes *(BB, B and F A Hannam, Dr and Mrs A K Clarke, Tom Evans, JWAC, J Iorwerth Davies)*

LLANDEILO [SN6226]

Angel [Salem; unclassified rd N, off B4302]: Attractive open-plan U-shaped bar, busy and well run, with good blackboard menu of home-made bar food using fresh produce from baguettes, well filled pitta breads and lunchtime bargain specials up, more imaginative dishes in back bistro, four real ales inc local Evan Evans, friendly helpful service; tables outside, lovely country setting *(Mike Pugh, Anne Morris)*

☆ *Cottage* [Pentrefelin (A40 towards Carmarthen)]: Welcoming and roomily refurbished open-plan beamed dining pub, huge log fire and lots of horsey prints, plates and brasses, good generous well priced food from sandwiches and baked potatoes through homely favourites to some interesting dishes, local fish and welsh black beef, well kept real ales, decent house wines, friendly service, well appointed back dining room; piped music *(Norman and Sarah Keeping, Tom Evans)*

White Horse [Rhosmaen St]: Friendly 16th-c local with several rooms, popular for its particularly well kept ales such as Breconshire and Charles Wells Bombardier, occasional live music; tables outside front and back *(the Didler)*

LLANDOVERY [SN7634]

Red Lion [Market Sq]: One basic welcoming room with no bar, well kept Brains Buckleys and a guest beer tapped from the cask, jovial landlord; cl Sun, may cl early evening if no customers *(the Didler, BB, RWC)*

LLANFIHANGEL-AR-ARTH [SN4539]

Cross [B4336/B4459 N of Pencader]: Well kept Fullers London Pride, enjoyable food inc bargain Sun lunch *(Martin Griffin)*

LLANGAIN [SN3613]

Pant yr Athro [B4312 towards Llanstephan]: Enjoyable food in pub/restaurant attached to main house used for weddings, great coast views to the Gower *(Stuart Lane)*

Pant yr Derwen [School Rd (B4312 S of Carmarthen)]: Emphasis on good varied food, freshly cooked, also small bar with real ale; attractive village location *(anon)*

LLANSTEPHAN [SN3510]

Castle: Cosy pleasant local with low-priced simple tasty food, real ale, long-serving owners, attractive open-plan restaurant area; tables on front terrace *(Stuart Lane)*

Sticks: Doing well under newish management, long attractive bar with real ale, popular food, compact restaurant;

newly done bedrooms with own bathrooms
(Stuart Lane)

LLANYCHAER [SM9835]

Bridge End [Bridge St (B4313 SE of
Fishguard)]: Former watermill in attractive
hamlet, friendly enthusiastic staff, one or
two real ales, good choice of food from
lunchtime snacks to full evening meals inc
popular roast Sunday lunches *(Colin Moore)*

LLWYNDAFYDD [SN3755]

✩ *Crown* [off A486 S of Newquay]: Stripped
stone, red plush banquettes and copper-
topped tables, popular bar food, well kept
Flowers IPA and Original and one or two
guest beers, friendly helpful service, big
woodburner, darts in winter; piped music;
children in family room, picnic-sets and
terrace in pretty garden with good play area,
lane down to attractive cove, cl Sun evening
in winter *(Gene and Kitty Rankin,
Mr and Mrs W E Cross, Brian Mills,
B and M Kendall, LYM)*

MATHRY [SM8732]

✩ *Farmers Arms* [Brynamlwg, off A487
Fishguard—St David's]: Creeper-covered
pub with beams, flagstones and dark
woodwork in carefully renovated homely
bar, enjoyable low-priced food freshly made
by landlady from good crab sandwiches to
reasonably priced hot dishes esp fish,
cheerful welcoming landlord and staff, well
kept Brains Rev James, Felinfoel Double
Dragon and a guest beer, fair range of
reasonably priced wines, log fire, children
welcome in large no smoking dining vine-
covered conservatory; piped music; tables in
small walled garden, open all day, cl till 4
Mon-Weds in winter *(David Field,
Robert Wivell, Alan and Paula McCully,
Patrick Renouf)*

NEW QUAY [SN3859]

Black Lion [Glanmor Terr]: Pub favoured by
Dylan Thomas, perched on cliffside above
little harbour, friendly staff and cheap food
in neat bar; superb sea view from big garden
with terrace picnic-sets *(Keith John Ryan)*

NEWPORT [SN0539]

Castle [Bridge St]: Rambling local with well
kept real ales, typical pub food and some
more interesting home-made specials,
generous helpings, fair prices, pleasant
service; handy for Parrog Estuary walk
(especially for birdwatchers) *(Mike Pugh)*

✩ *Golden Lion* [East St (A487)]: Nicely
refurbished pub with good local atmosphere
in cosy series of linked rooms, generous
enjoyable well priced food from sandwiches
to local welsh black beef, several well kept
real ales, some distinctive old settles,
children allowed in popular dining rooms
and games bar; good disabled access and
facilities, very good value comfortable
bedrooms, big breakfast *(Keith John Ryan,
LYM)*

✩ *Royal Oak* [West St (A487)]: Bustling and
well run sizeable pub with friendly helpful
landlady and staff, good choice of good
generous food inc lunchtime light dishes,

local lamb and lots of authentic curries, Tues
OAP lunch, well kept Greene King Old
Speckled Hen and guest beers, children
welcome in no smoking lounge with eating
areas, separate stone and slate bar with pool
and games, upstairs dining room; some
tables outside, an easy walk from the beach
(Colin Moore, Helene and Richard Lay)

PUMSAINT [SN6540]

Dolaucothi Arms: Well kept Bass and a
guest beer, enjoyable food, low prices,
pleasant helpful service and friendly
landlord, comfortable lounge, pleasantly
plain bar, restaurant *(John and
Joan Nash)*

RHANDIRMWYN [SN7843]

Royal Oak: 17th-c stone-built inn in remote
and peaceful walking country, comfortable
bar with log fire, up to six changing well
kept ales, enjoyable reasonably priced food
inc welsh black beef, big dining area (can
book); 60s music on free juke box; dogs
and children welcome, plenty of hanging
baskets and flowering tubs, hill views from
front garden and from good big bedrooms,
handy for Brecon Beacons *(Chris Power,
Geoff Palmer, BB, JWAC)*

ROBESTON WATHEN [SN0915]

Bridge Inn [just off A40 – B4314 towards
Narberth]: Cottagey and comfortable,
entirely no smoking now, with wide choice
of enjoyable reasonably priced food inc
popular Sun lunch, friendly attentive staff,
well kept real ale, large eating area; children
welcome *(John and Enid Morris)*

SOLVA [SM8024]

Harbour Inn [Main St]: Basic three-bar
beamed pub in delightful setting by small
sailing harbour, splendid views, wide choice
of reasonably priced food from quickly
served sandwiches up, Greene King Old
Speckled Hen, lots of local pictures, staff
helpful to families and cope well with the
holiday crowds, children's area with pool
table; piped music; plenty of tables on
suntrap terrace, bedrooms, open all day
*(David Field, B and F A Hannam,
Mike Pugh, Norma and Noel Thomas)*

Ship [Main St, Lower Solva]: Quaintly set in
attractive if touristy harbourside village,
interesting low-beamed bar with big log fire,
lots of old photographs, nautical artefacts
and bric-a-brac, well kept real ales,
enjoyable generous food with emphasis on
fish, friendly attentive service, big back
family dining room; games machine; little
garden has play area over stream, public car
park just down road *(Dave Irving)*

ST DAVID'S [SM7525]

✩ *Farmers Arms* [Goat St]: Bustling old-
fashioned low-ceilinged pub by cathedral
gate, cheerful and properly pubby, mainly
drinking on the left and eating on the right,
central servery with real ales such as Brains
Rev James and Worthington, wide choice of
good value straightforward food from
baguettes and ploughman's with local
cheeses to steaks, busy young staff, chatty

landlord and locals; pool room, TV for rugby; cathedral view from large tables on big back suntrap terrace, and lack of car park means no tour bus groups (though the surfers swell the numbers in summer), open all day *(Simon Watkins, David Field, Dave Irving, Michael and Alison Sandy, Giles and Annie Francis)*

Grove [High St]: Bars with own side entrance behind hotel and restaurant, good value generous food, well kept Brains Rev James and local farm cider, log fires; piped music may be loud; garden tables, bedrooms, open all day *(Dave Irving)*

ST DOGMAELS [SN1646]

Ferry: Old stone building with spectacular views of Teifi estuary and hills from picture-window dining extension; now taken over by Brains and run by pleasant new couple, three real ales inc Greene King Old Speckled Hen, decent wines inc small bottles, good value food from sandwiches up (in summer best to book for evenings and popular Sun lunch), character bar, pine tables, nice clutter of bric-a-brac with many old advertising signs; children welcome, tables out on decking *(LYM, Gene and Kitty Rankin, Colin Moore, Helene and Richard Lay)*

STACKPOLE [SR9896]

☆ *Stackpole Inn* [off B4319 S of Pembroke]: Good modern cooking in relaxing L-shaped dining pub on four levels, partly no smoking, with well kept Bass, Brains Rev James and Felinfoel Single and Double Dragon, simple décor, neat light oak furnishings, ash beams in low ceilings, shove-ha'penny and dominoes; piped music; children welcome, disabled access and facilities, tables out in attractive gardens, good woodland and coastal walks in the Stackpole estate, open all day (Sun afternoon break), plans for four-bedroom annexe *(LYM, Geoff Palmer, Comus and Sarah Elliott)*

TENBY [SN1300]

Hope & Anchor [Julian St]: Pleasant pub nr seafront, friendly staff, generous well presented food from sandwiches (inc crab from Caldy Island) to fresh fish, three or four changing guest beers, coal fire; children welcome in upstairs dining room, tables out on terrace, open all day *(Brian and Ruth Archer)*

TREGARON [SN6859]

Talbot [The Square]: Character bar with cosy rooms off, long-serving landlord and friendly thoughtful service, good range of food from snacks to full meals, well kept Greene King and other real ales; pleasant garden, interesting town *(Ann and Colin Hunt)*

TRESAITH [SN2751]

☆ *Ship*: Tastefully decorated bistro-style pub on Cardigan Bay with magnificent views of sea, beach, famous waterfall, perhaps even dolphins and seals; good generous home-made food from ploughman's with local cheeses to local fish, well kept Buckleys and

two changing guest beers often from Ceredigion, good photographs, no smoking dining area; tables with heaters out on decking stepped down to garden *(David and Nina Pugsley, Helene and Richard Lay)*

TREVINE [SM8332]

Ship [off A487 at Croes-Goch or via Penparc; Ffordd y Felin]: Nice atmosphere, with reasonably priced food inc fresh local crab, friendly helpful staff *(B Pike, Pat and Robert Watt)*

GWENT

ABERGAVENNY [SO2914]

Angel [Cross St, by Town Hall]: Well restored bar with thriving atmosphere, efficient pleasant bar staff, some big comfortable settees, lovely bevelled glass behind servery, good service, popular restaurant and adjacent lounge areas *(Pamela and Merlyn Horswell)*

Coliseum [Lion St/Frogmore St]: Steps up to modest Wetherspoons cinema conversion, very light and spacious, with low-priced real ales and good coffee, pleasant service, their usual food, lots of panelling, raised areas one end; wheelchair lift *(Mike Pugh)*

Hen & Chickens [Flannel St]: Unpretentious and relaxed traditional local, well kept Bass and Brains from bar unusually set against street windows, basic wholesome cheap lunchtime food (not Sun), mugs of tea and coffee, friendly efficient staff, interesting side areas, popular darts, cards and dominoes; TV, very busy on market day *(Pete Baker, the Didler)*

ABERSYCHAN [SO2603]

White Hart [Broad St (A4043 Pontypool—Blaenavon)]: Unchanged front parlour, basic but cosy, with well kept Buckleys IPA, perhaps a guest beer and summer farm cider, friendly local feel, pool in one of two back rooms; meeting place for several local societies *(Pete Baker)*

BASSALEG [ST2787]

Tredegar Arms [Caerphilly Rd (A468, nr M4 junction 28 via A467)]: Old-fashioned panelled bar, small comfortable area with sofa, steps up to attractive no smoking dining area, wide range of good value food inc interesting dishes, up to half a dozen or more well kept changing ales, enthusiastic landlord; picnic-sets in pleasant garden with trees and shrubs and some play equipment *(Mike Pugh, Michael and Alison Sandy)*

BRYNGWYN [SO4008]

☆ *Cripple Creek* [off old A40 W of Raglan]: Smartly extended and civilised old country dining pub with wide range of good reasonably priced food from simple things to more elaborate meals inc fresh fish and choice of four Sun roasts, efficient cheerful staff, well kept ales such as Adnams Broadside, Brains and Tetleys, decent wines, teas and coffees, pleasant no smoking dining room; country views from small terrace, play area, open all day *(Ann and Colin Hunt,*

Eryl and Keith Dykes, Pamela and Merlyn Horswell)

CHEPSTOW [ST5394]

Castle View [Bridge St]: Hotel bar with white-painted walls and some exposed stonework, plush chairs and stools, good value bar food inc good sandwich range, well kept Wye Valley Hereford PA from small bar counter, daily papers; opp castle and its car park, tables in pretty back garden with fountain, 13 bedrooms with own bathrooms *(BB, Ian Phillips, B M Eldridge)*

GWEHELOG [SO3903]

☆ *Hall* [old rd Usk—Raglan, S of village]: Neatly kept small former coaching inn, olde-worlde décor with beams and log fire, very friendly landlord, good fairly priced choice of unusual fresh food using local ingredients esp fresh fish, Bass and Brains Buckleys and SA, couple of steps up to dining area, separate games area *(Gwyneth and Salvo Spadaro-Dutturi, Mike Pugh)*

KEMEYS COMMANDER [SO3405]

Chainbridge [B4598 Usk—Abergavenny]: Splendid riverside setting by historic bascule-bridge, Bass and Hancocks HB, usual food from baguettes and baked potatoes to steaks, spacious bar area with open fire at top level and views of river and hills from lower level; plenty of tables on verandah, extensive grounds with adventure play area, fishing and caravan site *(Richard Fendick, Ian Phillips)*

LLANDENNY [SO4103]

☆ *Raglan Arms*: Good fresh food inc some rather unusual dishes cooked to order for sturdily furnished linked rooms of extensive dining area leading through to conservatory, also terracotta-walled flagstoned bar with big log fire in handsome stone fireplace, polite efficient service, relaxed atmosphere, three well kept real ales, good wine choice, serious dailies, leather sofas around low table on oriental rug, neat separate public bar with pool and wide-screen TV; garden tables, cl Tues in Jan-Mar *(BB, Pamela and Merlyn Horswell, Colin Morgan)*

LLANDEWI SKIRRID [SO3416]

☆ *Walnut Tree* [B4521]: Restaurant rather than pub, so scarcely eligible for the main entries, though it does have a nice small flagstoned bar with fireside seats as well as the airy main dining room; very good inventive italian-flavoured food at a price inc lovely puddings, very good wines and good cider (but no real ale), nice coffee and pleasantly relaxed and individual service; children welcome, cl Sun evening and Mon *(Bernard Stradling, Duncan Cloud, JHW, LYM, LM, Mrs R Pearson)*

LLANFIHANGEL CRUCORNEY [SO3220]

☆ *Skirrid* [signed off A465]: One of Britain's oldest pubs, dating partly from 1110; ancient studded door to high-ceilinged main bar, stone, flagstones and panelling, dark feel accentuated by furniture inc pews (some padded), huge log fire, separate dining room; well kept Marstons Pedigree and Ushers

Founders and Best, efficient cheerful staff, bar food from sandwiches up; open all day summer, children and dogs welcome, tables on attractive terrace and small sloping back lawn, well equipped bedrooms *(LYM, Richard Fendick, John and Joan Nash, Mark and Mary Fairman)*

LLANISHEN [SO4703]

Carpenters Arms: Small cottagey pub with enjoyable usual bar food (packet sauces) in comfortable bar/lounge, well kept Timothy Taylors Landlord, pleasant friendly staff, coal fire, pool table in back area; stone seats and small chrome tables and chairs on new back flagstone terrace, small side lawn up a few steps, a couple of front picnic-sets *(LM)*

LLANTHONY [SO2928]

☆ *Abbey Hotel* [Llanthony Priory; off A465, back rd Llanvihangel Crucorney—Hay]: Unique idyllic setting for plain bar in dim-lit vaulted flagstoned crypt of graceful ruined Norman abbey, lovely in summer, with lawns around and the peaceful border hills beyond; well kept Brains and perhaps a guest beer, farm cider in summer, good coffee, simple lunchtime bar food, evening restaurant; no children, occasional live music; bedrooms in restored parts of abbey walls, open all day Sat and summer Sun, cl winter Mon-Thurs and Sun evening, great walks all around *(LYM, the Didler, Mark and Mary Fairman)*

LLANTRISANT FAWR [ST3997]

☆ *Greyhound* [off A449 nr Usk]: Prettily set 17th-c country inn with relaxed homely feel in three linked bar rooms of varying sizes, steps between two, nice mix of furnishings and rustic decorations, wide choice of consistently good home cooking at sensible prices, good sandwiches and baguettes too, well kept Bass, Flowers Original, Greene King Abbot and a weekly guest beer, decent wines by the glass, friendly helpful staff, log fires, colourful prints in pleasant grey-panelled dining room; picnic-sets in attractive garden with big fountain, hill views, adjoining pine shop, good bedrooms in small attached motel *(Andy Sinden, Louise Harrington, BB, M Joyner, B M Eldridge, Colin McKerrow)*

MONMOUTH [SO5012]

Kings Head [Agincourt Sq]: Well run Wetherspoons in former substantial coaching inn, plenty of well spaced seating, their usual good deals on food and drink *(Geoff Pidoux, Ann and Colin Hunt, B M Eldridge)*

Punch House [Agincourt Sq]: Relaxed and chatty open-plan beamed bar, generous food, prompt efficient service service, well kept Bass and Brains Bitter and Rev James, decent wines, red leatherette settles, old bound *Punch* volumes, big fireplace, no smoking area, restaurant; discreet piped music; children in eating areas, tables out on cobbles overlooking square, open all day (cl Sun afternoon) *(Duncan Cloud, Ian Phillips)*

PANDY [SO3322]

Park Hotel: Hotel rather than pub, but well worth knowing for reasonably priced enjoyable food inc authentic austrian and hungarian dishes, decent low-priced wine, a well kept real ale and exotic lager, relaxed atmosphere and service; bedrooms *(Mike Pugh)*

PANTYGELLI [SO3017]

Crown [Old Hereford Rd, N of Abergavenny]: Good service from charming new licensees, three well kept real ales and Stowford Press farm cider, interesting choice of enjoyable lunchtime food, more extensive evening menu, plenty of local produce, bowls of mixed nuts sold, dark woody interior with nice old furnishings; immaculate seats out in front *(Guy Vowles, Mike Pugh)*

PONTYPOOL [ST3398]

Carpenters Arms [Coedypaen, just SE of Llandegfedd reservoir]: Pretty country pub doing well under current landlord, well kept real ales, good wine range, imaginative food with plenty for vegetarians; well behaved dogs and children welcome, pleasant seating outside *(Gwyneth and Salvo Spadaro-Dutturi, Mike Pugh)*

☆ *Open Hearth* [The Wern, Griffithstown, off A4051]: Caledonian Deuchars IPA, Greene King Abbot and lots of changing guest beers, plenty of malt whiskies, decent choice of wines and very wide food choice in comfortably modernised lounge bar, back bar and no smoking downstairs restaurant; TV; children and dogs welcome, seats out overlooking ducks on shallow stretch of Monmouthshire & Brecon Canal, adventure play area, open all day *(Gwyneth and Salvo Spadaro-Dutturi, Mike Pugh, LYM)*

ROCKFIELD [SO4614]

Stonemill: Enjoyable food (not Mon, nor Fri-Sun evenings) inc good family Sun lunches in attractively converted raftered 16th-c barn with up-to-date furnishings and décor *(Mrs R Pearson)*

ROGERSTONE [ST2788]

Tredegar Arms [Cefn Rd (B4591, off A467 nr M4 junction 27)]: Family-run low-beamed suburban pub, cosy and friendly public bar, bigger comfortable lounge, wide blackboard food choice from baguettes and baked potatoes up, good value pies and Sun lunch, well kept Bass, Courage Best and a guest beer, welcoming licensees *(Pete Baker)*

TINTERN [SO5301]

☆ *Moon & Sixpence* [A466 Chepstow—Monmouth]: Flower-decked small pub, attractively furnished and largely smoke-free, with lots of stripped stone, beams and steps, one room with sofas and wicker armchairs, natural spring feeding indoor goldfish pool, good choice of good value generous food inc Thurs curry night, well kept Archers and Wye Valley Butty Bach from back bar, friendly helpful service; quiet piped music; children welcome, terrace tables under arbour look along River Wye to abbey, good

walks *(Di and Mike Gillam, BB, Tim and Ann Newell, Bruce Bird)*

USK [SO3801]

Castle Inn [Twyn Sq]: Relaxed and pubby front bar with sofas, locals reading newspapers, interesting carved chair and comfortable window seats, big mirrors, lots of dried hops, well organised quick service, changing ales such as Bass and Wadworths 6X, freshly squeezed orange juice; big back area now functioning as a good chinese restaurant, piped music may be loud; pavement tables, garden behind with parakeets and lop-eared rabbits *(Mike Pugh, Ian Phillips, BB)*

Kings Head [Old Market St]: Busy pub with fine choice of well kept real ales inc Fullers London Pride, enjoyable food, welcoming staff, huge log fire in superb fireplace; open all day, bedrooms *(Mike Pugh, Gwyneth and Salvo Spadaro-Dutturi)*

☆ *Royal Hotel* [New Market St]: Comfortably traditional, with old china and pictures, old-fashioned fireplaces, wide choice of reasonably priced enjoyable food (not Sun evening; worth booking Sat and Sun lunch), well kept Bass, Hancocks HB and Felinfoel Double Dragon from deep cellar, friendly service; may be piped music; well behaved children welcome, has been cl Mon lunchtime *(Peter and Audrey Dowsett, LYM, Mike Pugh, Chris Flynn, Wendy Jones)*

Three Salmons [Porthycarne St/Bridge St]: Two-bar pub with thriving atmosphere, good service, enjoyable food; good disabled access *(Pamela and Merlyn Horswell)*

GWYNEDD

ABERDOVEY [SN6196]

Dovey [Sea View Terr]: Bay-window estuary views from bright clean front rooms, big helpings of good moderately priced imaginative food inc children's, pleasant helpful staff; three terraces, comfortably refurbished bedrooms, good breakfast *(Mr and Mrs M Brooksbank)*

ABERGYNOLWYN [SH6706]

Railway [Tywyn—Talyllyn pass]: Old-fashioned two-bar village pub in lovely setting, friendly staff, enjoyable honest food from sandwiches to hearty main meals, Greene King Abbot and Tetleys, big fire in pleasant lounge, small no smoking restaurant; nice outside seating but close to the road, handy for good walks and Talyllyn railway *(Di and Mike Gillam)*

BARMOUTH [SH6115]

Tal-y-Don [High St]: Congenial and attractive bare-boards bar with mainstream and local real ales, enjoyable food from baguettes to fresh local fish here and in simple carpeted restaurant, efficient welcoming staff, darts; children welcome, good garden with water feature, terrace, nice metal tables and heaters, fenced play area with wendy house, five bedrooms *(Stephen Woad)*

BETHESDA [SH6266]
Llangollen [High St (A5)]: Busy town-centre pub with well kept beers, wide choice of well presented tasty food *(John Tavernor)*

BETWS-Y-COED [SH7956]
Pont y Pair: Welcoming mix of diners and local drinkers, reasonably priced satisfying food (cooked fresh, so may be a wait if busy) from good lunchtime baked potatoes up in small cosy bar and separate no smoking dining room (not always open), Tetleys, decent wine, no piped music *(KC)*
Ty Gwyn [A5 just S of bridge to village]: Restaurant with rooms rather than pub (you must eat or stay overnight to be served alcohol), but pubby feel in beamed lounge bar with ancient cooking range, easy chairs, antique prints and interesting bric-a-brac, interesting meals (they do sandwiches too), well kept ales such as Brains and Youngs, partly no smoking restaurant; piped music, nr busy road junction; children welcome (high chair and toys), cl Mon-Weds in Jan *(LYM, Revd D Glover, J C Poley, Jack Clark)*

CAERNARFON [SH4762]
Black Boy [Northgate St]: Attractive recently renovated pub by castle walls, good value food all day from filled baguettes and huge doorstep sandwiches up, prompt friendly service, local real ale, cheery fire, beams from ships wrecked here in 16th c, bare floors, cosy lounge bar, restaurant, public bar with TV; a couple of pavement picnic-sets, bedrooms *(Michael and Alison Sandy, Mike and Mary Carter, Tony and Maggie Harwood)*
Palace Vaults [Palace St, opp castle]: Flower-decked pub with helpful service, enjoyable low-priced basic food till 4 (later in season), well kept Banks's and Camerons Strongarm, good mix of locals and visitors, old-fashioned bar fittings, family dining area; open all day, nr castle entrance and Welsh Highland Railway *(Dave Braisted, Craig Turnbull)*

CONWY [SH7878]
Bridge Hotel [Rose Hill St]: Typical neat town pub with good value home-made bar lunches and more restauranty evening choices, well kept Burtonwood and a guest ale such as Adnams, helpful service, no smoking dining area; bedrooms *(Michael and Alison Sandy, Craig Turnbull)*
Castle Hotel [High St]: Plenty of well spaced tables in interesting old building's cosy bars, good food here and in restaurant, three real ales, decent wines, friendly atmosphere and good informed service; own car parks (which helps here), 29 bedrooms with own bathrooms *(E G Parish, Peter Cole)*

DOLGELLAU [SH7318]
Royal Ship [Queens Sq]: Traditional small central hotel with helpful young staff and enjoyable food inc good puddings, compact bar, lounge with dining area, more formal restaurant *(Rona Murdoch)*

GELLILYDAN [SH6839]
Bryn Arms: Unpretentious place with enjoyable cheap bar food from sandwiches up, Wye Valley Butty Bach, friendly landlord *(Mike and Mary Carter)*

LLANDUDNO [SH7882]
Palladium [Gloddaeth St]: Spacious Wetherspoons in impressive converted former theatre, boxes and seats intact, spectacular ceilings, good value food and drinks, plenty of seating *(Keith and Chris O'Neill, E G Parish, Mike and Lynn Robinson)*

LLANDUDNO JUNCTION [SH7977]
Old Station Hotel [under a mile from A55 junction 19; Conway Rd (A547)]: Late Victorian pub/hotel with welcoming helpful service, relaxed atmosphere, traditional food in warm well furnished dining area, separate bar with pool tables (and big-screen TV); 13 bedrooms *(E G Parish)*

LLANUWCHLLYN [SH8730]
☆ *Eagles* [aka Eryrod; A494/B4403]: Good reasonably priced food from sandwiches to traditional and more enterprising dishes, helpful and courteous young staff, thriving atmosphere in small front bar and plush back lounge, neat décor with beams and some stripped stone, no smoking dining area, back picture-window view of mountains with Lake Bala in distance, limited wine list, strong coffee, no music; disabled access, picnic-sets under cocktail parasols on flower-filled back terrace *(Michael and Jenny Back, Mike and Mary Carter)*

MARIANGLAS [SH5084]
Parciau Arms: Decent bar food from sandwiches up, light and airy family dining lounge with log fire, four well kept ales inc a Mild, good range of other drinks, cheerful service, comfortable built-in banquettes and other seating, old coaching prints, interesting bric-a-brac inc lots of gleaming brass, pub games in busy bar; terrace and good-sized garden with excellent play area, open all day *(BB, John Tavernor)*

MENAI BRIDGE [SH5773]
☆ *Gazelle* [Glyngarth; A545, half way towards Beaumaris]: Outstanding waterside situation looking across to Snowdonia, good straightforward food inc fresh fish, well kept Robinsons, helpful staff, lively main bar, smaller rooms off and restaurant; children welcome, steep and aromatic mediterranean garden behind, children allowed away from serving bar; good bedrooms *(LYM, J Roy Smylie, Peter and Liz Holmes)*

MORFA NEFYN [SH2939]
Bryncynan: Modernised pub concentrating (particularly in summer) on good choice of quickly served enjoyable food, well kept ales such as Greene King Old Speckled Hen and Wadworths 6X, friendly service, quiet in winter with good log fire in the partly tiled bar, restaurant, children allowed, rustic seats outside, has been cl Sun *(LYM, John Mitchell)*

PENMAENPOOL [SH6918]

☆ *George III* [just off A493, nr Dolgellau]: Lovely views over Mawddach estuary from attractive inn, new licensees doing light lunches as well as other food from baguettes up in no smoking lower bar with beams, flagstones and stripped stone, well kept ales such as Bass, good choice of wines by the glass, also civilised partly panelled upstairs bar opening into cosy inglenook lounge, with same food, and separate restaurant; may be piped music downstairs; sheltered terrace, good walks, good bedrooms inc some (allowing dogs) in quiet and interesting conversion of former station on disused line now a walkway, open all day *(Dennis Jenkin, LYM, GSB, Stephen Woad, Comus and Sarah Elliott)*

PORTH DINLLAEN [SH2741]

☆ *Ty Coch* [beach car park signed from Morfa Nefyn, then 15-min walk]: Stunning spot on curving beach, far from the roads (and quite a long walk from the nearest car park), with great view along coast to mountains; pub itself full of attractive salvage, RNLI memorabilia, lamps and mugs, good prawn and crab salads and other usual lunchtime food, decent coffee; keg beer (and plastic beakers if you drink outside); cl winter exc Sat lunchtimes, but open all day summer and very popular then – idyllic on a hot still day *(LYM, Jason Caulkin, Tony and Maggie Harwood)*

PORTHMADOG [SH5639]

Spooners [Harbour Station]: Decent pub lunches inc good filled baguettes and Thurs-Sat evening meals at reasonable prices (Sun lunch may be booked early), virtually a museum of railway memorabilia inc full-size narrow-gauge locomotive, particularly well kept Marstons Bitter and Pedigree and quickly changing interesting guest beers, overflow into no smoking station buffet; children welcome, tables out on steam railway platform, open all day *(Keith and Chris O'Neill, Tony Hobden)*

RHYD DDU [SH5753]

☆ *Cwellyn Arms* [A4085 N of Beddgelert]: Comfortably basic 18th-c Snowdon pub not far below Welsh Highland Railway top terminus, with log fire in huge ancient fireplace to dry wet walkers, seven or eight well kept changing ales such as Banks's, Boggart Hole Clough, Conwy, Cottage, Dorset and Wye Valley, Leffe and Hoegaarden on tap, friendly licensees, wide choice of popular straightforward food from filled rolls and baked potatoes up – several different menus inc pizzas and children's; flagstones, several rooms inc pleasant restaurant area, small games bar with pool, darts and TV; children and walkers welcome, spectacular Snowdon views from garden tables with barbecue, babbling stream just over wall, big adventure playground, bedrooms, usually open all day *(Michael and Alison Sandy, A J Law, Martin Grosberg, Tony Hobden, Tony and*

Maggie Harwood, Stephen Dadswell)

TALYLLYN [SH7210]

☆ *Tynycornel* [B4405, off A487 S of Dolgellau]: Comfortably civilised hotel tucked below mountains, picture windows overlooking attractive lake, deeply comfortable sofas and armchairs, enjoyable bar lunches from good sandwiches up, courteous service, central log fire, no smoking restaurant and conservatory, nice pictures; children welcome, prettily planted side courtyard, open all day, good bedrooms *(Jacquie and Jim Jones, Peter and Anne Hollindale, J C Poley, LYM, Peter Cole)*

TREFRIW [SH7863]

Old Ship: Friendly local atmosphere, enjoyable generous food, well kept Banks's, Marstons Pedigree and guest beers *(Jane Smith)*

TREMADOG [SH5640]

☆ *Golden Fleece* [off A487 just N of Porthmadog; Market Sq]: Neat stone-built inn bustling with families and locals, quick friendly service, well kept Worthington and a guest beer, decent wines, partly partitioned rambling dark-beamed lounge with open fire, nice little snug (reserved seats for regulars Fri/Sat night), intriguing barrel-vaulted cellar bar, good value generous home-made bar food inc fish (ordered from back bistro, off sheltered inner courtyard with more tables), games room; children welcome, bedrooms and flats, on attractive square *(LYM, Tony Hobden, GSB)*

TUDWEILIOG [SH2336]

☆ *Lion* [Nefyn Rd (B4417), Lleyn Peninsula]: Cheerfully busy village inn with wide choice of good value straightforward food and some nice specials in bar and no smoking family dining conservatory (small helpings for children, who have a pretty free rein here), quick friendly service, well kept mainstream ales well described by helpful landlord, dozens of malt whiskies, decent wines, games in lively public bar; pleasant front garden, good value bedrooms with own bathrooms *(Sally and Dave Bates, LYM, Revd D Glover)*

WAUNFAWR [SH5359]

Snowdonia Parc [A4085 Caernarfon—Beddgelert]: Family atmosphere, straightforward pub food inc enormous hot beef baguettes, well kept real ales sometimes inc their own strong Welsh Highland Bitter, children's room with playthings; children and dogs welcome, overlooks and really part of Welsh Highland Railway terminus, bustling campsite, open all day *(Tony Hobden, Tony and Maggie Harwood)*

Y FELINHELI [SH5267]

Gardd Fôn [Beach Rd, off A487 SW of Bangor]: Nautical-theme local by Menai Straits, enjoyable food from good open sandwiches up in bar (which can be smoky) or no smoking bistro restaurant, Burtonwood and a guest beer; great views from tables out on grass *(Maurice and Gill McMahon, Gerry and Rosemary Dobson)*

MID GLAMORGAN

CAERPHILLY [ST1586]

Courthouse [Cardiff Rd]: 14th-c pub with superb view of classic castle from light and airy modern back café/bar and picnic-sets on grassy terrace above its moat; character original core has rugs on ancient flagstones, stripped stone walls, raftered gallery, enormous chimney breast, a real ale such as Shepherd Neame Spitfire, good coffee, lots of lagers, pub games, partly no smoking restaurant; quite a few special offer posters, cheap food all day (not Sun evening, not after 5.30 Mon, Fri or Sat) from baguettes up, piped pop music, virtually no nearby parking; children welcome in eating areas, open all day *(LYM, Ian Phillips)*

KENFIG [SS8383]

Prince of Wales [2¼ miles from M4 junction 37; A4229 towards Porthcawl, then right when dual carriageway narrows on bend, signed Maudlam and Kenfig]: New landlord in interesting ancient pub among sand dunes, well kept Bass and Brains Best or Worthington tapped from the cask, good choice of malt whiskies and decent wines, good straightforward food inc much enjoyed fish specials, stripped stone and log fire, lots of wreck pictures, traditional games, small upstairs dining room for summer and busy wknds; big-screen TV now; children and (in non-carpet areas) dogs welcome, handy for nature-reserve walks (awash with orchids in Jun) *(Phil and Sally Gorton, John and Joan Nash, the Didler, LYM, Ian Phillips)*

MERTHYR TYDFIL [SO0608]

Pant Cad Ifor [Pant Rd, Dowlais]: Good choice of food and drink, moderate prices; peaceful cemetery view *(Alan and Anita Thomas)*

MISKIN [ST0480]

Miskin Arms [handy for M4 junction 34, via A4119 and B4264]: Friendly and roomy village pub with well kept Everards Tiger, Hancocks HB and guest beers, good value bar food, popular restaurant Sun lunch and Tues-Sat evenings *(Colin Moore)*

NANT DDU [SO0015]

Nant Ddu Lodge [Cwmtaf; A470 Merthyr Tydfil—Brecon]: Hotel with popular adjacent brasserie and bar, wide range of enjoyable and imaginative reasonably priced food, good atmosphere, well kept Bass, cheerful landlord, no smoking lounge, large evening dining room; good bright well equipped bedrooms (some in separate block), good walking country by Taff Valley reservoirs *(V Brogden, Pamela and Merlyn Horswell)*

PEN-Y-CAE [SS9082]

Ty'r Isha [a mile from M4 junction 36, via A4061 towards Bridgend, then at Sainsburys roundabout take exit before Sainsbury's, towards Designer Village, and bear left down hill]: Biggish pub with enjoyable straightforward food inc attractively priced steaks, also children's dishes, in bar and restaurant, good service *(Andy Sinden, Louise Harrington)*

PONTYPRIDD [ST0790]

Bunch of Grapes [off A4054; Ynysangharad Rd]: Stripped-down pub with good choice of enterising eclectic food (not Sun evening) from French chef, well kept Bass, Hereford PA and guest beers, interesting bottled beers from around the world, reasonably priced wines, bare boards and simple décor, small easy-chair lounge, large no smoking dining area opening into grape-vine conservatory, public bar, coal fire; extension planned into pretty cottage behind, tables out on two terraces, open all day *(Pamela and Merlyn Horswell)*

Upper Boat Inn [Williams Pl, Upper Boat (off A470 S, roundabout at N end of retail park)]: Usefully placed Brewers Fayre, linked rooms and good long bar, good wines by the glass, their usual food, efficient service; easy disabled access, open all day *(Pamela and Merlyn Horswell)*

RUDRY [ST2087]

☆ *Maenllwyd* [off A468 Newport—Caerphilly in Lower Machen, halfway towards Caerphilly on minor rd]: Rambling olde-worlde Tudor Chef & Brewer recently reopened after major renovations giving easy access between its different levels, decent food all day, good choice of well kept real ales and of wines, low beams, panelling, huge log fireplace; piped music, can be very busy Fri/Sat; nice spot on the edge of Rudry Common, open all day from noon *(LYM, R Michael Richards, Dr and Mrs A K Clarke, Ian Phillips, David and Nina Pugsley)*

THORNHILL [ST1484]

☆ *Travellers Rest* [A469 S of Caerphilly]: Attractive thatched stone-built pub tucked into fold of the hillside, discreetly enlarged as welcoming Vintage Inn dining pub, well kept Bass and Hancocks HB, good sensibly priced wine choice, winter mulled wine, prompt friendly service, daily papers and magazines, reasonably priced food all day from sandwiches up, huge fireplace and nooks and crannies in low-beamed bar on right, no smoking area; piped music; children welcome lunchtimes, open all day, plenty of tables out on grass, good walks *(David and Nina Pugsley, Ian Phillips, R Michael Richards)*

POWYS

BEGUILDY [SO1979]

Radnorshire Arms [B4355 Knighton—Newtown]: Beautifully set pretty little black and white pub with very friendly newish licensees, well kept local beers and Fullers London Pride, nice house wine, enjoyable food inc wicked puddings (best to book Sun lunch), small spotless attractively decorated lounge and dining room *(Mike Pleass)*

BERRIEW [SJ1800]

☆ *Lion* [B4390; village signed off A483 Welshpool—Newtown]: Friendly newish licensees in comfortable village inn with nicely old-fashioned inglenook public bar and partly stripped stone lounge bar with open fire, home-made food (not Sun evening) here or in restaurant from sandwiches and baguettes up, Banks's and Marstons real ales, decent house wines, dominoes and cribbage; piped music, TV; children and dogs welcome, comfortable bedrooms with own bathrooms, open all day, nice riverside village with lively sculpture gallery *(Rodney and Norma Stubington, Simon Lawson, Geoffrey and Penny Hughes, DC, P Bottomley, LYM, Mark Killman)*

BRECON [SO0428]

Bulls Head [The Struet]: Friendly pub in attractive setting, notable for the constant stream of quickly changing guest ales as well as its well kept regular Breconshire, bar food; bedrooms, cl Mon lunchtime *(Mike Evans)*

George [George St]: Spacious town pub with three well kept changing ales, decent coffee, good blackboard choice of reasonably priced food all day from sandwiches and other snacks up, attentive service, log-effect gas fires in long bar, pleasant dining conservatory; very busy Sat night; tables in flower-filled back courtyard (with interesting cheeses etc from Welsh Food Centre), open all day *(Ann and Colin Hunt, Ian Phillips)*

CARNO [SN9697]

Aleppo Merchant [A470 Newtown— Machynlleth]: Very popular for decent low-priced food from good sandwiches to steaks, friendly helpful landlord, Boddingtons, occasional guest beer, tapestries in plushly modernised stripped stone bar, peaceful no smoking lounge on right with open fire, restaurant (well behaved children allowed here), back games room; piped music; tables in good-sized garden, bedrooms, nice countryside *(Michael and Jenny Back, LYM)*

CRICKHOWELL [SO2119]

☆ *White Hart* [Brecon Rd (A40 W)]: Stripped stone, beams and flagstones, welcoming local atmosphere, well kept Brains ales with a guest such as Shepherd Neame Spitfire, enjoyable food from lunchtime sandwiches up inc several welsh specialities in eating area (with TV) off one end, or sizeable no smoking restaurant, cheerful service, pub games; may be piped classical music, quiz night Mon; children in eating areas, open all day Sat, some tables outside *(Ann and Colin Hunt, LYM, Mrs N Atkins, R T and J C Moggridge)*

CWMDU [SO1823]

☆ *Farmers Arms* [A479 NW of Crickhowell]: Genuine friendly country local, popular with walkers, with welcoming licensees and regulars, unpretentious partly flagstoned bar with attractive prints and stove in big stone fireplace, good value hearty home cooking inc good local lamb and beef, welsh cheeses and children's dishes, several well kept changing real ales, decent wines by the glass,

plush restaurant; TV; tables in garden, bedrooms with own bathrooms and good breakfast, campsite nearby *(BB, Colin and Wendy John)*

DERWENLAS [SN7299]

☆ *Black Lion* [A487 just S of Machynlleth]: Friendly couple running cosy and peaceful 16th-c country pub, heavy black beams, thick walls and black timbering, attractive pictures and lion models, tartan carpet over big slate flagstones, great log fire, good range of good value food, efficient service, real ale, decent wines; piped music; garden up behind with play area and steps up into woods, bedrooms *(BB, Mike and Mary Carter)*

DINAS MAWDDWY [SH8514]

☆ *Llew Coch* [aka Red Lion; just off A470 E of Dolgellau]: Genuine country local surrounded by steep fir forests (good walks), charming timbered front bar sparkling with countless brasses, good log fire, well kept Brains Rev James and Worthington, quick friendly service, cheap cheerful food from good sandwiches to trout or salmon from River Dovey just behind; inner family room lively with video games, pool and Sat evening live music, dining extension (popular for Sun lunch); good wheelchair access, dogs on leads welcome, tables out on quiet lane *(Dennis Jenkin, LYM, Neil and Anita Christopher)*

GLADESTRY [SO2355]

Royal Oak [B4594 W of Kington]: Another change of management in two-bar beamed and flagstoned walkers' and locals' pub, well kept Brains Rev James, usual food from sandwiches up; picnic-sets in secluded garden behind, quiet village handy for Offa's Dyke Path *(LYM, Guy Vowles)*

HAY-ON-WYE [SO2242]

☆ *Blue Boar* [Castle St/Oxford Rd]: Good choice of generous home cooking (not Sun evening) in light and airy long no smoking dining room with food counter, lots of pictures for sale, bright tablecloths and cheery décor, big sash windows, good coffees and teas, also breakfasts; relaxed candlelit panelled medieval bar with pews and country chairs, well kept ales such as Brains SA and Flowers IPA, interesting bottled ciders inc organic, decent wines, friendly service, log fire; may be quiet piped music; children welcome *(John Whitehead, BB, Sue Demont, Tim Barrow, CMW, JJW)*

Three Tuns [Broad St]: Still closed and boarded up in summer 2005 as we went to press, following February fire damage; one of Hay's oldest buildings, and we hope the simple little quarry-tiled bar with its cider barrels and quaint old-fashioned appeal will be back in action soon – if not by the time this edition is published *(RWC, Bruce Bird, the Didler, Pete Baker)*

Wheatsheaf [Lion St]: Beams strung with hops, bric-a-brac in nooks and crannies, log fire, well kept real ale, attractively priced decent home-made food, cheerful friendly

staff; can get quite smoky when busy
(Martin and Sarah)

LIBANUS [SN9926]

☆ *Tai'r Bull* [A470 SW of Brecon]: Friendly
old well run pub, good helpings of food
using fresh produce from large ciabattas to
good up-to-date restaurant dishes, well kept
Brains SA and a guest such as Butcombe,
attentive young licensees, woodburner, light
and airy no smoking restaurant, great views
of Pen-y-Fan out in front; bedrooms well
appointed and comfortable, good breakfast
– good base for walking *(Michael and
Alison Sandy, Miss Joanne Mortimer,
Mr and Mrs L J Morgan-Hayes,
Stephen Funnell, J A Ellis)*

LLANFIHANGEL-NANT-MELAN [SO1958]

☆ *Red Lion* [A44 10 miles W of Kington]:
Warm and friendly stripped-stone 16th-c
roadside dining pub with good fresh food in
roomy main area beyond standing timbers
on right, smaller room with small pews
around tables, well kept changing real ale,
nice wine choice, sensible prices, good
obliging service, some tables in front sun
porch, back bar with pool; comfortable
simple chalet bedrooms, handy for Radnor
Forest walks, nr impressive waterfall, has
been cl Tues-Thurs lunchtime, Tues evening
*(Christopher J Darwent, BB, Rodney and
Norma Stubington)*

LLANGATTOCK [SO2118]

Vine Tree [signed from Crickhowell; Legar
Rd]: Small simple pub with reliable generous
food inc fresh fish and some unusual dishes
with masses of veg in bar and restaurant,
pleasant service, well kept Fullers London
Pride and Wadworths 6X, good coffee, coal-
effect gas fire; very busy wknds and bank
hols; children welcome, tables out under
cocktail parasols with lovely view of
medieval Usk bridge *(LYM, Nick and
Lynne Carter, R Michael Richards)*

LLANGYNIDR [SO1519]

Coach & Horses [Cwm Crawnon Rd (B4558
W of Crickhowell)]: Tidy and roomy flower-
decked dining pub with new Portuguese
licensees, wide choice of generous enjoyable
food from sandwiches and baguettes up,
plenty of cheerful young staff, well kept
Courage Best and Directors, Greene King
Ruddles County and Wadworths 6X,
comfortable banquettes and stripped stone,
nice big open fire, large attractive restaurant
with no smoking area; pub games, piped
music, TV; children and dogs welcome,
picnic-sets across road in safely fenced pretty
sloping garden by lock of Newport & Brecon
Canal; three good value comfortable
bedrooms, good breakfast, lovely views and
walks, open all day *(Ann and Colin Hunt,
LYM, Theocsbrian, M and J Lindsay,
David and Nina Pugsley, Andy and Yvonne
Cunningham, John and Joan Nash, R T and
J C Moggridge)*

LLANWDDYN [SJ0219]

Lake Vyrnwy Hotel: Comfortable pub
extension, well done in old tavern style,

behind smart late 19th-c country hotel in
remote beautiful spot with abundant fresh
air, lake view from big-windowed blue-
carpeted lounge and balcony, well kept
Brains, good house wines, wide range of
enjoyable generous food, attentive friendly
staff, darts; quiet piped music; bedrooms
(Simon Lawson, John and Sylvia Harrop)

LLANWRTHWL [SN9763]

Vulcan Arms [A470 S of Rhayader]: Large
partly divided open-plan bar with blazing
central log fire, warm décor, sofas and
armchairs, library restaurant, public area
with juke box and piped music, small
comfortable no smoking room with TV,
Greene King Abbot, usual pub food (new
licensees planning thai specialities –
landlady comes from Thailand) *(Dr and
Mrs M E Wilson)*

LLOWES [SO1941]

☆ *Radnor Arms* [A438 Brecon—Hereford]:
Attractive country dining pub with very
wide choice of good food served in local
pottery (for sale here) from good sandwiches
and choice of inventive soups to fine
restaurant-style dishes, dozens of puddings,
fair prices, friendly staff and long-serving
landlord on great form, well kept Felinfoel,
good coffee, cottagey bar with beams and
stripped stone, log fire, lots of knick-knacks,
stuffed toys and so forth, two small dining
rooms; tables in imaginatively planted
garden looking out over fields towards
the Wye, cl Sun pm, Mon *(Keith and
Jean Symons, Pat and Stewart Gordon,
Pam and David Bailey)*

MACHYNLLETH [SH7400]

☆ *White Lion* [Heol Pentrerhedyn; A489, nr
clock tower and junction with A487]: Big
friendly country-town bar with pink and
maroon décor, plush seats, shiny copper-
topped tables, big bay window seats
overlooking main street, inglenook log fire,
end eating area with enjoyable usual food all
day from sandwiches to roasts, well kept
Banks's Bitter and Mild and Marstons
Pedigree, decent wines by the glass, service
brisk and cheerful even on busy Weds
market day; piped music, silenced fruit
machine; children welcome, pretty views
from picnic-sets in attractive back garden,
some tables out by road too, neat stripped
pine bedrooms *(BB, Christine and
Phil Young)*

☆ *Wynnstay Arms* [Maengwyn St]: Well
established market-town hotel with good
sandwiches and interesting snacks in busy
and welcoming pubby annexe bar, friendly
service, three real ales, good choice of wines
by the glass, comfortable and relaxed hotel
lounge and good restaurant; courtyard
tables, bedrooms *(Dennis Jenkin, Mike and
Mary Carter, Mr and Mrs Richard Osborne,
Rodney and Norma Stubington)*

MALLWYD [SH8612]

Brigands: Stone-built Tudor-style hotel,
extensively and well refurbished, with linked
beamed rooms and separate restaurant, good

choice of reasonably priced food from bar snacks up inc good local beef and lamb, three real ales; tables outside with play area, newly refurbished bedrooms, three miles of sea trout fishing on River Dovey *(Ian and Deborah Carrington)*

MONTGOMERY [SO2296]

Brickys [Chirbury Road (B4386)]: Sadly this little dining pub, despite its good interesting food praised as a main entry in our last edition, never built up enough wkdy trade and closed in early summer 2005 *(LYM)*

Dragon [Market Sq]: Tall timbered 17th-c hotel with attractive prints and china in lively beamed bar, good wines and coffee, well kept Woods Special and guest beer, board games, restaurant; unobtrusive piped music, jazz most Weds; comfortable well equipped bedrooms and swimming pool, very quiet town below ruined Norman castle, open all day *(LYM, Mr and Mrs W E Cross)*

PENTRE BACH [SN9032]

☆ *Shoemakers Arms* [off A40 in Sennybridge]: Individual welcoming country pub in the middle of nowhere, well refurbished and reopened by consortium of local people, enjoyable lunchtime home cooking from good sandwiches up, reasonable prices, obliging service from helpful cheerful staff, well kept changing ales such as Thwaites Lancaster Bomber, small restaurant Sun lunchtime and Weds-Sat evenings; tables outside, good walks, open all day Sun, cl Mon/Tues lunchtime *(R Michael Richards, Annabel Pfeiffer, David Cosham)*

PENYBONT [SO0561]

Severn Arms [A44/A488, NE of Llandrindod Wells]: Welcoming hotel with real ales inc Brains Rev James, wide choice of good value straightforward food, friendly helpful landlady and staff, sizeable bar with games area, secluded lounge, restaurant; plenty of tables in sizeable garden by little River Ithon, bedrooms, own walks *(George Atkinson, Mike and Mary Carter)*

TALYBONT-ON-USK [SO1122]

☆ *Star* [B4558]: Fine choice of well kept changing real ales, usually about four in winter and more in summer, in relaxed and unpretentious stone-built local, straightforward food from good cheap filled rolls to some tasty main dishes, friendly attentive service, good log fire in fine inglenook with bread oven, Weston's Old Rosie farm cider, three bustling plain rooms off central servery inc brightly lit games area, lots of beermats, bank notes and coins on beams, monthly band night, winter quiz Mon; dogs and children welcome, picnic-sets in sizeable tree-ringed garden below Monmouth & Brecon Canal, bedrooms, open all day Sat and summer *(LYM, Pete Baker, the Didler, R Michael Richards, Elven Money, Neil and Anita Christopher, MLR)*

Usk: Good-sized comfortable bar with real ales, log fire, panelling and sporting prints,

cheerful service, pleasant staff, food in bar and restaurant; good value well equipped bedrooms *(Ann and Colin Hunt)*

TRECASTLE [SN8729]

☆ *Castle Hotel*: Pleasantly decorated Georgian inn, neatly kept lounge and dining room up a few stairs from tiled floor bar, enjoyable food from good sandwiches and ploughman's through appetising bar dishes to imaginative restaurant dishes, well kept Greene King Old Speckled Hen, good wines by the glass, choice of coffees, friendly service, roaring fire; unobtrusive piped music; terrace tables, comfortable bedrooms *(Richard and Anne Norris, Tony Davies)*

WELSHPOOL [SJ2107]

Raven [Raven Sq]: Good range of reasonably priced home-made food from baguettes and baked potatoes up in welcoming lounge bar/restaurant; handy for steam railway *(I D Barnett)*

SOUTH GLAMORGAN

ABERTHIN [ST0075]

Farmers Arms: Doing well under current newish landlord, well done usual bar food from sandwiches to fresh fish *(Alec and Barbara Jones)*

BARRY [ST1369]

Glenbrook [Dobbins Rd, off A4231]: Proper genuine suburban local, comfortable and clean, with well kept Brains Bitter and SA and lots of bottle-conditioned beers, sensibly priced wines, good value home-made bar food, friendly staff; sports TV, lots going on such as quiz nights, live music, karaoke; tables outside, good play area *(Larry Arthurs)*

CARDIFF [ST1776]

☆ *Cayo Arms* [Cathedral Rd]: Friendly, relaxed and shimmering with cleanliness, with well kept ales such as Bass, Brains Rev James and several from Tomos Watkins, good value food all day inc good range of sandwiches, a few hot dishes and Sun lunch, quick service, two raised areas separated by cast iron railings, comfortable seats inc fine old wooden armchairs, lots of prints, interesting stained glass, daily papers; piped music, very busy wknds; tables out in front, more in yard behind (with parking), open all day *(Ian Phillips, Roger Huggins, Tom and Alex McLean, Andy and Jill Kassube)*

Conway [Conway Rd/Mortimer Rd, Pontcanno]: Cheerfully relaxed corner pub with well kept Bass, Greene King Abbot and Timothy Taylors Landlord, usual food at low prices, small traditional front bar, drinking corridor to large comfortable back lounge/dining area, plenty of daily papers; sports TV; pavement picnic-sets *(Ian Phillips)*

Prince of Wales [St. Mary St/Wood St, nr station]: Very large stylish Wetherspoons cinema/theatre conversion, largely smoke-free, subdued dark brown and cream

décor, historical photographs, good choice of well priced beers, their usual food; disabled facilities, open all day *(Roger Huggins, Tom and Alex McLean)*
Yard [St Mary St]: Former Prince Albert, stylishly refurbished as Brains brewery flagship, their beers kept well, good value food cooked in front of you, prompt service, two-floor layout with functionalist décor; piped music may be loud, lighting dim; courtyard tables, open all day till late *(Andy and Jill Kassube)*

COWBRIDGE [SS9974]
Bear [High St, with car park behind off North St; signed off A48]: Neatly kept and very busy old coaching inn with well kept Bass, Hancocks HB and two guest beers, usually one from Wye Valley, decent house wines, friendly efficient young staff, three bars with flagstones, bare boards or carpet, some stripped stone and panelling, big hot open fires, enjoyable usual bar food from sandwiches up, barrel-vaulted cellar restaurant; children welcome, CCTV in car park, bedrooms quiet and comfortable, good breakfast *(V Brogden, David and Nina Pugsley, LYM, Ian Phillips)*

LISVANE [ST1883]
Ty Mawr Arms [follow Mill Rd into Graig Rd, then keep on]: Large neatly kept country pub with fairly wide choice of popular food from baguettes and baked potatoes through light dishes, familiar favourites and lots of curries to steaks, well kept Brains and guest ales, friendly service, great views over Cardiff from spacious bay-windowed dining area off traditional bar with big log fire; large attractive garden with good play area *(LYM, Sue and Gary Lay)*

LLANCARFAN [ST0570]
Fox & Hounds [signed off A4226; can also be reached from A48 from Bonvilston or B4265 via Llancadle]: Chef/landlord doing good carefully cooked food using local ingredients such as fresh fish, welsh black beef and farmhouse cheeses in neat comfortably modernised village pub, friendly open-plan bar rambling through arches, coal fire, Brains Bitter and Rev James, good wine choice, traditional settles and plush banquettes, candlelit bistro, more sparely furnished end family room; children welcome, unobtrusive piped music; tables out behind, pretty streamside setting by interesting church, eight comfortable well equipped bedrooms with own bathrooms, has been open all day wknds *(R Michael Richards, BB, Geoff and Carol Thorp)*

MICHAELSTON-Y-FEDW [ST2484]
Cefn Mably Arms [a mile off A48 at Castleton]: Brightly furnished country pub with good range of sensibly priced fresh food inc fish and imaginative dishes served with a smile in bar and pleasant dining room, well kept Bass and Hancocks HB, soft piped music; garden tables *(Richard Fendick, R Michael Richards, Alec and Barbara Jones)*

PENDOYLAN [ST0576]
Red Lion [2½ miles from M4 junction 34]: Friendly village pub, quiet and comfortable, with good standard home-made food in bar and restaurant, well kept real ale; good garden with play area, next to church in pretty vale *(Dr and Mrs A K Clarke)*

ST FAGANS [ST1277]
☆ **Plymouth Arms**: Stately Victorian pub reworked as rambling civilised Vintage Inn with plenty of dark wood and nice touches in bustling linked areas inc log fires, good range of generous food from smart sandwiches all day, Bass and Hancocks HB, decent wines by the glass at reasonable prices, prompt friendly service, daily papers; lots of tables on extensive back lawn, water-bowls outside for dogs, handy for Museum of Welsh Life *(Pamela and Merlyn Horswell, Michael and Alison Sandy)*

WEST GLAMORGAN

BISHOPSTON [SS5789]
☆ **Joiners Arms** [Bishopston Rd, just off B4436 SW of Swansea]: Thriving local brewing their own good value Swansea ales, usually three of these and four well kept changing guest beers, decent wines, good value generous simple food from panini to half a dozen changing daily specials, welcoming quarry-tiled bar with old-fashioned décor and furnishings, local paintings and massive solid fuel stove, late May bank hol beer and music festival; big-screen TV for rugby; children welcome, open all day *(LYM, Michael and Alison Sandy)*

BLACK PILL [SS6190]
Woodman [Mumbles Rd (A4067 Swansea—Mumbles)]: Good seafront dining pub attractively renovated with lots of wood, good value food all day from good sandwiches and baguettes to fresh local fish, well kept Courage Directors and guests such as Adnams and Greene King Old Speckled Hen, good choice of wines by the glass in two sizes, friendly efficient staff, several sensibly furnished linked areas opening out of bar, hundreds of wine bottles above panelled dado, airy restaurant and conservatory; car park across busy rd; children welcome in some areas, next to beautiful Clyne Gardens (great rhododendrons in May) *(Anne Morris, John and Vivienne Rice, Alan Davies, John and Joan Nash, Michael and Alison Sandy, Dave Braisted)*

OLDWALLS [SS4891]
Greyhound: Good value generous food with extra blackboards each for lots of curries, fresh fish and steaks, busy but spacious beamed and dark-panelled plush lounge bar and restaurant, well kept mainstream ales, good coffee inc decaf, decent wine, roaring coal fires, friendly service, back bar with display cases; big tree-shaded garden with terrace, play area and good views

(Michael and Alison Sandy)

OXWICH [SS4986]

Oxwich Bay Hotel: Large and pleasant food-oriented hotel bar with beautiful bay and beach views, above-average reasonably priced food all day inc good rib of welsh black beef, efficient friendly helpful staff, occasionally a real ale such as Felinfoel Double Dragon; good for families, tables in well kept garden, bedrooms *(Martin and Alison Stainsby)*

REYNOLDSTON [SS4889]

King Arthur [Higher Green, off A4118]: Large pub/hotel with cheery timbered main bar and hall, back family summer dining area (games room with pool in winter), food from lunchtime baguettes to popular Sun lunch, Bass, Felinfoel Double Dragon and Worthington Best, friendly helpful staff, country-house bric-a-brac and log fire, no smoking restaurant; lively local atmosphere evenings, piped music; tables outside with play area, open all day, bedrooms *(LYM, M G Hart)*

RHOSSILI [SS4188]

Worms Head Hotel: Stunning views over Rhossili Bay and three-mile sweep of beach from clifftop terrace tables, compact bar, well kept Hancocks HB, hearty food inc local fresh fish *(Dr C C S Wilson, Guy Consterdine)*

SWANSEA [SS6092]

Black Boy [Gower Rd (A4118), Killay]: Large well divided pub, lots of dark wood, Brains Bitter, SA, Rev James and Buckleys from long counter, good value food from wide choice of sandwiches, baguettes, ciabattas and baked potatoes to reliable steaks; TV for rugby *(Michael and Alison Sandy)*

No Sign Wine Bar [Wind St, 200 yds below Castle]: Four narrow old-fashioned rooms, first parlourish and welcoming, with mahogany cabinets and other fittings, large portrait in oils, cellars under bar; second more of an alcove, third full of church pews, fourth flagstoned and rather bare; some emphasis on fairly priced generous decent food (can get crowded lunchtimes), friendly service, good wines by the glass in two sizes, three real ales, daily papers *(Patrick Hancock, Rona Murdoch)*

Post Office address codings confusingly give the impression that some pubs are in Gwent or Powys, Wales when they're really in Gloucestershire or Shropshire (which is where we list them).

Channel Islands

This year for the first time the average price of a pint in the Channel Islands has topped the £2 barrier. So people coming here on holiday from Lancashire would now find their beers costing them slightly more than at home, and people from Cheshire and Nottinghamshire wouldn't notice a price difference. However, drinks prices are still among the lowest in the British Isles. It's particularly worth looking out for the local brews, Guernsey and Tipsy Toad (both actually brewed on Jersey) and Randalls (Guernsey), which can be a lot cheaper than imports from the mainland. And the islands' best pubs can compete on quality with those anywhere else. Jersey's top pub is now the Old Portelet, a bustling and well run family pub above the beach at St Brelade, very popular for its huge helpings of straightforward food at bargain prices. Guernsey's best pub, the Fleur du Jardin at King's Mills, takes its food on to a different quality level; this peaceful small hotel, with its nice bar, is the Channel Islands Dining Pub of the Year. One Jersey pub to note particularly in the Lucky Dip section at the end of the chapter is the Original Wine Bar in St Helier (nicely pubby despite its name); it now looks to us like making its way into the main entries before long.

KING'S MILLS Map 1
Fleur du Jardin 🍴 🍷 🛏

King's Mills Road

Channel Islands Dining Pub of the Year

This lovely old hotel is peacefully set in good-sized gardens, with picnic-sets among colourful borders, shrubs, bright hanging baskets and flower barrels. Comfortably civilised, its cosy relaxing rooms have low beams and thick granite walls, a good log fire in the public bar (popular with locals), and individual country furnishings in the hotel lounge bar. Bass or Fullers London Pride and Tipsy Toad Sunbeam are well kept on handpump, alongside a good wine list (with around 15 by the glass) and a local cider. A well balanced menu with quite a few choices includes beautifully prepared dishes such as soup (from £3.25), sandwiches (from £2.95), melon with bitter chocolate sorbet (£4.95), sautéed scallops with mango and coconut relish in a filo basket (£6.50), lasagne or steak baguette (£6.95), linguini with porcini mushrooms, tomatoes and spinach with garlic and truffle oil (£8.50), fish and chips (£8.75), sausage and mash or steak, kidney and ale pudding (£8.95), roast monkfish wrapped in prosciutto ham with roast vegetables (£13.95), and daily specials such as roast turbot with tomato and herb provençale sauce (£15.25). The menu in the partly no smoking restaurant amalgamates some bar menu items with other pricier more elaborate dishes; friendly efficient service. They have a large car park and there is a swimming pool for residents. *(Recommended by Phil and Sally Gorton, Sue Demont, Tim Barrow, Gordon Neighbour)*

Free house ~ Licensee Keith Read ~ Real ale ~ Bar food (12-2, 6-9.30(9 Sun)) ~ Restaurant ~ (01481) 257996 ~ Children in eating area of bar and restaurant ~ Open 10-11.45; 12-3, 6.30-10.30 Sun ~ Bedrooms: /£110B

Please let us know of any pubs where the wine is particularly good.

ROZEL Map 1

Rozel

This friendly inn, tucked away at the edge of a sleepy little fishing village and just out of sight of the sea, has a very pleasant steeply terraced and partly covered hillside garden. Inside, the bar counter (Bass, Charles Wells Bombardier and Courage Directors under light blanket pressure) and tables in the traditional-feeling and cosy little dark-beamed back bar are stripped to their original light wood finish, and there are dark plush wall seats and stools, an open granite fireplace, and old prints and local pictures on the cream walls. Leading off is a carpeted area with flowers on big solid square tables. Piped music, and TV, darts, pool, cribbage and dominoes in the games room. Food from a good value menu is served in generous helpings and includes dishes such as soup (£2.95), sandwiches (from £2.95), filled ciabattas (from £4.95, steak £5.50), half a dozen oysters (£6.50), salads and burgers (from £6.95), tempura cod (£7.50), braised lamb shank or fresh fish platter (£8.95), daily specials such as tagliatelle with creamy tomato sauce (£6.95), fillet steak (£14.50) and puddings such as iced parfait or sticky toffee (£3.95); Sunday roast (£8.95). The upstairs restaurant has a relaxed rustic French atmosphere, and a menu with up to ten fish dishes a day, and good value specials. (*Recommended by Mrs Romey Heaton, Dr and Mrs A K Clarke*)

Free house ~ Licensee Trevor Amy ~ Real ale ~ Bar food (12-2.30, 6-8.30) ~ Restaurant (not Sun evening) ~ (01534) 869801 ~ Children welcome ~ Dogs allowed in bar ~ Open 11-11

ST AUBIN Map 1 ⌂

Old Court House Inn ⇔

Harbour Boulevard

The pubby downstairs bar at this 15th-c hotel has cushioned wooden seats built against its stripped granite walls, low black beams, joists in a white ceiling, a turkey carpet, and an open fire. A dimly lantern-lit inner room has an illuminated rather brackish-looking deep well, and beyond that is the spacious cellar room which is open in summer. The conservatory enjoys delightful views over the tranquil harbour and on past St Aubin's fort right across the bay to St Helier, and the Westward Bar is elegantly constructed from the actual gig of a schooner and offers a restauranty menu with prices to match. The front rooms here were once the home of a wealthy merchant, whose cellars stored privateers' plunder alongside more legitimate cargo, and the upstairs restaurant still shows signs of its time as a courtroom. Bar food includes soup (£2.75), ciabattas (from £5.25), starters such as sautéed squid and chorizo with fresh chilli or pork and apple terrine with chickpea and shallot salsa (£6.25), and main courses such as vegetable lasagne (£4.95), lasagne (£5.50), sausage and mash (£8.95), fish and chips (£10.50), fruits de mer cocktail (£9.95), local plaice (£10.50) and grilled dover sole (£19.95). One or two well kept beers might be Bass and Jersey on handpump. It can be difficult to find parking near the hotel. (*Recommended by Mrs Ann Gray, Patrick Hancock*)

Free house ~ Licensee Jonty Sharp ~ Real ale ~ Bar food (12.30-2.30, 7-9; not Sun evening) ~ Restaurant ~ (01534) 746433 ~ Children in eating area of bar, restaurant and family room ~ Dogs allowed in bar ~ Open 11-11.30 ~ Bedrooms: £60B/£120B

ST BRELADE Map 1

Old Portelet Inn £

Portelet Bay

Particularly good for families, this 17th-c farmhouse can get very busy, but does have its quiet moments too. It's well placed at the head of a long flight of granite steps, giving views across Portelet (Jersey's most southerly bay) as you walk down to a sheltered cove. Children will find plenty to amuse them as there's a supervised indoor play area (half an hour 60p), another one outside, board games in the wooden-floored loft bar, and even summer entertainments arranged by the pub.

There are picnic-sets on the partly covered flower-bower terrace by a wishing well, and seats in the sizeable landscaped garden, with lots of scented stocks and other flowers. From a short snack menu, generous helpings of bar food, served by neatly dressed attentive staff includes sandwiches (from £2.30), soup (£2.75), filled baked potatoes (from £5.15), macaroni cheese (£5.20), ratatouille and goats cheese pancake (£5.25), ploughman's (£5.20) and chicken curry (£6.95). The low-beamed downstairs bar has a stone bar counter (well kept Bass and a guest such as Flowers Original kept under light blanket pressure and reasonably priced house wine), a huge open fire, gas lamps, old pictures, etched glass panels from France, and a nice mixture of old wooden chairs on bare oak boards and quarry tiles. It opens into the big timber-ceilinged no smoking barn restaurant, with standing timbers and plenty of highchairs; TV, cribbage, dominoes, and very audible piped music; disabled and baby-changing facilities. *(Recommended by Kay and Alistair Butler, Patrick Hancock, John Evans, Philip and June Caunt)*

Randalls ~ Manager Stephen Jones ~ Real ale ~ Bar food ~ Restaurant ~ (01534) 741899 ~ Children in restaurant and family room ~ Dogs allowed in bar ~ Open 11-11

Old Smugglers
Ouaisne Bay; OS map reference 595476

This straightforward pub is a conversion of a row of old fishermen's cottages, and is picturesquely set on a lane just above the beach. A weatherproof porch takes in interesting views over one of the island's many defence towers, and the welcoming bar has thick walls, black beams, log fires and cosy black built-in settles, as well as well kept Bass and two guests from brewers such as Charles Wells and Ringwood on handpump, and a farm cider; sensibly placed darts, cribbage and dominoes. Bar food includes soup (£2.95), vegetarian spring roll with sweet chilli dip (£4.90), filled baguettes (from £4.95), prawn cocktail (£5.25), steak and Guinness pie or battered haddock (£6.95), chicken curry or lasagne (£7.50), duck breast with orange and brandy sauce (£7.75), king prawns with garlic butter or black bean sauce (£8.95), steaks (from £9.50) and daily specials such as skate wing with prawns and capers (£7.95). The entire restaurant is no smoking. *(Recommended by Patrick Hancock, Darren Le Poidevin)*

Free house ~ Licensee Nigel Godfrey ~ Real ale ~ Bar food (12-2, 6-9; not Sun evening Oct-Mar) ~ Restaurant ~ (01534) 741510 ~ Children in eating area of bar, restaurant and family room ~ Dogs allowed in bar ~ Open 11-11.30

ST HELIER Map 1
Town House
New Street

Popular with locals, this big 1930s pub is fairly unassuming in appearance, the exterior being reminiscent of a converted cinema. More attractive inside, its two main bars are divided by heavy but airy glass and brass doors. The sports bar on the left has two giant TV screens, darts and pool and a juke box. To the right, the lounge area has parquet flooring, some attractive panelling and upholstered armchairs at low round glass tables. Bar food includes soup (£2.95), sandwiches (from £3.55), burgers (from £4.50), fish and chips (£5.75), steak and ale pie (£5.95), spinach and ricotta ravioli (£7.95), and puddings such as Baileys bread and butter pudding (£3.95). Well kept Tipsy Toad Jimmys, and sound house wines, and piped music. *(Recommended by Patrick Hancock)*

Jersey ~ Managers Jackie and Martin Kelly ~ Real ale ~ Bar food (12-2, 6.30-9.30 (not Mon evening or Sun)) ~ Restaurant ~ (01534) 615000 ~ Children after 6pm if eating ~ Live music Thurs evening Oct-Dec ~ Open 11-11

Pubs with outstanding views are listed at the back of the book.

ST JOHN Map 1
Les Fontaines
Le Grand Mourier, Route du Nord

Popular with families and locals, this former farmhouse is in a pretty spot on the north coast, and a nice place for a pint after a walk (well kept Bass and Charles Wells Bombardier). As you go in, look out for a worn, unmarked door at the side of the building, or as you go down the main entry lobby towards the bigger main bar go through the tiny narrow door on your right. These entrances take you into the best part, the public bar, (where you might even hear the true Jersey patois), which has very heavy beams in the low dark ochre ceiling, massively thick irregular red granite walls, cushioned settles on the quarry-tiled floor and antique prints. The big granite-columned fireplace with a log fire warming its unusual inglenook seats may date back to the 14th c, and still sports its old smoking chains and side oven. The carpeted main bar is a marked contrast, with plenty of wheelback chairs around neat dark tables, and a spiral staircase leading up to a wooden gallery under the high pine-raftered plank ceiling; the dining area is no smoking; piped music and board games. A bonus for families is Pirate Pete's, a play area for children. Bar food includes sandwiches (from £2.45), soup (£2.65), ploughman's (from £5.95), battered cod (£6.90), sweet and sour chicken or cumberland sausage (£6.95), baked lamb shank with mash (£8.35) and specials such as grilled mackerel (£7.25), grilled bass (£11) and lobster and prawn salad followed by strawberries and cream (all £12). Seats on a terrace outside have good views, although lorries from the nearby quarry can mar the atmosphere. *(Recommended by Darren Le Poidevin, Kay and Alistair Butler, BOB, Dr and Mrs A K Clarke)*

Randalls ~ Manager Hazel O'Gorman ~ Real ale ~ Bar food (12-2.15(2.45 Sun), 6-9(8.30 Sun)) ~ (01534) 862707 ~ Children welcome ~ Dogs allowed in bar ~ Open 11-11

ST OUENS BAY Map 1
La Pulente
Start of Five Mile Road; OS map reference 562488

With a drink on the terrace, watching the sun go down beyond the endless extent of Jersey's longest beach, this seaside pub makes a good place to end the day. The carpeted lounge (with ragged walls and scrubbed wood tables) and the conservatory share the same sweeping views, and it's the views that are the main reason for coming here. The cheerfully busy public bar has a surfing theme, with photographs and prints on the walls, well kept Bass on handpump, and a juke box, pool, games machine and TV; piped music. Bar food, served by friendly staff, includes sandwiches (from £2.50), soup (£2.50), baked potatoes (from £3.50), ploughman's (from £5), battered cod (£6.75), steak and ale pie (£6.95), thai chicken curry (£7.95), 8oz sirloin (£10.95) and daily specials such as roast duck breast (£11.50) and grilled lemon sole (£12.50). *(Recommended by John Evans, Dr and Mrs A K Clarke)*

Randalls ~ Manager Julia Wallace ~ Real ale ~ Bar food (12-2.15(2.45 Sun), 6-9; not Sun evening) ~ Restaurant ~ (01534) 744487 ~ Children in eating area of bar and restaurant ~ Dogs allowed in bar ~ Open 11-11

Several well known guide books make establishments pay for entry, either directly or as a fee for inspection. These fees can run to many hundreds of pounds. We do not. Unlike other guides, we never take payment for entries. We never accept a free meal, free drink, or any other freebie from a pub. We do not accept any sponsorship — let alone from commercial schemes linked to the pub trade. All our entries depend solely on merit.

LUCKY DIP

Besides the fully inspected pubs, you might like to try these Lucky Dips recommended to us and described by readers (if you do, please send us reports: www.goodguides.co.uk).

GUERNSEY

CASTEL
New Vazon Bay Hotel [Vazon Coast Rd]: Hotel nr stunning beach, pleasant bustling bar with dozens of whiskies, Randalls and Sam Smiths beers, enjoyable plentiful food inc popular fish and chips, sensibly priced restaurant; 25 bedrooms *(Geoff Pidoux, Gordon Neighbour)*

GRANDE HAVRE
Houmet [part of Houmet du Nord Hotel; Rte de Picquerel]: Friendly and well run, with good choice of reasonably priced food inc good fresh local scampi, big picture windows overlooking rock and sand beach; bedrooms some talk of possible redevelopment] *(BB, Gordon Neighbour)*

ST MARTIN
Auberge Divette [Jerbourg Rd]: Now restaurant-with-bar rather than pub, but worth knowing for glorious view of coast and Herm from floodlit garden high above sea and smartly refurbished picture-window lounge and dining room, good food, good range of wines by the glass, helpful staff; spectacular cliff walk to St Peter Port *(LYM, Geoff Pidoux)*

ST SAVIOUR
St Saviours Tavern [Grande Rue]: Popular with locals for good choice of reasonably priced food from baked potatoes to local seafood and steak *(Gordon Neighbour)*

TORTEVAL
Imperial [Pleinmont (coast rd, nr Pleinmont Point)]: Good choice of meals inc good seafood and traditional Guernsey bean jar in dining room which like the bar has a great sea view over Rocquaine Bay, Randalls beers; tables in untrap garden, bedrooms in hotel part separate from the pub, handy for good beach *(Mrs Romey Heaton, Gordon Neighbour)*

JERSEY

GOREY
Castle Green [steep climb to castle, above]: Former Randalls local above the village, now operating as a dining pub and already getting popular for its fresh local food *(anon)*

ST HELIER
☆ *Original Wine Bar* [Bath St]: Welcoming, informal and relaxed, with cheerful helpful staff, comfortable sofas and armchairs and great character, good choice of interesting lunchtime food (not Sun) inc good sandwiches and wraps, all-day home-made tapas, five well kept real ales from island and mainland, dutch lager on tap, very good choice of wines by the glass, coffees and teas, no smoking area; good wheelchair access *(BB, Peter Hopkins, Richard Ward)*

ST JOHN
Auberge du Nord [Route du Nord]: Old pub with good value tasty food such as pies, seafood and steaks upstairs, good snacks too, pool room off bar *(Darren Le Poidevin)*

ST MARTIN
☆ *Royal Hotel* [Gde Rte de Faldouet, by church]: Roomy and friendly family local by church in untouristy village, helpful landlord and staff, wide choice of generous popular well priced food in large efficiently run no smoking eating area, well kept Wadworths 6X as well as local beer, decent wines, toys and video games in small children's room off extended lounge, games in public bar, attractive upstairs restaurant, old prints and bric-a-brac; piped music, nightly live music; good disabled access and facilities, tables out on big terrace with play area, open all day *(LYM, Paul Goldman)*

ST PETER
☆ *Original Wine Bar* [St Peters Village]: Unpretentious four-room real ale pub with bare boards, stripped stonework, panelling, tasty and filling pubby food (not Sun) from sandwiches to steaks, friendly staff, games room with darts, pool etc, big-screen sports TV, family conservatory; Fri or Sat band nights; children welcome, disabled facilities, terrace and play area, open all day *(LYM, Darren Le Poidevin)*

Overseas Lucky Dip

We're always interested to hear of good bars and pubs overseas – preferably really good examples of bars that visitors would find memorable, rather than transplanted 'British pubs'. A star marks places we would be confident would deserve a main entry. It's common for good bars overseas, if they serve food, to serve it all day (a pleasant contrast to the UK, where most pubs outside big cities actually close for much of the day, let alone serve food all day). In many foreign bars, partly thanks to the fairly strong £, drinks are relatively cheap – note that this is not the case in Hong Kong, nor (surprisingly) in Dublin. On the other hand, the Republic of Ireland's new ban on smoking in pubs is now having a real effect. For this reason, we have this year separated the Ireland pubs listed into Republic (smoking ban) and Northern (no ban yet).

AUSTRALIA
SYDNEY
Australian [100 Cumberland St, The Rocks]: Substantial modernist 1913 Federation-style building, sturdily furnished two-level bar, a dozen beers on tap and over a hundred bottled beers, lots of wines by the glass (and a good 'bottle shop' or off licence specialising in fine wines), bar food inc unusual pizzas and kangaroo pie; roof-terrace views of opera house and Sydney Harbour Bridge, wicker chairs for terrace tables, bedrooms sharing bathrooms *(Ian Phillips)*

BELGIUM
ANTWERP
Hof Van Eden [Groenplats 11]: Smart café on main square below impressive cathedral tower, usual local beers and food (good value in comparison with Bruges establishments); tables outside *(Michael Dandy)*
Kumulator [Kleine Markt]: A must if you're interested in beer – they stock 550, either off the shelf or from the cellar; even the english bottled beers include ones that are very rare here (eg Courage Russian Stout) or virtually unobtainable (eg Bass Kings Ale), and the belgian and other continental ones are quite remarkable *(George Hamer)*
Paters Vaetje [1 Blaumoezelstraat]: Tall narrow bar in 17th-c building by cathedral, interesting old interior with marble-top tables on quarry tiles, carved wood counter, old beer advertisements, small panelled back gallery up steep spiral stairs (occasionally visited by an aloof cat), good beer list with four on tap and over 100 by the bottle, friendly helpful staff, pubby food; lavatories clean though not for the shy; tables outside ideal for the carillon concerts *(Brian and Anita Randall)*

BRUGES
Celtic Ireland [Burg 8]: Unusual multi-level irish theme pub with celtic décor, plenty of irish drinks and food from speciality sandwiches up – local specialities and beers etc too; TV, live music *(Michael Dandy)*
Civière d'Or [Markt 33]: Smart split-level café/restaurant behind crenellated façade, dark panelling, plenty of beers on tap inc Maes and Grimbergen, good wine and authentic local food from flemish stew and tasty waffles to lobsters from live tank – a civilised if pricey escape from the touristy market and the other day-tripping brits (the only blot on this delightful town with its polite locals speaking perfect English); heated and covered tables outside *(Michael Dandy)*
Erasmus [Wollestraat 35]: Small welcoming modernish hotel bar enlivened by friendly landlord's interest in his 300-plus helpfully described beers, enjoyable traditional belgian food in partly no smoking bistro area; piped classical music; comfortable bedrooms *(Mark and Ruth Brock)*
Fonteintje [Simon Stevin Plein 6]: Small good value bar/restaurant just off main shopping street, very helpful staff *(Michael Dandy)*
☆ *Garre* [1 de Garre, off Breidelstraat]: Attractive, welcoming and airy bar in 16th-c timbered building, stripped brickwork, no smoking upper gallery, elegant and civilised but very relaxed and unstuffy, well over 100 mainly local beers inc five Trappists and its own draught beer (each well served in its own glass with cheese nibbles), coffees and light snacks too, sensible prices, knowledgeable helpful staff; unobtrusive piped classical music no standing if tables are full – get there early; children welcome *(Jo Lilley, Simon Calvert, Mark and Ruth Brock)*
Pannier d'Or [Markt 28]: Typical café in main

square opp belfry tower, good belgian beer, nice omelettes and good chips, friendly service; not cheap *(Michael Dandy)*

Tom Pouce [Burg 17]: Large café in secondary square by some lovely old buildings, good choice of beers, snacks and main dishes inc lots of mussels, friendly service *(Michael Dandy)*

Vlissinghe [Blekersstraat]: Very old café away from the tourist centre, unspoilt décor and atmosphere, small choice of beers and snacks; some garden seating *(Mark and Ruth Brock)*

BRUSSELS

Bécasse [11 rue de Tabora]: Rather genteel brown café, ornate highly polished scrolled brass lamps showing its dark panelling and beams well, unblended Lambic (both white and sweet, young and old) served at the table in traditional blue and grey stone pitchers, also local fruit-flavoured Gueuze and other belgian beers such as Kwak served in its distinctive glass like a mini yard of ale, good cheap food such as croques monsieur or croustades made with beer and asparagus; open all day *(Tracey and Stephen Groves, Anthony Longden)*

Bon Vieux Temps [rue Marché aux Herbes 12]: Classy and relaxing L-shaped brown café down white-tiled passage, dating from 1695, with beautifully carved dark panelling, stained glass, several unspoiled nooks and crannies, old tables inlaid with delft tiles, eccentrically shaped stove in huge fireplace, friendly landlady and helpful staff, wide range of classic beers such as Duvel, Grimbergen Blonde and Brune, Leffe, Orval *(Anthony Longden)*

Imaige de Nostre-Dame [Impasse des Cadeaux, off rue du Marché aux Herbes]: Dark, relaxed and intriguing locals' bar tucked down alleyway nr Grand Place, through elaborate stone arch topped by weathered statue; two rough and ready rooms with right old mix of furniture, bags of character, wide range of belgian beers; outside lavatories; open till midnight *(Anthony Longden)*

Mort Subite [R Montagne aux Herbes Potagères; off Grand Place via ornate Galeries St Hubert]: Under same family since 1928, long highly traditional fin de siècle room divided by two rows of pillars into nave with double rows of small polished tables and side aisles with single row, huge mirrors on all sides, leather seats, brisk uniformed waiters and waitresses bustling from lovely mirrored serving counter on dais on right; lots of belgian beers inc Duvel, Gueuze, Grimbergen, Orval, Westmalle and their own speciality Kriek and other fruit beers brewed nearby (served by the bucket if you want), good straightforward food inc big omelettes, croques monsieur or madame, and local specialities such as brawn and rice tart, no piped music *(Anthony Longden)*

WESTVLETEREN

In de Vrede [Donkerstraat – follow Abdij St Sixtus signs off Poperinge rd]: Airy modern café in open country opp St Sixtus monastery, Trappist beer, simple snacks, useful for lunch when visiting World War I sites; shop, cl Fri *(Mark and Ruth Brock)*

HAVANA

Hotel Nacional: Hotel built 1930 as casino in flamboyant Spanish Colonial style, included for its Bar of Fame, hundreds of former customers from Winston Churchill to Nat King Cole, Yuri Gagarin to the Manic Street Preachers, pictured in floor-to-ceiling paintings in decade order around the bar, good range of drinks, cigars in various sizes, pubby food in another bar downstairs; bedrooms *(Keith and Chris O'Neill)*

PRAGUE

Café Montmartre [Retezova 7]: Tucked nicely away in quiet street parallel to Karlova (between new town square and Charles Bridge), shabby-chic and convivial café-bar with the odd easy chair and sofa as well as bentwood tables and chairs, attractive décor and few if any brits, good drinks hot and cold inc the usual beers from long bar, friendly laid-back staff and customers – some food, but primarily a place where people spin out a drink or a coffee for hours of chat *(BB, Ian Martin)*

Cerneho Vola [Loretanske Namesti 1]: Up steps above castle, still unspoilt, friendly and jolly, with beams, leaded lights, long dark benches or small stand-up entrance bar, good Kozel Pale and Dark 12 black beer, and Velkopopovicky Korel lager, local snacks; can get very busy (though rarely too touristy), cl 9 *(the Didler, J M Tansey)*

Fleku [Kremencova 11, Nove Mesto]: Brewing its own strong tasty black Flekovsky Dark 13 since 1843 (some say 1499); waiters will try to sell you a schnapps with it – say Ne firmly; huge, with benches and big refectory tables in two big dark-beamed rooms – tourists on right with 10-piece oompah band, more local on left (music here too), also courtyard after courtyard; good basic food – sausages, pork, goulash with dumplings; open early morning to late night, can be very busy and noisy with tourists *(the Didler, John Dwane)*

Medvidku [Na Perstyne 5, Stare Mesto]: Superb old building in red light district, namesake bears etched in stone over entry, lots of copper in left bar, bigger right room more for eating, Budvar Budweiser on tap *(Myke and Nicky Crombleholme, the Didler)*

Pivovarsky Dum [Lipova 15]: Brewpub with big windows showing fermentation room and brewing equipment, smart modern green décor and woodwork, interesting range inc wheat, banana, cherry and even coffee and champagne beers as well as classic lager (tempting brewing aromas out on the street), served by the gallon stick with its own tap if you wish, low prices, good choice of english-style food, friendly service; open all day *(the Didler, John Dwane)*

Senk Vrbovec [10 Wenceslas Sq (nr bottom, on right as you look up to National Museum at far end)]: Utterly untouristy and local, very small wine bar (coffee and beer too, but the very cheap good wine from the barrel is the main thing), tall deco stools at high peninsula tables, wine-related old photographs on dark cork-lined walls, mainly regulars inc just one or two women; foreigners seem sufficiently rare here to be worth an initial look, but not in the least unwelcoming *(BB)*

St Nicholas Café [Trziste 10]: Semi-basement café-bar, dark and snug, very friendly and relaxed, little more than candles at night, cosy and intimate seating, good snacks and light meals, good coffee as well as the usual beers and wines, well reproduced up-to-date piped music; a good escape from the stag party bars *(BB, Ian Martin)*

Vejvodu [Jilska 4]: Carefully rebuilt and extended next door, with thriving atmosphere, good service, well presented food, good value Pilsner Urquell; roomy but can get busy, handy for old town square *(the Didler, Myke and Nicky Crombleholme)*

FALKLAND ISLANDS
STANLEY

Malvina Hotel : Large pleasant lounge bar, neatly kept, friendly and locally popular, with australian lager and good chilean wine, adjoining restaurant *(Val and Alan Green)*

FRANCE
MEGÈVE

St-Paul [43 Quai du Prieuré]: Quiet central bar-tabac with more local flavour than usual for this smart resort, inexpensive lagers on tap, may be free peanuts *(Ian Phillips)*

PARIS

Grand Carnot [32 Avenue Carnot]: Good value convivial brasserie, friendly efficient service, reasonably priced beers, good choice of wines by the glass (best buys are beaujolais crus and lesser clarets), robust food inc good steaks *(Steve Whalley, Bob)*

GERMANY
COLOGNE

Café Reichard [Unter Fettenhannen 11]: Attractively decorated large café with decent food from light dishes through pasta to hearty main dishes, usual drinks inc mainly white and rosé wines by the glass; great cathedral views from terrace *(Michael Dandy)*

Kunibert der Fleise [Am Bollwerk]: One of several Rhine-side cafés, wide food and beer choice; tables out on the grass, bedrooms *(Michael Dandy)*

IRELAND (NORTHERN)
BELFAST

Botanic [Malone Rd]: Cavernous pub with Whitewater real ale from main room's curving bar counter, reasonably priced bar lunches inc three-course bargain Sun lunch, coal fire in cosy front bar with dark panelled ceiling and nicely carved bar counter; live music nightly and bouncy then (doormen on duty), very

popular with students *(David Crook, C J Fletcher)*

Bridge House [Bedford St]: Two-level Wetherspoons with two no smoking areas, usual good value food with regional variations, two real ales; piped music may be loud wknds or evening; children in family area *(C J Fletcher)*

☆ *Crown* [Gt Victoria St, opp Europa Hotel]: Well preserved ornate and bustling 19th-c National Trust gin palace with pillared entrance, opulent tiles outside and in, elaborately coloured windows, almost church-like ceiling, handsome mirrors, lots of individual snug booths with little doors and bells for waiter service (some graffiti too now, alas), gas lighting, mosaic tiled floor, well kept if pricey Whitewater real ale from imposing granite-top counter with colourful tiled facing, good lunchtime meals till 5 upstairs inc oysters; very wide and sometimes noisy range of customers (can take their toll on the downstairs gents'), and shame about the TV; open all day *(GLD, J M Tansey, Patrick Hancock, Joe Green, C J Fletcher)*

Deers Head [Lower Garfield St]: Preserved Victorian bar, enjoyable usual bar food, large restaurant area *(David Crook)*

John Hewitt [Donegall St]: Popular restaurant by day, vibrant bar with live music by night *(Keith and Chris O'Neill)*

Kitchen [Victoria St]: Spacious new bar (replacing original, demolished in redevelopment), three real ales inc Whitewater, different levels, leather-padded settles and smart leather armchairs; big-screen TV carefully tucked away so that it's invisible from most parts *(J M Tansey, C J Fletcher)*

McHughs [Queens Sq]: Extensively restored and extended (dates from 1711), with eclectic design in several linked rooms, comfortable leather chairs and settles around marble-top tables, Belfast Whitewater Ale and Porter *(C J Fletcher)*

Morning Star [Pottingers Entry]: Former coaching inn with large island bar, settles, mahogany stools at high tables, snug and side rooms, food specialising in fresh fish and steaks (even crocodile ones), with bar buffet 11.45-3.30 *(David Crook)*

Robinsons [Gt Victoria St]: Ground-floor saloon with quiet corners, high bar stools, good Guinness, upstairs restaurant with good window tables ideal for people-watching, above that a disco *(David Crook)*

Whites [Winecellar Entry]: Low-beamed alehouse, said to be town's oldest, very popular esp when there's live music, Hoegaarden and Guinness on tap; no real ale, can get quite smoky *(C J Fletcher)*

BUSHMILLS

Bushmills [Co Antrim]: Cosy inn with 17th-c core, linked rooms in various styles inc gaslit ochre-walled inner room with sofa, settles, windsor chairs and original cooking pots by huge peat fire, another in hallway inglenook, well kept beers, wide choice of wines and spirits, friendly efficient staff, good restaurant;

pleasant comfortable bedrooms, handy for
Giant's Causeway and the venerable Bushmills
Distillery *(Anthony Longden)*

LISBURN

Tuesday Bell [Lisburn Sq; Co Antrim]: Two-
level Wetherspoons with three well kept real
ales, prompt friendly service, low prices for
food and drink; lift for disabled access to upper
floor, in attractive old town *(C J Fletcher)*

IRELAND (REPUBLIC)

AVOCA

Fitzgeralds [just off R752; Co Wicklow]:
Coach trips come to this small ordinary village
to see this, the pub in TV's *Ballykissangel*;
lots of souvenirs, reasonable drinks prices
(Keith and Chris O'Neill)

BLARNEY

Blairs [Co Cork]: Warmly welcoming, with
enjoyable food in landlady's speciality
puddings in small dining room *(M and
R Thomas)*

CORK

Corner House [Coburg St]: Dark and
convivial, live music all week inc folk Weds
(Phil and Sally Gorton)
Sin ... [Coburg St]: Dark and cosy, traditional
brown décor with pictures and ephemera,
usual beers, friendly efficient service; live music
inc folk Tues *(Phil and Sally Gorton)*

CROOKHAVEN

O'Sullivans [Co Cork]: Very convivial, the
British Isles' most south-westerly pub, with
good fresh crab sandwiches, usual drinks; seats
out overlooking tiny village's harbour
(Geoff Calcott)

DUBLIN

Arlington [Bachelor's Walk, O'Connell St]:
Huge open-plan bar by River Liffey, several
areas, enjoyable food, efficient service, great
atmosphere, nightly live folk music and
dancing – several TVs show this live, then in
repeats next day *(Keith and Chris O'Neill)*
Brazen Head [Lower Bridge St]: Charming bar,
said to be oldest here, maze of dimly lit cosy
unspoilt rooms off attractive red and white
tiled passage, with old beams, mirrors, old
settles inc one given by Thin Lizzy's Phil
Lynnot, open fires; lunchtime bar food from
filled cobs to carvery, evening restaurant, well
served Guinness; peaceful front courtyard,
traditional music each night, main bar very
busy Sun lunchtime with music too *(Keith and
Chris O'Neill)*
Doheny & Nesbitt [Lower Baggot St, by the
Shelburne just below St Stephens Green]:
Friendly traditional pub, originally a grocer's,
close to Parliament; sensitively extended from
original core, with Victorian bar fittings,
marble-topped tables, wooden screens, old
whiskey mirrors etc; mainly drink (inc good
Guinness) and conversation, but has good
value toasties, panini, irish stew and so forth;
live music, can get very busy but worth the
wait *(Jo Lilley, Simon Calvert, J M Tansey)*
Gravity Bar [St James Gate Guinness Brewery]:
Great views from huge round glass-walled

tasting bar on top floor – effectively Dublin's
highest vantage-point; Guinness at its best;
culmination of up-to-date exhibition on firm's
history, brewing and advertising campaigns,
also lower Storehouse bar with lunchtime food
and gift shop *(Keith and Chris O'Neill,
David Crook)*
Ha'penny Bridge [Temple Bar]: Unchanged
18th-c corner pub with L-shaped bar, usual
drinks, tea, good coffee, soup, sandwiches and
snacks; may be piped radio, some live music –
and they don't play 'Wild Rover'; children
allowed till 7 *(David Crook)*
Madigans [O'Connell St]: Plenty of atmosphere
in relaxed traditional pub very near the historic
GPO of the 1916 Easter Rising; good choice of
snacks and light meals, friendly people, usual
drinks, good tea; may be piped pop music
(Keith and Chris O'Neill)
Messrs Maguires [O'Connell Bridge, S side]:
Well restored early 19th-c splendour, four
floors with huge staircase, superb woodwork
and ceilings, flame-effect gas fires, tasteful
décor inc contemporary irish prints and
functioning library; good own-brewed keg
beers inc Stout, Extra Stout, Red Ale, Rusty
Ale and lager, good coffee, enjoyable
reasonably priced food from interesting
sandwiches through very popular lunchtime
carvery to top-floor gourmet restaurant; two
TVs; irish music Sun-Tues from 9.30 *(CMW,
JJW, Phil and Sally Gorton, J M Tansey)*
☆ *O'Donoghues* [Merrion Row, off St Stephens
Green]: Small old-fashioned Victorian bar,
vibrant, noisy and crowded, with dark
panelling, mirrors, posters and snob screens,
musical instruments and other bric-a-brac on
ceiling, bank-note collection behind long side
counter; fine Guinness, long-armed landlord
ensures quick friendly service even when busy,
popular with musicians – perhaps an
impromptu riot of Celtic tunes played on
anything from spoons to banjo or pipes;
plainer back bar has live music too; open all
day *(David Crook)*
O'Neills [Suffolk St]: Spreading early Victorian
pub with lots of dark panelling and cubby-
holes off big lively bar, more rooms upstairs,
good lunchtime carvery (all day Sun), good
value doorstep sandwiches and home-made
soup, quick efficient service, good Guinness
*(Jo Lilley, Simon Calvert, Keith and
Chris O'Neill)*
O'Sheas [Talbot St]: Good Guinness, good live
irish music *(J M Tansey)*
Oliver St John Gogarty [Anglesea St, Temple
Bar]: Large bustling bare-boards bars, bric-a-
brac inc bicycle above counter, generous good
if not cheap food in fairly small cosy upper-
floor restaurant (former bank, interesting
preserved features) and at lunchtime in main
bar, friendly efficient service; rambles through
into adjoining Left Bank bar which has integral
heated terrace tables; live music upstairs
*(David Crook, Keith and Chris O'Neill,
J M Tansey)*
Porterhouse [Parliament St, nr Wellington
Quay]: Vibrant three-storey modern pub, lots

of pine and brass for café-bar feel, brewing half a dozen good beers inc several Porters (particularly good) and usually a cask-conditioned real ale, guest beers such as Shepherd Neame, dozens of foreign bottled beers, friendly efficient service, lots of anti-Guinness propaganda; high tables and equally high seats, good food from ciabatta sandwiches to steaks, upstairs restaurant; piped music, nightly live music, can be standing room only wknds *(Keith and Chris O'Neill, Jo Lilley, Simon Calvert, Emma and Will, J M Tansey)*
Temple Bar [Temple Bar]: Rambling multi-levelled, many-roomed pub, much extended at back; rather bohemian, usually crowded; tables out in big yard, good live music from 4pm *(Keith and Chris O'Neill)*

ISLE OF MAN
DOUGLAS [SC3876]
Cornerhouse [Ridgeway St, between Lord St bus station and Peel Rd railway station]: Open-plan brasserie feel, lots of little nooks and crannies as well as larger areas, lunchtime food, good atmosphere and friendly staff, decent wines in baby bottles, pool and darts; live music; open all day *(Dr J Barrie Jones)*

ITALY
ROME
Café Greco [Via Condotti]: Ornate marble-floored rooms with red flock wallpaper, gilding, pictures, busts and silhouette reliefs, stretching back from front bar with espresso etc, great atmosphere and long history; reassuringly expensive *(Anthony Longden)*

LATVIA
RIGA
Alus Seta [6 Tirgonu Iela, by Dome Sq]: Now all no smoking, with cheap Lido (brewed at another establishment in this Lido chain – most of which are more restaur, Aldaris and excellent Uzavas, also tea and coffee, all-day self-service food bar inc shashliks and local specialities as well as lasagne and steaks, beams, timbers and panelling, sliding windows to pavement tables, narrow passage to back drinking hall with own bar, décor of old prints, latvian sayings, bric-a-brac and a constellation of small lights; tables outside (where you can hear bands playing for the nearby more expensive Dome beer gardens), open all day, very wide range of customers *(Martin Grosberg)*

MADEIRA
FUNCHAL
Prince Albert [off Avenida do Infante, nr Savoy Hotel]: Refuge for homesick brits, owned by ex-pats, with Victorian-style dark panelling, wicker chairs and cast-iron-framed tables on tiled floor, old-fashioned curved bar, lots of advertising mirrors and colonial prints, good

value sandwich snacks with chips until midnight, a dozen unusual though pricey british bottled beers as well as Guinness, local lagers and keg beers, darts, books for sale; several screens for SkyTV sports, piped local and 60s music, quiz nights; open all day *(Kevin Thorpe, W W Burke)*

MALTA
RABAT
Jubilee Café [P Indipendenza; Gozo]: Old-fashioned café-bar with tea, coffee and snacks as well as beers and wines, friendly staff, good mix of customers *(Jo Lilley, Simon Calvert)*

NETHERLANDS
ALKMAAR
Grand Café [Houtill]: Typical brown café with dark panelling, books and old pictures, usual drinks, good food choice inc baguettes, pancakes and well made omelettes, friendly service *(Michael Dandy)*
AMSTERDAM
Dantzig [Waterlooplein]: Large modern café with usual good choice of beers and other drinks, food from good sandwiches to steak; plenty of tables outside overlooking River Amstel and canals, handy for concert hall and opera house *(Michael Dandy)*
Grand Café [Kleine Gartmanplantsoen]: Large café with good beer choice, good value food from breakfasts and sandwiches up, conservatory; tables out by square at end of main shopping street *(Michael Dandy)*
Pantry [Leidsekruisstraat 21]: Small cosy café with usual drinks, good choice of traditional dutch food, friendly helpful service *(Michael Dandy)*
Passage [Niewwnedijk]: Small café nr palace, beers and coffees, enjoyable food inc some dutch specialities; seats out behind overlooking main square *(Michael Dandy)*
Prins [Prinsengracht 124]: Friendly and appealing brown café on one of the most picturesque canals, well prepared generous food from good lunchtime sandwiches and fashionable snacks to steaks, wider evening choice (can be hard to get a table then), mainly dutch beers with one or two belgians such as La Chouffe, nice local atmosphere; seats out on both sides of street, opp Anne Frank Museum *(Christine and Neil Townend, Michael Dandy)*
LEIDEN
Scarlati [Stille Mare 4]: Good choice of drinks and food, friendly service, handy for canals and picturesque town centre *(Michael Dandy)*
Van der Werff [Steenstraat 2]: Modern riverside café with usual drinks, food from generous baguettes to some dutch specialities, friendly helpful service *(Michael Dandy)*

NEW ZEALAND
QUEENSTOWN
Speights Old Ale House [Stanley St]: Copper dome and stone fireplace, high bar stools, good

riendly service, six local beers on tap, massive elpings of enjoyable food such as liver and acon with their own bread; piped music may e loud, SkyTV; old tractor seats as outside eating *(David Crook)*

OTORUA

ig & Whistle [Tutanekai/Haupapa St; North sland]: Former police station, rare example of 940s architecture, good local beers on tap inc peights Gold, enjoyable generous simple food; ve music wknds; large covered outdoor eating area *(David Crook)*

OLAND

DANSK

romenada [Kotwkz Powroz Ponczosz]: riendly café-bar with nice views over enovated waterfront, local lagers and easonably priced lunches; handy for Arthus Court and City Hall *(Andrew York)*

NGAPORE

NGAPORE

affles [Beach Rd]: Magnificent national onument, lavishly restored: Long Bar well worth a visit for its atmosphere, Singapore ings, waving 'leaf' fans overhead, and nderfoot peanut shells (they're said to polish ie floor); also sedate Billiards Bar, Tiffin .oom with elaborate changing buffets, more xpensive meals in the Writer's Room, and five ther food outlets each with its own style of ooking; cultural and Raffles displays, striking hristmas displays out in front; prices can be aunting if you stay *(Roger and enny Huggins, Paul Humphreys)*

OUTH AFRICA

APE TOWN

litchells [Dock Rd, Foreshore]: Two-floor ub, smart but straightforward, with balcony verlooking own brewery in converted arehouse, good Bosun, Forresters and pecial, also fine Knysna beers, imported keg eers and food at attractive prices for this aterfront area; nr aquarium *(Tracey and tephen Groves)*

TORMS RIVER VILLAGE

sitsikamma Village Inn [Garden Route]: ubby bar by handsomely appointed hotel's ool, good value snacks and good Knysna eers, friendly inside with dark panelling, rints and stuffed animals; attractive Cape olonial style chalets in lovely gardens *Tracey and Stephen Groves)*

PAIN

ARCELONA

ar del Pi [Pl Sant Josep]: Small dark tapas ar, stand at counter for wines, good local beer nd tapas; tables out in lively square, old town r cathedral *(Ian Phillips)*

oria Café [Pl Major, Poble Espanyol]: afé/bar with tapas and good local beer under

shady arcade, overlooking square in 1929 re-creation of regional spanish building styles *(Ian Phillips)*

Font de Prades [Pl de la Font]: Friendly bar/restaurant with good very reasonably priced food and wine, in tiny square with fountain; tables out in sheltered courtyard *(Ian Phillips)*

NERJA

Bar Okey [Gloria 9]: Enjoyable food in nice surroundings, ex-pat managers, good choice of whiskies and whiskeys and of UK keg beers, plenty of regulars – even genuine locals *(D and M T Ayres-Regan)*

ST HELENA

GEORGETOWN

Obsidian Hotel [Ascension Island]: Good-sized seating areas inside and out, small well stocked bar with decent lager and good south african wine, food lunchtime and evening if you book (not necessary Sat lunchtime); incidentally the island's airport bar has the irresistible name of Terminal Drinks *(Val and Alan Green)*

SWEDEN

STOCKHOLM

Absolut Icebar [Nordic Sea Hotel, Vasaplan 2-4]: Unique: you wear thermal hooded coats and gloves and are served vodka (non-alcoholic cocktails too) in glasses made from ice; numbers limited, so best to book, no food *(Andy and Jill Kassube)*

SWITZERLAND

CHÂTEL-ST-DENIS

Lac des Joncs [Les Paccots]: Idyllic bar/restaurant overlooking its own quiet little lake, local beer on tap, good food esp local trout, lovely views *(Ian Phillips)*

USA

NEW YORK

Burp Castle [41 East 7th St, East Village]: Excuse the name: tremendous range of mainly bottled beers (even beer-haters will find one they like – try the peach beer on tap), weekly-changing food menu, good music, entertaining murals, waiters wearing friars' robes *(Jan Dobris)*

ORLANDO

George & Dragon [International Dr]: US staff but landlord from Stoke-on-Trent, and even an old red british telephone box; food all day inc bangers and mash, terrace tables *(Colin Gooch)*

TOPSHAM

Maine Sea Dog [Main St]: Big mill conversion, arched windows, huge beams and timbers, bare boards, good food and ten or so of their interesting Sea Dog beers, friendly service, pool room; tables out on side deck overlooking Androscoggin River rapids *(Dr and Mrs M E Wilson)*

Special Interest Lists

The pubs listed here have bigger or more beautiful gardens, grounds or terraces than are usual for their areas. Note that in a town or city this might be very much more modest than the sort of garden that would deserve a listing in the countryside.

BEDFORDSHIRE
Milton Bryan, Red Lion
Northill, Crown
Old Warden, Hare & Hounds
Ridgmont, Rose & Crown
Riseley, Fox & Hounds

BERKSHIRE
Aldworth, Bell
Ashmore Green, Sun in the Wood
Frilsham, Pot Kiln
Hurst, Green Man
Inkpen, Crown & Garter
Marsh Benham, Red House
Shinfield, Magpie & Parrot
White Waltham, Beehive
Winterbourne, Winterbourne Arms

BUCKINGHAMSHIRE
Bennett End, Three Horseshoes
Bovingdon Green, Royal Oak
Denham, Swan
Dorney, Palmer Arms
Ford, Dinton Hermit
Hawridge Common, Full Moon
Hedgerley, White Horse
Mentmore, Stag
Oving, Black Boy
Penn, Crown
Skirmett, Frog

CAMBRIDGESHIRE
Elton, Black Horse
Fowlmere, Chequers
Heydon, King William IV

CHESHIRE
Aldford, Grosvenor Arms
Bunbury, Dysart Arms
Haughton Moss, Nags Head
Macclesfield, Sutton Hall Hotel

CORNWALL
Helford, Shipwrights Arms
Mousehole, Old Coastguard
St Agnes, Turks Head
St Kew, St Kew Inn
St Mawgan, Falcon
Trematon, Crooked Inn
Tresco, New Inn

CUMBRIA
Ambleside, Wateredge
Barbon, Barbon Inn
Bassenthwaite Lake, Pheasant
Bouth, White Hart
Staveley, Eagle & Child

DERBYSHIRE
Hathersage, Plough
Melbourne, John Thompson
Woolley Moor, White Horse

DEVON
Berrynarbor, Olde Globe
Broadhembury, Drewe Arms
Clayhidon, Merry Harriers
Clyst Hydon, Five Bells
Cornworthy, Hunters Lodge
Exeter, Imperial
Exminster, Turf Hotel
Haytor Vale, Rock
Lower Ashton, Manor Inn
Lydford, Castle Inn
Newton Abbot, Two Mile Oak
Newton Ferrers, Dolphin
Poundsgate, Tavistock Inn
Sidbury, Hare & Hounds
Sidford, Blue Ball
Torbryan, Old Church House

DORSET
Cerne Abbas, Royal Oak
Chideock, George
Marshwood, Bottle
Osmington Mills, Smugglers
Plush, Brace of Pheasants
Shave Cross, Shave Cross Inn
Shroton, Cricketers
Tarrant Monkton, Langton Arms

ESSEX
Castle Hedingham, Bell
Chappel, Swan
Fyfield, Queens Head
Great Yeldham, White Hart
Hastingwood, Rainbow & Dove
Mill Green, Viper
Stock, Hoop
Wendens Ambo, Bell

GLOUCESTERSHIRE
Blaisdon, Red Hart
Ewen, Wild Duck
Nailsworth, Egypt Mill
Nether Westcote, New Inn
Northleach, Wheatsheaf
Upper Oddington, Horse & Groom

HAMPSHIRE
Bramdean, Fox
Exton, Shoe
Ovington, Bush
Steep, Harrow
Stockbridge, Grosvenor, Three Cups
Tichborne, Tichborne Arms

HEREFORDSHIRE
Aymestrey, Riverside Inn
Sellack, Lough Pool
Ullingswick, Three Crowns
Woolhope, Butchers Arms

HERTFORDSHIRE
Ashwell, Three Tuns
Chapmore End, Woodman
Potters Crouch, Holly Bush
Preston, Red Lion
Sarratt, Cock

ISLE OF WIGHT
Shorwell, Crown

KENT
Biddenden, Three Chimneys
Bough Beech, Wheatsheaf
Boyden Gate, Gate Inn
Brookland, Woolpack
Chiddingstone, Castle Inn
Dargate, Dove
Fordcombe, Chafford Arms
Groombridge, Crown
Hucking, Hook & Hatchet
Newnham, George
Penshurst, Bottle House
Selling, Rose & Crown
Ulcombe, Pepper Box

LANCASHIRE
Newton, Parkers Arms
Whitewell, Inn at Whitewell

LEICESTERSHIRE AND RUTLAND
Barrowden, Exeter Arms
Exton, Fox & Hounds
Lyddington, Old White Hart
Medbourne, Nevill Arms
Peggs Green, New Inn
Stathern, Red Lion

LINCOLNSHIRE
Billingborough, Fortescue Arms
Coningsby, Lea Gate Inn
Lincoln, Victoria
Newton, Red Lion
Stamford, George of Stamford

NORFOLK
Burnham Thorpe, Lord Nelson
Ringstead, Gin Trap
Snettisham, Rose & Crown
Stanhoe, Crown
Stow Bardolph, Hare Arms
Woodbastwick, Fur & Feather

NORTHAMPTONSHIRE
Bulwick, Queens Head
East Haddon, Red Lion
Farthingstone, Kings Arms
Wadenhoe, Kings Head

NORTHUMBRIA
Anick, Rat
Blanchland, Lord Crewe Arms
Diptonmill, Dipton Mill Inn
Greta Bridge, Morritt Arms
Newburn, Keelman
Thropton, Three Wheat Heads
Weldon Bridge, Anglers Arms

NOTTINGHAMSHIRE
Caunton, Caunton Beck

OXFORDSHIRE
Burford, Lamb
Clifton, Duke of Cumberlands Head
Fyfield, White Hart
Highmoor, Rising Sun
Hook Norton, Gate Hangs High
Kelmscott, Plough
Sibford Gower, Bishop Blaize
Stanton St John, Star
Swalcliffe, Stags Head
Tadpole Bridge, Trout

SHROPSHIRE
Bishop's Castle, Castle Hotel, Three Tuns
Hopton Wafers, Crown
Norton, Hundred House

SOMERSET
Axbridge, Lamb
Chiselborough, Cat Head
Compton Martin, Ring o' Bells
East Lyng, Rose & Crown
Shepton Montague, Montague Inn

STAFFORDSHIRE
Salt, Holly Bush
Stourton, Fox

SUFFOLK
Brome, Cornwallis
Dennington, Queens Head
Lavenham, Angel
Laxfield, Kings Head
Rede, Plough
Stoke-by-Nayland, Crown
Walberswick, Bell
Waldringfield, Maybush

SURREY
Charleshill, Donkey
Coldharbour, Plough
Compton, Withies
Eashing, Stag
Forest Green, Parrot
Laleham, Three Horseshoes
Lingfield, Hare & Hounds
Mickleham, King William IV
Newdigate, Surrey Oaks
Ockley, Kings Arms
Ottershaw, Castle
West End, Inn at West End
Worplesdon, Jolly Farmer

SUSSEX
Alfriston, George
Amberley, Black Horse
Balls Cross, Stag
Berwick, Cricketers Arms
Blackboys, Blackboys Inn
Byworth, Black Horse
Elsted, Three Horseshoes
Fittleworth, Swan
Fletching, Griffin
Heathfield, Star
Oving, Gribble Inn
Rushlake Green, Horse & Groom
Rye, Ypres Castle
Singleton, Partridge
Wineham, Royal Oak

WARWICKSHIRE
Edge Hill, Castle
Farnborough, Inn at Farnborough
Ilmington, Howard Arms
Preston Bagot, Crabmill
Priors Marston, Holly Bush
Wharf, Wharf Inn

WILTSHIRE
Berwick St James, Boot
Brinkworth, Three Crowns
Chicksgrove, Compasses
Ebbesbourne Wake, Horseshoe
Horton, Bridge Inn
Kilmington, Red Lion
Lacock, George, Rising Sun
Norton, Vine Tree
Seend, Barge
Whitley, Pear Tree

WORCESTERSHIRE
Bretforton, Fleece

YORKSHIRE
East Witton, Blue Lion
Egton Bridge, Horse Shoe
Halifax, Shibden Mill
Heath, Kings Arms
Sutton upon Derwent, St Vincent Arms

LONDON
Central London, Cross Keys
East London, Prospect of Whitby
North London, Spaniards Inn
South London, Crown & Greyhound,
   Founders Arms, Old Jail
West London, Colton Arms, Dove,
   Windsor Castle

SCOTLAND
Badachro, Badachro Inn
Edinburgh, Starbank
Gairloch, Old Inn
Gifford, Tweeddale Arms
Glenelg, Glenelg Inn
Skeabost, Skeabost House Hotel
Thornhill, Lion & Unicorn

WALES
Colwyn Bay, Pen-y-Bryn
Crickhowell, Bear, Nantyffin Cider Mill
Gresford, Pant-yr-Ochain
Llanfrynach, White Swan
Llangedwyn, Green Inn
Llangollen, Corn Mill
Mold, Glasfryn
Old Radnor, Harp
Presteigne, Radnorshire Arms
Raglan, Clytha Arms
Rosebush, Tafarn Sinc
Skenfrith, Bell
St Hilary, Bush
Tintern, Cherry Tree
Ty'n-y-groes, Groes

CHANNEL ISLANDS
King's Mills, Fleur du Jardin
Rozel, Rozel

WATERSIDE PUBS
The pubs listed here are right beside the sea, a
sizeable river, canal, lake or loch that contributes
significantly to their attraction.

BERKSHIRE
Kintbury, Dundas Arms

CAMBRIDGESHIRE
Sutton Gault, Anchor

CHESHIRE
Chester, Old Harkers Arms
Wrenbury, Dusty Miller

CORNWALL
Bodinnick, Old Ferry
Helford, Shipwrights Arms
Malpas, Heron
Mousehole, Old Coastguard
Mylor Bridge, Pandora
Polkerris, Rashleigh
Port Isaac, Port Gaverne Inn, Slipway
Porthleven, Ship
Porthtowan, Blue
Sennen Cove, Old Success
St Agnes, Turks Head
Tresco, New Inn

CUMBRIA
Ambleside, Wateredge
Staveley, Eagle & Child
Ulverston, Bay Horse

DERBYSHIRE
Hathersage, Plough

DEVON
Buckfast, Abbey Inn
Culmstock, Culm Valley
Exminster, Turf Hotel
Newton Ferrers, Dolphin
Noss Mayo, Ship
Torcross, Start Bay

ESSEX
Burnham-on-Crouch, White Harte
Chappel, Swan
Fyfield, Queens Head

GLOUCESTERSHIRE
Ashleworth Quay, Boat

HAMPSHIRE
Exton, Shoe
Ovington, Bush
Portsmouth, Still & West

HEREFORDSHIRE
Aymestrey, Riverside Inn

ISLE OF WIGHT
Bembridge, Crab & Lobster
Seaview, Seaview Hotel
Ventnor, Spyglass

KENT
Deal, Kings Head
Oare, Shipwrights Arms

LANCASHIRE
Little Eccleston, Cartford
Liverpool, Baltic Fleet
Manchester, Dukes 92
Whitewell, Inn at Whitewell

NORFOLK
Brancaster Staithe, White Horse

NORTHAMPTONSHIRE
Wadenhoe, Kings Head

NORTHUMBRIA
Newcastle upon Tyne, Head of Steam @ The Cluny
Newton-by-the-Sea, Ship

NOTTINGHAMSHIRE
Ranby, Chequers

OXFORDSHIRE
Tadpole Bridge, Trout

SHROPSHIRE
Ludlow, Unicorn
Shrewsbury, Armoury

SOMERSET
Churchill, Crown
Compton Martin, Ring o' Bells
Portishead, Windmill

SUFFOLK
Chelmondiston, Butt & Oyster
Nayland, Anchor
Southwold, Harbour Inn
Waldringfield, Maybush

SURREY
Eashing, Stag

WARWICKSHIRE
Lapworth, Navigation
Wharf, Wharf Inn

WILTSHIRE
Horton, Bridge Inn
Seend, Barge

WORCESTERSHIRE
Knightwick, Talbot
Wyre Piddle, Anchor

YORKSHIRE
Hull, Minerva
Whitby, Duke of York

LONDON
East London, Grapes, Prospect of Whitby
South London, Cutty Sark, Founders Arms
West London, Bulls Head, Dove

SCOTLAND
Aboyne, Boat
Badachro, Badachro Inn
Edinburgh, Starbank
Elie, Ship
Gairloch, Old Inn
Glenelg, Glenelg Inn
Isle of Whithorn, Steam Packet
Kingholm Quay, Swan
Plockton, Plockton Hotel
Shieldaig, Tigh an Eilean Hotel
Skeabost, Skeabost House Hotel
Stein, Stein Inn
Tayvallich, Tayvallich Inn
Ullapool, Ferry Boat

WALES
Aberaeron, Harbourmaster
Abercych, Nags Head
Aberdovey, Penhelig Arms

Abergorlech, Black Lion
Cresswell Quay, Cresselly Arms
Llangedwyn, Green Inn
Llangollen, Corn Mill
Overton Bridge, Cross Foxes
Pembroke Ferry, Ferry Inn
Red Wharf Bay, Ship
Skenfrith, Bell

CHANNEL ISLANDS
St Aubin, Old Court House Inn
St Ouens Bay, La Pulente

PUBS IN ATTRACTIVE SURROUNDINGS

These pubs are in unusually attractive or
interesting places – lovely countryside, charming
villages, occasionally notable town surroundings.
Waterside pubs are listed again here only if their
other surroundings are special, too.

BEDFORDSHIRE
Old Warden, Hare & Hounds

BERKSHIRE
Aldworth, Bell
Frilsham, Pot Kiln

BUCKINGHAMSHIRE
Bovingdon Green, Royal Oak
Hawridge Common, Full Moon
Skirmett, Frog
Turville, Bull & Butcher

CAMBRIDGESHIRE
Elton, Black Horse
Reach, Dyke's End

CHESHIRE
Barthomley, White Lion
Bunbury, Dysart Arms

CORNWALL
Altarnun, Rising Sun
Blisland, Blisland Inn
Helston, Halzephron
St Agnes, Turks Head
St Kew, St Kew Inn
St Mawgan, Falcon
Tresco, New Inn

CUMBRIA
Bassenthwaite Lake, Pheasant
Bouth, White Hart
Broughton Mills, Blacksmiths Arms
Buttermere, Bridge Hotel
Cartmel, Kings Arms
Chapel Stile, Wainwrights
Elterwater, Britannia
Hawkshead, Drunken Duck, Kings Arms
Hesket Newmarket, Old Crown
Ings, Watermill
Langdale, Old Dungeon Ghyll
Little Langdale, Three Shires
Loweswater, Kirkstile Inn
Mungrisdale, Mill Inn
Santon Bridge, Bridge Inn
Seathwaite, Newfield Inn
Stonethwaite, Langstrath
Troutbeck, Queens Head
Ulverston, Bay Horse

DERBYSHIRE
Alderwasley, Bear
Brassington, Olde Gate
Foolow, Bulls Head
Froggatt Edge, Chequers
Hardwick Hall, Hardwick Inn
Hathersage, Plough, Scotsmans Pack
Hayfield, Lantern Pike
Kirk Ireton, Barley Mow
Ladybower Reservoir, Yorkshire Bridge
Litton, Red Lion
Monsal Head, Monsal Head Hotel
Over Haddon, Lathkil
Sheldon, Cock & Pullet
Woolley Moor, White Horse

DEVON
Branscombe, Fountain Head
Buckland Monachorum, Drake Manor
Culmstock, Culm Valley
East Budleigh, Sir Walter Raleigh
Exminster, Turf Hotel
Haytor Vale, Rock
Holne, Church House
Horndon, Elephants Nest
Iddesleigh, Duke of York
Lower Ashton, Manor Inn
Lustleigh, Cleave
Lydford, Castle Inn
Molland, London
Parracombe, Fox & Goose
Peter Tavy, Peter Tavy Inn
Postbridge, Warren House
Rattery, Church House
Sandy Park, Sandy Park Inn
Slapton, Tower
Widecombe, Rugglestone
Wonson, Northmore Arms

DORSET
Corscombe, Fox
East Chaldon, Sailors Return
Marshwood, Bottle
Osmington Mills, Smugglers
Pamphill, Vine
Plush, Brace of Pheasants
Worth Matravers, Square & Compass

ESSEX
Mill Green, Viper

GLOUCESTERSHIRE
Ashleworth Quay, Boat
Bisley, Bear
Bledington, Kings Head
Chedworth, Seven Tuns
Chipping Campden, Eight Bells
Eastleach Turville, Victoria
Glasshouse, Glasshouse Inn
Guiting Power, Hollow Bottom
Miserden, Carpenters Arms
Nailsworth, Weighbridge
Newland, Ostrich
Northleach, Wheatsheaf
Sapperton, Bell

HAMPSHIRE
East Tytherley, Star
Fritham, Royal Oak
Hawkley, Hawkley Inn
Lymington, Kings Head
Micheldever, Half Moon & Spread Eagle
Ovington, Bush
Tichborne, Tichborne Arms

HEREFORDSHIRE
Aymestrey, Riverside Inn
Dorstone, Pandy
Sellack, Lough Pool
Titley, Stagg
Walterstone, Carpenters Arms
Weobley, Salutation
Woolhope, Butchers Arms

HERTFORDSHIRE
Frithsden, Alford Arms
Sarratt, Cock

KENT
Brookland, Woolpack
Chiddingstone, Castle Inn
Elham, Rose & Crown
Groombridge, Crown
Hucking, Hook & Hatchet
Newnham, George
Selling, Rose & Crown

LANCASHIRE
Blackstone Edge, White House
Bury, Lord Raglan
Little Eccleston, Cartford
Newton, Parkers Arms
Sawley, Spread Eagle
Tunstall, Lunesdale Arms
Uppermill, Church Inn
Whitewell, Inn at Whitewell

LEICESTERSHIRE AND RUTLAND
Barrowden, Exeter Arms
Exton, Fox & Hounds
Upper Hambleton, Finches Arms

LINCOLNSHIRE
Dry Doddington, Wheatsheaf

NORFOLK
Blakeney, White Horse
Burnham Market, Hoste Arms
Thornham, Lifeboat
Woodbastwick, Fur & Feather

NORTHAMPTONSHIRE
Harringworth, White Swan

NORTHUMBRIA
Allenheads, Allenheads Inn
Blanchland, Lord Crewe Arms
Diptonmill, Dipton Mill Inn
Great Whittington, Queens Head
Haltwhistle, Milecastle Inn
Langley on Tyne, Carts Bog Inn
Newton-by-the-Sea, Ship
Romaldkirk, Rose & Crown
Stannersburn, Pheasant

NOTTINGHAMSHIRE
Laxton, Dovecote

OXFORDSHIRE
Checkendon, Black Horse
Great Tew, Falkland Arms
Kelmscott, Plough
Oxford, Turf Tavern

Swalcliffe, Stags Head
Swinbrook, Swan

SHROPSHIRE
Bridges, Horseshoe
Cardington, Royal Oak
Picklescott, Bottle & Glass

SOMERSET
Appley, Globe
Axbridge, Lamb
Batcombe, Three Horseshoes
Crowcombe, Carew Arms
Exford, White Horse
Luxborough, Royal Oak
Triscombe, Blue Ball
Wells, City Arms

STAFFORDSHIRE
Alstonefield, George
Stourton, Fox

SUFFOLK
Dennington, Queens Head
Dunwich, Ship
Lavenham, Angel
Walberswick, Bell

SURREY
Blackbrook, Plough
Cobham, Cricketers
Englefield Green, Fox & Hounds
Esher, Marneys
Forest Green, Parrot
Lingfield, Hare & Hounds
Mickleham, King William IV
Reigate Heath, Skimmington Castle

SUSSEX
Alfriston, George
Amberley, Black Horse
Burpham, George & Dragon
Chilgrove, White Horse
Ditchling, Bull
East Dean, Tiger
Fletching, Griffin
Heathfield, Star
Rye, Mermaid, Ypres Castle
Wineham, Royal Oak

WARWICKSHIRE
Edge Hill, Castle
Himley, Crooked House
Priors Marston, Holly Bush

WILTSHIRE
Axford, Red Lion
Donhead St Andrew, Forester
Ebbesbourne Wake, Horseshoe
Lacock, Rising Sun
Newton Tony, Malet Arms
Stourton, Spread Eagle

WORCESTERSHIRE
Berrow Green, Admiral Rodney
Broadway, Crown & Trumpet
Kidderminster, King & Castle
Knightwick, Talbot
Pensax, Bell

YORKSHIRE
Beck Hole, Birch Hall
Blakey Ridge, Lion

Bradfield, Strines Inn
Byland Abbey, Abbey Inn
Chapel le Dale, Hill Inn
Cray, White Lion
East Witton, Blue Lion
Grinton, Bridge Inn
Halifax, Shibden Mill
Heath, Kings Arms
Langthwaite, Charles Bathurst
Lastingham, Blacksmiths Arms
Linton in Craven, Fountaine
Litton, Queens Arms
Lund, Wellington
Masham, Kings Head
Middleham, Black Swan
Osmotherley, Golden Lion
Ripley, Boars Head
Robin Hood's Bay, Laurel
Shelley, Three Acres
Thornton in Lonsdale, Marton Arms
Thornton Watlass, Buck
Wath in Nidderdale, Sportsmans Arms
Widdop, Pack Horse

LONDON
Central London, Olde Mitre
North London, Spaniards Inn
South London, Crown & Greyhound

SCOTLAND
Applecross, Applecross Inn
Gairloch, Old Inn
Kilberry, Kilberry Inn
Kingholm Quay, Swan
Kirk Yetholm, Border
Stein, Stein Inn

WALES
Abergorlech, Black Lion
Capel Curig, Bryn Tyrch
Crickhowell, Nantyffin Cider Mill
Llanberis, Pen-y-Gwryd
Llangedwyn, Green Inn
Old Radnor, Harp
Red Wharf Bay, Ship
Rhyd-y-Meirch, Goose & Cuckoo
Tintern, Cherry Tree

CHANNEL ISLANDS
St Brelade, Old Portelet Inn, Old Smugglers
St John, Les Fontaines

PUBS WITH GOOD VIEWS

These pubs are listed for their particularly good
views, either from inside or from a garden or
terrace. Waterside pubs are listed again here only
if their view is exceptional in its own right – not
just a straightforward sea view for example.

BUCKINGHAMSHIRE
Oving, Black Boy
Penn, Crown

CHESHIRE
Higher Burwardsley, Pheasant
Langley, Hanging Gate

CORNWALL
Falmouth, 5 Degrees West
Sennen Cove, Old Success

St Agnes, Turks Head
St Anns Chapel, Rifle Volunteer

CUMBRIA
Cartmel Fell, Masons Arms
Hawkshead, Drunken Duck
Keswick, Swinside Inn
Langdale, Old Dungeon Ghyll
Loweswater, Kirkstile Inn
Mungrisdale, Mill Inn
Stonethwaite, Langstrath
Troutbeck, Queens Head
Ulverston, Bay Horse

DERBYSHIRE
Alderwasley, Bear
Foolow, Barrel, Bulls Head
Monsal Head, Monsal Head Hotel
Over Haddon, Lathkil

DEVON
Brixham, Maritime
Newton Ferrers, Dolphin
Portgate, Harris Arms
Postbridge, Warren House
Sidbury, Hare & Hounds
Strete, Kings Arms

DORSET
Worth Matravers, Square & Compass

ISLE OF WIGHT
Bembridge, Crab & Lobster
Ventnor, Spyglass

KENT
Tunbridge Wells, Beacon
Ulcombe, Pepper Box

LANCASHIRE
Blackstone Edge, White House
Bury, Lord Raglan
Newton, Parkers Arms
Sawley, Spread Eagle
Uppermill, Church Inn

NORFOLK
Brancaster Staithe, White Horse

NORTHUMBRIA
Anick, Rat
Newfield, Fox & Hounds
Seahouses, Olde Ship
Thropton, Three Wheat Heads

OXFORDSHIRE
Sibford Gower, Bishop Blaize

SOMERSET
Portishead, Windmill
Shepton Montague, Montague Inn

SUFFOLK
Erwarton, Queens Head

SURREY
Mickleham, King William IV

SUSSEX
Byworth, Black Horse
Elsted, Three Horseshoes
Fletching, Griffin
Icklesham, Queens Head
Rye, Ypres Castle

WILTSHIRE
Axford, Red Lion
Box, Quarrymans Arms
Donhead St Andrew, Forester
Lacock, Rising Sun

WORCESTERSHIRE
Malvern, Nags Head
Pensax, Bell
Wyre Piddle, Anchor

YORKSHIRE
Blakey Ridge, Lion
Bradfield, Strines Inn
Kirkham, Stone Trough
Langthwaite, Charles Bathurst
Litton, Queens Arms
Shelley, Three Acres
Whitby, Duke of York

LONDON
South London, Founders Arms

SCOTLAND
Applecross, Applecross Inn
Badachro, Badachro Inn
Edinburgh, Starbank
Glenelg, Glenelg Inn
Kilberry, Kilberry Inn
Shieldaig, Tigh an Eilean Hotel
Stein, Stein Inn
Ullapool, Ferry Boat
Weem, Ailean Chraggan

WALES
Aberdovey, Penhelig Arms
Capel Curig, Bryn Tyrch
Colwyn Bay, Pen-y-Bryn
Llanberis, Pen-y-Gwryd
Llanferres, Druid
Llangollen, Corn Mill
Llannefydd, Hawk & Buckle
Mold, Glasfryn
Old Radnor, Harp
Overton Bridge, Cross Foxes
Rhyd-y-Meirch, Goose & Cuckoo
Ty'n-y-groes, Groes

CHANNEL ISLANDS
St Aubin, Old Court House Inn

PUBS IN INTERESTING BUILDINGS

Pubs and inns are listed here for the particular interest of their building – something really out of the ordinary to look at, or occasionally a building that has an outstandingly interesting historical background.

BUCKINGHAMSHIRE
Forty Green, Royal Standard of England

DERBYSHIRE
Kirk Ireton, Barley Mow

DEVON
Dartmouth, Cherub
Rattery, Church House

ESSEX
Great Yeldham, White Hart

LANCASHIRE
Liverpool, Philharmonic Dining Rooms

LINCOLNSHIRE
Grantham, Angel & Royal
Stamford, George of Stamford

NORTHUMBRIA
Blanchland, Lord Crewe Arms

NOTTINGHAMSHIRE
Nottingham, Olde Trip to Jerusalem

OXFORDSHIRE
Banbury, Reindeer
Fyfield, White Hart

SOMERSET
Norton St Philip, George

SUFFOLK
Laxfield, Kings Head

SUSSEX
Rye, Mermaid

WARWICKSHIRE
Himley, Crooked House

WILTSHIRE
Salisbury, Haunch of Venison

WORCESTERSHIRE
Bretforton, Fleece

YORKSHIRE
Hull, Olde White Harte

LONDON
Central London, Black Friar, Cittie of Yorke
South London, George

SCOTLAND
Edinburgh, Café Royal, Guildford Arms

PUBS THAT BREW THEIR OWN BEER

The pubs listed here brew their own beer on the premises; many others not listed have beers brewed for them specially, sometimes an individual recipe (but by a separate brewer). We mention these in the text.

BERKSHIRE
Frilsham, Pot Kiln

CAMBRIDGESHIRE
Peterborough, Brewery Tap

CUMBRIA
Cockermouth, Bitter End
Hawkshead, Drunken Duck
Hesket Newmarket, Old Crown
Loweswater, Kirkstile Inn
Tirril, Queens Head

DERBYSHIRE
Derby, Brunswick
Melbourne, John Thompson

DEVON
Branscombe, Fountain Head

HAMPSHIRE
Cheriton, Flower Pots

HEREFORDSHIRE
Hereford, Victory

KENT
West Peckham, Swan on the Green

LANCASHIRE
Bury, Lord Raglan
Little Eccleston, Cartford
Liverpool, Baltic Fleet
Manchester, Marble Arch
Uppermill, Church Inn
Wheelton, Dressers Arms

LEICESTERSHIRE AND RUTLAND
Barrowden, Exeter Arms
Oakham, Grainstore

LINCOLNSHIRE
South Witham, Blue Cow

NORTHUMBRIA
Diptonmill, Dipton Mill Inn
Newburn, Keelman

NOTTINGHAMSHIRE
Caythorpe, Black Horse
Nottingham, Fellows Morton & Clayton

SHROPSHIRE
Bishop's Castle, Six Bells

STAFFORDSHIRE
Burton upon Trent, Burton Bridge Inn

SUFFOLK
South Elmham, St Peters Brewery

SURREY
Coldharbour, Plough

WARWICKSHIRE
Sedgley, Beacon

WORCESTERSHIRE
Knightwick, Talbot

YORKSHIRE
Cropton, New Inn
Goose Eye, Turkey
Linthwaite, Sair
Sheffield, Fat Cat

SCOTLAND
Houston, Fox & Hounds
Pitlochry, Moulin

WALES
Abercych, Nags Head
Llanddarog, White Hart

OPEN ALL DAY (at least in summer)

We list here all the pubs that have told us they plan to stay open all day, even if it's only Saturday. We've included the few pubs which close just for half an hour to an hour, and the many more, chiefly in holiday areas, which open all day only in summer. The individual entries for the pubs themselves show the actual details.

BEDFORDSHIRE
Henlow, Engineers Arms
Old Warden, Hare & Hounds
Ridgmont, Rose & Crown
Stanbridge, Five Bells

BERKSHIRE
Bray, Hinds Head
East Ilsley, Swan
Frilsham, Pot Kiln
Reading, Hobgoblin
Remenham, Little Angel
Ruscombe, Royal Oak
Stanford Dingley, Old Boot
Windsor, Two Brewers
Winterbourne, Winterbourne Arms

BUCKINGHAMSHIRE
Bennett End, Three Horseshoes
Bovingdon Green, Royal Oak
Chalfont St Giles, White Hart
Denham, Swan
Dorney, Palmer Arms
Easington, Mole & Chicken
Ford, Dinton Hermit
Forty Green, Royal Standard of England
Hawridge Common, Full Moon
Hedgerley, White Horse
Ley Hill, Swan
Mentmore, Stag
Penn, Crown
Soulbury, Boot
Stoke Mandeville, Woolpack
Turville, Bull & Butcher
Wooburn Common, Chequers

CAMBRIDGESHIRE
Cambridge, Eagle
Elton, Black Horse
Godmanchester, Exhibition
Helpston, Blue Bell
Hemingford Grey, Cock
Huntingdon, Old Bridge Hotel
Kimbolton, New Sun
Longstowe, Red House
Peterborough, Brewery Tap, Charters

CHESHIRE
Aldford, Grosvenor Arms
Astbury, Egerton Arms
Aston, Bhurtpore
Barthomley, White Lion
Bunbury, Dysart Arms
Chester, Albion, Old Harkers Arms
Cotebrook, Fox & Barrel
Eaton, Plough
Haughton Moss, Nags Head
Higher Burwardsley, Pheasant
Langley, Hanging Gate
Macclesfield, Sutton Hall Hotel
Peover Heath, Dog
Prestbury, Legh Arms
Tarporley, Rising Sun
Wettenhall, Boot & Slipper
Wincle, Ship
Wybunbury, Swan

CORNWALL
Altarnun, Rising Sun
Blisland, Blisland Inn
Bodinnick, Old Ferry
Lostwithiel, Royal Oak
Mitchell, Plume of Feathers
Mithian, Miners Arms
Mousehole, Old Coastguard
Mylor Bridge, Pandora

Polkerris, Rashleigh
Port Isaac, Port Gaverne Inn, Slipway
Porthleven, Ship
Porthtowan, Blue
Sennen Cove, Old Success
St Agnes, Turks Head
Tregadillett, Eliot Arms
Trematon, Crooked Inn
Tresco, New Inn
Truro, Old Ale House

CUMBRIA
Ambleside, Golden Rule, Wateredge
Armathwaite, Dukes Head
Bouth, White Hart
Broughton Mills, Blacksmiths Arms
Buttermere, Bridge Hotel
Cartmel, Kings Arms
Cartmel Fell, Masons Arms
Chapel Stile, Wainwrights
Cockermouth, Bitter End
Dalton-in-Furness, Black Dog
Elterwater, Britannia
Hawkshead, Kings Arms, Queens Head
Ings, Watermill
Langdale, Old Dungeon Ghyll
Little Langdale, Three Shires
Loweswater, Kirkstile Inn
Mungrisdale, Mill Inn
Santon Bridge, Bridge Inn
Seathwaite, Newfield Inn
Stonethwaite, Langstrath
Tirril, Queens Head
Troutbeck, Queens Head
Ulverston, Bay Horse, Farmers Arms
Yanwath, Gate Inn

DERBYSHIRE
Alderwasley, Bear
Beeley, Devonshire Arms
Castleton, Castle Hotel
Derby, Alexandra, Brunswick, Olde Dolphin
Eyam, Miners Arms
Fenny Bentley, Coach & Horses
Foolow, Barrel, Bulls Head
Froggatt Edge, Chequers
Hardwick Hall, Hardwick Inn
Hathersage, Plough, Scotsmans Pack
Hayfield, Lantern Pike, Royal
Holbrook, Dead Poets
Ladybower Reservoir, Yorkshire Bridge
Litton, Red Lion
Monsal Head, Monsal Head Hotel
Over Haddon, Lathkil
Wardlow, Three Stags Heads
Woolley Moor, White Horse

DEVON
Branscombe, Fountain Head, Masons Arms
Cockwood, Anchor
Culmstock, Culm Valley
Dartmouth, Cherub
Drewsteignton, Drewe Arms
Exeter, Imperial
Exminster, Turf Hotel
Haytor Vale, Rock
Holbeton, Dartmoor Union
Iddesleigh, Duke of York
Lydford, Castle Inn

Marldon, Church House
Newton Abbot, Two Mile Oak
Nomansland, Mount Pleasant
Noss Mayo, Ship
Parracombe, Fox & Goose
Postbridge, Warren House
Poundsgate, Tavistock Inn
Rockbeare, Jack in the Green
Sandy Park, Sandy Park Inn
Sidbury, Hare & Hounds
Sidford, Blue Ball
Stoke Gabriel, Church House
Strete, Kings Arms
Torbryan, Old Church House
Torcross, Start Bay
Widecombe, Rugglestone
Winkleigh, Kings Arms
Wonson, Northmore Arms
Woodbury Salterton, Diggers Rest
Woodland, Rising Sun

DORSET
East Chaldon, Sailors Return
Middlemarsh, Hunters Moon
Mudeford, Ship in Distress
Osmington Mills, Smugglers
Poole, Cow
Shave Cross, Shave Cross Inn
Tarrant Monkton, Langton Arms
Worth Matravers, Square & Compass

ESSEX
Burnham-on-Crouch, White Harte
Castle Hedingham, Bell
Chappel, Swan
Chelmsford, Alma
Clavering, Cricketers
Dedham, Sun
Fingringhoe, Whalebone
Langham, Shepherd & Dog
Little Braxted, Green Man
Little Walden, Crown
Mill Green, Viper
Stock, Hoop
Stow Maries, Prince of Wales
Wendens Ambo, Bell
Youngs End, Green Dragon

GLOUCESTERSHIRE
Almondsbury, Bowl
Awre, Red Hart
Barnsley, Village Pub
Brimpsfield, Golden Heart
Chedworth, Seven Tuns
Chipping Campden, Eight Bells
Cowley, Green Dragon
Didmarton, Kings Arms
Dursley, Old Spot
Ewen, Wild Duck
Fairford, Bull
Ford, Plough
Guiting Power, Hollow Bottom
Nailsworth, Egypt Mill, Weighbridge
Nether Westcote, New Inn
Northleach, Wheatsheaf
Oldbury-on-Severn, Anchor
Tetbury, Snooty Fox
Upper Oddington, Horse & Groom
Winchcombe, White Hart

HAMPSHIRE
Bank, Oak
Bentley, Bull
Bentworth, Sun
Boldre, Red Lion
Braishfield, Wheatsheaf
Easton, Chestnut Horse
Fritham, Royal Oak
Littleton, Running Horse
Lower Wield, Yew Tree
Lymington, Kings Head
Monxton, Black Swan
Portsmouth, Still & West
Rotherwick, Falcon
Rowland's Castle, Castle Inn
Southsea, Wine Vaults
Stockbridge, Grosvenor, Three Cups
Well, Chequers
Winchester, Wykeham Arms

HEREFORDSHIRE
Aymestrey, Riverside Inn
Bodenham, Englands Gate
Dorstone, Pandy
Hereford, Victory
Ledbury, Feathers
Lugwardine, Crown & Anchor
Weobley, Salutation

HERTFORDSHIRE
Aldbury, Valiant Trooper
Ashwell, Three Tuns
Batford, Gibraltar Castle
Chapmore End, Woodman
Cottered, Bull
Frithsden, Alford Arms
Hertford, White Horse
Royston, Old Bull
Sarratt, Cock

ISLE OF WIGHT
Arreton, White Lion
Bembridge, Crab & Lobster
Ventnor, Spyglass

KENT
Bough Beech, Wheatsheaf
Brookland, Woolpack
Chiddingstone, Castle Inn
Deal, Kings Head
Elham, Rose & Crown
Fordcombe, Chafford Arms
Groombridge, Crown
Hawkhurst, Queens
Hollingbourne, Windmill
Hucking, Hook & Hatchet
Iden Green, Woodcock
Langton Green, Hare
Penshurst, Bottle House
Pluckley, Rose & Crown
Shipbourne, Chaser
Smarden, Chequers
Stodmarsh, Red Lion
Tunbridge Wells, Beacon, Sankeys
West Peckham, Swan on the Green

LANCASHIRE
Barnston, Fox & Hounds
Belmont, Black Dog
Bispham Green, Eagle & Child

Blackstone Edge, White House
Bury, Lord Raglan
Chipping, Dog & Partridge
Goosnargh, Horns
Little Eccleston, Cartford
Liverpool, Baltic Fleet,
    Philharmonic Dining Rooms
Longridge, Derby Arms
Lydgate, White Hart
Lytham, Taps
Manchester, Britons Protection, Dukes 92,
    Marble Arch
Newton, Parkers Arms
Ribchester, White Bull
Stalybridge, Station Buffet
Uppermill, Church Inn
Wheelton, Dressers Arms
Yealand Conyers, New Inn

LEICESTERSHIRE AND RUTLAND

Ab Kettleby, Sugar Loaf
Belmesthorpe, Blue Bell
Clipsham, Olive Branch
Cottesmore, Sun
Empingham, White Horse
Mowsley, Staff of Life
Newton Burgoland, Belper Arms
Oadby, Cow & Plough
Oakham, Grainstore
Somerby, Three Crowns
Stathern, Red Lion
Stretton, Ram Jam Inn
Swithland, Griffin
Upper Hambleton, Finches Arms
Wing, Kings Arms

LINCOLNSHIRE

Grantham, Angel & Royal
Lincoln, Victoria, Wig & Mitre
Rothwell, Blacksmiths Arms
South Witham, Blue Cow
Stamford, George of Stamford
Surfleet, Mermaid
Woolsthorpe, Chequers

NORFOLK

Bawburgh, Kings Head
Blakeney, Kings Arms
Brancaster Staithe, White Horse
Burnham Market, Hoste Arms
Cawston, Ratcatchers
Larling, Angel
Norwich, Adam & Eve, Fat Cat
Snettisham, Rose & Crown
Swanton Morley, Darbys
Thornham, Lifeboat
Tivetshall St Mary, Old Ram
Upper Sheringham, Red Lion
Wells-next-the-Sea, Crown
Winterton-on-Sea, Fishermans Return
Woodbastwick, Fur & Feather
Wymondham, Green Dragon

NORTHAMPTONSHIRE

Badby, Windmill
Kilsby, George
Lowick, Snooty Fox
Nether Heyford, Olde Sun
Oundle, Ship
Woodnewton, White Swan

NORTHUMBRIA

Allenheads, Allenheads Inn
Blanchland, Lord Crewe Arms
Carterway Heads, Manor House Inn
Greta Bridge, Morritt Arms
Haltwhistle, Milecastle Inn
Langley on Tyne, Carts Bog Inn
Newburn, Keelman
Newcastle upon Tyne, Crown Posada,
    Head of Steam @ The Cluny
Newton-by-the-Sea, Ship
Newton-on-the-Moor, Cook & Barker Arms
Rennington, Masons Arms
Seahouses, Olde Ship
Stannington, Ridley Arms
Thropton, Three Wheat Heads
Weldon Bridge, Anglers Arms

NOTTINGHAMSHIRE

Beeston, Victoria
Caunton, Caunton Beck
Halam, Waggon & Horses
North Muskham, Muskham Inn
Nottingham, Bell, Fellows Morton & Clayton,
    Lincolnshire Poacher, Olde Trip to Jerusalem,
    Pit & Pendulum, Vat & Fiddle

OXFORDSHIRE

Banbury, Reindeer
Burford, Lamb
Chipping Norton, Chequers
Churchill, Chequers
Cuxham, Half Moon
Fyfield, White Hart
Great Tew, Falkland Arms
Henley, Anchor
Highmoor, Rising Sun
Kelmscott, Plough
Oxford, Turf Tavern
Tetsworth, Red Lion

SHROPSHIRE

Bishop's Castle, Six Bells, Three Tuns
Bridges, Horseshoe
Bromfield, Clive/Cookhouse
Hopton Wafers, Crown
Ironbridge, Malthouse
Ludlow, Church Inn
Much Wenlock, George & Dragon, Talbot
Shrewsbury, Armoury
Wentnor, Crown

SOMERSET

Axbridge, Lamb
Bath, Old Green Tree, Star
Chew Magna, Bear & Swan
Churchill, Crown
Clapton-in-Gordano, Black Horse
Congresbury, White Hart
Crowcombe, Carew Arms
Exford, White Horse
Holcombe, Ring o' Roses
Huish Episcopi, Rose & Crown
Norton St Philip, George
Portishead, Windmill
Stanton Wick, Carpenters Arms
Triscombe, Blue Ball
Wells, City Arms, Crown
Withypool, Royal Oak

STAFFORDSHIRE
Abbots Bromley, Goats Head
Alstonefield, George
Lichfield, Boat
Salt, Holly Bush
Stourton, Fox

SUFFOLK
Brome, Cornwallis
Bury St Edmunds, Nutshell
Chelmondiston, Butt & Oyster
Cotton, Trowel & Hammer
Dunwich, Ship
Lavenham, Angel
Nayland, Anchor
South Elmham, St Peters Brewery
Southwold, Crown, Harbour Inn, Lord Nelson
Stoke-by-Nayland, Angel, Crown
Walberswick, Bell
Waldringfield, Maybush

SURREY
Betchworth, Dolphin
Charleshill, Donkey
Cobham, Cricketers
Coldharbour, Plough
Eashing, Stag
Englefield Green, Fox & Hounds
Esher, Marneys
Forest Green, Parrot
Laleham, Three Horseshoes
Leigh, Plough
Lingfield, Hare & Hounds
Mickleham, King William IV, Running Horses
Ottershaw, Castle
Reigate Heath, Skimmington Castle
West End, Inn at West End
Worplesdon, Jolly Farmer

SUSSEX
Alfriston, George
Amberley, Black Horse
Arlington, Old Oak
Berwick, Cricketers Arms
Blackboys, Blackboys Inn
Brighton, Greys
Burpham, George & Dragon
Charlton, Fox Goes Free
Chiddingly, Six Bells
Ditchling, Bull
Donnington, Blacksmiths Arms
East Dean, Star & Garter, Tiger
East Hoathly, Foresters Arms
Fittleworth, Swan
Fletching, Griffin
Hermitage, Sussex Brewery
Horsham, Black Jug
Icklesham, Queens Head
Lodsworth, Halfway Bridge Inn
Oving, Gribble Inn
Rye, Mermaid, Ypres Castle
Singleton, Partridge
Wilmington, Giants Rest

WARWICKSHIRE
Aston Cantlow, Kings Head
Birmingham, Old Joint Stock
Brierley Hill, Vine
Easenhall, Golden Lion

Edge Hill, Castle
Farnborough, Inn at Farnborough
Gaydon, Malt Shovel
Himley, Crooked House
Lapworth, Navigation
Long Itchington, Duck on the Pond
Preston Bagot, Crabmill
Shipston-on-Stour, White Bear
Welford-on-Avon, Bell
Wharf, Wharf Inn

WILTSHIRE
Box, Quarrymans Arms
Devizes, Bear
Heytesbury, Angel
Hindon, Lamb
Lacock, George, Red Lion, Rising Sun
Luckington, Old Royal Ship
Malmesbury, Smoking Dog
Norton, Vine Tree
Salisbury, Haunch of Venison
Seend, Barge
Stourton, Spread Eagle

WORCESTERSHIRE
Berrow Green, Admiral Rodney
Bewdley, Little Pack Horse
Bretforton, Fleece
Broadway, Crown & Trumpet
Childswickham, Childswickham Inn
Clent, Fountain
Kempsey, Walter de Cantelupe
Kidderminster, King & Castle
Knightwick, Talbot
Malvern, Nags Head
Pensax, Bell
Wyre Piddle, Anchor

YORKSHIRE
Aldborough, Ship
Asenby, Crab & Lobster
Beck Hole, Birch Hall
Beverley, White Horse
Blakey Ridge, Lion
Boroughbridge, Black Bull
Bradfield, Strines Inn
Burn, Wheatsheaf
Cray, White Lion
Crayke, Durham Ox
Cropton, New Inn
East Witton, Blue Lion
Elslack, Tempest Arms
Ferrensby, General Tarleton
Goose Eye, Turkey
Grinton, Bridge Inn
Halifax, Shibden Mill
Harome, Star
Heath, Kings Arms
Hull, Minerva, Olde White Harte
Kettlesing, Queens Head
Kirkbymoorside, George & Dragon
Langthwaite, Charles Bathurst
Lastingham, Blacksmiths Arms
Ledsham, Chequers
Leeds, Whitelocks
Linthwaite, Sair
Linton, Windmill
Linton in Craven, Fountaine

Low Catton, Gold Cup
Masham, Black Sheep Brewery, Kings Head
Middleham, Black Swan, White Swan
Mill Bank, Millbank
Osmotherley, Golden Lion
Pickering, White Swan
Pickhill, Nags Head
Ripley, Boars Head
Ripponden, Old Bridge
Robin Hood's Bay, Laurel
Sheffield, Fat Cat, New Barrack
Thornton in Lonsdale, Marton Arms
Thornton Watlass, Buck
Whitby, Duke of York
Widdop, Pack Horse

LONDON

Central London, Admiral Codrington, Albert,
　Archery Tavern, Argyll Arms, Black Friar,
　Cittie of Yorke, Coopers Arms, Cross Keys,
　Dog & Duck, Eagle, Grapes, Grenadier,
　Guinea, Jerusalem Tavern, Lamb,
　Lamb & Flag, Lord Moon of the Mall,
　Nags Head, Old Bank of England,
　Olde Cheshire Cheese, Olde Mitre,
　Princess Louise, Red Lion (both pubs),
　Seven Stars, Star, Westminster Arms
East London, Crown, Grapes, Prospect of Whitby
North London, Chapel, Compton Arms,
　Drapers Arms, Duke of Cambridge, Flask,
　Holly Bush, Olde White Bear, Spaniards Inn
South London, Alma, Anchor & Hope,
　Boathouse, Crown & Greyhound, Cutty Sark,
　Fire Station, Founders Arms, Fox & Hounds,
　George, Market Porter, Royal Oak,
　White Cross
West London, Anglesea Arms (both pubs),
　Atlas, Bulls Head, Churchill Arms, Dove,
　Havelock Tavern, Portobello Gold,
　Warrington, White Horse, Windsor Castle

SCOTLAND

Aberdeen, Prince of Wales
Aboyne, Boat
Applecross, Applecross Inn
Badachro, Badachro Inn
Broughty Ferry, Fishermans Tavern
East Linton, Drovers
Edinburgh, Abbotsford, Bow Bar, Café Royal,
　Guildford Arms, Kays Bar, Starbank
Elie, Ship
Gairloch, Old Inn
Gifford, Tweeddale Arms
Glasgow, Babbity Bowster, Bon Accord,
　Counting House
Houston, Fox & Hounds
Inveraray, George
Isle of Whithorn, Steam Packet
Kilberry, Kilberry Inn
Kingholm Quay, Swan
Linlithgow, Four Marys
Lybster, Portland Arms
Pitlochry, Moulin
Plockton, Plockton Hotel
Shieldaig, Tigh an Eilean Hotel
Stein, Stein Inn
Swinton, Wheatsheaf

Tayvallich, Tayvallich Inn
Thornhill, Lion & Unicorn
Ullapool, Ferry Boat
Weem, Ailean Chraggan

WALES

Aberaeron, Harbourmaster
Abercych, Nags Head
Aberdovey, Penhelig Arms
Abergorlech, Black Lion
Beaumaris, Olde Bulls Head
Capel Curig, Bryn Tyrch
Colwyn Bay, Pen-y-Bryn
Cresswell Quay, Cresselly Arms
East Aberthaw, Blue Anchor
Felinfach, Griffin
Gresford, Pant-yr-Ochain
Hay-on-Wye, Kilverts, Old Black Lion
Llanberis, Pen-y-Gwryd
Llandeilo, Castle
Llandudno Junction, Queens Head
Llanferres, Druid
Llangedwyn, Green Inn
Llangollen, Corn Mill
Mold, Glasfryn
Monknash, Plough & Harrow
Overton Bridge, Cross Foxes
Pembroke Ferry, Ferry Inn
Porthgain, Sloop
Presteigne, Radnorshire Arms
Raglan, Clytha Arms
Red Wharf Bay, Ship
Rhyd-y-Meirch, Goose & Cuckoo
Rosebush, Tafarn Sinc
Saundersfoot, Royal Oak
Shirenewton, Carpenters Arms
St Hilary, Bush
Tintern, Cherry Tree
Ty'n-y-groes, Groes

CHANNEL ISLANDS

King's Mills, Fleur du Jardin
Rozel, Rozel
St Aubin, Old Court House Inn
St Brelade, Old Portelet Inn, Old Smugglers
St Helier, Town House
St John, Les Fontaines
St Ouens Bay, La Pulente

NO SMOKING PUBS

We have listed all the pubs which have told us
they are completely no smoking for at least part of
the day. Look at the individual entries for the pubs
themselves. The entries also show which parts of
other pubs are no smoking. All Scottish pubs will
become no smoking by law during 2006.

BERKSHIRE
Frilsham, Pot Kiln

BUCKINGHAMSHIRE
Haddenham, Green Dragon

CAMBRIDGESHIRE
Cambridge, Cambridge Blue, Free Press

CUMBRIA
Loweswater, Kirkstile Inn
Stonethwaite, Langstrath

DERBYSHIRE
Beeley, Devonshire Arms
Froggatt Edge, Chequers
Hardwick Hall, Hardwick Inn
Milltown, Miners Arms

DEVON
Haytor Vale, Rock
Lustleigh, Cleave
Marldon, Church House
Noss Mayo, Ship
Topsham, Bridge Inn

GLOUCESTERSHIRE
Ashleworth, Queens Arms
Ashleworth Quay, Boat

HEREFORDSHIRE
Ullingswick, Three Crowns

KENT
Hollingbourne, Windmill

LANCASHIRE
Mellor, Oddfellows Arms

LEICESTERSHIRE AND RUTLAND
Barrowden, Exeter Arms

NORTHAMPTONSHIRE
Fotheringhay, Falcon

SOMERSET
Lovington, Pilgrims Rest

SUFFOLK
Earl Soham, Victoria
Horringer, Beehive
Lavenham, Angel
Nayland, Anchor
Southwold, Crown

SUSSEX
Chilgrove, White Horse

WARWICKSHIRE
Easenhall, Golden Lion
Ilmington, Howard Arms
Long Itchington, Duck on the Pond

WILTSHIRE
Rowde, George & Dragon
West Lavington, Bridge Inn

WORCESTERSHIRE
Baughton, Jockey
Clent, Fountain

YORKSHIRE
Constable Burton, Wyvill Arms
Sawley, Sawley Arms

PUBS CLOSE TO MOTORWAY JUNCTIONS

The number at the start of each line is the
number of the junction. Detailed directions are
given in the main entry for each pub. In this
section, to help you find the pubs quickly before
you're past the junction, we give the name of the
chapter where you'll find the text.

MI
13: Ridgmont, Rose & Crown (Beds)
2 miles

16: Nether Heyford, Olde Sun (Northants)
1.8 miles
18: Crick, Red Lion (Northants) 1 mile; Kilsby,
George (Northants) 2.6 miles
29: Hardwick Hall, Hardwick Inn (Derbys)
3 miles

M2
5: Hucking, Hook & Hatchet (Kent) 3.5 miles

M3
3: West End, Inn at West End (Surrey) 2.4 miles
5: Rotherwick, Falcon (Hants) 4 miles
9: Easton, Chestnut Horse (Hants) 3.6 miles
10: Winchester, Black Boy (Hants) 1 mile

M4
7: Dorney, Palmer Arms (Bucks) 2.7 miles
9: Bray, Crown (Berks) 1.75 miles; Bray, Hinds
Head (Berks) 1.75 miles
11: Shinfield, Magpie & Parrot (Berks) 2.6 miles
13: Winterbourne, Winterbourne Arms (Berks)
3.7 miles
17: Norton, Vine Tree (Wilts) 4 miles

M5
4: Holy Cross, Bell & Cross (Worcs) 4 miles;
Crowle, Old Chequers (Worcs) 2 miles
7: Kempsey, Walter de Cantelupe (Worcs)
3.75 miles
9: Bredon, Fox & Hounds (Worcs) 4.5 miles
16: Almondsbury, Bowl (Glos) 1.25 miles
19: Portishead, Windmill (Somerset) 3.7 miles;
Clapton-in-Gordano, Black Horse (Somerset)
4 miles
26: Clayhidon, Merry Harriers (Devon)
3.1 miles
28: Broadhembury, Drewe Arms (Devon)
5 miles
30: Topsham, Bridge Inn (Devon) 2.25 miles;
Woodbury Salterton, Diggers Rest (Devon)
3.5 miles

M6
4: Shustoke, Griffin (Warwicks) 5 miles
T6: Lichfield, Boat (Staffs) 2.7 miles
16: Barthomley, White Lion (Cheshire) 1 mile
33: Bay Horse, Bay Horse (Lancs) 1.2 miles
35: Yealand Conyers, New Inn (Lancs) 3 miles
40: Yanwath, Gate Inn (Cumbria) 2.25 miles;
Tirril, Queens Head (Cumbria) 3.5 miles

M9
3: Linlithgow, Four Marys (Scotland) 2 miles

M11
7: Hastingwood, Rainbow & Dove (Essex)
0.25 mile
8: Birchanger, Three Willows (Essex) 0.8 mile
9: Hinxton, Red Lion (Cambs) 2 miles
10: Thriplow, Green Man (Cambs) 3 miles

M20
8: Hollingbourne, Windmill (Kent) 1 mile

M25
8: Reigate Heath, Skimmington Castle (Surrey)
3 miles
10: Cobham, Cricketers (Surrey) 3.75 miles
11: Ottershaw, Castle (Surrey) 2.6 miles
13: Laleham, Three Horseshoes (Surrey) 5 miles
16: Denham, Swan (Bucks) 0.75 mile

18: Chenies, Red Lion (Bucks) 2 miles
21A: Potters Crouch, Holly Bush (Herts) 2.3 miles

M27
  1: Fritham, Royal Oak (Hants) 4 miles

M40
  2: Hedgerley, White Horse (Bucks) 2.4 miles;
    Forty Green, Royal Standard of England
    (Bucks) 3.5 miles
  6: Lewknor, Olde Leathern Bottel (Oxon)
    0.5 mile; Crowell, Shepherds Crook (Oxon)
    2 miles; Cuxham, Half Moon (Oxon) 4 miles
  7: Tetsworth, Red Lion (Oxon) 2.7 miles
  12: Gaydon, Malt Shovel (Warwicks) 0.9 mile

M48
  1: Littleton-upon-Severn, White Hart (Glos)
    3.5 miles

M50
  1: Baughton, Jockey (Worcs) 4 miles
  3: Upton Bishop, Moody Cow (Herefs) 2 miles

M53
  3: Barnston, Fox & Hounds (Lancs) 3 miles

M61
  8: Wheelton, Dressers Arms (Lancs) 2.1 miles

M66
  1: Bury, Lord Raglan (Lancs) 2 miles

REPORT FORMS

REPORT FORMS

Please report to us: you can use the tear-out forms on the following pages, the card in the middle of the book, or just plain paper – whichever's easiest for you, or you can report to our website, **www.goodguides.co.uk**. We need to know what you think of the pubs in this edition. We need to know about other pubs worthy of inclusion. We need to know about ones that should not be included.

The atmosphere and character of the pub are the most important features – why it would, or would not, appeal to strangers, so please try to describe what is special about it. In particular, we can't consider including a pub in the Lucky Dip section unless we know something about what it looks like inside, so that we can describe it to other readers. And obviously with existing entries, we need to know about any changes in décor and furnishings, too. But the bar food and the drink are also important – please tell us about them.

If the food is really quite outstanding, tick the FOOD AWARD box on the form, and tell us about the special quality that makes it stand out – the more detail, the better. And if you have stayed there, tell us about the standard of accommodation – whether it was comfortable, pleasant, good value for money. Again, if the pub or inn is worth special attention as a place to stay, tick the PLACE-TO-STAY AWARD box.

If you're in a position to gauge a pub's suitability or otherwise for **disabled people**, do please tell us about that.

Please try to gauge whether a pub should be a main entry, or is best as a Lucky Dip (and tick the relevant box). In general, main entries need qualities that would make it worth other readers' while to travel some distance to them; Lucky Dips are the pubs that are worth knowing about if you are nearby. But if a pub is an entirely new recommendation, the Lucky Dip may be the best place for it to start its career in the *Guide* – to encourage other readers to report on it.

The more detail you can put into your description of a Lucky Dip pub that's only scantily described in the current edition (or not in at all), the better. A description of its character and even furnishings is a tremendous boon.

It helps enormously if you can give the full address for any new pub – one not yet a main entry, or without a full address in the Lucky Dip sections. In a town, we need the street name; in the country, if it's hard to find, we need directions. Even better for us is the post code. If we can't find out a pub's post code, we no longer include it in the *Guide* – and the Post Office directories we use will not yet have caught up with new pubs, or ones which have changed their names. With any pub, it always helps to let us know about prices of food (and bedrooms, if there are any), and about any lunchtimes or evenings when food is not served. We'd also like to have your views on drinks quality – beer, wine, cider and so forth, even coffee and tea; and do let us know about bedrooms.

If you know that a Lucky Dip pub is open all day (or even late into the afternoon), please tell us – preferably saying which days.

When you go to a pub, don't tell them you're a reporter for the *Good Pub Guide*; we do make clear that all inspections are anonymous, and if you declare yourself as a reporter you risk getting special treatment – for better or for worse!

Sometimes pubs are dropped from the main entries simply because very few readers have written to us about them – and of course there's a risk that people may not write if they find the pub exactly as described in the entry. You can use the forms at the front of the batch of report forms just to list pubs you've been to, found as described, and can recommend.

When you write to The Good Pub Guide, FREEPOST TN1569, WADHURST, East Sussex TN5 7BR, you don't need a stamp in the UK. We'll gladly send you more forms (free) if you wish.

Though we try to answer letters, please understand if there's a delay. And from June till September, when we are fully extended getting the next edition to the printers, we put all letters and reports aside, not answering them until the rush is over (and after our post-press-day late summer holiday). The end of May is the cut-off date for reports for the next edition, and we can still cope with reports to our web site during the following weeks. But it is much more helpful if you can send reports earlier, rather than storing them up till then.

We'll assume we can print your name or initials as a recommender unless you tell us otherwise.

I have been to the following pubs in *The Good Pub Guide 2006* in the last few months, found them as described, and confirm that they deserve continued inclusion:

Continued overleaf

PLEASE GIVE YOUR NAME AND ADDRESS ON THE BACK OF THIS FORM

Pubs visited continued...

Your own name and address *(block capitals please)*

Postcode

In returning this form I confirm my agreement that the information I provide may be used by
The Random House Group Ltd, its assignees and/or licensees in any media or medium whatsoever.

Please return to
The Good Pub Guide,
FREEPOST TN1569,
WADHURST,
East Sussex
TN5 7BR

IF YOU PREFER, YOU CAN SEND US
REPORTS THROUGH OUR WEB SITE:
www.goodguides.co.uk

I have been to the following pubs in *The Good Pub Guide 2006* in the last few months, found them as described, and confirm that they deserve continued inclusion:

Continued overleaf

PLEASE GIVE YOUR NAME AND ADDRESS ON THE BACK OF THIS FORM

Pubs visited continued…

Your own name and address *(block capitals please)*

Postcode

Please return to
The Good Pub Guide,
FREEPOST TN1569,
WADHURST,
East Sussex
TN5 7BR

IF YOU PREFER, YOU CAN SEND US
REPORTS THROUGH OUR WEB SITE:
www.goodguides.co.uk

REPORT ON (PUB'S NAME)

Pub's address

☐ **YES** MAIN ENTRY ☐ **YES** LUCKY DIP ☐ **NO** DON'T INCLUDE
Please tick one of these boxes to show your verdict, and give reasons and descriptive
comments, prices etc

☐ DESERVES **FOOD award** ☐ DESERVES **PLACE-TO-STAY award** 2006:1

PLEASE GIVE YOUR NAME AND ADDRESS ON THE BACK OF THIS FORM

✂ ···

REPORT ON (PUB'S NAME)

Pub's address

☐ **YES** MAIN ENTRY ☐ **YES** LUCKY DIP ☐ **NO** DON'T INCLUDE
Please tick one of these boxes to show your verdict, and give reasons and descriptive
comments, prices etc

☐ DESERVES **FOOD award** ☐ DESERVES **PLACE-TO-STAY award** 2006:2

PLEASE GIVE YOUR NAME AND ADDRESS ON THE BACK OF THIS FORM

Your own name and address *(block capitals please)*
In returning this form I confirm my agreement that the information I provide may be used by
The Random House Group Ltd, its assignees and/or licensees in any media or medium whatsoever.

DO NOT USE THIS SIDE OF THE PAGE FOR WRITING ABOUT PUBS

- -

Your own name and address *(block capitals please)*
In returning this form I confirm my agreement that the information I provide may be used by
The Random House Group Ltd, its assignees and/or licensees in any media or medium whatsoever.

DO NOT USE THIS SIDE OF THE PAGE FOR WRITING ABOUT PUBS

IF YOU PREFER, YOU CAN SEND US REPORTS THROUGH OUR WEB SITE:
www.goodguides.co.uk

REPORT ON (PUB'S NAME)

Pub's address

☐ **YES** MAIN ENTRY ☐ **YES** LUCKY DIP ☐ **NO** DON'T INCLUDE
Please tick one of these boxes to show your verdict, and give reasons and descriptive comments, prices etc

☐ DESERVES **FOOD** award ☐ DESERVES **PLACE-TO-STAY** award 2006:3

PLEASE GIVE YOUR NAME AND ADDRESS ON THE BACK OF THIS FORM

✂ ....

REPORT ON (PUB'S NAME)

Pub's address

☐ **YES** MAIN ENTRY ☐ **YES** LUCKY DIP ☐ **NO** DON'T INCLUDE
Please tick one of these boxes to show your verdict, and give reasons and descriptive comments, prices etc

☐ DESERVES **FOOD** award ☐ DESERVES **PLACE-TO-STAY** award 2006:4

PLEASE GIVE YOUR NAME AND ADDRESS ON THE BACK OF THIS FORM

Your own name and address *(block capitals please)*

In returning this form I confirm my agreement that the information I provide may be used by
The Random House Group Ltd, its assignees and/or licensees in any media or medium whatsoever.

DO NOT USE THIS SIDE OF THE PAGE FOR WRITING ABOUT PUBS

By returning this form, you consent to the collection, recording and use of the information you submit, by The Random House Group Ltd. Any personal details which you provide from which we can identify you are held and processed in accordance with the Data Protection Act 1998 and will not be passed on to any third parties. The Random House Group Ltd may wish to send you further information on their associated products. Please tick box if you do not wish to receive any such information.

✂ ···

Your own name and address *(block capitals please)*

In returning this form I confirm my agreement that the information I provide may be used by
The Random House Group Ltd, its assignees and/or licensees in any media or medium whatsoever.

DO NOT USE THIS SIDE OF THE PAGE FOR WRITING ABOUT PUBS

By returning this form, you consent to the collection, recording and use of the information you submit, by The Random House Group Ltd. Any personal details which you provide from which we can identify you are held and processed in accordance with the Data Protection Act 1998 and will not be passed on to any third parties. The Random House Group Ltd may wish to send you further information on their associated products. Please tick box if you do not wish to receive any such information.

IF YOU PREFER, YOU CAN SEND US REPORTS THROUGH OUR WEB SITE:
www.goodguides.co.uk

REPORT ON (PUB'S NAME)

Pub's address

☐ **YES** MAIN ENTRY ☐ **YES** LUCKY DIP ☐ **NO** DON'T INCLUDE

Please tick one of these boxes to show your verdict, and give reasons and descriptive comments, prices etc

☐ DESERVES **FOOD award** ☐ DESERVES **PLACE-TO-STAY award** 2006:5

PLEASE GIVE YOUR NAME AND ADDRESS ON THE BACK OF THIS FORM

✂

REPORT ON (PUB'S NAME)

Pub's address

☐ **YES** MAIN ENTRY ☐ **YES** LUCKY DIP ☐ **NO** DON'T INCLUDE

Please tick one of these boxes to show your verdict, and give reasons and descriptive comments, prices etc

☐ DESERVES **FOOD award** ☐ DESERVES **PLACE-TO-STAY award** 2006:6

PLEASE GIVE YOUR NAME AND ADDRESS ON THE BACK OF THIS FORM

Your own name and address *(block capitals please)*

In returning this form I confirm my agreement that the information I provide may be used by
The Random House Group Ltd, its assignees and/or licensees in any media or medium whatsoever.

DO NOT USE THIS SIDE OF THE PAGE FOR WRITING ABOUT PUBS

✂ ....

Your own name and address *(block capitals please)*

In returning this form I confirm my agreement that the information I provide may be used by
The Random House Group Ltd, its assignees and/or licensees in any media or medium whatsoever.

DO NOT USE THIS SIDE OF THE PAGE FOR WRITING ABOUT PUBS

IF YOU PREFER, YOU CAN SEND US REPORTS THROUGH OUR WEB SITE:
www.goodguides.co.uk

REPORT ON   (PUB'S NAME)

Pub's address

☐ **YES** MAIN ENTRY   ☐ **YES** LUCKY DIP   ☐ **NO** DON'T INCLUDE
Please tick one of these boxes to show your verdict, and give reasons and descriptive
comments, prices etc

☐ DESERVES **FOOD** award   ☐ DESERVES **PLACE-TO-STAY** award   2006:7

PLEASE GIVE YOUR NAME AND ADDRESS ON THE BACK OF THIS FORM

✂--

REPORT ON   (PUB'S NAME)

Pub's address

☐ **YES** MAIN ENTRY   ☐ **YES** LUCKY DIP   ☐ **NO** DON'T INCLUDE
Please tick one of these boxes to show your verdict, and give reasons and descriptive
comments, prices etc

☐ DESERVES **FOOD** award   ☐ DESERVES **PLACE-TO-STAY** award   2006:8

PLEASE GIVE YOUR NAME AND ADDRESS ON THE BACK OF THIS FORM

Your own name and address *(block capitals please)*

In returning this form I confirm my agreement that the information I provide may be used by
The Random House Group Ltd, its assignees and/or licensees in any media or medium whatsoever.

DO NOT USE THIS SIDE OF THE PAGE FOR WRITING ABOUT PUBS

✂ ....

Your own name and address *(block capitals please)*

In returning this form I confirm my agreement that the information I provide may be used by
The Random House Group Ltd, its assignees and/or licensees in any media or medium whatsoever.

DO NOT USE THIS SIDE OF THE PAGE FOR WRITING ABOUT PUBS

IF YOU PREFER, YOU CAN SEND US REPORTS THROUGH OUR WEB SITE:
www.goodguides.co.uk

REPORT ON (PUB'S NAME)

Pub's address

☐ **YES** MAIN ENTRY ☐ **YES** LUCKY DIP ☐ **NO** DON'T INCLUDE
Please tick one of these boxes to show your verdict, and give reasons and descriptive
comments, prices etc

☐ DESERVES **FOOD award** ☐ DESERVES **PLACE-TO-STAY award** 2006:9
PLEASE GIVE YOUR NAME AND ADDRESS ON THE BACK OF THIS FORM

✂

REPORT ON (PUB'S NAME)

Pub's address

☐ **YES** MAIN ENTRY ☐ **YES** LUCKY DIP ☐ **NO** DON'T INCLUDE
Please tick one of these boxes to show your verdict, and give reasons and descriptive
comments, prices etc

☐ DESERVES **FOOD award** ☐ DESERVES **PLACE-TO-STAY award** 2006:10
PLEASE GIVE YOUR NAME AND ADDRESS ON THE BACK OF THIS FORM

Your own name and address *(block capitals please)*

In returning this form I confirm my agreement that the information I provide may be used by
The Random House Group Ltd, its assignees and/or licensees in any media or medium whatsoever.

DO NOT USE THIS SIDE OF THE PAGE FOR WRITING ABOUT PUBS

✂ ....

Your own name and address *(block capitals please)*

In returning this form I confirm my agreement that the information I provide may be used by
The Random House Group Ltd, its assignees and/or licensees in any media or medium whatsoever.

DO NOT USE THIS SIDE OF THE PAGE FOR WRITING ABOUT PUBS

IF YOU PREFER, YOU CAN SEND US REPORTS THROUGH OUR WEB SITE:
www.goodguides.co.uk

REPORT ON _(PUB'S NAME)_

Pub's address

☐ **YES** MAIN ENTRY   ☐ **YES** LUCKY DIP   ☐ **NO** DON'T INCLUDE

Please tick one of these boxes to show your verdict, and give reasons and descriptive comments, prices etc

☐ DESERVES **FOOD award**   ☐ DESERVES **PLACE-TO-STAY award**   2006:11

PLEASE GIVE YOUR NAME AND ADDRESS ON THE BACK OF THIS FORM

✂ -

REPORT ON _(PUB'S NAME)_

Pub's address

☐ **YES** MAIN ENTRY   ☐ **YES** LUCKY DIP   ☐ **NO** DON'T INCLUDE

Please tick one of these boxes to show your verdict, and give reasons and descriptive comments, prices etc

☐ DESERVES **FOOD award**   ☐ DESERVES **PLACE-TO-STAY award**   2006:12

PLEASE GIVE YOUR NAME AND ADDRESS ON THE BACK OF THIS FORM

Your own name and address *(block capitals please)*

In returning this form I confirm my agreement that the information I provide may be used by
The Random House Group Ltd, its assignees and/or licensees in any media or medium whatsoever.

DO NOT USE THIS SIDE OF THE PAGE FOR WRITING ABOUT PUBS

✂ ....

Your own name and address *(block capitals please)*

In returning this form I confirm my agreement that the information I provide may be used by
The Random House Group Ltd, its assignees and/or licensees in any media or medium whatsoever.

DO NOT USE THIS SIDE OF THE PAGE FOR WRITING ABOUT PUBS

IF YOU PREFER, YOU CAN SEND US REPORTS THROUGH OUR WEB SITE:
www.goodguides.co.uk

REPORT ON (PUB'S NAME)

Pub's address

☐ **YES** MAIN ENTRY ☐ **YES** LUCKY DIP ☐ **NO** DON'T INCLUDE

Please tick one of these boxes to show your verdict, and give reasons and descriptive comments, prices etc

☐ DESERVES **FOOD award** ☐ DESERVES **PLACE-TO-STAY award** 2006:13

PLEASE GIVE YOUR NAME AND ADDRESS ON THE BACK OF THIS FORM

✂ ··

REPORT ON (PUB'S NAME)

Pub's address

☐ **YES** MAIN ENTRY ☐ **YES** LUCKY DIP ☐ **NO** DON'T INCLUDE

Please tick one of these boxes to show your verdict, and give reasons and descriptive comments, prices etc

☐ DESERVES **FOOD award** ☐ DESERVES **PLACE-TO-STAY award** 2006:14

PLEASE GIVE YOUR NAME AND ADDRESS ON THE BACK OF THIS FORM

Your own name and address *(block capitals please)*

In returning this form I confirm my agreement that the information I provide may be used by
The Random House Group Ltd, its assignees and/or licensees in any media or medium whatsoever.

DO NOT USE THIS SIDE OF THE PAGE FOR WRITING ABOUT PUBS

✂ ....

Your own name and address *(block capitals please)*

In returning this form I confirm my agreement that the information I provide may be used by
The Random House Group Ltd, its assignees and/or licensees in any media or medium whatsoever.

DO NOT USE THIS SIDE OF THE PAGE FOR WRITING ABOUT PUBS

IF YOU PREFER, YOU CAN SEND US REPORTS THROUGH OUR WEB SITE:
www.goodguides.co.uk

REPORT ON (PUB'S NAME)

Pub's address

☐ **YES** MAIN ENTRY ☐ **YES** LUCKY DIP ☐ **NO** DON'T INCLUDE
Please tick one of these boxes to show your verdict, and give reasons and descriptive
comments, prices etc

☐ DESERVES **FOOD** award ☐ DESERVES **PLACE-TO-STAY** award 2006:15

PLEASE GIVE YOUR NAME AND ADDRESS ON THE BACK OF THIS FORM

✂

REPORT ON (PUB'S NAME)

Pub's address

☐ **YES** MAIN ENTRY ☐ **YES** LUCKY DIP ☐ **NO** DON'T INCLUDE
Please tick one of these boxes to show your verdict, and give reasons and descriptive
comments, prices etc

☐ DESERVES **FOOD** award ☐ DESERVES **PLACE-TO-STAY** award 2006:16

PLEASE GIVE YOUR NAME AND ADDRESS ON THE BACK OF THIS FORM

Your own name and address *(block capitals please)*

In returning this form I confirm my agreement that the information I provide may be used by
The Random House Group Ltd, its assignees and/or licensees in any media or medium whatsoever.

DO NOT USE THIS SIDE OF THE PAGE FOR WRITING ABOUT PUBS

✄

Your own name and address *(block capitals please)*

In returning this form I confirm my agreement that the information I provide may be used by
The Random House Group Ltd, its assignees and/or licensees in any media or medium whatsoever.

DO NOT USE THIS SIDE OF THE PAGE FOR WRITING ABOUT PUBS

IF YOU PREFER, YOU CAN SEND US REPORTS THROUGH OUR WEB SITE:
www.goodguides.co.uk

REPORT ON (PUB'S NAME)

Pub's address

☐ **YES** MAIN ENTRY ☐ **YES** LUCKY DIP ☐ **NO** DON'T INCLUDE
Please tick one of these boxes to show your verdict, and give reasons and descriptive
comments, prices etc

☐ DESERVES **FOOD award** ☐ DESERVES **PLACE-TO-STAY award** 2006:17

PLEASE GIVE YOUR NAME AND ADDRESS ON THE BACK OF THIS FORM

REPORT ON (PUB'S NAME)

Pub's address

☐ **YES** MAIN ENTRY ☐ **YES** LUCKY DIP ☐ **NO** DON'T INCLUDE
Please tick one of these boxes to show your verdict, and give reasons and descriptive
comments, prices etc

☐ DESERVES **FOOD award** ☐ DESERVES **PLACE-TO-STAY award** 2006:18

PLEASE GIVE YOUR NAME AND ADDRESS ON THE BACK OF THIS FORM

Your own name and address *(block capitals please)*

In returning this form I confirm my agreement that the information I provide may be used by
The Random House Group Ltd, its assignees and/or licensees in any media or medium whatsoever.

DO NOT USE THIS SIDE OF THE PAGE FOR WRITING ABOUT PUBS

✂ --

Your own name and address *(block capitals please)*

In returning this form I confirm my agreement that the information I provide may be used by
The Random House Group Ltd, its assignees and/or licensees in any media or medium whatsoever.

DO NOT USE THIS SIDE OF THE PAGE FOR WRITING ABOUT PUBS

IF YOU PREFER, YOU CAN SEND US REPORTS THROUGH OUR WEB SITE:
www.goodguides.co.uk